The ARRL

ANTENNA BOOK

FOR RADIO COMMUNICATIONS

24th EDITION

Volume 1: Antenna Fundamentals — Ch. 1-8

Volume 2: Antennas for LF/MF/HF— Ch. 9-14

Volume 3: Antennas for VHF through Microwave and Specialty Antennas — Ch. 15-22

Volume 4: Transmission Lines and Building Antenna Systems, and Index — Ch. 23-28

Editor

H. Ward Silver, NØAX

Contributing Editors

Steven R. Ford, WB8IMY

Mark J. Wilson, K1RO

Editorial Assistant

Maty Weinberg, KB1EIB

Production

Michelle Bloom, WB1ENT

Sue Fagan, KB1OKW — Cover Art

Jodi Morin, KA1JPA

David F. Pingree, N1NAS

Contributors to the 24th Edition

Alan Applegate, KØBG
Gary Breed, K9AY
Jim Brown, K9YC
Glen Brown, W6GJB
David Conn, VE3KL
Remco den Besten, PA3FYM
Wyatt Dirks, ACØRA
James Duffey, KK6MC
Darryl Holman, WW7D
Justin Johnson, GØKSC
Matt Kastigar, N9ES
Steve Kostro, N2CEI
Sean Kutzko, KX9X
Carl Luetzelschwab, K9LA
Brian Machesney, K1LI
Paul Marsh, MØEYT
Tino Pavic, VK3EGN
Stu Phillips, K6TU
Tom Planer, KJ9P
Gilles Renucci, VA2EW
Ulrich Rohde, N1UL
Rick Rosen, K1DS
Rudy Severns, N6LF
Corey Shields, KB9JHU
Kai Siwiak, KE4PT
Andrea Slack, K2EZ
Steve Stearns, K6OIK
Steve Sutterer, AKØM
John Thompson, K3MD
Paul Wade, W1GHZ
Mike Willis, GØMJW
Ken Wolff, K1EA
Grant Zehr, AA9LC

Published by:

ARRL The national association for AMATEUR RADIO®

225 Main Street, Newington, CT 06111-1400 USA

www.arrl.org

Printed in the USA

ISBN: 978-1-62595-111-3 Softcover
978-1-62595-114-4 Four-Volume Boxed Set

Kindle eBook Editions
ISBN: 978-1-62595-115-1 — Volume 1
ISBN: 978-1-62595-116-8 — Volume 2
ISBN: 978-1-62595-118-2 — Volume 3
ISBN: 978-1-62595-119-9 — Volume 4

Twenty-Fourth Edition
First Printing

Contents

A more detailed Table of Contents is included at the beginning of each chapter.

VOLUME 2
ANTENNAS FOR LF/MF/HF

VOLUME 3
ANTENNAS FOR VHF THROUGH MICROWAVE AND SPECIALTY ANTENNAS

VOLUME 4
TRANSMISSION LINES AND BUILDING ANTENNA SYSTEMS, AND INDEX

Foreword

Welcome to the 24th edition of the *ARRL Antenna Book*! Since 1939's very first edition, the amateur's ever-expanding affection for and association with the "skyhook" has been chronicled in these pages. That first edition's 139 pages have grown to more than 1000 and even then, there is more that could be covered. Amateurs use the widest frequency range of any civilian service and being an inventive lot, also use the widest variety of antennas. In response, the *ARRL Antenna Book* provides the amateur with a reference source for a balance of practical designs supplemented with theory and rationale.

The inaugural *Antenna Book* was written by two well-known authors — George Grammer, W1DF, and Byron Goodman, W1DX (then W1JPE). They covered the basics of what amateurs needed to know as our signals spanned ever-greater distances on ever-higher frequencies: propagation, antenna fundamentals, effects of ground, transmission lines, all manner of antennas, special low-frequency and UHF antennas, as well as how to construct, aim, and turn them. Do those topics sound familiar? We have many of the same questions today.

As this edition is being developed, amateurs are expanding their reach higher and lower. We've been granted our first LF allocation at 2200 meters. (That full-size dipole sure will be impressive!) A second MF allocation at 630 meters brackets the AM broadcast band with 160 meters. Contrary to expectations of noisy, short range contacts, surprising propagation is being discovered daily. To help us "get out" with electrically short antennas, Rudy Severns, N6LF, who participated as a test station before these bands were opened for general use, discusses the basics of effective antennas at long wavelengths.

Coupled with some amazing software by the *WSJT-X* team, hams are more active on the "ultra-highs" than ever before. As consumer electronics pushes far into the microwave region, amateurs are moving right along with them. In response, the entire section of antennas for the shortest of the shortwaves has been rewritten by Paul Wade, W1GHZ. You'll find more about the microwave feed line systems and devices, too.

The way we operate is beginning to change, as well. Amateur Radio "on the go" is enjoying a renaissance from better equipment, better batteries, better antennas, and exciting award programs that encourage mobile, portable, and maritime operation. Recognizing the need for more coverage of antennas to suit these circumstances, chapters on antennas for Portable, Space, Mobile and Maritime stations have all expanded. VHF/UHF rover stations get more attention as veterans of this exciting aspect of radiosport describe what makes their stations work. Antenna restricted? We've got antennas for you in the Stealth and Limited Space Antennas chapter.

Along with the antennas themselves, the transmission line system — from the transmitter to the terminals of the antenna — gets more attention. Jim Brown, K9YC, and Glen Brown, W6GJB have built and tested dozens of ferrite-core choke designs and materials, updating the amateur state of the art. If your antenna tuner won't tune, Matt Kastigar, N9ES, explains how to troubleshoot and repair it. For deciding where that new antenna should go, you'll find simple instructions for using Stu Philips, K6TU's online service that generates terrain profiles for use with *HFTA*.

Along with the many new projects in the book itself, there is plenty of new supplementary material to be downloaded. Check the inside cover of your book to find the code that gives you access to many megabytes of articles and papers, as well as propagation prediction tables, antenna modeling files, and some useful software. Many familiar designs and sections from previous editions are here for reference. There are also articles from *QST*, *QEX*, and the ARRL's companion IARU societies around the world.

Even with all that new and expanded material, there is still so much more to learn. We are encouraged to experiment and develop, one of the only services with that mandate and opportunity. Antennas and propagation are so fundamental to radio and so accessible. Amateurs are hard at work fulfilling the Basis and Purpose by advancing "the state of the radio art." Thank you to all of our many contributors who enrich every edition. May it always be so!

73,
Ward Silver, NØAX
Lead Editor
June 2019

The ARRL Antenna Book Downloadable Supplemental

A wealth of additional material for this edition of *The ARRL Antenna Book* is available with the downloadable supplemental content. As a purchaser of the print edition, you are entitled to download this material — see the instructions for doing so on the insert at the front of the printed book.

Searchable Edition of *The ARRL Antenna Book*

The downloadable content includes a PDF version of this edition of *The ARRL Antenna Book*, including text, drawings, tables, illustrations, and photographs. Using *Adobe Reader*, you can view, print, or search the entire book.

Supplemental Files for Each Chapter

The downloadable content contains supplemental information for most chapters of this book. This includes articles from *QST, QEX* and other sources, material from previous editions of *The ARRL Antenna Book*, tables and figures in support of the chapter material, and files that contain information to build and test the projects provided in the chapters. The supplemental information is arranged in folders for each chapter.

ARRL Antenna Modeling Files

A set of *EZNEC* modeling files representing many of the antennas discussed in *The ARRL Antenna Book*. The models are grouped in folders named for the type of antenna they represent. Requires *EZNEC* antenna modeling software (**www.eznec.com**), not supplied.

Propagation Prediction Tables

Propagation-prediction tables generated by Dean Straw, N6BV, for more than 240 different transmitting locations throughout the world, including 42 locations in the USA. Each file is in PDF format for viewing and printing using Adobe *Acrobat Reader*.

Companion Software

The following software is also included with the downloadable supplemental content:

• *HFTA* (*HF Terrain Assessment for Windows*) — A ray-tracing program designed to evaluate the effect of foreground terrain on the elevation pattern of up to four multi-element HF monoband Yagis in a stack. See the **HF Antenna System Design** chapter in this book for details about the theory behind ray tracing and diffraction in *HFTA*.

• *TLW* (*Transmission Line for Windows*) — A sort of "Swiss Army Knife" for transmission line and antenna tuner calculations.

• *YW* (*Yagi for Windows*) — A special-purpose program, designed strictly for evaluation of monoband Yagis. It has the advantage of running many times more quickly than general-purpose programs such as *NEC*, but it has some attendant limitations.

ARRL Membership Benefits and Services

ARRL membership includes *QST* magazine, plus dozens of other services and resources to help you get involved and enjoy Amateur Radio to the fullest. Here are just a few…

Find…

…a License Exam Session
www.arrl.org/exam

…a Licensing Class
www.arrl.org/class

…a Radio Club (ARRL-affiliated)
www.arrl.org/clubs

…a Hamfest or Convention
www.arrl.org/hamfests

Members-Only Web Services

Enjoy exclusive access to members-only benefits on the ARRL website.

QST Digital Edition

In addition to the printed copy of *QST*, all members have access to the online, monthly digital version at no additional cost. *QST* apps are also available.

Archives

ARRL members can browse ARRL's extensive online *QST* archive, including downloading and viewing *QST* product reviews. *QST* Product Reviews help our members make smarter, more informed purchasing decisions for Amateur Radio equipment.

E-Mail Forwarding Service

E-mail sent to your arrl.net address will be forwarded to any e-mail account you specify.

E-Newsletters

Subscribe to the weekly **ARRL Letter** and a variety of other e-newsletters and announcements: ham radio news, radio clubs, public service, contesting and more!

ARRL as Advocate

ARRL supports legislation and regulatory measures that preserve and protect meaningful access to the radio spectrum. Our **Regulatory Information Branch** answers member questions concerning FCC rules and operating practices. ARRL's **Volunteer Counsel** and **Volunteer Consulting Engineer** programs open the door to assistance with antenna regulation and zoning issues.

Technical Information Service

Call or e-mail our expert ARRL Technical Information Service specialists for answers to all your technical and operating questions. This service is FREE to ARRL members.

Public Service

ARRL works closely with FEMA, Red Cross, and other agencies to keep Amateur Radio's emergency communications capabilities in disaster response plans. Public service and emergency communication volunteers enjoy support and training from ARRL.

Group Benefits*

- ARRL Ham Radio Equipment Insurance
- Liberty Mutual Auto and Home Insurance (*US Only)

About the ARRL

The seed for Amateur Radio was planted in the 1890s, when Guglielmo Marconi began his experiments in wireless telegraphy. Soon he was joined by dozens, then hundreds, of others who were enthusiastic about sending and receiving messages through the air — some with a commercial interest, but others solely out of a love for this new communications medium. The United States government began licensing Amateur Radio operators in 1912.

By 1914, there were thousands of Amateur Radio operators — hams — in the United States. Hiram Percy Maxim, a leading Hartford, Connecticut inventor and industrialist, saw the need for an organization to unify this fledgling group of radio experimenters. In May 1914 he founded the American Radio Relay League (ARRL) to meet that need.

ARRL is the national association for Amateur Radio in the US. ARRL numbers within its ranks the vast majority of active radio amateurs in the nation and has a proud history of achievement as the standard-bearer in amateur affairs. ARRL's underpinnings as Amateur Radio's witness, partner, and forum are defined by five pillars: Public Service, Advocacy, Education, Technology, and Membership. ARRL is also International Secretariat for the International Amateur Radio Union, which is made up of similar societies in 150 countries around the world.

ARRL's Mission Statement: To advance the art, science, and enjoyment of Amateur Radio.
ARRL's Vision Statement: As the national association for Amateur Radio in the United States, ARRL:

- Supports the awareness and growth of Amateur Radio worldwide;
- Advocates for meaningful access to radio spectrum;
- Strives for every member to get involved, get active, and get on the air;
- Encourages radio experimentation and, through its members, advances radio technology and education; and
- Organizes and trains volunteers to serve their communities by providing public service and emergency communications.

At ARRL headquarters in the Hartford, Connecticut suburb of Newington, the staff helps serve the needs of members. ARRL publishes the monthly journal *QST* and an interactive digital version of *QST*, as well as newsletters and many publications covering all aspects of Amateur Radio. Its headquarters station, W1AW, transmits bulletins of interest to radio amateurs and Morse code practice sessions. ARRL also coordinates an extensive field organization, which includes volunteers who provide technical information and other support services for radio amateurs as well as communications for public service activities. In addition, ARRL represents US radio amateurs to the Federal Communications Commission and other government agencies in the US and abroad.

Membership in ARRL means much more than receiving *QST* each month. In addition to the services already described, ARRL offers membership services on a personal level, such as the Technical Information Service, where members can get answers — by phone, e-mail, or the ARRL website — to all their technical and operating questions.

A bona fide interest in Amateur Radio is the only essential qualification of membership; an Amateur Radio license is not a prerequisite, although full voting membership is granted only to licensed radio amateurs in the US. Full ARRL membership gives you a voice in how the affairs of the organization are governed. ARRL policy is set by a Board of Directors (one from each of 15 Divisions). Each year, one-third of the ARRL Board of Directors stands for election by the full members they represent. The day-to-day operation of ARRL HQ is managed by a Chief Executive Officer and his/her staff.

Join ARRL Today! No matter what aspect of Amateur Radio attracts you, ARRL membership is relevant and important. There would be no Amateur Radio as we know it today were it not for ARRL. We would be happy to welcome you as a member! Join online at **www.arrl.org/join**. For more information about ARRL and answers to any questions you may have about Amateur Radio, write or call:

ARRL — The national association for Amateur Radio®
225 Main Street
Newington CT 06111-1400 USA
Tel: 860-594-0200
FAX: 860-594-0259
e-mail: **hq@arrl.org**
www.arrl.org

Prospective new radio amateurs call (toll-free):
800-32-NEW HAM (800-326-3942)
You can also contact ARRL via e-mail at **newham@arrl.org**
or check out the ARRL website at **www.arrl.org**

Common Schematic Symbols Used in Circuit Diagrams

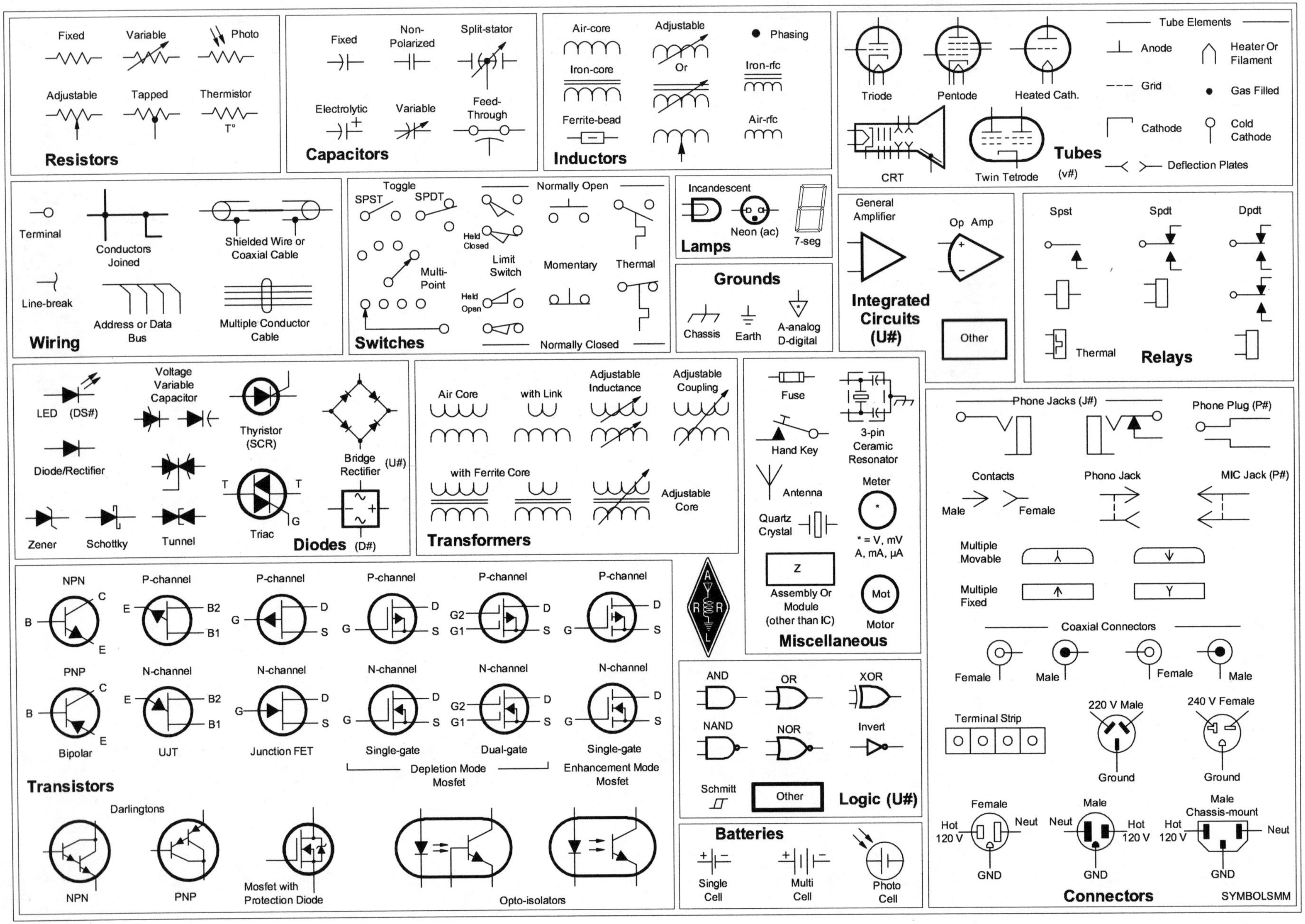

TABLE OF CONTENTS

Chapter 1 — Downloadable Supplemental Content

Supplemental Articles

- "Radio Mathematics" — supplemental information about math used in radio and a list of online resources and tutorials about common mathematics
- "Why an Antenna Radiates" by Kenneth MacLeish, W7TX

Chapter 1

Antenna Fundamentals

Where does the word "antenna" come from? As related by Dr. Ulrich Rohde, N1UL, the term originated with Guglielmo Marconi during early radio tests in 1895 during which he used wire "aerials" attached to a vertical tent pole. The aerial wire then ran down the pole to the transmitter. In Italian, a tent pole is known as "l'antenna central" and so the pole with the wire became simply, "l'antenna." In the beginning of radio, antennas were attached directly to generators and transmitters and were considered part of a common assembly. It wasn't until after 1900 that antennas began to be regarded as separate elements of the system, independent of the transmitter or receiver.

While there are an enormous variety of antennas, they share basic characteristics and all are designed to radiate and receive electromagnetic waves. In this chapter, we begin by defining what an electromagnetic wave is and how it is described. We then define the most important characteristics of an antenna — impedance, directivity and polarization — and show how those characteristics are measured and displayed. Finally, a section reviews how exposure to those waves affects the human body and the measures necessary for all amateurs to use antennas and electromagnetic waves safely.

1.1 INTRODUCTION TO ELECTROMAGNETIC FIELDS AND WAVES

1.1.1 E AND H FIELDS

In 1820 Hans Oerstad discovered that a current flowing in a wire would deflect the needle of a nearby compass. We attribute this effect to a magnetic or H-field, which at any given location is denoted by the letter H. The magnetic field's amplitude is expressed in A/m (Amperes/meter) along with a direction. (Direction can also be expressed as some value of phase with respect to a reference.) Because a magnetic field has *both* amplitude and direction, it is a *vector*. Symbols representing a vector are printed in bold-face.

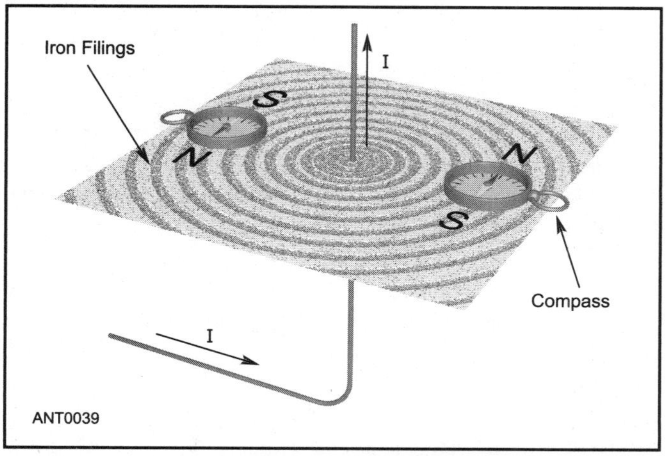

Figure 1.1 — Visualization of a magnetic field. The magnetic lines of force that surround a conductor with an electric current flowing in it are shown by iron filings and small compass needles. The needles point in the direction of the magnetic or H-field. The filings give a general view of the field distribution in the plane perpendicular to the conductor.

Figure 1.1 shows a typical experimental arrangement that demonstrates the presence of a magnetic field. The shape of the magnetic field is roughly shown by the distribution of the iron filings. This field distribution is very similar to that around a vertical antenna.

A compass needle (a small magnet itself) will try to align itself parallel to H. As the compass is moved around the conductor, the orientation of the needle changes accordingly. The orientation of the needle gives the direction of H. If you attempt to turn the needle away from alignment you will discover a torque trying to restore the needle to its original

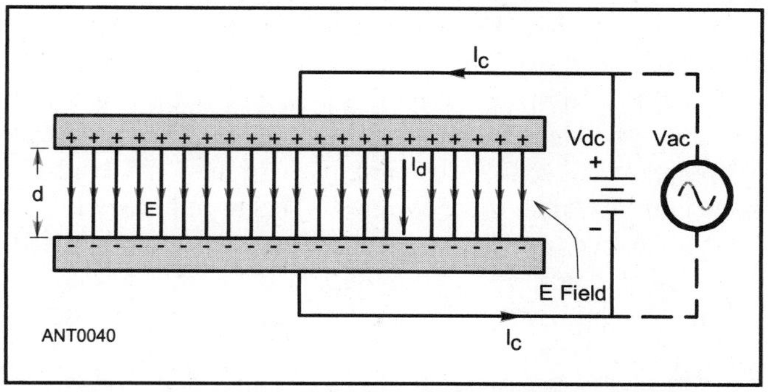

Figure 1.2 — Visualization of an electric field, $E=V_{dc}/d$. When the dc source is replaced with an ac source there will be a displacement current (I_d) flowing between the capacitor plates.

Math Tutorials

You will encounter a fair amount of intermediate-level mathematics in this book. If you would like to brush up on your math skills or learn about an unfamiliar topic, a list of free online math tutorials is included with the downloadable supplemental information for this book and on the ARRL website under "Math Tutorials" at **www.arrl.org/tech-prep-resource-library**.

position. The torque is proportional to the strength of the magnetic field at that point. This strength is called the *field intensity* or amplitude of H at that point. If a larger current flows in the conductor the amplitude of H will increase in proportion. Currents flowing in an antenna also generate an H-field.

An antenna will also have an electric or E-field, which can be visualized using a parallel-plate capacitor, as shown in **Figure 1.2**. If we connect a battery with a dc potential across the capacitor plates there will be an electric field E established between the plates, as indicated by the lines and directional arrows between the plates. (Like H, the electric field also has an amplitude and direction and so is a vector as well.) The magnitude of vector E is expressed in V/m (volts per meter), so for a potential of V volts and a spacing of d meters, E = V/d V/m. The amplitude of E will increase with voltage and/or a smaller separation distance (d). In an antenna, there will be ac potential differences between different parts of the antenna and from the antenna to ground. These ac potential differences establish the electric field associated with the antenna.

1.1.2 CONDUCTION AND DISPLACEMENT CURRENTS

If we replace the dc voltage source in Figure 1.2 with an ac source, an ac current will flow in the circuit. In the conductors between the ac source and the capacitor plates, current (I_c) flows, because of the movement of charge, usually electrons. But in the space between the capacitor plates (particularly in a vacuum) there are no charge carriers available to carry a conduction current. Nonetheless, current still flows in the complete circuit, and we attribute this to a *displacement current* (I_d) flowing between the capacitor plates to account for the continuity of current in the circuit. Displacement and conduction currents are two different phenomena but they both represent current, just two different kinds. Some observers prefer to call conduction currents "currents" and displacement currents "imaginary currents." That terminology is OK, but to account for the current flow in a closed circuit with capacitance you have to keep track of both kinds of current, whatever you call them. The accepted convention is to use the term "displacement current."

1.1.3 ELECTROMAGNETIC WAVES

An electromagnetic wave, as the name implies, is composed of both an electric field and a magnetic field that vary

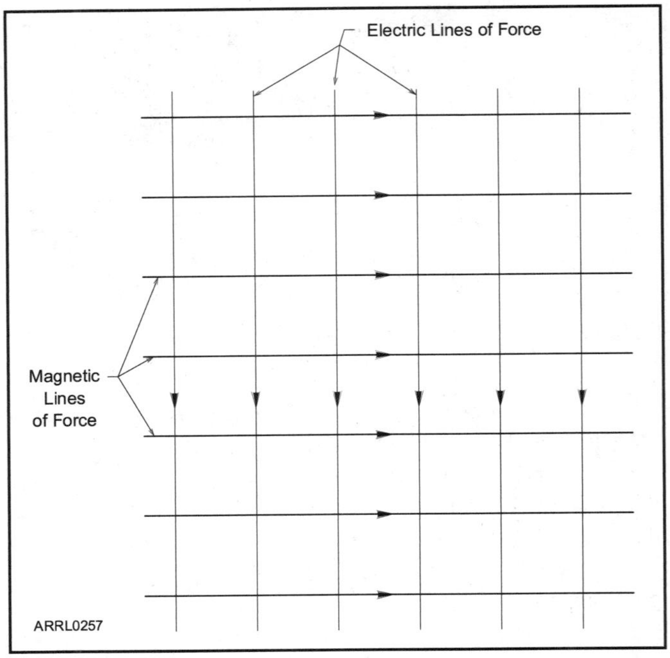

Figure 1.3 — Representation of electric and magnetic lines of force in an electromagnetic wavefront. Arrows indicate the instantaneous directions of the fields for a wavefront in a wave traveling toward you, out of the page. Reversing the direction of one of the fields would also reverse the direction of the wave.

with time. Electric and magnetic fields that do not change with time, such as those created by a dc current or voltage, are called *electrostatic fields*. The fields of a radio wave are created by an ac current in an antenna, usually having the form of a sine wave. As a result, the fields in a radio wave vary in the same sinusoidal pattern, increasing and decreasing in strength and reversing direction with the same frequency, f, as the ac current. It is the movement of electrons — specifically the acceleration and deceleration as the ac current moves back and forth — that creates the electromagnetic wave.

The two fields of the electromagnetic wave are oriented at right angles to each other as shown by **Figure 1.3**. The term "lines of force" in the figure means the direction in which a force would be felt by an electron (from the electric field) or by a magnet (from the magnetic field). The direction of the right angle from the electric field to the magnetic field, clockwise or counterclockwise, determines the direction the wave travels, as illustrated in the figure. This is called a *propagating wave*.

To an observer staying in one place, such as a stationary receiving antenna, the electric and magnetic fields of the wave appear to oscillate as the wave passes. That is, the fields create forces on electrons in the antenna that increase and decrease in a sine wave pattern. Some of the energy in the propagating wave is transferred to the electrons as the forces from the changing fields cause them to move. This creates a sine wave current in the antenna with a frequency determined by the rate at which the field strength changes as the wave passes.

If the observer is moving in the same direction as the wave and at the same speed, however, the strength of the fields will not change. To that observer, the electric and magnetic field strengths are fixed, as in a photograph. This is a *wavefront* of the electromagnetic wave; a flat surface or plane moving through space on which the electric and magnetic fields have a constant value as illustrated in Figure 1.3.

Just as an ac voltage is made up of an infinite sequence of instantaneous voltages, each slightly larger or smaller than the next, an infinite number of wavefronts make up a propagating electromagnetic wave, one behind another like a deck of cards. The direction of the wave is the direction in which the wavefronts move. The fields on each successive wavefront have a slightly different strength so as they pass a fixed location, the detected field strength changes as well. The fixed observer "sees" fields with strengths that vary as a sine wave.

Figure 1.4 is a drawing of what would happen if we could suddenly freeze all of the wave-fronts in the wave and take measurements of the electric and magnetic field strengths in each. In this example, the electric field is oriented vertically and the magnetic field horizontally. (Each of the vertical lines in the electric field can be thought of as representing an individual wavefront.) All of the wavefronts are moving in the direction indicated — the whole set of them moves together at the same speed. As the wave — the set of wavefronts — moves past the receiving antenna, the varying field strengths of the different wavefronts is perceived as a continuously changing wave. What we call a "wave" is really this entire group of wavefronts moving through space.

One more important note about electromagnetic waves: The electric and magnetic fields are *coupled*, that is they are both aspects of the same entity, the electromagnetic wave. They are not perpendicular electric and magnetic fields that simply happen to be in the same place at the same time! The fields cannot be separated, although the energy in the wave can be detected as electric or magnetic force. The fields are created as a single entity — an electromagnetic wave — by the motion of electrons in the transmitting antenna.

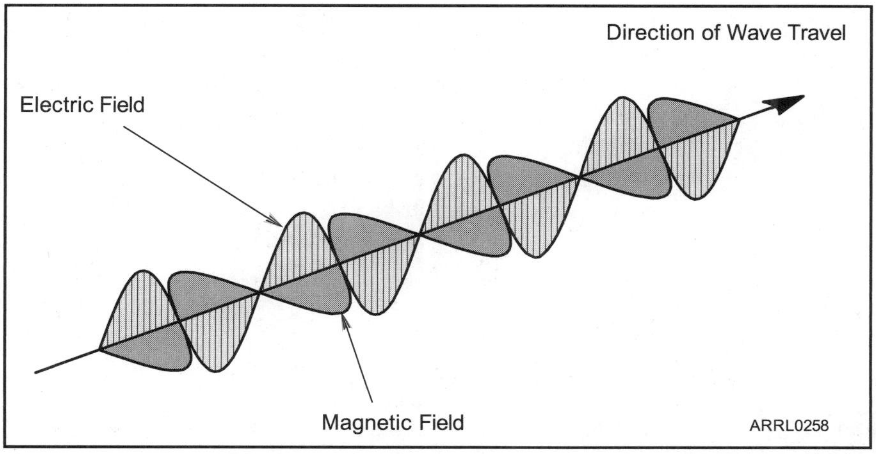

Figure 1.4 — Representation of the magnetic and electric field strengths of an electromagnetic wave. In the diagram, the electric field is oriented vertically and the magnetic field horizontally.

Speed of Propagation and Wavelength

Because the velocity of wave propagation is so great, we tend to ignore it. Only 1⁄7 of a second is needed for a radio wave to travel around the world — but in working with antennas the time factor is extremely important. The wave concept evolved because an alternating current flowing in a wire (antenna) creates propagating electric and magnetic fields. We can hardly discuss antenna theory or performance at all without involving travel time, consciously or otherwise.

The speed at which electromagnetic waves travel is called the *velocity of propagation*. It is determined by the permittivity (ε) and permeability (μ) of the medium in which the wave is traveling. This is commonly referred to as the "speed of light" and represented by *c*.

$$c = \frac{1}{\sqrt{\varepsilon\mu}} \qquad (1)$$

The speed of light is highest in the vacuum of free space, approximately 300 million or 3×10^8 meters per second and the special symbols ε_0 and μ_0 are used. It is often more convenient to remember this value as 300 m/µs (the actual value is 299.7925 m/µs).

It is also useful to know a radio wave's *wavelength* — the distance traveled during one complete cycle of a wave. Since one complete cycle takes 1/f the velocity of a wave is the speed of light, c, the wavelength, λ, is thus:

$$\lambda = c / f \qquad (2a)$$

In free-space

$$\lambda = 299.7925 \times 10^6 / f$$

where λ is the free-space wavelength in meters.

More convenient approximate formulas for use at radio frequencies are:

$$\lambda \text{ in meters} = 300 / f \text{ in MHz, and} \qquad (2b)$$

$$\lambda \text{ in feet} = 983.6 / f \text{ in MHz} \qquad (2c)$$

The ratio between the wave's velocity in a specific medium and that of free space is called the medium's *velocity factor* (VF) and is a value between 0 and 1. If the medium is air, the reduction in velocity of propagation can be ignored in most discussions of propagation at frequencies below 30 MHz. In the VHF range and higher, temperature and moisture content of the medium have increasing effects on the communication range, as will be discussed later in the **Radio Wave Propagation** chapter. In materials such as glass or plastic the wave's velocity can be quite a bit lower than that of free space. For example, in polyethylene (commonly used as a center insulator in coaxial cable), the velocity of propagation is about ⅔ that in free space. In distilled water (a good insulator) the speed is about 1/9 that of free space.

Phase of Waves

There will be few pages in this book where phase, wavelength and frequency do not enter the discussion. It is essential to have a clear understanding of their meaning in order to understand the design, installation, adjustment or use of antennas, matching systems or transmission lines in detail. In essence, *phase* means *time*. When something goes through periodic variations as an alternating current does, corresponding instants in succeeding periods are *in phase*.

It is important to distinguish between phase and *polarity*. Polarity is simply a convention that assigns a positive and negative direction or convention. Reversing the leads on a feed line reverses a signal's polarity but does not change its phase.

Phase is a relative measure of time within and between waveforms. The points A, B and C in **Figure 1.5** are all in phase. They are corresponding instants in the current flow, at intervals of 1 λ. The distance between A and B or between B and C is one wavelength. This is a conventional view of a sine wave alternating current, with time progressing to the right. It also represents the *instantaneous* value of intensity of the traveling fields, if distance is substituted for time in the horizontal axis. The field-intensity distribution follows the sine curve, in both amplitude and polarity, corresponding exactly to the time variations in the current that produced the fields. Remember that this is an *instantaneous* picture of the many wavefronts similar to Figure 1.4.

Waves used in radio communication may have frequencies from about 10,000 to several billion Hz. Suppose the frequency is 30 MHz. One cycle, or period, is completed in 1/30,000,000 second. The wave is traveling at 300,000,000 meters per second through the air, so it will move only 10 meters during the time that the current is going through one complete period of alternation. The electromagnetic field 10 meters away from the antenna is caused by the current that was flowing one period earlier in time. The field 20 meters away is caused by the current that was flowing two periods earlier, and so on.

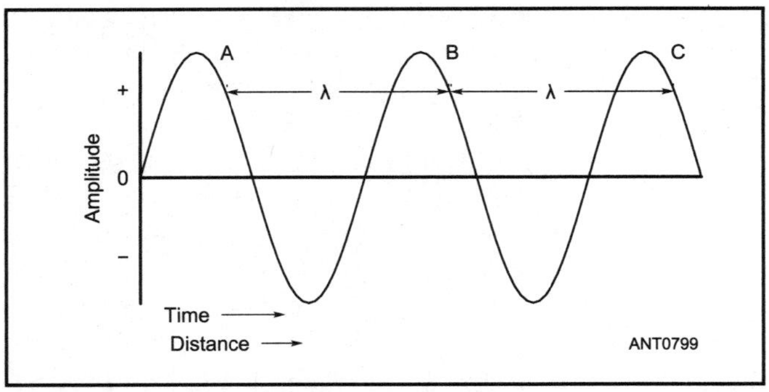

Figure 1.5 — The instantaneous amplitude of both fields (electric and magnetic) varies sinusoidally with time as shown in this graph. Since the fields travel at constant velocity, the graph also represents the instantaneous field intensity along the wave path. The distance between two points of equal phase such as A-B and B-C is the wave's wavelength.

If each period of the current is simply a repetition of the one before it, the currents at corresponding instants in each period will be identical. The fields caused by those currents will also be identical. As the fields move outward from the antenna they become more thinly spread over larger and larger spherical surfaces centered on the antenna. The field amplitudes decrease with distance from the antenna but they do not lose their identity with respect to the instant of the period at which they were generated. They are, and they remain, in phase. In the example above, on the spherical surfaces separated by intervals of 10 meters measured outward from the antenna, the phase of the waves at any given instant is identical.

These spherical surfaces are the wavefronts described earlier. When the sphere is so large that the surface is essentially flat, the wavefront is called a *plane wave*. On every part of this surface, the wavefront, the wave has the same phase. The wavelength is the distance between two wavefronts having the same phase at any given instant. This distance must be measured perpendicular to the wave fronts along the line that represents the direction of travel.

Wave Polarization

A wave like that in Figure 1.3 is said to be *polarized* in the direction of the electric lines of force. The polarization here is vertical, because the electric lines are perpendicular to the surface of the Earth. If the electric lines of force are horizontal, the wave is said to be horizontally polarized. Horizontally and vertically polarized waves may be classified generally under *linear polarization*. Linear polarization can be anything between horizontal and vertical. In free space, "horizontal" and "vertical" have no meaning, since the reference of the seemingly horizontal surface of the Earth has been lost.

In many cases the polarization of waves is not fixed, but rotates continually, sometimes at random. When this occurs the wave is said to be *elliptically polarized*. A gradual shift in polarization in a medium is known as *Faraday rotation*. For space communication, *circular polarization* is commonly used to overcome the effects of Faraday rotation. A circularly polarized wave rotates its polarization through 360° as it travels a distance of one wavelength in the propagation medium. The direction of rotation as viewed from the transmitting antenna defines the direction of circularity — right-hand (clockwise) or left-hand (counterclockwise). Linear and circular polarization may be considered as special cases of elliptical polarization.

Field Intensity

The energy from a propagated wave decreases with distance from the source. This decrease in strength is caused by the spreading of the wave energy over ever-larger spherical surfaces as the distance from the source increases.

A measurement of the strength of the wave at a distance from the transmitting antenna is its *field intensity*, which is synonymous with *field strength*. The strength of a wave is measured as the voltage between two points lying on an electric line of force in the plane of the wave front. The standard of measure for field intensity is the voltage developed in a wire that is 1 meter long, expressed as volts per meter. (If the wire were 2 meters long, the voltage developed would be divided by two to determine the field strength in volts per meter.)

The voltage in a wave is usually low so the measurement is made in millivolts or microvolts per meter. The voltage goes through time variations like those of the current that caused the wave. It is measured like any other ac voltage — in terms of the RMS value or, sometimes, the peak value. It is fortunate that in amateur work it is not necessary to measure actual field strength as the equipment required is elaborate. We need to know only if an adjustment has been beneficial, so relative measurements are satisfactory. These can be made easily with home-built equipment.

Wave Attenuation

In free space, the field intensity of the wave varies inversely with the distance from the source, once in the radiating far field of the antenna. If the field strength at 1 mile from the source is 100 millivolts per meter, it will be 50 millivolts per meter at 2 miles, and so on. The relationship between field intensity and power density is similar to that for voltage and power in ordinary circuits. They are related by the impedance of free space, which is approximately 377 Ω. A field intensity of 1 volt per meter is therefore equivalent to a power density of

$$P = \frac{E^2}{Z} = \frac{1\ (\text{volt}/\text{m})^2}{377\ \Omega} = 2.65\,\text{mW}/\text{m}^2 \qquad (3)$$

Because of the relationship between voltage and power, the power density varies with the square of the field intensity, or inversely with the *square* of the distance. If the power density at 1 mile is 4 mW per square meter, then at a distance of 2 miles it will be 1 mW per square meter.

It is important to remember this so-called *spreading loss* when antenna performance is being considered. Gain can come only from narrowing the radiation pattern of an antenna, which concentrates the radiated energy in the desired direction. There is no "antenna magic" by which the total energy radiated can be increased.

In practice, attenuation of the wave energy may be much greater than the inverse-distance law would indicate. The wave does not travel in a vacuum and the receiving antenna seldom is situated so there is a clear line of sight. The Earth is spherical and the waves do not penetrate its surface appreciably, so communication beyond visual distances must be by some means that will bend the waves around the curvature of the Earth. These means involve additional energy losses that increase the path attenuation with distance, above that for the theoretical spreading loss in a vacuum.

1.2 ANTENNA IMPEDANCE

1.2.1 RADIATION RESISTANCE AND EFFICIENCY

The power supplied to an antenna is dissipated in two ways: radiation of electromagnetic waves and heat losses in the wire and nearby conductors and dielectrics material. The radiated power is what we want, the useful part, but it represents a form of "loss" just as much as the power used in heating the wire or nearby dielectrics is a loss. In either case, the dissipated power is equal to I^2R.

In the case of heat losses, R is a real resistance. In the case of radiation, however, R is a "virtual" resistance, which, if replaced with an actual resistor of the same value, would dissipate the power actually radiated from the antenna. This resistance is called the *radiation resistance* to the radiated electromagnetic wave, also called the *radiation reaction.* Radiation resistance is discussed at great length in Chapter 2 of Kraus's *Antennas* (see Bibliography) for the interested reader. The total power in the antenna is therefore equal to $I^2 (R_r+R)$, where R_r is the radiation resistance and R represents the total of all the loss resistances. Radiation efficiency is defined as:

$$\eta = \frac{R_r}{R_r + R} \qquad (4)$$

where loss resistance (R) is calculated from (or normalized to) the same point at which R_r is determined. As R is reduced, the antenna's radiation efficiency increases.

In antennas that are not electrically small compared to the signal wavelength or that are close to or connected to the ground, the power lost as heat in the conductor does not exceed a few percent of the total power supplied to the antenna. Expressed in decibels, the loss is less than 0.1 dB. The RF loss resistance of copper wire even as small as #14 AWG is very low compared with the radiation resistance of an antenna that is reasonably clear of surrounding objects and is not too close to the ground. You can therefore assume that the ohmic loss in a reasonably well-located antenna is negligible and that the total resistance shown by the antenna (the feed point resistance) is radiation resistance. As a radiator of electromagnetic waves, such an antenna is a highly efficient device.

For antennas that are electrically small, incorporate loading or tuning circuits, or rely on the ground as a path for current, the power losses can be substantial. In these cases, such as small loops, mobile antennas, and vertical monopoles, it is important to reduce loss resistance wherever possible by using high-quality materials, insuring that connections are secure and low-loss, and providing the lowest-loss current path practical.

1.2.2 CURRENT AND VOLTAGE DISTRIBUTION

When power is fed to an antenna, the current and voltage vary along its length. The current is minimum at the ends,

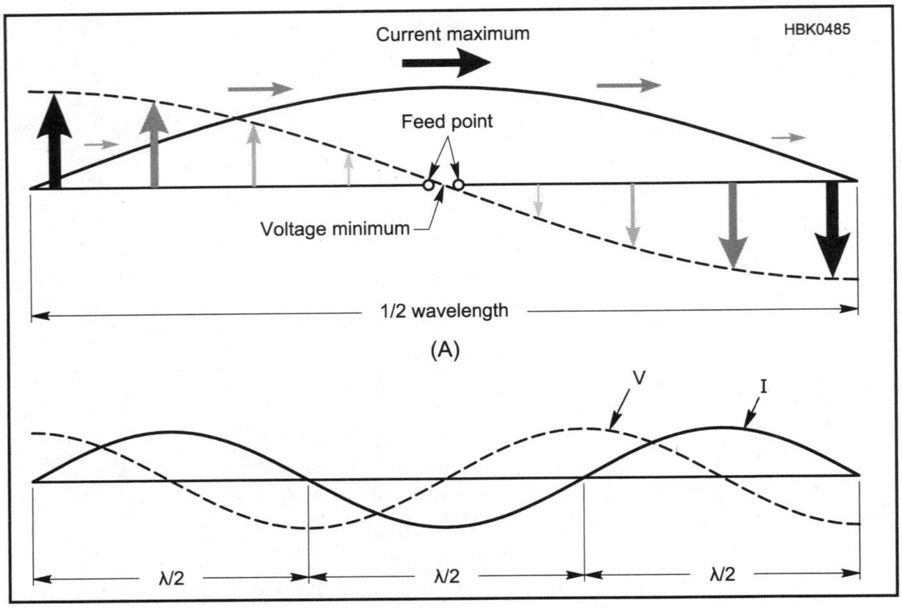

Figure 1.6 — The amplitude of voltage and current along a half-wavelength dipole (A) and along an antenna made from a series of half-wavelength sections. The curves show how voltage and current are distributed along the antenna.

regardless of the antenna's length. The current does not actually reach zero at the current minima, because of capacitance at the antenna ends. Insulators, loops at the antenna ends and support wires all contribute to this capacitance, which is also called the *end effect*. The opposite is true of the RF voltage. That is, there is a voltage maximum at the ends.

In the case of a half-wave antenna there is a current maximum at the center and a voltage minimum at the center as illustrated in **Figure 1.6**. The curved lines in the figure are not waveforms and do not represent the phase relationship of voltage and current. The curves only show the amplitude of the voltage and current at any point along the antenna. This is called the antenna's voltage and current *distribution*. The pattern of alternating current and voltage minima ¼ wavelength apart repeats every ½ wavelength along a linear antenna as shown in Figure 1.6B. The phase of the current and voltage are inverted in each successive half-wavelength section.

1.2.3 FEED POINT IMPEDANCE

Since amateurs are free to choose our operating frequencies within assigned bands we need to consider how the feed point impedance of a particular antenna varies with frequency within a particular band or even in several different bands if we intend to use one antenna on multiple bands. Impedance is simply the ratio of voltage to current. *Feed point impedance* is the ratio of voltage to current at the point where power is supplied to the antenna. As you can see from Figure 1.6, feed point impedance is high at the ends of a dipole where voltage is high and current is low. In the center of the dipole, feed point impedance is low, and it takes an intermediate value between those points. In the longer antenna of Figure 1.6B, there are several high-impedance and low-impedance points.

There are two forms of impedance associated with any antenna: *self impedance* and *mutual impedance*. As you might expect, self impedance is what is measured at the feed point terminals of an antenna located completely away from the influence of any other conductors.

Self Impedance

The current that flows into an antenna's feed point must be supplied at a finite voltage. The self impedance of the antenna is simply equal to the voltage applied to its feed point divided by the current flowing into the feed point according to Ohm's Law. Where the current and voltage are exactly in phase, the impedance is purely resistive with zero reactance and the antenna is *resonant*. (Amateurs often use the term "resonant" rather loosely, usually meaning "nearly resonant" or "close-to resonant." Resonance has nothing to do with the value of the impedance, only that it is purely resistive.)

Except at the one frequency where it is exactly resonant, the current in an antenna has a different phase compared to the applied voltage. In other words, the antenna exhibits a feed point impedance that is not just a pure resistance. The feed point impedance is composed of either capacitive or inductive reactance in series with a resistance.

Mutual Impedance

Mutual, or *coupled*, impedance is due to the parasitic effect of nearby conductors located within the antenna's reactive near field. This includes the effect of ground which is a lossy conductor, but a conductor nonetheless. Mutual impedance is defined using Ohm's Law, just like self impedance. However, mutual impedance is the ratio of voltage in one conductor, divided by the current in another (coupled) conductor. Mutually coupled conductors can distort the pattern of a highly directive antenna, as well as change the impedance seen at the feed point. Mutual impedance will be considered in detail in the chapter, **HF Yagi and Quad Antennas**, where it is essential for proper operation of these beam antennas.

Is Resonance Required?

An antenna need not be resonant in order to be an effective radiator. There is in fact nothing magic about having a resonant antenna, provided of course that you can devise some efficient means to feed the antenna. Many amateurs use non-resonant (even random-length) antennas fed with open-wire transmission lines and antenna tuners. They radiate signals just as well as those using coaxial cable and resonant antennas and as a bonus can usually be used on multiple frequency bands. It is important to consider an antenna and its feed line as a system in which all losses should be kept to a minimum.

1.3 ANTENNA DIRECTIVITY AND GAIN

1.3.1 THE ISOTROPIC RADIATOR

Before we can fully describe practical antennas, we must first introduce a completely theoretical antenna, the *isotropic radiator*. Envision, if you will, an infinitely small antenna at a point located in outer space, completely removed from anything else around it. Then consider an infinitely small transmitter feeding this infinitely small, point antenna. You now have an isotropic radiator.

The uniquely useful property of this theoretical point-source antenna is that it radiates equally well in all directions. That is to say, an isotropic antenna favors no direction at the expense of any other. In other words, it has absolutely no *directivity*, which is the property of radiating or receiving more strongly in some directions than in others. The isotropic radiator is useful for comparison with actual antenna systems.

You will find later that real, practical antennas all exhibit some degree of directivity. The radiation from a practical antenna never has the same intensity in all directions and may even have zero radiation in some directions. The fact that a practical antenna displays directivity (while an isotropic radiator does not) is usually desirable. The directivity of a real antenna is often carefully tailored to emphasize radiation in particular directions. For example, a receiving antenna that favors certain directions can discriminate against interference or noise coming from other directions, thereby increasing the signal-to-noise ratio for desired signals coming from the favored direction.

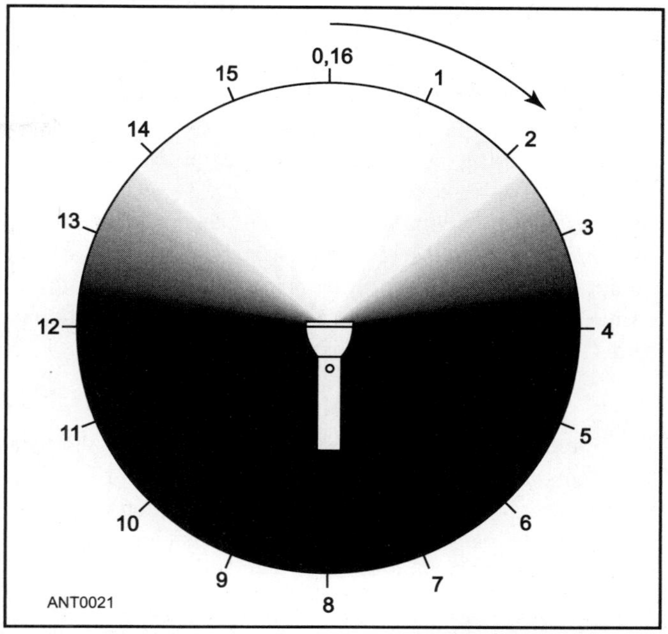

Figure 1.7 — The beam from a flashlight illuminates a totally darkened area a shown here. Readings taken with a photographic light meter at the 16 points around the circle may be used to plot the radiation pattern of the flashlight.

1.3.2 DIRECTIVITY AND THE RADIATION PATTERN

The directivity of an antenna is directly related to the pattern of its radiated field intensity in free space. A graph showing the actual or relative field intensity at a fixed distance as a function of the direction from the antenna system, is called a *radiation pattern*. Since we can't actually see electromagnetic waves making up the radiation pattern of an antenna, we can consider an analogous situation.

Figure 1.7 represents a flashlight shining in a totally darkened room. To quantify what our eyes are seeing we might use a sensitive light meter like those used by photographers, with a scale graduated in units from 0 to 10. We place the meter directly in front of the flashlight and adjust the distance so the meter reads 10, exactly full scale. We also carefully note the distance. Then, always keeping the meter the same distance from the flashlight and keeping it at the same height above the floor, we move the light meter around the flashlight, as indicated by the arrow, and take light readings at a number of different positions.

After all the readings have been taken and recorded, we plot those values on a sheet of polar graph paper, like that shown in **Figure 1.8**. The values read on the meter are plotted at an angular position corresponding to that at which each meter reading was taken. Following this, we connect the plotted points with a smooth curve, also shown in the figure. When this is finished, we have completed a radiation pattern for the flashlight.

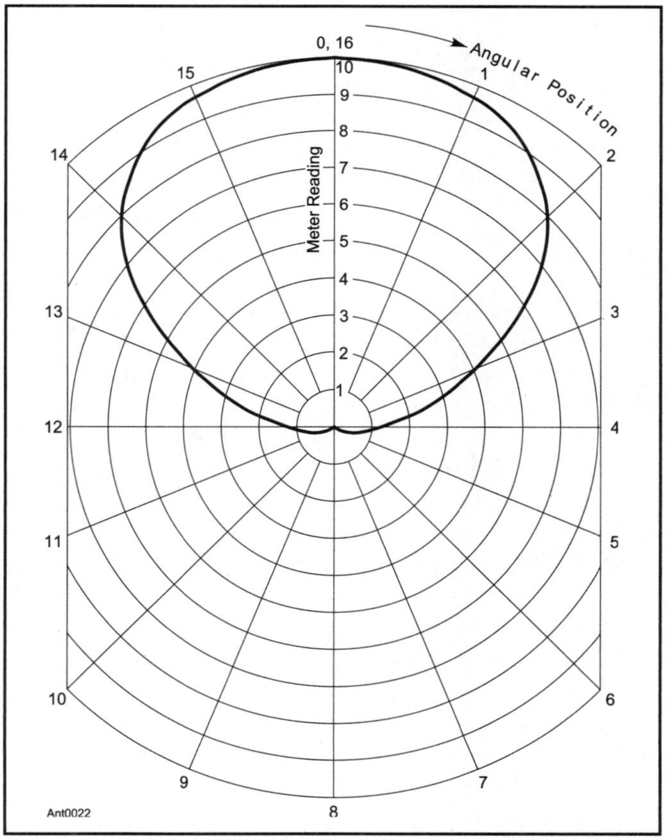

Figure 1.8 — The radiation pattern of the flashlight in Figure 1.7. The measured values are plotted and connected with a smooth curve.

Antenna radiation patterns can be constructed in a similar manner. Power is fed to the antenna under test and a field-strength meter indicates the amount of signal. We might wish to rotate the antenna under test, rather than moving the measuring equipment to numerous positions about the antenna. Since the pattern while receiving is the same as that while transmitting (see the section on Reciprocity later in this chapter), a source antenna fed by a low-power transmitter illuminates the antenna under test and the signal intercepted by the antenna under test is fed to a receiver and measuring equipment. Additional information on the mechanics of measuring antenna patterns is contained in the chapter **Antennas and Transmission-Line Measurements**.

1.3.3 NEAR AND FAR FIELDS

Some precautions must be taken to assure that the measurements are accurate and repeatable and one of the most important is to prevent mutual coupling between the source and receiving antennas that may alter the pattern you are trying to measure.

This sort of mutual coupling can occur in the region very close to the antenna under test. This region is called the *reactive near-field* region. The term "reactive" refers to the fact that the mutual impedance between the transmitting and receiving antennas can be either capacitive or inductive in nature. The reactive near field is sometimes called the "induction field," meaning that the magnetic field usually is predominant over the electric field in this region. The antenna acts as though it were a rather large, lumped-constant inductor or capacitor, storing energy in the reactive near field rather than propagating it into space.

For simple wire antennas, the reactive near field is considered to be within about a half wavelength from an antenna's radiating center. Later on, in the chapters dealing with arrays of antennas, you will find that mutual coupling between elements can be put to good use to purposely shape the radiated pattern. For making pattern measurements, however, we do not want to be too close to the antenna being measured.

The strength of the reactive near field decreases in a complicated fashion as you increase the distance from the antenna. Beyond the reactive near field, the antenna's radiated field is divided into two other regions: the *radiating near field* and the *radiating far field*. Historically, the terms *Fresnel* and *Fraunhöfer* fields have been used for the radiating near and far fields, but these terms have been largely supplanted by the more descriptive terminology used here. Even inside the reactive near-field region, both radiating and reactive fields coexist although the reactive field predominates very close to the antenna.

Because the boundary between the fields is not a precise distance, experts debate where one field begins and another leaves off but the boundary between the radiating near and far fields is generally accepted as:

$$D = \frac{2L^2}{\lambda} \tag{5}$$

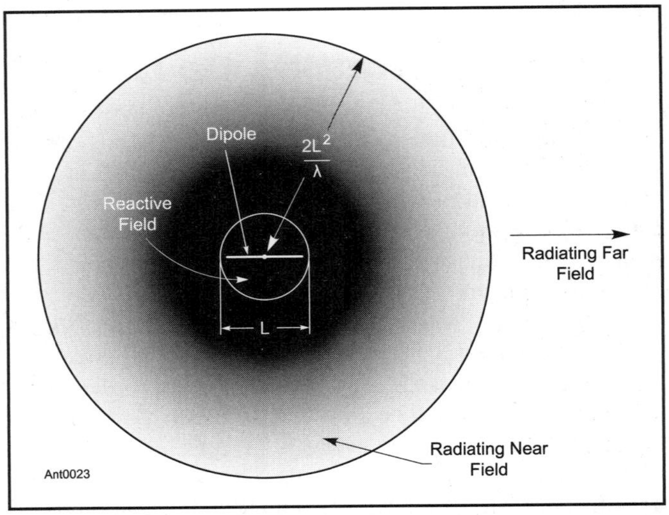

Figure 1.9 — The fields around a radiating antenna. Very close to the antenna, the reactive field dominates. Within this area mutual impedances are observed between the antenna and any other antennas or conductors. Outside the reactive near field, the radiating near field dominates up to the distance shown where L is the length of the largest dimension of the antenna. Beyond the near/far field boundary lies the radiating far field, where power density varies as the inverse square of radial distance.

where L is the largest dimension of the physical antenna expressed in the same units of measurement as the wavelength λ. Remember, many specialized antennas do not follow the rule of thumb in Eq 5 exactly. **Figure 1.9** depicts the three fields in front of a simple wire antenna. (An analysis of why this boundary is difficult to determine is provided in the article by Abdallah et al in the Bibliography.)

Throughout the rest of this book we will discuss mainly the radiating far fields, those forming the propagating electromagnetic waves and which will simply be referred to as the "far field." Far field radiation is distinguished by the fact that the intensity is inversely proportional to the distance, and that the electric and magnetic components, although perpendicular to each other in the wave front, are in phase as defined earlier. The total energy is equally divided between the electric and magnetic fields. Beyond several wavelengths from the antenna these are the only fields we need to consider. This is why for accurate measurement of radiation patterns, we must place our measuring instrumentation at least several wavelengths away from the antenna under test.

1.3.4 TYPES OF RADIATION PATTERNS

In the example of the flashlight, the plane of measurement was at one consistent height above the floor. In **Figure 1.10A** a similar radiation pattern is shown for a half-wavelength dipole (see the **Dipoles and Monopoles** chapter) in free-space, measured in a single plane containing the antenna wire. The antenna is located at the exact center of the plot with its orientation specified by the two-headed arrow. The antenna radiates best broadside to the wire axis and hardly at all off the ends of the wire.

Radiation patterns are graphic representations of an

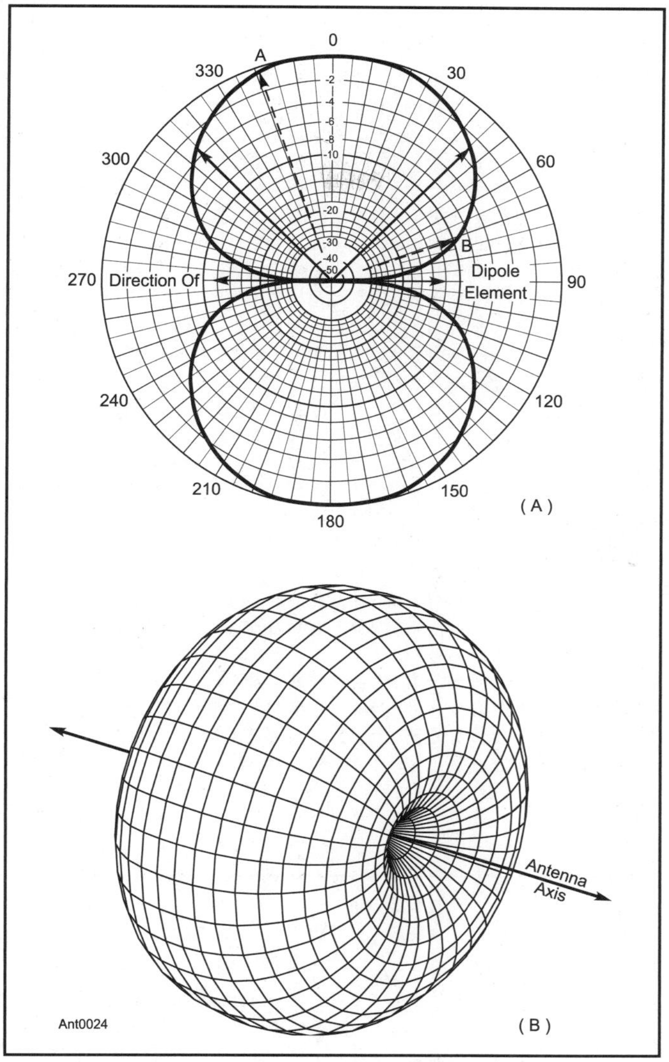

Figure 1.10 — Radiation patterns of a half-wavelength dipole in free-space. At A, the pattern in the plane containing the wire axis. The length of each dashed-line arrow represents the relative field strength in that direction, referenced to the direction of maximum radiation at right angles to the wire's axis. The arrows at approximately 45° and 315° are the half-power or –3 dB points. At B, a wire grid representation of the solid pattern for the same antenna.

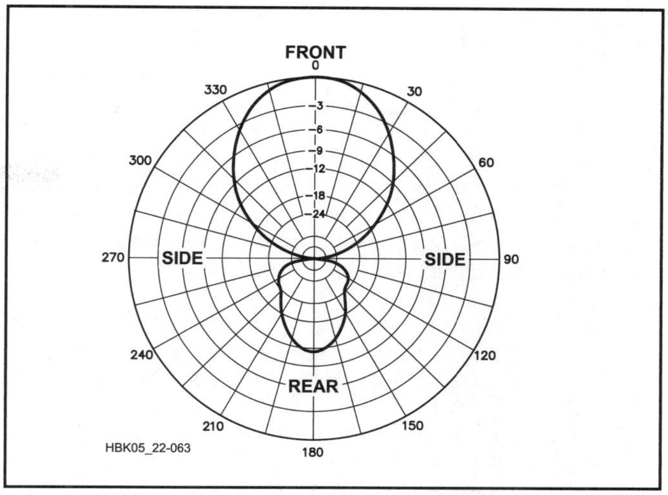

Figure 1.11 — Azimuthal pattern of a typical three-element Yagi beam antenna in free space. The Yagi's boom is aligned along the 0° to 180° axis and the beam's elements are in the plane of the pattern.

antenna's directivity. Shown in polar coordinates (see the math tutorial reference with the downloadable supplemental information for this book for information about polar coordinates), the angular scale shows direction and the scale from the center of the plot to the outer ring. The smooth line in the shape of a figure-8 shows the relative strength of the antenna's radiated signal at each angle.

The pattern in **Figure 1.11** shows both *nulls* (angles at which a pattern minimum occurs) and *lobes* (radiation at angles between nulls). The *main lobe* is the lobe with the highest amplitude unless noted otherwise and unless several plots are being compared, the peak amplitude of the main lobe is placed at the outer ring as a reference point. The peak of the main lobe can be located at any angle. All other lobes are *side lobes* which can be at any angle, including to the rear of the antenna. In addition to the labels showing the main lobe and nulls in the pattern, the so-called *half-power* points on the main lobe are shown. These are the angles at which the power is one-half of the peak value in the main lobe.

Actually, the pattern for any antenna is three-dimensional and therefore cannot be represented by a single-plane drawing. The total radiation pattern of an antenna in free space would be found by measuring the field strength at every point on the surface of an imaginary sphere having the antenna at its center. The information so obtained would then be used to construct a solid figure, where the distance from a fixed point (representing the antenna) to the surface of the figure is proportional to the field strength from the antenna in any given direction. Figure 1.10B shows a three-dimensional solid representation of the radiation pattern of a half-wave dipole. Figure 1.10A can be thought of as a cross-section of the solid pattern through the axis of the antenna. Two such diagrams, one in the plane containing the straight wire of a dipole and one in the plane perpendicular to the wire, can convey a great deal of information. After a little practice and with the exercise of some imagination, the complete solid pattern can be visualized with fair accuracy from inspection of the two planar diagrams, provided of course that the solid pattern of the antenna is smooth such as for simple antennas like the dipole of Figure 1.10.

Azimuth and Elevation Patterns

When a radiation pattern is shown for an antenna mounted over ground rather than in free space, we automatically gain two frames of reference: *an azimuth angle* and an *elevation angle*. The azimuth angle is usually referenced to 0° in the direction of maximum radiation from the antenna or it could be referenced to True North for an antenna oriented in a particular compass direction.

The elevation angle is referenced to the horizon at the Earth's surface, where the elevation angle is 0°. Of course,

Introduction to the Decibel

The power gain and pattern measurements such as front-to-back ratio of an antenna system are usually expressed in decibels (dB). The decibel is a practical unit for measuring power ratios because it is more closely related to the actual effect produced at a distant receiver than the power ratio itself. One decibel represents a just-detectable change in signal strength, regardless of the actual value of the signal voltage. A 20-decibel (20 dB) increase in signal, for example, represents 20 observable steps in increased signal. The power ratio (100 to 1) corresponding to 20 dB gives an entirely exaggerated idea of the improvement in communication to be expected. The number of decibels corresponding to any power ratio is equal to 10 times the common logarithm of the power ratio, or

$$dB = 10 \log_{10} \frac{P_1}{P_2}$$

If the voltage ratio is given, the number of decibels is equal to 20 times the common logarithm of the ratio. That is,

$$dB = 20 \log_{10} \frac{V_1}{V_2}$$

When a voltage ratio is used, both voltages must be measured across the same value of impedance. Unless this is done the decibel figure is meaningless, because it is fundamentally a measure of a power ratio.

The main reason a decibel is used is that successive power gains expressed in decibels may simply be added together. Thus a gain of 3 dB followed by a gain of 6 dB gives a total gain of 9 dB. In ordinary power ratios, the ratios must be multiplied together to find the total gain.

A reduction in power is handled simply by subtracting the requisite number of decibels. Thus, reducing the power to ½ is the same as subtracting 3 decibels. For example, a power gain of 4 in one part of a system and a reduction to ½ in another part gives a total power gain of 4 × ½ = 2. In decibels, this is 6 – 3 = 3 dB. A power reduction or loss is simply indicated by including a negative sign in front of the appropriate number of decibels.

When P_2 or V_2 are some fixed reference value, a letter is added to "dB" to indicate "decibels with respect to" the reference value. This allows absolute values of power and voltage to be expressed in dB, as well. You will often encounter dBm (P_2 = 1 mW) and dBμV (V_2 = 1 μV) in Amateur Radio.

For more information about the decibel, read "A Tutorial on the Decibel" available at **www.arrl.org/files/file/A%20Tutorial%20on%20the%20Decibel%20-%20Version%202_1%20-%20Formatted.pdf**.

the Earth is round but because its radius is so large, it can in this context be considered to be flat in the area directly under the antenna. An elevation angle of 90° is directly above the antenna (the *zenith*) and the angles then reduce back to 0° toward the horizon directly behind the antenna. (Professional antenna engineers often describe an antenna's orientation with respect to the point directly overhead — using the zenith angle, rather than the elevation angle. The elevation angle is computed by subtracting the zenith angle from 90°.)

Figure 1.11 is an *azimuthal* or *azimuth pattern* that shows the antenna's gain in all horizontal directions (azimuths) around the antenna. As with a map, 0° is at the top and bearing angle increases clockwise. (This is different from polar plots generated for mathematical functions in which 0° is at the right and the angle increases counter-clockwise.)

Figure 1.12 is an *elevation pattern* that shows the same antenna's directivity but this time at all vertical angles. In this case, the horizon at 0° is located to both sides of the antenna and the zenith (directly overhead) at 90°. The plot shown in Figure 1.12 assumes the presence of ground (drawn from 0° to 0°). The ground reflects or blocks radiation at negative elevation angles, making below-surface radiation plots unnecessary. In free-space, the plot would include the missing semicircle with –90° at the bottom. Without the ground reference, the term "elevation" has little meaning, however.

For amateur work, relative values of field strength (rather than absolute values) are quite adequate in pattern plotting. In other words, it is not necessary to know how many microvolts per meter a particular antenna will produce at a distance of 1 mile when excited with a specified power level. (This is the kind of specification that AM broadcast stations must meet to certify their antenna systems to the FCC.)

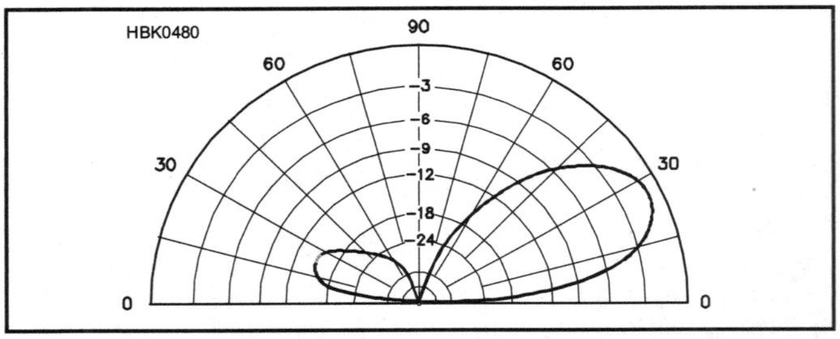

Figure 1.12 — Elevation pattern of a three-element Yagi beam antenna placed ½ wavelength above ground. The Yagi's boom lies on the 0°-0° axis and the elements are perpendicular to the page on the same axis.

Regardless of whether the data is collected by measurements, simulated by computer software, or calculated from theoretical equations, it is common to normalize the plotted values so the field strength in the direction of maximum radiation coincides with the outer edge of the chart. That way, on a given system of polar coordinate scales the shape of the pattern is not altered by proper normalization, only its size. (See the sidebar "Coordinate Scales for Radiation Patterns" later in this chapter for information about how radiation pattern scales are determined.)

Polar Coordinates

It is often helpful to consider the radiation pattern from an antenna in terms of polar coordinates, rather than trying to think in purely linear horizontal or vertical coordinates. The reference axis in the polar system shown in **Figure 1.13** is vertical to the Earth under the antenna. The zenith angle is usually referred to as θ (Greek letter theta) and the azimuth angle is referred to as ϕ (Greek letter phi). Instead of zenith angles, most amateurs are more familiar with elevation angles, where a zenith angle of 0° is the same as an elevation angle of 90°, straight overhead.

E and H-Plane Patterns

You'll also encounter *E-plane* and *H-plane radiation patterns*. These show the antenna's radiation pattern in the plane parallel to the E-field or H-field of the antenna. For antennas with horizontal elements, the E-field is in the horizontal plane so the E-plane radiation pattern is the same as an azimuthal pattern in the plane of the antenna. The H-field is perpendicular to the E-field, so the H-plane pattern is in a plane perpendicular to the E-plane pattern. If the E-plane pattern is an azimuthal pattern, then the H-plane pattern will be an elevation pattern.

It's important to remember that the E-plane and H-plane do not have a fixed relationship to the Earth's surface. For example, the E-plane pattern from a horizontal dipole is an azimuthal pattern but if the same dipole is oriented vertically, the E-plane pattern becomes an elevation pattern. For this reason, most E- and H-plane radiation patterns are created with the antenna in free space.

1.3.5 DIRECTIVITY AND GAIN

Let us now examine directivity more closely. As mentioned previously, all practical antennas, even the simplest types such as dipoles, exhibit directivity. Here's another picture that may help explain the concept of directivity. **Figure 1.14A** shows a balloon blown into its usual spherical shape. This represents a "reference" isotropic source. Squeezing the balloon in the middle in Figure 1.14B produces a dipole-like figure-8 pattern with peak levels at top and bottom larger than the reference sphere. Compare this

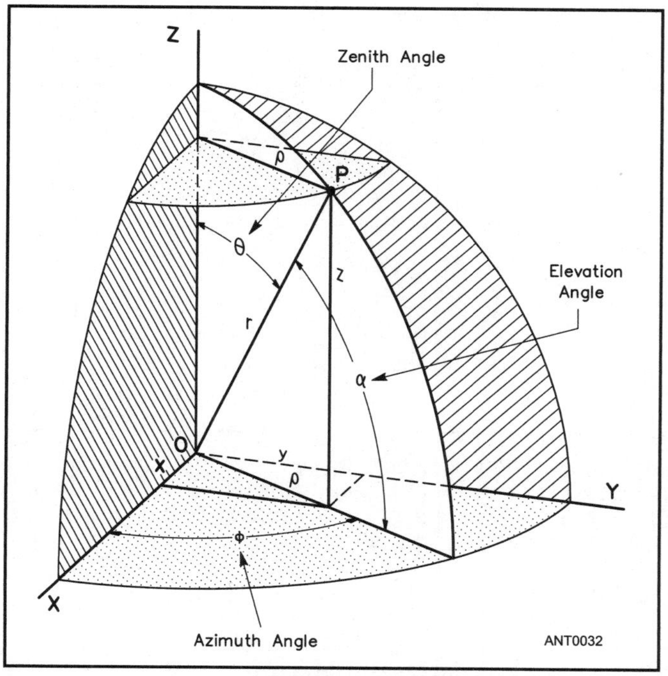

Figure 1.13 — Diagram showing polar representation of a point P lying on an imaginary sphere surrounding a point-source antenna. The various angles associated with the coordinate system are shown referenced to the x, y, and z-axes.

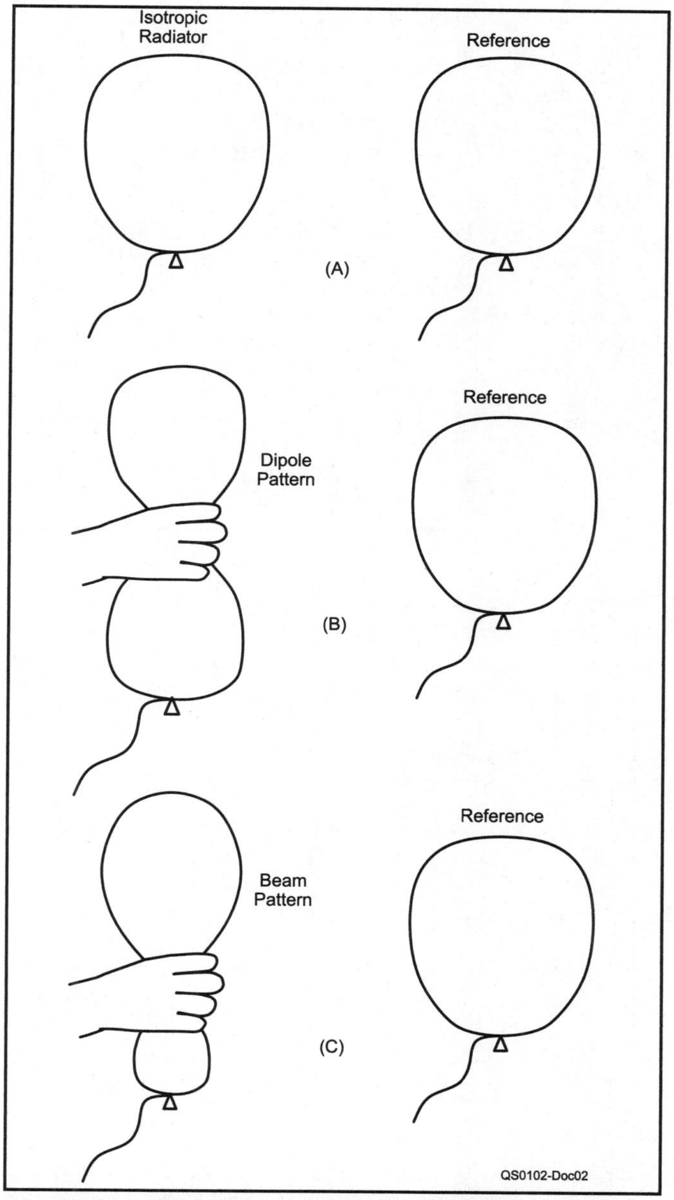

Figure 1.14 — Demonstrating antenna pattern gain with balloons. Take a balloon, blow it up so that it is roughly circular in shape and then declare that this is a radiation pattern from an isotropic radiator. Next, blow up another balloon to the same size and shape and tell the audience that this will be the "reference" antenna (A). Then, squeeze the first balloon in the middle to form a sort of figure-8 shape and declare that this is a dipole and compare the maximum size to that of the reference "antenna" (B). The dipole can be seen to have some "gain" over the reference isotropic. Next, squeeze the end of the first balloon to come up with a sausage-like shape to demonstrate the sort of pattern a beam antenna creates (C).

Coordinate Scales for Radiation Patterns

A number of different systems of coordinate scales or grids are in use for plotting antenna patterns. Antenna patterns published for amateur audiences are sometimes placed on rectangular grids, but more often they are shown using polar coordinate systems. Polar coordinate systems may be divided generally into three classes: linear, logarithmic and modified logarithmic.

A very important point to remember is that the shape of a pattern (its general appearance) is highly dependent on the grid system used for the plotting. This is exemplified in **Figure 1.A**, where the radiation pattern for a beam antenna is presented using three coordinate systems discussed in the paragraphs that follow.

Linear Coordinate Systems

The polar coordinate system in Figure 1.A (part A) uses linear coordinates. The concentric circles are equally spaced, and are graduated from 0 to 10. Such a grid may be used to prepare a linear plot of the power contained in the signal. For ease of comparison, the equally spaced concentric circles have been replaced with appropriately placed circles representing the decibel response, referenced to 0 dB at the outer edge of the plot. In these plots the minor lobes are suppressed. Lobes with peaks more than 15 dB or so below the main lobe disappear completely because of their small size. This is a good way to show the pattern of an array having high directivity and small minor lobes. Linear coordinate patterns are not common, however.

Logarithmic Coordinate System

Another coordinate system used by antenna manufacturers is the logarithmic grid, where the concentric grid lines are spaced according to the logarithm of the voltage in the signal. If the logarithmically spaced concentric circles are replaced with appropriately placed circles representing the decibel response, the decibel circles are graduated linearly. In that sense, the logarithmic grid might be termed a linear-log grid, one having linear divisions calibrated in decibels.

This grid enhances the appearance of the minor lobes. If the intent is to show the radiation pattern of an array supposedly having an omnidirectional response, this grid enhances that appearance. An antenna having a difference of 8 or 10 dB in pattern response around the compass appears to be closer to omnidirectional on this

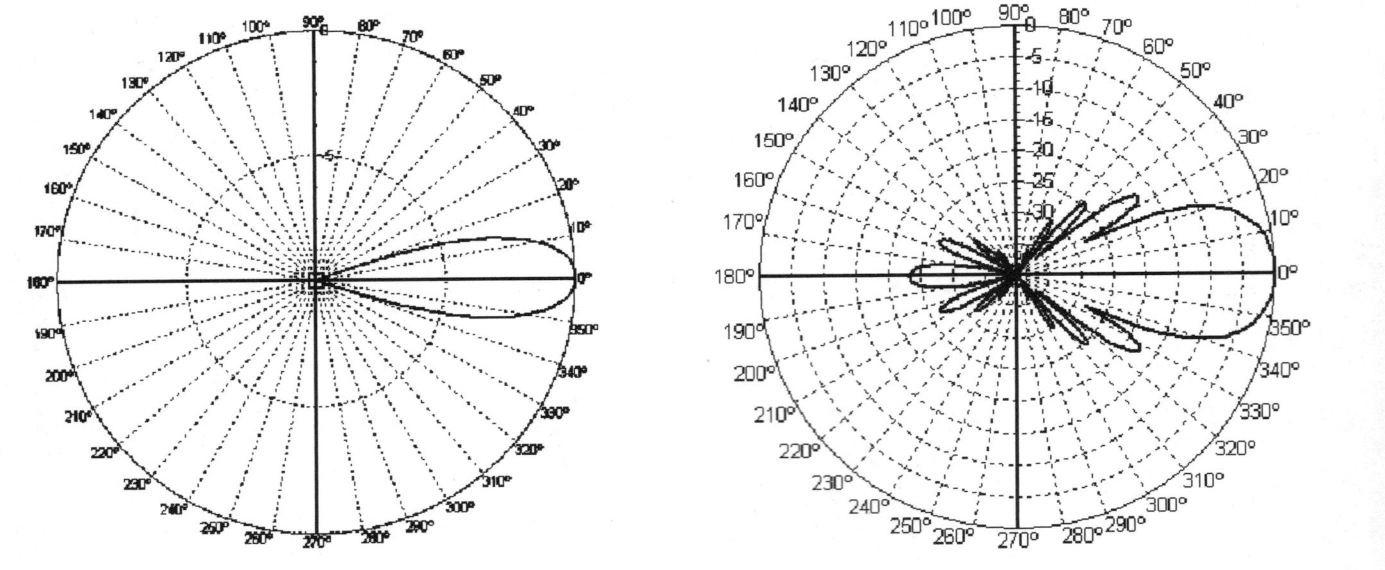

Figure 1.A — Radiation pattern plots for a high-gain Yagi antenna on different grid coordinate systems. At A, the pattern on a linear-power dB grid. Notice how details of side lobe structure are lost with this grid. At B, the same pattern on a grid with constant 5 dB circles. The side lobe level is exaggerated when this scale is employed. At C, the same pattern on the modified log grid used by ARRL. The side and rearward lobes are clearly visible on this grid. The concentric circles in all three grids

grid than on any of the others. See Figure 1.A (part B).

ARRL Log Coordinate System

The modified logarithmic grid used by the ARRL has a system of concentric grid lines spaced according to the logarithm of 0.89 times the value of the signal voltage. In this grid, minor lobes that are 30 and 40 dB down from the main lobe are distinguishable. Such lobes are of concern in VHF and UHF work. The spacing between plotted points at 0 dB and –3 dB is significantly greater than the spacing between –20 and –23 dB, which in turn is significantly greater than the spacing between –50 and –53 dB.

For example, the scale distance covered by 0 to –3 dB is about $\frac{1}{10}$ of the radius of the chart. The scale distance for the next 3-dB increment (to –6 dB) is slightly less, 89% of the first, to be exact. The scale distance for the next 3-dB increment (to –9 dB) is again 89% of the second. The scale is thus constructed so that the innermost two circles represent –36 and –48 dB and the chart center represents –100 dB.

The periodicity of spacing thus corresponds generally to the relative significance of such changes in antenna performance. Antenna pattern plots in this publication are made on the modified-log grid similar to that shown in Figure 1.A (part C).

To construct this pattern in software, the distance of a gain point from the center of the circle = radius × $0.89^{(-g/3)}$, where *radius* is the radius of the pattern's outer ring and g is the normalized gain in dB (g = 0 dB when g = maximum gain). When g is an integer multiple, n, of –3 dB, the distance is 0.89^n, which is equivalent to n times 89%. (Thanks to VA2EW for this formula.)

Rectangular Grid

Antenna radiation patterns can also be plotted on rectangular coordinates with gain on the vertical axis in dB and angle on the horizontal axis as shown in Figure 1.A (part D). Multiple patterns in polar coordinates can be difficult to read, particularly close to the center of the plot. Using a rectangular grid makes it easier to evaluate low-level minor lobes and is especially useful when several antennas are being compared.

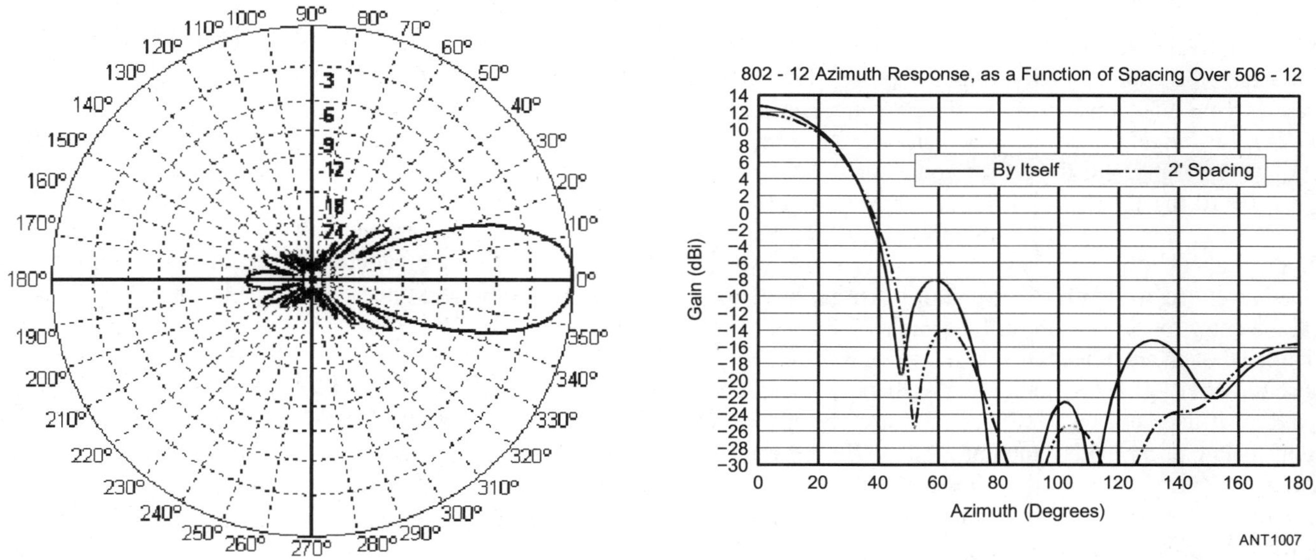

(C) (D)

are graduated in decibels referenced to 0 dB at the outer edge of the chart. The patterns look quite different, yet they all represent the same antenna response! D shows the rectangular azimuthal patterns of two VHF Yagi antennas. This example shows how a rectangular plot allows easier comparison of antenna patterns away from the main lobe.

with Figure 1.14C. Next, squeezing the bottom end of the balloon produces a pattern that gives even more "gain" compared to the reference.

Free-space directivity can be expressed quantitatively by comparing the three-dimensional pattern of the antenna under consideration with the perfectly spherical three-dimensional pattern of an isotropic antenna. For an isotropic antenna, the field strength (and thus power per unit area, or *power density*) is the same everywhere on the surface of an imaginary sphere having a radius of many wavelengths and centered on the antenna. For a directive antenna radiating the same total power as an isotropic antenna and surrounded by the same sphere, the directivity results in greater power density at some points on the sphere and less at others. The ratio of the maximum power density to the average power density taken over the entire sphere (which is the same as from the isotropic antenna under the specified conditions) is the numerical measure of the directivity of the antenna.

$$D = \frac{P}{P_{av}} \tag{6}$$

where
D = directivity
P = power density at its maximum point on the surface of the sphere
P_{av} = average power density

P_{av} is equivalent to the power density from a loss-free isotropic radiator with the same radiated power. D can be expressed in dB with respect to a reference antenna as 10 log [D/D_{ref}]. If the reference antenna is an isotropic antenna, then D_{dBi} = 10 log [D]. If the reference antenna is a dipole, then D_{dBd} = 10 log [D / 1.64]. The term *receive directivity factor* (*RDF*) is also used and is the difference between an antenna's peak gain and gain averaged over all directions. (See the **Receiving and Direction-Finding Antennas** chapter and the entry for Ordy in the Bibliography.)

The *gain* of an antenna is closely related to its directivity. Because directivity is based solely on the shape of the directive pattern, it does not take into account any power losses that may occur in an actual antenna system. To determine gain, these losses must be subtracted from the power supplied to the antenna. The loss is normally a constant percentage of the power input, so the antenna gain is:

$$G = k\frac{P}{P_{av}} = kD \tag{7}$$

where
G = gain (expressed as a power ratio, usually in dB)
D = directivity
k = efficiency (power radiated divided by power input) of the antenna
P and P_{av} are as above

For many of the antenna systems used by amateurs, the efficiency is quite high (the loss amounts to only a few percent of the total). In such cases the gain is essentially equal to the directivity. The more the directive diagram is compressed — or, in common terminology, the sharper the lobe — the greater the power gain of the antenna. This is a natural consequence of the fact that as power is taken away from a larger and larger portion of the sphere surrounding the radiator, it is added to the volume represented by the narrow lobes. Power is therefore concentrated in some directions at the expense of others. In a general way, the smaller the volume of the solid radiation pattern, compared with the volume of a sphere having the same radius as the length of the largest lobe in the actual pattern, the greater the power gain.

As stated above, the gain of an antenna is related to its directivity, and directivity is related to the shape of the directive pattern. A commonly used index of directivity, and therefore the gain of an antenna, is a measure of the width of the major lobe (or lobes) of the plotted pattern. The width is expressed in degrees at the half-power or –3 dB points and is often called the *beamwidth*.

This information provides only a general idea of relative gain, rather than an exact measure. This is because an absolute measure involves knowing the power density at every point on the surface of a sphere, while a single diagram shows the pattern shape in only one plane of that sphere. It is customary to examine at least the E-plane and the H plane patterns before making any comparisons between antennas.

A simple approximation for gain over an isotropic radiator can be used, but only if the side lobes in the antenna's pattern are small compared to the main lobe and if the resistive losses in the antenna are small.

$$G \approx \frac{41253}{H_{3dB} \times E_{3dB}} \tag{8}$$

where H_{3dB} and E_{3dB} are the half-power points, in degrees, for the H and E-plane patterns. When the radiation pattern is complex, numerical integration must be employed to give the actual gain.

1.3.6 RADIATION PATTERN MEASUREMENTS

Given the basic radiation pattern and scales, it becomes easy to define several useful measurements or metrics by which antennas are compared by using their azimuthal patterns.

Because an isotropic antenna has equal gain in all directions it is often used as a reference for gain measurements. Gain with respect to an isotropic antenna is stated as dBi. Another common gain reference is that of a dipole's maximum gain, broadside to the antenna. Gain with respect to this value is noted in dBd. The dipole's maximum gain is 2.15 dB greater than that of the isotropic antenna. To convert from gain given as dBi to dBd, subtract 2.15 dB. Note that to specify gain in dBd, the dipole must be at the same effective height as the antenna being specified. Alternately, the free-space values for gain could be used. Be sure to state clearly which set of values are used.

Next to gain, the most commonly-used metric for directional antennas is the *front-to-back ratio* (*F/B*) or just "front-to-back". This is the difference in dB between the antenna's gain in the specified "forward" direction and in the opposite direction. The front-to-back ratio of the antenna in Figure 1.11 is about 11 dB. *Front-to-side ratio* is also used and is the difference between the antenna's "forward" gain and gain at right angles to the forward direction. This assumes the radiation pattern is symmetric and is of most use to antennas such as Yagis and quads that have elements arranged in parallel planes. The front-to-side ratio of the antenna in Fig 1.11 is more than 30 dB. Because the antenna's rear-ward pattern can have large amplitude variations, the *front-to-rear ratio* is sometimes used. Front-to-rear uses the average of rear-ward gain over a specified angle, usually the 180° semicircle opposite the direction of the antenna's maximum gain, instead of a single gain figure at precisely 180° from the forward direction.

In Fig 1.11, the antenna's beamwidth is about 54°, since the pattern crosses the –3 dB gain scale approximately 27° to either side of the peak direction. Antenna patterns with comparatively small beamwidths are referred to as "sharp" or "narrow."

An antenna with an azimuthal pattern that shows equal gain in all directions is called *omnidirectional*. This is not the same as an isotropic antenna that has equal gain in all directions, both vertical both horizontal.

Because an isotropic antenna has equal gain in all directions it is often used as a reference for gain measurements. Gain with respect to an isotropic antenna is stated as dBi. Another common gain reference is that of a dipole's maximum gain, broadside to the antenna. Gain with respect to this value is noted in dBd. The dipole's maximum gain is 2.15 dB greater than that of the isotropic antenna. To convert from gain given as dBi to dBd, subtract 2.15 dB. Note that to specify gain in dBd, the dipole must be at the same effective height as the antenna being specified. Alternately, the free-space values for gain could be used. Be sure to state clearly which set of values are used.

1.4 ANTENNA POLARIZATION

We've now examined the first two of the three major properties used to characterize antennas: the impedance and the radiation pattern. The third general property is polarization. An antenna's polarization is defined to be that of its electric or E-field, in the direction where the field strength is maximum.

For example, if a half-wavelength dipole is mounted horizontally over the Earth, the electric field is strongest perpendicular to its axis (that is, at right angle to the wire) and parallel to the Earth. Thus, since the maximum electric field is horizontal, the polarization in this case is also considered to be horizontal with respect to the Earth. If the dipole is mounted vertically, its polarization will be vertical. See **Figure 1.15**. Note that if an antenna is mounted in free space, there is no frame of reference and hence its polarization is indeterminate.

Antennas composed of a number of elements arranged so that their axes lie in the same or parallel directions have the same polarization as that of any one of the elements. For example, a system composed of a group of horizontal dipoles is horizontally polarized. If both horizontal and vertical elements are used in the same plane and radiate in phase, however, the polarization is the resultant of the contributions made by each set of elements to the total electromagnetic field at a given point some distance from the antenna. In such a case the resultant polarization is still linear, but is tilted between horizontal and vertical.

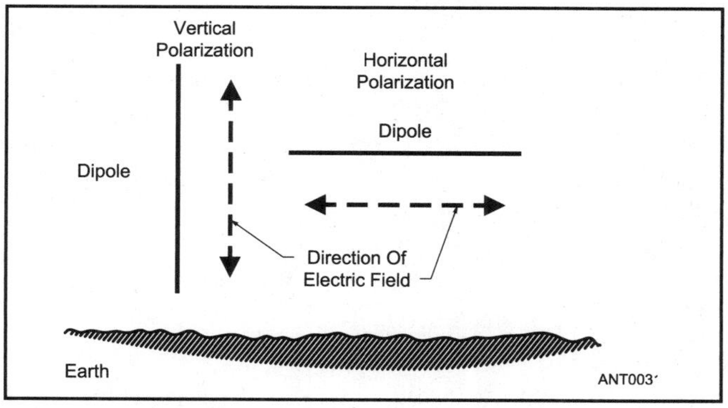

Figure 1.15 — Vertical and horizontal polarization of a dipole above ground. The direction of polarization is the orientation of the electric field in the direction of maximum field strength.

In directions other than those where the radiation is maximum, the resultant wave even for a simple dipole is a combination of horizontally and vertically polarized components. The radiation off the ends of a horizontal dipole is actually vertically polarized, albeit at a greatly reduced amplitude compared to the broadside horizontally polarized radiation — the sense of polarization changes with compass direction.

Circular Polarization

If vertical and horizontal elements in the same plane are fed out of phase (where the beginning of the RF period applied to the feed point of the vertical element is not in time phase with that applied to the horizontal), the resultant polarization is elliptical. Circular polarization is a special case of elliptical polarization. The wave front of a circularly polarized signal appears (to a stationary observer) to rotate every 90° between vertical and horizontal, making a complete 360° rotation once every period. *Instantaneous polarization* is the polarization of the wave at the stationary observer at a specific instant in time. Circular polarization is frequently used for space communications, and is discussed further in the chapter **Antennas for Space Communications**.

Effects of Sky-Wave Propagation

Sky-wave transmission usually changes the polarization of traveling waves. (This is discussed in the chapter **Radio Wave Propagation**.) The polarization of receiving and transmitting antennas in the 3 to 30 MHz range, where almost all communication is by means of sky wave, need not be the same at both ends of a communication circuit (except for distances of a few miles). In this range the choice of polarization for the antenna is usually determined by factors such as the height of available antenna supports, polarization of man-made RF noise from nearby sources, probable energy losses in nearby objects, the likelihood of interfering with neighborhood electronics and general convenience.

1.5 OTHER ANTENNA CHARACTERISTICS

Besides the three main characteristics of impedance, directivity and polarization, there are some other useful properties of antennas.

1.5.1 RECIPROCITY IN RECEIVING AND TRANSMITTING

Many of the properties of a resonant antenna used for reception are the same as its properties in transmission. It has the same directive pattern in both cases, and delivers maximum signal to the receiver when the signal comes from a direction in which the antenna has its best response. The impedance of the antenna is the same, at the same point of measurement, in receiving as in transmitting. This is the principle of *reciprocity*.

In the receiving case, the antenna is the source of power delivered to the receiver, rather than the load for a source of power (as in transmitting). Maximum possible output from the receiving antenna is obtained when the load to which the antenna is connected is the same as the feed point impedance of the antenna. We then say that the antenna is matched to its load.

The power gain in receiving is the same as the gain in transmitting, when certain conditions are met. One such condition is that both antennas must work into load impedances matched to their own impedances, so that maximum power is transferred in both cases. In addition, the comparison antenna should be oriented so it gives maximum response to the signal used in the test. That is, it should have the same polarization as the incoming signal and should be placed so its direction of maximum gain is toward the signal source.

In long-distance transmission and reception via the ionosphere, the relationship between receiving and transmitting, however, may not be exactly reciprocal. This is because the waves do not always follow exactly the same paths at all times and so may show considerable variation in the time between alternations between transmitting and receiving. Also, when more than one ionospheric layer is involved in the wave travel (see the chapter **Radio Wave Propagation**), it is sometimes possible for reception to be good in one direction and poor in the other over the same path.

Wave polarization usually shifts in the ionosphere. The tendency is for the arriving wave to be elliptically polarized, regardless of the polarization of the transmitting antenna. Vertically polarized antennas can be expected to show no more difference between transmission and reception than horizontally polarized antennas. On the average, however, an antenna that transmits well in a certain direction also gives favorable reception from the same direction, despite ionospheric variations.

1.5.2 ANTENNA BANDWIDTH

The *bandwidth* of an antenna refers generally to the range of frequencies over which the antenna can be used to obtain a specified level of performance. The bandwidth can be specified in units of frequency (MHz or kHz) or as a percentage of the antenna's design frequency.

Popular amateur usage of the term antenna bandwidth most often refers to the 2:1 SWR (standing wave ratio) bandwidth, such as, "The 2:1 *SWR bandwidth* is 3.5 to 3.8 MHz" or "The antenna has a 10% SWR bandwidth" or "On 20 meters, the antenna has an SWR bandwidth of 200 kHz." (Standing wave ratio is discussed in the **Transmission Lines** chapter.) Other specific bandwidth terms are also used, such as the *gain bandwidth* (the bandwidth over which gain is greater than a specified level) and the *front-to-back ratio bandwidth* (the bandwidth over which front-to-back ratio is greater than a specified level).

As operating frequency is lowered, an equivalent bandwidth in percentage becomes narrower in terms of frequency range in kHz or MHz. For example, a 5% bandwidth at 21 MHz is 1.05 MHz (more than wide enough to cover the whole band) but at 3.75 MHz only 187.5 kHz! Because of the wide percentage bandwidth of the lower frequency bands (160 meters is 10.5% wide, 80 meters is 13.4% wide) it is difficult to design an antenna with a bandwidth that covers the whole band.

It is important to recognize that SWR bandwidth does not always relate directly to gain bandwidth. Depending on the amount of feed line loss, an 80 meter dipole with a relatively narrow 2:1 SWR bandwidth can still radiate a good signal at each end of the band, provided that an antenna tuner is used to allow the transmitter to load properly. Broadbanding techniques, such as fanning the far ends of a dipole to simulate a conical type of dipole, can help broaden the SWR bandwidth.

Q of Antennas

As with circuits, antennas can also be considered to have Q which affects their SWR bandwidth. In an antenna, Q is a measure of how much energy is stored compared to how much is radiated during each cycle. Higher values of Q can result from low radiation resistance, as is the case for electrically small antennas, and result in reduced antenna bandwidth. High-Q antennas often have high voltage and currents due to the high stored energy, just as high-Q LC circuits have high voltages and circulating currents. This is discussed in detail in the paper by Yaghjian and Best, "Impedance, Bandwidth and Q of Antennas," listed in the Bibliography section of this chapter. Because of the high stored energy, high-Q antennas can create hazardous E and H field strengths in their near field. When using power levels of more than a few watts with a high-Q antenna, be cautious about people being close to the antenna.

1.5.3 FREQUENCY SCALING

Any antenna design can be scaled in size for use on another frequency or on another amateur band. The dimensions of the antenna may be scaled with Eq 9 below.

$$D = \frac{f1}{f2} \times d \qquad (9)$$

where

D = scaled dimension
d = original design dimension
f1 = original design frequency
f2 = scaled frequency (frequency of intended operation)

From this equation, a published antenna design for, say, 14 MHz can be scaled in size and constructed for operation on 18 MHz, or any other desired band. Similarly, an antenna design could be developed experimentally at VHF or UHF and then scaled for operation in one of the HF bands. For example, from Eq 9, an element of 39.0 inches length at 144 MHz would be scaled to 14 MHz as follows: D = 144/14 × 39 = 401.1 inches, or 33.43 feet.

To scale an antenna properly, all physical dimensions must be scaled, including element lengths, element spacings, boom diameters and element diameters. Lengths and spacings may be scaled in a straightforward manner as in the above example, but element diameters are often not as conveniently scaled. For example, assume a 14 MHz antenna is modeled at 144 MHz and perfected with ⅜-inch cylindrical elements. For proper scaling to 14 MHz, the elements should be cylindrical, of 144/14 × ⅜ or 3.86 inches diameter. From a realistic standpoint, a 4-inch diameter might be acceptable, but cylindrical elements of 4-inch diameter in lengths of 33 feet or so would be quite unwieldy (and quite expensive, not to mention heavy). Choosing another, more suitable diameter is the only practical answer.

Diameter Scaling

Simply changing the diameter of dipole type elements during the scaling process is not satisfactory without making a corresponding element-length correction. This is because changing the diameter results in a change in the length/diameter (l/d) ratio from the original design, and this alters the corresponding resonant frequency of the element. The element length must be corrected to compensate for the effect of the different diameter actually used.

To be more precise, however, the purpose of diameter scaling is not to maintain the same resonant frequency for the element, but to maintain the same ratio of self-resistance to self-reactance at the operating frequency — that is, the Q of the scaled element should be the same as that of the original element. This is not always possible to achieve exactly for elements that use several telescoping sections of tubing.

Tapered Elements

Rotatable beam antennas are usually constructed with elements made of metal tubing. The general practice at HF is to taper the elements with lengths of telescoping tubing. The center section has a large diameter, but the ends are relatively small. This reduces not only the weight, but also the cost of materials for the elements. Tapering of HF Yagi elements is discussed in detail in the chapter on **HF Yagi and Quad Antennas**.

Length Correction for Tapered Elements

The effect of tapering an element is to alter its electrical length. That is to say, two elements of the same length, one cylindrical and one tapered but with the same average diameter as the cylindrical element, will not be resonant at the same frequency. The tapered element must be made longer than the cylindrical element for the same resonant frequency.

A procedure for calculating the length for tapered elements has been worked out by Dave Leeson, W6NL, from work done by Schelkunoff at Bell Labs and is presented in Leeson's book, *Physical Design of Yagi Antennas*. On the *ARRL Antenna Book* website is a subroutine called *EFFLEN.FOR*. It is written in Fortran and is used in the *SCALE* program to compute the effective length of a tapered element. The algorithm uses the Leeson-Schelkunoff algorithm and is commented step-by-step to show what is happening. Calculations are made for only one half of an element, assuming the element is symmetrical about the point of boom attachment.

Also, read the documentation SCALE.PDF for the *SCALE* program, which will automatically do the complex mathematics to scale a Yagi design from one frequency to another, or from one taper schedule to another. (Both *SCALE* and EFFLEN.FOR are available for download from **www.arrl.org/antenna-book-reference**.)

1.5.4 EFFECTIVE RADIATED POWER (ERP)

In many instances it is important to evaluate the effectiveness of the total antenna system from the transmitter to the radiated signal. This is done by computing the system's *effective radiated power* (*ERP*). ERP is calculated by beginning with the *transmitter power output* (*TPO*), subtracting attenuation in the transmission line and all losses from connectors or other devices between the transmitter and antenna, and then adding the antenna gain. All of the gain and loss values are stated in decibels so that the calculations are straightforward additions and subtractions. If antenna gain is specified in dBi (decibels with respect to an isotropic antenna), the result is EIRP — Effective Isotropic Radiated Power. ERP and EIRP calculations are most often used in Amateur Radio in association with frequency coordination as described in the **Repeater Antenna Systems** chapter.

Here is an example calculation of a typical repeater antenna system
TPO = 100 watts = 50 dBm
Transmission line attenuation = 2.4 dB
Losses in RF connectors and antenna coupling network = 1.7 dB
Antenna gain = 7.5 dBi
EIRP = 50 dBm – 2.4 dB – 1.7 dB + 7.5 dB = 53.4 dBm = 219 watts

1.6 RF RADIATION AND ELECTROMAGNETIC FIELD SAFETY

Amateur Radio is basically a safe activity. In recent years, however, there has been considerable discussion and concern about the possible hazards of electromagnetic radiation (EMR), including both RF energy and power-frequency (50-60 Hz) electromagnetic (EM) fields. FCC regulations set limits on the maximum permissible exposure (MPE) allowed from the operation of radio transmitters. These regulations do not take the place of RF-safety practices, however. This section deals with the topic of RF safety.

This section was prepared by members of the ARRL RF Safety Committee and coordinated by Dr Robert E. Gold, WBØKIZ. It summarizes what is now known and offers safety precautions based on the research to date.

All life on Earth has adapted to survive in an environment of weak, natural, low-frequency electromagnetic fields (in addition to the Earth's static geomagnetic field). Natural low-frequency EM fields come from two main sources: the sun and thunderstorm activity. But in the last 100 years, man-made fields at much higher intensities and with a very different spectral distribution have altered this natural EM background in ways that are not yet fully understood. Researchers continue to look at the effects of RF exposure over a wide range of frequencies and levels.

Both RF and 60-Hz fields are classified as *nonionizing radiation,* because the frequency is too low for there to be enough photon energy to ionize atoms. (*Ionizing radiation*, such as X-rays, gamma rays and even some ultraviolet radiation has enough energy to knock electrons loose from their atoms. When this happens, positive and negative ions are formed.) Still, at sufficiently high power densities, EMR poses certain health hazards. It has been known since the early days of radio that RF energy can cause injuries by heating body tissue. (Anyone who has ever touched an improperly grounded radio chassis or energized antenna and received an *RF burn* will agree that this type of injury can be quite painful.) In extreme cases, RF-induced heating in the eye can result in cataract formation, and can even cause blindness. Excessive RF heating of the reproductive organs can cause sterility. Other health problems also can result from RF heating. These heat-related health hazards are called *thermal effects.* A microwave oven is a positive application of this thermal effect.

There also have been observations of changes in physiological function in the presence of RF energy levels that are too low to cause heating. These functions return to normal when the field is removed. Although research is ongoing, no harmful health consequences have been linked to these changes.

In addition to the ongoing research, much else has been done to address this issue. For example, FCC regulations set limits on exposure from radio transmitters. The Institute of Electrical and Electronics Engineers, the American National Standards Institute and the National Council for Radiation Protection and Measurement, among others, have recommended voluntary guidelines to limit human exposure to RF energy. The ARRL has established the RF Safety Committee, consisting of concerned medical doctors and scientists, serving voluntarily to monitor scientific research in the fields and to recommend safe practices for radio amateurs.

1.6.1 THERMAL EFFECTS OF RF ENERGY

Body tissues that are subjected to *very high* levels of RF energy may suffer serious heat damage. These effects depend on the frequency of the energy, the power density of the RF field that strikes the body and factors such as the polarization of the wave.

At frequencies near the body's natural resonant frequency, RF energy is absorbed more efficiently, and an increase in heating occurs. In adults, this frequency usually is about 35 MHz if the person is grounded, and about 70 MHz if insulated from the ground. Individual body parts may be resonant at different frequencies. The adult head, for example, is resonant around 400 MHz, while a baby's smaller head resonates near 700 MHz. Body size thus determines the frequency at which most RF energy is absorbed. As the frequency is moved farther from resonance, less RF heating generally occurs. *Specific absorption rate (SAR)* is a term that describes the rate at which RF energy is absorbed in tissue.

Maximum permissible exposure (MPE) limits are based on whole-body SAR values, with additional safety factors included as part of the standards and regulations. This helps explain why these safe exposure limits vary with frequency. The MPE limits define the maximum electric and magnetic field strengths or the plane-wave equivalent power densities associated with these fields, that a person may be exposed to without harmful effect — and with an acceptable safety factor. The regulations assume that a person exposed to a specified (safe) MPE level also will experience a safe SAR.

Nevertheless, thermal effects of RF energy should not be a major concern for most radio amateurs, because of the power levels we normally use and the intermittent nature of most amateur transmissions. Amateurs spend more time listening than transmitting, and many amateur transmissions such as CW and SSB use low-duty-cycle modes. (With FM or RTTY, though, the RF is present continuously at its maximum level during each transmission.) In any event, it is rare for radio amateurs to be subjected to RF fields strong enough to produce thermal effects, unless they are close to an energized antenna or un-shielded power amplifier. Specific suggestions for avoiding excessive exposure are offered later in this chapter.

1.6.2 ATHERMAL EFFECTS OF EMR

Research about possible health effects resulting from exposure to the lower level energy fields, the athermal effects, has been of two basic types: epidemiological research and laboratory research.

Scientists conduct laboratory research into biological mechanisms by which EMR may affect animals including humans. Epidemiologists look at the health patterns of large groups of people using statistical methods. These epidemiological studies have been inconclusive. By their basic design, these studies do not demonstrate cause and effect, nor do they postulate mechanisms of disease. Instead, epidemiologists look for associations between an environmental factor and an observed pattern of illness. For example, in the earliest research on malaria, epidemiologists observed the association between populations with high prevalence of the disease and the proximity of mosquito infested swamplands. It was left to the biological and medical scientists to isolate the organism causing malaria in the blood of those with the disease, and identify the same organisms in the mosquito population.

In the case of athermal effects, some studies have identified a weak association between exposure to EMF at home or at work and various malignant conditions including leukemia and brain cancer. A larger number of equally well designed and performed studies, however, have found no association. A risk ratio of between 1.5 and 2.0 has been observed in positive studies (the number of observed cases of malignancy being 1.5 to 2.0 times the "expected" number in the population). Epidemiologists generally regard a risk ratio of 4.0 or greater to be indicative of a strong association between the cause and effect under study. For example, men who smoke one pack of cigarettes per day increase their risk for lung cancer tenfold compared to nonsmokers, and two packs per day increases the risk to more than 25 times the nonsmokers' risk.

Epidemiological research by itself is rarely conclusive, however. Epidemiology only identifies health patterns in groups — it does not ordinarily determine their cause. And there are often confounding factors: Most of us are exposed to many different environmental hazards that may affect our health in various ways. Moreover, not all studies of persons likely to be exposed to high levels of EMR have yielded the same results.

There also has been considerable laboratory research about the biological effects of EMR in recent years. For example, some separate studies have indicated that even fairly low levels of EMR might alter the human body's circadian rhythms, affect the manner in which T lymphocytes function in the immune system and alter the nature of the electrical and chemical signals communicated through the cell membrane and between cells, among other things. Although these studies are intriguing, they do not demonstrate any effect of these low-level fields on the overall organism.

Much of this research has focused on low-frequency magnetic fields, or on RF fields that are keyed, pulsed or modulated at a low audio frequency (often below 100 Hz). Several studies suggested that humans and animals can adapt to the presence of a steady RF carrier more readily than to an intermittent, keyed or modulated energy source.

The results of studies in this area, plus speculations concerning the effect of various types of modulation, were and have remained somewhat controversial. None of the research to date has demonstrated that low-level EMR causes adverse health effects.

Given the fact that there is a great deal of ongoing research to examine the health consequences of exposure to EMF, the American Physical Society (a national group of highly respected scientists) issued a statement in May 1995 based on its review of available data pertaining to the possible connections of cancer to 60-Hz EMF exposure. This report is exhaustive and should be reviewed by anyone with a serious interest in the field. Among its general conclusions were the following:

1. The scientific literature and the reports of reviews by other panels show no consistent, significant link between cancer and power line fields.

2. No plausible biophysical mechanisms for the systematic initiation or promotion of cancer by these extremely weak 60-Hz fields has been identified.

3. While it is impossible to prove that no deleterious health effects occur from exposure to any environmental factor, it is necessary to demonstrate a consistent, significant and causal relationship before one can conclude that such effects do occur.

In a report dated October 31, 1996, a committee of the National Research Council of the National Academy of Sciences has concluded that no clear, convincing evidence exists to show that residential exposures to electric and magnetic fields (EMFs) are a threat to human health.

A National Cancer Institute epidemiological study of residential exposure to magnetic fields and acute lymphoblastic leukemia in children was published in the *New England Journal of Medicine* in July 1997. The exhaustive, seven-year study concludes that if there is any link at all, it is far too weak to be concerned about.

Readers may want to follow this topic as further studies are reported. Amateurs should be aware that exposure to RF and ELF (60 Hz) electromagnetic fields at all power levels and frequencies has not been fully studied under all circumstances. "Prudent avoidance" of any avoidable EMR is always a good idea. Prudent avoidance doesn't mean that amateurs should be fearful of using their equipment. Most amateur operations are well within the MPE limits. If any risk does exist, it will almost surely fall well down on the list of causes that may be harmful to your health (on the other end of the list from your automobile). It does mean, however, that hams should be aware of the potential for exposure from their stations, and take whatever reasonable steps they can take to minimize their own exposure and the exposure of those around them.

FCC RF-Exposure Regulations

FCC regulations control the amount of RF exposure that can result from your station's operation (§§97.13, 97.503, 1.1307 (b)(c)(d), 1.1310 and 2.1093). The regulations set limits on the maximum permissible exposure (MPE) allowed from operation of transmitters in all radio services. They also require that certain types of stations be evaluated to determine if they are in compliance with the MPEs specified in the rules. The FCC has also required that five questions on RF environmental safety practices be added to Novice, Technician and General license examinations.

These rules went into effect on January 1, 1998 for new stations or stations that file a Form 605 application with the FCC. Other existing stations had until September 1, 2000 to be in compliance with the rules.

THE RULES

Maximum Permissible Exposure (MPE)

All radio stations regulated by the FCC must comply with the requirements for MPEs, even QRP stations running only a few watts or less. The MPEs vary with frequency, as shown in **Table A**. MPE limits are specified in maximum electric and magnetic fields for frequencies below 30 MHz, in power density for frequencies above 300 MHz and all three ways for frequencies from 30 to 300 MHz. For compliance purposes, all of these limits must be considered separately. If any single limit is exceeded, the station is not in compliance.

The regulations control human exposure to RF fields, not the strength of RF fields. There is no limit to how strong a field can be as long as no one is being exposed to it, although FCC regulations require that amateurs use the minimum necessary power at all times (§97.311 [a]).

Environments

The FCC has defined two exposure environments — controlled and uncontrolled. A controlled environment is one in which the people who are being exposed are aware of that exposure and can take steps to minimize that exposure, if appropriate. In an uncontrolled environment, the people being exposed are not normally aware of the exposure. The uncontrolled environment limits are more stringent than the controlled environment limits.

Although the controlled environment is usually intended as an occupational environment, the FCC has determined that it generally applies to amateur operators and members of their immediate households. In most cases, controlled-environment limits can be applied to

Table A — (From §1.1310) Limits for Maximum Permissible Exposure (MPE)

(A) Limits for Occupational/Controlled Exposure

Frequency Range (MHz)	*Electric Field Strength (V/m)*	*Magnetic Field Strength (A/m)*	*Power Density (mW/cm^2)*	*Averaging Time (minutes)*
0.3-3.0	614	1.63	(100)*	6
3.0-30	1842/f	4.89/f	($900/f^2$)*	6
30-300	61.4	0.163	1.0	6
300-1500	—	—	f/300	6
1500-100,000	—	—	5	6

f = frequency in MHz
* = Plane-wave equivalent power density (see Note 1).

(B) Limits for General Population/Uncontrolled Exposure

Frequency Range (MHz)	*Electric Field Strength (V/m)*	*Magnetic Field Strength (A/m)*	*Power Density (mW/cm^2)*	*Averaging Time (minutes)*
0.3-1.34	614	1.63	(100)*	30
1.34-30	824/f	2.19/f	($180/f^2$)*	30
30-300	27.5	0.073	0.2	30
300-1500	—	—	f/1500	30
1500-100,000	—	—	1.0	30

f = frequency in MHz
* = Plane-wave equivalent power density (see Note 1).
Note 1: This means the equivalent far-field strength that would have the E or H-field component calculated or measured. It does not apply well in the near field of an antenna. The equivalent far-field power density can be found in the near or far field regions from the relationships: $P_d = |E_{total}|^2 / 3770$ mW/cm^2 or from $P_d = |H_{total}|^2 \times 37.7$ mW/cm^2.

your home and property to which you can control physical access. The uncontrolled environment is intended for areas that are accessible by the general public, such as your neighbors' properties.

The MPE levels are based on average exposure. An averaging time of 6 minutes is used for controlled exposure; an averaging period of 30 minutes is used for uncontrolled exposure.

Station Evaluations

The FCC requires that certain amateur stations be evaluated for compliance with the MPEs. Although an amateur can have someone else do the evaluation, it is not difficult for hams to evaluate their own stations. The ARRL book *RF Exposure and You* contains extensive information about the regulations and a large chapter of tables that show compliance distances for specific antennas and power levels. Generally, hams will use these tables to evaluate their stations. Some of these tables have been included in the FCC's information — OET Bulletin 65 and its Supplement B. If hams choose, however, they can do more extensive calculations, use a computer to model their antenna and exposure, or make actual measurements.

Table B — Power Thresholds for Routine Evaluation of Amateur Radio Stations

Wavelength Band	*Evaluation Required if Power* (watts) Exceeds:*
MF	
160 m	500
HF	
80 m	500
75 m	500
40 m	500
30 m	425
20 m	225
17 m	125
15 m	100
12 m	75
10 m	50
VHF	
All bands	50
UHF	
70 cm	70
33 cm	150
23 cm	200
13 cm	250
SHF	
All bands	250
EHF	
All bands	250

Repeater stations (all bands)
Non-building-mounted antennas: Height above ground level to lowest point of antenna < 10 m and power > 500 W ERP
Building-mounted antennas: Power > 500 W ERP

*Transmitter power = Peak-envelope power input to antenna. For repeater stations *only,* power exclusion based on ERP (effective radiated power).

Categorical Exemptions

Some types of amateur stations do not need to be evaluated, but these stations must still comply with the MPE limits. The station licensee remains responsible for ensuring that the station meets these requirements.

The FCC has exempted these stations from the evaluation requirement because their output power, operating mode and frequency are such that they are presumed to be in compliance with the rules.

Stations using power equal to or less than the levels in **Table B** do not have to be evaluated. For the 100-W HF ham station, for example, an evaluation would be required only on 12 and 10 meters.

Hand-held radios and vehicle-mounted mobile radios that operate using a push-to-talk (PTT) button are also categorically exempt from performing the routine evaluation. Repeater stations that use less than 500 W ERP or those with antennas not mounted on buildings, if the antenna is at least 10 meters off the ground, also do not need to be evaluated.

Correcting Problems

Most hams are already in compliance with the MPE requirements. Some amateurs, especially those using indoor antennas or high-power, high-duty-cycle modes such as a RTTY bulletin station and specialized stations for moonbounce operations and the like may need to make adjustments to their station or operation to be in compliance.

The FCC permits amateurs considerable flexibility in complying with these regulations. As an example, hams can adjust their operating frequency, mode or power to comply with the MPE limits. They can also adjust their operating habits or control the direction their antenna is pointing.

More Information

This discussion offers only an overview of this topic; additional information can be found in *RF Exposure and You* and on the ARRL website at **www.arrl.org/rf-exposure-regulations-news**. The ARRL website also has links to the FCC website, as well as OET Bulletin 65 and Supplement B and links to software that hams can use to evaluate their stations.

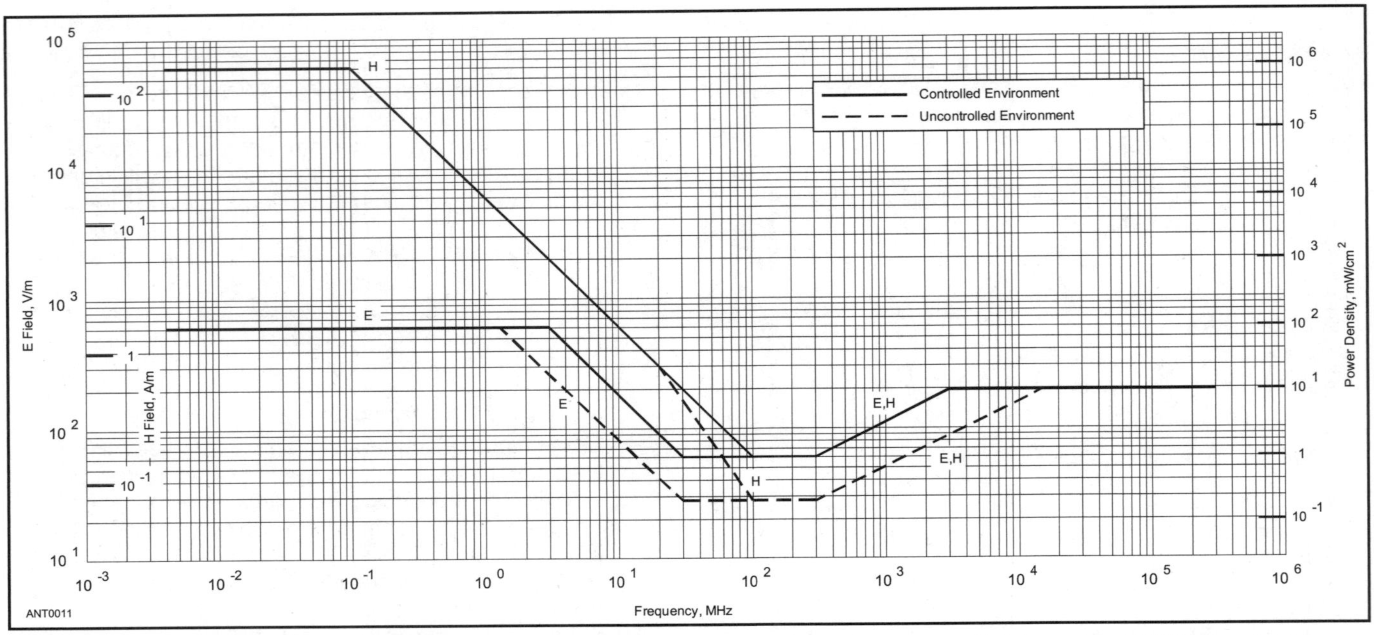

Figure 1.16 — 1991 RF protection guidelines for body exposure of humans. It is known officially as the "IEEE Standard for Safety Levels with Respect to Human Exposure to Radio Frequency Electromagnetic Fields, 3 kHz to 300 GHz."

Safe Exposure Levels

How much EM energy is safe? Scientists and regulators have devoted a great deal of effort to deciding upon safe RF-exposure limits. This is a very complex problem, involving difficult public health and economic considerations. The recommended safe levels have been revised downward several times over the years — and not all scientific bodies agree on this question even today. An Institute of Electrical and Electronics Engineers (IEEE) standard for recommended EM exposure limits was published in 1991 (see Bibliography). It replaced a 1982 American National Standards Institute (ANSI) standard. In the new standard, most of the permitted exposure levels were revised downward (made more stringent), to better reflect the current research. The new IEEE standard was adopted by ANSI in 1992.

The IEEE standard recommends frequency-dependent and time-dependent maximum permissible exposure levels. Unlike earlier versions of the standard, the 1991 standard recommends different RF exposure limits in controlled environments (that is, where energy levels can be accurately determined and everyone on the premises is aware of the presence of EM fields) and in uncontrolled environments (where energy levels are not known or where people may not be aware of the presence of EM fields). FCC regulations also include controlled/occupational and uncontrolled/general population exposure environments.

The graph in **Figure 1.16** depicts the 1991 IEEE standard. It is necessarily a complex graph, because the standards differ not only for controlled and uncontrolled environments but also for electric (E) fields and magnetic (H) fields. Basically, the lowest E-field exposure limits occur at frequencies between 30 and 300 MHz. The lowest H-field exposure levels occur at 100-300 MHz. The ANSI standard sets the maximum E-field limits between 30 and 300 MHz at a power density of 1 mW/cm^2 (61.4 V/m) in controlled environments — but at one-fifth that level (0.2 mW/cm^2 or 27.5 V/m) in uncontrolled environments. The H-field limit drops to 1 mW/cm^2 (0.163 A/m) at 100-300 MHz in controlled environments and 0.2 mW/cm^2 (0.0728 A/m) in uncontrolled environments. Higher power densities are permitted at frequencies below 30 MHz (below 100 MHz for H fields) and above 300 MHz, based on the concept that the body will not be resonant at those frequencies and will therefore absorb less energy.

In general, the 1991 IEEE standard requires averaging the power level over time periods ranging from 6 to 30 minutes for power-density calculations, depending on the frequency and other variables. The ANSI exposure limits for uncontrolled environments are lower than those for controlled environments, but to compensate for that the standard allows exposure levels in those environments to be averaged over much longer time periods (generally 30 minutes). This long averaging time means that an intermittently operating RF source (such as an Amateur Radio transmitter) will show a much lower power density than a continuous-duty station — for a given power level and antenna configuration.

Time averaging is based on the concept that the human body can withstand a greater rate of body heating (and thus, a higher level of RF energy) for a short time than for a longer period. Time averaging may not be appropriate, however, when considering nonthermal effects of RF energy.

The IEEE standard excludes any transmitter with an output below 7 W because such low-power transmitters would not be able to produce significant whole-body heating. (Recent studies show that hand-held transceivers often produce power densities in excess of the IEEE standard within the head.)

There is disagreement within the scientific community about these RF exposure guidelines. The IEEE standard is still intended primarily to deal with thermal effects, not exposure to energy at lower levels. A small but significant number of researchers now believe athermal effects also should be taken into consideration. Several European countries and localities in the United States have adopted stricter standards than the recently updated IEEE standard.

Another national body in the United States, the National Council for Radiation Protection and Measurement (NCRP), also has adopted recommended exposure guidelines. NCRP urges a limit of 0.2 mW/cm^2 for non-occupational exposure in the 30-300 MHz range. The NCRP guideline differs from IEEE in two notable ways: It takes into account the effects of modulation on an RF carrier and it does not exempt transmitters with outputs below 7 W.

The FCC MPE regulations are based on parts of the 1992 IEEE/ANSI standard and recommendations of the National Council for Radiation Protection and Measurement (NCRP). The MPE limits under the regulations are slightly different from the IEEE/ANSI limits. Note that the MPE levels apply to the FCC rules put into effect for radio amateurs on January 1, 1998. These MPE requirements do not reflect and include all the assumptions and exclusions of the IEEE/ANSI standard.

Cardiac Pacemakers and RF Safety

It is a widely held belief that cardiac pacemakers may be adversely affected in their function by exposure to electromagnetic fields. Amateurs with pacemakers may ask whether their operating might endanger themselves or visitors to their shacks who have a pacemaker. Because of this, and similar concerns regarding other sources of electromagnetic fields, pacemaker manufacturers apply design methods that for the most part shield the pacemaker circuitry from even relatively high EM field strengths.

It is recommended that any amateur who has a pacemaker, or is being considered for one, discuss this matter with his or her physician. The physician will probably put the amateur into contact with the technical representative of the pacemaker manufacturer. These representatives are generally excellent resources, and may have data from laboratory or "in the field" studies with specific model pacemakers.

One study examined the function of a modern (dual chamber) pacemaker in and around an Amateur Radio station. The pacemaker generator has circuits that receive and process electrical signals produced by the heart, and also generate electrical signals that stimulate (pace) the heart. In one series of experiments, the pacemaker was connected to a heart simulator. The system was placed on top of the cabinet of a 1-kW HF linear amplifier during SSB and CW operation. In another test, the system was placed in close proximity to several 1 to 5-W 2 meter hand-held transceivers. The test pacemaker was connected to the heart simulator in a third test, and then placed on the ground 9 meters below and 5 meters in front of a three-element Yagi HF antenna. No interference with pacemaker function was observed in these experiments.

Although the possibility of interference cannot be entirely ruled out by these few observations, these tests represent more severe exposure to EM fields than would ordinarily be encountered by an amateur — with an average amount of common sense. Of course, prudence dictates that amateurs with pacemakers, who use hand-held VHF transceivers, keep the antenna as far as possible from the site of the implanted pacemaker generator. They also should use the lowest transmitter output required for adequate communication. For high power HF transmission, the antenna should be as far as possible from the operating position, and all equipment should be properly grounded.

Table 1.1
Typical 60-Hz Magnetic Fields Near Amateur Radio Equipment and AC-Powered Household Appliances
Values are in milligauss.

Item	*Field*	*Distance*
Electric blanket	30-90	Surface
Microwave oven	10-100	Surface
	1-10	12"
Personal computer	5-10	Atop CRT monitor
	0-1	15" from screen
Electric drill	500-2000	At handle
Hair dryer	200-2000	At handle
HF transceiver	10-100	Atop cabinet
	1-5	15" from front
1-kW RF amplifier	80-1000	Atop cabinet
	1-25	15" from front

(Source: measurements made by members of the ARRL RF Safety Committee)

Table 1.2
Typical RF Field Strengths Near Amateur Radio Antennas

A sampling of values as measured by the Federal Communications Commission and Environmental Protection Agency, 1990

Antenna Type	*Freq (MHz)*	*Power (W)*	*E Field (V/m)*	*Location*
Dipole in attic	14.15	100	7-100	In home
Discone in attic	146.5	250	10-27	In home
Half sloper	21.5	1000	50	1 m from base
Dipole at 7-13 ft	7.14	120	8-150	1-2 m from Earth
Vertical	3.8	800	180	0.5 m from base
5-element Yagi	21.2	1000	10-20	In shack
			14	12 m from base at 60 ft
3-element Yagi	28.5	425	8-12	12 m from base at 25 ft
Inverted V	7.23	1400	5-27	Below antenna at 22-46 ft
Vertical on roof	14.11	140	6-9	In house
			35-100	At antenna tuner
Whip on auto roof	146.5	100	22-75	2 m antenna
			15-30	In vehicle
			90	Rear seat
5-element Yagi	50.1	500	37-50	10 m antenna at 20 ft

Low-Frequency Fields

Although the FCC doesn't regulate 60-Hz fields, some recent concern about EMR has focused on low-frequency energy rather than RF. Amateur Radio equipment can be a significant source of low-frequency magnetic fields, although there are many other sources of this kind of energy in the typical home. Magnetic fields can be measured relatively accurately with inexpensive 60-Hz meters that are made by several manufacturers.

Table 1.1 shows typical magnetic field intensities of Amateur Radio equipment and various household items. Because these fields dissipate rapidly with distance, "prudent avoidance" would mean staying perhaps 12 to 18 inches away from most Amateur Radio equipment (and 24 inches from power supplies with 1-kW RF amplifiers).

Determining RF Power Density

Unfortunately, determining the power density of the RF fields generated by an amateur station is not as simple as measuring low-frequency magnetic fields. Although sophisticated instruments can be used to measure RF power densities quite accurately, they are costly and require frequent recalibration. Most amateurs don't have access to such equipment, and the inexpensive field-strength meters that we do have are not suitable for measuring RF power density.

Table 1.2 shows a sampling of measurements made at Amateur Radio stations by the Federal Communications Commission and the Environmental Protection Agency in 1990. As this table indicates, a good antenna well removed from inhabited areas poses no hazard under any of the IEEE/ANSI guidelines. However, the FCC/EPA survey also indicates that amateurs must be careful about using indoor or attic-mounted antennas, mobile antennas, low directional arrays or any other antenna that is close to inhabited areas, especially when moderate to high power is used.

Ideally, before using any antenna that is in close proximity to an inhabited area, you should measure the RF power density. If that is not feasible, the next best option is make the installation as safe as possible by observing the safety suggestions listed in **Table 1.3**.

It also is possible, of course, to calculate the probable power density near an antenna using simple equations. Such calculations have many pitfalls. For one, most of the situations where the power density would be high enough to be of concern are in the near field. In the near field, ground interactions and other variables produce power densities that cannot be determined by simple arithmetic. In the far field, conditions become easier to predict with simple calculations.

The boundary between the near field and the far field depends on the wavelength of the transmitted signal and the physical size and configuration of the antenna. The boundary between the near field and the far field of an antenna can be as much as several wavelengths from the antenna.

Computer antenna-modeling programs are another approach you can use. *MININEC* or other codes derived from *NEC* (Numerical Electromagnetics Code) are suitable for estimating RF magnetic and electric fields around amateur antenna systems.

These models have limitations. Ground interactions must be considered in estimating near-field power densities, and the "correct ground" must be modeled. Computer modeling is generally not sophisticated enough to predict "hot spots" in the near field — places where the field intensity may be far higher than would be expected, due to reflections from

Table 1.3
RF Awareness Guidelines

These guidelines were developed by the ARRL RF Safety Committee, based on the FCC/EPA measurements of Table 1.2 and other data.

- Although antennas on towers (well away from people) pose no exposure problem, make certain that the RF radiation is confined to the antennas' radiating elements themselves. Provide a single, good station ground (earth), and eliminate radiation from transmission lines. Use good coaxial cable or other feed line properly. Avoid serious imbalance in your antenna system and feed line. For high-powered installations, avoid end-fed antennas that come directly into the transmitter area near the operator.
- No person should ever be near any transmitting antenna while it is in use. This is especially true for mobile or ground-mounted vertical antennas. Avoid transmitting with more than 25 W in a VHF mobile installation unless it is possible to first measure the RF fields inside the vehicle. At the 1-kW level, both HF and VHF directional antennas should be at least 35 ft above inhabited areas. Avoid using indoor and attic-mounted antennas if at all possible. If open-wire feeders are used, ensure that it is not possible for people (or animals) to come into accidental contact with the feed line.
- Don't operate high-power amplifiers with the covers removed, especially at VHF/UHF.
- In the UHF/SHF region, never look into the open end of an activated length of waveguide or microwave feed-horn antenna or point it toward anyone. (If you do, you may be exposing your eyes to more than the maximum permissible exposure level of RF radiation.) Never point a high-gain, narrow-bandwidth antenna (a paraboloid, for instance) toward people. Use caution in aiming an EME (moonbounce) array toward the horizon; EME arrays may deliver an effective radiated power of 250,000 W or more.
- With hand-held transceivers, keep the antenna away from your head and use the lowest power possible to maintain communications. Use a separate microphone and hold the rig as far away from you as possible. This will reduce your exposure to the RF energy.
- Don't work on antennas that have RF power applied.
- Don't stand or sit close to a power supply or linear amplifier when the ac power is turned on. Stay at least 24 inches away from power transformers, electrical fans and other sources of high-level 60-Hz magnetic fields.

nearby objects. In addition, "nearby objects" often change or vary with weather or the season, so the model so laboriously crafted may not be representative of the actual situation, by the time it is running on the computer.

Intensely elevated but localized fields often can be detected by professional measuring instruments. These "hot spots" are often found near wiring in the shack, and metal objects such as antenna masts or equipment cabinets. But even with the best instrumentation, these measurements also may be misleading in the near field.

One need not make precise measurements or model the exact antenna system, however, to develop some idea of the relative fields around an antenna. Computer modeling using close approximations of the geometry and power input of the antenna will generally suffice. Those who are familiar with *MININEC* can estimate their power densities by computer modeling, and those who have access to professional power-density meters can make useful measurements.

While our primary concern is ordinarily the intensity of the signal radiated by an antenna, we also should remember that there are other potential energy sources to be considered. You also can be exposed to RF radiation directly from a power amplifier if it is operated without proper shielding. Transmission lines also may radiate a significant amount of energy under some conditions. Poor microwave waveguide joints or improperly assembled connectors are another source of incidental radiation.

Further RF Exposure Suggestions

Potential exposure situations should be taken seriously. Based on the FCC/EPA measurements and other data, the "RF awareness" guidelines of Table 1.3 were developed by the ARRL RF Safety Committee. A longer version of these guidelines, along with a complete list of references, appeared in a *QST* article by Ivan Shulman, MD, WC2S ("Is Amateur Radio Hazardous to Our Health?" *QST*, Oct 1989, pp 31-34). For more information or background, see the list of RF Safety References in the next section.

In addition, the ARRL has published a book, *RF Exposure and You*, that is helping hams comply with the FCC's RF-exposure regulations. The ARRL also maintains an RF-exposure news page on its website. See **www.arrl.org/rf-exposure**. This site contains reprints of selected *QST* articles on RF exposure and links to the FCC and other useful sites.

1.7 BIBLIOGRAPHY

M. Abdallah et al, "Where Does the Far Field of an Antenna Start?," *IEEE Antennas and Propagation Magazine*, Oct 2016, pp 115-124.

C. A. Balanis, *Antenna Theory, Analysis and Design* (New York: Harper & Row, 1982).

L. Blake and M. Long, M., *Antennas: Fundamentals, Design, Measurement*, 3rd Ed., Scitech Publishing, 2009.

R. Collin, *Antennas and Radiowave Propagation*, Mcgraw-Hill College, 1985.

R. Collin and F. Zucker, *Antenna Theory, Part 1 & 2*, McGraw-Hill, 1969.

D. Fleisch, *A Student's Guide to Maxwell's Equations*, Cambridge University Press, 2008.

K. Iizuka, "Antennas for Non-Specialists," *IEEE Antennas and Propagation Magazine*, Feb 2004, pp 65-79, 112.

R. C. Johnson, *Antenna Engineering Handbook*, 3rd ed. (New York: McGraw-Hill, 1993).

E. C. Jordan and K. G. Balmain, *Electromagnetic Waves and Radiating Systems*, 2nd ed. (Englewood Cliffs, NJ: Prentice-Hall, Inc, 1968).

R. W. P. King, *Theory of Linear Antennas* (Cambridge, MA: Harvard Univ. Press, 1956).

J. D. Kraus, *Electromagnetics* (New York: McGraw-Hill Book Co).

J. D. Kraus, *Antennas*, 2nd ed. (New York: McGraw-Hill Book Co, 1988).

J. D. Kraus, "Antennas: Our Electronic Eyes and Ears," *Microwave Journal*, Jan 89, pp 77-92.

K. MacLeish, "Why an Antenna Radiates," *QST*, Nov 92, pp 59-63.

E. A. Laport, *Radio Antenna Engineering* (New York: McGraw-Hill Book Co, 1952).

G. Ordy, **www.seed-solutions.com/gregordy/Amateur%20Radio/Experimentation/RDFMetric.htm**

Ramo and Whinnery, *Fields and Waves in Modern Radio* (New York: John Wiley & Sons).

I. Straus and K. McDonald, "Near and Far Fields - from Statics to Radiation," *Antennex*, 2004.

F. E. Terman, *Radio Engineering*, 3rd ed. (New York: McGraw-Hill, 1947).

G. B. Welch, *Wave Propagation and Antennas* (New York: D. Van Nostrand Co, 1958), pp 180-182.

A. Yaghjian and S. Best, "Impedance, Bandwidth and Q of Antennas," Digest of IEEE Antennas and Propagation Society Symposium, Columbus, Ohio, Vol. 1, June 2003, pp. 501-504.

R. Zavrel, "Radiation Resistance, Feed Point Impedance and Mythology," *QEX*, Mar 2014, p 32.

R. Zavrel, *Antenna Physics: An Introduction*, ARRL, 2016.

Radio Broadcast Ground Systems, available from Smith Electronics, Inc, 8200 Snowville Rd, Cleveland, OH 44141.

TABLE OF CONTENTS

Chapter 2

Dipoles and Monopoles

Dipoles and monopoles are not only popular antennas, they are the basic elements from which most antennas used by amateurs are constructed, including beams. This chapter explores the basic characteristics of these antennas in support of the specific designs the reader will encounter later in the book. Material from previous editions is augmented by contributions from the dipole and vertical chapters of the 5th edition of *ON4UN's Low-Band DXing*.

2.1 DIPOLES

The *dipole* is a fundamental antenna — in its most common form it is about one-half wavelength long at the frequency of use. (See **Figure 2.1**.) Many types of more complex antennas are constructed from elements that approximate dipoles. Its name, di- meaning *two* and -pole meaning *electrical polarity*, describes the opposite voltages on each half of the antenna, creating two electrical halves.

Figure 2.2 shows how the magnitudes of voltage and current vary along a half-wave dipole. The dipole has opposite voltages on either side of center, reaching a maximum at each end. The current at each end of a dipole is zero. If the dipole is one-half wavelength long, the current is maximum at the center. This is the *distribution* of voltage and current. The distribution of current, in particular, determines how a dipole radiates.

If the dipole is *resonant*, the instantaneous waveforms of the voltage and current are exactly in phase. This means that the antenna's feed point impedance is purely resistive with no reactance. Another definition for resonance is that the stored energies in the electric and magnetic fields around the antenna are exactly equal.

2.1.1 EFFECTS OF CONDUCTOR DIAMETER

The physical length of a resonant ½-λ antenna will not be exactly equal to the half wavelength of a radio wave of that frequency in free space, but depends on the thickness of the conductor in relation to the wavelength as shown in **Figure 2.3**. **Table 2.1** gives resonant lengths for dipoles in free space, made of #12 AWG bare copper wire. If thinner wire is used, the resonant length will be a few percent longer, and vice versa.

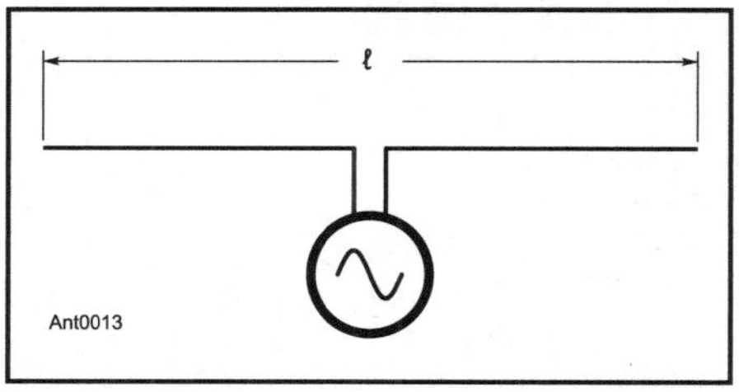

Figure 2.1 — The center-fed dipole antenna. It is assumed that the source of power is directly at the antenna feed point, with no intervening transmission line. Although λ/2 is the most common length for amateur dipoles, the length of a dipole antenna can be any fraction of a wavelength.

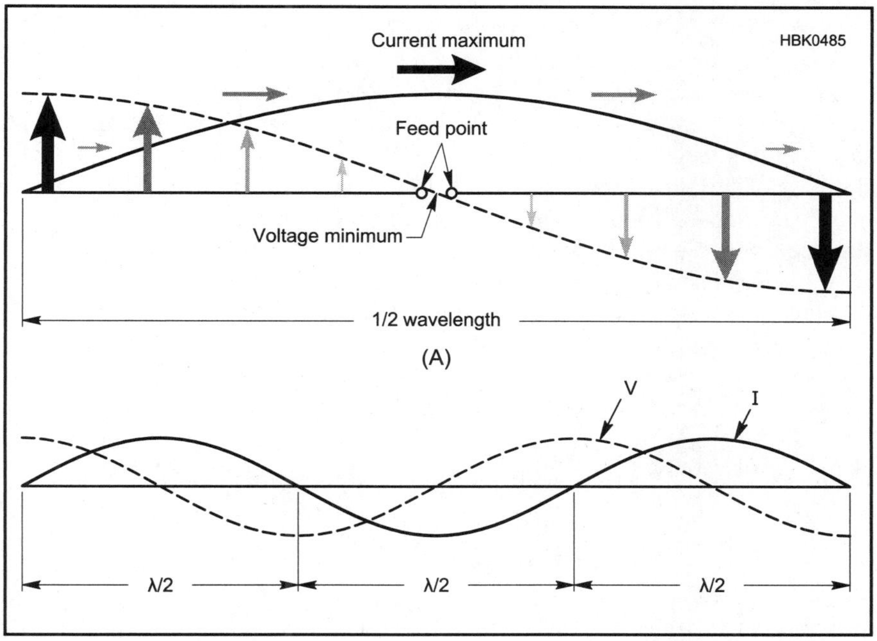

Figure 2.2 — The current and voltage distribution along a half-wave dipole (A) and for an antenna made from a series of half-wave dipoles (B).

Table 2.1
Resonant λ/2 Dipole Lengths in Free Space

Freq (MHz)	*½λ$_{fs}$ (ft)*	*L (ft)*	*L (m)*
1.82	270.3	263.8	80.4
3.6	136.7	133.0	40.5
3.85	127.8	124.4	37.9
5.35	92.0	89.5	27.3
7.15	68.8	66.9	20.4
10.1	48.7	47.3	14.4
14.15	34.8	33.7	10.3
18.1	27.2	26.3	8.0
21.2	23.2	22.5	6.9
24.9	19.8	19.1	5.8
28.3	17.4	16.8	5.1
51	9.6	9.3	2.8

Dipole constructed from #12 AWG bare copper wire
½λ$_{fs}$ is the free-space wavelength computed as 492/f(MHz)

An additional shortening effect occurs with wire antennas supported by insulators at the ends (and at the feed point) because of the capacitance added to the system by the loops of wire through the insulators. This shortening is called *end effect*.

K Factor

Based on the standard value for the speed of light, the wavelength λ of an electromagnetic wave in free-space at frequency *f* is given by:

$$\lambda(\text{in feet}) = \frac{983.571}{f(\text{in MHz})} \tag{1a}$$

and for one-half wavelength:

$$\frac{\lambda}{2}(\text{in feet}) = \frac{491.786}{f(\text{in MHz})} \tag{1b}$$

A dipole with a length of exactly one-half of a free-space wavelength λ/2 has an impedance of 73.079 + *j*42.515 Ω, essentially independent of wire diameter. The dipole must be shortened to achieve resonance where reactance is equal to zero. As the diameter of a conductor increases, its capacitance per unit length increases and inductance per unit length decreases. This increases the ratio of stored electric field energy to magnetic field energy, with the result of lowering the frequency at which the dipole is resonant. Stated another way: For a given frequency, the larger a conductor's diameter, the lower the frequency at which a dipole made of that conductor is resonant.

A dipole's resonant length is given by the product of the free-space half-wavelength and a constant, K:

$$L_{Resonant}(\text{in feet}) = K \times \frac{491.786}{f(\text{in MHz})} \quad \text{or} \tag{2}$$

$$L_{Resonant}(\text{in inches}) = K \times \frac{5901.43}{f(\text{in MHz})}$$

where K is a constant between zero and one, 0 < K < 1, that depends on the dipole's "thickness." There are several ways to express dipole thickness. Antenna builders prefer to specify dipole thickness in terms of the half-wavelength-to-diameter ratio (λ/2)/d because a builder generally knows d and wants to calculate L. (Antenna theorists use the parameter Ω = 2 × ln (2L/d), where ln( ) is the natural logarithm.) The graph in **Figure 2.3** satisfies this need and allows dipole resonant length to be determined for a given physical thickness and frequency. Most half-wavelength dipoles at HF typically have (λ/2)/d ratios in the range of

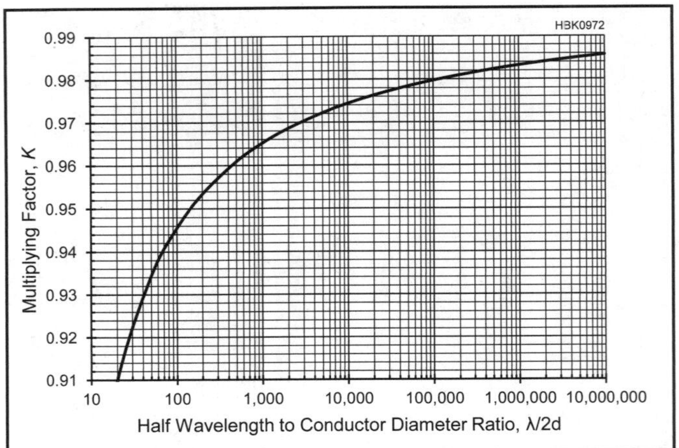

Figure 2.3 — Effect of antenna diameter on length for half-wavelength resonance in free-space, shown as a multiplying factor, K. The thicker the conductor relative to the wavelength, the shorter the physical length of the antenna at resonance. For antennas over ground, additional factors affect the antenna's electrical length.

History of the K Factor Graph

All *ARRL Handbooks* and *Antenna Books* from 1947 through 1996 published a graph of the K factor and dipole resonant resistance. The graphs were based on an early but approximate solution of Hallén's equation due to R.W.P King, F.G. Blake, and C.W. Harrison. Separately, the RSGB published a graph of the K factor based on R.A. Smith (1949) that was based on Schelkunoff's induced EMF (IEMF) equations. However, the ARRL and RSGB graphs did not agree.

In 1996, L.B. Cebik, W4RNL, pointed out that the ARRL's 70-year old K factor graph did not agree with *NEC2* calculations. So, from 1998 to 2018, the ARRL published a revised K factor graph that was based on *NEC2* modeling. Steve Stearns, K6OIK, discovered that although the original graph had overestimated *K*, the revised graph underestimated it! (See the discussion of Method of Moments accuracy in the **Antenna Modeling** chapter.) Consequently, the ARRL published a second revised graph in the 2019 *ARRL Handbook.* The new revised graph, which is shown here in Figure 2.3 and based on Eq 3, is the result of a re-analysis of Schelkunoff and the IEMF method and has been checked against authoritative theory, approximations, and data published by C.T. Tai, R.S. Elliott, and the late R.C. Hansen. — *Contributed by Steve Stearns, K6OIK*

2500 to 25,000 with values of K from 0.97 to 0.98.

While K can be determined exactly from the induced EMF method (see the Bibliography entry for Hansen), K6OIK gives a simple formula for K:

$$K = 1 - \frac{0.225706}{\ln\left(\frac{\lambda/2}{d}\right) - 0.429451} \quad (3)$$

Example 1: A half-wavelength dipole for 7.2 MHz has an uncorrected length of 491.786 / 7.2 = 68.3 feet. If it is made from #12 AWG wire (0.081 inch diameter), it has a (λ/2)/*d* ratio of:

$$\frac{491.786}{7.2}\text{ (ft)} \times \frac{12\text{ in/ft}}{0.081\text{ in}} = 10{,}119$$

From Figure 2.3 or Eq 3, a (λ/2)/d ratio of 10,119 gives K = 0.974. Thus, by Eq 2, the resonant length of the half-wavelength dipole is 0.974 × 68.3 = 66 feet 7 inches.

It should be understood that K is not a velocity factor because it is unrelated to waves or the speed of wave travel. Rather, K arises because if a dipole is exactly one-half wavelength long, the stored energies in the electric and magnetic fields are not exactly equal. A dipole must be shortened to obtain equality and resonance.

The graph shown in Figure 2.3 and Eq 3 were determined by Steve Stearns, K6OIK, who evaluated and compared theoretical and numerical methods for calculating dipole and monopole impedance. (See the Bibliography entries for Stearns, Tai and Long, Elliott, and Schelkunoff.) If better accuracy than the graph is needed, the formula in Eq 3 should be used.

Dipole Length Formulas

For wire dipoles for frequencies at and below 10 MHz and that are made of common wire sizes and are installed at heights of ⅛ to ¼ λ, the traditional "4-6-8" formula is:

$$L(\text{in feet}) = \frac{468}{f(\text{in MHz})} \quad (4)$$

This formula is an approximation that assumes the resonant length is 5% less than a half wavelength, i.e. K = 0.95, independent of wire thickness. 0.95 is outside the range of 0.97 to 0.98 that is typical for HF wire antennas. The next example illustrates the traditional formula.

Example 2: A half-wave dipole for 7200 kHz (7.2 MHz) is 468/7.2 = 65.0 feet. Note the traditional formula results in a dipole length that is 1 foot 7 inches too short compared to the more accurate calculation in Example 1 for the case of #12 AWG wire.

Example 3: Find the resonant length of a half-wave dipole antenna at 50.1 MHz, if the dipole is made of ½-inch diameter tubing. A half wavelength in space is 491.786 / 50.1 = 9.82 ft, and the ratio of half wavelength to conductor diameter (changing wavelength to inches) is (9.82 ft × 12 in/ft) / 0.5 in = 235.6. From Figure 2.3 or Eq 4, K = 0.955 for this ratio. The resonant length of the dipole is therefore 0.955 × 9.82 = 9.376 ft or 9 feet 4.5 inches. Calculated directly in inches, the resonant length is 0.955 × 5901.43 / 50.1 = 112.5 in.

The discussion and examples above are for antennas in free space. The effect of ground is not included. For single-wire HF antennas above ground, the free-space dipole length formulas can be inaccurate, but antenna modeling software can be used to come up with more accurate lengths. (See the **Antenna Modeling** chapter.) However, at VHF and UHF where the wavelength is short and antennas are several wavelengths above ground, the free-space dipole length formulas are accurate and useful.

2.1.2 RADIATION PATTERNS AND EFFECTS OF GROUND

The radiation pattern of a dipole antenna in free space is strongest at right angles to the wire as shown in **Figure**

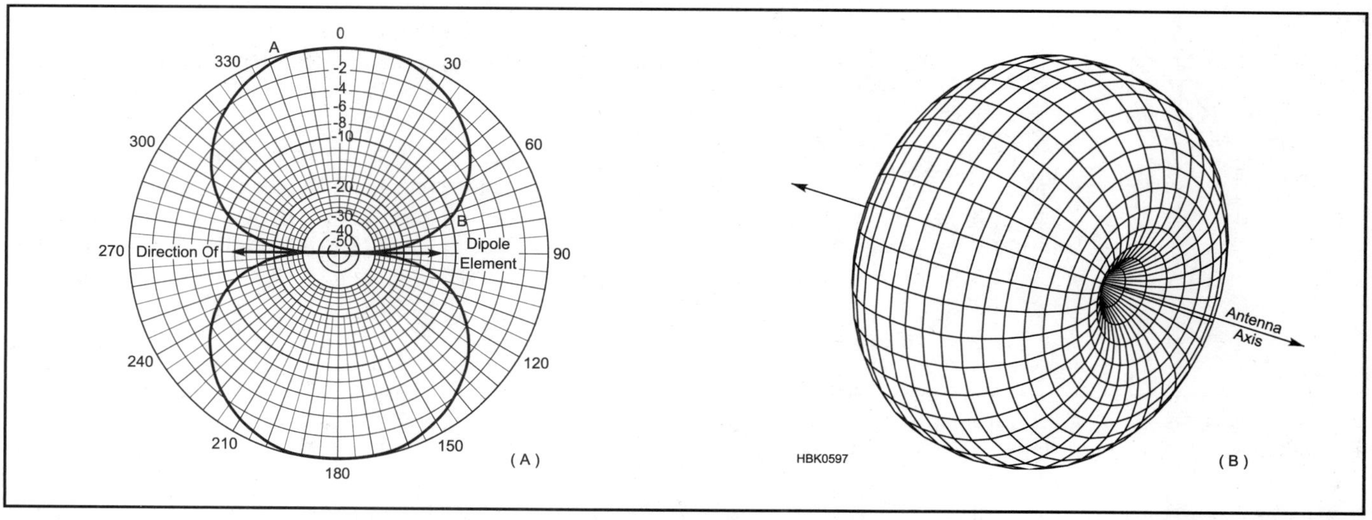

Figure 2.4 — Response of a dipole antenna in free space in the plane of the antenna with the antenna oriented along the 90° to 270° axis (A). The full three-dimensional pattern of the dipole is shown at (B). The pattern at A is a cross-section of the three-dimensional pattern taken directly through the axis of the antenna.

2.4, a free-space radiation pattern. The dipole in free space has a gain of 2.15 dBi.

In an actual installation, the figure-8 pattern is less directive due to reflections from ground and other conducting surfaces. As the dipole is raised to ½ λ or greater above ground, nulls off the ends of the dipole become more pronounced. Sloping the antenna above ground and coupling to the feed line tend to distort the pattern slightly.

As a horizontal dipole is brought closer to ground, reflections from the ground combine with the direct radiation to create lobes at different angles as shown in **Figure 2.5**. In addition, the directivity of the dipole also changes with height. For example, **Figure 2.6** shows the dipole's three-dimensional pattern at a height of ½ λ. The deep null along the axis of the wire in Figure 2.6 is filled in with a substantial amount of radiation.

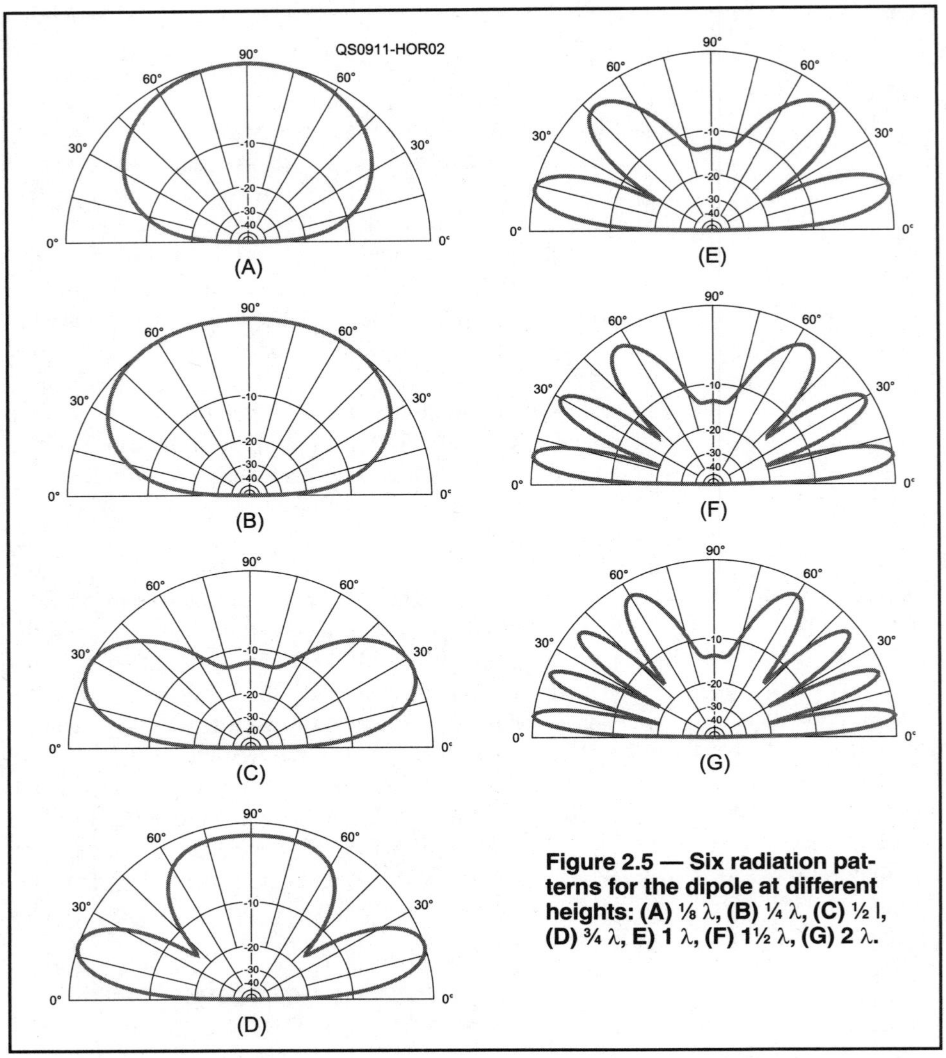

Figure 2.5 — Six radiation patterns for the dipole at different heights: (A) ⅛ λ, (B) ¼ λ, (C) ½ l, (D) ¾ λ, E) 1 λ, (F) 1½ λ, (G) 2 λ.

Figure 2.7 shows the radiation pattern for dipoles at different heights above ground and at four different elevation angles from 15° to 60°. You can see that for low heights (the H = ¼ λ figure) the dipole becomes almost omnidirectional at elevation angles of 60° and higher.

The type of ground under the dipole also affects the radiation pattern. **Figure 2.8** illustrates what happens over two different types of ground; very poor soil (desert) and saltwater. These two types of ground represent the extremes of what amateurs are likely to encounter and most installations will be somewhere in between these two examples.

For antennas over ground, the height above ground also affects the antenna's physical length as in the example of **Table 2.2** showing the resonant, half-wavelength length for a 20 meter dipole at various electrical heights. Nearby conducting surfaces and materials will also affect resonant length.

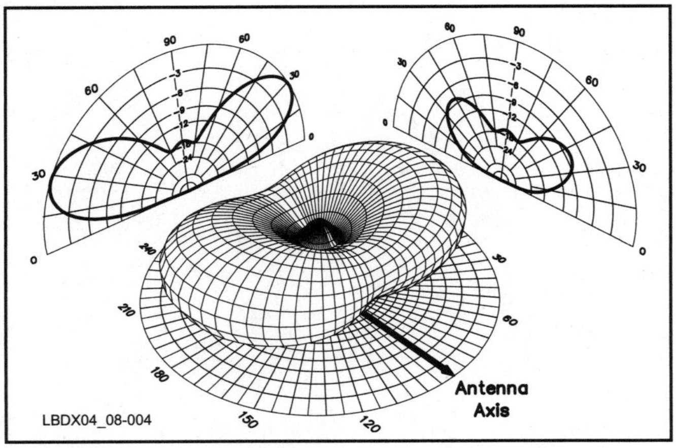

Figure 2.6 — Three-dimensional representation of the radiation patterns of a half-wave dipole, ½ λ above ground.

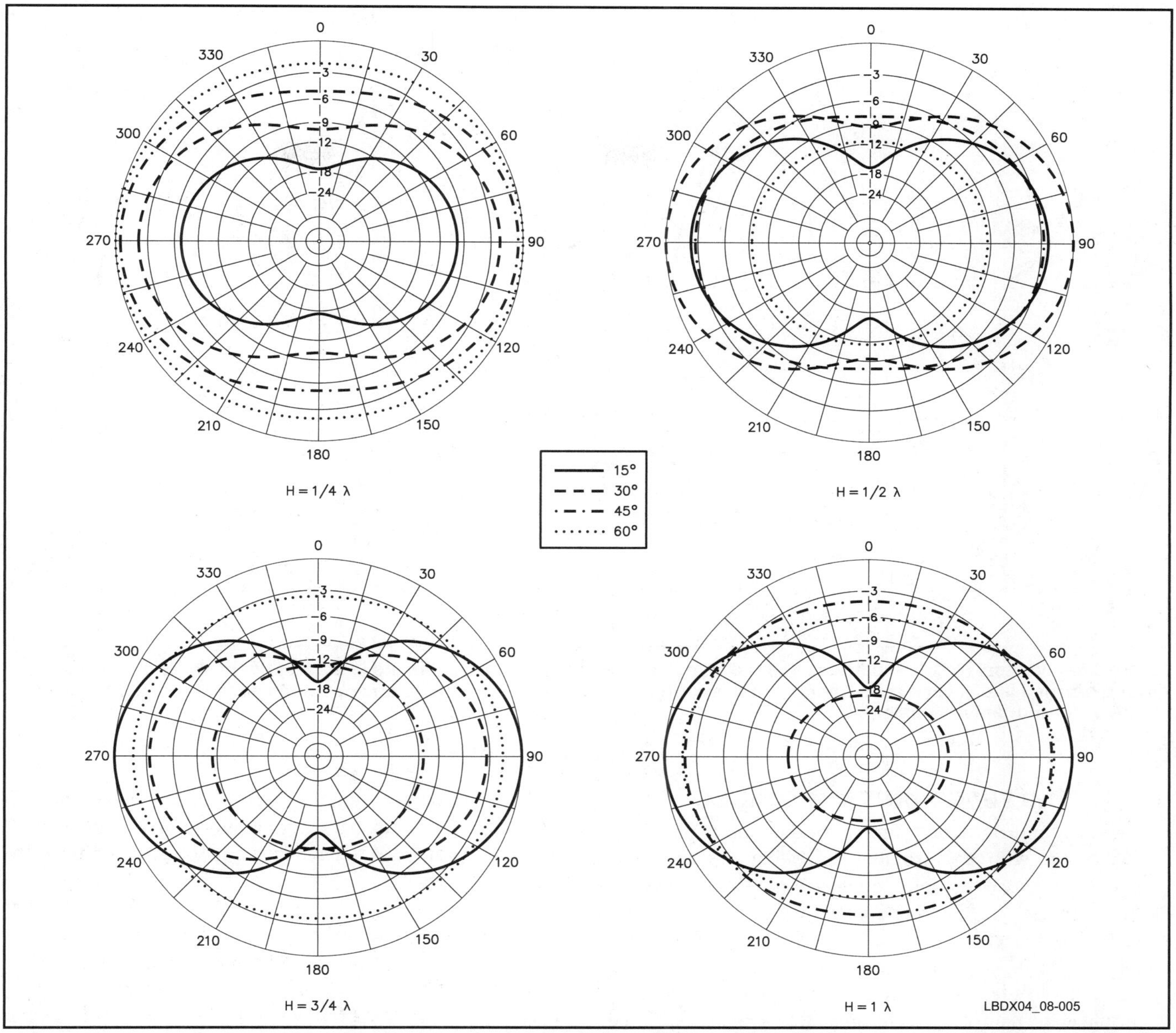

Figure 2.7 — Horizontal radiation pattern for ½-wave horizontal dipole at various heights above ground for wave angles of 15°, 30°, 45° and 60° (modeled over good ground).

Table 2.2
Variation in Dipole Performance with Height

Height in Wavelengths at 14.175 MHz (feet)	*Resonant Length in Feet (L x f)*	*Feed point Impedance in Ω (SWR)*	*Max Gain (dBi) at Angle (Degrees)*
⅛ (8.8)	33.0 (467.8)	31.5 (1.59)	8.3 @ 90
¼ (17.4)	32.9 (466.4)	81.7 (1.63)	6.5 @ 62
½ (34.7)	34.1 (483.4)	69.6 (1.39)	7.9 @ 28
¾ (52.0)	33.4 (473.4)	73.4 (1.47)	7.3 @ 18
1 (69.4)	33.9 (480.5)	71.9 (1.44)	7.7 @ 14
1½ (104.1)	33.8 (479.1)	72.0 (1.44)	7.8 @ 9
2 (138.8)	33.8 (479.1)	72.3 (1.45)	7.9 @ 7

Note: All gain values were calculated using *EZNEC*'s *MININEC* ground. These calculated gains and elevation angles are examples meant to illustrate the large effect that height above ground can have on antenna pattern. They are unlikely to be exactly correct for a real antenna in an actual installation.

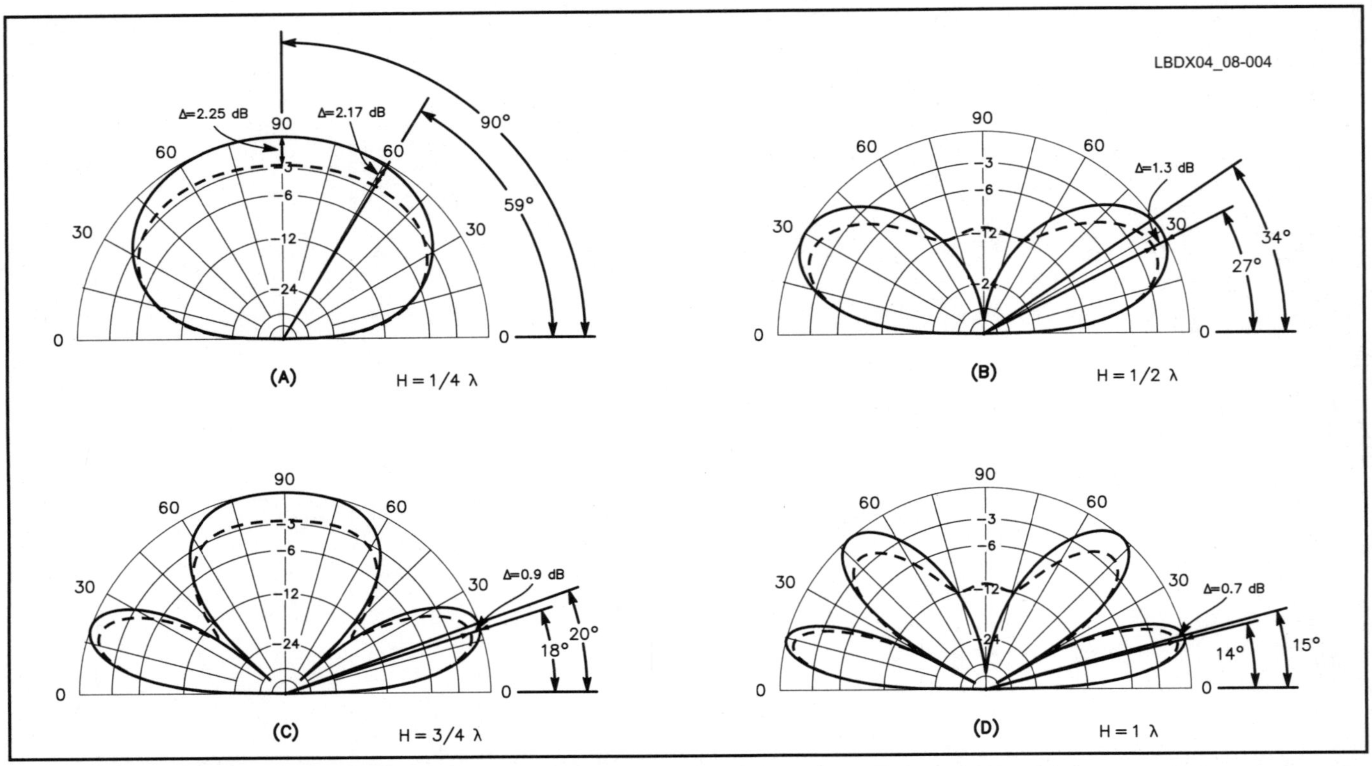

Figure 2.8 — Vertical radiation patterns over two types of ground: saltwater (solid line in each set of plots) and very poor ground (dashed line in each set of plots). The wave angles as well as the gain difference between saltwater and poor ground are given for four antenna heights.

2.1.3 FEED POINT IMPEDANCE

A feed line is attached directly to the dipole, generally at the center with an insulator separating the antenna's conductor into two sections. Such a dipole is referred to as being *center-fed*. One conductor of the feed line is attached to each section. The point at which the feed line is attached is the dipole's *feed point*.

The dipole's feed point impedance is the ratio of voltage to current at the feed point. Referring back to Figure 2.2A, the feed point impedance of a half-wave dipole will be low at the center (where voltage is minimum and current is maximum) and high on each end (where voltage is maximum and current is minimum).

If a dipole is fed at the center and excited (supplied with power) at the third harmonic, the situation changes to that of Figure 2.2B. The dipole's physical length has not changed but its electrical length at the third harmonic has tripled — it is now three half-wavelengths long. If fed in the center, the same low impedance (low voltage/high current) is presented to the feed line. This situation occurs for all odd harmonics of the dipole's fundamental frequency because the center of the dipole is at a low impedance point and will present a reasonably low SWR to coaxial feed lines.

The situation is reversed if the dipole is excited at an even harmonic. Remove the right-most half-wavelength section in Figure 2.2B as the dipole is now electrically one full wavelength long. At the center of this antenna, voltage is high and current is low so the impedance is high and SWR will be high on any common feed line, coaxial or parallel-conductor. This is the situation at all even harmonics of the dipole's fundamental frequency and is sometimes referred to as *anti-resonance*.

At frequencies in between harmonics, the feed point impedance will take some intermediate value. When fed with parallel-conductor line and a wide-range impedance-matching unit, a dipole can be used on nearly any frequency, including non-resonant frequencies. (An example of such an antenna system is presented in the chapter **Single Band MF and HF Antennas**.)

Feed Point Impedance in Free-Space

In free space the theoretical impedance of a half-wavelength antenna made of an infinitely thin conductor is $73 + j42.5\ \Omega$. This antenna exhibits both resistance and reactance. The positive sign in the $+ j42.5\ \Omega$ reactive term indicates that the antenna exhibits an inductive reactance at its feed point. The antenna is slightly long electrically, compared to the length necessary for exact resonance, where the reactance is zero.

The feed point impedance of any antenna is affected by the wavelength-to-diameter ratio (λ/dia) of the conductors used. Theoreticians like to specify an "infinitely thin" antenna because it is easier to handle mathematically.

What happens if we keep the physical length of an antenna constant, but change the thickness of the wire used in its construction? Further, what happens if we vary the frequency from well below to well above the half-wave resonance and measure the feed point impedance? **Figure 2.9** graphs the impedance of a 100-foot long, center-fed dipole in free space, made with extremely thin wire — in this case, wire that is only 0.001 inch in diameter. There is nothing particularly significant about the choice here of 100 feet. This is simply a numerical example.

We could never actually build such a thin antenna (and neither could we install it in free space), but we can model how this antenna works using a very powerful piece of computer software called *NEC-4.1*. (See the **Antenna Modeling** chapter for details on antenna modeling.)

The frequency applied to the antenna in Figure 2.9 is varied from 1 to 30 MHz. The x-axis has a logarithmic scale because of the wide range of feed point resistance seen over the frequency range. The y-axis has a linear scale representing the reactive portion of the impedance. Inductive reactance is positive and capacitive reactance is negative on the y-axis. The bold figures centered on the spiraling line show the frequency in MHz.

At 1 MHz, the antenna is very short electrically, with a resistive component of about 2 Ω and a series capacitive reactance about –5000 Ω. Close to 5 MHz, the line crosses the zero-reactance line, meaning that the antenna goes through half-wave resonance there. Between 9 and 10 MHz the antenna exhibits a peak inductive reactance of about 6000 Ω. It goes through full-wave resonance (again crossing the zero-reactance line) between 9.5 and 9.6 MHz. At about 10 MHz, the reactance peaks at about –6500 Ω. Around 14 MHz, the line again crosses the zero-reactance line, meaning that the antenna has now gone through 3/2-wave resonance.

Between 19 and 20 MHz, the antenna goes through 4/2-wave resonance, which is twice the full-wave resonance or four times the half-wave frequency. If you allow your mind's eye to trace out the curve for frequencies beyond 30 MHz, it eventually spirals down to a resistive component somewhere between 200 and 3000 Ω. Thus, we have another way of looking at an antenna—as a sort of transformer, one that transforms the free-space impedance into the impedance seen at its feed point.

Now look at **Figure 2.10**, which shows the same kind of spiral curve, but for a thicker-diameter wire, one that is 0.1 inch in diameter. This diameter is close to #10 AWG wire, a practical size we might actually use to build a real dipole. Note that the y-axis scale in Figure 2.10 is different from that in Figure 2.9. The range is from –3000 Ω in Figure 2.10, while it was –7000 Ω in Figure 2.9. The reactance for the thicker antenna ranges from +2300 to –2700 Ω over the whole frequency range from 1 to 30 MHz. Compare

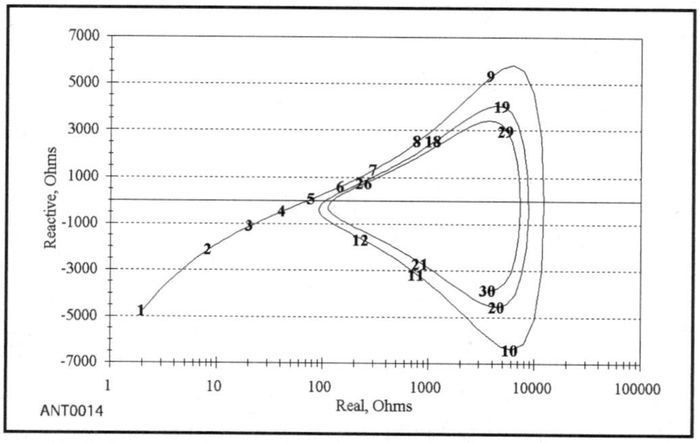

Figure 2.9 — Feed point impedance versus frequency for a theoretical 100-foot long dipole in free space, fed in the center and made of extremely thin 0.001-inch diameter wire. The y-axis is calibrated in positive (inductive) series reactance up from the zero line, and negative (capacitive) series reactance in the downward direction. The range of reactance goes from –6500 Ω to +6000 Ω. Note that the x-axis is logarithmic because of the wide range of the real, resistive component of the feed point impedance, from roughly 2 Ω to 10,000 Ω. The numbers placed along the curve show the frequency in MHz.

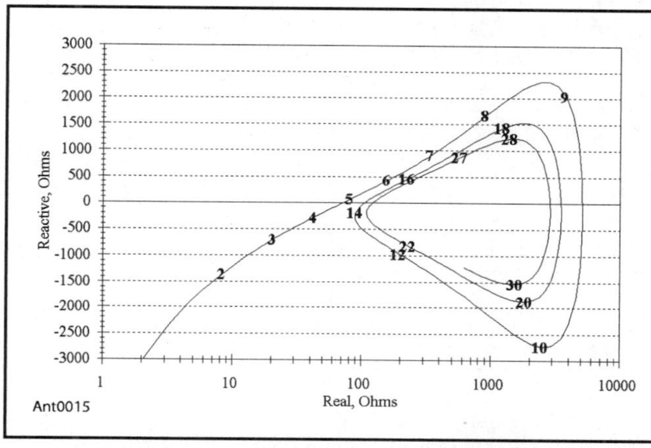

Figure 2.10 — Feed point impedance versus frequency for a theoretical 100-foot long dipole in free space, fed in the center and made of thin 0.1-inch (#10 AWG) diameter wire. Note that the range of change in reactance is less than that shown in Figure 2.9, ranging from –2700 Ω to +2300 Ω. At about 5000 Ω, the maximum resistance is also less than that in Figure 2.9 for the thinner wire, where it is about 10,000 Ω.

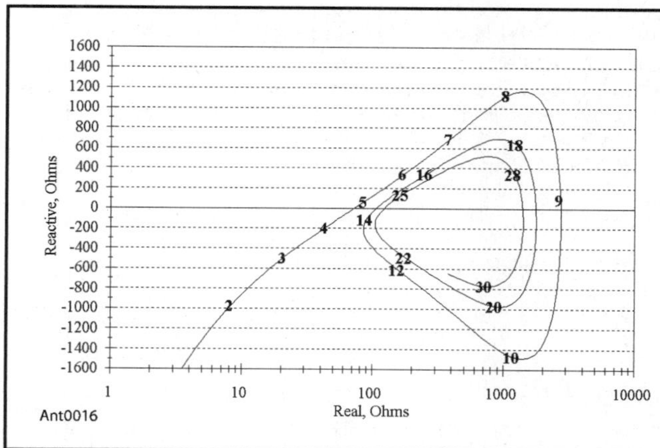

Figure 2.11 — Feed point impedance versus frequency for a theoretical 100-foot long dipole in free space, fed in the center and made of thick 1.0-inch diameter wire. Once again, the excursion in both reactance and resistance over the frequency range is less with this thick wire dipole than with thinner ones.

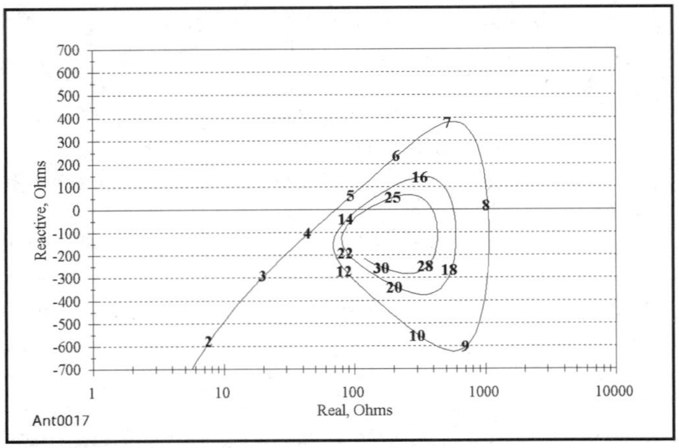

Figure 2.12 — Feed point impedance versus frequency for a theoretical 100-foot long dipole in free space, fed in the center and made of very thick 10.0-inch diameter wire. This ratio of length to diameter is about the same as a typical rod type of dipole element commonly used at 432 MHz. The maximum resistance is now about 1,000 Ω and the peak reactance range is from about –625 Ω to +380 Ω. This performance is also found in "cage" dipoles, where a number of paralleled wires are used to simulate a fat conductor.

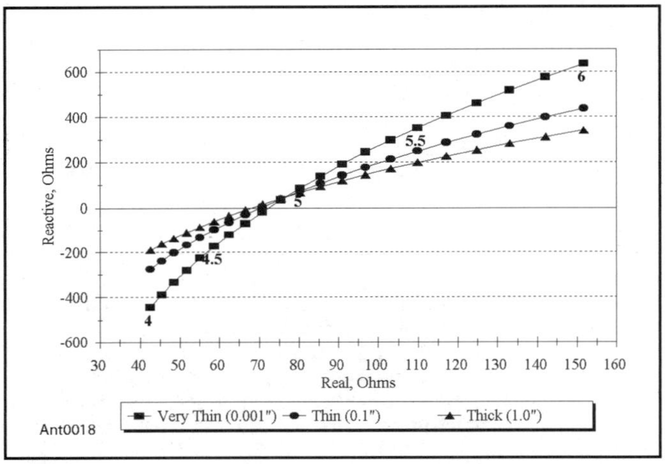

Figure 2.13 — Expansion of frequency range around half-wave resonant point of three center-fed dipoles of three different thicknesses. The frequency is shown along the curves in MHz. The slope of change in series reactance versus series resistance is steeper for the thinner antennas than for the thick 1.0-inch antenna, indicating that the Q of the thinner antennas is higher.

this with the range of +5800 to –6400 Ω for the very thin wire in Figure 2.9.

Figure 2.11 shows the impedance for a 100-foot long dipole using really thick, 1.0-inch diameter wire. The reactance varies from +1000 to –1500 Ω, indicating once again that a larger diameter antenna exhibits less of an excursion in the reactive component with frequency. Note that at the half-wave resonance just below 5 MHz, the resistive component of the impedance is still about 70 Ω, just about what it is for a much thinner antenna. Unlike the reactance, the half-wave radiation resistance of an antenna doesn't radically change with wire

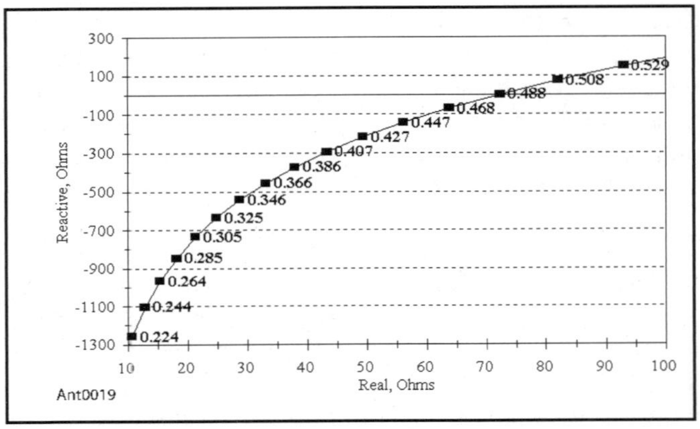

Figure 2.14 — Another way of looking at the data for a 100-foot, center-fed dipole made of #14 AWG wire in free space. The numbers along the curve represent the fractional wavelength, rather than frequency as shown in Figure 2.13. Note that this antenna goes through its half-wave resonance at about 0.488 λ, rather than exactly at a half-wave physical length.

diameter, although the maximum level of resistance at full-wave resonance is lower for thicker antennas.

Figure 2.12 shows the results for a very thick, 10-inch diameter wire. Here, the excursion in the reactive component is even less: about +400 to –600 Ω. Note that the full-wave resonant frequency is about 8 MHz for this extremely thick antenna, while thinner antennas have full-wave resonances closer to 9 MHz. Note also that the full-wave resistance for this extremely thick antenna is only about 1000 Ω, compared to the 10,000 Ω shown in Figure 2.9. All half-wave resonances shown in Figures 2.9 through 2.12 remain close to 5 MHz, regardless of the diameter of the antenna wire. Once again, the extremely thick, 10-inch diameter antenna has a resistive component at half-wave resonance close to 70 Ω. And once again, the change in reactance near this frequency is very much less for the extremely thick antenna than for thinner ones.

Now, we grant you that a 100-foot long antenna made with 10-inch diameter wire sounds a little odd! A length of 100 feet and a diameter of 10 inches represent a ratio of 120:1 in length to diameter. However, this is about the same length-to-diameter ratio as a 432 MHz half-wave dipole using 0.25-inch diameter elements, where the ratio is 109:1. In other words, the ratio of length-to-diameter for the 10-inch diameter, 100 foot long dipole is not that far removed from what might actually be used at UHF.

Another way of highlighting the changes in reactance and resistance is shown in **Figure 2.13**. This shows an expanded portion of the frequency range around the half-wave resonant frequency, from 4 to 6 MHz. In this region, the shape of each spiral curve is almost a straight line. The slope of the curve for the very thin antenna (0.001-inch diameter) is steeper than that for the thicker antennas (0.1 and 1.0-inch diameters). **Figure 2.14** illustrates another way of looking at the impedance data above and below the half-wave resonance. This is for a 100-foot dipole made of #14 AWG wire. Instead of showing the frequency for each impedance point, the wavelength is shown, making the graph more universal in application.

Just to show that there are lots of ways of looking at the same data, recall that Figure 2.8 graphs the constant "K" used to multiply the free-space half-wavelength as a function of the ratio between the half-wavelength and the conductor diameter. The curve approaches the value of 1.00 for an infinitely thin conductor, in other words an infinitely large ratio of half-wavelength to diameter.

The behavior of antennas with different λ/diameter ratios corresponds to the behavior of ordinary series-resonant circuits having different values of Q. When the Q of a circuit is low, the reactance is small and changes rather slowly as the applied frequency is varied on either side of resonance. If the Q is high, the converse is true. The response curve of the low-Q circuit is broad; that of the high-Q circuit sharp. So it is with antennas — the impedance of a thick antenna changes slowly over a comparatively wide band of frequencies, while a thin antenna has a faster change in impedance. Antenna Q is defined

$$Q = \frac{f_0 \Delta X}{2 R_0 \Delta f} \qquad (5)$$

where f_0 is the center frequency, ΔX is the change in the reactance for a Δf change in frequency, and R_0 is the resistance at f_0. For the "Very Thin," 0.001-inch diameter dipole in Figure 2.9, a change of frequency from 5.0 to 5.5 MHz yields a reactance change from 86 to 351 Ω, with an R_0 of 95 Ω. The Q is thus 14.6. For the 1.0-inch-diameter "Thick" dipole in Figure 2.11, ΔX = 131 Ω and R_0 is still 95 Ω, making Q = 7.2 for the thicker antenna, roughly half that of the thinner antenna.

A lower Q means the antenna's bandwidth is greater. This effect is can be exploited to increase an antenna's bandwidth. On the HF bands, one can make a dipole using multiple conductors in a cage or fan to increase its equivalent diameter d. On the VHF and UHF bands, one can build a dipole with copper pipe. The formulas in Eq 2 are particularly useful for antennas that are short and thick. Again, K is obtained from Figure 2.3 or Eq 3.

Let's recap. The dipole can be described as a transducer or as a sort of transformer to a range of free-space impedances. Now, we just compared the antenna to a series-tuned circuit. Near its half-wave resonant frequency, a center-fed λ/2 dipole exhibits much the same characteristics as a conventional series-resonant circuit. Exactly at resonance, the current at the input terminals is in phase with the applied voltage and the feed point impedance is purely resistive. If the frequency is below resonance, the phase of the current leads the voltage; that is, the reactance of the antenna is capacitive. When the frequency is above resonance, the opposite occurs; the current lags the applied voltage and the antenna exhibits inductive reactance. Just like a conventional series-tuned circuit, the antenna's reactance and resistance determines its Q.

Effect of Height Above Ground on Feed Point Impedance

The feed point impedance of an antenna varies with height above ground because of the effects of energy reflected from and absorbed by the ground. For example, a ½-λ (or half-wave) center-fed dipole will have a feed point impedance of approximately 75 Ω in *free space* far from ground, but **Figure 2.15** shows that only at certain electrical heights above ground will the feed point impedance be 75 Ω. The feed point impedance will vary from very low when the antenna is close to the ground to a maximum of nearly 100 Ω at 0.34 λ above ground, varying around 75 Ω as the antenna is raised farther. The 75-Ω feed point impedance is most likely to be realized in a practical installation when the horizontal dipole is approximately ½, ¾ or 1 λ above ground. This is why few amateur λ/2-dipoles exhibit a center-fed feed point impedance of 75 Ω, even though they may be resonant.

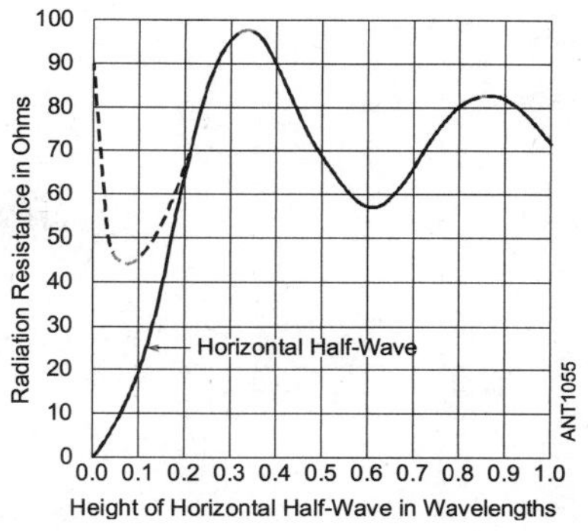

Figure 2.15 — Curves showing the radiation resistance of a horizontal half-wavelength dipole at various heights above ground. The broken-line portion of the curve for a horizontal dipole shows the resistance over *average* real earth, the solid line for perfectly conducting ground.

Figure 2.15 also compares the effects of perfect ground and typical soil at low antenna heights. The effect of height on the radiation resistance of a horizontal half-wave antenna is not drastic so long as the height of the antenna is greater than 0.2 λ. Below this height, while decreasing rapidly to zero over perfectly conducting ground, the resistance decreases less rapidly with height over actual lossy ground. At lower heights the resistance stops decreasing at around 0.15 λ, and thereafter increases as height decreases further. The reason for the increasing resistance is that more and more energy from the antenna is absorbed by the ground as the height drops below ¼ λ, seen as an increase in feed point impedance.

2.1.4 EFFECT OF FREQUENCY ON RADIATION PATTERN

Earlier, we saw how the feed point impedance of a fixed-length center-fed dipole in free space varies as the frequency is changed. What happens to the radiation pattern of such an antenna as the frequency is changed?

In general, the greater the length of a center-fed antenna, in terms of wavelength, the larger the number of lobes into which the pattern splits. A feature of all such patterns is the fact that the main lobe is always the one that makes the smallest angle with (is closest to) the antenna wire. Furthermore, this angle becomes smaller as the length of the antenna is increased.

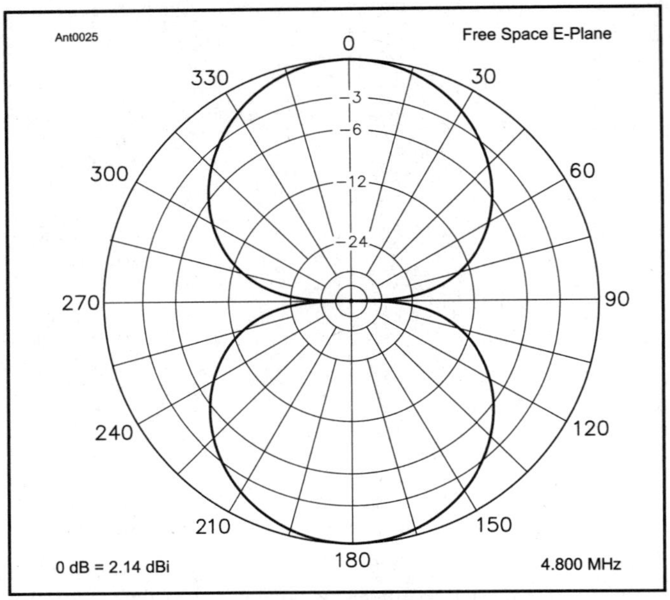

Figure 2.16 — Free-space E-Plane radiation pattern for a 100-foot dipole at its half-wave resonant frequency of 4.80 MHz. This antenna has 2.14 dBi of gain. The dipole is located on the line from 90° to 270°.

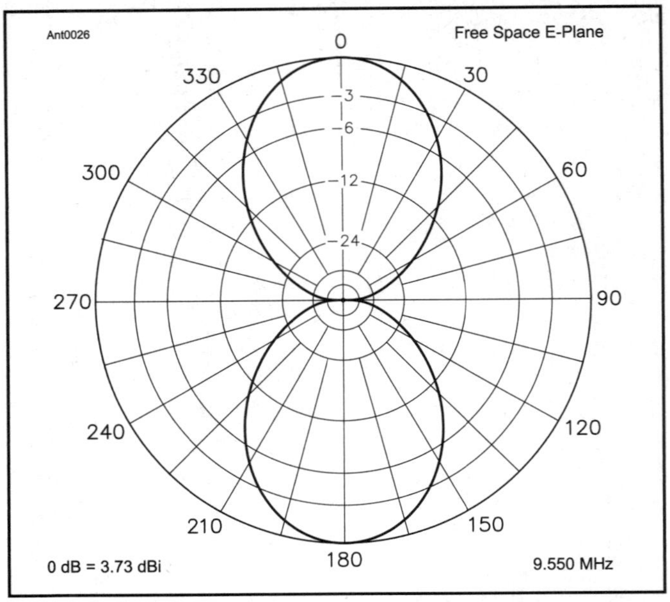

Figure 2.17 — Free-space E-Plane radiation pattern for a 100-foot dipole at its full-wave resonant frequency of 9.55 MHz. The gain has increased to 3.73 dBi, because the main lobes have been focused and sharpened compared to Figure 2.16.

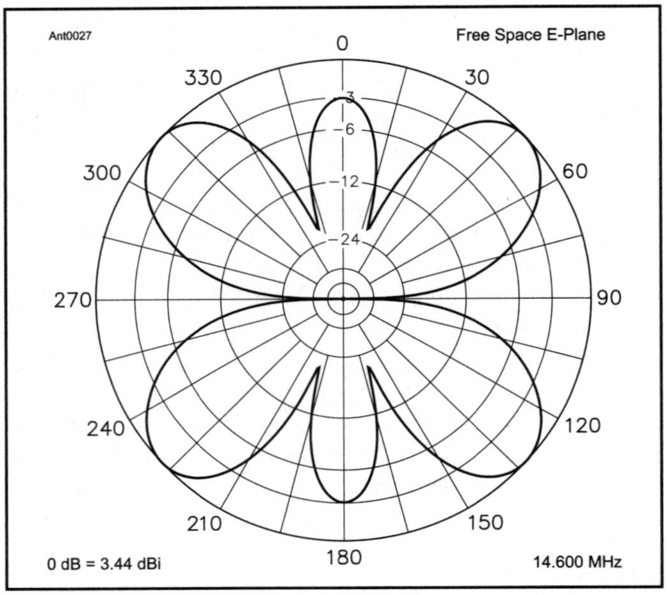

Figure 2.18 — Free-space E-Plane radiation pattern for a 100-foot dipole at its 3/2λ resonant frequency of 14.60 MHz. The pattern has broken up into six lobes, and thus the peak gain has dropped to 3.44 dBi.

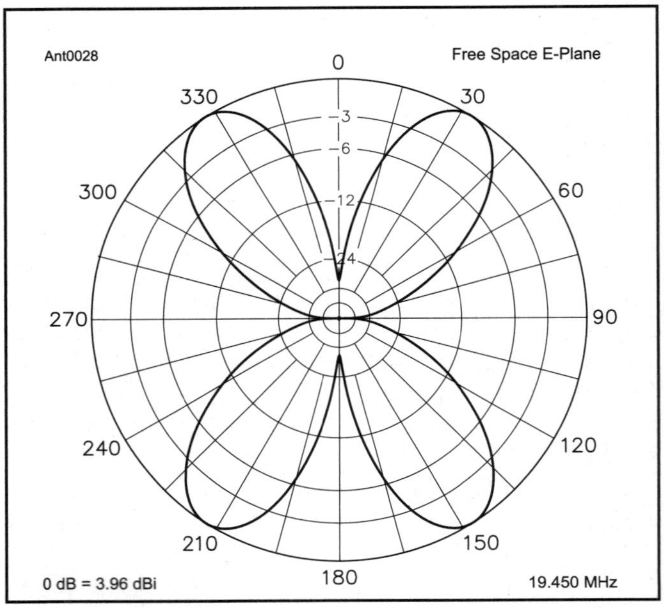

Figure 2.19 — Free-space E-Plane radiation pattern for a 100-foot dipole at twice its full-wave resonant frequency of 19.45 MHz. The pattern has been refocused into four lobes, with a peak gain of 3.96 dBi.

Let's examine how the free-space radiation pattern changes for a 100-foot long wire made of #14 AWG wire as the frequency is varied. (Varying the frequency effectively changes the electrical length of a fixed-length wire.) **Figure 2.16** shows the E-plane pattern at the λ/2 resonant frequency of 4.8 MHz. This is a classical dipole pattern, with a gain in free space of 2.14 dBi referenced to an isotropic radiator.

Figure 2.17 shows the free-space E-plane pattern for the same antenna, but now at the full-wave (2 λ/2) resonant frequency of 9.55 MHz. Note how the pattern has been pinched in at the top and bottom of the figure. In other words, the two main lobes have become sharper at this frequency, making the gain 3.73 dBi, higher than at the λ/2 frequency.

Figure 2.18 shows the pattern at the 3 λ/2 frequency of 14.6 MHz. More lobes have developed compared to Figure 2.16. This means that the power has split up into more lobes

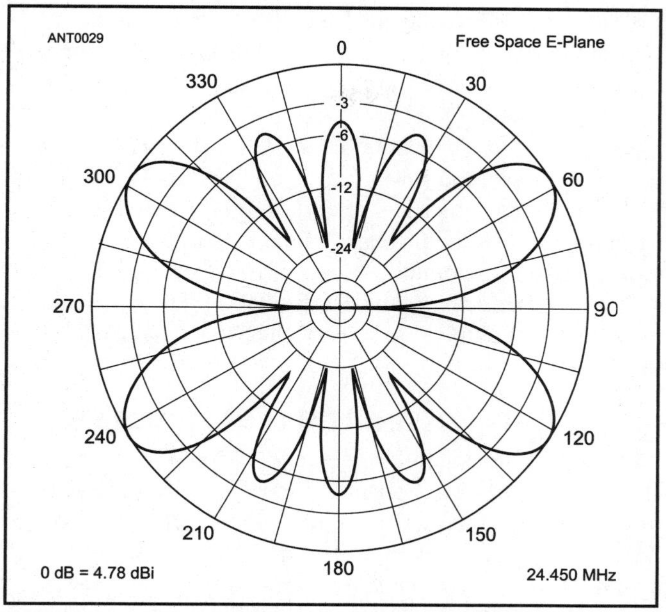

Figure 2.20 — Free-space E-Plane radiation pattern for a 100-foot dipole at its 5/2λ resonant frequency of 24.45 MHz. The pattern has broken down into ten lobes, with a peak gain of 4.78 dBi.

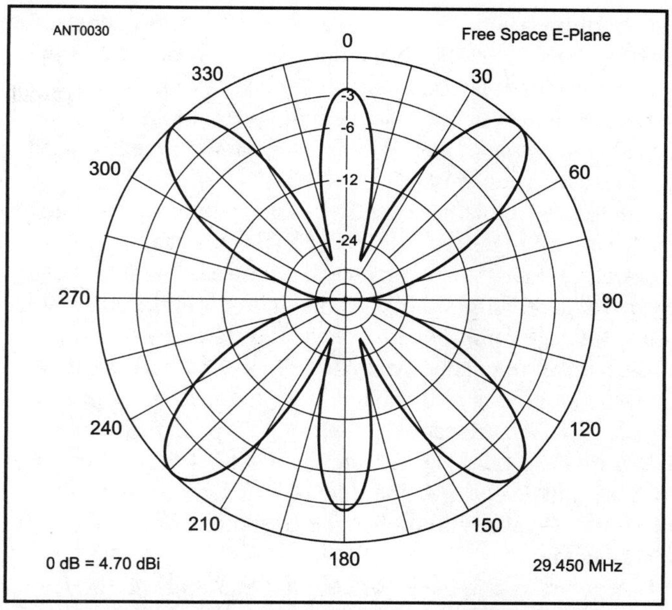

Figure 2.21 — Free-space E-Plane radiation pattern for a 100-foot dipole at three times its full-wave resonant frequency of 29.45 MHz. The pattern has returned to six lobes, with a peak gain of 4.70 dBi.

and consequently the gain decreases a small amount, down to 3.44 dBi. This is still higher than the dipole at its λ/2 frequency, but lower than at its full-wave frequency. **Figure 2.19** shows the E-plane response at 19.45 MHz, the 4 λ/2, or 2 λ, resonant frequency. Now the pattern has reformed itself into only four lobes, and the gain has as a consequence risen to 3.96 dBi.

In **Figure 2.20** the response has become quite complex at the 5 λ/2 resonance point of 24.45 MHz, with ten lobes showing. Despite the presence all these lobes, the main lobes now show a gain of 4.78 dBi. Finally, **Figure 2.21** shows the pattern at the 3λ (6 λ/2) resonance at 29.45 MHz. Despite the fact that there are fewer lobes taking up power than at 24.45 MHz, the peak gain is slightly less at 29.45 MHz, at 4.70 dBi.

The pattern — and hence the gain — of a fixed-length antenna varies considerably as the frequency is changed. Of course, the pattern and gain change in the same fashion if the frequency is kept constant and the length of the wire is varied. In either case, the wavelength is changing. It is also evident that certain lengths reinforce the pattern to provide more peak gain. If an antenna is not rotated in azimuth when the frequency is changed, the peak gain may occur in a different direction than you might like. In other words, the main lobes change direction as the frequency is varied.

2.1.5 FOLDED DIPOLES

Figure 21.22 shows a *folded dipole* constructed from open-wire transmission line. The dipole is made from a ½-λ

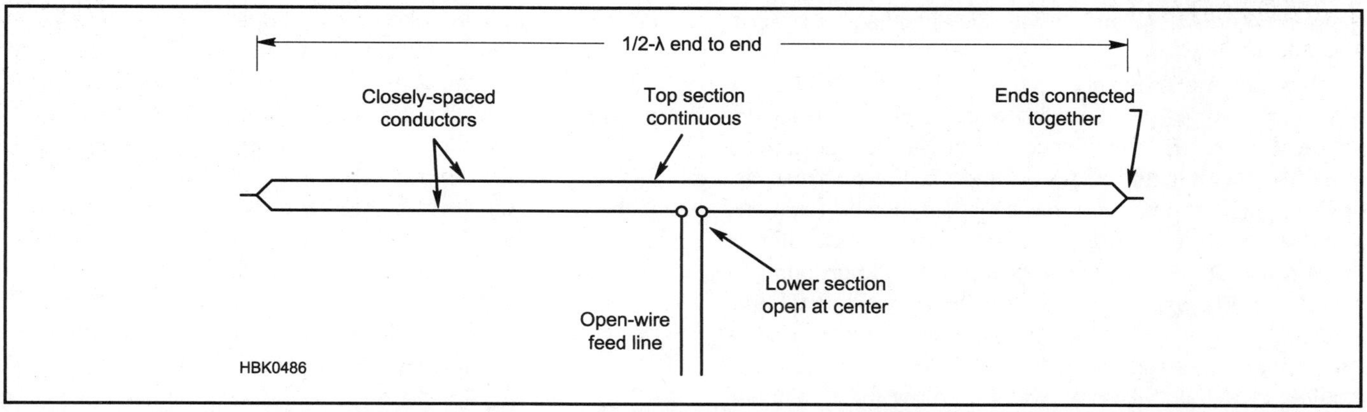

Figure 2.22 — The folded dipole is most often constructed from open-wire transmission line with the ends connected together. The close proximity of the two conductors and the resulting coupling act as an impedance transformer to raise the feed point impedance over that of a single-wire dipole by the square of the number of conductors used.

section of open-wire line with the two conductors connected together at each end of the antenna. The top conductor of the open-wire length is continuous from end to end. The lower conductor, however, is cut in the middle and the feed line attached at that point. Open-wire transmission line is then used to connect the transmitter.

A folded dipole has exactly the same gain and radiation pattern as a single-wire dipole. However, because mutual coupling divides the antenna current between the upper and lower conductors, the ratio of voltage to current at the feed point (the feed point impedance) is multiplied by the square of the number of conductors in the antenna. In this case, there are two conductors in the antenna, so the feed point impedance is $2^2 = 4$ times that of a single-wire dipole. A three-wire folded dipole would have a nine times higher feed point impedance and so forth. If the diameter of the conductors are different, the ratio will not be an exact square of the number of conductors.

A common use of the folded dipole is to raise the feed point impedance of the antenna to present a better impedance match to high impedance feed line. For example, if a very long feed line to a dipole is required, open-wire feed line would be preferable because of its lower loss. By raising the dipole's feed point impedance, the SWR on the open-wire line is reduced from that of a single-wire dipole fed with open-wire feed line.

2.1.6 VERTICAL DIPOLES

A half-wave dipole can also be oriented vertically over ground instead of horizontally, becoming a vertical dipole. The dipole's pattern becomes generally omnidirectional. In **Figure 2.23A** and B with the bottom of the vertical dipole very close ($\lambda/80$) to a saltwater ground plane the vertical dipole can have a gain of 6.1 dBi. Gain drops to about 0 dBi over good soil and lower over poorer soils. As with all vertical antennas, it is mainly the quality of the ground in the antenna's far field (several wavelengths from the antenna and beyond) that determines how good a low-angle radiator the vertical dipole will be as shown in Figure 2.23 and further discussed in the chapter **Effects of Ground**. Raising the $\lambda/2$ vertical higher above the ground introduces multiple lobes as shown in Figure 2.23C and D with the antenna's bottom tip $\lambda/8$ above ground.

The radiation resistance of the vertical dipole also depends on the height of its lower tip above ground as shown in **Figure 2.24**. The impedance of vertical and horizontal dipoles vary with height above ground for different reasons: The horizontal dipole receives reflected power from the ground affecting its mutual impedance. The vertical dipole, however, receives less reflected power from the ground and as it is lowered closer to ground, it is increasing its effective height and increasing its gain which has the effect of increasing its radiation resistance. As with the horizontal dipole, the radiation resistance varies above and below the free-space value of 73.5 Ω but not as much as for the horizontal dipole since its feed point is farther above ground. (Effective height of the dipole which is proportional to average current in the dipole divided by its physical length, increases as the antenna becomes lower because average current in the antenna increases. See Zavrel's referenced article on maximizing radiation resistance.)

In practice, it is not possible to obtain symmetrical currents in the upper and lower halves of the vertical dipole at HF due to the asymmetrical relationship of the two sections to ground. Further, the presence of the feed line introduces a third conductor for common-mode current that can influence the antenna's performance unless decoupled. Thus, the radiation patterns are unlikely to be very close to the ideal patterns shown here.

2.1.7 OFF-CENTER-FED (OCF) DIPOLES

The usual practice is to feed a $\lambda/2$ dipole in the center where the feed point impedance is low and makes a suitable match to coaxial cables. The dipole will accept energy from a feed point anywhere along its length, however. (See the section on Feed Point Impedance earlier in this chapter.) A common variation is the *off-center-fed* (*OCF*) dipole where the feed point is offset from the center by some amount and an impedance transformer used to match a coaxial feed line to the higher impedance that is presented away from the center point on several bands. The extreme example of an OCF dipole is the *end-fed Zepp* with the feed point moved all the way to one end.

The OCF dipole feed point and overall length are generally selected for a feed point impedance in the neighborhood of 150 to 300 Ω on several bands. A 4:1 or 6:1 impedance transformer is then used to match the antenna to 50 Ω coaxial cable. The feed point impedance will vary with height above ground and so will the SWR. A choke balun (see the **Transmission Line System Techniques** chapter) should also be used if the impedance transformer does not provide feed line isolation. The transformer creates a convenient point from which to suspend the antenna in an asymmetric inverted-V configuration.

Figure 2.25 shows the basic structure of the OCF dipole. Overall length is $\lambda/2$ on the lowest frequency of operation. Various formulas and conventions are used to determine how far from center the feed point is located. (See the Bibliography entry for Richter's in-depth article on the OCF Dipole.) The most common location for the feed point is approximately ⅓ of overall length from one end. Specific OCF dipole designs are presented in the chapter on **Multiband HF Antennas**.

The OCF dipole is often mistakenly referred to as a "Windom" or a "coax-fed Windom." The two antennas are not the same, however, since the Windom is essentially a short vertical loaded by an asymmetric flat-top, fed against ground at the base of the vertical section.

Richter also provides a formula for radiation resistance, R_r, at various locations for the feed point on its fundamental and harmonic frequencies. The antenna is assumed to be in free space:

$$R_r = \frac{73.1}{\sin^2\left(m\frac{2X}{\lambda}\times 180\right)} \qquad (6)$$

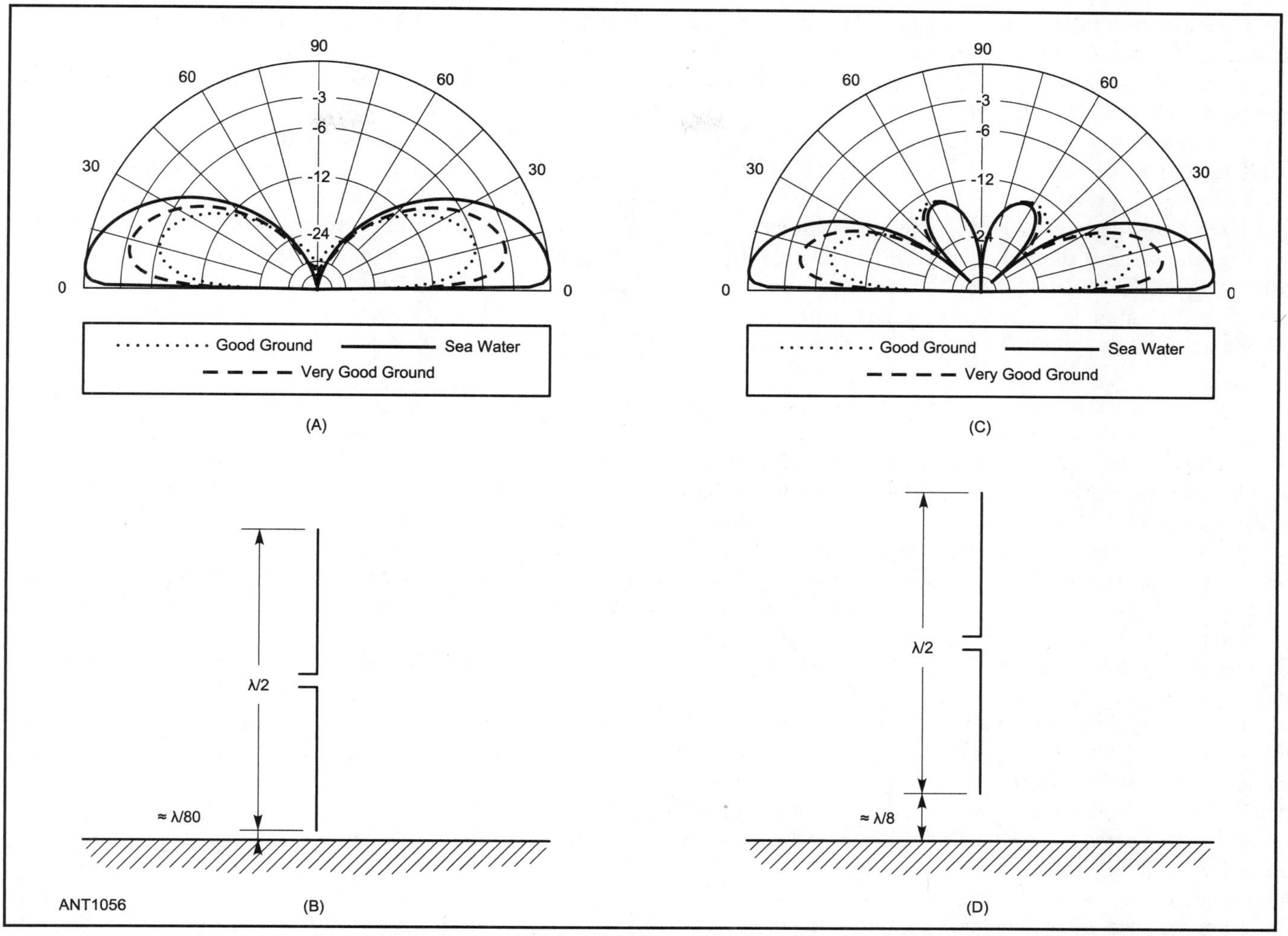

Figure 2.23 — At A and B, vertical radiation patterns over various grounds for a vertical half-wave center-fed dipole with the bottom tip just clearing the ground. The gain is as high as 6.1 dBi over ground and the feed point impedance is 100 Ω. At C and D, the vertical radiation patterns of the half-wave vertical dipole with the bottom tip ⅛ λ off the ground. Note the appearance of lobes in the radiation pattern at high elevation angles.

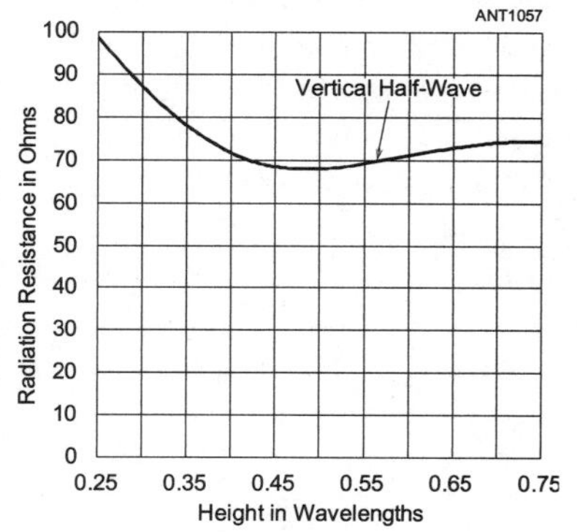

Figure 2.24 — The radiation resistance of a vertical half-wave dipole for various feed point heights above ground.

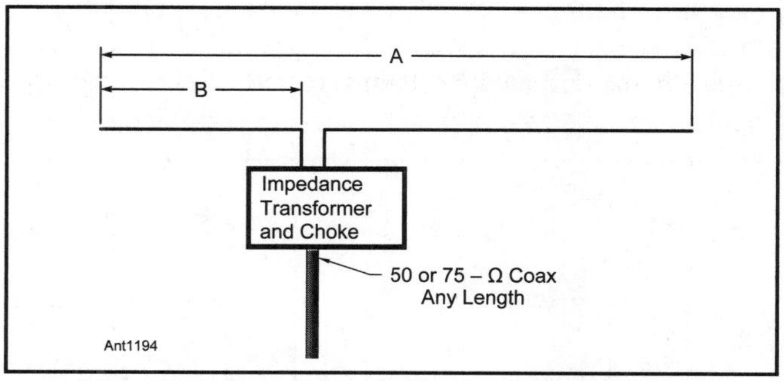

Figure 2.25 — An off-center-fed (OCF) dipole for use on several bands. Length A is generally λ/2 on the lowest frequency of operation. Length B is approximately ⅓ of A. The impedance transformer is usually a 4:1 or 6:1 design. A choke balun may be required for feed line isolation. Feed point impedance and SWR are affected by the antenna's height above ground.

where m is a multiplying factor (1 at the fundamental, 2 at the second harmonic, 3 at the third harmonic, etc.), λ is the full corrected wavelength, and X is the distance from the end of the antenna. Use the same units, meters or feet, for λ and X. The corrected wavelength includes the effect of the K factor (see the section Effects of Conductor Diameter earlier in this chapter).

Height above ground will affect the resonant length and R_r. The antenna is at different electrical heights on different bands, as well. Thus, it is difficult to make a precise calculation of feed point impedance or choose its location for a specific impedance on more than one band. Antenna modeling is probably the best practical method for designing an OCF dipole for a particular installation.

The OCF dipole is also an asymmetric or unbalanced antenna and there will be coupling to the feed line that affects the feed point impedance and radiation pattern. To minimize coupling use at least one feed line choke to isolate the feed line. One choke should be used at the feed point and others at intervals which prevent feed line resonances on the bands being used. Without decoupling, the antenna will still radiate a signal but the feed point impedance will likely vary a great deal from the design value.

2.2 MONOPOLES

Another simple form of antenna derived from a dipole is called a *monopole*. The name suggests that this is one half of a dipole, and so it is. The monopole is always used in conjunction with a ground plane, which acts as a sort of electrical mirror. See **Figure 2.26**, where a λ/2 dipole and a λ/4 monopole are compared. The image antenna for the monopole is the dotted line beneath the ground plane. The image forms the missing second half of the antenna, transforming a monopole into the functional equivalent of a dipole.

Monopoles are usually mounted vertically with respect to the surface of the ground. As such, they are called *vertical monopoles*, or simply *verticals*. A practical vertical is supplied power by feeding the radiator against a ground system, usually made up of a series of paralleled wires radiating from and laid out in a circular pattern around the base of the antenna. These wires are called *radials* since they extend radially from the base of the antenna.

The term *ground plane* is also used to describe a vertical antenna employing a vertical radiating element (usually λ/4 long) and a *counterpoise* system, another name for the ground plane that supplies the missing half of the antenna. The counterpoise for a ground-plane antenna usually consists of four λ/4-long radials elevated well above the ground. See **Figure 2.27**.

The chapter **Effects of Ground** devotes much attention to the requirements for an efficient grounding system for vertical monopole antennas. The chapter **Single Band MF and HF Antennas** gives more information on practical ground-plane verticals at HF. Ground-plane antennas at higher frequencies are discussed in the chapters **VHF and UHF Antenna Systems** and **Mobile VHF and UHF Antennas**.

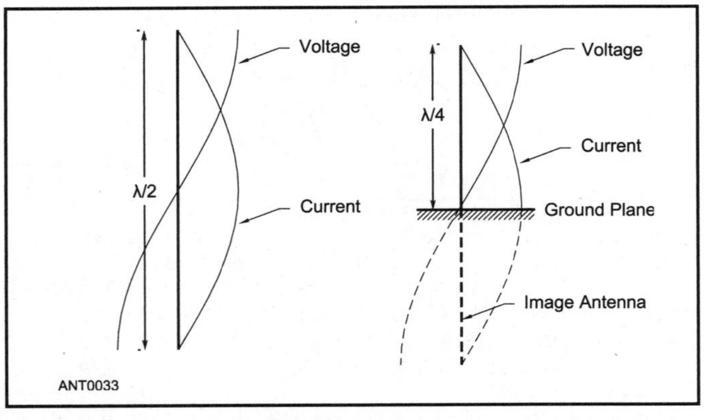

Figure 2.26 — The λ/2 dipole antenna and its λ/4 ground-plane counterpart. The "missing" quarter wavelength is supplied as an image in "perfect" (that is, high-conductivity) ground.

2.2.1 CHARACTERISTICS OF A λ/4 MONOPOLE

The free-space directional characteristics of a λ/4 monopole with its ground plane are very similar to that of a λ/2

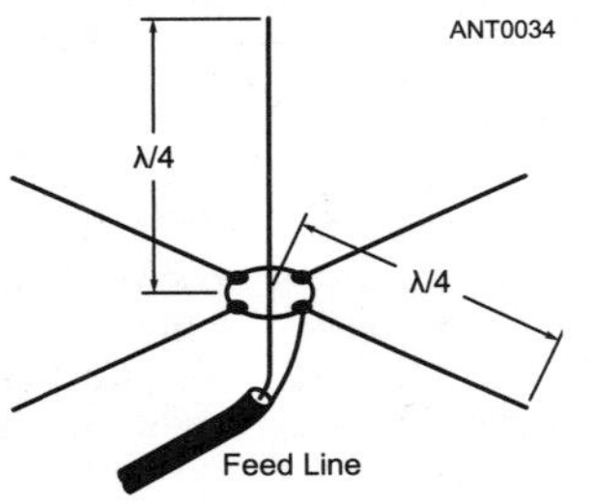

Figure 2.27 — The ground-plane antenna. Power is applied between the base of the vertical radiator and the center of the four ground plane wires.

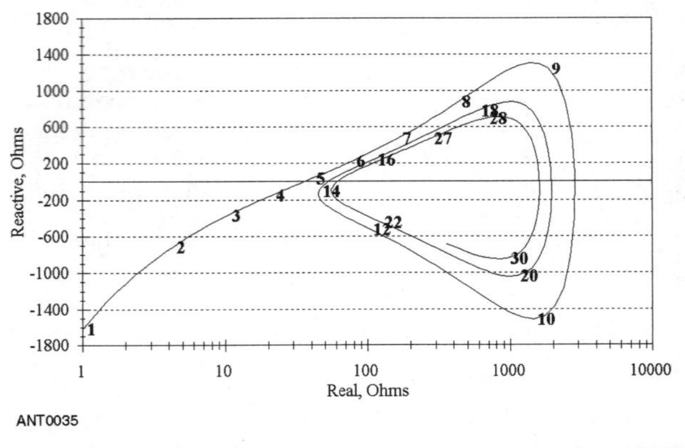

Figure 2.28 — Feed point impedance versus frequency for a theoretical 50-foot-high grounded vertical monopole made of #14 AWG wire. The numbers along the curve show the frequency in MHz. This was computed using "perfect" ground. Real ground losses will add to the feed point impedance shown in an actual antenna system.

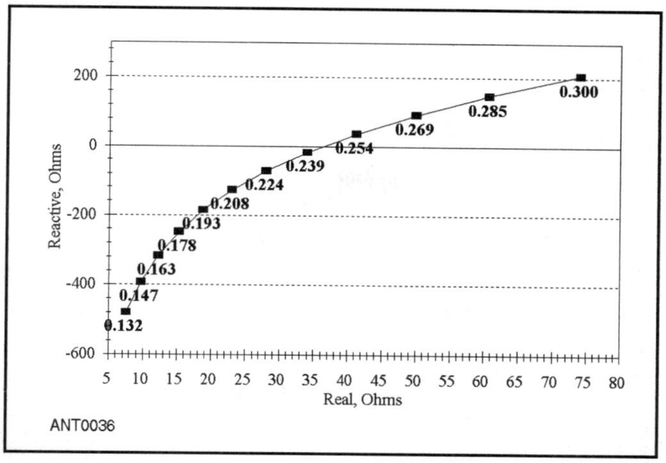

Figure 2.29 — Feed point impedance for the same antennas as in Figure 2.26, but calibrated in wavelength rather than frequency over the range from 0.132 to 0.300 λ, above and below the quarter-wave resonance.

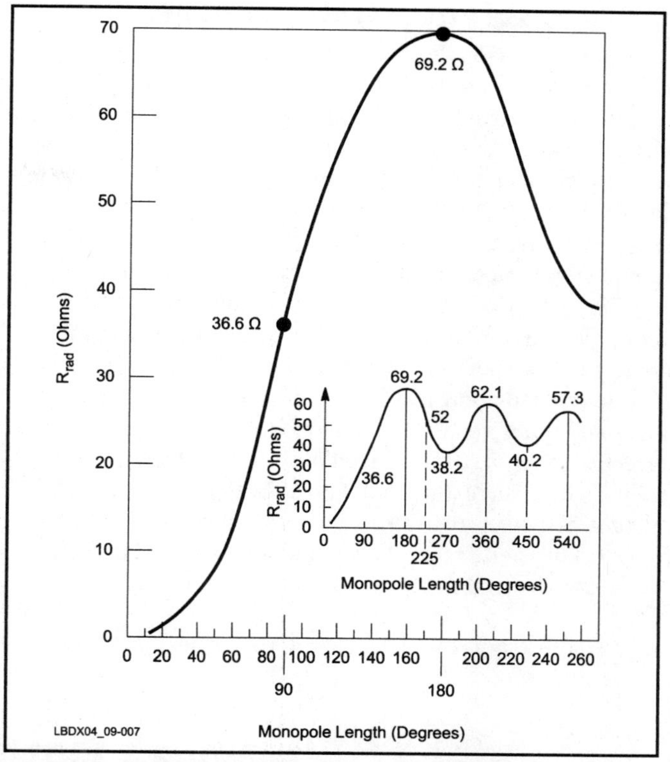

Figure 2.30 — Radiation resistances (at the current maximum) of monopoles with sinusoidal current distribution. The chart can be used for dipoles up to λ/2 in length, corresponding to the λ/4 monopole, but all values must be doubled.

antenna in free space. The directivity (*D*) and, thus, gain for the λ/4 monopole over a perfect, infinite ground plane is double that of the λ/2 dipole in free-space (assuming no losses) because there is no radiation in the hemisphere below the ground plane. Real monopoles over finite ground planes have less gain.

Like a λ/2 antenna, the λ/4 monopole has an omnidirectional radiation pattern in the plane perpendicular to the monopole.

The current in a λ/4 monopole varies practically sinusoidally (as is the case with a λ/2 dipole), and is highest at the ground-plane connection. The voltage is highest at the open (top) end and minimum at the ground plane. The feed point resistance close to λ/4 resonance of a vertical monopole over a perfect ground plane is one-half that for a λ/2 dipole at its λ/2 resonance. This is because half of the radiation resistance of a full-size λ/2 dipole has been replaced by an electrical image that does not actually exist and so cannot radiate power.

The word "height" applied to a vertical monopole antenna whose base is on or near the ground has the same meaning as length when applied to λ/2 dipole antennas. Some texts refer to heights in electrical degrees, referenced to a free-space wavelength of 360°, or height may be expressed in terms of the free-space wavelength.

Figure 2.28, which shows the feed point impedance of a vertical antenna made of #14 AWG wire, 50 feet long, located over perfect ground. Impedance is shown over the whole HF range from 1 to 30 MHz. Again, there is nothing special about the choice of 50 feet for the length of the vertical radiator; it is simply a convenient length for evaluation.

Figure 2.29 shows an expanded portion of the frequency range above and below the λ/4 resonance, but now calibrated in terms of wavelength. Note that this particular antenna goes through λ/4 resonance at a length of 0.244 λ, not at exactly 0.25 λ. The exact length for resonance varies with the diameter of the wire used, just as it does for the λ/2 dipole at its λ/2 resonance. The range shown in Figure 2.29 is from 0.132 λ to 0.300 λ, corresponding to a frequency range of 2.0 to 5.9 MHz.

The variation of a monopole's radiation resistance with electrical length or height is shown in **Figure 2.30** from 0° to 270°. Note that for the λ/4 monopole (a length of 90°) the radiation resistance is 36.6 Ω, one-half the radiation resistance of a λ/2 dipole. The radiation resistance is measured at the current maximum, which for monopoles longer than λ/4 will be located above the base of the antenna and have a different value than that at the base. (See the referenced articles by Zavrel for a more complete discussion of radiation resistance and feed point impedance.)

The reactive portion of the feed point impedance is highly dependent on the length/dia ratio of the conductor, as was discussed previously for a horizontal center-fed dipole. The impedance curve in Figures 2.26 and 2.27 is based on a #14 AWG conductor having a length/dia ratio of about 800 to 1. As usual, thicker antennas can be expected to show less reactance at a given height, and thinner antennas will show more.

The efficiency of a real vertical antenna over real earth often suffers dramatically compared with that of a λ/2 antenna. Without a fairly elaborate grounding system, the efficiency is not likely to exceed 50%, and it may be much less, particularly at monopole heights below λ/4. In addition, the gain of a monopole at angles close to the ground plane is highly dependent on the conductivity of the ground-plane. Both effects are discussed extensively in the chapter **Effects of Ground**.

2.2.2 FOLDED MONOPOLES

A folded monopole, shown in **Figure 2.31**, can be understood similarly to the folded dipole and the same increase in feed point impedance is achieved. Again, the ground-plane or counterpoise supplies the "missing half" of the antenna with an electrical image. The point opposite the feed point is electrically neutral in the λ/4 folded monopole and so is connected to the ground plane as in Figure 2.31A. An example of a commercial folded monopole is depicted in Figure 2.31B.

The increased feed point impedance of the folded monopole is often misunderstood as reducing ground losses due to the lower current at the feed point. This is incorrect because the radiation resistance and ground losses of both single and multiple-conductor monopoles is the same when correctly normalized to the feed point and so there is no difference when calculating radiation efficiency. For equivalent amounts of power, the same amount of current will flow in the ground system, regardless of the impedance transformation created by folding the conductor.

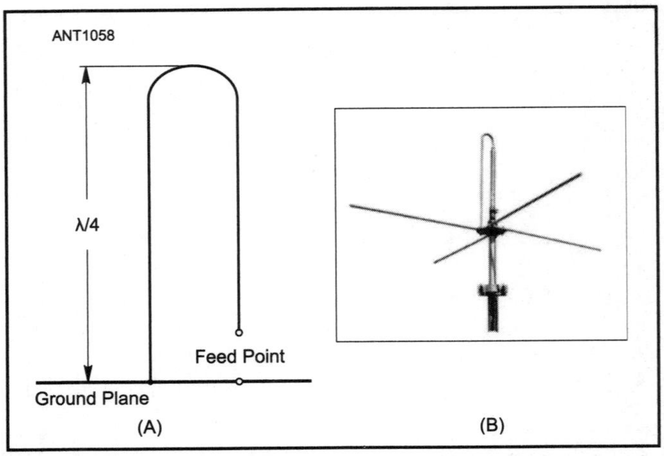

Figure 2.31 — The folded monopole antenna (A) can be nderstood similarly to the folded dipole with the ground-plane or counterpoise supplying the "missing half" of the antenna with an electrical image. An example of a commercial folded monopole is depicted in (B).

2.3 BIBLIOGRAPHY

The dipole and monopole are discussed extensively in the references listed in the Bibliography for the **Antenna Fundamentals** chapter.

J. Devoldere, *ON4UN's Low-Band DXing*, Fifth Edition (Newington: ARRL, 2010).

R.S. Elliott, *Antenna Theory and Design*, Wiley, 1981. Reissued by Wiley-IEEE, 2003, pp 297-304.

R.C. Hansen, "Carter Dipoles and Resonant Dipoles," *Allerton Antenna Applications Symposium*, pp 282-287, Monticello, IL, Sep 21-23, 2010.

P.H. Lee, *The Amateur Radio Vertical Antenna Handbook*, 2nd ed., CQ Publishing, 1984.

J. Richter, "Off-Center-Fed Dipole Antennas: Theory and Practice," *HF Dipole Antennas for Amateur Radio*, ARRL, 2019, pp 105-123.

S.A. Schelkunoff, "Theory of Antennas of Arbitrary Size and Shape," *Proceedings of the IRE*, Sep 1941; corrections Nov 1941 and Jan 1943. Republished in *Proc. IRE*, Sep 1984.

W. Silver, "Hands-On Radio: Experiment #84 — Antenna Height," *QST*, Nov 2009, pp 64-65.

W. Silver, "Hands-On Radio: Experiment #92 — The 468 Factor," *QST*, Sep 2010, pp 53-54.

S. Stearns, K6OIK, "Antennas: The Story from Physics to Computational Electromagnetics," *Antenna Seminar, ARRL Pacificon*, San Ramon, CA, Oct 19-21, 2019.

S. Stearns, K6OIK, "Antenna Modeling for Radio Amateurs," *Antenna Seminar, ARRL Pacificon*, San Ramon, CA, Oct 20-22, 2017. Archived at **www.fars.k6ya.org/docs**.

C.T. Tai and S.A. Long, "Dipoles and Monopoles," chapter 4 in *Antenna Engineering Handbook*, 3rd edition, R.C. Johnson editor, McGraw-Hill, 1993.

R. Zavrel, "Maximizing Radiation Resistance in Vertical Antennas," *QEX*, Jul/Aug 2009, pp 28-33.

R. Zavrel, "Radiation Resistance, Feed Point Impedance and Mythology," *QEX*, Mar/Apr 2014, pp 32-35.

TABLE OF CONTENTS

Chapter 3 — Downloadable Supplemental Content

Supplemental Articles

- "Determination of Soil Electrical Characteristics Using a Low Dipole" by Rudy Severns, N6LF
- "Maximum-Gain Radial Ground Systems for Vertical Antennas" by Al Christman, K3LC
- "Some Thoughts on Vertical Ground Systems over Seawater" by Rudy Severns, N6LF
- "Radiation and Ground Loss Resistances in LF, MF and HF Verticals: Parts 1 and 2" by Rudy Severns, N6LF
- "Determination of Soil Electrical Characteristics Using a Low Dipole" by Rudy Severns, N6LF
- "The Case of Declining Beverage-on-Ground Performance" by Rudy Severns, N6LF
- FCC Ground Conductivity Map Set

Chapter 3

The Effects of Ground

The **Antenna Fundamentals** chapter dealt mainly with ideal antennas in free space, completely removed from the influence of ground. Real antennas however, are placed over ground and in some cases have components right on or even buried in the ground. The presence of ground can have a profound effect on the behavior of an antenna, including the feed point impedance, the efficiency and the radiation pattern. This chapter is devoted to describing the interactions between antennas and ground and ways to reduce ground losses close to the antenna. For the purposes of this chapter the terms "soil" or "earth" are considered equivalent to "ground". In some cases "ground" may actually be fresh water or seawater.

We will begin by examining the characteristics of typical soils and then proceed to interactions between grounds and antennas. The interaction discussion is divided between two areas around the antenna: the *reactive near field* and the *radiating far field*. The reactive near field only exists very close to the antenna itself, essentially within one wavelength. In this region the antenna acts as though it were a large lumped-constant R-L-C tuned circuit where energy is stored in the fields close to the antenna. Only a portion of this energy is radiated. The RF current in the antenna will induce currents in the ground which in turn will affect the currents in the antenna. These interactions can modify the feed point impedance of an antenna and, due to the currents flowing in the ground, add power losses. This loss represents power supplied to the antenna from the transmitter but not radiated so there is a net reduction in signal for a given power input to the antenna. For vertical antennas located on or near ground, this can be very significant.

In the radiating far field, the presence of ground profoundly influences the radiation pattern of an antenna. (The radiating near field can be neglected as a transition zone between the reactive near field and radiating far field.) The interaction differs depending on the antenna polarization with respect to the ground. For horizontally polarized antennas, the shape of the radiated pattern in elevation plane depends primarily on the antenna's height above ground. For vertically polarized antennas, both the shape and the strength of the radiated pattern in the elevation plane strongly depend on the nature of the ground itself, as well as the height of the antenna above ground.

The material in this chapter assumes a flat ground surface surrounding the antenna. An extensive discussion of how to account for non-flat ground is presented in the chapter **HF Antenna System Design**, including use of the *HFTA* terrain analysis software by Dean Straw, N6BV.

3.1 EFFECTS OF GROUND IN THE REACTIVE NEAR FIELD

Sections 3.1 and 3.2 of this chapter have been expanded and reworked by the original author, Rudy Severns, N6LF to accommodate the results of work done since the previous version.

3.1.1 ELECTRICAL CHARACTERISTICS OF GROUND

One way to investigate the characteristics of a given sample of soil would be to fabricate a simple parallel plate capacitor as shown in **Figure 3.1**. First we might measure the capacitance (C_S) and the shunt resistance (R_S) without any soil between the plates. We would expect to get a very high value for R_S and some modest capacitance proportional to the plate areas and inversely proportional to the plate spacing. If we then fill the space between the plates with the soil we're interested in and repeat the R_S and C_S measurements, the chances are we will see a marked change in both: much lower R_S and higher C_S. What this experiment tells us is that soil acts like a lossy capacitor. When an RF current flows in the soil there will be some loss associated with R_S. The trick is to keep the RF current out of the soil at least near the antenna.

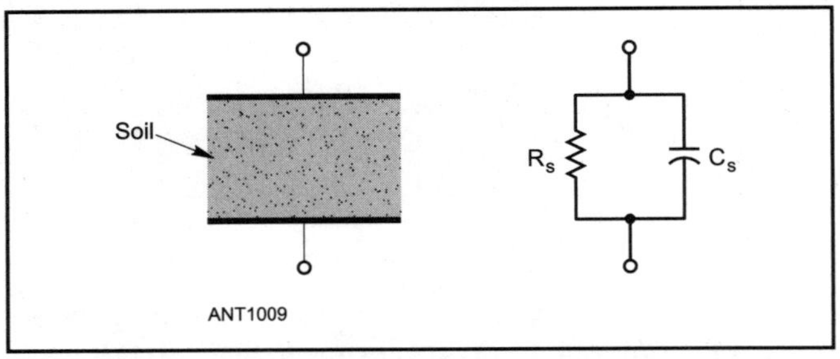

Figure 3.1 — Equivalent circuit for soil characteristics.

R_S is inversely related to the soil conductivity (σ) and C_S is directly related to the relative permittivity (dielectric constant) ($\varepsilon_{r\ or}$ Er as represented later in this chapter). We can infer values for σ and ε_r from measurements made on the capacitor with and without the soil between the plates. The unit for σ is Siemens per meter (S/m). ε_r is dimensionless. At HF both σ and ε_r are needed for the determination of ground losses or radiation patterns and are an important part of antenna modeling.

A century of measurements on different soils has shown that both σ and ε_r vary over a wide range depending on

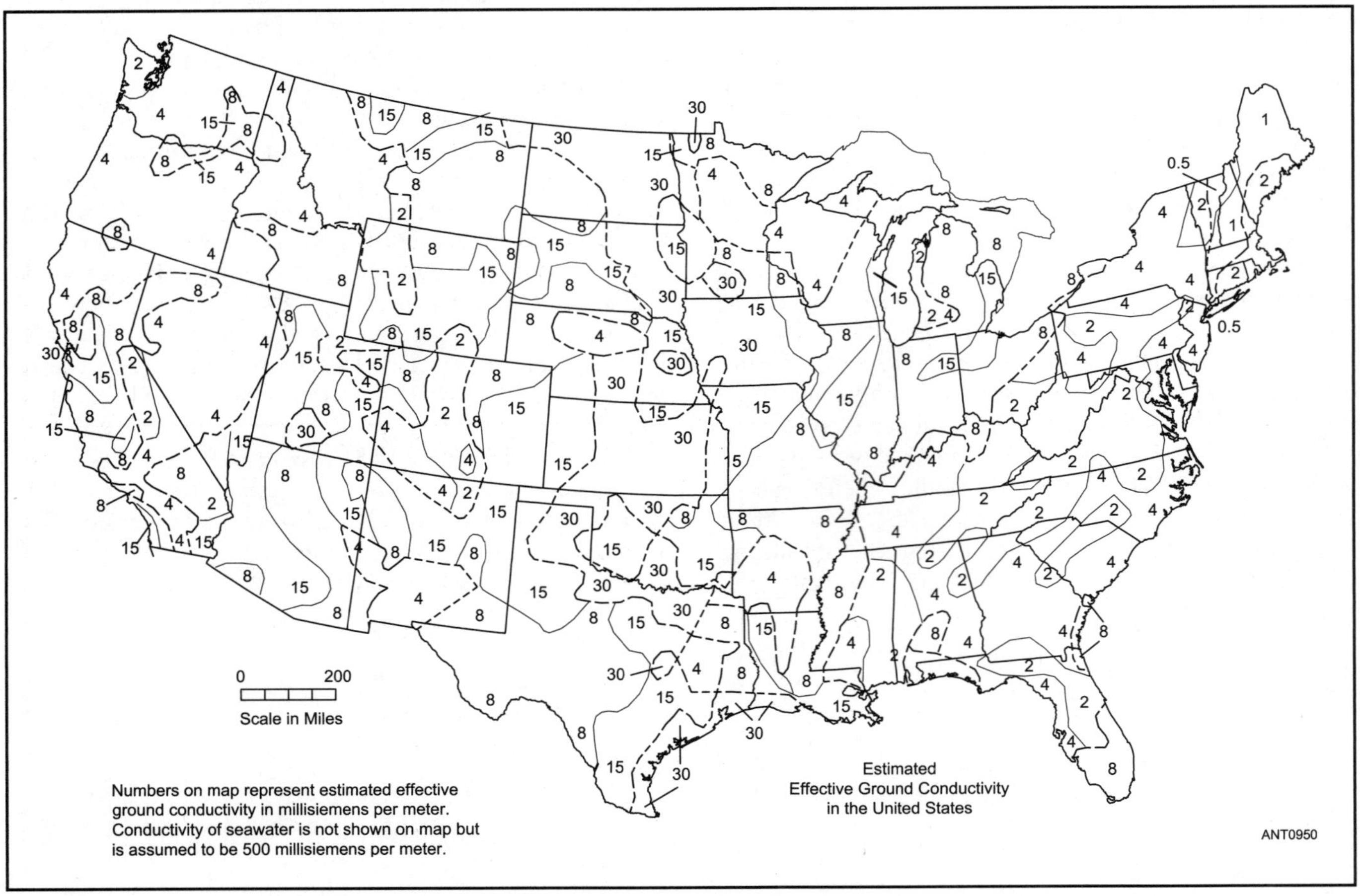

Figure 3.2 — Estimated effective ground conductivity in the United States. FCC map prepared for the Broadcast Service, showing typical conductivity for continental USA. Values are for the band 500 to 1500 kHz. Values are for flat, open spaces and often will not hold for other types of commonly found terrain, such as seashores, river beds, etc.

Table 3.1
Conductivities and Dielectric Constants for Common Types of Earth

Surface Type Constant	*Dielectric (S/m)*	*Conductivity Quality*	*Relative*
Fresh water	80	0.001	
Salt water	81	5.0	
Pastoral, low hills, rich soil, typ Dallas, TX, to Lincoln, NE areas	20	0.0303	Very good
Pastoral, low hills, rich soil typ OH and IL	14	0.01	
Flat country, marshy, densely wooded, typ LA near Mississippi River	12	0.0075	
Pastoral, medium hills and forestation, typ MD, PA, NY, (exclusive of mountains and coastline)	13	0.006	
Pastoral, medium hills and forestation, heavy clay soil, typ central VA	13	0.005	Average
Rocky soil, steep hills, typ mountainous	12-14	0.002	Poor
Sandy, dry, flat, coastal	10	0.002	
Cities, industrial areas	5	0.001	Very Poor
Cities, heavy industrial areas, high buildings	3	0.001	Extremely poor

location, soil composition, stratification of the soil, soil moisture content and many other variables. **Table 3.1** lists typical characteristics for a variety of typical grounds.

Real soils seldom have these exact pairs of σ and ε_r. For a given value of σ, ε_r can vary widely. Both σ and ε_r tend to increase with soil moisture content so it is normal to have higher ε_r when you have higher σ. However, it is also possible to have moderate values of σ but quite high values for ε_r. Soils with clay particles often have high ε_r. For fresh water at 23° C, $\varepsilon_r = 78$, so you may wonder how soil can have an ε_r higher than water. The higher values are the result of polarization effects that can occur in clay soils. It is quite possible to have $\varepsilon_r > 100$, at least at lower HF frequencies. In general, conductivity will increase with frequency and permittivity will decrease initially at lower HF but level out at higher frequencies.

Much of the data on soil conductivity stems from work at broadcast band frequencies. **Figure 3.2** is a graphic of typical ground conductivity for the United States. While useful for BC (AM broadcast) station planning this graphic is of limited use to amateurs because it averages the conductivity over large areas and the primary concern is ground wave propagation at BC frequencies. Amateurs are usually more concerned with the soil close to their antennas where the conductivity can vary dramatically from the large area average. (A set of detail maps showing ground conductivity is available as the file "FCC-GroundMap.zip" in this chapter's downloadable supplemental information.)

Soil characteristics vary not only with location and time of year but also with frequency. **Figures 3.3** and **3.4** show the

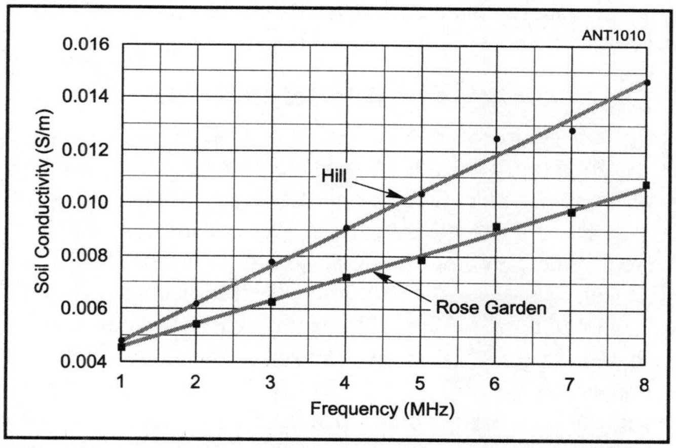

Figure 3.3 — Typical soil conductivity variation with frequency.

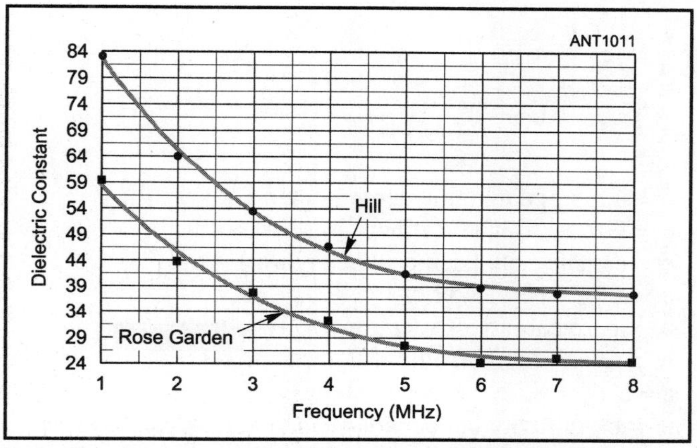

Figure 3.4 — Typical soil permittivity variation with frequency.

Soil Impedance vs Frequency

One of the limitations of presenting maps and charts of soil conductivity and permittivity is the extreme variability of soil. Not only does soil vary electrically from place to place but with frequency as well. In 1975, Longmire and Smith published "A Universal Impedance For Soils" (Nuclear Defense Agency report DNA3788T) that presented a consistent profile for changes in soil impedance with frequency that could be scaled and/or offset to match a specific soil type — the shape of a soil's impedance versus frequency graph was consistent. This report is discussed in Rudy Severn, N6LF's online report "Comments on Longmire and Smith." See the Bibliography for access information.

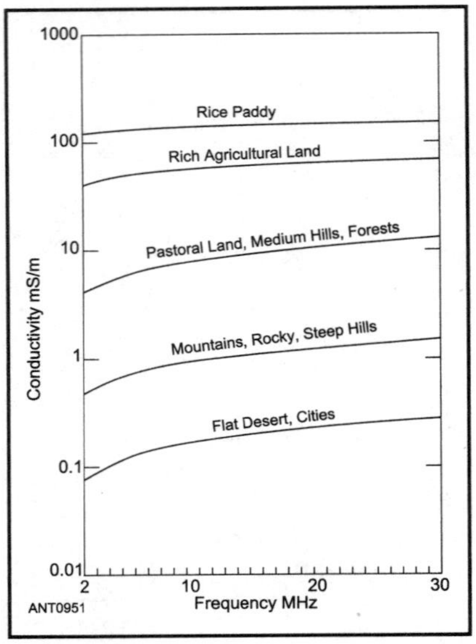

Figure 3.5 — Ground conductivity variation with frequency for different types of soils.

variation of σ and ε_r with frequency at two locations at a typical amateur QTH (N6LF). See this chapter's section "Ground Parameters for Antenna Analysis" for methods of measuring ground parameters for antenna modeling and design.

George Hagn and his associates at SRI have made a very large number of ground characteristic measurements at many different places in the world.[1] **Figure 3.5** shows the results of some of this work.

3.1.2 SKIN DEPTH IN SOIL

It is very probable that the soil at a given location will be stratified (vary with depth) so it will be necessary to take some average value. The question is then "how deep do I have to go to make the average?" This question is best answered by determining the depth to which the fields or the RF currents penetrate the soil. This penetration depth is often expressed in terms of the "skin depth" where the skin depth (δ) is the depth at which the current or the field has been attenuated to 1/e or 37% (e ≈ 2.71828) of its value at the ground surface. Skin depth is also used in the calculation of ground loss.

Knowing σ and ε_r, the skin depth in an arbitrary material can be determined from:

$$\delta = \left(\frac{\sqrt{2}}{\omega\sqrt{\mu\varepsilon}}\right)\left[\sqrt{1+\left(\frac{\sigma}{\omega\varepsilon}\right)^2}-1\right]^{-1/2} \qquad (1)$$

where

δ = skin or penetration depth [meters]
$\omega = 2\pi f$, f = frequency [hertz]
σ = conductivity [siemens/meter, S/m]
$\mu = \mu_r \mu_o$ = permeability
μ_o = permeability of vacuum = $4\pi 10^{-7}$ [henry/meter]
μ_r = relative permeability [dimensionless]
$\varepsilon = \varepsilon_r \varepsilon_o$ = permittivity [farad/meter]
ε_o = permittivity of vacuum = 8.854×10^{-12} [farad/meter]
ε_r = relative permittivity [dimensionless]

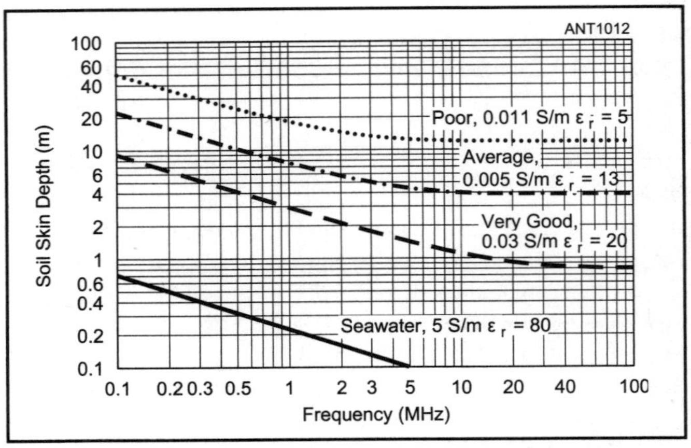

Figure 3.6 — Examples of skin depth variation with frequency for different grounds.

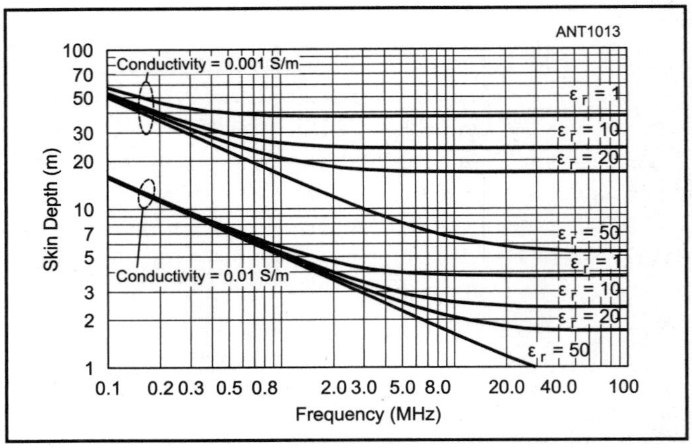

Figure 3.7 — Examples of skin depth as a function of ε_r for two different conductivities.

A graph of Eq 1 for typical grounds is given in **Figure 3.6**.

Skin depth varies with frequency and soil characteristics. For example, at 1.8 MHz δ varies from about 16 cm in seawater to 15 m in poor soil. As we go up in frequency the skin depth decreases, roughly proportional to $1/\sqrt{f}$, until at some point it flattens out.

The soil types in Figure 3.6 represent the typical values used in antenna modeling. An example of the effect of differing ε_r for soils with σ = 0.001 and 0.01 S/m is shown in **Figure 3.7**. In Figure 3.7, we can see several interesting things. At low frequencies (in the BC band) the values for δ converge and ε_r makes little difference. This is one reason why soil characteristics from BC data seldom include the permittivity. At high frequencies the curves are flat with a value that depends on σ and ε_r.

3.1.3 WAVELENGTH IN SOIL

Because soil is a complex medium where both σ and ε_r are significantly different from their values in free space, the wavelength in soil (λ) may differ greatly from the wavelength in free space (λ_o). This is important for antennas and radial systems close to or buried in the ground. In general the wavelength in soil will be considerably shorter than the

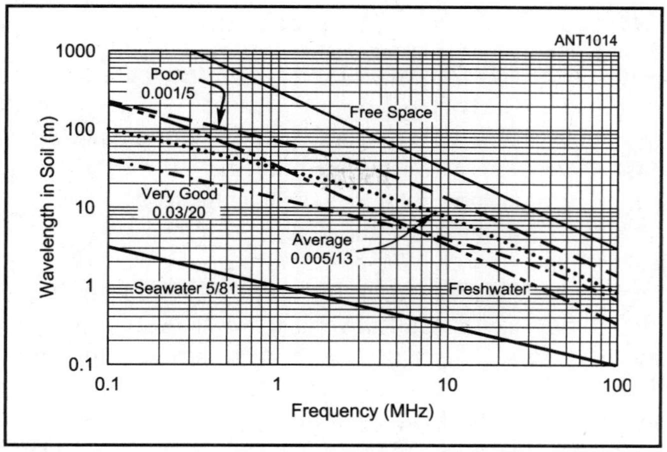

Figure 3.8 — Wavelength in typical soils as a function of frequency.

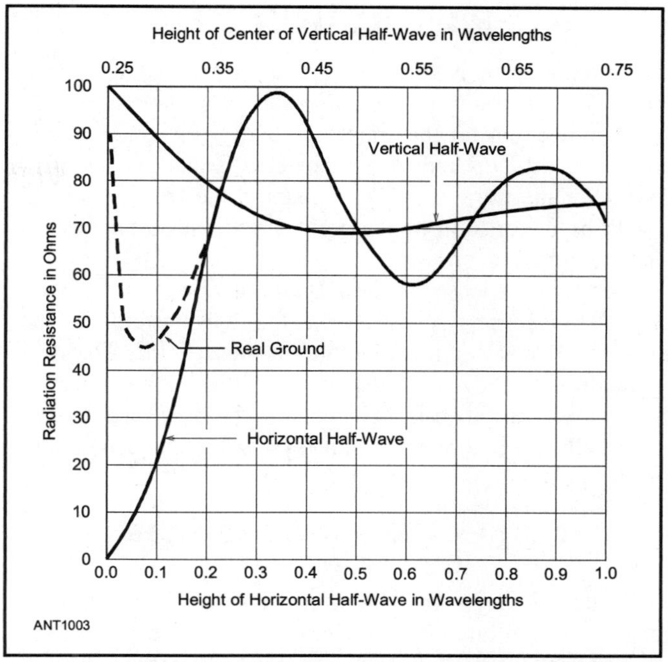

Figure 3.9 — Variation of feed point resistance with height for vertical and horizontal antennas.

free space wavelength and this must be taken into account for wire segmentation during modeling.

The wavelength in free space (λ_o) is:

$$\lambda_o = \frac{299.79}{f(\text{MHz})} \text{ in meters} \quad (2)$$

The wavelength in soil (λ) is:

$$\lambda = \frac{\lambda_o}{\left[\varepsilon_r^2 + \left(\frac{\sigma}{\omega \varepsilon_o}\right)^2\right]^{1/4}} \quad (3)$$

Figure 3.8 gives examples of wavelength as a function of frequency for different soils, salt and fresh water and free space. It can be seen that the wavelength in soil is typically much smaller than in free space.

3.1.4 FEED POINT IMPEDANCE VERSUS HEIGHT ABOVE GROUND

Radiation directly downward from the antenna will reflect vertically from the ground and, in passing the antenna on the upward journey, induce a current in it. The magnitude and phase of the current depends on the height of the antenna above the reflecting surface and the characteristics of the surface.[10] The total current in the antenna consists of two components: the amplitude of the first is determined by the excitation from the transmitter and the second component is induced in the antenna by the wave reflected from the ground. This second component of current, while considerably smaller than the first at most useful antenna heights, is by no means insignificant. At some heights, the two components will be in phase but at other heights the two components are out of phase. Changing the height of the antenna above ground will change the current amplitude at the feed point (we are assuming that the power input to the antenna is constant). A higher current at the same input power means that the effective resistance of the antenna is lower, and vice versa. In other words, the feed point resistance of the antenna is affected by the height of the antenna above ground because of mutual coupling between the antenna and the ground beneath it.

The electrical characteristics of the ground affect both the amplitude and the phase of reflected signals. For this reason, the electrical characteristics of the ground under the antenna will have some effect on the impedance of that antenna, the reflected wave having been influenced by the ground. Different impedance values may be encountered when an antenna is erected at identical heights but over soils with different characteristics.

Figure 3.9 gives an example of the way the feed point impedance of horizontal and vertical half-wave antennas can vary with height above ground. The height of the vertical half-wave is the distance from the bottom of the antenna to ground. For horizontally polarized half-wave antennas, the differences between the effects of perfect ground and real earth are negligible if the antenna height is greater than 0.2 λ. At lower heights, the feed point resistance over perfect ground decreases rapidly as the antenna is brought closer to a theoretically perfect ground. However, over real earth, the resistance actually begins increasing again at heights below about 0.08 λ as indicated by the dashed line. The reason for the increasing resistance at very low heights is that the field of the antenna interacts more strongly with the ground increasing ground losses. This increase in loss is reflected in an increased value for the feed point resistance.

3.2 GROUND SYSTEMS FOR VERTICAL MONOPOLES

In this section we look at vertical monopoles which are shorter than λ/2 and require some sort of ground system in order to make up for the "missing" part of the antenna and, just as importantly, reduce the power dissipated in the near field. (For the purposes of this chapter, the term "vertical" should be understood to represent a vertical monopole antenna mounted on or near the ground.)

Because the losses in the soil near a vertical are a function of the electric and magnetic field intensities close to the antenna we will begin by looking at these fields. The next step will be to show what the actual soil losses are and how that loss is distributed in the soil near the base of the vertical. Finally we'll describe ground systems which can greatly reduce this loss.

3.2.1 FIELDS NEAR THE BASE OF A VERTICAL

In this section we will be examining the E and H fields at ground level within λ/2 of the base of typical verticals. (See the **Antenna Fundamentals** chapter for a discussion of E and H fields.) This may seem like an abstract exercise but it's important because it allows us to visualize what's happening in the soil around the base of a vertical, giving us both the amplitude and location of the ground currents and their associated losses. This information will guide us in the design and optimization of ground systems.

A vertical antenna has two field components that induce currents in the ground around the antenna: E_z and H_Φ. **Figure 3.10** shows in a general way the electric-field component (E_z, in V/m) and magnetic-field component (H_Φ, in A/m) in the region near a vertical. Both of these field components will induce currents (I_V and I_H) in the soil. Because the soil near the antenna typically has relatively high resistance this results in power loss in the soil. Power dissipated in the ground is subtracted from the power supplied to the antenna weakening your signal.

As shown in Figure 3.10, the tangential component of the H-field (H_Φ) induces horizontal currents (I_H) flowing radially in the soil. The normal component (perpendicular to the ground surface) of the E-field (E_z) induces vertically flowing currents (I_v) in the soil. These field-induced ground currents will decrease as we go deeper into the soil with the rate of decrease a function of the skin depth in the particular soil.

We can determine E_z and H_Φ from either modeling (near-field calculations with *NEC*-based software, for example) or directly from equations. It turns out that the field intensities close to the base (<λ/2) of a vertical (within λ/2) over real ground are very close to the values for perfect ground. This allows us to use much simpler modeling or equations. The following graphs for field intensities assume perfect ground.

The base currents and the resistive part of the feed point impedance at the base of verticals with different heights (h) are given in **Table 3.2**. These are the values of current which result from an input power of 1.5 kW for an ideal vertical over perfect ground.

Figure 3.11 shows the H-field intensity within λ/2 of the base of the vertical for four different vertical heights (h): 0.05 λ, 0.125 λ, 0.250 λ and 0.375 λ. **Figure 3.12** shows the E-field intensity for the same values of h. Both of these graphs make the same two points:

1) Field intensity increases rapidly as you approach the base, particularly within a radius <λ/8, and

2) The shorter the antenna, the higher the fields for the same power input.

Table 3.2
Base Excitation Currents as a Function of Vertical Height (h) in Wavelengths
The input power is 1500 W.

h (λ)	I_o (A)	R_r (Ω)
0.050	39.7	0.95
0.125	15.1	6.57
0.250	6.45	36.1
0.375	2.53	234

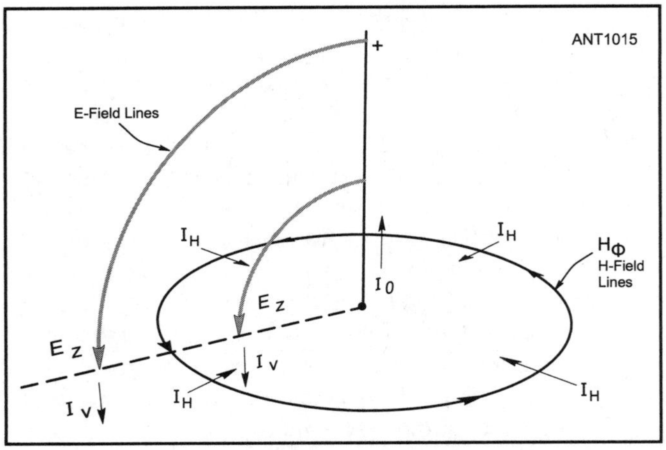

Figure 3.10 — Examples of the fields and currents close to a vertical.

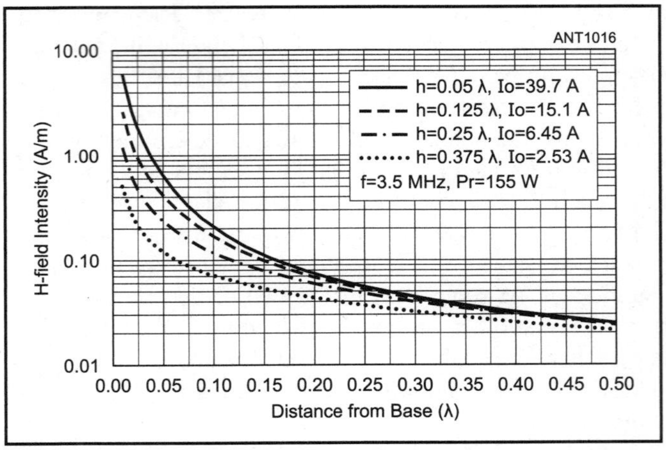

Figure 3.11 — H_Φ intensity as a function of distance from the base in wavelengths. Data is for a vertical at 3.5 MHz.

In the case of the E-field, the minimum field occurs for h = 0.25 λ and then increases again as h is increased beyond 0.25 λ. Ground losses are proportional to the square of the field intensity. In other words, if you double the intensity the power loss increases by 4 times! *This tells us that we must pay special attention to the ground system within λ/8 of the base and that short verticals require additional attention to the ground system.*

Another point which can be inferred from Figure 3.12 is the very high voltages which can be present on the antenna. The shorter the antenna and the higher the power level, the higher these voltages will be. Verticals taller than λ/4 can also have very high voltages near the base. This is a very real safety hazard! Touching a vertical while transmitting can lead to severe RF burns.

Figures 3.13 and **3.14** show the field intensities for a λ/4 vertical at frequencies from 1.8 to 28 MHz. At a given distance in λ, both E and H fields increase with frequency but, as the dashed line in Figure 3.13 indicates, at a given fixed physical distance the H-field intensity is constant, independent of frequency. However, as the dashed line in Figure 3.14 shows, the E-field at a given physical distance is not constant but increases with frequency.

This behavior may seem a bit strange because it says that the field distributions do not scale linearly with frequency! Keep in mind that the base current at all frequencies was set to 6.45 A (P_r = 1500 W, h = 0.250 λ). As the frequency was changed the height of the vertical was reduced from 135 feet at 1.8 MHz to 8.8 feet at 28 MHz. The high current point on a vertical (h ≤ λ/4) is at the base but the high voltage point is at the top. As we change frequency and alter h, the H-field is primarily influenced by the base current which does not change amplitude or location. However, the E-field is primarily influenced by the high voltage at the top of the vertical which is moving closer to ground as we go up in frequency. Normally we scale the dimensions of the ground system as we go up in frequency. If we elect to use λ/4 radials they will be approximately 34 feet on 40 meters, 17 feet on 20 meters, etc. The problem is that the fields are not scaling with frequency. At a given distance in λ the fields are higher as we go up in frequency. These observations tell us that for a given size (in λ) ground system *as we go up in frequency the ground loss will increase!*

As shown earlier, soil conductivity typically improves as we go up in frequency but that varies over a wide range and may not help as much as we would like. Better to be conservative and not count on the increase in σ unless you have actually measured your particular soil characteristics.

3.2.2 RADIATION EFFICIENCY AND POWER LOSSES IN THE SOIL

We can discuss the efficiency of an antenna by using an equivalent circuit model like that shown in **Figure 3.15** for the resistive part of the feed point impedance. We account for the radiated power (P_r) by assuming there is a resistor we call the *radiation resistance* (R_r) through which the antenna base current (I_o) flows. The radiated power (P_r) is then:

$$P_r = R_r I_o^2 \quad (4)$$

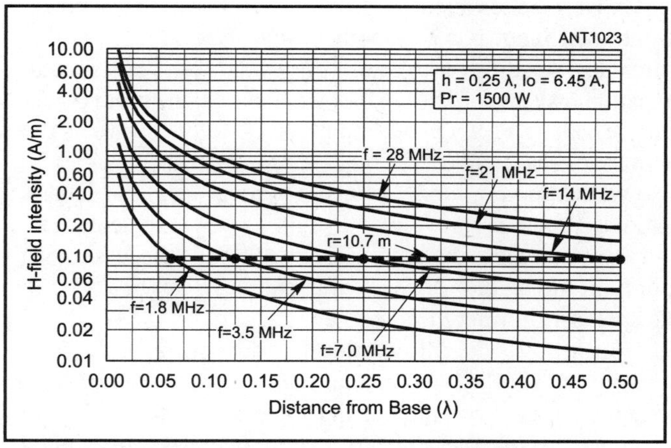

Figure 3.13 — H_Φ intensity as a function of distance from the base in wavelengths. Data is for a λ/4 vertical.

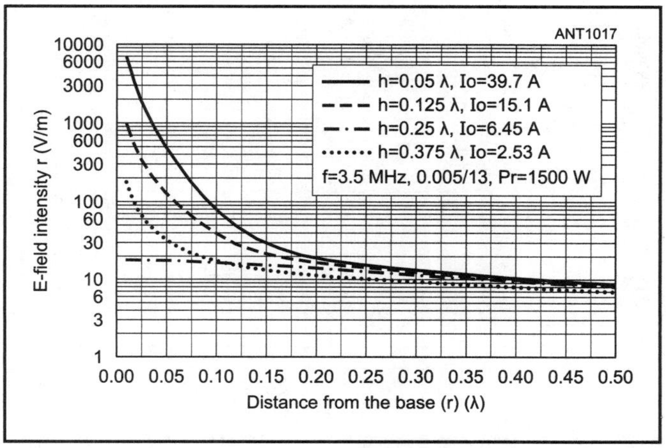

Figure 3.12 — E_z intensity as a function of distance from the base in wavelengths. Data is for a vertical at 3.5 MHz.

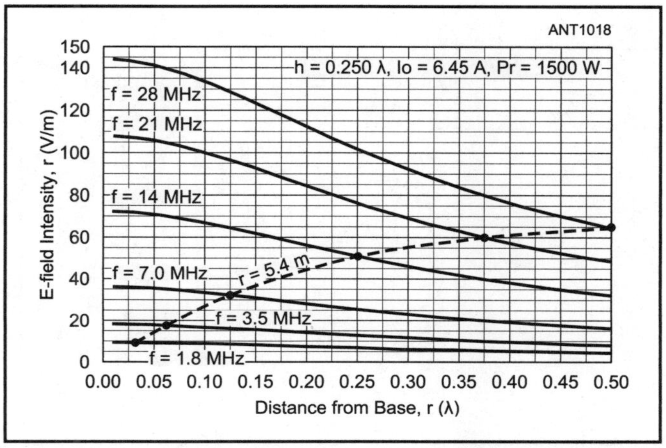

Figure 3.14 — E_z intensity as a function of distance from the base in wavelengths. Data is for a λ/4 vertical.

Similarly, we can account for the power dissipated in the ground (P_g) by adding a loss resistance (R_g) in series with R_r. The ground loss is:

$$P_g = R_g I_o^2 \tag{5}$$

Additional losses due to conductors, loading coils, etc can also be simulated by adding more series loss resistances to the equivalent circuit but for this discussion we will ignore these additional losses although they can be significant in real antennas. The total input power (P_T) is simply the sum of P_r and P_g

The efficiency (η) of a vertical can be expressed as:

$$\eta = \frac{P_r}{P_r + P_g} = \frac{P_r}{P_T} \tag{6}$$

This can be restated in terms of resistances as:

$$\eta = \frac{R_r}{R_r + R_g} = \frac{1}{1 + \frac{R_g}{R_r}} \tag{7}$$

In essence, efficiency is the ratio of the radiated power to the total input power. Another way of saying this is that efficiency depends on the ratio of ground loss resistance to radiation resistance. The smaller we make R_g the more power will be radiated for a given input power. Reducing R_g is the purpose of the ground system.

We can determine P_g near the vertical from the E- and H-fields shown earlier. Given P_g and I_o we can calculate R_g and from that the radiation efficiency. For this discussion we will omit the mathematical details but these can be found in the spreadsheet referenced earlier.

In the following discussion the radiated power is kept constant at 1.5 kW but the total input power may be much greater because it will include the power dissipated in the soil which can become very large for short antennas with limited ground systems. The ground losses shown in **Figures 3.16** and **3.17** are what you would see if the ground system were simply a long stake driven into the soil beneath the antenna.

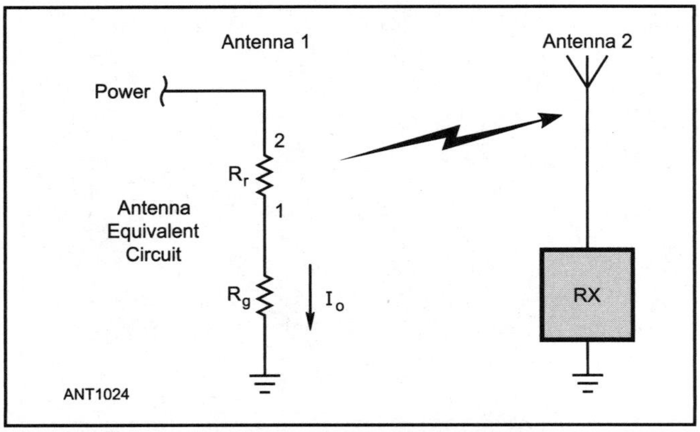

Figure 3.15 — Equivalent circuit for a vertical in terms of R_r and R_g.

The size of these losses makes it clear why we need to add a radial ground system around the base of a vertical.

Figure 3.16 shows the total ground loss (including both E- and H-field losses) within a radius r (in λ) around the base of verticals with different heights at 3.5 MHz, over average ground (σ = 0.005 S/m and ε_r = 13). For all heights the loss is significant but becomes almost astronomical for very short antennas. For example, the loss associated with the 0.050 λ vertical (about 13 feet for 3.5 MHz) amounts to a signal loss of almost 14 dB; in other words, over 20 kW of power is lost in the ground in order to produce 1.5 kW of radiated power. The efficiency of each antenna (using the values for R_r listed in Table 3.2) is listed in **Table 3.3**.

The efficiencies listed in Table 3.3 make it clear why some additional ground system beyond a simple ground stake is highly desirable in most installations. Keep in mind that these numbers are for one particular ground type (average). Poorer grounds will have even higher losses but better soils will have lower losses. Even a λ/4 vertical will have more

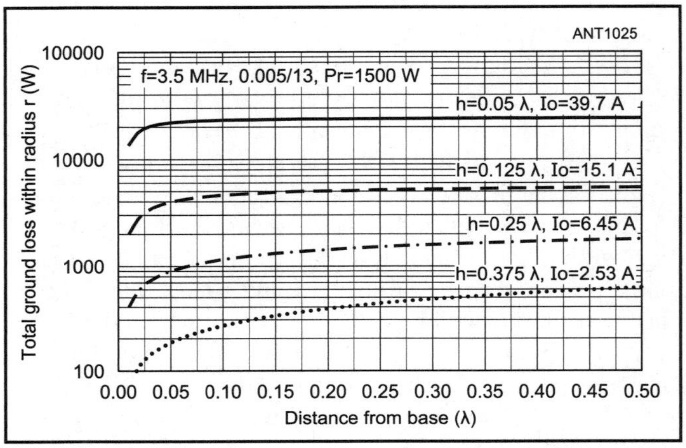

Figure 3.16 — Total ground loss within a fixed radius around verticals of different heights at 3.5 MHz.

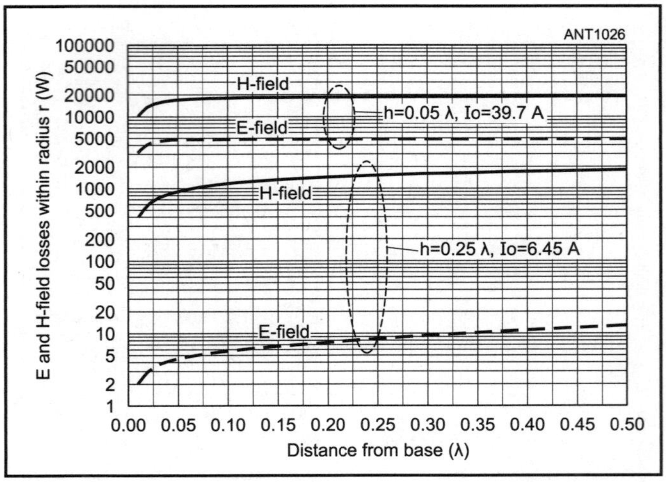

Figure 3.17 — Comparison between E- and H-field losses for two antenna heights.

Table 3.3
Efficiency for Verticals of Different Heights with Ground System Consisting of Only a Ground Stake in Average Soil

Height (h) (λ)	*Efficiency* (%)	*Power Loss* (dB)
0.050	4	–13.8
0.125	21	–6.7
0.250	46	–3.4
0.375	71	–1.5

Saltwater Grounds

Saltwater is often cited or imagined to be the very best ground for an HF vertical antenna. While very good, the issues to be considered are discussed by Rudy Severns, N6LF, in the paper "Some Thoughts on Vertical Ground Systems over Seawater," included with this book's downloadable supplemental information.

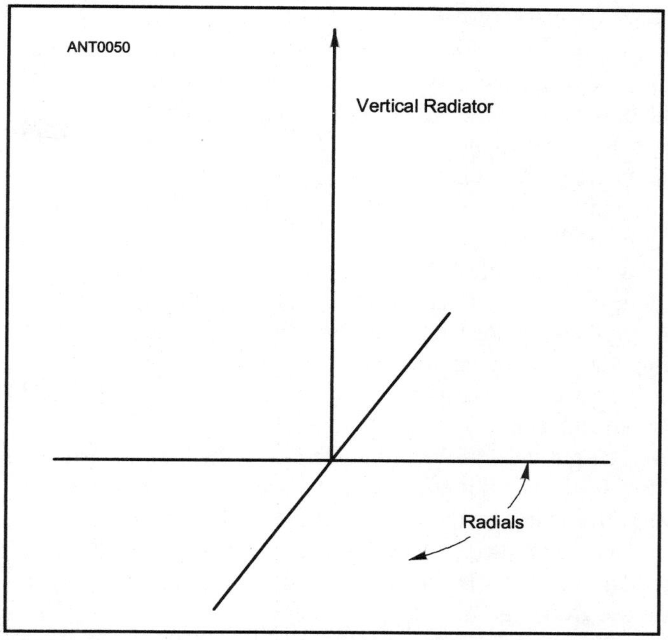

Figure 3.18 — Example of a radial wire ground system.

than 3 dB of signal loss for a given input power because over half the input power is dissipated in the soil. This shows us that *the shorter the vertical, the more critical the ground system is!*

Figure 3.16 also shows that most of the loss is occurring within $\lambda/8$ of the base which correlates with the field intensities shown in Figures 3.13 and 3.14. When designing radial ground systems this ground loss distribution is reflected in the need to increase the number of radials close to the base.

Figure 3.16 shows the total loss in the soil due to both E- and H-fields. However, the relative contribution of each field component to the total varies greatly with the height of the vertical. Figure 3.17 shows a comparison between the E and H losses for h = $\lambda/4$ and h = 0.05 λ. For the $\lambda/4$ vertical the E-field losses are very small compared to the H-field losses but for the shorter vertical both the E- and H-field losses increase dramatically and the E-field loss is comparable to the H-field loss. In very short verticals the E-field losses can become larger than the H-field losses.

3.2.3 WIRE GROUND SYSTEMS

Figure 3.18 illustrates what we mean by a "radial" ground system. The ground system wires are connected together at the base of the antenna and arranged radially outward from the base. Why radial wires? Why not wires in circles or some other shape? As shown in Figure 3.10, the H-field lines have the form of circles around the base of the vertical. When the H-field passes over a conductor there will be a current induced in the conductor which flows at right angles to the H-field vector. In a wire ground system the optimum orientation for the wires is at right angles to the field (i.e. radially). If the wire were oriented parallel to the field (in a circle) there would be no current induced in the wire and the current would simply flow in the soil instead. In some cases where multiple verticals are present (i.e. in an array for example) it may not be practical to use only radial wires. Some form of coarse mesh may be needed.

Buried or Ground Surface Radial Systems

There are different ways to install wire ground systems: the wires may be buried in the soil a few inches or lying on the ground surface or elevated several feet above ground or even some combination of these. In addition, in elevated systems there may be interconnections between the radial wires to form what is called a "counterpoise". Another possibility is to use a coarse rectangular mesh, either on the ground surface or elevated. We will discuss all these options but for the moment we'll focus on radial systems either buried or lying on the ground surface.

If we know the values for E and H, I_0 and the soil electrical characteristics we can determine P_g. We can then determine R_g directly from P_g:

$$R_g = \frac{P_g}{I_0^2} \tag{8}$$

R_g is *not* a resistance unique to a particular ground system that you can measure with some kind of ohmmeter. It is simply the relation between a given excitation current (I_0) and the power dissipated in the soil (P_g) for a given vertical. P_g in turn depends not only on the soil characteristics but on both I_0 *and* the details of the vertical itself, i.e. height, loading, etc. For this reason R_g for a given ground system *will change* as we change the vertical even if the soil characteristics and the physical ground system itself are kept constant.

Ideal Ground Screens

Initially we'll assume that the ground system is ideal: i.e. a high conductivity ground screen that covers the soil from the base out to some radius "r". This ideal ground screen will give us the minimum possible R_g for ground system of a given radius. Later we'll look at R_g for more practical wire ground systems with a limited number of radials to see how they compare. From the ideal ground screen information we will know what the ultimate limits are and can determine when adding more wire might result in only a small improvement. Surprisingly, it does not take a large number of radials to give a good approximation of an ideal ground screen.

Figure 3.19 is an example of R_g as a function of ground screen radius for several antenna heights at 3.5 MHz, over average ground. As we saw in Figure 3.16, near the base of the vertical the total ground loss is large but as we move outward from the base the *additional* ground loss becomes much smaller. This means that the values for R_g fall quickly as r initially increases but as the radius of the screen gets larger, the rate of decrease in R_g slows down.

If we take the values for R_r from Table 3.2 and combine these with the values for R_g in Figure 3.19 and use Eq 8, we can calculate the efficiency as shown in **Figure 3.20**. The efficiency is stated in dB so that this graph tells us directly how much our signal will improve as we expand the radius of the ground screen. For example, for h = 0.25 λ, expanding the screen radius from 0.01 λ to 0.125 λ increases the signal by 1.5 dB. If we further increase the radius to 0.250 λ we pick up another 0.6 dB and if we go to a screen radius of 0.375 λ the gain is an additional 0.4 dB. Clearly there is a substantial advantage to having a screen with a radius of at least λ/8 but as we increase the size, the incremental improvement gets smaller. In general for amateur applications expanding the ground screen radius beyond λ/4 is seldom worth the additional cost and effort at least on the lower bands (160 and 80 meters). But as pointed out earlier, we can make a case for larger ground systems (in terms of λ) at higher frequencies.

Figure 3.19 shows R_g for one frequency and one ground characteristic. **Figures 3.21** and **3.22** show what happens to R_g as we change frequency or ground characteristics for a given height (λ/4 in this example).

Figure 3.21 is a graph of the changes in R_g with frequency for several different screen radii. This graph is for a λ/4 vertical over average ground. What the figure shows us is that for a given antenna, screen radius (in wavelengths) and ground characteristic, R_g can increase significantly as we go to higher frequencies. For example with r = λ/4, R_g = 7 Ω at 3.5 MHz but at 28 MHz a λ/4 screen has an R_g = 12 Ω. If we increased the screen radius at 28 MHz to 0.375 λ, R_g drops back down to 5 Ω. Expanding the screen radius from λ/4 to 3λ/8 at 28 MHz means extending the radial lengths from 2.7 meters (8.8 feet) to 4 meters (13.2 feet) which is very practical. The message is: *as we go higher in frequency we should consider using a ground screen with a larger electrical radius (in terms of λ) and/or more radials.* Fortunately, as we go up in frequency the wavelength gets shorter so it's easier to add more and/or longer radials for a given total amount of wire.

From Figure 3.22 we see that with lower quality soils R_g

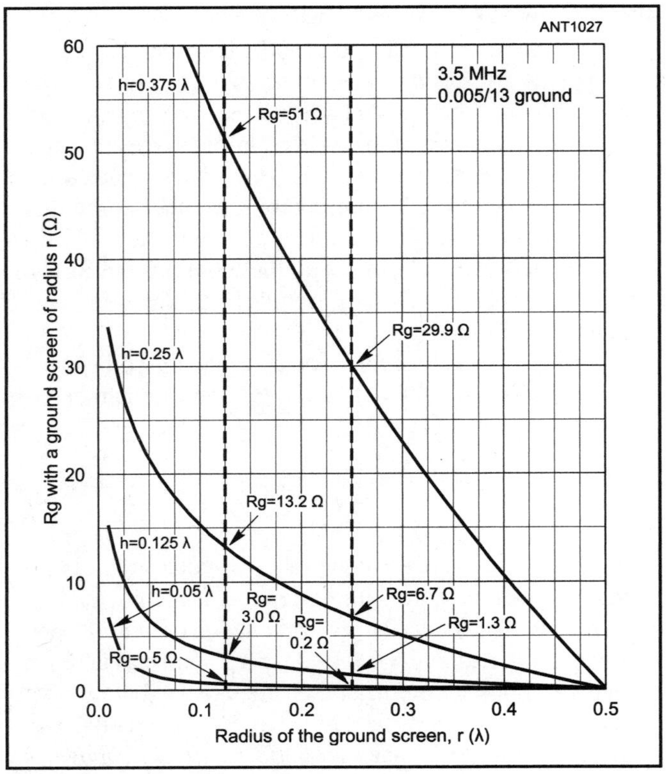

Figure 3.19 — Variation in R_g with ground screen radius. Normalized to include losses out to r = 0.5 λ.

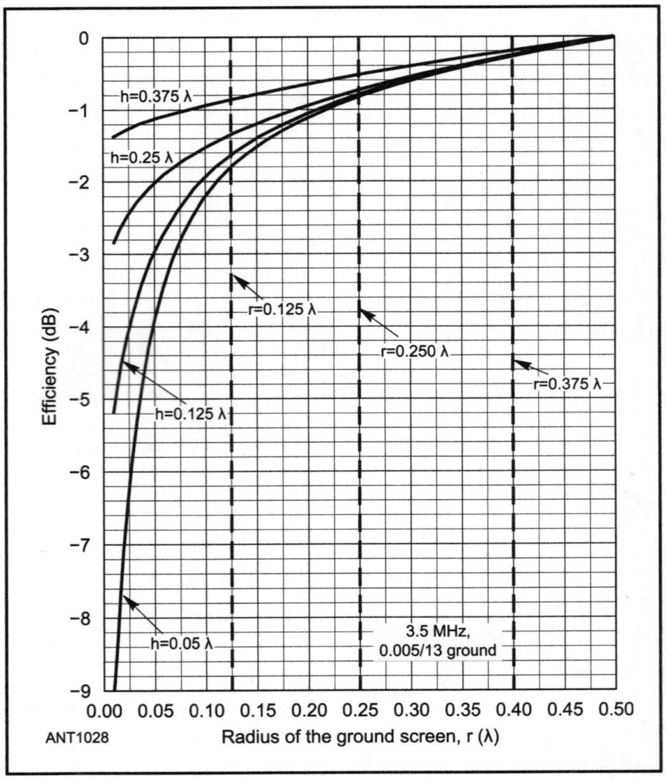

Figure 3.20 — Efficiency in dB as a function of ground screen radius.

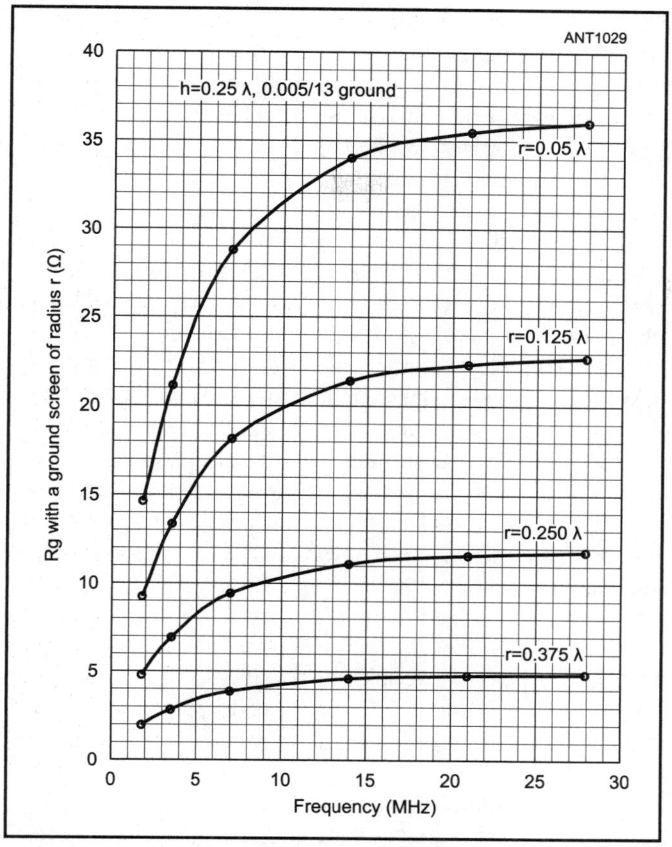

Figure 3.21 — Variation in R_g with frequency for h = λ/4 for several ground screen radii (in wavelengths) over average ground.

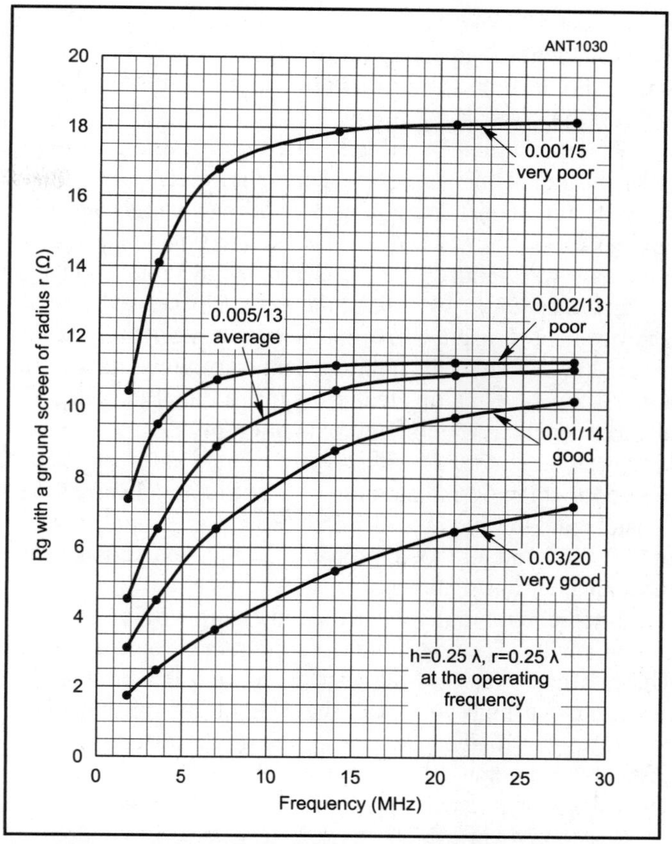

Figure 3.22 — Variation in R_g with frequency for h = r = λ/4 at the operating frequency.

Ground Radial System Design

Building an effective ground radial system is a study in compromises: space available, length of the radials, and available wire. The article "Maximum-Gain Radial Ground Systems for Vertical Antennas," by Al Christman, K3LC, shows you how to build the best radial system for the amount of wire you have available. It is available with this book's downloadable supplemental information. Appendix A for this chapter presents K3LC's results for average soil on the 40, 80, and 160 meter bands.

is significantly higher and it becomes increasingly important to use a more extensive ground system to maintain efficiency.

Real Wire Radial Systems

In practice, ground systems are usually made with wire in the form of a radial fan like that shown in Figure 3.18. How a particular ground system performs compared to an ideal ground screen can be determined using mathematical analysis or from *NEC* software modeling or from actual measurements on real antennas. All three routes give essentially the same answers but for this discussion we will use actual measurements on real antennas and also some *NEC* modeling results.

Figure 3.23 shows the measured signal improvement as λ/4 (33 feet) radials lying on the ground surface were added

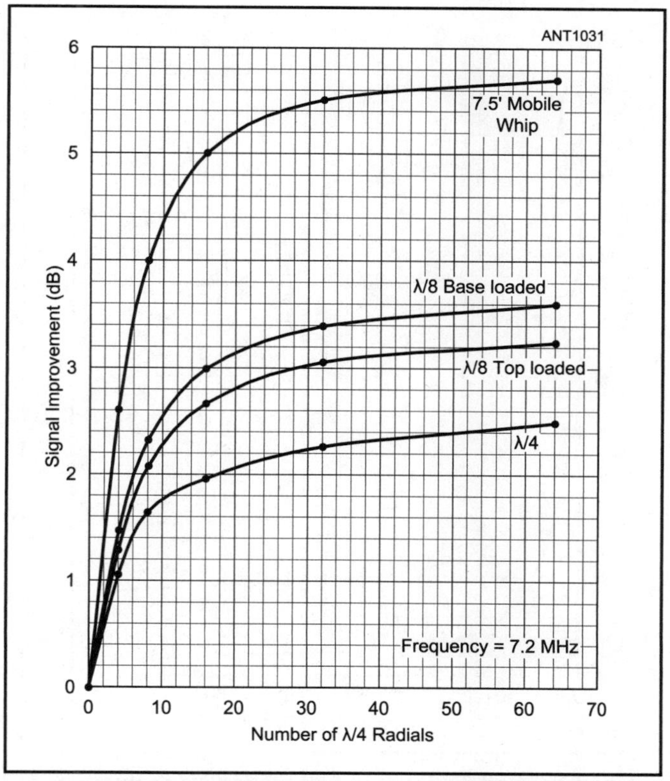

Figure 3.23 — Signal improvement for typical 40-meter verticals as the radial number is increased from 0 to 64.

to different 40 meter antennas: a λ/4 vertical, a λ/8 vertical with sufficient top-loading to resonate it, a λ/8 vertical resonated with an inductor at the base and a 7.5 foot 40 meter mobile whip.

The measurements began with only a single ground stake, no radials. Figure 3.23 shows the increase in signal strength (for a constant input power) for each antenna as the number of λ/4 radials was increased from 0 to 64. Initially, as radials were added, the signal improved rapidly but by the time there were 16 radials, the rate of increase in signal improvement turned a corner and started to decrease. Going from 32 to 64 radials the improvement was only a fraction of a dB (0.2 dB). What this tells us is that a radial fan with 32 or more radials is a good approximation of an ideal ground screen, at least for λ/4 radials. For short, loaded antennas over poor soils, 64 radials might be justified and should be considered. However, the standard broadcast ground system of 120, 0.4 λ radials would probably be a waste of copper for most amateur installations.

Another important thing we see in Figure 3.23 is that short loaded antennas benefit more from the same ground system. This is because (as shown earlier) the E- and H-field intensities are much higher close to the base of shorter antennas. Note also that in short antennas, moving the loading up the vertical, top-loading for example or placing the loading coil above the base, improves the signal for a given ground system.

The soil over which this experiment was conducted would be rated as very good ($\sigma = 0.015$ S/m, $\varepsilon_r = 30$). Over that soil the improvement going from 0 to 64 radials ranged from 2.5 to 5.7 dB. Over poor or even average soils the improvement would be substantially greater. Figure 3.23 also shows how important is to have at least a simple radial system. Sixteen radials is pretty much the practical minimum, especially over poor soils.

Measuring the signal strength for a given input power to the antenna, as radials are added to the ground system is a very direct way to gauge when adding more radials will give only a small improvement but for most amateurs that's not very practical. There is a simpler way to gauge when there are sufficient radials in the ground system. We can look at the feed point impedance which is a simple, direct measurement. An example of the variation of the resistive part (R_{in}) of the input impedance as radials are added to a ground system is given in **Figure 3.24**. The values are for the same antennas used in Figure 3.23. Note that for the 7.5 foot mobile whip, the series resistance of the loading coil has been subtracted from the measured feed point impedance.

If we assume that $R_{in} = R_r + R_g$ and that R_r is constant as we add radials (a reasonable approximation), then the leveling out of the curves for radial numbers above 16 can be interpreted as meaning that the minimum R_g for that radial length has been reached. Again, we see that 16 radials are pretty much the minimum but by the time we get to 32 radials the rate of change is quite small. Figures 3.23 and 3.24 tell the same tale.

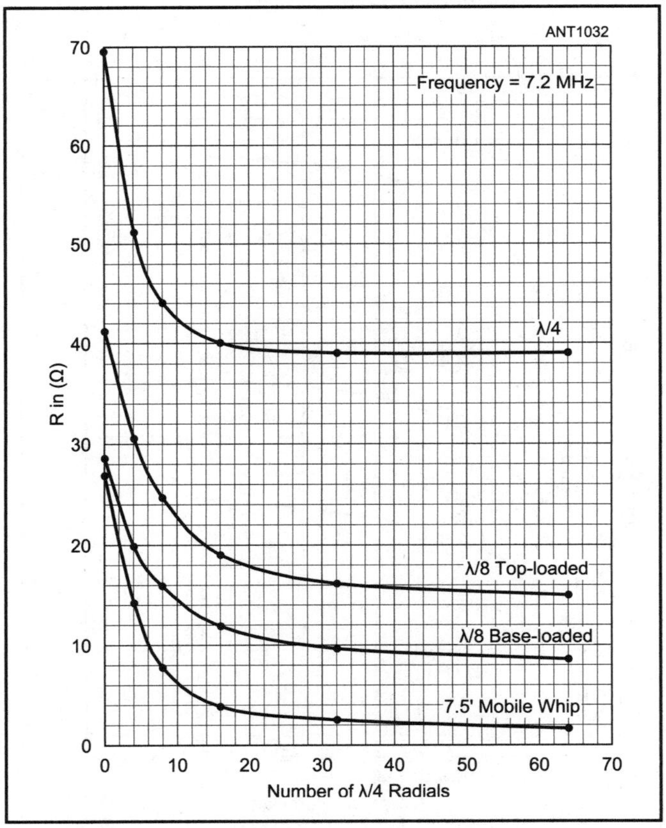

Figure 3.24 — Variation in R_g as a function of the number of λ/4 radials.

The Broadcast 120-Radial Ground System

The 1937 IRE study by Brown, Lewis, and Epstein is often cited as the origin of the "standard" broadcast ground system with 120 λ/4 radials. [11] This is a misunderstanding of what the report actually describes, which is 120 symmetrically laid-out radials of a length that results in 0.05 λ between the ends of the radials. This length happens to be close to λ/4 and so it was a natural assumption to assume it was specified to make the radial resonant as a λ/4 element. As is stated in this chapter, a radial laying on the ground will have an electrical length quite a bit longer than its physical length, so it is unlikely to act like a wire λ/4 long.

The importance of the ground radial system is to reduce ground losses by providing a low-loss path for current flowing to the feed point that would otherwise flow through soil. Broadcasters, having resources beyond the typical amateur and a strong economic reason to avoid ground losses, opt for the 120-radial system which is well beyond the point of reasonable return for amateurs. As you can see from the numerous graphs in this chapter, nothing special happens when a radial on or below the surface of the ground is λ/4 long. The *NCJ* article by K3LC on optimum radial systems referenced earlier in this section provides excellent guidance on how to get the best results from your radial system, even with far fewer than 120 radials!

Optimizing Radial Lengths

In the real world the amount of wire available for a ground system may be limited. How should we use the available wire: a few long radials or a bunch of short ones?[2,3,4] We can use *NEC* modeling to address this question. **Figures 3.25** and **3.26** show the signal improvement as both the number and the length of the radials are changed. Both figures assume f = 1.8 MHz and average ground (σ = 0.005 S/m, ε_r = 13). Figure 3.25 is for h = λ/8 and Figure 3.26 is for h = λ/4. These figures illustrate a number of important points and provide a guide to the optimal use of a given total length of radial wire in the ground system. The 0 dB reference is four λ/8 radials. In both figures we see that when only a few radials are employed (<16) there is very little increase in signal when longer radials are used. In general, from both modeling and experiments, we can say that a few long radials make a poor ground system.[5] From the graphs we can see that longer radials become effective only as we increase the number of radials.

These graphs show how to optimize your signal for a given total length of radial wire. The dashed lines connect points which have the same total wire length in the ground system. For example, if we have a total of 2 λ of wire we could make four λ/2 radials or eight λ/4 radials or 16 λ/8 radials. From the graphs we can see that with a total of 2 λ of wire the best radial system would be 16 λ/8 radials. That would be an improvement of over 3 dB for the λ/8 vertical and 1 dB for the λ/4 vertical. Similarly, if 4 λ of wire is available then the optimum use would be 32 λ/8 radials. When we go to 8 λ of wire, things change a bit. For the h = λ/8 antenna either 64 λ/8 or 32 λ/4 radials will work about the same. However, for the h = λ/4 antenna the best use of the wire would be 32 λ/4 radials. The reason that a large number of short radials are effective stems directly from the high field intensities close to the base of a vertical. The first priority is to reduce the losses close to the base. As more wire becomes available and the losses close to the base have been reduced then reducing the losses further out becomes useful.

A bit of long held conventional wisdom among amateurs is that "the length of the radials should be similar to the height of the vertical." Figures 3.25 and 3.26 give partial support to that belief. When 8 λ of wire is available, λ/8 radials will work fine for a λ/8 vertical but a smaller number of λ/4 radials work better for the λ/4 vertical. This stems from the much higher field intensities associated with the λ/8 vertical. In short antennas it's very important to use numerous radials close to the base. But in both cases, when sufficient wire is available, there comes a point where fewer but longer radials are a better choice.

Radial Screens with Missing Sectors

In many installations a vertical may have to be located close to an obstacle such as a building or a driveway and it may not be possible to have a full 360° symmetrical radial field. The lack of radials in a subsector of the radial system will increase ground loss because there aren't any radials in that sector to keep the field out of the soil! In addition

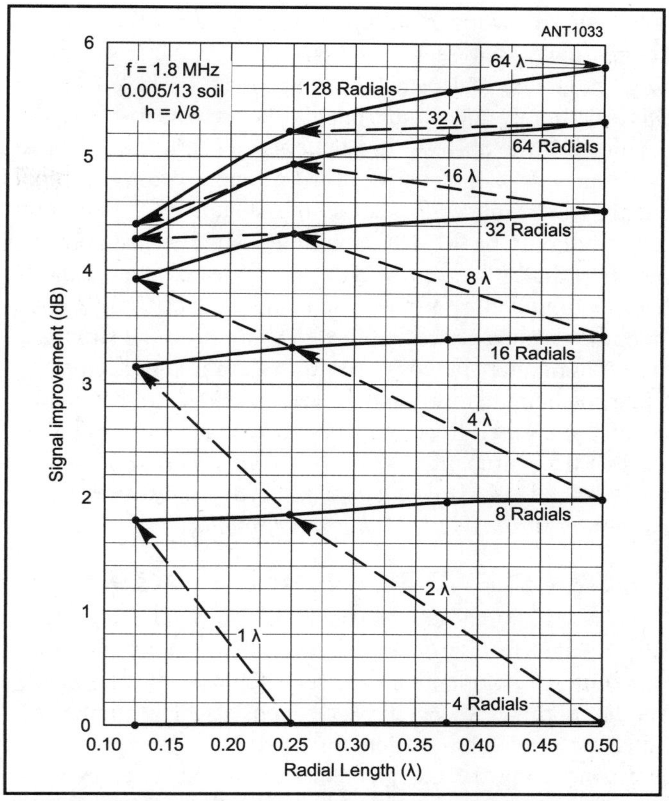

Figure 3.25 — Comparison of radial lengths and number versus signal improvement for a given total amount of radial wire (in λ). In this example h = λ/8.

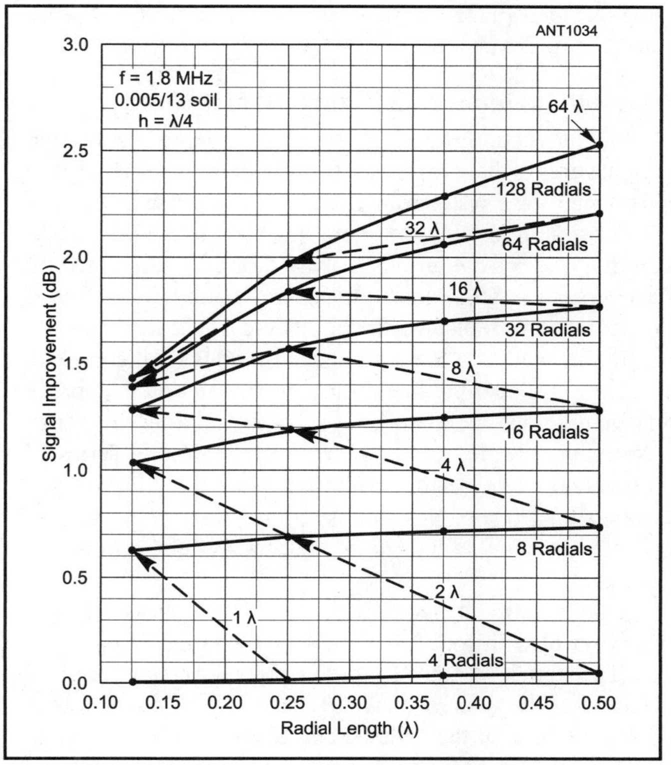

Figure 3.26 — Comparison of radial lengths and number versus signal improvement for a given total amount of radial wire (in λ). In this example h = λ/4.

there will be pattern distortion. Depending on the size of the missing radial sector and the soil characteristics the signal reduction and pattern distortion can be several dB.[6] This is definitely undesirable but may be unavoidable in some situations. If the obstacle is a building, locating the antenna along one side will result in a 180° missing sector but if the antenna can be moved to a corner of the building the missing sector will only be 90° which will be a significant improvement over the 180° case. From the earlier discussion we know that the ground close to the base is the most critical. If possible, the antenna should be moved away from the structure and a fan of short radials inserted in the missing sector. Of course the building itself may have considerable effect on the antenna. It's generally a good idea to keep antennas as far as possible from structures. *If space is limited in all directions, it may be better to move the antenna away from the structure and accept short radials all the way around.*

3.2.4 ELEVATED GROUND SYSTEMS

Ground systems can elevated above ground and electrically isolated from ground. The most common system uses four or more λ/4 radial wires placed a few feet above ground. Another form of elevated system consists of a number of radial wires, which have lengths <λ/4, perhaps with a skirt wire connecting the outer ends of the radial wires as well as interconnecting wires between the radials closer to the base. It is also possible to use an elevated wire mesh. These last two options are often referred to as a "counterpoise" or "capacitive" ground system. A λ/4 vertical with several λ/4 radials (usually four radials) is called a "ground-plane" antenna. Ground plane antennas are discussed in the **Dipoles and Monopoles** chapter.

Elevated Systems with Simple Radial Wires

In this section we discuss radial systems made from straight wires of the same length for single band use. Multiband and counterpoise systems are discussed in following sections.

For a number of years there has been much discussion regarding the relative merits of buried or ground surface radials versus elevated radials. Modeling using *NEC* software has consistently indicated that a few elevated radials should perform as well as a large number of radials on the ground. Modeling has also predicted that the signal would improve very quickly with height even for small elevations. To verify these modeling predictions a carefully controlled series of experiments were performed at 7.2 MHz directly comparing the signal from a vertical using either an on-the-ground system with many radials or an elevated system with only a few radials.[7]

The experiment began with the base of the vertical at ground level with four λ/4 radials lying on the ground surface. The signal strength at a remote point was recorded. This was used as the reference level (0 dB). The next step was to elevate the base of the antenna and the four radials in increments from zero to 48 inches. At each point the change in signal from the reference level was recorded. The second part of the experiment left all the radials on the ground surface but starting with four radials incrementally increased the number of radials. **Figure 3.27** shows the results of that experiment. The *NEC* modeling predictions agree well with the observed behavior:

1) Even a small elevation makes a considerable difference in signal and

2) The elevated system is equivalent to the ground system with 32 or more radials.

One additional point should be emphasized regarding this experimental work. For the 4-radial elevated system to work as well as the multiple radial ground based system, during the experiment it was found that very great care had to be taken to assure that the radial geometry was highly symmetric, the radial lengths identical and that the currents in the radials were all equal and in phase with the base current as discussed below.

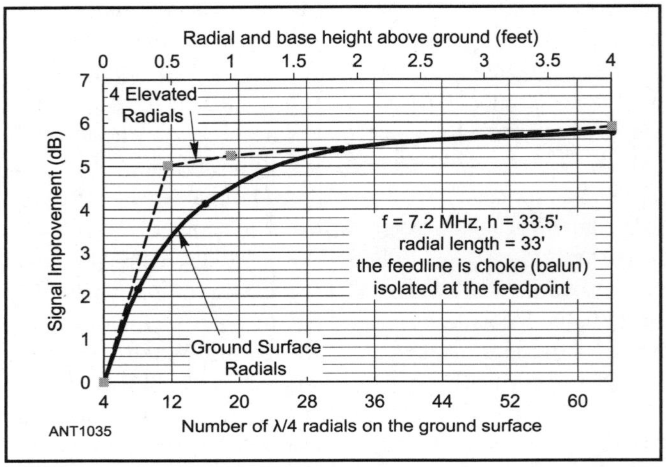

Figure 3.27 — Comparison between four elevated λ/4 radials and λ/4 radials on the ground surface. Note that this graph has two different horizontal axes. The arrows associate the plots with the appropriate horizontal axis.

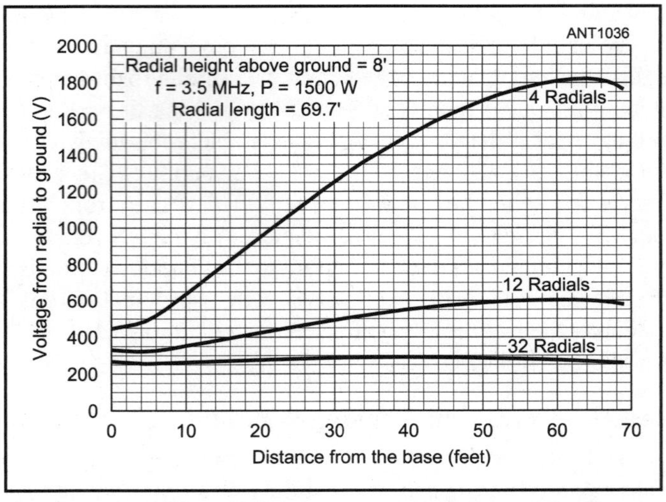

Figure 3.28 — Examples of the voltage from an elevated radial wire to ground with different numbers of radials. The input power to the vertical is 1500 W, the operating frequency is 3.5 MHz and the radial system is elevated 8 feet above ground.

Safety Consideration with Elevated Radials

Before looking more closely at the assertion that four elevated radials are equivalent to many ground-based radials we need to consider a safety issue. Like a vertical located at ground level, elevated verticals will have high voltages on the vertical but in addition, elevated radial systems can have very high fields and voltages on and near the radial wires. **Figure 3.28** gives examples of the voltage from a radial wire to ground for 4, 12 and 32 λ/4 radial systems.

Note that the voltages vary from 250 V_{RMS} to nearly 2000 V_{RMS}! These voltages are proportional to $\sqrt{P_{in}}$ so that if you drop the power from 1500 W to 100 W, a factor of 15:1, the voltages only drop by a factor of less than four. Even at 100 W, they are still very high! For safety reasons, elevated radial systems are usually placed well above head-height, 8 feet or more. This is done so that people or animals cannot accidentally run into the wires but also because the high voltages which are present on the radials, particularly at the ends, can cause severe RF burns. This hazard is typical of elevated ground systems.

Given the high potentials at the ends of the radials, high quality insulators should be used at the radial ends. In addition to the high voltages, the E-field intensities are also very high near the radial ends. This means there is a danger of corona discharge which can erode the wire or even damage a plastic insulator. Where the radial wires are attached to the insulators, care should be taken that the wire ends do not form any sharp points which could be sites for corona discharge. Usually a ball of solder is used to cover the wire end. This problem will become more acute as the altitude of the station increases.

Some Alternative Elevated Systems

It is not always practical to have the base of the antenna high above ground. For example, a 20 meter λ/4 vertical will only be about 17 feet long and made from small diameter aluminum tubing. Elevating this is not a great challenge. But a 160 meter λ/4 vertical will be about 130 feet high and probably made from tower sections or heavy tubing. It may not be possible to elevate the base of the larger antennas very high. As an alternative, the elevated radials can be arranged in several ways as shown in **Figure 3.29**. The simplest approach when the base is close to ground as shown in (B) is to just slope the radials out at an angle. While this approach can place the radial tips well above head height it still leaves a lot of the radial at low heights. Another approach (C) is to slope the initial portion of the radial upward at an angle of 45° until a height of 8 feet is reached and then to run the rest of the radial out at constant height. These are referred to as "gull wing" radials.[8]

Another problem that often arises (particularly on 80 and 160 meters) is that there may not be enough space for full λ/4 radials. That's OK because as shown in Figure 3.29D, shorter radials can be used and an inductor added at the base of the antenna to resonate it.[9] (Note, it is also possible to place individual inductors in each radial which may be helpful in balancing the current division between the radials.) Another alternative configuration is shown in Figure 3.29E.

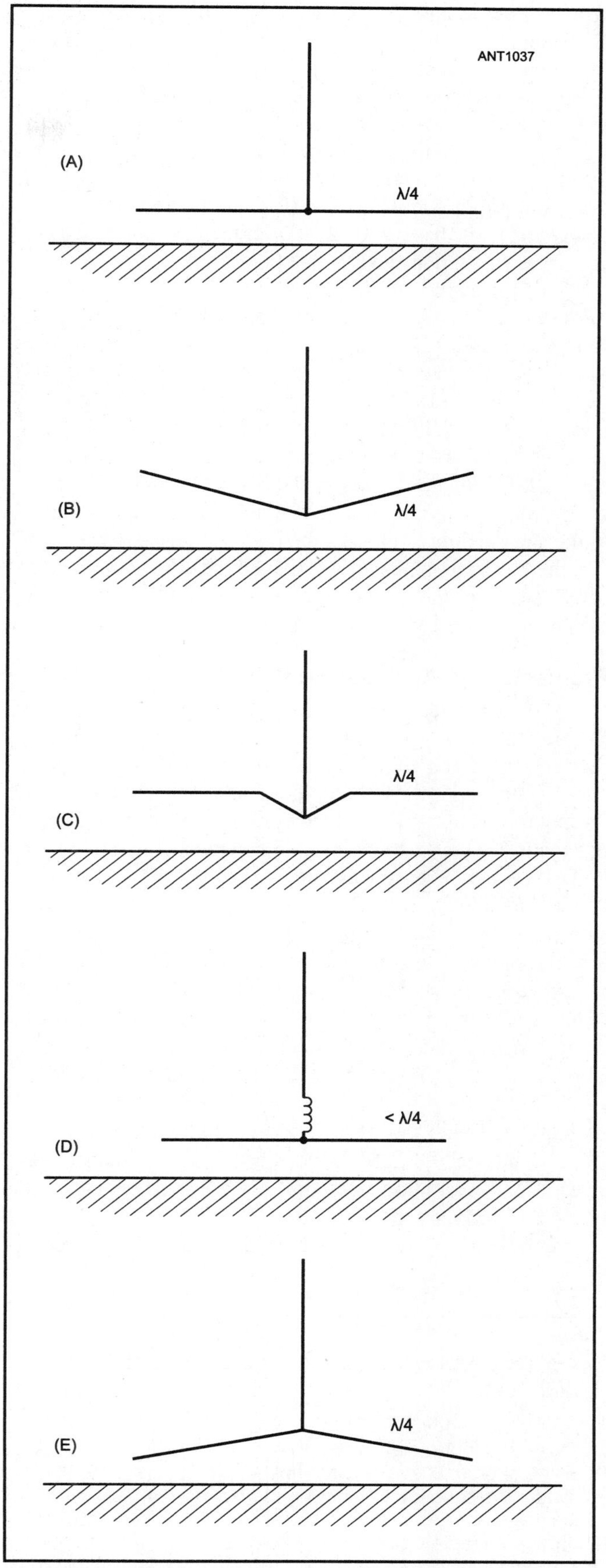

Figure 3.29 — Alternate elevated ground system configurations.

In this case the base is higher than the ends of the radials. This configuration is often used at 20 meters and above where the radials are self-supporting conductors. When the radials are anchored only at the base some droop to the outer end of the radials would be normal. In some cases the radials are deliberately sloped downward to increase the feed point impedance and provide a lower SWR. It should be pointed out that configurations (B) and (C), where the radials slope upward from the base, will have lower feed point impedances and somewhat reduced SWR bandwidths.[7]

This raises the question: how much is the antenna performance degraded by these alternate schemes? Again this can be addressed either with modeling or experimentally. The earlier experiment comparing elevated and ground surface radials on 40 meters was extended to compare the alternatives given in Figure 3.29. The results are listed in **Table 3.4**. All the alternatives were tested with four radials at 7.2 MHz. The base tuning inductor in option (D) had a Q of 350. The conventional system with all of the radials and the base elevated to the same height is used as the 0 dB reference. Except for (E), there is a small penalty associated with the alternate elevated radial configurations (on the order of –0.5 dB) which may be acceptable in many situations.

Problems with Elevated Radials

The simplicity of elevated systems with only three or four radials is very attractive because, at least in principle, they can be just as effective as much more extensive ground based systems. However, as pointed out above with regard to the experimental work, elevated systems with small numbers of radials are very sensitive to the mechanical details of the radials: i.e. length, droop, asymmetry in the radial fan, nearby conductors and so forth. The input impedance, current division between radials, radiation pattern, resonant frequency and efficiency of the antenna are all sensitive to even small asymmetries. It has been demonstrated experimentally that radial geometry asymmetry[9] and irregularities in ground characteristics under the radial fan[10] will cause problems. The following discussion explores some of these problems.

Typically a vertical with an elevated ground system will be fabricated with the vertical and the radial lengths calculated from L = 234/f in MHz which is 5% shorter than a free-space λ/4. The common wisdom that 5% shortening should be used is derived from work done in the 1930s but is only an approximation. When the base impedance of an actual antenna is checked, the resonant frequency will often be substantially different from what was expected and dependent on the number of radials as well as their length.

NEC modeling can be used to explore what's happening. The modeling is done in two steps: first model the vertical radiator element over a perfect ground and adjust its length to resonate at the desired frequency (7.2 MHz in this example). This example uses a #12 AWG wire and to be resonant at 7.2 MHz, h = 32.22 feet which is about 5.5% shorter than free space. The next step in the modeling is to add various numbers of horizontal #12 AWG wire radials. Each of the radials has the same length as the vertical (L = 32.22 feet). **Figure 3.30** shows the resonant frequency as a function of the number of radials from 2 to 128.

The resonant frequency of the complete antenna with the radials approaches the desired 7.2 MHz but doesn't quite get there. Even when a large number of λ/4 radials are used, the radial fan is not the same as an infinite ideal ground. In general, elevated systems should start with radials and perhaps

Table 3.4
Signal Comparison Between Different Elevated Radial Systems.

Radial System Configuration	*Relative Signal*
(A) Base and four radials elevated 4 ft	0.00 dB
(B) Base at ground level, radial ends at 4 ft	–0.47 dB
(C) Base at ground level, gull-wing-radials, ends at 4 ft	–0.65 dB
(D) Base and radials at 4 ft, λ/8 radials with L = 2.2 µH	–0.36 dB
(E) Base at 4 ft and radial ends at 3 ft	+0.10 dB

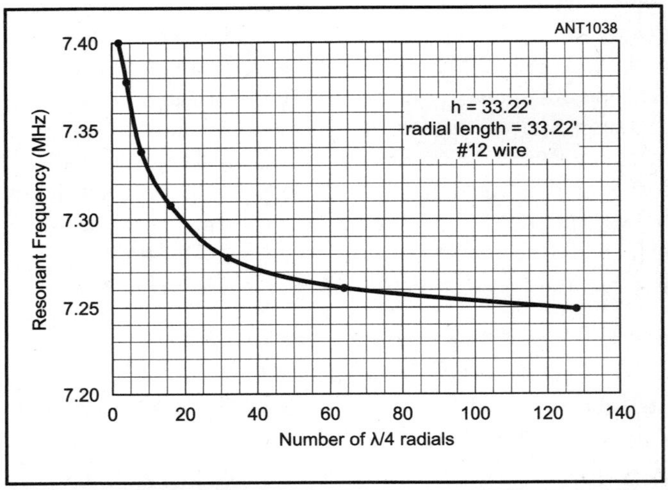

Figure 3.30 — Resonant frequency of a λ/4 vertical for different numbers of elevated radials.

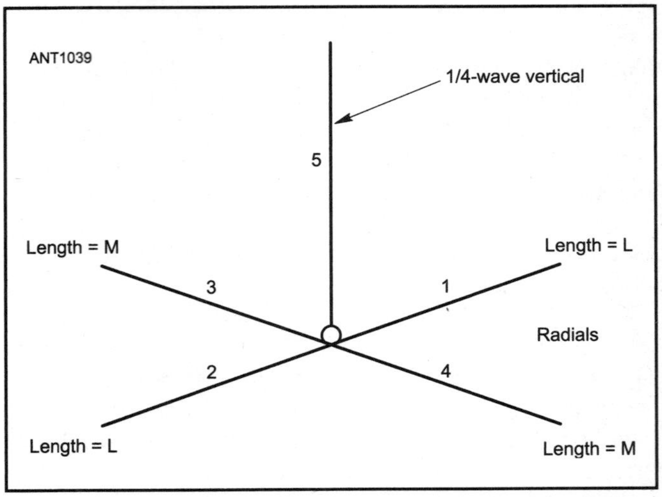

Figure 3.31 — 40-meter λ/4 vertical with four radials. Vertical height is 34.1 feet. The radial lengths are varied.

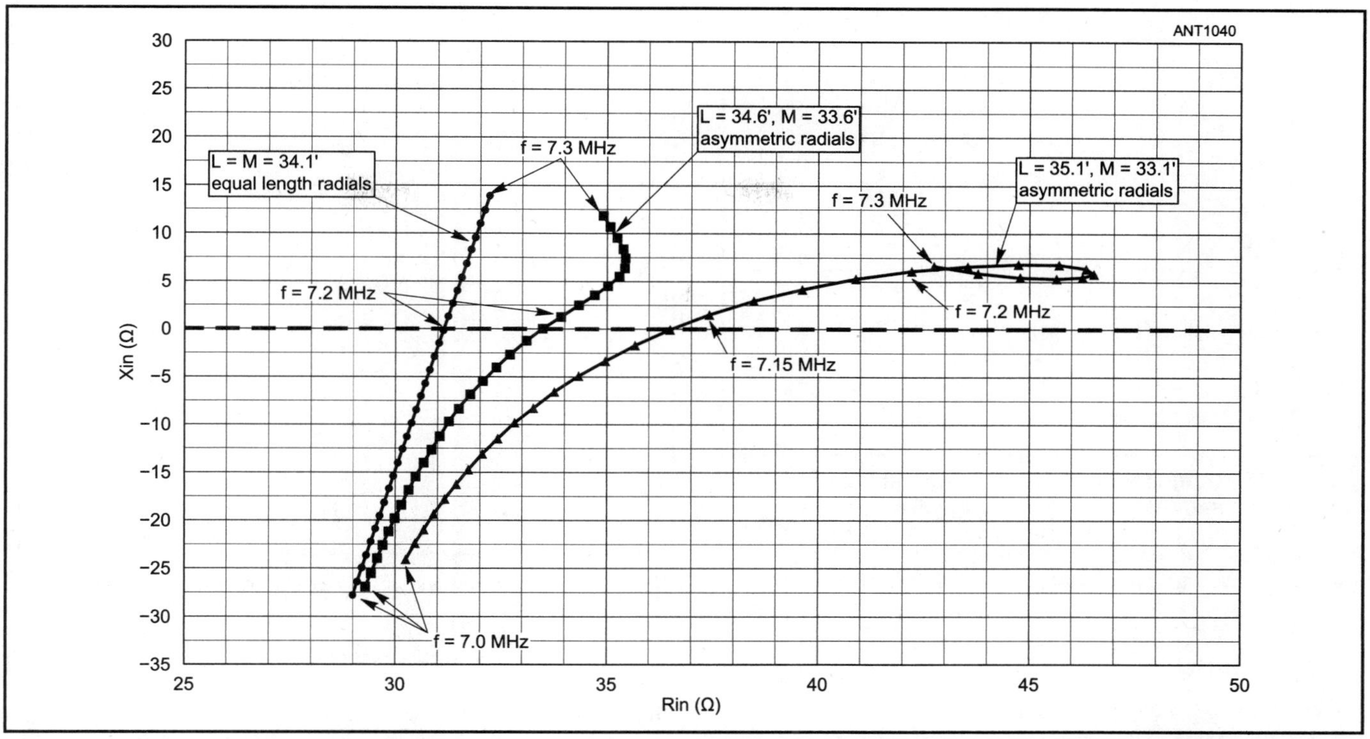

Figure 3.32 — A comparison of the input impedances ($Z_{in} = R_{in} + jX_{in}$) from 7.0 to 7.3 MHz at the feed point of the vertical for symmetric and asymmetric radial lengths.

the vertical radiator, with a length corresponding to the free space value for λ/4 (L = 246/f in MHz) and then trim the radials to resonate the antenna at the desired frequency. There is another reason for starting with a vertical that is a bit taller. When the radials are trimmed to resonate the antenna, the length of the radials will be somewhat shorter than might be expected. This saves wire and reduces the footprint.

A very common problem in elevated systems is that the radials may not all be exactly the same length. Experimentally this has been shown to cause non-uniform current division between the radials which can have a serious effect on the performance of the antenna.[9] We can model an example to demonstrate how severe this effect can be. Start with a 40 meter λ/4 vertical with four radials as shown in **Figure 3.31**, where the base of the vertical and the radials are placed 8 feet above average ground ($\sigma = 0.005$ S/m, $\varepsilon_r = 13$). Radials 1 and 2 form a pair of opposing radials with a length = L. Radials 3 and 4 are a second opposing pair of radials with length = M. First we model the antenna with all the radials the same length (L = M) and then with radials that differ in length (L ≠ M). The initial length for the vertical and the radials was made 34.1 feet to resonate the antenna at 7.2 MHz.

The modeled feed point impedances (from 7.0 to 7.3 MHz) for three different radial length configurations are compared in **Figure 3.32** which is a graph of R_{in} versus X_{in} ($Z_{in} = R_{in} + jX_{in}$ = feed point impedance) as the frequency is varied from 7.0 to 7.3 MHz. The plot on the left is for the case where all the radials are identical (L = M = 34.1 feet). The looping plot on the right is for case where L = 35.6 feet and M = 33.1 feet, this represents a length error of ±2.9%. The middle plot is for L = 34.6 feet and M = 33.6 feet, which is a length error of ±1.4%. Clearly even small radial length asymmetry can have a dramatic effect on the feed point impedance and resonant frequency. The resonant frequency is the point at which $X_{in} = 0$.

But feed point impedance is not the only problem created by asymmetric radial lengths. **Figure 3.33** compares modeled

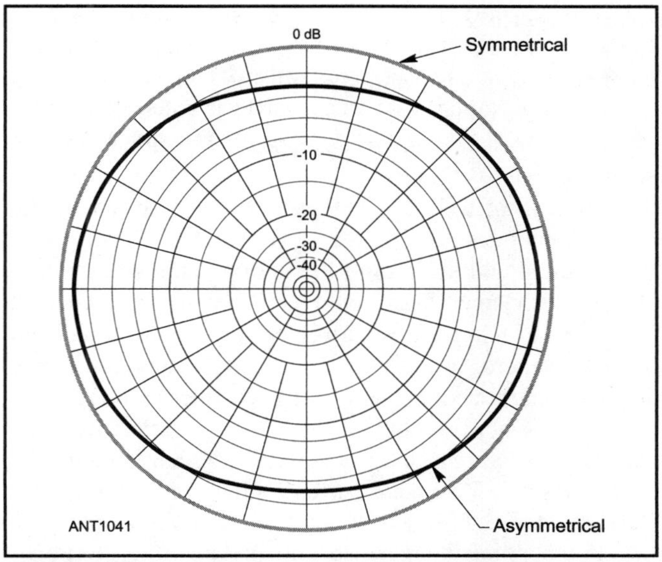

Figure 3.33 — Azimuthal radiation pattern at an elevation angle of 22 degrees, comparing symmetric (L = M = 34.1 feet) and asymmetric (L = 35.1 feet, M = 33.1 feet) radials at 7.25 MHz.

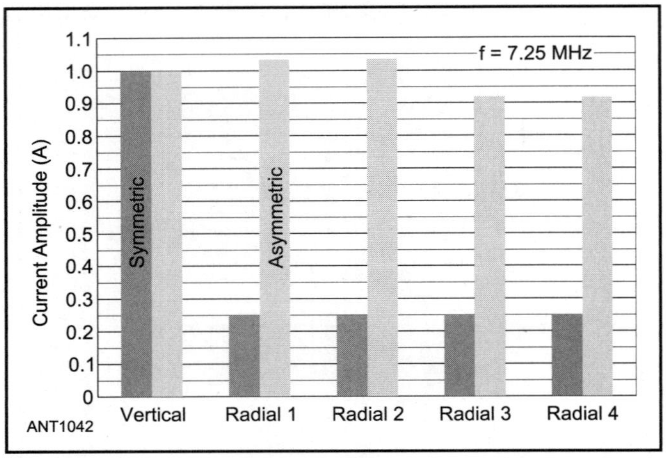

Figure 3.34 — Comparison of radial current at the bases of the vertical and the radials with symmetric (L = M = 34.1 feet) and asymmetric (L = 35.1 feet and M = 33.1 feet) radial lengths. The radials are numbered as shown in Figure 3.31. The current shown is the magnitude.

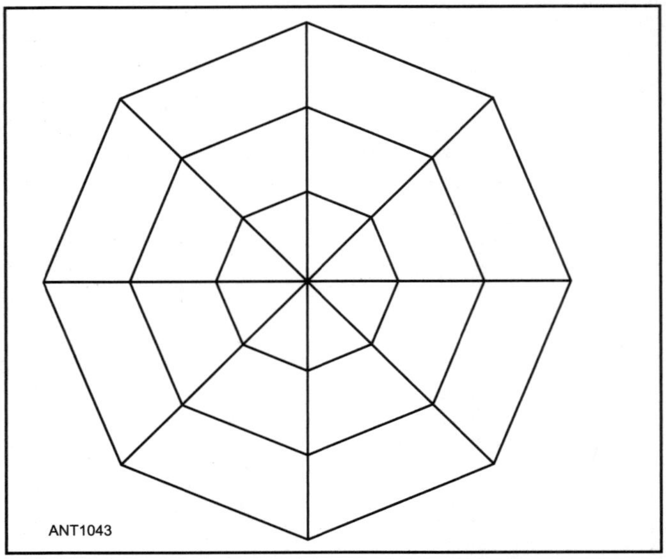

Figure 3.35 — Example of a wire counterpoise ground system.

radiation patterns between symmetric and asymmetric systems at 7.25 MHz. The amount of pattern distortion varies across the band from a fraction of a dB at 7.0 MHz to 3 dB at 7.25 MHz. Besides the distortion, the gain in all directions is smaller for the asymmetric case. Computing the average gains for the symmetric and asymmetric cases in Figure 3.33, there is about a 1.6 dB difference. What this tells us is that asymmetric radials can lead to significantly higher ground losses!

The pattern distortion and increased ground loss with asymmetric radials occurs because the radial currents with asymmetric radial lengths can be much different from the symmetric case. An example is given in **Figure 3.34**. The graph bars represent the current amplitudes at the base of the vertical and each of the radials immediately adjacent to the base of the vertical. The black bars are for symmetric radial lengths (L = M = 34.1 feet) and the red bars are for asymmetric radials (L = 35.1 feet and M = 33.1 feet). In the symmetric case each of the radials has a current of 0.25 A which sums to 1 A, the current at the base of the vertical. The radial currents are also in phase with the base current.

With asymmetric radials the picture is very different: the current amplitudes are different between radial pairs 1 and 2 and 3 and 4 and the sum of the current amplitudes is *not* 1 A, it is much larger! This would seem to violate Kirchhoff's current law which requires the **vector** sum of the currents at a node to be zero. In this case the radial currents in the two pairs of radials are not in phase with each other or the vertical base current. The current in radials 1 and 2 is shifted by –62° from the base current and the current in radials 3 and 4 is shifted by +89°. The radial currents still sum *vectorially* to 1 A however. These large asymmetric currents go a long way towards explaining the increased loss and pattern distortion.

How can we tell if there is a problem in an existing radial fan? One way is to measure the current amplitudes in the individual radials close to the base of the vertical.[13] If the current amplitudes are significantly different between the radials *and/or* if the sum of the current amplitudes in the radials is greater than the base current then you have a problem. These measurements can be made with a RF ammeter. More accurate measurements which also show the phase can be made using current transformers and an oscilloscope (see the section "Practical Aspects of Phased Array Design" in the **Multielement Arrays** chapter) or a vector network analyzer (see the **Antenna and Transmission Line Measurements** chapter).[13]

The sensitivity to asymmetric radial lengths is reduced when a larger number of radials are employed. The primary effect of additional elevated radials (>4) is to reduce the sensitivity to radial asymmetry, nearby conductors, variations in ground conductivity or objects under the radial fan, and, as shown in Figure 3.28, more numerous radials reduce the potentials on the radials. More numerous radials also reduce the E-field intensity below the radial fan. *Whenever possible an elevated ground system should use 10 or more radials.* If you follow that rule you are very likely to get the performance you expect. With small numbers of elevated radials the results can be hit or miss.

Sometimes it's not possible to have a symmetric radial fan of λ/4 radials. This is often the case on 160 or 80 meters. Because each installation will be unique it is difficult to give general advice but certainly the first step should be to model the proposed antenna with different radial options to get a feeling for how well they might work. One option is to keep the radial fan symmetric with a radius smaller than λ/4. You can then resonate the vertical with an inductor as shown in Figure 3.29D, add some top-loading to the vertical, make the vertical taller, or some combination of all three. With short radials it may be helpful to add a skirt wire at the ends of the radials as shown in **Figure 3.35**. Adding a skirt wire to the radial system will reduce the size of the base loading inductance.

Counterpoise Systems

In the early days of radio, operating wavelengths were in the hundreds or thousands of meters. Very often a ground system with λ/4 radials was not possible. Early on it was recognized that an elevated system of wires called a "counterpoise" or "capacitive ground" with dimensions much smaller than λ/4 could be very effective. Figure 3.35 shows a typical example that looks very much like a spider web. Rectangular counterpoises made with a coarse rectangular mesh were also very common. Amateurs have done some experimental work on counterpoise systems.[10] On 80 or 160 meters the normal λ/4 radial system may well be too large for many amateur locations so a counterpoise can be a practical option. However, it is recommended that the proposed installation be carefully modeled and optimized *before* construction to avoid surprises.

Isolation of Elevated Ground Systems

In an elevated ground system it is good practice to isolate the feed line with a common mode choke (i.e. a current balun — see the **Transmission Line System Techniques** chapter). Simply attaching a coaxial feed line to the antenna and running it back down to ground can increase ground loss and in some cases have a strong effect on the resonant frequency and behavior of the impedance across the band. The effects of not isolating the feed line vary from slight to severe depending on the details of each installation. Elevated systems with small numbers of radials are particularly sensitive. An additional problem with asymmetric radials is that they can greatly increase the voltage across the balun, leading to larger losses in the balun core.

3.2.5 DIFFERENCES BETWEEN RADIAL SYSTEMS

Ground systems using elevated radials, radials lying on the ground surface, or buried radials can all provide good performance but there are some differences with practical consequences which need to be recognized. As shown in **Figure 3.36**, the current distribution on a λ/4 radial is different for each of those arrangements.

When a radial is placed very close to the ground, the velocity of propagation along the radial is slower so that the radial is effectively electrically longer and the current maximum moves out onto the radial as shown in Figure 3.36B. This has two consequences: First, it can increase the ground loss and, second, it can affect the feed point impedance and resonant frequency of the vertical.[14,15] Note from the current distribution, that the ground surface radial behaves more like an elevated radial than a buried one. Ground surface radials can affect the resonant frequency of the antenna.

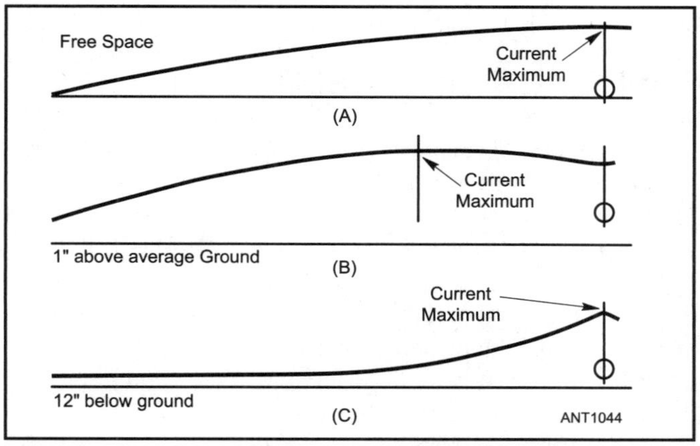

Figure 3.36 — Examples of current distribution on radials in elevated, ground surface and buried systems.

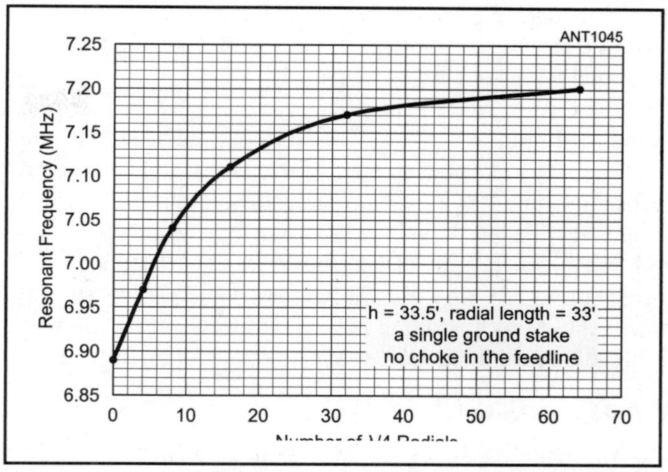

Figure 3.37 — A typical example of the effect on resonant frequency as the number of ground surface radials is varied.

An example of this is given in **Figure 3.37**. The experiment from which the data in Figure 3.37 was obtained began with no radials and only a single ground stake. As radials were added, the resonant frequency of the antenna was measured. Initially the change in resonant frequency was quite rapid but by 32 radials the rate of change slowed and the resonant frequency stabilized. The additional ground loss when <8 radials are used can be significant, providing another reason for not using a few long radials.[14]

For bare radials, well buried in the soil, the radial current distribution is exponential due to the damping effect of the soil conductivity (Figure 3.36C). In general, changing the radial number in buried systems does not greatly affect resonance except possibly in very low conductivity soils. The change in current distribution as a radial is taken from the surface into the soil is not abrupt. Radials just below the surface will behave much like radials right on the surface. The

Advice on Ground Systems

With so many configurations and options available, some advice on ground systems is in order: Buried, ground surface or elevated radial systems can all be very efficient. However, no matter which configuration is chosen, a few long radials are not likely to provide a satisfactory ground system. If you want an efficient ground system don't skimp on the radials! Try to use at least 20 or more radials on the ground and 10 or more in elevated systems.

rate of change depends on the soil characteristics so don't be surprised if you see some shift in resonance as more radials are added with shallow burial.

The goal of the radial system is to give current returning to the feed point a low-loss path through metal rather than soil. It is also more convenient for radials to be on the ground surface or buried. Figure 3.36 indicates that ground surface radials provide a reasonable compromise between efficiency and convenience. The discussion of radial systems in the **Single-Band MF and HF Antennas** chapter shows several practical options, including how to let grass and the animals living in the soil do the job of burying the radials for you.

Multiband Radial Systems

Multiband verticals are very popular which raises the question of what kind of ground system to use with them? In practice, the most common ground system, either on the ground or elevated, has four $\lambda/4$ radials *for each band.* For example if the vertical operates on 7, 14, 21 and 28 MHz there will be a total of 16 radials which is about 280 feet of radial wire. Multiband ground systems have been evaluated experimentally and shown to work very well.[15] Even though the most common system has only four radials on each band, coupling between the radials seems to minimize the elevated system problems discussed earlier. One alternative (for either on-the-ground or elevated systems) for a 40-10 meter vertical would be to use 30 or more 40 meter $\lambda/4$ radials without any of the shorter higher band radials. This also works well yielding an improvement of about 1 dB over the standard system. However, 30 radials on 40 meters total about 2100 feet of wire which is almost eight times the total wire in the standard system!

Radial Wire Size and Material

If the recommended number of radials is used, the wire size used in a radial system usually has only a small effect on the electrical performance. For a given amount of copper it is much better to use many small diameter radials instead of a few large ones. The practical issues are more mechanical than electrical: i.e. is the wire sturdy enough for installation and will it survive burial in the soil or lying on the soil surface for extended periods? In the case of elevated radial systems, is the wire strong enough to be stretched between the supports and, in climates where icing is a problem, is it strong enough for the possible ice load? The wire can be either insulated or bare although in the case of buried radials insulated wire may resist corrosion longer. Wire sizes as small as #22 AWG may be acceptable if there are a large number of radials. Either copper or aluminum wire can be used. Steel wire is very strong and inexpensive but both copper and aluminum wire have much better conductivity. Generally speaking galvanized fence wire should be viewed as an emergency measure. Although aluminum wire is attractive because it's much cheaper than copper, it has much lower corrosion resistance and may not be suitable for buried installations in most soils. Aluminum has the additional problem that it is difficult to solder and usually requires mechanical connections which may not be reliable when exposed to the weather for long periods. Either solid or stranded wire can be used in ground systems although in buried systems solid wire may be more corrosion resistant. For elevated systems where severe ice loading is expected Copperweld or Alumaweld wire can be used. These are steel wires with a thick copper or aluminum cladding. This construction gives both good conductivity and great strength. However, any damage to the cladding will expose bare steel to the elements, resulting in corrosion.

Insulated copper wire will frequently be less expensive than bare wire and in addition, insulated wire of many different kinds is often available inexpensively from surplus sources. It is not necessary to strip the insulation from the wire to use it for radials except to connect it at the base of the antenna or to other radials. In an elevated system loading by the insulation will make the radials electrically 2-3% longer but add little loss. For buried radials the insulation may provide some corrosion protection.

3.3 THE EFFECT OF GROUND IN THE FAR FIELD

The properties of the ground in the far field of an antenna are very important, especially for a vertically polarized antenna. Even if the ground-radial system for a vertical has been optimized to reduce ground-return losses in the reactive near field to an insignificant level, the electrical properties of the ground may still diminish far-field performance to lower levels than "perfect-ground" analyses might lead you to expect. The key is that *ground reflections* from horizontally and vertically polarized waves behave very differently.

This section, from earlier editions, uses an alternate convention in which k and ε_r refer to the same quantity and are interchangeable, as are σ and G. Both are in common use in the technical literature.

3.3.1 REFLECTIONS IN GENERAL

First, let us consider the case of flat ground. Over flat ground, either horizontally or vertically polarized downgoing waves launched from an antenna into the far field strike the surface and are reflected by a process very similar to that by which light waves are reflected from a mirror. As is the case with light waves, the angle of reflection is the same as the angle of incidence, so a wave striking the surface at an angle of, say, 15° is reflected upward from the surface at 15°.

The reflected waves combine with direct waves (those radiated at angles above the horizon) in various ways. Some of the factors that influence this combining process are the height of the antenna, its length, the electrical characteristics of the ground, and the polarization of the wave. At some elevation angles above the horizon the direct and reflected waves are exactly in phase — that is, the maximum field strengths of both waves are reached at the same time at the same point in space, and the directions of the fields are the same. In such a case, the resultant field strength for that angle is simply the sum of the direct and reflected fields. (This represents a theoretical increase in field strength of 6 dB over the free-space pattern at these angles.)

At other elevation angles the two waves are completely out of phase — that is, the field intensities are equal at the same instant and the directions are opposite. At such angles, the fields cancel each other. At still other angles, the resultant field will have intermediate values. Thus, the effect of the ground is to increase radiation intensity at some elevation angles and to decrease it at others. When you plot the results as an elevation pattern, you will see *lobes* and *nulls*, as described in the **Antenna Fundamentals** chapter.

The concept of an *image antenna* is often useful to show the effect of reflection. As **Figure 3.38** shows, the reflected ray has the same path length (AD equals BD) that it would if it originated at a virtual second antenna with the same characteristics as the real antenna, but situated below the ground just as far as the actual antenna is above it.

Now, if we look at the antenna and its image over perfect ground from a remote point on the surface of the ground, we will see that the currents in a horizontally polarized antenna and its image are flowing in opposite directions, or in other words, are 180° out of phase. But the currents in a vertically polarized antenna and its image are flowing in the *same* direction — they are *in* phase. This 180° phase difference between the vertically and horizontally polarized reflections off ground is what makes the combinations with direct waves behave so very differently.

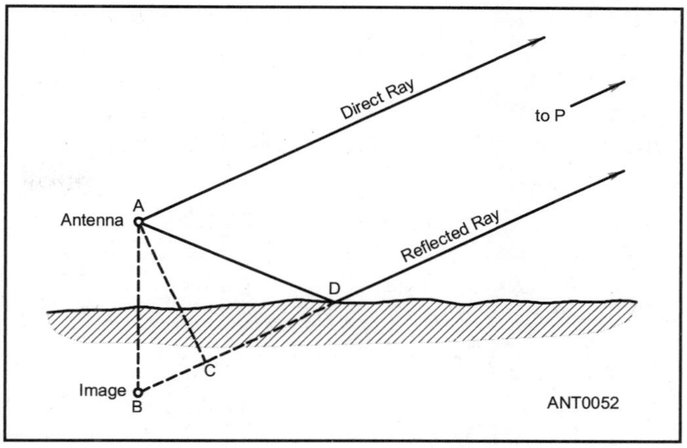

Figure 3.38 — At any distant point, P, the field strength will be the vector sum of the direct ray and the reflected ray. The reflected ray travels farther than the direct ray by the distance BC, where the reflected ray is considered to originate at the image antenna.

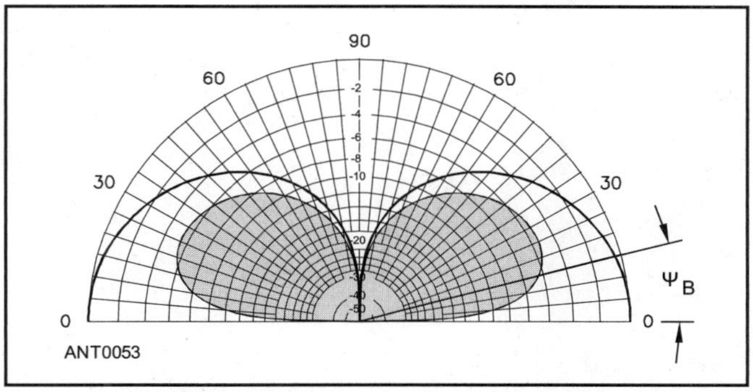

Figure 3.39 — Vertical-plane radiation pattern for a ground-mounted half-wave vertical. The solid line is the pattern for perfect earth. The shaded pattern shows how the response is modified over average earth (k = 13, G = 0.005 S/m) at 14 MHz. ψ is the pseudo-Brewster angle (PBA), in this case 14.8°.

3.3.2 FAR-FIELD GROUND REFLECTIONS AND THE VERTICAL ANTENNA

A vertical's azimuthal directivity is omnidirectional. A λ/2 vertical over ideal, perfectly conducting earth has the elevation-plane radiation pattern shown by the solid line in **Figure 3.39**. Over real earth, however, the pattern looks more like the shaded one in the same diagram. In this case, the low-angle radiation that might be hoped for because of perfect-ground performance is not realized in the real world.

Now look at **Figure 3.40A**, which compares the computed elevation-angle response for two half-wave dipoles at 14 MHz. One is oriented horizontally over ground at a height of λ/2 and the other is oriented vertically, with its center just over λ/2 high (so that the bottom end of the wire doesn't actually touch the ground). The ground is "average" in dielectric constant (13) and conductivity (0.005 S/m). At a 15° elevation angle, the horizontally polarized dipole has almost 7 dB more gain than its vertical brother. Contrast Figure 3.40A to the comparison in Figure 3.40B, where the peak gain of a vertically polarized half-wave dipole over seawater, which is virtually perfect for RF reflections, is quite comparable with the horizontal dipole's response at 15°, and exceeds the horizontally polarized antenna dramatically below 15° elevation.

Real-World Ground Surfaces

The material in this chapter deals with the effects of ground assuming that the ground surface around the antenna is flat. This is obviously not the case in the majority of actual installations! Accounting for the effects of non-flat ground is included in the chapter **HF Antenna System Design**, including an extensive discussion on the use of *HFTA* terrain analysis software by Dean Straw, N6BV.

To understand in a qualitative fashion why the desired low-angle radiation from a vertical is not delivered when the ground isn't "perfect," examine **Figure 3.41A**. Radiation from each antenna segment reaches a point P in space by two paths; one directly from the antenna, path AP, and the other by reflection from the earth, path AGP. (Note that P is so far away that the slight difference in angles is insignificant — for practical purposes the waves are parallel to each other at point P.)

If the earth were a perfectly conducting surface, there would be no phase shift of the vertically polarized wave upon reflection at point G. The two waves would add together with some phase difference because of the different path lengths. This difference in path lengths of the two waves is why the free-space radiation pattern differs from the pattern of the same antenna over ground.

Now consider a point P that is close to the horizon, as in Figure 3.41B. The path lengths AP and AGP are almost the same, so the magnitudes of the two waves add together, producing a maximum at zero angle of radiation. The arrows on the waves point both ways since the process works similarly for transmitting and receiving.

With real earth, however, the reflected wave from a vertically polarized antenna undergoes a change in both *amplitude* and *phase* in the reflection process. Indeed, at a low-enough elevation angle, the phase of the reflected wave will actually change by 180° and its magnitude will then subtract from that of the direct wave. At a zero takeoff angle, it will be almost equal in amplitude, but 180° out of phase with the direct wave.

Note that this is very similar to what happens with horizontally polarized reflected and direct waves at low elevation angles. Virtually complete cancellation will result in a deep null, inhibiting any radiation or reception at 0°. For real-world soils, the vertical loses the theoretical advantage it has at low elevation angles over a horizontal antenna, as Figure 3.40A so clearly shows.

The degree that a vertical works better than a horizontal antenna at low elevation angles is largely dependent on the characteristics of the ground around the vertical, as we'll next examine.

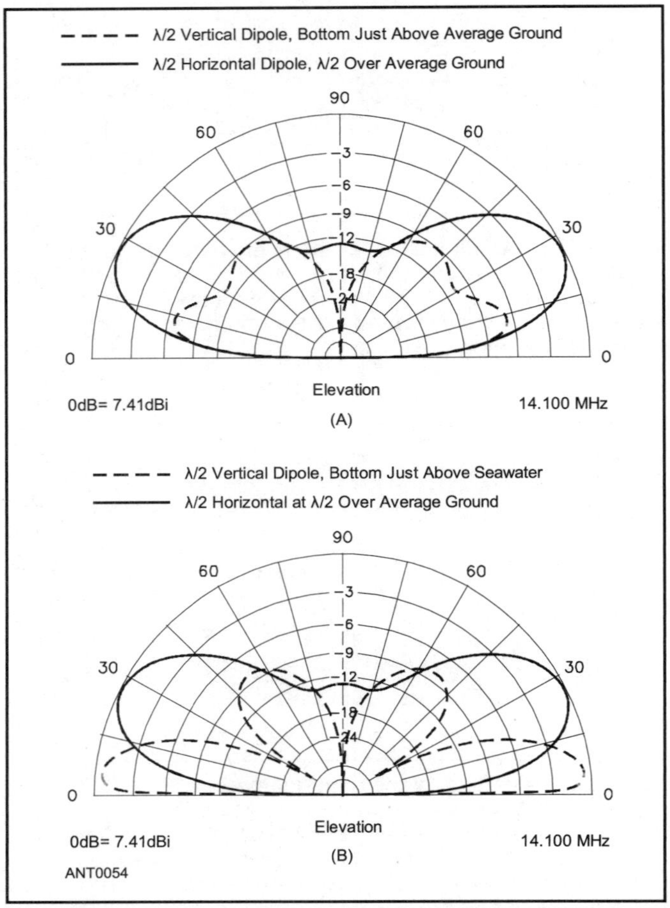

Figure 3.40 — At A, comparison of horizontal and vertical λ/2 dipoles over average ground. Average ground has conductivity of 5 mS/m and dielectric constant of 13. Horizontal dipole is λ/2 high; vertical dipole's bottom wire is just above ground. Horizontal antenna is much less affected by far-field ground losses compared with its vertical counterpart. At B, comparison of 20 meter λ/2 vertical dipole whose bottom wire is just above seawater with λ/2-high horizontal dipole over average ground. Seawater is great for verticals!

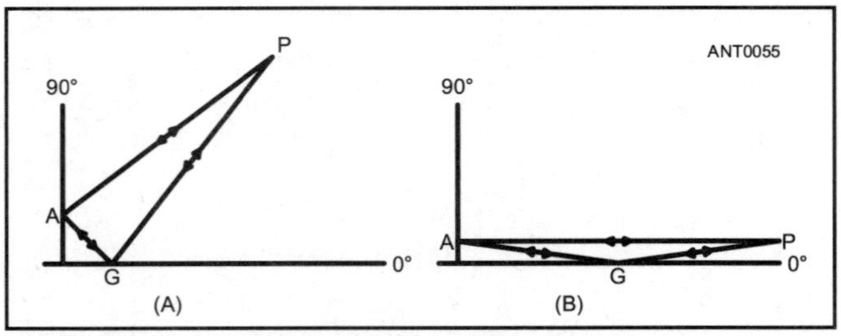

Figure 3.41 — The direct wave and the reflected wave combine at point P to form the pattern (P is very far from the antenna). At A the two paths AP and AGP differ appreciably in length, while at B these two path lengths are nearly equal.

3.3.3 THE PSEUDO-BREWSTER ANGLE (PBA) AND THE VERTICAL ANTENNA

Much of the material presented here regarding pseudo-Brewster angle was prepared by Charles J. Michaels, W7XC, and first appeared in July 1987 *QST*, with additional information in *The ARRL Antenna Compendium, Vol 3*.[12]

Most fishermen have noticed that when the sun is low, its light is reflected from the water's surface as glare, obscuring the underwater view. When the sun is high, however, the sunlight penetrates the water and it is possible to see objects below the surface of the water. The angle at which this transition takes place is known as the *Brewster angle*, named for the Scottish physicist, Sir David Brewster (1781-1868).

A similar situation exists in the case of vertically polarized antennas; the RF energy behaves as the sunlight in the optical system, and the earth under the antenna acts as the water. The *pseudo-Brewster angle* (PBA) is the angle at which the reflected wave is 90° out of phase with respect to the direct wave. "Pseudo" is used here because the RF effect is similar to the optical effect from which the term gets its name. Below this angle, the reflected wave is between 90°

and 180° out of phase with the direct wave, so some degree of cancellation takes place. The largest amount of cancellation occurs near 0°, and steadily less cancellation occurs as the PBA is approached from below.

The factors that determine the PBA for a particular location *are not related to the antenna itself, but to the ground around it*. The first of these factors is earth conductivity, σ, which is a measure of the ability of the soil to conduct electricity. Conductivity, measured in siemens/meter is the inverse of resistivity. The second factor is the dielectric constant, ε_r, which is a unit-less quantity that corresponds to the capacitive effect of the earth. (See the section "Electrical Characteristics of Ground" earlier in this chapter for a discussion of both σ and ε.) For both of these quantities, the higher the number, the better the ground (for vertical antenna purposes). The third factor determining the PBA for a given location is the frequency of operation. The PBA increases with increasing frequency, all other conditions being equal.

As the frequency is increased, the role of the dielectric constant in determining the PBA becomes more significant. **Table 3.5** shows how the PBA varies with changes in ground conductivity, dielectric constant and frequency. The table shows trends in PBA dependency on ground constants and frequency.

At angles below the PBA, the reflected vertically polarized wave subtracts from the direct wave, causing the radiation intensity to fall off rapidly. Similarly, above the PBA, the reflected wave adds to the direct wave, and the radiated pattern approaches the perfect-earth pattern. **Figure 3.42** shows the PBA, usually labeled ψ_B.

When plotting vertical-antenna radiation patterns over real earth, the reflected wave from an antenna segment is multiplied by a factor called the *vertical reflection coefficient*, and the product is then added vectorially to the direct wave to get the resultant. The reflection coefficient consists of an attenuation factor, A, and a phase angle, ϕ, and is usually expressed as A∠ϕ. (ϕ is always a negative angle, because the earth acts as a lossy capacitor in this situation.) The following equation can be used to calculate the reflection coefficient for vertically polarized waves, for earth of given conductivity and dielectric constant at any frequency and elevation angle (also called the wave angle in many texts).

Table 3.5
Pseudo-Brewster Angle Variation with Frequency, Dielectric Constant, and Conductivity

Frequency (MHz)	*Dielectric Constant*	*Conductivity (S/m)*	*PBA (degrees)*
7	20	0.0303	6.4
	13	0.005	13.3
	13	0.002	15.0
	5	0.001	23.2
	3	0.001	27.8
14	20	0.0303	8.6
	13	0.005	14.8
	13	0.002	15.4
	5	0.001	23.8
	3	0.001	29.5
21	20	0.0303	10.0
	13	0.005	15.2
	13	0.002	15.4
	5	0.001	24.0
	3	0.001	29.8

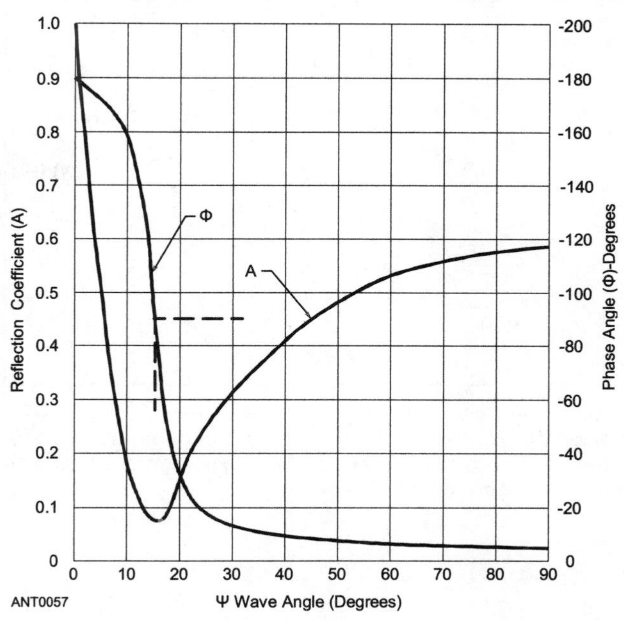

Figure 3.42 — Reflection coefficient for vertically polarized waves. A and ϕ are magnitude and angle for wave angles ψ. This case is for average earth, (k = 13, G = 0.005 S/m), at 21 MHz.

$$A_{Vert}\angle\phi = \frac{k'\sin\psi - \sqrt{k' - \cos^2\psi}}{k'\sin\psi + \sqrt{k' - \cos^2\psi}} \quad (9)$$

where

$A_{Vert}\angle\phi$ = vertical reflection coefficient

ψ = elevation angle

$$k' = k - j\left|\frac{1.8 \times 10^4 \times G}{f}\right|$$

k = dielectric constant of earth (k for air = 1)

G = conductivity of earth in S/m

f = frequency in MHz

j = complex operator ($\sqrt{-1}$)

(Reminder: k and ε_r refer to the same quantity and are interchangeable, as are σ and G. Both are in common use in the technical literature.)

Solving this equation for several points illustrates the effect of earth on vertically polarized signals at a particular location for a given frequency range. **Figure 3.42** shows the reflection coefficient as a function of elevation angle at 21 MHz over average earth (G = 0.005 S/m, and k = 13). Note that as the phase curve, ψ, passes through 90°, the attenuation curve (A) passes through a minimum at the same

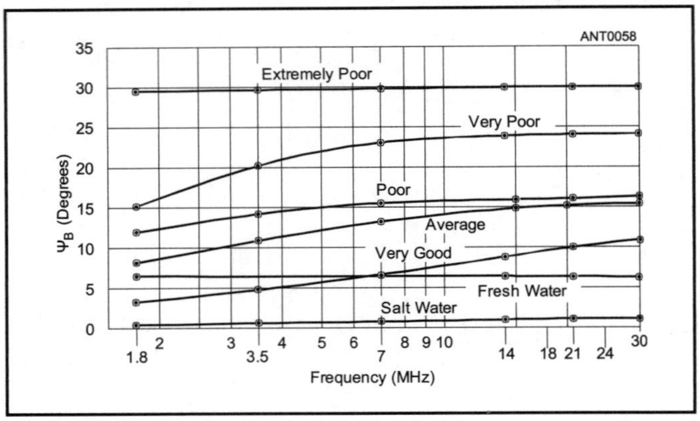

Figure 3.43 — Pseudo-Brewster angle (ψ) for various qualities of earth over the 1.8 to 30-MHz frequency range. Note that the frequency scale is logarithmic. The constants used for each curve are given in Table 3.5.

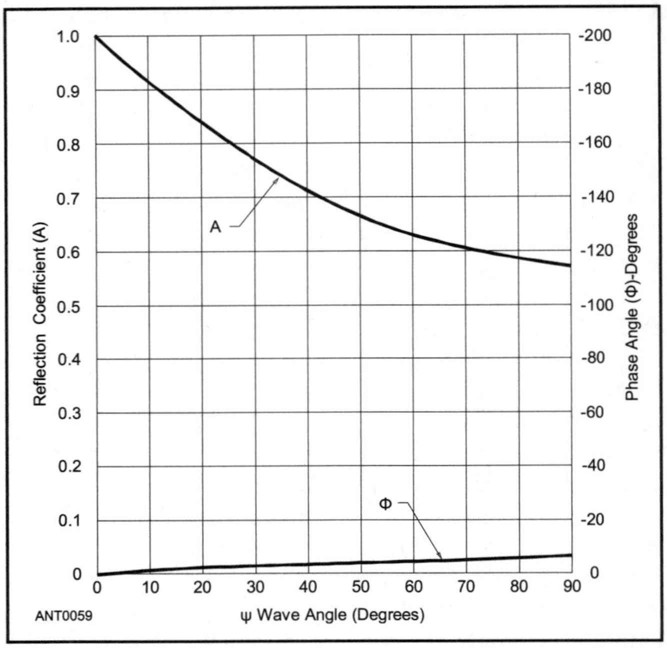

Figure 3.44 — Reflection coefficient for horizontally polarized waves (magnitude A at angle ϕ), at 21 MHz over average earth (k = 13, G = 0.005 S/m).

wave angle ψ. This is the PBA. At this angle, the reflected wave is not only at a phase angle of 90° with respect to the direct wave, but is so low in amplitude that it does not aid the direct wave by a significant amount. In the case illustrated in Figure 3.42 this elevation angle is about 15°.

Variations in PBA with Earth Quality

From Eq 9, it is quite a task to search for either the 90° phase point or the attenuation curve minimum for a wide variety of earth conditions. Instead, the PBA can be calculated directly from the following equation.

$$\psi_B = \arcsin\sqrt{\frac{k-1+\sqrt{\left(x^2+k^2\right)^2(k-1)^2+x^2\left[\left(x^2+k^2\right)^2-1\right]}}{\left(x^2+k^2\right)^2-1}} \qquad (10)$$

where k, G and f are as defined for Eq 9, and

$$x = \frac{1.8 \times 10^4 \times G}{f}$$

Figure 3.43 shows curves calculated using Eq 10 for several different earth conditions, at frequencies between 1.8 and 30 MHz. As expected, poorer earths yield higher PBAs. Unfortunately, at the higher frequencies (where low-angle radiation is most important for DX work), the PBAs are highest. The PBA is the same for both transmitting and receiving.

Relating PBA to Location and Frequency

Table 3.2 presented earlier in this chapter lists the physical descriptions of various kinds of earth with their respective conductivities and dielectric constants, as mentioned earlier. Note that in general, the dielectric constants and conductivities are higher for better earths. This enables the labeling of the earth characteristics as extremely poor, very poor, poor, average, very good, and so on, without the complications that would result from treating the two parameters independently.

Fresh water and salt water are special cases; in spite of high resistivity, the fresh-water PBA is 6.4°, and is nearly independent of frequency below 30 MHz. Salt water, because of its extremely high conductivity, has a PBA that never exceeds 1° in this frequency range. The extremely low conductivity listed for cities (the last case) in Table 3.5 results more from the clutter of surrounding buildings and other obstructions than any actual earth characteristic. The PBA at any location can be found for a given frequency from the curves in Figure 3.43. (The map presented earlier as Figure 3.2 shows approximate conductivity values for different areas in the continental United States.)

3.3.4 FLAT-GROUND REFLECTIONS AND HORIZONTALLY POLARIZED WAVES

The situation for horizontal antennas is different from that of verticals. **Figure 3.44** shows the reflection coefficient for horizontally polarized waves over average earth at 21 MHz. Note that in this case, the phase-angle departure from 0° never gets very large, and the attenuation factor that causes the most loss for high-angle signals approaches unity for low angles. Attenuation increases with progressively poorer earth types.

In calculating the broadside radiation pattern of a horizontal λ/2 dipole, the perfect-earth image current, equal to the true antenna current but 180° out of phase with it) is multiplied by the horizontal reflection coefficient given by Eq 11 below. The product is then added vectorially to the direct wave to get the resultant at that elevation angle. The reflection coefficient for horizontally polarized waves can be calculated using the following equation.

$$A_{Horiz}\angle\phi = \frac{\sqrt{k' - \cos^2\psi} - \sin\psi}{\sqrt{k' - \cos^2\psi} + \sin\psi} \qquad (11)$$

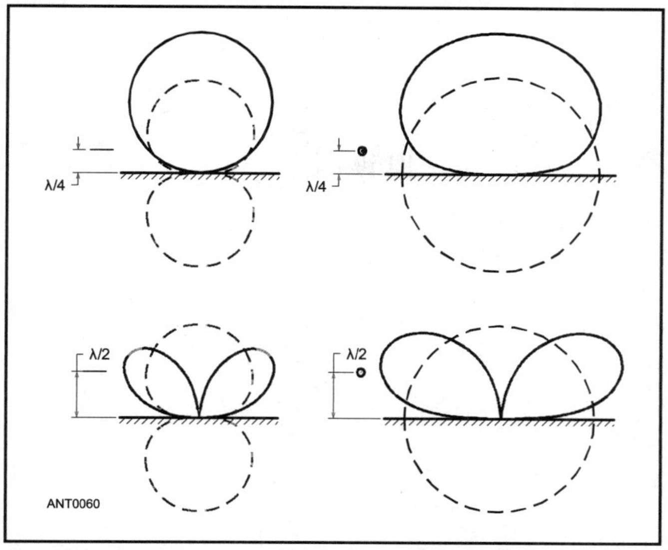

Figure 3.45 — Effect of the ground on the radiation from a horizontal half-wave dipole antenna, for heights of one-fourth and one-half wavelength. Broken lines show what the pattern would be if there were no reflection from the ground (free space).

where

$A_{Horiz} \angle \phi$ = horizontal reflection coefficient

ψ = elevation angle

$$k' = k - j\left|\frac{1.8 \times 10^4 \times G}{f}\right|$$

k = dielectric constant of earth

G = conductivity of earth in S/m

f = frequency in MHz

j = complex operator ($\sqrt{-1}$)

For a horizontal antenna near the earth, the resultant pattern is a modification of the free-space pattern of the antenna. **Figure 3.45** shows how this modification takes place for a horizontal λ/2 antenna over a perfectly conducting flat surface. The patterns at the left show the relative radiation when one views the antenna from the side; those at the right show the radiation pattern looking at the end of the antenna. Changing the height above ground from λ/4 to λ/2 makes a significant difference in the high-angle radiation, moving the main lobe down lower.

Note that for an antenna height of λ/2 (Figure 3.45, bottom), the out-of-phase reflection from a perfectly conducting surface creates a null in the pattern at the zenith (90° elevation angle). Over real earth, however, a *filling in* of this null occurs because of ground losses that prevent perfect reflection of high-angle radiation.

At a 0° elevation angle, horizontally polarized antennas also demonstrate a null, because out-of-phase reflection cancels the direct wave. As the elevation angle departs from 0°, however, there is a slight filling-in effect so that over other-than-perfect earth, radiation at lower angles is enhanced compared to a vertical. A horizontal antenna will often outperform a vertical for low-angle DX work, particularly over lossy types of earth at the higher frequencies.

Reflection coefficients for vertically and horizontally polarized radiation differ considerably at most angles above ground, as can be seen by comparison of Figures 3.42 and 3.44. (Both sets of curves were plotted for the same ground constants and at the same frequency, so they may be compared directly.) This is because, as mentioned earlier, the image of a horizontally polarized antenna is out-of-phase with the antenna itself, and the image of a vertical antenna is in-phase with the actual radiator.

The result is that the phase shifts and reflection magnitudes vary greatly at different angles for horizontal and vertical polarization. The magnitude of the reflection coefficient for vertically polarized waves is greatest (near unity) at very low angles, and the phase angle is close to 180°. As mentioned earlier, this cancels nearly all radiation at very low angles. For the same range of angles, the magnitude of the reflection coefficient for horizontally polarized waves is also near unity, but the phase angle is near 0° for the specific conditions shown in Figures 3.42 and 3.44. This causes reinforcement of low-angle horizontally polarized waves. At some relatively high angle, the reflection coefficients for horizontally and vertically polarized waves are equal in magnitude and phase. At this angle (approximately 81° for the example case), the effect of ground reflection on vertically and horizontally polarized signals will be the same.

3.3.5 DIRECTIVE PATTERNS OVER REAL GROUND

As explained in the **Antenna Fundamentals** chapter, because antenna radiation patterns are three-dimensional, it is helpful in understanding their operation to use a form of representation showing the elevation-plane directional characteristic for different heights. It is possible to show selected elevation-plane patterns oriented in various directions with respect to the antenna axis. In the case of the horizontal half-wave dipole, a plane running in a direction along the axis and another broadside to the antenna will give a good deal of information.

The effect of reflection from the ground can be expressed as a separate *pattern factor*, given in decibels. For any given elevation angle, adding this factor algebraically to the value for that angle from the free-space pattern for that antenna gives the resultant radiation value at that angle. The limiting conditions are those represented by the direct ray and the reflected ray being exactly in-phase and exactly out-of-phase, when both (assuming there are no ground losses) have equal amplitudes. Thus, the resultant field strength at a distant point may be either 6 dB greater than the free-space pattern (twice the field strength), or zero, in the limiting cases.

Horizontally Polarized Antennas

The way in which pattern factors vary with height for horizontal antennas over flat earth is shown graphically in the plots of **Figure 3.46**. The solid-line plots are based on perfectly conducting ground, while the shaded plots are based on typical real-earth conditions. These patterns apply

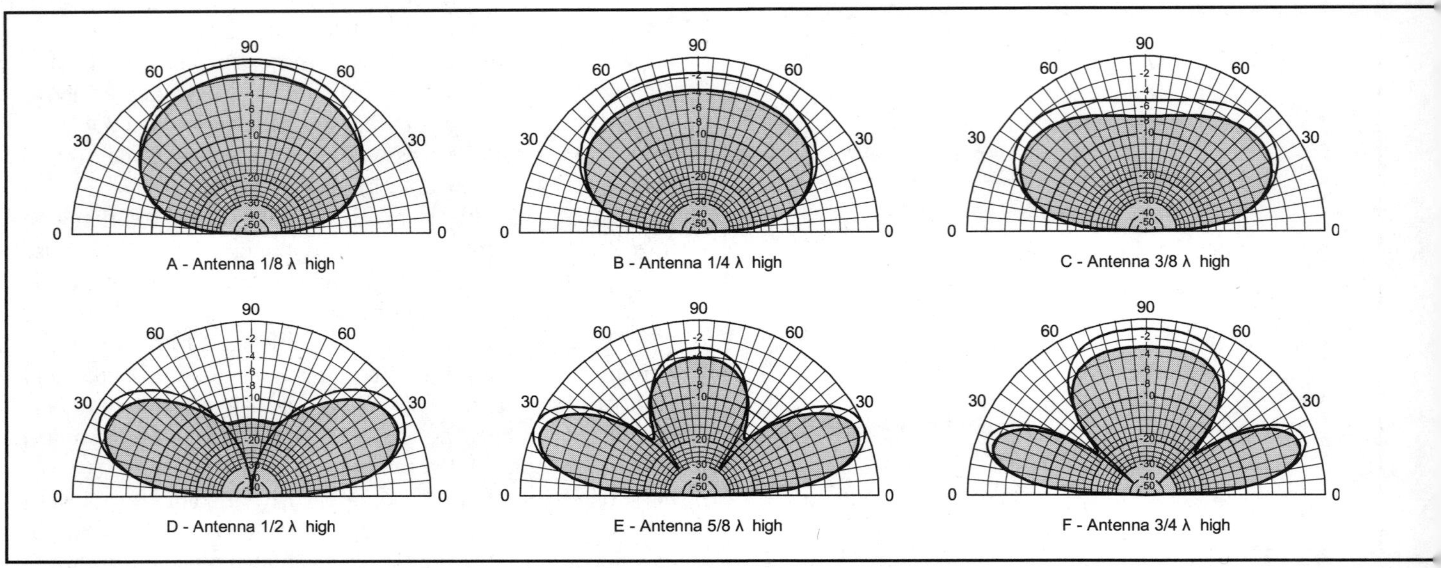

Figure 3.46 — Reflection factors for horizontal dipole antennas at various heights above flat ground. The solid-line curves are the perfect-earth patterns (broadside to the antenna wire); the shaded curves represent the effects of average earth (k = 13, G = 0.005 S/m) at 14 MHz. Add 7 dB to values shown for absolute gain in dBd referenced to dipole in free space, or 9.15 dB for gain in dBi. For example, peak gain over perfect earth at ⅝ λ height is 7 dBd (or 9.15 dBi) at 25° elevation.

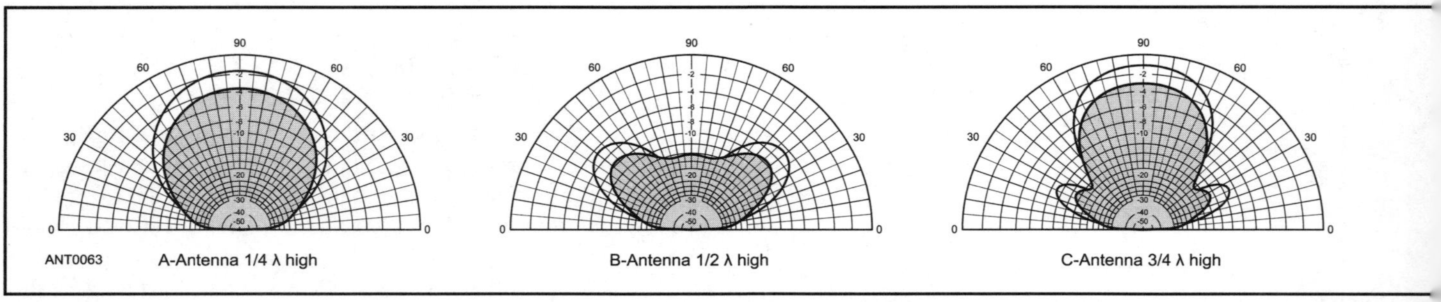

Figure 3.47 — Vertical-plane radiation patterns of horizontal half-wave dipole antennas off the ends of the antenna wire. The solid-line curves are the flat, perfect-earth patterns, and the shaded curves represent the effects of average flat earth (k = 13, G = 0.005 S/m) at 14 MHz. The 0-dB reference in each plot corresponds to the peak of the main lobe in the favored direction of the antenna (the maximum gain). Add 7 dB to values shown for absolute gain in dBd referenced to dipole in free space, or 9.15 dB for gain in dBi.

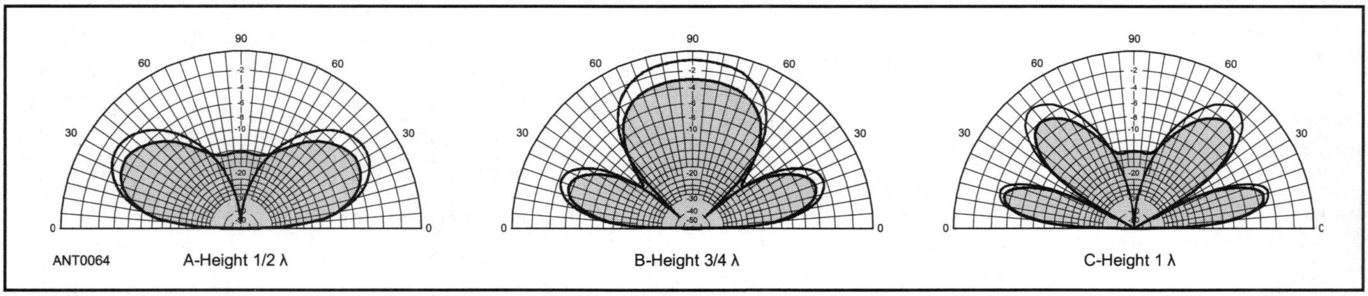

Figure 3.48 — Vertical-plane radiation patterns of half-wave horizontal dipole antennas at 45° from the antenna wire over flat ground. The solid-line and shaded curves represent the same conditions as in Figures 3.46 and 3.47. These patterns are scaled so they may be compared directly with those of Figures 3.46 and 3.47.

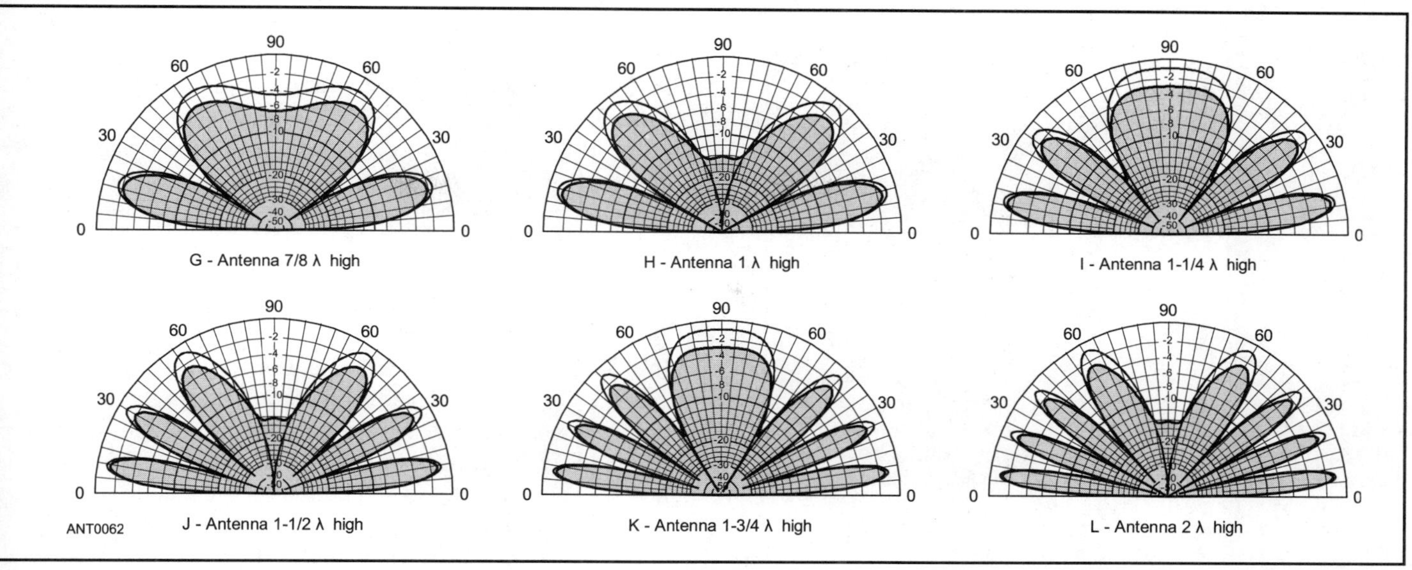

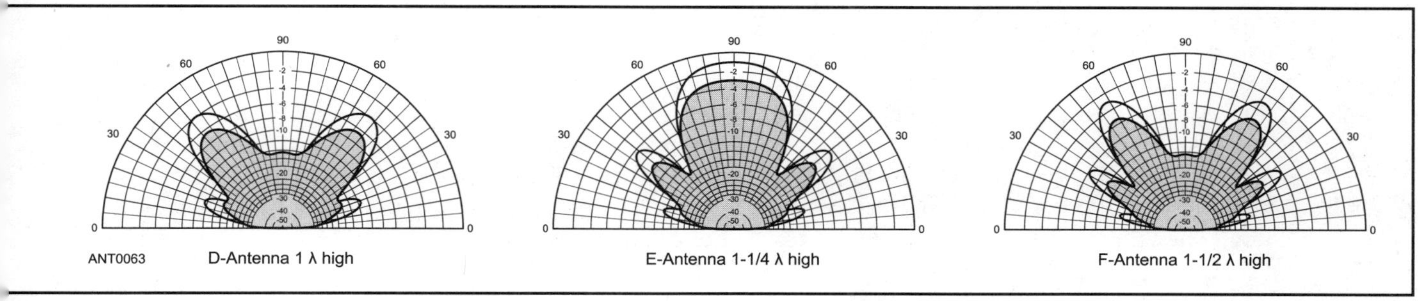

to horizontal antennas of any length. While these graphs are, in fact, radiation patterns of horizontal single-wire antennas (dipoles) as viewed from the axis of the wire, it must be remembered that the plots merely represent pattern factors.

Figure 3.47 shows vertical-plane radiation patterns in the directions off the ends of a horizontal half-wave dipole for various antenna heights. These patterns are scaled so they may be compared directly to those for the appropriate heights in Figure 3.46. Note that the perfect-earth patterns in Figures 3.46A and 3.46B are the same as those in the upper part of Figure 3.45. Note also that the perfect-earth patterns of Figures 3.47B and 3.46D are the same as those in the lower section of Figure 3.45. The reduction in field strength off the ends of the wire at the lower angles, as compared with the broadside field strength, is quite apparent. It is also clear from Figure 3.47 that, at some heights, the high-angle radiation off the ends is nearly as great as the broadside radiation, making the antenna essentially an omnidirectional radiator.

In vertical planes making some intermediate angle between 0° and 90° with the wire axis, the pattern will have a shape intermediate between the broadside and end-on patterns. By visualizing a smooth transition from the end-on pattern to the broadside pattern as the horizontal angle is varied from 0° to 90°, a fairly good mental picture of the actual solid pattern may be formed. An example is shown in **Figure 3.48**. At A, the elevation-plane pattern of a half-wave dipole at a height of $\lambda/2$ is shown through a plane 45° away from the favored direction of the antenna. At B and C, the pattern of the same antenna is shown at heights of $3\lambda/4$ and 1λ (through the same 45° off-axis plane). These patterns are scaled so they may be compared directly with the broadside and end-on patterns for the same antenna (at the appropriate heights) in Figures 3.47 and 3.48.

The curves presented in **Figure 3.49** are useful for determining heights of horizontal antennas that give either maximum or minimum reinforcement at any desired wave angle. For instance, if you want to place an antenna at a height so that it will have a null at 30°, the antenna should be placed where a broken line crosses the 30° line on the horizontal scale. There are two heights (up to 2 λ) that will yield this null angle: 1 λ and 2 λ.

As a second example, you may want to have the ground

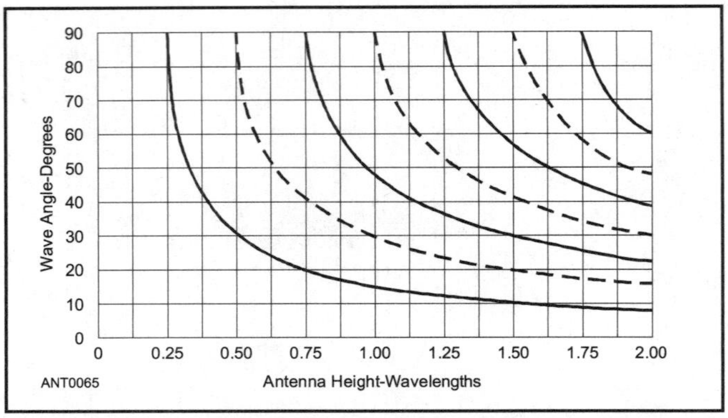

Figure 3.49 — Angles at which nulls and maxima (factor = 6 dB) in the ground-reflection factor appear for antenna heights up to two wavelengths over flat ground. The solid lines are maxima, dashed lines nulls, for all horizontal antennas. See text for examples. Values may also be determined from the trigonometric relationship θ = arc sin (A/4h), where θ is the wave angle and h is the antenna height in wavelengths. For the first maximum, A has a value of 1; for the first null A has a value of 2, for the second maximum 3, for the second null 4, and so on.

reflection give maximum reinforcement of the direct ray from a horizontal antenna at a 20° elevation angle. The antenna height should be 0.75 λ. The same height will give a null at 42° and a second lobe at 90°.

Figure 3.49 is also useful for visualizing the vertical pattern of a horizontal antenna. For example, if an antenna is erected at 1.25 λ, it will have major lobes (solid-line crossings) at 12° and 37°, as well as at 90° (the zenith). The nulls in this pattern (dashed-line crossings) will appear at 24° and 53°.

The Y-axis in Figure 3.49 plots the wave angle versus the height in wavelength above flat ground on the X-axis. Figure 3.49 doesn't show the elevation angles required for actual communications to various target geographic locations of interest. The **Radio Wave Propagation** chapter and this book's downloadable supplemental information give details about the range of angles required for target locations around the world. It is very useful to overlay plots of these angles together with the elevation pattern for horizontally polarized antennas at various heights above flat ground. This will be demonstrated in detail later in the **HF Antenna System Design** chapter.

Vertically Polarized Antennas

In the case of a vertical λ/2 dipole or a ground-plane antenna, the horizontal directional pattern is simply a circle at any elevation angle (although the actual field strength will vary, at the different elevation angles, with the height above ground). Hence, one vertical pattern is sufficient to give complete information (for a given antenna height) about the antenna in any direction with respect to the wire. A series of such patterns for various heights is given in **Figure 3.50**. Rotating the plane pattern about the zenith axis of the graph forms the three-dimensional radiation pattern in each case.

The solid-line curves represent the radiation patterns of the λ/2 vertical dipole at different feed point heights over perfectly conducting ground. The shaded curves in Figure 3.50 show the patterns produced by the same antennas at the same heights over average ground (G = 0.005 S/m, k = 13) at 14 MHz. The PBA in this case is 14.8°.

In short, far-field losses for vertically polarized antennas are highly dependent on the conductivity and dielectric constant of the earth around the antenna, extending far beyond the ends of any radials used to complete the ground return for the near field. Putting more radials out around the antenna may well decrease ground-return losses in the reactive near field for a vertical monopole, but will not increase radiation at

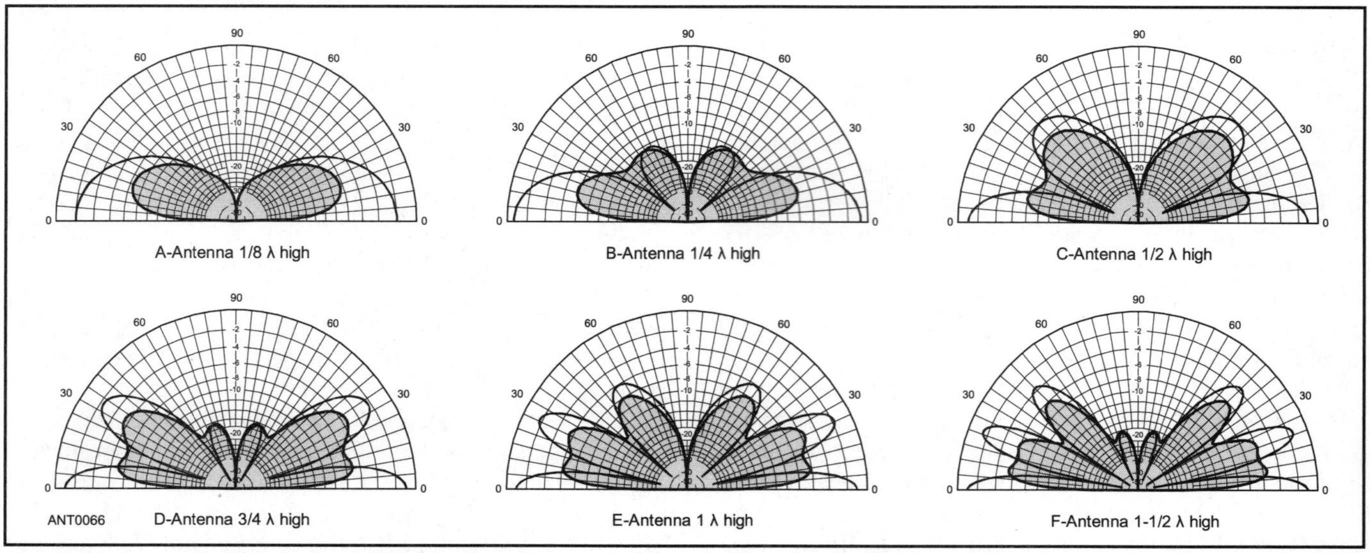

Figure 3.50 — Vertical-plane radiation patterns of a ground-plane antenna above flat ground. The height is that of the ground plane, which consists of four radials in a horizontal plane. Solid lines are perfect-earth patterns; shaded curves show the effects of real earth. The patterns are scaled — that is, they may be directly compared to the solid-line ones for comparison of losses at any wave angle. These patterns were calculated for average ground (k = 13, G = 0.005 S/m) at 14 MHz. The PBA for these conditions is 14.8°. Add 6 dB to values shown for absolute gain in dBd over dipole in free space.

low elevation launch angles in the far field, unless the radials can extend perhaps 100 wavelengths in all directions! Aside from moving to the fabled "salt water swamp on a high hill," there is very little that someone can do to change the character of the ground that affects the far-field pattern of a real vertical. Classical texts on verticals often show elevation patterns computed over an "infinitely wide, infinitely conducting ground plane." Real ground, with finite conductivity and less than perfect dielectric constant, can severely curtail the low-angle radiation at which verticals are supposed to excel.

While real verticals over real ground are not a surefire method to achieve low-angle radiation, cost versus performance and ease of installation are still attributes that can highly recommend verticals to knowledgeable builders. Practical installations for 160 and 80 meters rarely allow amateurs to put up horizontal antenna high enough to radiate effectively at low elevation angles. After all, a half-wave on 1.8 MHz is 273 feet high, and even at such a lofty height the peak radiation for a horizontal antenna would be at a 30° elevation angle, which is higher than desired for long-distance communication. A simple ground-mounted vertical with a reasonable radial field will almost always give much better results in this case.

3.4 GROUND PARAMETERS FOR ANTENNA ANALYSIS

The first part of this section is taken from an article in The ARRL Antenna Compendium, Vol 5 by R. P. Haviland, W4MB. The sections on direct and indirect soil measurements have been updated by R. Severns, N6LF.

In the past, amateurs paid very little attention to the characteristics of the earth (ground) associated with their antennas. There are two reasons for this. First, these characteristics are not easy to measure — even with the best equipment, care is needed. Second, most hams have to put up with what they have! Further, the ground is not a dominant factor for horizontally polarized antennas such as a tri-band Yagi at 40 feet or higher, or a 2 meter vertical at roof height. For vertically polarized antennas, however, the soil characteristics are very important for the design of ground systems, predictions of efficiency, and elevation radiation patterns. Ground data is useful for antennas mounted at low heights generally, and for such specialized ones as Beverage receiving antennas. The performance of such antennas changes significantly as the ground changes.

3.4.1 IMPORTANCE OF GROUND CONDITIONS

To see why ground conditions can be important, we can look at some values for ground wave attenuation with distance. At 10 MHz, *CCIR Recommendation 368* (see Bibliography), gives the distance at which the signal is calculated to drop 10 dB below its free-space level as:

Conductivity (mS/meter)	*Distance for 10 dB Drop (km)*
5000	100
30	15
3	0.3

The high-conductivity condition is for seawater. Inter-island work in the Caribbean on 40 and 80 meters is easy, whereas 40 meter ground-wave contact is difficult for much of the USA, because of much lower ground conductivity. On the other hand, the Beverage works because of poor ground conductivity.

Figure 3.51 shows a typical set of expected propagation curves for vertically polarized signals over a range of frequencies. This data is also from *CCIR Recommendation 368* for relatively poor ground, with a dielectric constant of 4 and a conductivity of 3 mS/m (one milliSiemens/meter is 0.001 mho/meter). The same data is available in the *Radio Propagation Handbook*. There are equivalent FCC curves, found in the book *Reference Data for Radio Engineers*, but only the ones near 160 meters are useful. In Florida the author has difficulty hearing stations across town on ground wave, an indication of the poor soil conditions — reflected sky-wave signals are often stronger.

3.4.2 SECURING GROUND DATA

There are two basic ways to approach this matter of ground data. One is to use generic ground data typical to the area. The second is to make direct measurements, which, with the introduction of moderately priced vector network analyzers (VNA), has become much easier. Some effort is still required however! For most amateurs the easiest approach a

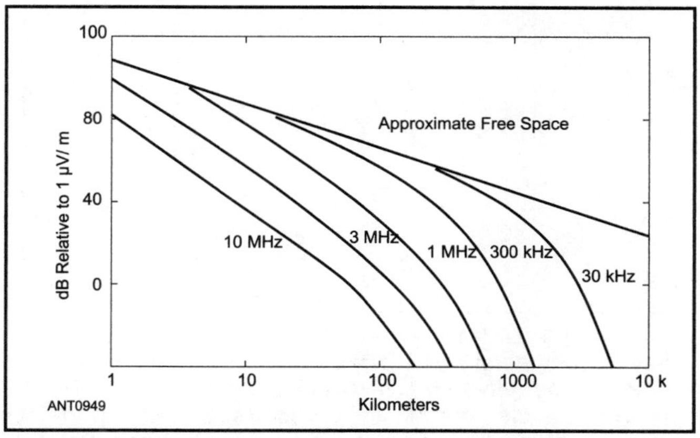

Figure 3.51 — Variation of field strength with distance. Typical field strengths for several frequencies are shown. This is from CCIR data for fairly poor soil, with dielectric constant of 4 and conductivity of 3 mS/m. The curves for good soil are closer to the free-space line, and those for sea water are much closer to the free-space line.

combination of these — make some simple measurements using the low frequency conductivity procedure outlined below and then combine this with the generic data to make a better estimate. For 220 meter and 630 meters the LF conductivity is adequate. For 160 meters and higher in frequency a more sophisticated measurement yielding both conductivity and permittivity can be helpful if an impedance measuring instrument is available. The simple approach of only measuring the LF conductivity may not be highly accurate for HF antennas but will still be much better than simply inserting some arbitrary preset values into an analysis program. Having a good set of values to plug into an analysis can be of great help in evaluating the true worth of a new antenna project, especially if the antenna is horizontally polarized.

Generic Data

In connection with its licensing procedure for broadcast stations, the FCC has published generic data for the entire country. This map was presented earlier as Figure 3.2, showing the "estimated effective ground conductivity in the United States." A range of 30:1 is shown, from 1 to 30 mS/m. An equivalent chart for Canada has been prepared, originally by DOT, now DOC.

Of course, some judgment is needed when trying to use this data for your location. Broadcast stations are likely to be in open areas, so the data should not be assumed to apply to the center of a city. And a low site near the sea is likely to have better conductivity than the generic chart for, say, the coast of Oregon. Other than such factors, this chart gives a good first value and a useful cross-check if some other method is used.

Still another FCC-induced data source is the license application of your local broadcast station. This includes calculated and measured coverage data. This may include specific ground data, or comparison of the coverage curves with the CCIR or FCC data to give the estimated ground conductivity. Another set of curves for ground conditions are those prepared by SRI (see References). These give the conductivity and dielectric constant versus frequency for typical terrain conditions. These are reproduced as **Figures 3.52** and **3.53**. By inspecting your own site, you may select the curve

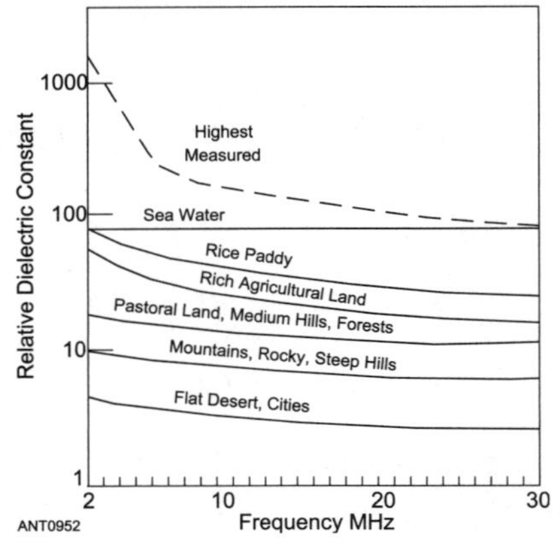

Figure 3.53 — Typical terrain relative dielectric constant for the 5 soil types of Figure 3.52, plus sea water. The dashed curve shows the highest measured values reported, and usually indicates mineralization.

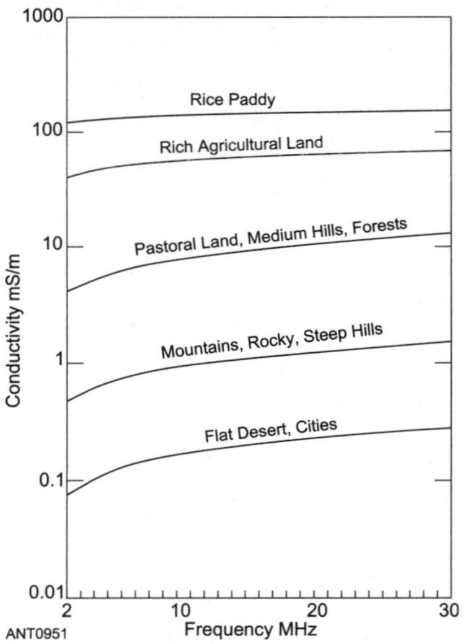

Figure 3.52 — Typical terrain conductivities versus frequency for 5 types of soils. This was measured by SRI. Units are mS/m. Conductivity of seawater is usually taken as 5000 mS/m. Conductivity of fresh water depends on the impurities present, and may be very low. To extrapolate conductivity values (for 500 to 1500 kHz) shown in Figure 3.2 for a particular geographic area to a different frequency, move from the conductivity at the left edge of this figure to the desired frequency. For example, in rocky New Hampshire, with a conductivity of 1 mS/m at BC frequencies, the effective conductivity at 14 MHz would be approximately 4 mS/m.

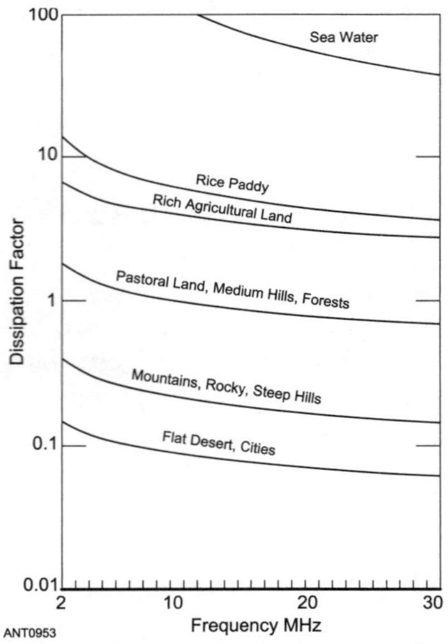

Figure 3.54 — Typical values of dissipation factor. The soil behaves as a leaky dielectric. These curves showing the dimensionless dissipation factor versus frequency for various types of soils and for sea water. The dissipation factor is inversely related to soil conductivity. Among other things, a high dissipation factor indicates that a signal penetrating the soil or water will decrease in strength rapidly with depth.

most appropriate to your terrain. The curves are based on measurements at a number of sites across the USA, and are averages of the measured values.

Figures 3.54 through **3.56** are data derived from these measurements. Figure 3.54 gives the ground-dissipation factor. Sea water has low loss (a high dissipation factor), while soil in the desert or in the city is very lossy, with a low dissipation factor. Figure 3.55 gives the skin depth, the distance for the signal to decease to 63% of its value at the surface. Penetration is low in high-conductivity areas and deep in low-conductivity soil. Finally, Figure 3.56 shows the wavelength in the earth. For example, at 10 meters (30 MHz), the wavelength in sea water is less than 0.3 meters. Even in the desert, the wavelength has been reduced to about 6 meters at this frequency. This is one reason why buried antennas have peculiar properties. Lacking other data, it is suggested that the values of Figure 3.52 and 3.53 be used in computer antenna modeling programs.

Measuring Ground Conditions

M.C. Waltz, W2FNQ developed a simple technique to measure low-frequency earth conductivity, which has been used by Jerry Sevick, W2FMI. The test setup is drawn in **Figure 3.57**, and uses a very old technique of 4-terminal resistivity measurements. For probes of 9⁄16-inch diameter (a standard grounding rod size), spaced 18 inches and penetrating 12 inches into the earth, the conductivity is:

$$G = 21\ V_1/V_2\ \text{mS/m} \qquad (12)$$

The voltages are conveniently measured by a digital voltmeter, to an accuracy of about 2%. In soil suitable for farming, the probes can be copper or aluminum. The strength of iron or Copperweld may be needed in hard soils. A piece of 2 × 6 inch or 4 × 4 inch lumber with guide holes drilled through it will help maintain proper spacing and vertical alignment of the probes, greatly speeding up the measurement process. Use care when measuring — there is a potential shock hazard! An isolating transformer with a 24 V secondary should be used instead of 120 V directly to reduce the danger. Ground conditions vary quite widely over even small areas. It is best to make a number of measurements around

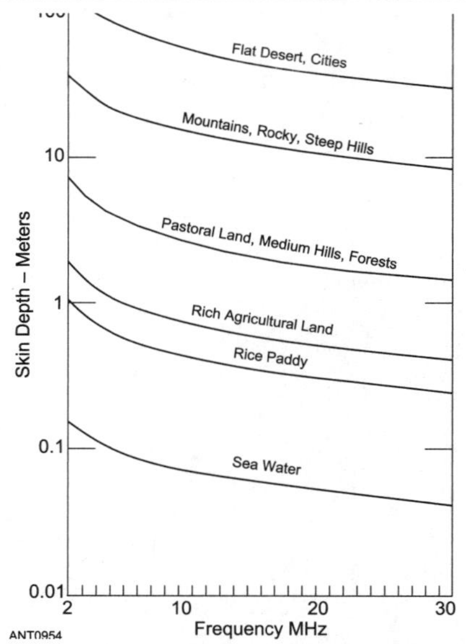

Figure 3.55 — Typical values of skin depth. The skin depth is the depth at which a signal will have decreased to 1/e of its value at the surface (to about 30%). The effective height above ground is essentially the same as the physical height for sea water, but may be much greater for the desert. For practical antennas, this may increase low-angle radiation, but at the same time will increase ground losses.

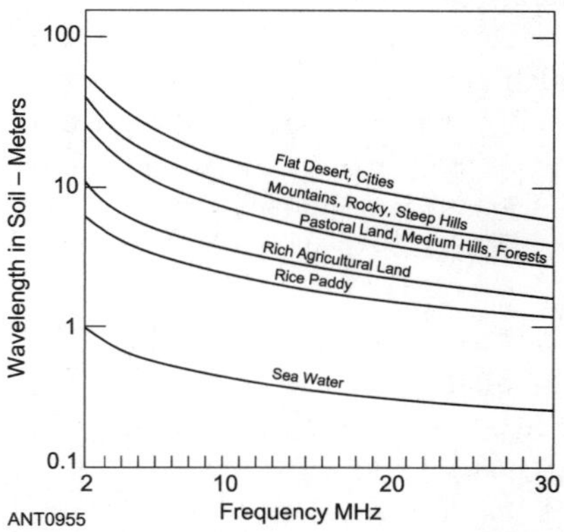

Figure 3.56 — Typical values of wavelength in soil. Because of its dielectric constant, the wavelength in soils and water will be shorter than that for a wave traveling in air. This can be important, since in a Method of Moment the accuracy is affected by the number of analysis segments per wavelength. Depending on the program being used, adjust the number of segments for antennas wholly or partly in the earth, for ground rods, and for antennas very close to earth.

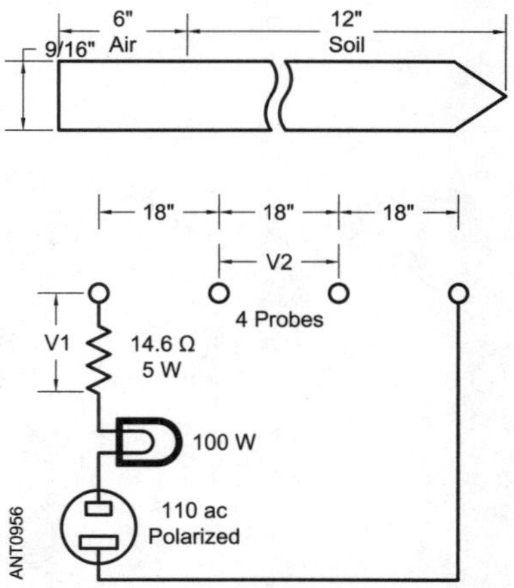

Figure 3.57 — Low-frequency conductivity measurement system. A 60-Hz measuring system devised by W2FNQ and used by W2FMI. The basic system is widely used in geophysics. Use care to be certain that the plug connection is correct. A better system would use a lower voltage and an isolation transformer. Measure the value of V_2 with no power applied — there may be stray ground currents present, especially if there is a power station or an electric railway close.

the area of the antenna, and average the measured values.

While this measurement gives only the low-frequency conductivity, it can be used to select curves in Figure 3.52 to give an estimate of the conductivity for the common ham bands. Assume that the 60 Hz value is valid at 2 MHz, and find the correct value on the left axis. Move parallel to the curves on the figure to develop the estimated curve for other soil conditions. This will give a value for conductivity which is a bit low but still very helpful.

A small additional refinement is possible. If the dielectric constant from Figure 3.53 is plotted against the conductivity from Figure 3.52 for a given frequency, a scatter plot develops, showing a trend to higher dielectric constant as conductivity increases which is mostly due to variations in moisture content. As the moisture content increases both conductivity and relative dielectric constant increase. At 14 MHz, the relation is:

$$k = \sqrt{1000 / G} \qquad (13)$$

where k is the dielectric constant and G is the measured conductivity. Using these values in *MININEC* or *NEC* calculations should give better estimates than countrywide average values.

Direct Measurement of Ground Properties

For really good values, both the conductivity and dielectric constant should be measured at the operating frequency. This is particularly important at HF. This can be done using conducting probes inserted into the soil. Two examples of amateur-made monopole probes are shown in **Figure 3.58.**

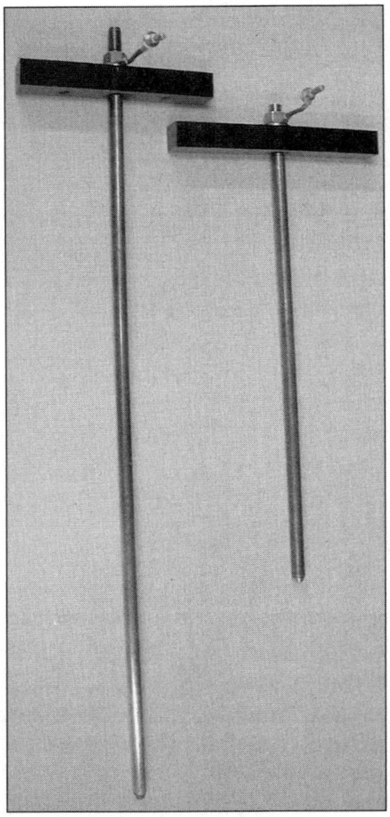

Figure 3.58 —Typical monopole probes, 12-inch and 19-inch examples.

The material for the probes can be aluminum, brass or even steel, the choice makes little difference in the measurement. The probes are inserted into the soil through a hole in a conducting sheet which can be a 36 × 36 inch galvanized mesh like that shown in **Figure 3.59**. The impedance, $Z = R + jX$, is then measured between the probe and the mesh as shown in **Figure 3.60**.

Another type of probe is the open-wire-line (OWL) technique described in George Hagn's article and Severn's *QEX* article from Nov/Dec 2006. (See the Reference section.) This was the technique used to secure the data for Figures 3.52 through 3.56. Examples of homemade OWL probes are shown in **Figure 3.61**.

Included in the photo is a simple coaxial common mode choke used to isolate the balanced probe terminals from an unbalanced measuring instrument. The short length of clothesline is placed around the horizontal wood shaft before inserting the probe into the soil, making it much easier to extract the probe when measurements are complete.

In practice both of these types of probes will be very short in terms of wavelength even taking into account the effect of the soil. The probes are essentially just capacitors. The impedance of the probe plus ground screen or between the two probes in the OWL is first measured in air and again when the probes are inserted in the soil. The soil electrical characteristics are derived from the changes in the two measurements. In air the probe impedances will be very high because there is very little resistive loss, so it is only necessary to measure the capacitance (C_o) not

Figure 3.59 — Ground probe inserted through the mesh sheet.

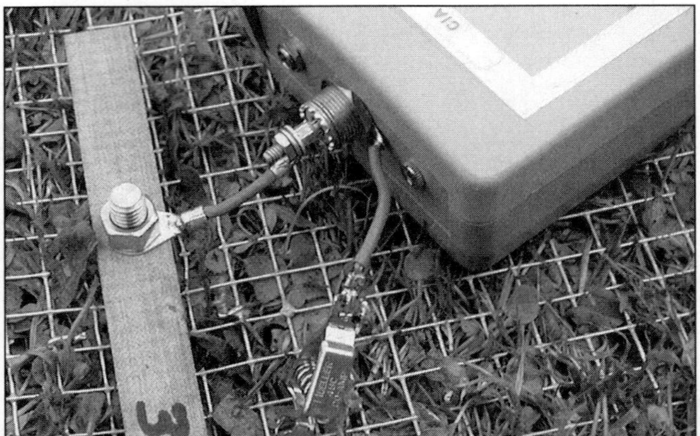

Figure 3.60 — Ground probe impedance measurement.

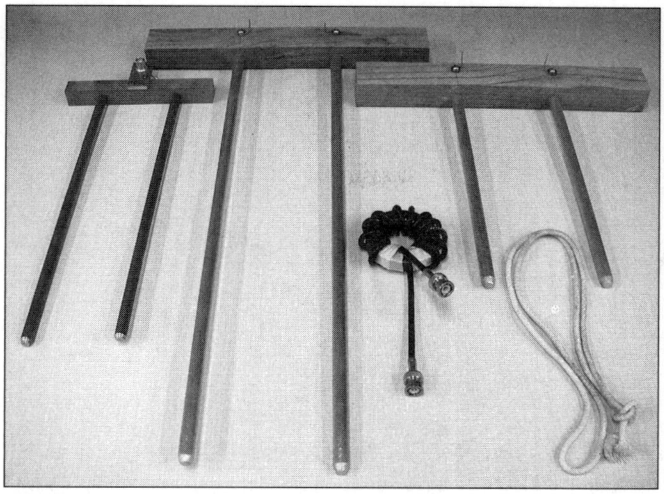

Figure 3.61 — Examples of OWL probes.

the full complex impedance. This can be done with a digital capacitance meter or, if that's not available, use the predetermined C_o value for a specific probe.

For example:

1) monopole probe — ⅜ × 19 inch rod, 36 × 36 inch groundsheet, C_o=7.4 pF

2) OWL probe — ⅜ × 12 inch rod, spaced 3 inches, C_o = 4 pF

It is also possible to compute the capacitance from the dimensions with sufficient accuracy. It should be kept in mind that we are not trying to make 1% measurements. Even at a single location the soil constants will vary widely with season and at different places around the site. Knowing σ and Er within 20% is a vast improvement over a random guess, but you don't need much better than that! When using the measured values for σ and Er in a model it is normal for the values to vary as much as ±25%, reflecting seasonal variations and measurement errors on the predicted performance.

Once you have a measurement for Z = R + *j*X and know C_o and the frequency (f_{MHZ}), σ and Er can be calculated from:

$$\sigma = \frac{8.84}{C_o}\left[\frac{R}{R^2+X^2}\right]$$

$$Er = \frac{10^6}{2\pi f_{MHZ} C_o}\left[\frac{X}{R^2+X^2}\right]$$

Indirect Measurement

The following material is a condensed version of the article "Determination of Soil Electrical Characteristics Using a Low Dipole" by R. Severns, N6LF, which is included with this book's downloadable supplemental information.

The direct measurements discussed in the previous section are effective for determining reasonable values for soil characteristics but the probe technique characterizes the soil in only a relatively small volume at one point in the site. You can get a more general characterization by repeating the measurements at several points spread over the site. This works, but there is another way to get average values over a large

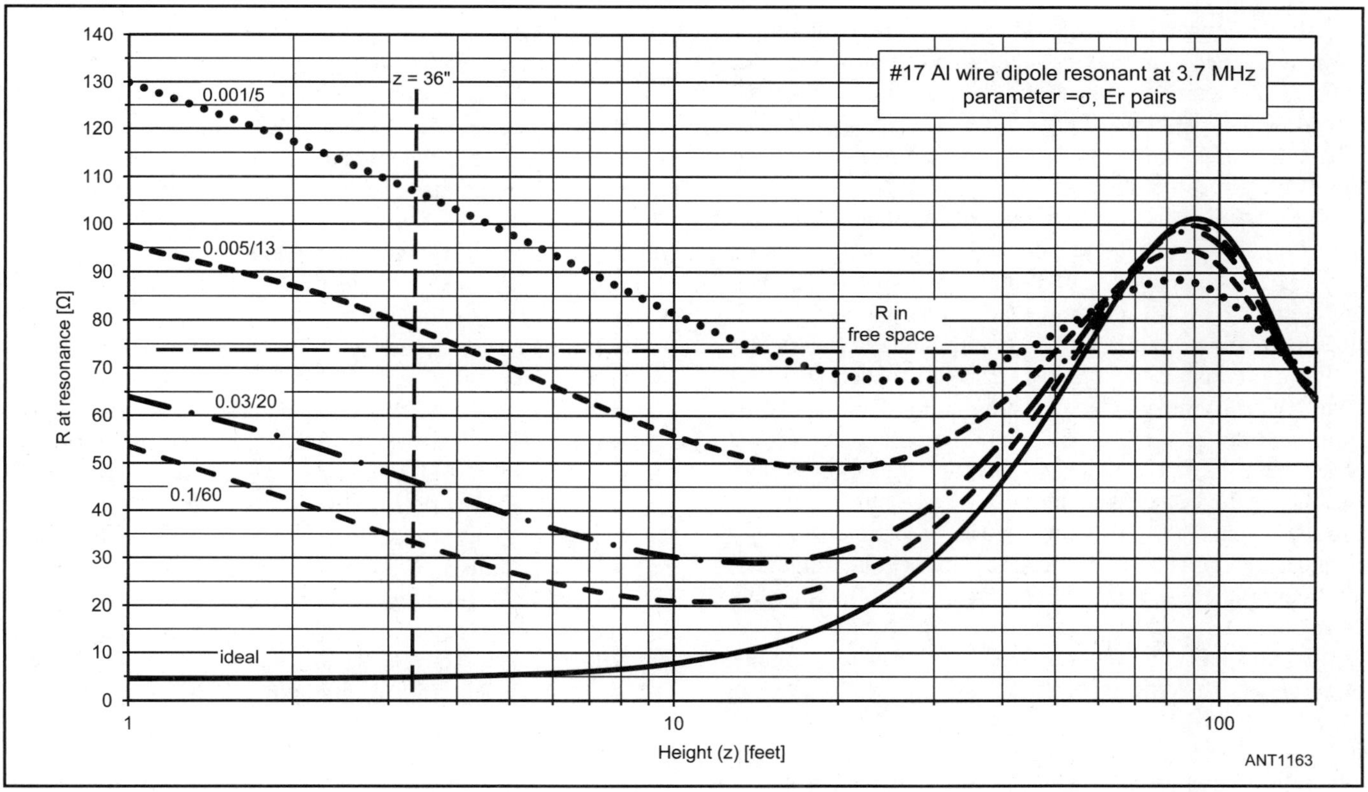

Figure 3.62 — Variation of feed point resistance, R, with height.

Figure 3.63 — Center connector and feed point support. Note use of a common mode choke at the feed point to isolate the feed line shield.

Figure 3.64 — Test antenna supported with fiberglass wands.

area. The terminal impedance and resonant frequency of an antenna will vary with both the height above ground and the electrical characteristics of the soil, it is possible to measure the feed point impedance of a low dipole and, from modeling of the antenna, determine the effective or average characteristics of the soil under the antenna.

The first question is "what height (z) should we use." Using a dipole with its length adjusted to maintain resonance at 3.7 MHz as the height and ground characteristics are varied, **Figure 3.62** illustrates how the feed point resistance, R, varies with height for a range of ground parameter pairs.

From Figure 3.62 it would appear that any height from 1 foot to 10 feet should give good resolution for determining the appropriate values of σ and Er. It should be noted that it is not necessary for the dipole to be resonant but if the dipole is close to resonance the values for R and X will be within the range of 10 to a few hundred ohms. That range is compatible with typical moderately priced impedance measurement instruments.

Erecting the test dipole can be greatly simplified if standard electric fence wire and insulating hardware are used. **Figures 3.63** and **3.64** are photos of a typical test antenna using standard electric fence hardware widely available in hardware and farm stores. #17 AWG aluminum electric fence wire is suspended at 36 inches from 5-foot fiberglass wands driven ≈1 foot deep, with yellow plastic wire clips which slide up/down the wands for height adjustment. The wands were spaced 10 to 20 feet apart and the wire anchored at the ends to steel fence posts 6 to 10 feet away from the ends of the wire. Multiple support points and significant wire tension can keep the droop to less than 0.25 inch. High quality insulators and non-conducting Dacron line were used at the wire ends. Figure 3.63 shows the Budwig center connecter and the common mode choke or choke balun at the feed point as described in the **Transmission Line System Techniques** chapter.

As an example of the procedure we'll assume a horizontal center-fed dipole made with #17 AWG aluminum wire at a convenient working height above ground (z) of 36 inches and the availability of antenna modeling software capable of properly calculating the effect of real ground, *NEC-4* for example.

After tuning to resonance at 3.5 MHz the length (L) is 131.11 feet. The measured feed point impedance (Z) at 3.5 MHz is $80.26 + j0\ \Omega$. With this information, we determine the values for soil conductivity (σ [S/m]) and relative dielectric constant (Er) at 3.5 MHz. The first step is to create a *NEC-4* model with #17 Al wire, L = 131.11 feet and z = 36 inches. Since we do not know the values for σ or Er we'll have to run the model repeatedly with a range of possible values for σ and Er. If we're too far off in our choice of values the process will show us and point the way to go! In this case the trial values will be $0.001 < \sigma < 0.01$ [S/m] and $1 < Er < 50$ which covers a wide range of typical soils. Running the model repeatedly we can determine Z for a matrix of σ and Er values. A spreadsheet is a good way to keep track as shown in **Table 3.6**.

A quick scan of the table shows that for Er > 20 and σ = 0.009 there are no resonances (ie, Xi transitions from + to –)

so we don't need to graph all the values. Using the spreadsheet we can graph a more restricted data as set shown in **Figure 3.65**, a graph of R versus X for the feed point impedance (Z = R + *j*X) with constant σ and Er contours. The solid lines are constant values of σ and the dashed lines constant values of Er.

The measured value of Z for the antenna at 3.5 MHz is 80.26 + *j*0 Ω. A dot with a label has been placed at that value on the graph. What we see is that our matrix of values has bracketed this value. The σ = 0.005 S/m line passes right through Z. We can also see that Z lies between Er = 10 and Er = 15 lines, with a bias towards Er = 15. Interpolation gives a value for Er ≈ 13. At this point we could repeat the process for multiple values of Er around Er = 13 to refine the answer further but from a practical point of view we're close enough! σ = 0.005 S/m and Er = 13, which is average soil.

Table 3.6
Calculated Values for R and X (in Ω)

sigma (σ)=	*0.001*		*0.002*		*0.003*		*0.004*		*0.005*	
Er	*Ri*	*Xi*	*Ri*	*Xi*	*Ri*	*Xi*	*Ri*	*Xi*	*Ri*	*Xi*
1	130.09	19.13	101.36	26.50	87.12	21.85	78.76	16.71	73.05	11.68
5	111.22	6.37	100.86	14.26	90.05	14.03	82.13	11.41	76.23	7.80
10	104.72	2.61	98.61	5.33	91.25	6.14	84.60	5.07	79.06	2.86
15	102.87	–2.21	97.34	–0.71	91.51	0.05	85.88	–0.54	80.89	–1.84
20	101.52	–7.01	96.45	–5.80	91.38	–5.29	86.51	–5.45	82.05	–6.16
30	98.60	–16.00	94.56	–14.75	90.58	–13.97	86.74	–13.62	83.09	–13.65
40	95.71	–23.00	92.50	–21.72	89.30	–20.79	86.17	–20.18	83.14	–19.86
50	93.00	–28.50	90.40	–27.27	87.77	–26.30	85.17	–25.60	82.62	–25.14

sigma (σ)=	*0.006*		*0.007*		*0.008*		*0.009*		*0.01*	
Er	*Ri*	*Xi*	*Ri*	*Xi*	*Ri*	*Xi*	*Ri*	*Xi*	*Ri*	*Xi*
1	68.88	7.27	65.65	3.47	63.06	0.18	60.90	–2.72	59.06	–5.29
5	71.75	4.30	68.23	1.11	65.36	–1.76	62.97	–4.35	60.94	–6.69
10	74.57	0.39	70.90	–2.06	67.84	–4.39	65.27	–6.58	63.06	–8.62
15	76.62	–3.51	72.99	–5.32	69.89	–7.15	67.22	–8.94	64.90	–10.69
20	78.07	–7.24	74.58	–8.53	71.52	–9.93	68.84	–11.36	66.47	–12.85
30	79.71	–13.99	76.60	–14.56	73.77	–15.30	71.20	–16.21	68.88	–17.21
40	80.26	–19.79	77.54	–19.96	75.00	–20.33	72.63	–20.84	70.45	–21.44
50	80.15	–24.88	77.78	–24.81	75.52	–24.88	73.39	–25.09	71.38	–25.39

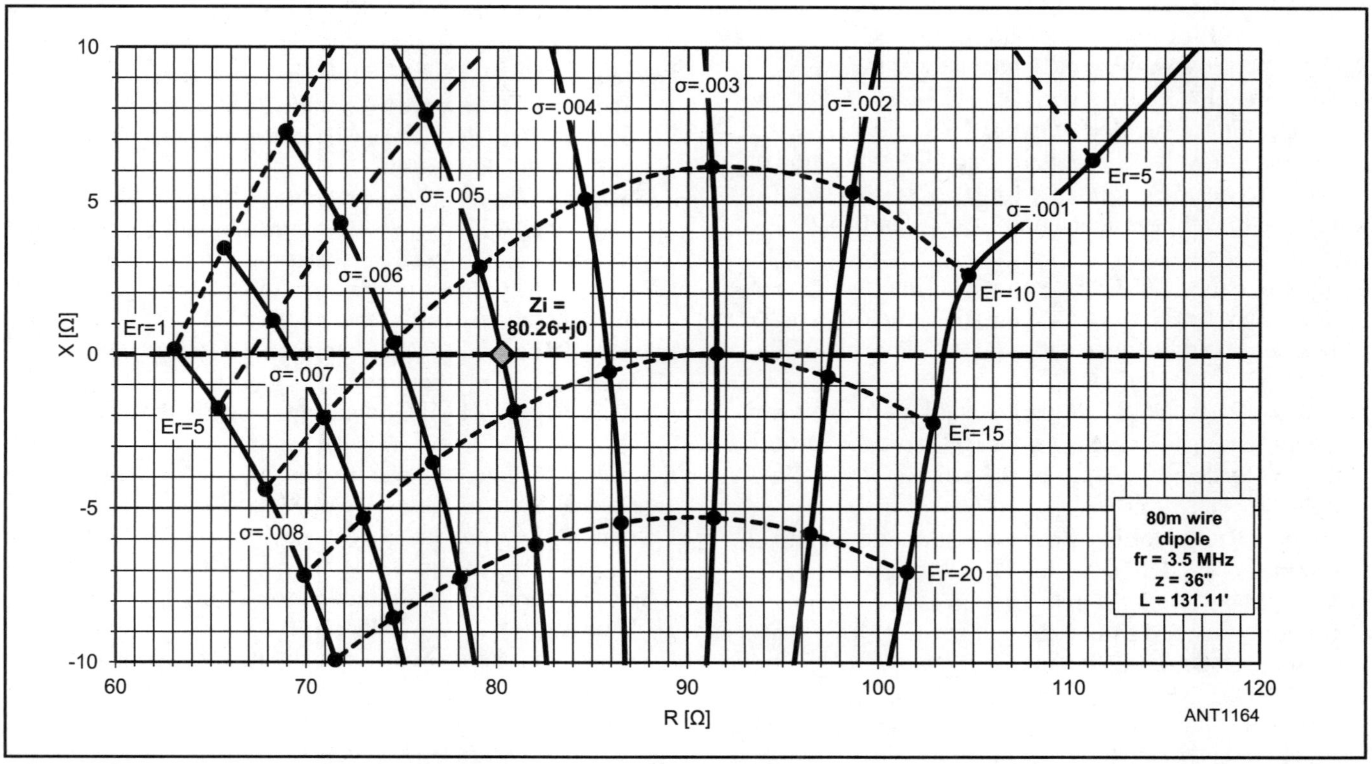

Figure 3.65 — Graph of Z = R + *j*X for a range of σ and Er values at 3.5 MHz.

3.5 REFERENCES AND BIBLIOGRAPHY

REFERENCES

1. George H. Hagn, SRI, "HF Ground Measurements at the Lawrence Livermore National Laboratory (LLNL) Field Site," *Applied Computational Electromagnetics Society Journal and Newsletter*, Vol 3, Number 2, Fall 1988.
2. Christman, Al, K3LC, "Ground System Configurations for Vertical Antennas," *QEX*, Jul/Aug 2005, pp 28-37
3. Christman, Al, K3LC, "Maximum-Gain Radial Ground Systems for Vertical Antennas," *National Contest Journal*, Mar/Apr 2004, pp 5-10.
4. Stanley, John, K4ERO, "Optimum Ground Systems for Vertical Antennas," *QST*, Dec 1976, pp 13-15.
5. Severns, Rudy, N6LF, "An Experimental Look at Ground Systems for HF Verticals," *QST*, Mar 2010, pp 30-33.
6. Severns, Rudy, N6LF, "Experimental Determination of Ground System Performance for HF Verticals, Part 7, Ground Systems with Missing Sectors," *QEX*, Jan/Feb 2010, pp 18-19.
7. Severns, Rudy, N6LF, "Experimental Determination of Ground System Performance for HF Verticals, Part 3, Comparisons Between Ground Surface and Elevated Radials," *QEX*, Mar/Apr 2009, pp 29-32.
8. Christman, Al, K3LC, "Gull-Wing Vertical Antennas," *National Contest Journal*, Nov/Dec 2000, pp 14-18.
9. Dick Weber, K5IU, "Optimum Elevated Radial Vertical Antennas," *Communications Quarterly*, Spring 1997, pp 9-27.
10. Doty, Frey and Mills, "Efficient Ground Systems for Vertical Antennas," *QST*, Feb 1983, pp 20-25.
11. Brown, Lewis and Epstein, "Ground Systems as a Factor in Antenna Efficiency," *Proc. IRE* , June 1937.
12. C. J. Michaels, "Horizontal Antennas and the Compound Reflection Coefficient," *The ARRL Antenna Compendium*, Vol 3 (Newington: ARRL, 1992).
13. Severns, Rudy, N6LF, "Experimental Determination of Ground System Performance for HF Verticals, Part 1, Test Setup and Instrumentation", *QEX*, Jan/Feb 2009, pp 21-25.
14. Severns, Rudy, N6LF, "Experimental Determination of Ground System Performance for HF Verticals, Part 2, Test Setup and Instrumentation," *QEX*, Jan/Feb 2009, pp 48-52.
15. Severns, Rudy, N6LF, "Experimental Determination of Ground System Performance for HF Verticals, Part 6, Ground Systems for Multi-band Verticals," *QEX*, Nov/Dec 2009, pg. 19-24
16. Severns, Rudy, N6LF, "Measurement of Soil Electrical Parameters at HF," *QEX*, Nov/Dec 2006, pp 3-8.
17. M. W. Maxwell, *Reflections III — Transmission Lines and Antennas*, 3rd edition (New York: CQ Communications, 2010).
18. I. Lindell, E. Alanen, K. Mannerslo, "Exact Image Method for Impedance Computation of Antennas Above the Ground," *IEEE Trans. On Antennas and Propagation*, AP-33, Sep 1985, pp 937-945.

BIBLIOGRAPHY

Source material and more extended discussion of the topics covered in this chapter can be found in the references listed below and in the textbooks listed at the end of the **Antenna Fundamentals** chapter.

B. Boothe, "The Minooka Special," *QST*, Dec 1974, pp 15-19, 28.

G. Brown, "The Phase And Magnitude Of Earth Currents Near Radio Transmitting Antennas," *Proc. IRE*, Feb 1935, pp 168-182.

CCIR Recommendation 368, Documents of the CCIR XII Plenary Assembly, ITU, Geneva, 1967.

R. Collin and F. Zucker, *Antenna Theory*, Chap 23 by J. Wait, Inter-University Electronics Series (New York: McGraw-Hill, 1969), Vol 7, pp 414-424.

T. Hulick, "A Two-Element Vertical Parasitic Array For 75 Meters," *QST*, Dec 1995, pp 38-41.

R. Jones, "A 7-MHz Vertical Parasitic Array," *QST*, Nov 1973, pp 39-43, 52.

T. Larsen, "The E-Field and H-Field Losses Around Antennas With a Radial Ground Wire System," *Journal of Research of the National Bureau of Standards*, D. Radio Propagation, Vol 66D, No. 2, Mar-Apr 1962, pp 189-204.

D. A. McNamara, C. W. I. Pistorius, J. A. G. Malherbe, *Introduction to the Geometrical Theory of Diffraction* (Norwood, MA: Artech House, 1994).

C. J. Michaels, "Some Reflections on Vertical Antennas," *QST*, Jul 1987, pp 15-19.

Radio Broadcast Ground Systems, available from Smith Electronics, Inc, 8200 Snowville Rd, Cleveland, OH 44141.

Reference Data for Radio Engineers, 5th edition (Indianapolis: Howard W. Sams, 1968), Chapter 28.

R. Severns, "Verticals, Ground Systems and Some History," *QST*, Jul 2000, pp 38-44.

R. Severns, "Comments on Longmire and Smith," Dec 2016. Available from **www.antennasbyn6lf.com/measurement_of_soil_characteristics/**.

J. Sevick, "The Ground-Image Vertical Antenna," *QST*, Jul 1971, pp 16-19, 22

J. Sevick, "The W2FMI 20-Meter Vertical Beam," *QST*, Jun 1972, pp 14-18.

J. Sevick, "The W2FMI Ground-Mounted Short Vertical," *QST*, Mar 1973, pp 13-18, 41.

J. Sevick, "A High Performance 20-, 40- and 80-Meter Vertical System," *QST*, Dec 1973, pp 30-33.

J. Sevick, "The Constant-Impedance Trap Vertical," *QST*, Mar 1974, pp 29-34.

J. Sevick, "Short Ground-Radial Systems for Short Verticals," *QST*, Apr 1978, pp 30-33.

J. Sevick, "Measuring Soil Conductivity," *QST*, Mar 1981, pp 38- 39.

J. Stanley, "Optimum Ground Systems for Vertical Antennas," *QST*, Dec 1976, pp 13-15.

F. E. Terman, *Radio Engineers' Handbook*, 1st ed. (New York, London: McGraw-Hill Book Co, 1943).

APPENDIX A

OPTIMUM RADIAL SYSTEMS WITH A GIVEN AMOUNT OF WIRE

The table and graph in this Appendix are taken from the March 2004 *National Contest Journal* article "Maximum-Gain Radio Ground Systems for Vertical Antennas," by Al Christman, K3LC. This table and graph contain results for average soil. (The full article is available in the downloadable supplemental information for this book.)

Table 3A.1 lists the "best" number of radials to maximize the gain, for each specific total wire length, on 40, 80, and 160 meters, in average soil. (Results for very poor to very good soil are provided in the original article.) For a given total length of wire, fewer (but longer) radials are needed as we go lower in frequency. Since the wavelength is greater at lower frequencies, the physical height of the quarter-wave vertical-monopole (radiator) also increases as we switch from 40 to 80 to 160 meters. As a result, the displacement currents leaving the vertical element intersect the earth farther from the base of the antenna, and longer radials are needed in order to collect this current.

Figure 3A.1 displays the same data in graphical form. Whenever the computer analysis showed that several different numbers of radials would provide the same peak gain, the average value was calculated and used for the graph. It is reasonable to extrapolate from this graph to 30, 20, and 17 meters for radial systems.

Table 3A.1
Optimum Number of Radials versus Total Wire Length For All Three Bands, in Average Soil

Total Wire	*Optimum number of radials for each band*		
Length (ft)	*40 meters*	*80 meters*	*160 meters*
125	9		
250	14	10	
500	21–22	15–16	11–12
1000	28–31	21–24	17–18
2000	39–43	29–32	23–28
4000	62–63	42–46	32–40
8000	100–104	63–67	45–55
16,000		99–111	76
32,000			99–122

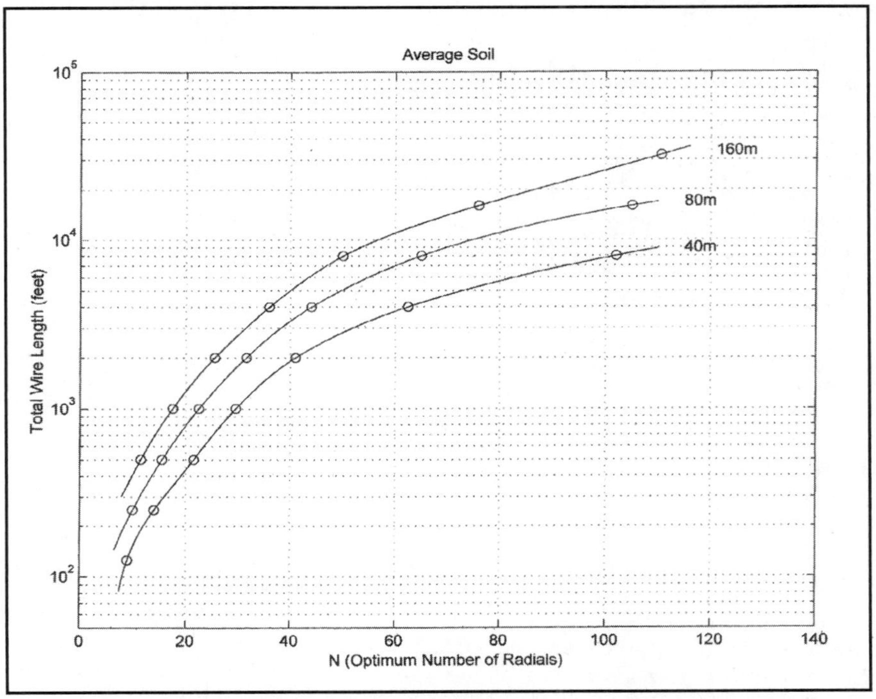

Figure 3A.1 — Optimum number of buried radials for quarter-wave vertical antennas over average soil, as the total wire length is varied, for the three "low bands" 40, 80, and 160 meters.

TABLE OF CONTENTS

Chapter 4 — Downloadable Supplemental Content

Supplemental Articles
- Antenna Book Table 4.3 expanded for other locations
- "Using Propagation Predictions for HF DXing" by Dean Straw N6BV

Chapter 4

Radio Wave Propagation

Because radio communication is carried on by means of electromagnetic waves traveling through the Earth's atmosphere, it is important to understand the nature of these waves and their behavior in the propagation medium. Most antennas will radiate the power applied to them efficiently, but no antenna can do all things equally well, under all circumstances. Whether you design and build your own antennas, or buy them and have them put up by a professional, you'll need propagation know-how for best results, both during the planning stages and while operating your station.

The material in this chapter has been updated for the 24th edition by Carl Luetzelschwab, K9LA, including a section on the new sunspot numbers, discussion of the above-the-MUF propagation mode, and more about propagation on our new bands at 630 and 2200 meters.

4.1 THE NATURE OF RADIO WAVES

The basic concepts and behavior of electromagnetic radio waves are presented in the chapter **Antenna Fundamentals**. This section discusses additional characteristics of radio waves that have particular importance to the study of how the waves propagate.

4.1.1 BENDING OF RADIO WAVES

Radio waves and light waves are both propagated as electromagnetic energy. Their major difference is in wavelength, since radio-reflecting surfaces are usually much smaller in terms of wavelength than those for light. In material of a given electrical conductivity, long waves penetrate deeper than short ones, and so require a thicker mass for good reflection. Thin metal however is a good reflector of even long-wavelength radio waves. With poorer conductors, such as the Earth's crust, long waves may penetrate quite a few feet below the surface.

The path of a *ray* traced from its source to any point on a spherical surface is considered to be a straight line — a radius of the sphere. An observer on the surface of the sphere would think of it as being flat, just as the Earth seems flat to us. A radio wave far enough from its source to appear flat is called a *plane wave*. From here on, we will be discussing primarily plane waves.

Reflection occurs at any boundary between materials of differing dielectric constant when the extent of the materials is on the order of at least one wavelength at the frequency being considered. (The surface should extend at least one wavelength from the point at which reflection takes place.) Familiar examples with light are reflections from water surfaces and window panes. Both water and glass are transparent for light, but their dielectric constants are very different from that of air. Light waves, being very short, seem to bounce off both surfaces. Radio waves, being much longer, are practically unaffected by glass, but their behavior upon encountering water may vary, depending on the purity of that medium. Distilled water is a good insulator; salt water is a relatively good conductor.

Depending on their wavelength (and thus their frequency), radio waves may be reflected by buildings, trees, vehicles, the ground, water, ionized layers in the upper atmosphere, or at boundaries between air masses having different temperatures and moisture content. Ionospheric and atmospheric conditions are important in practically all communication beyond purely local ranges.

Refraction is the bending of a ray as it passes from one medium to another at an angle when the extent of the mediums is much greater than one wavelength at the frequency being considered. (The material should extend much more than one wavelength around the region in which refraction takes place.) The appearance of bending of a straight stick, where it enters water at an angle, is an example of light refraction known to us all. The degree of bending of radio waves at boundaries between air masses increases with the radio frequency. There is slight atmospheric bending in our HF bands. It becomes noticeable at 28 MHz, more so at 50 MHz, and it is much more of a factor in the higher VHF range and in UHF and microwave propagation.

Scatter is the dispersion of an electromagnetic wave in many directions from a medium when the extent of the medium is much less than one wavelength at the frequency being considered. Scatter inherently implies additional loss. (The volume of material from which the scattering takes place is small compared to a wavelength.)

Diffraction of light over a solid wall prevents total darkness on the far side from the light source. This is caused largely by the spreading of waves around the top of the wall, due to the interference of one part of the beam with another. The dielectric constant of the surface of the obstruction may affect what happens to our radio waves when they encounter terrestrial obstructions — but the radio *shadow area* is never totally dark. See the chapter **Effects of Ground** for more information on diffraction.

The four terms reflection, refraction, scatter and diffraction were in use long before the radio age began. Radio propagation is nearly always a mix of these phenomena, and it may not be easy to identify or separate them while they are happening when we are on the air. This book tends to rely on the words *bending* (refraction) and *scattering* in its discussions, with appropriate modifiers as needed. The important thing to remember is that any alteration of the path taken by energy as it is radiated from an antenna is almost certain to affect on-the-air results — which is why this chapter on propagation is included in a book on antennas.

4.1.2 GROUND WAVES

As we have already seen, radio waves are affected in many ways by the media through which they travel. This has led to some confusion of terms in earlier literature concerning wave propagation. Waves travel close to the ground in several ways, some of which involve relatively little contact with the ground itself. The term *ground wave* has had several meanings in antenna literature, but it has come to be applied to any wave that stays close to the Earth, reaching the receiving point without leaving the Earth's lower atmosphere. This distinguishes the ground wave from a *sky wave*, which utilizes the ionosphere for propagation between the transmitting and receiving antennas.

The wave could also travel directly between the transmitting and receiving antennas, when they are high enough so they can "see" each other — this is commonly called the *direct wave*. The ground wave also travels between the transmitting and receiving antennas by reflections or diffractions off intervening terrain between them. The ground-influenced wave may interact with the direct wave to create a vector-summed resultant at the receiver antenna.

In the generic term ground wave, we also will include ones that are made to follow the Earth's curvature by bending in the Earth's lower atmosphere, or *troposphere*, usually no more than a few miles above the ground. Often called *tropospheric bending*, this propagation mode is a major factor in amateur communications above 50 MHz.

4.1.3 THE SURFACE WAVE

A ground wave could be traveling in actual contact with the ground where it is called the *surface wave*. As the frequency is raised, the distance over which surface waves can travel without excessive energy loss becomes smaller and smaller. The surface wave can provide coverage up to about 100 miles in the standard AM broadcast band during the daytime, but attenuation is high. As can be seen from **Figure 4.1**, the attenuation increases with frequency. The surface wave is of limited value in amateur communication, except possibly at 1.8 MHz (160 meters), 475 kHz (630 meters), and 137 kHz (2200 meters). Of course the better your station (in terms of your external noise level, your antenna gain, and transmit output power), the greater your surface wave range. Vertically polarized antennas are preferred, which tends to limit amateur surface-wave communication to the bands and installations for which large vertical antennas can be erected.

4.1.4 THE SPACE WAVE

Propagation between two antennas situated within line of sight of each other is shown in **Figure 4.2**. Energy traveling directly between the antennas is attenuated to about the same degree as in free space. Unless the antennas are very high or quite close together, an appreciable portion of the energy is reflected from the ground. This reflected wave combines with direct radiation to affect the actual signal received.

In most communication between two stations on the ground, the angle at which the wave strikes the ground will be small. For a horizontally polarized signal, such a reflection reverses the phase of the wave. If the distances traveled by

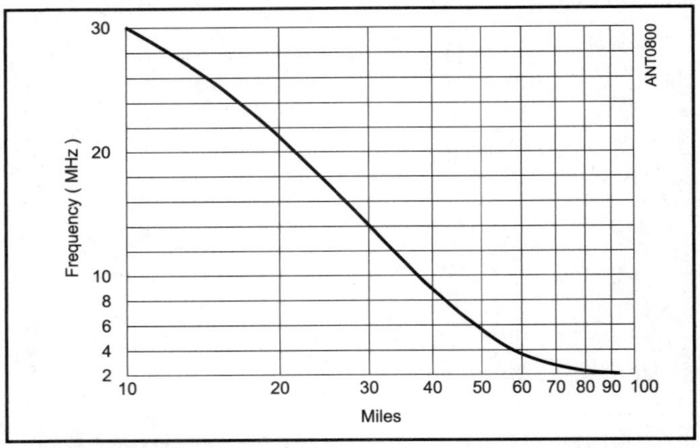

Figure 4.1 — Typical HF ground-wave range as a function of frequency.

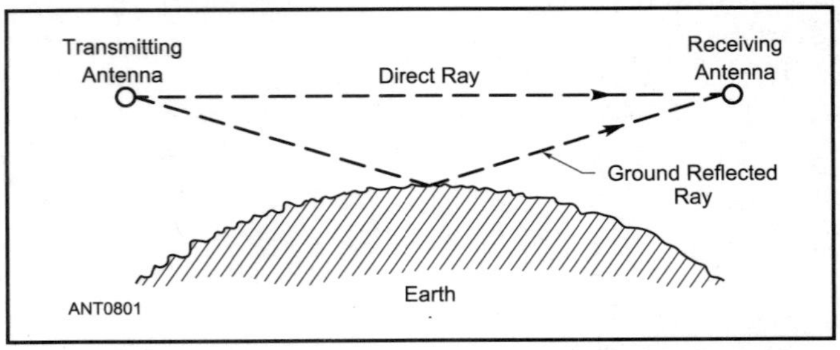

Figure 4.2 — The ray traveling directly from the transmitting antenna to the receiving antenna (direct wave) combines with a ray reflected from the ground (ground reflected ray) to form the space wave. For a horizontally polarized signal, a reflection as shown here reverses the phase of the ground-reflected ray.

both parts of the wave were the same, the two parts would arrive out of phase, and would therefore cancel each other. The ground-reflected ray in Figure 4.2 must travel a little further, so the phase difference between the two depends on the lengths of the paths, measured in wavelengths. The wavelength in use is important in determining the useful signal strength in this type of communication.

If the difference in path length is 3 meters, the phase difference with 160 meter waves would be only 360° × 3/160 = 6.8°. This is a negligible difference from the 180° shift caused by the reflection, so the effective signal strength over the path would still be very small because of cancellation of the two waves. But with 6 meter radio waves the phase length would be 360° × 3/6 = 180°. With the additional 180° shift on reflection, the two rays would add. Thus, the space wave is a negligible factor at low frequencies, but it can be increasingly useful as the frequency is raised. It is a dominant factor in local amateur communication at 50 MHz and higher.

Interaction between the direct and reflected waves is the principle cause of *mobile flutter* observed in local VHF communication between fixed and mobile stations. The flutter effect decreases once the stations are separated enough so that the reflected ray becomes inconsequential. The reflected energy can also confuse the results of field-strength measurements during tests on VHF antennas.

As with most propagation explanations, the space-wave picture presented here is simplified, and practical considerations dictate modifications. There is always some energy loss when the wave is reflected from the ground. Further, the phase of the ground-reflected wave is not shifted exactly 180°, so the waves never cancel completely. At UHF, ground-reflection losses can be greatly reduced or eliminated by using highly directive antennas. By confining the antenna pattern to something approaching a flashlight beam, nearly all the energy is in the direct wave. The resulting energy loss is low enough that microwave relays, for example, can operate with moderate power levels over hundreds or even thousands of miles. Thus we see that, while the space wave is inconsequential below about 20 MHz, it can be a prime asset in the VHF realm and higher.

4.1.5 VHF/UHF PROPAGATION BEYOND LINE OF SIGHT

From Figure 4.2 it appears that use of the space wave depends on direct line of sight between the antennas of the communicating stations. This is not literally true, although that belief was common in the early days of amateur communication on frequencies above 30 MHz. When equipment became available that operated more efficiently and after antenna techniques were improved, it soon became clear that VHF waves were actually being bent or scattered in several ways, permitting reliable communication beyond visual distances between the two stations. This was found true even with low power and simple antennas. The average communication range can be approximated by assuming the waves travel in straight lines, but with the Earth's radius increased by one-third. The distance to the *radio horizon* is then given as

$$D_{miles} = 1.415\sqrt{H_{feet}} \quad (1)$$

or

$$D_{km} = 4.124\sqrt{H_{meters}} \quad (2)$$

where H is the height of the transmitting antenna, as shown in **Figure 4.3**.

The formula assumes that the Earth is smooth out to the horizon, so any obstructions along the path must be taken into consideration. For an elevated receiving antenna the communication distance is equal to D + D1, that is, the sum

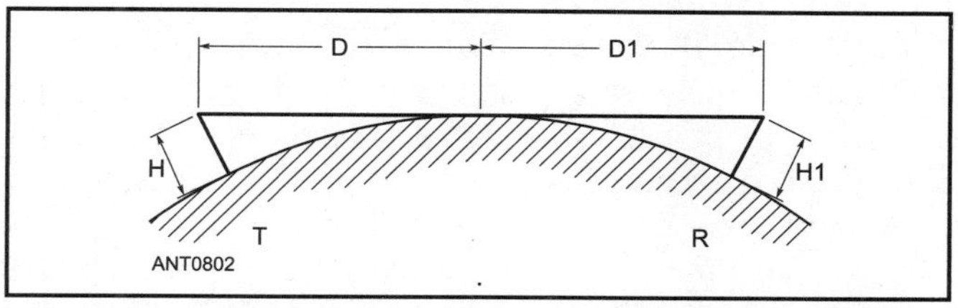

Figure 4.3 — The distance D to the horizon from an antenna of height H is given by equations in the text. The maximum line-of-sight distance between two elevated antennas is equal to the sum of their distances to the horizon as indicated here.

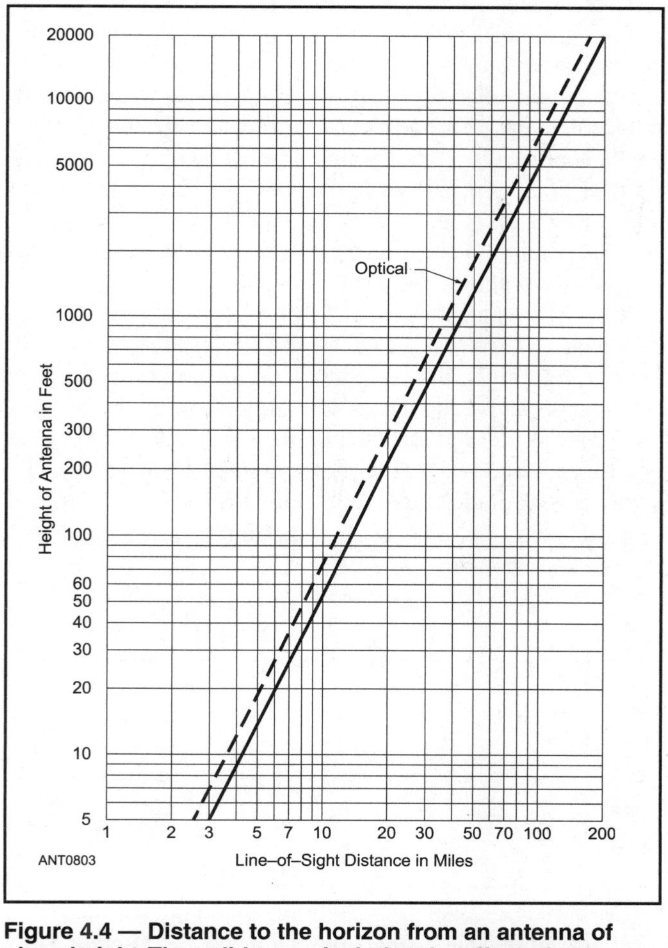

Figure 4.4 — Distance to the horizon from an antenna of given height. The solid curve includes the effect of atmospheric retraction. The optical line-of-sight distance is given by the broken curve.

of the distances to the horizon of both antennas. Radio horizon distances are given in graphic form in **Figure 4.4**. Two stations on a flat plain, one with its antenna 60 feet above ground and the other 40 feet, could be up to about 20 miles apart for strong-signal line-of-sight communication (11 + 9 mi). The terrain is almost never completely flat, however, and variations along the way may add to or subtract from the distance for reliable communication. Remember that energy is absorbed, reflected or scattered in many ways in nearly all communication situations. The formula or the chart will be a good guide for estimating the potential radius of coverage for a VHF FM repeater, assuming the users are mobile or portable with simple, omnidirectional antennas. Coverage with optimum home-station equipment, high-gain directional arrays, and SSB or CW is quite a different matter. A much more detailed method for estimating coverage on frequencies above 50 MHz is given later in this chapter.

For maximum use of the ordinary space wave it is important to have the antenna as high as possible above nearby buildings, trees, wires and surrounding terrain. A hill that rises above the rest of the countryside is a good location for an amateur station of any kind, and particularly so for extensive coverage on the frequencies above 50 MHz. The highest point on such an eminence is not necessarily the best location for the antenna. In the example shown in **Figure 4.5**, the hilltop would be a good site in all directions. But if maximum performance to the right is the objective, a point just below the crest might do better. This would involve a trade-off with reduced coverage in the opposite direction. Conversely, an antenna situated on the left side, lower down the hill, might do well to the left, but almost certainly would be inferior in performance to the right.

Selection of a home site for its radio potential is a complex business, at best. A VHF enthusiast dreams of the highest hill. The DX-minded HF ham may be more attracted by a dry spot near a salt marsh. A wide saltwater horizon, especially from a high cliff, just smells of DX. In shopping for ham radio real estate, a mobile or portable rig for the frequencies you're most interested in can provide useful clues. Two other helpful techniques to assess ham radio real estate are Google Earth (**www.google.com/earth/index.html**) and topographic maps (check with your local public library or go online for various sources of these maps).

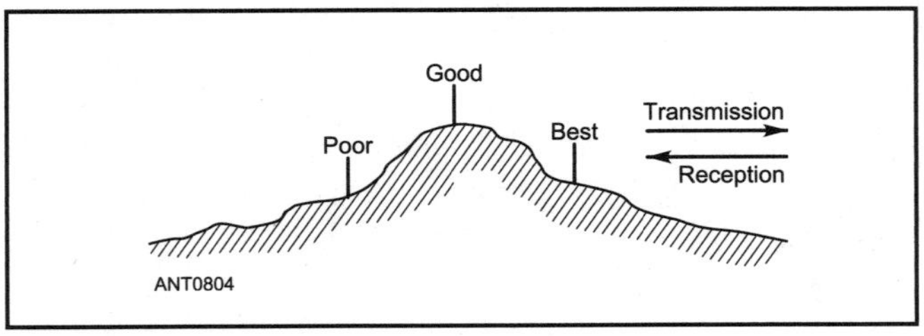

Figure 4.5 — Propagation conditions are generally best when the antenna is located slightly below the top of a hill on the side facing the distant station. Communication is poor when there is a sharp rise immediately in front of the antenna in the direction of communication.

4.1.6 ANTENNA POLARIZATION

If effective communication over long distances were the only consideration, we might be concerned mainly with radiation of energy at the lowest possible angle above the horizon. However, being engaged in a residential avocation often imposes practical restrictions on our antenna projects. As an example, our 1.8 and 3.5-MHz bands are used primarily for short-distance communication because they serve that purpose with antennas that are not difficult or expensive to put up. Out to a few hundred miles, simple wire antennas for these bands do well, even though their radiation is mostly at high angles above the horizon. Vertical systems might be better for long-distance use, but they require extensive ground systems for good performance.

Horizontal antennas that radiate well at low angles are most easily erected for 7 MHz and higher frequencies — horizontal wires and arrays are almost standard practice for work on 7 through 29.7 MHz. Vertical antennas, such as a single omnidirectional antenna of multiband design, are also used in this frequency range. An antenna of this type may be a good solution to the space problem for a city dweller on a small lot, or even for the resident of an apartment building.

High-gain antennas are almost always used at 50 MHz and higher frequencies, and most of them are horizontal. The principal exception is mobile communication with FM through repeaters, discussed in the chapter **Repeater Antenna Systems**. The height question is answered easily for VHF enthusiasts — the higher the better.

The theoretical and practical effects of height above ground at HF are treated in detail in the chapter **Effects of Ground**. Note that it is the height in *wavelengths* that is important — a good reason to think in the metric system, rather than in feet and inches, since our bands are generally referred to in terms of meters.

In working locally on any amateur frequency band, best results will be obtained with the same polarization at both stations, except on rare occasions when polarization shift is caused by terrain obstructions or reflections from buildings. Where such a shift is observed, mostly above 100 MHz or so, horizontal polarization tends to work better than vertical. This condition is found primarily on short paths, so it is not too important.

Although it has been stated by many that HF long distance communication by way of the ionosphere produces random polarization, the truth is there is more order to polarization than is generally acknowledged. The reason for this is the Earth's magnetic field.

The ionosphere, being immersed in this magnetic field, is a bi-refracting medium. That is, when an electromagnetic wave enters the ionosphere, it couples into two characteristic waves. These waves are the *ordinary wave* and the *extraordinary wave*.

On our HF bands (3.5 MHz and higher), both of these waves are circularly polarized (but rotate in opposite directions) and propagate with very similar ionospheric absorption. Thus the use of a horizontally-polarized or vertically-polarized (but rotate in opposite directions) and antenna on HF is moot with respect to polarization, as one or the other or both characteristic waves will propagate. This also suggests that a station using a circularly-polarized antenna will have a 3 dB advantage over a station using a linearly-polarized antenna (horizontal or vertical). Additionally fading may be negated to a large extent through the use of a circularly-polarized antenna. Three good articles to read for practical experience with circularly-polarized antennas are "The Enhancement of HF Signals by Polarization Control" by B. Sykes, G2HCG, in the November 1990 issue of *Communications Quarterly*, "Polarization Diversity Aerials" by George Messenger, K6CT, in the December 1962 issue of the *RSGB Bulletin*, and "So We Bought A Spiralray" by Joe Marshall, WA4EPY, in the January 1965 issue of *73 Magazine*.

On 1.8 MHz two interesting effects occur because the operating frequency is close to the ionosphere's electron gyro-frequency. (The *gyro-frequency* is the frequency at which an electron will spiral around a particular magnetic field line.) First, the extraordinary wave suffers significantly higher absorption than the ordinary wave, so for all intents and purposes only one characteristic wave propagates on 160 meters. Second, the ordinary wave is highly elliptical, approaching linear polarization. For stations at mid to high northern latitudes, vertical polarization couples the most energy into the ordinary wave — thus vertical polarization is generally the best way to go on Top Band. But other effects, like disturbances to propagation or high angle modes, sometimes dictate horizontal polarization. This is the origin of the oft-repeated statement on 160 meters that "you can't have enough antennas on Top Band."

Polarization Factors Above 50 MHz

In most VHF communication over short distances, the polarization of the space wave tends to remain constant. Polarization discrimination is high, usually in excess of 20 dB, so the same polarization should be used at both ends of the circuit. Horizontal, vertical and circular polarization all have certain advantages above 50 MHz, so there has never been complete standardization on any one of them.

Horizontal systems are popular, in part because they tend to reject man-made noise, much of which is vertically polarized. There is some evidence that vertical polarization shifts to horizontal in hilly terrain, more readily than horizontal shifts to vertical. With large arrays, horizontal systems may be easier to erect, and they tend to give higher signal strengths over irregular terrain, if any difference is observed.

Practically all work with VHF mobiles is now handled with vertical systems. For use in a VHF repeater system, the vertical antenna can be designed to have gain without losing the desired omnidirectional quality. In the mobile station a small vertical whip has obvious aesthetic advantages. Often a telescoping whip used for broadcast reception can be pressed into service for the 144-MHz FM rig. A car-top mount is preferable, but the broadcast whip is a practical compromise. Tests with at least one experimental repeater have shown that horizontal polarization can give a slightly larger service area, but mechanical advantages of vertical systems have made them the almost unanimous choice in VHF FM communication. Except for the repeater field, horizontal is the standard VHF system almost everywhere.

In communication over the Earth-Moon-Earth (EME) route the polarization picture is blurred, as might be expected with such a diverse medium. If the moon were a flat target, we could expect a 180° phase shift from the moon reflection process. But it is not flat. This plus the moon's *libration* (its slow oscillation, as viewed from the Earth), and the fact that waves must travel both ways through the Earth's entire atmosphere and magnetic field, provide other variables that confuse the phase and polarization issue. Building a huge array that will track the moon and give gains in excess of 20 dB is enough of a task that most EME enthusiasts tend to take their chances with phase and polarization problems. Where rotation of the element plane has been tried it has helped to stabilize signal levels, but it is not widely employed.

4.1.7 LONG-DISTANCE PROPAGATION OF VHF WAVES

The wave energy of VHF stations does not simply disappear once it reaches the radio horizon. It is scattered, but it can be heard to some degree for hundreds of miles, well beyond line-of-sight range. Everything on Earth, and in the regions of space up to at least 100 miles, is a potential forward-scattering agent.

Tropospheric scatter is always with us. Its effects are often hidden, masked by more effective propagation modes on the lower frequencies. But beginning in the VHF range, scatter from the lower atmosphere extends the reliable range markedly if we make use of it. Called *troposcatter*, this is what produces that nearly flat portion of the curves that will be described later (in the section where you can compute reliable VHF coverage range). With a decent station, you can consistently make troposcatter contacts out to 300 miles on the VHF and even UHF bands, especially if you don't mind weak signals and something less than 99% reliability. As long ago as the early 1950s, VHF enthusiasts found that VHF contests could be won with high power, big antennas and a good ear for signals deep in the noise. They still can.

Ionospheric scatter works much the same as the tropo version, except that the scattering medium is higher up, mainly the E region of the ionosphere but with some help from the D and F layers too. Ionospheric scatter is useful mainly above the MUF, so its useful frequency range depends on geography, time of day, season, and the state of the Sun. With near maximum legal power, good antennas and quiet locations, ionospheric scatter can fill in the skip zone with marginally readable signals scattered from ionized trails of meteors, small areas of random ionization, cosmic dust, satellites and whatever may come into the antenna patterns at 50 to 150 miles or so above the Earth. It's mostly an E-layer business, so it works all E-layer distances. Good antennas and keen ears help.

Transequatorial propagation (TE) was an amateur 50-MHz discovery in the years 1946-1947. (See Bibliography entry for *Beyond Line of Sight* by Pocock.) Amateurs

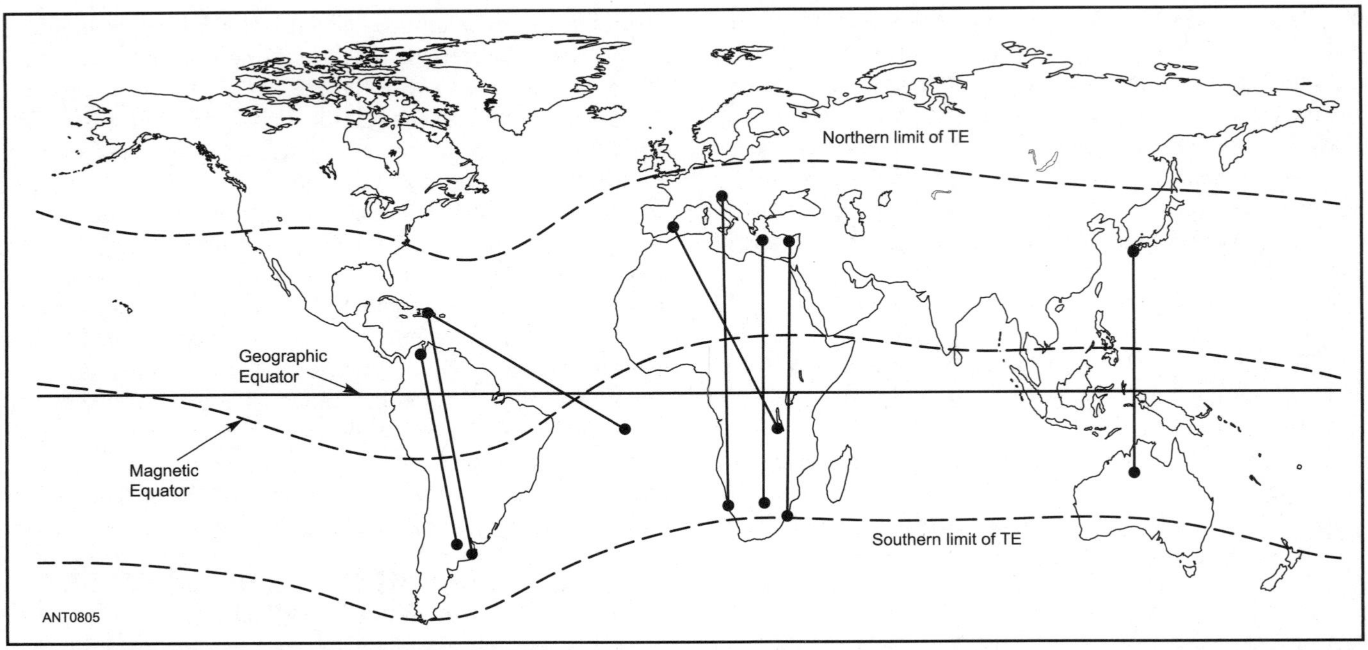

Figure 4.6 — Trans-equatorial propagation takes place between stations approximately equidistant across the geomagnetic equator. Distances up to 8000 km (5000 miles) are possible on 28 through 432 MHz. Note that the geomagnetic equator is considerably south of the geographic equator in the Western Hemisphere.

of all continents observed it almost simultaneously on three separate north-south paths. These amateurs tried to communicate at 50 MHz, even though the predicted MUF was around 40 MHz for the favorable daylight hours. The first success came at night, when the MUF was thought to be even lower. A remarkable research program inaugurated by amateurs in Europe, Cyprus, Zimbabwe and South Africa eventually provided technically sound theories to explain the then-unknown mode.

It has been known for years that the MUF is higher and less seasonally variable on transequatorial circuits, but the full extent of the difference was not learned until amateur work brought it to light. As will be explained in a later section in more detail, the ionosphere over equatorial regions is higher, thicker and denser than elsewhere. Because of its more constant exposure to solar radiation, the equatorial belt has high nighttime-MUF possibilities. TE can often work marginally at 144 MHz, and even at 432 MHz on occasion. The potential MUF varies with solar activity, but not to the extent that conventional F-layer propagation does. It is a late-in-the-day mode, taking over about when normal F-layer propagation goes out.

The TE range is usually within about 4000 km (2500 miles) either side of the geomagnetic equator. The Earth's magnetic axis is tilted with respect to the geographical axis, so the TE belt appears as a curving band on conventional flat maps of the world. See **Figure 4.6**. As a result, TE has a different latitude coverage in the Americas than that from Europe to Africa. The TE belt just reaches into the southern continental US. Stations in Puerto Rico, Mexico and even the northern parts of South America encounter the mode more often than those in favorable US areas. It is no accident that TE was discovered as a result of 50-MHz work in Mexico City and Buenos Aires.

Within its optimum regions of the world, the TE mode extends the usefulness of the 50-MHz band far beyond that of conventional F-layer propagation, since the practical TE MUF can be up to 1.5 times that of normal F2 based on analysis with ray tracing. Both its seasonal and diurnal characteristics are extensions of what is considered normal for 50-MHz propagation. In that part of the Americas south of about 20° North latitude, the existence of TE affects the whole character of band usage, especially in years of high solar activity. TE propagation is also discussed in the paper "Trans-Equatorial Propagation" by K9LA on his website, **k9la.us**.

Weather Effects on VHF/UHF Tropospheric Propagation

Changes in the dielectric constant of the medium can affect propagation. Varied weather patterns over most of the Earth's surface can give rise to boundaries between air masses of very different temperature and humidity characteristics. These boundaries can be anything from local anomalies to air-circulation patterns of continental proportions.

Under stable weather conditions, large air masses can retain their characteristics for hours or even days at a time. See **Figure 4.7**. Stratified warm dry air over cool moist air, flowing slowly across the Great Lakes region to the Atlantic Seaboard, can provide the medium for east-west communication on 144 MHz and higher amateur frequencies over as much as 1200 miles. More common, however, are communication distances of 400 to 600 miles under such conditions.

A similar inversion along the Atlantic Seaboard as a result of a tropical storm air-circulation pattern may bring VHF and UHF openings extending from the Maritime Provinces of Canada to the Carolinas. Propagation across the Gulf of Mexico, sometimes with very high signal levels, enlivens the VHF scene in coastal areas from Florida to Texas. The California coast, from below the San Francisco Bay Area to Mexico, is blessed with a similar propagation aid during the warmer months. Tropical storms moving west, across the Pacific below the Hawaiian Islands, may provide a transpacific long-distance VHF medium. Amateurs first exploited this on 144, 220 and 432 MHz, in 1957. It has been used fairly often in the summer months since, although not yearly.

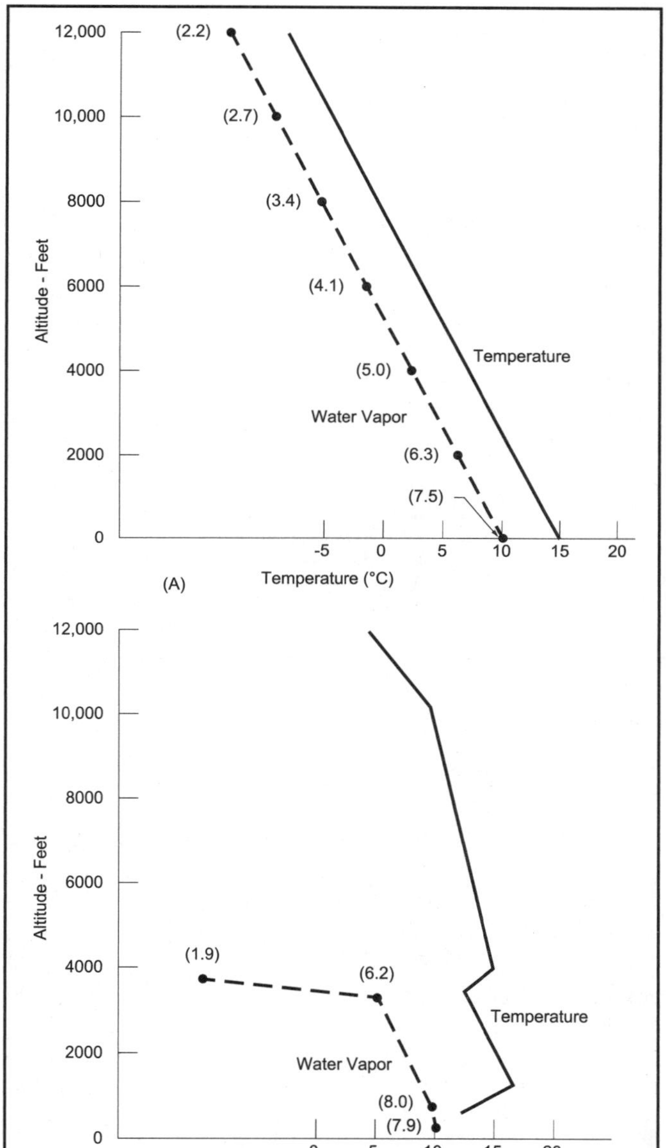

Figure 4.7 — Upper air conditions that produce extended-range communication on the VHF bands. At the top is shown the US Standard Atmosphere temperature curve. The humidity curve (dotted) is what would result if the relative humidity were 70%, from ground level to 12,000 feet elevation. There is only slight refraction under this standard condition. At the bottom is shown a sounding that is typical of marked refraction of VHF waves. Figures in parentheses are the "mixing ratio" — grams of water vapor per kilogram of dry air. Note the sharp break in both curves at about 3500 feet.

The examples of long-haul work cited above may occur infrequently, but lesser extensions of the minimum operating range are available almost daily. Under minimum conditions there may be little more than increased signal strength over paths that are workable at any time.

There is a diurnal effect in temperate climates. At sunrise the air aloft is warmed more rapidly than that near the Earth's surface, and as the Sun goes lower late in the day the upper air is kept warm, while the ground cools. In fair, calm weather such sunrise and sunset *temperature inversions* can improve signal strength over paths beyond line of sight as much as 20 dB over levels prevailing during the hours of high sun. The diurnal inversion may also extend the operating range for a given strength by some 20 to 50%. If you would be happy with a new VHF antenna, try it first around sunrise!

There are other short-range effects of local atmospheric and topographical conditions. Known as *subsidence*, the flow of cool air down into the bottom of a valley, leaving warm air aloft, is a familiar summer-evening pleasure. The daily inshore-offshore wind shift along a seacoast in summer sets up daily inversions that make coastal areas highly favored as VHF sites. Ask any jealous 144-MHz operator who lives more than a few miles inland.

Tropospheric effects can show up at any time, in any season. Late spring and early fall are the most favored periods, although a winter warming trend can produce strong and stable inversions that work VHF magic almost equal to that of the more familiar spring and fall events.

Regions where the climate is influenced by large bodies of water enjoy the greatest degree of tropospheric bending. Hot, dry desert areas see little of it, at least in the forms described above.

Tropospheric Ducting

Tropospheric propagation of VHF and UHF waves can influence signal levels at all distances from purely local to something beyond 4000 km (2500 miles). The outer limits are not well known. At the risk of over simplification, we will divide the modes into two classes — extended local and long distance. This concept must be modified depending on the frequency under consideration, but in the VHF range the extended-local effect gives way to a form of propagation much like that of microwaves in a waveguide, called *ducting*. The transition distance is ordinarily somewhere around 200 miles. The difference lies in whether the atmospheric condition producing the bending is localized or continental in scope. Remember, we're concerned here with frequencies in the VHF range, and perhaps up to 500 MHz. At 10 GHz, for example, the scale is much smaller.

In VHF propagation beyond a few hundred miles, more than one weather front is probably involved, but the wave is propagated between the inversion layers and ground, in the main. On long paths over the ocean (two notable examples

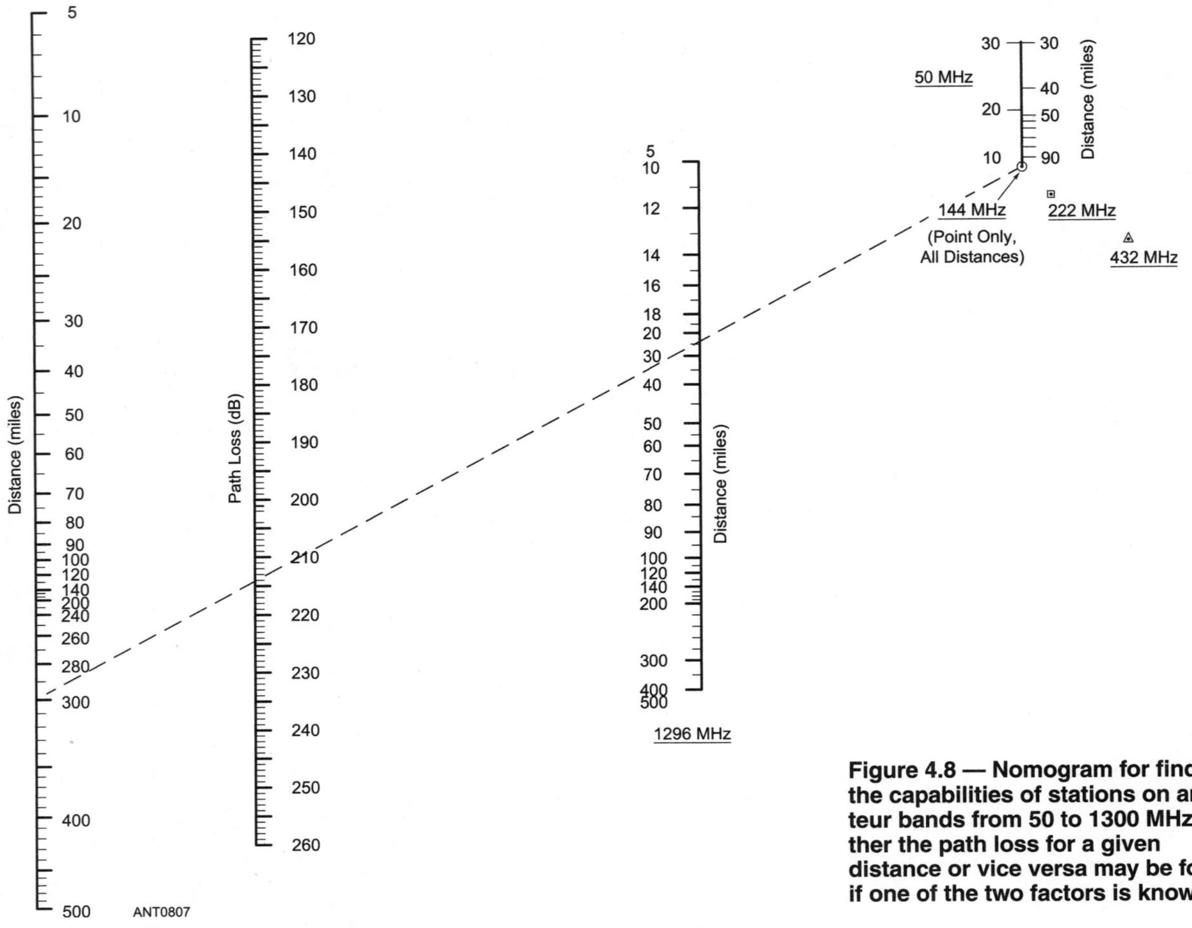

Figure 4.8 — Nomogram for finding the capabilities of stations on amateur bands from 50 to 1300 MHz. Either the path loss for a given distance or vice versa may be found if one of the two factors is known.

are California to Hawaii and Ascension Island to Brazil), propagation is likely to be between two atmospheric layers. On such circuits the communicating station antennas must be in the duct, or capable of propagating strongly into it. Here again, we see that the positions and radiation angles of the antennas are important. As with microwaves in a waveguide, the low-frequency limit for the duct is critical. In long-distance ducting it is also very variable. Airborne equipment has shown that duct capability exists well down into the HF region in the stable atmosphere west of Ascension Island. Some contacts between Hawaii and Southern California on 50 MHz are believed to have been by way of tropospheric ducts. Probably all contact over these paths on 144 MHz and higher bands is because of duct propagation.

Amateurs have played a major part in the discovery and eventual explanation of tropospheric propagation. In recent years they have shown that, contrary to beliefs widely held in earlier times, long-distance communication using tropospheric modes is possible to some degree on all amateur frequencies from 50 to at least 10,000 MHz. For forecasts of tropospheric ducting possibilities, visit **www.dxinfocentre.com/tropo.html**.

4.1.8 RELIABLE VHF COVERAGE

In the preceding sections we discussed means by which amateur bands above 50 MHz may be used intermittently for communication far beyond the visual horizon. In emphasizing distance we should not neglect a prime asset of the VHF band: reliable communication over relatively short distances. The VHF region is far less subject to disruption of local communication than are frequencies below 30 MHz. Since much amateur communication is essentially local in nature, our VHF assignments can carry a great load, and such use of the VHF bands helps solve interference problems on lower frequencies.

Because of age-old ideas, misconceptions about the coverage obtainable in our VHF bands persist. This reflects the thoughts that VHF waves travel only in straight lines, except when the DX modes described above happen to be present. However, let us survey the picture in the light of modern wave-propagation knowledge and see what the bands above 50 MHz are good for on a day-to-day basis, ignoring the anomalies that may result in extensions of normal coverage.

It is possible to predict with fair accuracy how far you should be able to work consistently on any VHF or UHF

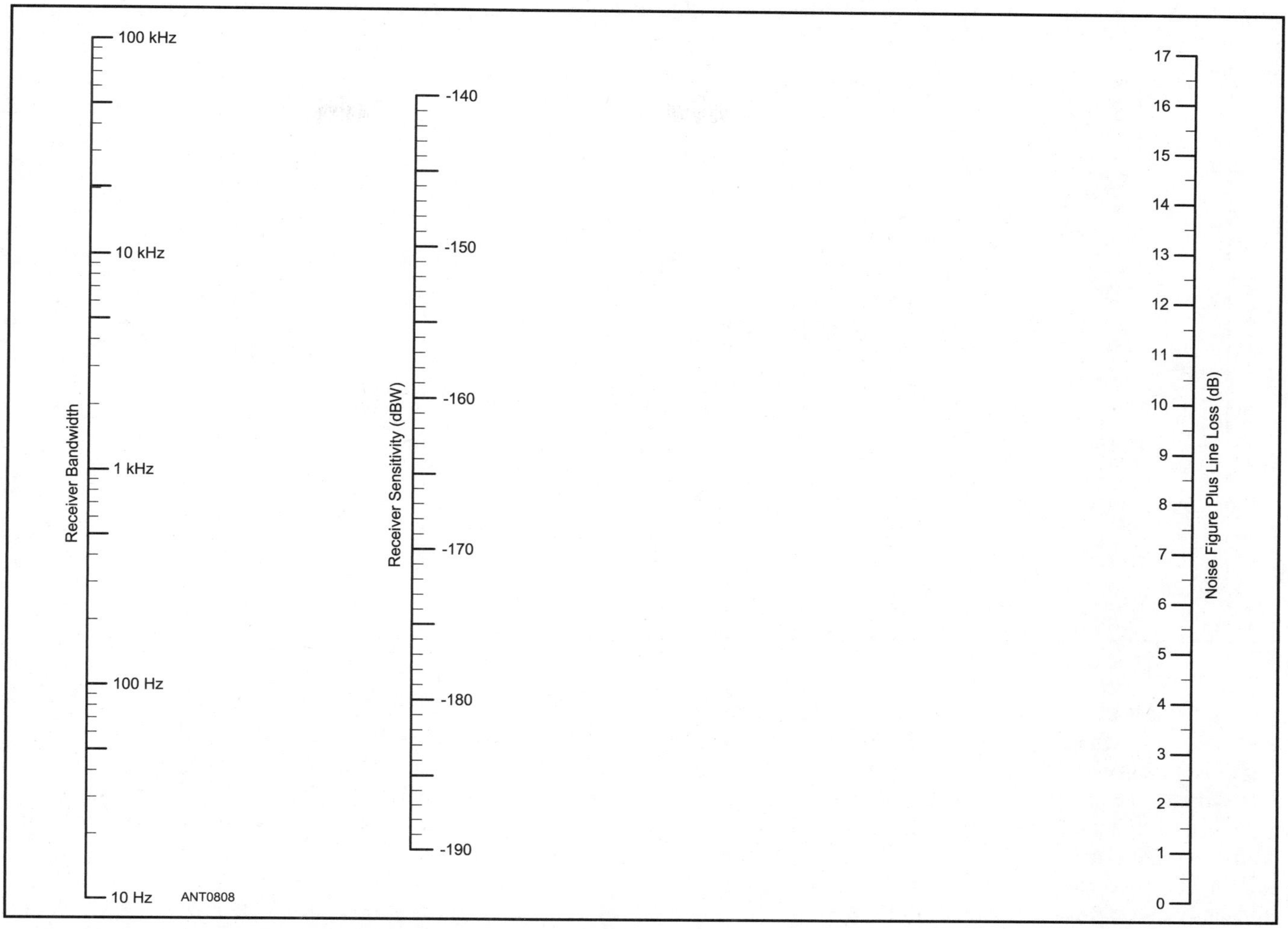

Figure 4.9 — Nomogram for finding effective receiver sensitivity.

band, provided a few simple facts are known. The factors affecting operating range can be reduced to graph form, as described in this section. The information was originally published in November 1961 *QST* by D. W. Bray, K2LMG, (see the Bibliography at the end of this chapter).

To estimate your station's capabilities, two basic numbers must be determined: station gain and path loss. Station gain is made up of seven factors: receiver sensitivity, transmitted power, receiving antenna gain, receiving antenna height gain, transmitting antenna gain, transmitting antenna height gain and required signal-to-noise ratio. This looks complicated but it really boils down to an easily made evaluation of receiver, transmitter, and antenna performance. The other number, path loss, is readily determined from the nomogram, **Figure 4.8**. This gives path loss over smooth Earth, for 99% reliability.

For 50 MHz, lay a straightedge from the distance between stations (left side) to the appropriate distance at the right side. For 1296 MHz, use the full scale, right center. For 144, 222 and 432, use the dot in the circle, square or triangle, respectively. Example: At 300 miles the path loss for 144 MHz is 214 dB.

To be meaningful, the losses determined from this nomogram are necessarily greater than simple free-space path losses. As described in an earlier section, communication beyond line-of-sight distances involves propagation modes that increase the path attenuation with distance.

VHF/UHF Station Gain

The largest of the eight factors involved in station design is receiver sensitivity. This is obtainable from **Figure 4.9**, if you know the approximate receiver noise figure and transmission-line loss. If you can't measure noise figure, assume 3 dB for 50 MHz, 5 for 144 or 222, 8 for 432 and 10 for 1296 MHz, if you know your equipment is working moderately well. These noise figures are well on the conservative side for modern solid-state receivers.

Line loss can be taken from information in the **Transmission Lines** chapter for the line in use, if the antenna system is fed properly. Lay a straightedge between the appropriate points at either side of Figure 4.9, to find effective receiver sensitivity in decibels below 1 watt (dBW). Use the narrowest bandwidth that is practical for the emission intended, with the receiver you will be using. For CW, an average value for effective work is about 500 Hz. Phone bandwidth can be taken from the receiver instruction manual, but it usually falls between 2.1 to 2.7 kHz.

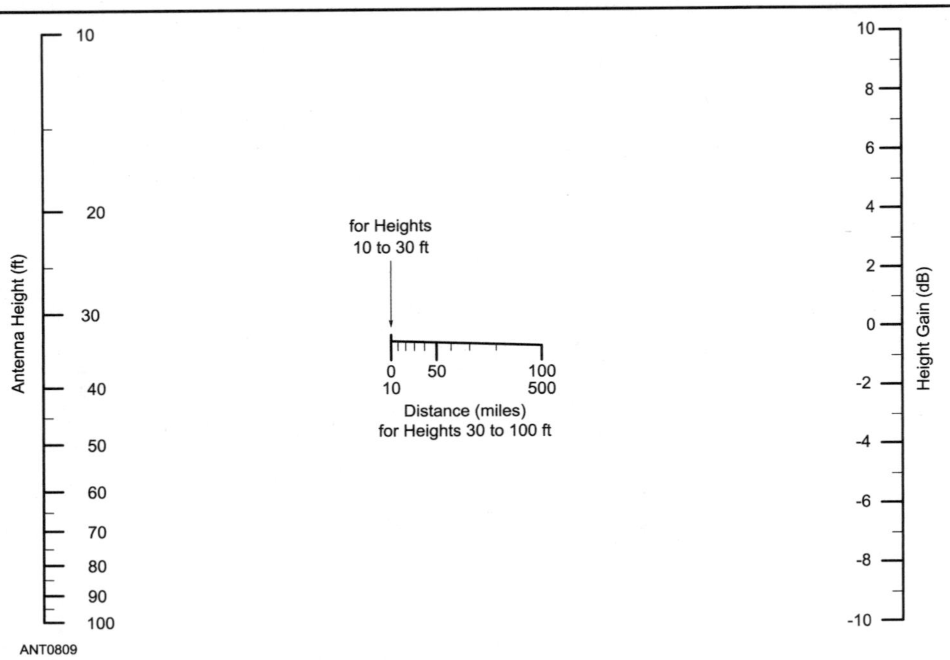

Figure 4.10 — Nomogram for determining antenna-height gain.

Antenna gain is next in importance. Gains of amateur antennas are often exaggerated. For well-designed Yagis the gain (over isotropic) run close to 10 times the boom length in wavelengths. (Example: A 24-foot Yagi on 144 MHz is 3.6 wavelengths long; 3.6 × 10 = 36, and 10 $\log_{10}$ 36 = 15.5 dBi in free space.) Add 3 dB for stacking, where used properly. Add 4 dB more for ground reflection gain. This varies in amateur work, but averages out near this figure.

We have one more plus factor — antenna height gain, obtained from **Figure 4.10**. Note that this is greatest for short distances. The left edge of the horizontal center scale is for 0 to 10 miles, the right edge for 100 to 500 miles. Height gain for 10 to 30 feet is assumed to be zero. For 50 feet the height gain is 4 dB at 10 miles, 3 dB at 50 miles, and 2 dB at 100 miles. At 80 feet the height gains are roughly 8, 6 and 4 dB for these distances. Beyond 100 miles the height gain is nearly uniform for a given height, regardless of distance.

Transmitter power output must be stated in decibels above 1 watt. If you have 500 W output, add 10 log (500/1), or 27 dB, to your station gain. The transmission-line loss must be subtracted from the station gain. So must the required signal-to-noise ratio. The information is based on CW work, so the additional signal needed for other modes must be subtracted. Use a figure of 3 dB for SSB. Fading losses must be accounted for also. It has been shown that for distances beyond 100 miles, the signal will vary plus or minus about 7 dB from the average level, so 7 dB must be subtracted from the station gain for high reliability. For distances under 100 miles, fading diminishes almost linearly with distance. For 50 miles, use –3.5 dB for fading.

What It All Means

Add all the plus and minus factors to get the station gain. Use the final value to find the distance over which you can expect to work reliably from the nomogram, Figure 4.8. Or work it the other way around: Find the path loss for the distance you want to cover from the nomogram and then figure out what station changes will be needed to overcome it.

The significance of all this becomes more obvious when we see path loss plotted against frequency for the various bands, as in **Figure 4.11**. At the left this is done for 50% reliability. At the right is the same information for 99% reliability. For near-perfect reliability, a path loss of 195 dB (easily encountered at 50 or 144 MHz) is involved in 100-mile communication. But look at the 50% reliability curve: The same path loss takes us out to well over 250 miles. Few amateurs demand near-perfect reliability. By choosing our times, and by accepting the necessity for some repeats or occasional loss of signal, we can maintain communication out to distances far beyond those usually covered by VHF stations.

Working out a few typical amateur VHF station setups with these curves will show why an understanding of these factors is important to any user of the VHF spectrum. Note that path loss rises very steeply in the first 100 miles or so. This is no news to VHF operators; locals are very strong, but stations 50 or 75 miles away are much weaker. What happens beyond 100 miles is not so well known to many of us.

From the curves of Figure 4.11, we see that path loss levels off markedly at what is the approximate limit of working range for average VHF stations using wideband modulation modes. Work out the station gain for a 50-W station with an average receiver and antenna, and you'll find that it comes out around 180 dB. This means you'd have about a 100-mile working radius in average terrain, for good but not perfect reliability. Another 10 dB may extend the range to as much as 250 miles. Changing from wideband modes such as FM or AM phone to SSB and CW makes a major improvement in daily coverage on the VHF bands.

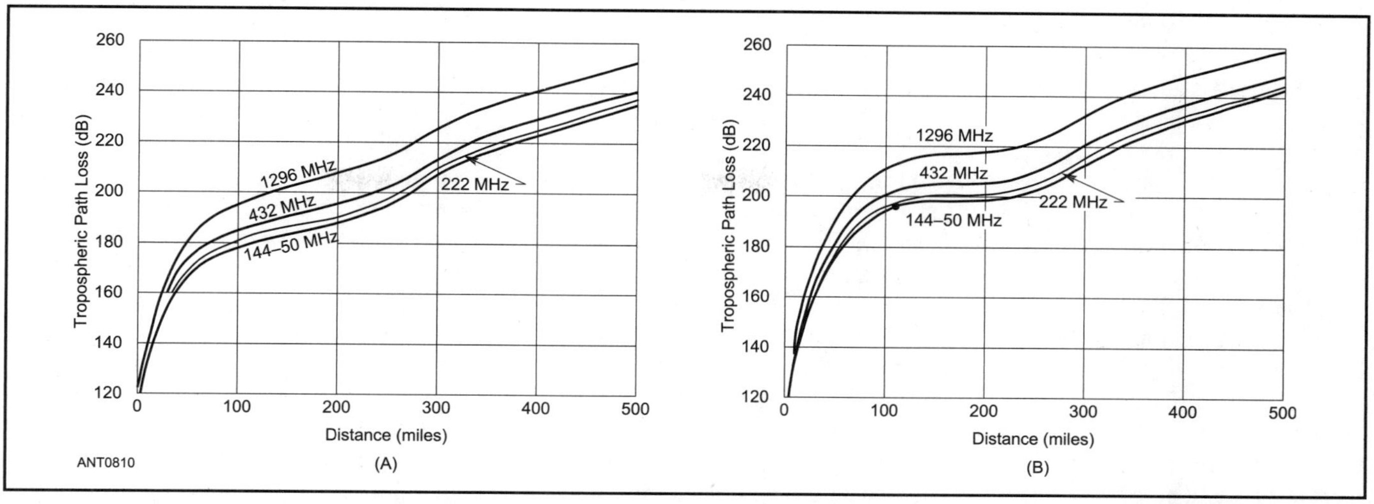

Figure 4.11 — Path loss versus distance for amateur frequencies above 50 MHz. At A are curves for 50% of the time; at B, for 99% of the time. The curves at A are more representative of Amateur Radio requirements.

A bigger antenna, a higher one if your present beam is not at least 50 feet up, an increase in power to 500 W from 50 W, an improvement in receiver noise figure if it is presently poor — any of these things can make a big improvement in reliable coverage. Achieve all of them, and you will have very likely tripled your sphere of influence, thanks to that hump in the path-loss curves. This goes a long way toward explaining why using a 10-W packaged station with a small antenna, fun though it may be, does not begin to show what the VHF bands are really good for.

Terrain at VHF/UHF

The coverage figures derived from the above procedure are for average terrain. What of stations in mountainous country? Although an open horizon is generally desirable for the VHF station site, mountain country should not be considered hopeless. Help for the valley dweller often lies in the optical phenomenon known as *knife-edge diffraction*. A flashlight beam pointed at the edge of a partition does not cut off sharply at the partition edge, but is diffracted around it, partially illuminating the shadow area. A similar effect is observed with VHF waves passing over ridges; there is a shadow effect, but not a complete blackout. If the signal is strong where it strikes the mountain range, it will be heard well in the bottom of a valley on the far side. (See **The Effects of Ground** chapter for a more thorough discussion of the theory of diffraction.)

This is familiar to all users of VHF communications equipment who operate in hilly terrain. Where only one ridge lies in the way, signals on the far side may be almost as good as on the near side. Under ideal conditions (a very high and sharp-edged obstruction near the midpoint of a long-enough path so that signals would be weak over average terrain), knife-edge diffraction may yield signals even stronger than would be possible with an open path.

The obstruction must project into the radiation patterns of the antennas used. Often mountains that look formidable to the viewer are not high enough to have an appreciable effect, one way or the other. Since the normal radiation pattern from a VHF array is several degrees above the horizontal, mountains that are less than about three degrees above the horizon, as seen from the antenna, are missed by the radiation from the array. Moving the mountains out of the way would have substantially no effect on VHF signal strength in such cases.

Rolling terrain, where obstructions are not sharp enough to produce knife-edge diffraction, still does not exhibit a complete shadow effect. There is no complete barrier to VHF propagation — only attenuation, which varies widely as the result of many factors. Thus, even valley locations are usable for VHF communication. Good antenna systems, preferably as high as possible, the best available equipment, and above all, the willingness and ability to work with weak signals may make outstanding VHF work possible, even in sites that show little promise by casual inspection.

4.1.9 AURORAL PROPAGATION

The Earth has a *magnetosphere* or magnetic field surrounding it. NASA scientists have described the magnetosphere as a sort of protective "bubble" around the Earth that shields us from the solar wind. Under normal circumstances, there are lots of electrons and protons moving in our magnetosphere, traveling along magnetic lines of force that trap them and keep them in place, neither bombarding the earth nor escaping into outer space.

Sudden bursts of activity on the Sun are sometimes accompanied by the ejection of charged particles, often from so-called *Coronal Mass Ejections (CME)* because they originate from the Sun's outer coronal region. These charged particles can interact with the magnetosphere, compressing and distorting it. If the orientation of the magnetic field contained in a large blast of solar wind or in a CME is aligned opposite to that of the Earth's magnetic field, the magnetic bubble can partially collapse and the particles normally trapped there can be deposited into the Earth's atmosphere along magnetic lines near the North or South poles. This produces a visible or radio *aurora*. An aurora is visible if the time of entry is after dark.

The visible aurora is, in effect, fluorescence at E-layer height — a curtain of ions capable of refracting radio waves in the frequency range above about 20 MHz. D-region absorption increases on lower frequencies during auroras. The exact frequency ranges depend on many factors: time, season, position with relation to the Earth's auroral regions, and the level of solar activity at the time, to name a few.

The auroral effect on VHF waves is another amateur discovery, this one dating back to the 1930s. The discovery came coincidentally with improved transmitting and receiving techniques then. The returning signal is diffused in frequency by the diversity of the auroral curtain as a refracting (scattering) medium. The result is a modulation of a CW signal, from just a slight burbling sound to what is best described as a "keyed roar." Before SSB took over in VHF work, voice was all but useless for auroral paths. A sideband signal suffers, too, but its narrower bandwidth helps to retain some degree of understandability. Distortion induced by a given set of auroral conditions increases with the frequency in use. Fifty-MHz signals are much more intelligible than those on 144 MHz on the same path at the same time. On 144 MHz, CW is almost mandatory for effective auroral communication.

The number of auroras that can be expected per year varies with the geomagnetic latitude. Drawn with respect to the Earth's magnetic poles instead of the geographical ones, these latitude lines in the US tilt upward to the northwest. For example, Portland, Oregon, is 2° farther north (geographic latitude) than Portland, Maine. The Maine city's geomagnetic latitude line crosses the Canadian border before it gets as far west as its Oregon namesake. In terms of auroras intense enough to produce VHF propagation results, Portland, Maine, is likely to see about 10 times as many per year. Oregon's auroral prospects are more like those of southern New Jersey or central Pennsylvania.

The antenna requirements for auroral work are mixed. High gain helps, but the area of the aurora yielding the best returns sometimes varies rapidly, so sharp directivity can be a disadvantage. So could a very low radiation angle, or a beam pattern very sharp in the vertical plane. Experience indicates that few amateur antennas are sharp enough in either plane to present a real handicap. The beam heading for maximum signal can change, however, so a bit of scanning in azimuth may turn up some interesting results. A very large array, such as is commonly used for moonbounce (with azimuth-elevation control), should be worthwhile.

The incidence of auroras, their average intensity, and their geographical distribution as to visual sightings and VHF propagation effects all vary to some extent with solar activity. Auroral activity is generated by CMEs (most prevalent at the peak of a solar cycle) and coronal holes (most prevalent during the declining phase of a solar cycle), with the maximum auroral activity tending to occur from coronal holes. Like sporadic E, an unusual auroral opening can come at any season. There is a marked diurnal swing in the number of auroras. Favored times are late afternoon and early evening, late evening through early morning, and early afternoon, in about that order. Major auroras often start in early afternoon and carry through to early morning the next day. It should be noted that auroral activity is most prevalent around the equinoxes.

4.2 HF SKY-WAVE PROPAGATION

As described earlier, the term *ground wave* is commonly applied to propagation that is confined to the Earth's lower atmosphere. Now we will use the term *sky wave* to describe modes of propagation that use the Earth's ionosphere. First, however, we must examine how the Earth's ionosphere is affected by the Sun.

4.2.1 THE ROLE OF THE SUN

Everything that happens in radio propagation, as with all life on Earth, is the result of radiation from the Sun. The variable nature of radio propagation here on Earth reflects the ever-changing intensity of ultraviolet and X-ray radiation, the primary ionizing agents in solar energy. Every day, solar nuclear reactions are turning hydrogen into helium, releasing an unimaginable blast of energy into space in the process. The total power radiated by the Sun is estimated at 4×10^{23} kW — that is, the number four followed by 23 zeroes. At its surface, the Sun emits about 60 *megawatts* per square meter. That is a very potent transmitter!

The Solar Wind

The Sun is constantly ejecting material from its surface in all directions into space, making up the so-called *solar wind*. Under relatively quiet solar conditions the solar wind blows around 200 miles per second (320 km per second) — 675,000 miles per hour — taking away about two million tons of solar material each second from the Sun. You needn't worry — the Sun is not going to shrivel up anytime soon. It's big enough that it will take many billions of years before that happens.

A 675,000 mile/hour wind sounds like a pretty stiff breeze, doesn't it? Lucky for us, the density of the material in the solar wind is very small by the time it has been spread out into interplanetary space. Scientists calculate that the density of the particles in the solar wind is less than that of the best vacuum they've ever achieved on Earth. Despite the low density of the material in the solar wind, the effect on the Earth, especially on its magnetic field, is very significant.

Before the advent of sophisticated satellite sensors, the Earth's magnetic field was considered to be fairly simple, modeled as if the Earth were a large bar magnet. The axis of this hypothetical bar magnet is oriented about 11° away from the geographic north-south pole. We now know that the solar wind alters the shape of the Earth's magnetic field significantly, compressing it on the side facing the Sun and elongating it on the other side — in the same manner as the tail of a comet is stretched out radially in its orientation from the Sun. In fact, the solar wind is also responsible for the shape of a comet's tail.

Partly because of the very nature of the nuclear reactions going on at the Sun itself, but also because of variations in the speed and direction of the solar wind, the interactions between the Sun and our Earth are incredibly complex. Even scientists who have studied the subject for years do not completely understand everything that happens on the Sun. Later in this chapter, we'll investigate the effects of the solar wind when conditions on the Sun are *not* "quiet." As far as amateur HF skywave propagation is concerned, the results of disturbed conditions on the Sun are not generally beneficial.

Sunspots

The most readily observed characteristic of the Sun, other than its blinding brilliance, is its tendency to have grayish black blemishes, seemingly at random times and at random places, on its fiery surface. (See **Figure 4.12**.) There are written records of naked-eye sightings of *sunspots* in the Orient back to more than 2000 years ago. As far as is known, the first indication that sunspots were recognized as part of the Sun was the result of observations by Galileo in the early 1600s, not long after he developed one of the first practical telescopes.

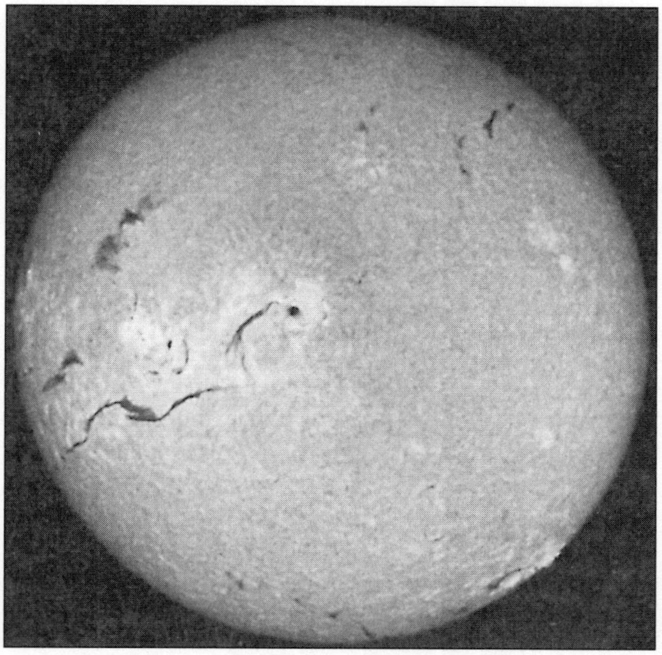

Figure 4.12 — Much more than sunspots can be seen when the Sun is viewed through selective optical filters. This photo was taken through a hydrogen-alpha filter that passes a narrow light segment at 6562 angstroms. The bright patches are active areas around and often between sunspots. Dark irregular lines are filaments of activity having no central core. Faint magnetic field lines are visible around a large sunspot group near the disc center. (Photo courtesy of Sacramento Peak Observatory, Sunspot, New Mexico).

Galileo also developed the projection method for observing the Sun safely, but probably not before he had suffered severe eye damage by trying to look at the Sun directly. (He was blind in his last years.) His drawings of sunspots, indicating their variable nature and position, are the earliest such record known to have been made. His reward for this brilliant work was immediate condemnation by church authorities of the time, which probably set back progress in learning more about the Sun for generations.

The systematic study of solar activity began about 1750, so a fairly reliable record of sunspot numbers goes back that far. (There are some gaps in the early data.) The record shows clearly that the Sun is always in a state of change. It never looks exactly the same from one day to the next. The most obvious daily change is the movement of visible activity centers (sunspots or groups thereof) across the solar disc, from east to west, at a constant rate. This movement was soon found to be the result of the rotation of the Sun, at a rate of approximately four weeks for a complete round. The average is about 27.5 days, the Sun's *synodic* rotation speed, viewed from the perspective of the Earth, which is also moving around the Sun in the same direction as the Sun's rotation.

Sunspot Numbers

Since the earliest days of systematic observation, our traditional measure of solar activity has been based on a count of sunspots. In these hundreds of years we have learned that the average number of spots goes up and down in cycles very roughly approximating a sine wave. In 1848, a method was introduced for the daily measurement of sunspot numbers. That method, which is still used today, was devised by the Swiss astronomer Johann Rudolph Wolf. The observer counts the total number of spots visible on the face of the Sun and the number of groups into which they are clustered, because neither quantity alone provides a satisfactory measure of sunspot activity. The observer's sunspot number for that day is computed by multiplying the number of groups he sees by 10, and then adding to this value the number of individual spots. Where possible, sunspot data collected prior to 1848 have been converted to this system.

As can readily be understood, results from one observer to another can vary greatly, since measurement depends on the capability of the equipment in use and on the stability of the Earth's atmosphere at the time of observation, as well as on the experience of the observer. A number of observatories around the world cooperate in measuring solar activity. A weighted average of the data is used to determine the *International Sunspot Number* or ISN for each day. (Amateur astronomers can approximate the determination of ISN values by multiplying their values by a correction factor determined empirically.)

A major step forward was made with the development of various methods for observing narrow portions of the Sun's spectrum. Narrowband light filters that can be used with any good telescope perform a visual function very similar to the aural function of a sharp filter added to a communications receiver. This enables the observer to see the actual area of the Sun doing the radiating of the ionizing energy, in addition to the sunspots, which are more a by-product than a cause. The photo of Figure 4.12 was made through such a filter. Studies of the ionosphere with instrumented probes, and later with satellites, manned and unmanned, have added greatly to our knowledge of the effects of the Sun on radio communication.

Daily sunspot counts are recorded, and monthly and yearly averages determined. The averages are used to see trends and observe patterns. Sunspot records were formerly kept in Zurich, Switzerland, and the values were known as *Zurich Sunspot Numbers*. They were also known as Wolf sunspot numbers. The official international sunspot numbers are now compiled at the Solar Influences Data Analysis Center (SIDC) in Brussels, Belgium.

The yearly means (averages) of sunspot numbers from 1700 through 2018 are plotted in **Figure 4.13** (these sunspot numbers are Version 1.0 values — more on this later). The cyclic nature of solar activity becomes readily apparent from this graph. The duration of the cycles varies from 9.0 to 12.7 years, but averages approximately 11.1 years, usually referred to as the 11-year solar cycle. The first complete cycle to be observed systematically began in 1755, and is numbered Cycle 1. Solar cycle numbers thereafter are consecutive. Cycle 23 began in October 1996 and peaked in April 2000 (this was the first peak — the second peak was in November 2001 but was a bit lower in terms of sunspot numbers). When this material was updated for the 24th edition of the *ARRL Antenna Book* in January 2019, Cycle 24 was very near solar minimum between Cycles 24 and 25.

The "Quiet" Sun

For more than 60 years it has been well known that radio propagation phenomena vary with the number and size of sunspots, and also with the position of sunspots on the surface of the Sun. There are daily and seasonal variations in the Earth's ionized layers resulting from changes in the amount of ultraviolet and X-ray radiation received from the Sun. The 11-year sunspot cycle affects propagation conditions because there is a direct correlation between sunspot activity and ionization.

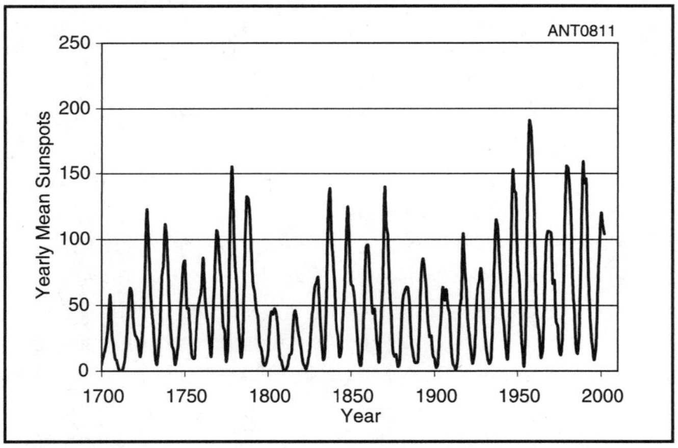

Figure 4.13 — Yearly means of smoothed sunspot numbers from data for 1700 through 2013. This plot clearly shows that sunspot activity takes place in cycles of approximately 11 years duration. There is also a longer-term periodicity in this plot, the Gleissberg 88-year (approximate) cycle. Cycle 1, the first complete cycle to be examined by systematic observation, began in 1755.

Activity on the surface of the Sun is changing continually. In this section we want to describe the activity of the so-called quiet Sun, meaning those times when the Sun is not doing anything more spectacular than acting like a "normal" thermonuclear ball of fusing matter. The Sun and its effects on Earthly propagation can be described in statistical terms — that's what the 11-year solar cycle does. You may experience vastly different conditions on any particular day compared to what a long-term average would suggest.

An analogy may be in order here. Have you ever gazed into a relatively calm campfire and been surprised when suddenly a flaming ember or a large spark was ejected in your direction? The Sun can also do unexpected and sometimes very dramatic things. Disturbances of propagation conditions here on Earth are caused by disturbed conditions on the Sun. More on this later.

Individual sunspots may vary in size and appearance, or even disappear totally, within a single day. In general, larger active areas persist through several rotations of the Sun. Some active areas have been identified over periods up to about a year. Because of these continual changes in solar activity, there are continual changes in the state of the Earth's ionosphere and resulting changes in propagation conditions. A short-term burst of solar activity may trigger unusual propagation conditions here on Earth lasting for less than an hour.

Smoothed Sunspot Numbers

Sunspot data are averaged or smoothed to remove the effects of short-term changes. For example, if a solar cycle is plotted in terms of the daily sunspot number or the monthly mean sunspot number, the resulting curve would be very spiky. Thus it would be somewhat difficult to ascertain when the solar cycle started, whether it had one or two peaks and when it ended. Additionally, the sunspot values that should be used for correlating propagation conditions are *Smoothed Sunspot Numbers* (also known as R_{12}), often called 12-month running average values. Data for 13 consecutive months are required to determine a smoothed sunspot number. Sometimes you'll see SSN used as the abbreviation for Smoothed Sunspot Number. Historically SSN has simply meant Sun Spot Number — not a smoothed value. It is best to use R_{12} as the abbreviation for the smoothed sunspot number.

Long-time users have found that the upper HF bands are reliably open for propagation only when the average number of sunspots is above certain minimum levels. For example, between mid-1988 to mid-1992 during Cycle 22, the SSN stayed higher than 100. The 10 meter band was open then almost all day, every day, to some part of the world. However, by mid-1996, few if any sunspots showed up on the Sun and the 10 meter band consequently was rarely open. Even 15 meters, normally a workhorse DX band when solar activity is high, was closed most of the time during the low point in Cycle 22. So far as propagation on the upper HF bands is concerned, the higher the sunspot number, the better the conditions.

Each smoothed number is an average of 13 monthly means, centered on the month of concern. The 1st and 13th months are given a weight of 0.5. A monthly mean is simply the sum of the daily ISN values for a calendar month, divided by the number of days in that month. We would commonly call this value a monthly average.

This may all sound very complicated, but an example should clarify the procedure. Suppose we wished to calculate the smoothed sunspot number for June 1986. We would require monthly mean values for six months prior and six months after this month, or from December 1985 through December 1986. The monthly mean ISN values for these months (again, these are Version 1.0 values) are:

Dec	85	17.3	Jul	86	18.1
Jan	86	2.5	Aug	86	7.4
Feb	86	23.2	Sep	86	3.8
Mar	86	15.1	Oct	86	35.4
Apr	86	18.5	Nov	86	15.2
May	86	13.7	Dec	86	6.8
Jun	86	1.1			

First we find the sum of the values, but using only one-half the amounts indicated for the first and 13th months in the listing. This value is 166.05. Then we determine the smoothed value by dividing the sum by 12: 166.05/12 = 13.8. (Values beyond the first decimal place are not warranted.) Thus, 13.8 is the smoothed sunspot number for June 1986. From this example, you can see that the smoothed sunspot number for a particular month cannot be determined until six months afterwards.

Generally the plots we see of sunspot numbers are averaged data. As already mentioned, smoothed numbers make it easier to observe trends and see patterns, but sometimes this data can be misleading. The plots tend to imply that solar activity varies smoothly, indicating, for example, that at the onset of a new cycle the activity just gradually increases. But this is definitely not so! On any one day, significant changes in solar activity can take place within hours, causing sudden band openings at frequencies well above the MUF values predicted from smoothed sunspot number curves. The durations of such openings may be brief, or they may recur for several days running, depending on the nature of the solar activity.

The New Sunspot Numbers

There has always been some concern about historical sunspot data because of the difficulty in counting individual sunspots, the evolution of better telescopes, and the bias of the official observers. A serious effort to understand the existing data started in the early 1990s when solar scientists Douglas Hoyt and Kenneth Schatten asked the simple question "Do we have the correct reconstruction of solar activity?" Their question came from the three problems noted above. To get around individual sunspot numbers, Hoyt and Schatten devised the Group Sunspot Number, which is based solely on the number of sunspot groups (sunspot areas) and normalized by a factor of 12 to match the Wolf numbers from 1874 to 1991.

Beginning in September 2011, there have been four Sunspot Number Workshops (sponsored by the National Solar Observatory, the Royal Observatory of Belgium, and the Air Force Research Laboratory) discussing the quality of the sunspot data. The last workshop reviewed the corrected time series of sunspot numbers from 1610 to the present, and the participants reached an agreement to publish the new data. The old data is designated Version 1.0 (V1.0), while the new data is designated Version 2.0 (V2.0). For more details on this effort, an explanation is provided by K9LA on his website (**k9la.us/Apr16_NEW_Sunspot_Numbers.pdf**). This paper also shows V1.0 vs V2.0 smoothed data (Figure 3 in the paper) from 1950 through 2015, and shows the difference in our lifetimes. V2.0 smoothed values are on average 1.4 times the V1.0 smoothed values for this period.

The Royal Observatory of Belgium (**sidc.oma.be/silso/datafiles**) began reporting V2.0 data on July 1, 2015. The Space Weather Prediction Center (part of NOAA) continues to report V1.0 data, and will transition to V2.0 data when solar minimum is reached between Cycles 24 and 25. At the solar minimum, for all intents and purposes the V2.0 values are equal to the V1.0 values.

Going forward in this chapter and edition, all sunspot numbers are V1.0 values unless otherwise noted as V2.0 data. A discussion of the impact of the new sunspot numbers with respect to propagation predictions will be addressed later.

Solar Flux

Since the late 1940s an additional method of determining solar activity has been put to use — the measurement of *solar radio flux*. The one amateurs are most familiar with is solar flux at a wavelength of 10.7 cm (2800 MHz). The quiet Sun emits radio energy across a broad frequency spectrum, with a slowly varying intensity. Solar flux is a measure of energy received per unit time, per unit area, per unit frequency interval. These radio fluxes, which originate from atmospheric layers high in the Sun's chromosphere and low in its corona, change gradually from day to day, in response to the activity causing sunspots. Thus, there is a degree of correlation between solar flux values and sunspot numbers.

One solar flux unit equals 10^{-22} joules per second per square meter per hertz. Values of solar flux at 10.7 cm are measured daily at The Dominion Radio Astrophysical Observatory, Penticton, British Columbia. Data have been collected since 1991. (Prior to June 1991, the Algonquin Radio Observatory, Ontario, made the measurements.) Measurements are also made at other observatories around the world, at several frequencies. With some variation, the daily measured flux values increase with increasing frequency of measurement, to at least 15.4 GHz. The daily 2800 MHz Penticton value is sent to Boulder, Colorado, where it is incorporated into WWV propagation bulletins (see later section). Solar flux, just like a sunspot number, is a proxy (substitute) for the true ionizing radiation at much shorter wavelengths, as solar flux at 2800 MHz does not have enough energy to ionize any atmospheric constituent. Solar flux and sunspots numbers will be discussed later in the section on computer-prediction programs.

Correlating Sunspot Numbers and Solar Flux Values

Based on historical data, an exact mathematical relationship does not exist to correlate sunspot data and solar flux values. Comparing daily values yields almost no correlation. Comparing monthly mean values (often called monthly averages since average = mean) produces a degree of correlation, but the spread in data is still significant. This is indicated in **Figure 4.14**, a scatter diagram plot of monthly mean V1.0 sunspot numbers versus the monthly means of solar flux values adjusted to one astronomical unit. (This adjustment applies a correction for differences in distance between the Sun and the Earth at different times of the year.)

A closer correlation exists when smoothed (12-month running average) sunspot numbers are compared with smoothed (12-month running average) solar flux values adjusted to one astronomical unit. A scatter diagram for smoothed V1.0 data appears in **Figure 4.15**. Note how the plot points establish a better defined pattern in Figure 4.15 as compared to Figure 4.14. The correlation is still not perfect, as records indicate a given smoothed sunspot number does not always correspond with the same smoothed solar flux value, and vice versa. **Table 4.1** illustrates some of the inconsistencies that exist in the historical data. Smoothed (12-month running average) V1.0 values are shown.

Even though there is no precise mathematical relationship between sunspot numbers and solar flux values, it is helpful to have some way to convert from one to the other. The primary reason is that sunspot numbers are valuable as a long-term link with the past, but the great usefulness of solar flux values are their immediacy, and their direct bearing on our field of interest. Remember, a smoothed sunspot number cannot be calculated until six months after the fact.

The following mathematical approximation has been derived to convert a V1.0 smoothed sunspot number to a smoothed solar flux value.

$$F_{12} = 63.75 + 0.728\ R_{12} + 0.00089\ R_{12}^2 \quad (3)$$

where

F_{12} = smoothed 10.7 cm solar flux number

R_{12} = V1.0 smoothed sunspot number

A graphic representation of this equation is given in **Figure 4.16**. Use this chart to make conversions graphically, rather than by calculations. With the graph, solar flux and sunspot number conversions can be made either way. The equation has been found to yield errors as great as 10% when historical data was examined. (Look at the August 1981 data in Table 4.1.) Therefore, conversions should be rounded to the nearest whole number, as additional decimal places are unwarranted. To make conversions from smoothed solar flux to smoothed sunspot number, the following approximation may be used.

$$R_{12} = 33.52\ (85.12 + F_{12})^{1/2} - 408.99 \quad (4)$$

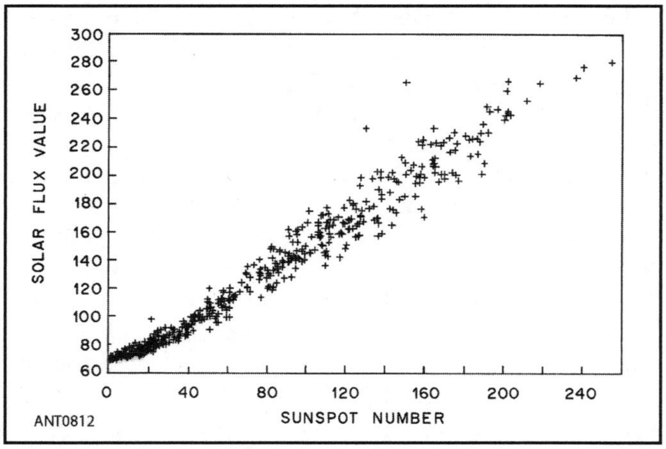

Figure 4.14 — Scatter diagram or X-Y plot of monthly mean sunspot numbers and monthly mean 2800-MHz solar flux values. Data values are from February 1947 through February 1987. Each "+" mark represents the intersection of data for a given month. If the correlation between the monthly mean sunspot number and monthly mean flux values was extremely high, all the marks would fall on or very near a single line.

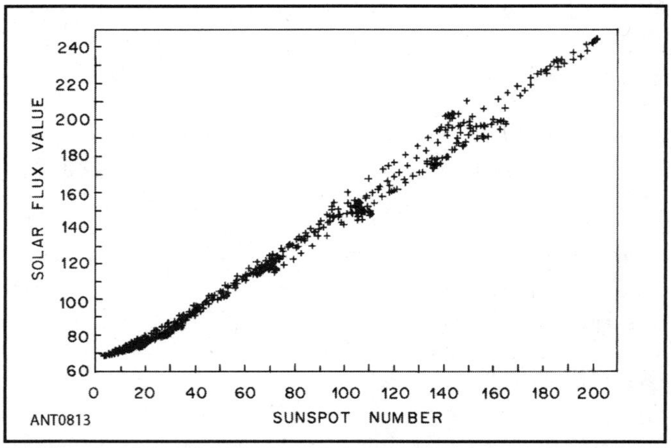

Figure 4.15 — Scatter diagram of smoothed (12-month running average) sunspot numbers versus smoothed 2800-MHz solar flux values. The correlation of smoothed values is much better than for the monthly means shown in Figure 4.14.

Table 4.1
Selected Historical Data Showing Inconsistent Correlation Between Smoothed Sunspot Number and Smoothed Solar Flux

Month	*Smoothed Sunspot Number*	*Smoothed Solar Flux Value*
May 1953	17.4	75.6
Sept 1965	17.4	78.5
Jul 1985	17.4	74.7
Jun 1969	106.1	151.4
Jul 1969	105.9	151.4
Dec 1982	94.6	151.4
Aug 1948	141.1	180.5
Oct 1959	141.1	192.3
Apr 1979	141.1	180.4
Aug 1981	141.1	203.3

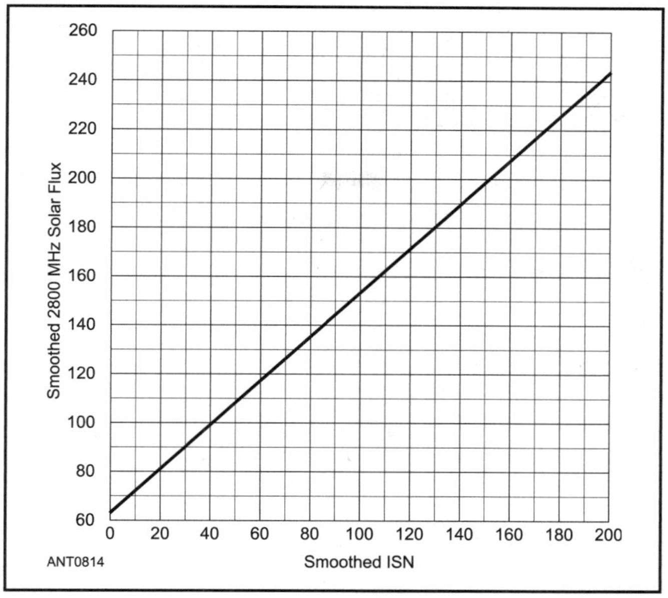

Figure 4.16 — Chart for conversions between smoothed International Sunspot Numbers and smoothed 2800-MHz solar flux. This curve is based on the mathematical approximation given in the text.

It should be obvious that Eq 3 and Eq 4 need to be changed for the V2.0 sunspot data. Perhaps solar scientists will do this in the future. For now, you can apply the average V2.0 / V1.0 ratio of 1.4 to the old sunspot numbers to convert between smoothed sunspot numbers and smoothed 10.7 cm solar flux.

4.2.2 THE IONOSPHERE

There will be inevitable "gray areas" in our discussion of the Earth's atmosphere and the changes wrought in it by the Sun and by associated changes in the Earth's magnetic field. This is not a story that can be told in neat equations, or values carried out to a satisfying number of decimal places. The story must be told, and understood — with its well-known limitations — if we are to put up good antennas and make them serve us well.

Thus far in this chapter we have been concerned with what might be called our "above-ground living space" — that portion of the total atmosphere wherein we can survive without artificial breathing aids, or up to about 6 km (4 miles). The boundary area is a broad one, but life (and radio propagation) undergo basic changes beyond this zone. Somewhat farther out, but still technically within the Earth's atmosphere, the role of the Sun in the wave-propagation picture is a dominant one.

This is the *ionosphere* — a region where the air pressure is so low that free electrons and ions can move about for some time without getting close enough to recombine into neutral atmospheric constituents. A radio wave entering this rarefied atmosphere, a region of relatively many free electrons, is affected in the same way as in entering a medium of different dielectric constant — its direction of travel is altered.

Extreme Ultraviolet (EUV) radiation (wavelengths of 10 to 100 nanometers or nm) from the Sun is the primary cause of ionization in the outer regions of the atmosphere, the ones most important for HF propagation. However, there are other forms of solar radiation as well, including both hard and soft x-rays (0.1 to 1 nm and 1 to 10 nm, respectively), gamma rays and cosmic rays. The radiated energy breaks up or *photoionizes* atoms and molecules of atmospheric gases into electrons and positively charged ions. The degree of ionization does not increase uniformly with distance from the Earth's surface. Instead there are relatively dense regions (layers) of ionization, each quite thick and more or less parallel to the Earth's surface, at fairly well-defined intervals outward from about 40 to 300 km (25 to 200 miles). These distinct layers are formed due to complex photochemical reactions of the various types of solar radiation with oxygen, ozone, nitrogen and nitrous oxide in the rarefied upper atmosphere.

Ionization is not constant within each layer, but tapers off gradually on either side of the maximum at the center of the layer. The total ionizing energy from the Sun reaching a given point, at a given time, is never constant, so the height and intensity of the ionization in the various regions will also vary. Thus, the practical effect on long-distance communication is an almost continuous variation in signal level, related to the time of day, the season of the year, the distance between the Earth and the Sun, and both short-term and long-term variations in solar activity. It would seem from all this that only the very wise or the very foolish would attempt to predict radio propagation conditions, but under quiet geomagnetic field conditions (low K indices) it is now possible to do so with a fair chance of success. It is possible to plan antenna designs, particularly the choosing of antenna heights, to exploit known propagation characteristics.

Ionospheric Layer Characteristics

The lowest known ionized region, called the *D layer* (or the *D region*), lies between 60 and 92 km (37 to 57 miles) above the Earth. In this relatively low and dense part of the atmosphere, atoms broken up into ions by sunlight (at appropriate wavelengths) recombine quickly, so the ionization level is directly related to sunlight. It begins at sunrise, peaks at local noon and disappears at sundown. When electrons in this dense medium are set in motion by a passing wave, collisions between particles are so frequent that a major portion of their energy may be used up as heat, as the electrons and disassociated ions recombine.

The probability of collisions depends on the distance an electron travels under the influence of the wave — in other words, on the wavelength. Thus, our 1.8- and 3.5-MHz bands, having the longest wavelengths, suffer the highest daytime absorption loss as they travel through the D layer, particularly for waves that enter the medium at the lowest angles. At times of high solar activity (peak years of the solar cycle) even waves entering the D layer vertically suffer almost total energy absorption around midday, making these bands almost useless for communication over appreciable distances during the hours of high sun. They "go dead" quickly in the morning, but come alive again the same way in late afternoon. The diurnal (daytime) D-layer effect is less at 7 MHz (though still marked), slight at 14 MHz and inconsequential on higher amateur frequencies.

The D region is ineffective in bending HF waves back to Earth, so its role in long-distance communication by amateurs is largely a negative one. (However, also see the later section on propagation at 2200 and 630 Meters — the D region is very involved in refraction at these low frequencies). It is the principal reason why our frequencies up through the 7-MHz band are useful mainly for short-distance communication during the high-Sun hours.

The lowest portion of the ionosphere useful for long-distance communication by amateurs is the *E layer* (also known as the *E region*) about 100 to 115 km (62 to 71 miles) above the Earth. In the E layer, at intermediate atmospheric density, ionization varies with the Sun angle above the horizon (the solar zenith angle), but solar EUV radiation is not the sole ionizing agent. Solar X-rays and meteors entering this portion of the Earth's atmosphere also play a part. Ionization increases rapidly after sunrise, reaches maximum around noon local time, and drops off quickly after sundown. The minimum is after midnight, local time. As with the D layer, the E layer absorbs wave energy in the lower-frequency amateur bands when the Sun angle is high, around mid day. The other varied effects of E-region ionization will be discussed later.

Most of our long-distance communication capability stems from the tenuous outer reaches of the Earth's atmosphere known as the *F layer* (also called the F region). At heights above 100 miles, ions and electrons recombine more slowly, allowing the region to hold its ability to reflect wave energy back to Earth well into the night. The *maximum usable frequency* (MUF) for F-layer propagation on east-west paths thus peaks just after noon at the midpoint, and the minimum occurs after midnight. We'll examine the subject of MUF in more detail later.

Judging what the F layer is doing is by no means that simple, however. The layer height may be from 160 to more than 500 km (100 to over 310 miles), depending on the season of the year, the latitudes, the time of day and, most capricious of all, what the Sun has been doing in the last few minutes and in perhaps the last three days before the attempt is made. The MUF between Eastern US and Europe, for example, has been anything from 7 to 70 MHz, depending on the conditions mentioned above, plus the point in the long-term solar-activity cycle at which the check is made.

During a summer day the F layer may split into two layers. The lower and weaker *F_1 layer*, about 160 km (100 miles) up, has only a minor role, acting more like the E than the *F_2 layer*. At night the F_1 region disappears and the F_2 region height drops somewhat. As a side note, the F_1 layer is more of an inflection point as opposed to a peak — just like the D layer.

Propagation information tailored to amateur needs is transmitted in all information bulletin periods by the ARRL Headquarters station, W1AW. Finally, solar and geomagnetic field data, transmitted hourly and updated eight times daily, are given in brief bulletins carried by the US Time Standard stations, WWV and WWVH, and also on Internet websites. More on these services later.

Bending in the Ionosphere

The degree of bending (refraction) of a wave path in an ionized layer depends on the density of the ionization and the length of the wave (inversely related to the square of its frequency). The bending at any given frequency or wavelength will increase with increased ionization density and will bend away from the region of most-intense ionization. For a given ionization density, bending increases with wavelength (that is, it decreases with frequency).

Two extremes are thus possible. If the intensity of the ionization is sufficient and the frequency is low enough, even a wave entering the layer perpendicularly will be reflected back to Earth. Conversely, if the frequency is high enough or the ionization decreases to a low-enough density, a condition is reached where the wave angle is not affected enough by the ionosphere to cause a useful portion of the wave energy to return to the Earth. The frequency at which this occurs is called the *vertical-incidence critical frequency*. Each region in the ionosphere has a critical frequency associated with it and this critical frequency will change depending on the date, time and state of the 11-year solar cycle. The D region also has a critical frequency, but it is so low that it does not come into play with respect to refraction on 160 meters and the HF bands. This is important as we move down to the new 630 meter and 2200 meter bands.

Figure 4.17 shows a simplified graph of the electron density (in electrons per cubic meter) versus height in the ionosphere (in km) for a particular set of daytime and nighttime conditions. This type of plot is also known as an *electron*

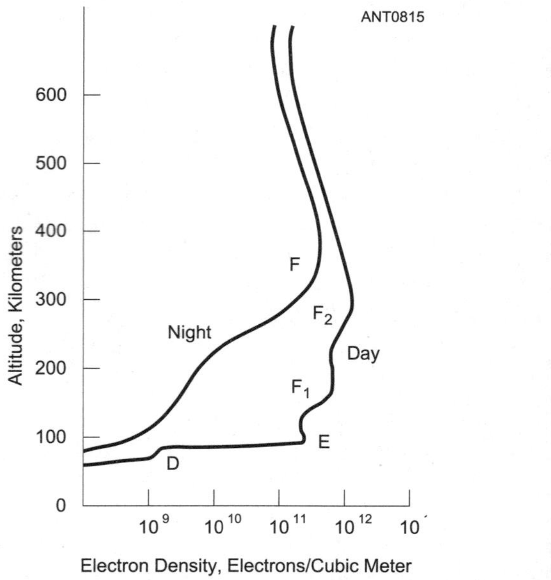

Figure 4.17 — Representative electron density profiles for nighttime and daytime conditions in the various ionospheric regions.

density profile. Free electrons are what return the signals you launch into the ionosphere back down to the Earth at some distance from your transmitter — the more free electrons in the ionosphere, the better propagation will be, particularly at higher frequencies. Remember, this is a simplified profile. It does not show the typical electron density valley above the E region peak in the nighttime profile. This valley is believed to be responsible for ducting on the low bands (160 meters and 80 meters — for details on ducting, visit the 160 meter link on K9LA's website, **k9la.us**). Also, as mentioned earlier, the the F_1 layer is more of an inflection point in the daytime profile — it is not a significant peak in electron density as is the F_2 layer.

In real life, electron-density profiles are extremely complicated and vary greatly from one location to the next, depending on a bewildering variety of factors. Of course, this sheer variability makes it all the more interesting and challenging for hams to work each other on ionospheric HF paths!

The following discussion about sounding the ionosphere provides some background information about the scientific instruments used to decipher the highly intricate mechanisms behind ionospheric HF propagation.

4.2.3 SOUNDING THE IONOSPHERE

For many years scientists have *sounded* the ionosphere to determine its communication potential at various elevation angles and frequencies. The word "sound" stems from an old idea — one that has nothing to do with the audio waves that we can hear as "sounds." Long ago, sailors sounded the depths beneath their boats by dropping weighted ropes, calibrated in fathoms, into the water. In a similar fashion, the instrument used to probe the height of the ionosphere is called an *ionosonde*, or ionospheric sounder. It measures distances to various layers by launching an electromagnetic wave directly up into the ionosphere.

Radar uses the same techniques as ionospheric sounding to detect targets such as airplanes. An ionosonde sends precisely timed pulses into the ionosphere over a range of MF and HF frequencies. The time of reception of an echo reflected from a region in the ionosphere is compared to the time of transmission. The time difference is multiplied by the speed of light to give the apparent distance that the wave has traveled from the transmitter to the ionosphere and back to the receiver. (Thus what is measured is an apparent or *virtual height* because in the real world the speed of a wave slows very slightly in the ionosphere, just as the speed of propagation through any medium other than a vacuum slows down because of that medium.)

Vertical-Incidence Sounders

Most ionosondes are *vertical-incidence sounders*, bouncing their signals perpendicularly off the various ionized regions above it by launching signals straight up into the ionosphere. The ionosonde frequency is swept upwards until echoes from the various ionospheric layers disappear, meaning that the critical frequencies for those layers have been exceeded, causing the waves to disappear into space.

Figure 4.18 shows a highly simplified ionogram for a typical vertical-incidence sounder. The echoes at the lowest height at the left-hand side of the plot show that the E region is about 100 km high. The F_1 region shown in the middle of the plot varies from about 200 to 330 km in this example, and the F_2 region ranges from just under 400 km to almost 600 km in height. [*In the amateur and professional literature, F_1 and F1 both refer to the same region — Ed.*] You can see that the F_1 and F_2 ionospheric regions take a "U" shape, indicating that the electron density varies throughout the layer. In this example, the peak in electron density is at a virtual height of the F_2 region of about 390 km, the lowest point in the F_2 curve.

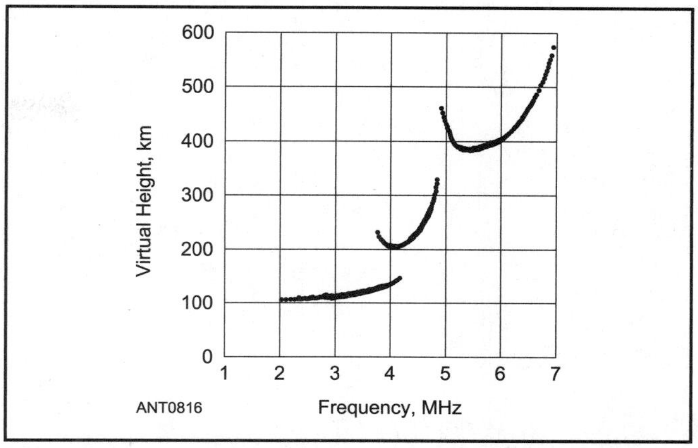

Figure 4.18 — Very simplified ionogram from a vertical-incidence sounder. The lowest trace is for the E region; the middle trace for the F_1 region and the upper trace for the F_2 region.

Scientists can derive a lot of information from a vertical-incidence ionogram, including the critical frequencies for each region, where raising the frequency any higher causes the signals to pass through that region. In Figure 4.18, the E-region critical frequency (abbreviated f_oE) is about 4.1 MHz. The F_1-region critical frequency (abbreviated f_oF_1) is 4.8 MHz. The F2-region critical frequency (abbreviated f_oF_2) is this simplified diagram is 6.8 MHz.

The observant reader may well be wondering what the subscripted "o" in the abbreviations f_oE, f_oF_1 and f_oF_2 mean. The abbreviation "o" means "ordinary." As explained previously, when an electromagnetic wave is launched into the ionosphere, the Earth's magnetic field splits the wave into two independent waves — the "ordinary" (o) and the "extraordinary" (x) components. The ordinary wave reaches the same height in the ionosphere whether the Earth's magnetic field is present or not, and hence is called "ordinary." The extraordinary wave, however, is greatly affected by the presence of the Earth's magnetic field, in a very complex fashion.

Figure 4.19 shows an example of an actual ionogram from the vertical Lowell Digisonde at Millstone Hill in Massachusetts, owned and operated by the Massachusetts Institute of Technology. This ionogram was made on June 18, 2000, and shows the conditions during a period of very high solar activity. The black-and-white rendition in Figure 4.19 of the actual color ionogram unfortunately loses some information. However, you can still see that a real ionogram

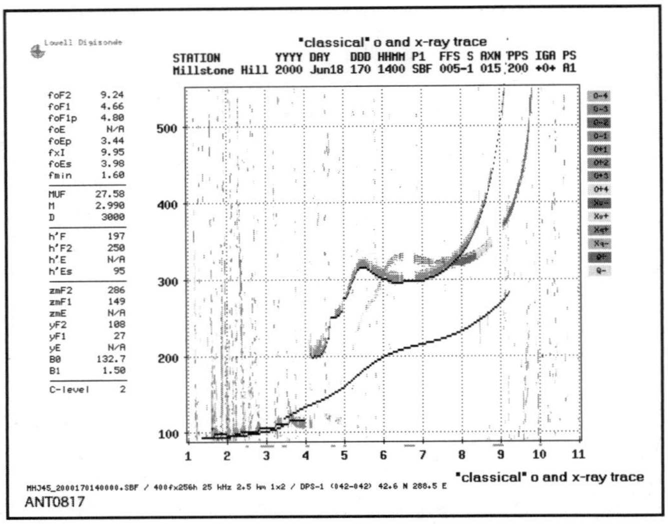

Figure 4.19 — Actual vertical-incidence ionogram from the Lowell Digisonde, owned and operated at Millstone Hill in Massachusetts by MIT (Massachusetts Institute of Technology). The ordinary (o) and extraordinary (x) traces are shown for heights greater than about 300 km. At the upper left are listed the computer-determined ionospheric parameters, such as f_oF_2 of 9.24 MHz and f_oF_1 at 4.66 MHz.

is a lot more complicated looking than the simple simulated one in Figure 4.18. This data is available at **www.digisonde.com/stationlist.html**.

The effects of noise and interference from other stations are shown by the many speckled dots appearing in the ionogram. The critical frequencies for various ionospheric layers are listed numerically at the left-hand side of the plot and the signal amplitudes are color-coded by the color bars at the right-hand side of the plot. The x-axis is the frequency, ranging from 1 to 11 MHz.

Compared to the simplified ionogram in Figure 4.18, Figure 4.19 shows another trace that appears on the plot from about 5.3 to 9.8 MHz, a trace shifted to the right of the darker ordinary trace. This second trace is the extraordinary (x) wave mentioned above. Since the x and o waves are created by the Earth's magnetic field, the difference in the ordinary and extraordinary traces is about 1/2 the *gyro-frequency*, the frequency at which an electron will spiral around a particular magnetic field line. The electron gyro-frequency is different at various places around the Earth, being related to the Earth's complicated and changing magnetic field (it varies from about 700 kHz to 1.7 MHz depending on location). The extraordinary trace always has a higher critical frequency than the ordinary trace on a vertical-incidence ionogram, and it is weaker than the ordinary trace, especially at frequencies below about 4 MHz because of heavy absorption.

The Big Picture Overhead

There are about 150 vertical-incidence ionosondes around the world. Ionosondes are located on land, even on a number of islands. There are gaps in sounder coverage, however, mainly over large expanses of open ocean. The compilation of all available vertical-incidence data from the worldwide network of ionospheric sounders results in global f_oF_2 maps, such as the 24th edition's updated map shown in **Figure 4.20**, a simulation from the highly sophisticated *PropLab Pro* computer program. (**spacew.com** — listed under Geophysical Software)

This simulation is for 1900 UTC, about four hours before East Coast sunset on September 15, 1998, with a high level of solar activity (SSN of 85) and a planetary A_p index

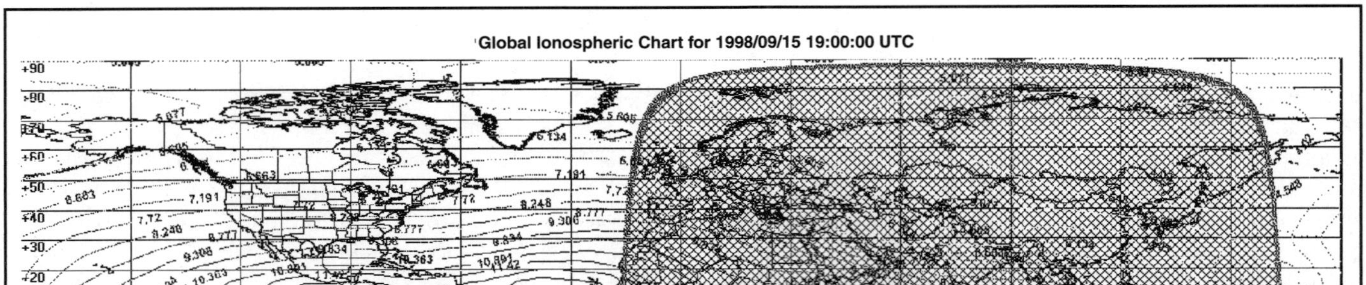

Figure 4.20 — Computer simulation of the f_oF_2 contours for 15 September 1998 at 1900 UTC, for an SSN of 85 and a quiet planetary Ap index of 5. Note the two regions of high f_oF_2 values in the South American sector (they can be seen better in a plot of MUF contours). These are the "equatorial anomalies," regions of high electronic density in the F2 region that often allow chordal-hop north-south propagation. See also Figure 4.6. (PropLab Pro V3 simulation courtesy of K9LA)

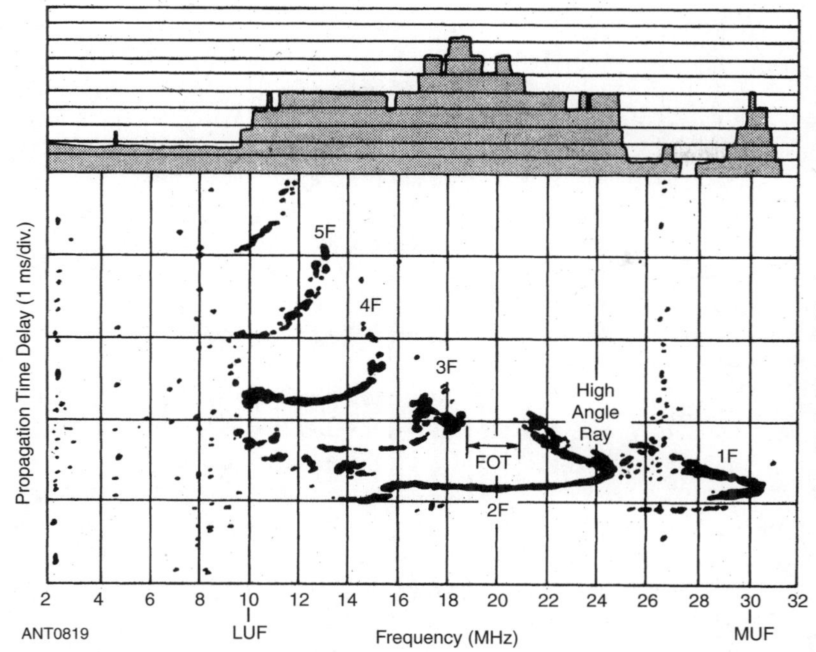

Figure 4.21 — HF oblique-sounder ionogram. This is a typical oblique ionosonde measurement on a 2500-mile path from Hawaii to southern California during mid-morning in March at a medium level of solar activity. Six possible modes (hops) are shown. The "FOT" is the frequency of optimum traffic, considered most reliable for this path/time.

of 5, indicating quiet geomagnetic conditions. The contours of f_oF_2 peak over the South American longitudes at around 12 MHz. If you look carefully, you'll see two peaks, or humps, on either side of the geomagnetic equator (or dip equator), at about –12 degrees geographic latitude in the South American sector.

These two "humps" in f_oF_2 form what is known as the "equatorial anomaly" and are caused by upwelling "fountains" of high electron concentration located in daylight areas about ±20° from the Earth's magnetic dip equator. The equatorial anomaly is important in transequatorial propagation. Those LU stations in Argentina that you can hear on 28 MHz from the US in the late afternoon, even during low portions of the solar cycle when other stations to the south are not coming through, are benefiting from transequatorial propagation, sometimes called *chordal hop* propagation, because signals going through this area remain in the ionosphere without lossy intermediate hops to the ground.

From records of f_oF_2 profiles, the underlying electron densities along a path can be computed. And from the electron density profiles computerized "ray tracing" may be done throughout the ionosphere to determine how a wave propagates from a transmitter to a particular receiver location. *ProPLab Pro* can do complex ray tracings that explicitly include the effect of the Earth's magnetic field, even taking into effect ionospheric stormy conditions.

Oblique-Angle Ionospheric Sounding

A more elaborate form of ionospheric sounder is the *oblique ionosonde*. Unlike a vertical-incidence ionospheric sounder, which sends its signals directly overhead, an oblique sounder transmits its pulses obliquely through the ionosphere, recording echoes at a receiver located some distance from the transmitter. The transmitter and distant receiver are precisely coordinated in GPS-derived time in modern oblique sounders.

Interpretation of ionograms produced by oblique sounders is considerably more difficult than for vertically incident ones. An oblique ionosonde purposely transmits over a continuous range of elevation angles simultaneously and hence cannot give explicit information about each elevation angle it launches. **Figure 4.21** shows a typical HF oblique-sounder ionogram for the path from Hawaii to California in March of 1973, during a period of medium-level sunspot activity. The y-axis is calibrated in time delay, in milliseconds. Longer distances involve longer time delays between the start of a transmitted pulse and the reception of the echo. The x-axis in this ionogram is the frequency, just like a vertical-incidence ionogram. Note that the frequency range for this plot extends to 32 MHz, while vertical-incidence ionograms usually don't sweep higher than about 12 MHz.

Six possible modes are shown in this ionogram: $1F_2$, $2F_2$, a High Angle Mode, $3F_2$, $4F_2$ and $5F_2$. These involve multiple modes of propagation (commonly called *hops*) between the ionosphere and reflections from the Earth. For example, at an operating frequency of 14 MHz, there are three modes open during the mid-morning: $2F_2$, $3F_2$ and $4F_2$. We'll discuss multiple hops later in more detail.

The lowest mode, $1F_2$ in Figure 4.21, employs a single F_2 hop to cover the 3900-km long path from Hawaii to California, but it is only open on 28-MHz. (Note that 3900 km is close to the maximum possible single-hop length for the F_2 region. We'll look at this in more detail later too.) In general, each mode that involves more than a single hop is weaker than a single hop. For example, you can see that the received $5F_2$ echo is weak and broken up because of the accumulation

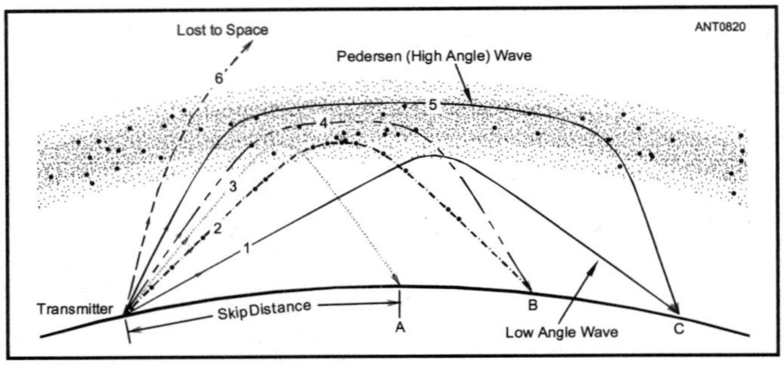

Figure 4.22 — Very simplified smooth-Earth/ionosphere diagram showing how the ground range from transmitter to receiver can vary as the elevation angle is gradually raised. The Pedersen wave, launched at a relatively high angle, has the same ground range as the low-angle wave #1. It may be slightly weaker and less stable, having traveled for a long distance in the ionosphere.

of losses at each ground-level reflection in its five hops, with absorption in the ionosphere all along its complicated path to the receiver.

The trace labeled "FOT" is the *frequency of optimum traffic*, considered the most reliable frequency for communications on this particular circuit and date/time (0.85 of the monthly median MUF of the most reliable mode, which results in a 90% probability — that is, 29 days of this March 1973 month). In this example, the FOT would be near the 21-MHz amateur band.

Another interesting point in Figure 4.21 is labeled "High Angle Ray." This refers to the *Pedersen ray*. Before we go into more details about the Pedersen high-angle wave, we need to examine how launch angles affect the way waves are propagated through the ionosphere.

Figure 4.22 shows a highly simplified situation, with a single ionospheric layer and a smooth Earth. This illustrates several important facts about antenna design for long-distance communication. In Figure 4.22, Wave #1 is launched at the lowest elevation angle (that is, most nearly horizontal to the horizon). Wave #1 manages to travel from the transmitter to the receiving location at point C in a single hop.

Wave #2 is launched at a higher elevation angle than Wave #1, and penetrates further into the ionospheric layer before it is refracted enough to return to Earth. The ground distance covered from the transmitter to point B is less for Wave #2 than for lower-angle Wave #1. Wave #3 is launched at a still-higher elevation angle. Like Wave #2 before it, Wave #3 penetrates further into the ionosphere and covers less ground downrange than #2.

Now, we see something very interesting happening for Wave #4, whose launch elevation angle is still higher than #3. Wave #4 penetrates even higher into the ionosphere than #3, reaching the highest level of ionization in our theoretical ionospheric layer, where it is finally refracted sufficiently to bend down to Earth. Wave #4 manages to arrive at the same point B as Wave #2, which was launched at a much lower elevation angle.

In other words, in the sequence from #1 to #3 we have been continually *increasing* the elevation launch angle and the ground range covered from the transmitter to the return of the signal back to Earth has been continually *decreasing*. However, starting with Wave #4, the ground range starts to *increase* with increased elevation angle. A further increase in the elevation angle causes Wave #5 to travel for an even longer distance through the ionosphere, exiting finally at point C, the same ground distance as lowest-angle Wave #1.

Finally, increasing the elevation angle even further results in Wave #6 being lost to outer space because the ionization in the layer is insufficient to bend the wave back to Earth. In other words, Wave #6 has exceeded the *critical angle* for this hypothetical ionospheric layer and this frequency of operation.

Both Waves #4 and #5 in Figure 4.22 are called "high-angle" or Pedersen waves (after the Danish physicist). Because Wave #5 has traveled a greater distance through the ionosphere, it is always weaker than Wave #1, the one launched at the lowest elevation angle. Pedersen waves are usually not very stable, since small changes in elevation angle can result in large changes in the ground range that these high-angle waves cover.

4.2.4 SKIP PROPAGATION

Figure 4.22 shows that we can communicate with the point on the Earth labeled "A" (where Wave #3 arrives), but not any closer to our transmitter site. When the critical angle is less than 90° (that is, directly overhead) there will always be a region around the transmitting site where an ionospherically propagated signal cannot be heard, or is heard weakly. This area lies between the outer limit of the ground-wave range and the inner edge of energy return from the ionosphere. It is called the *skip zone*, and the distance between the originating site and the beginning of the ionospheric return is called the *skip distance*. This terminology should not to be confused with ham jargon such as "the skip is in," referring to the fact that a band is open for sky-wave propagation.

The signal may often be heard to some extent within the skip zone, through various forms of scattering (discussed in detail later), but it will ordinarily be marginal in strength. When the skip distance is short, both ground-wave and sky-wave signals may be received near the transmitter. In such instances the sky wave frequently is stronger than the ground wave, even as close as a few miles from the transmitter. The ionosphere is an efficient communication medium under favorable conditions. Comparatively, the ground wave is not.

If the radio wave leaves the Earth at a radiation angle of zero degrees, just at the horizon, the maximum distance that may be reached under usual ionospheric conditions in the F_2 region is about 4000 km (2500 miles). This 4000 km value is for the higher HF frequencies — lower frequencies result in shorter hops.

Conversely, there is also a *critical frequency* below which waves are always returned to Earth even if the radiation angle is 90°. For signals below the critical frequency, there is no skip zone, making these frequencies very useful for regional communication. Deliberately launching a signal at high elevation angles in order to cover a region around the transmitting antenna is very useful for emergency and disaster relief communications, for example. This type of propagation is referred to as *Near Vertical Incidence Skywave* (NVIS) and antenna systems designed for NVIS are covered in the chapter on **HF Antenna System Design**.

4.2.5 MULTI-HOP PROPAGATION

As mentioned previously in the discussion about Figure 4.22, the Earth itself can act as a reflector for radio waves, resulting in multiple hops. Thus, a radio signal can be reflected from the reception point on the Earth back into the ionosphere, reaching the Earth a second time at a still more-distant point. This effect is illustrated in **Figure 4.23**, where a single ionospheric layer is depicted, although this time we show both the layer and the Earth beneath it as curved rather than flat. The wave identified as "Critical Angle" travels from the transmitter via the ionosphere to point A, in the center of the drawing, where it is reflected upwards and travels through the ionosphere to point B, at the right. This shows a two-hop signal.

As in the simplified case in Figure 4.22, the distance at which a ray eventually reaches the Earth depends on the launch elevation angle at which it left the transmitting antenna.

The information in Figure 4.23 is greatly simplified. On actual communication paths the picture is complicated by many factors. One is that the transmitted energy spreads over a considerable area after it leaves the antenna. Even with an antenna array having the sharpest practical beam pattern, there is what might be described as a *cone of radiation* centered on the wave lines (rays) shown in the drawing. The reflection/refraction in the ionosphere is also highly variable, and is the cause of considerable spreading and scattering.

Under some conditions it is possible for as many as four or five signal hops to occur over a radio path, as illustrated by the oblique ionogram in Figure 4.21. But no more than two or three hops is the norm. In this way, HF communication can be conducted over thousands of miles.

An important point should be recognized with regard to signal hopping. A significant loss of signal occurs with each hop — especially at lower HF frequencies. The D and E layers of the ionosphere absorb energy from signals as they pass through, and the ionosphere tends to scatter the radio energy in various directions, rather than confining it in a tight bundle. The roughness of the Earth's surface also scatters the energy at a reflection point.

Assuming that both waves do reach point B in Figure 4.23, the low-angle wave will contain more energy at point B. This wave passes through the lower layers just twice, compared to the higher-angle route, which must pass through these layers four times, plus encountering an Earth reflection. Measurements indicate that although there can be great variation in the relative strengths of the two signals — the one-hop signal will generally be from 7 to 10 dB stronger. The nature of the terrain at the mid-path reflection point for the two-hop wave, the angle at which the wave is reflected from the Earth, and the condition of the ionosphere in the vicinity of all the refraction points are the primary factors in determining the signal-strength ratio.

The loss per hop becomes significant at greater distances. It is because of these losses that no more than four or five propagation hops are useful; the received signal becomes too weak to be usable over more hops. Although modes other than signal hopping also account for the propagation of radio waves over thousands of miles, backscatter studies of actual radio propagation have displayed signals with as many as five hops. So the hopping mode is arguably the most prevalent method for long-distance communication.

Figure 4.24 shows another way of looking at propagation — a *geographic area* look. Figure 4.24 shows 15 meter

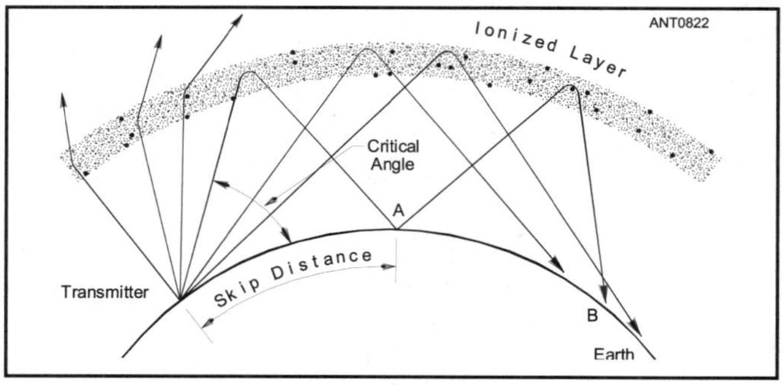

Figure 4.23 — Behavior of waves encountering a simple curved ionospheric layer over a curved Earth. Rays entering the ionized region at angles above the critical angle are not bent enough to be returned to Earth, and are lost to space. Waves entering at angles below the critical angle reach the Earth at increasingly greater distances as the launch angle approaches the horizontal. The maximum distance that may normally be covered in a single hop is 4000 km for low elevation angle signals at the upper end of HF. Greater distances are covered with multiple hops. Lower frequencies have shorter maximum hop distances due to more bending in the ionosphere.

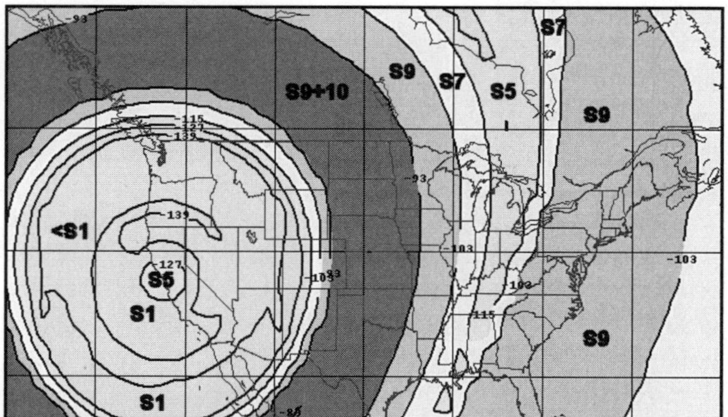

Figure 4.24 — Modified *VOAAREA* plot for 21.2 MHz from San Francisco to the rest of the US, annotated with signal levels in S units, as well as signal contours in dBW (dB below a watt). Antennas are assumed to be 3-element Yagis at 55 feet above flat ground; the transmitter power is 1500 W; the month is November with SSN = 50, a moderate level of solar activity, at 22 UTC. The most obvious feature is the large "skip zone" centered on the transmitter in San Francisco, extending almost one third of the distance across the US.

signal levels across the US as they propagate from a transmitting station in San Francisco. This simulation of propagation conditions is for the month of November, with a medium level of solar activity (SSN = 50) at 22 UTC. Figure 4.24 was created using the *VOAAREA* software program, part of the *VOACAP* software suite. Transmitter power is assumed to be 1500 W, with 3-element Yagis, 55 feet high, at the transmitter and at each receiving location.

From the transmitter out to about 50 miles, signals are moderate, at about S-5 on an S meter. Beyond that coverage area to almost 1/3 of the way across the country (to Colorado), there is a large and distinctive skip zone, where only very weak signals return to Earth (S-1 or less). Beyond Colorado, signals rapidly build up to S-9+10 dB across the middle of the US, falling to S-9 and then to S-7 in the vicinity of Chicago, Illinois. Beyond Chicago, the signals drop to S-5 in a swath from Michigan and part of Ohio down to Alabama. All along the US East Coast, signals come back strong at S-9.

The reason why the signals in Figure 4.24 drop down to S-5 in the Midwest is that the necessary elevation angles to cover this region in a single F2 hop are extremely low even at a moderate level of solar activity. To achieve launch angles as low as 1° requires either very high antenna heights or a high mountaintop location. Beyond the Midwest, out to the US East Coast, two F2 hops are required, with higher elevation angles and hence greater antenna gain for moderate antenna heights.

4.2.6 NON-HOPPING PROPAGATION MODES

Present propagation theory holds that for communication distances of many thousands of kilometers, signals do not always hop in relatively short increments from ionosphere-to-Earth-to-ionosphere and so forth along the entire path. Instead, the wave is thought to propagate *inside* the ionosphere throughout some portion of the path length, tending to be *ducted* in the ionized layer or between layers.

As was shown in Figure 4.22, the high-angle Pedersen ray can also penetrate an ionospheric layer farther than lower-angle rays. In the less-densely ionized upper edge of the layer, the amount of refraction is less, nearly equaling the curvature of the layer itself as it encircles the Earth.

Non-hopping theory of long-distance propagation is supported by studies of travel times for signals that go completely around the world and for the resultant signal strengths. The time required is significantly less than would be necessary to hop between the Earth and the ionosphere 10 or more times while circling the Earth, and the signal strength is stronger than multi-hop with its numerous transits through the absorbing region and numerous ground reflections.

Propagation between two points thousands of kilometers apart may in fact consist of a combination of ducting and hopping. It may involve combinations of refractions from the E layer and the F layer. Despite all the complex factors involved, most long-distance propagation can be seen to follow certain general rules. Thus, much commercial and military point-to-point communication over long distances employs antennas designed to make maximum use of known radiation angles and layer heights, even on paths where multihop propagation is assumed.

In amateur work, however, we usually try for the lowest practical radiation angle, hoping to keep reflection losses to a minimum. Years of amateur experience have shown this to be a decided advantage under most conditions — but there are times when a higher angle signal prevails.

The geometry of propagation by means of the F_2 layer limits our maximum distance along the Earth's surface to about 4000 km (2500 miles) for a single hop. For higher radiation angles, this same distance may require two or more hops (with higher reflection loss). And fewer hops are better, in most cases. If you have a nearby neighbor who consistently outperforms you on the longer paths, more energy radiated at lower elevation angles is probably the reason.

4.2.7 MAXIMUM USABLE FREQUENCY (MUF)

The vertical-incidence critical frequency is the *maximum usable frequency* for local sky-wave high-angle communication. It is also useful in the selection of optimum working frequencies and the determination of the maximum usable frequency for distant points at a given time. The abbreviation "MUF" for maximum usable frequency will be used hereafter.

In geographic middle latitudes, the vertical-incident critical frequency ranges between about 1 and 4 MHz for the E layer, and between 2 and 13 MHz for the F_2 layer. The lowest figures are for nighttime conditions in the lowest years of the solar cycle. The highest are for the daytime hours in the years of high solar activity. These are average figures. Critical frequencies have reached as high as 20 MHz briefly during exceptionally high solar activity in the middle latitudes. As was pointed out earlier in Figure 4.20, $f_o F_2$ levels approaching 40 MHz are possible at low latitudes.

While vertical-incidence critical frequencies are interesting from a scientific point of view, hams are far more concerned about how we can exploit propagation conditions to communicate, preferably at long distances. The MUF for a 4000-km (2500 miles) distance using the F_2 layer is about 3.5 times the vertical-incidence critical $f_o F_2$ frequency existing at the path midpoint. For one-hop signals, if a uniform ionosphere is assumed, the MUF decreases with shorter distances along the path. This is true because the higher-frequency waves must be launched at higher elevation angles for shorter ranges, and at these launch angles they are not bent sufficiently to reach the Earth. Thus, a lower frequency (where more bending occurs) must be used.

Precisely speaking, a maximum usable frequency or MUF is defined for communication between two specific points on the Earth's surface, for the conditions existing at the time, including the minimum elevation angle that the station can launch at the frequency in use. (This practical form of MUF is sometimes called the *operational MUF*). At the same time and for the same conditions, the MUF from either of these two points to a third point may be different.

Therefore, the MUF cannot be expressed broadly as a single frequency, even for any given location at a particular time. The ionosphere is never uniform, and in fact at a given time and for a fixed distance, the MUF changes significantly with changes in compass direction for almost any point on the Earth. Under usual conditions, the MUF will always be highest in the direction toward the Sun — to the east in the morning, to the south at noon (from northern latitudes), and to the west in the afternoon and evening.

For the strongest signals at the greatest distance, especially where the limited power levels of the Amateur Radio Service are concerned, it is important to work fairly near the MUF. It is at these frequencies where signals suffer the least loss. The MUFs can be estimated with sufficient accuracy by using the prediction charts that appear on the ARRL website (**www.arrl.org/propagation**) or by using a computer prediction program. This book's downloadable supplemental information includes detailed and summary tables for more than 175 transmitting locations around the world. (See the section "When and Where HF Bands Are Open" later in this chapter.)

MUFs can also be observed with the use of a continuous coverage communications receiver. Frequencies up to the MUFs are in round-the-clock use today. When you "run out of signals" while tuning upward in frequency from your favorite ham band, you have a pretty good clue as to which band is going to work well, right then. Of course, it helps to know the direction to the transmitters whose signals you are hearing. Shortwave broadcasters know what frequencies to use, and you can hear them anywhere, if conditions are good. Time-and-frequency stations are also excellent indicators, since they operate around the clock. See **Table 4.2**. WWV is also a reliable source of propagation data, hourly, as discussed in more detail later in this chapter. And the NCDXF/IARU beacon system (**www.ncdxf.org/pages/beacons.html**) can give you a real-time picture of worldwide propagation on our 20, 17, 15, 12, and 10 meter bands.

Other real-time methods to assess propagation *right now* include the world-wide DX spotting networks and the Reverse Beacon Network. A good example of a spotting network website is My DX Summit sponsored by Radio Arcala in Finland. Visit **www.dxsummit.fi** or **www.dxmaps.com** to see who is working what. You can filter spots by band and geographical area to mitigate being inundated with spots that likely don't help your cause.

For information on the Reverse Beacon Network (RBN), visit **www.reversebeacon.net**. This system consists of many software defined radios (SDRs) that monitor many bands at once. By transmitting a properly formatted short message using your call sign, spots from these monitoring stations will be published and logged, including your signal-to-noise ratio (SNR) at each location. This allows you to assess propagation to the various monitors, and can also be used for A/B antenna comparisons. The RBN is described in an October 2016 *QST* article by Pete Smith, N4ZR, and Ward Silver, NØAX (see the Bibliography).

The value of operating near the MUF is two-fold. Under undisturbed conditions, the absorption loss decreases proportional to the square of a change in frequency. For example, the absorption loss is four times higher at 14 MHz than it is at 28 MHz. Perhaps more important, the hop distance is considerably greater as the MUF is approached. A transcontinental contact is thus much more likely to be made on a single hop on 28 MHz than on 14 MHz, so the higher frequency will give the stronger signal most of the time. The strong-signal reputation of the 28-MHz band is founded on this fact.

Table 4.2
Time and Frequency Stations Useful for Propagation Monitoring

Call	*Frequency (MHz)*	*Location*
WWV	2.5, 5, 10, 15, 20	Ft Collins, Colorado
WWVH	Same as WWV except 20	Kekaha, Kauai, Hawaii
CHU	3.330, 7.850, 14.670	Ottawa, Ontario, Canada
RID*	5.004, 10.004, 15.004	Irkutsk, USSR*
RWM	4.996, 9.996, 14.996	Novosibirsk, USSR
VNG	2.5, 5, 8.634, 12.984, 16	Lyndhurst, Australia
BPM	2.5, 5, 10, 15	Xiang, China
BSF	5, 15	Taoyuan, Taiwan
LOL	5, 10, 15	Buenos Aires, Argentina

*The call, taken from an international table, may not be the one used during actual transmission. Locations and frequencies appear to be accurate as provided.

4.2.8 LOWEST USABLE FREQUENCY (LUF)

There is also a lower limit to the range of frequencies that provide useful communication between two given points by way of the ionosphere. *Lowest usable frequency* is abbreviated LUF. If it were possible to start near the MUF and work gradually lower in frequency, the signal would decrease in strength and eventually would disappear into the ever-present "background noise." This happens because signal absorption increases proportional to the square of the lowering of the frequency. The frequency nearest the point where reception became unusable would be the LUF. It is not likely that you would want to work at the LUF (although 160 meter aficionados are near the LUF on a regular basis!), although reception could be improved if the station could increase power by a considerable amount, if larger antennas could be used at both ends of the path, or if low-noise receive antennas are employed. Digital modes such as JT65 and FT8 that use coding techniques to reject noise can extend the LUF below what is available to analog modes, as well.

For example, when solar activity is very high at the peak of a solar cycle, the LUF often rises higher than 14 MHz on the morning Eastern US-to-Europe path on 20 meters. Just before sunrise in the US, the 20 meter band will be first to open to Europe, followed shortly by 15 meters, and then 10 meters as the Sun rises further. By mid-morning, however, when 10 and 15 meters are both wide open, 20 meters will become very marginal to Europe, even when both sides are running maximum legal power levels. By contrast, stations on 10 meters can be worked readily with a transmitter power of only 1 or 2 W, indicating the wide range between the LUF and the MUF.

Frequently, the *window* between the LUF and the MUF for two fixed points is very narrow, and there may be no ama-

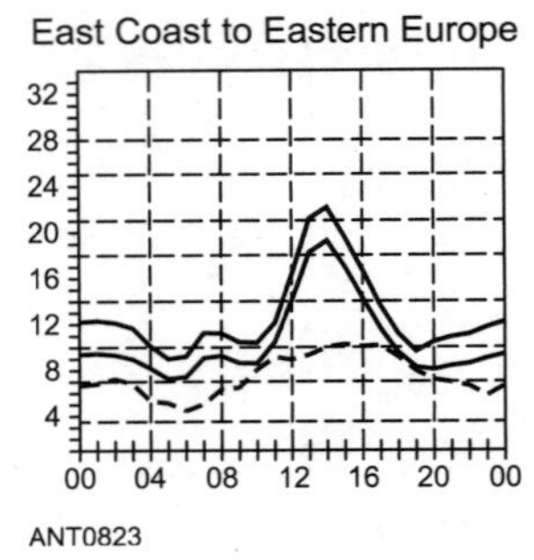

Figure 4.25 — Propagation prediction chart for East Coast of US to Europe. This appeared in December 1994 *QST*, where an average 2800-MHz (10.7-cm) solar flux of 83 was assumed for the mid-December to mid-January period. On 10% of these days, the highest frequency propagated was predicted at least as high as the uppermost curve (the Highest Possible Frequency, or HPF, approximately 21 MHz), and for 50% of the days as high as the middle curve, the median MUF. The broken lines show the Lowest Usable Frequency (LUF) for a 1500-W CW transmitter.

teur frequencies available inside the window. On occasion the LUF may be higher than the MUF between two points. This means that, for the highest possible frequency that will propagate through the ionosphere for that path, the absorption is so great as to make even that frequency unusable. Under these conditions it is impossible to establish amateur sky-wave communication between those two points, no matter what frequency is used. (It would normally be possible, however, to communicate between either point and other points on some frequency under the existing conditions.) Conditions when amateur sky-wave communication is impossible between two fixed points occur commonly for long distances where the total path is in darkness, and for very great distances in the daytime during periods of low solar activity.

Figure 4.25 shows a typical propagation prediction from the ARRL website (**www.arrl.org/propagation**). In this instance, the MUF and the LUF lines are blurred together at about 10 UTC, meaning that the statistical likelihood of any amateur frequency being open for that particular path at that particular time was not very good. Later on, after about 11 UTC, the gap between the MUF and LUF increased, indicating that the higher bands would be open on that path. Similar comments apply to around 18 UTC.

4.2.9 SOLAR AND GEOPHYSICAL DATA

At a minimum, an Amateur Radio operator interested in long-distance QSOs on any frequency should benefit by being aware of where we are in a solar cycle (solar data), the current state of the Sun's activity with respect to disturbances (geophysical data), and the fundamentals of propagation.

For solar and geophysical data, the internet can be very helpful. For example, the Space Weather Prediction Center (SWPC) website at **www.swpc.noaa.gov** can supply pretty much everything you need to know either directly or through links. Sites providing information on more specific propagation topics are referenced in the appropriate sections. Another source of useful information about solar disturbances is **www.spaceweather.com**.

The SWPC home page includes indexes for radio blackouts, solar radiation storm impacts, and geomagnetic storm impacts. (See the following section on disturbed conditions for more information about these disturbances.) Three videos are provided of recent X-ray activity (for assessment of solar radiation storms and radio blackouts), recent coronal mass ejections (for assessment of geomagnetic storms), and predicted visible aurora (which gives a general indication of radio aurora conditions). Plots of X-ray flux (for assessment of solar radiation storms and radio blackouts), proton flux (for assessment of solar radiation storms) and recent K-index activity (for assessment of geomagnetic storms) are also provided.

Under these six images are numerous links in three major categories of additional data: about space weather, products and data, and dashboards for specific interests. The "radio" dashboard is most suited to Amateur Radio.

There are also links to other sources of space weather information not on the SWPC website. For example, entering a specific topic (such as STEREO) in the search area in the upper right-hand corner of the home page brings up many links to NASA's STEREO mission (which allows us to look at the backside of the Sun).

Monitoring Geomagnetic Activity

Geomagnetic activity is monitored by devices known as *magnetometers*. These may be as simple as a magnetic compass rigged to record its movements. A worldwide network of magnetometers constantly monitors the Earth's magnetic field, because the Earth's magnetic field varies with location. Small variations in the geomagnetic field are scaled to two measures known as the K and A indices.

The K-Index

The *K-index* provides an indication of magnetic activity on a finite logarithmic scale of 0-9, updated every three hours. Very quiet conditions are reported as 0 or 1, while geomagnetic storm levels begin at 5. The K-index reflects readings of the Earth's geomagnetic field at Boulder, Colorado over the three hours just preceding the bulletin data changes. It is the nearest thing to current data on radio propagation available. With new data every three hours, the K-index trend is important. For HF propagation, rising is bad news; falling is good, especially related to propagation on paths involving latitudes above 30° north. Because this is a single-location reading of geomagnetic activity, it may not correlate closely with conditions in other areas.

The K-index is also a timely clue to aurora possibilities. Values of 4, and rising, warn that conditions associated with auroras and degraded HF propagation are present in the Boulder area at the time of the bulletin's preparation.

The *planetary K-index, K_p,* is a preliminary value that is updated every minute by the NOAA SWPC with an estimate of the measured K_p of the past three hours based on eight ground-based magnetometers around the world. Like the K-index, the estimated 3-hour planetary K_p-index ranges from 0 to 9. It is important to understand that this K_p-index isn't a forecast or an indicator of the current conditions, it always shows the K_p-value that was observed during a certain period.

The A-Index

Daily geomagnetic conditions are also summarized by the open-ended linear *A-index*, which corresponds roughly to the cumulative K-index values (it's the daily average of the eight K indices after converting the K indices to a linear scale).

The A-index is a daily figure for the state of activity of the Earth's magnetic field. The A-index tells you mainly how yesterday was, but it is very revealing when charted regularly because geomagnetic disturbances nearly always recur at approximately four-week intervals. The A-index commonly varies between 0 and 30 during quiet to active conditions, and up to 100 or higher during geomagnetic storms.

Geophysical Data on WWV and WWVH

At 18 minutes past the hour, radio station WWV broadcasts the solar flux measured at 2000 UTC, the prior day's planetary A-index and the latest mid-latitude K-index. (WWVH broadcasts the data at 45 minutes past the hour.) In addition, they broadcast a descriptive account of the condition of the geomagnetic field and a forecast for the next three hours. For more details about the broadcasts, visit **www.nist.gov/pml/time-and-frequency-division/radio-stations/wwv/wwv-and-wwvh-digital-time-code-and-broadcast**.

Interpreting Solar and Geophysical Data

You should keep in mind that the A-index is a description of what happened yesterday. Strictly speaking, the K-index is valid only for mid latitudes. However, the trend of the K-index is very important for propagation analysis and forecasting. A rising value foretells worsening HF propagation conditions, particularly for transpolar paths. At the same time, a rising value alerts VHF operators to the possibility of enhanced auroral activity, particularly when the K-index rises above 3.

A word of caution — it's easy to be overwhelmed with all this data. In fact, much of it has little direct relevance to radio propagation — but it certainly is colorful and interesting to look at! In this author's opinion, knowing the level and trends of the 10.7 cm solar flux and sunspot number, along with the level and trend of the K-Index, will give a good picture of HF propagation. The more esoteric parameters may serve to aid in the analysis of a particular propagation observation.

4.2.10 DISTURBED IONOSPHERIC CONDITIONS

So far, we have discussed the Earth's ionosphere when conditions at the Sun are undisturbed. Unfortunately, events on the Sun can disrupt propagation on Earth. These events cause three types of disturbances to propagation on Earth. These disturbances are *radio blackouts, solar radiation storms*, and *geomagnetic storms*. These three categories were defined by NOAA (National Oceanic and Atmospheric Administration) in early 2002 when they changed their format for solar disturbances to better align with the current understanding of these disturbances to propagation.

Geomagnetic storms (abbreviated G), solar radiation storms (abbreviated S), and radio blackouts (abbreviated R) are reported by NOAA on a scale of 1 to 5, with 1 being a minor disturbance and 5 being an extreme disturbance. Visit **www.swpc.noaa.gov/noaa-scales-explanation** for details. Although the above discussion of geomagnetic storms, solar radiation storms and radio blackouts gives you the fundamentals, reviewing the subject matter at the cited website will give you a much deeper understanding of the level of impact of each and how and what they impact

Radio Blackouts

Radio blackouts are caused by electromagnetic radiation at X-ray wavelengths from large flares (again mostly X-Class flares and big M-Class flares). This radiation causes additional D region ionization on that portion of the Earth in sunlight. Since the amount of absorption incurred is inversely proportional to the square of the frequency, the lower frequencies are affected the most. In other words, the higher frequencies recover first. So if you suspect a big flare has made the bands quiet, go higher in frequency and wait a bit for the recovery. Paths in darkness are not affected, so you may want to try a darkness path (for example, on 20 meters where the MUF might be high enough even in the dark ionosphere).

Radio blackouts are the least disruptive with respect to propagation. Their duration is only a couple hours. The higher bands are affected least, and radio blackouts only affect the daylight side of the Earth.

Solar Radiation Storms

Solar radiation storms are caused by very energetic protons from large flares (mostly X-Class flares and big M-Class flares). These protons coming from the Sun can funnel into the polar caps to increase D region absorption on over-the-pole paths (for example, the USA Midwest to India). Since these protons come from outside the Earth's magnetosphere, they do not necessarily affect the polar caps the same (unlike geomagnetic storms, which do). If your over-the-pole path is degraded, try the other way around.

Solar radiation storms are in the middle with respect to their impact to propagation. They can last for a couple days, but they only affect high-latitude, over-the-pole paths.

Geomagnetic Storms

Geomagnetic storms are caused by coronal mass ejections (CMEs — mostly occurring around solar maximum) and coronal holes (mostly occurring during the decline of a solar cycle). CMEs and coronal holes can result in increased geomagnetic field activity, which we see as higher A and K indices. This can cause electrons that are trapped in the Earth's magnetosphere to precipitate into the auroral zones, resulting in increased D and E region ionization. Generally, a similar effect is seen in both auroral zones since the precipitating electrons come from within the Earth's magnetosphere (they don't come directly from the Sun). Thus, as the A and K indices go higher, check for auroral VHF propagation. Storm levels range from a K value of 5 (minor) all the way to 9 (extreme). Extreme storms only occur for a few days during a typical solar cycle.

The K-index (and thus the A-index) can become elevated when the Bz component of the Earth's magnetic field (B is the symbol for magnetic field strength and z indicates the component perpendicular to the ecliptic) of the Interplanetary Magnetic Field (IMF) is oriented southward (negative). This condition best couples energy into the Earth's magnetic field, which then causes elevated K and A indices and geomagnetic storms.

An elevated K-index would also be a good time to check for skewed paths on the low bands — especially 160 meters since the amount of refraction by a given electron density profile is inversely proportional to the square of the frequency (the lower the frequency, the more the bending).

Additionally, when the K-index is high, F_2 region ionization generally is depleted at middle and high latitudes, thus moving down in frequency may minimize the impact to propagation. F_2 region ionization can also be enhanced at the low latitudes during geomagnetic storms, so check for enhanced low latitude (equatorial) propagation.

Geomagnetic storms are the most detrimental storms with respect to propagation, and can last for many days. In other words, it can take the ionosphere a long time to recover. Geomagnetic storms can affect the entire globe, day and night.

4.2.11 ONE-WAY PROPAGATION

One-way propagation is an interesting observation when it happens, but unfortunately it can be elusive in explaining. Possible explanations for one-way propagation are:

1. Receiver performance — perhaps one station has a receiver with less sensitivity than the other station
2. Transmitter power — one station is running the full legal limit, but the other station is only 100 W or even QRP
3. QRN — higher man-made and/or atmospheric noise at one end
4. Separate directional transmit and receive antennas — transmitting on a vertical so you're heard in every direction, but listening on a low-noise receive antenna with directivity
5. QRM — such as when North America can't work Europe when a band is just opening because of all the strong signals the Europeans are hearing from other Europeans
6. The ionosphere itself — the ionosphere looks different at each end of the path and has irregularities along the path which could cause a different (or prohibitive) hop structure or different absorption characteristics going one way and not the other way
7. Polarization coupling — ray tracing with sophisticated software suggests non-reciprocal paths could occur on the bands due to additional losses because the polarization of the transmit and receive antenna(s) does not match the polarization of the characteristic waves (ordinary and extraordinary) that propagate through the ionosphere.

4.2.12 LONG AND SHORT PATH PROPAGATION

Propagation between any two points on the Earth's surface is usually by the shortest direct route — the *great-circle path* found by stretching a string tightly between the two points on a globe. If an elastic band going completely around the globe in a straight line is substituted for the string, it will show another great-circle path, going "the long way around." The long path may serve for communication over the desired circuit when conditions are favorable along the longer route. There may be times when communication is possible over the long path but not possible at all over the short path. If there is knowledge of this potential at both ends of the circuit, long-path communication may work very well. Cooperation is almost essential, because both the aiming of directional antennas and the timing of the attempts must be right for any worthwhile result. The *IONCAP/VOACAP* predictions in Figure 4.25 were made for short-path azimuths only.

Sunlight is a required element in long-haul communication via the F layer above about 10 MHz, but due to recombination being a slow process after sunset, propagation may be supported in the dark ionosphere for several hours after sunset. This fact tends to define long-path timing and antenna aiming. Both are essentially the reverse of the "normal" for a given circuit. We know also that salt-water paths work better than overland ones. This can be significant in long-path work.

We can better understand several aspects of long-path propagation if you become accustomed to thinking of the Earth as a ball. This is easy if you use a globe frequently. A flat map of the world, of the *azimuthal-equidistant* projection type, is a useful substitute. The ARRL World Map is one, centered on Wichita, Kansas. A similar world map prepared by K5ZI and centered on Newington, Connecticut, is shown in **Figure 4.26**. These help to clarify paths involving those areas of the world. (NS6T provides an online service at **ns6t.net/azimuth/azimuth.html** to generate these maps centered on any location.

Long-Path Examples

There are numerous long-path routes well known to DX-minded amateurs. Two long paths that work frequently and well when 28 MHz is open from the northeastern US are New England to Perth, Western Australia, and New England to Tokyo. Although they represent different beam headings and distances, they share some favorable conditions. By the long path, Perth is close to halfway around the world; Tokyo is about three-quarters of the way. On 28 MHz, both areas come through in the early daylight hours, Eastern Time, but not necessarily on the same days. Both paths are at their best around the equinoxes. (The sunlight is more uniformly distributed over transequatorial paths at these times.) Probably the factor that most favors both is the nature of the first part of the trip at the US end. To work Perth by way of long path, northeastern US antennas are aimed southeast, out over salt

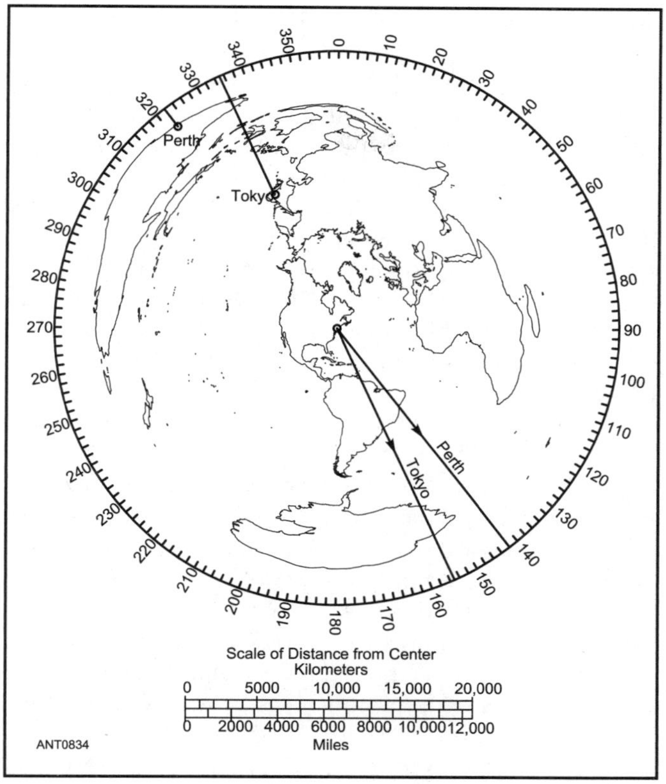

Figure 4.26 — K5ZI's computer-generated azimuthal-equidistant projection centered on Newington, Connecticut. Land masses and information showing long paths to Perth and Tokyo have been added. Notice that the paths in both cases lie almost entirely over water, rather than over land masses.

water for thousands of miles — the best low-loss start a signal could have. It is salt water essentially all the way, and the distance, about 13,000 miles, is not too much greater than the "short" path.

The long path to Japan is more toward the south, but still with no major land mass at the early reflection points. It is much longer, however, than that to Western Australia. Japanese signals are more limited in number on the long path than on the short, and signals on the average somewhat weaker, probably because of the greater distance.

On the short path, an amateur in the Perth area is looking at the worst conditions — away from the ocean, and out across the huge land mass of North America, unlikely to provide strong ground reflections. The short paths to both Japan and Western Australia, from most of the eastern half of North America, are hardly favorable. The first hop comes down in various western areas likely to be desert or mountains, or both, and not favored as reflection points.

A word of caution: Don't count on the long-path signals always coming in on the same beam heading. There can be notable differences in the line of propagation via the ionosphere on even relatively short distances. There can be more variations on long path, especially on circuits close to halfway around the world. Remember, for a point exactly halfway around (the antipode), all directions of the compass represent great-circle paths.

Other common long paths are the US Midwest to Western Australia and Japan on 10 meters after US sunrise, and the US West Coast to Europe on 10 meters several hours after US sunset. Of course high solar activity is needed for 10 meter propagation.

4.2.13 GRAY-LINE PROPAGATION

The *gray line*, sometimes called the *twilight zone*, is a band around the Earth between the sunlit portion and darkness. Astronomers call this the *terminator*. The terminator is a somewhat diffused region because the Earth's atmosphere tends to scatter the light into the darkness. **Figure 4.27** illustrates the gray line. Notice that on one side of the Earth, the gray line is coming into daylight (sunrise), and on the other side it is coming into darkness (sunset).

For many years, the belief has been that propagation along the gray line is very efficient — particularly on the lower bands (80 meters and 160 meters). Thus it was believed that greater distances could be covered than might be expected for the frequency in use. Unfortunately, when the physics of the ionosphere is properly understood, it becomes apparent that absorption along the terminator is prohibitive on the lower frequencies for the observed extremely long distance paths. What this says is the dark ionosphere is best for the lower frequencies. Thus there must be an alternative explanation for gray line propagation on the low bands that satisfies both the observations and the physics of the ionosphere.

This alternate explanation is that RF takes a short cut across the dark ionosphere by getting away from the terminator as quickly as possible to minimize absorption. This requires a skew area (or point) to connect the great circle path out of one end of the path to the great circle path out of the other end of the path. A possible skew area is the equatorward edge of the auroral oval. The old adages to look "southwest at sunrise" and "southeast at sunset" are still valid as our antenna azimuth patterns (even for directional transmit arrays) are broad enough to accept these paths that are somewhat deviated from the terminator.

In general, the gray line runs north and south, but varies as much as 23° either side of the north-south line. This varia-

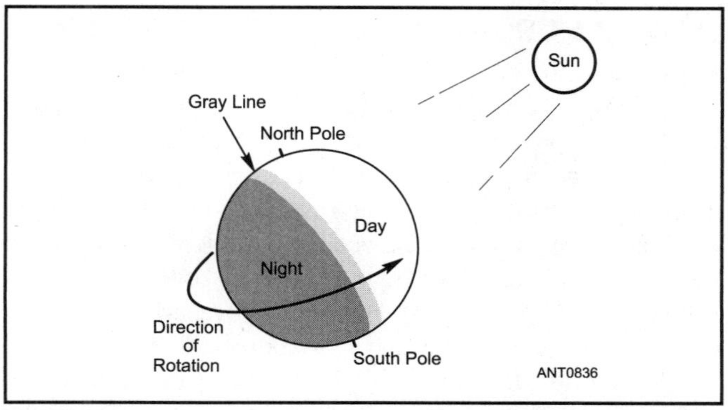

Figure 4.27 — The gray line or terminator is a transition region between daylight and darkness. One side of the Earth is coming into sunrise, and the other is just past sunset.

tion is caused by the tilt of the Earth's axis relative to its orbital plane around the Sun. The gray line will be exactly north and south at the equinoxes (March 21 and September 21). On the first day of Northern Hemisphere summer, June 21, it is tilted to the maximum of 23° one way, and on December 21, the first day of winter, it is tilted 23° the other way.

To an observer on the Earth, the direction of the terminator is always at right angles to the direction of the Sun at sunrise or sunset. It is important to note that, except at the equinoxes, the gray-line direction will be different at sunrise from that at sunset. This means you can work different areas of the world in the evening than you worked in the morning. Finally, it isn't necessary to be located inside the twilight zone in order to take advantage of gray-line propagation.

4.2.14 FADING

When all the variable factors in long-distance HF communication are taken in account, it is not surprising that signals vary in strength during almost every contact beyond the local range. In VHF communication we can also encounter some fading at distances greater than just to the visible horizon. These are mainly the result of changes in the temperature and moisture content of the air in the first few thousand feet above the ground.

On paths covered by HF ionospheric modes, the causes of fading are very complex — constantly changing layer height and density, random polarization shift, portions of the signal arriving out of phase, and so on. The energy arriving at the receiving antenna has components that have been acted upon differently by the ionosphere. Often the fading is very different for small changes in frequency. With a signal of a wideband nature, such as high-quality FM, or even double-sideband AM, the sidebands may have different fading rates from each other, or from the carrier. This causes severe distortion, resulting in what is termed *selective fading*. The effects are greatly reduced (but still present to some extent) when single-sideband (SSB) is used. Some immunity from fading during reception (but not to the distortion induced by selective fading) can be had by using two or more receivers on separate antennas, preferably with different polarizations, and combining the receiver outputs in what is known as a *diversity* receiving system.

4.2.15 SPORADIC E AND HF SCATTER MODES

In propagation literature there is a tendency to treat the various propagation modes as if they were separate and distinct phenomena. This they may be at times, but often there is a shifting from one to the other, or a mixture of two or more kinds of propagation affecting communication at one time. In the upper part of the usual frequency range for F-region work, for example, there may be enough tropospheric bending at one end (or both ends) to have an appreciable effect on the usable path length. There is the frequent combination of E and F-region propagation in long-distance work. And in the case of the E region, there are various causes of ionization that have very different effects on communication. Finally, there are weak-signal variations of both tropospheric and ionospheric modes, lumped under the term "scatter." We look at these phenomena separately here, but in practice we have to deal with them in combination, more often than not.

Sporadic E (E_s)

Note that sporadic E can also be written as *E-subscript-s* (E_s) but is often written simply as Es (pronounced E ess). *Sporadic E* is ionization at E-layer heights, but of different origin and communication potential from the E layer that affects mainly our lower amateur frequencies. *[The amateur and professional literature is not strict about the punctuation, with sporadic-E and Es used regularly — Ed.]*

The formative mechanism for sporadic E is believed to be wind shear. This explains ambient ionization (believed to be from meteor deposition) being distributed and compressed into a thin layer (a couple km thick) of high density, without the need for production of extra ionization. Neutral winds of high velocity, flowing in opposite directions at slightly different altitudes, produce shears. In the presence of the Earth's magnetic field, the ions are collected at a particular altitude, forming a thin, over-dense layer. Data from rockets entering E_s regions confirm the electron density, wind velocities and height parameters.

The ionization is formed in clouds of high density, lasting only a few hours at a time and distributed randomly. They vary in density and, in the middle latitudes in the Northern Hemisphere, move rapidly from southeast to northwest. Although E_s can develop at any time, it is most prevalent in the Northern Hemisphere between May and August, with a minor season about half as long beginning in December (the summer and winter solstices). The seasons and distribution in the Southern Hemisphere are not so well known. Australia and New Zealand seem to have conditions much like those in the US, but with the length of the seasons reversed, of course. Much of what is known about E_s came as the result of amateur pioneering in the VHF range.

Correlation of E_s openings with observed natural phenomena, including sunspot activity, is not readily apparent, although there is a meteorological tie-in with high-altitude winds. There is also a form of E_s, mainly in the northern part of the North Temperate Zone that is associated with auroral phenomena.

At the peak of the long E_s season, most commonly in late June and early July, ionization becomes extremely dense and widespread. This extends the usable range from the more common "single-hop" maximum of about 1400 miles to "double-hop" distances, mostly 1400 to 2500 miles. With 50-MHz techniques and interest improving in recent years, it has been shown that distances considerably beyond 2500 miles can be covered. Also, the evolution of the FT8 mode has opened up new possibilities on 50 MHz.

E_s can also "link-up" with other modes. For example, those in the northern continental US normally can't take advantage of TEP (trans-equatorial propagation — see the section Long-Distance Propagation of VHF Waves) because they are too far north. But E_s can provide a link to TEP. This hybrid mode is most likely to be experienced on our 50 MHz band. E_s can also provide a link to normal F_2 propagation.

When E_s is particularly strong and widespread, even the HF bands can suddenly support *short skip* producing exceptionally strong signals from distances that would normally be in the no-signal "skip zone." Dean Straw, N6BV, distinctly remembers a spectacular 20 meter E_s opening in September 1994, during the "Hiram Percy Maxim/125" anniversary celebration, when he was living in New Hampshire. Signals on 20 meters were 30 to 40 dB over S-9 from all along the Eastern Seaboard, from W2 to W4. One exasperated W3 complained that he had been calling in the huge pileup for 20 minutes. N6BV glanced at the S meter and saw that the W3 was 20 dB over S-9, normally a very strong 20 meter SSB signal, but not when almost everybody else was 40 dB over S-9! (See the Bibliography for N6BV's presentation on HF sporadic E.)

Such short-skip conditions caused by Sporadic E are more common on 10 meters than they are on 15 or 20 meters. They can result in excellent transatlantic 10 meter openings during the summer months — when 10 meters is not normally open for F_2 ionospheric propagation.

The MUF for E_s is not known precisely. It was long thought to be around 100 MHz, but in the last 25 years or so there have been thousands of 144-MHz contacts during the summer E_s season. Presumably, the possibility also exists at 222 MHz. The skip distance at 144 MHz does average much longer than at 50 MHz, and the openings are usually brief and extremely variable.

The terms "single" and "double" hop may not be accurate technically, since it is likely that cloud-to-cloud paths are involved. There may also be "no-hop" E_s. At times the very high ionization density produces critical frequencies up to the 50-MHz region, with no skip distance at all. It is often said that the E_s mode is a great equalizer. With the reflecting region practically overhead, even a simple dipole close to the ground may do as well over a few hundred miles as a large stacked antenna array designed for low-angle radiation. It's a great mode for low power and simple antennas on 28 and 50 MHz.

The summer E_s season in 2017 was unremarkable, but the summer E_s season in 2018 was spectacular. Undoubtedly the release and wide adoption of FT8 boosted participation in 2018, but CW and SSB openings in 2018 exceeded CW and SSB openings in 2017. Until scientists understand the complete E_s process, we can only speculate on why 2018 was so much better than 2017.

HF Scatter Modes

The term "skip zone" (where no signals are heard) should not be taken too literally. Two stations communicating over a single ionospheric hop can be heard to some degree by other stations at almost any point along the way, unless the two are running low power and using simple antennas. Some of the wave energy is *scattered* in all directions, including back to the starting point and farther.

Backscatter functions like a sort of HF ionospheric radar. **Figure 4.28** shows a schematic for a simple backscatter path. The signal launched from point A travels through the ionosphere back to earth at Point S, the scattering point. Here, the rough terrain of the land scatters signals in many directions, one of which propagates a weak signal back through the ionosphere to land at point B. Point B would normally be in the no-signal skip zone between A and S. Because backscatter signals arrive from multiple directions, through various paths through the ionosphere, they have a characteristic "hollow" sound, much like you get when you talk into a paper tube with its many internal reflections.

Because backscatter involves mainly scattering from the Earth at the point where the strong ionospherically propagated signal comes down, it is a part of HF over-the-horizon radar techniques. Amateurs using sounding techniques have shown that you can tell to what part of the world a band is usable (single-hop F) by probing the backscatter with a directive antenna and high transmitter power, even when the Earth contact point is over the open ocean. In fact, that's where the mode is at its best, because ocean waves can be efficient backscatter reflectors.

Backscatter is very useful on 28 MHz, particularly when that band seems dead simply because nobody is active in the right places. The mode keeps the 10 meter band lively in the low years of the solar cycle, thanks to the never-say-die attitude of some users. The mode is also an invaluable tool of 50 MHz DX aspirants, in the high years of the sunspot cycle, for the same reasons. On a high-MUF morning, hundreds of 6 meter beams may zero in on a hot spot somewhere in the Caribbean or South Atlantic, where there is no land, let alone other 6 meter stations — keeping in contact while they wait

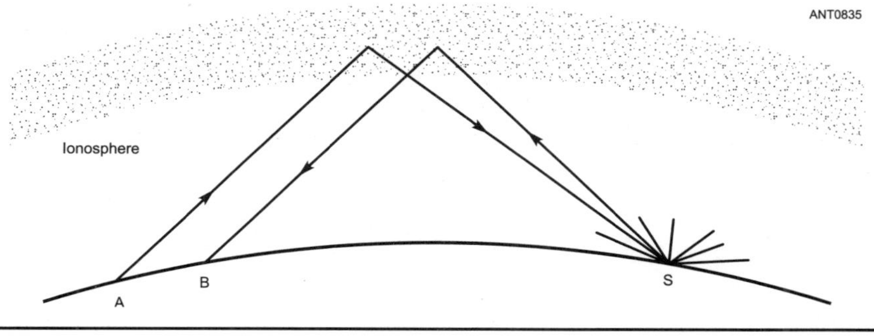

Figure 4.28 — Schematic of a simple backscatter path. Stations A and B are too close to make contact via normal F-layer ionospheric refraction. Signals scattered back from a distant point on the Earth's surface (S), often the ocean, may be accessible to both A and B to create a backscatter circuit.

for the band to open to a place where there is somebody.

Sidescatter is similar to backscatter, except the ground scatter zone is off the direct line between participants. A typical example, often observed during the lowest years of the solar cycle, is communication on 28 MHz between the eastern US (and adjacent areas of Canada) and much of the European continent. Often, this may start as "backscatter chatter" between Europeans whose antennas are turned toward the Azores. Then suddenly the North Americans join the fun, perhaps for only a few minutes, but sometimes much longer, with beams also pointed toward the Azores. Duration of the game can be extended, at times, by careful reorientation of antennas at both ends, as with backscatter. The secret, of course, is to keep hitting the highest-MUF area of the ionosphere and the most favorable ground-reflection points.

The favorable route is usually, but not always, south of the great-circle heading (for stations in the Northern Hemisphere). There can also be sidescatter from the auroral regions. Sidescatter signals are stronger than backscatter signals using the same general area of ground scattering.

Sidescatter signals have been observed frequently on the 14-MHz band, and can take place on any band where there is a large window between the MUF and the LUF. For sidescatter communications to occur, the thing to look for is a common area to which the band is open from both ends of the path (the Azores, in the above example), when there is no direct-path opening. It helps if the common area is in the open ocean, where there is less scattering loss than over land.

Forward scatter is similar to the other two scatter modes. In this case, the MUF may not be high enough for pure refraction to a distant point, but some scatter energy may go forward to complete the path.

With all these scatter modes, a propagation mode called *above-the-MUF* must come into play. Normally we believe the MUF must be equal to or greater than the operating frequency for propagation to occur. This assumes pure refraction. But the MUF can be below the operating frequency a certain amount — with additional loss incurred due to the scatter process. The *VOACAP* propagation prediction program includes this above-the-MUF mode, and it will be discussed later.

4.2.16 NEW AMATEUR BANDS AT LF AND MF

In late April 2015, the FCC proposed to allow Amateur Radio operators access to 2200 meters (135.7 to 137.8 kHz) and 630 meters (472 to 479 kHz). Related to this topic was the FCC in May 2014 denying a *Petition for Rule Making* to add a 4 meter band (70.0 to 70.5 MHz) to US Amateur Radio allocations at VHF. Although US amateurs can't transmit on 4 meters, we can certainly listen to that band to assess propagation across the Atlantic Ocean from stations in the United Kingdom, other European countries and African countries that do have authorization to transmit.

So how is propagation on these three bands? Propagation on 4 meters is the easiest to understand — it should be very similar to 6 meters. There should be sporadic E in the summer, just like on 6 meters, but with a slightly lower probability due to the slightly higher frequency. There should also be F_2 propagation, just like on 6 meters, in the fall and winter months in the northern hemisphere at high solar cycle levels. But just like E_s, the probability of an F_2 opening will be slightly lower due to the higher frequency.

As for 2200 meters and 630 meters, we can gain some insight into propagation on these bands by understanding two basic concepts in ionospheric physics. The first concept is that the amount of refraction incurred by an electromagnetic wave at a given frequency with a given electron density profile is inversely proportional to the square of the frequency. The second concept is that the amount of absorption incurred by an electromagnetic wave at a given frequency with a given electron density profile is also inversely proportional to the square of the frequency.

From the first concept, when the frequency decreases, the wave is bent more. Thus waves at MF and LF don't get as high into the ionosphere as an HF wave. This results in shorter hops. For example, a 28 MHz wave easily gets up to 300 km and gives maximum hops around and above 4000 km. A wave at 1.8 MHz only gets up to something like 200 km and gives maximum hops around 2000 km. And a wave at 150 kHz only gets up to around 80 km, with maximum hops of around 1400 km. Thus propagation on 2200 meters and 630 meters is via shorter hops than at HF.

From the second concept, when the frequency decreases, the wave incurs more absorption. This is why a long-distance signal on 10 meters can be well over S-9 while a long-distance signal on 160 meters is normally much nearer the noise level of your receive system. But an interesting phenomenon occurs below 160 meters, which is just above the electron gyro-frequency — the frequency at which an electron spirals around a magnetic field line. Absorption actually begins decreasing as the frequency goes below about 1.5 MHz. Also, as stated above, 150 kHz doesn't get too high into the absorbing region at night (the lower E region).

In summary, propagation on these two new bands is both at a disadvantage (shorter hops) and at an advantage (not as much absorption as expected). Unfortunately, on these bands antenna efficiency and man-made noise are tough to overcome. For more details, read the article titled "Physics of Propagation — Refraction Absorption Polarization" in the *Basic Concepts* link at the website **k9la.us**. Additionally, the December 2018 article titled "Propagation on 630m and 2200m" in the Monthly Feature link at **k9la.us** looks at both the ordinary wave and the extraordinary wave at these frequencies.

4.3 WHEN AND WHERE HF BANDS ARE OPEN

4.3.1 THE PROPAGATION BIG PICTURE

A newcomer to the HF bands could easily be overwhelmed with the sheer amount of data available in the Summary (and particularly the Detailed) prediction tables described in the following sections and provided with this book's downloadable supplemental information. So here's a long-term, "big-picture" view of HF propagation that might help answer some common questions. For example, what month really is the best for working DX around the clock? Or what level of solar activity is necessary to provide an opening between your QTH and somewhere in the South Pacific?

Table 4.3 is a table showing the number of hours in a day during each month when each major HF band is open to the same receiving areas shown in Tables 4.4 and 4.5 shown in a later section of this chapter. The listing is for New England, for three levels of solar activity: Very Low, Medium and Very High. The number of hours are separated in Table 4.3 by slashes. (Versions of Table 4.3 for other areas around the US are included with this book's downloadable supplemental information.)

Let's examine the conditions for New England to Europe on 15 meters for October. The entry shows "7/11/17," meaning that for a Very Low level of solar activity, 15 meters is open for 7 hours; for a Medium level, it is open for 11 hours and for a Very High level of solar activity it is open for 17 hours a day.

Even for a Very Low level of solar activity, the month with the most hours available per day from Boston to somewhere in Europe is October, with 7 hours, followed by the next largest month of March, with 6 hours. For a Very High level of solar activity, however, the 15 meter band is open to Europe for 18 hours in April, followed by 17 hours availability in September and October. Arguably, the CQ World Wide Contest Committee picked the very best month for higher-frequency propagation when they chose October for the Phone portion of that contest. November isn't too far behind, either.

You can easily see that even at a Very High level of solar activity, the summer months are not very good to work DX, particularly on east-west paths. For example, the 10 meter band is very rarely open from New England to Europe after the month of April, even when solar activity is at the highest levels possible. Things pick up after September, even for a Medium level of solar activity. Again, October looks like the most fruitful month in terms of the number of hours 10 meters is open to Europe under all levels of solar conditions.

Ten meters is open more regularly on north-south paths, such as from New England to South America or to southern Africa. It is open as much as 10 hours a day during March and October to far South America, and 7 hours a day in October to Africa — even during the lowest parts of the solar cycle. (Together with the sporadic-E propagation that 10 meters enjoys during the summer, this band can often be a lot of fun even during the sunspot doldrums. You just have to *be operating* on the band, rather than avoiding it because you know the sunspots are "spotty!")

Now, look at the 20 meter band in Table 4.3. From New England, twenty is open to somewhere in South America for 24 hours a day, no matter the level of solar activity. Note that Table 4.3 doesn't predict the level of signals available; it just shows that the band is open with a signal strength greater than 0 on the S meter.

Look ahead to Summary Table 4.4 for the predicted signal strengths in January at a Very Low level of solar activity. There, you can see that the signal strength from New England into deep South America is always S-8 or greater for a big gun station. A lot of the time during the night the band sounds dead, simply because everyone is either asleep or operating on a lower frequency.

For the 40 meter band in Table 4.3, during the month of January the band is open to Europe for 24 hours a day, whatever the level of solar activity is. Look now at Table 4.4, and you'll see that the predicted level for Very Low solar activity varies from S-4 to S-9. Local QRM or QRN would probably disrupt communications on 40 meters in Europe for stateside signals weaker than perhaps S-3 or S-4. Even though you might well be able to hear Europeans from New England during the day, they probably won't hear you because of local conditions, including local S-9+ European stations and atmospheric noise from nearby thunderstorms. New England stations with big antennas can often hear Europeans on 40 meters as early as noontime, but must wait until the late afternoon before the Europeans can hear them above their local noise and QRM.

Let's say that you want to boost your country total on 80 meters by concentrating on stations in the South Pacific. The best months would be from November to February in terms of the number of hours per day when the 80 meter band is open to Oceania. You can see by reading across the line for each month that the level of solar activity is not hugely important on 80 meters to any location (due to propagation taking place in the dark ionosphere). Common experience (backed by the statistical information in Table 4.6) is that the 80 meter band is open only marginally longer when sunspots are low.

This is true to a greater extent on 40 meters. Thus you may hear the generalization that the low bands tend to be better during periods of low solar activity, while the upper HF bands (above 10 MHz) tend to be better when the sun is more active.

Table 4.3 can give you a good handle on what months are the most productive for DXing and contesting. It should be no surprise to most veteran operators that the fall and winter months are the best times to work DX.

The 160 meter band is not covered in any of the tables since propagation in this frequency range can be quite difficult to predict and there is considerable uncertainty about the exact mechanisms involved. This is discussed further by Oler and Cohen in their paper on the vagaries of 160 meter propagation and why it is so different from propagation in the slightly higher HF bands. Also see the follow-on article by Luetzelschwab in the Bibliography.

Table 4.3

The number of hours per day when a particular band is open to the target geographic areas in Table 4.4, as related to the level of solar activity (Very Low, Medium and Very High). This table is customized for Boston to the rest of the world. Some paths are open 24 hours a day, plus or minus QRM and local QRN, no matter what the level of solar activity is. See this book's downloadable supplemental information for other transmitting locations.

MA (Boston)
Hours Open to Each Region for Very-Low/Medium/Very-High SSNs

80 Meters:

Month	Europe	Far East	So. Amer.	Africa	So. Asia	Oceania	No. Amer.
Jan	17/17/16	5/ 4/ 3	17/17/16	16/16/15	8/ 7/ 5	11/10/ 9	24/24/24
Feb	17/16/15	3/ 3/ 2	17/16/16	15/15/14	6/ 4/ 4	10/ 9/ 9	24/24/24
Mar	15/15/14	3/ 2/ 1	16/16/15	15/13/13	4/ 4/ 3	9/ 8/ 7	24/24/24
Apr	13/13/12	1/ 0/ 0	16/16/14	13/13/13	3/ 3/ 1	9/ 8/ 7	24/24/24
May	12/11/10	0/ 0/ 0	16/15/14	12/11/10	2/ 1/ 1	7/ 6/ 6	24/24/24
Jun	10/ 9/ 8	0/ 0/ 0	14/14/14	11/10/10	1/ 1/ 0	6/ 5/ 5	24/24/24
Jul	11/11/ 9	0/ 0/ 0	15/14/14	11/11/11	2/ 1/ 1	7/ 6/ 5	24/24/24
Aug	13/11/11	0/ 0/ 0	16/16/14	13/12/11	3/ 2/ 1	7/ 7/ 6	24/24/24
Sep	14/13/11	2/ 1/ 0	17/16/14	13/13/12	4/ 4/ 2	9/ 8/ 8	24/24/24
Oct	15/15/13	3/ 2/ 1	17/17/16	14/14/13	5/ 4/ 4	9/ 9/ 7	24/24/24
Nov	17/17/15	4/ 4/ 2	17/17/16	16/15/14	8/ 7/ 4	11/10/ 9	24/24/24
Dec	19/18/17	7/ 6/ 4	18/18/17	16/16/16	11/ 9/ 7	12/11/11	24/24/24

40 Meters:

Month	Europe	Far East	So. Amer.	Africa	So. Asia	Oceania	No. Amer.
Jan	24/24/24	15/16/15	24/24/21	21/20/19	21/21/19	19/18/15	24/24/24
Feb	24/24/21	13/11/11	24/23/20	20/19/18	19/19/17	16/15/14	24/24/24
Mar	23/22/19	10/ 9/ 7	24/21/18	19/17/17	17/17/13	13/13/13	24/24/24
Apr	21/19/18	8/ 6/ 4	22/20/18	17/16/15	16/11/ 8	13/13/11	24/24/24
May	19/17/17	5/ 4/ 3	22/18/17	17/16/14	9/ 8/ 5	12/11/10	24/24/24
Jun	17/15/13	4/ 2/ 2	22/18/16	16/15/14	7/ 5/ 5	11/10/ 9	24/24/24
Jul	18/16/15	5/ 4/ 2	24/18/17	17/15/14	8/ 7/ 5	12/11/10	24/24/24
Aug	19/17/16	7/ 5/ 4	24/19/18	18/16/15	11/10/ 6	13/12/11	24/24/24
Sep	22/21/17	9/ 8/ 5	23/20/18	18/17/16	14/11/ 7	13/13/12	24/24/24
Oct	24/23/20	12/11/ 8	24/23/19	20/18/17	17/16/14	16/13/13	24/24/24
Nov	24/24/22	14/13/12	24/24/20	21/19/18	21/20/17	17/17/13	24/24/24
Dec	24/24/24	18/19/22	24/24/21	23/21/19	24/23/22	21/19/18	24/24/24

4.3.2 ELEVATION ANGLES FOR HF COMMUNICATION

It was shown in connection with Figure 4.23 that the distance at which a ray returns to Earth depends on the elevation angle at which it left the Earth (also known by other names: takeoff, launch or wave angle). The chapter **HF Antenna System Design** deals with the effects of local terrain, describing how the elevation angle of a horizontally polarized antenna is determined mainly by its height above the ground.

Although it is not shown specifically in Figure 4.23, propagation distance also depends on the layer height at the time, as well as the elevation angle. As you can probably imagine, the layer height is a very complex function of the state of the ionosphere and the Earth's geomagnetic field. There is a large difference in the distance covered in a single hop, depending on the height of the E or the F_2 layer. The maximum single-hop distance by the E layer is about 2000 km (1250 miles) or about half the maximum distance via the F_2 layer. Practical communicating distances for single-hop E or F layer work at various wave angles are shown in graphic form in **Figure 4.29**.

Actual communication experience usually does not fit the simple patterns shown in Figure 4.23. Propagation by means of the ionosphere is an enormously complicated business (which makes it all the more intriguing and challenging to radio amateurs, of course), even when the Sun is not in a disturbed state. Until the appearance of sophisticated computer models of the ionosphere, there was little definitive information available to guide the radio amateur in the design

20 Meters:

Month	Europe	Far East	So. Amer.	Africa	So. Asia	Oceania	No. Amer.
Jan	13/16/22	15/22/22	24/24/24	20/21/21	18/20/22	18/23/22	24/24/24
Feb	12/18/23	13/21/24	24/24/24	22/22/24	15/21/24	18/23/24	24/24/24
Mar	15/18/24	17/20/24	24/24/24	22/24/24	18/21/24	16/24/24	24/24/24
Apr	15/20/24	19/22/24	24/24/24	21/24/24	19/22/24	18/24/24	24/24/24
May	19/23/24	22/24/24	24/24/24	23/24/24	23/24/24	21/24/24	24/24/24
Jun	22/24/24	24/24/24	24/24/24	24/24/24	24/24/24	24/24/24	24/24/24
Jul	19/24/24	24/24/24	24/24/24	21/24/24	24/24/24	23/24/24	24/24/24
Aug	15/20/24	20/24/24	24/24/24	20/24/24	20/24/24	19/24/24	24/24/24
Sep	16/19/24	17/21/24	24/24/24	21/24/24	18/21/24	17/24/24	24/24/24
Oct	15/21/24	16/20/24	24/24/24	22/24/24	19/22/24	17/24/24	24/24/24
Nov	14/20/23	14/22/24	24/24/24	20/24/24	17/21/24	19/23/24	24/24/24
Dec	11/17/24	13/22/24	24/24/24	17/23/24	12/22/24	16/24/24	24/24/24

15 Meters:

Month	Europe	Far East	So. Amer.	Africa	So. Asia	Oceania	No. Amer.
Jan	4/ 6/ 7	2/ 9/13	12/15/16	9/13/13	3/ 4/ 7	9/12/13	24/15/16
Feb	4/ 7/12	4/10/14	13/18/23	11/13/16	3/ 7/13	8/13/15	22/16/19
Mar	6/ 9/14	2/13/15	14/21/24	13/17/22	5/11/17	10/14/17	15/16/23
Apr	0/10/18	3/13/18	15/23/24	15/18/24	9/15/19	11/15/21	16/16/24
May	1/13/16	6/10/19	17/20/24	14/18/24	13/17/18	10/16/19	20/19/24
Jun	0/ 2/16	0/ 9/15	16/21/24	14/18/24	5/15/18	10/12/20	24/22/22
Jul	0/ 2/16	0/ 5/18	15/19/24	12/18/24	0/12/18	4/12/20	24/22/21
Aug	0/ 2/14	0/ 8/17	14/18/22	13/16/22	0/12/17	6/10/19	22/19/21
Sep	1/10/17	6/13/17	14/16/24	13/17/22	9/14/17	9/14/17	16/16/22
Oct	7/11/17	10/13/17	12/16/22	12/15/22	7/12/17	12/13/15	18/15/22
Nov	5/ 8/14	8/11/14	12/16/22	11/14/17	3/ 7/16	10/13/15	20/16/21
Dec	3/ 6/ 9	2/10/13	12/15/23	8/13/15	2/ 4/12	9/12/14	24/15/18

10 Meters:

Month	Europe	Far East	So. Amer.	Africa	So. Asia	Oceania	No. Amer.
Jan	0/ 1/ 4	0/ 1/ 8	6/11/13	0/ 7/10	0/ 1/ 3	0/ 3/11	23/24/24
Feb	0/ 2/ 7	0/ 2/10	8/12/14	0/ 9/13	0/ 3/ 5	0/ 7/13	24/24/24
Mar	0/ 0/ 8	0/ 1/10	10/14/20	1/11/14	0/ 0/ 8	0/ 7/13	23/24/24
Apr	0/ 0/ 8	0/ 0/ 8	7/14/21	0/12/17	0/ 0/13	0/ 5/11	18/24/24
May	0/ 0/ 0	0/ 0/ 1	7/12/20	1/10/17	0/ 1/12	0/ 2/11	17/20/22
Jun	0/ 0/ 0	0/ 0/ 0	7/11/18	0/ 3/17	0/ 0/ 0	0/ 0/ 2	21/19/23
Jul	0/ 0/ 0	0/ 0/ 0	2/ 9/19	0/ 2/18	0/ 0/ 7	0/ 0/ 6	16/16/24
Aug	0/ 0/ 0	0/ 0/ 0	2/10/17	0/ 1/16	0/ 0/10	0/ 0/ 8	17/17/24
Sep	0/ 0/ 8	0/ 1/10	7/13/18	0/11/16	0/ 0/10	0/ 2/ 9	19/24/24
Oct	0/ 5/ 9	0/ 2/11	10/12/16	7/12/14	0/ 5/ 9	0/ 8/12	24/24/24
Nov	0/ 4/ 8	0/ 3/11	9/12/15	5/10/13	0/ 3/ 6	4/10/12	24/24/24
Dec	0/ 3/ 6	0/ 1/ 8	8/11/13	1/ 8/12	0/ 1/ 4	2/ 7/12	23/23/24

of antenna systems for optimal performance over all portions of the 11-year solar cycle.

The *IONCAP* Computer Propagation Model

Since the 1960s several agencies of the US government have been working on a detailed computer program that models the complex workings of the ionosphere. The program has been dubbed *IONCAP*, short for "Ionospheric Communications Analysis and Prediction Program." *IONCAP* was originally written for a mainframe computer, but later versions have been rewritten to allow them to be run by personal computers. *IONCAP* incorporates a detailed database covering almost three complete solar cycles. The program allows the operator to specify a wide range of parameters, including detailed antenna models for multiple frequency ranges, noise models tailored to specific local environments (from low-noise rural to noisy residential QTHs), minimum elevation angles suitable for a particular location and antenna system, different months and UTC times, maximum levels of multipath distortion, and finally solar activity levels, to name the most significant of a bewildering array of options.

While *IONCAP* has a well-justified reputation for being very *unfriendly* to use, due to its mainframe, non-interactive background, it is also the one ionospheric model most highly regarded for its accuracy and flexibility, both by amateurs and professionals alike. It is the program used for many years to produce the long-term MUF charts available on the ARRL web page on Propagation (**www.arrl.org/propagation**).

IONCAP is not well suited for short-term forecasts of propagation conditions based on the latest solar indices re-

MHz frequency range were specified to be isotropic-type antennas, but with +6 dBi gain, representing a good amateur antenna on each frequency band. These theoretical antennas radiate uniformly from the horizon, up to 90° directly overhead. With response patterns like this, these are obviously not real-world antennas. They do, however, allow the computer program to explore all possible modes and elevation angles.

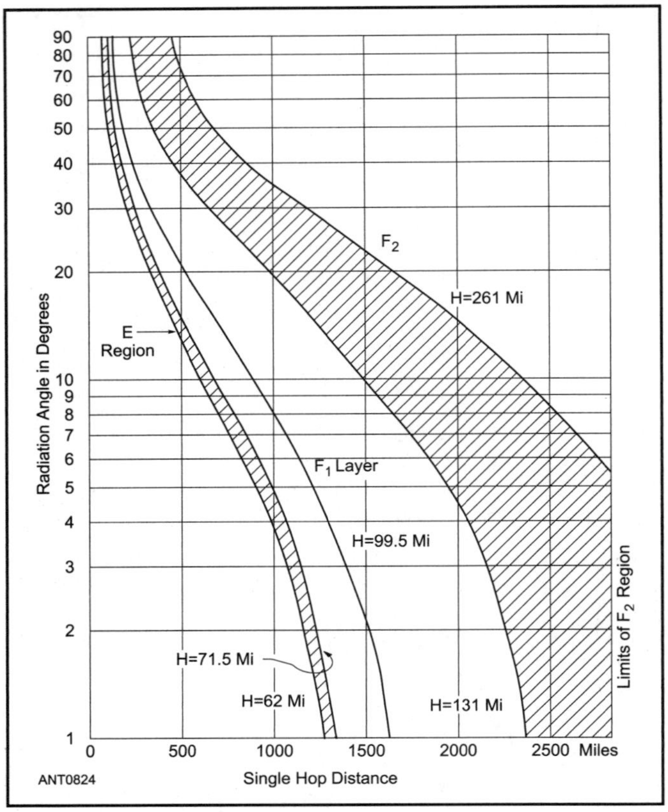

Figure 4.29 — Distance plotted against wave angle (one-hop transmission) for the nominal range of heights for the E, F_1 and F_2 layers.

ceived from WWV. (The model of the ionosphere in *IONCAP*, as well as the models in all other propagation prediction programs, is a monthly median model.) It is an excellent tool, however, for long-range, detailed planning of antenna systems and shortwave transmitter installations, such as that for the Voice of America, or for radio amateurs. See the section later in this chapter describing other computer programs that can be used for short-term, interactive propagation predictions.

IONCAP/VOACAP Parameters

The elevation-angle statistical information contained in this section was compiled from thousands of *VOACAP* runs (an improved version of *IONCAP* developed by scientists from VOA, the Voice of America). These runs were done for a number of different transmitting locations throughout the world to important DX locations throughout the world. See the Bibliography entry for Straw on use of propagation prediction software.

Some assumptions were needed for setting *VOACAP* parameters. The transmitting and receiving sites were all assumed to be located on flat ground, with "average" ground conductivity and dielectric constant. Each site was assumed to have a clear shot to the horizon, with a minimum elevation angle less than or equal to 1°. Electrical noise at each receiving location was also assumed to be very low.

Transmitting and receiving antennas for the 3.5 to 30-

Looking at the Elevation-Angle Statistical Data

Table 4.4 shows detailed statistical elevation information for the path from Boston, Massachusetts, near ARRL HQ in Newington, Connecticut, to all of Europe. The data incorporated into Table 4.4 shows the percentage of time versus elevation angle for all HF bands from 80 meters to 10 meters, over all portions of the 11-year solar cycle. This book's downloadable supplemental information includes more tables such as this for more than 150 transmitting sites around the world. These tables are used by the *HFTA* program (and earlier *YT* program) described in the **HF Antenna System Design** chapter and can also be imported into many programs,

Table 4.4
Boston, Massachusetts, to All of Europe

Elev	*80 m*	*40 m*	*30 m*	*20 m*	*17 m*	*15 m*	*12 m*	*10 m*
1	4.1	9.6	4.6	1.7	2.1	4.4	5.5	7.2
2	0.8	2.3	7.2	1.4	2.8	2.8	3.7	5.3
3	0.3	0.7	4.3	3.1	2.4	2.2	4.4	7.9
4	0.5	4.1	8.7	11.6	12.2	9.4	8.1	3.9
5	4.6	4.8	7.5	12.7	14.3	13.1	9.2	11.2
6	7.1	8.9	5.5	9.2	9.6	12.2	9.2	7.2
7	8.5	6.9	7.2	4.6	7.9	7.4	10.0	5.9
8	5.1	7.0	5.4	3.2	5.9	7.4	4.8	6.6
9	3.3	5.6	3.2	3.1	2.1	3.9	8.1	9.2
10	1.0	4.0	7.9	6.3	5.1	3.7	11.1	6.6
11	1.9	3.8	9.7	10.2	7.2	5.4	3.7	7.9
12	5.6	3.4	4.8	8.5	6.9	7.4	4.8	6.6
13	11.0	3.0	2.4	4.1	5.9	4.6	3.3	2.6
14	7.6	4.8	2.0	2.7	3.8	3.9	6.3	5.9
15	5.3	7.9	2.0	1.5	2.4	1.7	1.5	2.0
16	2.8	6.4	3.8	2.9	1.5	1.3	2.6	2.6
17	5.0	3.4	4.5	3.1	1.0	1.5	0.0	0.0
18	4.2	2.0	3.1	3.1	2.0	2.2	1.8	1.3
19	5.7	1.4	1.4	2.3	1.3	0.7	0.0	0.0
20	6.6	1.4	1.2	1.8	1.1	1.3	0.7	0.0
21	4.4	1.4	0.5	0.8	0.7	0.7	0.4	0.0
22	2.3	2.4	1.0	1.1	0.6	1.3	0.7	0.0
23	1.3	1.8	0.1	0.3	0.1	0.0	0.0	0.0
24	0.6	1.0	0.5	0.5	0.4	0.7	0.0	0.0
25	0.3	0.8	0.3	0.1	0.4	0.0	0.0	0.0
26	0.0	0.5	0.7	0.2	0.1	0.4	0.0	0.0
27	0.1	0.1	0.1	0.2	0.1	0.2	0.0	0.0
28	0.0	0.3	0.1	0.2	0.0	0.2	0.0	0.0
29	0.1	0.0	0.2	0.0	0.0	0.0	0.0	0.0
30	0.0	0.1	0.0	0.0	0.0	0.0	0.0	0.0
31	0.0	0.0	0.0	0.0	0.0	0.0	0.0	0.0
32	0.0	0.0	0.1	0.0	0.0	0.0	0.0	0.0
33	0.1	0.0	0.0	0.0	0.0	0.0	0.0	0.0
34	0.0	0.0	0.0	0.0	0.0	0.0	0.0	0.0
35	0.0	0.0	0.0	0.0	0.0	0.0	0.0	0.0

Percentage of time a particular frequency band is open on this specific propagation path.

such as word processors or spreadsheets. Six important areas throughout the world are covered, one per table: all of Europe (from London, England, to Kiev, Ukraine), the Far East (centered on Japan), South America (Paraguay), Oceania (Melbourne, Australia), Southern Africa (Zambia) and South Asia (New Delhi, India).

You may be surprised to see in Table 4.4 that angles lower than 10° dominate the possible range of incoming angles for this moderate-distance path from New England to Europe. In fact, 1.7% of all the times when the 20 meter band is open to Europe, the takeoff angle is as low as 1°. You should recognize that very few real-world 20 meter antennas achieve much gain at such an extremely low angle — unless they just happen to be mounted about 400 feet high over flat ground or else are located on the top of a tall, steep mountain.

The situation is even more dramatic on 40 and 80 meters. **Figure 4.30** shows the "cumulative distribution function" of the total percentage of time (derived from Table 4.4) when 40 meters is open from Boston to the rest of the world, plotted against the elevation angle. For example, into Europe from Boston, 50% of the time when the band is open, it is at 10° or less. Into Japan from Boston, the statistics are even more revealing: 50% of the time when the band is open, the angle is 6° or less, and 90% of the time the angle is 13° or less!

Figure 4.31 shows the same sort of information for 80 meters from Boston to the world. For 50% of the time from Boston to Europe the elevation angle is 13° or less; at the 90% level the angle is 20° or less. For the path to Japan on 80 meters from Boston, 50% of the time the angle is 8° or less; at the 90% level, the angle is 13° or less. Now, to achieve peak gain on 80 meters at an elevation angle of 8° over flat land, a horizontally polarized antenna must be 500 feet high. You can begin to see why verticals can do very well on long-distance contacts on 80 meters, even when they are mounted over poorly conducting, rocky ground. Clearly, low angles are very important for successful DXing.

The Ionosphere Controls Propagation

You should always remember that it is the *ionosphere* that controls the elevation angles, *not* the transmitting antenna. The elevation response of a particular antenna only determines how strong or weak a signal is, at whatever angle (or angles) the ionosphere is supporting at that particular instant, for that propagation path and for that frequency.

If only one propagation mode is possible at a particular time, and if the elevation angle for that one mode happens to be 5°, then your antenna will have to work satisfactorily at that very low angle or else you won't be able to communicate. For example, if your low dipole has a gain of –10 dBi at 5°, compared to your friend's Yagi on a mountain top with +10 dBi gain at 5°, then you will be down 20 dB compared to his signal. It's not that the elevation angle is somehow *too low* — the real problem here is that you don't have *enough gain* at that particular angle where the ionosphere is supporting propagation. Many "flatlanders" can vividly recall the times when their mountain-top friends could easily work DX stations, while they couldn't even hear a whisper.

Looking at the Data — Further Cautions

A single propagation mode is quite common at the opening and the closing of daytime bands like 20, 15 or 10 meters, when the elevation angle is often lower (but not always) than when the band is wide open. The lower-frequency bands tend to support multiple propagation modes simultaneously. For example, **Figure 4.32** plots the signal strength (in dBμV) and the elevation angle for the dominant mode (with the strongest

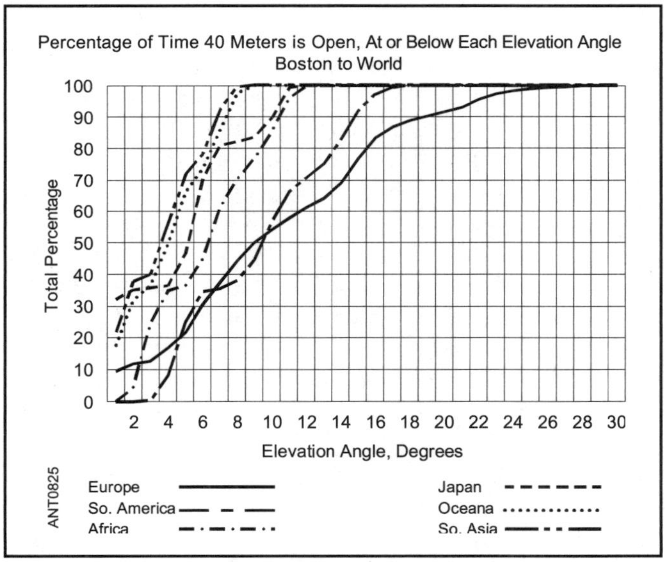

Figure 4.30 — The cumulative distribution function showing the total percentage of time that 40 meters is open, at or below each elevation angle, from Boston to the world. For example, 50% of the time the band is open to Europe from Boston at angles less than 10°. The angles for DX work are indeed low.

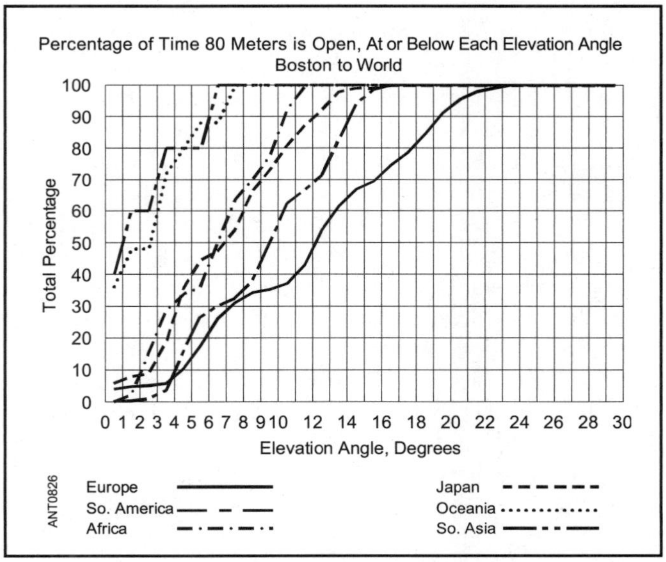

Figure 4.31 — The cumulative distribution function showing the total percentage of time that 80 meters is open, at or below each elevation angle, from Boston to the world. For example, 50% of the time the band is open to Europe from Boston at angles less than 13°.

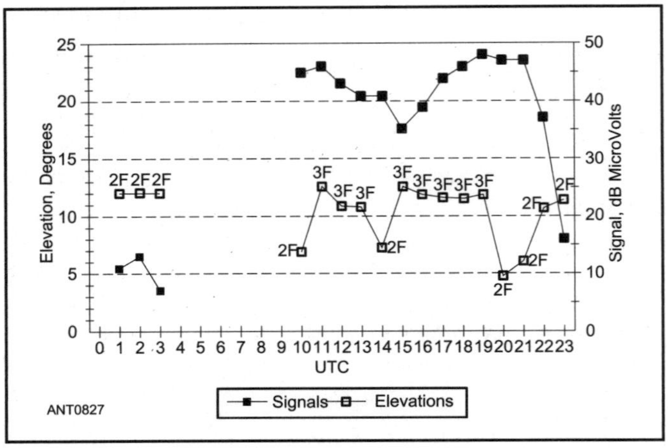

Figure 4.32 — Overlay of 20 meter signals and elevation angles, together with hop-mode information. This is for one month, October, at one level of solar activity, SSN=70, for the path from Newington, CT, to London, England. The mode of propagation does not closely follow the elevation angle. From 15 to 19 UTC the mode is 3F$_2$ hops, and the elevation angle is approximately 12°. The same elevation angle is required from 23 to 03 UTC, but here the mode is 2F$_2$ hops.

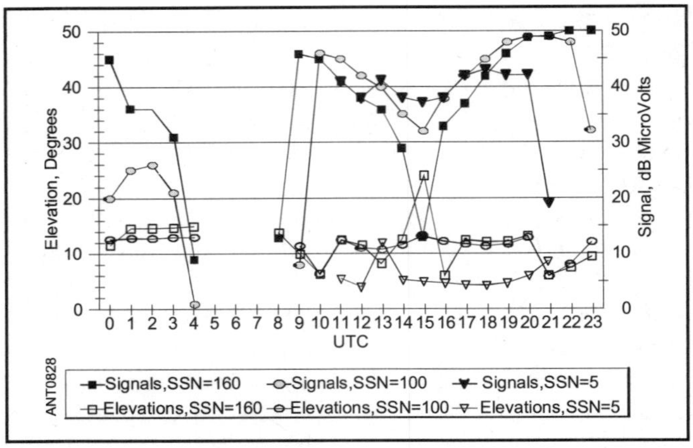

Figure 4.33 — October 20 meter signals and elevation angles for the full range of solar activity, from W1 to England. The elevation angle does not closely follow the level of solar activity. What is important in designing a station capable of covering all levels of solar activity is to have flexibility in antenna elevation pattern response — to cover a wide range of possible angles.

signal) over a 24-hour period from Newington to London in October, for a medium-level SSN = 70. The morning opening at 10 UTC starts out with a two-hop 2F$_2$ mode (labeled 2F) at an elevation angle of 6°. By 11 UTC the mode has changed to a three-hop 3F$_2$ (labeled 3F) at a 12° elevation angle. The band starts to close down with weaker signals after about 23 UTC. Note that this path actually supports both 2F$_2$ and 3F$_2$ modes most of the time. Either mode may be stronger than the other, depending on the particular time of day.

It is tempting to think that two-hop signals always occur at lower elevation launch angles, while three-hop signals require higher elevation angles. In reality, the detailed workings of the ionosphere are enormously complicated. From 22 UTC to 03 UTC, the elevation angles are higher than 11° for 2F$_2$ hops. During much of the morning and early afternoon in Newington (from 11 to 13 UTC, and from 15 to 19 UTC), the angles are also higher than 11°. However, 3F$_2$ hops are involved during these periods of time. The number of hops is not directly related to the elevation angles needed — changing layer heights account for this.

Note that starting around 15 UTC, the mid-morning 20 meter "slump" (down some 10 dB from peak signal level) is caused by higher levels of mainly D-layer absorption when the Sun is high overhead. This condition favors higher elevation angles, since signals launched at lower angles must travel for a longer time through the lossy lower layer.

How does the situation change with different levels of solar activity? **Figure 4.33** overlays predicted signals and elevation angles for three levels of solar activity in October, again for the Newington-London path. Figure 4.33 shows the mid-morning slump dramatically when the solar activity is at a very high level, represented by SSN = 160. At 15 UTC, the signal level drops 35 dB from peak level, and the elevation angle rises all the way to 24°. By the way, as a percentage of all possible openings, the 24° angle occurs only rarely, 0.5% of the time. It barely shows up as a blip in Table 4.4. Elevation angles are *not* closely related to the level of solar activity, but on the higher HF bands are generally lower at solar minimum than at solar maximum.

IONCAP/VOACAP demonstrates that elevation angles do not follow neat, easily identified patterns, even over a 24-hour period — much less over all portions of the solar cycle. Merely looking at the percentage of all openings versus elevation angle, as shown in Table 4.4, does not tell the whole story, although it is probably the most statistically valid approach to station design, and possibly the most emotionally satisfying approach too. Neither is the whole story revealed by looking only at a snapshot of elevation angles versus time for one particular month, or for one solar activity level.

What is important to recognize is that the most effective antenna system will be one that can cover the *full range* of elevation angles, over the whole spectrum of solar activity, even if the actual angle in use at any one moment in time may not be easy to determine. For this particular path, from New England to all of Europe, an ideal antenna would have equal response over the full range of angles from 1° to 28°. Unfortunately, real-world antennas have a tough time covering such a wide range of elevation angles equally well.

Antenna Elevation Patterns

Figures 4.34 through **4.38** show overlays of the same sort of elevation angle information listed in Table 4.4, together with the elevation response patterns for typical antennas for the HF amateur bands 80, 40, 20, 15 and 10 meters. For example, Figure 4.36 shows an overlay for 20 meters, with three different types of 20 meter antennas. These are a 4-element Yagi at 90 feet, a 4-element Yagi at 120 feet and a large stack of four 4-element Yagis located at 120, 90, 60 and 30 feet. Each antenna is assumed to be mounted over flat ground. Placement on a hill with a long slope in the direction of interest would lower the required elevation angle by the amount of the hill's slope. For example, if a 10° launch angle is desired, and the antenna is placed on a hill with a slope of –5°, the antenna itself should be designed for a height that would optimize the response at 15° over flat ground — one wavelength high.

In Figure 4.36, the large stack of four 20 meter Yagis over flat ground comes closest to being ideal, but even this large array will not work well for that very small percentage of time when the angle needed is higher than about 20°. Some hams might conclude that the tiny percentage of time when the angles are very high doesn't justify an antenna tailored for that response. However, when that new DX country pops up on a band, or when a rare multiplier shows up in a contest, doesn't it always seem that the desired signal only comes in at some angle your antenna doesn't cover well? What do you do then, if your only antenna happens to be a large stack?

The answer to this, perhaps unique, high-angle problem lies in switching to using only the top antenna in the stack. In this example, the second elevation lobe of the 120-foot high antenna would cover the angles from 20° to 30° well, much better than the stack does. Note that the top antenna by

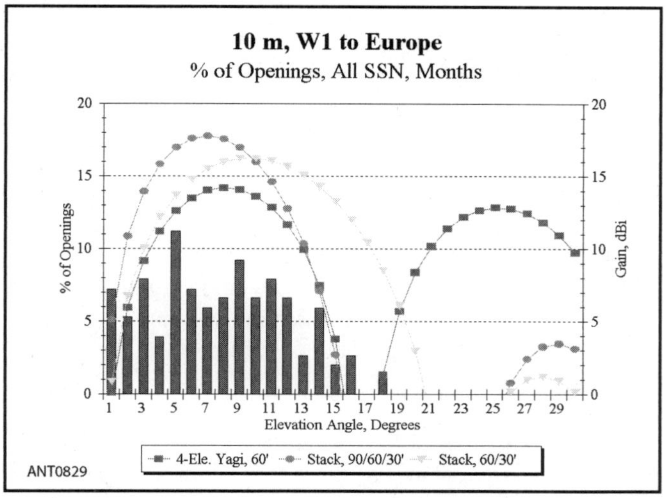

Figure 4.34 — 10 meter graph of the percentage of all openings versus elevation angles, together with overlay of elevation patterns over flat ground for three 10 meter antenna systems. Stacked antennas have wider "footprints" in elevation angle coverage for this example from New England to Europe.

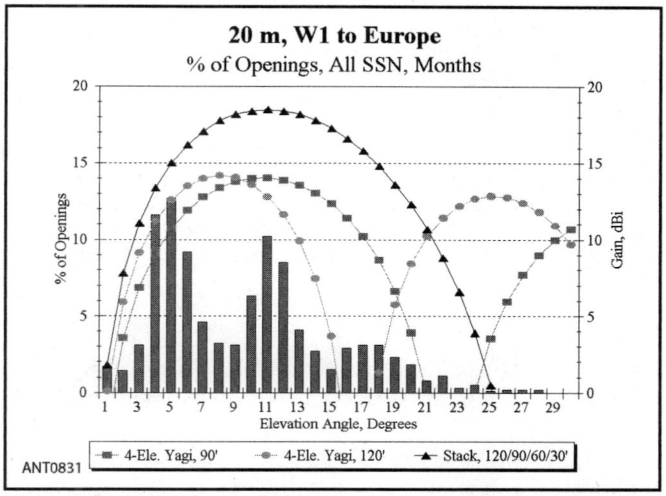

Figure 4.36 — 20 meter graph of the percentage of all openings from New England to Europe versus elevation angles, together with overlay of elevation patterns over flat ground for three 20 meter antenna systems.

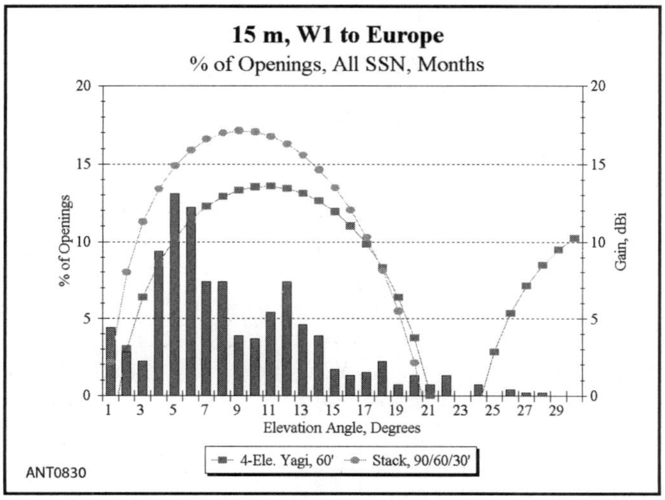

Figure 4.35 — 15 meter graph of the percentage of all openings versus elevation angles, together with overlay of elevation patterns over flat ground for two 15 meter antenna systems. Like 10 meters, 15 meter stacked antennas have wider footprints in elevation angle coverage for this example from New England to Europe.

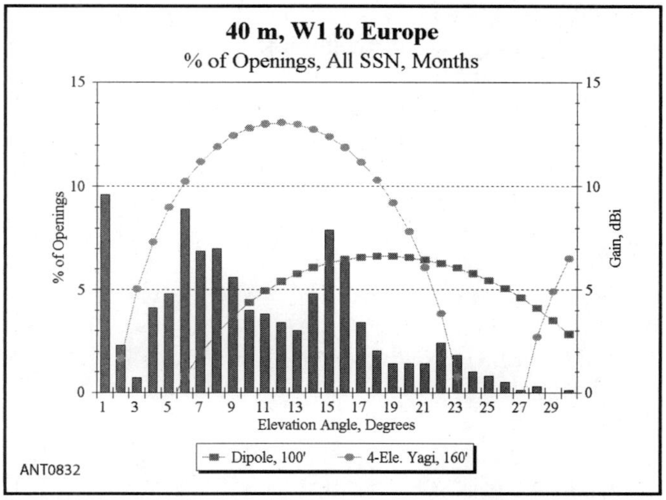

Figure 4.37 — 40 meter graph of the percentage of all openings from New England to Europe versus elevation angles, together with overlays of elevation patterns over flat ground for a 100-foot high dipole and a large 4-element Yagi at 160 feet. Achieving gain at very low elevation angles requires very high heights above ground.

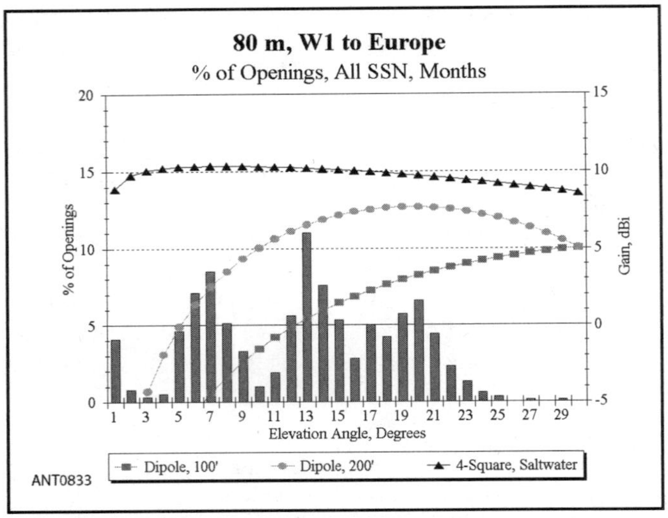

Figure 4.38 — 80 meter graph of the percentage of all openings from New England to Europe versus elevation angles, together with overlay of elevation patterns over flat ground for dipoles at two different heights. The 200-foot-high dipole clearly covers the necessary elevation angles better than does the 100-foot-high dipole, although a four-square vertical array located over saltwater is even better for all angles needed.

itself would not be ideal for all conditions. It is simply too high much of the time when the elevation angles are higher than about 12°. The experience of many amateurs on the US East Coast with high 20 meter antennas bears this out — they find that 60 to 90-foot high antennas are far more consistent performers into Europe.

4.3.3 PROPAGATION PREDICTION TABLES

This book's downloadable supplemental information includes summary and detailed propagation predictions for more than 150 transmitting locations around the world. This propagation data was calculated using *CapMAN*, an upgraded variety of the mainframe propagation program *IONCAP*. An expanded set of tables by N6BV is available from Radioware, **www.radio-ware.com**. The predictions were done for default antennas and powers that are representative of a "big-gun" station. Of course, not everyone has a big-gun station in his/her backyard, but this represents what the ultimate possibilities are, statistically speaking. After all, if the bands aren't open for the big guns, they are unlikely to be open for the "little pistols" too. (*CapMAN* was offered by Jim Tabor, KU5S, of Kangaroo Tabor Software — KU5S became a Silent Key in mid-2009, and his software is no longer supported.)

Let's see how propagation is affected if the smoothed sunspot number is 0 (corresponding to a smoothed solar flux of about 65), which is classified as a "Very Low" level of solar activity (in terms of SSN, the smoothed sunspot number). And we'll examine the situation for a sunspot number of 100 (a smoothed solar flux of 150), which is typical of a "Very High" portion of the solar cycle.

Five-Band Summary Predictions

Tables 4.5 and **4.6** are Summary tables showing the predicted signal levels (in S units) from Boston, Massachusetts, to the rest of the world for the month of January. The Boston transmitting site is representative of the entire New England area of the USA. The target geographic receiving regions for the major HF bands from 80 through 10 meters are tabulated versus UTC (Universal Coordinated Time) in hours. Table 4.5 represents a Very Low level of solar activity, while Table 4.6 is for a Very High level of solar activity.

Each transmitting location is organized by six levels of solar activity over the whole 11-year solar cycle:

- VL (Very Low: SSN between 0 to 20)
- LO (Low: SSN between 20 to 40)
- ME (Medium: SSN between 40 to 60)
- HI (High: SSN between 60 to 100)
- VH (Very High: SSN between 100 to 150)
- UH (Ultra High: SSN greater than 150)

The receiving geographic regions for each frequency band are abbreviated:

- EU — All of Europe
- FE — The Far East, centered on Japan
- SA — South America, centered on Paraguay
- AF — All of Africa, centered on Zambia
- AS — South Asia, centered on India
- OC — Oceania, centered on Sydney, Australia
- NA — North America, all across the USA

These propagation files show the highest predicted signal strength (in S-units) throughout the generalized receiving area, for a 1500-W transmitter and rather good antennas on both sides of the circuit. The standard antennas are:

- 100-foot high inverted-V dipoles for 80 and 40 meters
- 3-element Yagi at 100 feet for 20 meters
- 4-element Yagi at 60 feet for 15 and 10 meters

For example, Summary Table 4.5 shows that in January during a period of Very Low solar activity, 15 meters is open to somewhere in Europe from Boston for only 4 hours, from 13 to 16 UTC, with a peak signal level between S-4 and S-7. Now look at Table 4.6, where 15 meters is predicted to be open to Europe during a period of Very High solar activity for 7 hours, from 12 to 18 UTC, with peak signals ranging from S-9 to S-9+.

Both Tables 4.5 and 4.6 represent *snapshots* of predicted signal levels to generalized receiving locations — that is, they are computed for a particular month, from a particular transmitting location, and for a particular level of solar activity. These tables provide summary information that is particularly valuable for someone planning for an operating event such as a DXpedition or a contest.

What happens if you don't have a big-gun station with high antennas or the 1500-W power assumed in the analyses above? You can discount the S-Meter readings to reflect a smaller station:

- Subtract 2 S units for a dipole instead of a Yagi at same height on 20/15/10 meters
- Subtract 3 S units for a dipole at 50 feet instead of a Yagi at 100 feet on 20 meters

Table 4.5

Printout of Summary propagation table for Boston to the rest of the world, for a Very Low level of solar activity in the month of January. The abbreviations for the target geographic areas are: EU = Europe, FE = Far East, SA = South America, AF = Africa, sAS = south Asia, OC = Oceania, and NA = North America.

Jan., MA (Boston), for SSN = Very Low, Sigs in S-Units. By N6BV, ARRL.

	80 Meters							40 Meters							20 Meters							15 Meters							10 Meters							
UTC	EU	FE	SA	AF	AS	OC	NA	EU	FE	SA	AF	AS	OC	NA	EU	FE	SA	AF	AS	OC	NA	EU	FE	SA	AF	AS	OC	NA	EU	FE	SA	AF	AS	OC	NA	UTC
0	9	-	9+	9	9	-	9+	9	8	9+	9+	9	2	9+	-	8	9+	7	4	8	9+	-	-	-	-	-	-	1	-	-	-	-	-	-	2	0
1	9	-	9+	9	9	-	9+	9	6	9+	9+	9+	6	9+	-	4	9	4	2	6	9+	-	-	-	-	-	-	1	-	-	-	-	-	-	2	1
2	9	-	9+	9+	8	1	9+	9	6	9+	9+	9	8	9+	-	1	8	1	2	3	9+	-	-	-	-	-	-	1	-	-	-	-	-	-	2	2
3	9	-	9+	9+	8	6	9+	9	6	9+	9+	9	8	9+	-	-	8	2	2	-	9+	-	-	-	-	-	-	1	-	-	-	-	-	-	2	3
4	9	-	9+	9+	1	8	9+	9	8	9+	9+	9	9	9+	-	1	8	7	2	-	9+	-	-	-	-	-	-	1	-	-	-	-	-	-	2	4
5	9	-	9+	9+	-	9	9+	9	8	9+	9+	8	9	9+	-	1	9	8	2	-	9	-	-	-	-	-	-	1	-	-	-	-	-	-	2	5
6	9+	-	9+	9+	-	9	9+	7	8	9+	9+	8	9	9+	-	1	9+	8	-	-	9	-	-	-	-	-	-	1	-	-	-	-	-	-	2	6
7	9	7	9+	9	-	9	9+	7	8	9+	9	8	9	9+	-	1	9+	1	-	1	8	-	-	-	-	-	-	1	-	-	-	-	-	-	2	7
8	9	8	9+	9	-	9	9+	8	9	9+	9	8	9+	9+	-	1	9+	-	-	5	9	-	-	-	-	-	-	1	-	-	-	-	-	-	2	8
9	8	8	9+	7	6	9	9+	8	9	9+	9	9	9+	9+	-	-	9	1	-	7	9	-	-	-	-	-	-	1	-	-	-	-	-	-	2	9
10	5	8	9+	4	6	9	9+	9	9	9+	9	9	9+	9+	-	3	9	5	-	6	9	-	-	-	-	-	-	1	-	-	-	-	-	-	2	10
11	3	8	9+	-	5	9	9+	8	9	9+	7	9	9+	9+	5	-	9+	9	5	1*	8	-	-	-	-	-	-	1	-	-	-	-	-	-	2	11
12	1	8	9	-	4	9	9+	7	9	9+	4	8	9	9+	9	5	9+	9+	9	2*	8	-	-	5	6	-	-	1	-	-	-	-	-	-	2	12
13	-	6	1	-	-	7	9+	6	8	9+	1	8	9	9+	9+	9	9+	9	9	7	8	4	-	9+	9	7	-	1	-	-	-	-	-	-	1	13
14	-	-	-	-	-	1	9+	5	7	8	-	8	8	9+	9+	9	9+	9	9	9	9+	7	2*	9+	9	9	-	8	-	-	5	-	-	-	1	14
15	-	-	-	-	-	-	9+	4	6	5	-	6	7	9+	9+	9	9+	9	9	9	9+	7	5	9+	9	2	2	5	-	-	5	-	-	-	-	15
16	-	-	-	-	-	-	9+	5	6	4	2	5	4	9+	9+	8	9+	9+	9	9	9+	5	1	9+	8	2*	2	9	-	-	5	-	-	-	1	16
17	-	-	-	-	-	-	9+	6	5	5	5	6	1	9+	9+	5	9+	9+	3	9	9+	-	-	9+	9	-	3	9+	-	-	5	-	-	-	1	17
18	1	-	-	-	-	-	9+	8	6	6	7	6	-	9+	9+	6	9+	9+	4	9	9+	-	-	9+	9	-	7	9+	-	-	5	-	-	-	1	18
19	3	-	-	2	-	-	9+	9	7	8	8	8	-	9+	6	6	9+	9+	6	9	9+	-	-	9+	9	-	9	9+	-	-	2	-	-	-	1	19
20	5	-	7	5	-	-	9+	9	8	9+	9	8	4	9+	1	7	9+	9+	8	9	9+	-	-	9+	4	-	9	9	-	-	-	-	-	-	1	20
21	8	3	9	8	6	-	9+	9	8	9+	9+	9	7	9+	-	8	9+	9	8	9	9+	-	-	9+	-	-	9	6	-	-	-	-	-	-	1	21
22	9	3	9+	9	8	-	9+	9	8	9+	9+	9	5	9+	-	9+	9+	9	8	9	9+	-	-	9	-	-	7	1	-	-	-	-	-	-	1	22
23	9	2	9+	9	9	-	9+	9	8	9+	9+	9	4	9+	-	9+	9+	9	5	9	9+	-	1	6	-	-	2	3	-	-	-	-	-	-	2	23
	EU	FE	SA	AF	AS	OC	NA	EU	FE	SA	AF	AS	OC	NA	EU	FE	SA	AF	AS	OC	NA	EU	FE	SA	AF	AS	OC	NA	EU	FE	SA	AF	AS	OC	NA	

Table 4.6

Printout of Summary propagation table for Boston to the rest of the world, for a Very High level of solar activity in the month of January.

Jan., MA (Boston), for SSN = Very High, Sigs in S-Units. By N6BV, ARRL.

	80 Meters							40 Meters							20 Meters							15 Meters							10 Meters							
UTC	EU	FE	SA	AF	AS	OC	NA	EU	FE	SA	AF	AS	OC	NA	EU	FE	SA	AF	AS	OC	NA	EU	FE	SA	AF	AS	OC	NA	EU	FE	SA	AF	AS	OC	NA	UTC
0	9+	-	9+	9+	8	-	9+	9+	5	9+	9+	9	-	9+	1	9+	9+	9+	9+	9	9+	-	9	9+	2	2	9+	9+	-	1	8	-	-	8	9+	0
1	9+	-	9+	9+	8	-	9+	9+	4	9+	9+	9	2	9+	1	9	9+	8	9+	9+	9+	-	3	9	-	7	9+	9	-	-	-	-	-	4	2	1
2	9+	-	9+	9+	7	-	9+	9+	4	9+	9+	9	7	9+	1	9	9+	8	9	9+	9+	-	-	3	-	-	7	9	-	-	-	-	-	-	2	2
3	9+	-	9+	9+	1	2	9+	9+	4	9+	9+	9	9	9+	-	7	9+	7	8	9+	9	-	-	-	-	-	-	-	-	-	-	-	-	-	2	3
4	9+	-	9+	9+	-	7	9+	9+	5	9+	9+	8	9	9+	-	5	9+	9	9	9	9+	-	-	1	-	-	-	-	-	-	-	-	-	-	2	4
5	9+	-	9+	9+	-	8	9+	9+	6	9+	9+	7	9	9+	-	5	9+	9	9	5	9+	-	-	-	-	-	-	-	-	-	-	-	-	-	2	5
6	9+	-	9+	9+	-	8	9+	9+	7	9+	9+	7	9	9+	-	8	9+	8	9	5	9+	-	-	-	-	-	-	-	-	-	-	-	-	-	2	6
7	9+	-	9+	9+	-	8	9+	9	8	9+	9+	7	9+	9+	-	9	9+	-	7	9	9+	-	-	1	-	-	-	-	-	-	-	-	-	-	2	7
8	9	7	9+	9	-	8	9+	9	8	9+	9+	8	9+	9+	-	9	9+	-	4	9+	9+	-	-	1	-	-	-	2	-	-	-	-	-	-	2	8
9	8	7	9+	7	-	8	9+	9	9	9+	9	8	9+	9+	-	6	9+	-	1	9+	9+	-	-	-	-	-	-	1	-	-	-	-	-	-	2	9
10	5	8	9+	2	3	8	9+	9	9	9+	8	8	9	9+	4	-	9+	9+	1	5	9	-	-	-	-	-	-	-	-	-	-	-	-	-	2	10
11	1	8	9+	-	4	9	9+	8	9	9+	5	8	9	9+	9+	4*	9+	9+	7	-	8	-	-	9	9	-	-	-	-	-	-	-	-	-	2	11
12	-	7	8	-	1	9	9+	6	9	9+	1	8	9	9+	9+	9	9+	9	9	1*	9+	9	8*	9+	9+	9	5*	-	-	2*	9	9	1	1*	2	12
13	-	-	-	-	-	2	9+	4	8	8	-	7	9	9+	9+	9	9+	9	9	9+	9+	9+	7	9+	9+	9+	3*	9	9	5*	9+	9+	9	6*	2	13
14	-	-	-	-	-	-	9+	2	7	4	-	5	8	9+	9+	9	9+	8	9	9	9+	9+	9	9+	9+	9+	9	9+	9	6*	9+	9+	9	1*	1	14
15	-	-	-	-	-	-	9	1	5	-	-	4	5	9+	9+	9	9+	9	9	9	9+	9+	9+	9+	9+	9+	9	9+	9	5	9+	9+	6	6	8	15
16	-	-	-	-	-	-	8	3	4	-	-	3	1	9+	9+	8	9	9	9	9	9+	9+	9+	9+	9+	9	9+	9+	9	8	9+	9+	-	8	9	16
17	-	-	-	-	-	-	8	5	3	-	2	4	-	9+	9+	8	9+	9+	9	9	9+	9+	9	9+	9+	1*	9+	9+	-	8	9+	9+	-	8	9+	17
18	-	-	-	-	-	-	9	7	4	2	5	5	-	9+	9+	9	9+	9+	9	9	9+	9+	9	9+	9+	1	9+	9+	-	7	9+	9+	-	9+	9+	18
19	1	-	-	1	-	-	9+	8	5	6	8	7	-	9+	9+	9	9+	9+	9	9	9+	-	9+	9+	9+	2	9	9+	-	6	9+	9+	-	9+	9+	19
20	4	-	2	5	-	-	9+	9	6	9	9	8	-	9+	9+	9	9+	9+	9	9	9+	-	8	9+	9+	3	9	9+	-	1	9+	9	-	9	9+	20
21	7	-	8	7	1	-	9+	9+	7	9+	9+	8	1	9+	8	9	9+	9+	9	9	9+	-	6	9+	9+	3	9	9+	-	-	9+	5*	-	9+	9+	21
22	9	2	9+	9	8	-	9+	9+	7	9+	9+	9	4	9+	2	9+	9+	9+	9	9	9+	-	9+	9+	9	1	9+	9+	-	5	9+	4*	-	9	6	22
23	9	-	9+	9	8	-	9+	9+	7	9+	9+	9	-	9+	1	9+	9+	9+	9	9	9+	-	9+	9+	6	-	9	9+	-	7	9+	2*	-	9	2	23
	EU	FE	SA	AF	AS	OC	NA	EU	FE	SA	AF	AS	OC	NA	EU	FE	SA	AF	AS	OC	NA	EU	FE	SA	AF	AS	OC	NA	EU	FE	SA	AF	AS	OC	NA	

• Subtract 1 S unit for a dipole at 50 feet rather than a dipole at 100 feet on 40/80 meters

• Subtract 3 S units for 100 W rather than 1500 W

• Subtract 6 S units for 5 W (QRP) rather than 1500 W

For example, Table 4.5 predicts an S-7 signal into Boston from Europe on 15 meters at 14 UTC. If a European station is using a dipole at 50 feet, with 100 W of power, what would this do to the predicted signal level in Boston? You would compute: S-7 – 2 S units (for a dipole instead of Yagi) – 3 S units (100 W rather than 1500 W) = an S-2 signal in Boston. A QRP station with a 4-element 15 meter Yagi at 60 feet would yield: S-7 – 6 S units = an S-1 signal in Boston.

More Detailed Predictions

Let's now look at **Figure 4.39**, which is the Detailed 20 meter page for the same conditions in Table 4.6: January at a Very High level of solar activity from Boston to the world. There are six such pages per month/SSN level, covering 160, 80, 40, 20, 15 and 10 meters.

In a Detailed prediction table, the world is divided into the 40 CQ Zones, with a particular sample location in each zone. For example, Zone 14 in Western Europe is represented by a location in London, England (call sign G), while Zone 25 is represented by a location in Tokyo, Japan (call sign JA1). Note that Zones with large ham populations are highlighted with dark shadowing for easy identification. For example, Zones 3, 4 and 5 cover the USA, while Zones 14, 15 and 16 cover the majority of Europe. Zone 25 covers the big ham population in Japan.

Let's revisit the example above for computing the signal strength for a station in London, but this time on 20 meters. Again, we'll assume that the G station has a dipole at 50 feet and 100 W of transmitter power. At 14 UTC in Zone 14, the table in Figure 4.39 predicts a very healthy signal for the reference big-gun station, at S-9+. This is a signal at least S-9 + 10 dB. Here, we're going to round off the plus 10 dB to 2 S units, giving a fictional 11 S units to start. We discount this for the smaller station: S-11 – 3 S units (for a dipole at 50 feet instead of a 3-element Yagi at 100 feet) – 3 S units (100 W rather than 1500 W) = S-5 signal in Boston. This

20 Meters: Jan., MA (Boston), for SSN = Very High, Sigs in S-Units. By N6BV, ARRL.

UTC -->

Zone	00	01	02	03	04	05	06	07	08	09	10	11	12	13	14	15	16	17	18	19	20	21	22	23
KL7 = 01	9+	9+	9+	7	-	-	-	-	-	-	-	-	-	-	-	3	9+	9+	9+	9+	9+	9+	9+	9+
VO2 = 02	9+	9	9	9	9	9	8	7	5	3	2	1	5	9+	9+	9+	9+	9+	9+	9+	9+	9+	8	9+
W6 = 03	9+	9+	9+	7	7	1	1	5	8	8	3	-	-	1	9	9+	9+	9+	9+	9	9	9+	9+	9+
W9 = 04	9+	9+	8	9	9	9	9	9	8	5	2	1	1	9	9+	9+	9+	9+	9+	9+	9+	9+	9+	9+
W3 = 05	4	2	2	2	2	2	2	3	3	3	3	2	1	1	8	9+	9+	9+	9+	9+	9+	9+	9+	9
XE1 = 06	9+	9+	7	9	9+	9+	9+	9+	9+	9+	9	8	9+	9+	9+	9+	9	9	9	9	9+	9+	9+	9+
TI = 07	9+	9+	8	9	9	9	9	9	9	9+	9	9+	9+	9+	9+	9+	9	8	9	9	9+	9+	9+	9+
VP2 = 08	9+	9+	9+	9+	9+	9+	9+	9+	9+	8	9	9+	9+	9+	9+	9+	9	9+	9+	9+	9+	9+	9+	9+
P4 = 09	9+	9+	9+	9+	9+	9+	9+	9+	9+	9+	9+	9+	9+	9+	9+	9	9	9	9	9+	9+	9+	9+	9+
HC = 10	9+	8	9+	9	9	9	9	9	7	3	1	7	9+	9+	9	5	5	5	7	8	9+	9+	9+	9+
PY1 = 11	9+	9+	9+	9	9	9+	9+	9	8	6	9	9+	8	2	1	-	-	1	4	8	9	9+	9+	9+
CE = 12	9+	9+	9+	9+	9+	9+	9+	9+	9	8	8	9+	9	8	2	1	1	-	1	3	7	9	9+	9+
LU = 13	9+	9+	9+	9+	9+	9+	9+	9+	8	8	8	9+	8	4	2	1	-	-	1	4	8	9	9+	9+
G = 14	-	-	-	-	-	-	-	-	-	-	-	9+	9+	9+	9+	9+	9+	9+	9+	9+	9+	8	2	-
I = 15	-	-	-	-	-	-	-	-	-	-	4	9	9	9	9	9	9	9+	9+	9	8	2	-	-
UA3 = 16	1	1	1	-	-	-	-	-	-	-	-	8	9	9+	9+	9+	9	8	5	-	-	-	-	1
UN = 17	1	-	-	8	7	7	7	1	-	-	-	2	9	9	9	6	-	-	2	4	8	9	5	4
UA9 = 18	6	7	6	6	9	9	9	7	4	1	-	-	8	8	6	6	5	6	7	8	9	9	8	7
UA0 = 19	9+	9	9	6	5	5	8	8	8	4	-	-	2	6	8	8	8	7	4	4	7	9	9+	9+
4X = 20	8	6	3	1	-	3	4	-	-	-	1	8	8	8	8	8	9	9	9+	9	9	8	7	7
HZ = 21	9+	9	4	3	8	8	2	-	-	-	1	7	8	9	8	8	9	9	9	9	9	9	9	9
VU = 22	7	5	8	7	6	7	5	-	-	-	-	6	9	9	9	9	3	2	2	2	8	8	9	8
JT = 23	9	9+	9	5	7	8	8	6	3	-	-	2*	8	8	5	6	8	8	8	8	9	7	5	6
VS6 = 24	9	9	9	5	4	5	7	8	6	1	-	1*	5	7	1	1	1	1	4	2	-	-	-	9
JA1 = 25	9	9	8	7	5	5	8	9	9	6	-	1	1	2	7	7	6	2	-	-	7	9	9+	9
HS = 26	9	9	6	4	2	-	-	2	1	-	-	2*	9	9	9	9	8	7	5	4	5	-	1*	1
DU = 27	9	8	7	-	-	-	5	7	7	1	-	-	1*	9	9	7	6	4	5	3	1*	1*	8	9
YB = 28	9	8	1	-	-	-	-	-	-	-	-	4*	8	9	9	9	8	8	9	9	9	9	9+	9+
VK6 = 29	3*	4*	-	-	-	-	-	-	5	3	-	-	-	5	9	9	9	8	9	9	9	9	9	8
VK3 = 30	1*	-	-	-	-	-	1	3	9	9	4	-	-	9+	9	8	2	1	-	-	1	2*	5*	4*
KH6 = 31	9	9+	9+	9+	8	2	2	6	4	-	-	-	-	-	-	-	9	9	8	7	6	4	6	7
KH8 = 32	-	2	9	9	9	5	5	9	9+	9+	5	-	-	9+	9	9	8	5	3	1	-	-	-	-
CN = 33	-	-	-	-	-	-	-	-	-	-	9	9+	9	9	8	9	9	9+	9+	9+	9+	9+	9+	7
SU = 34	9	8	3	3	-	1	4	-	-	-	2	7	8	8	8	8	9	9	9+	9+	9+	9+	8	8
6W = 35	9+	8	-	-	2	7	5	-	-	-	9+	9+	8	5	4	3	7	9	9+	9+	9+	9+	9+	9+
D2 = 36	9+	9+	5	3	9	9	8	-	-	-	3	-	-	-	-	4	4	7	8	9	9+	9+	9+	9+
5Z = 37	9+	9	2	4	8	8	1	-	-	-	2	-	-	3	5	5	7	8	9	9	9+	9+	9+	9+
ZS6 = 38	9+	9+	8	7	8	9	6	-	-	-	-	-	-	-	1*	1	2	6	8	9	9+	9+	9+	9+
FR = 39	9+	8	2	1	4	1	-	-	-	-	-	-	-	2*	3*	1*	1	3	8	9	9+	9+	9+	9+
FJL = 40	9+	9+	7	4	7	8	7	1	-	-	-	1*	8	9	9	9	9	9	9	9	9+	9+	9+	9+
Zone	00	01	02	03	04	05	06	07	08	09	10	11	12	13	14	15	16	17	18	19	20	21	22	23

UTC --> * = Longpath

Expected signal levels using 1500 W and 3-element Yagis at 100 feet at each station.

Figure 4.39 — The 20 meter page from Detailed propagation-prediction for the month of January, during Very High solar conditions, from Boston to 40 CQ Zones throughout the world. There are similar pages for each month/SSN level for 160, 80, 40, 20, 15 and 10 meters. These Detailed tables are very useful for planning DX operation.

is a respectable signal and will probably get through, in the absence of stronger signals calling the Boston station at the same time, of course.

Here's another example of how to use the detailed propagation-prediction tables. Let's say that at 1230 UTC in January you work a VU2 station in New Delhi on 15 meters from Boston, where the local time is 7:30 AM. You need a 20 meter contact also for the 5-Band DXCC award, so you quickly check the table in Figure 4.39 for Zone 22 (VU) and find that the predicted signal strength is S-9. Your new VU2 friend is willing to jump to 20 meters and so you QSY to make the contact.

But perhaps you are late leaving for work and so you ask your new VU2 friend to make a schedule with you later that evening. Again, you consult the Detailed prediction table for 20 meters and find that signals are predicted to be S-8 or stronger from 20 to 23 UTC, dropping to S-7 at 00 UTC. You quickly ask your new friend whether he minds waking up at 4:30 AM his time to make a schedule with you at 2300 UTC, because New Delhi is 5½ hours ahead of UTC. You determined this using the program *GeoClock*, which runs in the background on *Windows*. *GeoClock* is a shareware program from **www.softpedia.com**. Luckily, he's a very gracious fellow and agrees to meet you on a specific frequency at that time.

The detailed propagation-prediction tables give you all the information needed to plan your operations to maximize your enjoyment chasing DX. You can use these tables to plan a 48-hour contest next month, or next year — or you can use them to plan a schedule with your ham cousin on the West Coast on Saturday afternoon.

4.4 PROPAGATION PREDICTION SOFTWARE

Very reliable methods of determining the MUF for any given radio path under quiet solar conditions have been developed over the last 50 years. As discussed previously, these methods are all based on the smoothed sunspot number (R_{12}) as the measure of solar activity. It is for this reason that smoothed sunspot numbers hold so much meaning for radio amateurs and others concerned with radio-wave propagation — they are the link to past (and future) propagation conditions.

We must also consider that we now have NEW sunspot numbers as discussed in Section 4.2.1. The model of the ionosphere was based on the correlation of monthly median ionospheric parameters (foE, hmE, foF2, hmF2, and so on) to the OLD smoothed sunspot numbers. If you use the new sunspot numbers in your propagation prediction software, the resulting outputs (usually monthly median signal strength and monthly median MUF) will be optimistic by about one band. In other words, if the old smoothed sunspot numbers gave a monthly median MUF of 21 MHz, then the new smoothed sunspot numbers will give a monthly median MUF of 24 MHz. Considering the dynamic nature of the ionosphere, this may not be as bad as one would think. Additionally, the Earth's magnetic poles are moving, the Earth's magnetic field strength is changing, and there are long-term trends in the ionospheric layers — thus there are three issues that may require the model to be adjusted. Until that happens, you can always divide the new smoothed sunspot numbers by 1.4 (again from Section 4.2.1) to get a good enough approximation to the old smoothed sunspot numbers for use in your propagation prediction software.

Early on, the prediction of propagation conditions required tedious work with numerous graphs, along with charts of frequency contours overlaid, or overprinted, on world maps. The basic materials were available from an agency of the US government. Monthly publications provided the frequency-contour data a few months in advance. Only rarely did amateurs try their hand at predicting propagation conditions using these hard-to-use methods.

Today's powerful PCs have given the amateur wonderful tools to make quick-and-easy HF propagation predictions, whether for a contest or a DXpedition. The summary and detailed prediction tables described earlier in this chapter were generated using *CAPMan*, a modernized version of the mainframe *IONCAP* program, on a PC. (*Capman* is no longer available.) You can also make use of *VOACAP* predictions online using the website **www.voacap.com/hf/** that was developed by OH6BG, HZ1JW, and OH8GLV. As mentioned earlier, *VOACAP* includes the above-the-MUF mode. If a path can withstand a bit more loss, the QSO may be completed although the MUF is *below* the operating frequency. And with FT8 having the ability to decode signals farther down into the noise than CW, it essentially says the MUF can be even lower than for CW. This will likely keep the 10 meter band livelier than ever before as we go through the solar minimum between Cycles 24 and 25. FT8 will certainly help in the summer sporadic E season, as well.

While tremendously useful to setting up schedules and for planning strategy for contests, both the Summary and Detailed prediction tables included with the downloadable supplemental information for this book show signal strength. They do not show other information that is also in the underlying databases used to generate them. They don't, for example, show the dominant elevation angles and neither do they show reliability statistics. You may want to run propagation-prediction software yourself to get into the really "nitty-gritty" details.

Modern programs are designed for quick-and-easy predictions of propagation parameters. See **Table 4.7** for a listing of a number of popular programs. (A larger collection of

Table 4.7
Features and Attributes of Propagation Prediction Programs

	ASAPS V. 6	*VOACAP Windows*	*W6ELProp V. 2.70*	*PropLab Pro V. 3*
User Friendliness	Good	Good	Good	Poor**
Operating System	Windows	Windows	Windows	Windows
Uses K or A index	No*	No	Yes	Yes
User library of QTHs	Yes	Yes	Yes	No
Bearings, distances	Yes	Yes	Yes	Yes
MUF calculation	Yes	Yes	Yes	Yes
LUF calculation	Yes	Yes	No	Yes
Wave angle calculation	Yes	Yes	Yes	Yes
Vary minimum wave angle	Yes	Yes	Yes	Yes
Path regions and hops	Yes	Yes	Yes	Yes
Multipath effects	Yes	Yes	No	Yes
Path probability	Yes	Yes	Yes	Yes
Signal strengths	Yes	Yes	Yes	Yes
S/N ratios	Yes	Yes	Yes	Yes
Long-path calculation	Yes	Yes	Yes	Yes
Antenna selection	Yes	Yes	Indirectly	Yes
Vary antenna height	Yes	Yes	ndirectly	Yes
Vary ground characteristics	Yes	Yes	No	No
Vary transmit power	Yes	Yes	Indirectly	Yes
Graphic displays	Yes	Yes	Yes	2D/3D
UT-day graphs	Yes	Yes	Yes	Yes
Area Mapping	Yes	Yes	Yes	Yes
Documentation	Yes	On-line	Yes	Yes
Price class	$385 AUD	free	free	$290

Price classes are current as of early 2019 and subject to change.
ASAPS - **www.sws.bom.gov.au/Products_and_Services**
VOACAP - **www.voacap.com**
W6ELProp - **www.qsl.net/w6elprop**
PropLab Pro - **shop.spacew.com/l**

*Uses T-index available from IPS.
***Proplab Pro* is more of a propagation analysis program, and a good understanding of the ionosphere is needed to use it properly.

propagation prediction software is also available at **astrosurf.com/luxorion/qsl-review-propagation-software.htm**.) The basic input information required is the smoothed sunspot number (R_{12}) or smoothed solar flux (F_{12}), the date (month and day), and the latitudes and longitudes at the two ends of the radio path. The latitude and longitude, of course, are used to determine the great-circle radio path. Most commercial programs tailored for ham use allow you to specify locations by the call sign. The date is used to determine the latitude of the Sun, and this, with the smoothed sunspot number (or smoothed 10.7 cm solar flux converted to a smoothed sunspot number), is used to determine the properties of the ionosphere at critical points on the path.

Of course, just because a computer program predicts that a band will be open on a particular path, it doesn't follow that the Sun and the ionosphere will always cooperate! Under disturbed solar conditions, a coronal mass ejection or big solar flare can affect HF communication anywhere from hours to days (see the sections Disturbed Ionospheric Conditions and Ionospheric Storms). There is still art, as well as a lot of science, in predicting propagation. In times of quiet geomagnetic activity, however, the prediction programs are good at forecasting band openings and closings. To help explain how predication software may be applied to real-life operating, a presentation "Using Propagation Predictions for HF DXing" by Dean Straw, N6BV, is included with this book's downloadable supplemental information.

4.4.1 SOLAR ACTIVITY DATA

Our propagation prediction programs were developed based on the very high correlation between a smoothed solar index (originally the smoothed sunspot number, but equally good is the smoothed solar flux) and monthly median ionospheric parameters. Thus to use our prediction programs properly, you must use a smoothed solar index and understand that the outputs (usually signal strength and MUF) are statistical in nature over a month's time frame.

Future smoothed solar indices are available at **ftp://ftp.swpc.noaa.gov/pub/weekly/Predict.txt**. The "Predicted" values at this website for both indices are most likely what you should use. The "High" and "Low" values give the upper and lower boundary of the predicted parameter. If the solar activity is greater than expected, use the "High" value. If the solar activity is lower than expected, use the "Low" value.

Using the daily 10.7 cm solar flux or the daily sunspot number doesn't provide a more accurate picture of propagation. This comment is true even when including the K or A index. The reason for this is the significant day-to-day variation

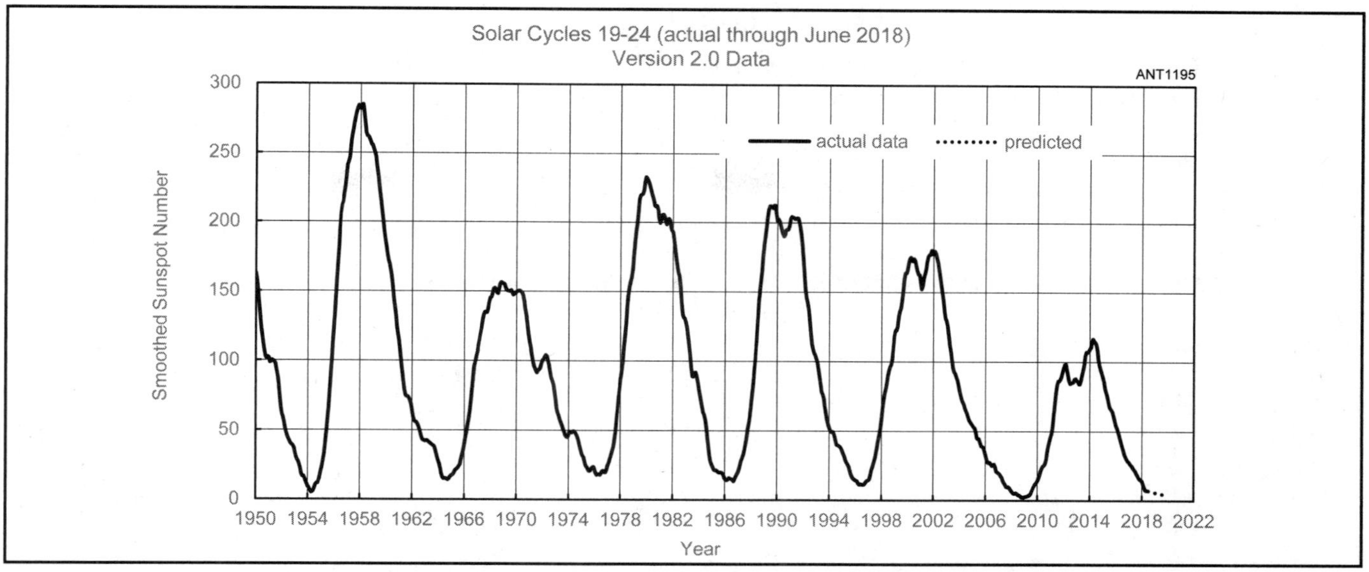

Figure 4.40 — Historical and predicted V2.0 smoothed sunspot numbers for Cycles 19 through 24.

of the ionosphere, especially the F_2 region. The F_2 region varies on a day-to-day basis not only due to solar ionizing radiation, but due to events in the lower atmosphere coupling up to the ionosphere and due to a more complicated response to the K or A index than a single value.

Using values of 10.7 cm solar flux averaged over 7 days or even longer (3 months, for example) will drive the prediction results more towards how they were intended to be used — with a smoothed solar index. These results will be better than using a daily solar index, but there will still be a discrepancy between the index used and what the ionosphere is doing.

Smoothed V2.0 sunspot numbers from July 1749 to the latest data are available at **sidc.oma.be/silso/datafiles**. **Figure 4.40** plots the smoothed V2.0 sunspot number starting with Cycle 19 and including the Cycle 24 actual data (through June 2018 at the time of this writing) and predicted data (July 2018 through the end of 2019).

For the most current data on what the Sun is doing, National Institute of Standards and Technology stations WWV and WWVH broadcast information on solar activity at 18 and 45 minutes past each hour, respectively. These propagation bulletins give the solar flux, geomagnetic A-index, Boulder K-index, and a brief statement of solar and geomagnetic activity in the past and coming 24-hour periods, in that order. The solar flux and A-index are changed daily with the 2118 UT bulletin, the rest every three hours — 0018, 0318, 0618 UT and so on. On the web, up-to-date WWV information can be found at: **ftp://ftp.swpc.noaa.gov/pub/latest/wwv.txt** or on the NOAA web page **www.swpc.noaa.gov**.

Some other useful websites are: **dx.qsl.net/propagation**, **www.solen.info/solar**, **www.qrz.com**, and **hfradio.org/propagation.html**. The Solar Terrestrial Dispatch page contains a wealth of propagation-related information: **www.spacew.com**. You may also access propagation information via your preferred spotting network website. Use the command SH/WWV/*n*, where *n* is the number of spots you wish to see (five is the default).

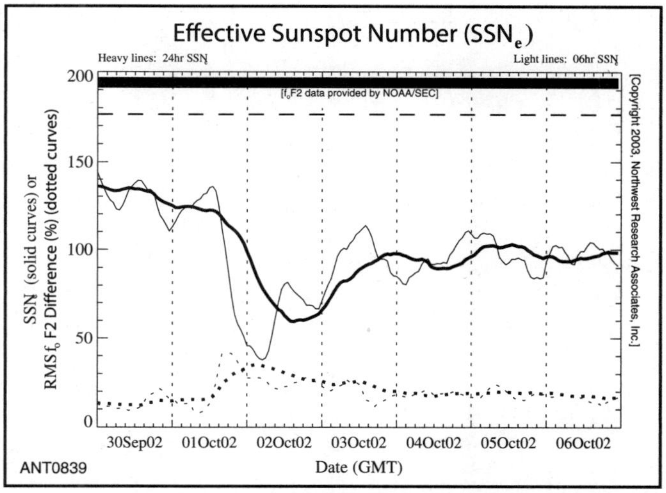

Figure 4.41 — Effective Sunspot Number (SSN_e) produced by NWRA. Note the large drop in effective SSN due to a geomagnetic storm commencing Oct 1, 2002.

Another excellent method for obtaining an "equivalent sunspot number" (SSN_e) is to go to the Space Weather site of Northwest Research Services at **spawx.nwra.com/spawx/ssne24.html**. NWRA compares real-time ionospheric sounder data around the world with predictions using various levels of SSN looking for the best match. They thus "back into" the actual effective sunspot number. Note that this is necessarily a best fit of ionospheric sounder data to an equivalent sunspot number — it's not a perfect fit for all the data due to the dynamic hour-to-hour variability of the worldwide F2 region. **Figure 4.41** is a typical NWRA graph, which covers the week ending 6 October 2002. Note the sudden decrease in SSNe after a geomagnetic storm depressed SSNe by more than 50%.

4.5 BIBLIOGRAPHY

Source material and more extended discussion of topics covered in this chapter can be found in the references given below.

E. V. Appleton and W.R. Piggott, "Ionospheric Absorption Measurements during a Sunspot Cycle," *J. Atmos. Terr. Phys.*, Vol 3, p 141, 1954.

D. Bilitiza, *International Reference Ionosphere (IRI 90)*, National Space Science Data Center, Greenbelt, MD, 1990.

D. Bray, "Method of Determining VHF/HF Station Capabilities," *QST*, Nov 1961.

A. Brekke, "Physics of the Upper Polar Atmosphere," (New York, 1997: John Wiley and Sons).

R. R. Brown, "Demography, DXpeditions and Magneto-Ionic Theory," *The DX Magazine*, Vol. X, No. 2, p 44, Mar/Apr 1998.

R. R. Brown, *The Little Pistol's Guide to HF Communication* (Sacramento: WorldRadio Books, 1996). [Out of print, but it can be downloaded at **https://k9la.us**]

R. R. Brown, "Signal Ducting on the 160 Meter Band," *Communications Quarterly*, p 65, Spring 1998.

R. R. Brown, "Unusual Low-Frequency Signal Propagation at Sunrise," *Communications Quarterly*, p 67, Fall 1998.

R. R. Brown, "Atmospheric Ozone, a Meteorological Factor in Low-Frequency and 160 Meter Propagation," *Communications Quarterly*, Spring 1999.

K. Davies, *Ionospheric Radio* (London: Peter Peregrinus Ltd, 1990). Excellent technical reference.

R. Garcia, S. Solomon, S. Avery, G. C. Reid, "Transport of Nitric Oxide and the D-Region Winter Anomaly," *J. Geophys. Res.*, Vol 92, p 977, 1987.

J. Hall, "Propagation Predictions and Personal Computers," Technical Correspondence, *QST*, Dec 1990, pp 58-59 (description of *IONCAP* as used for ARRL publications).

E. Harper, *Rhombic Antenna Design* (New York: D. Van Nostrand Co, Inc, 1941).

H. Hertz, *Electric Waves*, translated by D. E. Jones (London: MacMillan, 1893).

R. D. Hunsucker, *Radio Techniques for Probing the Terrestrial Ionosphere* (New York: Springer-Verlag).

R. D. Hunsucker, J. K. Hargreaves, *The High Latitude Ionosphere and Its Effects on Radio Propagation* (Cambridge: Cambridge University Press, 2003).

T.L. Killeen, R.M. Johnsson, "Upper Atmospheric Waves, Turbulence, and Winds: Importance for Mesospheric and Thermospheric Studies."

R. C. Luetzelschwab, K9LA's Amateur Radio Propagation website, **https://k9la.us**. Contains many articles and presentations about solar issues and MF, HF and VHF propagation.

R. C. Luetzelschwab, "Ducting and Spotlight Propagation on 160 Meters," *CQ Magazine*, Dec 2005.

J. L. Lynch, "The Maunder Minimum," *QST*, Jul 1976, p 24-26.

J. C. Maxwell, *A Treatise on Electricity and Magnetism*, Vols I and II (Oxford: Oxford University Press, 1873).

M. W. Maxwell, *Reflections — Transmission Lines and Antennas* (Newington, CT: ARRL, 1990) [out of print].

M. W. Maxwell, *Reflections II — Transmission Lines and Antennas* (Sacramento, CA: 2001). [Out of print. *Reflections III* is available on CD from **store.cq-amateur-radio.com**.]

L. F. McNamara, *The Ionosphere: Communications, Surveillance, and Direction Finding* (Malabar, FL: Krieger Publishing Company, 1991). Another excellent technical reference on propagation.

L. F. McNamara, *Radio Amateur's Guide to the Ionosphere* (Malabar, FL: Krieger Publishing Company, 1994). Excellent, quite-readable text on HF propagation.

C. Oler, T. Cohen, "The 160-Meter Band: An Enigma Shrouded in Mystery, Parts 1 and 2," *CQ Magazine*, Mar and Apr 1998.

A. K. Paul, "Medium Scale Structure of the F Region," *Radio Science*, Volume 24, No. 3, p. 301, 1989.

W. R. Piggott, K. Rawer, "URSI Handbook of Ionogram Interpretation and Reduction," Report UAG-50. World Data Center A for Solar-Terrestrial Physics, Boulder, CO, 1975.

E. Pocock, Ed., *Beyond Line of Sight: A History of VHF Propagation from the Pages of QST* (ARRL: 1992). [Out of print]

E. Pocock, "Sporadic-E Propagation at VHF: A Review of Progress and Prospects," *QST*, Apr 1988, pp 33-39.

E. Pocock, "Auroral-E Propagation at 144 MHz," *QST*, Dec 1989, pp 28-32.

E. Pocock, "Propagation Forecasting During Solar Cycle 22," *QST*, Jun 1989, pp 18-20.

G. C. Reid, "Ion Chemistry of the D-region," *Advances in Atomic and Molecular Physics*, Vol 12, Academic Press, 1976.

R. B. Rose, "MINIMUF: A Simplified MUF-Prediction Program for Microcomputers," *QST*, Dec 1982, pp 36-38

M. L. Salby, "Fundamentals of Atmospheric Physics," (Academic Press: Boulder, CO, 1996).

S. C. Shallon, *W6ELProp*, available from **www.qsl.net/w6elprop**.

P. Smith and W. Silver, "The Reverse Beacon Network," *QST*, Oct 2016, pp 30-32.

R. D. Straw, *All the Right Angles* (New Bedford, PA: LTA, 1993). Out of print.

R. D. Straw, "*ASAPS* and *CAPMAN*: HF Propagation-Prediction Software for the IBM PC," *QST*, Dec 1994, pp 79-81.

R. D. Straw, "Heavy-Duty HF Propagation-Prediction/Analysis Software," Part 1: *QST*, Sep 1996, pp 28-32; Part 2: *QST*, Oct 1996, pp 28-30.

R. D. Straw, "Using Propagation Predictions for DXing," available from **www.voacap.com**.

TABLE OF CONTENTS

Chapter 5 —
Supplemental Downloadable Content

Supplemental Articles

Chapter 5

Loop Antennas

A loop antenna is a closed-circuit antenna independent of a counterpoise — that is, one in which a conductor is formed into one or more turns so its two ends are close together. Loops can be divided into two general classes — large loops in which both the conductor length and the loop dimensions are comparable with the wavelength and small loops in which both the total conductor length and the maximum linear dimension of a turn are very small compared with the wavelength.

Material on quad and delta loops is adapted from Chapter 10 of *Low-Band DXing,* 5th edition by John Devoldere, ON4UN. Material on small HF gap-resonated loops was written by Kai Siwiak, KE4PT, based on the *QEX* and *QST* loop articles with coauthor Rich Quick, W4RQ, and includes material from earlier editions that was contributed by Domenic Mallozzi, N1DM. Additional discussion of loop antennas can be found in these chapters: **Single-Band MF and HF Antennas**, **Multiband HF Antennas,** and **Receiving and Direction-Finding Antennas**.

5.1 LARGE LOOPS

Resonant loop antennas have a circumference of 1 λ. The exact shape of the loop is not particularly important. In free space, the loop with the highest gain, however, is the loop with the shape that encloses the largest area for a given circumference. This is a circular loop, which is difficult to construct. Second best is the square loop (quad), and in third place comes the equilateral triangle (delta) loop (see the reference for Dietrich and for Stanley, K4ERO).

The maximum gain of a 1 λ loop over a λ/2 dipole in free space is approximately 1.35 dB. Delta loops are used extensively on the low bands at apex heights of λ/4 to 3λ/8 above ground. At such heights the vertically polarized loops far outperform dipoles or inverted-V dipoles for low-angle DXing, assuming good ground conductivity.

Loops are generally erected with the plane of the loop perpendicular to the ground. Whether or not the loop produces a vertically or a horizontally polarized signal (or a combination of both) depends only on how (or on which side) the loop is being fed.

Another variety of large loop antenna comprises the horizontally mounted loops, which have the plane of the loop parallel to the ground. These antennas produce horizontal radiation with takeoff angles determined, as usual, by the height of the horizontal loop over ground.

5.1.1 THE SQUARE OR QUAD LOOP

Belcher, WA4JVE; Casper, K4HKX; and Dietrich, WAØRDX, have published studies comparing the horizontally polarized vertical quad loop with a dipole. (See the Bibliography section.) A horizontally polarized quad loop antenna (**Figure 5.1A**) can be seen as two short, end-loaded dipoles stacked λ/4 apart, with the top antenna at λ/4 and the bottom one just above ground level. The total length for a resonant loop is approximately 5 to 6% longer than the free-space wavelength.

There is no broadside radiation from the vertical wires of the quad because of the current opposition in the vertical members. In a similar manner, the vertically polarized quad loop consists of two top-loaded, λ/4 vertical dipoles, spaced λ/4 apart. Figure 5.1 shows how the current distribution along the elements produces cancellation of radiation from certain parts of the antenna, while radiation from other parts (the horizontally or vertically stacked short dipoles) is reinforced.

The square quad can be fed for either horizontal or vertical polarization merely by placing the feed point at the center of a horizontal arm or at the center of a vertical arm. At the higher frequencies in the HF range, where the quads are typically half to several wavelengths high, quad loops are usually fed to produce horizontal polarization, although there is no specific reason for this except maybe from a mechanical standpoint. Polarization by itself is of little importance at HF because of random rotation in the ionosphere.

Quad Loop Impedance

The radiation resistance of an equilateral quad loop in free space is approximately 120 Ω. The radiation resistance for a quad loop as a function of its height above ground is

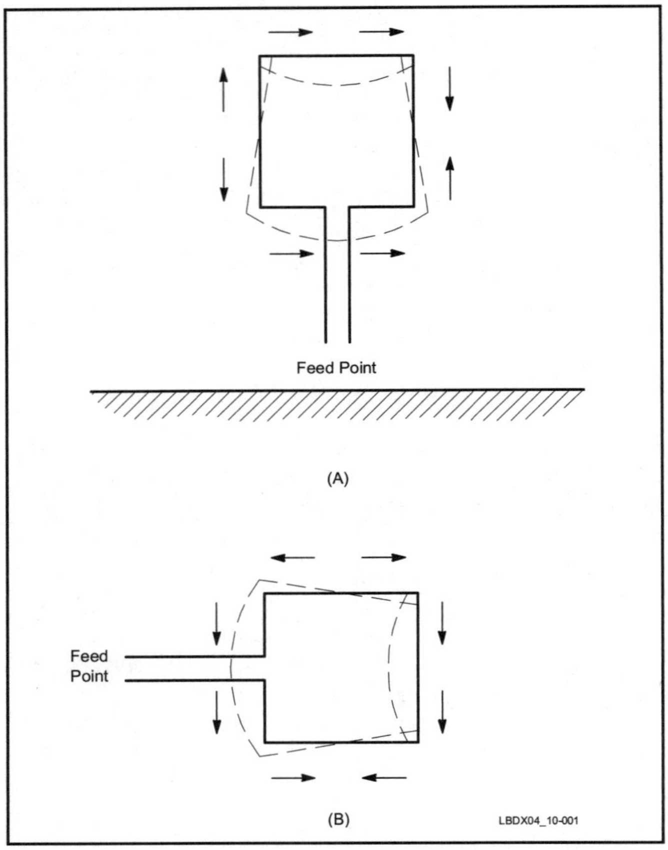

Figure 5.1 — Quad loops with a 1-λ circumference. The current distribution is shown for (A) horizontal and (B) vertical polarization. Note how the opposing currents in the two legs result in cancellation of the radiation in the plane of those legs, while the currents in the other legs are in-phase and reinforce each other in the broadside direction (perpendicular to the plane of the antenna).

given in **Figure 5.2**. The impedance data were obtained by modeling an equilateral quad loop over three types of ground (very good, average, and very poor ground) using *NEC*.

The reactance data can assist you in evaluating the influence of the antenna height on the resonant frequency. The loop antenna was first modeled in free space to be resonant at 3.75 MHz and the reactance data were obtained with those free-space resonant-loop dimensions.

For the vertically polarized quad loop, the resistive part of the impedance changes very little with the type of ground under the antenna. The feed point reactance is influenced by the ground quality, especially at lower heights. For the horizontally polarized loop, the radiation resistance is noticeably influenced by the ground quality, especially at low heights. The same is true for the reactance.

Quad Loop Patterns — Vertical Polarization

The vertically polarized quad loop in Figure 5.1B can be considered as two shortened top-loaded vertical dipoles, spaced λ/4 apart. Broadside radiation from the horizontal elements of the quad is canceled, because of the opposition of currents in the vertical legs. The wave angle in the broadside direction will be essentially the same as for either of the vertical members. The resulting radiation angle will depend on the quality of the ground up to several wavelengths away from the antenna, as is the case with all vertically polarized antennas.

The quality of the reflecting ground will also influence the gain of the vertically polarized loop to a great extent. The quality of the ground is as important as it is for any other vertical antenna, meaning that vertically polarized loops close to the ground will not work well over poor soil.

Figure 5.3 shows both the azimuth and elevation radiation patterns of a vertically polarized quad loop with a top height of 0.3 λ (bottom wire at approximately 0.04 λ). This

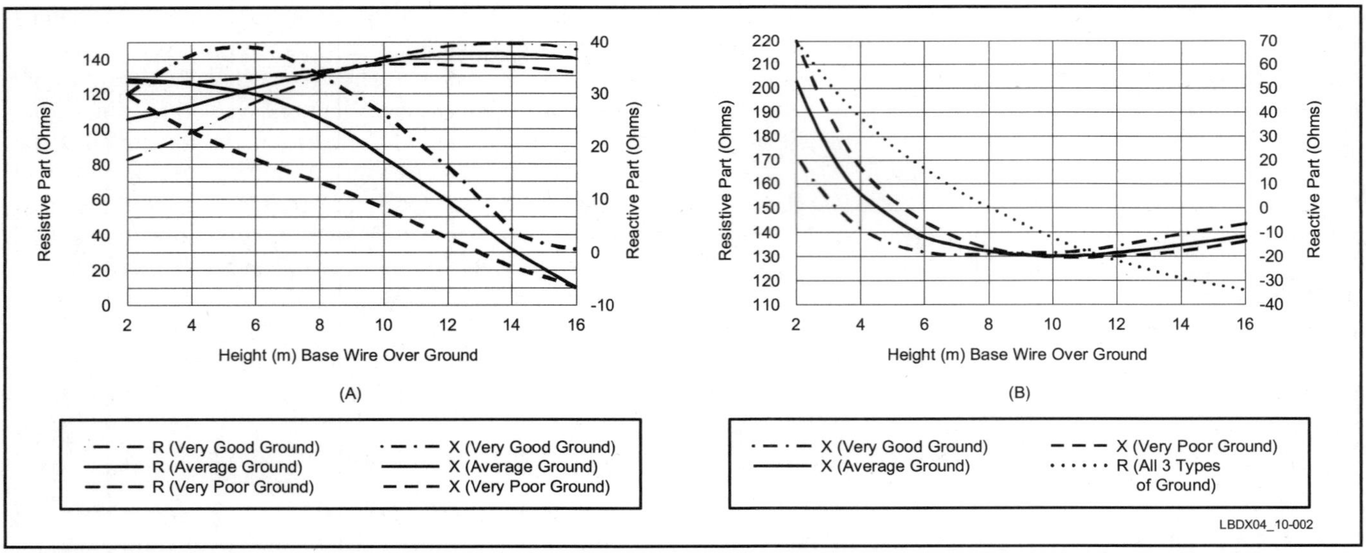

Figure 5.2 — Radiation resistance and feed point resistance for square loops at different heights above real ground. The loop was first dimensioned to be resonant in free space (reactance equal to zero), and those dimensions were used for calculating the impedance over ground. At A, for horizontal polarization, and at B, for vertical polarization. Analysis was with *NEC* at 3.75 MHz.

is a very realistic situation, especially on 80 meters. The loop radiates an excellent low-angle wave (lobe peak at approximately 21°) when operated over average ground. Over poorer ground, the wave angle would be closer to 30°. The horizontal directivity, Figure 5.3C, is rather poor, and amounts to approximately 3.3 dB of side rejection at any wave angle.

Quad Loop Patterns — Horizontal Polarization

A horizontally polarized quad-loop antenna (two stacked short dipoles) produces a wave angle that is dependent on the height of the loop. The low horizontally polarized quad (top at 0.3 λ) radiates most of its energy right at or near zenith angle (straight up).

Figure 5.4 shows directivity patterns for a horizontally polarized loop. The horizontal pattern, Figure 5.4C, is plotted for a takeoff angle of 30°. At low wave angles (20° to 45°), the horizontally polarized loop shows more front-to-side ratio (5 to 10 dB) than the vertically polarized rectangular loop.

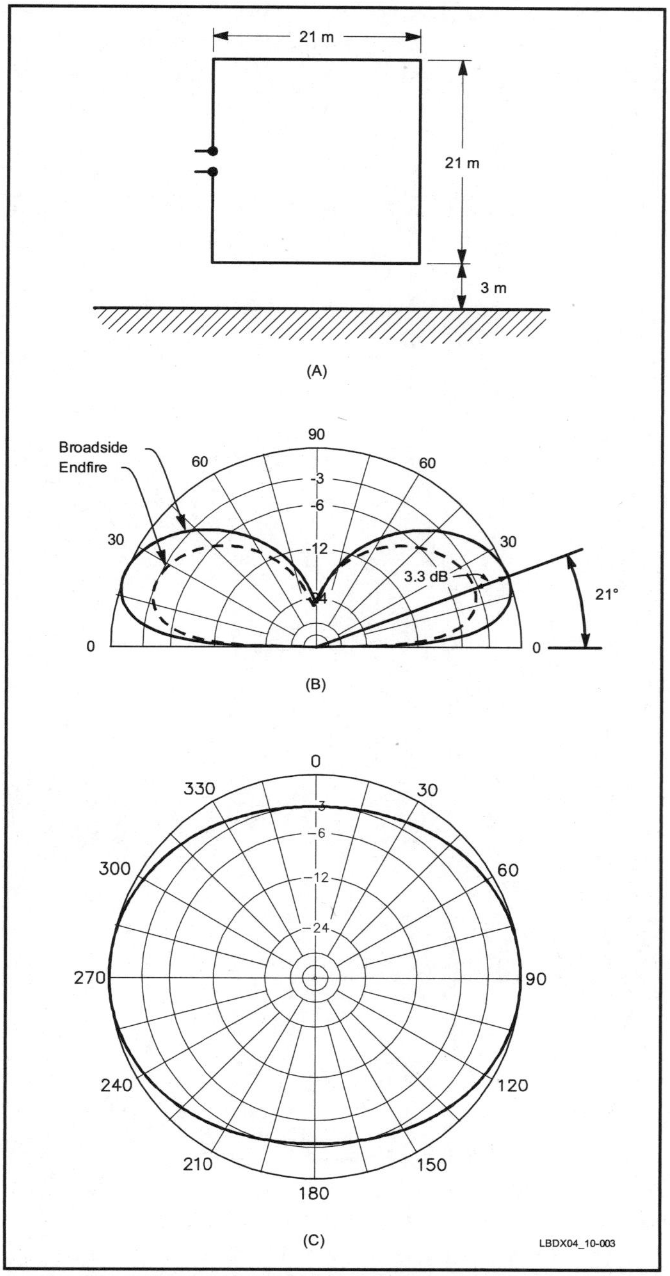

Figure 5.3 — Shown at A is a square loop, with its elevation-plane pattern at B and azimuth pattern at C. The patterns are generated for good ground. The bottom wire is 0.0375 λ above ground (3 meters or 10 feet on 80 meters). At C, the pattern is for a wave angle of 21°.

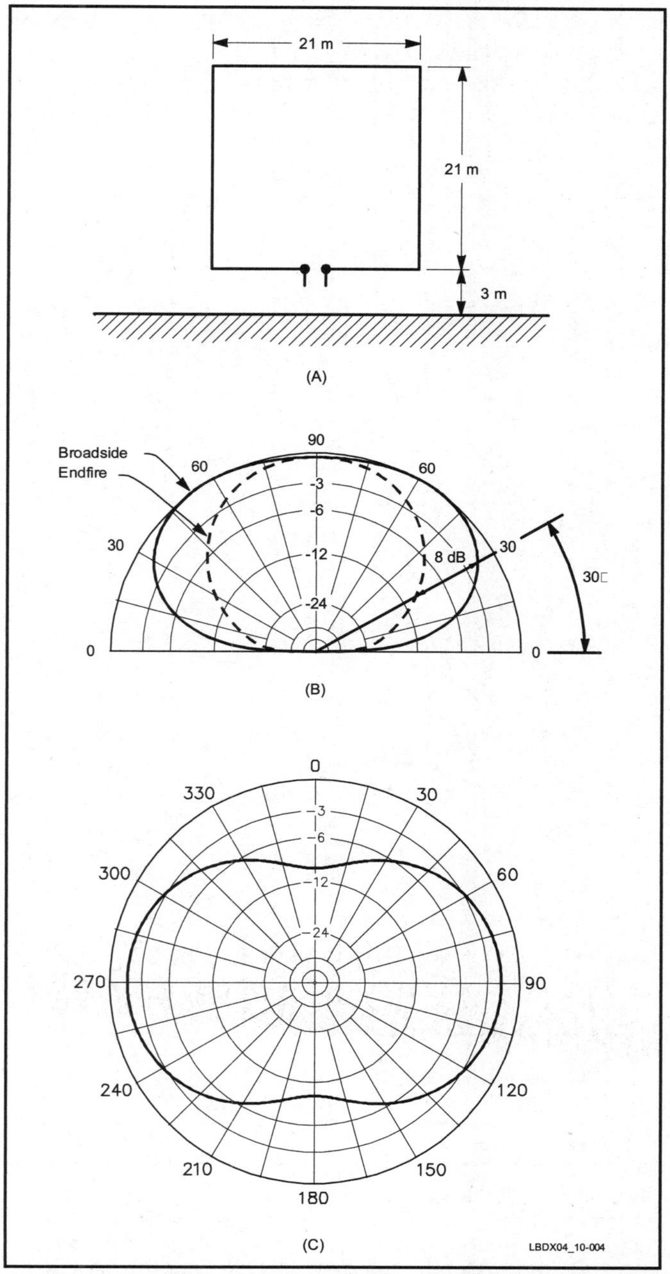

Figure 5.4 — Azimuth and elevation patterns of the horizontally polarized quad loop at low height (bottom wire 0.0375 λ above ground). At an elevation angle of 30°, the loop has a front-to-side ratio of approximately 8 dB.

Vertical versus Horizontal Polarization — Quad Loops

Vertically polarized loops should be used only where very good ground conductivity is available. From **Figure 5.5A** we see that the gain of the vertically polarized quad loop, as well as the wave angle, does not change very much as a function of the antenna height. This makes sense, since the vertically polarized loop is in the first place two phased verticals, each with its own radial.

However, the gain is drastically influenced by the quality of the ground. At low heights, the gain difference between very poor ground and very good ground is a solid 5 dB! The wave angle for the vertically polarized quad loop at a low height (bottom wire at 0.03 λ) varies from 25° over very poor ground to 17° over very good ground. Vertically polarized delta loops at low height always require a good ground screen underneath the antenna (unless they are over excellent or perfect ground), exactly in the same way that a vertical with only one or two radials requires a good ground underneath the radials.

With a horizontally polarized quad loop the wave angle is very dependent on the antenna height, but not so much on the quality of the ground. At very low heights, the main wave angle varies between 50° and 60° (but is rather constant all the way up to 90°). As far as gain is concerned, there is a 2.5-dB gain difference between very good and very poor ground, which is only half the difference we found with the vertically polarized loop. Comparing the gain to the gain of the vertically polarized loop, we see that at very low antenna heights the gain is about 3-dB better than for the vertically polarized loop. But this gain exists at a high wave angle (50° to 90°), while the vertically polarized loop at very low heights radiates at 17° to 25°.

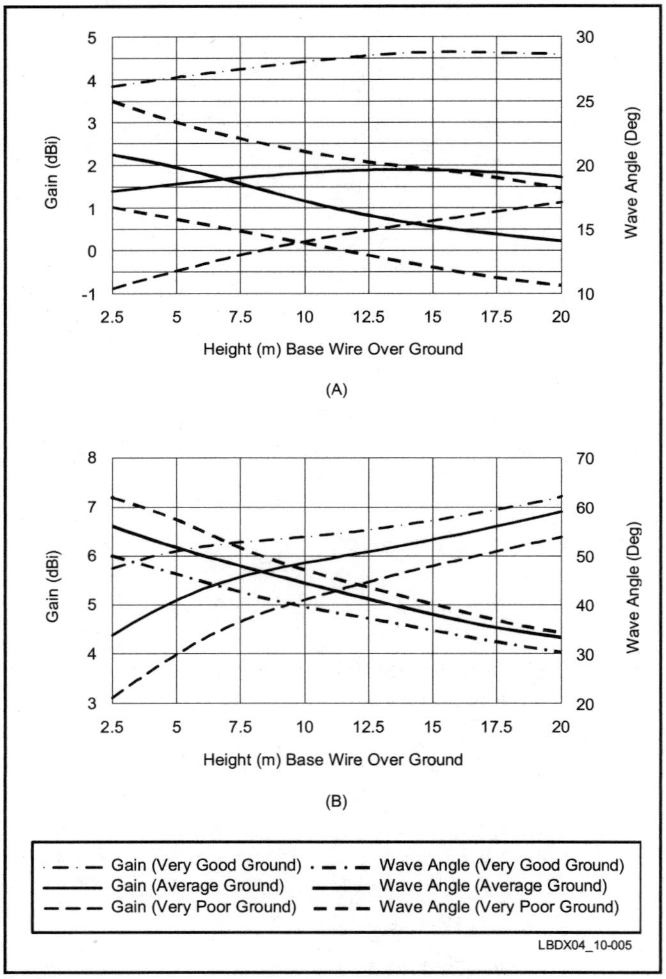

Figure 5.5 — Radiation angle and gain of the horizontally and the vertically polarized square loops at different heights over good ground. At A, for vertical polarization, and at B, for horizontal polarization. Note that the gain of the vertically polarized loop never exceeds 4.6 dBi, but its wave angle is low for any height (14 to 20°). The horizontally polarized loop can exhibit a much higher gain provided the loop is very high. Modeling was done over average ground for a frequency of 3.75 MHz, using *NEC*.

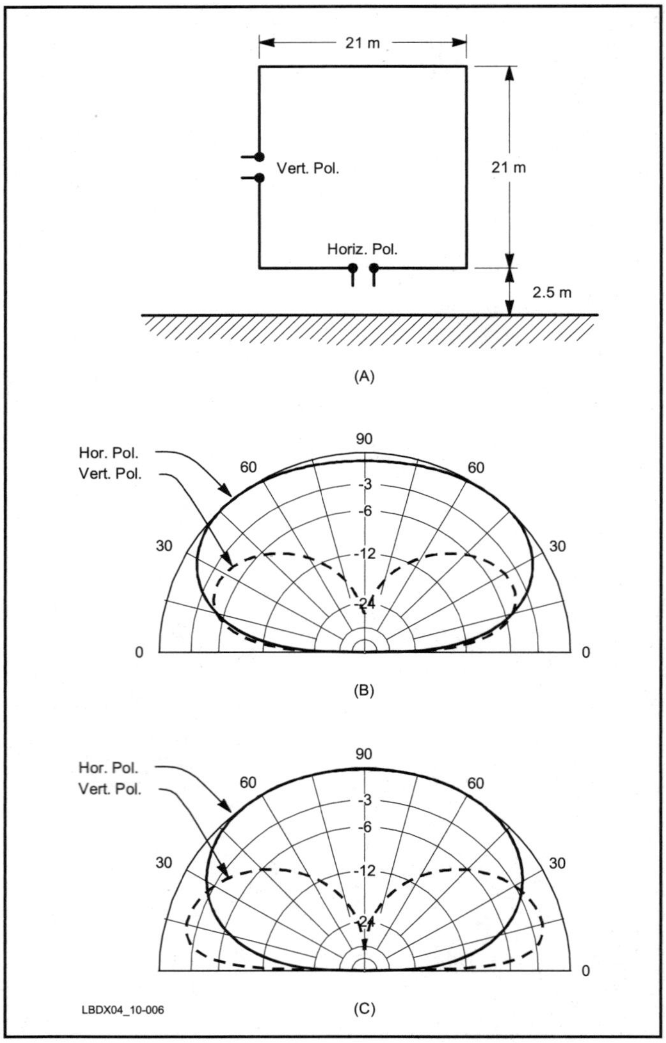

Figure 5.6 — Superimposed patterns for horizontally and vertically polarized square quad loops (shown at A) over very poor ground (B) and very good ground (C). In the vertical polarization mode the ground quality is of utmost importance, as it is with all verticals.

Figure 5.6 shows the vertical-plane radiation patterns for both types of quad loops over very poor ground and over very good ground on the same dB scale.

Rectangular Quad Loops

A rectangular quad loop with unequal side dimensions can be used with very good results on the low bands. The vertical and the horizontal radiation patterns for this quad loop over good ground are shown in **Figure 5.7**. The horizontal directivity is approximately 6 dB (front-to-side ratio).

Even in free space, the feed point impedance of the two configurations of this rectangular loop is not the same. When fed in the center of a short side, the radiation resistance of the antenna in Figure 5.7 at resonance is 44 Ω. When fed in the center of one of the long sides, the resistance is 215 Ω. Over real ground the feed point impedance is different in both configurations as well; depending on the quality of the ground, the impedance can vary by 40 to 90 Ω.

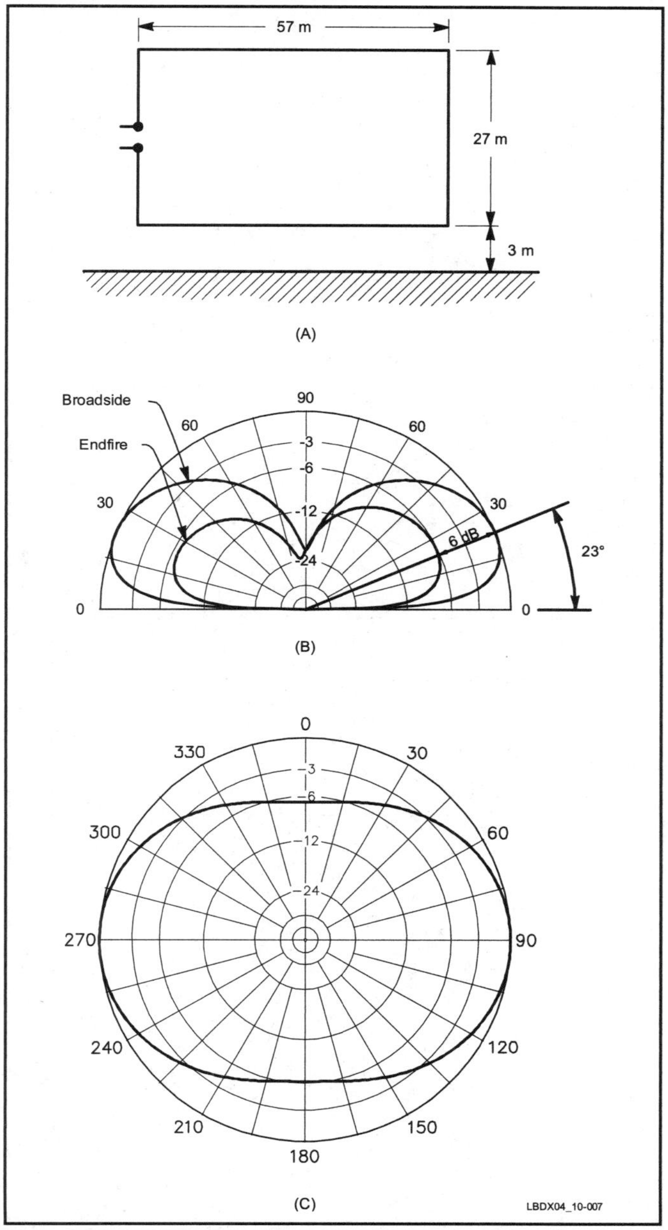

Figure 5.7 — At A, a rectangular loop with its baseline approximately twice as long as the vertical height. At B and C, the vertical and horizontal radiation patterns, generated over good ground. The loop was dimensioned to be resonant at 1.83 MHz. The azimuth pattern at C is taken at a 23° elevation angle.

Feeding the Quad Loop

The quad loop feed point should be in the middle of the vertical or the horizontal wire. A balun should be used as described in the **Transmission Line System Techniques** chapter. Alternatively, you could use open-wire feeders (for example, 450-Ω line). The open-wire-feeder alternative has the advantage of being a lightweight solution. With a tuner you will be able to cover a wide frequency range with no compromises. (See Feeding Large Loops following the section on Delta Loops.)

5.1.2. TRIANGULAR OR DELTA LOOPS

Because of its shape, the delta loop with the apex on top is a very popular antenna as it needs only one support. As for the quad configuration, the length of the resonant delta loop is approximately 1.05 to 1.06 λ.

In free space the equilateral triangle produces the highest gain and the highest radiation resistance for a three-sided loop configuration. As we deviate from an equilateral triangle toward a triangle with a long baseline, the effective gain and the radiation resistance of the loop will decrease for a bottom corner-fed delta loop. In the extreme case (where the height of the triangle is reduced to zero), the loop has become a half-wavelength-long transmission line that is shorted at the end, which shows a zero-Ω input impedance (radiation resistance), and thus zero radiation.

Just as with the quad loop, we can switch from horizontal to vertical polarization by changing the position of the feed point on the loop. For horizontal polarization the loop is fed either at the center of the baseline or at the top of the loop. For vertical polarization the loop should be fed on one of the sloping sides, at λ/4 from the apex of the delta. **Figure 5.8** shows the current distribution in both cases.

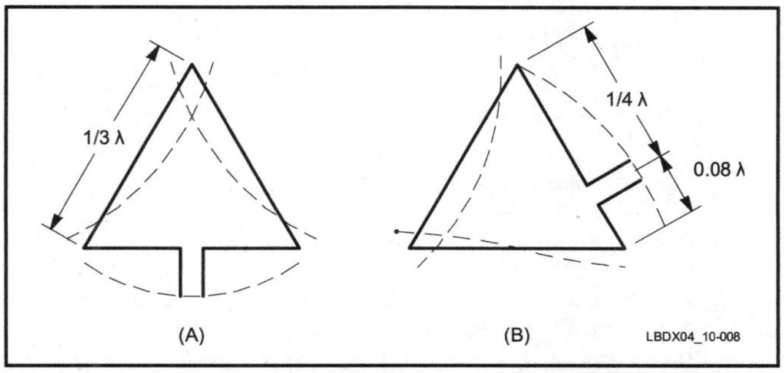

Figure 5.8 — Current distribution for equilateral delta loops fed for (A) horizontal and (B) vertical polarization.

Delta Loop Patterns — Vertical Polarization

As shown in **Figure 5.9**, in the vertical-polarization mode the delta loop can be seen as two sloping quarter-wave verticals (their apexes touch at the top of the support), while the baseline (and the part of the sloping section under the feed point) takes care of feeding the "other" sloping section with the correct phase. The top connection of the sloping verticals can be left open without changing anything about the operation of the delta loop. The same is true for the baseline, where the middle of the baseline could be opened without changing anything. These two points are the high-impedance points of the antenna. Either the apex or the center of the baseline must be shorted, however, in order to provide feed voltage to the other half of the antenna. Normally, of course, we use a fully closed loop in the standard delta loop, although for single-band operation this is not strictly necessary.

Assume we construct the antenna with the center of the horizontal bottom wire open. Now we can see the two half baselines as two λ/4 radials, one of which provides the necessary low-impedance point for connecting the shield of the coax. The other radial is connected to the bottom of the second sloping vertical, which is the other sloping wire of the delta loop. This is similar to a λ/4 vertical using a single elevated radial. The current distribution in the two quarter-wave radials is such that all radiation from these radials is effectively canceled.

The vertically polarized delta loop is really an array of two λ/4 verticals, with the high-current points spaced 0.25 λ to 0.3 λ, and operating in phase. The fact that the tops of the verticals are close together does not influence the performance to a large degree. The reason is that the current near the apex of the delta is at a minimum (it is current that creates radiation!). You can open the apex and move the vertical wires apart if you have a very tall support, in which case you will increase the gain of the antenna somewhat.

Considering a pair of phased verticals, we know from the chapter **Effects of Ground** that the quality of the ground will be very important as to the efficient operation of the antenna. This does not mean that the delta loop requires radials. It has two elevated radials that are an integral part of the loop and take care of the return currents. The presence of the (lossy) ground under the antenna is responsible for near-field losses, unless we can shield it from the antenna by using a ground screen or a radial system, which should not be connected to the antenna.

As with all vertically polarized antennas, the quality of the ground within a radius of several wavelengths will determine the low-angle radiation of the loop antenna.

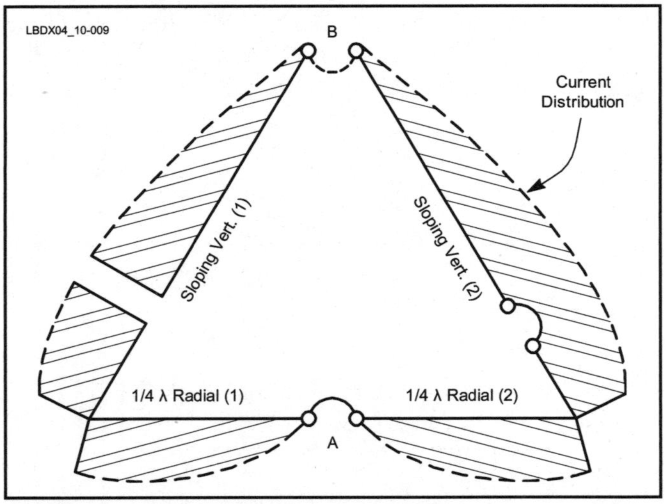

Figure 5.9 — The delta loop can be seen as two λ/4 sloping verticals, each using one radial. Because of the current distribution in the radials, the radiation from the radials is effectively canceled.

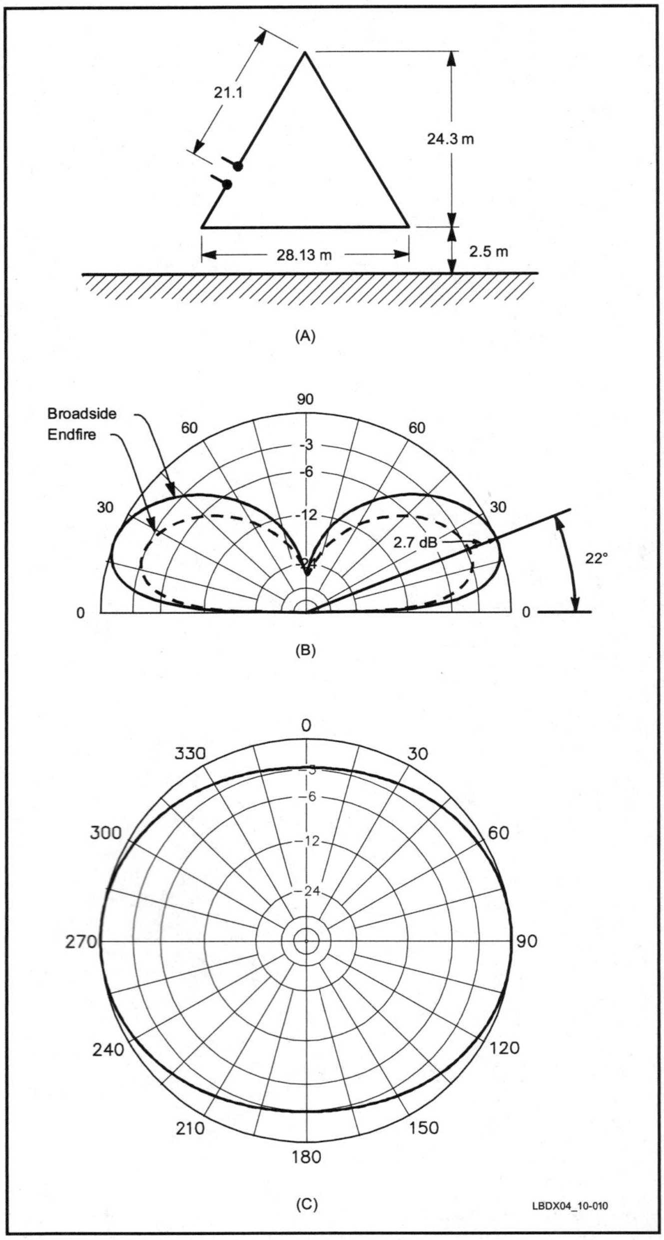

Figure 5.10 — Configuration and radiation patterns for a vertically polarized equilateral delta loop antenna. The model was calculated over good ground, for a frequency of 3.8 MHz. The elevation angle for the azimuth pattern at C is 22°.

The Equilateral Triangle

Figure 5.10 shows the configuration as well as both the broadside and the end-fire vertical radiation patterns of the vertically polarized equilateral-triangle delta loop antenna. The model was constructed for a frequency of 3.75 MHz. The baseline is 2.5 meters above ground, which puts the apex at 26.83 meters. The model was made over good ground. The delta loop shows nearly 3 dB front-to-side ratio at the main wave angle of 22°. With average ground the gain is 1.3 dBi.

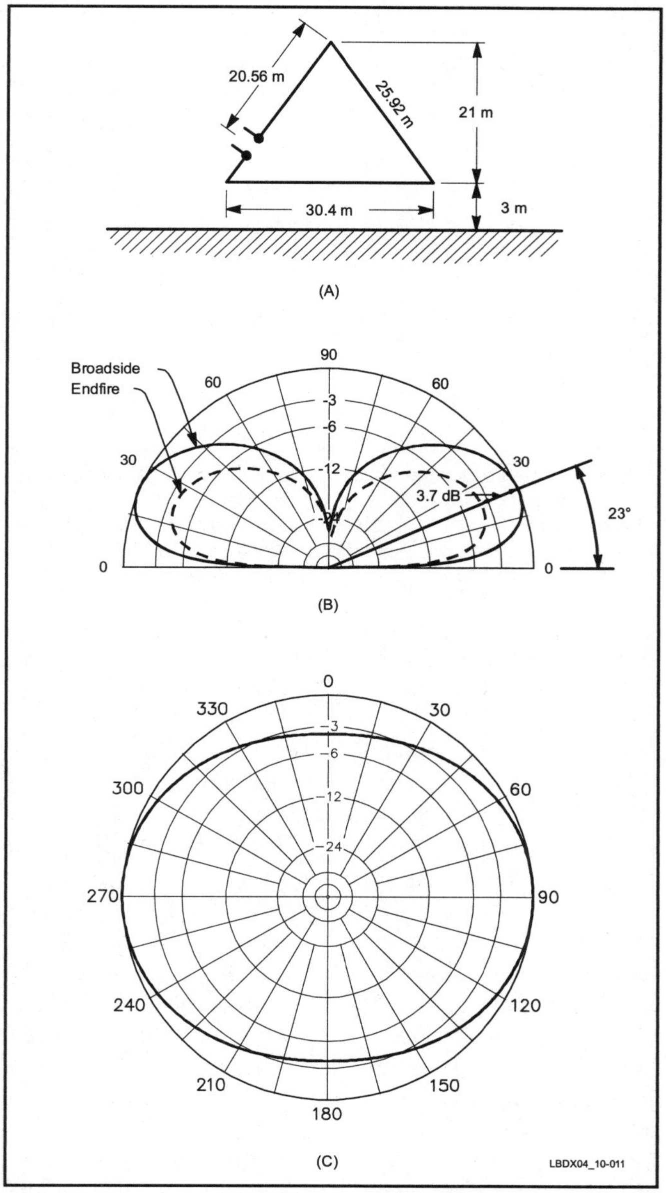

Figure 5.11 — Configuration and radiation patterns for the "compressed" delta loop, which has a baseline slightly longer than the sloping wires. The model was dimensioned for 3.8 MHz to have an apex height of 24 meters and a bottom wire height of 3 meters. Calculations are done over good ground at a frequency of 3.8 MHz. The azimuth pattern at C is for an elevation angle of 23°. Note that the correct feed point remains at λ/4 from the apex of the loop.

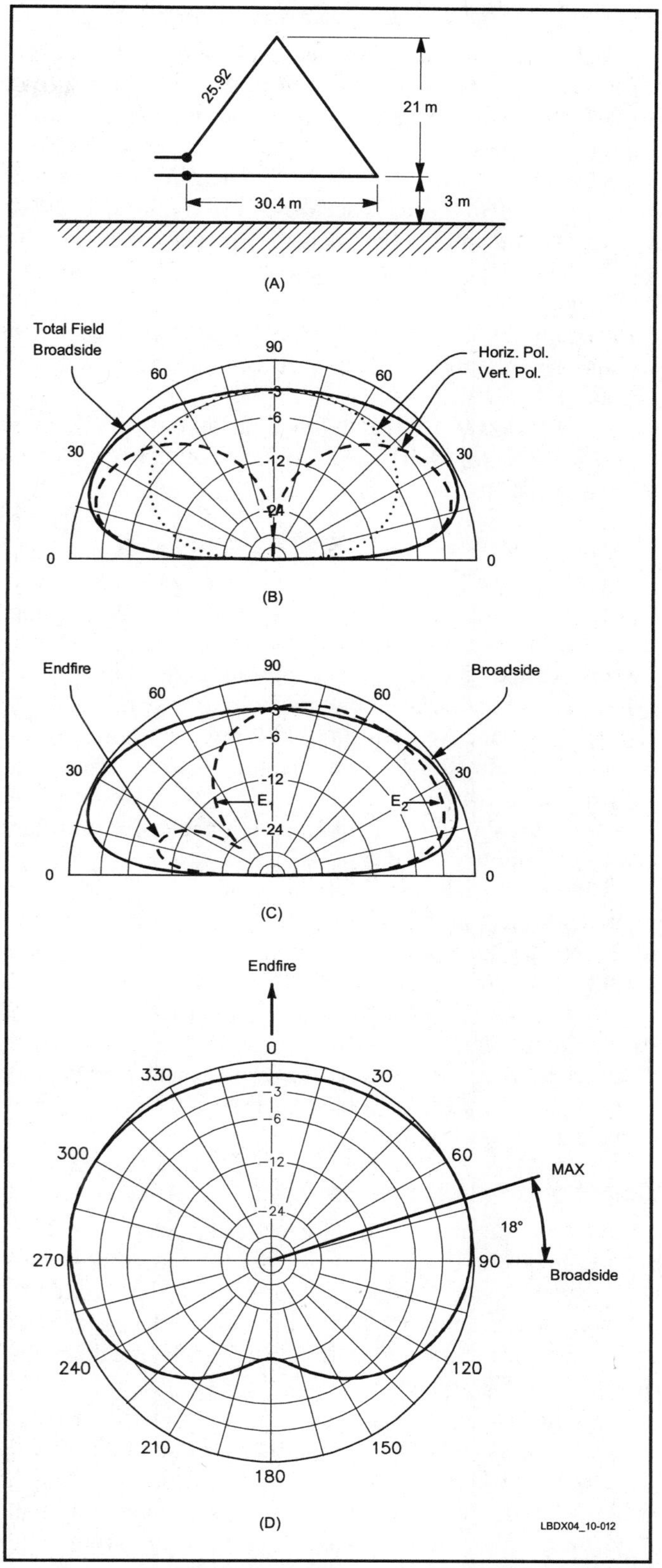

Figure 5.12 — Configuration and radiation patterns for the compressed delta loop of Figure 5.11 when fed in one of the bottom corners at a frequency of 3.75 MHz. Improper cancellation of radiation from the horizontal wire produces a strong high-angle horizontally polarized component. The delta loop now also shows a strange horizontal directivity pattern (at D), the shape of which is very sensitive to slight frequency deviations. This pattern is for an elevation angle of 29°.

The Compressed Delta Loop

Figure 5.11 shows an 80 meter delta loop with the apex at 24 meters and the baseline at 3 meters. This delta loop has a long baseline of 30.4 meters. The feed point is again located λ/4 from the apex.

The front-to-side ratio is 3.8 dB. The gain with average ground is 1.6 dBi. In free space the equilateral triangle gives a higher gain than the "flat" delta. Over real ground and in the vertically polarized mode, the gain of the flat delta loop is 0.3 dB better than the equilateral delta, however. This must be explained by the fact that the longer baseline yields a wider separation of the two "sloping" verticals, yielding a slightly higher gain.

For a 100-kHz bandwidth (on 80 meters) the SWR rises to 1.4:1 at the edges. The 2:1 SWR bandwidth is approximately 175 kHz.

The Bottom-Corner-Fed Delta Loop

Figure 5.12 shows the layout of the delta loop being fed at one of the two bottom corners. The antenna has the same apex and baseline height as the compressed delta loop. Because of the "incorrect" location of the feed point, cancellation of radiation from the base wire (the two "radials") is not 100% effective, resulting in a significant horizontally polarized radiation component. The total field has a uniform gain coverage (within 1 dB) from 25° to 90°. This may be a disadvantage for the rejection of high-angle signals when working DX at low wave angles.

Due to the "incorrect" feed point location, the end-fire radiation (radiation in line with the loop) has become asymmetrical. The horizontal radiation 2pattern shown in Figure 5.12D is for a wave angle of 29°. Note the deep side null (nearly 12 dB) at that wave angle. The loop actually radiates its maximum signal about 18° off the broadside direction. This feed point configuration (in the corner of the compressed loop) is to be avoided, as it really degrades the performance of the antenna.

Delta Loop Patterns — Horizontal Polarization

In the horizontal polarization mode, the delta loop can be seen as an inverted-V dipole on top of a very low dipole with its ends bent upward to connect to the tips of the inverted V. The loop will act as any horizontally polarized antenna over real ground; its wave angle will depend on the height of the antenna over the ground.

Figure 5.13 shows the vertical and the horizontal radiation patterns for an equilateral-triangle delta loop, fed at the center of the bottom wire. As anticipated, the radiation is maximum at the zenith. The front-to-side ratio is around 3 dB for a 15 to 45° wave angle. Over average ground the gain is 2.5 dBi. So far we have only spoken about relative patterns. What about real gain figures from the vertically and the horizontally polarized delta loops?

Vertical versus Horizontal Polarization — Delta Loops

Figure 5.14 shows the superimposed elevation patterns for vertically and horizontally polarized low-height equilateral triangle delta loops over two different types of ground (same dB scale).

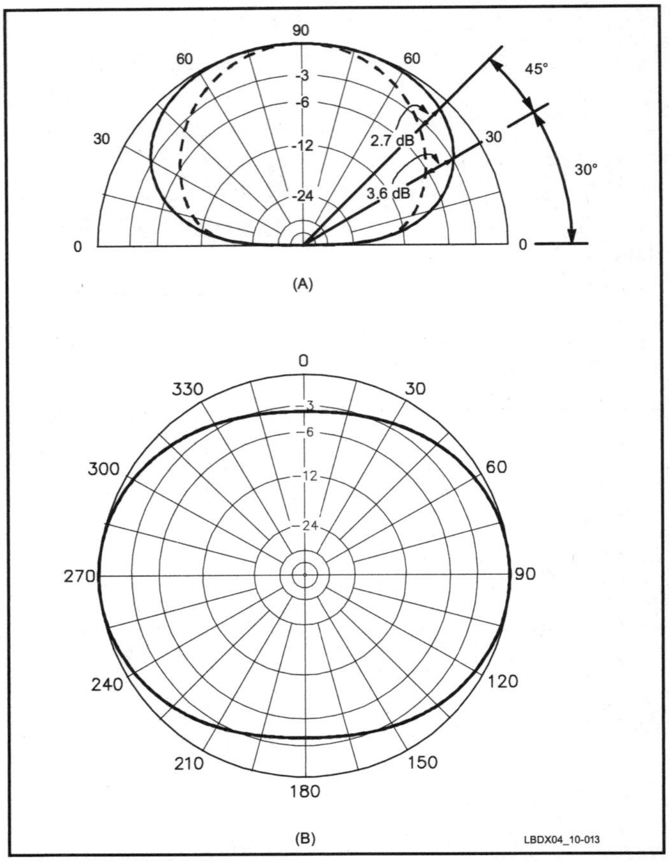

Figure 5.13 — Vertical and horizontal radiation patterns for an 80 meter equilateral delta loop fed for horizontal polarization, with the bottom wire at 3 meters. The radiation is essentially at very high angles, comparable to what can be obtained from a dipole or inverted-V dipole at the same (apex) height.

Over very poor ground, the horizontally polarized delta loop is better than the vertically polarized loop for all wave angles above 35°. Below 35° the vertically polarized loop takes over, but quite marginally. The maximum gain of the vertically and the horizontally polarized loops differs by only 2 dB, but the big difference is that for the horizontally polarized loop, the gain occurs at almost 90°, while for the vertically polarized loop it occurs at 25°.

One might argue that for a 30° elevation angle, the horizontally polarized loop is as good as the vertically polarized loop. It is clear, however, that the vertically polarized antenna gives good high-angle rejection (rejection against local signals), while the horizontally polarized loop will not.

Over very good ground, the same thing that happens with any vertical happens with a vertically polarized delta: The performance at low angles is greatly improved with good ground. The vertically polarized loop is still better at any wave angle under 30° than when horizontally polarized. At a 10° radiation angle, the difference is as high as 10 dB.

In conclusion, over very poor ground, vertically polarized loops do not provide much better low-angle radiation when compared to the horizontally polarized loops. They have the advantage of giving substantial rejection at high angles, however. Over good ground, Figure 5.14 shows that the vertically polarized loop will give up to 10 dB and more gain at low radiation angles as compared to the horizontally polarized loop, in addition to its high-angle rejection.

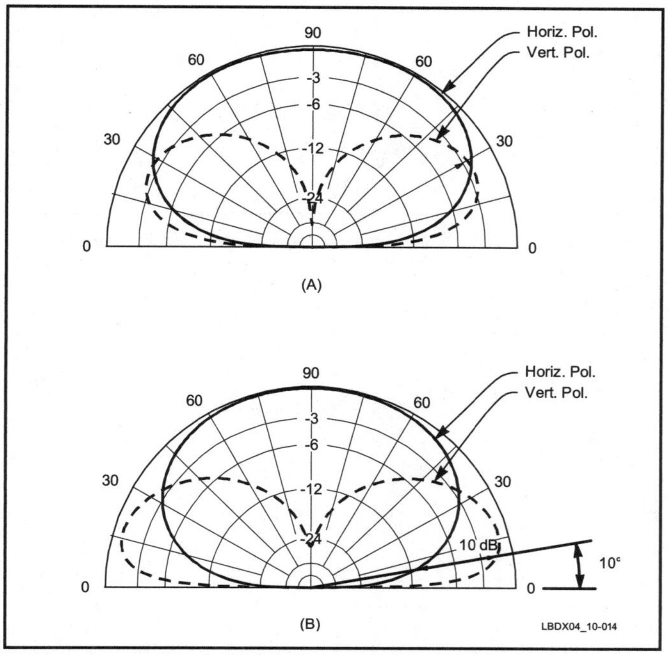

Figure 5.14 — Radiation patterns of vertically and horizontally polarized delta loops on the same dB scale. At A, over very poor ground, and at B, over very good ground. These patterns illustrate the tremendous importance of ground conductivity with vertically polarized antennas. Over better ground, the vertically polarized loop performs much better at low radiation angles, while over both good and poor ground the vertically polarized loop gives good discrimination against high-angle radiation. This is not the case for the horizontally polarized loop.

Feeding the Delta Loop

The feed point of the delta loop in free space is symmetrical. At high heights above ground the loop feed point is to be considered as symmetrical, especially when we feed the loop in the center of the bottom line (or at the apex), because of its full symmetry with respect to the ground.

Figure 5.15 shows the radiation resistance and reactance for both the horizontally and the vertically polarized equilateral delta loops as a function of height above ground. At low heights, when fed for vertical polarization, the feed point is to be considered as asymmetric, whereby the "cold" point is the point to which the "radials" are connected. The center conductor of a coax feed line goes to the sloping vertical section. Many users have, however, used (symmetric) open-wire line to feed the vertically polarized loop (for example, 450-Ω line).

Delta Loop Gain and Radiation Angle

Figure 5.16 shows the gain and the main-lobe radiation angle for the equilateral delta loop at different heights. The values were obtained by modeling a 3.8-MHz loop over average ground using *NEC*.

Cunningham, K6SE, investigated different configurations of single element loops for 160 meters, and came up with the results listed in **Table 5.1** (modeling done with *EZNEC* over good ground). These data correspond surprisingly well with those shown in Figure 5.16 (where the ground was average), which explains the slight difference in gain.

5.1.3 FEEDING LARGE LOOPS

Most practical 1 λ loops present a feed point impedance between 50 and 150 Ω, depending on the exact geometry and coupling to other antennas. Delta loops tend to have impedances at the low end of the range and quads somewhat higher. The shape of the loop and proximity to the ground will affect the feed point impedance.

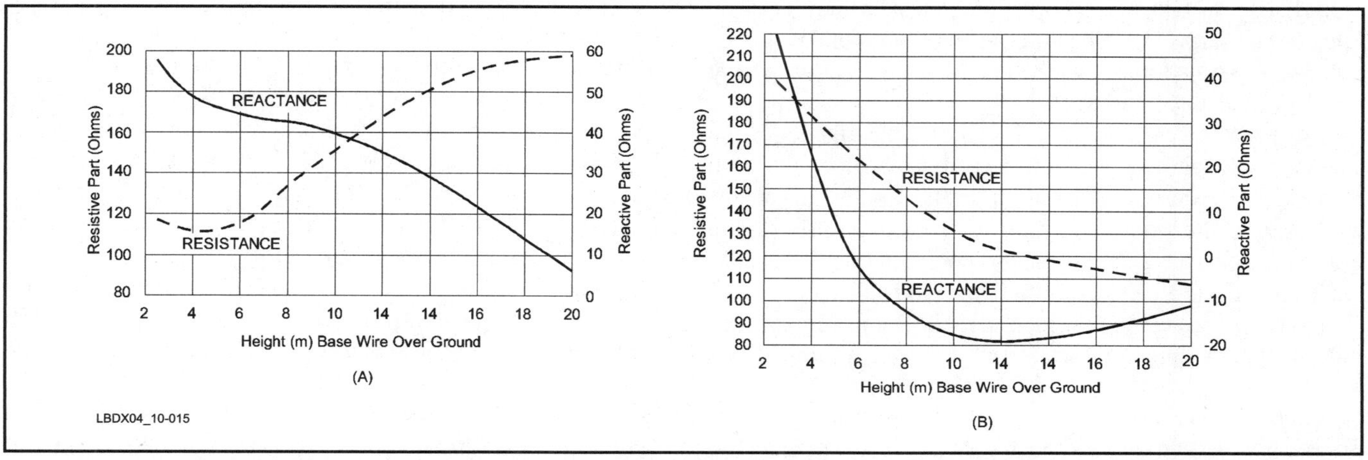

Figure 5.15 — Radiation resistance of (A) horizontally and (B) vertically polarized equilateral delta loops as a function of height above average ground. The delta loop was first dimensioned to be resonant in free space (reactance equals zero). Those dimensions were then used for calculating the impedance over real ground. Modeling was done at 3.75 MHz over good ground, using *NEC*.

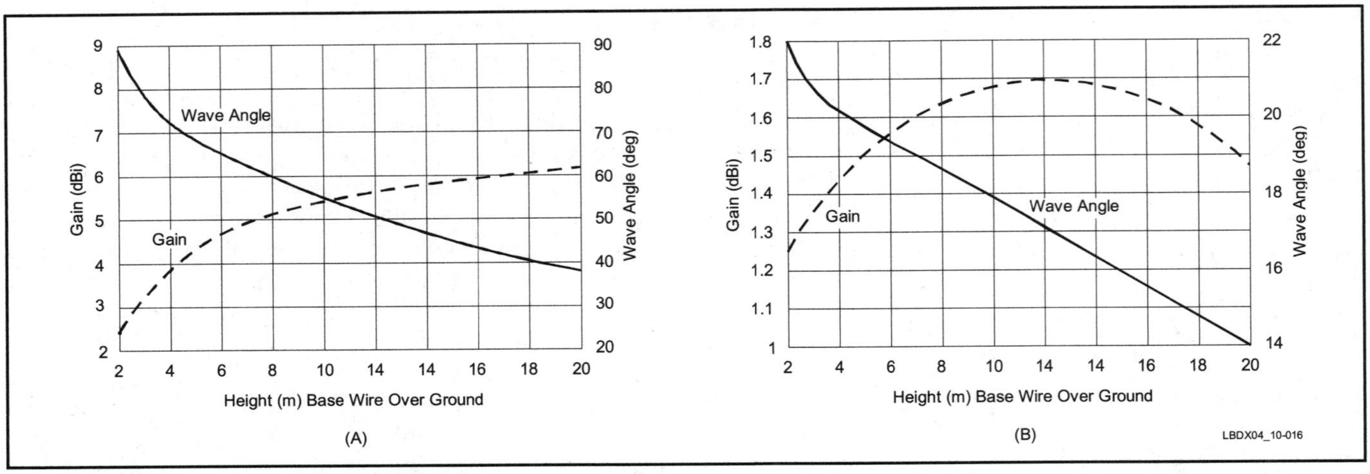

Figure 5.16 — Gain and radiation angle of (A) horizontally and (B) vertically polarized equilateral delta loops as a function of the height above ground. Modeling was done at 3.75 MHz over average ground, using *NEC*.

Table 5.1
Loop Antennas for 160 Meters

Description	*Feeding Method*	*Gain (dBi)*	*Elevation Angle (degrees)*
Diamond loop, bottom 2.5 meters high	Fed in side corner	2.15	18.0
Square loop, bottom 2.5 meters high	Fed in center of one vertical wire	2.06	20.5
Inverted equilateral delta loop (flat wire on top)	Fed λ/4 from bottom	1.91	20.9
Regular equilateral delta loop	Fed λ/4 from top	1.90	18.1

Measure the feed point impedance using a noise bridge or antenna analyzer connected directly to the antenna terminals. A section of feed line that is λ/2 long (or an integer multiple of λ/2) connected to the feed point will also allow direct measurement of feed point impedance if the feed point can't be reached directly.

If the impedance exceeds 50 to 70 Ω, a λ/4 feed line transformer can be used to reduce the feed point impedance to a more acceptable value (see the **Transmission Line System Techniques** chapter). If the impedance is much higher than 150 Ω, feeding via 450 Ω open-wire feeders may be warranted. Alternatively, you could use an unun (unbalanced-to-unbalanced) transformer, which can be made to cover a very wide range of impedance ratios.

To keep RF current from flowing on the outside of the coaxial feed line, use a balun or current choke at the loop feed point. RF current flowing on the feed point can distort the pattern of the loop and result in unnecessary noise pickup. For details on ununs, baluns, and common mode chokes see the **Transmission Line System Techniques** chapter.

It is important to consider that the loop's impedance will likely vary quite a bit from band to band. An impedance matching scheme such as a fixed-ratio transformer or tuned feed line sections is not likely to work well on multiple bands. To use a large loop on multiple bands, it is more practical to use a low-loss feed line (window or ladder line are recommended) connected to an adjustable impedance matching unit at a convenient location as described in the following section.

5.1.4 HORIZONTAL LOOPS

A large loop, installed horizontally over ground is an excellent multiband antenna. A 1 λ circumference loop installed at a height of λ/2 or lower has a radiation pattern similar to a λ/2 dipole at the same height — omnidirectional, high-angle radiation. As the frequency of operation increases the current distribution around the loop and the radiation pattern become more complex. The radiation lobes peak at lower elevation angles, generally approximating the angle of peak radiation for a dipole at the same electrical height.

The exact performance of the loop depends on shape, height, and frequency of use. Radiation patterns for a square, horizontal loop cut for 3.8 MHz at a height of 30 feet (about λ/8) over average ground are shown in **Figure 5.17**. On the fundamental, the pattern is essentially omnidirectional at high-angles, making it an excellent choice for regional communications using NVIS propagation. On the higher bands (patterns are shown for 14.2 and 28.3 MHz) the patterns break up into multiple lobes at lower elevation angles. In practice, the deep nulls are filled in to some degree by reflections from terrain and scatter propagation. See the **Multiband HF Antennas** chapter for examples of horizontal loops for the HF bands.

Feed point impedance on the 1 λ resonant frequency is approximately 100 Ω and rises to a few hundred ohms or higher at higher frequencies. Because of the varying feed point impedance, it is recommended that the antenna be fed with parallel conductor transmission line to reduce feed line

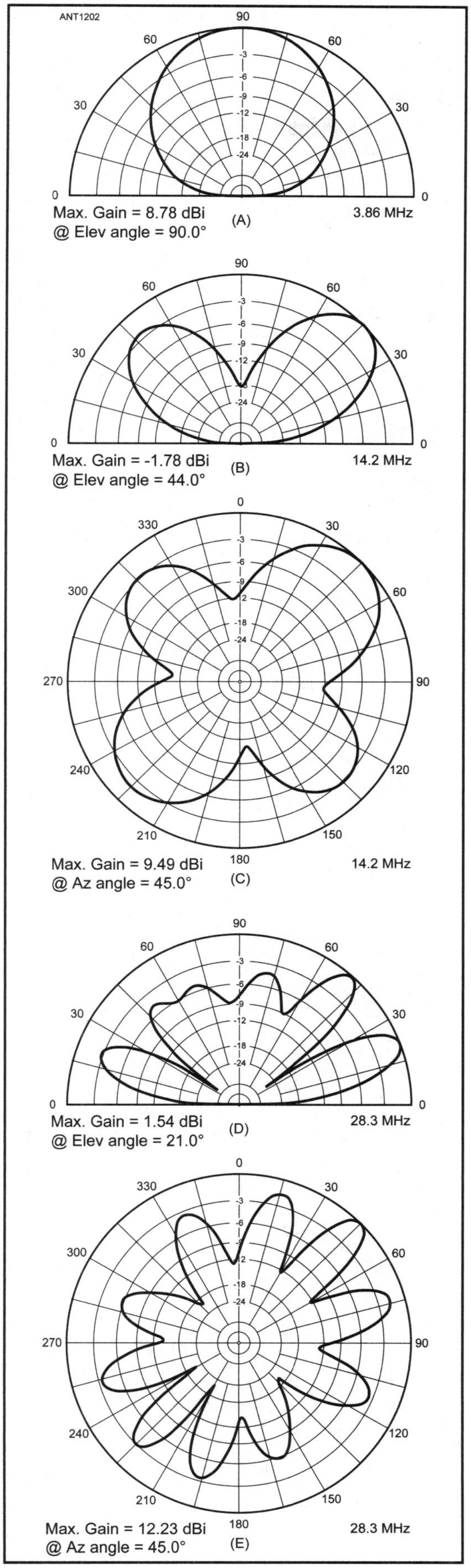

Figure 5.17 — Radiation patterns for a 1 λ square, horizontal loop cut for 3.8 MHz and installed at 30 feet above average ground. On the fundamental (A), the loop has an omnidirectional, high-angle pattern. At higher frequencies (B – 14.2 MHz, C – 28.3 MHz) the pattern breaks up into multiple lobes at lower elevation angles. NOTE: data to be included with each pattern is indicated by arrow.

loss. An impedance matching unit can then be used to convert whatever impedance is presented by the feed line to 50 Ω for coaxial cable.

5.1.5 HALF-WAVE LOOPS

The smallest size of "large" loop generally used is one having a conductor length of ½ λ. The conductor is usually formed into a square, as shown in **Figure 5.18**, making each side ⅛ λ long. When fed at the center of one side, the current flows in a closed loop as shown in Figure 5.18A. The current distribution is approximately the same as on a ½ λ wire, and so is a maximum at the center of the side opposite the terminals X-Y, and a minimum at the feed point. This current distribution causes the field strength to be a maximum in the plane of the loop and in the direction looking from the low-current side to the high-current side. (See the referenced article by Cebik for additional discussion of this configuration.)

If the side opposite the feed point is opened at the center as shown in Figure 5.18B (strictly speaking, it is then no longer a loop because it is no longer a closed circuit), the direction of current flow remains unchanged but the maximum current flow and lowest impedance occurs at the feed point. This reverses the direction of maximum radiation.

The radiation resistance at a current maximum (which is also the resistance at X-Y in Figure 5.18B) is on the order of

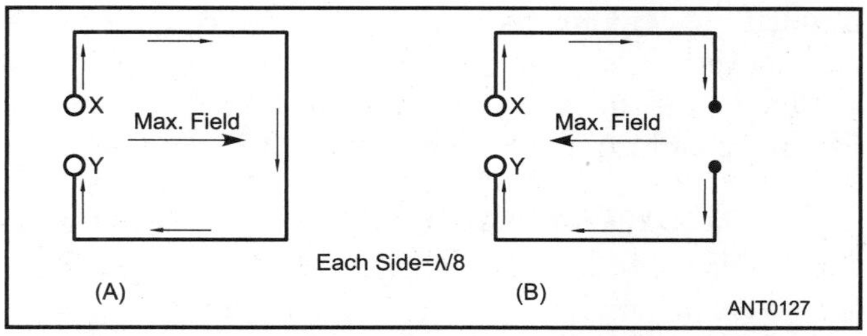

Figure 5.18 — Half-wave loops, consisting of a single turn having a total length of ½ λ.

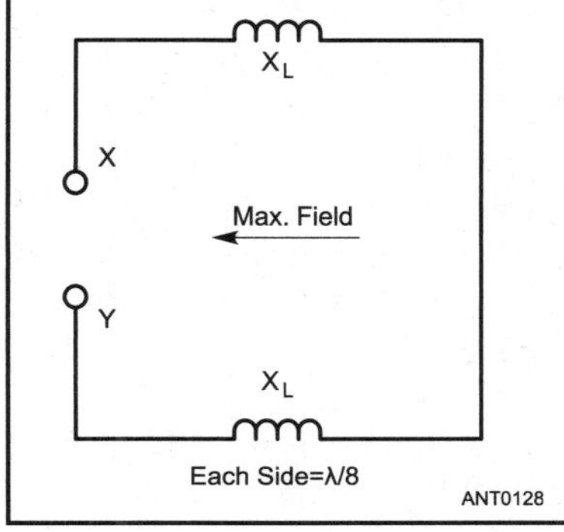

Figure 5.19 — Inductive loading in the sides of a ½-λ loop to increase the directivity and gain. Maximum radiation or response is in the plane of the loop, in the direction shown by the arrow.

50 Ω. The impedance at the feed point in Figure 5.18A is a few thousand ohms. This can be reduced by using two identical loops side by side with a few inches spacing between them and applying power between terminal X on one loop and terminal Y on the other.

Unlike a ½ λ dipole or a small loop, there is no direction in which the radiation from a loop of the type shown in Figure 5.18 is zero. There is appreciable radiation in the direction perpendicular to the plane of the loop, as well as to the "rear" — the opposite direction to the arrows shown. The front-to-back (F/B) ratio is approximately 4 to 6 dB. The small size and the shape of the directive pattern result in a loss of about 1 dB when the field strength in the optimum direction from such a loop is compared with the field from a ½ λ dipole in its optimum direction.

The ratio of the forward radiation to the backward radiation can be increased, and the field strength likewise increased at the same time to give a gain of about 1 dB over a dipole, by using inductive reactances to "load" the sides joining the front and back of the loop. This is shown in **Figure 5.19**. The reactances, which should have a value of approximately 360 Ω, decrease the current in the sides in which they are inserted and increase it in the side with the feed point. This increases the directivity and thus increases the efficiency of the loop as a radiator. Lossy coils can reduce this advantage greatly.

5.2 SMALL RECEIVING LOOPS

A "small" loop can be considered to be simply a rather large coil, and the current distribution in such a loop is the same as in a coil. That is, the current has the same phase and the same amplitude in every part of the loop. To meet this condition, the total length of conductor in the loop must not exceed about 0.085 λ. Loops with circumference up to 0.3 λ and intended for transmitting are described in the Small Transmitting Loops section.

The electrically small loop antenna has existed in various forms for many years. Amateur applications of the small loop include direction finding and low-noise directional receiving antennas for 3.5 MHz and below. Because the design of transmitting and receiving loops requires some different considerations, the two situations are examined separately, beginning with receiving loops in this section.

Applications of small loops are presented in the **Receiving and Direction-Finding Antennas** and the **Stealth and Limited-Space Antennas** chapters. Ferrite-core receiving loop antennas, such as the ferrite *loopstick* found in portable AM broadcast-band receivers, are discussed in the chapter on **Receiving and Direction-Finding Antennas**.

5.2.1 THE BASIC SMALL LOOP

A loop is considered electrically small when the current around the perimeter of the loop is in phase (i.e. assumed to be constant). This requires the total conductor length to be less than 0.085 λ. This constraint results in a very predictable figure-eight radiation pattern, shown in **Figure 5.20**. For greater circumferences, the current can no longer be treated as having a constant phase.

The simplest loop is a 1-turn untuned loop with a load connected to a pair of terminals located in the center of one of the sides, as shown in **Figure 5.21**. How its pattern is developed is easily pictured if we look at some "snapshots" of the antenna relative to a signal source. **Figure 5.22** shows a loop from above and the instantaneous received voltage wave. Note that points A and B of the loop are receiving the same instantaneous voltage. This means that no current will flow through the loop, because there is no current flow between points of equal potential. A similar analysis of **Figure 5.23**, with the loop turned 90° from the position represented in Figure 5.22, shows that this position of the loop provides maximum response. Figure 5.20 shows the ideal radiation pattern for a small loop.

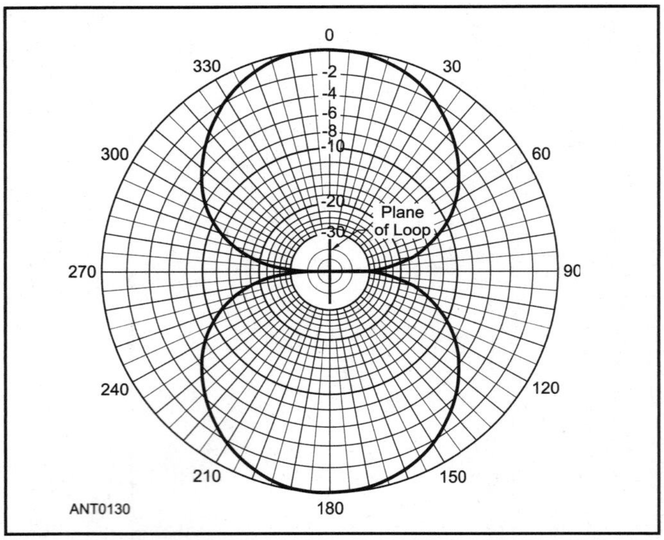

Figure 5.20 — Calculated small loop antenna radiation pattern.

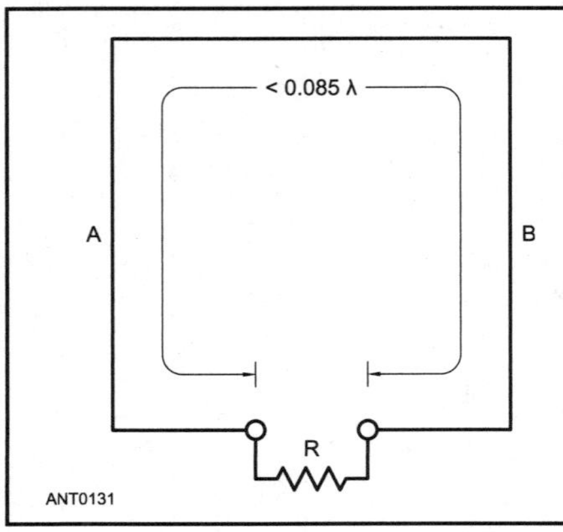

Figure 5.21 — Simple untuned small loop antenna.

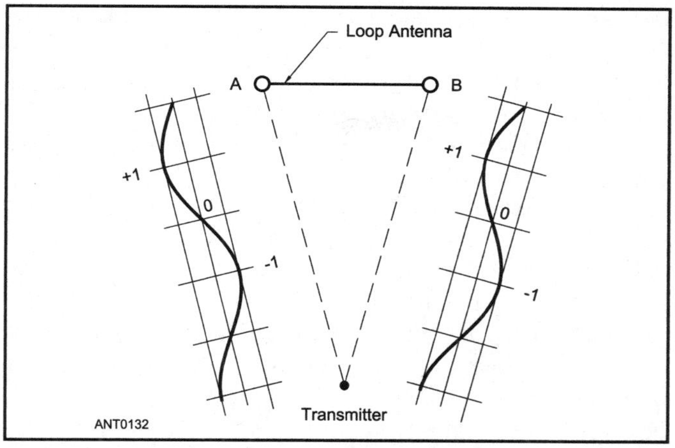

Figure 5.22 — Example of orientation of loop antenna that does not respond to a signal source (null in pattern).

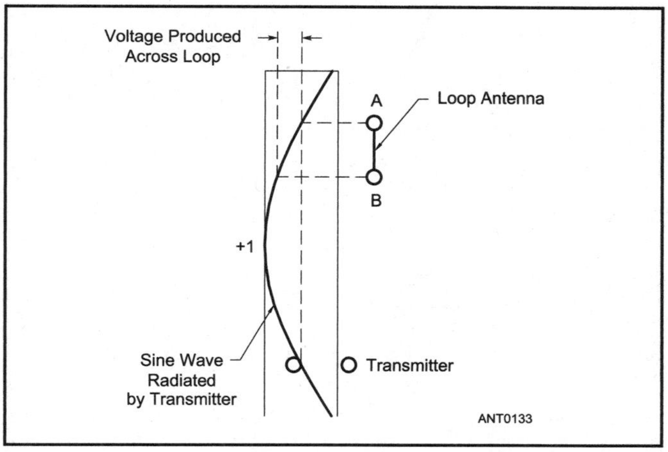

Figure 5.23 — Example of orientation of loop antenna for maximum response.

Table 5.2
Inductance Equations for Short Coils (Loop Antennas)

Triangle:

$$L\,(\mu H) = 0.006\,N^2\,s\left[\ln\left(\frac{1.1547\,s\,N}{(N+1)\,\ell}\right) + 0.65533 + \frac{0.1348\,(N+1)\,\ell}{s\,N}\right]$$

Square:

$$L\,(\mu H) = 0.008\,N^2\,s\left[\ln\left(\frac{1.4142\,s\,N}{(N+1)\,\ell}\right) + 0.37942 + \frac{0.3333\,(N+1)\,\ell}{s\,N}\right]$$

Hexagon:

$$L\,(\mu H) = 0.012\,N^2\,s\left[\ln\left(\frac{2\,s\,N}{(N+1)\,\ell}\right) + 0.65533 + \frac{0.1348\,(N+1)\,\ell}{s\,N}\right]$$

Octagon

$$L\,(\mu H) = 0.016\,N^2\,s\left[\ln\left(\frac{2.613\,s\,N}{(N+1)\,\ell}\right) + 0.75143 + \frac{0.07153\,(N+1)\,\ell}{s\,N}\right]$$

where
- N = number of turns
- s = side length in cm
- ℓ = coil length in cm

The small loop is insensitive to the electric field. The voltage across the loop terminals is given by

$$V = \frac{2\pi ANH\eta_0 \cos(\theta)}{\lambda} \qquad (1)$$

where
- V = voltage across the loop terminals
- A = area of loop in square meters
- N = number of turns in the loop
- H = RF magnetic field strength in amperes per meter
- η_0 = 376.73 Ω, the intrinsic impedance of free space
- θ = angle between the plane of the loop and the signal source (transmitting station)
- λ = wavelength of operation in meters

This equation comes from a term called *effective height*. The effective height refers to the height (length) of a vertical piece of wire above ground that would deliver the same voltage to the receiver. The equation for effective height is

$$h = \frac{2\pi NA}{\lambda} \qquad (2)$$

where h is in meters and the other terms are as for Eq 1.

A few minutes with a calculator will show that, with the constraints previously stated, the loop antenna will have a very small effective height. This means it will deliver a relatively small voltage to the receiver, even with a large transmitted signal.

Inductance of the Small Loop

The loop forms an inductor having a very small ratio of winding length to diameter. The equations for calculating inductance given in most radio handbooks assume that the inductor coil is longer than its diameter. However, F. W. Grover of the US National Bureau of Standards has provided equations for inductors of common cross-sectional shapes and small length-to-diameter ratios. (See the Bibliography at the end of this chapter.) Grover's equations are shown in **Table 5.2**. Their use will yield relatively accurate results which are easily worked out with a scientific calculator or PC.

5.2.2 TUNING THE SMALL LOOP

We can tune the loop by placing a capacitor across the antenna terminals. This causes a larger voltage to appear across the loop terminals because of the Q of the parallel resonant circuit that is formed with the loop inductance. The resulting voltage is that given by Eq 1 multiplied by the loaded Q of the resonant circuit. Loaded Q values of 100 or greater are easy to obtain with careful loop construction.

The value of a tuning capacitor to resonate a loop is easy to calculate from the standard resonance equations. The total tuning capacitance, however, must also include the value of distributed capacitance of the loop winding. This capacitance is caused by the slight voltage difference between adjacent turns of the coil. The distributed capacitance appears as a capacitance across the loop terminals in parallel with and adding to the tuning capacitor's value. Therefore, when determining the value of the tuning capacitor, the distributed capacitance must be subtracted from the total capacitance required to resonate the loop. The distributed capacitance also determines the highest frequency at which a particular loop can be used, because it is the minimum capacitance obtainable.

As with all other capacitances, the value of the distributed capacitance is based on the physical dimensions of the coil. An exact mathematical analysis of its value is a complex problem. A simple approximation is given by Medhurst (see Bibliography) as:

Table 5.3
Values of the Constant H for Distributed Capacitance

Length to Diameter Ratio	*H*
0.10	0.96
0.15	0.79
0.20	0.78
0.25	0.64
0.30	0.60
0.35	0.57
0.40	0.54
0.50	0.50
1.00	0.46

$$C = HD \quad (3)$$

where

C = distributed capacitance in pF

H = a constant related to the length-to-diameter ratio of the coil (**Table 5.3** gives H values for length-to-diameter ratios typical of receiving loops.)

D = diameter of the winding in cm

Medhurst's work was with coils of round cross section. For loops of square cross section the distributed capacitance is given by Bramslev (see Bibliography) as

$$C = 60S \quad (4)$$

where

C = the distributed capacitance in pF

S = the length of the side in meters

If you convert the length in this equation to centimeters, you will find Bramslev's equation gives results in the same order of magnitude as Medhurst's equation.

5.2.3 ELECTROSTATICALLY SHIELDED LOOPS

Many receiving loop antennas include an electrostatic shield. This shield generally takes the form of a tube around the winding, made of a conductive but nonmagnetic material (such as copper or aluminum). Its purpose is to maintain loop balance with respect to ground, by forcing the capacitance between all portions of the loop and ground to be identical. This is illustrated in **Figure 5.24**. It is necessary to maintain electrical loop balance to eliminate what is referred to as the *antenna effect*. When the antenna becomes unbalanced it appears to act partially as a small vertical antenna. This vertical pattern gets superimposed on the ideal figure-eight pattern, distorting the pattern and filling in the nulls. The type of pattern that results is shown in **Figure 5.25**. Since the null is used to reject noise or interference, it is important to preserve balance in the loop's construction for best performance.

Adding the shield has the effect of reducing the loop's terminal voltage somewhat, but this loss is generally offset by the increase in null depth of the loops. Proper balance of the loop antenna requires that the load on the loop also be balanced. This is usually accomplished by use of a balun or a balanced input preamplifier.

One important point regarding the shield is that it cannot form a continuous electrical path around the loop perimeter, or it will appear as a shorted coil turn. Usually the insulated break is located opposite the feed point to maintain symmetry. (The loop conductor itself is not broken.) Another point to be considered is that the shield should have a much larger cross-sectional diameter than the loop conductor, or it will lower the Q of the loop.

Various construction techniques have been used in making shielded loops. Genaille located his loop winding inside aluminum conduit, while True constructed an aluminum shield can around his winding. Others have used pieces of semi-flexible hard line to form a loop, using the outer

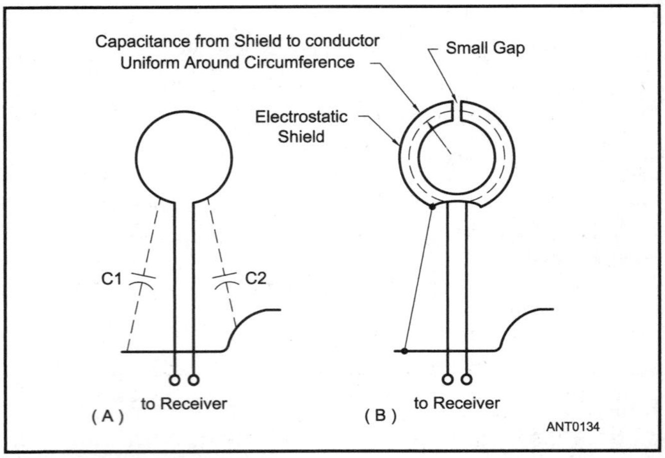

Figure 5.24 — At A, the loop is unbalanced by capacitance to its surroundings. At B, the use of an electrostatic shield overcomes this effect.

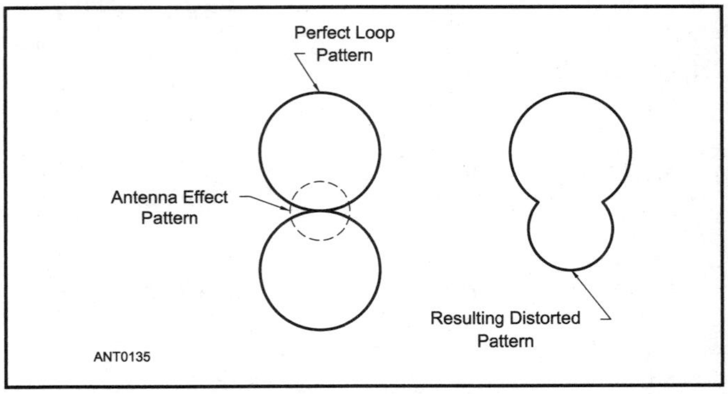

Figure 5.25 — Distortion in loop pattern resulting from antenna effect.

conductor as a shield. DeMaw used flexible coax with the shield broken at the center of the loop conductor in a multi-turn loop for 1.8 MHz. Goldman uses another shielding method for broadcast receiver loops. His shield is in the form of a cylindrical "barrel" made of hardware cloth, with the loop in its center. (See Bibliography for articles by DeMaw and Goldman.) All these methods provide sufficient shielding to maintain the balance.

It is important to consider the effect of the shield configuration on antenna Q. A short letter by N1DM in *QEX* (July/Aug 1998, see Bibliography) discusses the Q of a loop antenna with a U-type shield versus a full box shield. His data shows between 54% and 89% degradation of Q for the full box case on an otherwise identical antenna configuration.

The extra capacitance of coaxial cable (flexible or hardline) used to construct a shielded loop will limit the loop's higher frequency tuning range. Those designing a loop of this type should consider this when selecting the loop inductance. This parasitic capacitance must be taken into account to obtain the desired higher frequency tuning point.

It is possible, as Nelson shows, to construct an unshielded loop with good nulls (60 dB or better) but only if the loop circumference is very small (less than 0.0005λ) and by paying great attention to symmetry.

5.2.4 SMALL LOOP LOSS FACTORS

Loop losses include several factors: (1) the Q of the loop conductor by itself, (2) the effect of the load, (3) the effect of the electrostatic shield, and (4) the Q of the tuning capacitor. The major loss factor is the resistance of the loop conductor. The ac resistance of the conductor caused by skin effect is the major consideration. For a copper conductor, ac resistance is:

$$R_{ac} = \frac{0.996 \times 10^{-6} \sqrt{f}}{d} \qquad (5)$$

where

R_{ac} = ac resistance in ohms per foot
f = frequency in Hz
d = conductor diameter in inches

Inductor Q is then the reactance of the inductor (X_L = 2pfL) divided by the ac resistance. Ac resistance for other metals can be obtained by multiplying R_{ac} by the resistance of the metal relative to that of copper. (Multi-turn loops also experience loss from the proximity effect described later in this section.)

Improvement in Q can be obtained in some cases by the use of Litz wire (short for Litzendraht). Litz wire consists of strands of individual insulated wires that are woven into bundles in such a manner that each conductor occupies each location in the bundle with equal frequency. Litz wire has a reduced ac resistance when compared to an equivalent cross section solid or stranded wire, taking into account the skin depth of conductors as frequency increases.

Litz wire's improvement in ac resistance is due to the fact that the insulated individual strands result in more area of the total cross section of the conductor being in the skin depth region than for an equivalent diameter solid or stranded wire. (Stranded wire at ac acts the same as a solid wire of the same outside diameter.) Over 60% of the ac current is in this skin depth region. Therefore, skin depth is more important to the calculation of ac resistance than the total conductor diameter.

Figure 5.26 shows an example of the skin depth of a solid conductor with radius R and a piece of Litz wire with an equivalent radius R. You can see that the cross-sectional area of the current carrying skin effect region is double that of the solid wire. Litz wire is available in many configurations and the determining factor for the selection of a particular Litz wire starts with determining the optimum diameter of the individual insulated wire strands used in the construction of the particular cable. **Table 5.4** gives the values of optimum wire size based on frequency of use.

Properly-sized Litz wire results in improved Q over solid or stranded wire of equivalent size, up to about 2.8 MHz. Above 2.8 MHz other effects quickly reduce the advantage of Litz wire. When using Litz wire it is important to realize that the ends of the Litz wire must be properly prepared so that all the strands of the wire are soldered to the connections of the capacitor and output connector. For those interested in the use of Litz wire the most common modern application is in high-efficiency transformers and inductors in the kHz and low MHz range. Technical journals on transformer and magnetic design still present articles on the use of Litz wire with some regularity.

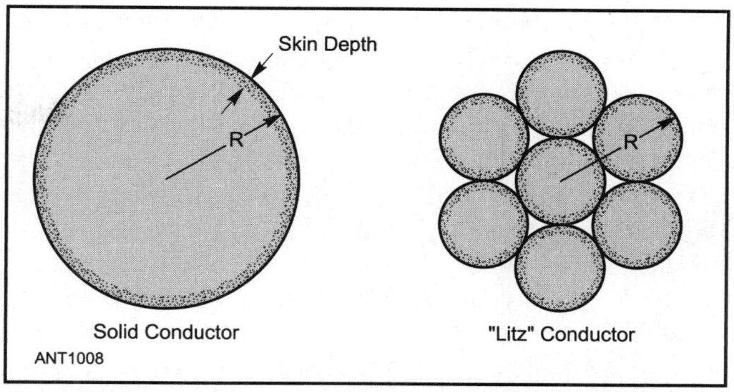

Figure 5.26 — Comparison of skin depth between conventional (A) and Litz wire (B).

Table 5.4
Optimum Sizes of Individual Wires Used in Litz Wire

Frequency Range	*Optimum AWG*
60 Hz to 1 kHz	28
1 kHz to 10 kHz	30
10 kHz to 20 kHz	33
20 kHz to 50 kHz	36
50 kHz to 100 kHz	38
100 kHz to 200 kHz	40
200 kHz to 350 kHz	42
350 kHz to 850 kHz	44
850 kHz to 1.4 MHz	46
1.4 MHz to 2.8 MHz	48

(After Table 2 from New England Wire Technologies "Litz Wire Technical Information")

The Q of the tuned circuit of the loop antenna is also determined by the Q of the capacitors used to resonate it. In the case of air variables or dipped micas typically used this is not usually a problem. But if variable-capacitance diodes are used to remotely tune the loop, pay particular attention to the manufacturer's specification for Q of the diode at the frequency of operation. The tuning diodes can have a significant effect on circuit Q.

Now we consider the effect of load impedance on loop Q. In the case of a directly coupled loop (as in Figure 5.21), the load is connected directly across the loop terminals, causing it to be treated as a parallel resistance in a parallel-tuned RLC circuit. Obviously, if the load is of a low value, the Q of the loop will be low. A simple way to correct this is to use a transformer to step up the load impedance that appears across the loop terminals. In fact, if we make this transformer a balun, it also allows us to use our unbalanced receivers with the loop and maintain loop symmetry. Another solution is to use what is referred to as an inductively coupled loop, such as DeMaw's four-turn electrostatically shielded loop. A one-turn link is connected to the receiver. This turn is wound with the four-turn loop. In effect, this builds the transformer into the antenna.

Another solution to the problem of load impedance on loop Q is to use an active preamplifier with balanced input and unbalanced output. This method also has the advantage of amplifying the low-level output voltage of the loop to where it can be used with a receiver of even mediocre sensitivity.

In recent years, there has been a significant amount of technical interest in this area driven by low-band DXers and AM band DXers. They have discovered that one of the critical issues to maximize performance of a loop/preamp combination is the dynamic range of the preamp. A poorly designed preamp may overload from local broadcast stations or have a poor noise figure itself which limits the ultimate performance observed with the loop antenna. Chris Trask, N7ZWY, has covered this in some detail with regards to the shortwave bands. Trask's excellent two-part article in the July/Aug and Sep/Oct 2003 issues of *QEX* (see the Bibliography and the articles included with this book's downloadable supplemental content) includes a discussion of preamp requirements in Part 2. His design resulted in a noise figure of less than 2 dB from 6 to 14 MHz while obtaining a third order intercept of +5 dBm. The interested experimenter should consult that article.

In fact, the Q of the loop when used with a balanced preamplifier having high input impedance may be so high as to be unusable in certain applications. An example of this situation would occur where a loop is being used to receive a 5 kHz wide AM signal at a frequency where the bandwidth of the loop is only 1.5 kHz. In this case the detected audio might be very distorted. The solution to this is to connect a loading resistor across the loop terminals to reduce Q and match the antennas bandwidth to the signal. The chapter **Receiving and Direction-Finding Antennas** also contains information about preamplifiers for use with loop antennas.

Proximity Loss

In the case of multi-turn loops there is an additional loss related to a term called *proximity effect*. The proximity effect occurs in cases where the turns are closely spaced (such as being spaced one wire diameter apart). As these current-carrying conductors are brought close to each other, the current density around the circumference of each conductor is redistributed. The result is that more current per square meter is flowing at the surfaces adjacent to other conductors. This means that the loss is higher than a simple skin-effect analysis would indicate, because the current is bunched so it flows through a smaller cross section of the conductor than if the other turns were not present.

As the efficiency of a loop approaches 90%, the proximity effect is less serious. But unfortunately, the less efficient the loop, the worse the effect. For example, an 8-turn transmitting loop with an efficiency of 10% (calculated by the skin-effect method) actually only has an efficiency of 3% because of the additional losses introduced by the proximity effect. It is for this reason that the transmitting loop is typically just one turn. The higher inductance of multi-turn loops also limits the higher frequency range unless the circumference is very small. This generally limits the use of multi-turn loops to receiving applications.

If you are contemplating construction of a multi-turn transmitting loop, you might want to consider spreading the conductors apart to reduce this effect. G. S. Smith includes graphs that detail this effect in his 1972 IEEE paper and Trask examined the details of this loss for receiving antennas and recommends spacing turns at least five wire diameters to reduce this effect. His recommendation also applies to the transmitting variety of the loop antenna.

5.2.5 USING SMALL TUNED LOOPS

Most amateur receiving loops are of the tuned variety, consisting of one or more turns. You can use a small tuned loop antenna to improve reception under certain conditions, especially at the lower amateur frequencies. This is particularly true when high levels of man-made noise are prevalent, when harmonic energy from a nearby AM broadcast station falls in the band, or when interference is created by a strong amateur signal in the immediate area. A properly constructed and tuned small loop will exhibit approximately 30 dB of front-to-side response, the minimum response being at right angles to the plane of the loop. Therefore, noise and interference can be reduced significantly or completely nulled out, by rotating the loop so that it is sideways to the noise or interference source.

Generally speaking, small balanced loops are far less responsive to man-made noise than are the larger antennas used for transmitting and receiving. But a trade-off in performance must be accepted when using the loop, for the strength of received signals will be 10 or 15 dB less than when using a full-size resonant antenna. This condition is not a handicap on 1.8 or 3.5 MHz, provided the station receiver has normal sensitivity and overall gain. Adding a preamp may increase signal level but also re-introduces the possibility of overload and intermodulation.

Loop Selectivity

The loop's narrow frequency response can also become an advantage in rejecting unwanted signals. Not only are out-of-band signals rejected, but unwanted signals within an amateur band can also be attenuated by the loop's narrow bandwidth.

Consider a situation where the inherent selectivity due to the loop's frequency response is helpful. Assume we have a loop with a loaded Q of 100 at 1.805 MHz. While listening to a DX station on 1.805 MHz we are suffering strong interference from a local station 10 kHz away. Switching from a dipole to a small loop will reduce the strength of the off-frequency signal by 6 dB (approximately one S unit) compared to the DX station. This, in effect, increases the receiver's dynamic range. In fact, that farther off-frequency the interfering station is, the greater the attenuation.

Interfering Signal Rejection

Another use of the tuned loop is by using the nulls in its pattern to reject on-frequency (or slightly off-frequency) interference. For example, say we are working a DX station to the north, and another local station to our west is engaged in a contact is just 1 kHz away. We can simply rotate our loop to aim its null to the west, and now the DX station should be readable while the local will be knocked down by several tens of dB. This is quite a noticeable difference.

Of course, this method of nulling will be effective only if the interfering station and the desired station are not in the same direction (or in exact opposite directions) from our location. If the two stations are in the same direction, both stations would be in the null. Luckily the nulls are very sharp, so as long as the station directions are different by at least 10°, using the loop null will be helpful in reducing interference.

Reducing Noise

A similar use of the nulling capability is to eliminate local noise interference, such as that from a neighbor's house or other nearby noise source. By aiming the null at the noise source, the noise should be greatly reduced. It is important to realize that the loop will only reject noise or interference in one direction at a time. Noise from multiple directions, as is common from power lines and in urban or suburban locations, will only be partially rejected.

The noise from approaching or regional storms (with attendant atmospheric noise) could be reduced considerably by rotating the loop nulls away from the location of the storm. If the storm is sufficiently distant, the noise may be received as sky-wave signals as discussed in the next section.

Propagation Effects on Null Depth

After building a balanced loop you may find it does not approach the theoretical performance in the null depth. Small loops oriented vertically do not exhibit meaningful directivity when receiving sky-wave signals.

When mounted vertically, the loop's directivity relates primarily to ground-wave signals since the nulls are in the horizontal plane. This is a feature in disguise, for when

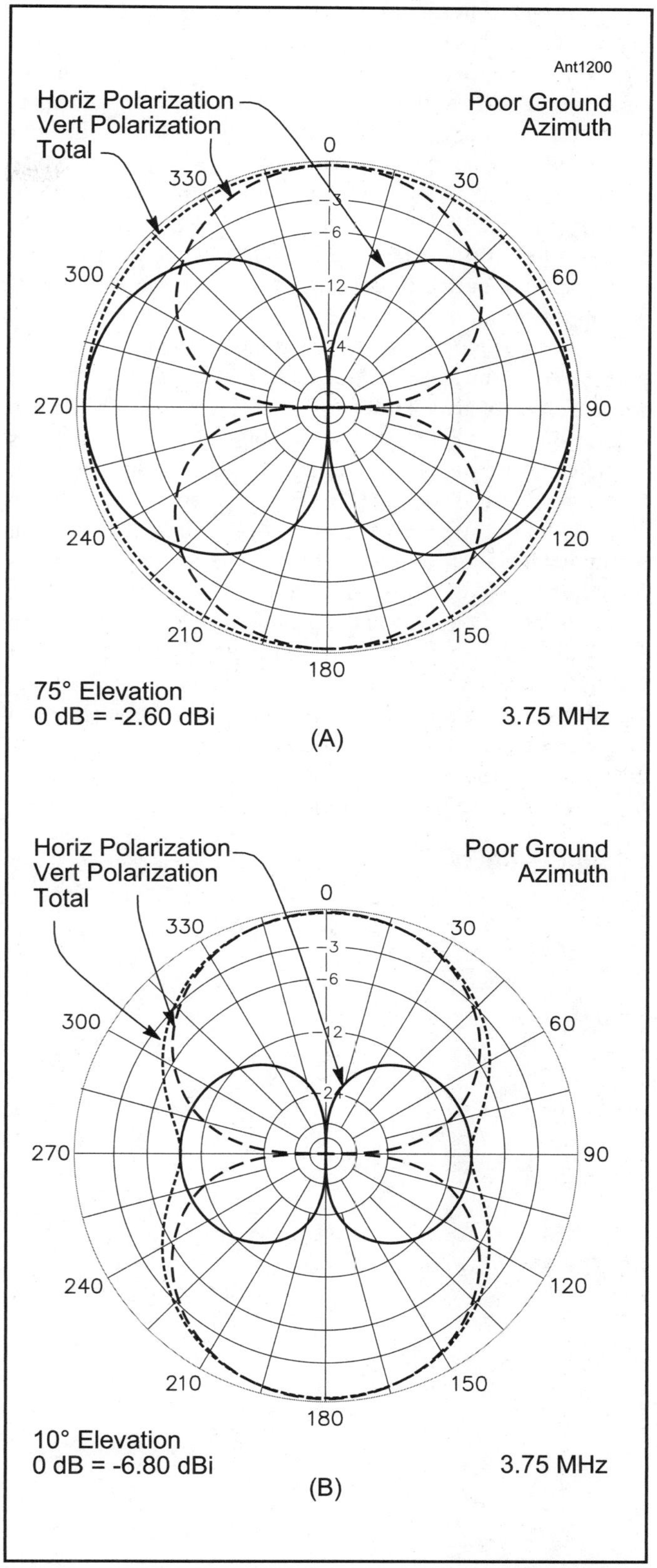

Figure 5.27 — The total azimuthal pattern for a vertically-oriented (along 0° and 180° axis) 3.4 meter diameter loop mounted with its center 2.5 meters over poor ground (3 mS/m conductivity and dielectric constant of 13). The total pattern for an elevation angle of 75° (A) and 10° (B). See the Bibliography entry for Belrose from Nov 1993 *QST* for the full article.

nulling out local noise or interference, one is still able to copy sky-wave signals from any direction.

Nulls have their full effect only when the signal is arriving perpendicular to the axis of rotation of the loop. At incidence angles other than perpendicular, the position and depth of the nulls deteriorate. Bond explained this issue in his book on direction finding in 1944 along with the math to calculate the performance. (See the Bibliography) The problem can be even further influenced by the fact that if the loop is situated over less than perfectly conductive ground, the wave front will appear to tilt or bend.

Tilting the loop away from vertical may improve performance under some propagation conditions, to account for the vertical angle of arrival. **Figure 5.27** illustrates the difference in total antenna response at low and high elevation angles for a small transmitting loop over real ground, typical of small receiving loops as well. (The 1993 *QST* article by Belrose listed in the Bibliography is included in the downloadable set of supplemental articles.) The high-angle response is nearly omnidirectional, while the low-angle response shows the pattern nulls at right angles to the plane of the loop.

Another cause of apparent poor performance in the null depth can be from polarization error. If the polarization of the signal is not completely linear, the nulls will not be sharp. In fact, for circularly polarized signals, the loop might appear to have almost no nulls. Propagation effects are discussed further in the **Receiving and Direction-Finding Antennas** chapter.

Siting Effects on the Loop

The location of the loop has an influence on its performance that at times may become quite noticeable. For ideal performance the loop should be located outdoors and clear of any large conductors, such as metallic downspouts and towers. A VLF loop, when mounted this way, will show good sharp nulls spaced 180° apart if the loop is well balanced.

Most hams locate their loop antennas near their operating position. If you choose to locate a small loop indoors, its performance may show nulls of less than the expected depth, and some skewing of the pattern. For precision direction finding there may be some errors associated with wiring, plumbing, and other metallic construction members in the building. Also, a strong local signal may be reradiated from the surrounding conductors so that it cannot be nulled with any positioning of the loop. There appears to be no known method of curing this type of problem. All this should not discourage you from locating a loop indoors; this information is presented here only to give you an idea of some pitfalls. Many hams have reported excellent results with indoor mounted loops, in spite of some of the problems.

Locating a receiving loop in the field of a transmitting antenna may cause a large voltage to appear at the receiver antenna terminals. This may be sufficient to destroy sensitive RF amplifier transistors or front-end protection diodes. This can be solved by disconnecting your loop from the receiver or shorting it during transmit periods. This can obviously be done automatically with a relay that operates when the transmitter is activated, controlled by a PTT or amplifier relay signal.

5.3 SMALL TRANSMITTING LOOPS

This section addresses small loops with a physical circumference of less than 0.3 λ that are used for both transmitting and receiving. As a consequence of their relatively large size (compared to a very small receiving loop), transmitting loops have a non-uniform current distribution along their circumference. This leads to some performance changes from the small receiving loops discussed in the preceding section.

While there are several practical loop designs, this section is primarily concerned with the popular gap-resonated loop designs that are fed with a small coupling loop inside the main loop. The loop is generally tuned with a variable capacitor across a gap in the loop conductor.

The analysis presents expressions for the loop impedance and the effects of the secondary feeding loop. Formulas for the loop current and loop impedance are given which lead to an accurate determination of close-near-fields and far field null depths for loops with circumference up to 0.3 λ. Details are also provided about the loop near fields and far-field null filling that are a direct result of including the non-uniform loop current. The material also covers how loop currents can couple to the coaxial feed line shield, and also to the ground. Additional recent articles are included in the Bibliography, as well.

Amateurs using small transmitting loops should also be cautious about RF exposure from high field strengths near the antenna. The antenna's high Q means that a lot of energy is present near the antenna, even at low power. DeNeef (see the Bibliography) used *NEC* to model and analyze fields from a small loop to determine the minimum compliance distances for a 1.0 meter loop at 7, 14, 18, 21, and 28 MHz using power levels of 10, 100, and 400 watts. The ICNIRP distances calculated in **Table 5.5** are more conservative than the IEEE standards used by the FCC, but not dramatically. (ICNIRP, or International Commission on Non-Ionizing Radiation Protection, standards use the terms "occupational" and "general public" where the IEEE uses "controlled" and "uncontrolled," respectively.) Because these loops are often used in portable operation and close to living areas, careful attention should be paid to ensuring RF exposure limits are not exceeded and that people cannot inadvertently get too close to the antenna.

Table 5.5
Minimum Compliance Distances from Small (1.0 m diameter) Transmitting Loops

Freq (MHz)	*Controlled Distance (m)*	*Uncontrolled Distance (m)*
Power = 10 watts		
7	2.1	2.9
14	2.1	2.9
18	1.9	2.7
21	1.8	2.5
28	1.5	2.1
Power = 100 watts		
7	3.3	4.3
14	3.4	4.7
18	3.1	4.4
21	2.9	4.2
28	2.5	3.9*
Power = 400 watts		
7	4.2	5.7
14	4.5	6.5
18	4.2	6.9*
21	4.0	7.1*
28	3.7*	7.3*

** - Electric field limit*

UK ICNIRP compliance distances from "Safety distances for small HF loop antennas," AE7PD, Radcom, June 2017, pages 46 and 47.

Evolution of Small Transmitting Loops

The small gap-resonated circular loop antenna with a circumference of less than 0.3 λ has received much attention for use on HF since John H. Dunlavy, Jr. (see the Bibliography) patented his efficient small loop that can be tuned over wide bandwidths. The now-expired patent spawned a multitude of homebrew loops and several commercial products aimed at hams.

Loop studies and analyses date back more than a century to the earliest days of radio. The recent loop antennas theme issue of *QEX* (see the Bibliography) features articles from several authors who investigate the patterns, efficiency, matching, coupling to ground, and other aspects of small HF gap-resonated loops.

In the March 1968 *QST*, Lew McCoy, W1ICP, introduced the so-called "Army Loop" to radio amateurs. This was an amateur version of a loop designed for portable use by Patterson of the US Army and described in 1967. The Army Loop is diagrammed in **Figure 5.28A**, showing that this is a parallel tuned circuit fed by a tapped-capacitance impedance-matching network. As shown in the figure, the loop does not illustrate the best low-loss construction practices and is included here only in reference to the loop antenna's history with amateurs.

The Hart "high-efficiency" loop was introduced in the June 1986 *QST* by Ted Hart, W5QJR. It is shown schematically in Figure 5.28B and has the series-tuning capacitor separate from the matching network. The Hart matching network is basically a form of gamma match.

The most popular design today is a smaller loop connected to the transmission line to couple into the larger transmitting loop as shown in Figure 5.28C. In addition, Steve Yates, AA5TB, has published a website (**www.aa5tb.com/loop.html**) with a great deal of information on these small antennas and links to many designs.

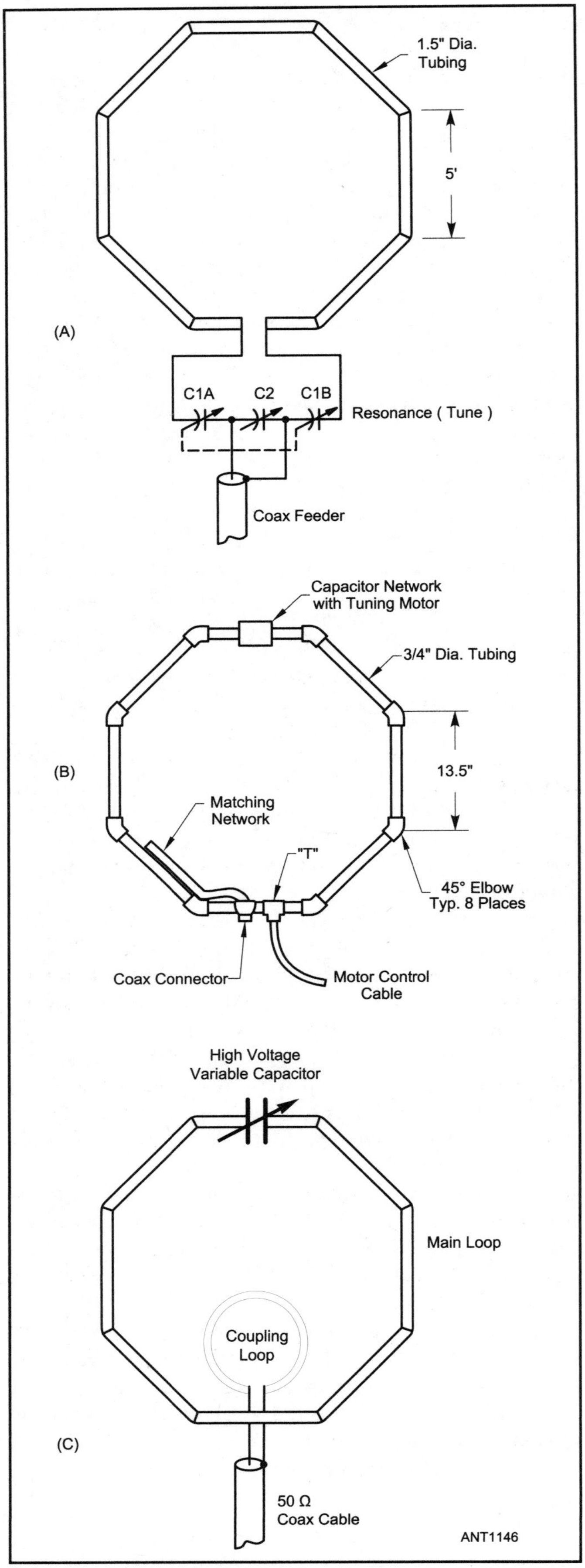

Figure 5.28 — At A, a simplified diagram of the Army Loop. At B, the W5QJR loop. At C, using a smaller loop connected to the transmission line to couple into the larger transmitting loop.

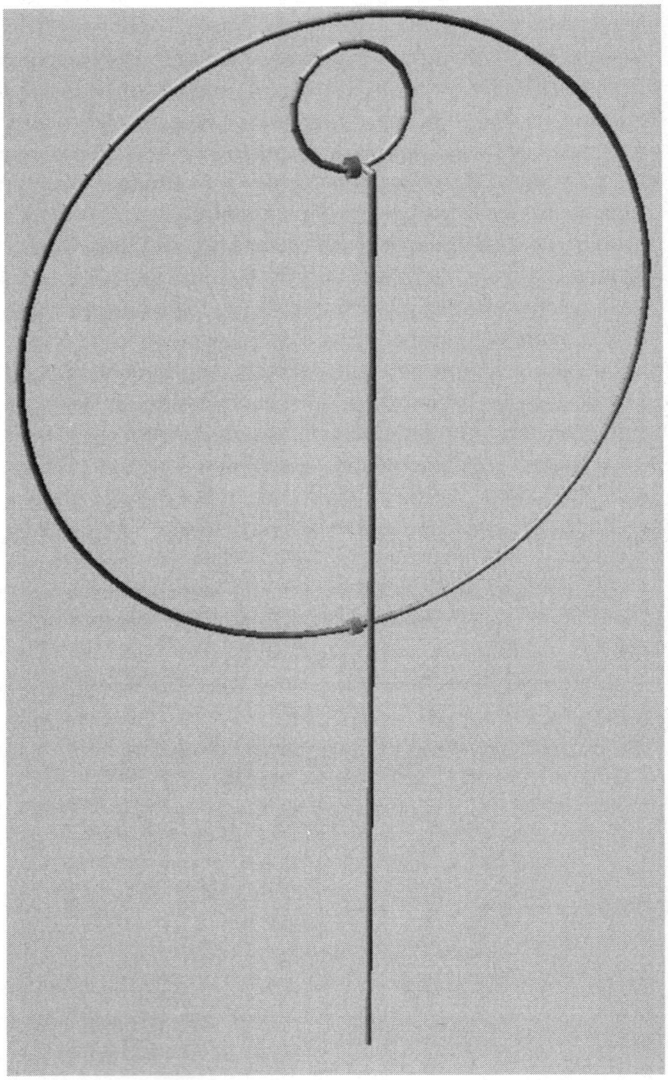

Figure 5.29 — The electrically small HF loop includes a primary loop and a secondary feeding loop in slightly displaced parallel planes, so that the feeding cable does not touch the bottom of the primary loop. A resonating capacitor connects across a gap at the bottom of the primary loop.

5.3.1 LOOP CURRENT

Figure 5.29 shows the circular loop geometry rendered in *4nec2* software. In their *QEX* article, K. Siwiak, KE4PT and R. Quick, W4RQ studied the effect of current variation on loops up to 0.3 λ in circumference. (See the Bibliography and the article is included in the downloadable supplemental material for this book.) In their article, the primary loop radius is b = 0.4534 m (a loop diameter of 3 ft), the loop conductor radius is a = 0.00406 m, the angular extent along the loop circumferences is ϕ, with the loop gap located at ϕ = 0. The resonating capacitor, with a Q_c = 2400 in the model, connects across the gap at the bottom of the primary loop. The secondary feeding loop radius is b_2 = 0.077 m (diameter of 6 inches) and the conductor radius is a_2= 0.002 m. A coaxial cable feed line connects across a gap at the bottom of the smaller secondary loop. The loop centers are displaced by 0.343 m. The length of the coax feed line can be varied to study the effect on the common mode current coupling to the shield of the feeding coax cable.

The Dunlavy Loop Patent

John Dunlavy revealed in his US patent 3,588,905 that a one-turn primary loop antenna having a circumference of less than three-eighths of a wavelength and interrupted along its length by a gap, with a tuning capacitor connected across the gap, can be tuned over a wide tuning range. A single-turn secondary loop, much smaller than the primary loop, is inductively coupled to the primary loop. Both loops are in the same or parallel planes. The secondary loop diameter is selected to bear an optimum relationship to the diameter of the primary loop so that variation in feed impedance is minimized over the band of operation. A low-impedance transmission line (50 Ω) connects to the terminals of the secondary loop.

Loop Current Density

Unlike the small receiving loops discussed previously, the current around the loop is not a constant (I_0), but varies around the loop,

$$I(\phi) = I_o \left\{1 - 2C_\lambda{}^2 \cos(\phi)\right\} \quad (6)$$

where C_λ is the loop circumference in wavelengths and ϕ is the angular position around the loop. The full description of loop current is a Fourier series. Eq 6 is an abbreviated result, and the detailed equations are in the original *QEX* article by Siwiak and Quick (see Bibliography).

The current's amplitude variation depends solely on the loop circumference in wavelengths. The bigger the loop, the more current varies around the loop. **Figure 5.30** shows the loop current for our loop at 7, 14, and 30 MHz, where C_λ is 0.067, 0.133, and 0.285 λ respectively. The loop current Eq 6 is valid for $C_\lambda < 0.3$, and is used to solve for the loop fields in classical fashion.

5.3.2 LOOP IMPEDANCE AND Q

The transmitting loop is treated as a parallel-tuned circuit with a large inductor acting as the radiator. Calculation of the loop inductance may be carried out with the approximate equations in Table 5.2. Avoid equations for long solenoids found in most texts. Other fundamental equations for transmitting loops are given in **Table 5.6.**

Loop Radiation Resistance

The approximate radiation resistance of a loop is given in Table 5.6. The radiation resistance of a small transmitting loop is usually very small. For example, a 1-meter diameter, single-turn circular loop has a radius of 0.5 meters and an enclosed area of $\pi \times 0.5^2 = 0.785$ m². Operated at 14.0 MHz, the free-space wavelength is 21.4 meters and this

Figure 5.30 — Loop currents at 7, 14, and 30 MHz along the loop circumference.

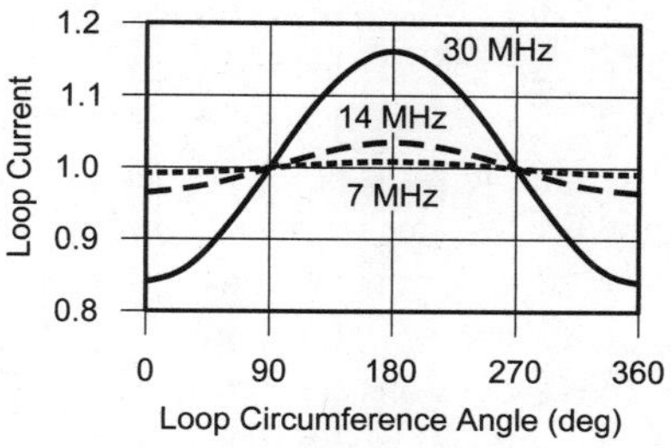

Table 5.6
Transmitting Loop Equations

$$X_L = 2\pi f L$$

$$Q = \frac{f}{\Delta f} = \frac{X_L}{2(R_R + R_L)}$$

$$R_R = 3.12 \times 10^4 \left(\frac{NA}{\lambda^2}\right)^2 = 197 C_\lambda^4 N^2$$

$$V_C = \sqrt{2PX_L Q}$$

$$I_L = \sqrt{\frac{PQ}{X_L}}$$

where
- X_L = inductive reactance in ohms
- f = frequency in Hz
- Df = bandwidth in Hz
- R_R = radiation resistance in ohms
- R_L = loss resistance in ohms (see text)
- C_λ = loop circumference in wavelengths
- N = number of turns
- A = area enclosed by loop in square meters
- λ = wavelength at operating frequency in meters
- V_C = peak voltage across capacitor
- P = power in watts
- I_L = resonant circulating RMS current in the loop

leads to a computed radiation resistance of only $3.12 \times 10^{-4} (0.785/21.4^2)^2 = 0.092\ \Omega$. (The *QEX* article by Siwiak and Quick article provides a more accurate treatment of radiation resistance.)

The loop also has losses, both ohmic and from skin effect. By using this information, the radiation efficiency of a loop can be calculated from the simple formula:

$$\eta = \frac{R_R}{R_R + R_L} \quad (7)$$

where

η = antenna efficiency

R_r = radiation resistance in Ω

R_l = loss resistance in Ω, which includes the loop's conductor loss plus the loss in the tuning capacitor and any current-carrying mechanical connections.

A simple ratio of R_R versus R_L shows the effects on the efficiency, as can be seen from **Figure 5.31**. This graph is presented as a general illustration of how losses affect loop efficiency and is not a representation of any specific design. See the discussion on loop efficiency at the end of this section which compares a simulation, calculation, and measurement of efficiency.

The loss resistance is primarily the ac resistance of the conductor (Eq 5). A transmitting loop generally requires the use of copper conductors of at least ½ inch in diameter in order to obtain reasonable efficiency. Tubing is as useful as a solid conductor because high-frequency currents flow only along a very small depth of the surface of the conductor; the center of the conductor has almost no effect on current flow. Note that the R_L term above must also include the effect of the loss in the tuning capacitor and mechanical connections. Practical details for curbing losses are covered later in this chapter in the section on loop construction.

Loop Impedance and Q

The loop impedance with just radiation loss is

$$Z_{loop} = [\text{Radiation resistance}] + j[\text{Loop reactance}] \quad (8)$$

The loaded radiation Q of the antenna is,

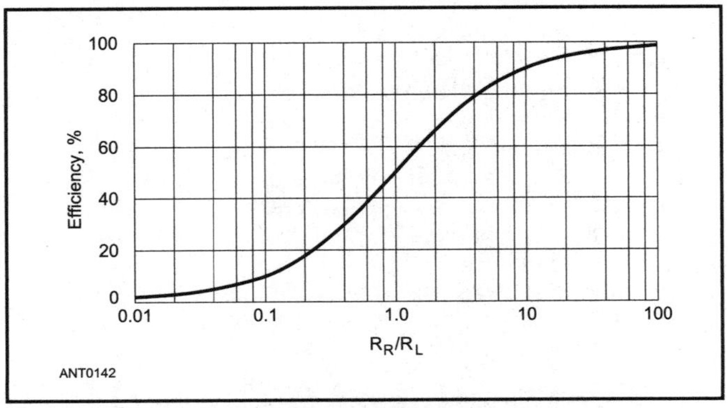

Figure 5.31 — Effect of ratio of R_R/R_L on loop efficiency.

$$Q_{rad} = \frac{1}{2}\frac{\text{Loop reactance}}{\text{Radiation resistance}} \quad (9)$$

The primary loop loss resistance is due to the main loop conductor losses represented by R_{loss}. The Q_c of the resonating capacitor also contributes to losses in the form of parallel resistance across the capacitor, so that the net loaded Q_L of the antenna is

$$Q_L = \frac{0.5}{\frac{1}{Q_C} + \frac{[\text{Radiation resistance}] + R_{loss}}{[\text{Loop reactance}]}} \quad (10)$$

from which we can determine the loop radiation efficiency in dB as,

$$\text{eff}_{dB} = 10\log\left[\frac{Q_L}{Q_{rad}}\right] \quad (11)$$

The value of Q_L can be obtained from Eq 10 or from direct measurements. See the referenced Siwiak and Quick article for a complete discussion of the loop's radiation resistance.

Loop Bandwidth

It is important to note that small transmitting loops (like their receiving cousins) have very narrow 2:1 SWR bandwidths. If you wish to operate across a wide range of frequencies, expect to do some tuning. In commercial loops this is usually done remotely using a small stepper or gear motor to adjust the tuning capacitor. This type of antenna may require retuning for frequency changes as small as 5 kHz. If you are using any wide-band mode such as AM or a high-speed digital mode, you might wish to sacrifice a little efficiency to obtain the required bandwidth.

5.3.3 THE SECONDARY FEEDING LOOP

For the given example loop dimensions, the mutual coupling inductance M_{12} between the main and feeding loops is 57.3 nH, and the secondary feed loop inductance L_{feed} is 0.361 µH, obtained using the Jordan and Balmain high frequency extension to the Neumann formula, see the Bibliography. The main loop impedance, including the resonating capacitor, is transformed using a circuit model developed by Milton Cram, W8NUE, (see Bibliography) to the feed point impedance by,

$$R_{feed} = j\omega L_{feed} + \frac{(\omega M_{12})^2}{R_{total} + j\Delta} \quad (12)$$

R_{total} is the sum of the radiation resistance and conductor and capacitor series equivalent losses and ω = 2pf. Interestingly, the feed point reactance is not zero when the main loop is resonant because of the feed-loop inductance L_{feed} term in Eq 12. The $j\Delta$ term simulates the tuning of the main loop to bring R_{feed} close to 50 Ω. Apply Eq 12 and choose Δ at each frequency for a best match to 50 Ω. In practice, this is accomplished by adjusting the main loop resonating capacitor.

Figure 5.32 shows that the load resistance presented to the coax feed line stays close to 50 Ω (SWR is under 1.3:1) across the 7 to 29.7 MHz operating range of this loop. This illustrates a key characteristic taught by Dunlavy in his 1971 patent — the feeding loop diameter and location bear an optimum relationship to the diameter of the primary loop so that variation in feed impedance is minimized over the band of operation.

5.3.4 FIELDS AT THE LOOP CENTER AND IN THE FAR FIELD NULL

Since the loop current term varies with ϕ an electric field E_{center} and a magnetic field H_{center} can be found at the loop center, and the magnetic field can be approximated from the single turn solenoid equation, -both equations are in the *QEX* article. The resulting wave impedance Z_W at the loop center is a measure of how well the loop discriminates between the electric and magnetic fields and is,

$$Z_W = \frac{E_{center}}{H_{center}} = -j\eta_0 C_\lambda \quad (13)$$

clearly revealing the dependence of Z_W on the loop circumference. Without the ϕ dependent current variation term E_{center} and Z_W would be erroneously reported as zero!

Likewise, the far-field peak-to-null ratio depends on the current variation term in a simple manner for $C_\lambda < 0.3$,

$$N_{dB} = -20\log(2C\lambda) \quad (14)$$

Figure 5.33 shows the null depth across 7 to 30 MHz.

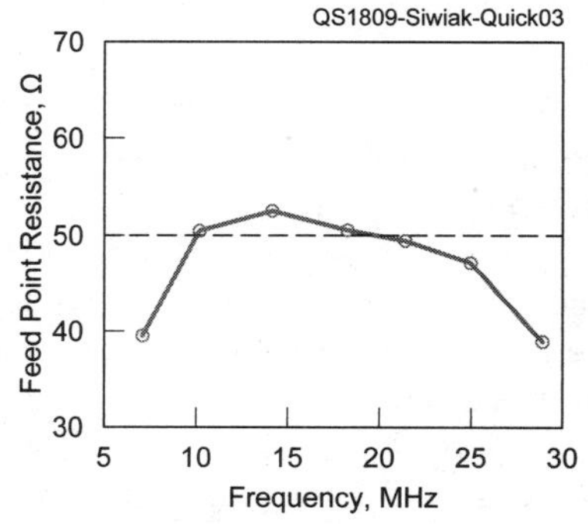

Figure 5.32 — The approximate impedance presented to the coax feed line is not much different from 50 Ω across the entire 7 to 29.7 MHz tuning and operating range of this loop.

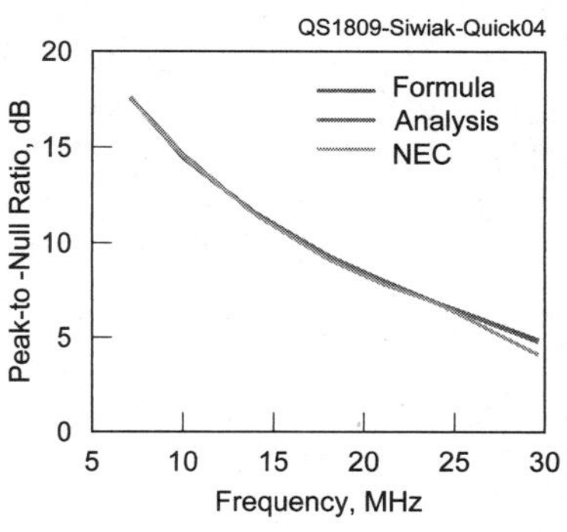

Figure 5.33 — The depth of the null steadily decreases across the 7 to 30 MHz operating band. Omitting the current variation term results in an erroneous infinite null depth.

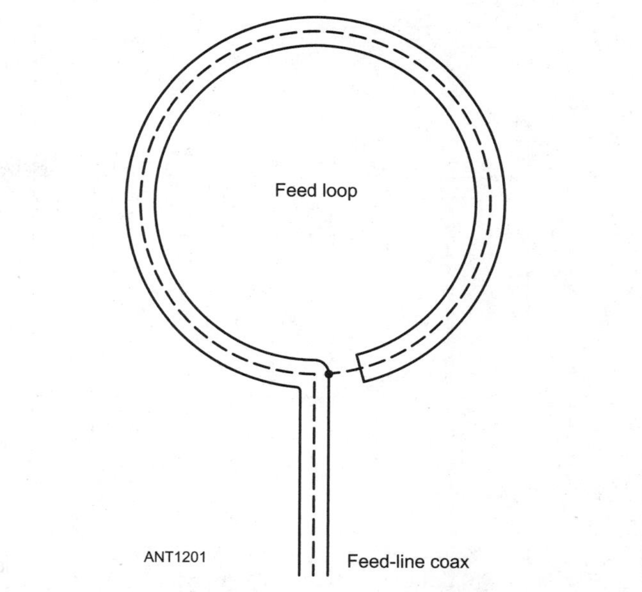

Figure 5.34 — Detail of the secondary feeding loop.

The null depth using Eq 14 is compared to the null depth found with a detailed loop near-field analysis, and the null simulated by a *4nec2* model. The polarization at the horizon of the vertically oriented loop is vertical. The far-field null and E_{center}, however, are horizontally polarized — same as the orientation of the electric field across the main loop gap for the geometry of Figure 5.29. The null becomes shallower as the frequency increases for a fixed-size loop, and at $C_\lambda = 1$ — the classic one wavelength circumference loop — becomes the peak gain (in horizontal polarization) of about +4 dBi in the broadside direction.

5.3.5 COUPLING TO A COAXIAL FEED LINE

A coaxial cable feeds the secondary loop directly as shown in **Figure 5.34**, so common-mode currents (CMC) can be picked up on the coax feed line shield. Vary the length of the coax and search for the maximum current on the coax cable shield, just like on a previous *QST* study (see Bibliography) by Quick and Siwiak involving common-mode currents on the feed line to a dipole. They found that the maximum CMC occurs for a coaxial feed line length of 0.45 λ and recommend that common-mode chokes (ferrites) should be installed on the feed line coax at least a loop diameter away from the loop, and at intervals of less than about 0.3 λ (at the highest frequency).

5.3.6 VERTICAL LOOP COUPLING TO THE GROUND

Siwiak and Quick estimated the loop coupling to the ground by calculating the mutual inductance between the primary loop and its image in the ground, normalized to the loop self-inductance and expressed in percent. That coupling affects the impedance of the loop antenna system. They calculated the coupling for a perfect electric conductor (PEC)

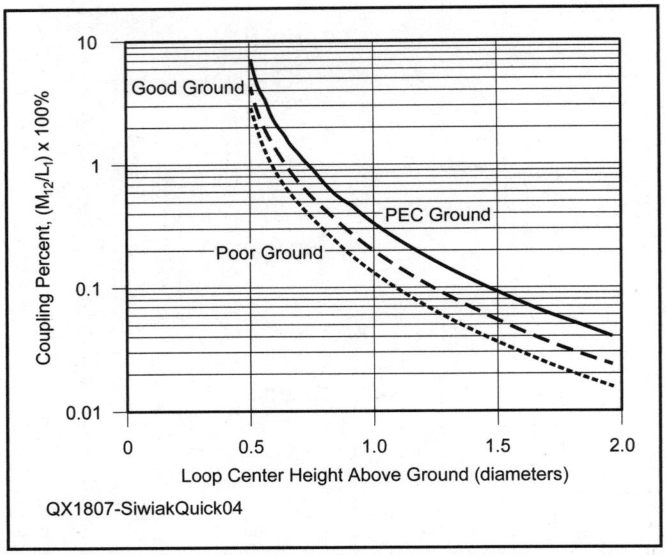

Figure 5.35 — The percent coupling to ground for this small HF loop is insignificant when the loop center is at least one loop diameter above the ground. Coupling is strongest for a PEC ground, and decreases significantly for realistic ground parameters.

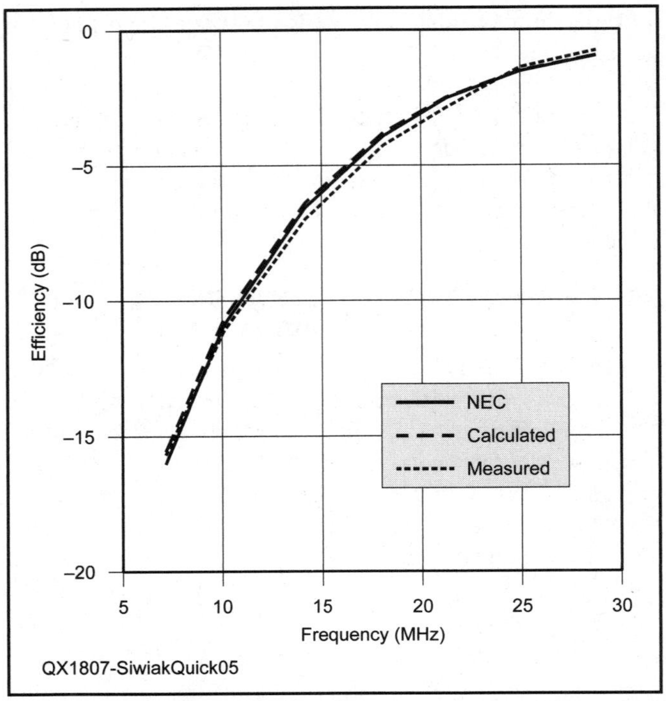

Figure 5.36 — Small loop efficiency simulated in *NEC* (solid), calculated from loop equations (long dashes), and measured using the Q method (short dashes). The close agreement among three methods validates the analysis, the Q measurements, and the completely independent *NEC* model.

ground, and then estimated the effects over an "average" ground, and a "poor" ground, by reducing the PEC ground coupling by the magnitude of the refection coefficient for normal incidence on the ground. The reflection coefficient magnitude is 1.0 for the PEC, 0.59 for the "average" ground, and 0.39 for "poor" ground at 14.1 MHz. See **Figure 5.35**.

Coupling of the vertical loop to a perfect ground is small, and decreases for realistic ground parameters. Even for a worst-case PEC ground, the coupling is less than 0.5% for a loop with its center more than one loop diameter above ground. Additional discussion of loop-ground coupling is available in the article by DeNeef listed in the Bibliography.

5.3.7 EFFICIENCY OF THE SMALL LOOP

Three methods are compared to estimate the radiation efficiency of the small loop. In one *calculated* method the total loaded Q_L is found using Eq 10 and compared that to the loaded Q_{rad} of Eq 9, and then Eq 11 is applied for the efficiency.

In a second method measure *loaded* Q_L using a matched transmitter, and apply the classic bandwidth formula,

$$Q_L = \frac{\sqrt{F_H F_L}}{F_H - F_L} = \frac{\text{Frequency}}{\text{Bandwidth}} \qquad (15)$$

where F_H and F_L correspond to the 2.236:1 SWR points on each side of the center frequency.

Finally, the completely independent NEC model is used to simulate efficiency. **Figure 5.36** shows that all three methods of determining efficiency are within 0.5 dB of each other across 7 to 29.7 MHz, inspiring confidence in all three methods.

Austin, Boswell, and Perks published a short paper discussing loss mechanisms for small loops (see the Bibliography) recognizing the extremely low radiation resistance made any resistive losses a major factor in antenna efficiency. Losses in the tuning capacitor contacts were found to be a major source of resistive loss. Ground losses were found to decrease rapidly as the loop was raised above ground and inconsequential above 0.1 λ. Those authors also used a toroidal coupling transformer to couple to the loop.

In addition, Boswell, Tyler, and White published an article in a professional journal which considers the efficiency of a simple 1-meter diameter loop made from 22 mm diameter copper tube from 3–10 MHz. (See the Bibliography) Their results were 0.25 percent on 80 meters and 18 percent on 30 meters. The low numbers should not preclude considering the loop as in many cases this is the only reasonable solution to transmitting for the amateurs in a restricted space antenna situation.

5.4 CONSTRUCTION GUIDELINES FOR SMALL TRANSMITTING LOOPS

This section is based on material contributed by Rich Quick, W4RQ. There is an optimum balance between the size of the HF loop, the thickness of the conductor and the relative size of the feeding loop that results in an antenna that has the widest tuning range with close to 50 Ω feeding impedance. Small HF loops are typically between 0.08 and 0.4 in circumference over the operating range. That works out to approximately 3 m in circumference for an HF loop the covers 7 to 30 MHz. All else equal, a larger loop will be more efficient than a smaller loop.

It is important to note that the usual construction techniques for antennas can create excessive losses in small loops. Loop radiation resistance is on the order of fraction of an ohm. To minimize resistive losses, solder or weld all connections that carry antenna current. Sliding contacts, clamped joints and connections, and undersized conductors can hurt performance significantly. Bolted connections should be avoided because at RF these joints generally have high resistance, especially after being subjected to weathering.

A circular shape provides the best radiation resistance to conductor loss resistance ratios, hence is most efficient. Loop conductor diameter should be between 1 and 5 cm. Larger conductors help reduce losses. For a given cross-section, tubular conductors will be less lossy than flat conductors because of current bunching at flat conductor edges.

The lowest loss material practical for HF antennas is pure electrical grade copper. T60 aluminum has 66% the conductivity of electrical grade copper. Avoid the high loss of construction grade aluminum and soft copper tubing. Trask has also noted that some flexible copper tubing is made from a lead/copper alloy. This should be avoided due to increased resistivity. Rigid copper tubing, refrigeration tubing or large copper wire should be used. Often it is convenient to fashion loops from RG-213, LMR-400, LMR-500, or LMR-600 coax cable. These work well, especially for portable loop antennas.

Components in a resonant transmitting loop are subject to both high currents and voltages as a result of the large circulating currents found in the high-Q tuned circuit formed by the antenna. Loop circulating current can range from about 8 A at 10 W to more than 25 A at 100 W RF input power. This makes it important that any fixed capacitors have a high RF current rating, such as transmitting micas or the Centralab 850 series. Be aware that even a 100-W transmitter can develop currents in the tens of amperes, and peak voltages across the tuning capacitor in excess of 5000 V. This consideration also applies to any conductors used to connect the loop to the capacitors. A piece of #14 AWG used as a jumper and carrying a high current may create more loss than the rest of the loop conductor! It is therefore best to use copper strips or large diameter wire to make any connections. Make the best electrical connection possible, using soldered or welded joints.

The tuning capacitor should be very high Q — greater than 1000 to 4000. For example, a very high-quality tuning capacitor with no mechanical wiping contacts, such as a vacuum-variable or a transmitting butterfly capacitor, might have an unloaded Q of about 5000. This implies a series loss resistance of less than about 0.02 Ω for a capacitive reactance of 100 Ω. This relatively tiny loss resistance can become significant, however, when the radiation resistance of the loop is only on the order of 0.1 Ω!

The highest Q capacitors are vacuum variables, followed by butterfly air dielectric capacitors. Both are hard to find and can be expensive. Often an inexpensive but lower-Q dual-stator capacitor is used. The key is to find a variable range that can resonate with the loop inductance over the desired tuning range. Avoid capacitors that have mechanical 'wiper' connections in the circuit path. They are lossy. Ensure that the capacitor peak voltage rating is sufficient for the loop transmitter power. Use heavy gauge wire to connect the capacitor to the loop.

Because of the sensitivity to loss in the tuning capacitor, there is a lot of interest in designs that avoid sliding or wiping contacts. For example, a "trombone" tuning capacitor design uses concentric copper tubing to construct the linear version of a butterfly capacitor, controlled by a dc motor similarly to a screwdriver mobile antenna.

An enclosure surrounding the capacitor can affect the Q, and therefore losses, dramatically. Use a polymeric enclosure that does not absorb RF energy. Wooden enclosures might be inexpensive and look good, but some types of wood can absorb RF energy.

If you are not sure about an enclosure's effect on RF, place a piece of the material in a microwave oven together with a glass of water. (The material must *not* have any metal fasteners or fittings.) The water provides a load for the oven in the case of a low-loss material. Run the oven on high for about 1 minute. If the material heats up, it absorbs RF, don't use it. Be careful, a piece of lossy material can become hot enough to burn you!

For portable loops that use coax and coaxial connectors for portable assembly, use gold plated connectors since gold will not corrode or oxidize.

A secondary feeding loop circumference should be about 20% of the main loop circumference, and located opposite the capacitor resonated gap. A gamma-type feeding arrangement is also possible for single band operation, but the gamma match can distort the radiation pattern of the loop. A toroidal transformer match might also be suitable for single-band operation.

5.5 BIBLIOGRAPHY

Source material and more extended discussion of topics covered in this chapter can be found in the references given below and the textbooks listed in the Bibliography section of the **Antenna Fundamentals** chapter.

C. F. W. Anderson, "A Crossed-Loop/Goniometer DF Antenna for 160 Meters," *The ARRL Antenna Compendium, Vol 1* (Newington: ARRL, 1985), pp 127-132.

B. Austin, et al, "Loss Mechanisms in the Electrically Small Loop Antenna," *IEEE Antennas & Propagation Magazine*, Aug 2014, pp 142-147.

D. Belcher, "Loops vs Dipole Analysis and Discussion," *QST*, Aug 1976, pp 34-37.

J. S. Belrose, "Ferromagnetic Loop Aerials," *Wireless Engineer*, Feb 1955, pp 41-46.

J. S. Belrose, "An Update on Compact Transmitting Loops," *QST*, Nov 1993, pp 37-40.

D. S. Bond, *Radio Direction Finders*, 1st edition (New York: McGraw-Hill Book Co).

A. Boswell, A. Tyler, and A. White, "Performance of a Small Loop Antenna in the 3-10 MHz Band," *IEEE Antennas and Propagation Magazine*, Apr 2005, pp 51-56.

B. Bowers and J. Bryant, "Very Large Ferrite Loops," *Fine Tuning Proceeding 1994-1995* (John H. Bryant, 1994), pp 18-1 to 18-6.

LB Cebik, "A Comparison of Closed and Interrupted Loop Antennas for 40 Meters," 15 Jan 2006.

B. S. Collins, "A New High Performance HF Receiving Antenna," *Proceedings of the International Conference on Antennas and Propagation*, 28-30 Nov 1978, (London, UK: Institution of Electrical Engineers), pp 80-81

M. E. Cram, W8NUE, "Small Transmitting Loop Antennas: a Different Perspective on Determining Q and Efficiency", *QEX*, July/Aug, 2018, pp 3-8.

P. DeNeef, AE7PD, "Safety distances for small HF loop antennas," *Radcom*, June 2017, pp 46-47.

D. DeMaw, "Beat the Noise with a Scoop Loop," *QST*, Jul 1977, pp 30-34.

D. DeMaw and L. Aurick, "The Full-Wave Delta Loop at Low Height," *QST*, Oct 1984, pp 24-26.

P. DeNeef, "Effects Due to Ground for Small Transmitting Loop Antennas", *QEX*, Jul/Aug 2018, pp 9-11.

J. Dietrich, "Loops and Dipoles: A Comparative Analysis," *QST*, Sep 1985, pp 24-26.

John H. Dunlavy, Jr., "Wide Range Tunable Transmitting Loop Antenna", US Patent 3,588,905, issued June 28, 1971.

D. Fischer, "The Loop Skywire," *QST*, Nov 1985, pp 20-22. Also "Feedback," *QST*, Dec 1985, p 53.

R. A. Genaille, "V.L.F. Loop Antenna," *Electronics World*, Jan 1963, pp 49-52.

R. S. Glasgow, *Principles of Radio Engineering* (New York: McGraw-Hill Book Co, Inc, 1936).

S. Goldman, "A Shielded Loop for Low Noise Broadcast Reception," *Electronics*, Oct 1938, pp 20-22.

F. W. Grover, *Inductance Calculation-Working Formulas and Tables* (New York: D. VanNostrand Co, Inc, 1946).

J. V. Hagan, "A Large Aperture Ferrite Core Loop Antenna for Long and Medium Wave Reception," *Loop Antennas Design and Theory*, M.G. Knitter, Ed. (Cambridge, WI: National Radio Club, 1983), pp 37-49.

S. Harwood, "The Horizontal Loop — An Effective Multipurpose Antenna," *QST*, Nov 2006, pp 42-44.

H. Hawkins, "A Low Budget, Rotatable 17 Meter Loop," *QST*, Nov 1997, p 35.

B. Jones, "A Home-Brew Loop Tuning Capacitor," *QST*, Nov 1994, pp 30-32.

E.C. Jordan and K. G. Balmain, Chapter 10, *Electromagnetic Waves and Radiating Systems*, Second Edition, 1968, Prentice–Hall, Inc., Englewood Cliffs, NJ.

J. A. Lambert, "A Directional Active Loop Receiving Antenna System," *Radio Communication*, Nov 1982, pp 944-949.

F. Langford-Smith (ed.), *Radiotron Designers Handbook*, 4th ed, (Wireless Press: Australia, 1953), p 466

D. Lankford, "Loop Antennas, Theory and Practice," *Loop Antennas Design and Theory*, M. G. Knitter, Ed. (Cambridge, WI: National Radio Club, 1983), pp 10-22.

Loop Antenna Issue, *QEX*, Jul/Aug 2018.

D. M. Mallozzi, "Q of Shielded Loop Antennas," *QEX*, Jul/Aug 1998, pp 59-60.

R. Q. Marris, "The Optima 160/80-Meter Receive Antenna," *The ARRL Antenna Compendium Vol 6*, (Newington: ARRL), pp 45-48.

New England Wire Technologies, Litz Wire Technical Information (**www.newenglandwire.com**)

W. J. Polydoroff, High *Frequency Magnetic Materials — Their Characteristics and Principal Applications* (New York: John Wiley and Sons, Inc, 1960).

R. Quick, W4RQ, and K. Siwiak, KE4PT, "Does Your Antenna Need a Choke or a Balun?," *QST*, Mar, 2017, pp. 30-33.

Reference Data for Radio Engineers, 6th ed. (Indianapolis: Howard W. Sams & Co, subsidiary of ITT, 1977).

T. Simpson and J. Cahill, "The Electrically Small Elliptical Loop with an Oblate Spheroidal Core," *IEEE Antennas and Propagation Magazine*, Vol 49, No 5: Oct 2007, pp 83 to 92.

T. Simpson and Y. Zhu, "The Electrically Small Multi-Turn Loop with a Spheroidal Core," *IEEE Antennas and Propagation Magazine*, Vol 48, No 5: Oct 2006, pp 54 to 65.

K. Siwiak, KE4PT, and R. Quick, W4RQ, "Small Gap-resonated HF Loop Antenna Fed by a Secondary Loop", *QEX*, July/Aug, 2018, pp 12-17.

K. Siwiak, KE4PT, and R. Quick, W4RQ, "Small Gap-resonated HF Loop Antennas", *QST*, Sep 2018, pp 30-33.

G. S. Smith, "Radiation Efficiency of Electrically Small Multiturn Loop Antennas," *IEEE Trans on Ant and Prop*, Sep 1972, pp 656-657.

J. Stanley, K4ERO, "Some Additional Geometries for Loop Antennas," *QEX*, July/Aug, 2018, pp 31-36.

C. R. Sullivan, "Optimal Choice for the Number of Strands in a Litz-Wire Transformer Winding," *IEEE Transactions on Power Electronics*, Mar 1999, Vol 14, No 2, pp 283-291 (available from **engineering.dartmouth.edu/inductor/papers/litzj.pdf**)

C. Trask, "Active Loop Aerials for HF Reception Part 1: Practical Loop Aerial Design," *QEX*, Jul/Aug 2003, pp 35-42.

C. Trask, "Active Loop Aerials for HF Reception Part 2: High Dynamic Range Aerial Amplifier Design," *QEX*, Sep/Oct 2003, pp 44-49.

J. R. True, "Low-Frequency Loop Antennas," *Ham Radio*, Dec 1976, pp 18-24.

TABLE OF CONTENTS

Chapter 6 — Downloadable Supplemental Content

Supplemental Articles

- Appendix B — Manual Calculations for Arrays
- "A Wire Eight-Circle Array (for 7 MHz)" by Tony Preedy, G3LNP
- "A Study of Tall Verticals" by Al Christman, K3LC
- "Tall Vertical Arrays" by Al Christman, K3LC
- "The Simplest Phased Array Feed System — That Works" by Roy Lewellan, W7EL

Support Files

- *EZNEC* modeling files for examples in this chapter

Chapter 6

Multielement Arrays

6.1 CREATING GAIN AND DIRECTIVITY

The gain and directivity offered by an array of elements represents a worthwhile improvement both in transmitting and receiving. Power gain in an antenna is the same as an equivalent increase in the transmitter power. But unlike increasing the power of your own transmitter, antenna gain works equally well on signals received from the favored direction. In addition, the directivity reduces the strength of signals coming from the directions not favored, and so helps discriminate against interference.

One common method of obtaining gain and directivity is to combine the radiation from a group of $\lambda/2$ dipoles to concentrate it in a desired direction. A few words of explanation may help make it clear how power gain is obtained.

In **Figure 6.1**, imagine that the four circles, A, B, C and D, represent four dipoles so far separated from each other that the coupling between them is negligible. Also imagine that point P is so far away from the dipoles that the distance from P to each one is exactly the same (obviously P would have to be much farther away than it is shown in this drawing). Under these conditions the fields from all the dipoles will add up at P if all four are fed RF currents in the same phase.

Let us say that a certain current, I, in dipole A will produce a certain value of field strength, E, at the distant point P. The same current in any of the other dipoles will produce the same field at P. Thus, if only dipoles A and B are operating, each with a current I, the field at P will be 2E. With A, B and C operating, the field will be 3E, and with all four operating with the same I, the field will be 4E. Since the power received at P is proportional to the square of the field strength, the relative power received at P is 1, 4, 9 or 16, depending on whether one, two, three or four dipoles are operating.

Now, since all four dipoles are alike and there is no coupling between them, the same power must be put into each in order to cause the current I to flow. For two dipoles the relative power input is 2, for three dipoles it is 3, for four dipoles 4, and so on. The actual gain in each case is the relative received (or output) power divided by the relative input power. Thus we have the results shown in **Table 6.1**. The power ratio is directly proportional to the number of elements used.

It is well to have clearly in mind the conditions under which this relationship is true:

1) The fields from the separate antenna elements must be in-phase at the receiving point.

2) The elements are identical, with equal currents in all elements.

3) The elements must be separated in such a way that the

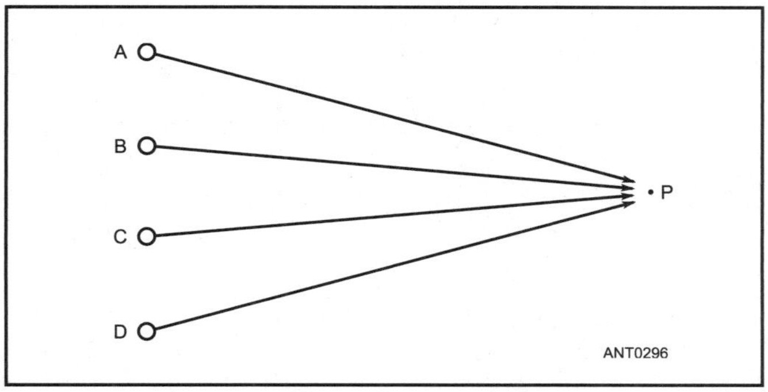

Figure 6.1 — Fields from separate antennas combine at a distant point, P, to produce a field strength that exceeds the field produced by the same power in a single antenna.

Table 6.1
Comparison of Dipoles with Negligible Coupling (See Figure 6.1)

Dipoles	*Relative Output Power*	*Relative Input Power*	*Power Gain*	*Gain in dB*
A only	1	1	1	0
A and B	4	2	2	3
A, B and C	9	3	3	4.8
A, B, C and D	16	4	4	6

current induced in one by another is negligible; that is, the radiation resistance of each element must be the same as it would be if the other elements were not there.

Very few antenna arrays meet all these conditions exactly. However, the power gain of a directive array using dipole elements with optimum values of element spacing is approximately proportional to the number of elements. Another way to say this is that a gain of approximately 3 dB will be obtained each time the number of elements is doubled, assuming the proper element spacing is maintained. It is possible, though, for an estimate based on this rule to be in error by a ratio factor of two or more (gain error of 3 dB or more), especially if mutual coupling is not negligible.

6.1.1 DEFINITIONS

Some definitions are repeated here from the **Antenna Fundamentals** chapter for the convenience of the reader. Refer to that chapter for more extensive discussion of basic concepts.

An *element* in a multi-element directive array is usually a $\lambda/2$ radiator or a $\lambda/4$ vertical element above ground. The length is not always an exact electrical half or quarter wavelength, because in some types of arrays it is desirable that the element show either inductive or capacitive reactance. However, the departure in length from resonance is ordinarily small (not more than 5% in the usual case) and so has no appreciable effect on the radiating properties of the element.

Antenna elements in multi-element arrays of the type considered in this chapter are always either *parallel*, as in **Figure 6.2A**, or *collinear* (end-to-end), as in Figure 6.2B. Figure 6.2C shows an array combining both parallel and collinear elements. The elements can be either horizontal or vertical, depending on whether horizontal or vertical polarization is desired. Except for space communications, there is seldom any reason for mixing polarization, so arrays are customarily constructed with all elements similarly polarized.

A *driven element* is one supplied power from the transmitter, usually through a transmission line. A parasitic element is one that obtains power solely through coupling to another element in the array because of its proximity to such an element.

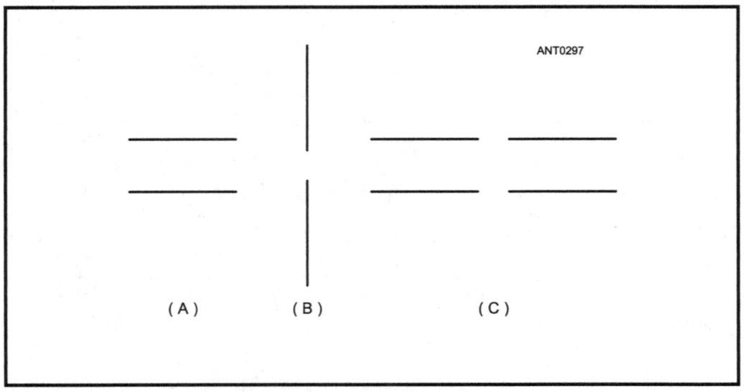

Figure 6.2 — At A, parallel and at B, collinear antenna elements. The array shown at C combines both parallel and collinear elements.

A *driven array* is one in which all the elements are driven elements. A *parasitic array* is one in which one or more of the elements are parasitic elements. At least one element must be a driven element, since you must somehow introduce power into the array.

A *broadside array* is one in which the principal direction of radiation is perpendicular to the axis of the array and to the plane containing the elements, as shown in **Figure 6.3**. The elements of a broadside array may be collinear, as in Figure 6.3A, or parallel (two views in Figure 6.3B).

An *end-fire array* is one in which the principal direction of radiation coincides with the direction of the array axis. This definition is illustrated in **Figure 6.4**. An end-fire array must consist of parallel elements. They cannot be collinear, as $\lambda/2$ elements do not radiate straight off their ends. A Yagi is a familiar form of an end-fire array.

A *bidirectional array* is one that radiates equally well in either direction along the line of maximum radiation. A bidirectional pattern is shown in **Figure 6.5A**. A *unidirectional array* is one that has only one principal direction of radiation, as the pattern in Figure 6.5B shows.

The *major lobes* of the directive pattern are those in which the radiation is a maximum. Lobes of lesser radiation intensity are called *side* or *minor* lobes. The *beamwidth* of a directive antenna is the width, in degrees, of the major lobe between the two directions at which the relative radiated power is equal to one half its value at the peak of the lobe. At these *half-power points* the field intensity is equal to 0.707 times its maximum value, or in other words, is down 3 dB from the maximum. **Figure 6.6** shows a lobe having a beamwidth of 30°.

Unless specified otherwise, the term *gain* as used in this

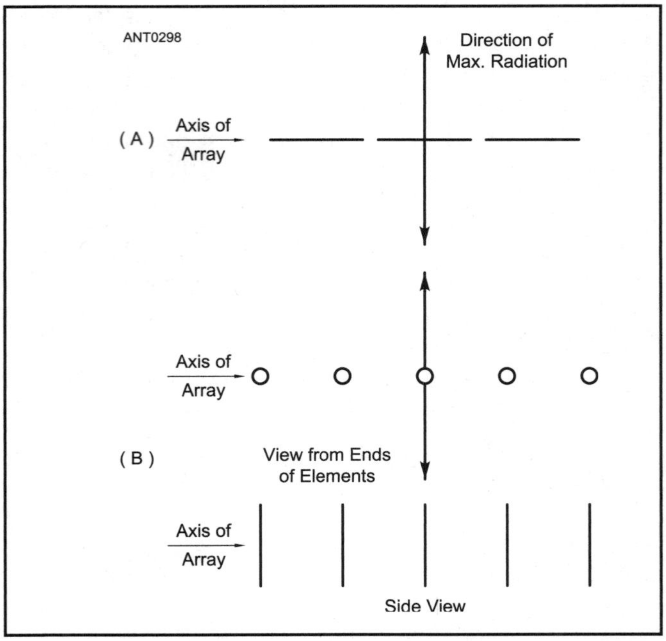

Figure 6.3 — Representative broadside arrays. At A, collinear elements, with parallel elements at B.

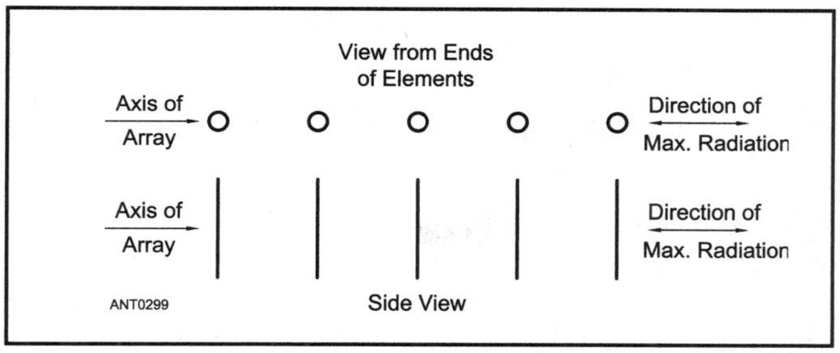

Figure 6.4 — An end-fire array. Practical arrays may combine both broadside directivity (Figure 6.3) and end-fire directivity, including both parallel and collinear elements.

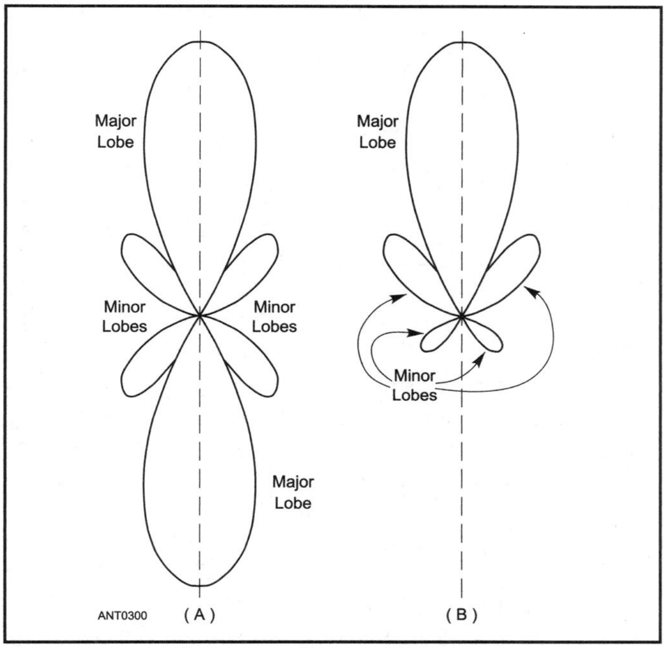

Figure 6.5 — At A, typical bidirectional pattern and at B, unidirectional directive pattern. These drawings also illustrate the application of the terms *major* and *minor* to the pattern lobes.

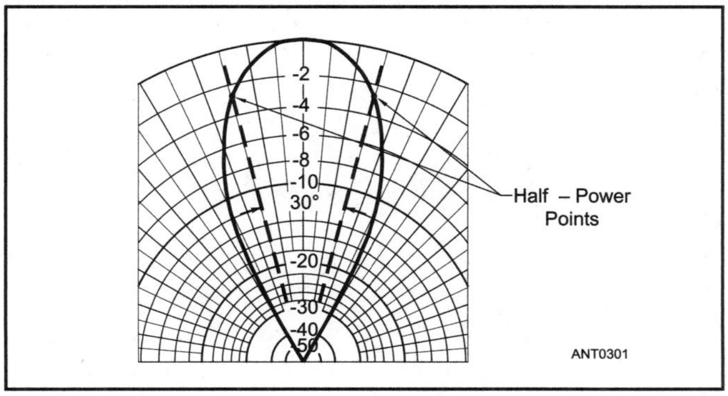

Figure 6.6 — The width of a beam is the angular distance between the directions at which the received or transmitted power is half the maximum power (–3 dB). Each angular division of the pattern grid is 5°.

section is the power gain over an isotropic radiator in free space. The gain can also be compared with a λ/2 dipole of the same orientation and height as the array under discussion and having the same power input. Gain may either be measured experimentally or determined by calculation. Experimental measurement is difficult and often subject to considerable error, for two reasons. First, errors normally occur in measurement because the accuracy of simple RF measuring equipment is relatively poor — even high-quality instruments suffer in accuracy compared with their low-frequency and dc counterparts. And second, the accuracy depends considerably on conditions — the antenna site, including height, terrain characteristics, and surroundings — under which the measurements are made.

Calculations are frequently based on the measured or theoretical directive patterns of the antenna. The theoretical gain of an array may be determined approximately from:

$$G \approx \frac{41253}{H_{3dB} \times E_{3dB}} \qquad (1)$$

where

G = decibel gain over a dipole in its favored direction

H_{3dB} = half-power beamwidth in degrees of the H-field pattern

E_{3dB} = vertical half-power beamwidth in degrees of the E-field pattern.

This equation, strictly speaking, applies only to lossless antennas having approximately equal and narrow E- and H-plane beam widths — up to about 20° — and no large minor lobes. The error may be considerable when the formula is applied to simple directive antennas having relatively large beam widths. The error is in the direction of making the calculated gain larger than the actual gain.

Phase and Polarity

The term *phase* has the same meaning when used in connection with the currents flowing in antenna elements as it does in ordinary circuit work. For example, two currents at the same frequency are in-phase when they reach their maximum values, flowing in the same direction, at the same instant. The direction of current flow depends on the way in which power is applied to the element. Reiterating from the **Antenna Fundamentals** chapter, it is important to distinguish between phase and *polarity*. Polarity is simply a convention that assigns a positive and negative direction or convention. Reversing the leads on a feed line reverses a signal's polarity.

This is illustrated in **Figure 6.7**. Assume that by some means an identical voltage is applied to each of the elements at the ends marked A. Assume also that the coupling between the elements is negligible, and that the instantaneous polarity of the voltage is such that the current is flowing away from the point at which the voltage is applied. The arrows show the assumed current directions. Then the currents in elements 1 and 2 are in-phase, since they are flowing in the

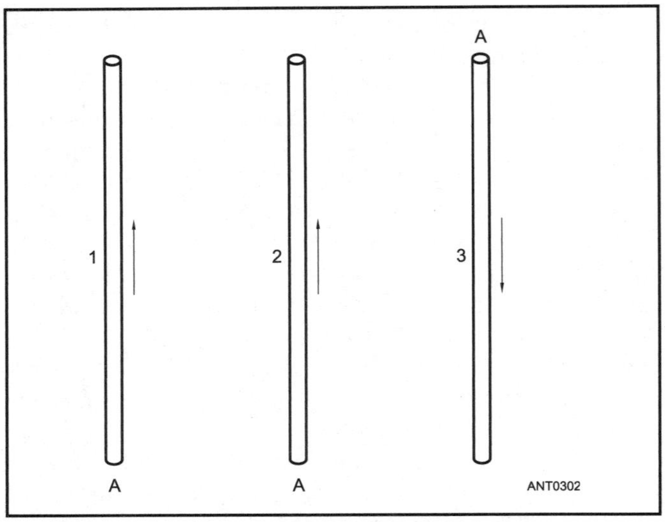

Figure 6.7 — This drawing illustrates the phase of currents in antenna elements, represented by the arrows. The currents in elements 1 and 2 are in phase, while that in element 3 is 180° out of phase with 1 and 2.

same direction in space and are caused by the same voltage. However, the current in element 3 is flowing in the *opposite* direction in space because the voltage is applied to the opposite end of the element. The current in element 3 is therefore 180° out-of-phase with the currents in elements 1 and 2.

The phasing of driven elements depends on the direction of the element, the phase of the applied voltage, and the point at which the voltage is applied. In many systems used by amateurs, the voltages applied to the elements are exactly in or exactly out-of-phase with each other. Also, the axes of the elements are nearly always in the same direction, since parallel or collinear elements are invariably used. The currents in driven elements in such systems therefore are usually either exactly in or exactly out-of-phase with the currents in other elements.

It is possible to use phase differences of less than 180° in driven arrays. One important case is where the current in one set of elements differs by 90° from the current in another set. However, making provision for proper phasing in such systems is considerably more complex than in the case of simple 0° or 180° phasing, as described in a later section of this chapter.

In parasitic arrays the phase of the currents in the parasitic elements depends on the spacing and tuning, as described later.

Ground Effects

The effect of the ground is the same with a directive antenna as it is with a simple dipole antenna. The reflection factors discussed in the chapter **Effects of Ground** may therefore be applied to the vertical pattern of an array, subject to the same modifications mentioned in that chapter. In cases where the array elements are not all at the same height, the reflection factor for the mean height of the array may be used for a close approximation. The mean height is the average of the heights measured from the ground to the centers of the lowest and highest elements.

6.1.2 MUTUAL IMPEDANCE

Consider two λ/2 elements that are fairly close to each other. Assume that power is applied to only one element, causing current to flow. This creates an electromagnetic field, which induces a voltage in the second element and causes current to flow in it as well. The current flowing in element 2 will in turn induce a voltage in element 1, causing additional current to flow there. The total current in 1 is then the sum (taking phase into account) of the original current and the induced current.

With element 2 present, the amplitude and phase of the resulting current in element 1 will be different than if element 2 were not there. This indicates that the presence of the second element has changed the impedance of the first. This effect is called *mutual coupling*. Mutual coupling results in a mutual impedance between the two elements. The mutual impedance has both resistive and reactive components. The actual impedance of an antenna element is the sum of its self-impedance (the impedance with no other antennas present) and its mutual impedances with all other antennas in the vicinity.

The magnitude and nature of the feed point impedance of the first antenna depends on the amplitude of the current induced in it by the second, and on the phase relationship between the original and induced currents. The amplitude and phase of the induced current depend on the spacing between the antennas and whether or not the second antenna is tuned to resonance.

In the discussion of the several preceding paragraphs, power is applied to only one of the two elements. Do not interpret this to mean that mutual coupling exists only in parasitic arrays! It is important to remember that mutual coupling exists between any two conductors that are located near one another.

Amplitude of Induced Current

The induced current will be largest when the two antennas are close together and are parallel. Under these conditions the voltage induced in the second antenna by the first, and in the first by the second, has its greatest value and causes the largest current flow. The coupling decreases as the parallel antennas are moved farther apart.

The coupling between collinear antennas is comparatively small, and so the mutual impedance between such antennas is likewise small. It is not negligible, however.

Phase Relationships

When the separation between two antennas is an appreciable fraction of a wavelength a measurable period of time elapses before the field from antenna 1 reaches antenna 2. There is a similar time lapse before the field set up by the current in number 2 gets back to induce a current in number 1. Hence the current induced in antenna 1 by antenna 2 will have a phase relationship with the original current in antenna 1 that depends on the spacing between the two antennas.

The induced current can range all the way from being completely in-phase with the original current to being completely out-of-phase with it. If the currents are in-phase, the total current is larger than the original current and the antenna feed point impedance is reduced. If the currents are out-of-phase, the total current is smaller and the impedance is increased. At intermediate phase relationships the impedance will be lowered or raised depending on whether the induced current is mostly in or mostly out-of-phase with the original current.

Except in the special cases when the induced current is exactly in or out-of-phase with the original current, the induced current causes the phase of the total current to shift with respect to the applied voltage. Consequently, the presence of a second antenna nearby may cause the impedance of an antenna to be reactive — that is, the antenna will be detuned from resonance — even though its self-impedance is entirely resistive. The amount of detuning depends on the magnitude and phase of the induced current.

Tuning Conditions

A third factor that affects the impedance of antenna 1 when antenna 2 is present is the tuning of number 2. If antenna 2 is not exactly resonant, the current that flows in it as a result of the induced voltage will either lead or lag the phase it would have if the antenna were resonant. This causes an additional phase advance or delay that affects the phase of the current induced back in antenna 1. Such a phase lag has an effect similar to a change in the spacing between self-resonant antennas. However, a change in tuning is not exactly equivalent to a change in spacing because the two methods do not have the same effect on the amplitude of the induced current.

6.1.3 MUTUAL IMPEDANCE AND GAIN

The mutual coupling between antennas or antenna elements can have a significant effect on the amount of current that will flow for a given amount of power supplied, which then determines the radiated field strength from the antenna. Mutual coupling, as used in this section, assumes that the mutual impedance between elements is taken into account, along with the added effects of propagation delay due to element spacing and the effects of element tuning or phasing.

Other things being equal, if the mutual coupling between two antennas is such that the currents are greater for the same total power than would be the case if there was no coupling, the power gain will be greater will be greater than shown in Table 6.1. If mutual coupling results in a reduction of current, the gain will be less than if there was no coupling.

The calculation of mutual impedance between antennas is a complex problem. Data for two simple but important cases are graphed in Figures 6.8 and 9. These graphs do not show the mutual impedance, but instead show a more useful quantity — the feed point resistance measured at the center of an antenna as it is affected by the spacing between two antennas.

As shown by the solid curve in **Figure 6.8**, the feed point resistance at the center of either antenna, when the two are *self-resonant*, parallel, and operated in-phase, decreases as the spacing between them is increased until the spacing is about 0.7 λ. This is a broadside array. The maximum gain is achieved from a pair of such elements when the spacing is in this region, because the current is larger for the same power and the fields from the two elements arrive in-phase at a distant point placed on a line perpendicular to the line joining the two antennas. (Self-resonance means the antenna is resonant in the absence of mutual coupling with any other antenna.)

The dashed line in Figure 6.8, representing two antennas operated 180° out-of-phase (end-fire), cannot be interpreted quite so simply. The feed point resistance decreases with spacing decreasing less than about 0.6 λ in this case. However, for the range of spacings considered, only when the spacing is 0.5 λ do the fields from the two antennas add up exactly in phase at a distant point in the favored direction. At smaller spacings the fields become increasingly out-of-phase, so the total field is less than the simple sum of the two. Smaller spacings thus decrease the gain at the same time that the reduction in feed point resistance is increasing it. For a lossless antenna, the gain goes through a maximum when the spacing is in the region of ⅛ λ.

The feed point resistance curve for two collinear elements in-phase, **Figure 6.9**, shows that the feed point resistance decreases and goes through a broad minimum in the region of 0.4 to 0.6 λ spacing between the adjacent ends of the antennas. As the minimum is not significantly less than the feed point resistance of an isolated antenna, the gain will not exceed the gain calculated on the basis of uncoupled antennas. That is, the best that two collinear elements will give, even with optimum spacing, is a power gain of about 2 (3 dB). When the separation between the ends is very small — the usual method of operation — the gain is reduced.

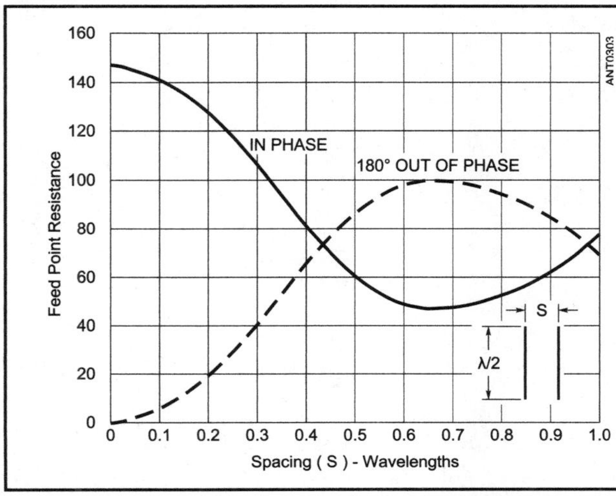

Figure 6.8 — Feed point resistance measured at the center of one element as a function of the spacing between two parallel ½-λ self-resonant antenna elements. For ground-mounted ¼-λ vertical elements, divide these resistances by two.

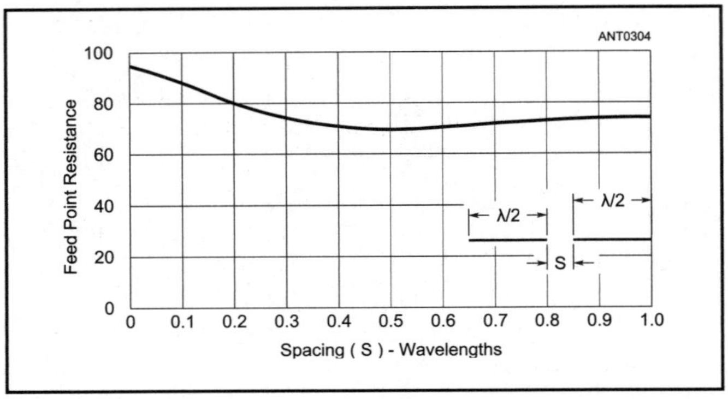

Figure 6.9 — Feed point resistance measured at the center of one element as a function of the spacing between the ends of two collinear self-resonant ½-λ antenna elements operated in phase.

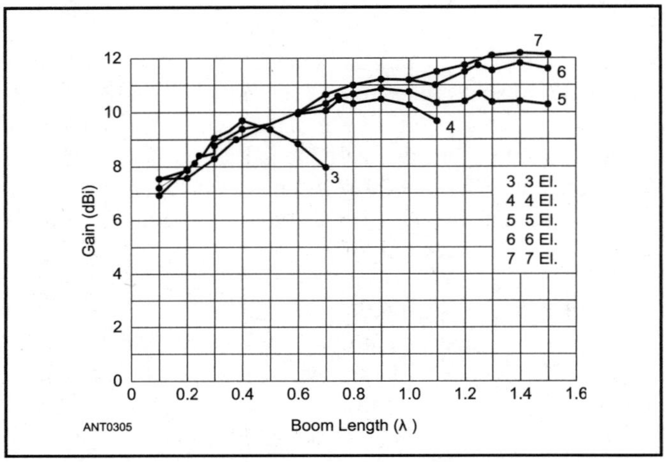

Figure 6.10 — Yagi gain for 3, 4, 5, 6 and 7-element beams as a function of boom length. (From *Yagi Antenna Design*, J. Lawson, W2PV.)

6.1.4 GAIN AND ARRAY DIMENSIONS

The gain of an array is principally determined by the dimensions of the array, so long as there are a minimum number of elements. A good example of this is the relationship between boom length, gain and number of elements for an array such as a Yagi. **Figure 6.10** compares the gain versus boom length for Yagis with different numbers of elements. For given number of elements, notice that the gain increases as the boom length increases, up to a maximum. Beyond this point, longer boom lengths result in less gain for a given number of elements. This observation does not mean that it is always desirable to use only the minimum number of elements. Other considerations of array performance, such as front-to-back ratio, minor lobe amplitudes or operating bandwidth, may make it advantageous to use more than the minimum number of elements for a given array length. A specific example of this is presented in a later section in a comparison between a half-square, a bobtail curtain and a Bruce array.

In a broadside array the gain is a function of both the length and width of the array. The gain can be increased by adding more elements (with additional spacing) or by using longer elements (>λ/2), although the use of longer elements requires proper attention to current phase in the elements. In general, in a broadside array the element spacing that gives maximum gain for a minimum number of elements, is in the range of 0.5 to 0.7 λ. Broadside arrays with elements spaced for maximum gain will frequently have significant side lobes and associated narrowing of the main lobe beamwidth. Side lobes can be reduced by using more than the minimum number of elements, spaced closer than the maximum gain distance.

Additional gain can be obtained by expanding the array into a third dimension. An example of this is the stacking of end-fire arrays in a broadside configuration. In the case of stacked short end-fire arrays, maximum gain occurs with spacings in the region of 0.5 to 0.7 λ. However, for longer higher-gain end-fire arrays, larger spacing is required to achieve maximum gain. This is important in VHF and UHF arrays, which often use long-boom Yagis.

6.2 DRIVEN ARRAYS

Definitions in the preceding section apply to multielement arrays of both types, driven and parasitic. However, there are special considerations for driven arrays that do not necessarily apply to parasitic arrays, and vice versa. Such considerations for Yagi and quad parasitic arrays are presented in the **HF Yagi and Quad Antennas** chapter. The remainder of this chapter is devoted to driven arrays.

Driven arrays in general are either broadside or end-fire, and may consist of collinear elements, parallel elements, or a combination of both. From a practical standpoint, the maximum number of usable elements depends on the frequency and the space available for the antenna. Fairly elaborate arrays, using as many as 16 or even 32 elements, can be installed in a rather small space when the operating frequency is in the VHF range and more at UHF. At lower frequencies the construction of antennas with a large number of elements is impractical for most amateurs.

Of course the simplest of driven arrays is one with just two elements. If the elements are collinear, they are always fed in-phase. The effects of mutual coupling are not great, as illustrated in Figure 6.9. Therefore, feeding power to each element in the presence of the other presents no significant problems. This may not be the case when the elements are parallel to each other. However, because the combination of spacing and phasing arrangements for parallel elements is infinite, the number of possible radiation patterns is endless.

This is illustrated in **Figure 6.11**. When the elements are fed in-phase, a broadside pattern always results. At spacings of less than ⅝ λ with the elements fed 180° out-of-phase, an end-fire pattern always results. With intermediate amounts of phase difference, the results cannot be so simply stated. Patterns evolve that are not symmetrical in all four quadrants.

Because of the effects of mutual coupling between the two driven elements, for a given power input greater or lesser currents will flow in each element with changes in spacing and phasing, as described earlier. This, in turn, affects the gain of the array in a way that cannot be shown merely by plotting the *shapes* of the patterns, as has been done in Figure 6.11. Therefore, supplemental gain information is also shown in Figure 6.11, adjacent to the pattern plot for each combination of spacing and phasing. The gain figures shown are referenced to a single element. For example, a pair of elements fed 90° out of phase with a spacing of λ/4 will have a gain in the direction of maximum radiation of 3.1 dB over a single element.

6.2.1 CURRENT DISTRIBUTION IN PHASED ARRAYS

In the plots of Figure 6.11, the two elements are assumed to be identical and self-resonant. In addition, currents of equal amplitude are assumed to be flowing at the feed point of each element, a condition that most often will not exist in practice without devoting special consideration to the feeder system. Such considerations are discussed in the next section of this chapter.

Most literature for radio amateurs concerning phased arrays is based on the assumption that if all elements in the array are identical, the *current distribution* in all the elements will be identical. This distribution is presumed to be that of a single, isolated element, or nearly sinusoidal. However, information published in the professional literature as early as the 1940s indicates the existence of dissimilar current distributions among the elements of phased arrays. (See Harrison and King references in the Bibliography.) Lewallen, in July 1990 *QST*, pointed out the causes and effects of dissimilar current distributions.

In essence, even though the two elements in a phased array may be identical and have exactly equal currents of the desired phase flowing at *the feed point*, the amplitude and phase relationships degenerate with departure from the feed point. This happens any time the phase relationship is not 0° or 180°. Thus, the field strengths produced at a distant point by the individual elements may differ. This is because the field from each element is determined by the *distribution* of the current, as well as its magnitude and phase.

The effects are minimal with shortened elements — verticals less than λ/4 or dipoles less than λ/2 long. The effects on radiation patterns begin to show at the above resonant lengths, and become profound with longer elements — λ/2 or longer verticals and 1 λ or longer center-fed elements. These effects are less pronounced with thin elements. The amplitude and phase degeneration takes place because the currents in the array elements are not sinusoidal. Even in two-element arrays with phasing of 0° or 180°, the currents are not sinusoidal, but in these two special cases they do remain identical.

The pattern plots of Figure 6.11 take element current distributions into account. The visible results of dissimilar distributions are incomplete nulls in some patterns and the development of very small minor lobes in others. For example, the pattern for a phased array with 90° spacing and 90° phasing has traditionally been published in amateur literature as a cardioid with a perfect null in the rear direction. Figure 6.11, calculated for 7.15-MHz self-resonant dipoles of #12 AWG wire in free space, shows a minor lobe at the rear and only a 33-dB front-to-back ratio.

It is characteristic of broadside arrays that the power gain is proportional to the length of the array but is substantially independent of the number of elements used, provided the optimum element spacing is not exceeded. This means, for example, that a five-element array and a six-element array will have the same gain, provided the elements in both are spaced so the overall array length is the same. Although this principle is seldom used for the purpose of reducing the number of elements because of complications introduced in feeding power to each element in the proper phase, it does illustrate the fact that there is nothing to be gained, in terms of more gain, by increasing the number of elements if the space occupied by the antenna is not increased proportionally.

Generally speaking, the maximum gain in the smallest linear dimensions will result when the antenna combines both broadside and end-fire directivity and uses both parallel and collinear elements. In this way the antenna is spread over a greater volume of space, which has the same effect as extending its length to a much greater extent in one linear direction.

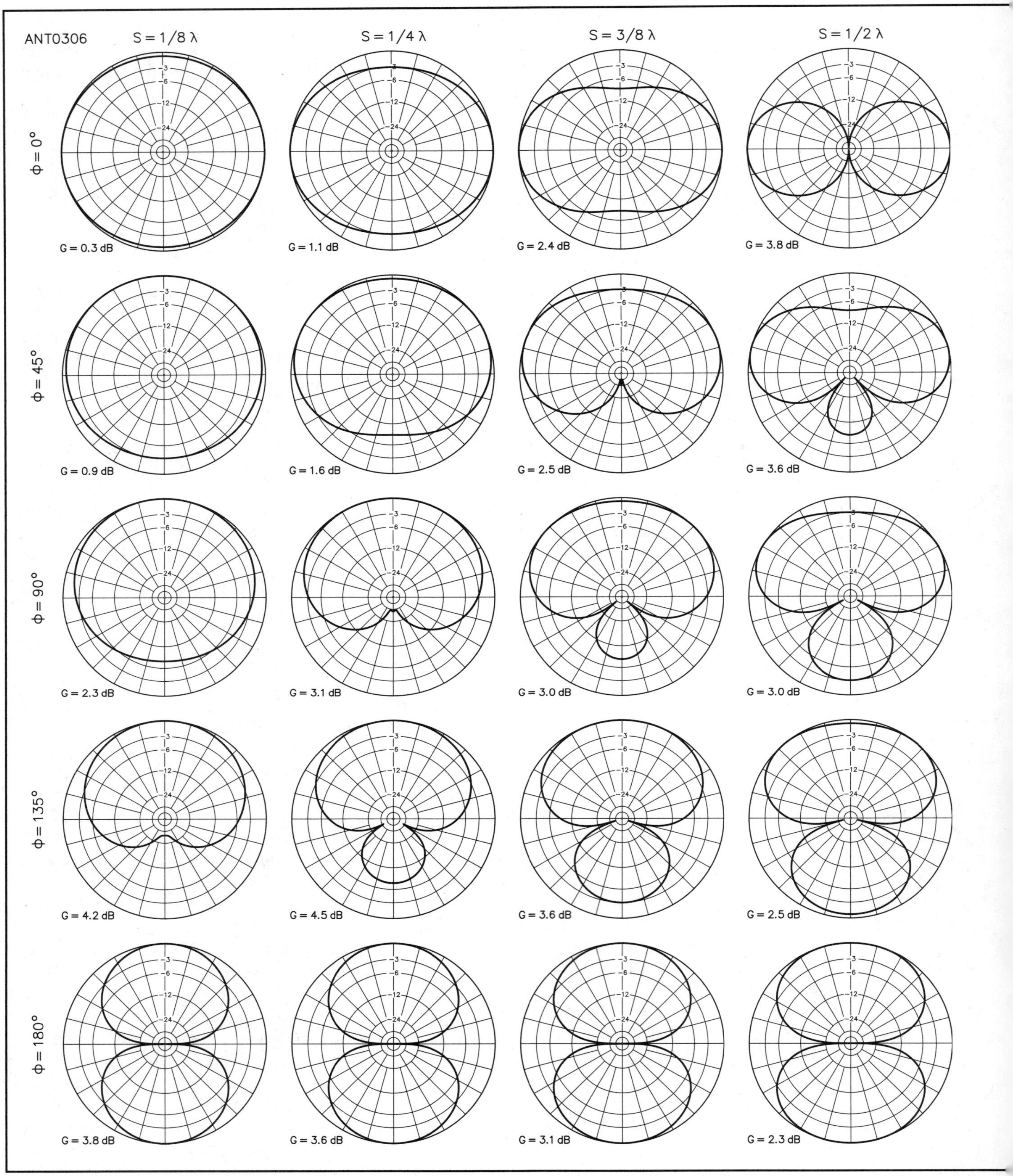

Figure 6.11 — H-plane patterns of two identical parallel driven elements, spaced and phased as indicated (S = spacing, φ = phasing). The elements are aligned with the vertical (0°-180°) axis, and the element nearer the 0° direction (top of page) is of lagging phase at angles other than 0°. The two elements are assumed to be thin and self-resonant, with equal-amplitude currents flowing at the feed point. See text regarding current distributions. The gain figure associated with each pattern

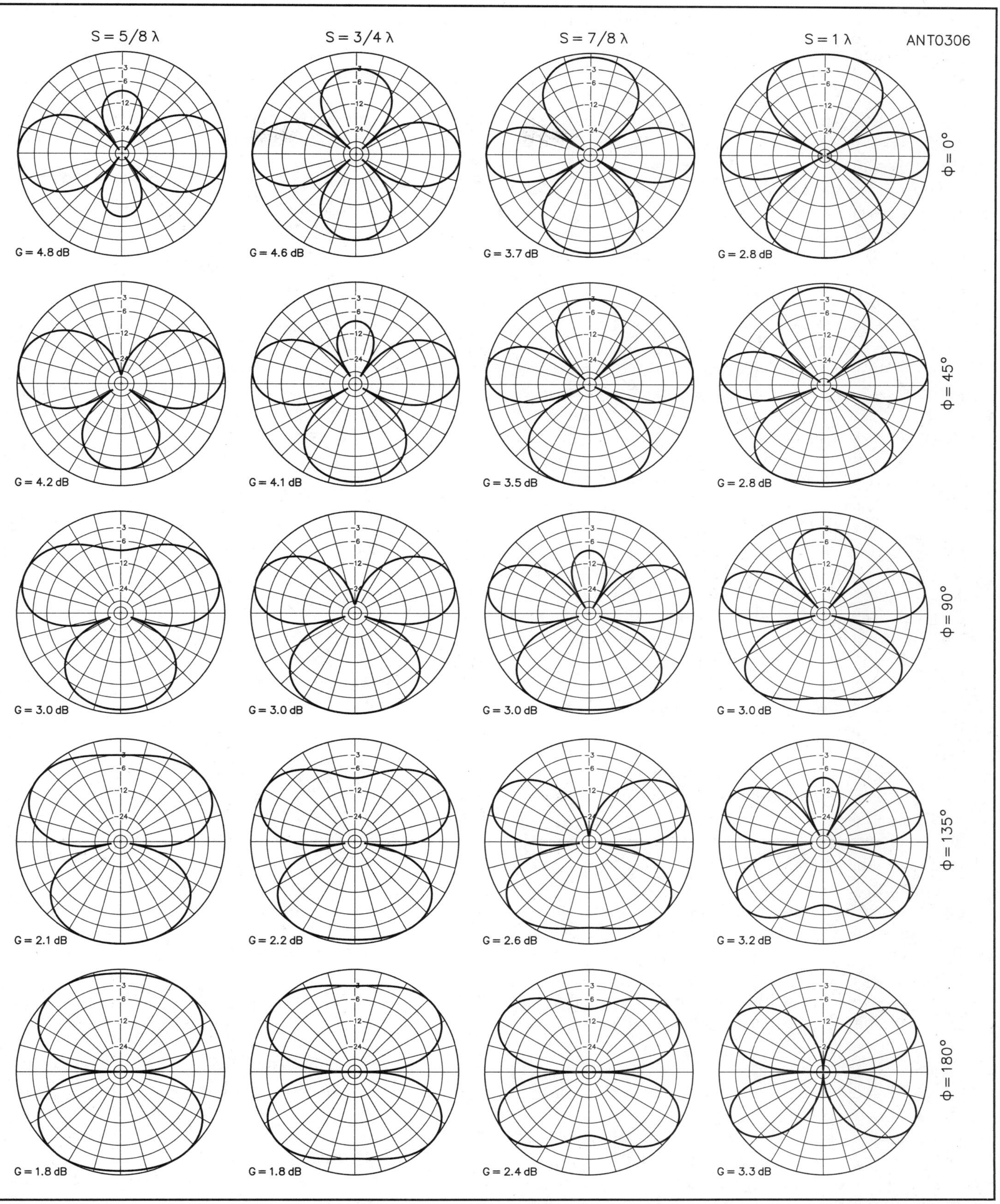

indicates that of the array over a single element. The plots represent the horizontal or azimuth pattern at a 0° elevation angle of two ¼-λ vertical elements over a perfect conductor, or the free-space vertical or elevation pattern of two horizontal ½-λ elements when viewed on end, with one element above the other. (Patterns computed with *ELNEC* — the predeccessor to *EZNEC*.)

6.3 PHASED ARRAY TECHNIQUES

Phased antenna arrays have become increasingly popular for amateur use, particularly on the lower frequency bands, where they provide one of the few practical methods to obtain substantial gain and directivity. This section on phased-array techniques was written by Roy Lewallen, W7EL, and updated for this edition.

The operation and limitations of phased arrays, how to design feed systems to make them work properly and how to make necessary tests and adjustments are discussed in the pages that follow. The examples deal primarily with vertical HF arrays, but the principles apply to VHF/UHF arrays and arrays made from other element types as well.

6.3.1 OVERVIEW

Much of this chapter is devoted to techniques for feeding phased arrays. Many people who have a limited acquaintance with phased array techniques believe this is a simple problem, consisting only of connecting array elements through "phasing lines" consisting of transmission lines of the desired electrical lengths. Unfortunately, except for a very few special cases, this approach won't achieve the desired array pattern.

Other proposed universal solutions, such as hybrid couplers or Wilkinson or other power dividers, also usually fail to achieve the necessary phasing. These approaches sometimes produce — often more by accident than design — results good enough to mislead the user into believing that the simple approach is working as planned. Confusion can result when an approach fails to work in different circumstances. This section will explain why the simple solutions don't work as often thought, and how to design feed systems that do consistently produce the desired results.

Very briefly, the reason why the simple phasing line approach fails is that the delay of current or voltage in a transmission line equals the line's electrical length only if the line is terminated in its characteristic impedance. And in phased arrays, element feed point impedances are profoundly affected by mutual coupling.

Consequently, even if each element has the correct impedance when isolated, it won't when all elements are excited. Furthermore, transmission lines that are not terminated in their characteristic impedance will transform both the voltage and current magnitude. The net result is that the array elements will have neither the correct magnitudes nor phases of current necessary for proper operation except in a few special cases. This isn't a minor effect of concern only to perfectionists, but often a major one that causes significant pattern distortion and poor or mis-located nulls. The problem is examined in greater depth later.

Power dividers and hybrid couplers also fail to achieve the desired result for different reasons which will be discussed below although in one common application hybrid couplers fortuitously provide results that are acceptable to many users. This chapter will show how to design array feed systems that will produce predicted element currents and array patterns.

Various *EZNEC* models are provided to illustrate concepts presented in this chapter. The models are included with the downloadable supplemental information for this book, and they may be used with the demo version of *EZNEC* v. 6 available from **www.eznec.com**.Step-by-step instructions for the examples are given in **Appendix A**.

6.3.2 FUNDAMENTALS OF PHASED ARRAYS

The performance of a phased array is determined by several factors. Most significant among these are the characteristics of a single element, reinforcement or cancellation of the fields from the elements and the effects of mutual coupling. To understand the operation of phased arrays, it is first necessary to understand the operation of a single antenna element.

Of primary importance is the strength of the field produced by the element. The field radiated from a linear (straight) element, such as a dipole or vertical monopole, is proportional to the sum of the elementary currents flowing in each part of the antenna element. For this discussion it is important to understand what determines the current in a single element.

The amount of current flowing at the base of a ground mounted vertical or ground-plane antenna is given by the familiar formula

$$I = \sqrt{\frac{P}{R}} \qquad (2)$$

where

P is the power supplied to the antenna

R is the feed point resistance.

R consists of two parts, the loss resistance and the radiation resistance. The loss resistance, R_L, includes losses in the conductor, in the matching and loading components and dominantly (in the case of ground-mounted verticals) in ground losses. The power "dissipated" in the radiation resistance, R_r, is actually the power that is radiated, so maximizing the power dissipated by the radiation resistance is desirable. However, the power "dissipated" in the loss resistance truly is lost as heat, so resistive losses should be made as small as possible.

The radiation resistance of an element can be derived from electromagnetic field theory, being a function of antenna length, diameter and geometry. Graphs of radiation resistance versus antenna length are given in the **Dipoles and Monopoles** chapter. The radiation resistance of a thin resonant λ/4 ground-mounted vertical is about 36 Ω. A resonant λ/2 dipole in free space has a radiation resistance of twice this amount, about 73 Ω. Reducing the antenna lengths by one-half drops the radiation resistances to approximately 7 and 14 Ω, respectively.

The radiation resistance of a large variety of antennas can easily be determined by using *EZNEC*. The radiation resistance is simply the feed point resistance (the resistive part of the feed point impedance) when all losses have been set to zero.

Radiation Efficiency

To generate a stronger field from a given radiator, it is necessary to increase the power P (the brute-force solution), decrease the loss resistance R_L (by putting in a more elaborate ground system for a vertical, for instance) or to somehow decrease the radiation resistance R_r so more current will flow with a given power input. This can be seen by expanding the formula for base current as

$$I = \sqrt{\frac{P}{R_R + R_L}} \quad (3)$$

Splitting the feed point resistance into components R_r and R_L easily leads to an understanding of element efficiency. The efficiency of an element is the proportion of the total power that is actually radiated. The roles of R_r and R_L in determining efficiency can be seen by analyzing a simple equivalent circuit, shown in **Figure 6.12**.

The power dissipated in R_r (the radiated power) equals I^2R_r. The total power supplied to the antenna system is

$$P = I^2 (R_r + R_L) \quad (4)$$

so the efficiency (the fraction of supplied power that is actually radiated) is

$$\text{Eff } (\eta) = \frac{I^2 R_r}{I^2 (R_r + R_L)} = \frac{Rr}{R_r + R_L} \quad (5)$$

Efficiency is frequently expressed in percent, but expressing it in decibels relative to a 100%-efficient radiator gives a better idea of what to expect in the way of signal strength. The field strength of an element relative to a lossless but otherwise identical element, in dB, is

$$\text{FSG} = 10 \log \frac{R_r}{R_r + R_L} \quad (6)$$

where FSG = field strength gain in dB.

For example, information presented by Sevick in March 1973 *QST* shows that a λ/4 ground-mounted vertical antenna with four 0.2-λ radials has a feed point resistance of about 65 Ω (see the Bibliography at the end of this chapter). The efficiency of such a system is 36/65 = 55.4%. It is rather disheartening to think that, of 100 W fed to the antenna, only 55 W is being radiated, with the remainder literally warming up the ground. Yet the signal will be only 10 log (36/65) = –2.57 dB relative to the same vertical with a perfect ground system. In view of this information, trading a small reduction in signal strength for lower cost and greater simplicity may become an attractive consideration.

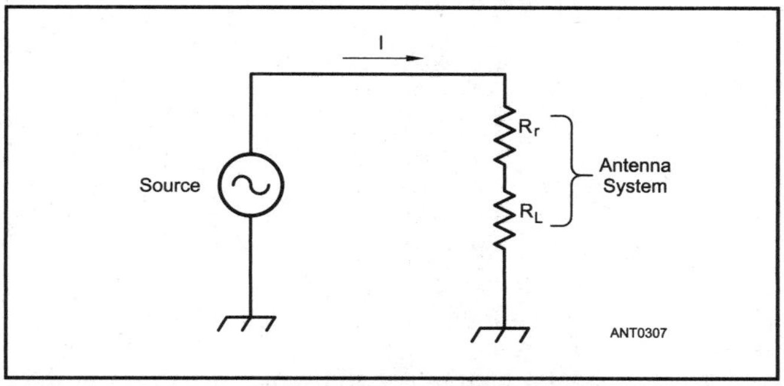

Figure 6.12 — Simplified equivalent circuit for a single-element resonant antenna. R_r represents the radiation resistance, and R_L the ohmic losses in the total antenna system.

So far, only the current at the base of a resonant antenna has been discussed, but the field is proportional to the sum of currents in each tiny part of the antenna. The field is a function of not only the magnitude of current flowing at the feed point, but also the distribution of current along the radiator and the length of the radiator. Nothing can be done at the feed point to change the current distribution, so for a given element the field strength is proportional to the feed point current. However, changing the radiator length or loading it at some point other than the feed point will change the current distribution.

More information on shortened or loaded radiators may be found in the **Antenna Fundamentals** and **Single-Band MF and HF Antennas** and in the Bibliography references of this chapter. The current distribution is also changed by mutual coupling to other array elements, although for most arrays this has only a minor effect on the pattern. This is discussed later in more detail. A few other important facts follow.

1) If there is no loss, the field from even an infinitesimally short radiator is less than ½ dB weaker than the field from a half-wave dipole or quarter-wave vertical. Without loss, all the supplied power is radiated regardless of the antenna length, so the only factor influencing gain is the slight difference in the patterns of very short and λ/2 antennas. The small pattern difference arises from different current distributions. A short antenna has a very low radiation resistance, resulting in a heavy current flow over its short length. In the absence of loss, this generates a field strength comparable to that of a longer antenna. Where loss is present — that is, in practical antennas — shorter radiators usually don't do so well, since the low radiation resistance leads to lower efficiency for a given loss resistance. Nevertheless, reasonably short antennas can achieve good efficiency if care is taken.

2) Caution must be used in calculating the efficiency of folded antennas. Folding transforms both the radiation resistance and loss resistance by the same factor, so their ratio and therefore the efficiency remains the same. It's easy to show that in a ground-mounted vertical array, folding reduces the current flowing from the feed line to the ground system by a factor of two due to the impedance transformation. However, the folded antenna has an additional connection to ground, which also carries half the original ground current. The result is that the same amount of current flows into the ground system, whether unfolded or folded, resulting in the same ground system loss. Analyses purporting to show otherwise invariably transform the radiation resistance but neglect to also transform the loss resistance and reach an incorrect conclusion.

3) The current flowing in an element with a given power input can be increased or decreased by mutual coupling to other elements. The effect is equivalent to changing the element radiation resistance. Mutual coupling is sometimes thought of as a minor effect, but often it is not minor!

Field Reinforcement and Cancellation

The mechanism by which phased arrays produce gain, and the role of mutual coupling in determining gain, were covered earlier in this chapter. One important point that can't be emphasized enough is that all antennas must abide by the law of *conservation of energy*. No antenna can radiate more power than supplied to it. The total amount of power it radiates is the amount it's supplied, less the amount lost as heat. This is true of all antennas, from the smallest "rubber ducky" to the most gigantic array.

Gain

Gain is strictly a relative measure, so the term is completely meaningless unless accompanied by a statement of just what it is relative to. One useful measure for phased array gain is *gain relative to a single similar element*. This is the increase in signal strength that would be obtained by replacing a single element by an array made from elements just like it. In some instances, such as investigating what happens to array performance when all elements become more lossy, it's useful to state gain relative to a more absolute, although unattainable standard: a lossless element.

And the most universal reference for gain is another unattainable standard, the *isotropic radiator*. This fictional antenna radiates absolutely equally in all directions. It's very useful because the field strength resulting from any power input is readily calculated, so if the gain relative to this standard is known, the field strength is also known for any radiated power. Gain relative to this reference is referred to as dBi, and it's the standard used by most modeling programs including *EZNEC*. To find the gain of an array relative to a single element or other reference antenna such as a dipole, model both the array and the single element or other reference antenna in the same environment and subtract their dBi gains. Don't rely on some assumption about the gain of a single element — many people assume values that can be very wrong.

Nulls

Pattern nulls are very often more important to users of phased arrays than gain because of their importance in reducing both man-made and natural interference when receiving. Consequently, a good deal of emphasis is, and should be, placed on achieving good pattern nulls. Unfortunately, good nulls are much more difficult to achieve than gain and they are much more sensitive to array and feed-system imperfections.

As an illustration, consider two elements that each produce a field strength of, say, exactly 1 millivolt per meter (mV/m) at some distance many wavelengths from the array. In the direction in which the fields from the elements are in-phase, a total field of 2 mV/m results. In the direction in which they're out-of-phase, zero field results. The ratio of maximum to minimum field strength of this array is 2/0, or infinity.

Now suppose, instead, that one field is 10% high and the other 10% low — 1.1 and 0.9 mV/m, respectively. In the forward direction, the field strength is still 2 mV/m, but in the canceling direction, the field will be 0.2 mV/m. The front-to-back ratio has dropped from infinity to 2/0.2, or 20 dB. (Actually, slightly more power is required to redistribute the field strengths this way, so the forward gain is reduced — but by only a small amount, less than 0.1 dB.) For most arrays, unequal fields from the elements have a minor effect on forward gain, but a major effect on pattern nulls. This is illustrated by ***EZNEC* Example: Nulls** in Appendix A.

Even with perfect current balance, deep nulls aren't assured. **Figure 6.13** shows the minimum spacing required for total field reinforcement or cancellation. If the element spacing isn't adequate, there may be no direction in which the fields are completely out-of-phase (see curve B of Figure 6.13). Slight physical and environmental differences between elements will invariably affect null depths, and null depths will also vary with elevation angle.

However, a properly designed and fed array can produce very impressive nulls. The key to producing good nulls, like producing gain, is controlling the strengths and phases of the fields from the elements. Just how to accomplish that is the subject of most of the remainder of this section. But be sure to keep in mind that producing good nulls is generally a much more difficult task than producing approximately the predicted gain.

Mutual Coupling

Mutual coupling was discussed briefly earlier in this chapter. Because it has an important and profound effect on both the performance and feed system design of phased arrays, it will be covered in greater depth here.

Mutual coupling refers to the effects which the elements in an array have on each other. Mutual coupling can occur intentionally or entirely unintentionally. People with multiple

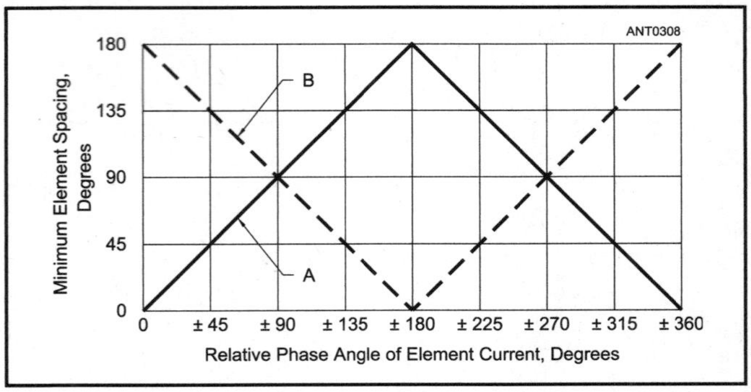

Figure 6.13 — Minimum element spacing required for total field reinforcement, curve A, or total field cancellation, curve B. Total cancellation results in pattern nulls in one or more directions. Total reinforcement does not necessarily mean there is gain over a single element, as the effects of loss and mutual coupling must also be considered.

antennas on a small lot (or car top) often discover that a better description of their system is a single antenna with multiple feed points. Current is induced in conductors in various antennas by mutual coupling, causing them to act like parasitic elements, which re-radiate and distort the antenna's pattern. The effects of mutual coupling are present whether or not the elements are driven.

Suppose that two driven elements are many wavelengths from each other. Each has some voltage and current at its feed point. For each element, the ratio of this voltage to current is the element self-impedance. If the elements are brought close to each other, the current in each element will change in magnitude and phase because of coupling with the field from the other element. The field from the first element changes the current in the second. This changes the field from the second, which alters the current in the first, and so forth until an equilibrium condition is reached in which the currents in all elements (hence, their fields) are totally interdependent.

The feed point impedances of all elements also are changed from their values when far apart, and all are dependent on each other. In a driven array, the changes in feed point impedances can cause additional changes in element currents, because the operation of many feed systems depends on the element feed point impedances. Significant mutual coupling occurs at spacings as great as a wavelength or more.

Connecting the elements to a feed system to form a driven array does not eliminate the effects of mutual coupling. In fact, in many driven arrays the mutual coupling has a greater effect on antenna operation than the feed system does. All feed-system designs must account for the impedance changes caused by mutual coupling if the desired current balance and phasing are to be achieved.

Several general statements can be made regarding the effects of mutual coupling on phased-array systems (unless loss is high enough to swamp mutual coupling effects as discussed in the next section).

1) The resistances and reactances of all elements of an array generally will be substantially different from the values when the elements are isolated (that is, very distant from other elements).

2) If the elements of a two-element array are identical and have equal currents that are in-phase or 180° out-of-phase, the feed point impedances of the two elements will be equal. But they will be different than for an isolated element. If the two elements are part of a larger array, their impedances can be very different from each other.

3) If the elements of a two-element array have currents that are neither in-phase (0°) nor out-of-phase (180°), their feed point impedances will not be equal. The difference will be considerable in typical amateur arrays.

4) The feed point resistances of the elements in a closely spaced, 180° out-of-phase array will be very low, resulting in poor efficiency due to ohmic losses unless care is taken to minimize loss. This is also true for any other closely spaced array with significant predicted gain.

It's essential to realize that this is not a minor effect and one that can be overlooked or ignored. See ***EZNEC* Example — Mutual Coupling** in Appendix A for an illustration of these phenomena.

Loss Resistance, Mutual Coupling and Antenna Gain

Loss reduces the effects of mutual coupling because the feed point impedance change resulting from mutual coupling is effectively in series with loss resistance. If the loss is great enough, two important results occur. First, the feed point impedance becomes independent of the presence of nearby current-carrying elements. This greatly simplifies feed system design — the simple "phasing-line" or hybrid-coupler feed system described below is adequate *provided that all elements are physically identical and the feed point of each element is matched to the* Z_0 *of the feed line and, if used, the hybrid coup*ler.

The impedance matching restrictions are necessary to insure that the phasing line or hybrid coupler performs as expected. Identical elements are needed so that equal element currents will result in equal fields from the elements.

In the absence of mutual coupling effects, the maximum gain of an array of identical elements relative to a single (similarly lossy) element is simply 10 log(N), where N is the number of elements — providing that spacing is adequate for the fields to fully reinforce in some direction. If spacing is less, maximum gain will also be less. Of course, the array gain relative to a single lossless element will be very low, most likely a sizeable negative number when expressed in dB. So intentionally introducing loss isn't a wise idea for a transmitting array. It is sometimes an advantageous thing to do for a receiving array, however, as explained in the following section.

High-gain close-spaced arrays, such as the W8JK phased array (see *EZNEC* example file **ARRL_W8JK.EZ** and accompanying Antenna Notes file), and most parasitic arrays depend heavily on mutual coupling to achieve their gain. Introduction of any loss to these arrays, which reduces the mutual coupling effects, has a profound effect on the gain. Consequently, parasitic or close-spaced driven arrays often produce disappointing results when made from grounded vertical elements unless each has a fairly elaborate (and therefore very low-loss) ground system.

If you place two low-loss elements very close together and feed them in-phase, mutual coupling reduces the array gain to essentially that of a single element, so there's no advantage to this configuration over a single element. However, if you have a single lossy element, for example a short vertical having a relatively poor ground system, you can improve the gain by up to 3 dB by adding a second, close spaced, element and ground system and feeding the two in-phase. Another way to look at this technique is that you're putting two equal ground system resistances in parallel, which effectively cuts the loss in half. The gain you can realize in practice depends on such things as the ground system overlap, but it might be a practical way to improve transmitting array performance in some situations.

6.3.3 FEEDING PHASED ARRAYS

The previous section explains why the fields from the elements must be very close to the ratios required by the array design. Since the field strengths are proportional to the currents in the elements, controlling the fields requires controlling the element currents. Since the desired current ratio is 1:1 for virtually all two-element and for most (but not all) larger amateur arrays, special attention is paid to methods of assuring equal element currents. But we will examine other current ratios also.

The Role of Element Currents

The field from a conductor is proportional to the current flowing on it. So if we're to control the relative strengths and phases of the fields from the elements, we have to control their currents. We usually do this by controlling the currents at the element feed points. But because the field from an element depends on the current everywhere along the element, elements having identical feed point currents will produce different fields if they have different current distributions — that is, if the way the current varies along the lengths of the elements is different.

A previous section explained that mutual coupling alters the current distribution, so in many arrays the current distributions will be different on the elements and consequently the relationship between the overall fields won't be the same as that between the feed point currents. Fortunately, this effect is relatively minor in thin, λ/4 monopole or λ/2 dipole elements. The most common arrays are made from elements in this category, so we can generally get very nearly the desired ratio of fields by creating the same ratio of feed point currents. Exceptions are detailed in the following section.

Feed Point vs Element Current

For most antennas, environmental factors are likely to cause greater performance anomalies than current distribution differences, and both can be corrected with minor feed system adjustments. The difference between field and feed point current ratios can become very significant, however, if the elements are very fat and/or close to λ/2 (monopole) or 1 λ (dipole) long. In those cases, most of the feed systems described here won't produce the desired field ratios without major adjustment or modification, except in the special cases of 2-element arrays with identical elements having feed point currents in-phase or 180° out-of-phase. In those special cases, the element current distributions are the same for the same reason the feed point impedances are equal. This is explained later in the feed system sections.

To get an idea of just how large an element must be to disturb the pattern of an array with correct feed point currents, a two-element cardioid array of quarter wave vertical elements was modeled at 10 MHz. With thin, 0.1-inch diameter elements the front-to-back ratio was 35 dB, the very small reverse lobe caused by slightly unequal element current distributions. Increasing the element diameter to 20 inches decreased the front-to-back ratio to 20 dB. Returning the front-to-back ratio of the array of 20-inch elements to >35 dB required changing the feed point current ratio from the nominal value of 1.0 at an angle of 90° to 0.88 at 83°.

The same array was first modeled with 0.1-inch diameter elements, where it has a front-to-back ratio of 35 dB, then the elements were lengthened. The front-to-back ratio dropped to 20 dB at an element length of 36 feet, or about 0.37 λ. In that case, adjustment of the feed point current ratio to about 0.9 at about 83° restored a good front-to-back ratio.

In the discussion and development which follow, the assumption is made that the fields will be very nearly proportional to the feed point currents. If the elements are fat or long enough to make this assumption untrue, some adjustment of feed point current ratio will be necessary to achieve the desired pattern, particularly nulls. Most feed systems can be designed for any current ratio. Modeling will reveal the ratio required for the desired pattern, and then the feed system can be designed accordingly.

6.3.4 COMMON PHASED ARRAY FEED SYSTEMS

This section will first describe several popular approaches to feeding phased arrays that often don't produce the desired results. It will describe why they don't work as well as hoped. It also briefly discusses systems that could be used, but that often aren't appropriate or optimum for amateur arrays.

This will be followed in the next section by detailed descriptions of array feed systems that do produce the predicted element current ratios and array patterns.

The "Phasing-Line" Approach

For an array to produce the desired pattern, the element currents must have the required magnitude and the required phase relationship. As explained above, this can generally be achieved well enough by causing the feed point currents to have that same relationship.

On the surface, this sounds easy — just make sure that the difference in electrical lengths of the feed lines to the elements equals the desired phase angle. Unfortunately, this approach doesn't necessarily achieve the desired result. The first problem is that the phase shift through the line is not equal to its electrical length. The current (or, for that matter, voltage) delay in a transmission line is equal to its electrical length in only a few special cases — cases which don't exist in most amateur arrays! The impedance of an element in an array is frequently very different from the impedance of an isolated element and the impedances of all the elements in an array can be different from each other.

See the *EZNEC* Example — Mutual Coupling in Appendix A for a graphic illustration of the effect of mutual coupling on feed point impedance. Also look at the Four-Square array example in the Phased Array Design Examples section. The array in that example has one element with a *negative* feed point resistance, if ground loss is low. Without mutual coupling, the resistance of that same element would be about 36 Ω plus ground loss.

Because of mutual coupling, the elements seldom provide a matched load for the element feed lines. The effect of mismatch on phase shift can be seen in **Figure 6.14**. Observe

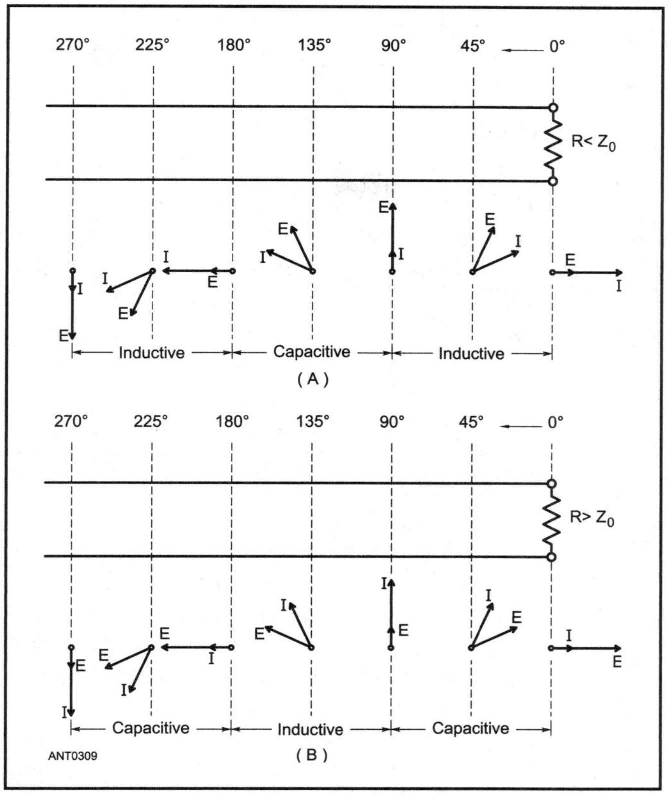

Figure 6.14 — Resultant voltages and currents along a mismatched line. At A, R less than Z_0, and at B, R greater than Z_0.

what happens to the phase of the current and voltage on a line terminated by a purely resistive impedance that is lower than the characteristic impedance of the line (Figure 6.14A). At a point 45° from the load the current has advanced less than 45°, and the voltage more than 45°. At 90° from the load both are advanced 90°. At 135° the current has advanced more and the voltage less than 135°. This apparent slowing down and speeding up of the current and voltage waves is caused by interference between the forward and reflected waves. It occurs on any line that is not terminated with a pure resistance equal to its characteristic impedance. If the load resistance is greater than the characteristic impedance of the line, as shown in Figure 6.14B, the voltage and current exchange angles. Adding reactance to the load causes additional phase shift. *The only cases in which the current (or voltage) delay is equal to the electrical length of the line are*

1) When the line is flat; that is, terminated in a purely resistive load equal to its characteristic impedance;

2) When the line length is an integral number of half wavelengths;

3) When the line length is an odd number of quarter wavelengths and the load is purely resistive; and

4) When other specific lengths are used for specific load impedances.

Just how much phase error can be expected if two feed lines are simply hooked up to form an array? There is no simple answer. Some casually designed feed systems might deliver satisfactory results, but most will not. See the *EZNEC* Example — "Phasing-Line" Feed in Appendix A for the typical consequences of using this sort of feed system.

A second problem with simply connecting feed lines of different lengths to the elements is that the lines will change the *magnitudes* of the currents. The magnitude of the current (or voltage) out of a line does not equal the magnitude into that line, except in cases 1, 2 and 4 above. The feed systems presented later in this chapter assure currents that are correct in both magnitude and phase.

The elementary phasing-line approach *will* work in three very special but common situations. If the array consists of only two identical elements and those elements are fed in-phase, mutual coupling will modify the element impedances, but both will be modified exactly the same amount. Consequently, if the two elements are fed through equal-length transmission lines, the lines will transform and delay the currents by the same amount and result in equal, in-phase currents at the element feed points.

Similarly, an array of two identical elements fed 180° out of phase will have the same feed point impedances and can be fed with two lines of any length so long as one line is an electrical half wavelength longer than the other. But this can't be extended to any two elements in a larger array, since mutual coupling to the other elements can result in different feed point impedances. Methods will be described later which do assure a correct current ratio in this situation.

The third application in which the phasing-line approach works is in receiving arrays where the elements are very short in terms of wavelength and/or very lossy. In either of these cases, mutual coupling between elements is much less than an element's self-impedance. This allows the elements to be individually matched to the feed lines, with no significant change taking place when the elements are formed into an array. Under those conditions, the transmission lines can be matched and the lines used as simple delay lines with easily predictable phase shift and with no transformation of current or voltage magnitude other than cable loss. This is discussed in the later section on receiving antennas.

ON4UN's *Low-Band DXing* (see Bibliography) describes a modified phasing-line feed system method which works in some special cases where the feed point resistances are favorable to the approach. First, a quarter wave transmission line is connected to each element. Then a shunt inductor or capacitor is added at the input of the line to the lagging element in order to make the impedance at that point purely resistive. If the resulting resistance is close to the characteristic impedance of an available transmission line (e.g., 50 or 75 Ω), a simple delay line can be used to feed that element. See *EZNEC* example **ARRL_Cardioid_Modified_Phasing_Line_Feed.EZ** and its accompanying Antenna Notes file for an example. When impedance values allow this feed method, it saves only one component compared to the L network feed method and isn't fully adjustable. And it has one component more than the "simplest" method to be described. The bandwidth of arrays fed using this method isn't significantly different from the other feed systems, so there's no clear advantage to using it. However, it might be a viable approach under some circumstances. More design information is available in *Low-Band DXing*.

The interested reader is encouraged to consult *Low-Band DXing* as it contains examples of additional feed system design approaches that produce a desired element magnitude and phase ratio.

Many arrays *can* be correctly fed with a feed system consisting of only transmission lines, but the technique requires knowledge of the element feed point impedances in a correctly fed array. Line lengths can then be computed that provide the correct ratio of currents into those particular load impedances. The line lengths generally differ by amount that's considerably different from the element phase angle difference, and appropriate line lengths can't always be found for all arrays. This technique is described more fully in the section The Simplest Phased Array Feed System — That Works later in this chapter and illustrated in the examples in Phased Array Design Examples.

The Wilkinson Divider

The *Wilkinson divider*, sometimes called the *Wilkinson power divider*, was once heavily promoted as a means to distribute power among the elements of a phased array. While it's a very useful device for other purposes, it won't produce the desired current ratios in antenna elements. In most phased arrays, element feed point resistances are different and therefore require different amounts of power to achieve the desired equal magnitude currents. (See the section on mutual coupling above.) A Wilkinson divider is intended to deliver equal powers, not currents, to multiple loads. And it won't even do that when the load impedances are different. It might be useful in combining element outputs in receiving arrays in which element losses are high enough to swamp mutual coupling effects and effect impedance matches.

The Hybrid Coupler

Hybrid couplers are promoted as solving the problem of achieving equal magnitude currents with a 90° phase difference between elements. Unfortunately, standard 90° hybrids provide equal magnitude, quadrature (90° phased) currents only when the load impedances are equal and correct. And this simply isn't true of arrays with quadrature-fed elements, except for arrays consisting of short and/or lossy elements, usually suitable only for receiving. In those arrays, the hybrid coupler can be useful for the same reasons as the phasing-line approach, discussed in an earlier section.

Hybrid couplers can, however, be useful for feeding transmitting or low-loss phased arrays if suitably modified to function when terminated with the particular impedances presented by an array's elements. In *Low-Band DXing* (see the Bibliography), methods are described to modify the standard 90° hybrid design to provide approximate hybrid functionality when terminated in typical phased array impedance values. Methods are quite involved, as evidenced by more than 20 pages devoted to the topic. It is important to realize that no passive network, including the hybrid coupler, is capable of providing equal magnitude 90° phased currents in loads with arbitrary impedances. See The Magic Bullet below for more information.

"Crossfire" Feed Method

Tom Rauch, W8JI, has described a "crossfire" feed system which is capable of producing a deep null in one direction over an exceptionally wide bandwidth. This method, generally suitable only for lossy receiving arrays, is described in more detail in this chapter's section Receiving Arrays and Broadbanding.

Large Array Feed Systems

The author once worked on a radar system where the transmit array consisted of over 5000 separate dipole elements and the receive array over 4000 pairs of crossed dipoles, all over a metal reflecting plane, which was the sloping side of a 140 foot high building. In such large arrays, each element is in essentially the same environment as every other element except near the array edges, so almost all elements have very nearly the same feed point impedance. While producing the phase shifts and magnitude tapers is a considerable mathematical challenge, the problem of unequal element feed point impedances can largely be ignored. Consequently, feed methods for these large arrays are generally not suitable for typical amateur arrays of a few elements.

The Broadcast Approach

Networks can be designed to transform the element base impedances from their values in an excited array to, say, 50 Ω resistive. Then another network can be inserted at the junction of the feed lines to properly divide the power among the elements (not necessarily equally!). And finally, additional networks must be added to correct for the phase shifts and magnitude transformations of the other networks. This general approach is used by the broadcast industry, in installations that are typically adjusted only once for a particular frequency and pattern.

Although this technique can be used to correctly feed any type of array, design is difficult and adjustment is tedious since all adjustments interact. When the relative currents and phasing are adjusted, the feed point impedances change, which in turn affect the element currents and phasing, and so on. A further disadvantage of using this method is that switching the array direction is generally impossible. Information on applying this technique to amateur arrays can be found in Paul Lee's book on verticals, listed in the Bibliography.

The "Magic Bullet"

More than 15 years ago, the *Antenna Book* published specifications for a circuit that would provide equal-magnitude, 90° phased currents into two loads without respect to the load impedances. This would be a circuit that would guarantee exactly the correct currents in any two elements. In 1996, Kevin Schmidt, W9CF, formulated a mathematical proof that such a circuit — in fact, one resulting in any relative phase other than 0° or 180° — cannot exist if restricted to reciprocal elements. (That is, it can't exist unless directional components such as ferrite circulators are used.) Thus, in order to design a network to feed elements with currents of any other phase angle other than 0 or 180°, we must know the impedance of at least one element and correct feed system operation depends on that impedance. There's no way around this requirement. At the time of this writing, Schmidt's proof can be found at **fermi.la.asu.edu/w9cf/articles/magic/index.html**.

6.3.5 RECOMMENDED FEED METHODS FOR AMATEUR ARRAYS

The following feed methods are able to produce element feed point currents having a desired magnitude and phase relationship, resulting in desirable and predictable patterns. Most methods require knowing the feed point impedance of one or more array elements *when the array element currents are the correct values*. This isn't possible to measure directly, because if the element currents were correct, the feed system would already be working properly and no further design would be necessary.

By far the easiest way to get this information, if possible, is by computer modeling. Modeling programs such as *EZNEC* allow you to construct an ideal array with perfect element currents then look at the resulting feed point impedances. Because of its simplicity and versatility, this approach is highly recommended and it's the one used for the array design examples in this chapter.

Some feed systems allow adjustment, so even an approximate result provides an adequate starting point on which to base the feed-system design. There are several other alternatives to computer modeling. One is to first eliminate the effects of coupling of the element to be measured from all other elements, usually by open circuiting the feed points of the other elements. Then the feed point impedance of the element is measured. Next, the impedance change due to mutual coupling from all other elements has to be calculated, based on the intended currents in the other elements, their lengths and their distances from the element being measured. Mutual impedance (which is not the same as the impedance change due to mutual coupling) between each pair of elements must be known for this calculation and it can be determined by measurement, calculation or from a graph.

The latter two methods are possible only for the simplest element types and measurement is very difficult to do accurately because it involves resolving very small differences between two relatively large values. Accuracy of a calculated result will be reduced if any elements are relatively fat (that is, they have a large diameter, because this impacts the current distribution) or they aren't perfectly straight and parallel.

So the only situations where you're likely to get good results from approaches other than modeling are the very easiest ones to model! Modeling also allows determination of the feed point impedances of many antennas that are impossible to calculate by manual or graphical methods. Therefore, the manual approach isn't discussed or used here. Appendix B, with the downloadable supplemental information for this book, contains equations and manual techniques from previous editions of *The ARRL Antenna Book*, for those who are interested. You can also find a great deal of additional information in many of the texts listed in the Bibliography, particularly Jasik and Johnson.

Current Forcing with λ/4 Lines — Elements In-Phase or 180° Out-of-Phase

The feed method introduced here has been used in its simplest form to feed television receiving antennas and other arrays, as presented by Jasik, pages 2-12 and 24-10 or Johnson, on his page 2-14. However, until first presented in the *ARRL Antenna Book*, this feed method was not widely applied to amateur arrays.

The method takes advantage of an interesting property of λ/4 transmission lines. (All references to lengths of lines are electrical length and lines are assumed to have negligible loss.) See **Figure 6.15**. The magnitude of the *current out* of a λ/4 transmission line is equal to the *input voltage* divided by the characteristic impedance of the line. This is independent of the load impedance. In addition, the phase of the output current lags the phase of the input voltage by 90°, also independent of the load impedance. These properties can be used to advantage in feeding arrays with certain phase angles between elements.

If any number of loads are connected to a common driving point through λ/4 lines of equal impedance, the currents in the loads will be *forced* to be equal and in-phase, regardless of the load impedances. So any number of in-phase elements can be correctly fed using this method, regardless of how their impedances might have been changed by mutual coupling. Arrays that require unequal currents can be fed through λ/4 lines of unequal impedances to achieve other current ratios.

The properties of λ/2 lines also are useful. Since the current out of a λ/2 line equals the input current shifted 180°, regardless of the load impedance, any number of half wavelengths of line may be added to the basic λ/4, and the current and phase forcing property will be preserved. For example, if one element is fed through a λ/4 line and another element is fed from the same point through a 3λ/4 line of the same characteristic impedance, the currents in the two elements will be forced to be equal in magnitude and 180° out-of-phase, regardless of the feed point impedances of the elements.

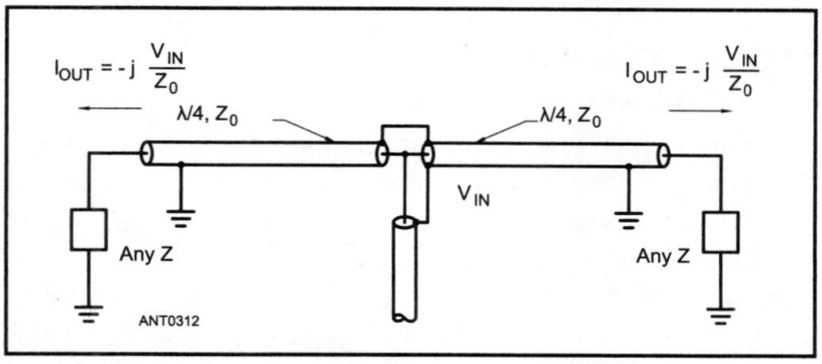

Figure 6.15 — A useful property of λ/4 transmission lines; see text. This property is utilized in the "current-forcing" method of feeding an array of coupled elements.

If an array of two, and only two, identical elements is fed in-phase or 180° out-of-phase with equal magnitude currents, both elements have the same feed point impedance. The reason is that each element sees exactly the same thing when looking at the other. In an in-phase array, each sees another element with an identical current; in an out-of-phase array, each sees another element with an equal magnitude current that's 180° out-of-phase, the same distance away in both cases. This isn't true in something like a 90° fed array, where one element sees another with a current leading its current by 90°, while the other sees another element with a lagging current.

With arrays fed in-phase or 180° out-of-phase, feeding the elements through equal lengths of feed line (in-phase) or lengths differing by 180° (out-of-phase) will lead to the correct current magnitude ratio and phase difference, regardless of the line length and regardless of how much the element feed point impedances depart from the lines' Z_0.

Unless the feed point impedances equal the line Z_0 or the lines are an integral number of half wavelengths long, the magnitudes of the currents out of the lines will not be equal to the input magnitudes, and the phase will not be shifted an amount equal to the electrical lengths of the lines. But both lines will produce the same transformation and phase shift because their load impedances are equal, resulting in a properly fed array. In practice, however, feed point impedances of elements frequently are different even in these arrays, because of such things as different ground systems (for ground mounted vertical elements), proximity to buildings or other antennas, or different heights above ground (for horizontal or elevated vertical elements).

In many larger arrays, two or more elements must be fed either in-phase or out-of-phase with equal currents, but coupling to other elements can cause their impedances to change unequally — sometimes extremely so. Using the current-forcing method allows the feed system designer to ignore all these effects, while guaranteeing equal and correctly phased currents in any combination and number of 0° and 180° fed elements.

This method is used to develop feed systems for the Four-Square and 4-element rectangular arrays in the Practical Array Design section. The front and rear elements of a Four-Square antenna provide a good example of elements having very different feed point impedances that are forced to have equal out-of-phase currents.

"The Simplest Phased Array Feed System — That Works"

This is the title of an article in *The ARRL Antenna Compendium, Vol 2*, which describes how arrays can be fed with a feed system consisting of only transmission lines. (The article is available for viewing at **www.eznec.com/Amateur/Articles/Simpfeed.pdf** and is also with the downloadable supplemental information for this book, and supported by the program *Arrayfeed1*, available at **www.arrl.org/antenna-book-reference**, which solves the equations presented in the article.)

As explained earlier in the Phasing Line section, this method requires knowing what the element feed point impedances will be in a correctly fed array. Feed line lengths can then be computed, for most but not all arrays. These lengths will produce the desired current ratio in array elements that do present those feed point impedances. If you know the load impedances connected to transmission lines whose inputs are connected to a common source, it's simple to calculate the resulting load currents for any transmission line lengths. However, the reverse problem is much more difficult; that is, given the load impedances and desired currents to calculate the required cable lengths.

One way to solve the problem is to choose some feed line lengths, solve for the currents, examine the answer, adjust the feed line lengths, and try again until the desired currents are obtained. The author used this iterative approach, using first a programmable calculator and later a computer, for some time before developing a direct way of solving for the transmission-line lengths. The direct solution method is described briefly in the *Compendium* article.

Figure 6.16 shows the basic so-called "simplest" system applied to a two-element array. Although it resembles an elementary phasing-line system as described earlier, the critical difference is that the lengths of Lines 1 and 2 are calculated to provide the correct current relative magnitude transformation and phase shift when terminated with the actual feed point impedances.

The advantage to using this "simplest" feed system is indeed its simplicity. It's no more complicated than the

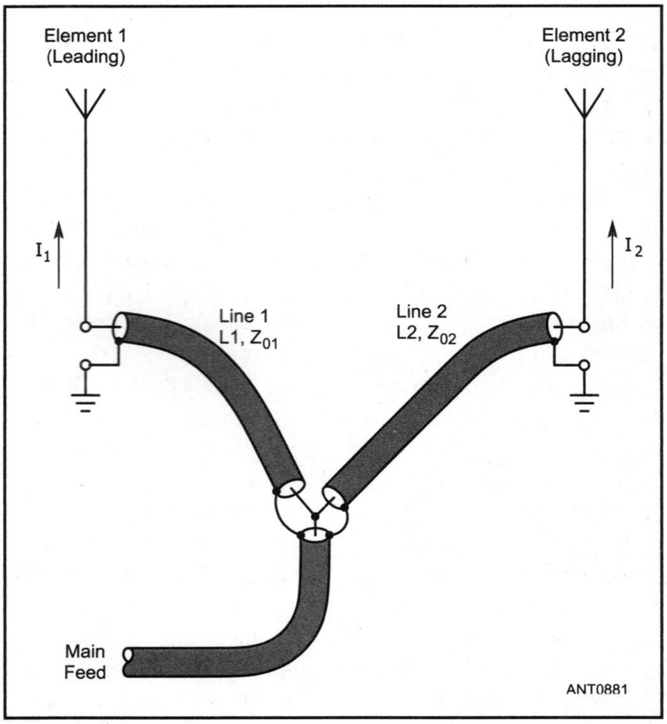

Figure 6.16 — "Simplest" feed system for 2-element array. No matching or phasing network is used here, only transmission lines.

elementary phasing-line approach but actually works as planned. The disadvantage over some other methods is that there's no convenient adjustment to compensate for environment factors, array imperfections or inaccurately known feed point impedances.

Also, while unusual, it's possible that no suitable feed line lengths can be found for some arrays, or at least none with practical feed line characteristic impedances. The difference in electrical feed line lengths almost never equals the difference in phase angles between element currents. This is because of the different line delays resulting from different feed point impedances.

Arrayfeed1 can do the calculations for any two elements (alone or in a larger array), a Four-Square array or a rectangular array in which two in-phase elements are driven at any current magnitude and phase relative to the other two in-phase elements. These possibilities cover a large number of common arrays.

Arrayfeed1 can also be applied to other types of arrays using the method described in the Feeding Larger Arrays"section in Appendix B (with the downloadable supplemental information for this book). The required knowledge of element feed point impedances in a correctly fed array can be obtained using *EZNEC*. Examples of the design of a "simplest" feed system for several different arrays using *EZNEC* and *Arrayfeed1* can be found in the Phased Array Design Examples section.

When a solution is possible for a given choice of line characteristic impedances, a second solution with different lengths is always available. See the comments in the introductory part of the Phased Array Design Examples section about choosing the solution to use.

An Adjustable L-Network Feed System

Adjustment of the current ratio of any two elements requires varying two independent quantities; for example, the magnitude and phase of the current ratio. Two degrees of freedom — adjustments that are at least partially independent — are required. The "simplest" all-transmission line feed system described earlier adjusts the lengths of the two transmission lines to achieve the correct ratio.

But if the antenna characteristics aren't well known — for example, if the ground resistance isn't known even approximately — then the initial "simplest" design won't be optimum and adjustment can be difficult and tedious. The current-forcing method produces correct currents independently of the element characteristics, so it doesn't require adjustment as long as the elements are identical. But it's suitable only for feeding elements in-phase or 180° out-of-phase and a few fixed current-magnitude ratios.

The addition of a simple network as shown in **Figure 6.17** allows you to easily adjust feeding of element pairs at other relative phase angles and/or magnitude ratios. Any desired current ratio (magnitude and phase) can be obtained with two elements fed with any lengths of wire, equal or unequal, by adding a network.

However, calculations for the general case are complex.

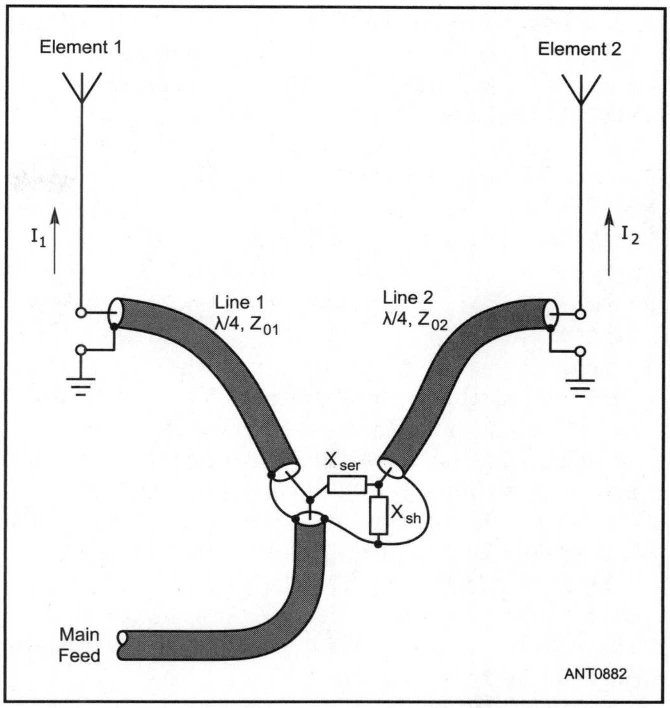

Figure 6.17 — The addition of a simple L network to Figure 6.16 allows you to easily adjust feeding of element pairs at other relative phase angles and/or magnitude ratios.

The problem becomes much simpler if the transmission lines are restricted to lengths of odd multiples of λ/4, forming a modified "forcing" system that includes an added network. There are at least three additional advantages of this scheme. One is that a λ/4 line is easy to measure, even if the velocity factor isn't known. This is described in the Practical Aspects of Phased Array Design section.

Second is that the feed system becomes completely insensitive to the feed point impedance of one of the two elements. And the third is that the transmission lines of "forcing" systems feeding groups of elements in larger arrays can be used in place of the normal λ/4 lines. This greatly simplifies both the design of feed systems for larger arrays and the feed systems themselves. Note that both lines can be changed to 3λ/4 if necessary to span the physical distance between elements, but both lines must be the same 3λ/4 length.

This basic feed method can be used for any pair of elements, or for two groups of elements having forced equal currents. (See Feeding Four Element and Larger Arrays below) Many networks can accomplish the desired function, but a simple L network is adequate for most feed systems. The network can be designed to produce a phase lead or phase lag. The basic two-element L network feed system is shown in Figure 6.17. Many variations of this general method can be used, but the equations, program, and method to be discussed here apply only to the feed system shown.

If the phase angle of I_2/I_1 is negative (element 2 is lagging element 1), the L network will usually resemble a low-pass network (X_{ser} is an inductor and X_{sh} is a capacitor). But if the phase angle is positive (element 2 lagging element 1), the L network will resemble a high-pass network (X_{ser} is a capacitor and X_{sh} is an inductor). However, some current ratios and feed point impedances could result in both components being inductors or both being capacitors.

If it's desired to maintain symmetry in the feed system, X_{ser} can be divided into two components, each being inserted in series with a transmission line conductor. If X_{ser} is an inductor, the new components will each have half the value of the original X_{ser}, as shown in **Figure 6.18**. If X_{ser} is a capacitor, each of the new components will be twice the original value of X_{ser}.

Because of the current-forcing properties of λ/4 lines, we need to make the ratio of voltages at the inputs of the lines equal to the desired ratio of currents at the output ends of the lines; that is, at the element feed points. The job of the L network is to provide the desired voltage transformation. If the output-to-input voltage ratio of the network is, say, 2.0 at an angle of –60°, then the ratio of element currents (I_2/I_1) will be 2.0 at an angle of –60°. The voltage transformation of the network is affected by the impedance of element 2, but not by the impedance of element 1. So only the impedance of element 2 must be known to design the feed system.

Equations for designing the L network are given in Appendix B (with the downloadable supplemental information for this book), but the program *Arrayfeed1* makes it unnecessary to solve them. The feed point impedance of the lagging element or group of elements must be known in order to design the network. This can best be determined by modeling the array with *EZNEC*. The impedance can be manually calculated for some simple element and array types by using the equations in Appendix B, but those same types of element and array are simple to model.

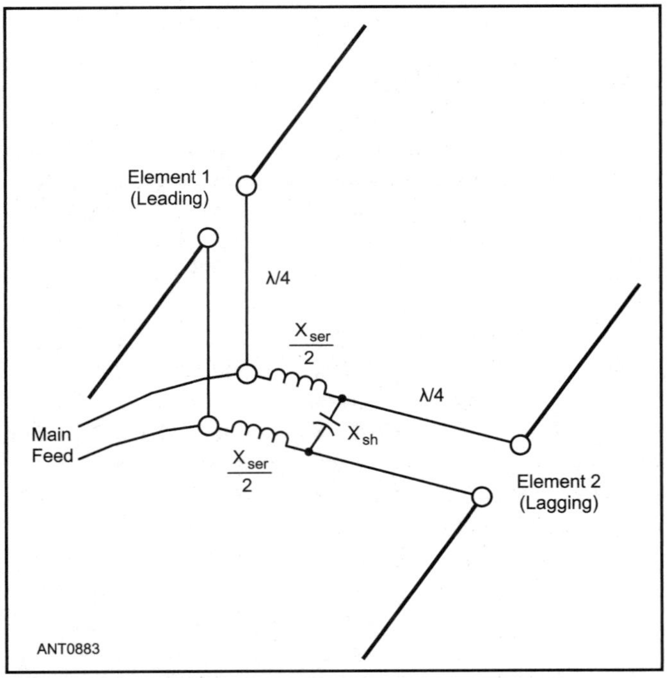

Figure 6.18 — Symmetrical feed system similar to Figure 6.17, in which the feed network is split into two symmetrical parts.

Examples of the design of L network feed systems for several different arrays using *EZNEC* and *Arrayfeed1* can be found in the Phased Array Design Examples section. A similar application of this feed system and a spreadsheet program for calculation was developed by Robye Lahlum, W1MK, and described in *Low-Band DXing* (see the Bibliography). *Arrayfeed1* can be used for the applications of the feed system described in that book if desired.

Additional Considerations

Feeding 4-Element and Larger Arrays

Both the simplest and L network feed systems described above can be extended to feeding larger arrays having two groups of elements in which all the elements in a group are in-phase or 180° out-of-phase with each other — basically, any group that can be fed with the current-forcing method. The elements in each group are connected to a common point with λ/4 or 3λ/4 lines to force the currents to be in the correct ratio within the group. Then the "simplest" or L network feed system can be used to produce the correct phasing between the two groups, just as it does between two individual elements.

Two common arrays that fit this description are the Four-Square and the 4-element rectangular array. But more elaborate arrays could be constructed and fed using this method, such as a pair of binomial arrays. (A single binomial array is described in the Phased Array Design Example section below.) The *Arrayfeed1* program incorporates additional calculations necessary for designing Four-Square and 4-element rectangular arrays. The general procedure for adapting the feed methods to other larger arrays can be found in Appendix B with the downloadable supplemental information for this book.

What If the Elements Aren't Identical?

Getting the desired pattern requires getting the correct relative magnitude and phase of the fields from the elements. If the elements are identical, which we've generally assumed up to this point, then producing currents of the desired magnitude and phase will create the desired *fields* (neglecting mutual coupling current distribution effects, discussed elsewhere).

But what if the elements aren't identical? Fortunately, the feed systems described here can still be used for any 2-element array and some more complex arrays, provided that the system can be accurately modeled. But a slightly different approach is required than for identical elements.

The first step is to model the array with a current source at the feed point of each element. Next, the magnitudes and phases of the model source currents are varied until the desired pattern is achieved. Then the ratio of feed point (source) currents is calculated. This value and the feed point impedances reported by the model are used for the feed system design. The feed system will produce the same ratio of currents as the model, resulting in the same pattern.

In general, this approach won't work with shunt fed towers or gamma-fed elements because of the difficulty of accurately modeling those structures as described in the following section.

Shunt- and Gamma-Fed Towers and Elements

In a shunt-, gamma-, or similarly fed tower or element, the feed point current isn't the same as the main current flowing in the element. The ratio between the feed point current and element current isn't a constant, but depends on a number of factors. The ratio of currents in shunt- or gamma-fed elements is typically different — often vastly different — from the currents at the feed points. This complicates the design of feed systems for arrays of these elements.

An even more limiting problem is that the feed point impedances are difficult to determine. The feed point impedances of one or more elements in a properly fed array must be known in order to design a feed system for anything but 2-element in-phase or 180° out-of-phase arrays.

The only practical way to get this information for a shunt or gamma fed array is by modeling an array having the desired element currents. But Cebik has pointed out ("Two Limitations of NEC-4" — see the Bibliography) that many common antenna analysis programs, including *EZNEC*, have difficulty accurately modeling folded dipoles with unequal diameter wires. The same problem applies to shunt and gamma-fed elements when the element diameter is significantly different from the diameter of the shunt or gamma feed wire. Without accurate feed point impedances, feed systems can't be designed to work without adjustment. It might be possible to get reasonably accurate results from a *MININEC*-based modeling program, but there are a number of issues which must be given great care when using one. (See Lewallen, "*MININEC* — The Other Edge of the Sword," listed in the Bibliography.)

If such a *MININEC* program is available, you would have to model the complete array including feed system, with sources at the normal feed points in the shunt or gamma wires. Next, you would have to adjust the magnitudes and phases of the sources to produce the desired pattern. The reported source impedances and currents would be the ones you would use to design the feed system. It's likely that some adjustment would be necessary, so an adjustable system such as the L network feed system described later would be best.

Loading, Matching and Other Networks

Adding a component such as a loading inductor in series with an element or element feed point won't change the ratio of element current to feed point current. As a result, a feed system designed to produce a particular ratio of element currents will still function properly if the elements contain series components. The extra feed point impedance introduced by the loading component(s) must be considered when designing the feed system, however. Similarly, end or top loading won't alter the relationship between feed point and element current, provided that the current distribution in the elements is essentially the same. (See Feed point vs Element Current previously.)

However, insertion of any *shunt* component, or a network containing a shunt component, *will* alter the relationship between feed point and element current because it will divert part of the feed line current that would otherwise flow into the antenna. As a result, a feed system designed to deliver correct currents at the feed points will produce incorrect element currents and therefore an incorrect pattern. Therefore, any components or networks other than a series loading component should be avoided at any place in the feed system on the antenna side of the point at which the feed system splits to go to the various elements.

There are a few exceptions to this rule. If the feed point impedances of the elements when in the excited array are equal, then identical networks with or without shunt components can be put at the feed points of the elements and the proper element current ratio maintained — so long as the feed system is designed to deliver the proper feed point current ratio with the networks in place. Equal element impedances occur in arrays having only two identical elements fed in-phase or 180° out-of-phase, or arrays of any number of elements where the elements are electrically short and/or very lossy.

Baluns in Phased Arrays

For purposes of achieving the correct array pattern, baluns aren't usually required when feeding grounded vertical elements with coaxial cable feed lines. However, a balun might be desirable if current induced onto the outside of the feed line by mutual coupling to the elements is causing RF in the shack. And with arrays of dipole or other elevated elements, baluns can be important to achieve the proper element current ratio, as explained below.

First, however, the general rules for using baluns in phased arrays will be stated. Here, "main feed line" means the feed line going from the transmitter or receiver to the common point where the system splits to feed the various elements. "Phasing-system lines" means any transmission lines between that common point and any element. The rules are:

Rule 1: A balun or baluns (more specifically, a current balun, sometimes called a choke balun) should be used as necessary to suppress unbalanced current on the main feed line. Unbalanced current can occur on either coax or parallel-conductor lines. A balun usually isn't required when feeding grounded elements with coaxial feed line from an unbalanced transceiver or tuner. If current on the shield of a coaxial feed line to a grounded element is a problem, the feed line can be buried or run in buried conduit to reduce coupling to the antenna or to the radial system. Additional chokes can be added anywhere along the feed line. See the **Transmission Line System Techniques** chapter and the Bibliography entry for Brown to obtain more information on choke baluns.

"Baluns: What They Do and How They Do It", listed in the Bibliography, describes conducted-imbalance (common-mode) currents. Imbalance can also be caused by mutual coupling to the array elements. Common-mode currents have at least two undesirable effects on array performance. First, the imbalance current can flow from the main feed line to the phasing system lines, not necessarily splitting in the right proportion to maintain the correct element current ratio. This can affect the array pattern. In practice, however, this effect is likely to be small unless the common-mode current is unusually large. Even a small common-mode current, however, results in main feed line radiation, and even a small amount of radiation can significantly degrade array pattern nulls. Any type of current balun can be used on the main feed line, at any place along the line, without any effect on the array pattern except to the extent that it reduces common mode current.

Rule 2: No balun or any other component or network should be inserted in any phasing system line that will alter the line length or characteristic impedance. This means that baluns in phasing system lines must be of a type made from the phasing line itself. Options are the W2DU or "bead" balun, consisting of ferrite beads placed along the outside of the feed line; an air-core or "choke" balun made by winding part of the line into an approximately self-resonant or otherwise high-impedance coil; or winding part of the line onto a ferrite core or rod to make a several-turn winding. When coaxial cable is used, the feed system characteristics are dictated by the conditions *inside* the cable. Any cores placed on or winding of the *outside* prevents common-mode current on the outside but otherwise have no effect on the phasing performance. This rule applies equally to parallel-wire line, where the balun affects only common-mode current (equivalent to current on the outside of coax) while the phasing performance depends on differential mode current (equivalent to the current on the inside of coax).

Baluns are important when feeding dipole or other elevated arrays, unless a fully balanced tuner is used. This is because common-mode current represents a diversion of some of the current that should be going to the array elements. The presence of common-mode current means that the element currents are being altered from the desired ratio and therefore the pattern won't be as intended. A balun should be placed wherever a path for current exists other than along a parallel-line conductor or on the inside of a coaxial line. Such a path exists, for example, where a coaxial cable connects to a dipole, as shown in Figure 1 of the balun article referenced above. Or a path can exist where a parallel-conductor transmission line connects to an unbalanced tuner or to a coaxial line, as shown in Figure 2 of that article. In both those cases, a path exists for a common-mode current to flow on the outside of the coax cable. A balun presents a high impedance to this current, thereby reducing its magnitude, but remember that all baluns must conform to the rules above. **Figure 6.19** shows recommended balun locations for a coax-fed dipole array using an L network feed system.

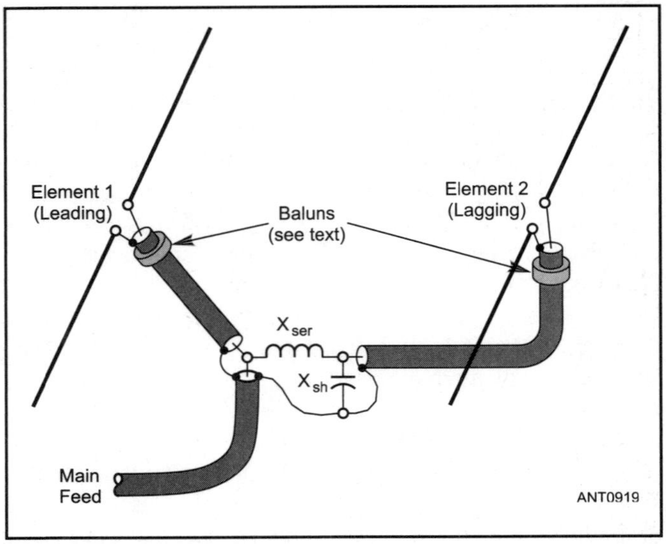

Figure 6.19 — Adding choke baluns to a two-dipole feed system to get rid of common-mode currents induced onto the coax shields.

Receiving Arrays and Broadbanding

While it might not be entirely intuitive, an array designed for a particular gain and pattern for transmitting that considers mutual coupling, element currents, field reinforcement and cancellation, and so forth, will perform exactly the same when receiving. So a receiving array can be designed by approaching the problem as though the array were to be used for transmitting.

However, at HF and below, the system requirements for transmitting and receiving antennas are different, so receiving-only arrays can be designed that aren't suitable for transmitting but are perfectly adequate for receiving in that frequency range. The reason, described in more detail in the **Long Wire and Traveling-Wave Antennas** chapter, is that at HF and below atmospheric noise is typically much greater than a receiver's internally generated noise. Lowering a receiving antenna's gain and efficiency reduces the signal and atmospheric noise both by the same factor. Because the overall noise is for practical purposes all atmospheric noise, the signal/noise ratio isn't affected by antenna efficiency.

Of course, a point can be reached where the atmospheric noise is so reduced by inefficiency that the receiver itself becomes the dominant source of noise, but this typically doesn't happen until the antenna is extremely inefficient. When transmitting, reduced efficiency lowers the transmitted signal, but it has no effect on the receiving station's noise. So reduced efficiency of a transmitting antenna results in a reduced signal/noise ratio at the receiving end, and consequently should be avoided.

Mutual coupling effects can be minimized by increasing the loss (and therefore reducing the efficiency) of the elements, or by reducing the element sizes to a small fraction of a wavelength. Doing the second without the first isn't usually a good idea because the feed point impedance tends to change rapidly with frequency for very small elements, making an antenna that works well over only a narrow bandwidth. But increasing loss broadens the bandwidth, even for small elements, as well as reducing mutual coupling effects. So this approach is often taken for designing a receiving-only array. With mutual coupling effects minimized because of loss, feed-system design becomes relatively simple, provided a few simple rules are followed. (See Loss Resistance, Mutual Coupling, and Antenna Gain above.)

The "crossfire" feed method described by Tom Rauch, W8JI (**www.w8ji.com/crossfire.phasing.htm**), delivers an array with very wide pattern bandwidth. That is, the pattern shape, particularly null direction and depth, stay nearly constant over a very large range of frequencies. The method requires elements whose feed point impedances stay nearly constant over the frequency range, which for a wide range requires high loss and low efficiency. As explained earlier, however, this is acceptable for receiving arrays and receiving arrays are usually the case for which deep and predictable pattern nulls are the most important. The basic idea for two elements is to use a delay line between the two whose delay in electrical degrees equals the element spacing in degrees then add a frequency-independent phase inversion to the line. A distant signal arriving at the first element creates a wave in the delay line connected to its feed point. That same signal arrives at the second element at the same time the wave from the first element reaches the end of the delay line. The signal from the second element is added to the inverted wave from the first element and, if the two are the same amplitude, complete cancellation occurs. This is independent of the frequency, and also of the element spacing provided that the delay line's electrical length is the same as the element spacing. See the design examples for additional information.

For ungrounded elements like dipoles, the inversion can easily be effected simply by reversing the feed line connections to one element by giving the phasing line a half twist. Or a broadband inverting transformer can be used for either grounded or ungrounded elements.

Feed Line Shield Connections

It is common for antenna system designs to assume that the shields of coaxial feed lines and phasing lines are isolated from the antennas. (See the previous discussion on "Baluns in Phased Arrays.") It is also often assumed that the shield connections are so short that the connection length can be ignored. However, an unintended or uncontrolled current path between the feed line shields may upset the array's phasing and current levels. See this chapter's "Practical Aspects of Phased Array Design" subsection on "Improving Array Switching Systems."

If the shields of the feed lines are switched, the feed lines should be run directly to the relays or switches and connected there. If several shields are to be connected together, use a single terminal or an electrically short strip of copper or brass as a common connecting point. Keep shield connections as short as possible. If the antenna switching and control circuits are placed in metal enclosures, use caution when using bulkhead or feedthrough connectors since they will create an uncontrolled connection between the feed line shields. Do not use bulkhead connectors in a metal enclosure if the shields are also switched, since the enclosure connection will bypass the switched connection.

If a plastic or fiberglass enclosure is used, bulkhead connectors may be used. Remember that the entire length of the feed line includes the connectors and any internal lengths of cable that must be accounted for.

Lightning protection is another source of unwanted connections between feed lines. For example, the ground connection of gas-discharge tube lightning arrestors in a system of multiple feed lines creates a connection between the shields. For ground-mounted vertical arrays, such as a four-square, a lightning arrestor should be located at the antenna feed point, where there is a ground connection in parallel with the arrestor. Otherwise, the arrestor should be located on the array's main feed line from the transmitter.

6.4 PHASED ARRAY DESIGN EXAMPLES

This section, also written by Roy Lewallen, W7EL, presents examples of feed-system design for several kinds of array using the design principles given in previous sections. All but the dipole example array are assumed to be made of $\lambda/4$ vertical elements. The dipole example illustrates that exactly the same method can be used for arrays of any shape of elements, including dipole, square (quad) and triangular. Likewise, the methods shown here apply equally well to VHF and UHF arrays. The first example includes more detail than the remaining ones, so you should read it before the others. Following the array design examples using the "simplest" and L network feed systems is an example of a receiving array using two different configurations of "crossfire" feed.

EZNEC has the capability of incorporating L networks in the model, so the L network fed array can also be analyzed for accuracy and the effects of component and ground loss variation. **ARRL_Cardioid_L_Network_Example.EZ** models the cardioid array with L network feed system.

EZNEC also has provision for including transmission line loss. It can be instructive to add various amounts of loss to see the effect on pattern and bandwidth. The effect of loss will generally be most apparent on lines running with a high SWR, i.e., when terminated in an impedance very different from the characteristic impedance.

In the following sections, text in SMALL CAPS denotes menu or function button label or an input to the *EZNEC* software used in the creation and modeling of these examples.

In addition to the set of examples, there is a great deal of additional information and numerous other array designs in Chapter 11, "Phased Arrays" of *Low-Band DXing* by John Devoldere, ON4UN (see the Bibliography at the end of this chapter). Al Christman, K3LC, has also written two excellent articles (included with the downloadable supplemental information for this book) examining the effect of lengthening $\lambda/4$ monopoles to $\frac{5}{8}\lambda$, both for single elements and for the 2-element cardioid pattern and 4-square array on 80 meters. His study of phased vertical arrays also provides useful information to the antenna system builder (see the Bibliography).

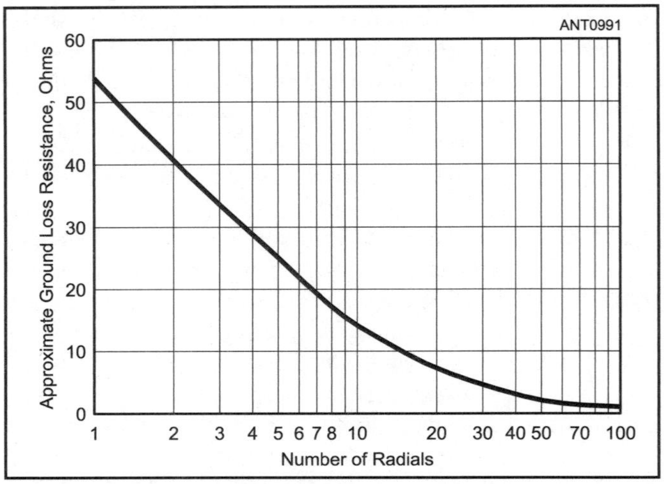

Figure 6.20 — Approximate ground system loss resistance of a resonant λ/4 ground-mounted vertical element versus the number of radials, based on measurements by Jerry Sevick, W2FMI. Moderate length radials (0.2 to 0.4 λ) were used for the measurements. The exact resistance, especially for only a few radials, will depend on the nature of the soil under the antenna. Add 36 Ω for the approximate feed point resistance of a thin resonant λ/4 vertical.

6.4.1 GENERAL ARRAY DESIGN CONSIDERATIONS

If either the "simplest" feed system (Figure 6.16) or L network feed system (Figure 6.17) is used, the feed point impedance of one or more elements — *when the array elements all have the correct currents* — must be known. By far the best way to determine this is by modeling. If accurate modeling isn't practical for some reason, an estimate should be made from an approximate model, and you should expect to have to adjust the feed system after building and installing it.

Manual calculation methods for some simple configurations are given in Appendix B (with the downloadable supplemental information for this book), but calculation is tedious and, as stated earlier, the configurations for which this method works are the very ones which are easiest to model. *EZNEC* is used in the following examples to determine feed point impedance. Space doesn't permit detailed instructions here on creating the models, so they are included in complete form. They should provide a convenient starting point for any variations you might like to try. See the *EZNEC* manual (accessed by clicking HELP/CONTENTS in the main *EZNEC* window) for help in using this program.

In the following examples, vertical elements are close to λ/4 high and dipole elements close to λ/2, and their lengths have been adjusted for resonance when all other elements are absent or open circuited. There's actually no need in practice to make the elements self-resonant — it's simply used as a convenient reference point for these examples. You'll also find it interesting to see how much reactance is present at the feed points of the elements when in the arrays, knowing that it's very nearly zero when only one element is present.

In any real grounded vertical array, there is ground loss associated with each element. The amount of loss depends on the length and number of ground radials, and on the type and wetness of the ground under and around the antenna. This resistance becomes part of the feed point resistance, so it must be included in the model used to determine feed point impedance. The 90° Fed, 90° Spaced Array example below discusses how this is done. **Figure 6.20** gives resistance values for typical ground systems, based on measurements by Sevick (July 1971 and March 1973 *QST*). The values of feed system components based on Figure 6.20 will be reasonably close to correct, even if the ground characteristics are somewhat different than Sevick's.

Feed systems for the design example arrays to follow are based on the resistance values given below.

Number of Radials	*Loss Resistance, Ω*
4	29
8	18
16	9
Infinite	0

Elevated radial systems also have some ground loss, although it can be considerably less than a system with the same number of buried radials. This loss will be automatically included in the feed point impedance of a model which includes the elevated radials, so no further estimation is required. Be sure to use Perfect, High-Accuracy ground type when modeling an elevated radial system with *EZNEC*. In other *NEC-2* based programs, this might be referred to as Sommerfeld type ground. More information can be found in the *EZNEC* manual.

The matter of matching the array for the best SWR on the feed line to the station is not dealt with here, since it's a separate problem from that of the main topic, which is designing feed systems to produce a desired pattern. Some of the simpler arrays provide a match that is close to 50 or 75 Ω, so no further matching is required. However, as shown by program *Arrayfeed1*, many larger arrays present a less favorable impedance for direct connection and will require matching if a low SWR on the main feed line is required. If matching is necessary, the appropriate network should be placed in the single feed line running to the station. Attempts to improve the match by adjustment of the phasing L network, individual element lengths, matching at the element feed points or individual element feeder lengths will usually ruin the current balance of the array. Program *TLW*, included with the downloadable supplemental information for this book, can be used for designing an appropriate matching network. Additional information on impedance matching may be found in the **Transmission Line System Techniques** chapter.

Choosing *Arrayfeed1* Solutions

When designing a feed system for a two-element array, *Arrayfeed1* program allows you to choose the characteristic impedances of the two transmission lines going to the elements, which don't have to be equal, so you have your choice of more than one solution. However, directional array switching is much more difficult if the lines have different impedances, so in general you should use the same characteristic impedances.

For larger arrays, *Arrayfeed1* requires the feed lines to all elements to have the same impedance. In choosing the transmission line impedance values, usually you can simply use convenient impedances. But in general, you should avoid solutions where component reactance (X) values are vastly different (say, more than three times or less than one third as large) as the line characteristic impedances. Such networks will become more critical to adjust, and both the impedance and pattern will change more rapidly with changes in frequency. You can usually avoid this situation by choosing feed line impedances that are in the same ballpark as the element feed point impedances. The last example in the Practical Array Design section illustrates this problem and its solution.

When designing a "simplest" feed system, the most broadbanded and least critical system is usually one where the difference in electrical feed line lengths is closest to the relative element phase angle. Here, "broadbanded" means that the pattern changes less with frequency, not necessarily that the SWR changes less. However, an array that's broadbanded in the pattern sense is usually also relatively broadbanded with respect to SWR.

Arrayfeed1 reports the impedance seen at the main array feed point. While it might be tempting to choose the solution producing the lowest SWR on the main feed line, you'll end up with a less critical and more broadbanded system if you base your choice on the criteria given above, and provide separate impedance matching at the array's main feed point when necessary.

6.4.2 90° FED, 90° SPACED VERTICAL ARRAY

This example illustrates the design of both "simplest" and L network feed systems for a 2-element, 90° spaced and fed vertical array. The first task when using either feed system is to determine the feed point impedances of the elements when placed in an array having the desired element currents. The "simplest" feed system method requires knowledge of both element impedances, while the L network system requires you to know only one. Actually, it's equally easy to determine both as it is to find just one, using *EZNEC*. (Appendix B with the downloadable supplemental information contains equations for those interested in manual methods or for more insight as to how the impedances come about.) The first step is to specify the antenna we want. For this example, we'll specify:

- Frequency: 7.15 MHz.
- Two identical, one inch (2.54 cm) diameter, 33 feet (10.06 meter) long elements spaced 90 electrical degrees, with element currents equal in magnitude and 90° apart in-phase.
- 8 buried radial wires, 0.3 λ long, under each element.

A model of this antenna has been created and furnished with *EZNEC*. So the next step is to start *EZNEC*, click the OPEN button, enter ARRL_CARDIOID_EXAMPLE in the text box (or double-click it in the file list) to open example file **ARRL_Cardioid_Example.EZ**.

This *EZNEC* example model uses a *MININEC*-type ground, which is the same as perfect ground when calculating antenna currents and impedances. A real antenna would have some additional resistive loss due to the finite conductivity of the ground system. The only way to model a buried radial ground system with an *NEC-2* based program like *EZNEC* is to create radial wires just above the ground (using the Real, High-Accuracy ground type), because *NEC-2* can't handle buried conductors.

This provides only a moderate approximation of a buried system. Another way to estimate ground-system resistance is to measure the feed point impedance of a single element, then subtract from that the resistance reported for a model of that element over perfect (or *MININEC*-type) ground. For most uses, however, an adequate approximation can be made by simply referring to the graph of Figure 6.20. As stated previously, the feed system design depends on the feed point impedances of the elements, which in turn depend on the ground system resistance. So the ground system resistance must be known, approximately anyway, before designing the feed system. At the end of this example we'll investigate the effect of changes in the ground system or errors in estimating the resistance on the pattern.

For 8 radials, Figure 6.20 shows the ground system resistance to be about 18 Ω. This is included in the example model as a simple resistive load at the feed point of each element. Click the SRC DAT button to see the feed point impedances of the two elements. In this model, Source 1 is at the base of Wire 1 (element 1), and Source 2 is at the base of Wire 2 (element 2). Notice in the SOURCE DATA display that the Source 1 current has been specified at 1 amp at 0°, and Source 2 is 1 amp at –90°. So the Source 2-element is the lagging element. You should see impedances of 37.53 – *j*19.1 Ω for element 1 and 68.97 + *j*18.5 Ω for element 2. These are the feed point impedances resulting when the array is ideally fed, with equal magnitude and 90° phased currents. Record these values for use in *Arrayfeed1*.

Click the FF PLOT button to generate a plot of the azimuth pattern at an elevation angle of 10°. In the 2D Plot Window, open the FILE menu and select SAVE TRACE AS. Enter CARDIOID_IDEAL FEED in the FILE NAME box, then click SAVE. This saves the cardioid pattern plot so you can compare it later to the pattern you get with the transmission line feed system.

Now it's time to design the feed system. Refer to the appropriate subheading below for the design of each of the two kinds of feed systems. Both systems use program *Arrayfeed1* program.

"Simplest" (Transmission Line Only) Feed System

Start *Arrayfeed1*. In the ARRAY TYPE frame, select TWO ELEMENT. In FEED SYSTEM TYPE, select SIMPLEST. In the INPUTS frame, enter the following values:

Frequency MHz = 7.15; Feed point impedances – Leading Element: R ohms = 37.53, X ohms = –19.1; Lagging Element: R ohms = 68.97, X ohms = 18.5 (these are the element R and X values from *EZNEC*). We'll be discussing the array input impedance, so check the CALC ZIN box near the lower left corner of the main window if it's not already checked.

We're free to choose any transmission-line characteristic impedances we want, so long as we can get cables with those impedances. And the two cables don't have to have the same characteristic impedances. Each choice will lead to a different set of solutions. But sometimes a solution isn't possible, which then requires choosing different line impedances. Let's try 50 Ω for both lines. Enter 50 in both Z0 boxes.

Finally, enter 1 for the LAGGING:LEADING I MAG, and –90 for the PHASE. Click FIND SOLUTIONS. The result is no solution! So enter 75 into both the line impedance boxes and click FIND SOLUTIONS again. You should now see two sets of results in the Solutions frame, electrical lengths of 68.80° and 156.03° for the first solution and 131.69° and 185.00° for the second. (Notice that the difference in length between the two lines isn't 90° for either solution, although the first solution is quite close. It's normal for the feed line length difference to be different than the phase difference, due to the unequal element feed point impedances caused by mutual coupling.)

The solution with a line length difference closest to the element phase difference is usually preferable. Also, all else being equal, the solution with shortest lines is better providing that the lines will physically reach the elements. This is because the current magnitude and phase will change less with frequency than for a longer-length solution. However, there might be some cases where the change with frequency luckily compensates for the changing electrical distance between elements, so it's not a bad idea to model both solutions unless you plan on using the antenna over only a narrow frequency range.

In this case, the first solution looks best in all respects. The sum of the two lines in the first solution is about 225 electrical degrees. Assuming the lines have a velocity factor of 0.66, the total length of the lines will be more than 148 physical degrees. Since our two elements are spaced 90 physical degrees apart, the lines will comfortably reach. If they didn't, we could either use the second solution's lengths, use cable with a higher velocity factor or add a half wavelength to both the line lengths in the first solution.

The impedance ZIN shown by *Arrayfeed1* is the impedance at the input to the feed system, so it's the impedance that will be seen by the main feed line. The second solution provides nearly a perfect match for a 50-Ω transmission line. But the first solution is good for nearly all applications. Also a 50-Ω line connected to the first solution's feed system would have an SWR of only 1.65:1, which wouldn't require any matching under most circumstances. Normal line loss would reduce the SWR even more at the transmitter end of the feed coax.

To find the required physical line lengths, enter the cable velocity factor and make your choice of units in the PHYSICAL LENGTHS frame. The design is now complete; all you have to do is cut two lines to the specified lengths and connect one from a common feed point to each element as shown in Figure 6.16, or the screen capture from *Arrayfeed1* shown in **Figure 6.21**.

Next, we'll design an L network feed system for the same array.

L Network Feed System

In *Arrayfeed1*, select L NETWORK in the FEED SYSTEM TYPE frame. The program doesn't need to know the leading element impedance to calculate the L network values, but it does need it to calculate the array input impedance. If you want to know the impedance, check the ZIN box at the lower left corner of the main window, otherwise you can uncheck it and the input box for the leading element Z will disappear. The values from the "Simplest" analysis should still be present in the appropriate boxes; if not, refer to the "Simplest" feed system design above and re-enter the values. Again, we'll use 75 Ω for the line impedances, since that gave us a solution for the "Simplest" feed system. This feed system is more versatile, though, so we could use 50-Ω lines with this feed system if desired.

Click FIND SOLUTION and see the results in the SOLUTION frame. See screen capture in **Figure 6.22**. With 75-Ω lines,

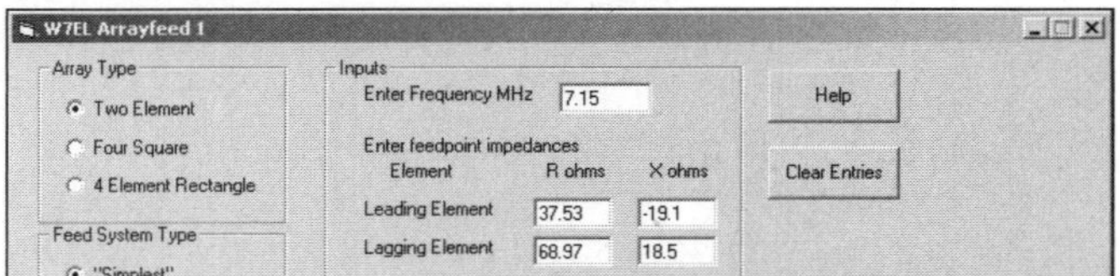

Figure 6.21 — Screen capture from *Arrayfeed1* program for "Simplest" 2-element phased array shown in Figure 6.16 and whose feed point impedances are modeled by *EZNEC*.

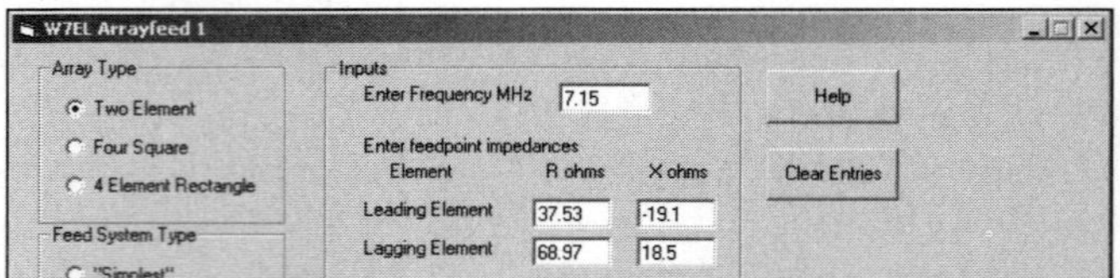

Figure 6.22 — Screen capture from *Arrayfeed1* program for L network feed system using "current-forcing" properties of λ/4 feed lines.

the L network consists of a series inductor of 1.815 µH and a shunt capacitor of 199.7 pF, connected as shown in the diagram in the left part of the program window. To find the physical length of the λ/4 lines, enter the velocity factor and choice of units in the PHYSICAL LENGTHS frame.

The main feed point impedance of 31.37 + *j* 25.94 Ω would result in about a 2.2:1 SWR on a 50-Ω feed line, which would be acceptable for many applications. It could easily be reduced to 1.6:1 by the simple addition of a series capacitor of 25.94 Ω reactance (858 pF) at the main feed point or, of course, reduced to 1:1 with a simple L network or other matching system designed with the *TLW* program.

Pattern Verification and Effect of Loss Resistance

L network *EZNEC* model **ARRL_Cardioid_TL_Example.EZ** has been created to model the "simplest" feed system just designed. Open it with *EZNEC*. In the VIEW ANTENNA DISPLAY, you can see the boxes representing the transmission lines placed at the element bases. The other ends of the transmission lines are shown going to "virtual segment" (connection point) V1. The source is also connected to V1. In *EZNEC*, the physical locations of the ends of transmission line models don't have to be the same as the physical locations, so the view isn't a precise representation of what the actual setup would look like. (You can find more about this in **ARRL_Cardioid_TL_Example.txt**, the Antenna Notes file that accompanies example file **ARRL_Cardioid_TL_Example.EZ.**)

Click FF PLOT to generate a 2D pattern of the antenna. In the 2D Plot Window, open the FILE menu and select ADD TRACE. Select CARDIOID — IDEAL FEED (which you saved earlier) and click OPEN. The added plot overlays perfectly, indicating that the pattern using this feed system is identical to the pattern we got with perfect current sources at each feed point.

To check the feed point currents, click the CURRENTS button. In the resulting table, you can see that WIRE 1 SEGMENT 1 current is 0.56467 A at a phase of –56.73° and WIRE 2 SEGMENT 1 current is 0.56467 A at –146.7°. (If you get the correct phase angles but wrong magnitudes, open the main window OPTIONS menu, select POWER LEVEL, and make sure the ABSOLUTE V, I SOURCES box is checked.) The ratio is 1.0000 at an angle of –89.97°, which is within normal error bounds for the desired 1 at –90°.

As a check on *Arrayfeed1*, click the SRC DAT button to find the impedance seen by the source. This would be the impedance at the main feed line connection in the real array. *EZNEC* reports 33.96 + j13.11 Ω, very close to the 33.94 + j13.13 Ω given by *Arrayfeed1* in Figure 6.21. Small differences of this order are normal and to be expected. This provides a further check that the *EZNEC* model is correctly analyzing the *Arrayfeed1* feed system.

This *EZNEC*-model uses lossless transmission lines of a fixed physical length rather than a fixed electrical length (number of degrees), so they'll behave like real lines as the frequency is changed. By changing the *EZNEC* frequency and re-running the 2D plot, you can see that the front-to-back ratio degrades at 7.0 and 7.3 MHz. A slight adjustment of one or more line lengths, or a new *Arrayfeed1* solution at a slightly different frequency might produce a better compromise for some uses.

Other things you can try are to evaluate the second *Arrayfeed1* solution, or to try using different line impedances. (Keep the two line impedances equal if you anticipate doing array direction switching.) The effect of varying ground system resistance can also be evaluated by clicking the LOADS line in the main window and changing the load resistance values. For example, if the ground system resistance were 9 Ω instead of the 18 Ω we have assumed, the front-to-back ratio would drop from about 32 to about 20 dB. Note that changing the *EZNEC* ground conductivity in this model has no effect on the feed point current ratio. With a *MININEC* type ground, it's used only for pattern calculation — the ground is assumed perfect during impedance and current calculations, and the only ground system loss resistance in the model is what we've specifically put in as loads.

Not surprisingly, the forward gain is affected very little by changes in frequency or ground system loss. To find the gain relative to a single element, compare the reported dBi gain of **ARRL_Cardioid_Example** with the same model with one of the elements deleted. You'll find it's very close to 3.0 dB. The 90° fed, 90° spaced array is a special case of array where the effects of mutual coupling on the two elements are opposite and cancel, resulting in the same gain as if mutual coupling didn't exist. But mutual coupling most certainly does exist!

The second solution presented a more favorable main feed point impedance, so it would be tempting to use that one instead of the first solution. Replacing the feed line lengths with the second solution lengths to model the second solution shows that the front-to-back ratio deteriorates more at the band edges when the second solution is used. This might be tolerable if restricted frequency use is anticipated. But it does illustrate that the solution with shorter lines is generally more broadbanded and that the choice of solution shouldn't in general be based on the one giving the most favorable impedance.

6.4.3 A THREE-ELEMENT BINOMIAL BROADSIDE ARRAY

An array of three in-line elements spaced λ/2 apart and fed in-phase gives a pattern that is generally bidirectional. If the element currents are equal, the resulting pattern has a forward gain of 5.7 dB (for lossless elements) compared to a single element, but it has substantial side lobes. If the currents are tapered in a binomial coefficient 1:2:1 ratio (twice the current in the center element as in the two end elements), the gain drops slightly to just under 5.3 dB, the main lobes widen and the side lobes disappear.

The array is shown in **Figure 6.23**, and an *EZNEC* model of the antenna over perfect ground to show the ideal pattern is provided as **ARRL_Binomial_Example.EZ**. To obtain a 1:2:1 current ratio in the elements, each end element is fed through a 3λ/4 line of impedance Z_0. Line lengths of 3λ/4 are chosen because λ/4 lines will not physically reach. The center element is fed from the same point through two parallel 3λ/4 lines of the same characteristic impedance. This is equivalent to feeding it through a line of impedance $Z_0/2$. The currents are thus forced to be in-phase and to have the correct ratio. **ARRL_Binomial_TL_Example.EZ** is an *EZNEC* model that shows this feed system with lossless transmission lines. The reader is encouraged to experiment with this model to see the effect of changes in frequency, the addition of loss resistance (as resistive loads at the element feed points), transmission line loss, and other alterations on the array pattern and gain. You should also replace the perfect ground with *MININEC* type of ground to show how radiation patterns over real ground differ from the theoretical perfect-ground pattern.

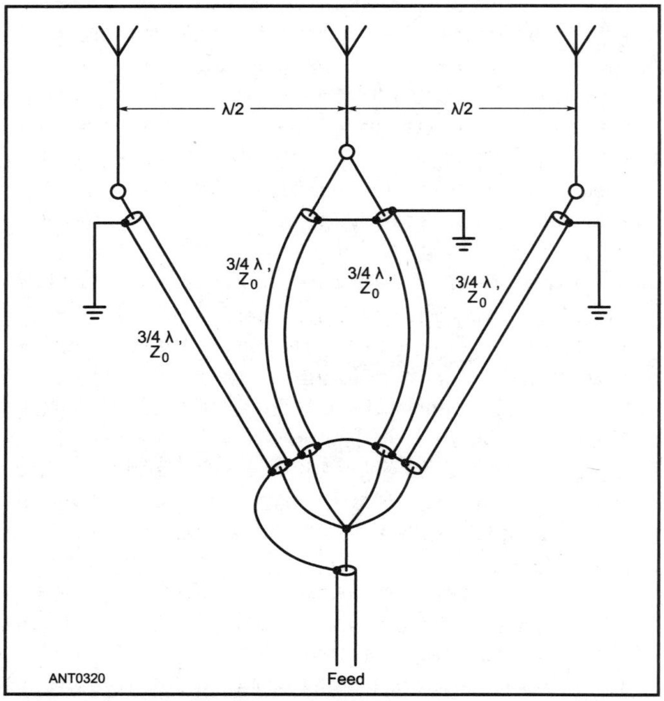

Figure 6.23 — Feed system for the three element 1:2:1 binomial array. All feed lines are ¾ electrical wavelength long and have the same characteristic impedance.

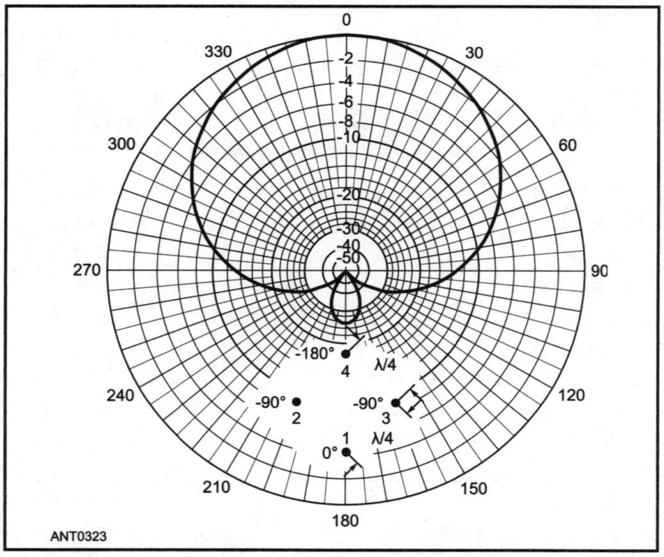

Figure 6.24 — Pattern and layout of the four-element Four-Square array. Gain is referenced to a single similar element; add 5.5 dB to the scale values shown.

6.4.4 A FOUR-SQUARE ARRAY

Several types of feed system are used for feeding this popular array, and most share a common problem — they don't provide the correct element current ratio — although a number of them produce a workable approximation. The feed systems described here are capable of producing exactly the correct current ratio. The only significant variable is the element feed point impedances, so the quality of the result depends on your ability to model the feed point impedances of a correctly fed array. As in the examples above, *EZNEC* will be used for that purpose and *Arrayfeed1* for the design of the feed system itself.

In this array (see **Figure 6.24**), four elements are placed in a square with λ/4 sides. (A variation of the Four-Square uses wider spacing.) The rear and front elements (1 and 4) are 180° out-of-phase with each other. The side elements (2 and 3) are in phase with each other and 90° delayed from the front element. The magnitudes of the currents in all four elements are equal. The front and rear elements can be forced

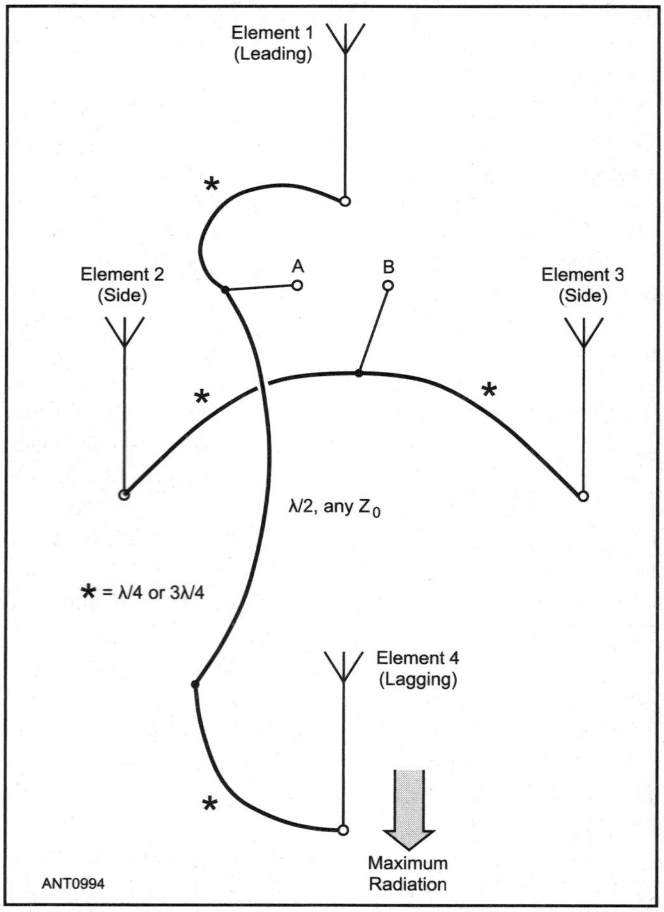

Figure 6.25 — "Simplest" feed system for the Four-Square array in Figure 6.24. Grounds and cable shields have been omitted for clarity.

to be 180° out-of-phase and to have equal currents by using the current-forcing method described earlier. One element is connected to a line that is either λ/4 or 3λ/4 long, the other to a line that is λ/2 longer, and the two lines to a common point.

Likewise, the two side element currents are forced to be equal by connecting them to a common point via λ/4 or 3λ/4 lines. **Figure 6.25** shows the basic current-forcing system.

If the pattern is to be electrically rotated, it is necessary to bring lines from all four elements to a common location. If solid-polyethylene dielectric coaxial cable, which has a dielectric constant of 0.66, is used, λ/4 lines won't reach the center of the array. So 3λ/4 lines must be used. Alternatively, you can use λ/4 lines with foam or other dielectric having a velocity factor of more than about 0.71 (plus a little extra margin). These will reach to the center. Whatever your choice, three of the lines must be the same length and the fourth must be λ/2 longer.

In this array, the side elements (2 and 3) have equal impedances, but the rear and front (1 and 4) are different from each other, and both are different from the side elements. We have to know the feed point impedances of the front, rear and side elements in order to design the "simplest" feed system, but only the side element impedances are needed to design the L network system. Knowledge of all feed point impedances is necessary if the array main feed point impedance ZIN is to be calculated. *EZNEC* model **4Square_Example.EZ** shows a 40-meter Four-Square array with 18 Ω of loss resistance at each element, to approximate an 8-radial per element ground system. (See the cardioid array example above for more information about modeling ground system loss.) Opening the file in *EZNEC* and clicking the SRC DAT button gives the following impedances:

Source 1: 16.4 – *j*15.85 Ω

Sources 2 and 3: 57.47 – *j*19.44 Ω

Source 4: 77.81 + *j*54.8 Ω

It's interesting to note that the resistive part of source 1 is less than the 18 Ω of loss resistance we intentionally added to simulate ground system loss. That means that the element 1 feed point resistance would be negative if the ground resistance were about 1.5 Ω. This isn't uncommon in phased arrays and simply means that the element is feeding power into the feed system. This power is coming via mutual coupling from the other elements.

"Simplest" (Transmission Line Only) Feed System

To design a "simplest" feed system, start *Arrayfeed1*. In the ARRAY TYPE frame, select 4 SQUARE, and select SIMPLEST in the FEED SYSTEM TYPE frame. In the INPUTS frame, enter the frequency and the impedances from *EZNEC*:

Frequency = 7.15 MHz

Leading Element: R = 16.4, X = –15.85

Side elements: R = 57.47, X = –19.44

Lagging Element: R = 77.81, X = 54.8

We'll try using 50 Ω for all lines, so enter 50 into the next three boxes.

Enter 1 for the lagging:leading I magnitude and –90 for the phase.

Click FIND SOLUTIONS.

The result is shown in the SOLUTIONS frame, shown in **Figure 6.26**. As always when any solution exists, there are two to choose from. The one with the shortest lines is generally preferable, so we'll choose it. For this example, we'll use λ/4 lines with velocity factor of 0.82. So enter 0.82 in the VELOCITY FACTOR box in the PHYSICAL LENGTHS frame, and read the physical lengths from the bottom of that frame. The λ/4 lines (marked in the *Arrayfeed1* diagram with an asterisk) are 28.2 feet, line 1 is 7.483 feet and line 2 is 51.668 feet. The "simplest" feed system is shown in Figure 6.26, and the complete feed system consists of this connected to the array of Figure 6.25.

EZNEC model **ARRL_4Square_TL_Example.EZ** simulates the array fed with this system. Comparison of the pattern plot to one from ideal-current model **ARRL_4Square_Example.EZ** and examination of the element currents verify that the feed system is producing the desired pattern and element currents. You can use **ARRL_4Square_Example.EZ** to investigate the effect of frequency change, ground loss and other changes on the array gain and pattern.

L Network Feed System

To design the L network feed system, simply change the FEED SYSTEM TYPE to L NETWORK and click FIND SOLUTIONS. The results you should see are a 0.484 μH inductor for the series component X_{ser}, and a 1369.6 pF capacitor for the shunt component X_{sh}. The L network feed system is shown in **Figure 6.27**, and the complete feed system consists of this L network connected to the array of Figure 6.25.

EZNEC model **ARRL_4Square_L_Network_Example.EZ** simulates the array fed with this system. You can compare it with the idealized feed system array and use it to see the effects of various parameter changes as you did with the

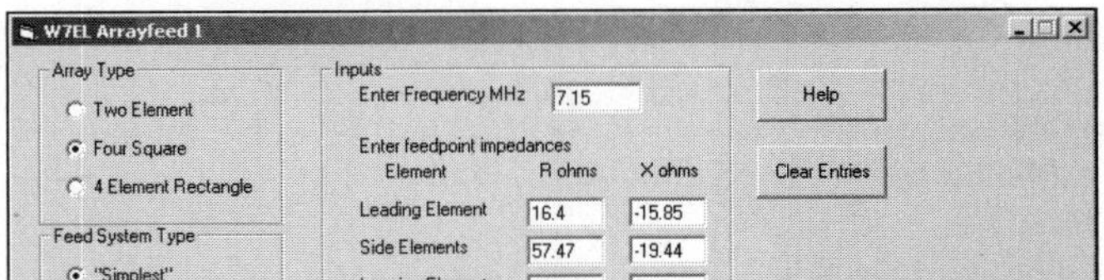

Figure 6.26 — Screen capture from *Arrayfeed1* for "Simplest" feed system for Four-Square feed system shown in Figure 6.25.

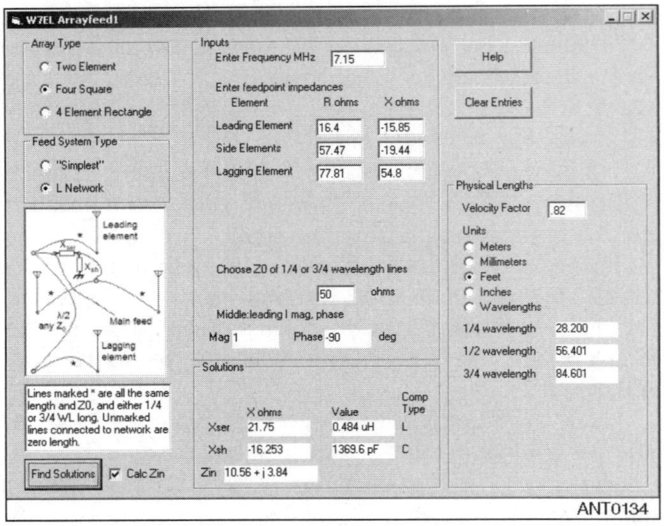

Figure 6.27 — L network setup for Four-Square array in Figure 6.25, fed with λ/4 (or 3λ/4) current-forcing feed system.

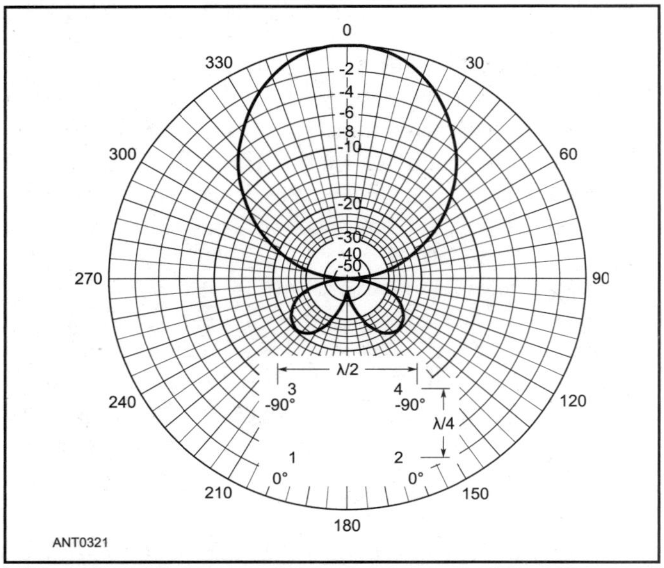

Figure 6.28 — Pattern and layout of the four-element rectangular array. Gain is referenced to a single similar element; add 6.8 dB to the scale values shown.

"simplest" feed system model. Arrays have also been built using this feed system and the element currents measured, with exactly the expected results.

This array is more sensitive to adjustment than the 2-element 90° fed, 90° spaced array. Adjustment procedures and a method of remotely switching the pattern direction are described in the Practical Aspects of Phased Array Design section below.

6.4.5 A 4-ELEMENT RECTANGULAR ARRAY

The 4-element rectangular array shown with its pattern in **Figure 6.28** has appeared numerous times in amateur publications. However, many of the accompanying feed systems fail to deliver currents in the proper amounts and phases to the various elements. The array can be correctly fed using the principles discussed in this chapter and the design methods that follow.

Elements 1 and 2 can be forced to be in-phase and to have equal currents by feeding them through 3λ/4 lines. (As in the binomial and Four-Square array examples, 3λ/4 lines are chosen because λ/4 lines won't physically reach.) The currents in elements 3 and 4 can similarly be forced to be equal and in-phase. **Figure 6.29** shows the "current-forcing" feed system. Elements 3 and 4 are made to have currents of equal magnitude but of 90° phase difference from elements 1 and 2 by use of either a "simplest" all-transmission line feed system or an L network feed system. Both will be designed in this example.

For this array, we have to know the feed point impedances of two elements (one of each pair) in order to design either type of feed system. *EZNEC* model **Rectangular_Example.EZ** shows a 20-meter rectangular array with 18 Ω of loss resistance at each element, again to approximate an 8-radial per element ground system. (See the cardioid array example above for more information about modeling ground system loss.) Open the file in *EZNEC* and click the SRC DAT button to find the following feed point impedances:

Sources 1 and 2: 21.44 – *j* 21.29 Ω
Sources 3 and 4: 70.81 – *j* 5.232 Ω

"Simplest" (Transmission-Line Only) Feed System

To design a "simplest" feed system, start program *Arrayfeed1*. In the ARRAY TYPE frame, select 4 ELEMENT RECTANGLE, and select SIMPLEST in the FEED SYSTEM TYPE frame. In the INPUTS frame, enter the frequency and the impedances from *EZNEC*:

Frequency = 14.15 MHz
Leading Elements R = 21.44, X = –21.29
Lagging Elements R = 70.81, X = –5.232

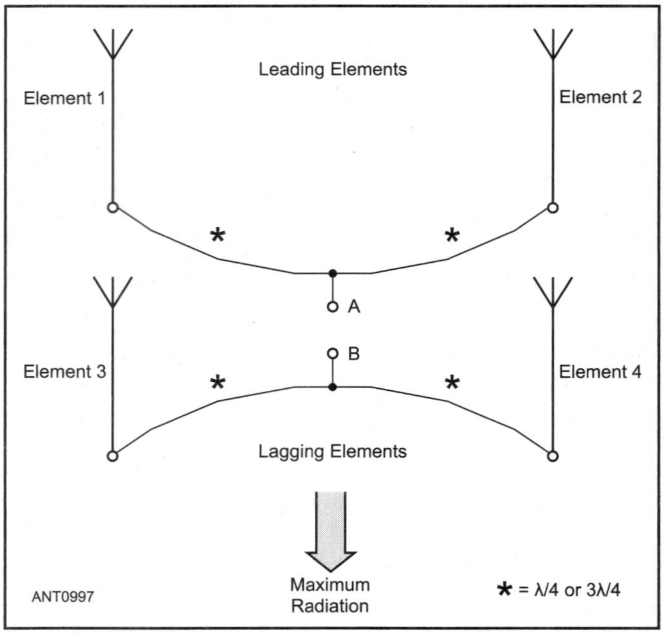

Figure 6.29 — "Simplest" feed system for four-element rectangular array, using four equal-length λ/4 (or 3λ/4) cables.

We'll use 50 Ω for all lines, so enter 50 into the next three boxes.

Enter 1 for the LAGGING:LEADING I MAGNITUDE and –90 for the phase.

Click FIND SOLUTIONS.

The result will be "No Solution" — indicating this combination of line impedances can't be used. Several other combinations also produce this result, but making lines 1 and 2 each 75 Ω and the 3λ/4 lines 50 Ω does produce a solution. Enter 75 into the LINE 1 Z0 and LINE 2 Z0 boxes, and leave 50 in the CHOOSE Z0 OF 1/4 OR 3/4 WAVELENGTH LINES box, then click the FIND SOLUTIONS button. There won't be any problem making lines 1 and 2 reach, so we'll choose the first solution because the lines are shorter. The physical lengths of all the lines are shown in the PHYSICAL LENGTHS frame when the velocity factor is entered in the appropriate box. Assuming that we use coax with a velocity factor of 0.66 (and the example frequency of 14.15 MHz), the lengths are:

Line 1: 4.982 feet

Line 2: 20.153 feet

3λ/4 lines (marked with an asterisk in the *Arrayfeed1* diagram): 34.408 feet

The lines are connected following the diagram in the upper left part of the *Arrayfeed1* window. This completes the "simplest" feed system design. *EZNEC* model **Rectangular_TL_Example.EZ** simulates an array fed with this system.

Comparison of the pattern plot to one from ideal-current **Rectangular_Example.EZ**, and examination of the element currents verify that the feed system is producing the desired pattern and element currents.

L-Network Feed System

To design the L network feed system using *Arrayfeed1*, change the FEED SYSTEM TYPE to L NETWORK and click FIND SOLUTIONS. The resulting L network values are a 0.199 µH inductor for the series component X_{ser} and a 684.2 pF capacitor for the shunt component X_{sh}. *EZNEC* model **ARRL_Rectangular_L_Network_Example.EZ** simulates an array fed with this system.

6.4.6 120° FED, 60° SPACED DIPOLE ARRAY

This example shows the design of "simplest" and L network feed systems for a 2-element 20 meter dipole array, rather than a vertical array. No special accommodation is required for the array made from dipoles rather than vertical elements — the same methods can be used regardless of element shape. This example also shows that both the "simplest" and L network feed systems can readily be applied to elements that use phase angles other than 90°.

Any 2-element array made with identical elements spaced λ/2 or closer and having equal magnitude currents with a relative phase angle of 180° minus the spacing will produce a unidirectional pattern with a good null to the rear. In practice, very close spacings lead to very low feed point resistances, with consequent losses and very narrowband characteristics. But this 60° spaced array is well within the range of practical realization. File **ARRL_Dipole_Array_Example.EZ** is a model created for this array, with ideal element currents. Open this file in *EZNEC* and click FF PLOT to show the pattern at an elevation angle of 10°. You can save this pattern for later comparison to the pattern with a "simplest" feed system by opening the FILE menu in the 2D PLOT window, selecting SAVE TRACE AS, entering a name for the trace file and clicking SAVE.

Following the same procedure as in the previous examples, we begin the array design by finding the element feed point impedances in the ideally fed array using *EZNEC* numbers. Having already opened **ARRL_Dipole_Array_Example.EZ**, all that's needed is to click SRC DAT. The results are:

Leading element (source 1): 36.16 – j 46.05 Ω

Lagging element (source 2): 49.56 + j 51.47 Ω

"Simplest" (Transmission Line Only) Feed System

Select TWO ELEMENT for the ARRAY TYPE in *Arrayfeed1* and "SIMPLEST" for the FEED SYSTEM TYPE. Enter the frequency of 14.15 MHz and enter the element feed point impedances from *EZNEC* into the appropriate boxes in the INPUTS frame. For line impedances, the section describing the "simplest" feed system recommends against choosing one which is very different from the element feed point impedances, but for fun let's try 300 Ω for the two lines and see what happens. Enter 300 in the LINE 1 Z0 and LINE 2 Z0 boxes. Finally, enter the LAGGING:LEADING I MAG, PHASE of 1 for MAG and –120 for PHASE.

Click FIND SOLUTIONS. For this example we'll assume that TV-type twinlead with a velocity factor of 0.8 is being used. So enter 0.8 for the VELOCITY FACTOR and read the physical line lengths in the PHYSICAL LENGTHS frame. A model of the array using the first solution has been created as **ARRL_Dipole_Array_TL_Example.EZ**. Open this file in *EZNEC* and click FF Tab. You should see that the plot is virtually identical to the one saved earlier from the ideal-current model. Note the gain and front-to-back ratio or 8.79 dBi and 31.01 dB respectively reported in the data box below the 2D plot.

Don't subtract 2.15 dB to find the gain relative to a single element! This isn't a free-space model, and the gain of a single dipole over ground is much greater than 2.15 dBi. Instead, delete one of the elements in **ARRL_Dipole_Array_Example.EZ** to find the gain of a single element and subtract that value from the array gain. You can use the undo feature or re-open the file to restore the array.

Now, go back to the model with the "simplest" feed system in *EZNEC* and change the Frequency to 14.0 MHz. Click FF TAB again. The gain has decreased a little, to 8.54 dBi and the front-to-back ratio has also decreased, to 21.8 dB. At 14.3 MHz, the gain is slightly higher, 9.04 dBi, but the front-to-back is again worse, down to 18.64 dB. But this isn't bad overall.

Let's take a look at the second solution. Click the TRANS LINES line in the main *EZNEC* window to open the TRANSMISSION LINES window. Change the length of the first line to 26.856 feet, the second to 28.356 feet, and press the Enter key to complete the change. Change the FREQUENCY back to 14.15 MHz and click FF TAB. You should see exactly the same pattern as for both the first solution and for the ideal current model. But now change the FREQUENCY to 14.0 MHz, click FF TAB, and look at the pattern.

What happened? The gain has dropped to 5.95 dBi and the front-to-back to only 3.1 dB. The array is now nearly bi-directional! It's almost as bad at 14.3 MHz. So we've created a terribly touchy system. The chance of its working correctly even at the design frequency is slim, because there are inevitably some differences between the model and real antenna.

We did have a clue this might happen. As stated in the section describing the "simplest" feed system, the best choices for line Z_0 and for the resulting solution give a difference in electrical line lengths about equal to the desired phase delay of the current. The difference in electrical line lengths for the first solution was about 152° — not as close to the 120° current phase difference as we'd like, but much better than the mere 9.7° difference of the lines for the second solution. While the 300-Ω line Z_0 is quite different from the element feed point impedances, the first solution result is quite good. If desired, you can try other line impedance values into *Arrayfeed1* and evaluate the results with *EZNEC.*

Please see the information about baluns in the Baluns in Phased Arrays section. Baluns are placed the same as in Figure 6.19, which shows the L network feed system.

L-Network Feed System

To design an L network feed system, change the *Arrayfeed1* FEED SYSTEM TYPE to L NETWORK and click FIND SOLUTIONS. The results aren't good ones to use. The component reactance magnitudes of about 1573 and 2619 Ω are more than five times the 300-Ω Z_0 of the feed lines. As explained in the section describing the L network feed system, it's undesirable to have such a large ratio of component reactance to line Z_0. Among other problems, the inductor and capacitor values are quite extreme and capacitor stray inductance and inductor capacitance would have a significant impact on performance.

The problem occurs because the feed line impedance we chose is much larger than the element feed point impedances, so the λ/4 lines transform the feed point impedances to much higher values at the L network and main feed point. This feed system would be extremely critical, narrowbanded and difficult to adjust. We can do better by choosing feed line impedances that aren't too drastically different than the element feed point impedances. In this case, 50 or 75 Ω would be a much better choice than 300. Let's try 75.

In *Arrayfeed1*, change the LINE 1 Z0 and LINE 2 Z0 impedances from 300 to 75 and click FIND SOLUTIONS. L network component reactance magnitudes are now about 98 and 164 Ω, much better than before. This will be a relatively uncritical and broadbanded feed system.

Again, be sure to read the information about baluns in the Baluns in Phased Arrays section. Figure 6.19 shows the completed feed system including baluns. *EZNEC* example file **ARRL_Dipole_Array_L_Network_Example.EZ** is a model of the array with L network feed. It does not include baluns, since the transmission line models support only differential mode currents and therefore have the implicit effect of including ideal baluns.

6.4.7 CROSSFIRE RECEIVING ARRAY

While any transmitting array can be used for receiving with the same gain and directivity, inefficient (lossy) arrays do well for HF and MF receiving but not for transmitting. High loss brings the potential for exceptionally wide bandwidth, simplified feed systems and compact size, so receive-only arrays are worth considering for many installations. The following example is for a simple 2-element array using the "crossfire" phasing principle discussed earlier. The same methods can be used for more complex arrays.

The general principle of "crossfire" phasing is to connect the elements together with a delay line with an electrical length equal to the distance between the elements. A frequency-independent phase inversion (such as a wide-band transformer or physical connection reversal of one of the transmission lines) is added somewhere in the feed system path to one but not both of the elements, causing frequency-independent cancellation of the signals from the two elements when the signal is coming from one end-fire direction. The result is a potentially deep pattern null in one direction over a wide range of frequencies. The pattern can be reversed using methods described later and more elaborate arrays such as the Four-Square can be designed to allow additional null directions by directional switching. Since transmission lines invariably have velocity factors less than one, a single delay line of the proper electrical length is too short in practice to reach between the elements. The method works equally well, however, using a line to each element from a common point, the only requirement being that the difference in their electrical lengths equals the correct delay length. That is how these example designs were created.

There are a number of ways to create a time delay but about the only practical way of achieving a constant time delay over a wide frequency range is to use a transmission line terminated in its characteristic impedance. The termination must, of course, maintain its impedance over the wide frequency range. The straightforward method of designing a receiving antenna therefore requires that the transmission lines from the elements to somehow be added together but with each properly terminated. This could be done with active circuits, for example, by terminating each line with a terminating resistor connected to the high impedance input of an amplifier or buffer circuit whose outputs can then be added (or subtracted, since an inversion is required somewhere) without affecting the transmission line termination. Passive methods include terminating each transmission line with a matched attenuator, then resistively combining the attenuator outputs. This effectively isolates the terminating impedance from the summing circuitry. Another passive method is to use a hybrid combiner (see **Figure 6.30**) The potential advantage of this method is its relative efficiency, resulting in higher signal (and noise) level output than the attenuator method. This is important only if the received signal level is otherwise

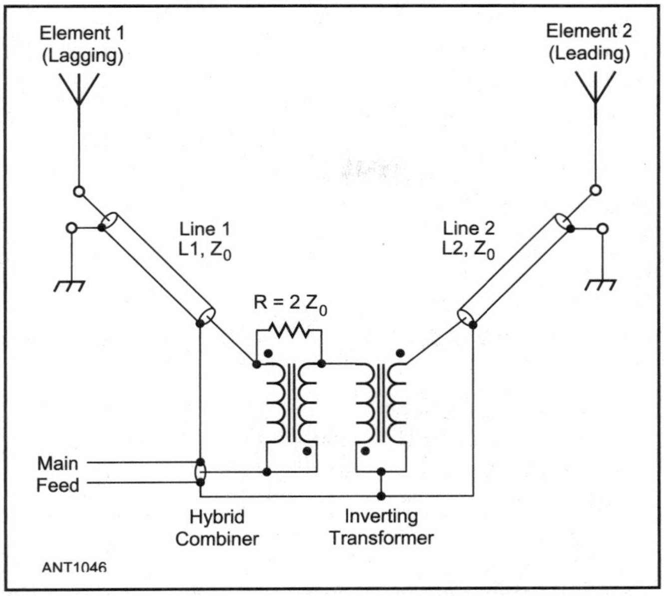

Figure 6.30 — "Crossfire" array with hybrid termination.

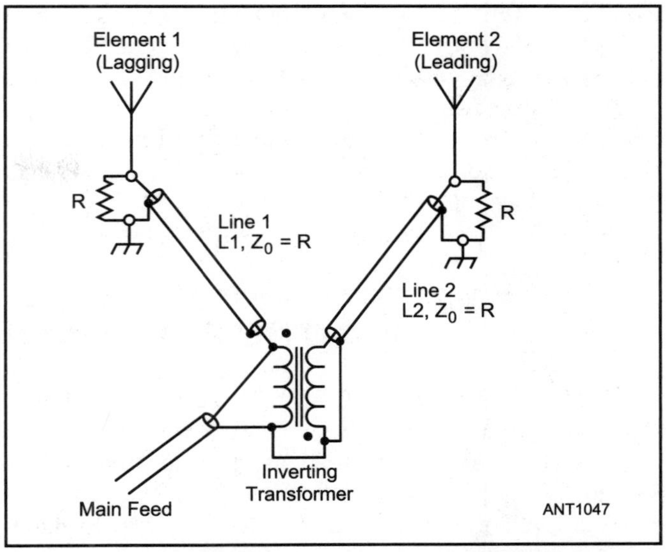

Figure 6.31 — "Crossfire" array with transmitting-type design.

small enough that receiver noise becomes apparent.

Another approach to the "crossfire" system is to design the array as though it were to be used for transmitting, even though its low efficiency would make it impractical for that purpose. The difference in this approach is that the transmission line termination is done at the element feed points rather than at the summing point (see **Figure 6.31**) Reciprocity assures that the same directional properties will exist when using the array for receiving, even though the transmission lines are properly terminated at their source rather than load ends. The following examples show this approach and the hybrid-terminated receiving array approach for comparison and to illustrate that the reciprocal principle applies. Both arrays have the same pattern when receiving as they do for the modeled transmitting case.

Transmitting Array Type Design

A two-element "crossfire" array with transmitting-type design is included as *EZNEC* example file **ARRL_Crossfire1_Example.EZ**. The array consists of two 30-foot-high vertical elements spaced 60 feet apart. These correspond to approximately 1⁄16 wavelength and 1⁄8 wavelength respectively at 1.85 MHz. Two transmission lines are used. This is being called a "transmitting array type design" because the transmission lines are terminated at the load end when driven by a transmitter, but are terminated at the load end in some other impedance when receiving.

Because the elements are electrically short, they have high feed point impedances, so parallel 50-Ω resistors at each feed point provide stable, near-50-Ω terminations for the transmission lines regardless of mutual coupling effects. The difference between the electrical lengths of the lines is 60 feet, the same as the line spacing. An ideal transformer is used in the model to effect the required phase inversion to one of the elements.

The model could be simplified by deleting the transformer and specifying a reverse connection of one of the transmission lines, and the result would be the same. However, the included model more closely represents how the antenna would actually be implemented. The model shows a front-to-back ratio of better than 30 dB at 1 and 1.85 MHz, dropping to just over 20 dB at 4 MHz. Degradation at the higher frequency is due to the lower feed point impedance as the element becomes electrically longer. This dilutes the effectiveness of the 50-Ω feed point swamping resistors. Modeling with a program having plane-wave excitation capability confirms that the front-to-back ratio is the same when receiving as when transmitting.

An 18-Ω resistor is included at each element base to simulate the resistance of a moderately good ground system. However, because its value is small compared to the large impedance of a short element, it has no significant effect on the array performance. This indicates that the array will work well (for receiving) without an elaborate ground system.

Receiving Array Type Design — Hybrid Termination

EZNEC example **ARRL_Crossfire_Hybrid_Feed_Example.EZ** uses the opposite design approach from the previous example. Instead of being terminated at the elements, the transmission lines are terminated at the ends where a receiver would be connected. Termination and signal addition are done with a hybrid combiner circuit consisting of a transformer and resistor. The inverting transformer is replaced in this model with a connection reversal of one of the transmission lines, for simplicity, as explained in the previous example. This model shows an improved front-to-back ratio of about 29 dB at 4 MHz compared to about 22 dB for the transmitting-type design, due to reduced sensitivity to mutual coupling and element impedance effects.

Front-to-back ratio of the two examples is about the same at 1 and 1.85 MHz. This system is more efficient than the transmitting-type design, with signal (and noise) levels of about 5 dB greater at 4 MHz increasing to 14 dB greater at 1 MHz. This won't improve system signal-to-noise ratio unless the level of atmospheric noise is so low that receiver noise is audible.

Note: Modeling of the hybrid circuit and similar structures is difficult, requiring some experimenting and compromising to satisfy the requirements of the *NEC* calculating engine which isn't designed for analysis of loaded electrically small structures. Often, a suitable compromise isn't possible. This design is included for illustration only, not as encouragement to attempt to construct similar models.

6.5 PRACTICAL ASPECTS OF PHASED ARRAY DESIGN

With almost any type of antenna system, there is much that can be learned from experimenting with, testing and using various array configurations. In this section, Roy Lewallen, W7EL, extends his contribution to this book, sharing the benefit of years of his experience from actually building, adjusting and using phased arrays. There is much more work to be done in most of the areas covered here, and Roy encourages the reader to build on this work.

6.5.1 ADJUSTING PHASED ARRAY FEED SYSTEMS

If a phased array is constructed only to achieve forward gain, adjusting it is seldom worthwhile. This is because the forward gain of most arrays is quite insensitive to either the magnitude or phase of the relative currents flowing in the elements. If, however, good rejection of unwanted signals is desired, adjustment may be required. And achieving very deep nulls will almost surely require some adjustment.

The in-phase and 180° out-of-phase current-forcing method supplies very well-balanced and well-phased currents to elements without adjustment. If the pattern of an array fed using this method is unsatisfactory, it's generally the result of environmental differences — where the elements, even though furnished with correct currents, aren't generating the correct fields. Such an array can be optimized in a single direction, but a more general approach than the current-forcing method must be taken. Some possibilities are described by Paul Lee and Forrest Gehrke (see Bibliography).

Unlike the current-forcing method, the "simplest" and L network feed systems described earlier in this chapter are dependent on the self and mutual impedance of one or more elements. The required transmission-line lengths or L network component values can be computed to a high level of precision, but the results are only as good as the knowledge of the relevant feed point impedances.

While the simplest feed system doesn't readily lend itself to adjustment, the components of an L network can easily be made adjustable or can be experimentally changed in increments. A practical approach is to model the array as accurately as possible, design and build the feed system based on the model results and then adjust the network for the best performance.

Simple arrays such as the two-element 90° fed and spaced array can be adjusted as follows. Place a low-power signal source at a distance from the array (preferably several wavelengths), in the direction a null should be. While listening to the signal on a receiver connected to the array, alternately adjust the two L network components for the best rejection of the signal.

This has proved to be a very good way to adjust 2-element arrays. However, variable results were obtained when a Four-Square array was adjusted using this technique. The probable reason is that more than one combination of current balance and phasing can produce a null in a given direction but each produces a different overall pattern. So a different method must be used for adjusting more complex arrays. This involves actually measuring the element currents in some way, and adjusting the network until the currents are correct. After adjusting the currents, small adjustments can be made to deepen the null(s) if desired.

Measuring Element Currents

You can measure the element currents two ways. One way is to measure them directly at the element feed points, as shown in **Figure 6.32**. A dual-channel oscilloscope is required to monitor the currents. This method is the most

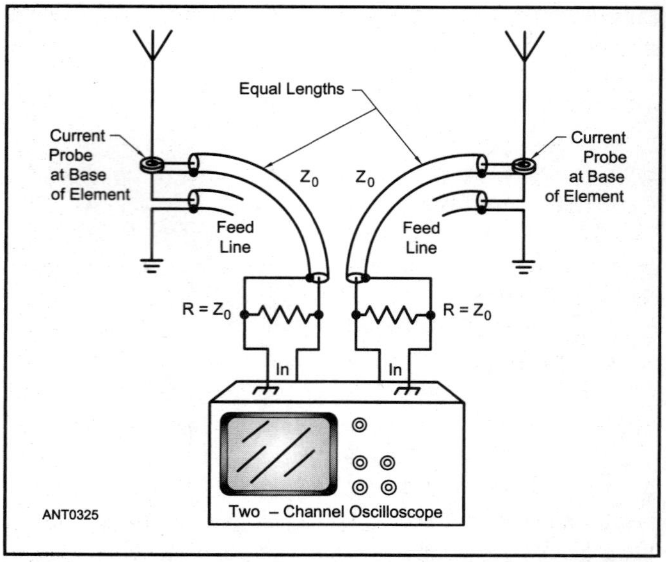

Figure 6.32 — One method of measuring element currents in a phased array. Details of the current probe are given in Figure 6.33. Caution: Do not run high power to the antenna system for this measurement, or damage to the test equipment may result.

accurate and it provides a direct indication of the actual relative magnitudes and phases of the element currents. The current probe is shown in **Figure 6.33**. (Another current probe design by W8JI is presented at **www.w8ji.com/building_a_current_meter.htm**.)

Instead of measuring the element currents directly, you could measure them indirectly by measuring the voltages on the feed lines an electrical λ/4 or 3λ/4 distance from the array. The voltages at these points are directly proportional to the element currents. This introduces additional variables that can reduce the accuracy of the result, but the method generally produces adequate performance. The 2-element arrays fed with the L network system and all the four-element arrays presented earlier have λ/4 or 3λ/4 lines from all elements to a common location, making this second measurement method convenient. The voltages can be observed with a dual-channel oscilloscope, or, to adjust for equal-magnitude currents and 90° phasing, you can use the test circuit shown in **Figure 6.34**.

The test circuit is connected to the feed lines of two elements that are to be adjusted for 90° phasing (such as elements 1 and 2, or 2 and 4 of the Four-Square array of Figures 6.24 and 25). Adjust the L network components alternately until both meters read zero. Proper operation of the test circuit can be verified by disconnecting one of the inputs. The phase output should remain close to zero. If not, there is an undesirable imbalance in the circuit, which must be corrected. Another means of verification is to first adjust the L network so the tester indicates correct phasing (zero volts at the phase output). Then reverse the tester input connections to the elements. The phase output should remain close to zero.

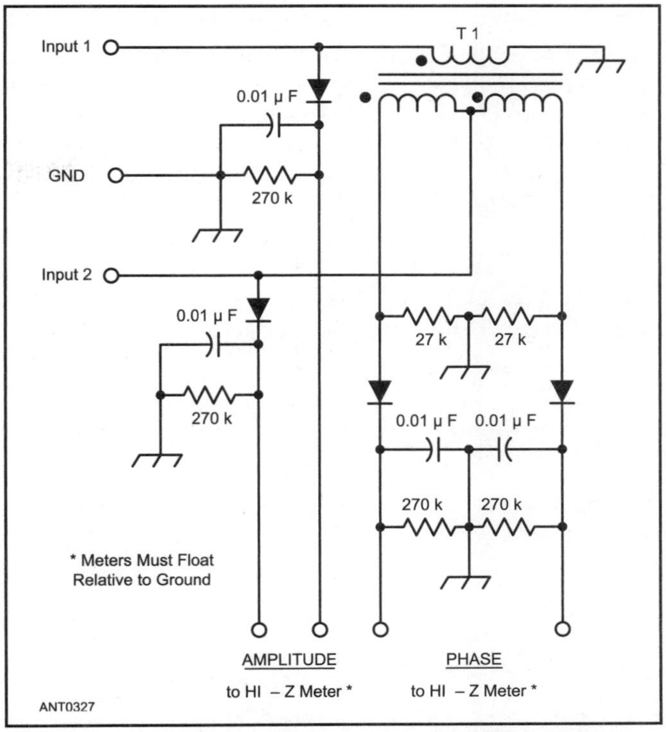

Figure 6.34 — Quadrature test circuit. All diodes are germanium, such as 1N34A, 1N270, or equiv. Hot carrier or silicon diodes can be used at higher power levels. All resistors are ¼ or ½ W, 5% tolerance. Capacitors are ceramic. Alligator clips are convenient for making the input and ground connections to the array.

T1 — 7 trifilar turns on an Amidon FT-37-43, -75, -77, or equivalent ferrite toroid core.

6.5.2 DIRECTIONAL SWITCHING OF ARRAYS

One ideal directional-switching method would take the entire feed system, including the lines to the elements and physically rotate it. The smallest possible increment of rotation would depend on the symmetry of the array — the feed system would need to rotate until the array again looks the same to it. For example, any 2-element array can be rotated 180° (although that wouldn't accomplish anything if the array is bidirectional to begin with). The 4-element rectangular array of Figures 6.28 and 29 can also be reversed, and the Four-Square array of Figures 6.24 and 25 can be switched in 90° increments.

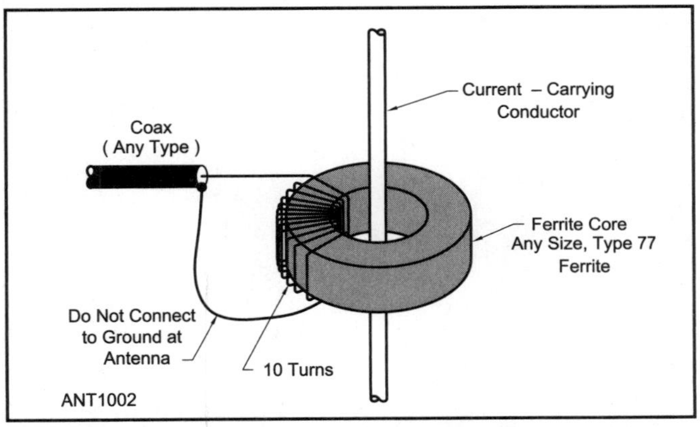

Figure 6.33 — The current probe for use in the test setup of Figure 6.32. The ferrite core is of type 77 ferrite or type 2 powdered iron and may be any size. The coax line must be terminated at the opposite end with a resistor equal to its characteristic impedance. You should build this probe in a plastic or metal box to provide mechanical ruggedness.

Smaller switching increments can be accomplished only by reconfiguring the feed system, including any network if used, effectively creating a different kind of array. Switching in smaller increments than dictated by symmetry will create a different pattern in some directions than in others, and must be thoughtfully done to maintain equal and properly phased element currents. The methods illustrated here will deal only with switching in increments related to the array symmetry, except for one: a 2-element broadside/end-fire array.

In all arrays, the success of directional switching depends on the elements and ground systems being identical so that equal element currents result in equal fields. It's even more important in arrays fed with any method other than current forcing, because the effectiveness of those methods depends on the element feed point impedances. Few of us can afford the luxury of having an array many wavelengths away from all other conductors, so an array will nearly always perform somewhat differently in each direction. The array should be adjusted when steered in the direction requiring the most signal rejection in the nulls. Forward gain will, for all practical purposes, be equal in all the switched directions, since gain is much more tolerant of error than are nulls.

Basic Switching Methods

Following is a discussion of basic switching methods, how to power relays through the main feed line and other practical considerations. In diagrams, grounds are frequently omitted to aid clarity, but connections of the ground conductors must be carefully made. In fact, it is recommended that the ground conductors be switched just as the center conductors are, as explained in more detail in Improving Array Switching Systems below. In all cases, interconnecting lines must be very short.

A pair of elements spaced λ/2 apart can readily be switched between broadside and end-fire bidirectional patterns, using the current-forcing properties of λ/4 lines. The method is shown in **Figure 6.35**. The switching device can be a relay powered via a separate cable or by dc sent along the main feed line.

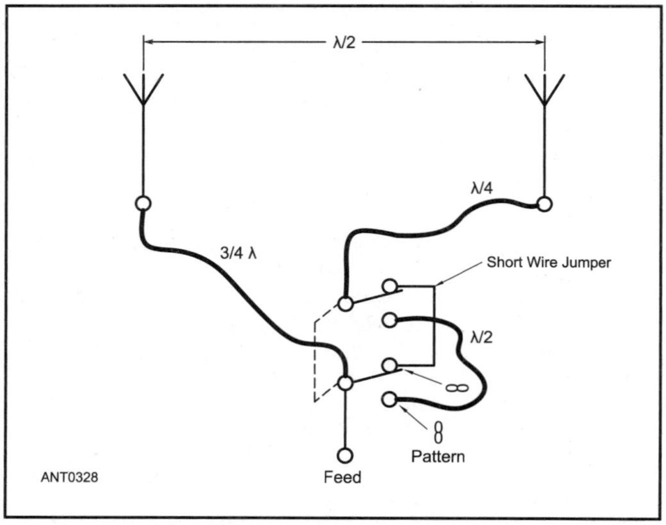

Figure 6.35 — Two-element broadside/end-fire switching. All lines must have the same characteristic impedance. Grounds and cable shields have been omitted for clarity.

Figure 6.36 shows directional switching of a 90° fed, 90° spaced array fed with a "simplest" feed system, where L1 and L2 are the required lengths of the two feed lines. **Figure 6.37** shows how to switch the same array when fed with an L network, current-forcing system.

The rectangular array of Figure 6.28 can be switched in a similar manner, as shown in **Figure 6.38**. To switch a "simplest" fed rectangular array, use the switching circuit of Figure 6.36, but connect the two equal length lines to points A and B of Figure 6.29 in place of the two elements shown in Figure 6.36.

Switching the direction of an array in increments of 90°, when permitted by symmetry, requires at least two relays. A method of 90° switching of the Four-Square array with L network feed is shown in **Figure 6.39**.

Powering Relays Through Feed Lines

All of the above switching methods can be implemented without additional wires to the switch box. A single-relay system is shown in **Figure 6.40A**, and a two-relay system in Figure 6.40B. Small 12 or 24-V dc power relays can be used in either system at power levels up to at least a few hundred watts. Do not attempt to change directions while transmitting,

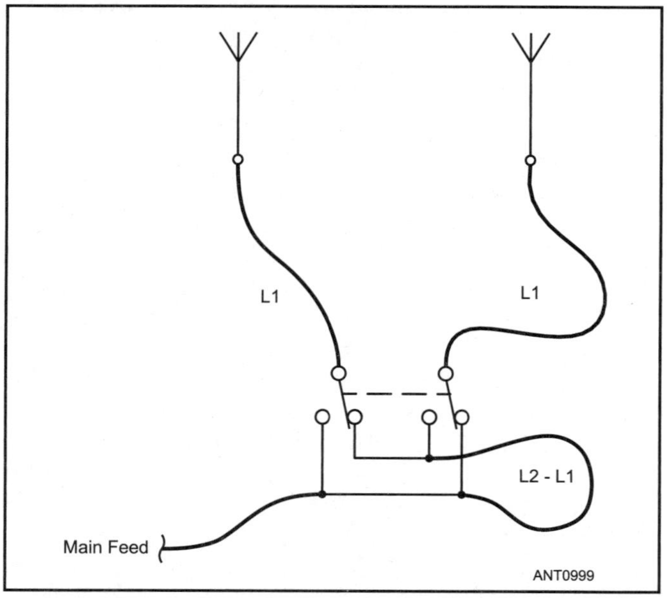

Figure 6.36 — Directional switching for 90°, 90° spaced 2-element array fed with a "simplest" feed system. The switch adds line to create a total length of L2 to the right-hand element.

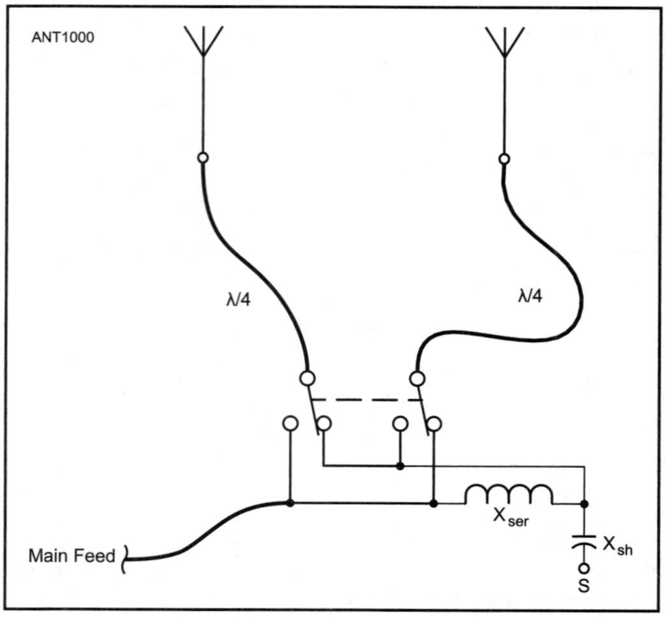

Figure 6.37 — Directional switching for 90°, 90° spaced 2-element array fed with an L network, current-forcing feed system.

however. Blocking capacitors C1 and C2 should be good quality ceramic or transmitting mica units of 0.01 to 0.1 µF. No problems have been encountered using 0.1 µF, 300-V monolithic ceramic units at RF output levels up to 300 W. C2 may be omitted if the antenna system is an open circuit at dc. C3 and C4 should be ceramic, 0.001 µF or larger.

In Figure 6.40B, capacitors C5 through C8 should be selected with the ratings of their counterparts in Figure 6.40A, as given above. Electrolytic capacitors across the relay coils, C9 and C10 in Figure 6.40B, should be large enough to prevent the relays from buzzing, but not so large as to make relay operation too slow. Final values for most relays will be in the range from 10 to 100 µF. They should have a voltage rating of at least double the relay coil voltage. Some relays do not require this capacitor. All diodes are 1N4001 or similar. A rotary switch may be used in place of the two toggle switches in the two-relay system to switch the relays in the desired sequence.

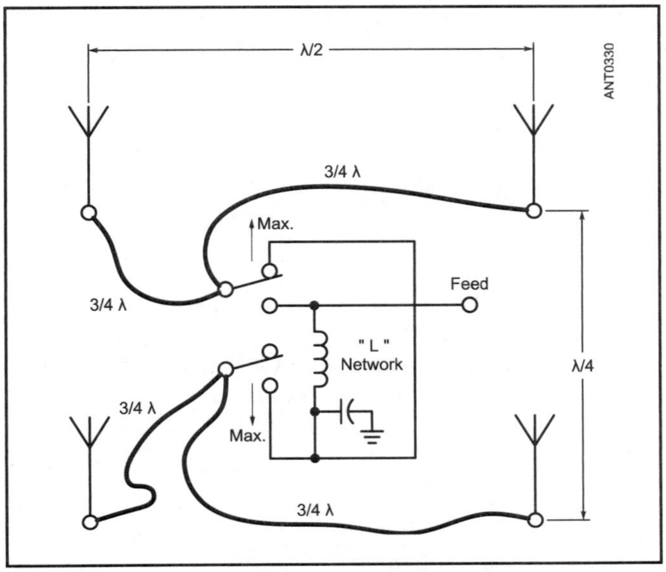

Figure 6.38 — Directional switching of a four-element rectangular array. All interconnections must be very short. As usual, grounds and cable shields have been omitted for clarity.

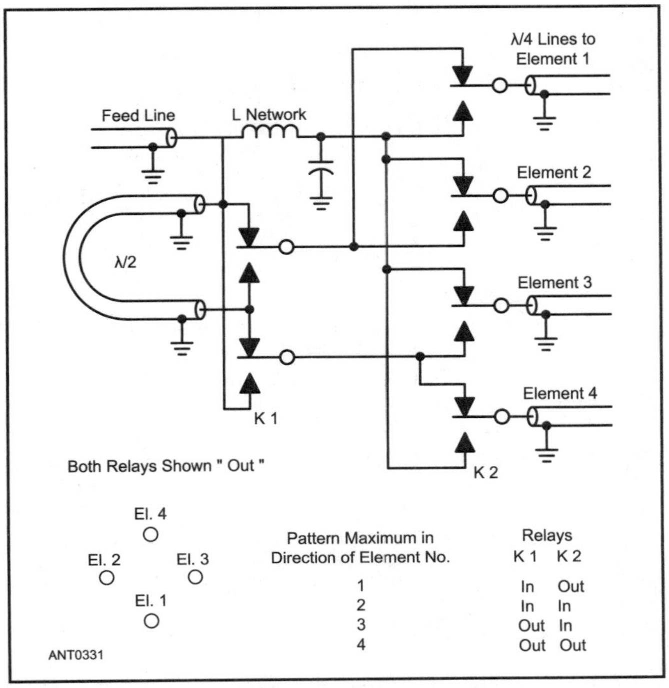

Figure 6.39 — Directional switching of the Four-Square array. All interconnections must be very short.

Improving Array-Switching Systems

The extra circuitry involved in switching arrays can degrade array performance by altering the relative currents fed to each element. One common cause is current sharing in common ground conductors, even when connections are kept

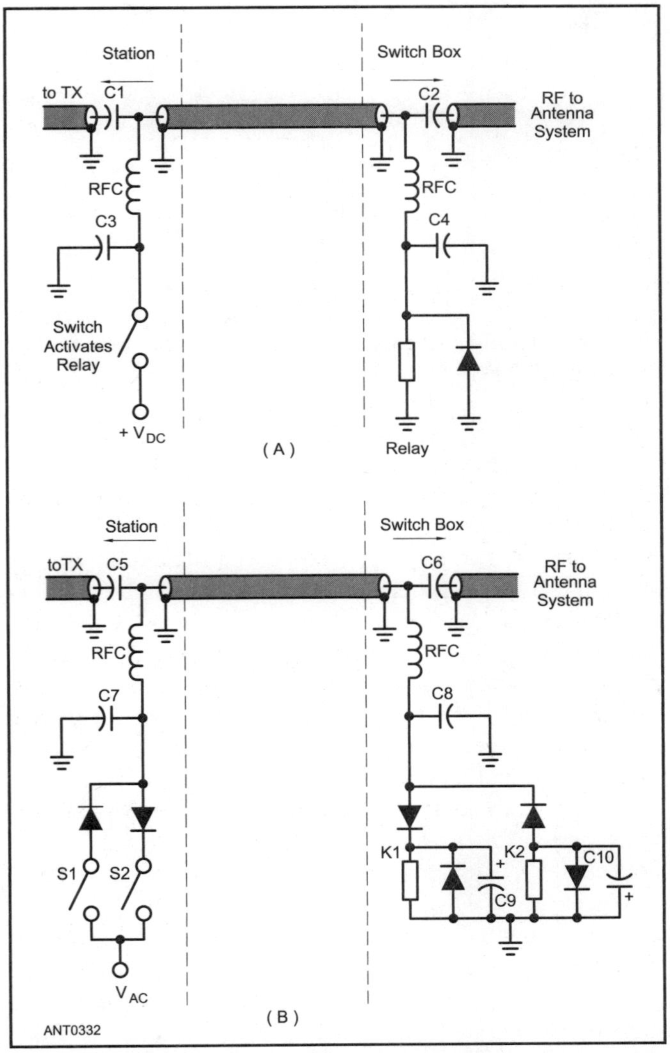

Figure 6.40 — Remote switching of relays. See text for component information. A one-relay system is shown at A, and a two-relay system at B. In B, S1 activates K1, and S2 activates K2. In addition, it is recommended to bypass each diode with a 0.001 - 0.01 µF disc ceramic capacitor to avoid generating harmonics and mixing products when transmitting.

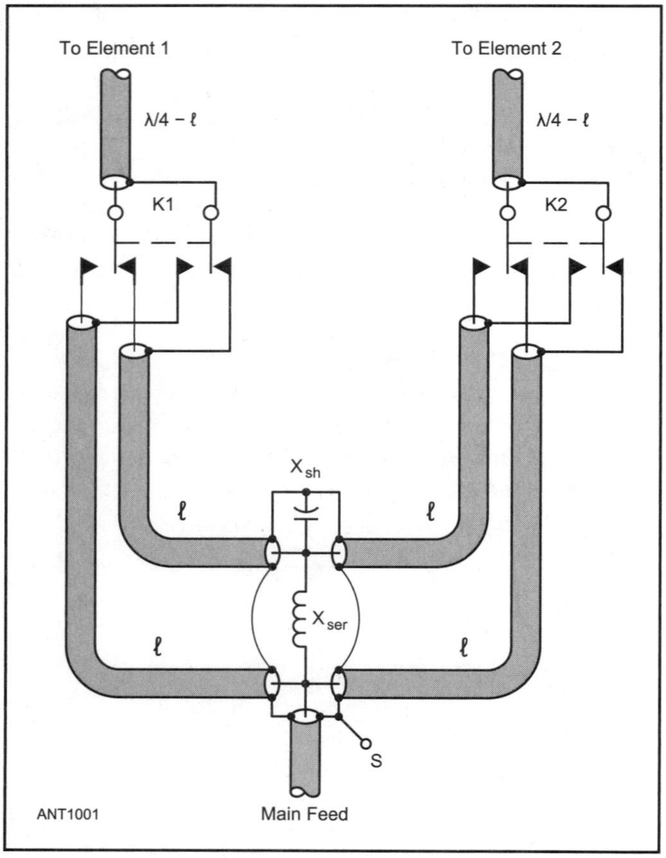

Figure 6.41 — A carefully designed L network, current-forcing switching system that switches both hot and shield conductors in feed coaxes.

very short. The author has seen a 30° phase shift in voltage along a 4-inch piece of #12 AWG wire in a 40 meter array feed system.

When the two conductors of a feed line are physically separated from each other the characteristic impedance increases. This is especially true when the main lines are coaxial cables. If currents from two elements share the ground conductor of a split line a relatively large voltage drop results. Voltage changes λ/4 from the elements translate to current changes at the elements. Although keeping all leads extremely short is sometimes adequate, the best way to reduce current sharing problems is to keep the two conductors of each transmission line as close together as possible, and switch both conductors of each line rather than just a single or "hot" conductor.

An example of a carefully designed switching system is shown in **Figure 6.41**. It avoids the problem of shared ground conductor currents, as well as another common problem, namely that effective line lengths are often different along different switching paths. Notice how the path from the main feed point travels through a single line to each element with no common ground connections to other lines except at the main feed point. Notice also that the distance doesn't change as the direction is switched. The λ/4 lines going to the two elements must be shortened by the length ℓ of the lines on the feed side of the relays so that the total line length from the main feed point to each element is λ/4 (or 3λ/4).

You can see that in either relay position, there's an open ended stub of length ℓ connected at the main feed point and another at the output end of the L network. These will add capacitance at those points. Extra capacitance at the main feed point will alter the overall impedance seen by a transmitter, but won't otherwise have any effect on the array or its performance. The one at the output of the L network will, however, change the transformation and phase shift properties of the network. But it's easy to compensate — the value of the shunt capacitor element is simply reduced by the amount of capacitance added by the stub. The amount of capacitance for any kind of transmission line can be calculated from:

$$C\,(\mathrm{pF/ft}) = \frac{1017}{Z_0\ \mathrm{VF}}$$

or

$$C\,(\mathrm{pF/m}) = \frac{3336}{Z_0\ \mathrm{VF}}$$

where Z_0 = the characteristic impedance of the line and VF = the velocity factor. This works out to 31 pF/foot or 101 pF/

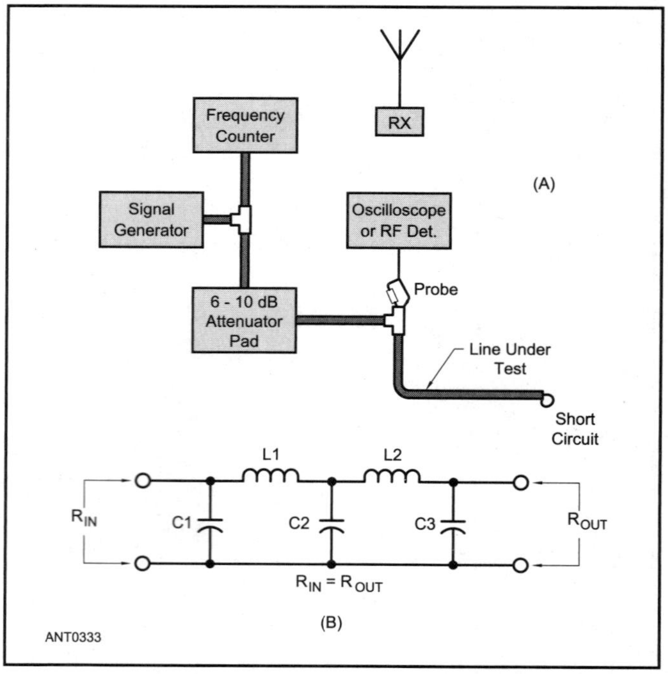

Figure 6.42 — At A, the setup for measurement of the electrical length of a transmission line. The receiver may be used in place of the frequency counter to determine the frequency of the signal generator. The signal generator output must be free of harmonics; the half-wave harmonic filter at B may be used outboard if there is any doubt. It must be constructed for the frequency band of operation. Connect the filter between the signal generator and the attenuator pad.

C1, C3 — Value to have a capacitive reactance = R_{IN}.
C2 — Value to have a capacitive reactance = ½ R_{IN}.
L1, L2 — Value to have an inductive reactance = R_{IN}.

meter for 50-Ω solid polyethylene insulated coax which has a velocity factor of 0.66.

The general principles illustrated in Figure 6.41 can be extended to other switching systems. If switching the ground conductors as described above isn't practical, use of a metal box for the switching circuitry is recommended, so that the relatively large surface area of the box can be used for the common ground conductors, minimizing their inductance. Always keep leads extremely short.

6.5.3 MEASURING THE ELECTRICAL LENGTH OF FEED LINES

When using the feed methods described earlier the feed lines must be very close to the correct length. For best results, they should be correct within 1% or so. This means that a line that is intended to be, say, λ/4 at 7 MHz, should actually be λ/4 at some frequency within 70 kHz of 7 MHz. A simple but accurate method to determine at what frequency a line is λ/4 or λ/2 is shown in **Figure 6.42A**. The far end of the line is short circuited with a very short connection. A signal is applied to the input and the frequency is swept until the impedance at the input is a minimum. This is the frequency at which the line is λ/2. Either the frequency counter or the receiver may be used to determine this frequency. The line is, of course, λ/4 at one half the measured frequency.

The detector can be a simple diode detector or an oscilloscope may be used if available. A 6 to 10 dB attenuator pad is included to prevent the signal generator from looking into a short circuit at the measurement frequency. The signal generator output must be free of harmonics. If there is any doubt, an outboard low-pass filter, such as a half-wave harmonic filter, should be used. The half-wave filter circuit is shown in Figure 6.42B, and must be constructed for the frequency band of operation.

Another satisfactory method is to use a noise or resistance bridge or antenna analyzer at the input of the line, again looking for a low impedance at the input while the output is short circuited. Simple resistance bridges are described in the **Antenna and Transmission Line Measurements** chapter.

Dip oscillators have been found to be unsatisfactory. The required coupling loop has too great an effect on measurements.

6.5.4 MEASURING ELEMENT SELF AND MUTUAL IMPEDANCES

The need for measuring element self and mutual impedances has been made largely unnecessary with the ready availability of modeling software. Few amateurs appreciate the considerable difficulty of making accurate impedance measurements and accurate mutual impedance measurements are very difficult even with professional test equipment and skills. Despite the limitations of computer modeling, results very often are better than measured values because of the multiple factors affecting measurement accuracy.

Those who are interested in measuring self and mutual impedances can find more detailed information about doing so in Appendix B with the downloadable supplemental information for this book. The information there is from earlier editions of *Antenna Book*.

6.6 BIBLIOGRAPHY

Source material and more extended discussion of topics covered in this chapter can be found in the references given below and in the textbooks listed at the end of the **Antenna Fundamentals** chapter.

D. W. Atchley, H. E. Stinehelfer, and J. F. White, "360°-Steerable Vertical Phased Arrays," *QST*, Apr 1976, pp 27-30.

G. H. Brown, "Directional Antennas," *Proc. IRE*, Vol 25, No. 1, Jan 1937, pp 78-145.

G. H. Brown, R. F. Lewis and J. Epstein, "Ground Systems as a Factor in Antenna Efficiency," *Proc. IRE*, Jun 1937, pp 753-787.

G. H. Brown and O. M. Woodward, Jr., "Experimentally Determined Impedance Characteristics of Cylindrical Antennas," *Proc. IRE*, Apr 1945.

J. Brown, "A New Choke Cookbook for the 160-10M Bands," **k9yc.com/publish.htm**.

L. B. Cebik, "Two Limitations of NEC-4", various online sources.

A. Christman, "Feeding Phased Arrays: An Alternate Method," *Ham Radio*, May 1985, pp 58-59, 61-64.

A. Christman, "Tall Vertical Arrays," *QEX*, Nov/Dec 2012, pp 24-35.

A. Christman, "A Study of Tall Verticals," *QEX*, May/Jun 2011, pp 26-31.

A. Christman, "A Study of Tall Verticals (Letters to the Editor)," *QEX*, Sep/Oct 2011, pp 38-39.

A. Christman, "A Study of Phased Vertical Arrays," *QEX*, Mar/Apr 2006, pp 46-51.

J. Devoldere, *ON4UN's Low-Band DXing*, 5th ed. (Newington, CT: ARRL, 2010).

EZNEC is an antenna-modeling computer program for Microsoft *Windows*. See **www.eznec.com** for full information.

F. Gehrke, "Vertical Phased Arrays," in six parts, *Ham Radio*, May-Jul, Oct and Dec 1983, and May 1984.

C. Harrison, Jr, and R. King, "Theory of Coupled Folded Antennas," *IRE Trans on Antennas and Propagation*, Mar 1960, pp131-135.

W. Hayward and D. DeMaw, *Solid State Design for the Radio Amateur* (Newington, CT: ARRL, 1977).

W. Hayward, *Radio Frequency Design* (Newington, CT: ARRL, 1994).

H. Jasik, *Antenna Engineering Handbook*, 1st ed. (New York: McGraw-Hill, 1961). Later editions are edited by Richard C. Johnson.

R. King and C. Harrison, Jr, "Mutual and Self-Impedance for Coupled Antennas," *Journal of Applied Physics*, Vol 15, Jun 1944, pp 481-495.

R. King, "Self- and Mutual Impedances of Parallel Identical Antennas," *Proc. IRE*, Aug 1952, pp 981-988.

R. W. P. King, *Theory of Linear Antennas* (Cambridge, MA: Harvard Univ Press, 1956), p 275ff.

H. W. Kohler, "Antenna Design for Field-Strength Gain," *Proc. IRE*, Oct 1944, pp 611-616.

J. D. Kraus, "Antenna Arrays with Closely Spaced Elements," *Proc. IRE*, Feb, 1940, pp 76-84.

J. D. Kraus, *Antennas*, 2nd ed. (New York: McGraw-Hill Book Co, 1988).

Johnson, Richard C., *Antenna Engineering Handbook*, 3rd ed. (New York: McGraw-Hill Inc, 1993). This is a later edition of the volume by the same name edited by H. Jasik.

E. A. Laport, *Radio Antenna Engineering* (New York: McGraw-Hill Book Co, 1952).

J. L. Lawson, "Simple Arrays of Vertical Antenna Elements," *QST*, May 1971, pp 22-27.

P. H. Lee, *The Amateur Radio Vertical Antenna Handbook*, 2nd ed. (Hicksville, NY: CQ Publishing, Inc., 1984).

R. W. Lewallen, "Baluns: What They Do and How They Do It," *The ARRL Antenna Compendium, Vol 1* (Newington: ARRL, 1985). Also available for viewing at **www.eznec.com/Amateur/Articles/Baluns.pdf**.

R. Lewallen, "The Impact of Current Distribution on Array Patterns," Technical Correspondence, *QST*, Jul 1990, pp 39-40. Also available for viewing at **www.eznec.com/Amateur/Articles/Current_Dist.pdf**.

R. Lewallen, "*MININEC* — The Other Edge of the Sword," *QST*, Feb 1991, pp 18-22. *ELNEC*, referenced in the article, is no longer available.

M. W. Maxwell, "Some Aspects of the Balun Problem," *QST*, Mar 1983, pp 38-40.

J. Sevick, "The Ground-Image Vertical Antenna," *QST*, Jul 1971, pp 16-19, 22.

J. Sevick, "The W2FMI Ground-Mounted Short Vertical," *QST*, Mar 1973, pp 13-28,41.

E. J. Wilkinson, "An N-Way Hybrid Power Divider," *IRE Transactions on Microwave Theory and Techniques*, Jan, 1960.

Radio Broadcast Ground Systems, available from Smith Electronics, Inc, 8200 Snowville Rd, Cleveland, OH 44141.

APPENDIX A — *EZNEC* EXAMPLES

This appendix contains step-by-step procedures using *EZNEC* to illustrate various topics discussed in the main chapter. The various example modeling files described in the text are available with the downloadable supplemental information for this book. They may be opened and used with the demo version of *EZNEC* v. 6, which is available for download from **www.eznec.com**. A full version of *EZNEC* v. 4.0 or later may also be used. Different versions, program types and calculating engines may give results that are slightly different from those shown in the examples. However, any differences should be insignificantly small.

EZNEC Example — Mutual Coupling

This example illustrates the effect of mutual coupling on feed point impedance. Open the **ARRL_Cardioid.EZ** file, which is mounted over "perfect" ground. Click the VIEW ANT button to see a diagram of the antenna, a 2-element array of vertical elements. Click on the WIRES line in the main window to open the Wires Window. Click the button at the left of the Wire 2 line, and then press the DELETE key on your keyboard to delete wire #2. After clicking OK, note that one of the verticals has disappeared from the View Antenna display, leaving a single element. Click SRC DAT and note that the feed point impedance of this single vertical is about $37 + j\,1\ \Omega$ — it's very nearly resonant.

Next, in the Wires Window, open the EDIT menu at the top and click UNDO DELETE WIRE(S) to restore the second element. Click SRC DAT again and notice that the feed point impedance of wire #1 is now about $21 - j\,19\ \Omega$. The feed point impedance of the second element, which is identical to the first, is about $52 + j\,21\ \Omega$. This difference, and the change from the self-impedance of $37 + j\,1\ \Omega$, is due to mutual coupling. As you see, it's not at all a minor effect.

As an additional exercise, change the magnitude or phase angle of the source at the base of wire #2 (click SOURCES in the main window), and see how this changes the feed point impedances of both elements. You should be able to confirm each of the four points enumerated in the "Mutual Coupling" section.

EZNEC Example — Nulls

This example illustrates the effect of current magnitude on nulls and gain. Again, open the **ARRL_Cardioid.EZ** file. Click the FF PLOT button to generate the azimuth pattern of an ideal array. Save the plot for future reference as follows: In the plot window, open the FILE menu and select SAVE TRACE AS. Enter the name CARDIOID and click SAVE. Now, in the main window click on the SOURCES line to open the Sources Window. Change the magnitude of source 1 from 1 to 1.1, and of source 2 from 1 to 0.9 and press ENTER on your keyboard so that *EZNEC* will accept the last change.

Click FF PLOT to generate a pattern with the new currents. In the plot window, open the File menu and select ADD TRACE. Enter the name CARDIOID and click Open. You should now see the original plot and new plot overlaid. Notice that the null is much less deep with the altered currents, but the forward patterns are nearly identical. By clicking on the names of the traces, PRIMARY and CARDIOID, you can see in turn the gain and front-to-back ratio of each of the traces. The original, CARDIOID, has a front-to-back ratio of about 32 dB, while Primary, the new plot, has a ratio of about 22.5 dB. The forward gain, however, differs by only 0.02 dB, a completely insignificant amount.

EZNEC Example — "Phasing-Line" Feed

This example illustrates the effect of using a "phasing-line" feed. Open the **ARRL_CardTL.EZ** file. This is a model of an array fed with transmission lines whose lengths were designed using the *Arrayfeed1* program to take into account the actual load impedances of elements in a phased array. This model is mounted over "perfect" ground.

Click the VIEW ANT button to show the array. Note that the lengths of the lines from the source (circle) to the elements don't represent the actual physical lengths of the lines. In the main window, click on the TRANS LINES line to open the Transmission Lines window. In it you can see that the lengths of the feed lines, both of which are connected to the same source, are about 81° and 155°, a difference of 74° rather than 90°.

In the main window, click the CURRENTS button and take a look at the current shown for segment 1 of wires 1 and 2. These are the currents at the element feed points. The ratio of the magnitude of currents is 4.577/4.561 = 1.003, and the phase difference is –56.3°–(–147.5°) = 91.2°. (A more accurate determination of feed line lengths with program *Arrayfeed1* gives lengths of 80.61° and 153.70°, resulting in a current ratio of 1.000 at a phase of 90.02°. But the resulting pattern is very nearly the same.) But let's see what happens when we make the lines exactly 90° different in length.

First, click the FF PLOT button to generate the azimuth pattern of the original model. Save the plot for future reference as follows: In the plot window, open the FILE menu and select SAVE TRACE AS. Enter the name CARDTL and click SAVE. Now in the Transmission Lines Window, change the length of line number 1 from 80.56° to 90°. *Important:* In the line 1 Length box, enter 90D to make the line 90° long. If you omit the "d," it will become 90 meters long! Similarly, change the length of line 2 to 180° by entering 180D in the line 2 Length box, then press ENTER on your keyboard so that *EZNEC* will accept the last change.

Click FF PLOT to generate a pattern with the new line lengths. In the plot window, open the FILE menu and select ADD TRACE. Enter the name CARDTL and click OPEN. You should now see the original plot and new plot overlaid together. Notice that the gain of the modified model is about 1 dB greater than the original but the front-to-back ratio has deteriorated to about 10 dB.

Experiment with different combinations of line lengths that differ by 90°—for example, 45° and 135° (don't forget the 'd'!), or change the impedance of one or both lines and you'll see that you can get a wide variety of patterns. None, however, are likely to be as close to the ideal cardioid pattern as the original.

TABLE OF CONTENTS

Chapter 7 — Downloadable Supplemental Content

Supplemental Articles

- 5-Band LPDA Construction Project and Telerana Construction Project
- "An Updated 2 Meter LPDA" by Andrzej Przedpelsi, KØABP
- Log Periodic-Yagi Arrays
- "Practical High-Performance HF Log Periodic Antennas" by Bill Jones, K8CU
- "Six Band, 20 through 6 Meter LPDA" by Ralph Crumrine, NØKC
- "The Log Periodic Dipole Array" by Peter Rhodes, K4EWG
- "Using LPDA TV Antennas for the VHF Ham Bands" by John Stanley, K4ERO
- "Vee Shaped Elements vs Straight Elements" by John Stanley, K4ERO

Chapter 7

Log-Periodic Dipole Arrays

Log Periodic Dipole Array (*LPDA*) is one of a family of frequency-independent antennas. The LPDA forms a directional antenna with relatively constant characteristics across a wide frequency range. It may also be used with parasitic elements to achieve specific characteristics within a narrow frequency range. Common names for such hybrid arrays are the *log-cell Yagi* or the *Log-Yagi*. (Information on the log-cell Yagi is included with this book's downloadable supplemental information.) Designs for log-periodic antennas at HF and VHF-UHF are presented in the **Multiband HF Antennas** and **VHF and UHF Antenna Systems** chapters. This chapter was contributed originally by L. B. Cebik, W4RNL, with additional contributions from John Stanley, K4ERO. The Band-Optimized Log-Periodic Array (BOLPA) developed by Justin Johnson, GØKSC, is introduced as a design method for using LPDAs as design elements.

7.1 BASIC LPDA DESIGN

The LPDA is the most popular form of log-periodic systems which also include zigzag, planar, trapezoidal, slot, and V forms. The appeal of the LPDA version of the log periodic antenna owes much to its structural similarity to the Yagi-Uda parasitic array. This permits the construction of directional LPDAs that can be rotated — at least within the upper HF and higher frequency ranges. Nevertheless, the LPDA has special structural as well as design considerations that distinguish it from the Yagi. Different construction techniques for both wire and tubular elements are illustrated later in this chapter.

The LPDA in its present form derives from the pioneering work of D. E. Isbell at the University of Illinois in the late 1950s. Although you may design LPDAs for large frequency ranges — for example, from 3 to 30 MHz or a little over 3 octaves — the most common LPDA designs that radio amateurs use are limited to a one-octave range, usually from 14 to 30 MHz. Amateur designs for this range tend to consist of linear elements. However, experimental designs for lower frequencies have used elements shaped like inverted Vs and some versions use vertically oriented ¼-λ elements over a ground system.

Figure 7.1 shows the parts of a typical LPDA. The structure consists of a number of linear elements, the longest of which is approximately ½ λ long at the lowest design frequency. The shortest element is usually about ½ λ long at a frequency well above the highest operating frequency. The antenna feeder, also informally called the *phase-line*, connects the center points of each element in the series, with a

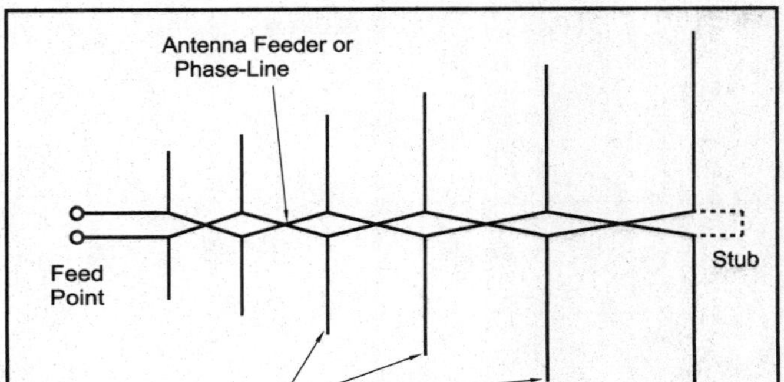

Figure 7.1 — The basic components of a log periodic dipole array (LPDA). The forward direction is to the left in this sketch. Many variations of the basic design are possible.

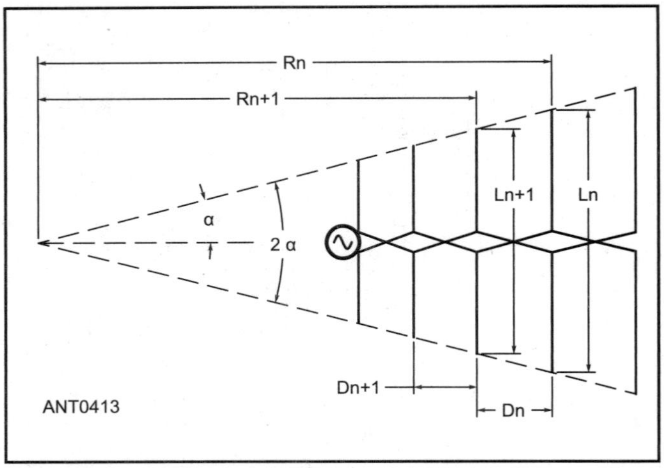

Figure 7.2 — Some fundamental relationships that define an array as an LPDA. See the text for the defining equations.

phase reversal or *crossover* between each element. A stub consisting of a shorted length of parallel-wire feed line is often added at the back of an LPDA.

The arrangement of elements and the method of feed yield an array with relatively constant gain and front-to-back ratio across the designed operating range. In addition, the LPDA exhibits a relatively constant feed point impedance, simplifying matching to a transmission line.

For the amateur designer, the most fundamental facets of the LPDA revolve around three interrelated design variables: α (alpha), τ (tau), and σ (sigma). Any one of the three variables may be defined by reference to the other two.

Figure 7.2 shows the basic components of an LPDA. The angle α defines the outline of an LPDA and permits every dimension to be treated as a radius or the consequence of a radius (R) of a circle. The most basic structural dimensions are the element lengths (L), the distance (R) of each

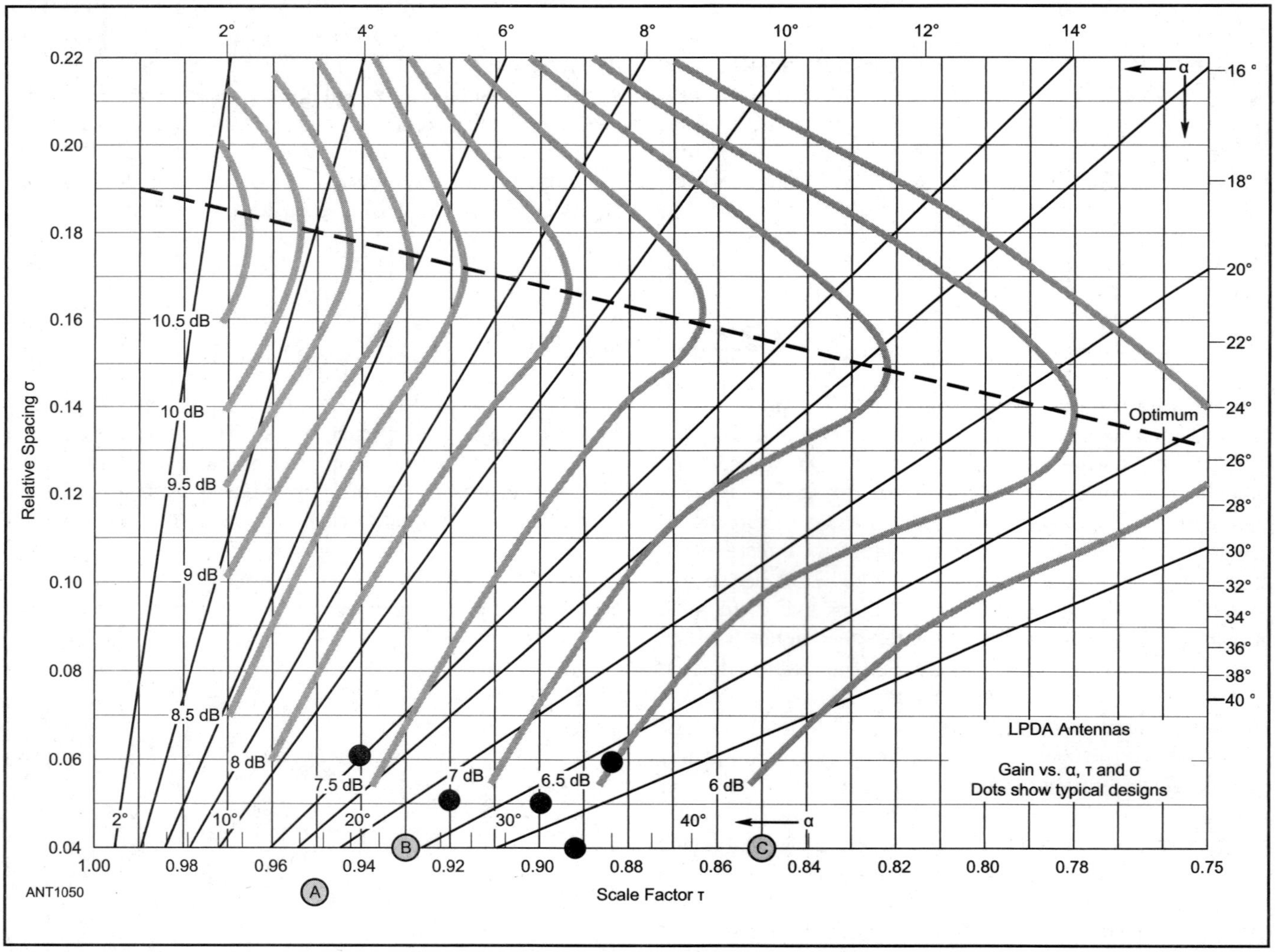

Figure 7.3 — The optimum value for σ lies on the straight line that intersects the constant-gain curves at different values of τ. Using the optimum value of σ to design an LPDA usually results in antenna that is impractically large at HF (see text). Points labeled "A", "B", and "C" represent values of σ and τ are given for the three design examples in this chapter; "9302", "8904", and "8504", respectively. (Graphic after Carrel, et al; see Bibliography.)

element from the apex of angle α, and the distance between elements (D). A single design constant, τ, defines all of these relationships in the following manner:

$$\tau = \frac{R_{n+1}}{R_n} = \frac{D_{n+1}}{D_n} = \frac{L_{n+1}}{L_n} \tag{1}$$

where element n and n+1 are successive elements in the array working toward the apex of angle α. The value of τ is always less than 1.0 although effective LPDA design requires values as close to 1.0 as may be feasible.

The variable τ defines the relationship between successive element spacings but it does not itself determine the initial spacing between the longest and next longest elements upon which to apply τ successively. The initial spacing also defines the angle α for the array. Hence, we have two ways to determine the value of σ, the relative spacing constant:

$$\sigma = \frac{1-\tau}{4\tan\alpha} = \frac{D_n}{2L_n} \tag{2}$$

where D_n is the distance between any two elements of the array and L_n is the length of the longer of the two elements. From the first of the two methods of determining the value of σ, we may also find a means of determining α when we know both τ and σ.

For any value of τ, we may determine the optimal value of σ:

$$\sigma_{opt} = 0.243\tau - 0.051 \tag{3}$$

The combination of a value for τ and its corresponding optimal value of σ yields the highest performance of which an LPDA is capable. For values of τ from 0.80 through 0.98, the value of optimal σ varies from 0.143 to 0.187, in increments of 0.00243 for each 0.01 change in τ. This is illustrated by the graph in **Figure 7.3**, originally published by Carrel and updated by Butson and Thompson (see the Bibliography).

Practically however, using the optimal value of σ usually yields a total array length that is beyond amateur construction or tower/mast support capabilities. A design procedure more likely to result in a useful design at HF is to reduce σ until maximum gain begins to fall significantly. Consequently, amateur LPDAs usually employ compromise values of τ and σ that yield lesser but acceptable performance. The sidebar "Determining LPDA Design Parameters Quickly" shows how to arrive at acceptable values of τ and σ for use in *LPCAD* and similar software.

For a given frequency range, increasing the value of τ increases both the gain and the number of required elements. Increasing the value of σ increases both the gain and the overall boom length. A τ of 0.96 — which approaches the upper maximum recommended value for τ — yields an optimal σ of about 0.18, and the resulting array grows to over 100 feet long for the 14 to 30 MHz range. The maximum free space gain is about 11 dBi, with a front-to-back ratio that approaches 40 dB. Normal amateur practice, however, uses values of τ from about 0.88 to 0.95 and values of σ from about 0.03 to 0.06.

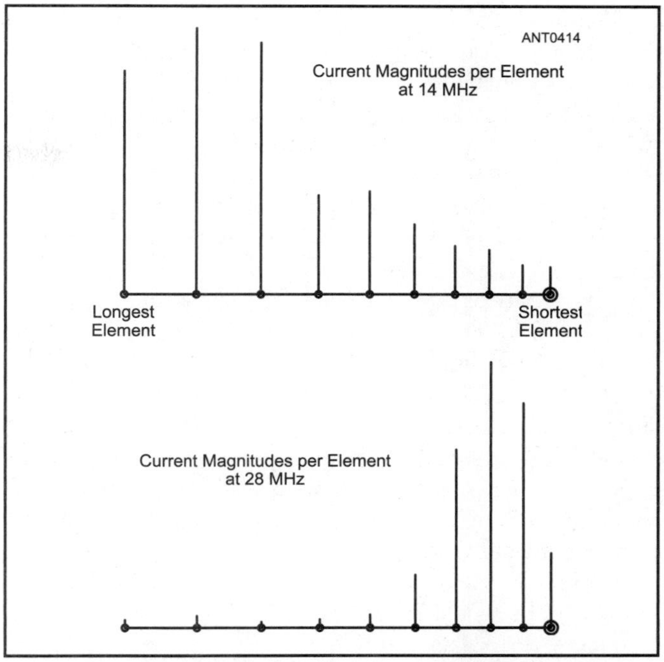

Figure 7.4 — The relative current magnitude on the elements of an LPDA at the lowest and highest operating frequencies for a given design. Compare the number of "active" elements, that is, those with current levels at least ⅒ of the highest level.

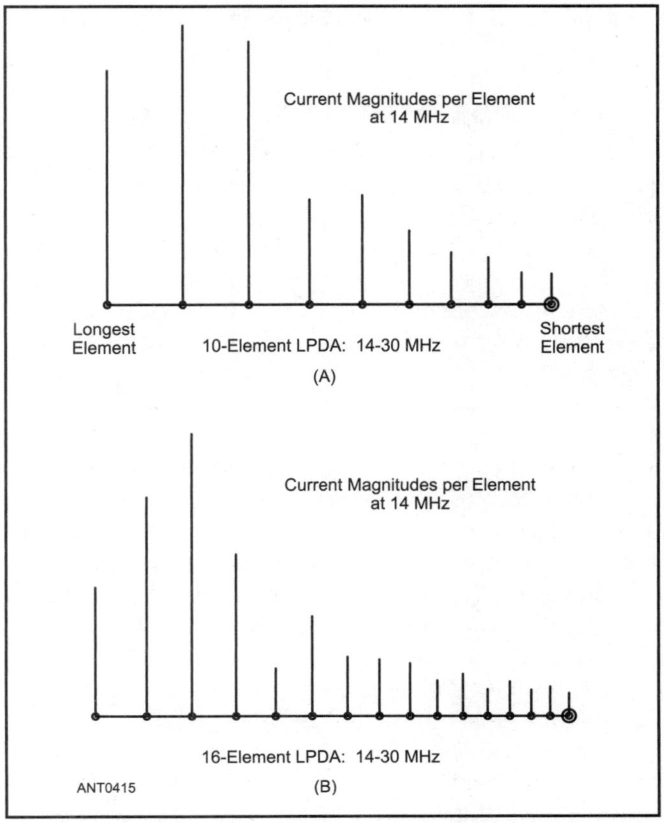

Figure 7.5 — Patterns of current magnitude at the lowest operating frequency of two different LPDA designs: a 10-element low-τ design and a 16-element higher-τ design.

Standard design procedures usually assign to the rear element a resonant frequency about 7% lower than the lowest design frequency with a physical length 5% lower than a free-space half wavelength. The upper frequency limit of the design is ordinarily set at about 1.3 times the highest design frequency. Since τ and σ set the increment between successive element lengths, the number of elements becomes a function of when the shortest element reaches the dipole length for the adjusted upper frequency.

The adjusted upper frequency limit results from the behavior of LPDAs with respect to the number of active elements. See **Figure 7.4**, which shows an edge view of a 10-element LPDA for 20 through 10 meters. The vertical lines represent the peak relative current magnitude for each element at the specified frequency. At 14 MHz, virtually every element of the array shows a significant current magnitude. However, at 28 MHz, only the forward 5 elements carry significant current. Without the extended design range to nearly 40 MHz, the number of elements with significant current levels would be severely reduced, along with upper frequency performance.

The need to extend the design equations below the lowest proposed operating frequency varies with the value of τ. In **Figure 7.5**, we can compare the current on the rear elements of two LPDAs, both with a σ value of 0.04. The upper design uses a τ of 0.89, while the lower design uses a value of 0.93. The most significant current-bearing element moves forward with increases in τ, reducing (but not wholly eliminating) the need for elements whose lengths are longer than a dipole for the lowest operating frequency.

7.1.1 LPDA DESIGN AND COMPUTERS

Originally, LPDA design proceeded through a series of design equations intended to yield the complete specifications for an array. More recent techniques available to radio amateurs include basic LPDA design software and antenna modeling software. One good example of LPDA design software is *LPCAD* by Roger Cox, WBØDGF, available for downloading from **www.w8io.com/LPCAD.htm**. The user begins by specifying the lowest and highest frequencies in the design. The user then selects values for τ and σ or choices for the number of elements and the total length of the array. With this and other input data, the program provides a table of element lengths and spacings, using the adjusted upper and lower frequency limits described earlier. (A spreadsheet to assist with performing the calculations in this chapter was contributed by Dennis Miller, KM9O, and is available for downloading from **www.arrl.org/antenna-book**.)

The program also requests the diameters of the longest and shortest elements in the array, as well as the diameter of average element. From this data, the program calculates a recommended value for the characteristic impedance of the phase-line connecting the elements and the approximate resistive value of the input impedance. Among the additional data that *LPCAD* makes available is the spacing of conductors to achieve the desired characteristic impedance of the phase-line. These conductors may be round — as we would

Determining LPDA Design Parameters Quickly

LPCAD provides a very efficient method of arriving at a preliminary design for an LPDA. When using the program, it is much faster to use the boom length and number of elements input method rather than the τ and σ data entry method. Those parameters will be calculated along with all dimensions. For those wishing to better understand the tradeoffs or who wish to use the formulas in this chapter to calculate all dimensions, the following procedure will help you to arrive at starting values of τ and σ that will make your progress towards a final design much more rapid.

The first consideration is the frequency range to be covered. Many ham LPDA designs cover about a 2:1 frequency range, for example, 14 to 29 MHz. Extending the high end of the frequency range adds little to the size and cost and can smooth out operation at the higher frequencies of interest. An LPDA with an 8:1 range will be only 1.8 times longer than an antenna with a 2:1 range, while the frequency range is 4 times more. However, use of a very wideband LPDA only at its high frequency end means most of the size and weight of the antenna is wasted since the largest parts of the antenna are inactive. Covering only the desired frequencies reduces boom length. **Figure 7.A** illustrates the different sizes of arrays having the same gain but different frequency coverage.

The lowest frequency determines the longest element length, which will be somewhat more than ½ wavelength at that frequency. An approximate length in feet can be gotten by dividing 500 by the frequency in MHz. This dimension is pretty much fixed, although in some large designs it is reduced somewhat by inductive or capacitive loading of the lowest frequency elements.

The boom length is the next logical parameter to be determined and will be based on what you can afford to build, raise, support and rotate versus the performance to be expected for various boom options. For a given frequency ratio — the longer the boom, the higher the gain. **Figure 7.B** will give

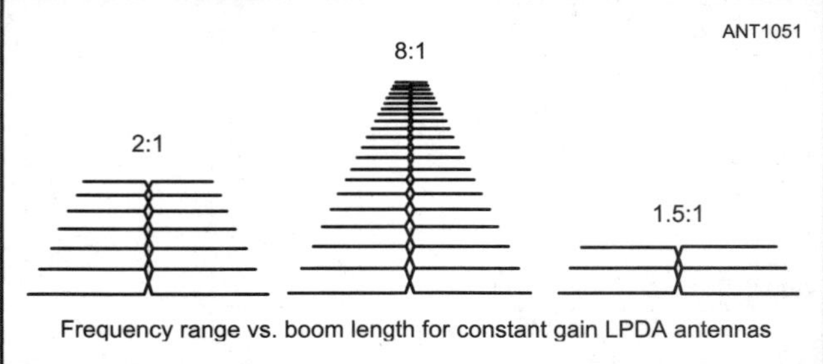

Figure 7.A — Comparison of boom length for several LPDA designs with the same gain but different ratios of maximum to minimum frequency coverage.

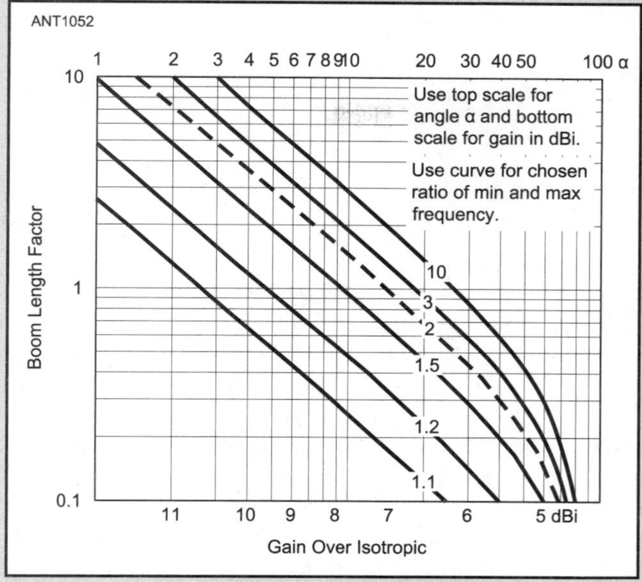

Figure 7.B — A chart relating gain, boom length factor, and α.

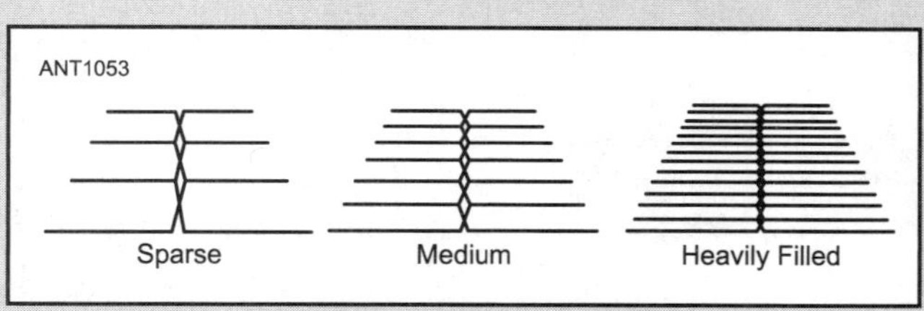

Figure 7.C — Illustration of sparse to heavily filled arrays.

some guidance as to the gain to be expected for a given boom length. The boom length factor (BLF) represents the boom length compared to the length of the longest element. As a rough rule of thumb, each doubling of the boom length will add about 1 dB of gain. Beyond a certain point, doubling the boom length to add 1 dB will be uneconomical. Keeping the boom to a reasonable length means accepting either a reduced frequency range or a lower gain.

Once a boom length is chosen, based on a trade-off between mechanical limits and the desired gain value and frequency range ratio, we can also read off the angle using this same graph, since gain is closely associated with α.

Once α is determined along with the frequency coverage, the shape and size of the antenna is defined. We must now decide how to fill up this outlined shape with elements. In other words, determine the number, length and spacing of the elements. The chart of Figure 7.3 is useful in this. This chart plots gain as a function of τ, σ and α. The α values are represented by the slanted lines between the marked degree values on the chart. Since we have determined the desired value of α, we can use that value to choose values of τ and σ.

For a given α value (slanted lines), follow the corresponding line diagonally along and you will see the lower part of the line lies more or less parallel to a constant gain curve. The portion of a constant-α line on the bottom left represents a heavily filled array (more elements, closely spaced) while upper right portion of the constant, a line represents a sparsely filled array (fewer elements). (**see Figure 7.C**)

Notice that as the number of elements decreases (moving right and upwards on the constant-α gain may fluctuate a bit but will reach a point where it quickly falls off as you cross the "optimum σ" line. Values above this line represents a design that has too few elements to realize good performance. The interpretation of this "optimum σ" value is not obvious and perhaps its name was poorly chosen. It may be intended to give the value of σ for maximum gain for a given value of τ. However, this approach disregards the boom length factor. Designs that first choose τ and then use the optimum σ will be outrageously long — of course they will have high gain!

For a given antenna outline (length vs. width or constant-α) "optimum σ" is optimum only in that it indicates the point where further reduction in the number of elements will cause the gain to drop off. Thus, it gives a design with the least number of elements for a given gain. However, this design will not have the smoothest gain and SWR vs. frequency and the F/B ratio may be inadequate. For this reason, very few practical designs fall near the "optimum σ" line. All of the designs in this chapter fall well below the "optimum σ" as shown by the dots on the chart.

For designs with a higher α value, the gain should increase a bit with the more heavily filled arrays. Very narrow (long boom) arrays may have less gain if too heavily filled. It is not wise to approach the "optimum σ" line too closely in an attempt to reduce the element number. On the other hand, designs too far down the sloping a curve will be more expensive to build and will have greater wind load due to having more elements than necessary.

Having selected from the chart some τ and σ combinations that give us the design we want, we can now use software such as *LPCAD* to generate a detailed design using those values of τ and σ. This should result in a boom length fairly close to that desired. A second pass through the program may use the exact boom length desired and the number of elements calculated in the first pass, plus or minus one element. The program will then give us all of the mechanical dimensions, and also generate files for *NEC* analysis. Alternatively, we can proceed with the manual method given elsewhere in this chapter. If using that method we should come out close to the desired design on the first try and avoid multiple guesses as to where to start.

Several different designs that are close to that desired should be prepared as *NEC* files and an analysis done using *NEC*. This may show that a sparsely filled array may have excessive variation of gain and SWR vs. frequency or an inadequate F/B ratio or have other problems such as a weakness on an important frequency.
— *John Stanley, K4ERO*

use for a wire phase-line — or square — as we might use for double-boom construction.

An additional vital output from *LPCAD* is the conversion of the design into antenna modeling input files of several formats, including versions for *AO* and *NEC4WIN* (both *MININEC*-based programs), and a version in the standard *.NEC format usable by many implementations of *NEC-2* and *NEC-4*, including *NECWin Plus*, *GNEC*, and *EZNEC Pro*. Every proposed LPDA design should be verified and optimized by means of antenna modeling, since basic design calculations rarely provide arrays that require no further work before construction. Moreover, some of the design equations are based upon approximations and do not completely predict LPDA behavior. Despite these limitations, most of the sample LPDA designs shown later in this chapter are based directly upon the fundamental calculations.

Modeling LPDA designs is most easily done on a version of *NEC*. The transmission line (TL) facility built into *NEC-2* and *NEC-4* alleviates the problem of modeling the phase-line as a set of physical wires, each section of which has a set of constraints in *MININEC* at the right-angle junctions with the elements. Although the *NEC* TL facility does not account for losses in the lines, the losses are ordinarily low enough to neglect.

NEC models do require some careful construction to obtain the most accurate results. Foremost among the cautions is the need for careful segmentation, since each element has a different length. The shortest element should have about 9 or 11 segments, so that it has sufficient segments at the highest modeling frequency for the design. Each element behind the shortest one should have a greater number of segments than the preceding element by the inverse of the value of τ. However, there is a further limitation. Since the transmission line is at the center of each element, *NEC* elements should have an odd number of segments to hold the phase-line centered. Hence, each segmentation value calculated from the inverse of τ must be rounded up to the nearest odd integer.

Initial modeling of LPDAs in *NEC-2* should be done with uniform-diameter elements, with any provision for stepped-diameter element correction turned off. Since these correction factors apply only to elements within about 15% of dipole resonance at the test frequency, models with stepped-diameter elements will correct for only a few elements at any test frequency. The resulting combination of corrected and uncorrected elements will not yield a model with assured reliability.

Once one has achieved a satisfactory model with uniform-diameter elements, the modeling program can be used to calculate stepped-diameter substitutes. Each uniform-diameter element, when extracted from the larger array, will have a resonant frequency. Once this frequency is determined, the stepped-diameter element to be used in final construction can be resonated to the same frequency. Although *NEC-4* handles stepped diameter elements with much greater accuracy than *NEC-2*, the process just described is also applicable to *NEC-4* models for the greatest precision.

7.1.2 LPDA BEHAVIOR

Although LPDA behavior is remarkably uniform over a wide frequency range compared to narrow-band designs, such as the Yagi-Uda array, it nevertheless exhibits very significant variations within the design range. **Figure 7.6** shows several facets of these behaviors. Figure 7.6 shows the free-space gain for three LPDA designs using 0.5-inch diameter aluminum elements. The designations for each model list the values of τ (0.93, 0.89, and 0.85) and of σ (0.02, 0.04, and 0.06) used to design each array. The resultant array lengths are listed with each designator. The total number of elements varies from 16 for "9302" to 10 for "8904" to 7 for "8504."

First, the gain is never uniform across the entire frequency span. The gain tapers off at both the low and high ends of the design spectrum. Moreover, the amount of gain undulates across the spectrum, with the number of peaks dependent upon the selected value of τ and the resultant number of elements. The front-to-back ratio tends to follow the gain level. In general, it ranges from less than 10 dB when the free-space gain is below 5 dBi to over 20 dB as the gain approaches 7 dBi. The front-to-back ratio may reach the high 30 dBs when the free-space array gain exceeds 8.5 dBi. Well-designed arrays, especially those with high values of τ and σ, tended to have well-controlled rear patterns that result in only small differences between the 180° front-to-back ratio and the averaged front-to-rear ratio.

Since array gain is a mutual function of both τ and σ, average gain becomes a function of array length for any given frequency range. Although the gain curves in Figure 7.6 interweave, there is little to choose among them in terms of average gain for the 14 to 18-foot range of array lengths. Well-designed 20 to 10 meter arrays in the 30-foot array length region are capable of about 7 dBi free-space gain, while 40-foot arrays for the same frequency range can achieve about 8 dBi free-space gain.

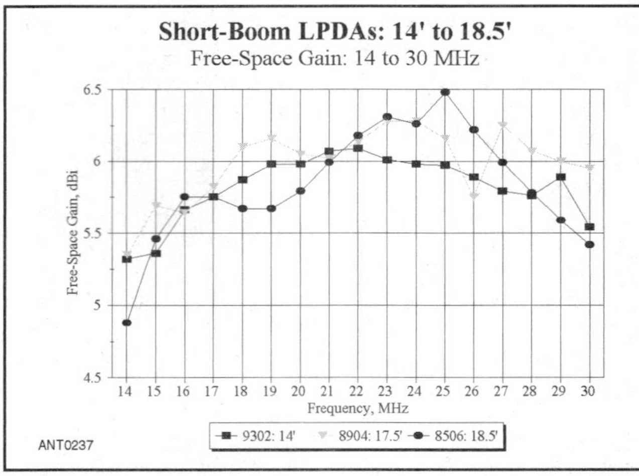

Figure 7.6 — The modeled free-space gain of three relatively small LPDAs of different design. Note the relationship of the values of τ and of σ for these arrays with quite similar performance across the 14-30 MHz span.

Exceeding an average gain of 8.5 dBi requires at least a 50-foot array length for this frequency range. Long arrays with high values of τ and σ also tend to show smaller excursions of gain and of front-to-back ratio in the overall curves. In addition, high-τ designs tend to show higher gain at the low frequency end of the design spectrum.

The frequency sweeps shown in Figure 7.6 are widely spaced at 1 MHz intervals. The evaluation of a specific design for the 14 to 30-MHz range should decrease the interval between check points to no greater than 0.25 MHz in order to detect frequencies at which the array may show a *performance weakness*. Weaknesses are frequency regions in the overall design spectrum at which the array shows unexpectedly lower values of gain and front-to-back ratio. In Figure 7.6 note the unexpected decrease in gain of model "8904" at 26 MHz. The other designs also have weak points, but they fall between the frequencies sampled.

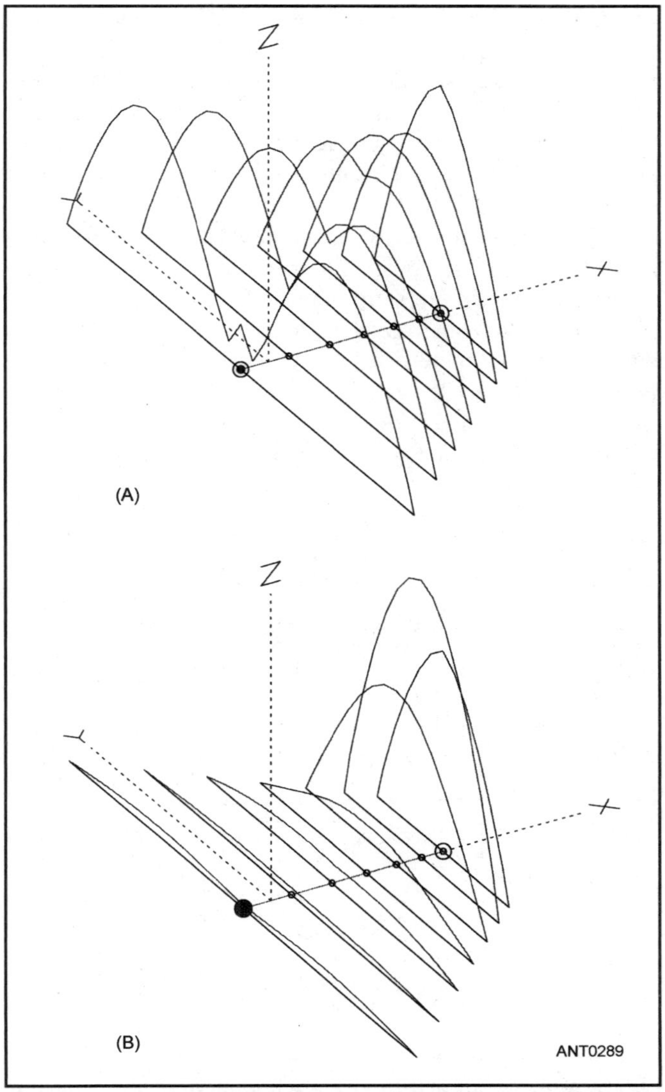

Figure 7.7 — The relative current magnitude on the elements of model "8504" at 28 MHz without and with a stub. Note the harmonic operation of the rear elements before a stub is added to suppress such operation.

In large arrays, these regions may be quite small and may occur in more than one frequency region. The weakness results from the harmonic operation of longer elements to the rear of those expected to have high current levels. Consider a 7-element LPDA with a boom about 12.25-feet long for 14 to 30 MHz using 0.5-inch aluminum elements. At 28 MHz, the rear elements operate in a harmonic mode as shown by the high relative current magnitude curves in **Figure 7.7**. The result is a radical decrease in gain, as shown in the "No Stub" curve of **Figure 7.8**. The front-to-back ratio also drops as a result of strong radiation from the long elements to the rear of the array.

Early designs of LPDAs called for terminating transmission-line stubs as standard practice to help eliminate such weak spots in frequency coverage. In contemporary designs, their use tends to be more specific for eliminating or moving frequencies that show gain and front-to-back weakness. (Stubs have the added function of keeping both sides of each element at the same dc level of static charge or discharge.) The model dubbed "8504" was fitted (by trial and error) with an 18-inch shorted stub of 600-Ω transmission line. As Figure 7.7B shows, the harmonic operation of the rear elements is attenuated. The "stub" curve of Figure 7.8 shows the smoothing of the gain curve for the array throughout the upper half of its design spectrum. In some arrays showing multiple weaknesses, a single stub may not eliminate all of them. However, it may move the weaknesses to unused frequency regions. Where full-spectrum operation of an LPDA is necessary, additional stubs located at specific elements may be needed.

Most LPDA designs benefit (with respect to gain and front-to-back ratio) from the use of larger-diameter elements. Elements with an average diameter of at least 0.5-inch are desirable in the 14 to 30 MHz range. However, standard designs usually presume a constant element length-to-diameter ratio. In the case of *LPCAD*, this ratio is about 125:1, which assumes an even larger diameter. To achieve a relatively constant length-to-diameter ratio in the computer models, you

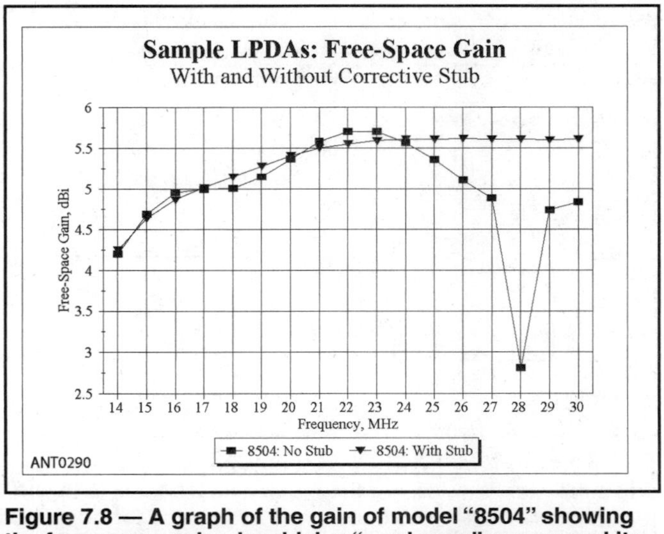

Figure 7.8 — A graph of the gain of model "8504" showing the frequency region in which a "weakness" occurs and its absence once a suitable stub is added to the array.

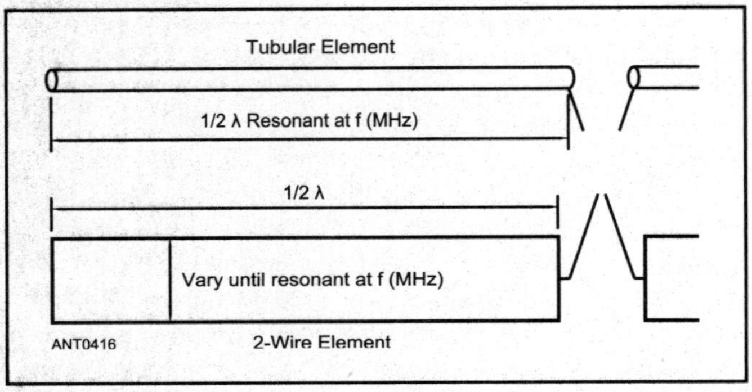

Figure 7.9 — A substitute for a large-diameter tubular element composed of two wires shorted at both the outer ends and at the center junction with the phase-line.

can set the diameter of the shortest element in a given array design and then increase the element diameter by the inverse of τ for each succeeding longer element. This procedure is often likely to result in unreasonably large element diameters for the longest elements, relative to standard amateur construction practices.

Since most amateur designs using aluminum tubing for elements employ stepped-diameter (tapered) elements, roughly uniform element diameters will result unless the LPDA mechanical design tries to lighten the elements at the forward end of the array. This practice may not be advisable, however. Larger elements at the high end of the design spectrum often counteract (at least partially) the natural decrease in high-frequency gain and show improved performance compared to smaller diameter elements.

An alternative construction method for LPDAs uses wire throughout. At every frequency, single-wire elements reduce gain relative to larger-diameter tubular elements. An alternative to tubular elements appears in **Figure 7.9**. For each element of a tubular design, there is a roughly equivalent 2-wire element that may be substituted. The spacing between the wires is determined by taking one of the modeled tubular elements and finding its resonant frequency. A two-wire element of the same length is then constructed with shorts at the far ends and at the junctions with the phase-line. The separation of the two wires is adjusted until the wire element is resonant at the same frequency as the original tubular element. The required separation will vary with the wire chosen for the element. Models used to develop these substitutes must pay close attention to segmentation rules for *NEC* due to the short length of segments in the end and center shorts, and to the need to keep segment junctions as exactly parallel as possible with close-spaced wires.

7.1.3 FEEDING AND CONSTRUCTING THE LPDA

Original design procedures for LPDAs used a single, ordinarily fairly high, characteristic impedance for the phase-line (antenna feeder). Over time, designers realized that other values of impedance for the phase-line offered both mechanical and performance advantages for LPDA performance. Consequently, for the contemporary designer, phase-line choice and construction techniques are almost inseparable considerations.

High-impedance phase-lines (roughly 200 Ω and higher) are amenable to wire construction similar to that used with ordinary parallel-wire transmission lines. They require careful placement relative to a metal boom used to support individual elements (which themselves must be insulated from the support boom). Connections also require care. If the phase-line is given a half-twist between each element, the construction of the line must ensure constant spacing and relative isolation

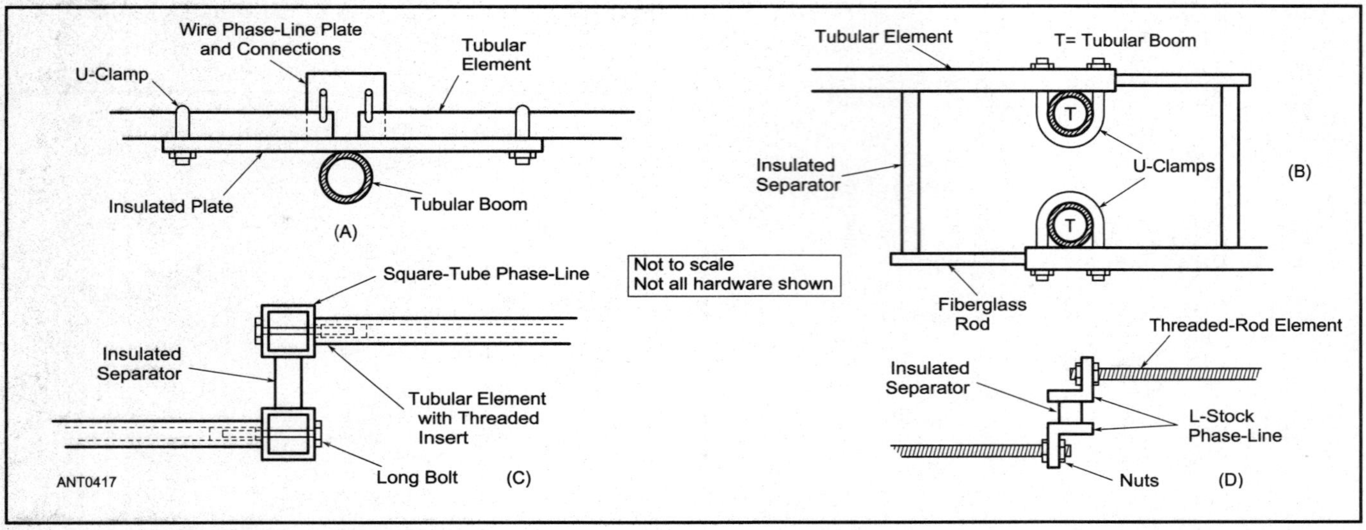

Figure 7.10 — Four (of many) possible construction techniques, shown from the array end. In A, an insulated plate supports and separates the wires of the phase-line, suitable with wire or tubular elements. A dual circular boom phase-line also supports the elements, which are cross-supported for boom stability. Square tubing is used in C, with the elements joined to the boom/phase-line with through-bolts and an insert in each half element. The L-stock shown in D is useful for lighter VHF and UHF arrays.

from metal supports to maintain a constant impedance and to prevent shorts.

Along with the standard parallel-wire line, shown in **Figure 7.10A**, there are a number of possible LPDA structures using booms to support the elements and to create relatively low-impedance (under 200 Ω) phase-lines. Figure 7.10B shows the basics of a twin circular tubing boom with the elements cross-supported by insulated rods. Figure 7.10C shows the use of square tubing with the elements attached directly to each tube by through-bolts. Figure 7.10D illustrates the use of L-stock, which may be practical at VHF frequencies. Each of these sketches is incomplete, however, since it omits the necessary stress analyses that determine the mechanical feasibility of a structure for a given LPDA project.

The use of square boom material requires some adjustment when calculating the characteristic impedance of the phase-line. For conductors with a circular cross-section,

$$Z_0 = 120 \cosh^{-1} \frac{D}{d} \qquad (4)$$

where D is the center-to-center spacing of the conductors and d is the outside diameter of each conductor, both expressed in the same units of measurement. Since we are dealing with closely spaced conductors, relative to their diameters, the use of this version of the equation for calculating the characteristic impedance (Z_0) is recommended. For a square conductor,

$$d \approx 1.18 \text{ w} \qquad (5)$$

where d is the approximate equivalent diameter of the square tubing and w is the width of the tubing across one side. Thus, for a given spacing, a square tube permits you to achieve a lower characteristic impedance than round conductors. However, square tubing requires special attention to matters of strength, relative to comparable round tubing.

Electrically, the characteristic impedance of the LPDA phase-line tends to influence other performance parameters of the array. Decreasing the phase-line Z_0 also decreases the feed point impedance of the array. For small designs with few elements, the decrease is not fully matched by a decrease in the excursions of reactance. Consequently, using a low impedance phase-line may make it more difficult to achieve a 2:1 or less SWR for the entire frequency range. However, higher-impedance phase-lines may result in a feed point impedance that requires the use of an impedance-matching balun.

Decreasing the phase-line Z_0 also tends to increase LPDA gain and front-to-back ratio. There is a price to be paid for this performance improvement — weaknesses at specific frequency regions become much more pronounced with reductions in the phase-line Z_0. For a specific array you must weigh carefully the gains and losses, while employing one or more transmission line stubs to get around performance weaknesses at specific frequencies.

Depending upon the specific values of τ and σ selected for a design, you can sometimes select a phase-line Z_0 that provides either a 50-Ω or a 75-Ω feed point impedance, holding the SWR under 2:1 for the entire design range of the LPDA. The higher the values of τ and σ for the design, the lower the reactance and resistance excursions around a central value. Designs using optimal values of σ with high values of τ show a very slight capacitive reactance throughout the frequency range. Lower design values obscure this phenomenon due to the wide range of values taken by both resistance and reactance as the frequency is changed.

At the upper end of the frequency range, the source resistance value decreases more rapidly than elsewhere in the design spectrum. In larger arrays, this can be overcome by using a variable Z_0 phase-line for approximately the first 20% of the array length. This technique is, however, difficult to implement with anything other than wire phase-lines. Begin with a line impedance about half of the final value and increase the wire spacing evenly until it reaches its final and fixed spacing. This technique can sometimes produce smoother impedance performance across the entire frequency span and improved high-frequency SWR performance.

Designing an LPDA requires as much attention to designing the phase-line as to element design. It is always useful to run models of the proposed design through several iterations of possible phase-line Z_0 values before freezing the structure for construction.

7.1.4 SPECIAL DESIGN CORRECTIONS

The curve for the sample 8504 LPDA in Figure 7.8 revealed several deficiencies in standard LPDA designs. The weakness in the overall curve was corrected by the use of a stub to eliminate or move the frequency at which rearward elements operated in a harmonic mode. In the course of describing the characteristics of the array, we have noted several other means to improve performance. Fattening elements (either uniformly or by increasing their diameter in step with τ) and reducing the characteristic impedance of the phase-line are capable of small improvements in performance. However, they cannot wholly correct the tendency of the array gain and front-to-back ratio to fall off at the upper

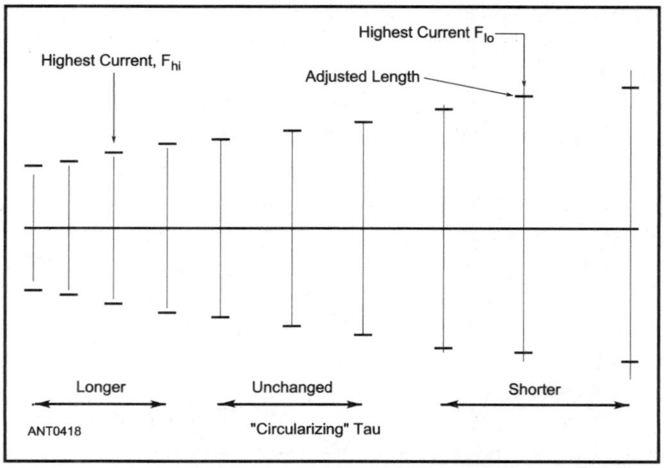

Figure 7.11 — A before and after sketch of an LPDA, showing the original lengths of the elements and their adjustments from diminishing the value of τ at both ends of the array. See the text for the amount of change applicable to each element.

and lower limits of the LPDA frequency range.

One technique sometimes used to improve performances near the frequency limits is to design the LPDA for upper and lower frequency limits much higher and lower than the frequencies of use. This technique unnecessarily increases the overall size of the array and does not eliminate the downward performance curves. Increasing the values of τ and σ will usually improve performance at no greater cost in size than extending the frequency range. Increasing the value of τ is especially effective in improving the low frequency performance of an LPDA.

Working within the overall size limits of a standard design, one may employ a technique of *circularizing* the value of τ for the rear-most and forward-most elements. See **Figure 7.11**, which is not to-scale relative to overall array length and width. Locate (using an antenna-modeling program) the element with the highest current at the lowest operating frequency, and the element with the highest current at the highest operating frequency. The adjustments to element lengths may begin with these elements or — at most — one element further toward the array center. For the first element (counting from the center) to be modified, reduce the value of τ by about 0.5%. For a rearward element, use the inverse of the adjusted value of τ to calculate the new length of the element relative to the unchanged element just forward of the change. For a forward element, use the new value of τ to calculate the new length of the element relative to the unchanged element immediately to the rear of it.

For succeeding elements outward, calculate new values of τ from the adjusted values, increasing the increment of decrease with each step. Second adjusted elements may use values of τ about 0.75% to 1.0% lower than the values just calculated. Third adjusted elements may use an increment of 1.0% to 1.5% relative to the preceding value.

Not all designs require extensive treatment. As the values of τ and σ increase, fewer elements may require adjustment to obtain the highest possible gain at the frequency limits, and these will always be the most outward elements in the array. A second caution is to check the feed point impedance of the array after each change to ensure that it remains within design limits.

Figure 7.12 shows the free-space gain curves from 14 to 30 MHz for a 10-element LPDA with an initial τ of 0.89 and a σ of 0.04. The design uses a 200-Ω phase-line, 0.5-inch aluminum elements, and a 3-inch 600-Ω stub. The lowest curve shows the modeled performance across the design frequency range with only the stub. Performance at the frequency limits is visibly lower than within the peak performance region. The middle curve shows the effects of circularizing τ. Average performance levels have improved noticeably at both ends of the spectrum.

In lieu of, or in addition to, the adjustment of element lengths, you may also add a parasitic director to an LPDA, as shown in **Figure 7.13**. The director is cut roughly for the highest operating frequency. It may be spaced between 0.1 λ and 0.15 λ from the forward-most element of the LPDA. The exact length and spacing should be determined experimentally (or from models) with two factors in mind. First, the element should not adversely affect the feed point impedance at the highest operating frequencies. Close spacing of the director has the greatest effect on this impedance. Second, the exact spacing and element length should be set to have the most desired effect on the overall performance curve of the array. The mechanical impact of adding a director is to increase overall array length by the spacing selected for the element.

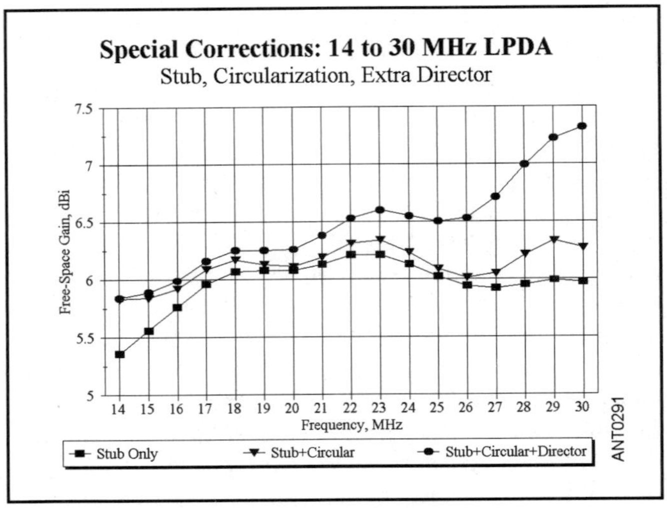

Figure 7.12 — The modeled free space gain from 14 to 30 MHz of an LPDA with τ of 0.89 and σ of 0.04. Squares: just a stub to eliminate a weakness; Triangles: with a stub and circularized elements, and Circles: with a stub, circularized elements and a parasitic director.

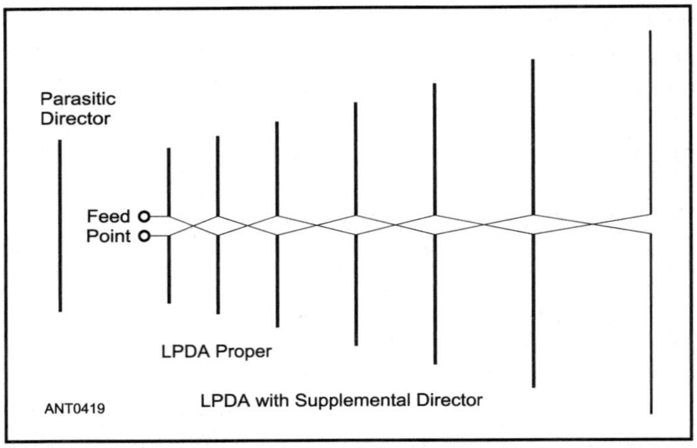

Figure 7.13 — A generalized sketch of an LPDA with the addition of a parasitic director to improve performance at the higher frequencies within the design range.

The upper curve in Figure 7.12 shows the effect of adding a director to the circularized array already equipped with a stub. The effect of the director is cumulative, increasing the upper range gain still further. Note that the added parasitic director is not just effective at the highest frequencies within the LPDA design range. It has a perceptible effect almost all the way across the frequency span of the array, although the effect is smallest at the low-frequency end of the range.

The addition of a director can be used to enhance upper frequency performance of an LPDA, as in the illustration, or simply to equalize upper frequency performance with mid-range performance. High-τ designs, with good low-frequency performance, may need only a director to compensate for high-frequency gain decrease. One potential challenge to adding a director to an LPDA is sustaining a high front-to-back ratio at the upper frequency range. (See this book's downloadable supplemental information for more information on such log-Yagi arrays.)

Throughout the discussion of LPDAs, the performance curves of sample designs have been treated at all frequencies alike, seeking maximum performance across the entire design frequency span. Special compensations are also possible for ham-band-only LPDA designs. They include the insertion of parasitic elements within the array as well as outside the initial design boundaries. In addition, stubs may be employed not so much to eliminate weaknesses, but only to move them to frequencies outside the range of amateur interests.

7.1.5 BAND-OPTIMIZED LPDA (BOLPA)

The traditional approach to designing LPDAs assumes that the antenna parameters for gain, pattern ratios, feed point impedance, and so on are maintained across the entire range of frequencies. For example, the usual amateur HF LPDA covers 14 to 30 MHz in one continuous range. This approach allows the antenna manufacturer to provide the same antenna to all services within that range — a very reasonable thing to do from a business standpoint. The amateur service, however, only makes use of a few bands within that range: 20, 17, 15, 12, and 10 meters. Relaxing the continuous-coverage requirement to only cover the amateur bands allows the antenna designer some flexibility.

The wide bandwidth of log-periodics was adapted to the design of single-band Yagi antennas by replacing the single driven element with a two- or three-element array called a "log-cell." (See the Bibliography entry for Cebik.) The log-cell acted as a single compound element with the active dipole moving back and forth within the log-cell from one end of the band to the other. This technique was mostly used on 20 meters to give better performance from 14.0 to 14.35 MHz. The movement of the active region back and forth along the axis of the antenna with frequency made it difficult to optimize the pattern ratios and gain across the band, since the reflector and director elements were fixed in place.

The log-cell Yagi was replaced by the Optimized Wideband Array (OWA) design, created by Jim Breakall, WA3FET. Using the "open sleeve" method of very closely-spaced elements, the OWA Yagi moved the first director very close to the driven element, creating a compound driven element. This enabled a 50-Ω feed point impedance and stabilized gain and other pattern ratios across a wider bandwidth. The open-sleeve technique is discussed for dipoles in the **Single-Band MF and HF Antennas** chapter. It is a popular technique on the VHF and UHF bands, as well. (See the Bibliography entry for Cebik.)

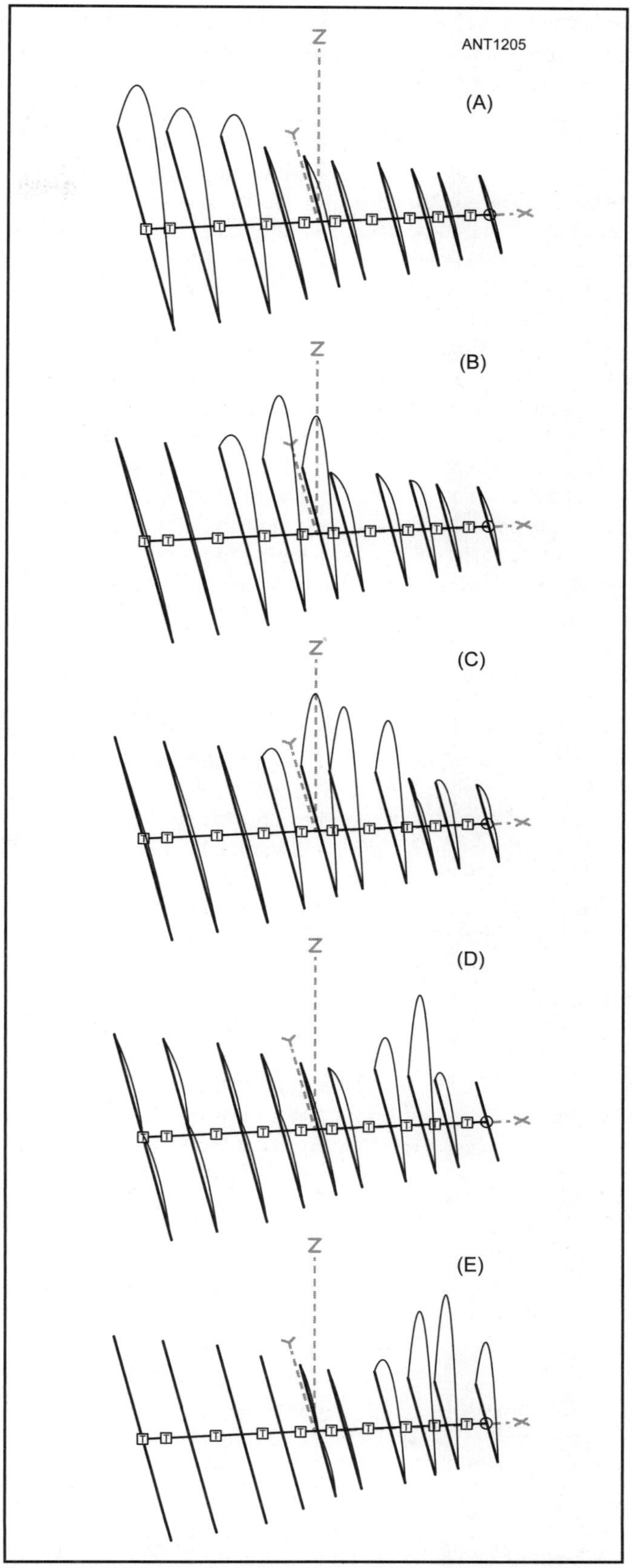

Figure 7.14 — Individual single-band LPDA cells are arranged along a single boom producing consistent performance across the amateur bands in one antenna. These *EZNEC Pro/4* models show current amplitudes on each element from 20 meters (A) through 10 meters (E).

The Band-Optimized LPDA or BOLPA revisits the log-cell concept by creating individual monoband LPDA cells along the antenna axis. Each cell is a short-boom three-element LPDA for a single amateur band. The cells are designed for 50-Ω direct feed, optimized across the band, and spaced for minimal interaction. Additional elements are inserted between the cells to provide coverage of intermediate bands. A 50-Ω feed point impedance also eliminates the LPDA's usual 4:1 impedance transformer. The BOLPA is best explained in terms of the process by which the design was created by Justin Johnson, GØKSC (**www.g0ksc.co.uk**).

The initial design consisted of monoband log cells for 20, 15, and 10 meters along a single common feed line that serves as the boom. Each cell has three elements and was optimized for performance. Then the spacing between the cells was optimized along the boom and the individual cells re-optimized. This produced good performance on the three contest bands but 17 and 12 meters were left out.

The next step was to add a single 17 meter element between the 20 meter cell and the 15 meter cell. (The 17 meter element is the fourth from the left with the highest current in **Figure 7.14A**.) With the 17 meter element present, the original three cells were shifted on the boom to maintain performance without adjusting any element lengths except that of the 17 meter element. The additional element acted as a fourth element on 15 meters with some improvement in gain. The process is continued to add 12 meters with another element between the 15 and 10 meter cells. Final boom length is 26 feet and free-space gain is approximately 7 dBi with front-to-back ratios of 20 dB or more.

The sequence of current models in Figures 7.14A-E shows how the active area of the antenna moves forward along the boom with increasing frequency — typical of LPDA antennas. Depending on the designer's requirements and resources a BOLPA covering 40-30-20 meters is possible or the BOLPA described here could be extended to 6 meters with another cell in front of the 10 meter cell. Start with a basic log cell and treat it as a fixed component as the additional bands are added. Automatic optimizer software (see the **Antenna Modeling** chapter) makes this job a lot easier.

7.2 DESIGNING AN LPDA

The following presents a systematic step-by-step design procedure for an LPDA with any desired bandwidth. The procedure requires some mathematical calculations, but a common calculator with square-root, logarithmic, and trigonometric functions is completely adequate. The notation used in this section may vary slightly from that used earlier in this chapter.

1) Decide on an operating bandwidth B between f_1, lowest frequency and f_n, highest frequency:

$$B = \frac{f_n}{f_1} \tag{6}$$

2) Choose τ and σ to give the desired estimated average gain.

$$0.8 \le \tau \le 0.98 \text{ and } 0.03 \le \sigma \le \sigma_{opt} \tag{7}$$

where σ_{opt} is calculated as noted earlier in this chapter.

3) Determine the value for the cotangent of the apex half-angle α from

$$\cot\alpha = \frac{4\sigma}{1-\tau} \tag{8}$$

Although α is not directly used in the calculations, cot α is used extensively.

4) Determine the bandwidth of the active region B_{ar} from

$$B_{ar} = 1.1 + 7.7\,(1-\tau)^2 \cot\alpha \tag{9}$$

5) Determine the structure (array) bandwidth B_s from

$$B_S = B \times B_{ar} \tag{10}$$

6) Determine the boom length L, number of elements N, and longest element length ℓ_1.

$$L_n = \left(1 - \frac{1}{B_S}\right) \cot\alpha \times \frac{\lambda_{max}}{4} \tag{11}$$

$$\lambda_{max} = \frac{984}{f_1} \tag{12}$$

$$N = 1 + \frac{\log B_S}{\log \frac{1}{\tau}} = 1 + \frac{\ln B_S}{\ln \frac{1}{\tau}} \tag{13}$$

$$\ell_{1ft} = \frac{492}{f_1} \tag{14}$$

Usually the calculated value for N will not be an integral number of elements. If the fractional value is more than about 0.3, increase the value of N to the next higher integer. Increasing the value of N will also increase the actual value of L over that obtained from the sequence of calculations just performed.

Examine L, N and ℓ_1. to determine whether or not the array size is acceptable for your needs. If the array is too large, increase f_1 or decrease σ or τ and repeat steps 2 through 6. Increasing f_1 will decrease all dimensions. Decreasing σ will decrease the boom length. Decreasing τ will decrease both the boom length and the number of elements.

7) Determine the terminating stub Z_t. (Note: For many HF arrays, you may omit the stub, short out the longest element with a 6-inch jumper, or design a stub to overcome a specific performance weakness.) For VHF and UHF arrays calculate the stub length from

$$Z_t = \frac{\lambda_{max}}{8} \tag{15}$$

8) Solve for the remaining element lengths from

$$\ell_n = \tau \ell_{n-1} \qquad (16)$$

9) Determine the element spacing d_{1-2} from

$$d_{1-2} = \frac{(\ell_1 - \ell_2)\cot\alpha}{2} \qquad (17)$$

where ℓ_1 and ℓ_2 are the lengths of the rearmost elements, and d_{1-2} is the distance between the elements with the lengths ℓ_1 and ℓ_2. Determine the remaining element-to-element spacings from

$$d_{(n-1)-n} = \tau\, d_{(n-2)-(n-1)} \qquad (18)$$

10) Choose R_0, the desired feed point resistance, to give the lowest SWR for the intended balun ratio and feed line impedance. R_0, the mean radiation resistance level of the LPDA input impedance, is approximated by:

$$R_0 = \frac{Z_0}{\sqrt{1 + \frac{Z_0}{4\sigma' Z_{AV}}}} \qquad (19)$$

where the component terms are defined and/or calculated in the following way.

From the following equations, determine the necessary antenna feeder (phase-line) impedance, Z_0:

$$Z_0 = \frac{R_0^{\,2}}{8\sigma' Z_{AV}} + R_0 \sqrt{\left(\frac{R_0}{8\sigma' Z_{AV}}\right)^2 + 1} \qquad (20)$$

σ' is the mean spacing factor and is given by

$$\sigma' = \frac{\sigma}{\sqrt{\tau}} \qquad (21)$$

Z_{AV} is the average characteristic impedance of a dipole and is given by

$$Z_{AV} = 120\left[\ln\left(\frac{\ell_n}{\mathrm{diam}_n}\right) - 2.25\right] \qquad (22)$$

The ratio, ℓ_n/diam_n is the length-to-diameter ratio of the element n.

11) Once Z_0 has been determined, select a combination of conductor size and spacing to achieve that impedance, using the appropriate equation for the shape of the conductors. If an impractical spacing results for the antenna feeder, select a different conductor diameter and repeat step 11. In severe cases it may be necessary to select a different R_0 and repeat steps 10 and 11. Once a satisfactory feeder arrangement is found, the LPDA design is complete.

The resultant design should be subjected to extensive modeling tests to determine whether there are performance deficiencies or weaknesses that require modification of the design before actual construction.

7.3 LPDA HF PROJECTS

This section presents a pair of LPDA designs — a fixed array of wire dipoles for the 3.5 and 7 MHz bands and a rotatable array for the five amateur bands from 14 through 30 MHz. In addition, the *QST* article "Practical High Performance HF Log Periodic Antennas" by Bill Jones, K8CU is provided with this book's downloadable supplemental information for additional design information.

7.3.1 LPDA FOR 3.5 OR 7 MHZ

These wire log-periodic dipole arrays for the lower HF bands are simple in design and easy to build. They are designed to have reasonable gain, be inexpensive and lightweight, and may be assembled with stock items found in large hardware stores. They are also strong — they can withstand a hurricane! These antennas were first described by John J. Uhl, KV5E, in *QST* for August 1986. **Figure 7.15** shows one method of installation. You can use the information here as a guide and point of reference for building similar LPDAs.

If space is available, the antennas can be rotated or repositioned in azimuth after they are completed. A 75-foot tower and a clear turning radius of 120 feet around the base of the tower are needed. The task is simplified if you use only three anchor points, instead of the five shown in Figure 10.51. Omit the two anchor points on the forward element, and extend the two nylon strings used for element stays all the way to the forward stay line.

Design of the Log-Periodic Dipole Arrays

Design constants for the two arrays are listed in **Tables 7.1** and **7.2.** More information about the design procedure

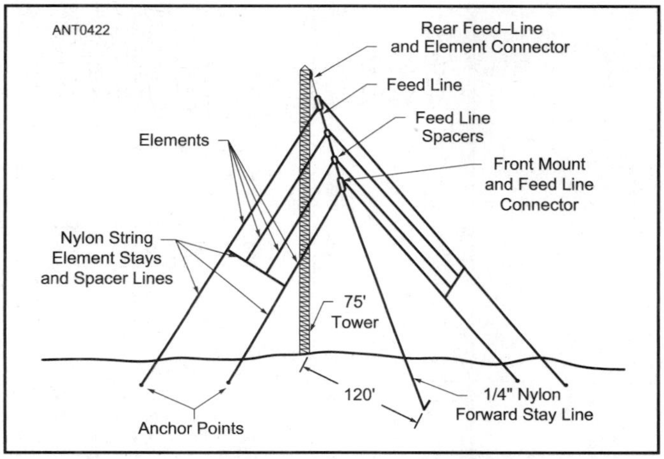

Figure 7.15 — Typical lower-HF wire 4-element log periodic dipole aray erected on a tower.

Table 7.1
Design Parameters for the 3.5-MHz Single-Band LPDA

f1 = 3.3 MHz	Element lengths:
f_n = 4.1 MHz	$\ell1$ = 149.091 feet
B = 1.2424	$\ell2$ = 125.982 feet
τ = 0.845	$\ell3$ = 106.455 feet
σ = 0.06	$\ell4$ = 89.954 feet
Gain = 5.9 dBi = 3.8 dBd	Element spacings:
cot α = 1.5484	d_{12}=17.891 feet
B_{ar} = 1.3864	d_{23} = 15.118 feet
B_s = 1.7225	d_{34} = 12.775 feet
L = 48.42 feet	Element diameters
N = 4.23 elements (decrease to 4)	All = 0.0641 inches
Z_t = 6-inch short jumper	ℓ/diameter ratios:
R_0 = 208 Ω	ℓ/diam$_4$ = 16840
Z_{AV} = 897.8 Ω	ℓ/diam$_3$ = 19929
σ' = 0.06527	ℓ/diam$_2$ = 23585
Z_0 = 319.8 Ω	ℓ/diam$_1$ = 27911
Antenna feeder: #12 AWG wire spaced 0.58 inches	
Balun: 4:1	
Feed line: 52-Ω coax	

Table 7.2
Design Parameters for the 7-MHz Single-Band LPDA

f1 = 6.9 MHz	Element lengths:
f_n = 7.5 MHz	$\ell1$ = 71.304 feet
B = 1.0870	$\ell2$ = 60.252 feet
τ = 0.845	$\ell3$ = 50.913 feet
σ = 0.06	$\ell4$ = 43.022 feet
Gain = 5.9 dBi = 3.8 dBd	Element spacings:
cot α = 1.5484	d_{12} = 8.557 feet
B_{ar} = 1.3864	d_{23} = 7.230 feet
B_s = 1.5070	d_{34} = 6.110 feet
L = 18.57 feet	Element diameters:
N = 3.44 elements (increase to 4)	All = 0.0641 inches
Z_t = 6-inch short jumper	ℓ/diameter ratios:
R_0 = 208 Ω	$\ell4$/diam$_4$ = 8054
Z_{AV} = 809.3 Ω	$\ell3$/diam$_3$ = 9531
σ' = 0.06527	$\ell2$/diam$_2$ = 11280
Z_0 = 334.2 Ω	$\ell1$/diam$_1$ = 13349
Antenna feeder: #12 AWG wire spaced 0.66 inches	
Balun: 4:1	
Feed line: 52-Ω coax	

for arriving at the dimensions and other parameters of these arrays was presented earlier in this chapter. The primary differences between these designs and one-octave upper HF arrays are the narrower frequency ranges and the use of wire, rather than tubing, for the elements. As design examples for the LPDA, you may wish to work through the step-by-step procedure and check your results against the values in Tables 7.1 and 7.2. You may also wish to compare these results with the output of an LPDA design software package such as *LPCAD*.

From the design procedure, the feeder wire spacings for the two arrays are slightly different, 0.58 inch for the 3.5-MHz array and 0.66 inch for the 7-MHz version. As a compromise toward the use of common spacers for both bands, a spacing of ⅝ inch is quite satisfactory. Surprisingly, the feeder spacing is not at all critical here from a matching standpoint, as may be verified from the equations presented earlier in this chapter. Increasing the spacing to as much as ¾ inch results in an R_0 SWR of less than 1.1:1 on both bands.

Constructing the Arrays

Construction techniques are the same for both the 3.5 and the 7-MHz versions of the array. Once the designs are completed, the next step is to fabricate the fittings; see **Figure 7.16** for details. Cut the wire elements and feed lines to the proper sizes and mark them for identification. After the wires

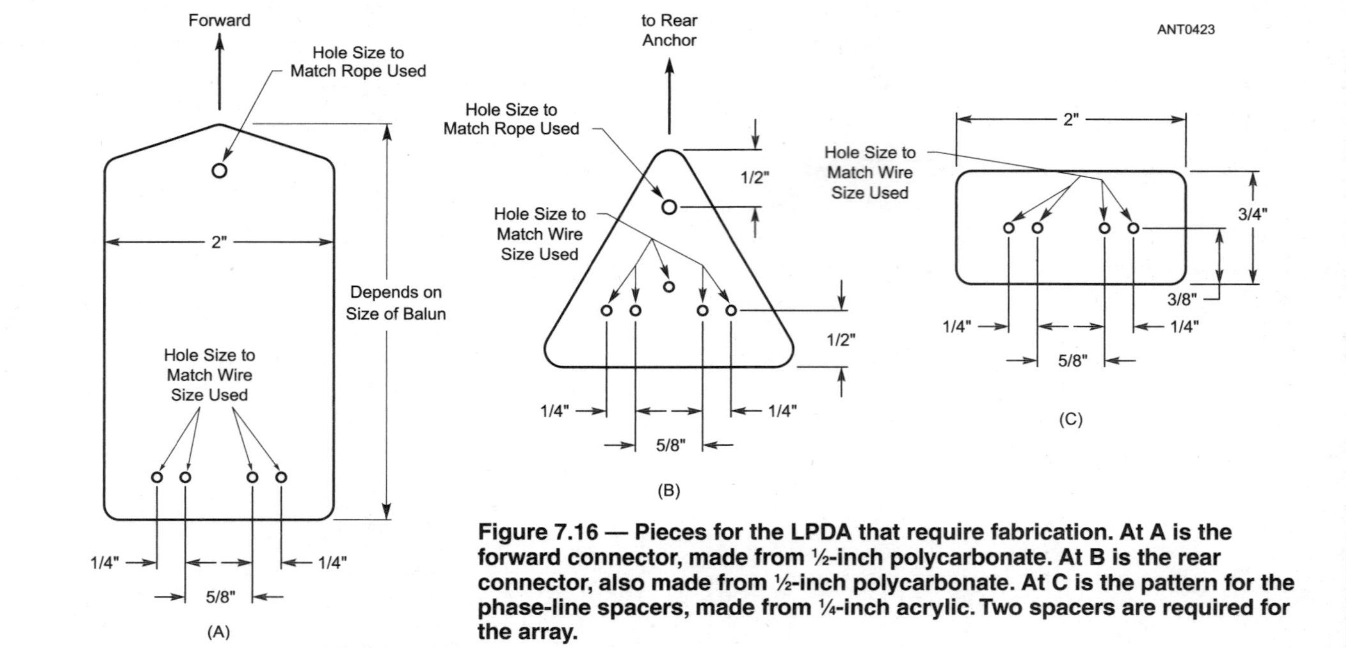

Figure 7.16 — Pieces for the LPDA that require fabrication. At A is the forward connector, made from ½-inch polycarbonate. At B is the rear connector, also made from ½-inch polycarbonate. At C is the pattern for the phase-line spacers, made from ¼-inch acrylic. Two spacers are required for the array.

are cut and placed aside, it will be difficult to remember which is which unless they are marked. When you have finished fabricating the connectors and cutting all of the wires, the antenna can be assembled. Use your ingenuity when building one of these antennas; it isn't necessary to duplicate these LPDAs precisely.

The elements are made of standard #14 AWG stranded copper wire. The two parallel-wire feed lines are made of #12 AWG solid copper-clad steel wire, such as Copperweld. Copperweld will not stretch when placed under tension. The front and rear connectors are cut from ½-inch thick polycarbonate sheeting, and the feed line spacers from ¼-inch acrylic sheeting.

Study the drawings carefully and be familiar with the way the wire elements are connected to the two feed lines, through the front, rear and spacer connectors. Details are sketched in **Figures 7.17** and **7.18**. Connections made in the way shown in the drawings prevent the wire from breaking. All of the rope, string, and connectors must be made of materials that can withstand the effects of tension and weathering. Use nylon rope and strings, the type that yachtsmen use. Figure 10.51 shows the front stay rope coming down to ground level at a point 120 feet from the base of a 75-foot tower. Space may not be available for this arrangement in all cases. An alternative installation technique is to put a pulley 40 feet up in a tree and run the front stay rope through the pulley and down to ground level at the base of the tree. The front stay rope will have to be tightened with a block and tackle at ground level.

Putting an LPDA together is not difficult if it is assembled in an orderly manner. It is easier to connect the elements to the feeder lines when the feed line assembly is stretched between two points. Use the tower and a block and tackle. Attaching the rear connector to the tower and assembling the LPDA at the base of the tower makes raising the antenna into place a much simpler task. Tie the rear connector securely to the base of the tower and attach the two feeder lines to it. Then thread the two feed line spacers onto the feed line. The spacers will be loose at this time, but will be positioned properly when the elements are connected. Now connect the front connector

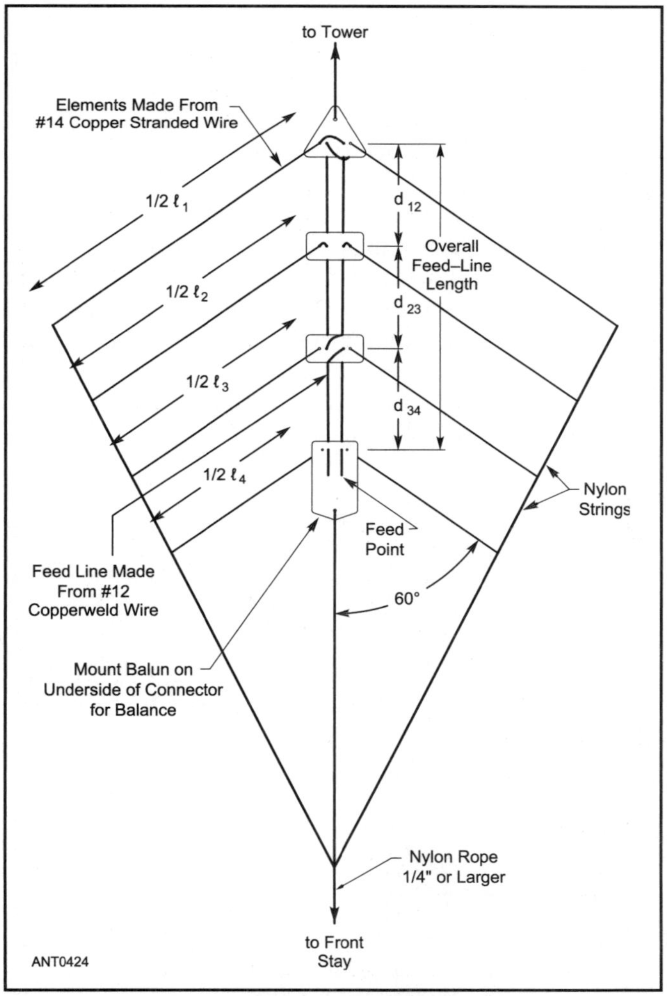

Figure 7.17 — The generic layout for the lower HF wire LPDA. Use a 4:1 balun on the forward connector. See Tables 7.1 and 7.2 for dimensions.

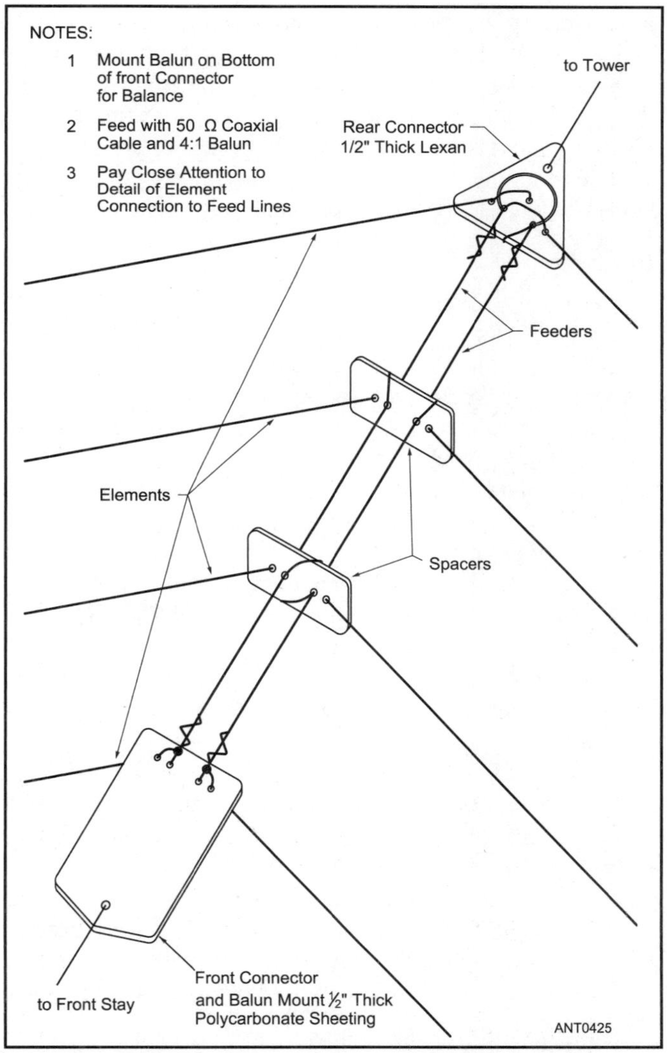

Figure 7.18 — Details of the electrical and mechanical connections of the elements to the phase-line. Knots in the nylon rope stay line are not shown.

to the feed lines. A word of caution: Measure accurately and carefully! Double-check all measurements before you make permanent connections.

Connect the elements to the feeder lines through their respective plastic connectors, beginning with element 1, then element 2, and so on. Keep all of the element wires securely coiled. If they unravel, you will have a tangled mess of kinked wire. Recheck the element-to-feeder connections to ensure proper and secure junctions. (See Figures 7.17 and 7.18.) Once you have completed all of the element connections, attach the 4:1 balun to the underside of the front connector. Connect the feeder lines and the coaxial cable to the balun.

You will need a separate piece of rope and a pulley to raise the completed LPDA into position. First secure the eight element ends with nylon string, referring to Figures 7.15 and 7.17. The string must be long enough to reach the tie-down points. Connect the front stay rope to the front connector, and the completed LPDA is now ready to be raised into position. While raising the antenna, uncoil the element wires to prevent their getting away and tangling up into a mess. Use care! Raise the rear connector to the proper height and attach it securely to the tower, then pull the front stay rope tight and secure it. Move the elements so they form a 60° angle with the feed lines, in the direction of the front, and space them properly relative to one another. By adjusting the end positions of the elements as you walk back and forth, you will be able to align all the elements properly. Now it is time to hook your rig to the system and make some contacts.

Performance

The reports received from these LPDAs were compared with an inverted-V dipole. All of the antennas are fixed; the LPDAs radiate to the northeast, and the dipole to the northeast and southwest. The apex of the dipole is at 70 feet, and the 40- and 80-meter LPDAs are at 60 and 50 feet, respectively. Basic array gain was apparent from many of the reports received. During pileups, it was possible to break in with a few tries on the LPDAs, yet it was impossible to break the same pileups using the dipole. The gain of the LPDAs is several dB over the dipole. For additional gain, experimenters may wish to try a parasitic director about ⅛ λ ahead of the array. Director length and spacing from the forward LPDA element should be field-adjusted for maximum performance while maintaining the impedance match across each of the bands.

Wire LPDA systems offer many possibilities. They are easy to design and to construct: real advantages in countries where commercially built antennas and parts are not available at reasonable cost. The wire needed can be obtained in all parts of the world, and cost of construction is low. If damaged, the LPDAs can be repaired easily with pliers and solder. For those who travel on DXpeditions where space and weight are large considerations, LPDAs are lightweight but sturdy, and they perform well.

7.3.2 LPDA FOR 13 TO 30 MHz

A rotatable log periodic array designed to cover the frequency range from 13 to 30 MHz is pictured in **Figure 7.19**. This is a large array having a free-space gain that varies from 6.6 to over 6.9 dBi, depending upon the operating portion of the design spectrum. This antenna system was originally described by Peter D. Rhodes, K4EWG, in November 1973 *QST*.

The characteristics of this array are:

1) Half-power beamwidth, 43° (14 MHz)
2) Design parameter $\tau = 0.9$
3) Relative element spacing constant $\sigma = 0.05$
4) Boom length, L = 26 feet
5) Longest element $\lambda 1$ = 37 feet 10 inches.
6) Total weight, 116 pounds
7) Wind-load area, 10.7 square feet
8) Required input impedance (mean resistance), $R_0 = 72\ \Omega$, Z_t = 6-inch jumper #18 AWG wire
9) Average characteristic dipole impedance, Z_{AV}: 337.8 Ω
10) Impedance of the feeder, Z_0: 117.1 Ω
11) Feeder: #12 AWG wire, close spaced
12) With a 1:1 toroid balun at the input terminals and a 72-Ω coax feed line, the maximum SWR is 1.4:1.

The mechanical assembly uses materials readily available from most local hardware stores or aluminum supply houses. A complete set of tables and assembly drawings are included in the original article included with this book's downloadable supplemental content.

Experimenters may wish to improve the performance of the array at both the upper and lower frequency ends of the design spectrum so that it more closely approaches the performance in the middle of the design frequency range. The most apt general technique for raising both the gain and the front-to-back ratio at the frequency extremes would be to circularize τ as described earlier in this chapter. However, other techniques may also be applied.

Figure 7.19 — The 13-30 MHz log periodic dipole array.

7.4 BIBLIOGRAPHY

Source material and more extended discussion of the topics covered in this chapter can be found in the references listed below and in the textbooks listed at the end of the **Antenna Fundamentals** chapter.

D. Allen, "The Log Periodic Loop Array (LPLA) Antenna," *The ARRL Antenna Compendium, Vol 3*, pp 115-117.

C. A. Balanis, *Antenna Theory, Analysis and Design*, 2nd Ed. (New York: John Wiley & Sons, 1997) Chapter 9.

P. C. Butson and G. T. Thompson, "A Note on the Calculation of the Gain of Log-Periodic Dipole Antennas," *IEEE Trans on Antennas and Propagation*, Vol AP-24, No. 1, Jan 1976, pp 105-106.

R. L. Carrel, "The Design of Log-Periodic Dipole Antennas," *1961 IRE International Convention Record.*

L. B. Cebik, "Notes on Standard Design LPDAs for 3-30 MHz," *QEX*, Part 1, May/Jun 2000, pp 23-38; Part 2, Jul/Aug 2000, pp 17-31.

L. B. Cebik, "The Monoband Log-Cell Yagi Revisited, Part 1: An Introduction to the Log-Cell Yagi and Some Standards of Comparison and Part 2: Element Phasing and Log-Cell Design," various sources online.

L. B. Cebik, "Notes on the OWA Yagi," *QEX*, Jul-Aug 2002, pp 22-34.

R. H. DuHamel and D. E. Isbell, "Broadband Logarithmically Periodic Antenna Structures," *1957 IRE National Convention Record*, Part 1.

J. Fisher, "Development of the W8JF Waveram: A Planar Log-Periodic Quad Array," *The ARRL Antenna Compendium, Vol 1*, pp 50-54.

K. Heitner, "A Wide-Band, Low-Z Antenna — New Thoughts on Small Antennas," *The ARRL Antenna Compendium, Vol 1*, pp 48-49.

D. E. Isbell, "Log-Periodic Dipole Arrays," *IRE Transactions on Antennas and Propagation*, Vol. AP-8, No. 3, May 1960.

J. Johnson, "Enhancing performance of stacked Yagi arrays and BOLPA Development," Dayton Hamvention Antenna Forum 2017, **www.kkn.net/dayton2017/Yagi-Stack-Enhance-BOLPA-Dayton-2017.pdf**.

J. D. Kraus, *Antennas*, 2nd Ed. (New York: McGraw-Hill, 1988), Chapter 15.

R. A. Johnson, ed., *Antenna Engineering Handbook*, 3rd Ed. (New York: McGraw-Hill, 1993), Chapters 14 and 26.

C. Luetzelschwab, "Log Periodic Dipole Array Improvements," *The ARRL Antenna Compendium, Vol 6*, pp 74-76.

C. Luetzelschwab, "More Improvements to an LPDA," *The ARRL Antenna Compendium, Vol 7,* pp 121-122.

P. E. Mayes and R. L. Carrel, "Log Periodic Resonant-V Arrays," *IRE Wescon Convention Record*, Part 1, 1961.

P. E. Mayes, G. A. Deschamps, and W. T. Patton, "Backward Wave Radiation from Periodic Structures and Application to the Design of Frequency Independent Antennas," *Proc. IRE.*

C. T. Milner, "Log Periodic Antennas," *QST*, Nov 1959, pp 11-14.

W. I. Orr and S. D. Cowan, *Beam Antenna Handbook*, pp 251-253.

V. H. Rumsey, *Frequency Independent Antennas* (New York: Academic Press, 1966).

W. L. Stutzman and G. A. Thiele, *Antenna Theory and Design*, 2nd Ed. (New York: John Wiley & Sons, 1998), Chapter 6.

TABLE OF CONTENTS

Chapter 8 — Downloadable Supplemental Content

Supplemental Articles

- "How to Start Modeling Antennas Using *EZNEC*" by Greg Ordy, W8WWV

Chapter 8

Antenna Modeling

8.1 OVERVIEW: ANTENNA ANALYSIS BY COMPUTER

As pointed out in **The Effects of Ground** chapter, irregular local terrain can have a profound effect on the launch of HF signals into the ionosphere. A *system approach* as described in the **HF Antenna System Design** chapter is needed to create a scientifically planned station. Antenna modeling programs do not generally take into account the effects of irregular terrain and by "irregular" we mean any sort of ground that is not flat. Most modeling programs based on *NEC-2* or *MININEC* do model reflections, but they do not model diffractions.

On the other hand, while a ray-tracing program like *HFTA* (HF Terrain Assessment by Dean Straw, N6BV — described in the **HF Antenna System Design** chapter) does take into account diffraction, it doesn't explicitly factor in the mutual impedance between an antenna and the ground. Instead, *HFTA* makes the basic assumption that the antenna is mounted sufficiently high above ground so that the mutual impedance between an antenna and the ground is minimal.

In this chapter we'll look at modeling the antennas themselves on the PC. We'll evaluate some typical antennas over flat ground and also in free space. Once characterized — or even optimized for certain characteristics — these antennas can then be analyzed over real terrain using *HFTA* and the other tools discussed in the **HF Antenna System Design** chapter.

Previous editions of this book have included *EZNEC-ARRL*, a version of *EZNEC* antenna modeling software that worked with a special set of model files. Effective with this edition, the demo version of *EZNEC 6.0* will run all *EZNEC-ARRL* models, subject to the limitations spelled out in the demo version documentation. The demo version of *EZNEC 6.0* is free and can be downloaded from **www.eznec.com**. Previous versions of *EZNEC-ARRL* will continue to operate properly with *EZNEC-ARRL* files as before. Model files including those referenced in this chapter are included with this book's downloadable supplemental information.

8.1.1 A SHORT HISTORY OF ANTENNA MODELING

With the proliferation of personal computers since the early 1980s, amateurs and professionals alike have made significant strides in computerized antenna system analysis. It is now possible for the amateur with a relatively inexpensive computer to evaluate even complicated antenna systems. Amateurs can obtain a keener grasp of the operation of antenna systems — a subject that has been a great mystery to many in the past. We might add that modern computing tools allow hams to debunk overblown claims made about certain antennas.

The most commonly encountered programs for antenna analysis are those derived from a program developed at US government laboratories called *NEC*, short for "Numerical Electromagnetics Code." *NEC* uses a so-called *Method of Moments (MoM)* algorithm. (The name derives from a numerical method of dealing with accumulated errors in fields generated by current distributed along an antenna.) If you want to delve into details about the Method of Moments, see the excellent chapter in *Antennas*, 2nd edition, by John Kraus, W8JK. See also the article "Programs for Antenna Analysis by the Method of Moments," by Bob Haviland, W4MB, in *The ARRL Antenna Compendium*, Vol 4.

The mathematics behind the MoM algorithm are pretty formidable, but the basic principle is simple. An antenna is broken down into a number of straight-line wire segments, and the field resulting from the RF current in each segment is evaluated by itself and also with respect to other mutually coupled segments. Finally, the field from each contributing segment is vector-summed to yield the total field, which can be computed for any elevation or azimuth angle desired. The effects of flat-earth ground reflections, including the effect of ground conductivity and dielectric constant, may be evaluated as well.

In the early 1980s, *MININEC* was written in *BASIC* for use on personal computers. Because of limitations in memory and speed typical of personal computers of the time, several simplifying assumptions were necessary in *MININEC*, limiting potential accuracy. Perhaps the most significant limitation was that perfect ground was assumed to be directly under the antenna, even though the radiation pattern in the far field did take into account real ground parameters. This meant that antennas modeled closer to ground than approximately 0.2 λ sometimes gave erroneous impedances and

Antenna and Electromagnetic Modeling Software

By Steve Stearns, K6OIK

Originally developed at Lawrence Livermore National Laboratory (LLNL) in the 1970s, the program *Numerical Electromagnetics Code* or *NEC* is publicly available for general use and is available for personal computers running Windows, Linux, and macOS. The public version is *NEC-2* (**www.nec2.org**). An updated version, *NEC-4*, is only available as a compiled binary program under license agreement with LLNL and is best-known to amateurs in the *EZNEC-Pro* software. More information about *NEC* is available from **en.wikipedia.org/wiki/Numerical_Electromagnetics_Code**.

The *NEC* program family (*NEC, NEC-BSC, NEC-2, NEC-3, NEC-4*) and the alternative implementation *MININEC* are examples of "thin wire" codes, which are limited to modeling antennas made of wires, rods, and tubes, with materials limited to non-magnetic metals.

Other programs have appeared since *NEC* was developed. For example, a series of programs started from B.D. Popovic's modeling program *WireZeus*, including *AWAS, WIPL, WIPL-D,* and *HOBBIES*. *WireZeus* and *AWAS* are thin-wire programs. *WIPL* and *WIPL-D* are professional modeling programs. *HOBBIES* was released in 2012 and is the newest member of the family. Most of these programs are characterized as electromagnetic "solvers" or simulators that use advanced numerical algorithms to handle general geometries and arbitrary materials.

Programs such as *WIPL-D*, *FEKO*, and *HOBBIES* have, in addition to a thin-wire code, the ability to model surfaces. Just as a thin-wire code divides a wire into segments, a surface code divides a surface into elementary patches by using a process called *meshing*. Surface meshing allows one to model irregularly shaped antennas on irregularly shaped platforms such as automobiles, airplanes, ships, and even irregular terrain. Consequently, models can include structural features such as buildings, trees, hills, and valleys, which a thin-wire code cannot model.

Figure 8.A shows a mesh model of a car's surface modeled as metal skin over ground. A 2-meter whip is mounted on the car's roof. The surface has been meshed into small triangular patches by the modeling program *FEKO*. A source placed at the base of the whip feeds it against the roof. *FEKO* computes RF current in each triangular patch. **Figure 8.B** shows the computed currents. Magnitude is shown as shades of grey and current direction is depicted by small arrows. Note how current concentrates around the edges of the windows. (See KI6BDR's October 2016 *QST* article for more about this type of modeling.)

HOBBIES is an acronym for "Higher Order Basis Based Integral Equation Solver." It runs on an ordinary Windows PC, is feature rich, and is affordable for amateurs. However, it does require learning modern CAD geometry modeling and uses *GiD* version 10 for specifying model geometries.

Modern programs for computational electromagnetics do a better job of telling us what is going on with antennas and structures. Such programs not only allow more complex models, but their graphical output can improve our understanding of electromagnetic physics, fields, and wave propagation. An expanded discussion of modeling software and automated shell programs such as *AutoEZ* is available on the *Antenna Book* web page: **www.arrl.org/arrl-antenna-book-reference**. See K6OIK's 2017 Pacificon presentation on antenna modeling, "Antenna Modeling for Radio Amateurs," at **www.fars.k6ya.org/docs/k6oik**.

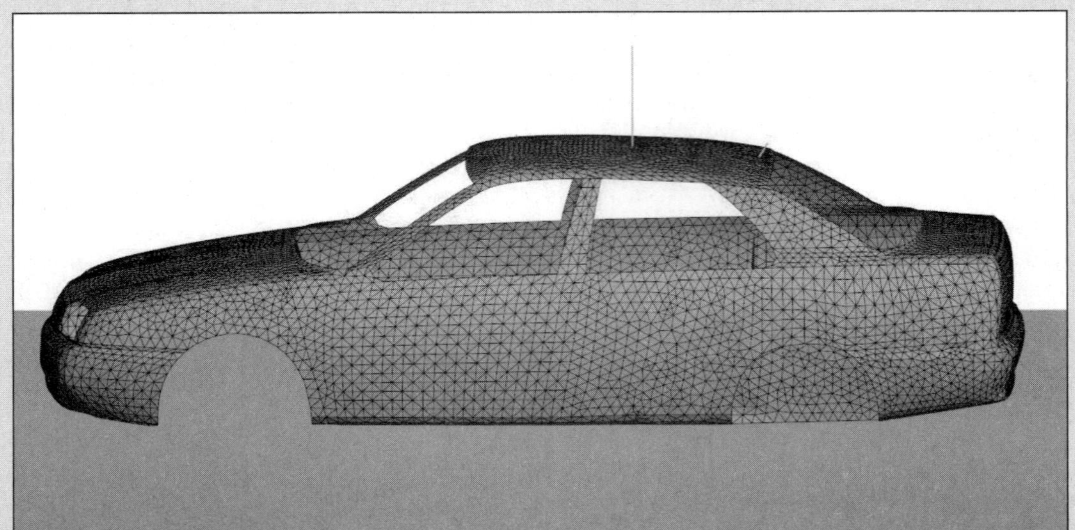

Figure A — *FEKO* model of a 2 meter whip on the roof of a car.

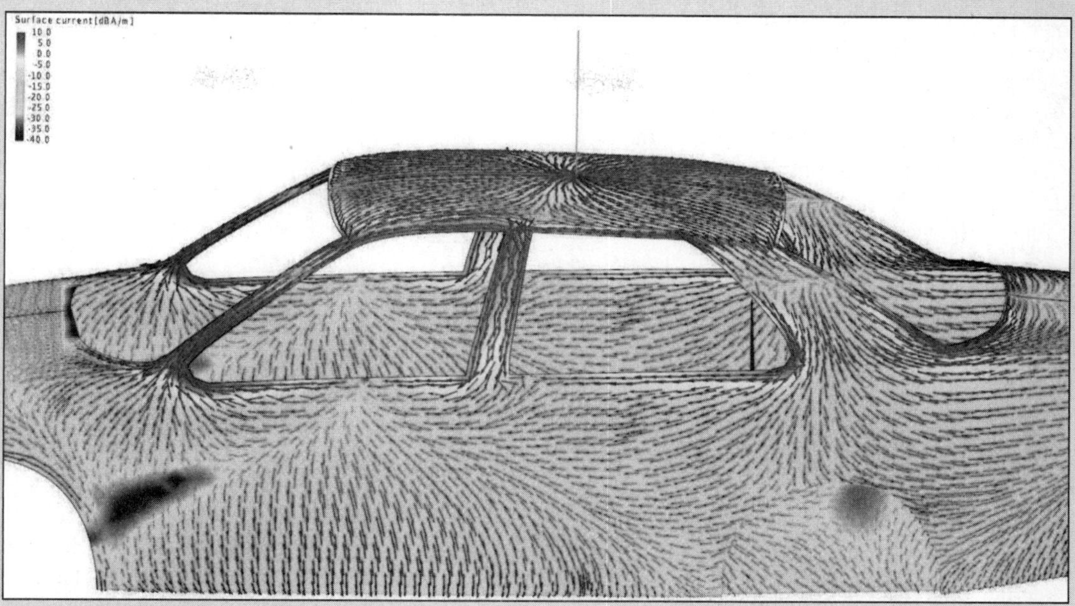

Figure B — Skin currents in car are concentrated around the windows.

Table 8.A
Antenna and Electromagnetic Modeling Software

Program	*Website*	*Notes*
4NEC2	**www.qsl.net/4nec2**	
EZNEC, *EZNEC-Pro*	**www.eznec.com**	
AutoEZ	**www.ac6la.com/autoez.html**	Automated shell for *EZNEC*, based on *Excel*
YW — Yagi for Windows	**www.arrl.org/arrl-antenna-book-reference**	
YagiCAD	**www.yagicad.com/yagicad/YagiCAD.htm**	Calculator for VHF/UHF Yagi design
Yagi Calculator	**www.vk5dj.com/yagi.html**	Calculator for DL6WU long-Yagi VHF/UHF design
CocoaNEC	**www.w7ay.net/site/Applications/cocoaNEC/**	macOS version of *NEC*
MMANA-GAL, *MMANA-GAL PRO*	**gal-ana.de**	
NEC2GO	**www.nec2go.com/**	Simplified user interface
NEC 4.2	**ipo.llnl.gov/technologies/nec**	
NEC archives by WB6TPU	**www.qsl.net/wb6tpu** **Nec-archives.pa3kj.com**	Unofficial archives

Electromagnetic solver/modeling/simulation

HOBBIES	**www.em-hobbies.com/**
WIPL, WIPL-D	**wipl-d.com/**
FEKO	**altairhyperworks.com/product/FEKO**

See also **en.wikipedia.org/wiki/Comparison_of_EM_simulation_software** inflated gains, especially for horizontal polarization. Despite some limitations, *MININEC* represented a remarkable leap forward in analytical capability. See Roy Lewallen's (W7EL) "*MININEC* — the Other Edge of the Sword" in Feb 1991 *QST* for an excellent treatment on pitfalls when using *MININEC*.

Because source code was made available when *MININEC* was released to the public, a number of programmers produced some very capable commercial versions for the amateur market, many incorporating exciting graphics showing antenna patterns in 2D or 3D. These programs also simplify the creation of models for popular antenna types, and several come with libraries of sample antennas.

By the end of the 1980s, the speed and capabilities of personal computers had advanced to the point where PC versions of *NEC* became practical, and several versions are now available to amateurs. The most recent public-domain version is *NEC-2* and this is the computational core that we'll use as an example throughout this chapter.

Like *MININEC*, *NEC-2* is a general-purpose modeling package and it can be difficult to use and relatively slow in operation for certain specialized antenna forms. Thus, custom commercial software has been created for more user-friendly and speedier analysis of specific antenna varieties, mainly Yagi arrays described in the chapter on **HF Yagi and Quad Antennas**. Also see the sidebar, "Commercial Implementations of *MININEC* and *NEC-2* Programs."

The following material on antenna modeling is by necessity a summary since entire books have been written on this subject. Additional antenna modeling resources may be found on the ARRL website at **www.arrl.org/antenna-modeling**. We also strongly recommend that you read the HELP files available with the demo version of *EZNEC*. It contains a wealth of practical information on the finer points of antenna modeling.

8.1.2 COMPARING *NEC-2* TO *NEC-4*

The following section was contributed by Greg Ordy, W8WWV, for the 23rd edition. Another article by Greg, "How to Start Modeling Antennas Using EZNEC," is included with this book's downloadable supplemental information.

Two popular antenna modeling programs are *EZNEC* and *4nec2*. They are GUI (graphical user interface) shells or wrappers that use an *NEC* modeling engine to perform the antenna simulation. (See the Reference section of this chapter for website URLs for these and other programs referenced in this sidebar.)

NEC versions 2 and 4 are the engines available to both modeling programs. I know of no antenna model where *NEC-2* would be preferred to *NEC-4*. *NEC-2* survives because it is free software in the public domain and *NEC-4* is licensed software that costs at least several hundred dollars. Programs such as *EZNEC* and *4nec2* have augmented *NEC-2* with extensions that address the most serious of the *NEC-2* deficiencies in many models.

For a wide range of models, the choice between the *NEC-2* and *NEC-4* engines makes little difference. There are models, however, where the choice of engine becomes very important if the highest accuracy is desired.

This section highlights the differences between *NEC-2* and *NEC-4*. Most of the information comes from the references included at the end of this chapter.

History

The acronym "NEC" (pronounced *neck*) stands for Numerical Electromagnetics Code. It is not related to the other popular use of "NEC," which is used to refer to the National Electrical Code.

- *NEC-1* was developed at the Lawrence Livermore National Lab (LLNL) in 1977. *NEC-1* built upon versions 1 and 2 of the *Antenna Modeling Program* (*AMP*). They date back to 1974.
- *NEC-2* was released in 1980, with its user manual dated January, 1981.
- *NEC-3* was released in 1983. It addressed one of the two major problems with *NEC-2*. It accepts buried wires and wires that penetrate a lossy media (such as ground).
- *NEC-4* was released in 1992. It extends and improves *NEC-3*. In particular, it corrects the problem that *NEC-2* and *NEC-3* have with stepped-radius wires and junctions of tightly coupled wires.

NEC-2 is the most recent version that was released in source form without restriction into the public domain. It has been used as part of many commercial and freeware software packages. It's safe to say that more models have been run using *NEC-2* than any other modeling engine.

NEC-4 supersedes *NEC-3*. *NEC-4* remains licensed software. To use *NEC-4* legally it is necessary to obtain a license from the Lawrence Livermore National Laboratory (LLNL). The one-time license fee is a function of the intended use of the software (personal/commercial/foreign). The cost ranges from $300 to $1500 (as of early 2015). The license is non-transferable.

It is worth mentioning the *MININEC* modeling engine. *MININEC* was developed as a personal computer antenna modeling engine in 1982. It is written in the *BASIC* programming language as opposed to *FORTRAN*. Despite the name, it is not a cut down version of *NEC*. While it has its own set of issues and concerns, in some areas it is considered to be superior to *NEC-2* and potentially even *NEC-4*. In particular, *MININEC* models stepped-radius wires accurately. *MININEC* has its place in the world of antenna modeling. It is available in packages such as *MMANA-GAL*.

In recent years, the specific version of *NEC-4* that has been in common use is version 4.1. In 2011, version 4.2 was released, and is included along with version 4.1 as part of the licensed package from LLNL. Version 4.2 adds a new ground option. In some cases, it can be more accurate than the 4.1 version. Using it, however, does slow down running the model. Look for *NEC* version 4.2 to be adopted by modeling packages in the future.

The modeling engine software dates back to the time before the explosive expansion of the power and capacity of the personal computer (PC). To provide the highest performance at the time, programmers included options such as using single-precision (32-bit) floating point computations as opposed to double-precision (64-bit) computations. After almost 30 years of PC evolution, there are very few cases where using the single-precision modeling engine makes sense. There are cases, however, where the added precision of the double-precision engine improves accuracy.

NEC-4 is more "idiot proof" than *NEC-2*. It has fewer idiosyncrasies and modeling guidelines to follow. To use *NEC-2* effectively, you have to be smarter about how to use it, and even when to use it.

It has always been possible to directly use the *NEC* engines and skip the wrapper or shell programs. Be aware, however, that the original interface to *NEC* is a deck of punch cards on the input and a long plain-text output file intended for a line printer.

Average Gain Test

Regardless of the engine in use, it's always a good idea to use the Average Gain Test to evaluate and increase the confidence in a model. When a model is inappropriate due to guideline violations or using an engine incorrectly, the Average Gain Test can highlight the problem.

A lossless antenna in a lossless environment radiates all incoming power in some direction. To perform the average gain test all loss is removed from the model. When run, all of the power supplied to the antenna should be captured in the pattern. If not, then the lossless antenna is acting like an amplifier or attenuator, and since it is neither, something is wrong with the results.

Details on running the Average Gain Test can be found in the program documentation. Often times the model can be adjusted to pass the test. If that is not possible, then the numeric results of the test can be used to correct the reported gain. If your model results are way out of line with common sense expectations, then it is a good time to run the Average Gain Test.

Differences Between *NEC-2* and *NEC-4*

Stepped Wire Diameters

Perhaps the biggest failing with *NEC-2* is its handling of stepped-diameter wire connections. If this sounds esoteric, please remember that telescoping aluminum tubing is used to construct many of our antennas — including the Yagi and ground-mounted vertical. When an aluminum tube slides into the next size tube, a stepped diameter situation is created. This problem was finally addressed in *NEC-4*, and *MININEC* does a good job of handling it appropriately too. If not for the ability to compensate or correct for this problem, I think it's fair to say that *NEC-2* would have been abandoned — certainly for this class of antenna.

The correction approach used was developed by Dr David Leeson, W6NL. It is detailed in Chapter 8 of his book *Physical Design of Yagi Antennas*. Although more than 20 years old, it is still a valuable reference for anyone who is serious about the mechanical or electrical aspects of a Yagi.

The stepped-diameter correction algorithm converts a set of coaxial and stepped wires into a single wire with a uniform diameter. The before and after elements are considered to be equivalent. The shell programs such as *EZNEC* and *4nec2* identify correction opportunities and apply the algorithm automatically. The corrected model is sent to the engine. Although this tight integration makes it painless to use the correction algorithm, there are a set of conditions that have to be true in order for the correction to be used. Needless to say, if you believe that the correction is being used, but it isn't, the results will contain more error than expected.

The *EZNEC* Help documentation contains a complete list of the constraints on the use of the stepped diameter correction algorithm. The program also indicates when the correction is in use, but in the heat of modeling the antenna it's possible to lose track of the status information.

Over-simplified, the correction can only be applied to a set of two or more wires that are all collinear with more than one diameter. In addition, if there the model includes a Source or Load or Transmission Line, they must be connected in the middle of the element. These constraints allow for many antenna designs, but not all.

Situations that would disable the correction include:

1. Phasing lines running down and connecting to a set of elements.

2. Loading coils or traps not located at the center of an element.

3. Wires located near the feed point used in matching networks such as the gamma or hairpin (beta) match.

4. Non-collinear wires, such as squares or rectangles in antennas such as quads or the Moxon Rectangle.

5. Wires groups that are not within 15% of the half-wave resonant length (or quarter-wave resonant length for wire groups with one end grounded).

If a particular model cannot use stepped diameter correction where needed, and the highest accuracy is desired, then moving to *NEC-4* (or possibly *MININEC*) is the solution.

While on the topic of modeling Yagis, two more correction or compensation situations warrant mention. They are compensating for the metal boom and the metal element clamps. The metal present in the boom and clamps changes the electrical length of the element.

Boom compensation for the typical HF Yagi is on the order of 1/8 inch per half-element. This might be smaller than the construction accuracy and is often ignored. On VHF and UHF antennas, however, where the ratio between element length and boom diameter is much lower, boom compensation is an important consideration.

The element clamping scheme also creates a need for compensation, even at HF. There are a number of clamp styles and sizes in use. Chapter 9 of Leeson's book tackles the problem of clamp compensation. The approach converts the dimensions of a set of clamp styles into a wire length and diameter that can be located at the center of the element in the model. This is a clever way to incorporate the effect of the clamp by turning it into something that can be modeled — a fat and short wire located at the middle of the element.

The *AutoEZ* program from Dan Maguire, AC6LA, is a very powerful antenna modeling tool that uses *EZNEC* as its engine. *AutoEZ* incorporates the Leeson clamp models. By selecting a clamp style and then entering the dimensions, *AutoEZ* will compute the equivalent wire and add it to the model.

When you come across a model for a Yagi, especially an existing commercial product, and if you find a relatively short and fat wire at the center of an element it's safe to assume that it is a proxy for the element to boom mounting clamp. This is most certainly true if the wire is not part of the mechanical specification. It's intended to represent the effect of the actual metal clamp in the model.

The errors introduced by not using stepped diameter correction (*NEC-2* only) or boom compensation, or clamp compensation, all shift the model performance in the same direction. If they are not used the model results will be shifted downward in frequency. The natural response to this result is to scale the design up in frequency, usually by shortening the elements. Now, the model results line up with the target frequency. Unfortunately, if you build the antenna using those dimensions and then measure characteristics such as SWR, you will find that the antenna performance characteristics have been shifted above the target frequency. This leads to the sad realization that your elements are too short.

In several monoband HF Yagi projects the author has been involved with over the past few years, the impact on the actual antenna is on the order of 1/2 inch per each element end on 15 meters, a little bit more on 20 meters and a little bit less on 10 meters. This is for antennas modeled using *NEC-4*, but without clamp or boom compensation added to the model. The size and shape of the clamps will influence the amount of compensation needed.

If the short and fat wire representing the clamp contains a *NEC* Source, representing the feed point, then even with *NEC-4* there can be additional error in the results depending upon the segment length to diameter ratio. One approach is to use the average gain as a correction factor, or, use the stepped diameter correction algorithm even with the *NEC-4* engine.

Wires Below Ground

Since before the classic paper "Ground Systems as a Factor in Antenna Efficiency" was published by Brown, Lewis and Epstein in 1937 (see the Bibliography for the chapter **Effects of Ground**), the topic of ground wires and radials for ground mounted vertical antennas has been discussed. If you wish to explore what modeling predicts about wires very near to the surface of the ground or buried below the surface, you must use *NEC-4*.

Rudy Severns, N6LF, has written extensively on the topic of radial systems, using both *NEC-4* models and field measurements. His work is an excellent place to start any investigation of this topic, including the material in this book's chapter, **Effects of Ground**.

If it's not possible to model ground radial systems with *NEC-2* then that should surely imply that vertical antennas with ground radials can only be modeled with *NEC-4*. Fortunately, that is not the case. *NEC-2* has been modified to include a ground type that was first used with the *MININEC* engine. This is called the *MININEC*-type ground. In this case, the approach is to directly connect the vertical to *MININEC* ground, and then add a resistive Load at the base with a value chosen to simulate the expected ground resistance for the presumed radial system. Many sources such as the *ARRL Antenna Book* and ON4UN's *Low-Band DXing* explore the topic of ground resistance for radial fields.

The use of the *MININEC*-type ground turns out to be a good solution because the truth is that in most cases precise modeling of radial fields is work. The *MININEC* solution works well for investigating vertical antennas and arrays of vertical antennas.

If you are investigating buried wires with *NEC-4*, but sure to use the real/high accuracy ground model. There is a general admonition against using the *MININEC* ground with any horizontal wire less than 0.2 wavelength above ground. Elevated radials can be modeled with either *NEC-2* or *NEC-4*.

Other Differences

Here are two other differences between *NEC-2* and *NEC-4* that should be kept in mind while modeling. Quoting from the *EZNEC* Help documentation, "*NEC* has some difficulty in accurately modeling multiple wires joining at a very acute angle, such as with a 'fan' antenna, the difficulty being greater with *NEC-2* than with *NEC-4*."

Similarly, quoting from the *NEC-4.2* User's Manual, "The size of the segments determines the resolution in solving for the current on the model, since the current is computed at the center of each segment. Earlier versions of *NEC* suffered a loss of precision or complete failure of the solution when very short segments were used, but this problem has been corrected in *NEC-4*. The extremely short segments can be used with *NEC-4*, subject to limitations related to the wire radius as discussed below."

Geometry and Segmentation Checks

NEC models are built out of wires. Wires are divided into segments. The number of segments on a wire is specified by the modeler. The number of segments on a wire is an important factor in determining the accuracy of the results as well as the time it takes to run the model.

Segments are like the story of Goldilocks and the Three Bears — you do not want to use too few or too many segments. There are many trade-offs in determining the best number of segments to use.

1. Reducing the number of segments speeds up the *NEC* engine. Past some point, accuracy suffers because the model becomes too coarse.

2. Increasing the number of segments slows down the *NEC* engine. The maximum number of allowed segments may be limited by the modeling package. At some point, too many segments can reduce the accuracy of the results. This is especially true with *NEC-2*. Blindly using more segments is not a solution.

3. There are situations where it's desirable to align segments between closely-spaced wires.

Fortunately the programs that drive the *NEC* engines

include a number of checks that follow the *NEC* segmentation guidelines. You should observe their warnings related to the segment count. It is also possible to have the program automatically segment the wires in a model.

If there is any concern about the number of segments being used, you should perform segment convergence testing. The idea is to run a model, note the results (SWR, impedance, gain, F/B, and so on), change the number of segments, and run it again. As you move from too few toward too many segments, the results should converge. Once they do, there is little point in increasing the number of segments. If you notice that the results are very sensitive to segmentation, then it may signal a model that challenges the *NEC* engines, and might have less trustworthy results. *4nec2* has a convergence test option that automates much of the process. Getting segmentation correct is more important with *NEC-2* than *NEC-4*.

In addition to the material here, an additional tutorial on antenna modeling using *EZNEC* has been contributed by Greg Ordy, W8WWV and is included with this book's downloadable supplemental information. It features alternate perspectives on topics in this chapter and covers additional material in depth. The tutorial was originally presented in support of a presentation at Contest University in 2011.

8.2 THE BASICS OF ANTENNA MODELING

This chapter will discuss the following antenna-modeling topics for *NEC-2*-based modeling software, using *EZNEC* as an example:

- Program outputs
- Wire geometry
- Segmentation, warnings and limitations
- Source (feed point) placement
- Environment, including ground types and frequency
- Loads and transmission lines
- Testing the adequacy of a model

While *EZNEC* is very popular among amateurs, two other programs also based on *NEC-2* are available and widely used. *4nec2* is a free application by Arie Voors that offers a graphical interface for design and a 3-D color radiation pattern display many find useful. For Apple Macintosh users, Kok Chen, W7AY, has published *cocoaNEC 2.0*. Both can use the *NEC-4* engine, assuming licensing permission has been obtained. See the Reference section of this chapter for more modeling software and links to the websites for these and other programs. Actively supported programs such as *4nec2* also offer tutorials via the website and user groups may also be available online to help with questions and share model files.

8.2.1 PROGRAM OUTPUTS

Instruction manuals for software programs traditionally start out describing in detail the input data needed by the program. They then demonstrate the output data the program can generate. We feel it is instructive, however, to turn things around and start out with a brief overview of the output from a typical antenna-modeling program.

We'll look at the output from public-domain *NEC-2*. Next, we'll look at the output information available from commercial adaptations of *NEC-2*, using *EZNEC* as an example. (From now on in this chapter we'll refer merely to *EZNEC* rather than *EZNEC 6.0*, the official name, or the *EZNEC* demo version. Both programs function identically.) After this brief overview of the output data, we'll look in detail at the input data needed to make a modeling program work. In the following discussions it will be very instructive if you to bring up *EZNEC* on your computer and open the specific modeling files used in each example.

Native *NEC-2*

Native *NEC-2* was written in the Fortran language, which stands for *Formula Translation*. The original program used Hollerith punch-cards to enter the program and input data. The output of the program was raw numeric data printed on many sheets of paper. Commercial software that uses the *NEC-2* computational core algorithms shields provides much easier methods of entering antenna design information and generates graphic output that is much easier to understand. Numerical tables are provided where they are useful, such as for source impedance and SWR at a single frequency, or the characteristics of a load or a transmission line. *EZNEC* produces the following types of graphs:

- Polar (linear-dB or ARRL-style) graphs of the far-field elevation and azimuth responses.
- 3-D wire-frame graph of the total far-field response.
- Graph of the SWR across a frequency band.
- Graphical display of the RF currents on various conductors in a model.
- Rotatable, zoom-able 3-D views of the wires used to make a model.
- Output to programs capable of generating Smith charts and performing other analysis

Figure 8.1 shows the computed far-field 2-D elevation and azimuth patterns for a 135-foot long horizontal dipole, mounted in a flattop configuration 50 feet above flat ground.

These figures were generated using *EZNEC* at 3.75 MHz. Figure 8.1C shows a 3-D wire-frame picture of the far-field response, but this time at 14.2 MHz.

Figure 8.2 shows the computed SWR curve over the frequency range 3.0 to 4.0 MHz for this dipole, fed with lossless 50-Ω transmission line. *EZNEC* generated this plot using the "SWR" button. Figures 8.1 and 8.2 are typical of the kind of graphical outputs that commercial implementations of the *NEC-2* computing core can produce — a vast improvement over tables of numbers from a mainframe computer's line printer! Now, let's get into the details of what kind of input data is required to run a typical method-of-moments antenna-modeling program.

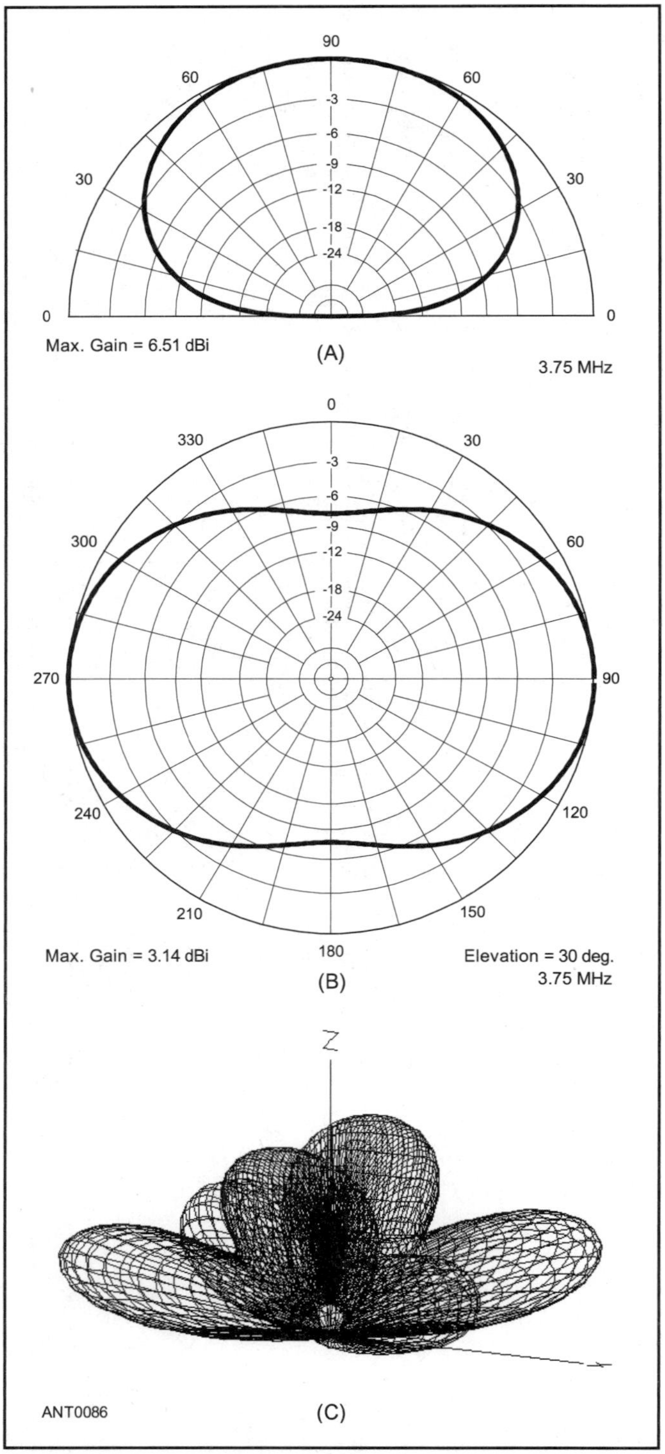

Figure 8.1 — At A, far-field elevation-plane pattern for a 135- foot-long horizontal dipole, 50 feet above flat ground, at 3.5 MHz. At B, the far-field azimuth-plane pattern at an elevation angle of 30°.

8.2.2 PROGRAM INPUTS: WIRE GEOMETRY

Coordinates in an X, Y and Z World

The most difficult part of using a *NEC*-type of modeling program is setting up the antenna's geometry — you must condition yourself to think in three-dimensional, Cartesian coordinates. Each end point of a wire is represented by three numbers: an x, y and z coordinate. These coordinates represent the distance from the origin (x-axis), the width of an antenna (y-axis), and the height (z-axis).

An example should help sort things out. **Figure 8.3** shows a simple model of a 135-foot center-fed dipole, made of #14 copper wire placed 50 feet above flat ground. The common term for this antenna is "flattop dipole." For convenience, the ground is located at the origin of the coordinate system, at (0, 0, 0) feet, directly under the center of the dipole. **Figure 8.4** shows the *EZNEC* spreadsheet-like input data for this antenna. (Use model file: **Ch8-Flattop Dipole.EZ.**) *EZNEC* allows you to specify the type of conductor material from its main window, using the WIRE LOSS button to open a new window. We will click on the COPPER button for this dipole.

Above the origin, at a height of 50 feet on the z-axis, is the dipole's *feed point*, called a *source* in *NEC* terminology. The width of the dipole goes toward the left (that is, in the "negative-y" direction) one-half the overall length of 135 feet, or –67.5 feet. Toward the right, our dipole's other end is at +67.5 feet. The x-axis dimension of our dipole is zero, meaning that the dipole wire is parallel to and directly

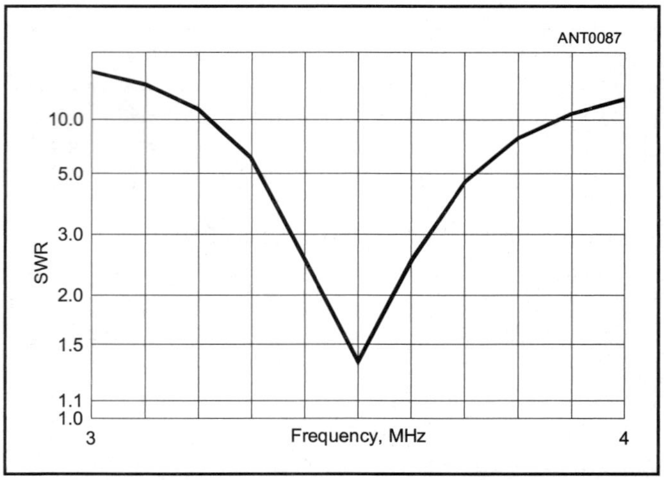

Figure 8.2 — SWR curve for 135-foot flattop dipole over the frequency range 3.0 to 4.0 MHz for a 50-Ω feed line. This antenna is an example and is not optimized for the amateur band.

above the x-axis. The dipole's ends are thus represented by two points, whose coordinates are (0, –67.5, 50) and (0, 67.5, 50) feet. The use of parentheses with a sequential listing of (x, y, z) coordinates is a common practice among antenna modelers to describe a wire end point.

Figure 8.3B includes some other useful information about this antenna beyond the wire geometry. Figure 8.3B overlays the wire geometry, the current distribution along the wire and the far-field azimuth response, in this case at an elevation angle of 30°.

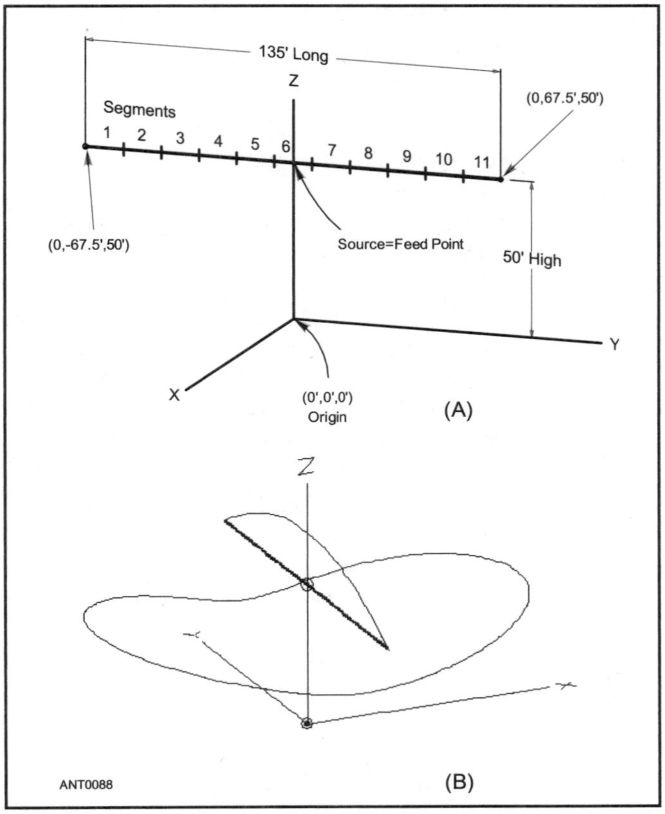

Figure 8.3 — At A, simple model for a 135-foot long horizontal dipole, 50 feet above the ground. The dipole is over the y-axis. The wire has been segmented into 11 segments, with the center of segment number 6 as the feed point. The left-hand end of the antenna is –67.5 feet from the center feed point and that the right-hand end is at 67.5 feet from the center. At B, *EZNEC* "View Antenna" screen, showing geometry of wire and the x, y and z axes. Overlaid on the wire geometry drawing are the current distribution along the wire and the far-field azimuthal response at an elevation angle of 30°.

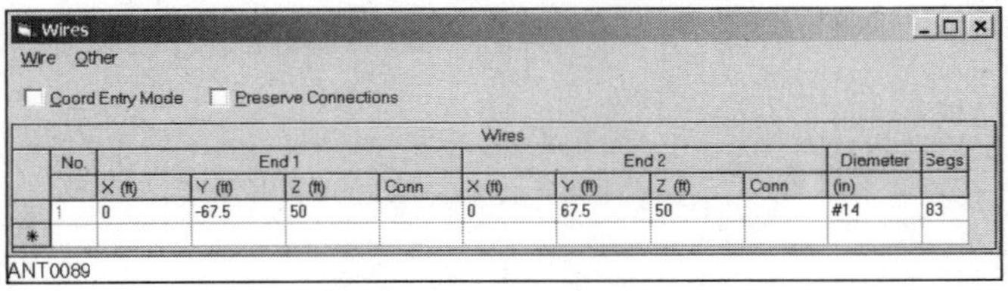

Figure 8.4 — *EZNEC* "View Wires" data entry screen for simple flattop dipole in Figure 8.3. The numbers shown are in feet, except for the wire diameter, which *EZNEC* allows you to specify as an AWG gauge, in this case #14. Note that 83 segments have been specified for this antenna for analysis over the range from 3.5 to 29.7 MHz.

Although not shown specifically in Figure 8.3, the thickness of the antenna is the diameter of the wire, #14 AWG. Note that native *NEC* programs specify the *radius* of the wire, rather than the diameter, but programs like *EZNEC* use the more intuitive diameter of a wire rather than the radius. *EZNEC* (and other commercial programs) also allows the user to specify the wire as an AWG gauge, such as #14 or #22, for example.

We've represented our simple dipole in Figure 8.3 using a single, straight wire. In fact, all antenna models created for method-of-moments programs are made of combinations of straight wires. This includes even complex antennas, such as helical antennas or round loops. (The mathematical basis for modeling complex antennas is that they can be simulated using straight-wire polygons. A circular loop, for example, can be modeled using an octagon.)

Segmentation and Specifying a Source Segment

We've specified the physical geometry of this simple one-wire dipole. Now several more modeling details surface — you must specify the number of *segments* into which the dipole is divided for the method-of-moments analysis and you must somehow feed the antenna. The *NEC-2* guideline for setting the number of segments is to use at least 10 segments per half-wavelength. This is a general rule of thumb, however, and in many models more dense segmentation is mandatory for good accuracy.

In Figure 8.3, we've specified that the dipole be divided into 11 segments for operation on the 80 meter band. This follows the rule of thumb above, since the 135-foot dipole is about one half-wavelength long at 3.5 MHz.

Setting the Source Segment

The use of 11 segments, an odd rather than an even number such as 10, places the dipole's feed point (a feed point is referred to as a *source* in *NEC*-speak, a word choice that can befuddle beginners) right at the antenna's center, at the center of segment number six. In concert with the "EZ" in its name, *EZNEC* makes choosing the source segment easy by allowing the user to specify a percentage along the wire, in this case 50% centers the source in the middle of the segment.

At this point you may very well be wondering why no center insulator is shown in the middle of our center-fed dipole. After all, a real dipole would have a center insulator. However, method-of-moments programs assume that a source generator is placed across an infinitely small gap in the antenna wire. While this is convenient from a mathematical point of view, the unstated use of such an infinitely small gap often confuses newcomers to the world of antenna modeling. We'll get into more details, caveats and limitations in source placement later in this chapter. For now, just trust that the model we've just described with 11 segments, fed at segment 6, will work well over the entire amateur band from 3.5 to 4.0 MHz.

Now, let's consider what would happen if we want to use our 135-foot long dipole on all HF amateur bands from 3.5 to 29.7 MHz, rather than just from 3.5 to 4.0 MHz. Instead of feeding such an antenna with coax cable, we would feed it with open-wire line and use an antenna tuner in the shack to create a 50-Ω load for the transmitter. To comply with the segmentation rule above, the number of segments used in the model should vary with frequency — or at least be segmented at or above the minimum recommended level at the highest frequency used. This is because a half-wavelength at 29.7 MHz is 16.6 feet, while a half-wavelength at 3.5 MHz is 140.6 feet. So the number of segments for proper operation on 29.7 MHz should be 10 × 135/16.6 = 81. We'll be a little more conservative than the minimum requirement and specify 83 segments. Figure 8.4 shows the *EZNEC* input spreadsheet for this model. (Use model file: **Ch8-Multiband Dipole.EZ**.)

The penalty for using more segments in a program like *NEC* is that the program slows down roughly as the square of the segments — double the number of segments and the speed drops by a factor of four (two squared). Using too few segments will result in inaccuracies, particularly in computing the feed point impedance. We'll delve into the area of segmentation density in more detail later when we discuss testing the adequacy of a model.

Segment Length-to-Wire-Diameter Ratio

Even if you're willing to live with the slowdown in computing speed for situations involving a large number of wire segments, you should make sure the ratio between the segment length and the diameter of any wire is greater than 1:1. This is to say that the length of each segment should be longer than the diameter of the wire to avoid internal limitations in the *NEC* program.

For the #14 wire specified in this simple 135-foot long dipole, it's pretty unlikely that you'll bump up against this limitation for any reasonable level of segmentation. After all, #14 wire has a diameter of 0.064 inch and 135 feet is 1620 inches. To stay above a segment length of 0.064 inch, the maximum number of segments is 1620/0.064 = 25,312. This is a very large number of segments and it would take a very long time to compute, assuming that your program can handle that many segments.

Staying above a 1:1 ratio in segment length to wire diameter can be more challenging at VHF/UHF frequencies, however. This is particularly true for fairly large "wires" made of aluminum tubing. Incidentally, this is another point where newcomers to antenna modeling can be led astray by the terminology. In a *NEC*-type program, all conductors in a model are considered to be wires, even if they consist of hollow aluminum or copper tubes. The skin effect keeps the RF current in any conductor confined to the outer surface of that conductor, and thus it doesn't matter whether the conductor is hollow or solid, or even a number of wire strands twisted together.

Let's look at a half-wave dipole at 420 MHz. This would be about 14.1 inches long. If you use ¼-inch diameter tubing for this dipole, the maximum segment length meeting the 1:1 diameter-to-length ratio requirement is also ¼ inch long. The maximum number of segments then would be 14.1/0.25 = 56.4, rounded down to 56. From this discussion you should now understand why method-of-moments programs are known for using a "thin-wire approximation." Really fat conductors can get you into trouble, particularly at VHF/UHF.

Some Caveats and Limitations Concerning Geometry

Example: Inverted-V Dipole

Now, let's get a little more complicated and specify another 135-foot-long dipole, but this time configured as an inverted V. As shown in **Figure 8.5**, you must now specify two wires. The two wires join at the top, at (0, 0, 50) feet. (Again, the program doesn't use a center insulator in the model.)

If you are using a native version of *NEC*, you may have to go back to your high-school trigonometry book to figure out how to specify the end points of our "droopy" dipole, with its 120° included angle. Figure 8.5 shows the details, along with the trigonometric equations needed. *EZNEC* is indeed more "easy" here since it allows you to tilt the ends of each wire downward an appropriate number of degrees (in this case –30° at each end of the dipole) to automatically create an inverted-V configuration. **Figure 8.6A** shows the *EZNEC* spreadsheet describing this inverted-V dipole with a 120° included angle between the two wires.

See the *EZNEC* HELP section under "Wire Coordinate Shortcuts" for specific instructions on how to use the "elevation rotate end" shortcut "RE-30" to create the sloping wires easily by rotating the end of the wire down 30°. Now the specification of the source becomes a bit more complicated. The easiest way is to specify two sources, one on each end segment at the junction of the two wires. *EZNEC* does this automatically if you specify a so-called *split-source* feed. Figure 8.6B shows the two sources as two open circles at the top ends of the two wires making up the inverted-V dipole.

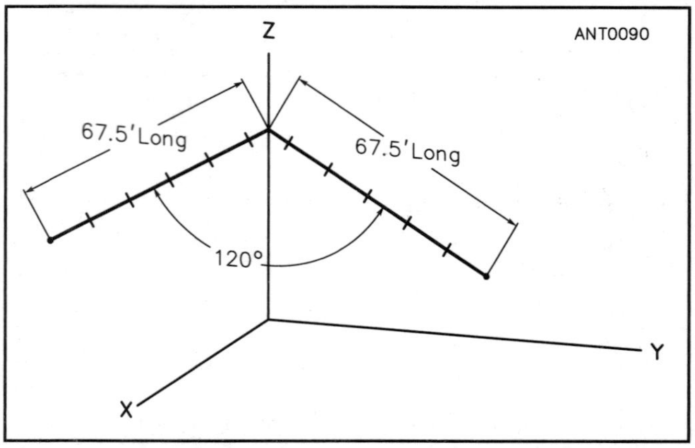

Figure 8.5 — Model for an inverted-V dipole with an included angle between the two legs of 120° apex at 50' high. Sine and cosine functions are used to describe the heights of the end points for the sloping arms of the antenna.

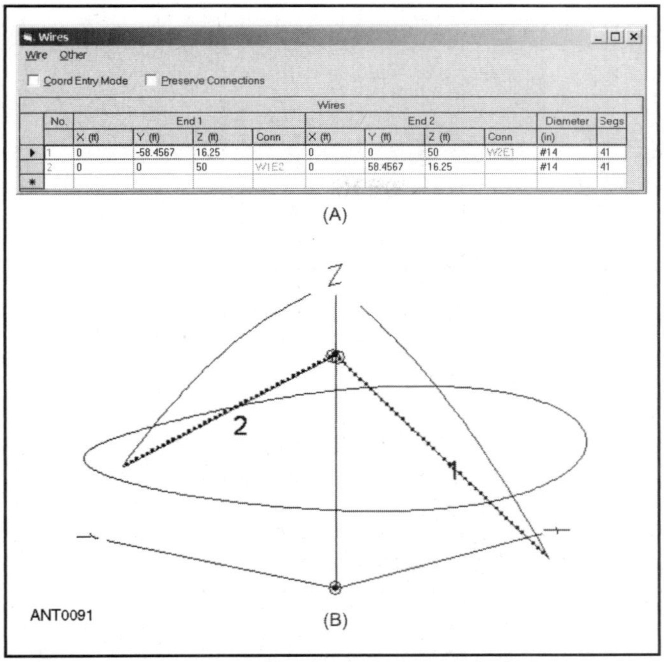

	Wires									
No.	End 1				End 2				Diameter	Segs
	X (ft)	Y (ft)	Z (ft)	Conn	X (ft)	Y (ft)	Z (ft)	Conn	(in)	
1	0	-58.4567	16.25		0	0	50	W2E1	#14	41
2	0	0	50	W1E2	0	58.4567	16.25		#14	41
*										

Figure 8.6 — At A, *EZNEC* "View Wires" data entry screen for inverted-V dipole in Figure 8.5. Now the ends of the inverted-V dipole are 16.25 feet above ground, instead of 50 feet for the flattop dipole. At B, *EZNEC* "View Antenna" screen, with overlay of geometry, current distribution and azimuth plot.

What *EZNEC* is doing is creating two sources, one in each of the segments immediately on either side of the junction of the two wires. *EZNEC* sums up the two source impedances to provide a single result.

Navigating in the View Antenna Window

At this point it's worthwhile to explore some of the ways you can look at the antenna you've designed using the *EZNEC* VIEW ANT button on the main window. Bring up the file **Ch8-Inverted V Dipole.EZ** in *EZNEC*, and click on the VIEW ANT button. You will see a small inverted-V dipole raised over the (0, 0, 0) origin on the ground directly under the feed point of the inverted-V dipole. First, "rotate" the dipole by holding down the left-mouse button and moving the mouse. You can orient the picture any way you wish.

Let's take a closer look at the junction of the two wires at the feed point. Click the CENTER ANT IMAGE checkbox toward the bottom of the window to anchor the center of the image at the center of the window, then move the *Zoom* slider upward to zoom in on the image. At some point the junction of the two slanted wires will move up beyond the edge of the window, so you will need to click on the left-hand side of the Z MOVE IMAGE slider to bring the junction back into view. You should be able to see a zoomed view of the junction along with the two open circles that represent the location of the split sources in the middle of the segments adjacent to the wire junction.

Place the mouse cursor over one of the slanted wires and double click the left-mouse button. *EZNEC* will now identify that wire and show its length, as well as the length of each segment on that wire. Pretty slick, isn't it?

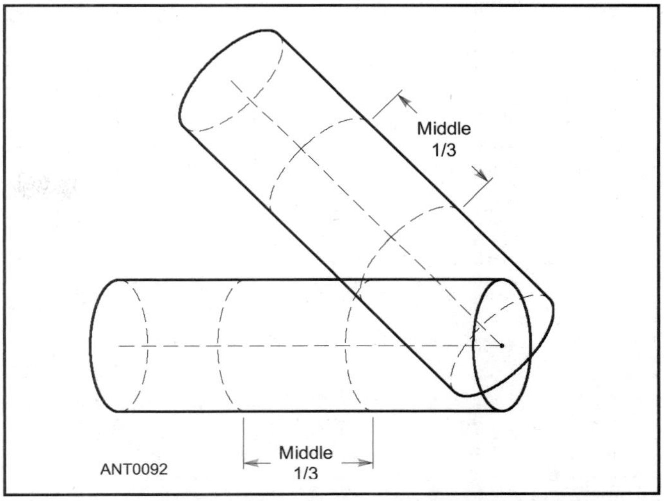

Figure 8.7 — A junction of two short, fat wire segments at an acute angle. This results in inter-penetration of the two wire volumes beyond the middle-⅓ recommended limit.

Short, Fat Wires and the Acute-Angle Junction

Another possible complication can arise for wires with short, fat segments, particularly ones that have only a small included angle between them. These wire segments can end up inter-penetrating within each other's volumes, leading to problems in a model. Once you think of each wire segment as a thick cylinder, you can appreciate the difficulty in connecting two wires together at their ends. The two wires always inter-penetrate each other's volume to some extent. **Figure 8.7** depicts this problem graphically for two short, fat wires joined at their ends at an acute angle. A rule of thumb is to avoid creating junctions where more than ⅓ of the wire volumes inter-penetrate. You can achieve this by using longer segment lengths or thinner wire diameters.

Some Other Practical Antenna Geometries

A Vertical Half-Wave Dipole

If you turn the 135-foot-long horizontal dipole in Figure 8.1 on its end you will create a vertical half-wave dipole that is above the origin of the x, y and z axes. See **Figure 8.8**, where the bottom end of the dipole is placed 8 feet off the ground to keep it away from humans and animals at (0, 0, 8) feet. The top end is thus at 8 + 135 = 143 feet off the ground at (0, 0, 143). Figure 8.8 also shows the current distribution and the elevation pattern for this antenna. (Use *EZNEC* model file: **Ch8-Vertical Dipole.EZ**.)

A Ground-Plane Antenna

The ground-plane model is more complicated than previous ones because a total of five wires are now needed: one for

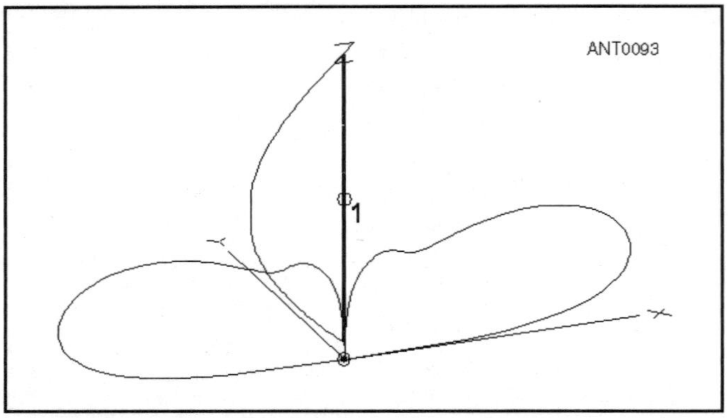

Figure 8.8 — A vertical half-wave dipole, created by turning the dipole in Figure 8.3 on its end, with a minimum height at the lower end of 8 feet to keep the antenna away from people and animals. The current distribution and the elevation pattern for this antenna are also shown overlaid on the wire geometry.

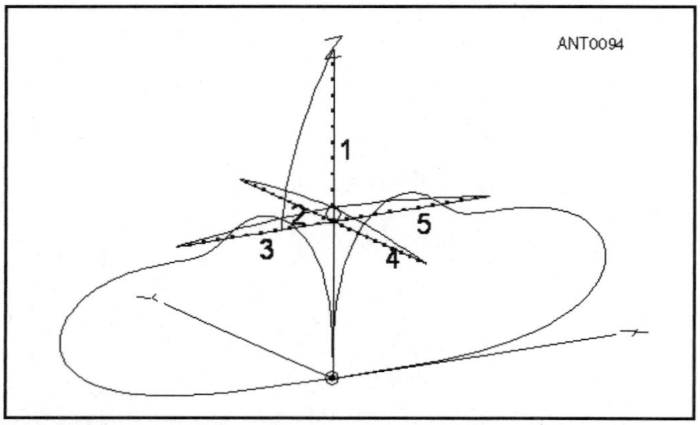

Figure 8.9 — A vertical ground-plane antenna. The radials and the bottom of the vertical radiator are located 15 feet off the ground in this model. The current distribution along each wire and the far-field elevation-plane pattern are overlaid on the antenna geometry.

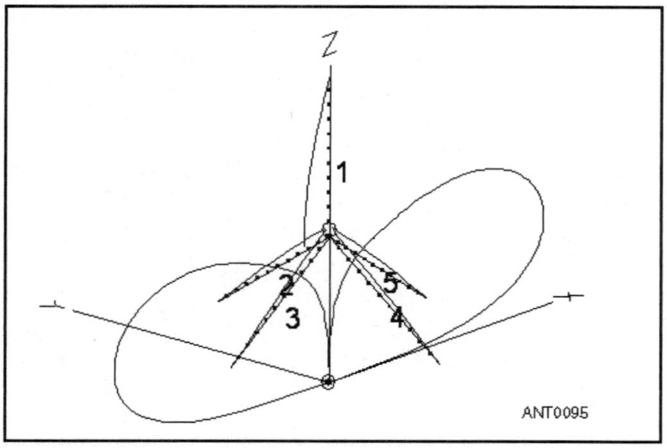

Figure 8.10 — *EZNEC* "View Antenna" screen for the ground-plane antenna with its four radials tilted downward by 40° to improve the SWR at the feed point.

Table 8.1

520-40W.YW, using #14 AWG wire from 520-40H.YW
14.000 14.174 14.350 MHz

5 elements	inches
Spacing	.064
0.000	210.923
72.000	200.941
72.000	199.600
139.000	197.502
191.000	190.536

the vertical radiator and four for the radials. **Figure 8.9** shows the *EZNEC* view for a 20 meter ground plane mounted 15 feet off the ground (perhaps on a garage roof), with the overlay of both the current distribution and the elevation-plane plot. (Use *EZNEC* model file: **Ch8-GP.EZ.**) Note that the source has been placed at the bottom segment of the vertical radiator. Once again, the program needs no bottom insulator since all five wires are connected together at a common point. *EZNEC* reports that this antenna has a resonant feed-point impedance of about 22 Ω, which would show an SWR of 2.3:1 for a 50-Ω coax feed line if no matching system is used, such as a gamma or hairpin match.

Figure 8.10 shows the same antenna, except that the radials have now been tilted downward by 35° to raise the feed point impedance to present an almost perfect 50-Ω match (SWR = 1.08:1). In addition, the length of the radiator in this model was shortened by 6 inches to re-resonate the antenna. (Use *EZNEC* model file: **Ch8-Modified GP.EZ.**) The trick of tilting the radials downward for a ground-plane antenna is an old one, and the modeling programs validates what hams have been doing for years.

A 5-Element Horizontal Yagi

This is a little more challenging modeling exercise. Let's use a 5-element design on a 40-foot boom, but rather than using telescoping aluminum tubing for the elements, we'll use #14 wire. The *SCALE* program (available for download from **www.arrl.org/antenna-book**) converted the aluminum-tubing 520-40.YW to a design using #14 copper wire. **Table 8.1** shows the element lineup for this antenna. (Later in this chapter we'll see what happens when telescoping aluminum tubing is used in a real-world Yagi design.)

Some explanations of what Table 8.1 means are in order. First, only one half of each element is shown. The *YW* program (*Yagi for Windows*), included with this book's downloadable supplemental information, computes the other half of the Yagi automatically, essentially mirroring the other half on the opposite side of the boom. Having to enter the dimensions for only half of a real-world Yagi element that uses telescoping aluminum tubing is much easier this way.

Second, the placement of the elements along the boom starts at 0.0 inches for the reflector. The distance between adjacent elements defined in this particular file is the spacing between the element itself and the element just before

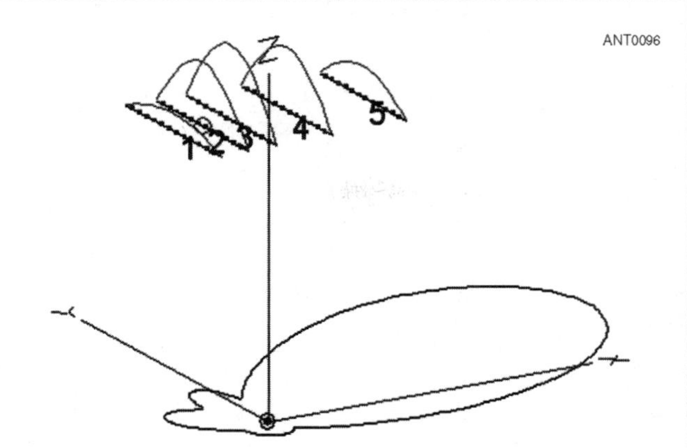

(A)

Wires

Wire Other

Coord Entry Mode Preserve Connections

	No.	End 1				End 2				Diameter	Segs
		X (in)	Y (in)	Z (in)	Conn	X (in)	Y (in)	Z (in)	Conn	(in)	
▶	1	-237.188	-210.923	720		-237.188	210.923	720		0.064	13
	2	-165.188	-200.941	720		-165.188	200.941	720		0.064	13
	3	-93.188	-199.6	720		-93.188	199.6	720		0.064	13
	4	45.812	-197.502	720		45.812	197.502	720		0.064	13
	5	236.812	-190.536	720		236.812	190.536	720		0.064	13
*											

(B)

Figure 8.11 — At A, geometry for 5-element Yagi on a 40-foot boom, mounted 720 inches (60 feet) above flat ground, with an overlay of current and the azimuth pattern. At B, *EZNEC* "View Wires" screen for this antenna. This design uses #14 wire for simplicity.

it. For example, the spacing between the driven element and the reflector is 72 inches and the spacing between the first director and the driven element is also 72 inches. The spacing between the second director and the first director is 139 inches.

Figure 8.11A shows the wire geometry for this Yagi array when it is mounted 720 inches (60 feet) above flat ground and Figure 8.11B shows the *EZNEC* Wires spreadsheet that describes the coordinates. (Use *EZNEC* model file: **Ch8-520-40W.EZ.**) You can see that the x-axis coordinates for the elements have been automatically moved by the *SCALE* program so that the center of the boom is located directly above the origin. This makes it easier to evaluate the effects of stacking different monoband Yagis on a rotating mast in a typical "Christmas Tree" arrangement, such as 20, 15 and 10 meter monobanders on a single rotating mast sticking out of the top of the tower.

Figure 8.12 shows the computed azimuth pattern for this Yagi at 14.175 MHz, at an elevation angle of 15°, the angle at which the peak of the forward lobe occurs for this height above flat ground. The antenna exhibits excellent gain at 13.1 dBi, as well as a clean pattern behind the main lobe. The worst-case front-to-rear ratio at any point from 90° to 270° in azimuth is better than 23 dB. *EZNEC* says the feed point impedance is 25 – *j* 23 Ω, just the right impedance suited for a simple hairpin or gamma match.

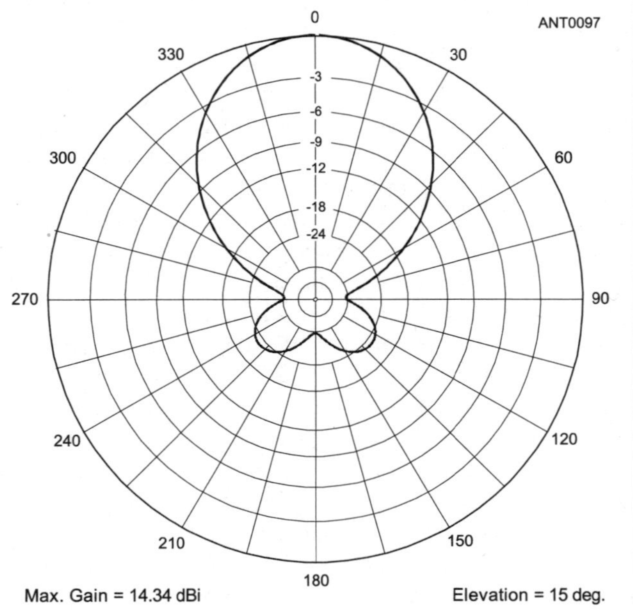

Figure 8.12 — *EZNEC* azimuth-plane pattern at an elevation angle of 15° for #14 AWG wire Yagi described in Figure 8.11.

A Monoband 2-Element Quad

Unlike a Yagi, with its elements existing only in the x-y plane, a quad type of beam is a three-dimensional antenna. A quad loop has height in the z-axis, as well as width and length in the x-y plane. Each individual loop for a monoband quad consists of four wires, joined together at the corners. **Figure 8.13** shows the coordinates for a 2-element 15-meter quad, consisting of a reflector and a driven element on a 10-foot boom.

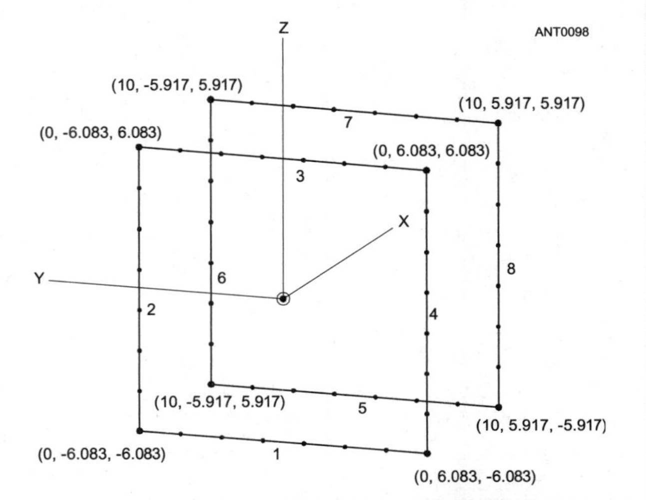

Figure 8.13 — Wire geometry for a 2-element quad, with a reflector and driven element. The x-axis is the axis of symmetry for this free-space model.

Wires

Wire Other

Coord Entry Mode   Preserve Connections

No.	End 1				End 2				Diameter	Segs
	X (ft)	Y (ft)	Z (ft)	Conn	X (ft)	Y (ft)	Z (ft)	Conn	(in)	
1	0	-6.083	-6.083	W4E2	0	6.083	-6.083	W2E1	#12	7
2	0	6.083	-6.083	W1E2	0	6.083	6.083	W3E1	#12	7
3	0	6.083	6.083	W2E2	0	-6.083	6.083	W4E1	#12	7
4	0	-6.083	6.083	W3E2	0	-6.083	-6.083	W1E1	#12	7
5	10	-5.917	-5.917	W8E2	10	5.917	-5.917	W6E1	#12	7
6	10	5.917	-5.917	W5E2	10	5.917	5.917	W7E1	#12	7
7	10	5.917	5.917	W6E2	10	-5.917	5.917	W8E1	#12	7
8	10	-5.917	5.917	W7E2	10	-5.917	-5.917	W5E1	#12	7

ANT0099

Figure 8.14 — *EZNEC* "View Wires" screen showing the coordinates used for the quad in Figure 8.13. Note how the x-axis describes the position of an element on the 10-foot boom and also is the axis of symmetry for each element. The values for the z-axis and y-axis vary above and below the axis of symmetry.

You can see that the axis of symmetry, the x-axis, runs down the center of this model, meaning that the origin of this particular x, y and z-coordinate scheme is in the center of the reflector. The (0, 0, 0) origin is placed this way for convenience in assigning corner coordinates for each element. For actual placement of the antenna at a particular height above real ground, the heights of all z-axis coordinates are changed accordingly. *EZNEC* has a convenient built-in function to change the height of all wires at a single stroke.

Figure 8.14 shows the input *EZNEC* spreadsheet for this quad in free space, clearly showing the symmetrical nature of the corner coordinates. (Use *EZNEC* model file: **Ch8-Quad.EZ.**) This is a good place to emphasize that you should enter the wire coordinates in a logical sequence. The most obvious example in this particular model is that you should group all the wires associated with a particular element together — for example, the four wires associated with the reflector should be in one place. In Figure 8.14 you can see that all four wires with an x-coordinate of zero represent the reflector.

It's best to follow a convention in entering wires in a loop structure in a logical fashion. The easiest way is to connect the end point of one wire to the starting point of the next wire. For example, in Figure 8.13 you can see that the left-hand end of Wire 1 is connected to the bottom of Wire 2, and that the top of Wire 2 connects to the left-hand end of Wire 3. In turn, Wire 3 connects to the top of Wire 4, whose bottom end connects to the right-hand end of Wire 1. The pattern is known as "going around the horn" meaning that the connections proceed smoothly in one direction, in this case in a clockwise direction.

You can see that the entry for the wires making up the elements in the 5-element Yagi in Figure 8.11B also proceeded in an orderly fashion by starting with the reflector, then the driven element, then director 1, then director 2 and finally director 3. This doesn't mean that you couldn't mix things up, say by specifying the driven element first, followed by director 3, and then the reflector, or whatever. But it's a pretty good bet that doing so in this quasi-random fashion will result in some confusion later on when you revisit a model, or when you let another person use or review your model.

8.2.3 THE MODELING ENVIRONMENT

The Ground

Above, when considering the 135-foot dipole mounted 50 feet above flat earth, we briefly mentioned the most important environmental item in an antenna model — the ground beneath it. Let's examine some of the options available in the *NEC-2* environment in *EZNEC*:

- Free space
- Perfect ground
- *MININEC* type ground
- "Fast" type ground
- Sommerfeld-Norton ground.

The free space environment option is pretty self-explanatory — the antenna model is placed in free space away from the influence of any type of ground. This option is useful when you wish to optimize certain characteristics of a particular antenna design. For example, you might wish to optimize the front-to-rear ratio of a Yagi over an entire amateur band and this might entail many calculation runs. The free-space option will run the fastest because there is no ground interaction to compute.

Perfect ground is useful as a reference case, especially for vertically polarized antennas over real ground. Antenna evaluations over perfect ground are shown in most classical antenna textbooks, so it is useful to compare models for simple antennas over perfect ground to those textbook cases.

MININEC type ground is useful when modeling vertical wires, or horizontal wires that are higher than 0.2 λ above ground. A *MININEC* type ground will compute faster than either a "Fast" ground or a Sommerfeld-Norton type of ground because it assumes that the ground under the antenna is perfect, while still taking into account the far-field reflections for ground using user-specified values of ground conductivity and dielectric constant. The fact that the ground under the antenna is treated as perfect allows the *NEC-2* user of a *MININEC* type ground to specify wires that touch (but don't go below) the ground surface, something that only users of the advanced *NEC-4* program can do with the more accurate Sommerfeld-Norton type of ground described below. (*NEC-4* is presently not in the public domain. Software based on *NEC-4*, such as *EZNEC-PRO*, requires an additional license from the copyright holder — the US government. See the section Comparing *NEC-2* to *NEC-4* at the beginning of this chapter.) The ability to model grounded wires is useful with vertical antennas. The modeler must be wary of the feed-point source impedances reported for either horizontally or vertically polarized wires because of the perfect-ground assumption inherent in a *MININEC*-type ground.

The "Fast" type of ground is a hybrid type of ground that makes certain simplifying assumptions to speed up calculations, provided that horizontal wires are higher than about 0.1 λ above ground. With today's high-speed computers, the simplifications are no longer required and the Sommerfeld-Norton model is preferred.

The Sommerfeld-Norton ground (referred to in *EZNEC* as "High Accuracy" ground) is preferable to the other ground models because it has essentially no practical limitations for wire height. It has the disadvantage that it runs about four times slower than a *MININEC* type of ground but today's fast computers make that almost a non-issue. Again, *NEC-2*-based programs cannot model wires that penetrate into the ground (although there are workarounds described below).

As mentioned above, for any type of ground other than perfect ground or free space the user must specify the conductivity and dielectric constant of the soil. (See the section "Ground Parameters for Antenna Analysis" in the chapter **The Effects of Ground**.) *EZNEC* allows selection of several user-friendly categories, where σ is conductivity in siemens/meter and ε is dielectric constant:

- Extremely poor: cities, high buildings (σ = 0.001, ε = 3)
- Very Poor: cities, industrial (σ = 0.001, ε = 5)
- Sandy, dry (σ = 0.002, ε = 10)
- Poor: rocky, mountainous (σ = 0.002, ε = 13)
- Average: pastoral, heavy clay (σ = 0.005, ε = 13)
- Pastoral: medium hills and forestation (σ = 0.006, ε = 13)
- Flat, marshy, densely wooded (σ = 0.0075, ε = 12)
- Pastoral, rich soil, US Midwest (σ = 0.010, ε = 14)
- Very Good: pastoral, rich, central US (σ = 0.0303, ε = 20)
- Fresh water (σ = 0.001, ε = 80)
- Saltwater (σ = 5, ε = 80)

Let's use *EZNEC*'s ability to overlay one or more plots together on one graph to compare the response of the vertical ground plane antenna in Figure 8.9 for two different types of ground: Saltwater and Poor. Open the **Ch8-GP.EZ** file in *EZNEC*. Click the GROUND DESCRIP button and then right-click anywhere in the Media window that opens up. Choose first the "Poor: rocky, mountainous" option button, click OK and then FF PLOT. When the elevation plot appears, click the File menu at the top of the main window, and then SAVE AS. Choose an appropriate name for the trace, perhaps "Poor Gnd. PF."

Go back and select saltwater using GROUND DESCRIP and follow the same procedure to compute the far-field plot for saltwater ground. Now, add the Poor Gnd.PF trace, by clicking menu selection FILE, ADD TRACE. **Figure 8.15** shows this comparison, which greatly favors the saltwater environment, particularly at low elevation angles. At 5° the ground plane mounted over saltwater has about a 10 dB advantage compared to its landlocked cousin.

You might be wondering what happens if we move the ground-plane antenna down closer to the ground. The lower limit to how closely radials may approach lossy ground is 0.001 λ or twice the diameter of the radial wire. A distance of 0.001 λ is about 6 inches at 1.8 MHz and 0.4 inch at 30 MHz. While *NEC-2*-based programs cannot model wires that penetrate the ground, radial systems just above the ground with more than about eight radial wires can provide a work-around to simulate a direct-ground connection.

Modeling Environment: Frequency

It's always a good idea to evaluate an antenna over a range of frequencies, rather than simply at a single spot frequency.

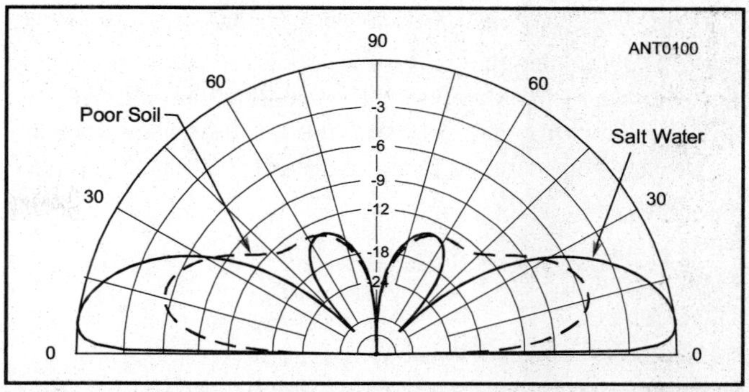

Figure 8.15 — A comparison of the elevation response for the vertical ground plane in Figure 8.9 over saltwater and over "poor: rocky, mountainous" soil. Saltwater works wonders for verticals, providing excellent low-angle signals.

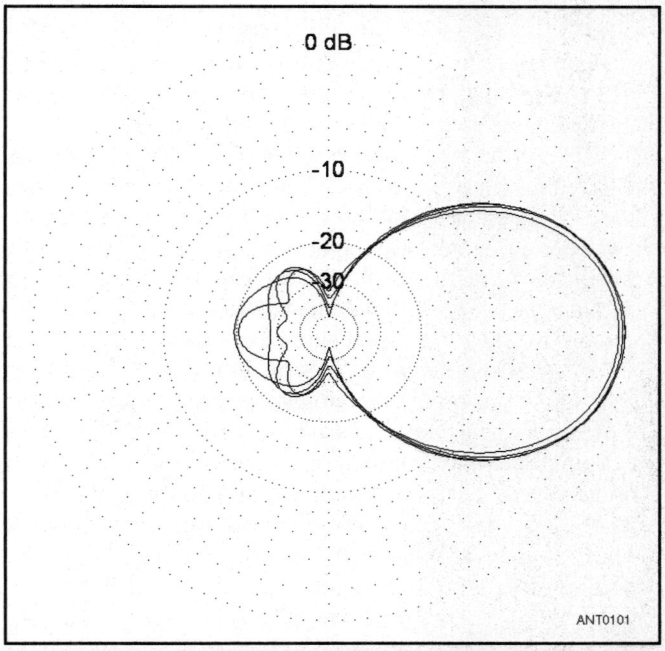

Figure 8.16 — Frequency sweep of 5-element Yagi described in Figure 8.11, showing how the azimuth pattern changes with frequency.

Trends that become quite apparent on a frequency sweep are often lost when looking simply at a single frequency. Native *NEC-2* has built-in frequency sweep capabilities but once again the commercial programs make the process easier to use and understand. You saw in the SWR curve of Figure 8.2 the result of one such frequency sweep using *EZNEC*. **Figure 8.16** shows a frequency sweep of the azimuth response for the 5-element Yagi in Figure 8.11 across the 20 meter band, using steps of 117 kHz so there are four evaluation frequencies. At 14.0 MHz this Yagi's gain is down a small amount compared to the gain at 14.351 MHz but the rearward pattern is noticeably degraded, dropping to a front-to-back ratio of just under 20 dB.

EZNEC can save frequency sweeps of elevation (or azimuth) patterns to a series of output plot files. In essence, the program automates the process described above for saving a plot to disk and then overlaying it on another plot. *EZNEC* can save the following parameters to a text file for later analysis (or perhaps importation into a spreadsheet) chosen by the user:

- Source data
- Load data
- Pattern data
- Current data
- *MicroSmith* numeric data
- Pattern analysis summary.

Frequency Scaling

EZNEC has a very useful feature that allows you to create new models scaled to a new frequency. You invoke the algorithm used to scale a model from one frequency to another by checking the RESCALE box after you've clicked the FREQUENCY button. *EZNEC* will scale all model dimensions (wire length, height and diameter) except for one specific situation — if you originally specified wire size by AWG gauge, the wire diameter will stay the same at the new frequency. For example, #14 copper wire for a half-wave 80-meter dipole will stay #14 copper wire when the antenna is scaled to become a 20-meter half-wave dipole. If, however, you specified diameter as a floating point numeric value originally (such as 0.064 inch), the diameter will be scaled by the ratio of new to old frequency, along with wire length and height.

Start up *EZNEC* and open up the file **Ch8-520-40W.EZ** for the 5-element 20-meter Yagi on a 40-foot boom. Click the FREQUENCY box and then check the RESCALE check box. Now, type in the frequency of 28.4 MHz and click OK. You have quickly and easily created a new 5-element 10-meter Yagi, that is mounted 29.9949 feet high, the exact ratio of 28.4 MHz to 14.1739 MHz, the original design frequency on 20 meters. Click the FF PLOT button to plot the azimuth pattern for this new Yagi. You will see that it closely duplicates the performance of its 20 meter sibling. Click SRC DAT to see that the source impedance is $25.38 - j\,22.19\ \Omega$, again very close to the source data for the 20-meter version.

8.2.4 REVISITING SOURCE SPECIFICATION

Sensitivity to Source Placement

Earlier, we briefly described how to specify a source on a particular segment using *EZNEC*. The sources for the relatively simple dipole, Yagi and quad models investigated so far have been in the center of an easy-to-visualize wire. The placement for the source on the vertical ground plane was at the bottom of the vertical radiator, an eminently logical place. In the other cases we specified the position of the source at 50% of the distance along a wire, given that the wire being fed had an odd number of segments. Please note that in each case so far, the feed point (source) has been placed at a relatively low-impedance point, where the current changes relatively slowly from segment to segment.

Now we're going to examine some subtler source-placement problems. *NEC-2* is well-known as being very sensitive

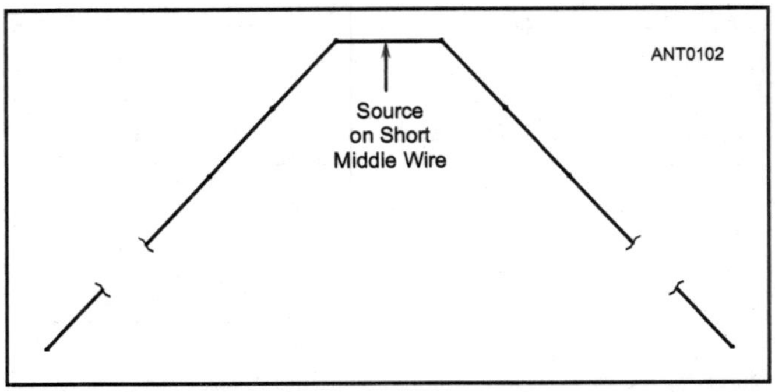

Figure 8.17 — Model of inverted-V dipole using a short center wire on which the source is placed.

Table 8.2
135-Foot Inverted-V Dipole at 3.75 MHz

Case	*Segments*	*Source Impedance (Ω)*	*Max. Gain (dBi)*
1	82	$72.64 + j\,128.2$	4.82
2	246	$73.19 + j\,128.9$	4.82
3	67	$73.06 + j\,129.1$	4.85
4	401	$76.21 + j\,135.2$	4.67

to source placement. Significant errors can result from a haphazard choice of the source segment and the segments surrounding it.

Let's return to the inverted-V dipole in Figure 8.5. The first time we evaluated this antenna (**Ch8-Inverted V Dipole.EZ**) we specified a split source in *EZNEC*. This function uses two sources, one on each of the segments immediately adjacent to the junction of the two downward slanting wires.

Another common method to create a source at the junction of two wires that meet at an angle is to separate these two slanted wires by a short distance and bridge that gap with a short straight wire which is fed at its center. **Figure 8.17** shows a close-up of this scheme in which the length of the segments surrounding the short middle wire are purposely made equal to the length of the middle wire bridging the gap between them. The segmentation for the short middle wire is set to one. **Table 8.2** lists the source impedance and the maximum gain the *EZNEC* computes for four different models:

1. **Ch8-Inverted V Dipole.EZ** (the original model)
2. **Ch8-Inverted V Dipole Triple Segmentation.EZ**
3. **Ch8-Modified Inverted V Dipole.EZ** (as shown in Figure 8.17, for the middle wire set to be 2 feet long)
4. **Ch8-Mod Inverted V Poor Segmentation.EZ** (where the number of segments on the two slanted wires have been increased to 200)

Case 2 shows the effect of tripling the number of segments in Case 1. This is a check on the segmentation, to see that the results are stable at a lower level compared to a higher level of segmentation (which theoretically is better although slower in computation). We purposely set up

Table 8.3
135-Foot Inverted-V Dipole at 7.5 MHz

Case	*Segments*	*Source Impedance (Ω)*	*Max. Gain (dBi)*
1	82	2297 – *j* 2668	5.67
2	246	1822 – *j* 2553	5.66
3	67	1960 – *j* 2583	5.66
4	401	2031 – *j* 2688	5.48

Case 4 so that the lengths of the segments on either side of the single-segment middle wire are significantly different (0.33 feet) compared to the 2-foot length of the middle wire.

The feed point and gain figures for the first three models are close to each other. But you can see that the figures for the fourth model are beginning to diverge from the first three, with about a 5% overall change in the reactance and resistance compared to the average values, and about a 3% change in the maximum gain. This illustrates that it is best to keep the segments surrounding the source equal or at least close to equal in length. We'll soon examine a figure of merit called the *Average Gain* test, but it bears mentioning here that the average gain test is very close for the first three models and begins to diverge for the fourth model.

Things get more interesting if the source is placed at a high-impedance point on an antenna — for example, in the center of a full-wave dipole — the value computed for the source impedance will be high and the results will be quite sensitive to the segment lengths. We'll repeat the computations for the same inverted-V models, but this time at twice the operating frequency, at 7.5 MHz.

Table 8.3 summarizes the results. The source impedance is high, as expected. Note that the resistance term varies quite a bit for all four models with a range of about 23% around the average value. Interestingly, the poorly segmented model's resistance falls in between the other three. The reactive terms are closer for all four models but still cover a range of 4% around the average value. Maximum gain shows the same tendency to be somewhat lower in the fourth model compared to the first three and thus looks as potentially untrustworthy at 7.5 MHz as it does at 3.75 MHz.

This is, of course, a small sampling of segmentation schemes and caution dictates that you shouldn't take these results as being representative of all possibilities. Nevertheless, the lesson to be learned here is that the feed-point (source) impedance can vary significantly at a point where the current is changing rapidly, as it does at a high impedance point on the antenna. Another general conclusion that can be drawn from Tables 8.2 and 8.3 is that more segments, particularly if they surround the source segment improperly, is not necessarily better.

Voltage and Current Sources

Before we leave the topic of sources, you should be aware that programs like *EZNEC* and others have the ability to simulate both voltage sources and current sources. Although native *NEC-2* has several source types, voltage sources are the most commonly used by amateurs. Native *NEC-2* doesn't have a current source but a current source is nothing more than a voltage source delivering current through a high impedance. Basic network theory says that every Thevenin voltage source has a Norton current source equivalent.

Various commercial implementations of *NEC-2* approach the creation of a current source in slightly different fashions. Some use a high value of inductive reactance as a series impedance, while others use a high value of series resistance. Why would we want to use a current source instead of a voltage source in a model? The general-purpose answer is that models containing a single source at a single feed point can use a voltage source with no problems. Models that employ multiple sources, usually with different amplitudes and different phase shifts, do best with current sources.

For example, *driven arrays* feed RF currents at different amplitudes and phase shifts into two or more elements. The impedances seen at each element may be very different — some impedances might even have negative values of resistance, indicating that power is flowing out of that element into the feed system due to mutual coupling to other elements. Having the ability to specify the amplitude and phase of the current rather than a feed voltage at a feed point in a program like *EZNEC* is a valuable tool.

Next, we examine one more important aspect of building a model — setting up loads. After that, we'll look into two tests for the potential accuracy of a model. These tests can help identify source placement, as well as other problems.

8.2.5 LOADS

Many ham antennas, in particular electrically short ones, employ some sort of *loading* to resonate the system. Sometimes loading takes the form of *capacitance hats*, but these can and should be modeled as wires connected to the top of a vertical radiator. A capacitance hat is not the type of loading we'll explore in this section.

Here, the term *loads* refers to discrete inductances, capacitances and resistances that are placed at some point (or points) in an antenna system to achieve certain effects. One fairly common form of a load is a *loading coil* used to resonate an electrically short antenna. Another form of load often seen in ham antennas is a *trap*. *EZNEC* has a special built-in function to evaluate parallel-resonant traps, even at different frequencies beyond their main parallel resonance.

Just for reference a more subtle type of load is a *distributed* material load. We encountered just such a load in our first model antenna, the 135-foot long flattop dipole — although we didn't identify it specifically as a load at that time. Instead, it was identified as a "wire loss" associated with copper.

The *NEC-2* core program has the capability of simulating a number of built-in loads, including distributed material and discrete loads. *EZNEC* implements the following discrete loads:

- Series R ± *j* X loads.
- Series R-L-C loads, specified in Ω of resistance, μH of

inductance and pF of capacitance.

- Parallel R-L-C loads, specified in Ω of resistance, μH of inductance and pF of capacitance.
- Trap loads, specified in Ω of resistance in series with μH of inductance, shunted by pF of capacitance, at a specific frequency.
- Laplace loads, specified as mathematical Laplace coefficients (sometimes used in older modeling programs and left in *EZNEC* for backward compatibility).

It is important to recognize that the discrete loads in an antenna modeling program *do not radiate* and they have zero size which is why *NEC-2* discrete loads are described as being *mathematical loads*. The fact that *NEC-2* loads do not radiate means that the popular mobile antennas that use helical loading coils wound over a length of fiberglass whip cannot be modeled accurately with *NEC-2* because such coils do radiate.

Let's say that we want to put an air-wound loading coil with an unloaded Q of 400 at the center of a 40-foot long, 50-foot high, flattop dipole so that it is resonant at 7.1 MHz. The schematic of this antenna is shown in **Figure 8.18**. Examine the modeling file **Ch8-Loaded Dipole.EZ** to see how a discrete series-RL load is used to resonate this short dipole at 7.1 MHz, with a feed-point (source) impedance of 25.3 Ω. This requires a series resistance of 1.854 Ω and an inductive reactance of +741.5 Ω. Note that we again used a single wire to model this antenna, and that we placed the load at a point 50% along the length of the wire.

Specifying this value of reactance represents a 16.62 μH coil with an unloaded Q of 741.5/1.854 = 400 which is just what we wanted. Let's assume for now that we use a perfect transformer to transform the 25.3-Ω source impedance to 50 Ω. If we now attempt to run a frequency sweep over the whole 40 meter band from 7.0 to 7.3 MHz, the load reactance and resistance will not change, since we specified fixed values for reactance and resistance. Hence, the source impedance will be correct only at the frequency where the reactance and resistance are specified since the reactance of an actual coil changes with frequency.

Let's use a different type of load, a 16.62 μH coil with a series 1.854-Ω resistance at 7.1 MHz. We'll let *EZNEC* take care of the details of computing both the reactance and the changing series resistance at various frequencies. The degree that both reactance and series loss resistance of the coil change with frequency may be viewed using the LOAD DAT button from the main *EZNEC* window. By specifying inductance or capacitance, the model's reactance will change with frequency as expected.

Figure 8.19 shows the computed SWR curve for a 25.3-Ω ALT SWR Z0 reference resistance. The 2:1 SWR bandwidth is about 120 kHz. As could be expected, the antenna has a rather narrow bandwidth because it is electrically short.

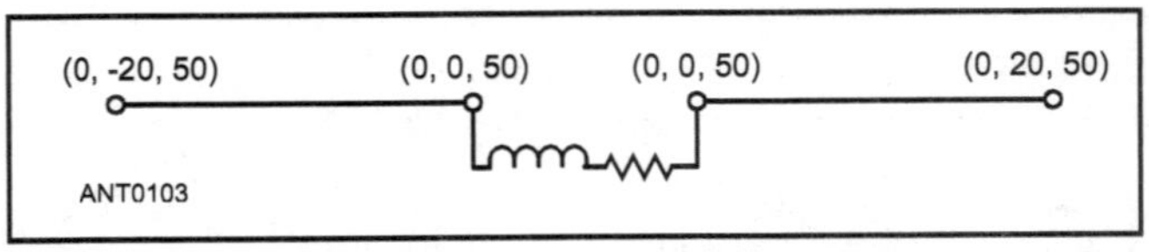

Figure 8.18 — Schematic diagram of a 40-foot long flattop dipole with a loading coil placed at the center. This coil has an unloaded Q of 400 at 7.1 MHz.

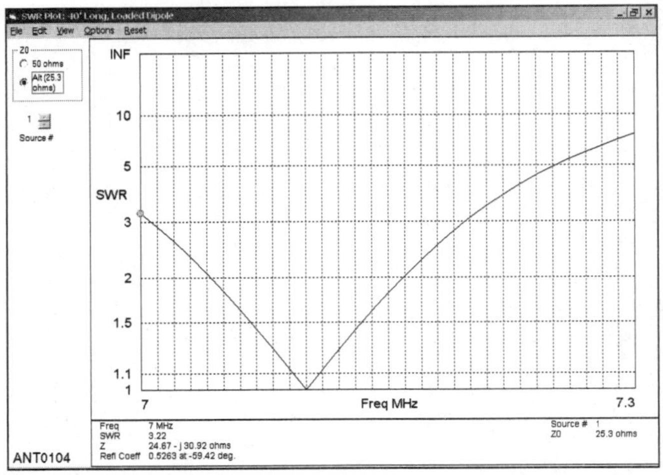

Figure 8.19 — SWR graph of the loaded 40-foot long flattop dipole shown in Figure 8.18.

8.2.6 ACCURACY TESTS

There are two tests that can help identify accuracy problems in a model:

- The Convergence test.
- The Average Gain test.

Convergence Test

The idea behind the Convergence test is simple: If you increase the segmentation in a particular model and the results change more than you'd like, increase the segmentation until the computations converge to a consistent answer. This process has the potential for being subjective but simple antenna models do converge quickly. In this section, we'll review several more of the antennas discussed previously to see how they converge.

Let's go back to the simple dipole in Figure 8.3. The original segmentation was 11 segments, but we'll start with a very low value of segmentation of three, well below the minimum recommended level. **Table 8.4** shows how the source impedance and gain change with increase in segmentation at 3.75 MHz. For this simple antenna, the gain levels off at 6.50 dBi when segmentation has reached 11 segments. Going to ten times the minimum-recommended level (to 111 segments) results in an increase of only 0.01 dBi in the gain.

Arguably, the impedance has also stabilized by the time we reach a segmentation level of 11 segments, although purists may opt for 23 segments. The tradeoff is a slowdown in computational speed.

Let's see how the 5-element Yagi model converges with changes in segmentation level. **Table 8.5** shows how the source impedance, gain, 180° front-to-back ratio and worst-case front-to-rear ratio change with segmentation density. By the time the segmentation has reached 11 segments per wire,

Table 8.4
135-Foot Flattop Dipole at 3.75 MHz

Segments	*Source Impedance (Ω)*	*Max. Gain (dBi)*
3	85.9 + *j* 128.0	6.34
5	86.3 + *j* 128.3	6.45
7	86.8 + *j* 128.8	6.48
11	87.9 + *j* 129.5	6.50
23	88.5 + *j* 130.3	6.51
45	89.0 + *j* 130.8	6.51
101	89.4 + *j* 131.1	6.51

Table 8.5
5-element Wire Yagi at 14.1739 MHz

Segments	*Source Impedance (Ω)*	*Max. Gain (dBi)*	*180° F/B (dB)*	*F/R (dB)*
3	28.5 – *j* 30.6	12.79	23.2	22.4
5	26.3 – *j* 25.6	13.02	30.5	23.1
7	25.6 – *j* 24.0	13.07	34.8	23.1
11	25.1 – *j* 22.9	13.09	39.9	23.1
25	24.9 – *j* 22.0	13.10	43.7	23.1
99	24.7 – *j* 21.5	13.10	44.2	23.1

the impedance and gain have stabilized quite nicely, as has the F/R. The 180° F/B is still increasing with segmentation level until about 25 segments, but a relatively small shift in frequency will change the maximum F/B level greatly. For example, with 11 segments per wire, shifting the frequency to 14.1 MHz — a shift of only 0.5% — will change the maximum 180° F/B from almost 50 dB down to 27 dB. For this reason the F/R is considered a more reliable indicator of the adequacy of the segmentation level than is F/B.

Average Gain Test

The theory behind the Average Gain test is a little more involved. Basically, if you remove all intentional losses in a model and if you place the antenna either in free space or over perfect ground, then all the power fed to the antenna should be radiated by it. Internally, the program runs a full 3-D analysis, adding up the radiated power in all directions and dividing that sum by the total power fed to the antenna. Ideally, the ratio of input power to radiated power should be unity. Since *NEC-2* is very sensitive to source placement, as mentioned before, the Average Gain test is a good indicator if something is wrong with the specification of the source.

Various commercial versions of *NEC-2* handle the Average Gain test in different ways. *EZNEC* requires the operator to turn off all distributed losses in wires or set to zero any discrete resistive losses in loads. Next set the ground environment to free space (or perfect ground) and request a 3-D pattern plot. *EZNEC* will then report the average gain, which will be 1.000 if the model has no problems. Average gain can be lower or higher than 1.000 but if it falls within the range 0.95 to 1.05 it is usually considered adequate.

As L. B. Cebik, W4RNL has stated: "Like the convergence test, the average gain test is a necessary but not a sufficient condition of model reliability." Pass both tests, however, and you can be pretty well sure that your model represents reality. Pass only one test, and you have reason to worry about how well your model represents reality.

Once again, open the model file **Ch8-Mod Inverted V Poor Segmentation.EZ** and set WIRE LOSS to zero, GROUND TYPE to FREE SPACE and PLOT TYPE to 3-DIMENSIONAL. Click on the FF PLOT button. *EZNEC* will report that the Average Gain is 0.955 = –0.2 dB. This is very close to the lower limit of 0.95 considered valid for excellent accuracy. This is a direct result of forcing the segment lengths adjacent to the source segment to be considerably shorter than the source segment's length. The gain reported using this test would be approximately –0.2 dB from what it should be — just what Table 8.3 alludes to also.

Now, let's revisit the basic model **Ch8-Inverted V Dipole.EZ** and look at Case 2 in Table 8.3. Case 2 amounts to a Convergence test for the basic inverted-V model. Since the impedance and gain changes were small comparing the basic model to the one using three times the number of segments, the model passed the Convergence test. The Average Gain test for the basic model yields a value of 0.991, well within the limits for good accuracy. This model has thus passed both tests and can be considered accurate.

Running the Average Gain test for the 5-element Yagi (using 11 segments per wire and whose convergence we examined in Table 8.5) yields a value of 0.996, again well within the bounds indicating a good model. The simple flat-top dipole with 11 segments at 3.75 MHz yields an Average Gain result of 0.997, again indicating a very accurate model.

8.2.7 OTHER POSSIBLE MODEL LIMITATIONS

Programs based on the *NEC-2* core computational code have several well-documented limitations that you should know about. Some limitations have been removed in the restricted-access *NEC-4* core (which is not generally available to users), but other limitations still exist, even in *NEC-4*.

Closely Spaced Wires

If wires are spaced too close to each other, the *NEC-2* core can run into problems. If the segments are not carefully aligned, there also can be problems with accuracy. The worst-case situation is where two wires are so close together that their volumes actually merge into each other as we discussed earlier for wire junctions. This can happen where wires are thick, parallel to each other and close together. You should keep parallel wires separated by at least several wire diameters.

For example, #14 AWG wire is 0.064 inch in diameter. The rule then is to keep parallel #14 wires separated by more than 2 × 0.064 = 0.128 inch. And you should run the Convergence test to assure yourself that the solution is indeed converging when you have closely spaced wires, especially if the two wires have different diameters. To model antennas containing closely spaced wires, very often you will need many more segments than usual and you must also carefully ensure that the segments align with each other.

Things can get a little more tricky when wires cross over or under each other, simply because such crossings are sometimes difficult to visualize. Again, the rule is to keep crossing wires separated by more than two diameters from each other and if you intend to join two wires together, make sure you do so at the ends of the two wires, using identical end coordinates. When any of these rules are violated, the Convergence and Average Gain tests will usually warn you of potential inaccuracies.

Parallel-Wire Transmission Lines and LPDAs

A common example of problems with closely spaced wires is when someone attempts to model a parallel-wire transmission line. *NEC-2*-based programs usually do not work as well in such situations as do *MININEC*-based programs. The problems are compounded if the diameters are different for the two wires simulating a parallel-wire transmission line. In *NEC-2* programs, it is usually better to use the built-in "perfect transmission line" function than to try to model closely spaced parallel wires as a transmission line.

For example, a Log Periodic Dipole Array (LPDA) is composed of a series of elements fed using a transmission line that reverses the phase 180° at each element. (See the **Log Periodic Antennas** chapter.) In other words, the elements are connected to a transmission line that reverses connections left-to-right at each element. It is cumbersome to do so, but you could model such a transmission line using separate wires in *EZNEC* but it is a potentially confusing and a definitely painstaking process. Further, the accuracy of the resulting model is usually suspect, as shown by the Average Gain test.

It is far easier to use the TRANS LINES function from the *EZNEC* main window to accurately model an LPDA. See **Figure 8.20**, which shows the TRANS LINES window for the **9302A.EZ** 16-element LPDA. There are 15 transmission lines connecting the 16 elements, placed at the 50% point on each element, with a 200-Ω characteristic impedance and with Reversed connections.

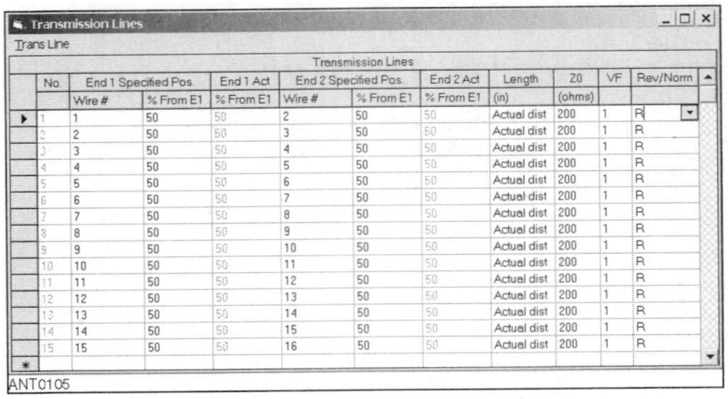

No.	End 1 Specified Pos. Wire #	End 1 Specified Pos. % From E1	End 1 Act % From E1	End 2 Specified Pos. Wire #	End 2 Specified Pos. % From E1	End 2 Act % From E1	Length (in)	Z0 (ohms)	VF	Rev/Norm
1	1	50	50	2	50	50	Actual dist	200	1	R
2	2	50	50	3	50	50	Actual dist	200	1	R
3	3	50	50	4	50	50	Actual dist	200	1	R
4	4	50	50	5	50	50	Actual dist	200	1	R
5	5	50	50	6	50	50	Actual dist	200	1	R
6	6	50	50	7	50	50	Actual dist	200	1	R
7	7	50	50	8	50	50	Actual dist	200	1	R
8	8	50	50	9	50	50	Actual dist	200	1	R
9	9	50	50	10	50	50	Actual dist	200	1	R
10	10	50	50	11	50	50	Actual dist	200	1	R
11	11	50	50	12	50	50	Actual dist	200	1	R
12	12	50	50	13	50	50	Actual dist	200	1	R
13	13	50	50	14	50	50	Actual dist	200	1	R
14	14	50	50	15	50	50	Actual dist	200	1	R
15	15	50	50	16	50	50	Actual dist	200	1	R

Figure 8.20 — Transmission-line data entry screen for the 9302A.EZ 16-element LPDA. Note that the transmission lines going between elements are "reversed," meaning that they are 180° out-of-phase at each element, a requirement for properly feeding an LPDA.

Fat Wires Connected to Skinny Wires

Another inherent limitation in the *NEC-2* computational core shows up when modeling many Yagis and some quads: popular amateur antennas.

Tapered Elements

As mentioned before, many Yagis are built using telescoping aluminum tubing. This technique saves weight and makes for a more flexible and usually stronger element, one that can survive wind and ice loading better than a single-diameter "monotaper" element design. Many vertical antennas are also constructed using telescoping aluminum tubing.

Unfortunately, native *NEC-2* doesn't model accurately such *tapered elements*, as they are commonly called. There is, however, a sophisticated and accurate workaround for such elements, called the *Leeson corrections*. Derived by Dave Leeson, W6NL, from pioneering work by Schelkunoff at Bell Labs, these corrections compute the diameter and length of an element that is electrically equivalent to a tapered element. This monotaper element is much easier to use in a program like *NEC-2*. (See the **HF Yagi and Quad Antennas** chapter for more information on tapered elements.)

EZNEC and other *NEC-2* programs can automatically invoke the Leeson corrections, providing that some basic conditions are met — and happily, these conditions are true for the telescoping aluminum-tubing elements commonly used as Yagi elements. *EZNEC* gives you the ability to disable or enable Leeson corrections, under the OPTION menu, under STEPPED DIAMETER CORRECTION, *EZNEC*'s name for the Leeson corrections. Open the modeling file **520-40H.EZ**, which contains tapered aluminum tubing elements and compare the results using and without using the Leeson corrections.

Table 8.6 lists the differences over the 20-meter band, with the 5-element Yagi at a height of 70 feet above flat ground. You can see that the non-Leeson corrected figures are very different from the corrected ones. At 14.3 MHz, the pattern for the non-corrected Yagi has degenerated to a F/R of 3.1 dB, while at 14.4 MHz, just outside the top of the amateur band, the pattern for the non-corrected antenna actually has reversed. Even at 14.2 MHz, the non-corrected antenna shows a low source impedance, while the corrected version exhibits smooth variations in gain, F/R and impedance across the whole band, just as the actual antenna exhibits.

Some Quads

Some types of cubical quads are made using a combination of aluminum tubing and wire elements, particularly in Europe where the "Swiss" quad has a wide following. Again, *NEC-2*-based programs don't handle such tubing/wire elements well. It is best to avoid modeling this type of antenna,

Table 8.6
5-element Yagi at 14.1739 MHz with Telescoping Aluminum Elements

	With Leeson Corrections			*Without Leeson Corrections*		
Freq (MHz)	*Source Impedance (Ω)*	*Gain (dBi)*	*F/R (dB)*	*Source Impedance (Ω)*	*Gain (dBi)*	*F/R (dB)*
14.0	23.2 – *j* 26.5	14.82	23.3	22.4 – *j* 12.7	14.92	23.1
14.1	22.7 – *j* 20.5	14.87	22.8	18.6 – *j* 12.5	14.70	21.6
14.2	22.8 – *j* 14.8	14.87	22.7	6.6 – *j* 4.6	14.01	16.2
14.3	22.5 – *j* 11.9	14.76	21.5	1.9 + *j* 10.6	10.61	3.1
14.4	14.5 – *j* 10.5	14.45	19.9	1.6 + *j* 23.7	11.15	–11.4

although there are some ways to attempt to get around the limitations, ways that are beyond the scope of this chapter.

8.2.8 NEAR-FIELD OUTPUTS

FCC regulations set limits on the maximum permissible exposure (MPE) allowed from the operation of radio transmitters. These limits are expressed in terms of the electric (V/m) and magnetic fields (A/m) close to an antenna. *NEC-2*-based programs can compute the electric and magnetic near fields and the FCC accepts such computations to demonstrate that an installation meets their regulatory requirements. See the section "RF Radiation and Electromagnetic Field Safety" in the **Antenna Fundamentals** chapter.

We'll continue to use the 5-element Yagi at 70 feet to demonstrate a near-field computation. Open **Ch8-520-40H.EZ** in *EZNEC* and choose SETUPS and then NEAR FIELD from the menu at the top of the main window. Let's calculate the E-field and H-field intensity for a power level of 1500 W (chosen using the OPTIONS, POWER LEVEL choices from the main menu) in the main beam at a fixed distance, say 50 feet, from the tower base. We'll do this at various heights, using 10-foot increments of height, in order to see the lobe structure of the Yagi at 70 feet height.

Table 8.7
E- and H-Field Intensities for 1500 W into 5-Element Yagi at 70 Feet on 14.2 MHz

Height (Feet)	*H-Field (A/m)*	*E-Field (V/m)*
0	0.04	4.1
10	0.03	13.8
20	0.04	20.6
30	0.06	22.6
40	0.08	25.8
50	0.10	33.8
60	0.12	41.5
70	0.12	44.3

Table 8.7 summarizes the total H- and E-field intensities as a function of height. As you might expect, the fields are strongest directly in line with the antenna at a height of 70 feet. At ground level, the total fields are well within the FCC limits for RF exposure for both fields. In fact, the fields are within the FCC limits if someone were to stand at the tower base, directly under the antenna.

8.3 REFERENCES AND BIBLIOGRAPHY

Steve Stearns, K6OIK, contributed this set of references for the 23rd edition of the *Antenna Book.*

Amateur Radio Literature

1) J.L. Lawson, W2PV, "Yagi Antenna Design Experiments Confirm Computer Analysis," *Ham Radio*, Feb 1980, pp 19-27.
2) R. Lewallen, W7EL, "MININEC: The Other Side of the Sword," *QST*, Feb 1991, pp 18-22.
3) L.B. Cebik, W4RNL, "A Beginner's Guide to Using Computer Antenna Modeling Programs," *ARRL Antenna Compendium*, Vol 3, ARRL, 1992, pp 148-155.
4) J.S. Belrose, VE2CV, "Modeling HF Antennas with MININEC: Guidelines and Tips from a Code-Users Notebook," *ARRL Antenna Compendium*, Vol 3, ARRL, 1992, pp 156-164.
5) R.P. Haviland, W4MB, "Programs for Antenna Analysis by the Method of Moments," *ARRL Antenna Compendium*, Vol 4, ARRL, 1995, pp 69-73.
6) R.P. Haviland, W4MB, "Ground parameters for Antenna Analysis," *ARRL Antenna Compendium*, Vol. 5, ARRL, 1996, pp 96-100.
7) L.B. Cebik, W4RNL, "NEC and MININEC Antenna Modeling Programs: A Guide to Further Information," *QEX*, Mar/Apr 1998, pp 47-49.
8) J. Rockway and J. Logan, N6BRF, "Wire Modeling Limitations of NEC and MININEC for Windows," *QEX*, May/Jun 1998, pp 17-21.
9) M. Tracy, KC1SX, "EZNEC 3.0 for Windows," Short Takes, *QST*, Sep 2000, p 66.
10) L.B. Cebik, W4RNL, "A Beginners Guide to Modeling with *NEC*," a four part series in *QST*: Part 1, Nov 2000, pp 34-38; Part 2, Dec 2000, pp 40-44; Part 3,Jan 2001, pp 44-48; Part 4, Feb 2001, pp 31-35.
11) L.B. Cebik, W4RNL, *ARRL Antenna Modeling Course*, ARRL, 2003.
12) L.B. Cebik, W4RNL, "Notes on Modeling LPDAs in MININEC," *QST*, Jun 2004, pp 72-73.
13) L.B. Cebik, W4RNL, "Antenna Options: A Yagi Case Study Part 1 — Design Options," first of a three part article in *QEX*, Jul/Aug. 2004, pp 55-59.
14) L.B. Cebik, W4RNL, "Antenna Options: Modeling Software," a two-part series in *QEX*: Part 1, Sep/Oct 2005, pp 54-59; Part 2, Nov/Dec 2005, pp 50-56.
15) S. Stearns, K6OIK, "Antenna Modeling for Radio Amateurs," *ARRL Pacificon Antenna Seminar*, San Ramon, CA, Oct 17-19, 2008. Download from **www.fars.k6ya.org/docs/k6oik**
16) W. Silver, NØAX, *Antenna Modeling for Beginners: An Introductory Guide to Using Antenna Modeling Software*, ARRL, 2012.
17) S. Nichols, GØKYA, *An Introduction to Antenna Modeling*, RSGB, 2014.
18) K. Snyder, "Near Fields of a Mobile Mounted 2 Meter Antenna," *QST*, Oct 2016, pp 33-35.

Professional Literature

18) J.H. Richmond, "A Wire-Grid Model for Scattering by Conducting Bodies," *IEEE Transactions on Antennas and Propagation*, Vol 14, No 6, Nov 1966, pp 782-786.
19) R.F. Harrington, "Matrix Methods for Field Problems," *Proc. IEEE*, Vol 55, No 2, Feb 1967, pp 136-149.
20) R.F. Harrington, *Field Computation by Moment Methods*, Macmillan, 1968. Republished by Krieger, 1981, and IEEE-Wiley, 1993.
21) J.P.Y. Lee and K.G. Balmain, "Wire Antennas Coated with Magnetically and Electrically Lossy Material," *Radio Science*, Vol 14, No 3, May-June 1979, pp 437-445. Download from **onlinelibrary.wiley.com/journal/10.1002/(ISSN)1944-799X/issues**
22) G.J. Burke and A.J. Poggio, *Numerical Electromagnetics Code (NEC)-Method of Moments*, Part I: Program Description-Theory; Part II: Program Description-Code; Part III, Users Guide, Tech. Rept. UCID-18834, Lawrence Livermore Laboratory, Jan 1981. Download all parts as DTIC document ADA956129 from **www.dtic.mil/dtic/tr/fulltext/u2/a956129.pdf**
23) S.M. Rao, D.R. Wilton, and A.W. Glisson, "Electromagnetic Scattering by Surfaces of Arbitrary Shape," *IEEE Transactions on Antennas and Propagation*, Vol 30, No 3, May 1982, pp 409-418.
24) A.J. Julian, J.C. Logan, and J.W. Rockway, *MININEC: A Mini-Numerical Electromagnetics Code*, Tech Doc 516, DTIC ADA121535, Naval Ocean Systems Center, Sep 6, 1982. Download from **www.dtic.mil/dtic/tr/fulltext/u2/a121535.pdf**
25) B.D. Popovic and A. Nešic, "Generalisation of the Concept of Equivalent Radius of Thin Cylindrical Antennas," *IEE Proc.*, Part H, Vol 131, No 3, Jun 1984, pp 153-158.
26) J.C. Logan and J.W. Rockway, *The New MININEC (Version 3): A Mini-Numerical Electromagnetic Code*, Tech. Doc. 938, DTIC ADA181682, Naval Ocean Systems Center, Sep 1986. Download from **www.dtic.mil/dtic/tr/fulltext/u2/a181682.pdf**
27) A.C. Ludwig, "Wire Grid Modeling of Surfaces," *IEEE Transactions on Antennas and Propagation*, Vol 35, No 9, Sep 1987, pp 1045-1048.
28) J.W. Rockway, J.C. Logan, S.T. Li, and D.W.S. Tam, *The MININEC System: Microcomputer Analysis of Wire Antennas*, Artech House, 1988.
29) G.J. Burke, *Numerical Electromagnetics Code – NEC-4, Method of Moments*, Part I: User's Manual (NEC 4.1); Part II: Program Description-Theory, Tech. Report UCRL-MA-109338, Jan 1992. Download both parts from **puhep1.princeton.edu/~mcdonald/examples/NEC_Manuals**
30) U. Jakobus, DG6SHF, "Numerical Computation of the Near-Field of Typical Amateur Radio Antennas and Comparison with Approximate Results of Far-Field Formulas Applied in the Near-Field Region," 2000. Online.

31) J.M. Stamm and J.K. Breakall, "Comparison of Results for the NEC4, WIPL-D, and EIGER Antenna Modeling Programs," *17th Annual Review of Progress in Applied Computational Electromagnetics*, Monterey, CA, Mar 19-23, 2001, pp 269-276.

32) G.J. Burke, E.K. Miller, and A.I. Poggio, "The Numerical Electromagnetics Code (NEC) — A Brief History," *IEEE International Symposium on Antennas and Propagation*, Monterey, CA, Jun 20-26, 2004, pp 2871-2874. Download from **e-reports-ext.llnl.gov/pdf/304278.pdf**

33) A. Rubinstein, F. Rachidi, and M. Rubinstein, "On Wire-Grid Representation of Solid Metallic Surfaces," *IEEE Transactions on Electromagnetic Compatibility*, Vol 47, No 1, Feb. 2005, pp 192-195.

34) B.M. Kolundzija, J.S. Ognjanovic, and T.K. Sarkar, WIPL-D Microwave: Circuit and 3D EM Simulation for RF & Microwave Applications — Software and User's Manual, Artech House, 2006.

35) W.D. Rawle, "The Method of Moments: A Numerical Technique for Wire Antenna Design," *High Frequency Electronics*, Feb. 2006, pp 42-47. Download from **www.highfrequencyelectronics.com**

36) D. García-Doñoro, Y. Zhang, W. Zhao, T.K. Sarkar, L.E. García-Castillo, and M. Salazar-Palma, "HOBBIES: A New Electromagnetic Simulator," *IEEE International Symposium on Antennas and Propagation* (APS-URSI), July 2010.

37) G.J. Burke, *Ground Model Options in the NEC-4.2 Antenna Code*, Tech. Report LLNL-TR-490316, Lawrence Livermore National Laboratory, July 6, 2011. Download from **e-reports-ext.llnl.gov/pdf/498709.pdf**

38) Y. Zhang, T.K. Sarkar, X. Zhao, D. Garcia-Doñoro, W. Zhao, M. Salazar-Palma, and S. Ting, *Higher Order Basis Based Integral Equation Solver (HOBBIES)*, Wiley, 2012.

39) A.Z. Elsherbeni, P. Nayeri, and C.J. Reddy, *Antenna Analysis and Design using FEKO Electromagnetic Simulation Software*, SciTech Publishing, 2014.

40) T.K. Sarkar, W.M. Dyab, M.N. Abdallah, M. Salazar-Palma, M.V.S.N. Prasad, and S-W. Ting, "Application of the Schelkunoff Formulation to the Sommerfeld Problem of a Vertical Electric Dipole Radiating Over an Imperfect Ground," *IEEE Transactions on Antennas and Propagation*, Vol 62, No 8, Aug 2014, pp 4162-4170.

Notes

Notes

Notes

Supplemental Material

Download Included with Purchase of This Book

The ARRL Antenna Book

24th Edition

You may download supplemental material that includes the fully searchable digital edition of this printed book, as well as expanded content, software, PC board templates, and other support files.

System Requirements: The digital edition and expanded content (PDF files) are viewed using Adobe *Acrobat Reader* software and are compatible with any Windows or Macintosh system with that software installed. *Acrobat Reader* is a free download at **www.adobe.com**. PDF files are *Linux* readable and can also be viewed on iOS and Android devices. Other included software is Windows compatible, only. Antenna modeling files require *EZNEC* software (not included).

Important: This material is protected by copyright. It is unlawful to reproduce or copy this software, except for making a backup copy for your personal use.

How to Redeem Your Coupon and Download the Supplemental Material:

1. Go to the following ARRL e-store link:
   www.arrl.org/shop/ARRL-Antenna-Book-eBook/
2. Click the "Add to Cart" button.
3. Enter the Coupon Code found below, and click the "Submit Coupon Code" button. **This code will discount the full purchase price of the download.** The code may only be used one time.
4. Follow the on-screen instructions to Checkout. Upon completing your order, you will receive instructions to download and save the installation file. We recommend saving the file to a new folder on your computer. Double-click the installation file to begin the software installation, and follow the instructions.

Code expires December 31, 2023.

Coupon Code:

ABB860846

The ARRL

ANTENNA BOOK

FOR RADIO COMMUNICATIONS

24th EDITION

Volume 1: **Antenna Fundamentals — Ch. 1-8**

Volume 2: **Antennas for LF/MF/HF— Ch. 9-14**

Volume 3: **Antennas for VHF through Microwave and Specialty Antennas — Ch. 15-22**

Volume 4: **Transmission Lines and Building Antenna Systems, and Index — Ch. 23-28**

Editor

H. Ward Silver, NØAX

Contributing Editors

Steven R. Ford, WB8IMY
Mark J. Wilson, K1RO

Editorial Assistant

Maty Weinberg, KB1EIB

Production

Michelle Bloom, WB1ENT
Sue Fagan, KB1OKW
— Cover Art
Jodi Morin, KA1JPA
David F. Pingree, N1NAS

Contributors to the 24th Edition

Alan Applegate, KØBG
Gary Breed, K9AY
Jim Brown, K9YC
Glen Brown, W6GJB
David Conn, VE3KL
Remco den Besten, PA3FYM
Wyatt Dirks, ACØRA
James Duffey, KK6MC
Darryl Holman, WW7D
Justin Johnson, GØKSC
Matt Kastigar, N9ES
Steve Kostro, N2CEI
Sean Kutzko, KX9X
Carl Luetzelschwab, K9LA
Brian Machesney, K1LI
Paul Marsh, MØEYT
Tino Pavic, VK3EGN
Stu Phillips, K6TU
Tom Planer, KJ9P
Gilles Renucci, VA2EW
Ulrich Rohde, N1UL
Rick Rosen, K1DS
Rudy Severns, N6LF
Corey Shields, KB9JHU
Kai Siwiak, KE4PT
Andrea Slack, K2EZ
Steve Stearns, K6OIK
Steve Sutterer, AKØM
John Thompson, K3MD
Paul Wade, W1GHZ
Mike Willis, GØMJW
Ken Wolff, K1EA
Grant Zehr, AA9LC

Published by:

ARRL The national association for AMATEUR RADIO®

225 Main Street, Newington, CT 06111-1400 USA

www.arrl.org

Printed in the USA

ISBN: 978-1-62595-111-3 Softcover
978-1-62595-114-4 Four-Volume Boxed Set

Kindle eBook Editions
ISBN: 978-1-62595-115-1 — Volume 1
ISBN: 978-1-62595-116-8 — Volume 2
ISBN: 978-1-62595-118-2 — Volume 3
ISBN: 978-1-62595-119-9 — Volume 4

Twenty-Fourth Edition
First Printing

Contents

A more detailed Table of Contents is included at the beginning of each chapter.

VOLUME 1
ANTENNA FUNDAMENTALS

VOLUME 2
ANTENNAS FOR LF/MF/HF

VOLUME 3
ANTENNAS FOR VHF THROUGH MICROWAVE AND SPECIALTY ANTENNAS

VOLUME 4
TRANSMISSION LINES AND BUILDING ANTENNA SYSTEMS, AND INDEX

TABLE OF CONTENTS

Chapter 9 — Downloadable Supplemental Content

Supplemental Articles

- "Designing a Shortened Antenna" by Luiz Duarte Lopes, CT1EOJ
- "A 6-Foot-High 7-MHz Vertical" by Jerry Sevick, W2FMI
- "A Horizontal Loop for 80-Meter DX" by John Belrose, VE2CV
- "A Gain Antenna for 28 MHz" by Brian Beezley, K6STI
- "A Low-Budget, Rotatable 17 Meter Loop" by Howard Hawkins, WB8IGU
- "A Simple Broadband Dipole for 80 Meters" by Frank Witt, AI1H
- "A Wideband Dipole for 75 and 80 Meters" by Ted Armstrong, WA6RNC
- "A Wideband 80 Meter Dipole" by Rudy Severns, N6LF
- "Broad-Band 80-Meter Antenna" by Allen Harbach, WA4DRU
- "Broad-banding a 160 m Vertical Antenna" by Grant Saviers, KZ1W
- "Inductively Loaded Dipoles"
- "Off-Center Loaded Antennas" by Jerry Hall, K1PLP
- "The 3/8-Wavelength Vertical — A Hidden Gem" by Joe Reisert, W1JR
- "The 160-Meter Sloper System at K3LR" by Al Christman, KB8I, Tim Duffy, K3LR and Jim Breakall, WA3FET
- "The 'C-Pole' — A Ground Independent Vertical Antenna" by Brian Cake, KF2YN
- "The Compact Vertical Dipole"
- "The Half-Delta Loop — A Critical Analysis and Practical Deployment" by John Belrose, VE2CV and Doug DeMaw, W1FB
- "The K1WA 7-MHz Sloper System"
- "The K4VX Linear-Loaded Dipole for 7 MHz" by Lew Gordon, K4VX
- "The Story of the Broadband Dipole" by Dave Leeson, W6NL
- "The W2FMI Ground-Mounted Short Vertical" by Jerry Sevick, W2FMI
- "Use Your Tower as a Dual-Band, Low-Band DX Antenna" by Ted Rappaport, N9NB, and Jim Parnell, W5JAW

Chapter 9

Single-Band MF and HF Antennas

The antennas in this chapter are based on the dipole and the ground-plane monopole — the theory of which is covered in the first group of chapters in this book. These antennas can be combined into arrays for additional directivity as described in the **Multielement Arrays** and **Broadside and End-Fire Arrays** chapters. (Loops are covered in the chapter on **Loop Antennas**.)

This chapter presents practical designs most often used as single-band antennas on the amateur bands below 30 MHz. This is not to say that the antennas can *only* be used on a single band or below 30 MHz — many can be used on several bands as discussed in the **Multiband HF Antennas** chapter and the same principles can be used to create VHF and UHF antennas. Nevertheless, in these examples the discussion will be mainly concerned with use on the LF/MF and HF bands. See the chapter **Antenna Materials and Construction** for information on the techniques used to build practical antennas.

The antennas in this chapter are generally installed to radiate either horizontally or vertically polarized signals. Several antennas, such as the dipole, can be installed in either orientation or some intermediate fashion. For most amateurs, the choice of what type of antenna to install and whether it is installed horizontally or vertically is one of necessity and is driven by constraints such as whether trees or a tower are available, restrictions on external antennas, and esthetic concerns. The goal of this chapter is to present a variety of options so that given the circumstances, the best choice or choices for the desired purpose can be made.

As shown in the chapter **Effects of Ground**, radiation angles from horizontally polarized antennas are strongly affected by their height above ground in wavelengths. On the lower frequency bands, a horizontally polarized antenna at low heights (in terms of wavelengths) provides good regional coverage via NVIS propagation. As a result, horizontal antennas are very popular on the lower bands for short range and regional communications, nets, and rag chewing. Also horizontal antennas do not require extensive ground systems to be efficient.

For a horizontally polarized antenna to be effective for typical DX communications, heights of $\lambda/2$ to 1 λ are considered to be a minimum. As we go down in frequency these heights become harder to realize. For example, a 160 meter dipole at 70 feet is only 0.14 λ high, the equivalent of a 20 meter dipole only 9 feet off the ground! This antenna will be very effective for local and short distance QSOs but not very good for DXing.

On our MF bands (630 and 160 meters) and the lower HF bands, vertical antennas become increasingly attractive — especially for making DX contacts — because they provide a means for lowering the radiation angle. This is especially true where practical heights for horizontally polarized antennas are too low. On our LF band with a wavelength of 2200 meters, vertical antennas are the only practical option, requiring special loading techniques to resonate at that low frequency.

Performance of a vertically polarized antenna is determined by several factors:

- Electrical height of the vertical portion of the radiator
- The ground or counterpoise system efficiency, if one is used
- Ground characteristics in the near- and far-field regions
- The efficiency of loading elements and matching networks

Determining whether a horizontal or vertical antenna is appropriate depends on the intended use of the antenna. The chapter **HF Antenna System Design** will extend the discussion beyond individual antennas to the selection of antennas for a desired purpose, such as DX versus local or continental coverage.

9.1 HORIZONTAL ANTENNAS

9.1.1 DIPOLE ANTENNAS

Half-wave dipoles and variations of these can be a very good choice for an HF antenna. Where only single-band operation is desired, the λ/2 antenna fed with 50- or 75-Ω coaxial cable is a popular and inexpensive antenna. It can also be used on the third harmonic with some adjustment as explained in the project at the end of this section. The basic and most common construction for MF and HF dipoles is shown in **Figure 9.1**. For more information about constructing wire antennas in general, see the **Antenna Materials and Construction** chapter.

The length of the λ/2 dipole in feet is often stated as ℓ = 468/f (MHz) although this rarely results in an antenna resonant at the desired frequency as discussed in the chapter **Dipoles and Monopoles**. It is more practical to begin with a length of 485/f or 490/f (**Table 9.1** gives lengths for each of the ham bands from 1.8 through 50 MHz) and then adjust the

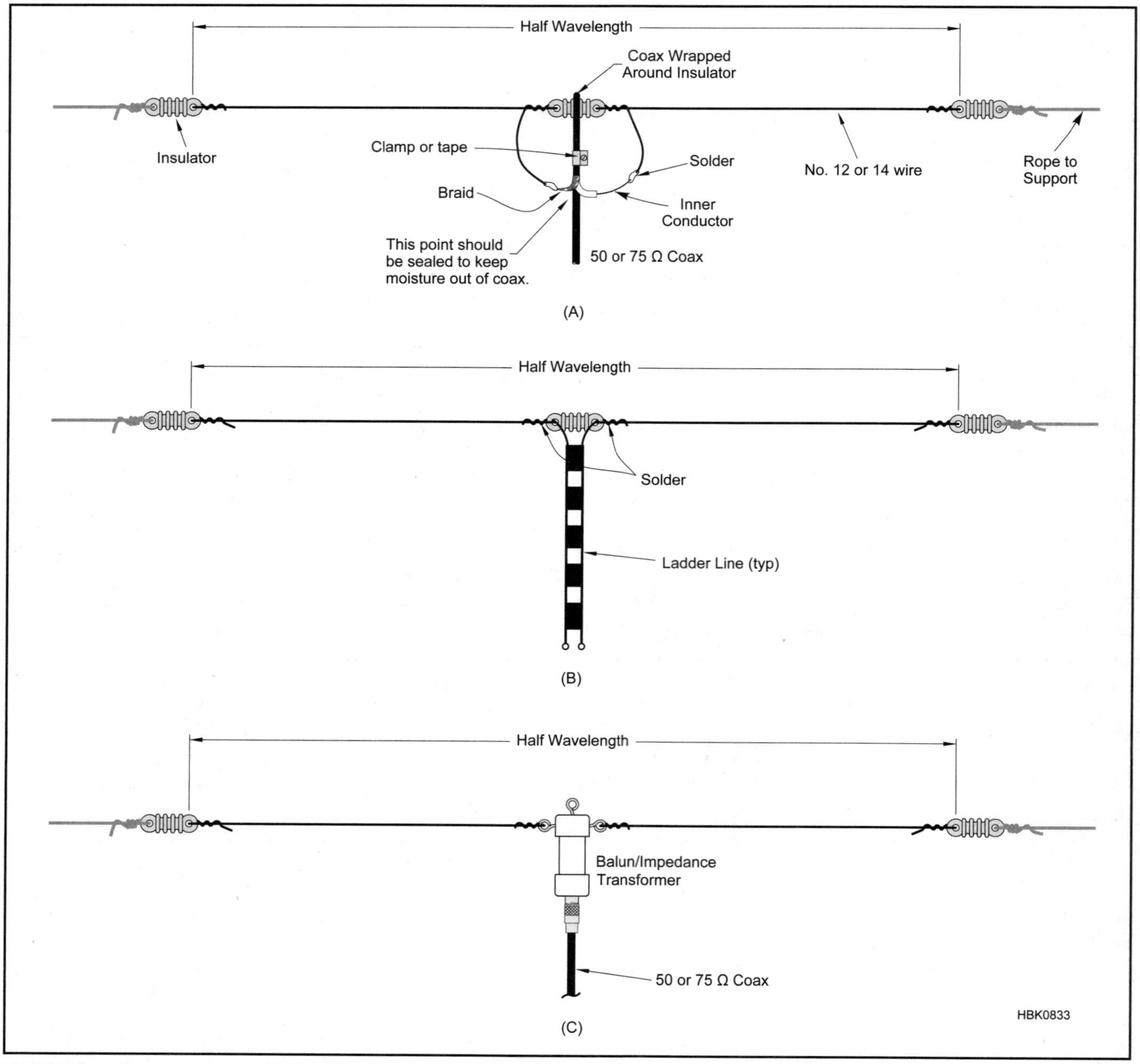

Figure 9.1 — Details of center-fed coax-fed dipole construction. The dipole at B can also be fed with open-wire or ladder-line. Note that the electrical length of the dipole extends to the tips of the loops of wire attached to the insulators.

antenna according to the following procedure:

1) Assemble the antenna with length l_1 for a desired frequency of f_1 but do not make the attachments to the end insulators permanent. Twisting or clamping the antenna wire at the insulators will suffice during adjustment.

2) Raise the antenna to its desired position and determine the frequency of lowest SWR, f_2.

3) Assuming that f_2 is too low (the antenna is too long), calculate the desired length $l_2 = l_1 \times f_2 / f_1$. Trim the antenna to the desired length by removing equal amounts of wire on each end to maintain electrical balance at the feed point.

Example: A dipole intended to be used at 14.250 MHz is initially built with a physical length of 490 / 14.250 = 34.4 feet (34 feet 5 in). Once in place, f_2 is determined to be 13.795 MHz. Using step 3, the desired length should be 34.4 × 13.795 / 14.250 = 33.3 feet and the antenna is 34.4 – 33.3 = 1.1 feet (1 foot 1 inch) too long. Remove 6.5 inches from each end of the antenna.

Coaxial lines present support problems as a concentrated weight at the center of the antenna, tending to pull the center of the antenna down, so care must be taken to make the feed point connections strong and provide support for the cable. If a center support or conveniently located tree is available, insulators with a rope attachment point can be used to support the weight.

The feed line should come away from the antenna at right angles for the longest practical distance so as to preserve electrical balance and minimize coupling of the antenna to the feed line shield's outer surface. Adding a choke balun at the feed point helps to electrically isolate the shield surface and prevent common-mode current from flowing on the feed line. (See the **Transmission Line System Techniques** chapter for a discussion of the use of choke baluns.)

Table 9.1
Starting Lengths for Amateur Band Dipoles

Freq (MHz)	*Length in feet 468/f*	*485/f*	*490/f*
1.85	253.0	262.2	264.9
3.6	130.0	134.7	136.1
3.9	120.0	124.4	125.6
5.3	88.3	91.5	92.5
7.1	65.9	68.3	69.0
10.1	46.3	48.0	48.5
14.15	33.1	34.3	34.6
18.1	25.9	26.8	27.1
21.2	22.1	22.9	23.1
24.9	18.8	19.5	19.7
28.2	16.6	17.2	17.4
29	16.1	16.7	16.9
50.1	9.3	9.7	9.8

Dipole or Doublet?

When does a dipole become a doublet and vice versa? There is no formal difference — these are just two different names for the same antenna. The term "doublet" is often applied to symmetrical center-fed antennas that are not resonant or that are used on multiple bands to distinguish them from the resonant center-fed dipole. This is a matter of convention only.

"Dipole" means "two poles" with the poles being the opposite polarity voltages on either side of the dipole. From the Wikipedia entry (**en.wikipedia.org/wiki/Dipole**) "An electric dipole is a separation of positive and negative charges. The simplest example of this is a pair of electric charges of equal magnitude but opposite sign, separated by some (usually small) distance."

The antenna feed line supplies voltages with opposite polarity on either side of the feed point, creating the pair of electric poles. The poles cause current to flow in the antenna, creating the radiation. As the length increases beyond a half-wavelength, the situation is much less clear because multiple poles eventually appear. For example, a 3/2-wavelength wire is really a tri-pole!

Bending a Dipole

If you do not have sufficient length between the supports, simply hang as much of the center of the antenna as possible between the supports and let the ends hang down as in **Figure 9.2**. The ends can be straight down or may be at an angle as indicated but in either case should be secured so that they do

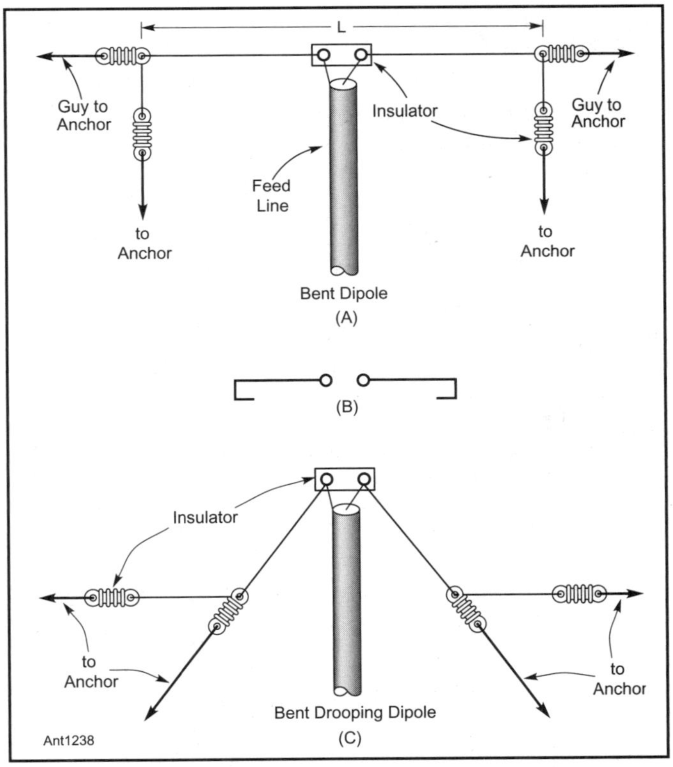

Figure 9.2 — When space is limited, the ends may be bent downward as shown at A, or back on the radiator as shown at B. The bent dipole ends may come straight down or be led off at an angle away from the center of the antenna. An inverted-V as shown in C can be erected with the ends bent parallel to the ground when the support structure is not high enough.

not move in the wind. As long as the center portion between the supports is at least λ/4, the radiation pattern will be very nearly the same as a full-length dipole.

The resonant length of the wire will be somewhat shorter than a full-length dipole and can best be determined by experimentally adjusting the length of ends, which may be conveniently near ground. Keep in mind that there can be very high voltages at the ends of the wires and for safety the ends should be kept out of reach.

Letting the ends hang down as shown is a form of capacitive *end loading*. Folding the ends back on the antenna is a type of *linear loading*. Both types of loading are discussed later in this chapter. While both techniques are efficient, it will also reduce the matching bandwidth — as does any form of loading.

A 40 – 15 Meter Dual-Band Dipole

As mentioned earlier, dipoles have harmonic resonances near odd multiples of their fundamental resonances. Because 21 MHz is the third harmonic of 7 MHz, 7-MHz dipoles are harmonically resonant in the popular ham band at 21 MHz. This is attractive because it allows you to install a 40 meter dipole, feed it with coax, and use it without an antenna tuner on both 40 and 15 meters.

But there's a catch: The third harmonic resonance is actually higher than three times the fundamental resonant frequency. This is because there is no end effect in the center portion of the antenna where there are no insulators.

An easy fix for this, as shown in **Figure 9.3**, is to add capacitive loading to the antenna about ¼-λ wavelength (at 21.2 MHz) away from the feed point in both halves of the dipole. Known as *capacitance hats*, the simple loading wires lower the antenna's resonant frequency on 15 meters without substantially affecting resonance on 40 meters. This scheme can also be used to build a dipole that can be used on 80 and 30 meters and on 75 and 10 meters.

Measure, cut, and adjust the dipole to resonance at the desired 40 meter frequency. Then, cut two 2-foot-long pieces of stiff wire (such as #12 or #14 AWG house wire) and solder the ends of each one together to form loops. Twist the loops in the middle to form figure-8s, and strip and solder the wires where they cross. Install these capacitance hats on the dipole by stripping the antenna wire (if necessary) and soldering the hats to the dipole about a third of the way out from the feed point (placement isn't critical) on each wire. To resonate the antenna on 15 meters, adjust the loop shapes until the SWR is acceptable in the desired segment of the 15 meter band. Conversely, you can move the hats back and forth along the antenna until the desired SWR is achieved and then solder or clamp the hats to the antenna.

9.1.2 INVERTED-V DIPOLE

If only a single support is available, the halves of a dipole may be sloped to form an inverted-V dipole, as shown in **Figure 9.4**. This also reduces the horizontal space required for the antenna.

There will be some difference in performance between a horizontal dipole and the inverted-V as shown by the radiation patterns in **Figure 9.5**. There is small loss in peak gain and the pattern is less directional.

Bringing a dipole's wires toward each other results in a decrease of the resonant frequency and a decrease in feed point impedance and bandwidth. (This is true whether the dipole is constructed as an inverted-V or not.) Thus, to maintain the same resonant frequency, the length of the dipole must be decreased somewhat over that of the horizontal configuration.

The amount of shortening required varies with the circumstances of the installation but a reasonable rule of thumb would be 5% for every 45 degrees that the legs of the dipole are lowered from horizontal. Start with an initial length for a horizontal dipole and then trim it in the inverted-V configuration according to the procedure given for horizontal dipoles.

The angle at the apex is not critical, although angles smaller than 90° begin to compromise performance significantly. Because of the lower feed point impedance, a 50-Ω feed line should be used.

If a close match to the feed line impedance is desired, the usual procedure is to adjust the angle for lowest SWR while keeping the dipole resonant by adjusting its length. Bandwidth may be increased by using multiconductor elements, such as a cage or fan configuration as discussed below.

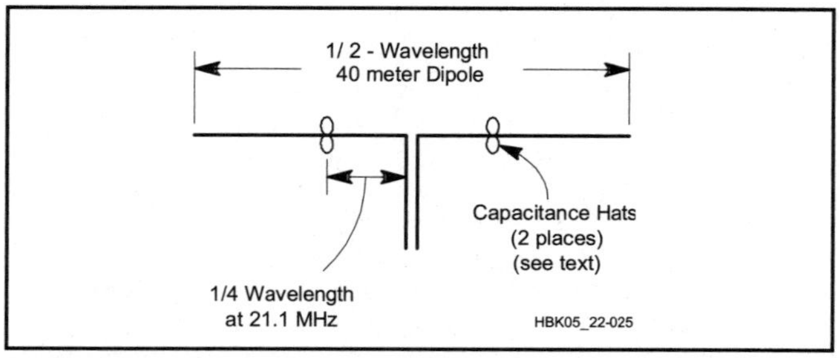

Figure 9.3 — Figure-8-shaped capacitance hats made and placed as described in the text, can make a 40 meter dipole resonate anywhere in the 15 meter band.

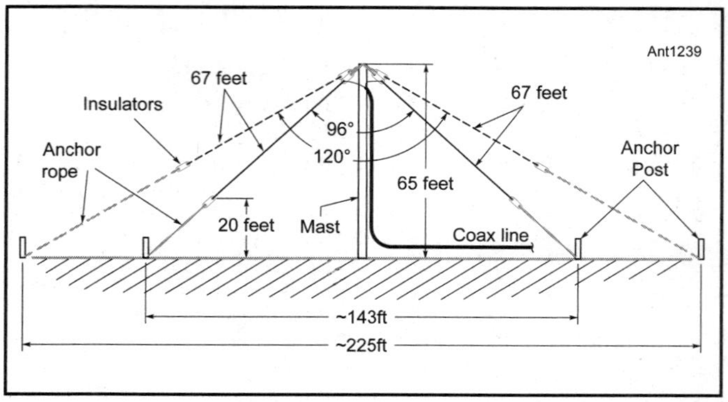

Figure 9.4 — The inverted-V dipole. Two different configurations for 80 meter inverted-V dipoles are shown — one for a 120° apex angle and one for a 96° apex angle.

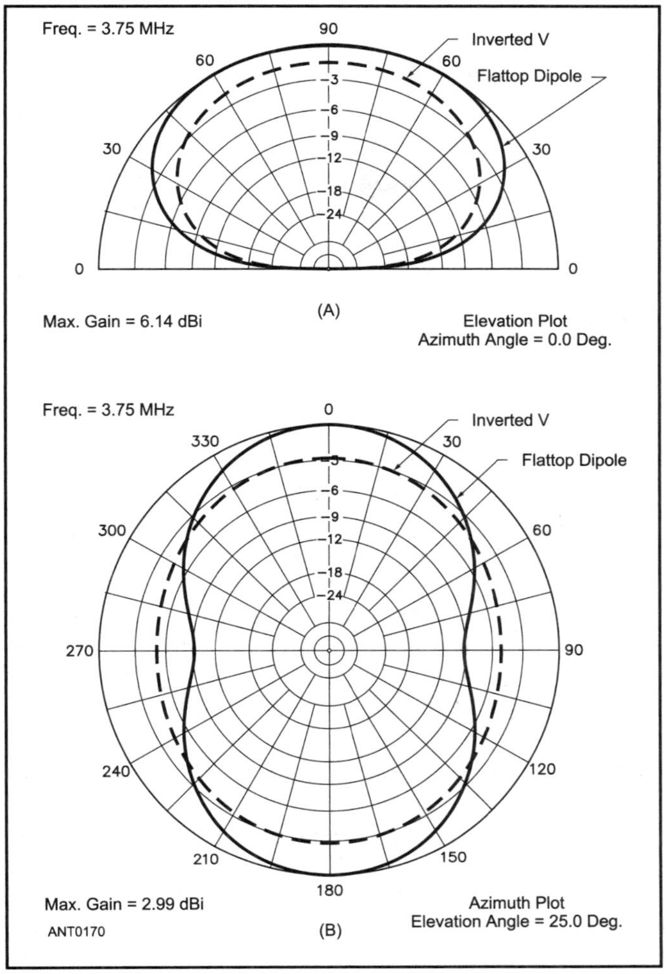

Figure 9.5 — At A, elevation and at B, azimuthal radiation patterns comparing a normal 80 meter dipole and an inverted-V dipole. The center of both dipoles is at 65 feet and the ends of the inverted-V are at 20 feet. The frequency is 3.750 MHz.

9.1.3 SLOPING DIPOLES

Another variation of the single-support configuration is the λ/2 *sloping dipole* shown in **Figure 9.6A**. This antenna is also known as a *sloper* or *half-wave sloper* to distinguish it from the *half sloper* described in the section on vertically-polarized antennas. The feed point impedance depends on the height of the antenna above ground, the characteristics of the ground, and the angle the antenna makes with the ground. In most cases, an acceptable SWR for coaxial cable can be achieved by altering the direction and height. Losses increase

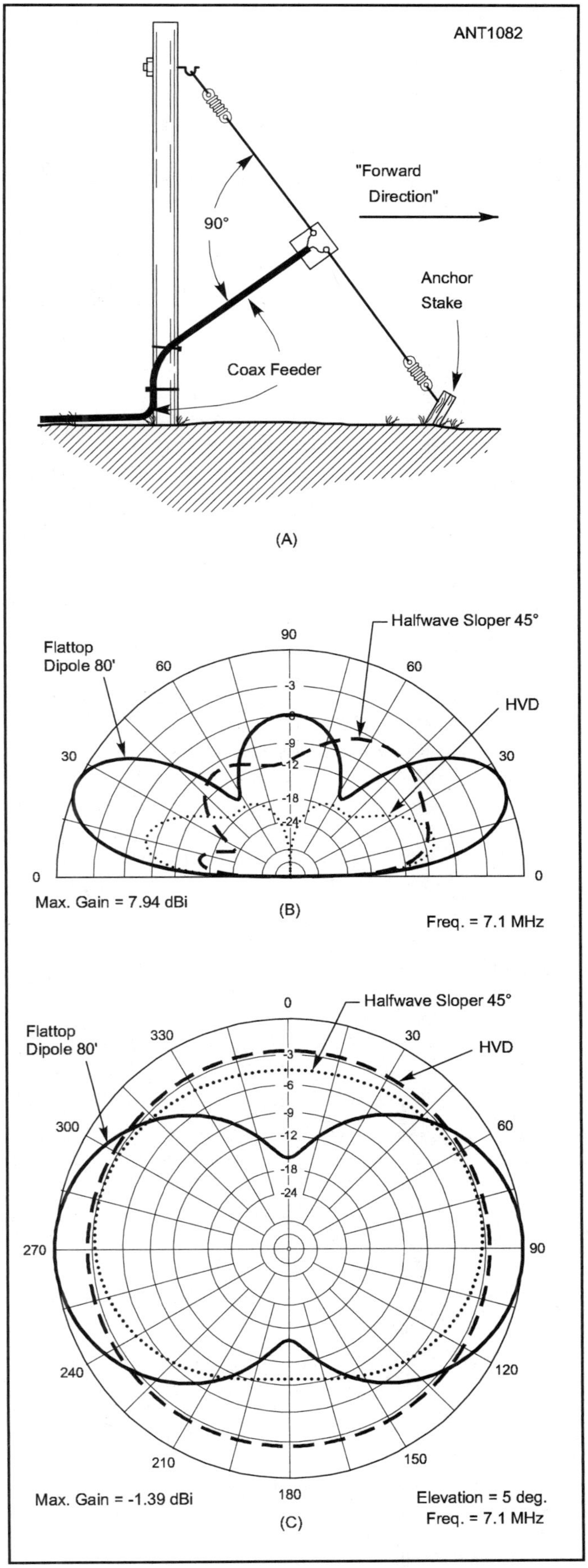

Figure 9.6 — Example of a sloping λ/2 dipole, or *full sloper*. On the lower HF bands, maximum radiation over poor to average ground is off the sides and in the *forward direction* indicated if a non-conductive support is used. A metal support will alter this pattern by acting as a parasitic element. B compares the 40 meter azimuthal patterns at a DX takeoff angle of 5° for three configurations: a flattop dipole, a dipole tilted down 45° and an HVD (half wave vertical dipole). C shows the elevation patterns for the same antennas. Note that the sloping half wave dipole has more energy at higher elevation angles than either the flattop dipole or HVD.

as the antenna ends approach the support or the ground, so the same cautions about the height of the antenna ends apply as for the inverted-V antenna.

The amount of slope from horizontal can vary from 0°, where the dipole is in a flattop configuration, all the way to 90°, where the dipole becomes fully vertical. The latter configuration is sometimes called a *Halfwave Vertical Dipole* (*HVD*) and is discussed in the section on vertically polarized antennas.

This antenna slightly favors the direction of the antenna's slope as shown in Figure 9.6B. With a non-conducting support and average to poor ground, signals off the back are weaker than those off the front. With a non-conducting mast and good ground, the response is approximately omnidirectional with no gain in any direction.

A conductive support such as a tower acts as a parasitic element. The parasitic effects vary with ground quality, support height, and other conductors on the support (such as a beam at the top or other wire antennas). With such variables, performance is very difficult to predict but that is no reason not to put up the antenna and experiment with it. Many hams report good results with a sloper. To prevent coupling to the feed line, route the coax away from the feed point at 90° from the antenna as far as possible and use a choke balun at the feed point.

An intensive modeling study on feeding the closely-related HVD was done for the book *Simple and Fun Antennas for Hams* (see Bibliography). This study indicated that directing the feed line at an angle down to the ground of as little as 30° from the antenna can work with only minor interaction, provided that feed line chokes were employed at the feed point and a quarter-wavelength down the line from the feed point. (See the **Transmission Line System Techniques** chapter.)

The sloping half-wave dipole in Figure 9.6 exhibits about 5 dB of front-to-back ratio, although even at its most favored direction it doesn't quite have the same maximum gain as the HVD or the flattop dipole.

Two systems of multiple sloping dipoles are presented in articles included with this book's downloadable supplemental information. A system designed for 7 MHz by K1WA and another for 1.8 MHz by K3LR give the builder some directivity while only requiring a single support. These systems can also be adapted to other bands. See also the Bibliography entry for *Sloper Antennas* by Juergen Weigl, OE5CWL.

9.1.4 END-FED ZEPP

Other than to obtain a convenient feed point impedance and to be somewhat balanced, there is no reason why a dipole has to be fed exactly at the center. In the early days, the λ/2 dipole (then called a "Hertz" or "Hertzian" antenna) was often fed at one end where it was called an "End-fed Zepp" after the Zeppelin airships from which it was first deployed. (See the discussion on end-fed half-wave (EFHW) antennas in the **Portable Antennas** chapter.)

Figure 9.7 shows a typical end-fed Zepp with a parallel-wire feed line. Since the feed line is connected at a low-current/high-voltage point on the antenna, the feed point impedance is quite high and often in the neighborhood of 3000-5000 Ω. This is too high to present a match to even the widest-spaced parallel-wire lines, so *tuned feeders* are often employed in which the feed line is an odd number of quarter-wavelengths long. Such a feed line transforms a high impedance into a low impedance as described in the **Transmission Lines** chapter, allowing low-impedance feed lines such as coax to be connected at a point with a more manageable SWR.

Coax feed lines can connect directly to an end-fed Zepp or EFHW by using an impedance transformer at the antenna's feed point. Because of the high impedance, a high transformation ratio is required. Turn ratios of 8:1 (64:1 Z ratio) or higher are required and transformer losses can be significant. Owen Duffy, VK1OD, presents an 8:1 autotransformer in his article "Small efficient matching transformer for an EFHW" at **owenduffy.net**.

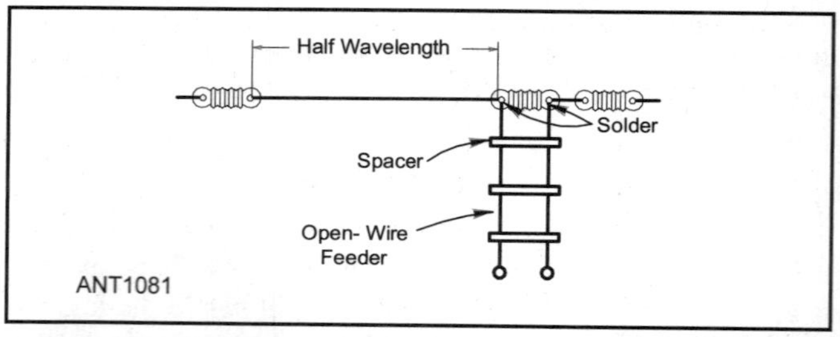

Figure 9.7 — An end-fed Zepp with a parallel-wire feed line connected at one end. Tuned feeders can be used to create a low impedance point for connecting coax as described in the text.

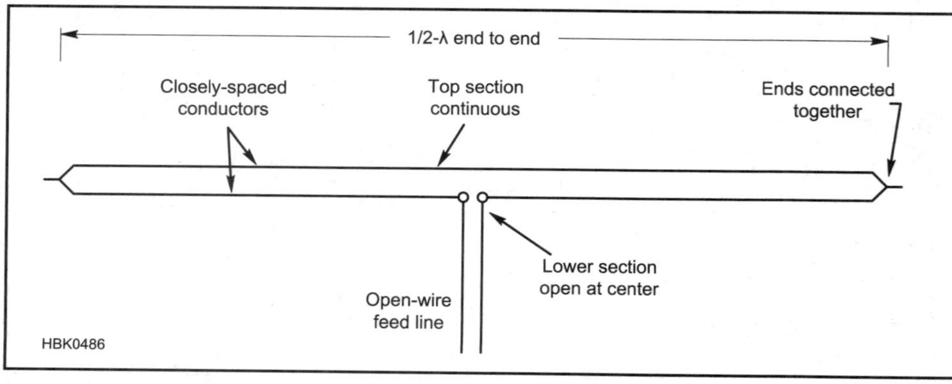

Figure 9.8 — The folded dipole is constructed from open-wire transmission line with the ends connected together. The close proximity of the two conductors and the resulting coupling act as an impedance transformer to raise the feed point impedance over that of a single-wire dipole by the square of the number of conductors used.

Feed points that are not in the center of the antenna (i.e. – asymmetric) are intrinsically unbalanced and significant amounts of common-mode current will flow on the feed line, whether parallel-conductor or coaxial, unless blocked by choke baluns as described in the **Transmission Line System Techniques** chapter. End-fed antennas require the feed line's common-mode path as part of the antenna system. Off-center-fed antennas may or may not include the common-mode path depending on the antenna design.

9.1.5 FOLDED DIPOLES

Figure 9.8 shows a *folded dipole* constructed from a ½-λ section of two wires spaced 4 to 6 inches apart and connected together at each end of the antenna. Plastic spacers are generally used to separate the conductors and open-wire line can also be used. The top conductor is continuous from end to end. The lower conductor, however, is cut in the middle and the feed line attached at that point. Parallel-wire transmission line is then used to connect the transmitter.

A folded dipole has exactly the same gain and radiation pattern as a single-wire dipole. However, because of mutual coupling, feed point current, I, is divided equally between the upper and lower conductors. If the current at the feed point is divided by 2 the feed point impedance goes up by $2^2 = 4$. Feed point impedance in a folded dipole is multiplied from a single-wire dipole by number of wires squared, assuming the wires have the same diameter. Using three wires increases feed point impedance by $3^2 = 9$ and so forth.

The higher feed point impedance allows a low-loss parallel-conductor line to be used with low SWR instead of coaxial cable when a very long feed line is required and using coax would result in too much loss. For example, a three-wire folded dipole would present a feed point impedance close to that of 450-Ω ladder line. VHF and UHF Yagis may use a folded-dipole element to increase the feed point impedance without a matching network.

Another advantage of the two- and three-wire folded dipoles over the single-wire dipole is that they offer a better match over a wider band. This is particularly important if full coverage of the 3.5-MHz band is contemplated.

9.1.6 BROADBAND DIPOLES

Producing a dipole with an SWR bandwidth covering an entire amateur band is difficult for the 160 meter and 80 meter bands due to their relative spans: approximately 10.5% for the 160 meter band and 13.4% for the 80 meter band from the lowest to the highest frequency of the allocation. Most single-wire dipoles have an SWR bandwidth of a few percent in comparison, making it difficult to cover these widest of our bands with just one antenna. Given the importance of 80 meters to a wide variety of operating activities, that band has received the most attention. The higher HF bands are much narrower in comparison and generally can be covered by a single-wire dipole.

As Dave Leeson, W6NL, notes in his *QEX* article "The Story of the Broadband Dipole," the search for a broadband 80 meter dipole antenna has a long history, culminating in a series of articles by Frank Witt, AI1H. Beginning with the antennas seen in early radio, a wide range of broadbanding concepts has been explored. Here are some major categories:

- Cage, parallel wire, fan or bow-tie dipoles that have a large equivalent diameter or that approximate conical dipoles
- Multiple dipoles with staggered resonances connected in parallel
- Dipoles with a coupled resonator "open sleeve" element
- "Bazooka" dipoles with coaxial radiating elements
- Dipoles with lumped reactive matching networks
- Dipoles with coaxial radiating and matching elements
- Dipoles with resonant feed line matching

There are mechanical and reliability problems associated with many of the broadbanding schemes. Cage and multiple dipole configurations have a tendency to become twisted in the wind, are difficult to construct and install, take up more space, and have greater visual impact than a simple dipole. Coaxial radiating elements require sealing from the weather, are heavy to support and are not necessarily strong enough to avoid stretching under load. In addition, some of the published designs don't have sufficient broadband response, while others are broadband mainly because of losses in the matching network.

The remainder of this section will present examples of each, focusing on the first and last categories as giving the best performance. See Leeson's article for a thorough list of references. All of these methods are discussed in the article "Broadband Antenna Matching" by Frank Witt, AI1H, which is included with the **Transmission Line System Technique** chapter's supplemental material.

Increasing Antenna Diameter

The simplest way to increase the SWR bandwidth of a single-wire dipole is to increase the thickness of the wire (the length-to-diameter ratio) as discussed in the **Antenna Fundamentals** and **Dipoles and Ground-Planes** chapters. This reduces the change in reactance with frequency, causing the SWR to vary more gradually with frequency, as well. Since the range of available wire sizes is quite limited in the potential effect on bandwidth at MF and HF, the technique of employing multiple wires is used to create a larger-diameter conductor.

There are three common methods of using multiple wires in this way: the cage, the fan and the open-sleeve. The cage shown in **Figure 9.9** is a very old design, having been employed during the early days of "wireless" to increase bandwidth of antennas used for spark signals with their very wide bandwidths. The cage consists of several wires (three or more) held apart by spreaders (insulating or non-insulating) and connected together at the ends and at the feed point. A project describing the cage dipole in use at W1AW on 80 meters is included at the end of this section. The "flat-top" antenna of several wires in parallel instead of in a cage was also used in this way.

In fact, to increase bandwidth it is not necessary to increase the antenna's diameter over the entire length, just near the ends. Thus, a simplified variation on the cage is to create

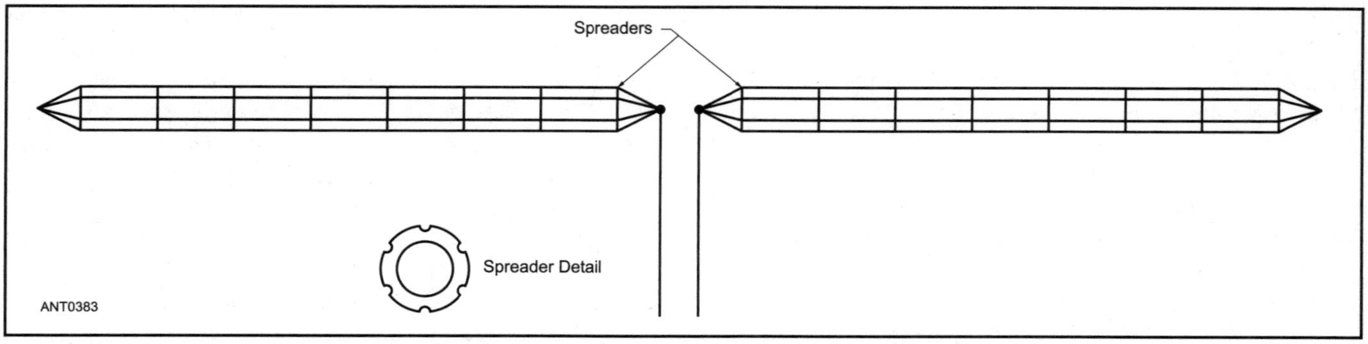

Figure 9.9 — Construction of a cage dipole. The spreaders need not be of conductive material and should be lightweight. Between adjacent conductors, the spacing should be 2% of overall length or less. The number of spreaders and their spacing along the dipole should be sufficient to maintain a relatively constant separation of the radiator wires. The spreaders can be round as shown in the detail or any suitable cross arrangement.

a "bow-tie" with just two wires in each leg of the dipole. The wires are tied together at the feed point and spread apart up to 10 feet at the ends of the dipole where they may be connected together or left separate. The bow-tie or "skeleton biconical dipole" was discussed by Hallas in May 2005 *QST*. (See the Bibliography.)

In both cases, extra tethers are usually required at the ends of the cage or fan to keep the antenna from twisting in the wind. This is less of a problem with the cage design which uses multiple spreaders to keep the wires apart. Such antennas provide excellent electrical performance at the cost of some mechanical complexity and extra weight. They may not be suitable in areas where heavy icing or high wind speed is common.

A second method creates a fan of two or more dipoles with close but not identical resonant frequencies. This is illustrated in **Figure 9.10** in which three dipoles are cut for the bottom, middle and top frequencies in the 80 meter band (3.5, 3.75, and 4 MHz) and fed in parallel at the feed point. This is similar to the bow-tie mentioned in the previous paragraph but the ends of the dipoles are not connected together. A non-conducting spreader is used to hold the wires apart.

The dipole impedances interact to some degree depending on how different the resonant frequencies are. Modeling is recommended at the expected height above ground but may not give completely accurate results due to the very shallow angle at which the wires join at the feed point. Expect some adjustments as the three dipoles are adjusted to give the desired SWR curve across the band. Two dipoles can cover approximately two-thirds of the band.

The third method is to place a parasitic dipole extremely close to the driven dipole so that it couples to the driven dipole and essentially operates in parallel with it. This technique has been refined in several recent articles. **Figure 9.11** shows an implementation by Ted Armstrong, WA6RNC, from the March 2013 issue of *QST*. (This article is included with this book's downloadable supplemental information along with a previous design from Rudy Severns, N6LF. Check the

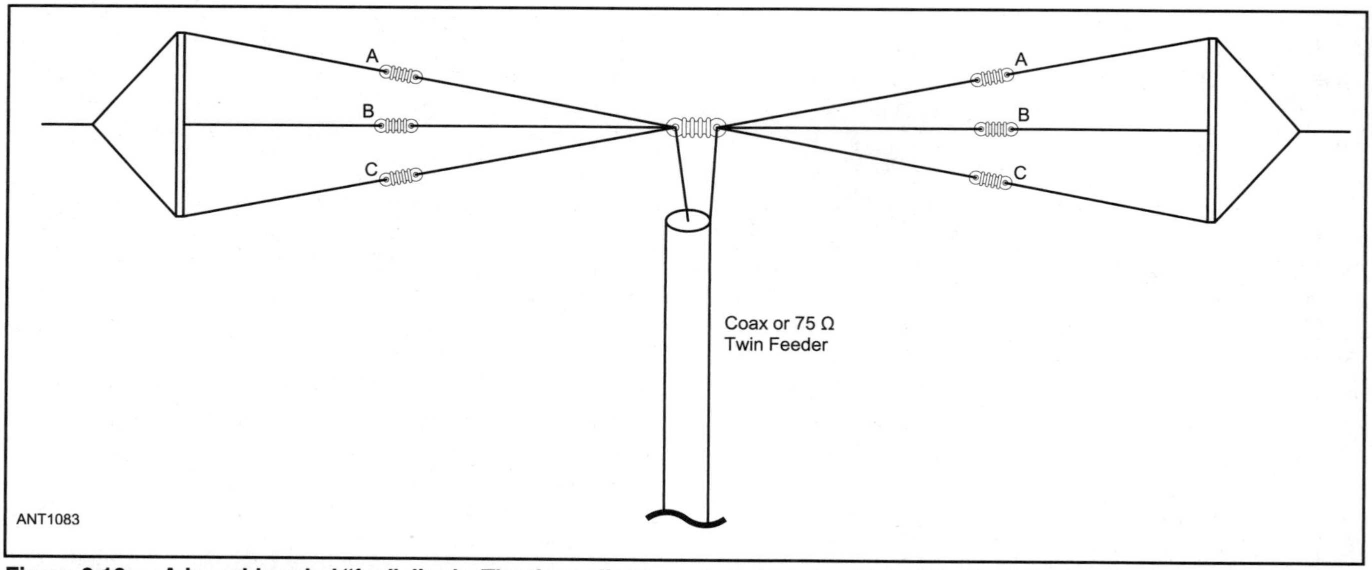

Figure 9.10 — A broad-banded "fan" dipole. The three dipoles a, b and c are cut to resonate at the band edges and center band frequency. This creates a single antenna that can be used over the entire 3.5 MHz band. On 80 meters, the dipole cut for 3.5 MHz will be approximately 7 feet longer than the one cut for 4 MHz. (Figure 9.10 from *Practical Wire Antennas*, courtesy RSGB — see Bibliography.)

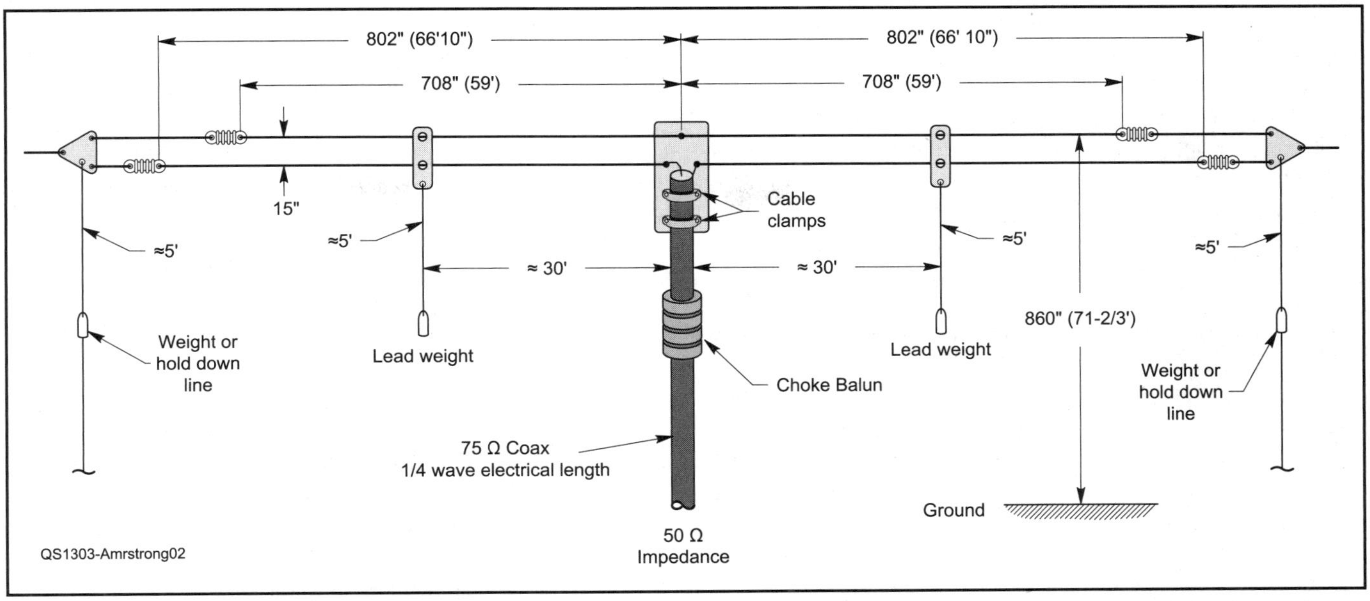

Figure 9.11 — Construction details and dimensions of the coupled resonator 75/80 meter antenna including a λ/4 impedance transformer of 75 Ω coax. Based on a coax velocity factor of 0.66 (66%) for solid polyethylene dielectric coax, the λ/4 transformer should be 43.3 feet long at 3.75 MHz. Measure and build the λ/4 transformer as described in the Transmission Line System Techniques chapter. The original article recommended type #43 but type #31 will provide more choking impedance at these frequencies.

Antenna Book's website at **www.arrl.org/arrl-antenna-book-reference** for more information about broadband designs for antennas on 160 through 40 meters.)

An isolated wire is placed next to a dipole cut for the low end of the band. The shorter wire has a higher resonant frequency than that of outer, longer folded dipole and so acts as the radiator at the higher frequency. This antenna's SWR was less than 1.7:1 across the entire 75/80 meter band and lower at most frequencies. .

W1AW 80 Meter Cage Dipole

The 80 meter cage antenna used at W1AW is based loosely on a design that appeared in a December 1980 *QST* article by Allen Harbach, WA4DRU. (See the Bibliography and this book's downloadable supplemental information.) The antenna is used primarily for W1AW's scheduled transmissions. It is also used for regular visitor operations as well. The resonant frequency of the antenna is 3627 kHz but the overall SWR is less than 2:1 from 3580 to 3995 kHz.

The W1AW cage antenna differs from the original article in that it's meant to be in place for a long period of time. So, most parts of the antenna are designed more ruggedly than in the Harbach design.

Each leg of the dipole is a cage made of four 80 meter dipole antennas of #14 AWG stranded copper wire tied together both at the ends and at the feed point as shown in **Figure 9.12**. Although Copperweld or an equivalent heftier wire could have been used, this size wire was easy to work with. The four wires forming each leg of the dipole are separated using a similar crosspiece. There is a crosspiece near the feed point and the ends. The spacing between the wires is three feet.

Each cage wire passes through one leg of each crosspiece.

Figure 9.12 — The center insulator is constructed from a PVC pipe tee with end caps covering each end. A similar crosspiece separates the wires at the ends of the antenna. Stainless steel eyebolts are used to hold the ends of the cage and solder lugs with jumpers connect to the cage wires. Inside the tee, jumpers connect the eyebolts to the SO-239 on the third pipe cap. A piece of PVC pipe is U-bolted to the inner crosspieces of both cage sections. The entire assembly is supported by a sidearm from one of the W1AW towers. The antenna was constructed by W1AW Chief Operator Joe Carcia, NJ1Q.

A keeper wire is soldered across around the end of the PVC tube to the antenna wire on either side. This keeps the crosspiece from moving up and down the antenna. Exterior silicone caulk is applied to the hole in the tubing to seal it from moisture. Inside the crosspieces are oak dowels and the ends of the crosspieces are also capped. This adds rigidity to the crosspiece.

The feed point assembly is a homebrew PVC center insulator consisting of a pair of 2-inch end caps attached to both ends of a 6-inch long, 2-inch PVC pipe tee. A stainless steel eyebolt with two solder lugs is mounted in the middle of each cap. One solder lug is on the outside of the cap for a connection to the antenna and the other is inside for connection to the SO-239 coax connector. The SO-239 is mounted on a third cap attached to the middle tee section.

An 8-turn coaxial choke is connected to the antenna at the center insulator. The choke is made from RG-213 coax using designs included in the **Transmission Line System Techniques** chapter.

The center insulator assembly is bolted to a 4-foot length piece of 1-inch PVC pipe. The inner crosspieces are also bolted to this section of pipe as shown in the figure. This provides added support to the antenna. The center insulator and length of PVC are secured to the tower using a side-arm.

At the feed point, the four wires of each leg are brought together and looped through the eye-bolt. They are then twisted and soldered together and a short jumper of wire connects the twisted wires to a solder lug on the eyebolt. Inside each end cap, a jumper wire connects a second solder lug on the eyebolt to the SO-239 on the remaining cap.

At the outside ends of the cage, all four wires are brought to a common point, twisted together, and then attached to a strain insulator. The strain insulator and two of the crosspiece arms are tied off to the supports. This keeps the antenna legs from twisting in the breeze.

Tuning the antenna can be a bit tricky since each leg (wire) must be trimmed the same amount. It is best to start off with wire lengths calculated using the lowest operating frequency (for example, 3500 kHz). After trimming, the overall length of the antenna will be slightly smaller than that of a single-wire 80 meter dipole. This is because the radiating element is three feet in diameter — much thicker than a single-wire dipole.

While construction of this antenna is a bit more involved than that of a regular dipole, the result is a broadband antenna that doesn't require a tuner. The design specifications can also be recalculated to fit other amateur bands.

"Bazooka" Dipoles

The initial design for the "Double Bazooka" antenna was published in 1968 by W8TV (see the Bibliography). It uses twin matching stubs of RG-58 coax connected in series with each leg of the dipole at the feed point (see **Figure 9.13A**) A variation called the "Crossed Bazooka" (Figure 9.13B) connects the stubs in parallel across the feed point. Each stub is electrically λ/4 inside the coax, shorted at the outside end. The outer surface of the coax shield and the extension wires from the shorted end of the coax form the radiating surface of the dipole. The original article suggested parallel-conductor extensions but most builders use a single wire today.

The theory of the double bazooka is presented as follows: The shorted stubs act as open circuits at their resonant frequency. As the frequency is increased, the stubs are electrically longer and become capacitive above resonance. The feed point impedance of the antenna, however, becomes inductive. So, the reactance of the stubs acts to cancel some of the antenna's reactance, increasing the SWR bandwidth of the antenna.

Bandwidths of 250 to 500 kHz are reported for the double bazooka, but most of the increased bandwidth is due to loss and effects other than reactance cancelling, which analysis shows to be fairly minor. The addition of the reactance in parallel with the feed point does not result in simple cancellation but also raises the feed point resistance, similarly to how an L-network behaves.

Walt Maxwell, W2DU addressed these issues in a *QST* Technical Correspondence and a *Ham Radio* article (see Bibliography), attributing the reported larger bandwidth primarily to feed line losses and increased conductor diameter. A similar analysis by Owen Duffy, VK1OD (**owenduffy.net/antenna/DoubleBazooka/index.htm**) yields the same conclusions. Nevertheless, the antenna is fairly popular as a single-band low-band HF antenna and gives adequate service.

Table 9.2 gives lengths for the various parts of the double bazooka on three bands where the antenna is commonly used.

Table 9.2
Double Bazooka Component Lengths

Frequency (MHz)	*End Wire Length*	*Stub Length*	*Overall Length*
3.80	17 ft 9.1 in	42 ft 9.2 in	121 ft 0.6 in
5.37	12 ft 6.8 in	30 ft 3.1 in	85 ft 7.9 in
7.15	9 ft 5.4 in	22 ft 8.8 in	64 ft 4.1 in

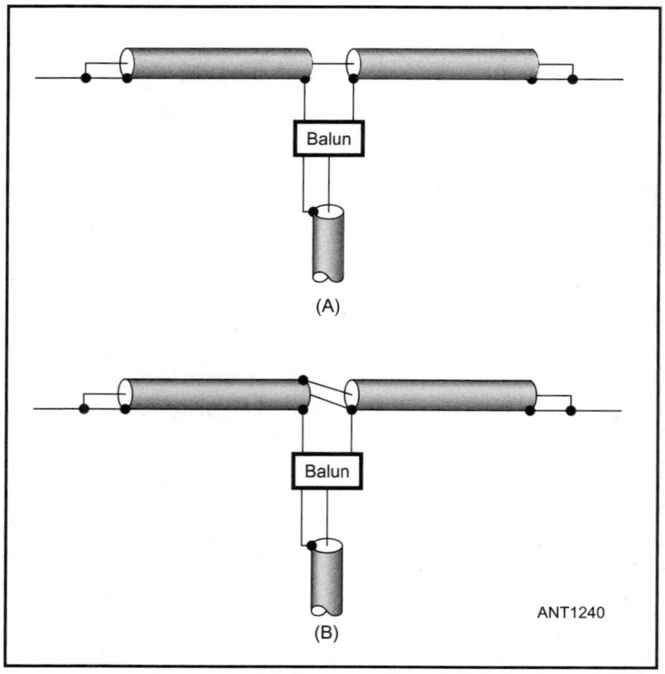

Figure 9.13 — The construction of a double bazooka dipole (A) showing the construction of the stubs and connection to the feed line. A variation is the crossed bazooka antenna at B.

Values are from the online calculator "Double Bazooka NVIS Antenna Calculator" provided by West Mountain Radio at **www.westmountainradio.com/antenna_calculator_bazooka.php**. Height above ground will also affect tuning of the antenna and may require adjustment of the end wire sections. The coaxial stubs must also be carefully waterproofed.

LC Matching Network

This matching technique in **Figure 9.14** uses a parallel LC circuit for reactance compensation instead of stubs. It also acts as a step-up transformer voltage balun — see the **Transmission Line System Techniques** section on Three-Winding Voltage Baluns. The network is connected across the feed point of a single-wire dipole and adjusted for best performance.

The 3:1 SWR points can be kept entirely within the 80-meter band, rising to near 3:1 at 3.5 and 4 MHz. The version known as the "DXer's Delight" sacrifices low SWR at the high end of the band for low SWR near 3.5 and 3.8 MHz — both prime frequencies for DXing and contesting. The DXer's Delight version uses a 400 pF / 4 kV transmitting capacitor for C1 and a 4.7 µH inductor made from 8½ turns of B&W type 3029 coil stock (6 turns per inch, 2½ inch diameter, #12 AWG wire). Regardless of which version you prefer, use a variable capacitor and tapped coil to perform adjustments at low power levels and then replace the components with high-power equivalents.

Transmission Line Resonator (TLR) Matching

The TLR system was introduced to amateurs by Frank Witt, AI1H, in the article "A Simple Broadband Dipole for 80 Meters." (The article is excerpted here and is included in this chapter's downloadable supplemental information along with a more complete treatment of broadband matching techniques in the article "Broadband Antenna Matching" in the supplemental material for the **Transmission Line System Techniques** chapter.) In this system-level approach, the single-wire dipole antenna itself is not modified. The system uses a broadband match as shown in **Figure 9.15A**. The key broadbanding element is the *transmission line resonator* (TLR). Part of the transmission line compensates for the reactance presented by the dipole away from its resonant frequency. This part of the line is a multiple of an electrical half-wavelength. The quarter-wavelength segment acts as a synchronous transformer to present an appropriate source impedance to the TLR. (See the **Transmission Line System Techniques** chapter.) See the Bibliography entry for Cebik's more detailed analysis and modeling of the TLR match.

The antenna is a center-fed half-wavelength dipole trimmed for resonance at 3.75 MHz. The transmission line is segmented into one electrical wavelength of 50-Ω coax and an electrical quarter-wavelength of 75-Ω coax. The values in **Table 9.3** were calculated using standard formulas for electrical length of feed lines (see the **Transmission Lines** chapter) with a velocity factor (VF) of 0.66, corresponding to coax with a solid polyethylene dielectric, such as RG-11 and RG-213. The actual values resulted from tuning the antenna, manufacturing variations in VF from published values, and stretching of the coax. The antenna was installed as an inverted-V with an included angle of 140° and a height of 60 feet. Dipole wire size was #14 AWG but that is not critical.

The system's SWR at the transmitter is shown in Figure 9.15B. The SWR curve labeled "Conventional System" is the same dipole fed with about ¾-wavelength of RG-213. The broadband system's SWR bandwidth is 2.2 times that of the conventional system. Additional mismatch loss caused by SWR in the matching sections is less than 0.5 dB anywhere in the band. Witt's 1993 article shows loss for several system configurations, including an unmatched system.

The feed line length may be extended by adding any

Table 9.3
Broadband 80 Meter Dipole Calculated and Actual Lengths

	Calculated	*Actual*
¼-λ Coax	43.3 ft	43.3 ft
1-λ Coax	173.1 ft	170.5 ft*
Dipole	124.5 ft	122.7 ft

* includes feed line used for choke balun

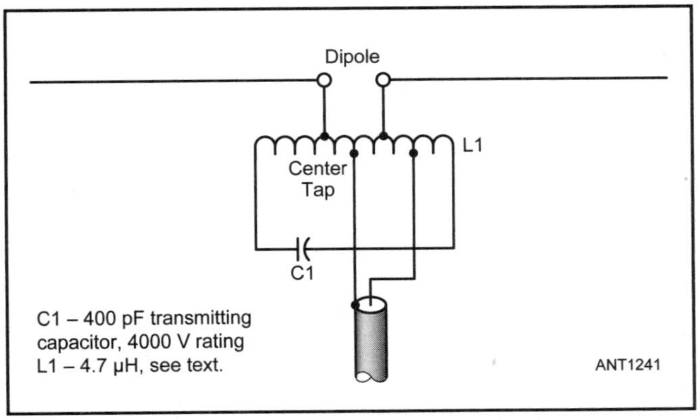

Figure 9.14 — The matching network for the DXer's Delight.

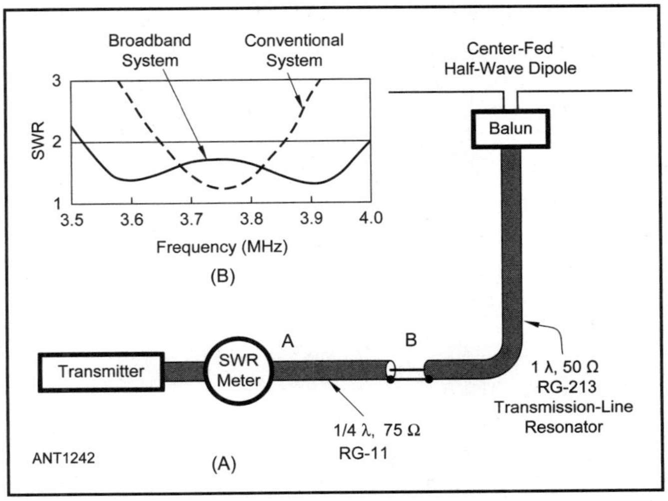

Figure 9.15 — Broadband TLR-based feed line match (see text).

required length of 50-Ω coax between the transmitter and the quarter-wave segment (point A in Figure 9.15A). A choke balun should be installed at the antenna's feed point. If the feed line is formed into a coiled-coax choke, that length of line must be included in the one-wavelength segment.

Tuning is accomplished by adjusting the dipole and resonator lengths. You can tune the antenna without connectors at the junction of the resonator and ¼-wavelength section by tack-soldering them together and testing with an antenna analyzer or very low power. Start with the dipole legs each 2 feet longer than calculated and the extra wire wrapped back around the antenna — it can be trimmed after adjustment is complete. (Existing 80 meter dipoles can be converted to the TLR system by trimming them to resonance at a mid-band frequency and adding the necessary resonator segments.

Begin by adjusting the dipole legs, each by the same amount, so that the SWR curve measured at the transmitter is symmetrical about the center frequency. To offset the frequency of minimum SWR, adjust the length of the one-wavelength resonator using the formula $L_{NEW} = L_{OLD} (f_0 - \Delta f) / f_0$, where f_0 is the design frequency of the antenna system and Δf is the required offset. The length of the quarter-wavelength segment does not need to be changed to shift the SWR curve.

9.2 VERTICAL ANTENNAS

9.2.1 THE HALF-WAVE VERTICAL DIPOLE (HVD)

The simplest form of vertical is that of a half-wave vertical dipole, an HVD. This is a horizontal dipole turned 90° so that it is perpendicular to the ground under it. Of course, the top end of such an antenna must be at least a half wave above the ground or else it would be touching the ground. This poses quite a construction challenge if the builder wants a free-standing low-frequency antenna. Hams fortunate enough to have tall trees on their property can suspend wire HVDs from these trees. Similarly, hams with two tall towers can run rope catenaries between them to hold up an HVD.

A vertical half-wave dipole has some operational advantages compared to a more-commonly used vertical configuration — the quarter-wave vertical used with some sort of above-ground counterpoise or an on-ground radial system. See **Figure 9.16**, which shows the two configurations discussed here. In each case, the lowest part of each antenna is 8 feet above ground, to prevent passersby from being able to touch any live wire. Each antenna is assumed to be made of #14 AWG wire resonant on 80 meters.

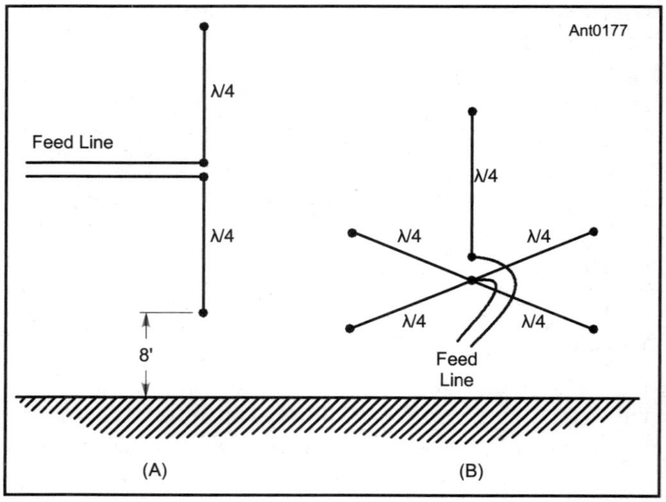

Figure 9.16 — At A, an 80 meter half-wave vertical dipole elevated 8 feet above the ground. The feed line is run perpendicularly away from the dipole. At B, a "ground plane" type of quarter-wave vertical, with four elevated resonant radials. Both antennas are mounted 8 feet above the ground to keep them away from passersby.

Figure 9.17 compares elevation patterns for the two antennas for "average ground." You can see that the half-wave vertical dipole has about 1.5 dB higher peak gain, since it compresses the vertical elevation pattern down somewhat closer to the horizon than does the quarter-wave ground plane. Another advantage to using a half-wave radiator besides higher gain is that less horizontal "real estate" is needed compared to a quarter-wave vertical with its horizontal radials.

The obvious disadvantage to an HVD is that it is taller than a quarter-wave ground plane. This requires a higher support (such as a taller tree) if you make it from wire, or a longer element if you make it from telescoping aluminum tubing.

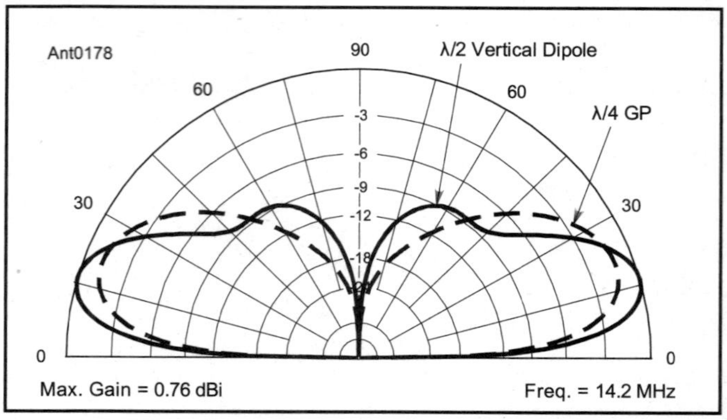

Figure 9.17 — A comparison of the elevation patterns for the two antennas in Figure 9.16. The peak gain of the HVD is about 1.5 dB higher than that for the quarter-wave ground-plane radiator with radials.

Center-Feeding a Vertical Dipole

To minimize coupling between the feed line and the antenna, you must arrange the feed line so that it is perpendicular to the half-wave radiator. This means you must support the coax feed line above ground for some distance before bringing the coax down to ground level. A question immediately arises: How far must you go out horizontally with the feed line before going to ground level to eliminate common-mode currents that are radiated onto the coax shield? Such common-mode currents will affect the feed point impedance as well as the radiation pattern for the antenna system. Quite a bit of distortion in the azimuthal pattern can be created if common-mode currents aren't suppressed, usually by using a common-mode choke balun.

Constructing such a choke is very simple: ferrite beads of an approximate mix are slipped over the coax (before the connectors are soldered on or else they won't fit!) and taped in place. The only problem with this scheme is that an additional support (some sort of "skyhook") is required to support the coax horizontally. Let's try to simplify the installation, by slanting the feed line coax down to ground from the feed point at a fairly steep angle of about 30° from vertical. See **Figure 9.18**.

Note that the bottom end of the coax in Figure 9.18 is grounded to a ground rod. This serves as a mechanical connection to hold the coax in place and it provides some protection against lightning strikes. Now, as a purely practical matter, just how picky are we being here? What if we skip the second common-mode choke and just use one at the feed point? The computer model predicts that there will be some distortion in the azimuthal pattern — about 1.1 dB worth. Whether this is serious is up to you. However, you may find other problems with common-mode currents on the coax shield — problems such as "RF in the shack" or variable SWR readings depending on the way coax is routed in the station. The addition of three extra ferrite beads to suppress the common-mode currents is cheap insurance.

A variation on the HVD that is shortened through the use of capacitive loading is the *Compact Vertical Dipole (CVD)*. An article describing the CVD is included with this book's downloadable supplemental information.

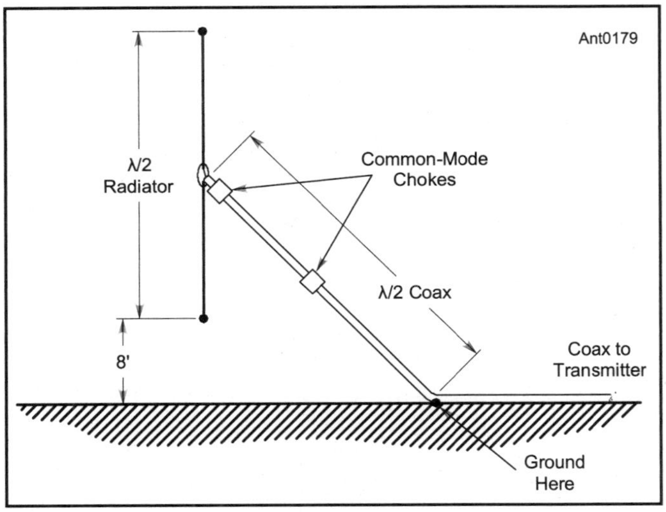

Figure 9.18 — A 20 meter HVD whose bottom is 8 feet above ground. This is fed with a λ/2 of RG-213 coax. This system uses a common-mode choke at the feed point and another λ/4 down the line. The resulting azimuthal radiation pattern is within 0.4 dB of being perfectly circular. The "wingspan" of this antenna system is 27 feet from the radiator to the point where the coax comes to ground level.

End-Feeding a Vertical Dipole

The problem of coupling between the feed line and the antenna is minimized by making the feed line part of the antenna as shown in **Figure 9.19**. In this design by Jim Brown, K9YC, and Glen Brown, W6GJB, a quarter-wavelength of

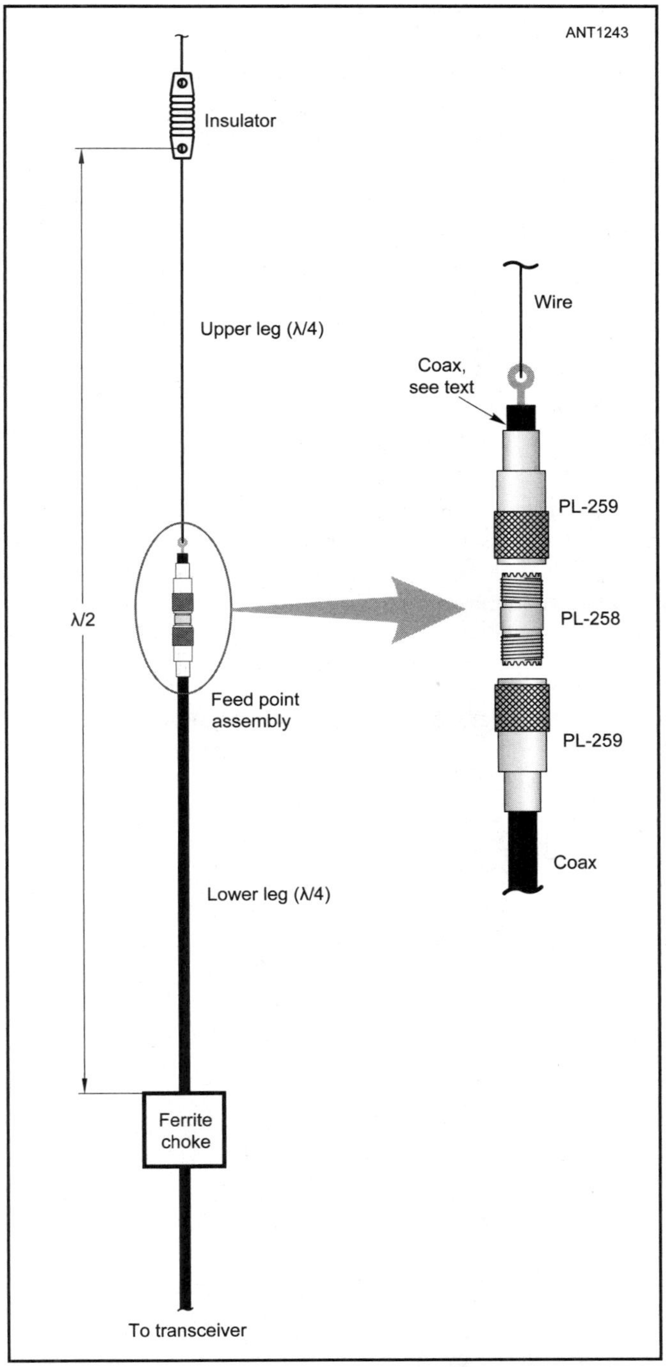

Figure 9.19 — The vertical dipole shown here uses coaxial cable as the lower leg. The upper and lower leg are connected together by using a PL-259 on each and a PL-258 to join them. A ferrite choke acts as a insulator for the bottom leg (see text).

coaxial cable forms the bottom leg of the dipole and is terminated by a high-impedance ferrite choke. The upper leg is a conventional quarter-wave wire. This design requires just the single support and has none of the issues with trying to run the feed line at right angles to the antenna. The full presentation by K9YC is available at **k9yc.com/VerticalDipole.pdf**.

The challenge with this design is to ensure that the ferrite choke at the bottom of the antenna has enough choking impedance at the frequency of use to act like an insulator and to not overheat from the high voltage across it. The choke can be made of type #31 or #43 ferrite and should be resonant (for maximum impedance) near the operating frequency. If the choking impedance is not high enough, the choke will overheat. For 1500 W operation, at least 10 kΩ is needed; for 500 W, 5 kΩ; and for 100 W or less, 1–2 kΩ is sufficient. (See the sections on ferrite chokes in the **Transmission Line System Techniques** chapter.)

Use coaxial cable with a copper braid shield for power levels above QRP. Do not use cable with only a foil or thin braid shield. The dipole's impedance will be around 70 Ω so either 75-Ω or 50-Ω coax will work.

The center connection is shown as a detail in Figure 9.19 and consists of two PL-259 plugs connected by a PL-258 "barrel" connector. The upper PL-259 should have a short piece of RG-8 or RG-213 inserted with only the center conductor soldered to the connector pin. The coax should extend out of the body of the connector for at least ¼ inch so that the center conductor is insulated from the body by the coax jacket. Extend the center conductor for an inch or so and form a small loop. The upper leg wire is then soldered to this loop. The lower PL-259 is fitted to the coax feed line as usual.

9.2.2 MONOPOLE VERTICALS WITH GROUND-PLANE RADIALS

For best performance the vertical portion of a ground-plane type of antenna should be λ/4 or more, but this is not an absolute requirement. With proper design, antennas as short as 0.1 λ or even less can be efficient and effective. Antennas shorter than λ/4 will be reactive and some form of loading and perhaps a matching network will be required.

If the radiator is made of wire supported by nonconducting material, the approximate length for λ/4 resonance can be found from:

$$\ell_{feet} = \frac{234}{f_{MHz}} \qquad (1)$$

The same cautions about the effects of ground and wire or tubing diameter apply to this equation for verticals. For a tower, the resonant length will be shorter still. It is recommended that the builder start a few percent long and trim the antenna to length based on measurements taken with the antenna in place. (See the **Dipoles and Monopoles** chapter.)

The effect of ground characteristics on losses and elevation pattern is discussed in detail in the chapter **Effects of Ground**. The most important points made in that discussion are the effect of ground characteristics on the radiation pattern and the means for achieving low ground-loss resistance in a buried ground system. As ground conductivity increases, low-angle radiation improves. This makes a vertical very attractive to those who live in areas with good ground conductivity. If your QTH is on a saltwater beach, then a vertical would be very effective, even when compared to horizontal antennas at great height.

When a radial ground system is used, the efficiency of the antenna will be limited by the loss resistance of the ground system. The ground can be a number of radial wires extending out from the base of the antenna for about λ/4. Note that radial wires on or in the ground are not tuned or resonant in the conventional sense because they couple strongly to the soil. That they are often specified to be λ/4 long stems from a study of broadcast antenna systems in the 1930s that resulted in the current standard of 120 radials, each long enough such that their ends are approximately 0.05-λ apart. That system was designed to minimize ground losses and the radials are approximately ¼-λ long but it is not resonant or tuned.

If the radials are to be buried, only enough depth to keep them in the ground throughout the year is required. Burying radials more than a few inches deep reduces their effectiveness, particular on the higher HF bands. Radial wires should be close to or on the surface for maximum effectiveness.

Radial Spacing

Figuring out how to space radials equally around a circle is explained in this sidebar. The information was originally published on the Towertalk reflector by Rod Ehrhart, WN8R, of DX Engineering.

Begin by determining the radius of the circle in which the radials will be installed. If your area is irregular, choose the minimum radial length. An example is the best way of illustrating the process:

If your minimum radial length is 25 feet, establish a circle that has a radius (r) of 25 feet from the antenna mount. The circumference (C) of that circle is 2πr or C = (2) × (3.14) × (25 feet), which equals 157 feet. If you have decided to install 60 radials (N = 60), the spacing (S) between each radial on the 25-foot radius circle is calculated as S = C / N or S = 157 feet / 60 radials = 2.6 feet or about 2 feet, 7 inches between each radial on the circle. Use string to draw the circle and measure 2 feet, 7 inches spacing around the circle. If the radial is longer than 25 feet, stretch it straight out from the antenna mount so that it crosses the circle at the marked point.

If you want to install 90 radials, then it would be 157 feet / 90 radials = 1.74 feet/radial, or a little less than 1 foot 9 inches between each radial wire on the circle at 25 feet from the antenna mount.

Working this out in advance, you will not need to worry about how far apart the radials are where they end, or trying to eye-ball their spacing. When filling an irregular area with radials, each one will have a different spacing where they end. By using this measurement method, you will be able to make all of the radials evenly spaced, and as long as they can be, for maximum antenna system performance.

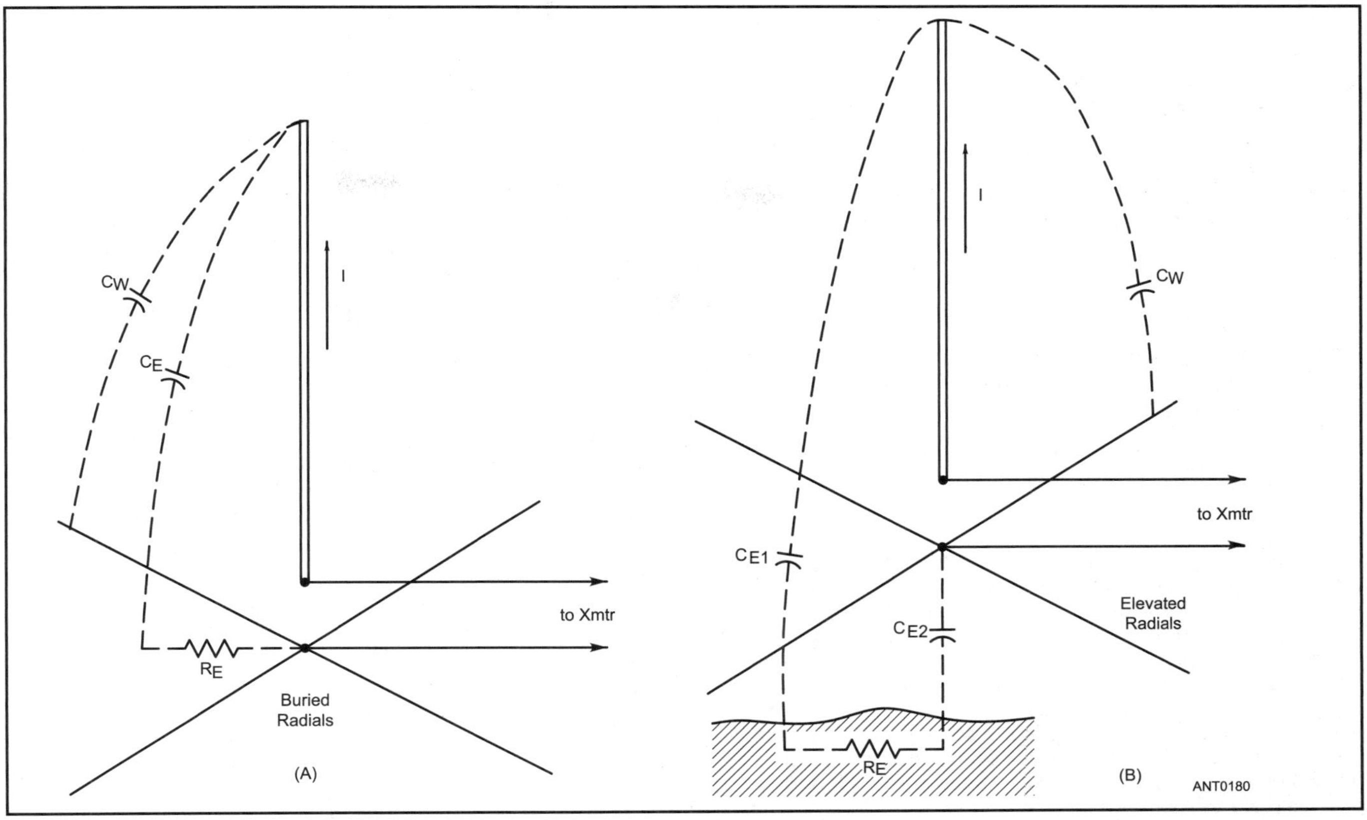

Figure 9.20 — How earth currents affect the losses in a short vertical antenna system. At A, the current through the combination of C_E and R_E may be appreciable if C_E is much greater than C_W, the capacitance of the vertical to the ground wires. This ratio can be improved (up to a point) by using more radials. By raising the entire antenna system off the ground, C_E (which consists of the series combination of C_{E1} and C_{E2}) is decreased while C_W stays the same. The radial system shown at B is sometimes called a counterpoise.

Radials can be effectively hidden by mowing grass or cutting vegetation as short as practical, then laying down the radials and holding them against the ground with lawn staples or short lengths of iron rebar-tie wire bent double. Grass will quickly grow over the radials, effectively hiding them while keeping them close to the soil surface. The action of plant growth, insects, and worms will eventually bury the radials in soil.

Driven ground rods, while needed for electrical safety and for lightning protection, are of little value as an RF ground for a vertical antenna, except perhaps in marshy or beach areas. As pointed out, many long radials are desirable. In general, however, a large number of short radials are preferable to only a few long radials, although the best system would have 60 or more radials longer than λ/4. An elevated system of radials or a ground screen (*counterpoise*) may be used instead of buried radials, and can result in an efficient antenna. **Figure 9.20** illustrates the difference between buried and elevated radial systems. The reader is directed to the chapter Effects of Ground for a discussion of ground plane radial systems for vertical monopole antennas.

9.2.3 GROUND-PLANE ANTENNAS

The ground-plane antenna is a λ/4 vertical with four radials, as shown in **Figure 9.21**. The entire antenna is elevated above ground. A practical example of a 7-MHz ground-plane antenna is given in **Figure 9.22**. As explained earlier, elevating the antenna reduces the ground loss and lowers the radiation angle somewhat. The radials are sloped downward to make the feed point impedance closer to 50 Ω. (Also see the discussion of elevated radial systems in the chapter **Effects of Ground**.)

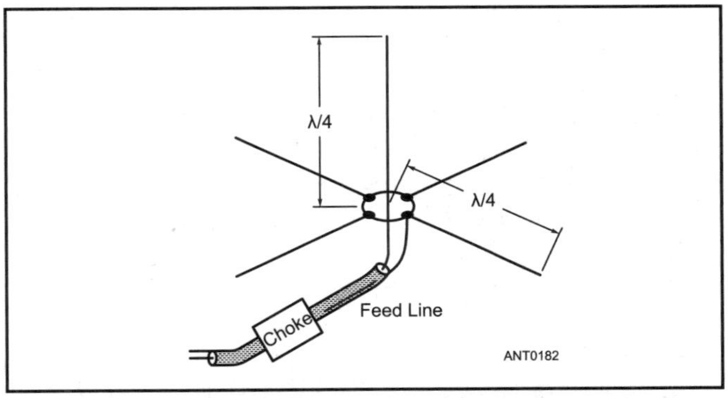

Figure 9.21 — The ground-plane antenna. Power is applied between the base of the vertical radiator and the center of the ground plane, as indicated in the drawing. Decoupling from the transmission line and any conductive support structure is highly desirable.

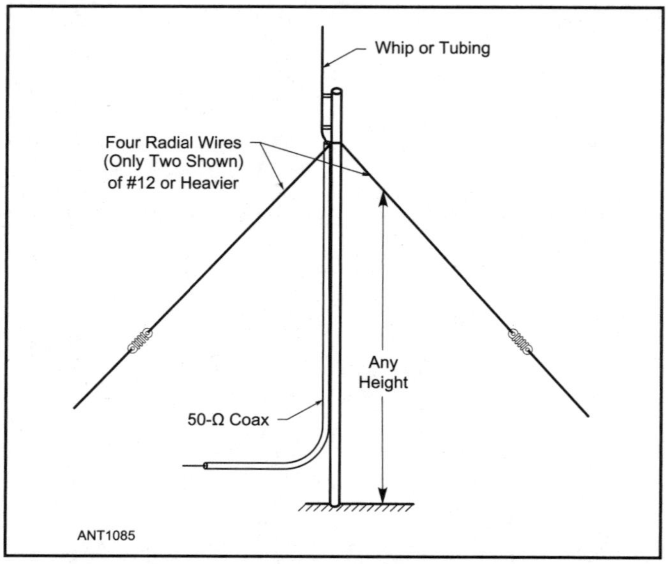

Figure 9.22 — A ground-plane antenna is effective for DX work on 7 MHz. Although its base can be any height above ground, losses in the ground underneath will be reduced by keeping the bottom of the antenna and the ground plane as high above ground as possible. Feeding the antenna directly with 50-Ω coaxial cable will result in a low SWR. The vertical radiator and the radials are all λ/4 long electrically. The radial's physical length will depend on their length-to-diameter ratios, the height over ground and the length of the vertical radiator, as discussed in text.

The feed point impedance of the antenna varies with the height above ground, and to a lesser extent varies with the ground characteristics. **Figure 9.23** is a graph of feed point resistance (R_R) for a ground-plane antenna with the radials parallel to the ground. R_R is plotted as a function of height above ground. Notice that the difference between perfect ground and average ground ($\varepsilon = 13$ and $\sigma = 0.005$ S/m) is small, except when quite close to ground. Near ground R_R is between 36 and 40 Ω. This is a reasonable match for 50-Ω feed line but as the antenna is raised above ground R_R drops to approximately 22 Ω, which is not a very good match. The feed point resistance can be increased by sloping the radials downward, away from the vertical section.

The effect of sloping the radials is shown in **Figure 9.24**. The graph is for an antenna well above ground (> 0.3 λ). Notice that $R_R = 50$ Ω when the radials are sloped downward at an angle of 45°, a convenient value. The resonant length of the antenna will vary slightly with the angle. In addition, the resonant length will vary a small amount with height above the ground. It is for these reasons, as well as the effect of conductor diameter, that some adjustment of the radial lengths is usually required. When the ground-plane antenna is used on the higher HF bands and at VHF, the height above ground is usually such that a radial sloping angle of 45° will give a good match to 50-Ω feed line.

The effect of height on R_R with a radial angle of 45° is shown in **Figure 9.25**. Below 7 MHz, it is seldom possible to elevate the antenna a significant portion of a wavelength and the radial angle required to match to 50-Ω line is usually

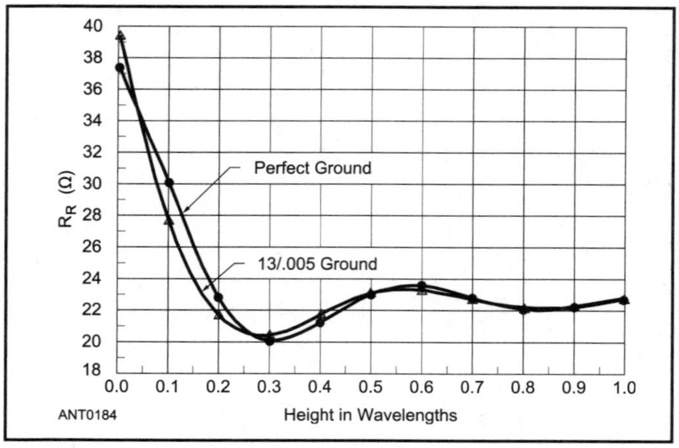

Figure 9.23 — Radiation resistance of a 4-radial ground-plane antenna as a function of height over ground. Perfect and average ground are shown. Frequency is 3.525 MHz. Radial angle (θ) is 0°.

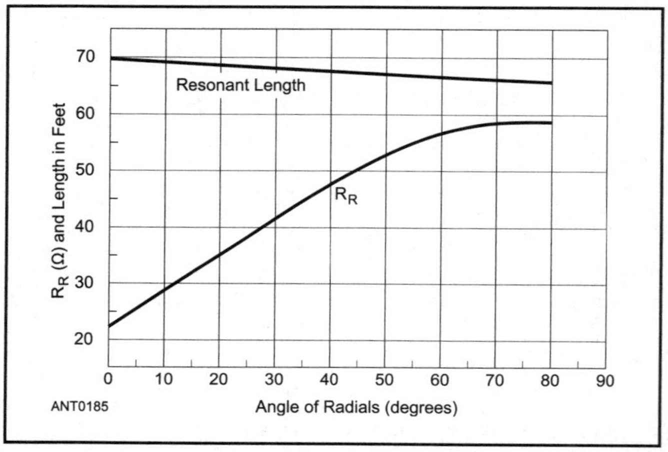

Figure 9.24 — Radiation resistance and resonant length for a 4-radial ground-plane antenna > 0.3 λ above ground as a function of radial droop angle (θ).

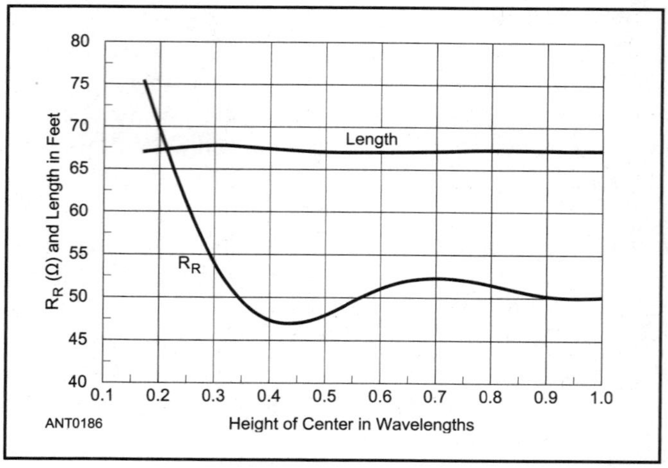

Figure 9.25 — Radiation resistance and resonant length for a 4-radial ground-plane antenna for various heights above average ground for radial droop angle θ = 45°.

of the order of 10° to 20°. To make the vertical portion of the antenna as long as possible, it may be better to accept a slightly poorer match and keep the radials parallel to ground.

The principles of the folded dipole discussed earlier can also be applied to the ground-plane antenna, as shown in **Figure 9.26**. This is the *folded monopole* antenna. The feed point resistance can be controlled by the number of parallel vertical conductors and the ratios of their diameters.

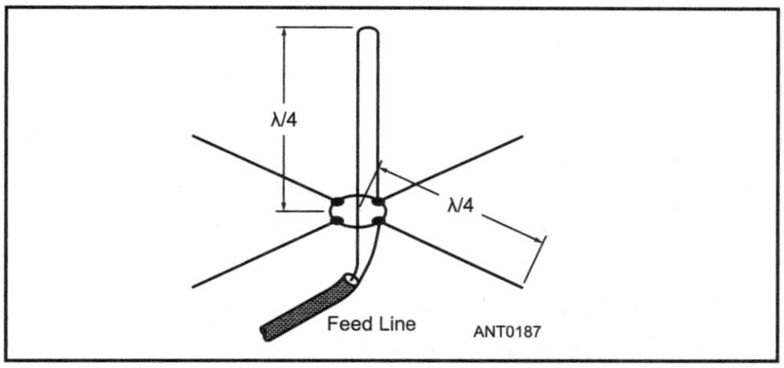

Figure 9.26 — The folded monopole antenna. Shown here is a ground plane of four λ/4 radials. The folded element may be operated over an extensive counterpoise system or mounted on the ground and worked against buried radials and the earth. As with the folded dipole antenna, the feed point impedance depends on the ratios of the radiator conductor sizes and their spacing.

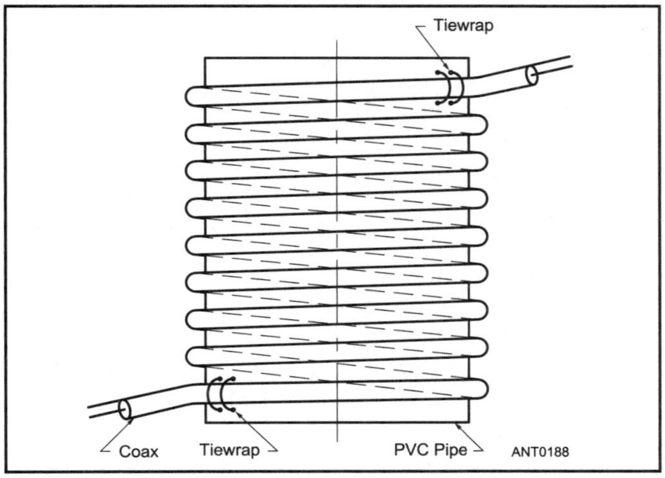

Figure 9.27 — A wound-coax choke balun with sufficient impedance to isolate the antenna properly can be made by winding coaxial cable around a section of plastic pipe. Suitable dimensions are given in the text.

As mentioned earlier, it is important in most installations to isolate the antenna from the feed line and any conductive supporting structure. This is done to minimize the return current conducted through the ground. A return current on the feed line itself or the support structure can drastically alter the radiation pattern, usually for the worse. For these reasons, a choke balun (see the chapter **Transmission Line System Techniques**) or other isolation scheme must be used. 1:1 baluns are effective for the higher bands but at 3.5 and 1.8 MHz commercial baluns often have insufficient impedance to provide adequate isolation. It is very easy to recognize when the isolation is inadequate. When the antenna is being adjusted while watching an isolated impedance or SWR meter, adjustments may be sensitive to your touching the instrument. After adjustment and after the feed line is attached, the SWR may be drastically different. When the feed line is inadequately isolated, the apparent resonant frequency or the length of the radials required for resonance may also be significantly different from what you expect because the feed line's outer surface has become part of the antenna.

In general, a choke balun impedance of 5000 Ω will provide adequate isolation of the feed line as discussed in the **Transmission Line System Techniques** chapter. A ferrite choke with resistive material is preferred but the wound-coax choke shown in **Figure 9.27** will do the job on a single-band antenna. For 1.8 MHz, 30 turns of RG-213 wound on a 14-inch length of 8-inch diameter PVC pipe will make a very good choke balun that can handle full legal power continuously. A smaller choke could be wound on 4-inch diameter plastic drain pipe using RG-8X or a Teflon insulated cable. The important point here is to isolate or decouple the antenna from the feed line and support structure.

9.2.4 THE 3/8-λ VERTICAL

The ⅜-wavelength vertical shown in **Figure 9.28** is often overlooked. It has several advantages over the ¼-λ vertical while adding just 50% to the height. When ground-mounted, its vertical takeoff angle is a few degrees lower than the ¼-λ

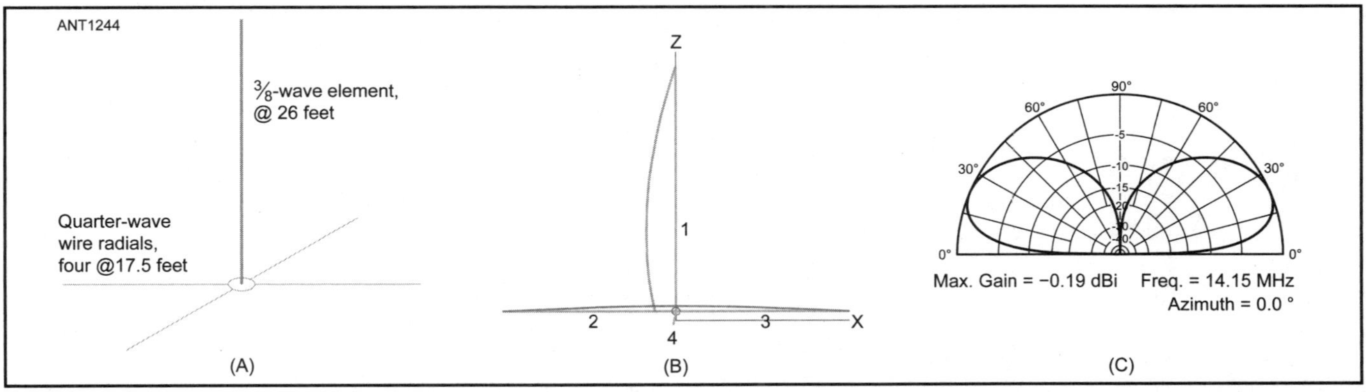

Figure 9.28 — The ⅜-λ vertical (A) is 50 % taller than the ¼-λ vertical. Note that the current distribution on the vertical (B) shows the current maximum to be about ¼ λ above the base. The elevation pattern of the ground mounted ⅜-λ wavelength vertical is shown at C.

which is important for DX contacts. The current maximum is above the ground by ¼-λ which keeps the maximum radiation point clear of ground clutter. It is easily matched with a wide operating bandwidth and has a high radiation resistance so that an extensive ground radial system is unnecessary.

For 14 MHz and higher-frequency operation, the antenna can be constructed from copper wire or aluminum tubing as shown in **Figure 9.29A**. This is an easy antenna to construct from the pieces of old antennas on the upper HF bands. A complete construction article by Joe Reisert, W1JR, is included in this chapter's downloadable supplementary information.

The antenna has a series impedance of approximately 200 Ω of resistance in series with an inductive reactance of 300 to 700 Ω. A series capacitor will cancel the inductive reactance and a 4:1 impedance transformer will convert the remaining resistance to approximately 50 Ω for attaching a coaxial feed line. At 14 MHz, the typical series capacitance required is 40 to 50 pF and is not critical. See the **Transmission Line System Techniques** chapter for 4:1 transformer designs.

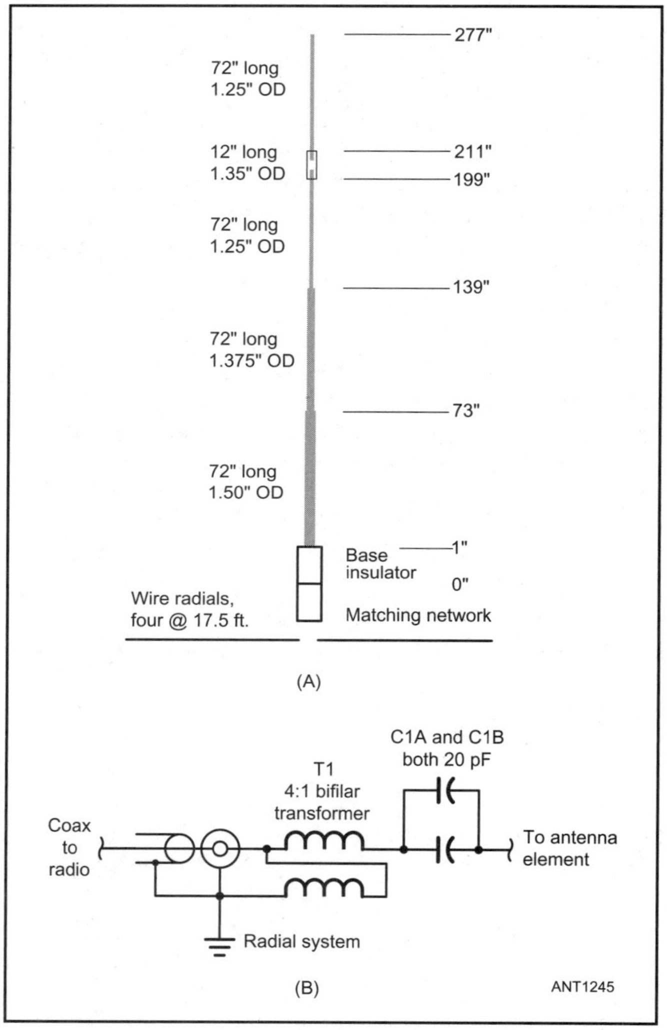

Figure 9.29 — Tubing construction for the 3/8-λ vertical (A) can use clamps, rivets, or screws to hold the sections together. The 12-inch section near the top is a splice to connect the top section. The impedance matching network is shown at B — see text for component values and rating.

Ground radials can be made of wire or any gauge or material. PVC-insulated #14 AWG is recommended so that the ground characteristics will have little effect on long-term performance. Only four radials are needed, approximately 15–17 feet long at 14 MHz, and length is not critical.

9.2.5 VERTICALS FOR 3.5 AND 1.8 MHz

There are many possible ways to build a vertical antenna — the limits are set by your ingenuity. The primary problem is creating the vertical portion of the antenna with sufficient height. Some of the more common means are:

- A dedicated tower
- Using an existing tower with an HF Yagi on top
- A wire suspended from a tree limb or the side of a building
- A vertical wire supported by a line between two trees or other supports
- Flagpoles
- Irrigation pipe

If you have the space and the resources, the most straightforward means is to erect a dedicated tower for a vertical. While this is certainly an effective approach, many amateurs do not have the space or the funds to do this, especially if they already have a tower with an HF antenna on the top. The existing tower can be used as a top-loaded vertical, using shunt feed and a ground radial system.

For those who live in an area with tall trees, it may be possible to install a support rope between two trees, or between a tree and an existing tower. (Under no circumstances should you use an active utility pole!) The vertical portion of the antenna can be a wire suspended from the support line to ground. If top loading is needed, some or all of the support line can be used, creating a T antenna.

Freestanding (unguyed) flagpoles are available in heights exceeding 100 feet. These are made of fiberglass, aluminum or galvanized steel. All of these are candidates for verticals. Flagpole suppliers are listed under "Flags and Banners" in your Yellow Pages. Like a wooden pole, a fiberglass flagpole does not require a base insulator, but metal poles do.

Aluminum irrigation tubing, which comes in diameters of 3 and 4 inches and in lengths of 20 to 40 feet, is widely available in rural areas. One or two lengths of tubing connected together can make a very good vertical when guyed with non-conducting line. It is also very lightweight and relatively easy to erect.

1.8 to 3.5-MHz Vertical Using an Existing Tower

A tower can be used as a vertical ground plane antenna, provided that a good ground system is available. The shunt-fed tower is at its best on 1.8 MHz, where a full λ/4 vertical antenna is rarely possible. Almost any tower height can be used. If the beam structure provides some top loading, so much the better, but anything can be made to radiate — if it is fed properly. A detailed discussion of using towers as vertical antennas for low-band operation can be found in the fifth edition of ON4UN's *Low-Band DXing*. A 30-minute video on shunt-feeding towers by VE6WZ is available online at **www.youtube.com/watch?v=cHlc5MTGTFM&feature=youtu.be**.

Earl Cunningham, K6SE, used a self-supporting, aluminum, crank-up, tilt-over tower, with a TH6DXX tribander mounted at 70 feet. Measurements showed that the entire structure has about the same properties as a 125-foot vertical. It thus works quite well as an antenna on 1.8 and 3.5 MHz for DX work requiring low-angle radiation. Except for dealing with the moving tower sections, the description applies to shunt-feeding a fixed tower, as well.

Ted Rappaport, N9NB, and Jim Parnell, W5JAW, have developed a system for using a 65-foot tower on both 3.5 and 1.8 MHz with a single feed line. Their approach is detailed in the article "Use Your Tower as a Dual-Band, Low-Band DX Antenna" which is included in the downloadable supplemental material for this chapter. **Figure 9.30** shows the basic approach.

Preparing the Structure

Usually some work on the tower system must be done before shunt-feeding is tried. If present, metallic guys should be broken up with insulators. They can be made to simulate top loading, if needed, by judicious placement of the first insulators. Don't overdo it; there is no need to "tune the radiator to resonance" in this way since a shunt feed is employed. If the tower is fastened to a house at a point more than about one-fourth of the height of the tower, it may be desirable to insulate the tower from the building. Plexiglas or Lexan sheet, ¼-inch or more thick, can be bent to any desired shape for this purpose if it is heated in an oven and bent while hot.

All cables should be taped tightly to the tower, on the inside, and run down to the ground level. It is not necessary to bond shielded cables to the tower electrically except for lightning protection, but there should be no exceptions to the down-to-the-ground rule. It is also not necessary to bond the nested sections of a crank-up tower together.

A good system of radials is very desirable. The ideal would be 120 radials, each 250 feet long, but fewer and shorter ones must often suffice. You can lay them around corners of houses, along fences or sidewalks, wherever they can be put a few inches under the surface, or even on the ground. The radials should be tied into the tower's ground system and provide extra paths to ground for lightning. Contact with the soil is not important as described earlier but burying the radials at a shallow depth works well.

Copper wire is preferred because it lasts longer when in direct contact with the soil. Aluminum clothesline wire may be used extensively in areas where it will not be subject to corrosion. Neoprene-covered aluminum wire will be better in highly acid soils. Deep-driven ground rods and connection to underground copper water pipes may be helpful, if available, especially to provide some protection from lightning.

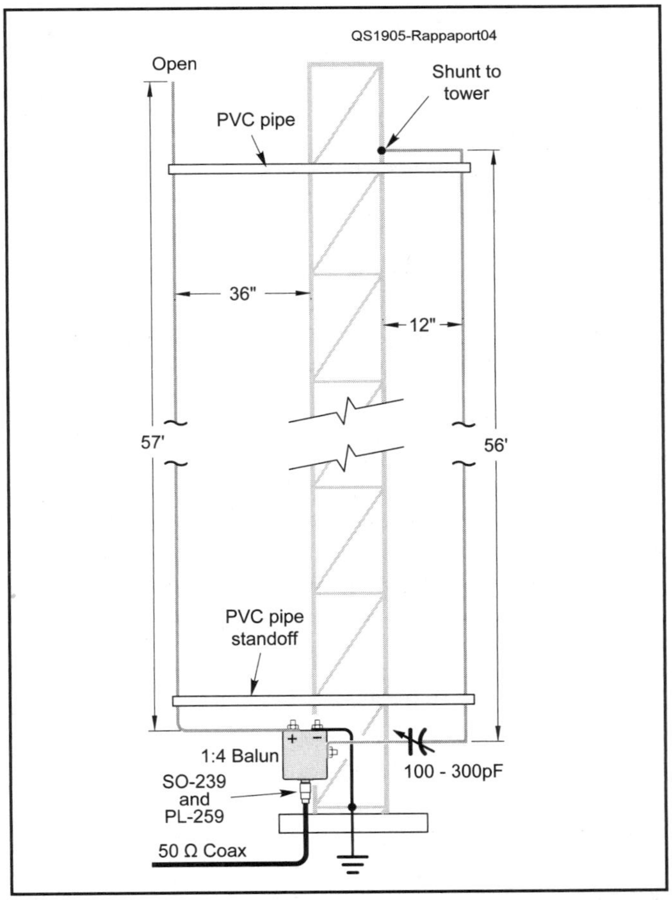

Figure 9.30 — Feed system design of the dual-band 80/160 meter vertical antenna using an existing tower and single coax feed line.

Installing the Shunt Feed

A shunt-fed tower for 1.8 and 3.5 MHz is shown in **Figure 9.31**. The shunt feed network is basically a gamma or omega match as used on Yagis but feeds a vertical monopole here. Rigid rod or tubing can be used for the shunt conductor, but heavy gauge aluminum or copper wire is easier to work with.

If the feed point impedance at the tower base can be estimated, it is possible to use the *GAMMAMW4* software as described in the **Transmission Line System Techniques** chapter. Antenna modeling software can provide the necessary impedance estimate.

The Effect of Trees

Wire verticals and vertical dipoles are often used close to trees which make great supports for them. While the absorption of VHF and UHF signals by foliage is well-known, the effect at HF is less pronounced. In a recent *QST* article (see Bibliography), Kai Siwiak, KE4PT, and Richard Quick, W4RQ, studied the effects of placing HF antennas close to live trees. The tree acts as a parasitic element if the antenna is closer than 0.2 λ to the trunk of the tree with the effect diminishing quickly at larger distances. Loss through a group of trees depends on foliage and tree density so there is a summer/winter variation. Trees also affect propagation as the top of the forest canopy may act to guide waves along the foliage "surface."

For a crank-up tower, flexible stranded #8 AWG copper wire is used at K6SE for the 1.8-MHz feed, because when the tower is cranked down, the shunt wire must come down with it. Connection is made at the top, 68 feet, through a 4-foot horizontal length of aluminum tubing clamped to the top of the tower. The wire is clamped to the tubing at the outer end, and runs down vertically through standoff insulators. These are made by fitting 12-inch lengths of PVC plastic water pipe over 3-foot lengths of aluminum tubing. These are clamped to the tower at 15- to 20-foot intervals, with the bottom clamp about 3 feet above ground. These lengths allow for adjustment of the tower-to-wire spacing over a range of about 12 to 36 inches, for impedance matching.

The gamma-match capacitor for 1.8 MHz is a 250-pF variable with about ⅙-inch plate spacing. This is adequate for power levels up to about 200 W. A large transmitting or a vacuum-variable capacitor should be used for high-power applications.

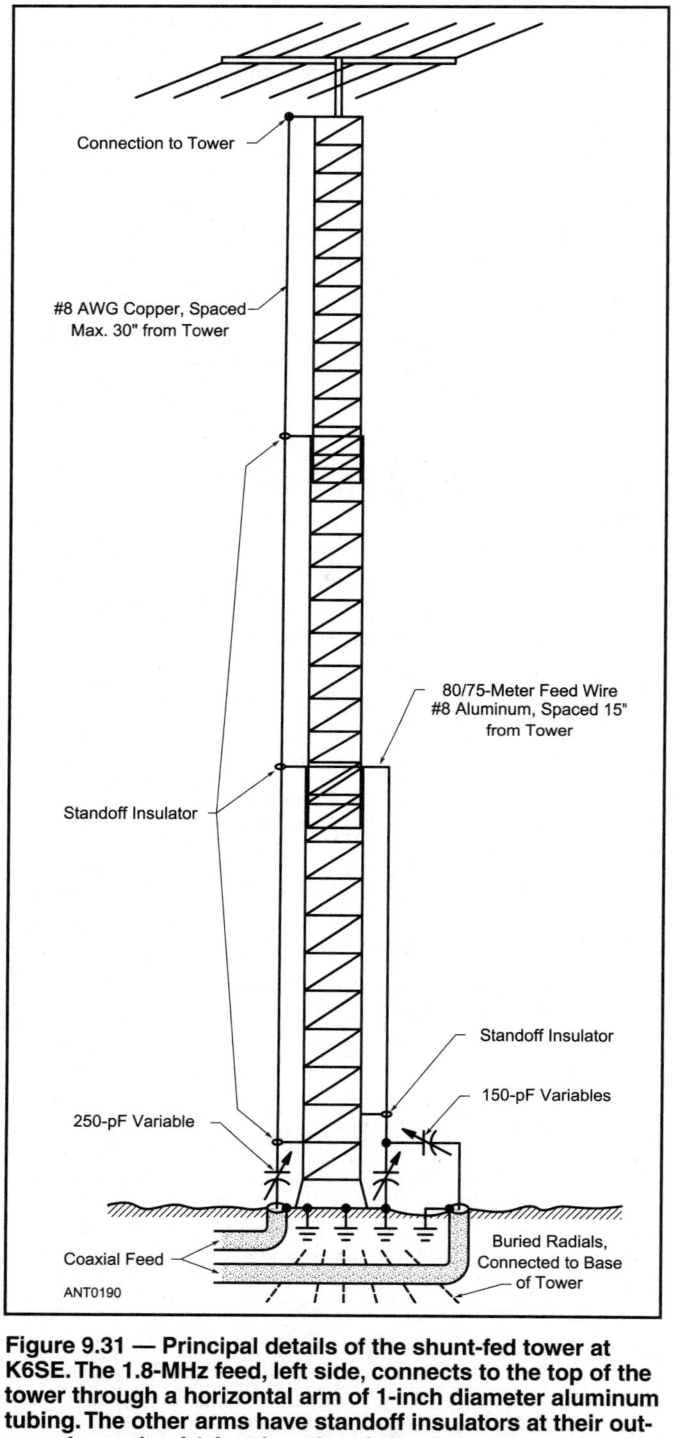

Figure 9.31 — Principal details of the shunt-fed tower at K6SE. The 1.8-MHz feed, left side, connects to the top of the tower through a horizontal arm of 1-inch diameter aluminum tubing. The other arms have standoff insulators at their outer ends, made of 1-foot lengths of plastic water pipe. The connection for 3.5 to 4 MHz, right, is made similarly, at 28 feet, but two variable capacitors are used to permit adjustment of matching with large changes in frequency.

Tuning Procedure

The 1.8-MHz feed wire should be connected to the top of the structure if it is 75 feet tall or less. Mount the standoff insulators so as to have a spacing of about 24 inches between wire and tower. Pull the wire taut and clamp it in place at the bottom insulator. Leave a little slack below to permit adjustment of the wire spacing, if necessary.

Adjust the series capacitor in the 1.8-MHz line for minimum reflected power, as indicated on an SWR meter connected between the coax and the connector on the capacitor housing. Make this adjustment at a frequency near the middle of your expected operating range. If a high SWR is indicated, try moving the wire closer to the tower. Just the lower part of the wire need be moved for an indication as to whether reduced spacing is needed. If the SWR drops, move all insulators closer to the tower, and try again.

If the SWR goes up, increase the spacing. There will be a practical range of about 12 to 36 inches. If going down to 12 inches does not give a low SWR, try connecting the top a bit farther down the tower. If wide spacing does not enable a match, the omega match shown for 3.5 MHz should be tried. No adjustment of spacing is needed with the latter arrangement, which may be necessary with short towers or installations having little or no top loading.

The two-capacitor arrangement in the omega match is also useful for working in more than one 25-kHz segment of the 160 meter band. Tune up on the highest frequency, say 1990 kHz, using the single capacitor, making the settings of wire spacing and connection point permanent for this frequency. To move to the lower frequency, say 1810 kHz, connect the second capacitor into the circuit and adjust it for the new frequency. Switching the second capacitor in and out then allows changing from one segment to the other, with no more than a slight retuning of the first capacitor.

Broadbanding 1.8 and 3.5 MHz Verticals

As with dipoles, the SWR bandwidth of a vertical antenna can be increased by making the antenna thicker. For example, a wire about a foot from and in parallel with a tower used as a vertical will increase the SWR bandwidth noticeably. Up to three wires will have a similar effect. Even so, it is unlikely for the antenna to cover the entire band without some form of retuning.

In the article "Broad-banding a 160 m Vertical Antenna," Grant Saviers, KZ1W, shows a method of switching in different values of series capacitance using relays. Series capacitance is a common matching technique for inverted-L and top-loaded antennas. Rather than use a continuously-adjustable, motor-driven capacitor, KZ1W switches between several band segments. He also discusses the use of inexpensive relays to perform the switching. (The article is included in the downloadable supplemental material.)

In an email on the AntennaWare reflector from September 2018, Guy Olinger, K2AV, discusses modifying a DPDT relay to become a *shorting-bar relay*. These relays have two sets of contacts that are shorted together by a direct, low-impedance conductor when the relay is activated. This is ideal for selecting series capacitors or inductor taps. Not all DPDT relays are suitable for modification in this way. A graphic is available at **www.qsl.net/ei7ba/images/Remote/Relaymod.GIF** and more discussion is available in the original post which is available in the searchable archives for the reflector during September 2018 at **lists.contesting.com/_antennaware**. You can read more about switching tuning networks with high voltage or current present in the Folded Counterpoise (FCP) web pages at **k2av.com**.

9.2.6 ELEVATED GROUND-PLANE ANTENNAS

This section describes a simple and effective means of using a grounded tower, with or without top-mounted antennas, as an elevated ground-plane antenna for 80 and 160 meters. It first appeared in a June 1994 *QST* article by Thomas Russell, N4KG.

From Sloper to Vertical

Recall the quarter-wavelength sloper, also known as the *half sloper*. (The half sloper is covered later in this chapter in more detail.) It consists of an isolated quarter wavelength of wire, sloping from an elevated feed point on a grounded tower. Best results are usually obtained when the feed point is somewhere below a top-mounted Yagi antenna. You feed a sloper by attaching the center conductor of a coaxial cable to the wire and the braid of the cable to the tower leg. Now, imagine four (or more) slopers, but instead of feeding each individually, connect them together to the center conductor of a single feed line. Voilà! Instant elevated ground plane.

Now, all you need to do is determine how to tune the antenna to resonance. With no antennas on the top of the tower, the tower can be thought of as a fat conductor and should be approximately 4% shorter than a quarter wavelength in free space. Calculate this length and attach four insulated quarter-wavelength radials at this distance from the top of the tower. For 80 meters, a feed point 65 feet below the top of an unloaded tower is called for. The tower guys must be broken up with insulators for all such installations. For 160 meters, 130 feet of tower above the feed point is needed.

What can be done with a typical grounded-tower-and-Yagi installation? A top-mounted Yagi acts as a large capacitance hat, top loading the tower. Fortunately, top loading is the most efficient means of loading a vertical antenna.

The examples in **Table 9.4** should give us an idea of how much top loading might be expected from typical amateur antennas. The values listed in the *Equivalent Loading* column tell us the approximate vertical height replaced by the antennas listed in a top-loaded vertical antenna. To arrive at the remaining amount of tower needed for resonance, subtract these numbers from the non-loaded tower height needed for resonance. Note that for all but the 10 meter antennas, the equivalent loading equals or exceeds a quarter wavelength on 40 meters. For typical HF Yagis, this method is best used only on 80 and 160 meters.

Table 9.4
Effective Loading of Common Yagi Antennas

Antenna	*Boom Length (feet)*	*S (area, ft²)*	*Equivalent Loading (feet)*
3L 20	24	768	39
5L 15	26	624	35
4L 15	20	480	31
3L 15	16	384	28
5L 10	24	384	28
4L 10	18	288	24
3L 10	12	192	20
TH7	24	—	40 (estimated)
TH3	14	—	27 (estimated)

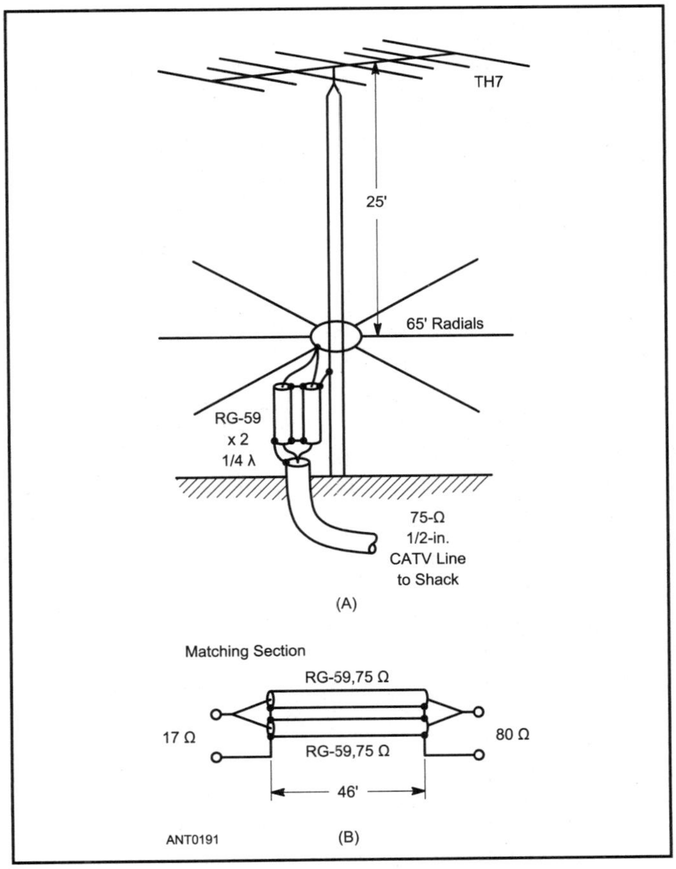

Figure 9.32 — At A, an 80 meter top-loaded, reverse-fed elevated ground plane, using a 40-foot tower carrying a TH7 triband Yagi antenna. At B, dimensions of the 3.6-MHz matching network, made from RG-59.

Construction Examples

Consider this example: A TH7 triband Yagi mounted on a 40-foot tower. The TH7 has approximately the same overall dimensions as a full-sized 3-element 20 meter beam, but has more interlaced elements. Its equivalent loading is estimated to be 40 feet. At 3.6 MHz, 65 feet of tower is needed without loading. Subtracting 40 feet of equivalent loading, the feed point should be 25 feet below the TH7 antenna.

Ten $\lambda/4$ (65-foot) radials were run from a nylon rope tied between tower legs at the 15-foot level, to various supports 10 feet high. Nylon cord was tied to the insulated, stranded, #18 AWG wire, without using insulators. The radials are all connected together and to the center of an exact half wavelength (at 3.6 MHz) of RG-213 coax, which will repeat the antenna feed impedance at the other end. **Figure 9.32** is a drawing of the installation. The author used a Hewlett-Packard low-frequency impedance analyzer to measure the input impedance across the 80 meter band. An exact resonance (zero reactance) was seen at 3.6 MHz, just as predicted. The radiation resistance was found to be 17 Ω. The next question is, how to feed and match the antenna.

One good approach to 80 meter antennas is to tune them to the low end of the band, use a low-loss transmission line, and switch an antenna tuner in line for operation in the higher portions of the band. With a 50-Ω line, the 17-Ω radiation resistance represents a 3:1 SWR, meaning that an antenna tuner should be in-line for all frequencies. For short runs, it would be permissible to use RG-8 or RG-213 directly to the tuner. If you have a plentiful supply of low-loss 75-Ω CATV rigid coax, you can take another approach.

Make a quarter-wave (70 feet × 0.66 velocity factor = 46 feet) 37-Ω matching line by paralleling two pieces of RG-59 and connecting them between the feed point and a run of the rigid coax to the transmitter. The magic of quarter-wave matching transformers is that the input impedance (R_i) and output impedance (R_o) are related by:

$$Z_0^2 = R_i \times R_o \qquad (2)$$

For $R_i = 17\ \Omega$ and $Z_0 = 37\ \Omega$, $R_o = 80\ \Omega$, an almost perfect match for the matching section made from 75-Ω CATV coax. The resulting 1.6:1 SWR at the transmitter is good enough for CW operation without a tuner.

160 Meter Operation

On the 160 meter band, a resonant quarter-wavelength requires 130 feet of tower above the radials. That's a pretty tall order. Subtracting 40 feet of top loading for a 3-element 20 meter or TH7 antenna brings us to a more reasonable 90 feet above the radials. Additional top loading in the form of more antennas will reduce that even more.

Another installation, using stacked TH6s on a 75-foot tower, is shown in **Figure 9.33**. The radials are 10 feet off the ground.

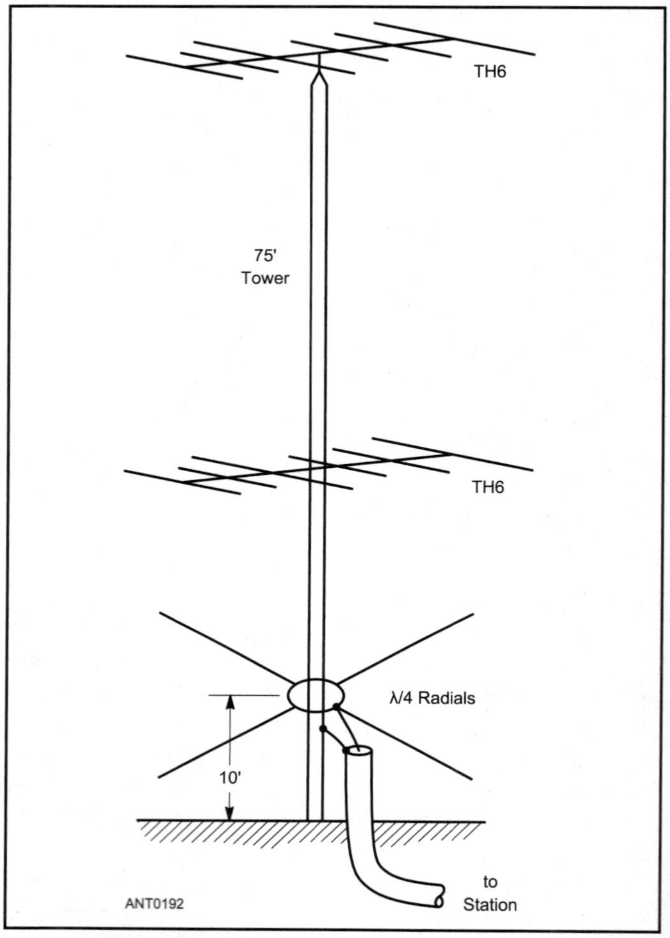

Figure 9.33 — A 160 meter antenna using a 75-foot tower carrying stacked triband Yagis.

9.3 LOADING TECHNIQUES FOR SHORT ANTENNAS

The following section was contributed by Rudy Severns, N6LF, who is well-known for his work with vertical antennas and the effects of ground. The article "The W2FMI Ground-Mounted Short Vertical" by Jerry Sevick, W2FMI, considered one of the best on the subject of short verticals, is included in this chapter's downloadable supplemental material, as well.

9.3.1 SHORT VERTICAL ANTENNAS

A λ/4 vertical can be a simple and efficient antenna but at lower operating frequencies it becomes increasingly difficult to accommodate the full λ/4 height and a set of full-length λ/4 radials. For example, at 3.7MHz λ/4 ≈ 66 feet, at 1.83 MHz λ/4 ≈ 134 feet, at 475 kHz λ/4 ≈ 518 feet and at 137 kHz λ/4 ≈ 1800 feet – more than ¼ mile! Fortunately it's not necessary to make the antenna full-size (λ/4). With careful design the size of the antenna can be reduced by half or even much more while retaining reasonable efficiency and radiation pattern. Some form of loading, inductive and/or capacitive, will be needed both for matching and to maximize efficiency. When height falls below 0.1 λ, such as for typical suburban locations, design becomes more difficult but usable antennas are still possible.

The operating bandwidth of a shortened antenna will be reduced because shortened antennas have higher Q. This translates into a more rapid increase of reactance away from resonance. The effect can be mitigated to some extent by using larger-diameter conductors but bandwidth will still be a problem, particularly on the 3.5 to 4 MHz band which is very wide (13.3%) in proportion to the center frequency of 3.75 MHz.

This section discusses vertical antennas with heights (H) < λ/4 employing inductive and/or capacitive loading. The focus is on antennas for the current US amateur bands of 80 and 160 meters, along with anticipated allocations at 630 and 2200 meters. The loading techniques discussed here can also be used at higher frequencies and for horizontal antennas.

One word of advice: very short verticals rely on heavy capacitive top-loading to obtain reasonable efficiency. The details of the loading arrangements will vary at each location due to wide variations in available supports (poles, trees, and so on) or lack thereof. While it is possible to make approximate calculations for each structure to approximate the efficacy of a particular choice, it is much easier to model multiple possibilities using antenna modeling software and then choose the best design. Suitable software is available both free and at modest cost. (See the chapter on **Antenna Modeling**.) The use of modeling software can be of great help in optimizing a design for a particular installation and is strongly recommended.

9.3.2 EFFICIENCY OF SHORT VERTICALS

The essential problem of short antennas, generally, is that of efficiency. **Table 9.5** illustrates the dramatic effect of reducing an 80 meter vertical's physical height by adding base loading inductance. (Perfect ground and conductors are assumed in this design. The vertical section is 2 inches in diameter.) **Figure 9.34** graphs the feed point resistance (R_r), the magnitude of the capacitive reactance ($|X_C|$) and Q (Q_a) for an ideal vertical as a function of height (H in wavelengths), where $Q_a = |X_C|/R_r$. At resonance $R_r = 36\ \Omega$ and $X_C = 0$ but as H is reduced below resonance R_r falls quickly and $|X_C|$ increases very rapidly. For example when H = 0.125 λ, $R_r \approx 6.5\ \Omega$ and $|X_C| \approx 500\ \Omega$. As H is reduced further, R_r decreases proportional to H^2 and $|X_C|$ increases proportional to 1/H. As a result, Q_a increases proportional to $1/H^3$! Short antennas have low radiation resistances and high capacitive reactances at the feed point which becomes especially acute on 2200 meters where only very short (in terms of λ) verticals are practical. Short antennas also have very high Q resulting in narrow operating bandwidths.

From Figure 9.34 we can see that a short vertical is essentially a capacitor in series with a resistance as shown by the electrical model in **Figure 9.35**.

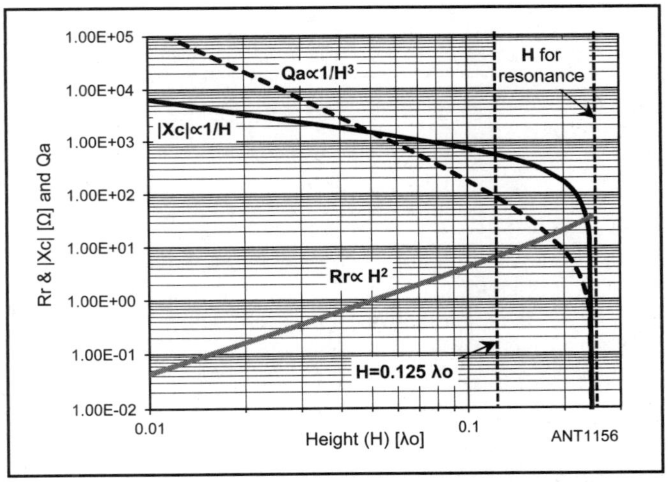

Figure 9.34 — Base impedances and Q of a lossless vertical over perfect ground.

Table 9.5
Effect of Shortening a Vertical Radiator Below λ/4 Using Inductive Base Loading.
Frequency is 3.525 MHz and for the Inductor Q_L = 200.
Ground and conductor losses are omitted.

Length (feet)	*Length (λ)*	*R_r (Ω)*	*X_C (Ω)*	*R_L (Ω)*	*Efficiency (%)*	*Loss (dB)*
14	0.050	0.96	–761	3.8	20	–7.0
20.9	0.075	2.2	–533	2.7	45	–3.5
27.9	0.100	4.2	–395	2.0	68	–1.7
34.9	0.125	6.8	–298	1.5	82	–0.86
41.9	0.150	10.4	–220	1.1	90	–0.44
48.9	0.175	15.1	–153	0.77	95	–0.22
55.8	0.200	21.4	–92	0.46	98	–0.09
62.8	0.225	29.7	–34	0.17	99	–0.02

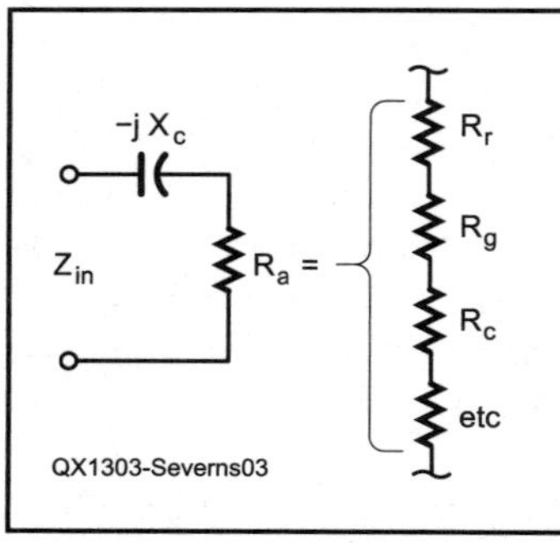

Figure 9.35 — Equivalent circuit for a short vertical including loss elements.

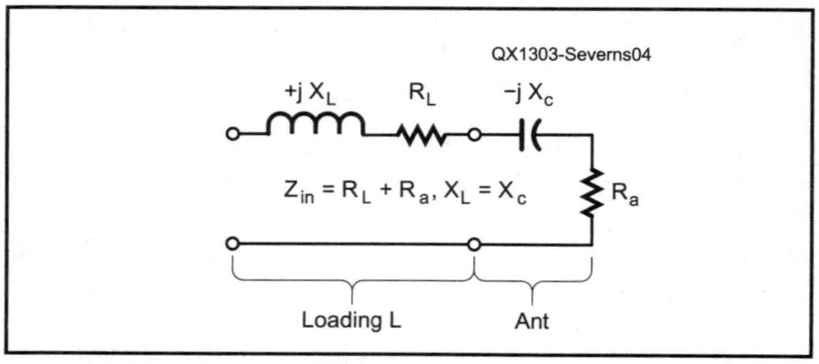

Figure 9.37 — Equivalent circuit for inductive base loading.

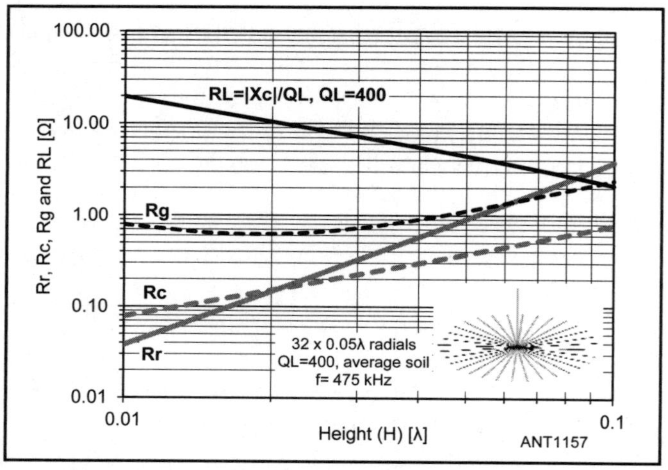

Figure 9.36 — Typical values for R_r, R_c, R_L and R_g as a function of H.

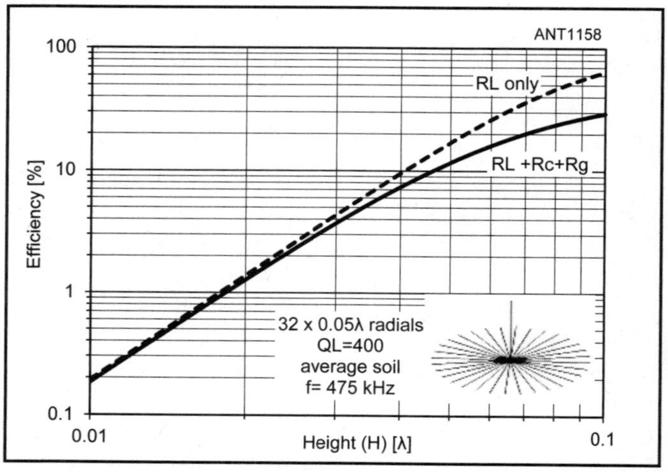

Figure 9.38 — Example of efficiency as a function of height.

In addition to R_r and X_C a real antenna will have several sources of loss:

- R_L — loading coil series resistance where RL = XL/QL, QL = inductor Q.
- R_g — equivalent ground loss resistance.
- R_c — conductor resistance.
- R_l — losses due to leakage across the base insulator and insulators at wire ends.
- R_{cor} — corona loss at high voltage points. This can be a problem at higher altitudes.
- R_n — Matching network losses

Figure 9.36 shows an example of typical values of R_r, R_c, R_g and R_L for a short vertical with a radial ground system over average soil. This example is for 630 meters but 160 and 80 meter verticals of the same electrical heights (in λ) will be similar.

Antenna efficiency (η) can be expressed as:

$$\eta = \frac{R}{R_r + (R_L + R_g + R_c + R_l + R_{cor} + R_n)} = \frac{R_r}{R_r + R_{loss}} \quad (3)$$

The design goal is to increase efficiency by increasing R_r and decreasing R_{loss}.

9.3.3 BASE LOADING

A vertical with $H < l_o/4$ will require some form of loading and matching. The base of the antenna is a convenient point at which to add a loading inductor as shown in **Figure 9.37**.

Ignoring R_l, R_{cor} and R_n for the present, we can use Eq 3 and the loss resistance values in Figure 9.36 to graph the efficiency of that antenna as shown in **Figure 9.38**. H=0.01λ corresponds to a 72 foot vertical at 137 kHz. The efficiency is <0.2%!

The dashed line in Figure 9.38 shows the efficiency when only R_L is included compared to the sum of R_L and R_g (the solid line). This graph has a strong message: *Make the vertical as tall as possible (when H<λ/4) because even small increases in H can substantially improve efficiency.*

This graph also illustrates the low efficiency intrinsic to short base-loaded verticals. The efficiency of very short verticals is dominated by R_L because the resonating inductance value is large and therefore R_L is large ($R_L = X_C/Q_L$). We can increase Q_L to reduce R_L but there are practical limits.

The base of the antenna is a convenient point at which to add a loading inductor, but it's usually not the lowest loss point at which an inductor could be placed. There is an extensive discussion of the optimum location for the loading coil in a short vertical as a function of ground loss and Q_L in the **Mobile and Maritime HF Antennas** chapter. This information should be reviewed before using inductive loading. Available for download from **www.arrl.org/arrl-antenna-book-reference** is the program *MOBILE.EXE*. This is an excellent tool for designing short, inductively loaded antennas.

A loading inductor at the base has no effect on R_r but moving the loading coil from the base to near the middle can increase R_r significantly.

9.3.4 CAPACITIVE TOP-LOADING

As shown above, inductive loading is not a very efficient way to compensate for reduced antenna height. Capacitive top loading can be much more effective as shown in the example illustrated by **Table 9.6** for a top-loaded 3.525 MHz vertical made of 2-inch tubing. The vertical section is L_1 and the horizontal top-loading section is L_2, also a piece of 2-inch tubing adjusted to make the antenna resonant. As with the previous example, perfect ground and conductors are assumed.

A simple example using a wire suspended between two supports forming a "T" antenna is shown in **Figure 9.39**. We can model this antenna varying H and adjusting L to resonate the antenna to illustrate the advantages of top-loading. A comparison of R_r between capacitive top-loading and inductive base loading is given in **Figure 9.40**. The dashed line shows the ratio of R_r-top to R_r-base. For a given vertical height, resonating the antenna with top-loading results in much higher radiation resistance R_r.

Compared to inductive base loading, top-loading significantly increases R_r while base loading does not. For Example, if H=20 feet (≈0.04λ @1.83 MHz) R_r with top-loading is over four times that for base loading. Besides increasing R_r, top-loading can reduce or eliminate R_L due to reduction in value of the base inductor. The net result can be a dramatic improvement in efficiency! As shown in **Figure 9.41** we can use multiple wires to obtain even more top-loading.

Figure 9.42 compares the span (= 2L, see Figure 9.39) of the top-loading wire(s) when using one or two wires. The use of two wires with conductive spreaders such as aluminum tubing significantly reduces the spacing (span) required between the supports for the top-loading wires. The span can

Table 9.6
Effect of Shortening a Vertical Using Top Loading

Frequency is 3.525 MHz and vertical is made of 2-inch tubing

L1 (feet)	*L2 (feet)*	*Length (λ)*	*R_r (Ω)*
14.0	48.8	0.050	4.0
20.9	38.6	0.075	8.5
27.9	30.1	0.100	14.0
34.9	22.8	0.125	19.9
41.9	17.3	0.150	25.5
48.9	11.9	0.175	30.4
55.8	7.0	0.200	33.9
62.8	2.4	0.225	35.7

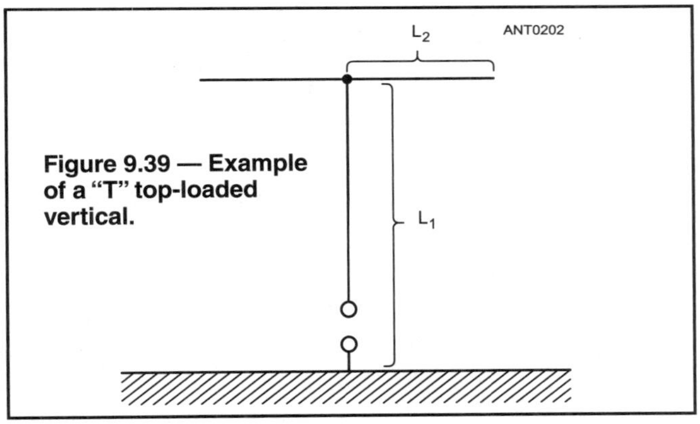

Figure 9.39 — Example of a "T" top-loaded vertical.

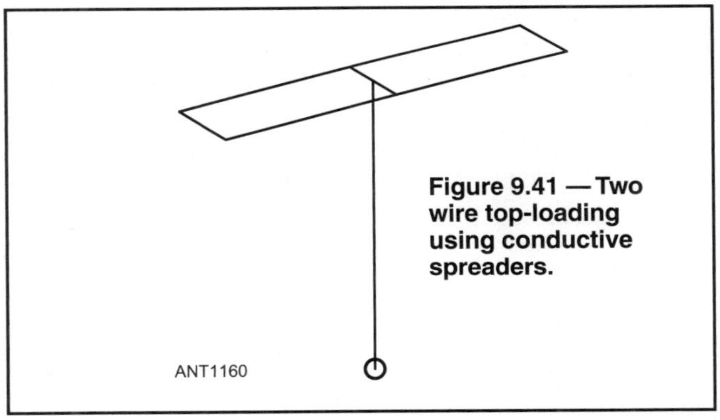

Figure 9.41 — Two wire top-loading using conductive spreaders.

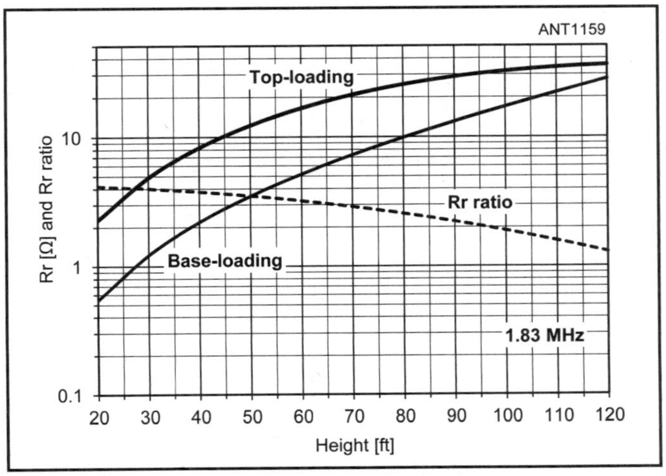

Figure 9.40 — R_r comparison between top and base loading.

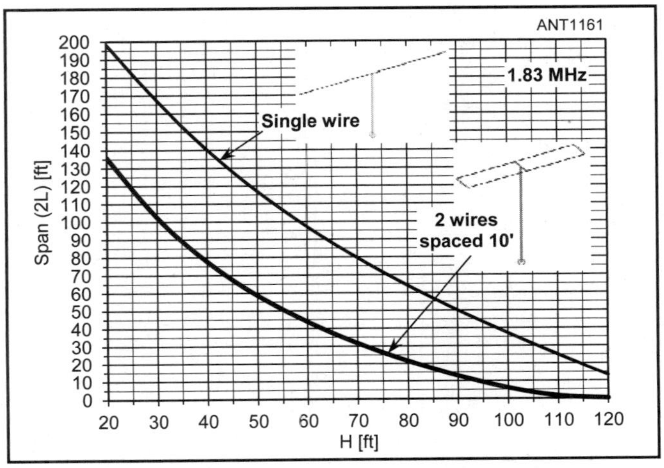

Figure 9.42 — Span (=2L) of the top hat for one or two wires.

be further reduced by using longer spreaders and additional well-spaced parallel wires. The design of this kind of top-loading will vary with every installation. Antenna modeling software will be of great assistance for optimizing the design. (L.B. Cebik, W4RNL, also analyzed top-hat loading, comparing it to inductive loading. See the Bibliography.)

When no supports other than the vertical itself are available a top-hat using rigid spreaders can be used. **Figure 9.43** is a sketch of this kind of "wagon-wheel" top-hat along with the required radius for resonance at 1.83 MHz for a range of vertical heights. A simple way to make a capacitance hat would be to take four to six 8-foot CB mobile whips, arrange them like spokes in a wagon wheel and connect the ends with a peripheral wire. This arrangement will produce a 16-foot diameter hat that is economical and very durable. The whip lengths can be extended further with lengths of aluminum tubing. Another approach for a large hat would be to salvage the hub and spreaders from an old 20 meter quad and use them for the wagon-wheel.

Unfortunately, radii greater than ≈15 feet become increasingly impractical. The rigid supports can be replaced with wires sloping downward as shown in **Figure 9.44** to form what is called an "umbrella" vertical. To increase the loading effect of the umbrella more wires can be used as well as a skirt wire like that shown in Figure 9.43. The wires can also be made longer but there is a point where the reduction in R_L due to a smaller resonating inductor is offset by the decreasing value of R_r due to canceling currents flowing in the umbrella wires. This is situation where optimization is best done using modeling software.

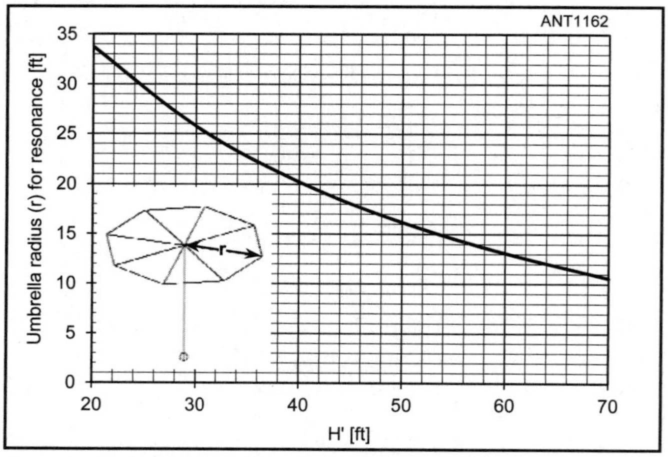

Figure 9.43 — Wagon wheel top-hat example.

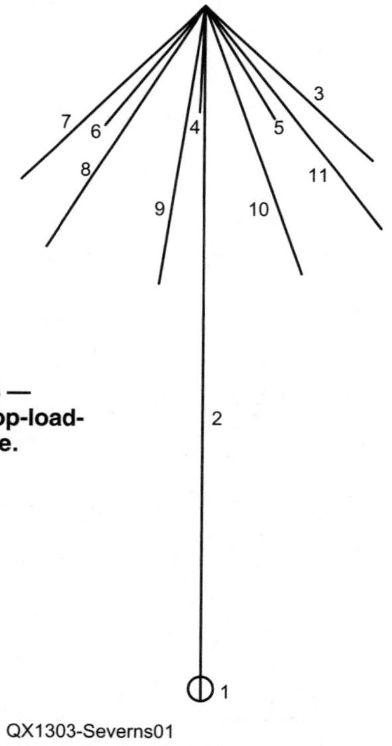

Figure 9.44 — Umbrella top-loading example.

Finding Capacitance Hat Size

Practically any sufficiently large metallic structure can be used for capacitive loading and the structure doesn't even have to be symmetric, but simple geometric forms such as the sphere, cylinder and disc are preferred because of the relative ease with which their capacitance can be calculated.

While antenna modeling software is very helpful for the design of top-loading structures the capacitance of common geometric forms can be estimated from the curves of **Figure 9.45** as a function of size. For the cylinder, the length is specified equal to the diameter. The sphere, disc and cylinder can be constructed from sheet metal, if such construction is feasible, but the capacitance will be almost the same if a "skeleton" type of construction with screen or wire networks or tubing is used.

The required value of the capacitance may be determined

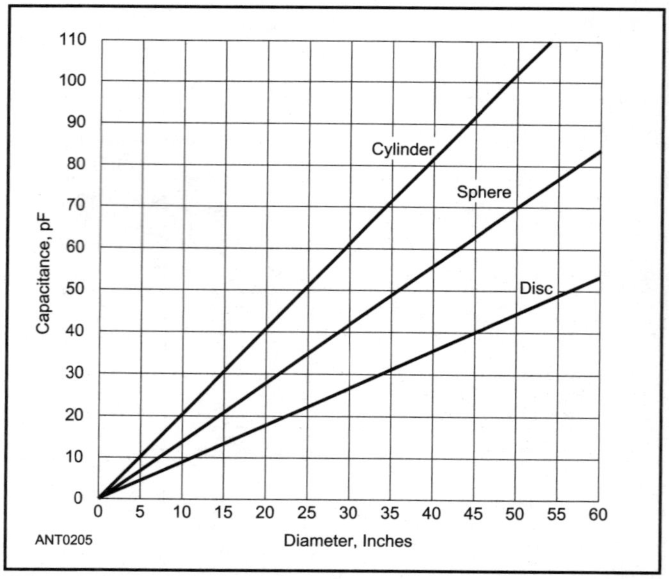

Figure 9.45 — Capacitance of sphere, disc and cylinder as a function of their diameters. The cylinder length is assumed equal to its diameter.

using the following procedure. The information in this section is based on a September 1978 *QST* article by Walter Schulz, K3OQF. (see Bibliography) The physical length of a shortened antenna can be found from:

$$h_{inches} = \frac{11808}{F_{MHz}} \times \lambda \qquad (4)$$

where h is length in inches and λ is the electrical length in wavelengths.

Thus, using an example of 7 MHz and a shortened length of 0.167 λ, h = 11808/7 × 0.167 = 282 inches, equivalent to 23.48 feet.

Consider the vertical radiator as an open-ended transmission line, so the impedance and top loading may be determined. The characteristic impedance of a vertical antenna can be found from

$$Z_0 = 60\left[\ln\left(\frac{4h}{d}\right) - 1\right] \qquad (5)$$

where

ln = natural logarithm

h = length (height) of vertical radiator in inches (as above)

d = diameter of radiator in inches

The vertical radiator for this example has a diameter of 1 inch. Thus, for this example,

$$Z_0 = 60\left[\ln\left(\frac{4 \times 281}{1}\right) - 1\right] = 361\,\Omega$$

The capacitive reactance required for the amount of top loading can be found from

$$X_C = \frac{Z_0}{\tan\theta} \qquad (6)$$

where

X_C = capacitive reactance, ohms

Z_0 = characteristic impedance of antenna (from Eq 4)

θ = amount of electrical loading, degrees.

This value for a 30° hat is 361/tan 30° = 625 Ω. This capacitive reactance may be converted to capacitance with the following equation,

$$C = \frac{10^6}{2\,\pi\, f\, X_C} \qquad (7)$$

where

C = capacitance in pF

f = frequency, MHz

X_C = capacitive reactance, ohms (from above).

For this example, the required C = $10^6/(2\ \pi \times 7 \times 625)$ = 36.4 pF, which may be rounded to 36 pF. A disc capacitor is used in this example. The appropriate diameter for 36 pF of hat capacitance can be found from Figure 9.45. The disc diameter that yields 36 pF of capacitance is 40 inches.

Combined Loading

As an antenna is shortened, the size of the top-loading device will become larger and at some point it will become impractical to resonate the antenna with top-loading only. In that situation inductive loading, usually placed either at the base or directly between the capacitance "hat" and the top of the antenna, can be added to resonate the antenna. An alternative would be to use linear loading in place of inductive loading.

Shortening Radials

Very often the space required by full-length radials is not available. Like the vertical portion of the antenna, the radials can also be shortened and loaded in very much the same way. An example of end-loaded radials is given in **Figure 9.46A**. Radials half the usual length can be used with little reduction in efficiency but, as in the case of top loading, the antenna Q will be higher and the bandwidth reduced. As shown in Figure 9.46B**,** inductive loading can also be used. As long as they are not made too short (down to 0.1 λ) loaded radials can be efficient — with careful design.

9.3.5 GENERAL RULES FOR LOADING VERTICAL ANTENNAS

Sound advice on the design of LF and MF antennas was given many years ago by Woodrow Smith: "The main object in the design of low frequency transmitting antenna systems

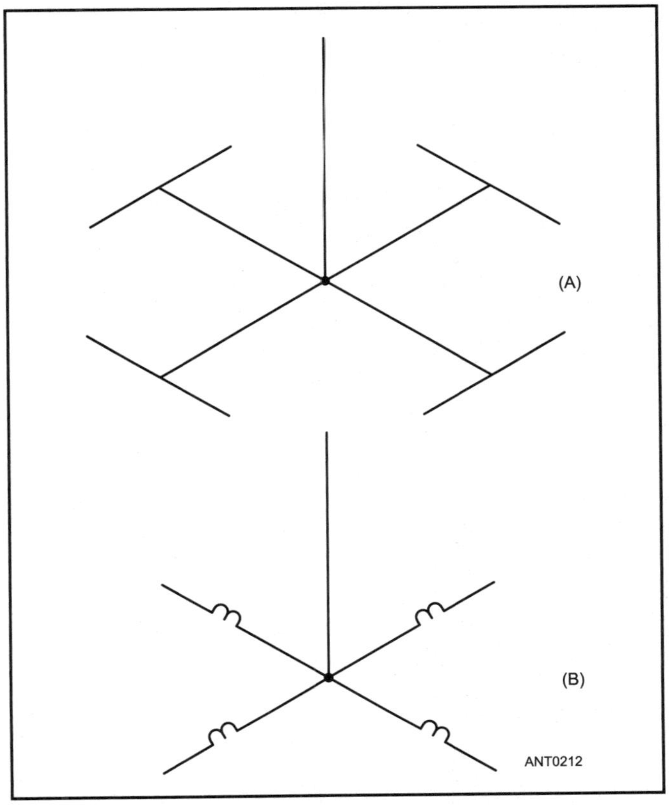

Figure 9.46 — Radials may be shortened by using either capacitive (A) or inductive (B) loading. In extreme cases both may be used but the operating bandwidth will be limited.

can be summarized briefly by saying that the general idea is to get as much wire as possible as high in the air as possible and to use excellent insulation and an extensive ground system."

We can codify this advice in order of priority:

• Make the height as great as practical up to the point where H = λ/4.

• Provide as much top loading as possible.

• Make the diameter of the vertical section large. Tubing or a cage of smaller wires will work well.

• If the capacitive loading is insufficient, resonate the antenna with a high-Q inductor placed between the hat and the top of the antenna.

• For buried-ground systems, use as many radials (>0.2 λ) as possible, 32 or more is best.

• If an elevated ground plane is used, use 12 or more radials, 5 or more feet above ground.

• Use of high-quality insulators at the base and wire ends.

• If shortened radials must be used, capacitive loading is preferable to inductive loading.

9.3.6 LINEAR LOADING

Another alternative to inductive loading is *linear loading*. This method of shortening radiators can be applied to almost any antenna configuration — including parasitic arrays. Linear loading is basically folding the antenna to reduce its physical length while attempting to preserve overall signal radiation. Depending on what section of the antenna is folded and the spacing of the conductors, radiation from the folded section is relatively low because of field cancellation but because current is not constant over the length of the folded section, cancellation is not total and there is some radiation from the folded sections. Careful selection of what sections to fold and the use of modeling can result in an effective antenna.

Linear loading can be used to advantage in many antennas because it introduces relatively little loss, does not degrade directivity patterns, and has low enough Q to allow reasonably good bandwidth. Some examples of linear-loaded antennas are shown in **Figure 9.47**. Note that linear loading increases the mechanical complexity of the antenna which can cause reliability problems.

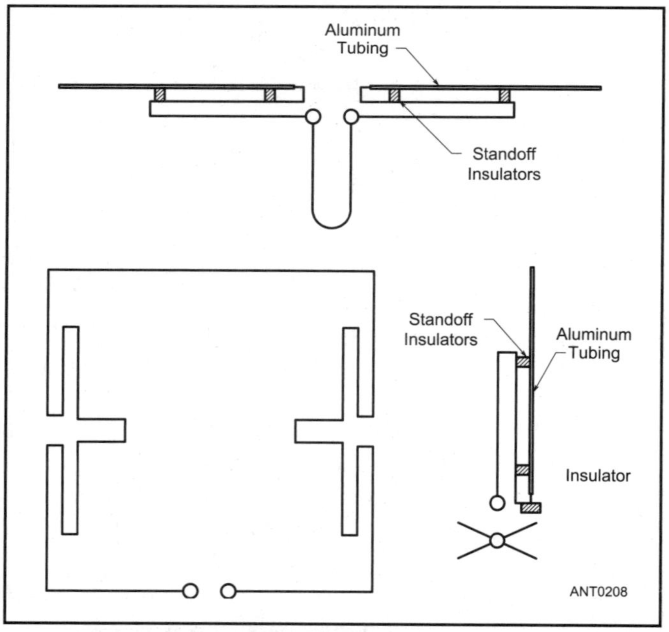

Figure 9.47 — Some examples of linear loading. The small circles indicate the feed points of the antennas.

Since the dimensions and spacing of linear-loading devices vary greatly from one antenna installation to another, the best way to employ this technique is to try a length of conductor 10% to 20% longer than the difference between the shortened antenna and the full-size dimension for the linear-loading device. Then use the "cut-and-try" method, varying both the spacing and length of the loading device to optimize the match. A hairpin match at the feed point can be useful in achieving a 1:1 SWR at resonance.

Linear-Loaded Short Wire Antennas

More detail on linear loading is provided in this section, which was originally presented in *The ARRL Antenna Compendium Vol 5* by John Stanford, NNØF. Linear loading can significantly reduce the required length for resonant antennas. For example, it is easy to make a resonant antenna that is as much as 30 to 40% shorter than an ordinary dipole for a given band. The shorter overall lengths come from bending back some of the wire. The increased self-coupling lowers the resonant frequency. These ideas are applicable to short antennas for restricted space or portable use.

Experiments

The results of the measurements are shown in **Figure 9.48** and are also consistent with values given by Rashed and Tai from an earlier paper. This shows several simple wire antenna configurations, with resonant frequencies and impedance (radiation resistance). The reference dipole has a resonant frequency f_0 and resistance R = 72 Ω. The f/f_0 values give the effective reduced frequency obtained with the linear loading in each case. For example, the two-wire linear-loaded

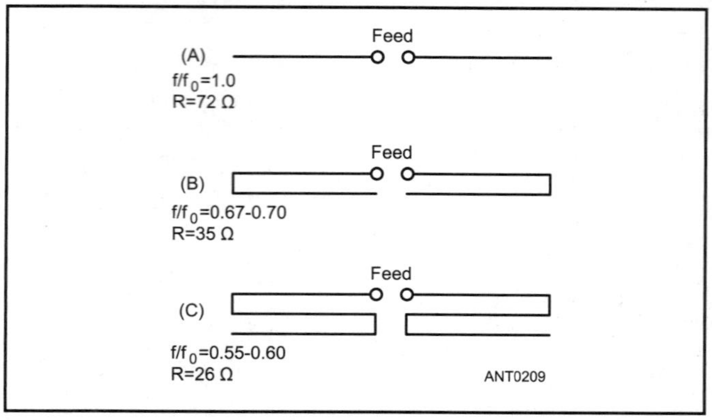

Figure 9.48 — Linearly-loaded wire dipole antennas. The ratio f/f_0 is the measured resonant frequency divided by frequency f_0 of a standard dipole of same length. R is radiation resistance in ohms. At A, standard single-wire dipole. At B, two-wire linear-loaded dipole, similar to folded dipole except that side opposite feed line is open. At C, three-wire linear-loaded dipole.

dipole has its resonant frequency lowered to about 0.67 to 0.70 that of the simple reference dipole of the same length.

The three-wire linear-loaded dipole has its frequency reduced to 0.55 to 0.60 of the simple dipole of the same length. As you will see later, these values will vary with conductor diameter and spacing.

The two-wire linear-loaded dipole (Figure 9.48B) looks almost like a folded dipole but, unlike a folded dipole, it is open in the middle of the side opposite where the feed line is attached. Measurements show that this antenna structure has a resonant frequency lowered to about two-thirds that of the reference dipole, and R equal to about 35 Ω. A three-wire linear-loaded dipole (Figure 9.48C) has even lower resonant frequency and R about 25 to 30 Ω.

Linear-loaded monopoles (half of the dipoles in Figure 9.48) working against a radial ground plane have similar resonant frequencies, but with only half the radiation resistance shown for the dipoles.

The Linear-Loaded Short Dipole (LLSD)

Based on these results, NNØF next constructed a linear loaded dipole as in Figure 9.48B, using 24 feet of 1-inch 450-Ω window line for the dipole length. He hung the system from a tree using nylon fishing line, about 4 feet from the tree at the top, and about 8 feet from the ground on the bottom end. It was slanted at about a 60° angle to the ground. This antenna resonated at 12.8 MHz and had a measured resistance of about 35 Ω. After the resonance measurements, he fed it with 1-inch ladder open-wire line (a total of about 100 feet to the shack).

For brevity, this is called a vertical LLSD (linear-loaded short dipole). A tuner resonated the system nicely on 20 and 30 meters. On these bands the performance of the vertical LLSD seemed comparable to his 120-foot long, horizontal center-fed Zepp, 30 feet above ground. In some directions where the horizontal, all-band Zepp has nulls, such as toward Siberia, the vertical LLSD was definitely superior. This system also resonates on 17 and 40 meters. However, from listening to various signals, NNØF had the impression that this length LLSD is not as good on 17 and 40 meters as the horizontal 120-foot antenna.

Any of the linear-loaded dipole antennas can be mounted either horizontally or vertically. The vertical version can be used for longer skip contacts — beyond 600 miles or so — unless you have rather tall supports for horizontal antennas to give a low elevation angle. Using different diameter conductors in linear-loaded antenna configurations yields different results, depending on whether the larger or small diameter conductor is fed.

Linear Loaded Dipole for 7 MHz

Lew Gordon, K4VX, designed a simple 40 meter dipole using linear loading with 450-Ω window line as the folded section. Complete details are available in his article "The K4VX Linear-Loaded Dipole for 7 MHz" that is included in the downloadable supplemental material for this chapter.

Linear loading is added at the center of the dipole in order to simplify the mechanical design and avoid extra insulators along the antenna if the loading was added midway along the antenna. Modeling with *NEC-2* and *NEC-4* showed little difference between these two approaches. **Figure 9.49** shows the overall approach and a construction detail at the center.

Rather than place the window line below the main single-wire span, K4VX threaded the single-wire span through holes in the window line spaced every 6 inches or so. This keeps the single wire centered in the window line. Concerns that the three conductors are spaced too closely were not realized in practice on the air.

9.3.7 INDUCTIVELY LOADED DIPOLES

Similar to inductive loading of vertical antennas, dipoles can also be shortened by inserting loading coils in the antenna. Two identical coils are used, one on each side of the feed point, placed equal distances from the feed point. To accomplish a specific amount of shortening, the farther from the feed point the coils are placed, the more reactance they must have.

The most serious drawback associated with inductive

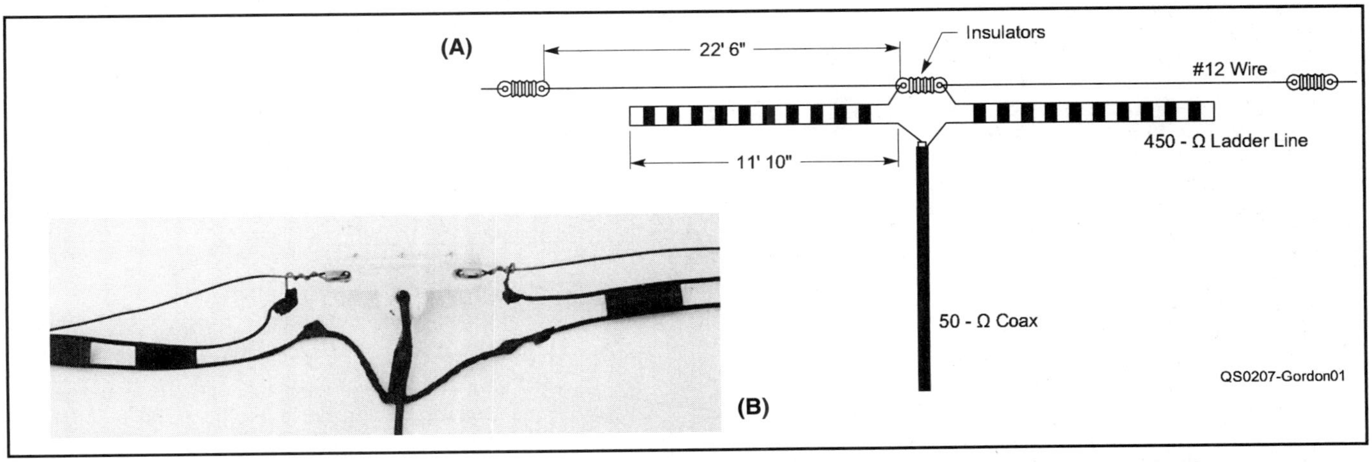

Figure 9.49 — Layout of the K4VX linear-loaded dipole (A). The #12 AWG wire is threaded through the window line but is shown separately for clarity. (See text.) At B are details of the feed point. Note that the coax feed line requires mechanical support to make the connections to the window line, which must be carefully waterproofed.

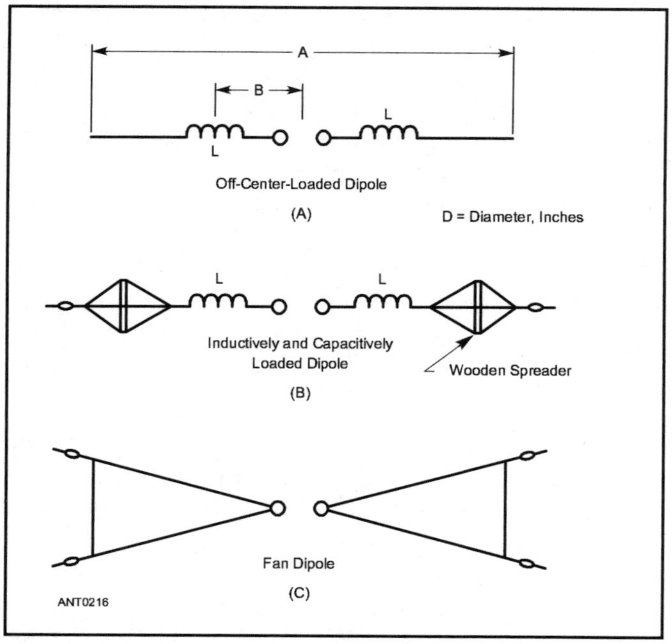

Figure 9.50 — At A is a dipole antenna lengthened electrically with off-center loading coils. For a fixed dimension A, greater efficiency will be realized with greater distance B, but as B is increase, L must be larger in value to maintain resonance. At B, capacitive loading of the ends will reduce the required inductance of the coils.

loading is loss in the coils themselves. It is important that you use "high-Q" inductors made from reasonably large wire or tubing to minimize this problem. Close winding of turns should also be avoided if possible. A good compromise is to use some off-center inductive loading in combination with capacitive end loading, keeping the inductor losses small and the efficiency as high as possible.

Some examples of off-center coil loading and capacitive-end loading are shown in **Figure 9.50.** This technique was described by Jerry Hall, K1TD in September 1974 *QST* and by Luiz Duarte Lopes, CT1EOJ in October 2003 *QST*. (These articles are included with this book's downloadable supplemental information and are listed in the Bibliography.) Approximate inductive reactances for single-band resonance (for the antenna in Figure 9.50A only) may be determined with the aid of **Figure 9.51**. The final values will depend on the proximity of surrounding objects in individual installations and must be determined experimentally.

The use of high-Q low-loss coils is important for maximum efficiency. This is particularly important if high power is to be used. Several calculators and online articles are available to guide the antenna builder. Serge Stroobandt, ON4AA, has made available a sophisticated inductor design calculator web page at **hamwaves.com/antennas/inductance.html** which takes into account a number of important effects that affected the accuracy of earlier calculators. Tom Rauch, W8JI, has published a great deal of information about loading coils at **www.w8ji.com/loading_inductors.htm**. And as an example of building high-performance loaded antennas,

Figure 9.51 — Chart for determining approximate inductance values for off-center-loaded dipoles shown in Figure 9.50A. At the intersection of the appropriate curve from the body of the chart for dimension A and proper value for the coil position from the horizontal scale at the bottom of the chart, read the required inductive reactance for resonance from the scale at the left. Dimension A is expressed as percent length of the shortened antenna with respect to the length of a half-wave dipole of the same conductor material (that is, how much shorter than a full-size λ/2 dipole). Dimension B is expressed as the percentage of coil distance from the feed point to the end of the antenna. For example, a shortened antenna, which is 50% or half the size of a half-wave dipole (λ/4 overall) with loading coils positioned midway between the feed point and each end (50% out), would require coils having an inductive reactance of approximately 950 Ω at the operating frequency for antenna resonance.

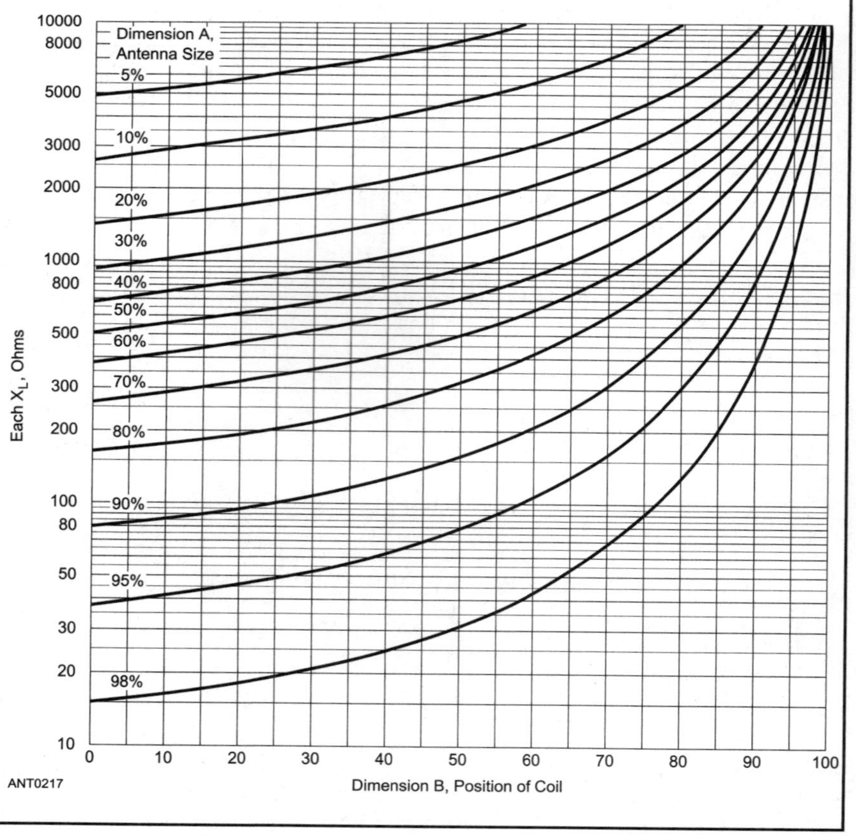

Steve Babcock, VE6WZ, shows construction methods for some rugged 80 meter Yagi loading coils at **www.qsl.net/ve6wz/coil.htm**. One caveat for the coil winder — if you use copper tubing instead of wire, it is specified by its inside diameter, not the outside diameter, as is done for wire.

An antenna analyzer is recommended for use during adjustment of the system. Note that the minimum inductance required is for a center-loaded dipole where the coil is at the feed point (B=0). If the inductive reactance is read from Figure 9.51 for a dimension B of zero, one coil having approximately twice this reactance can be used near the center of the dipole.

9.4 INVERTED-L AND T ANTENNAS

The antenna shown in **Figure 9.52** is called an inverted-L antenna. It is simple and easy to construct and is a good antenna for the beginner or the experienced 1.8-MHz DXer. This antenna is a form of top-loaded vertical, where the top loading is asymmetrical. This results in both vertical and horizontal polarization because the currents in the top wire do not cancel like they would in a symmetrical-T vertical. This is not necessarily a bad thing because it eliminates the zenith null present in a true vertical. This allows for good communication at short ranges as well as for DX. The azimuthal radiation pattern is slightly asymmetrical with »1 to 2 dB increase in the direction opposite to the horizontal wire. This antenna requires a good buried ground system or elevated radials and will have a 2:1 SWR bandwidth of about 50 kHz on 160 meters.

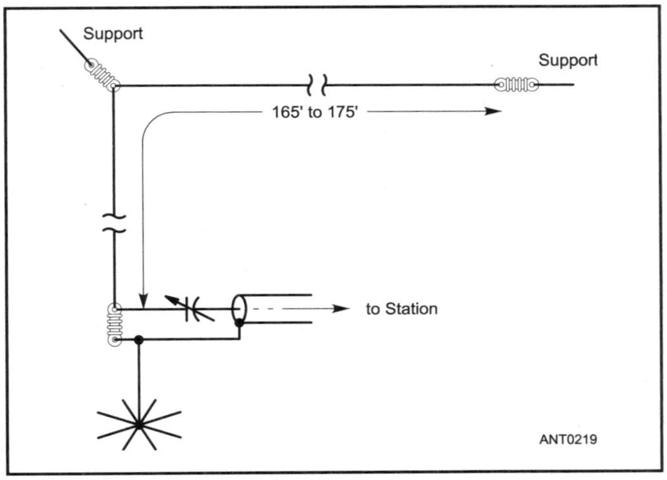

Figure 9.52 — The 1.8-MHz inverted-L. Overall wire length is 165 to 175 feet. The variable capacitor has a capacitance range from 100 to 800 pF, at 3 kV or more. Adjust antenna length and variable capacitor for lowest SWR.

Table 9.7
Inverted L Dimensions for 50-Ω Feed Point Resistance at 1.82 MHz

Vertical Height (m)	*Horizontal Length (m)*	*Inductive Reactance (Ω)*	*Capacitance Required (pF)*
10	59.9	1238	71
20	39.7	517	169
30	21	235	372

Results modeled by *EZNEC 5.0* over real ground
Capacitance specified as series value to cancel inductive reactance

Because the overall electrical length is made somewhat greater than λ/4, the feed point resistance is on the order of 50 Ω, with an inductive reactance. A resonant λ/4 vertical monopole has a feed point impedance of approximately 36 Ω. To raise that impedance for a better match to 50 Ω, the antenna is lengthened.

At an electrical length of 102° a vertical wire antenna will have a feed point impedance of approximately 50 + *j*100 Ω over good ground. As an exercise, the inverted-L is designed at 1.82 MHz as a 45.6-meter (149.6-foot) vertical if constructed from #12 AWG wire.) That reactance is canceled by a series capacitor as indicated in the figure.

Bending part of the vertical so that it is parallel to the ground or sloping will change the feed point impedance and lower the resistive component. For example, with a 20-meter (65.6-foot) vertical section and the horizontal wire parallel to the ground, the resonant antenna (now 41.25 meters long overall) has a feed point impedance of only 20 Ω. As with the vertical antenna, the length is increased to raise the feed point impedance. With the horizontal section extended to 39.7 meters (130.25 feet) the feed point impedance becomes 50 + *j* 517 Ω. This requires a series capacitor of 169 pF to cancel the inductive reactance and reduce SWR to 1:1. Various other combinations of vertical and horizontal lengths behave similarly as shown in **Table 9.7**. (The dimensions can be scaled to 80 meters with approximately half the series capacitance required.) The inverted-L is an excellent antenna on which to practice modeling and matching skills.

As for other wire antennas, the bandwidth of the antenna can be improved by increasing its effective diameter. For example, making the vertical radiator out of window or ladder line with both conductors tied together at the top and bottom will show some increase in operating bandwidth, the horizontal section remaining a single wire. Jim Brown, K9YC, reports using a pair of #10 AWG wires spaced 10 inches apart increased the 1.5:1 SWR bandwidth of his L to 100 kHz. A tower can also be used as the vertical section as described below.

A yardarm attached to a tower or a tree limb can be used to support the vertical section. As with any vertical, for best results the vertical section should be as long as possible. A good ground system is necessary for good results — the better the ground, the better the results.

If you don't have the space for the inverted-L shown in Figure 9.52 (with its 115-foot horizontal section) and if you don't have a second tall supporting structure to make the top wire horizontal, consider sloping the top wire down toward ground. **Figure 9.53** illustrates such a setup, with a 60-foot high vertical section and a 79-foot sloping wire. As always, you will have to adjust the length of the sloping wire to fine-tune the resonant frequency. For a good ground radial system, the feed point impedance is about 12 Ω, which may be transformed to 50 Ω with a 25-Ω quarter-wave transformer consisting of two paralleled 50-Ω quarter-wave coaxes. The peak gain will decrease about 1 dB compared to the inverted-L shown in Figure 9.52. **Figure 9.54** overlays the elevation responses for average ground conditions. The 2:1 SWR bandwidth will be about 30 kHz, narrower than the larger system in Figure 9.52.

If a large ground system is not practical, you can use a single elevated radial as shown in **Figure 9.55**. For the

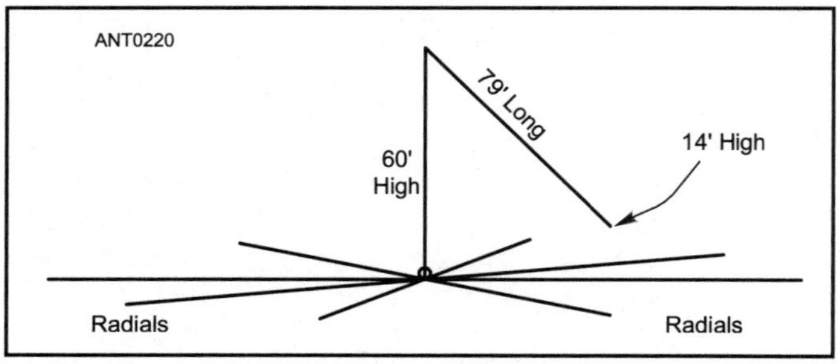

Figure 9.53 — Sketch showing a modified 160 meter inverted-L, with a single supporting 60-foot high tower and a 79-foot long slanted top-loading wire. The feed point impedance is about 12 Ω in this system, requiring a quarter-wave matching transformer made of paralleled 50-Ω coaxes.

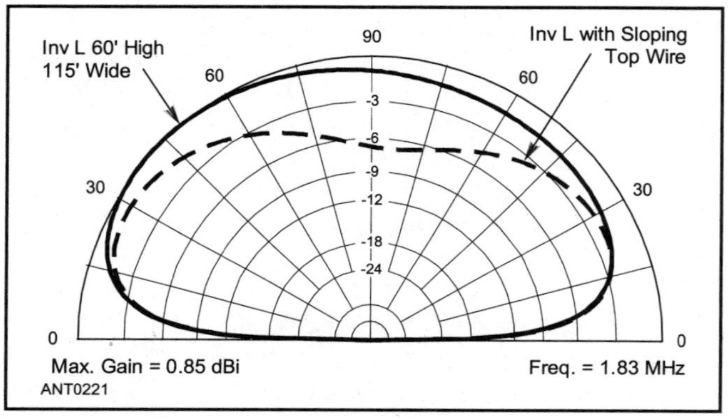

Figure 9.54 — Overlay of the elevation responses for the inverted-L antennas in Figure 9.52 (solid line) and Figure 9.53 (dashed line). The gains are very close for these two setups, provided that the ground radial system for the antenna in Figure 9.53 is extensive enough to keep ground losses low.

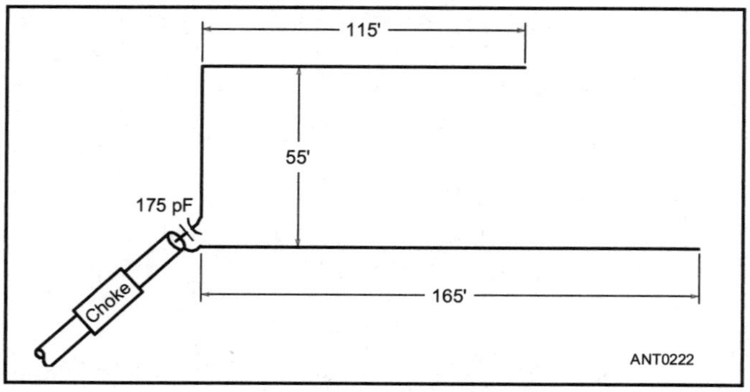

Figure 9.55 — A single elevated radial can be used for the inverted-L. This changes the directivity slightly. The series tuning capacitor is approximately 175 pF for this system.

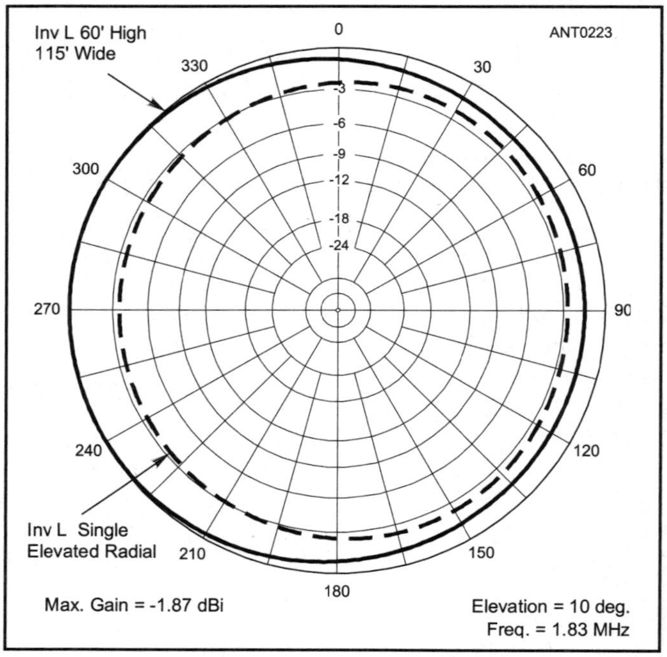

Figure 9.56 — Azimuthal pattern comparison for inverted-L antennas shown in Figure 9.52 (solid line) and the compromise, single-radial system in Figure 9.55 (dashed line). This is for a takeoff angle of 10°.

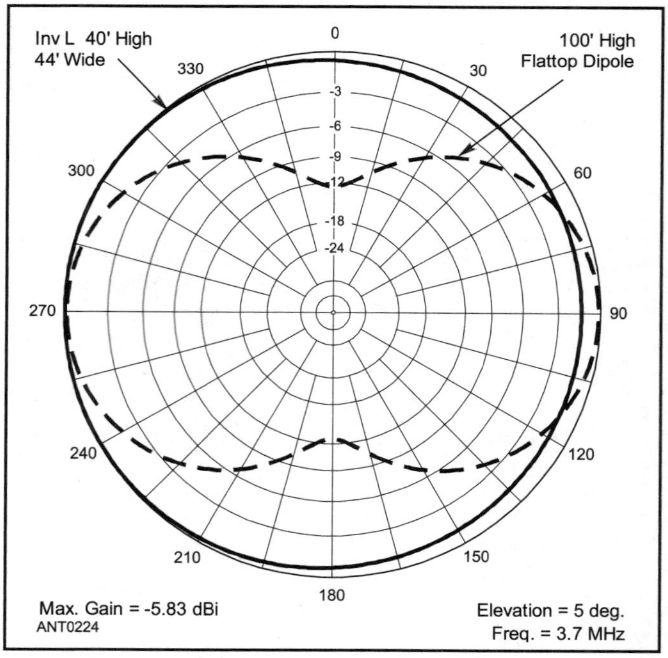

Figure 9.57 — Azimuthal pattern at a takeoff angle of 5° for an 80 meter version of the inverted-L (solid line) in Figure 9.52, compared to the response for a 100-foot high flattop dipole (dashed line).

dimensions shown in the figure, $Z_i = 50 + j\,498\ \Omega$, requiring a 175-pF series resonating capacitor. The azimuthal radiation pattern is shown in **Figure 9.56** compared to the inverted-L in Figure 9.52. Note that the 1 to 2 dB asymmetry is now in the direction of the horizontal wires, just the opposite of that for a symmetrical ground system. The 2:1 SWR bandwidth is about 40 kHz, assuming that the series capacitor is adjusted at 1.83 MHz for minimum SWR.

Figure 9.57 shows the azimuthal response at a 5° elevation angle for an 80 meter version of the inverted-L in Figure 9.52. The peak response occurs at an azimuth directly behind the direction in which the horizontal portion of the inverted-L points. For comparison, the response for a 100-foot high flattop dipole is also shown. The top wire of this antenna is only 40 feet high and the 2:1 SWR bandwidth is about 150 kHz wide with a good, low-loss ground-radial system.

Figure 9.57 illustrates that the azimuth response of an inverted-L is nearly omnidirectional. This gives such an antenna an advantage in certain directions compared to a flattop dipole, which is constrained by its supporting mounts (such as trees or towers) to favor fixed directions. For example, the flattop dipole in Figure 9.57 is at its weakest at azimuths of 90° and 270°, where it is down about 12 dB compared to the inverted-L. Hams who are fortunate enough to have high rotary dipoles or rotatable low-band Yagis have found them to be very effective antennas indeed.

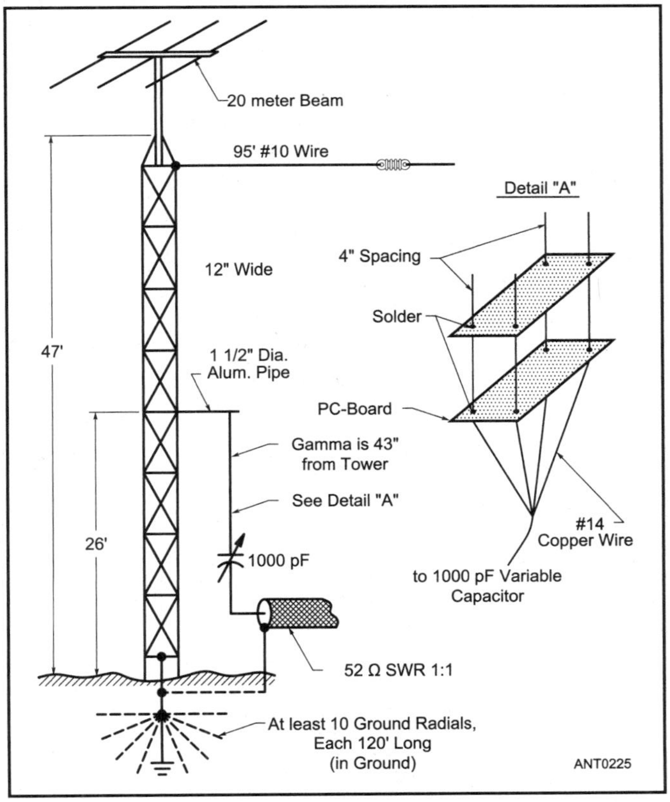

Figure 9.58 — Details and dimensions for gamma-match feeding a 50-foot tower as a 1.8-MHz vertical antenna. The rotator cable and coaxial feed line for the 14-MHz beam is taped to the tower legs and run into the shack from ground level. No decoupling networks are necessary.

9.4.1 TOWER-BASED INVERTED-L

Figure 9.58 shows the method used by Doug DeMaw, W1FB, to gamma match his self-supporting 50-foot tower operating as an inverted-L. A wire cage simulates a gamma rod of the proper diameter. The tuning capacitor is fashioned from telescoping sections of 1¼ and 1½-inch aluminum tubing with polyethylene tubing serving as the dielectric. This capacitor is more than adequate for power levels of 100 W. The horizontal wire connected to the top of the tower provides the additional top loading.

9.4.2 T ANTENNAS

The T is basically a shortened ¼-λ vertical with the flat-top T section acting as capacitive loading to length the antenna electrically. **Figure 9.59** shows a flat-top T vertical. As with the inverted-L, the vertical section (H) should be as large as possible (up to ¼-λ) for best results. Length of the horizontal T section is then adjusted to achieve resonance. Maximum radiation is polarized vertically despite the horizontal top-loading wire because current in each symmetrical half creates out-of-phase radiation that cancels.

A sidearm or a length of line attached to a tower can be used to support the vertical section of the T antenna. (Keep the vertical section of the antennas as far from the tower as is practical. Certain combinations of tower height and top loading can create a resonance that interacts severely with the antennas — a 70-foot tower and a 5-element Yagi, for example.) If the tower has an insulated base or is shunt-fed, it can be used as a T antenna by attaching horizontal or sloping wires at the top of the tower.

An ordinary dipole can be used as a T antenna by shorting the feed line terminals together and driving the single resulting wire against the station ground system as shown in **Figure 9.60A**. A photo of a typical feed-through panel configured for using a dipole fed with window line in this way is shown in Figure 9.60B. Feed line to the antenna tuner is reconnected with one conductor connected to the shorted external feed line and the other conductor is connected to the station ground system outside. A good ground plane is required just as for any other ground-plane antenna and can be provided by radials attached to the ground system either temporarily or as part of the station ground.

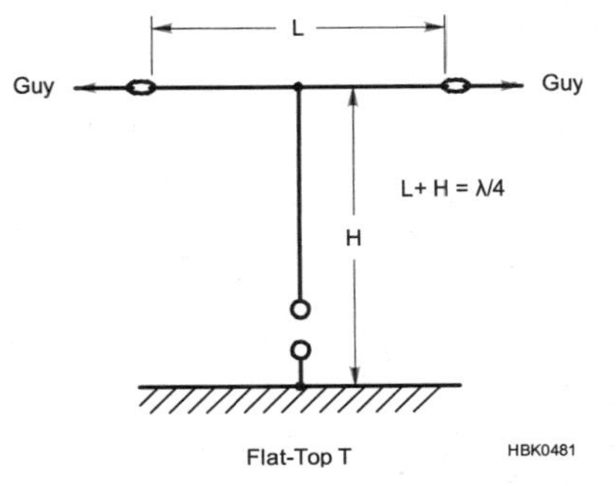

Figure 9.59 — The T antenna is basically a shortened ¼-λ vertical with the flat-top T section acting as capacitive loading to length the antenna electrically.

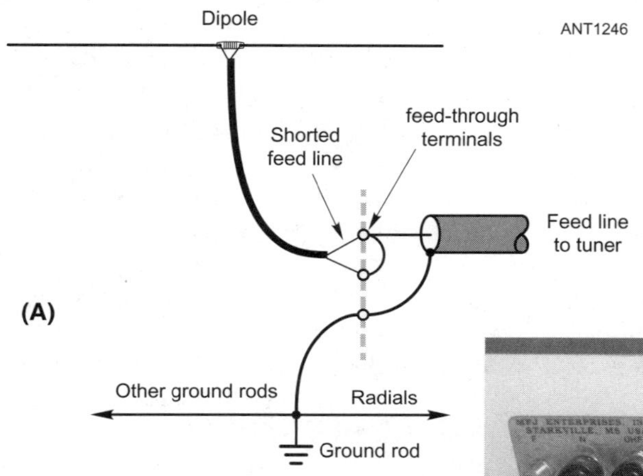

(A)

(B)

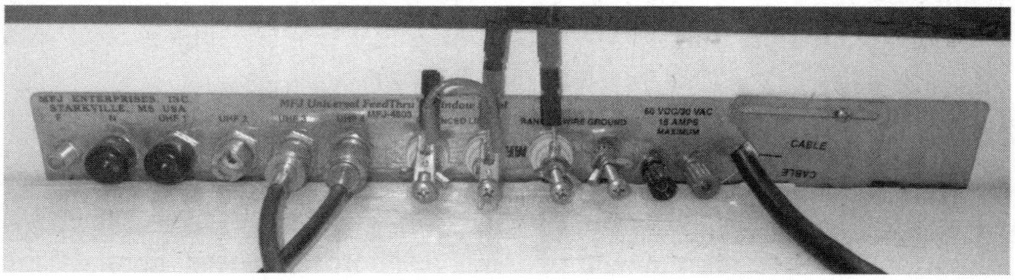

Figure 9.60 — Converting a dipole to a T antenna (A) can be done by shorting the feed line terminals and driving both conductors against the station ground. B shows a typical feed-through panel with a shorting jumper attached to the feed-through terminals. One conductor of the feed line to a balanced tuner is attached to the shorted terminals and the other to the station ground terminal. Powerpole connectors are used to allow quick feed line configuration changes.

9.5 HALF-SLOPER ANTENNAS

Sloping dipoles and λ/2 dipoles can be very useful antennas on the low bands. These antennas can have one end attached to a tower, tree or other structure and the other end near ground level, elevated high enough so that passersby can't contact them, of course. The following section gives a number of examples of these types of antennas. The book *Sloper Antennas* by Juergen Weigl, OE5CWL, contains analysis and many designs of half-sloper antennas. (See the Bibliography.)

Perhaps one of the easiest antennas to install is the λ/4 sloper shown in **Figure 9.61**. As pointed out above, a sloping λ/2 dipole is known among radio amateurs as a *sloper* or sometimes as a *full sloper*. If only one half of it is used, it becomes a *half sloper*. The performance of the two types of sloping antennas is similar — they exhibit some directivity in the direction of the slope and radiate vertically polarized energy at low angles respective to the horizon. The amount of directivity will range from 3 to 6 dB, depending upon the individual installation, and will be observed in the slope direction.

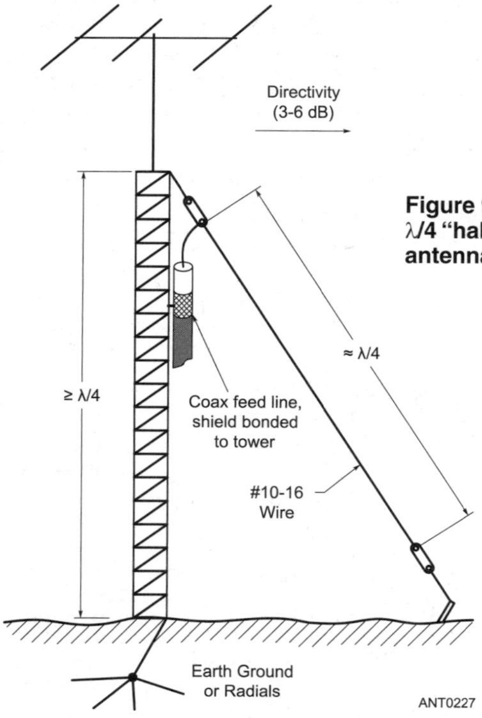

Figure 9.61 — The λ/4 "half sloper" antenna.

The main advantage of the half sloper over the full half wave-long sloping dipole is that its supporting tower needn't be as high. Both the half sloper and the full sloper place the feed point (the point of maximum current) high above lossy ground. But the half-sloper only needs half as much wire to build the antenna for a given amateur band. The disadvantage of the half sloper is that it is sometimes difficult or even impossible to obtain a low SWR when using coaxial-cable feed, especially without a good isolating choke balun. (See the section above on isolating ground-plane antennas.)

Other factors that affect the feed-impedance are tower height, height of the attachment point, enclosed angle between the sloper and the tower, and what is mounted atop the tower (HF or VHF beams). Further, the quality of the ground under the tower (ground conductivity, radials, etc) has a marked effect on the antenna performance. The final SWR can vary (after optimization) from 1:1 to as high as 6:1. Generally speaking, the closer the low end of the slope wire is to ground, the more difficult it will be to obtain a good match.

The half sloper can be an excellent DX type of antenna. Hams usually install theirs on a metal supporting structure such as a mast or tower. Assuming coax feed line, the center conductor is connected to the sloping wire and the shield to the support. The support needs to be grounded at the lower end, preferably to a buried or on-ground radial system. If a nonconductive support is used, the outside of the coax braid becomes the return circuit and should be grounded at the base of the support.

As a starting point you can attach the sloper so the feed point is approximately λ/4 above ground. If the tower is not high enough to permit this, the antenna should be fastened as high on the supporting structure as possible. Start with an enclosed angle of approximately 45°, as indicated in Figure 9.61. Cut the wire to the length determined from

$$\ell = \frac{260}{f_{MHz}}$$

This will allow sufficient extra length for pruning the wire for the lowest SWR. A metal tower or mast becomes an operating part of the half sloper system. In effect, it and the slope wire function somewhat like an inverted-V dipole antenna. In other words, the tower operates as the missing half of the dipole. Hence its height and the top loading (beams) play a significant role.

Detailed modeling indicates that a sufficiently large mass of metal (that is, a large, "Plumber's Delight" Yagi) connected to the top of the tower acts like enough of a "top counterpoise" that the tower may be removed from the model with little change in the essential characteristics of the half-sloper system. Consider an installation using a freestanding 50-foot tower with a large 5-element 20 meter Yagi on top. This Yagi is assumed to have a 40-foot boom oriented east-west, 90° from the north-facing slanted 80 meter half-sloper. The best SWR that could be reached by changing the length and slant angle for this sloper is 1.67:1, representing a feed point impedance of $30.1 - j\,2.7\ \Omega$. The peak gain at 3.8 MHz is 0.97 dBi at an elevation angle of 70°. **Figure 9.62** shows the azimuth-plane pattern for this half sloper, compared to a 100-foot high flat-top dipole for reference, at an elevation angle of 5°.

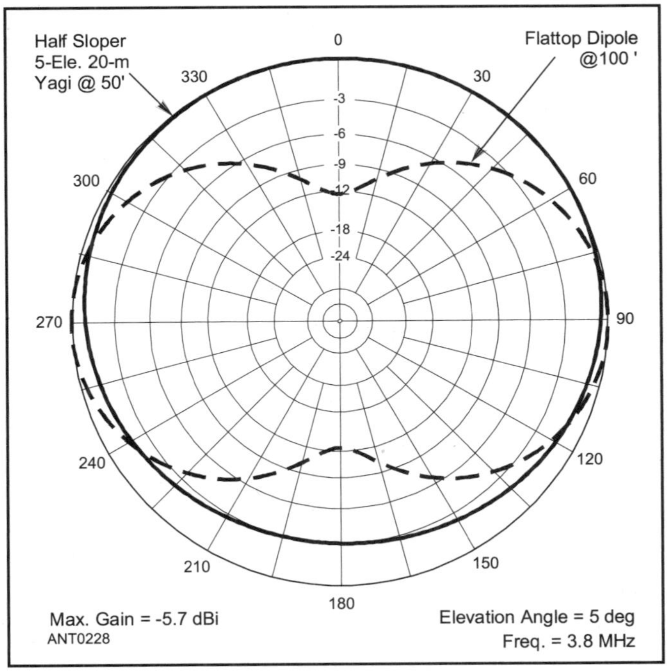

Figure 9.62 — Radiation pattern for a typical half sloper (solid line) mounted on a 50-foot high tower with a large 5-element 20 meter beam on the top compared to that for a flattop dipole (dashed line) at 100 feet. At a 5° takeoff angle typical for DX work on 80 meters, the two antennas are pretty comparable in the directions favored by the high dipole. In other directions, the half sloper has an advantage of more than 10 dB.

Removing the tower from the model resulted in a feed point impedance of $30.1 - j\,1.5\ \Omega$ and a peak gain of 1.17 dBi. The tower is obviously not contributing much in this setup, since the mass of the large 20 meter Yagi is acting like an elevated counterpoise all by itself. It's interesting to rotate the boom of the model Yagi and observe the change in SWR that occurs on the half-sloper antenna. With the boom turned 90°, the SWR falls to 1.38:1. This level of SWR change could be measured with amateur-type instrumentation.

On the other hand, substituting a smaller 3-element 20 meter Yagi with an 18-foot boom in the model does result in significant change in feed point impedance and gain when the tower is removed from the model, indicating that the "counterpoise effect" of the smaller beam is insufficient by itself. Interestingly enough, the best SWR for the half sloper/tower and the 3-element Yagi (with its boom in line with the half sloper is 1.33:1), changing to 1.27:1 with the boom turned 90°. Such a small change in SWR would be difficult to measure using typical amateur instrumentation.

In any case, the 50-Ω transmission line feeding a half sloper should be taped to the tower leg at frequent intervals to make it secure. The best method is to bring it to earth level, then route it to the operating position along the surface of the ground if it can't be buried. This will ensure adequate RF decoupling, which will help prevent RF energy from affecting the equipment in the station. Rotator cable and other feed lines on the tower or mast should be treated in a similar manner.

Adjustment of the half sloper is done with an SWR indicator in the 50-Ω transmission line. A compromise can usually be found between the enclosed angle and wire length, providing the lowest SWR attainable in the center of the chosen part of an amateur band. If the SWR "bottoms out" at 2:1 or lower, the system will work fine without using an antenna tuner, provided the transmitter can work into the load. Typical

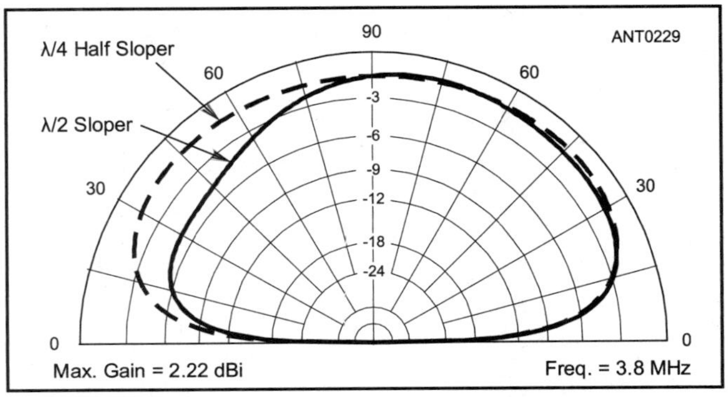

Figure 9.63 — Comparison of elevation patterns for a full-sized half wave sloper (solid line) on a 100-foot tower and a half sloper (dashed line) on a 50-foot tower with a 5-element 20 meter Yagi acting as a top counterpoise. The performance is quite comparable for these two systems.

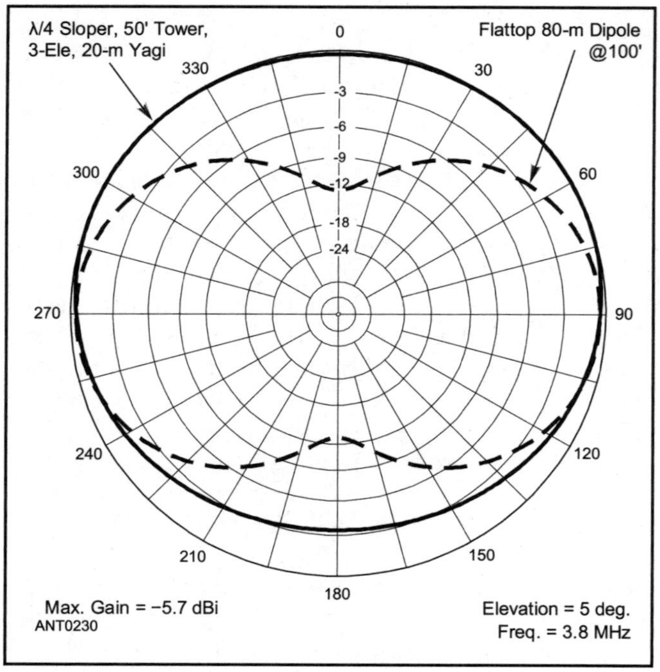

Figure 9.64 — Comparing the azimuthal response of a half sloper (solid line) on a 50-foot tower with a 3-element 20 meter Yagi on top to that of a flattop dipole (dashed line) at 100 feet. The two are again quite comparable at a 5° takeoff angle.

optimum values of SWR for 3.5 or 7-MHz half slopers are between 1.3:1 and 2:1. A 100-kHz bandwidth is normal on 3.5 MHz, with 200 kHz being typical at 7 MHz.

If the lowest SWR possible is greater than 2:1, the attachment point can be raised or lowered to improve the match. Readjustment of the wire length and enclosed angle may be necessary when the feed point height is changed. If the tower is guyed, the guy wires will need to be insulated from the tower and broken up with additional insulators to prevent resonance.

At this point you may be curious about which antenna is better — a full sloper or a half sloper. The peak gain for each antenna is very nearly identical. **Figure 9.63** overlays the elevation-plane pattern for the full-sized half wave sloper on a 100-foot tower and for the half sloper shown in Figure

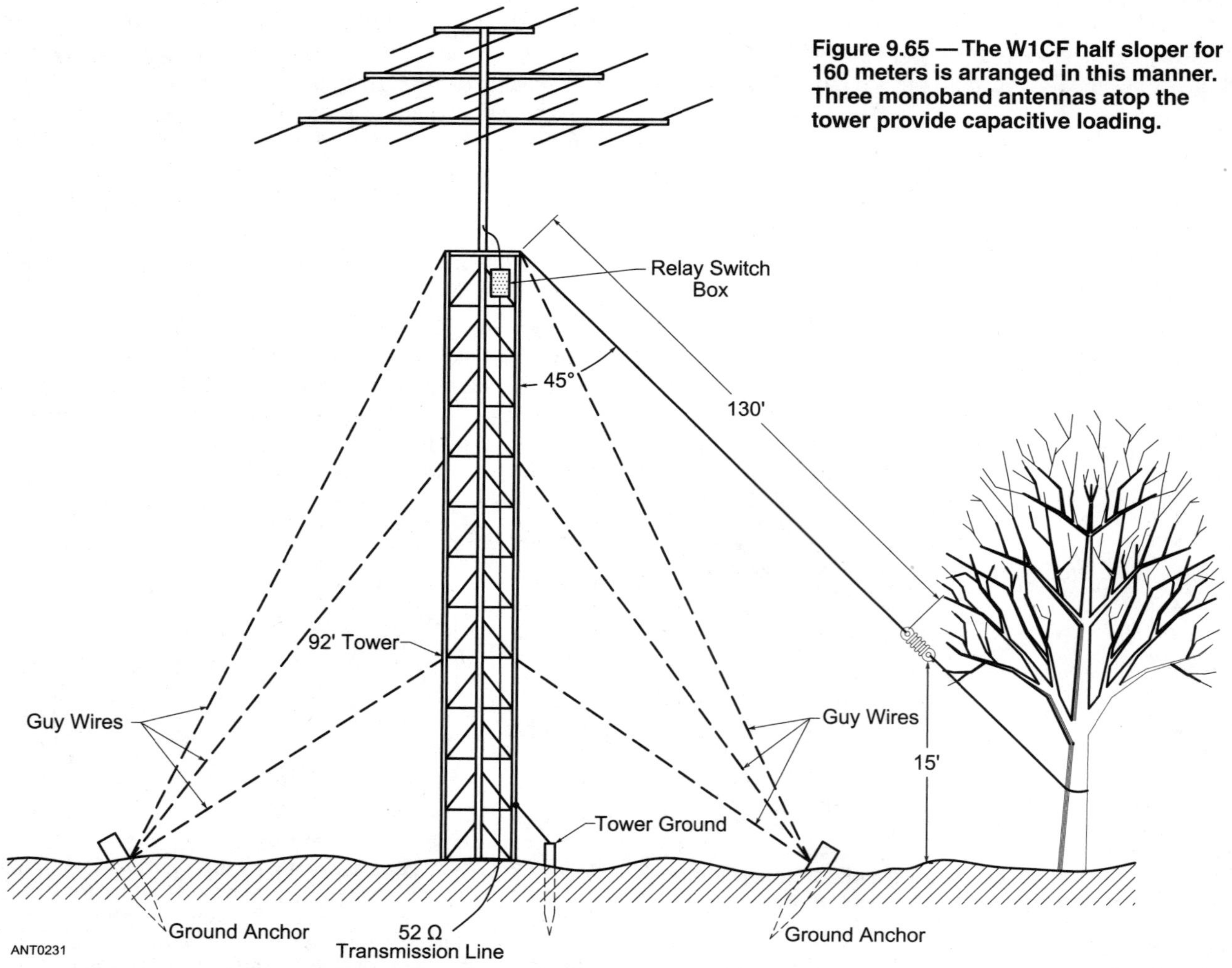

Figure 9.65 — The W1CF half sloper for 160 meters is arranged in this manner. Three monoband antennas atop the tower provide capacitive loading.

9.61 on a 50-foot tower with a 5-element 20 meter Yagi on top. The full-sized half wave sloper has more front-to-back ratio, but it is only a few dB more than the half sloper. **Figure 9.64** compares the azimuthal patterns at a 5° takeoff angle for a 100-foot high flattop dipole and a half-sloper system on a 50-foot tower with a 3-element 20 meter Yagi on top.

Despite the frustration some have experienced trying to achieve a low SWR with some half-sloper installations, many operators have found the half sloper to be an effective and low-cost antenna for DX work.

9.5.1 1.8-MHZ HALF-SLOPERS USING TOWERS

The half sloper discussed above for 80 or 40 meter operation will also perform well on 1.8 MHz where vertically polarized radiators can achieve the low takeoff angles needed on Top Band. Prominent 1.8-MHz operators who have had success with the half sloper antenna suggest a minimum tower height of 50 feet. Dana Atchley, W1CF, used the configuration sketched in **Figure 9.65**. He reported that the uninsulated guy wires act as an effective counterpoise for the sloping wire. In **Figure 9.66** is the feed system used by Doug DeMaw, W1FB, on a 50-foot self-supporting tower. The ground for the W1FB system is provided by buried radials connected to the tower base. Jack Belrose, VE2CV and DeMaw also described an interesting method of using a sloping wire to create a "half delta" usable on the lower HF bands. The system is described in the Sep 1982 *QST* article, "The Half-Delta Loop: A Critical Analysis and Practical Deployment" which is also included with this book's downloadable supplemental information.

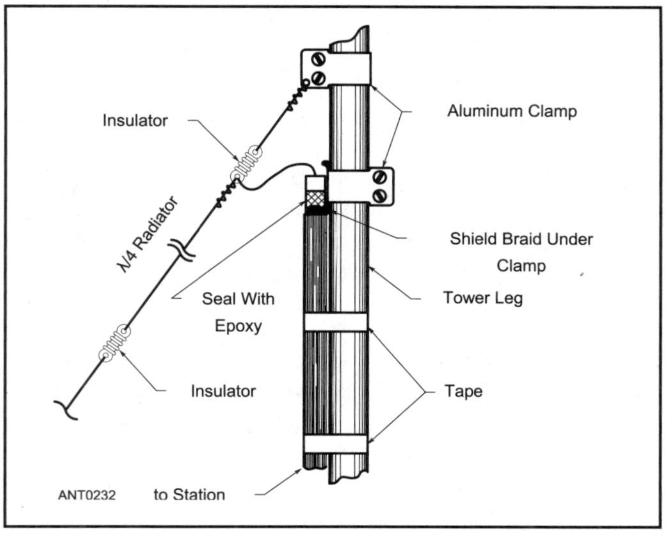

Figure 9.66 — Feed system used by W1FB for 1.8 MHz half sloper on a 50-foot self-supporting tower.

As described previously, a tower can also be used as a true vertical antenna, provided a good ground system is used. The shunt-fed tower is at its best on 1.8 MHz, where a full λ/4 vertical antenna is rarely possible. Almost any tower height can be used. An HF beam at the top provides some top loading.

9.6 LF AND MF ANTENNAS

This material is excerpted and summarized from "LF and MF Antennas for Amateurs" by Rudy Severns, N6LF. Rudy participated as experimental licensee WD2XSH/20 during the evaluation period for the new bands and gained much valuable experience. This section is a collection of theory and practical recommendations for transmitting antennas at the long wavelengths below the AM broadcast band. The full document is downloadable from ***www.antennasbyn6lf.com*** *and the interested reader is urged to read the full presentation.*

A hundred years ago, amateurs were restricted to wavelengths below 200 meters (f >1.5 MHz). We now have allocations at 2200 meters (135.7-137.8 kHz, LF) and 630 meters (472-479 kHz, MF). However, amateurs have very little experience at these frequencies and it turns out that design and construction of antennas for the new bands is substantially different from HF. The primary purpose of these notes is practical advice on LF/MF transmitting antennas. There is a perception that substantial acreage is required for the antennas on these bands. That is not the case! Those with small properties can be successful,but we have to know how!

There are differences between LF/MF and HF which impact antenna design:

1) Wavelengths are much longer so that any practical antenna will be electrically small.

2) Soil electrical characteristics change substantially going from HF down to LF/MF.

3) Power limitations are in terms of power radiated from the antenna rather than maximum transmitter output power although there are also limits on transmitter power.

Long Wavelengths

At 1.9 MHz, the wavelength (λ) ≈ 518 feet, so a λ/4 vertical will be ≈ 130 feet high. If you divide 1.9 MHz by 4 you get 475 kHz, right in the middle of the new 630 meter band. λ/4 on 160 meters is only ≈ λ/16 at 475 kHz. The 2200-meter band is another factor of 3.5 lower in frequency, so a λ/4 vertical on 160 meters is only ≈ 0.018 λ on 137 kHz. At 475 kHz, λ ≈ 2071 feet, so a λ/4 vertical would be ≈ 500 feet high. At 137 kHz λ/4 ≈ 1800 feet! In any case, the FCC has limited the maximum height to 197 feet (60 meter), which is still only 0.095 λ at 137 kHz.

The focus of this discussion is on antennas with heights (H) practical for amateurs, i.e. H = 20–100 feet (H ≈ 0.01 – 0.05 λ at 475 kHz and H ≈ 0.003 – 0.015 λ at 137 kHz). In terms of electrical height these are certainly "short" antennas, with very low radiation resistance (R_r), narrow matched SWR bandwidth and low efficiency. A major part of the design effort for LF/MF antennas is directed towards obtaining adequate efficiency.

Soil Characteristics

Because ground electrical characteristics have a profound effect, some basic information on soil electrical characteristics will be needed. At 100 Hz soil conductivity $\sigma \approx 0.09$ S/m and is relatively constant up to ≈1 MHz but beyond that point σ increases rapidly with frequency. Relative permittivity of soil, ε_r behaves just the opposite, with a value of approximately 200 at 137 kHz that decreases with frequency, reaching approximately 70 at 475 kHz. Permittivity continues to decrease with an approximate value of 50 at 1 MHz and 23 at 10 MHz. At a given QTH, with the same soil, the electrical characteristics will be very different between HF and LF/MF.

EIRP and Radiated Power

Power limits on 2200 and 630 meters are stated in terms of *effective isotropic radiated power* (EIRP). The "isotropic" in EIRP refers to an idealized antenna in free space which radiates power uniformly in all directions. On 630 meters 5 W EIRP is allowed and on 2200 meters the allowed EIRP is 1 W, which means the total radiated power, P_r, is about 1.7 W on 630 meters and 0.33 W on 2200 meters.

At HF, antenna efficiencies are typically >90% and the focus is on antenna gain. On LF/MF our goal is to achieve sufficient efficiency that we can radiated the allowed power with the available transmitter power. This is a fundamentally different mindset! We have the choice of a large efficient antenna with small input power (P_i) or a small inefficient antenna with a large input power. Most installations will be a balance between the two extremes.

A transmitter output power of 100 W is generally pretty easy to obtain, and 100 W is frequently assumed in later chapters unless stated otherwise. In addition to the EIRP power limit, the FCC has also limited the input power to the antenna to 500 W PEP on 630 meters and 1.5 kW PEP on 2200 meters. However, given limitations due to the high voltages associated with these power levels, from a practical point of view these limits are moot. (P_r can be measured directly as described in Severn's material.)

A major part of the design effort for LF/MF antennas is directed at obtaining adequate efficiency. Given practical height limitations, most LF/MF antennas will require loading inductors for resonance and matching. In many cases the losses in this inductor will determine the efficiency of the antenna. Much of the design effort is directed towards first minimizing the required inductance (L) with height and top-loading and then maximizing inductor "Q" (Q_L)

Fundamental Advice

Repeating Woodrow Smith's summary of LF/MF antenna design given earlier in the discussion on short verticals:

"The main object in the design of low frequency transmitting antenna systems can be summarized briefly by saying that the general idea is to get as much wire as possible as high in the air as possible and to use excellent insulation and an extensive ground system."

This simple advice should be taken literally! This advice can be organized in order of priority:

1) Make the vertical as tall as you can.

2) Use as much capacitive top-loading as practical.

3) Use carefully placed high-Q loading coils.

4) Put substantial effort into the ground system, with the radial density high near the base of the vertical and under the top-loading hat.

5) Minimize conductor losses by using multiple wires and/or large diameter conductors.

6) Use high quality insulators, at the base and at wire ends.

9.6.1 EFFICIENCY OF VERY SHORT VERTICALS

The material on short verticals earlier in this chapter applies to LF/MF verticals, especially the discussion of losses and efficiency. Refer to Chapter 2 of N6LF's notes for detailed discussion of the material in this section.

Efficiency of a short vertical antenna depends on the radiation resistance (R_r), ground resistance (R_g) and the loss resistance in the antenna itself (R_{loss}):

$$\eta = \frac{R_r}{R_r + R_g + R_{loss}} \quad (8)$$

Figure 9.67 graphs R_r for a lossless #12 AWG wire vertical for H = 20 to 100 feet at 137 and 475 kHz. We can see that R_r is very small even for heights of 100 feet. A λ/4 vertical would have $R_r \approx 36\ \Omega$ but in LF/MF antennas R_r is typically

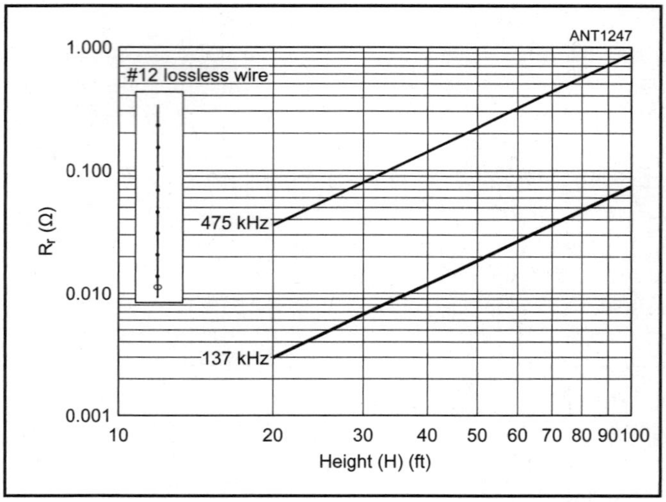

Figure 9.67 — Example of R_r variation with vertical height (H).

smaller by a factor of 100 to 1000!

Conductors larger than #12 wire are often employed by using multiple parallel wires (up to a few inches spacing) or a cage of vertical wires is created with all of the wires connected together at the top. For diameters up to a few feet, eight wires are more than adequate but for very large diameters, say 10 to 40 feet, adding more wires to the cage may be worth doing. Using a larger diameter conductor or more wires has the immediate benefit of reducing conductor loss (R_c) which is a component of R_{loss}. The bottom ends of the vertical wires are typically connected together with a skirt wire like similarly to the top of the cage. The bottom skirt wire is then driven against ground or inductors are placed in each downlead and only one or two are driven. **Figure 9.68** shows the variation in R_r at 475 and 137 kHz as the conductor diameter is varied from #12 wire to 40 feet over heights from 20 to 100 feet. For a thin wire vertical (no inductor or capacitive loading) with a triangular current distribution:

$$R_r \approx 0.003{G_v}^2\ \Omega$$

where G_v is the electrical length of the wire in degrees.

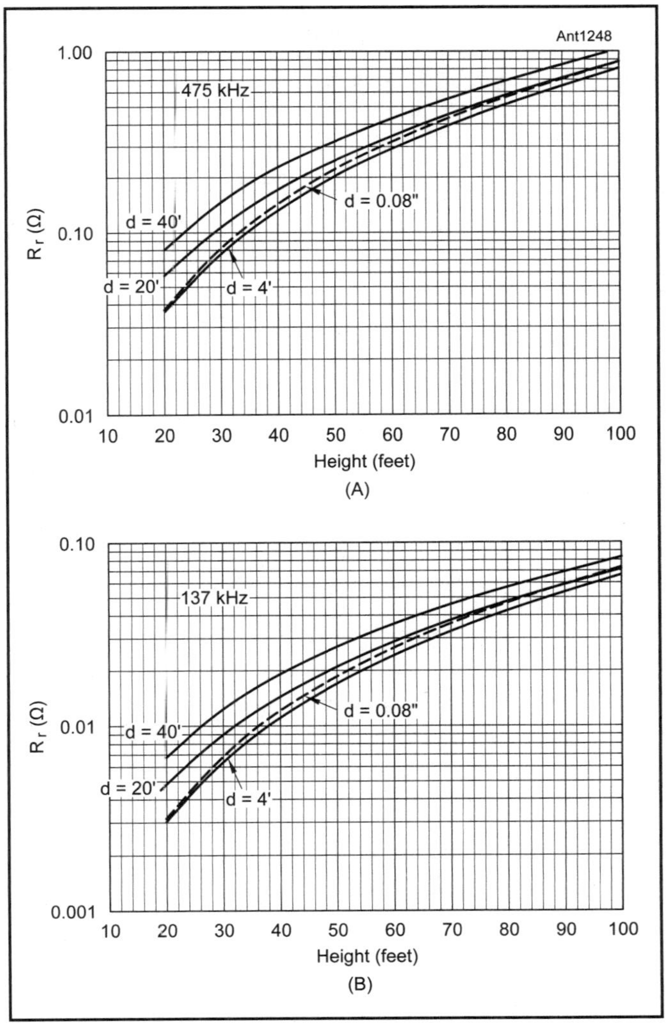

Figure 9.68 — Effects of conductor diameter on R_r at 475 kHz (A) and 137 kHz (B).

Loading Inductors

Loaded Q (Q_L) can range from 100 to >1000. In general, for a given inductor, Q_L at 137 kHz will be ≈0.54 Q_L at 475 kHz or a little less if the Q_L at 475 kHz is near a peak value due to the effects of self-resonance. While very high Q_L inductors are possible most of this discussion will assume Q_L=200 at 137 kHz and 400 at 475 kHz because these values are practical with modest effort but keep in mind that higher values are possible.

We can get a good feeling for the effect of loading inductor losses (R_L) on efficiency by assuming input $R = R_L + R_r$ (i.e. ignoring other losses) and calculate the efficiency. Q_L = 200 at 137 kHz and 400 at 475 kHz are assumed. With H = 20 feet, at 137 kHz η = 0.0024% and at 475 kHz η = 0.20% even without accounting for any other losses! Increasing H to 100 feet makes a great difference. At 137 kHz η = 0.24% which is still very low but a factor of 100 improvement. With 100 W output from the transmitter, to radiate the maximum allowed power the antenna will have to have η > 2% at 475 kHz and η >0.33% at 137 kHz.

To radiate the maximum allowed power, a minimum height of 45 feet on 630 meters and >100 feet on 2200 meters is needed. A small change in height means a large change in efficiency! Maximizing height is a vital for improving efficiency.

R_L is the dominant loss throughout this range of H, especially as we go lower in frequency. This observation is important because it tells us what our design priorities must be. The value of R_L is tied directly to the value of X_L ($|X_L| \approx |X_C|$) through Q_L. Again, the message is very clear: To reduce R_L we must reduce X_C! Once height has been maximized, top-loading becomes the primary tool for reducing X_C.

Chapter 6 of the online notes, "Design and Fabrication of High-Q Tuning Inductors for LF/MF Antennas" goes into detail about the construction of high-Q inductors for transmitting use at LF/MF. The information in the chapter can also be applied to inductors for the lower HF bands, as well. The chapter also covers the design and construction of variable inductors and variometers.

Feed Point Voltages and Currents

Unfortunately, low efficiency is not the only challenge. Base currents (I_O) and feed point voltages (V_O) can be very high. The following discussion is for a simple vertical without the top-loading that significantly reduces I_O and V_O.

Figure 9.69A shows base current (I_O in A RMS) as a function of H. These are the RMS currents required to produce the allowed radiated power on each band. Figure 9.69B shows the input power, P_i, required to produce the allowed radiated power, P_r, on each band for a given loading inductor Q. If you wish to use a simple 20 feet vertical on 137 kHz radiating the maximum allowed power you'll have to provide $P_i \approx 9$ kW!

The input current (I_O) flows through the short-vertical series circuit of the sum of radiation resistance and all losses (R_a), the antenna's inductive reactance ($+X_a$) and capacitive reactance ($-X_c$). In short antennas R_a and X_a are very small

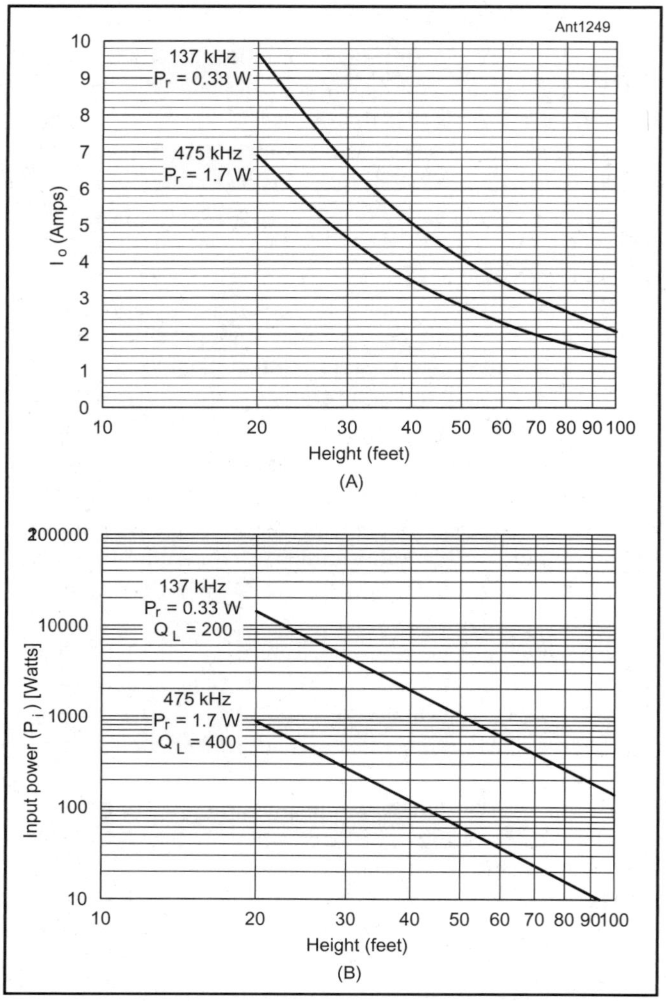

Figure 9.69 — Base current (I_O) and voltage (V_O) versus antenna height (H) at A. B shows the required input power (P_i) to radiate the maximum allowed power, (P_r) versus height with the same loading inductors as in the previous section.

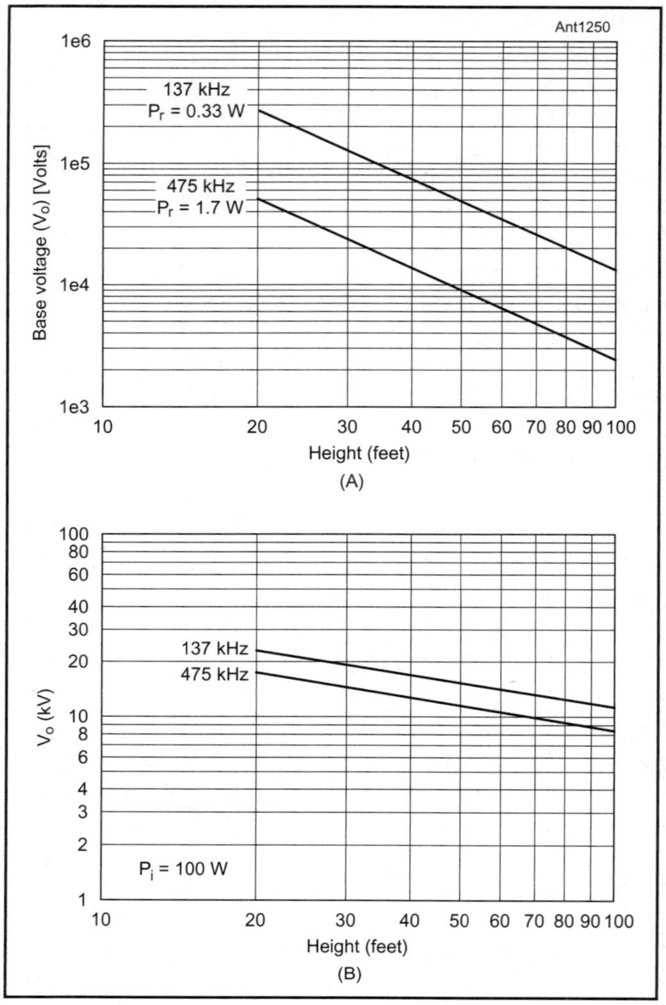

Figure 9.70 — Base voltage when radiating allowed P_r (A) and with P_i = 100 W (B).

compared to X_C. The input reactance is thus $X_i \approx X_C$ and X_C will be very large. The voltage across the feed point ($V_O = I_O \times X_i$) will be very high as indicated in **Figure 9.70A**. A 20-foot vertical at 137 kHz with $P_i \approx 9$ kW and $P_r = 0.33$ W will have $V_O \approx 300$kV! Given the very modest radiating power allowed, these voltage levels can come as an unpleasant surprise when an increase in transmitter power unexpectedly causes the loading coil to go up in flames or there is arcing across the base insulator or within tuning network components! For most amateurs $P_i \leq 100$ W is more realistic but even at this greatly reduced power V_O can still be many kV as shown in Figure 9.70B. This further reinforces the advice to minimize X_C. We must be very respectful of the voltages present on these antennas even at seemingly low power levels. *Be careful*!

9.6.2 CAPACITIVE TOP-LOADING

A critical part of achieving higher efficiency is the reduction of capacitive reactance at the feed point because this reduces the size of the loading inductor and its associated R_L. In addition, steps to reduce inductance can also increase R_r at the same time. Other top-loading schemes which reduce X_i also reduce R_r rather than increase it and at some point the efficiency may actually start to fall even though we continue to reduce X_i. This happens in top-loading schemes with sloping wires with currents opposing the current in the main vertical conductor.

For amateurs new to LF/MF the first antenna needs to be as simple as possible to get on the air. We'll start by keeping it simple and assuming only one or two supports, a roll of wire and some insulators. We'll begin with an example showing R_r, X_i and efficiency and then go on to explain why top-loading is so effective in reducing X_i and increasing R_r.

It is assumed that height (H) has been made as tall as practical and we are now turning to capacitive top-loading to improve efficiency. The same tuning inductor Q_L = 400 at 475 kHz and 200 at 137 kHz is assumed. Many different variables affect the capacitance introduced by the top-loading structure:

• The number and/or length of umbrella wires

• Whether or not there is a skirt tying the ends of the wires together

• The location of the tuning inductor along the vertical conductor

• Conductor size

Keep in mind that efficiency determined from only R_L and R_r is an upper limit, i.e. the best we can do. Adding more losses only reduces efficiency. Once we've reduced R_L as much as possible we can deal with other losses. Reducing X_i has the further benefit of reducing the voltages and currents at the base. For the most part, if you make some change in your antenna which reduces the inductance required to resonate the antenna that change is likely to improve your efficiency. This is a useful guide when experimenting. One important point, most examples have symmetric wire arrangements because it's easier to model but symmetry is not required!

Efficiency with Top-loading

The T antenna shown in **Figure 9.71A** and B illustrates how effective capacitive top-loading is. Efficiency is shown in percent (%) as a function of the length of the top wire (L) at 475 and 137 kHz. The L = 0 trace represents the case with no top-loading, just the bare vertical with a loading coil at the base. In these models the value of the tuning inductor was adjusted to maintain resonance as L and H were changed. #12 wire conductors are assumed. Even a small amount of top-loading increases efficiency. As an example, for L = 0 and H = 20 feet, $\eta = 0.19\%$ at 475 kHz. Keeping H = 20 feet but adding a 40 foot top-wire, $\eta = 1.3\%$, a factor of 6.8! Taking L to 100 feet increases the efficiency by a factor of 18! Height and capacitive top-loading are keys to improving efficiency!

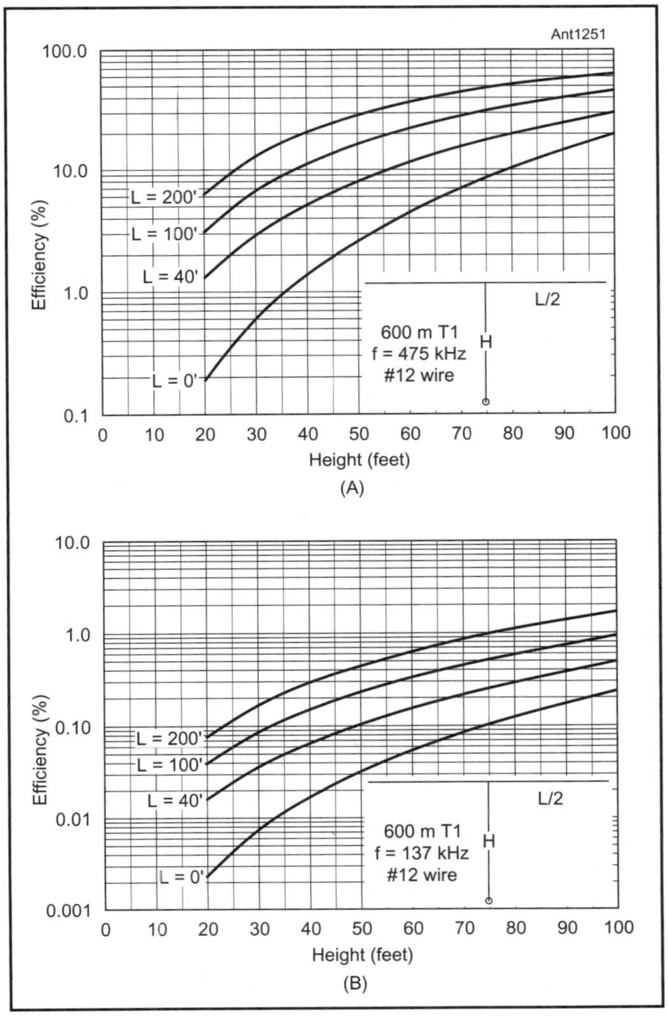

Figure 9.71 — Efficiency at 475 kHz (A) and 137 kHz (B) with base tuning.

Rr with Top-loading

Top-loading can also improve R_r. R_r increases substantially as we add more top wire. **Figure 9.72** shows a graph for R_r as a function of antenna height with the current ratio I_t/I_O as a parameter (I_t is the current at the top of the antenna). The I_t/I_o ratio is varied from 0 (no top-loading) to 1, which corresponds to heavy top-loading and constant current on the vertical radiator (i.e. $I_t/I_O = 1$). As I_t/I_O goes from zero to 1, R_r increases by a factor of 4.

What happens to V_O and I_O when top-loading is present?

$$I_O = \sqrt{\frac{P_r}{R_r}} \text{ and}$$

$$V_O = X_i I_O = X_i \sqrt{\frac{P_r}{R_r}}$$

Even a small amount of top-loading significantly reduces I_O and greatly reduces V_O! This is important because despite the low radiated powers V_O can easily approach 1 kV on 630 meters and be even higher on 2200 meters. This must be kept in mind when selecting a base insulator. It's clear that substantial height (H) and top-loading are required on 2200 meters if V_O is to be kept below 10 kV. Given that we are trying to radiate only 330 mW that may come as a shock!

Top-loading and Symmetry

In the real world, the T antenna will not be perfectly symmetric and there will be some sag in the support wire, as

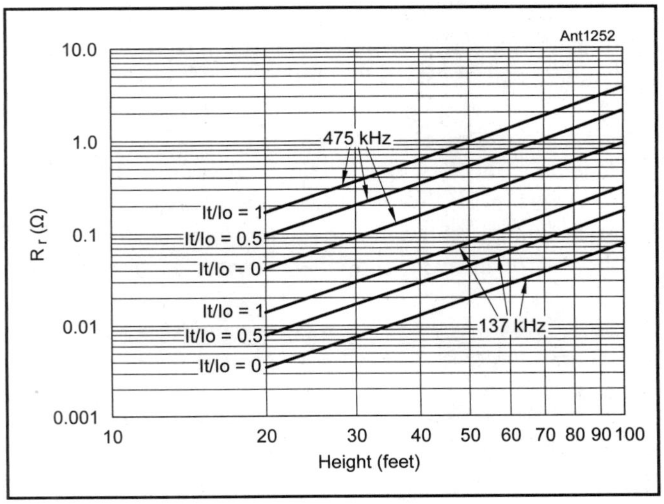

Figure 9.72 — R_r as a function of height in feet.

well. With 5 feet of sag in the 475 kHz antenna the efficiency drops by ≈1.5%. At 137 kHz the efficiency drops from 0.23% to 0.20%.

In some installations it may be more convenient to attach the vertical portion of the antenna at a point other than the center of the top-wire. We can attach the downlead anywhere along the wire and we are also free to place the ground end of the downlead pretty much where we want with little effect on efficiency.

Using supports already on hand (trees, poles, structures), the two ends of the top-wire are likely to be at different heights. For example, the top-wire might slope downward from one end to the other. This is not necessarily a bad thing. For a given center height of 50 feet (see the graphs in the online notes), when we raise one end of the top wire the efficiency goes up even though we've lowered the other end.

Sometimes only one support will be available and the top-wires will have to slope downward from the center support. If the height of the vertical is assumed to be 50 feet and the two top-wires are 50 feet long, efficiency is a strong function of the height of the top-wire ends. The higher the better! This is a case where the current in the top-wires has a component that partially cancels the current in the vertical, reducing R_r. The ends of the top-loading wires can also be bent toward the ground without significant effects on efficiency.

Using a Tower as a Support

What is the effect of coupling between a grounded tower and the vertical downlead? The simple answer is that it will reduce the efficiency somewhat but usually only a few percent because the tower, even with multiple Yagis for loading, is unlikely to be resonant anywhere near 475 kHz, not to mention 137 kHz. The coupling can be minimized by spacing the top anchor point as far out from the tower as possible; several feet would be helpful. Pulling the bottom and/or the top of the download away from the tower as shown in **Figure 9.73** can also help. The effect on a specific installation is best explored with modeling.

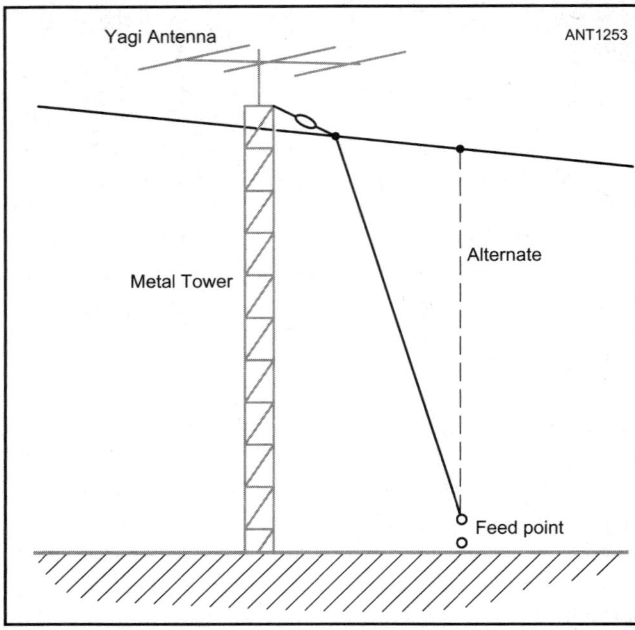

Figure 9.73 — Using a grounded tower as a center support.

9.6.3 MORE COMPLICATED TOP-LOADING

While a vertical with a single top-wire is attractive, we're not limited to a single wire for top-loading. More complex top-loading can substantially improve efficiency. For example, we can add spreaders and use two or more wires in a rectangular arrangement.

One note, the T models in this section use only a single conductor down-lead. When multiple top wires are used, the down-lead can also have multiple wires for at least part of its length which can make a small improvement in efficiency by reducing conductor loss, R_C. One of the problems with spreaders is that they tend to rotate and twist. Extra down-leads can act as stabilizers. Light non-conducting lines can also be used to stabilize the spreaders.

Adding more wire to the hat reduces X_C and leads to higher efficiency but as can be seen in the test cases shown in **Figure 9.74**, for a given spreader length the rate of improvement falls pretty quickly and in this case using more than five wires gains very little. Adding more wire to the top-hat helps to reduce X_C but there's an important drawback to more wire up in the air: if you live in a area with ice storms, the antenna becomes much more vulnerable.

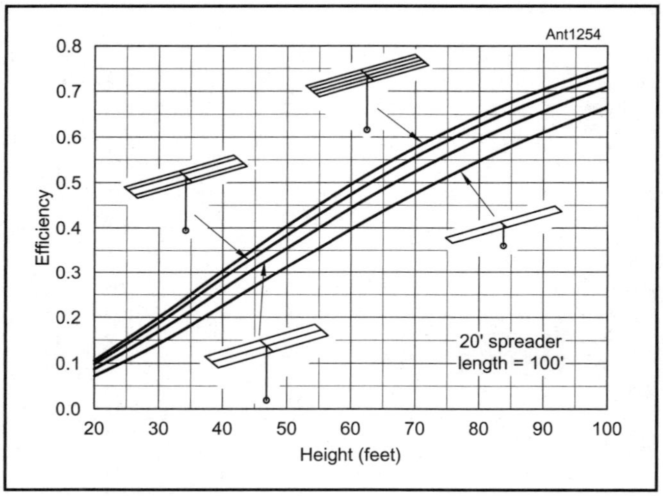

Figure 9.74 — Comparison of top-loaded verticals using a single wire or multiple horizontal wires with 20-foot spreaders.

Umbrella Top-loading

Top-loading structures like umbrellas are often used when only one support (the vertical itself for example) is available. There are many ways to construct an umbrella top-hat:

- Use several rigid radial supports like a wagon wheel. For example, the supports can be aluminum tubing or fiberglass poles supporting wires or some combination of the two. The practical limit for a self-supporting structure is probably a radius of 20 feet or so. Using the hub(s) and spreaders from an old HF quad can be a very simple way to fabricate an umbrella.

- Set up a circle of poles (3 to 8) at some distance from the base of the vertical to support the far ends of the umbrella wires. The radial dimension of the umbrella could be quite large but the length of the poles, which establishes the height of the outer rim of the umbrella, is a limiting factor.
- Attach a number of wires to the top of the vertical, sloping them downward at an angle towards anchor points located at some distance from the base of the vertical.
- You can add sloping wires to the outer rim of a horizontal umbrella to increase the loading.
- You do not have to connect the outer ends of the umbrella radial wires together with a "skirt" wire but a skirt-wire significantly increases the loading effect of an umbrella of a given radius.
- While most of this discussion shows symmetric umbrellas, symmetry is not required. Supports at different distances with different heights can also be used to good effect. Take advantage of what's on site!

As few as three wires (with a skirt!) can make a useful umbrella but the performance improves substantially as you go from three to four and then eight wires. While the jump from four to eight wires gives a useful improvement the law of diminishing returns starts to set in and sixteen wires is about the useful limit. The online notes go into some detail about umbrellas that slope downward from the center hub.

9.6.4 CONDUCTOR LOSS, R_C

Copper or aluminum wire and aluminum tubing are typical conductors. The wire may be bare or insulated. The choice of conductor is usually a matter of what's on hand and/or what's economical. Insulated wire intended for home wiring is of often the most economic choice for copper wire. Aluminum electric fence wire, available in #14 or #17 AWG, is a less expensive choice but aluminum has greater resistance than copper and because soldering aluminum is often not satisfactory, joints require special attention. We can work around the resistance issue by using multiple, well-spaced, wires in parallel.

Given the very low efficiencies compared to typical antennas at HF and above, some attention must be made to the loss created skin effect, δ, which forces ac current to flow in a thin layer on the outside of a conductor. At 137 kHz δ = 7.03 mils (0.00703 inches) and at 475 kHz δ = 3.78 mils. (1 mil = 0.001 inch) At RF, ac resistance can be calculated as $R_{ac} = R_{dc} \times K_s$, where K_s is a factor attributed to skin effect that depends on the ratio of conductor thickness, d, to skin depth, δ. **Table 9.8** shows K_S on both bands for several wire sizes.

Table 9.8
K_s for Typical Wire Sizes

Wire #	*137 kHz* K_s	*475 kHz* K_s
8	4.82	8.76
10	3.87	7.00
12	3.10	5.55
14	2.53	4.49
16	2.06	3.61
18	1.15	1.93

9.6.5 LOADING INDUCTOR PLACEMENT

Top-loading is not the only means for increasing Rr. We can move the tuning inductor or even only a portion of it, from the base up into the vertical. We can also move the feed point higher in the vertical. Multiple inductors can be useful in what referred to as "multiple-tuning", a technique using multiple inductors in multiple downleads to manipulate the feed point impedance and distribution of current between parallel wires.

In HF mobile verticals it has long been standard practice to move the loading inductor from the base up into the vertical to increase R_r. We can do the same for LF/MF verticals. Traditionally the entire loading inductance is moved up. However, there are advantages to moving only a portion of the loading inductance up into the antenna and retaining the remainder (L_{base}) at the base. For a given Q_L, R_L will increase as the inductor is moved up. Despite this increase in R_L moving the inductor up generally improves efficiency. The peak efficiency occurs for heights of 40 to 50% of H. How much does this increase our signal? For L_{base} = 0, i.e. we move all the inductance up, we can get about 0.74 dB of improvement at a height of ≈35%. By making L_{base}=1500 Ω of the total reactance we can pick up another 0.25 dB for a total improvement of almost 1 dB which is probably worth doing.

Even if a modest increase in signal is not compelling there are other reasons for using two inductors. Even when resonated it will still be necessary to match the feed point impedance to the feed line which can be done very simply by tapping the base inductance as shown in **Figure 9.75**.

A base inductor is also a convenient point to retune the antenna when necessary. Over the course of the seasons as the soil characteristics change, the tuning often shifts, primarily due to variations in effective loading capacitance as the soil conductivity changes with moisture content. Small heavily loaded verticals typically have very narrow bandwidths. In most cases some arrangement for adjusting the inductance will be needed. This can be readily done by using a variometer (Figure 9.75B) or a separate small roller inductor in series. One additional advantage of not putting all the inductance up high is the reduced weight of the elevated inductor.

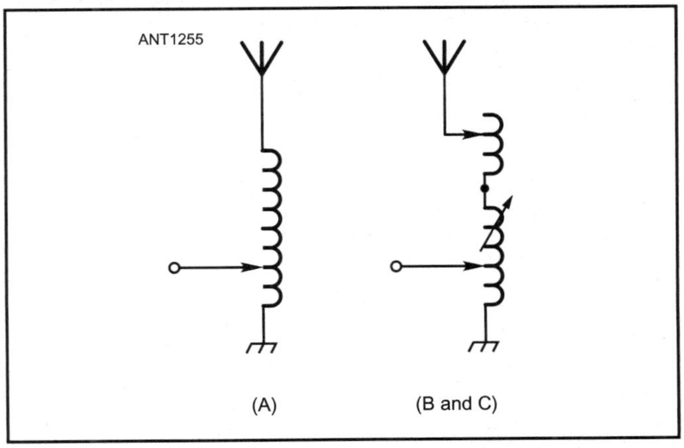

Figure 9.75 — Feed point impedance matching with the base inductor.

Top-loading Combined with Inductor Top-loading

Moving the inductor higher into a heavily top-loaded vertical has less effect on the current distribution. As a result efficiency improvements are much smaller. For the example of a T antenna with H = 50 feet and a single 100-foot top-wire, as the inductor is moved up there is some improvement in the signal but not a lot, only 0.4 dB even when two inductors are used.

When there is a much larger top-hat (for example, three wires 100 feet long by 20 feet wide) the improvement from elevating the inductor is even smaller, <0.15 dB This small an improvement is not worth the hassle of mounting an inductor high in the antenna.

In heavily top-loaded verticals there appears to be little improvement in efficiency from elevating the loading inductor. On the other hand if the top-loading is less, I_t/I_O ratio <0.4 – 0.5, and more top-loading is not practical then moving the coil up may help. This has to be evaluated on a case-by-case basis using modeling.

9.6.6 GROUNDED TOWER VERTICALS FOR LF/MF

A grounded tower with attached HF antennas and associated cabling is sometimes available. For an LF/MF antenna the tower may be simply a support but it can also be a radiator. One way we might do this is shown in **Figure 9.76** where the loading inductor and the feed point have been moved to the top of the tower. The top-loading wires are insulated from the tower and connected to one end of the loading inductor. The other end of the inductor is connected to the top of the tower. A coaxial feed line runs up the tower with the shield connected to the top of the tower. The coax center conductor is connected to a tap on the loading inductor to provide a match. Although not shown, it is possible to have a mast with HF Yagis extending above the top of the tower which will add some additional capacitive loading. The downside of this scheme is that all the adjustments must be made at the top of the tower.

A common alternative for exciting a grounded tower often used on 80 and 160 meters is the shunt-fed tower. Unfortunately, this scheme works only if H >0.7 λ/4 at the operating frequency. At 475 kHz that would mean H >350 feet, much taller than most amateur towers. See the online notes for an extended discussion of this situation including creating and tuning a folded monopole.

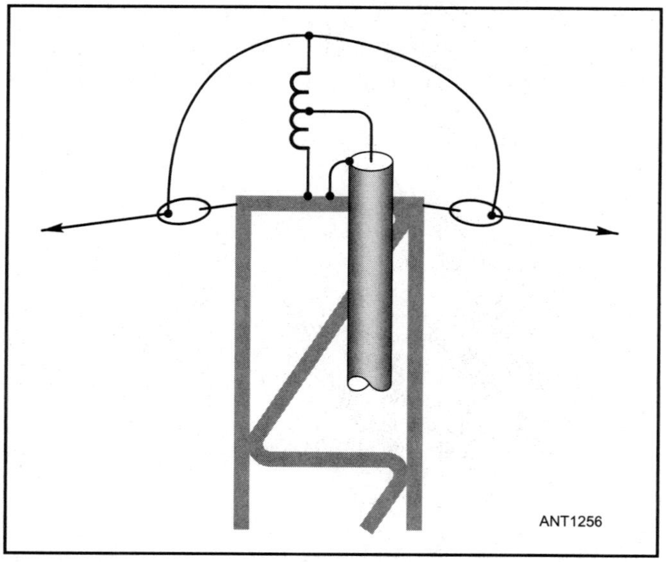

Figure 9.76 — A grounded tower radiator with the feed point and loading inductor at the top with top-loading.

9.6.7 LOOP ANTENNAS AT MF

Ground systems are a nuisance and sometimes impractical. We might consider using a transmitting loop like that shown in **Figure 9.77**. In this example the horizontal wires are 100 feet long and the vertical wires 50 feet, all #12 AWG copper wire. The bottom wire is 8 feet above average ground (0.005/13) and f = 475 kHz. The antenna is resonated with a capacitive load at the center of the upper wire (point 3) where X_C = 537 Ω. As is typical for small loops the current amplitude around the loop varies only ±5% with very little phase difference and for the values given, the radiation efficiency will be ≈1.8%. John Andrews, W1TAG and WE2XGR/3, has used a similar loop made with RG-8 coax (diameter ≈ 0.3 inch). This increases the efficiency to ≈ 3.1%. Not great but if 100 W of input power is available then the maximum EIRP can be reached. Even if we used superconducting wire the efficiency would still be limited to ≈ 4.2% due to near-field ground losses, a factor often overlooked in transmitting loops. Poorer soil would mean even lower efficiency. These efficiencies are not very encouraging but then transmitting loop antennas are not known for their efficiency! Inductive and capacitive loading can also be used, increasing efficiency to 9 to 12%.

9.6.8 LF/MF GROUND SYSTEMS

The discussion of efficiency focused on loss introduced by the tuning inductor which is reasonable given that R_L often represents a major loss in short antennas. While much can done to reduce X_i and increase R_r, there are practical limits and at some point we have to start thinking about reducing other losses. A substantial portion of the power supplied to the antenna may be absorbed in the soil near the base. To reduce this loss we install a ground system:

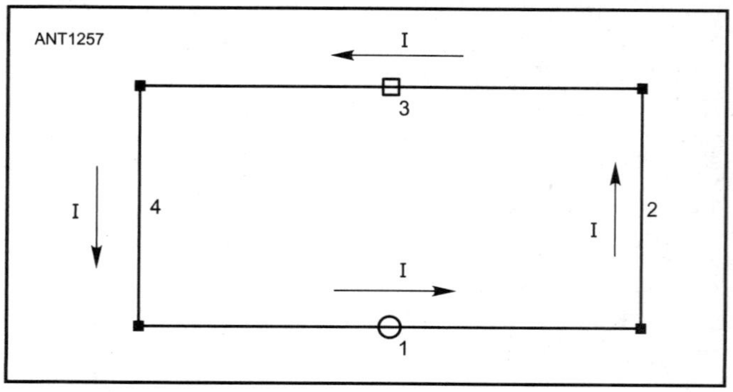

Figure 9.77 — Loop antenna for LF/MF operation.

- what type of ground system?
- how many radials?
- radial lengths?
- what performance can we expect?
- optimum use of a fixed amount of wire?

A range of examples have been chosen to provide general guidance but none should be taken as exact numerical descriptions for all cases. You will have to do some measurements, modeling and/or calculations to arrive at the best solution for your unique situation.

Choices for Ground Systems

Ground systems can take several forms:

1. A radial wire fan lying on the ground surface or buried a few inches.
2. A rectangular grid of wires
3. Single or multiple ground rods.
4. Elevated wires in the form of a counterpoise or "capacitive" ground.
5. Combinations of the above. Limited only by imagination!

The choice of ground system will be dictated by the operating wavelength, available space, soil mechanical characteristics (i.e. sandy loam or tree stumps and boulders), available resources, etc. Because of the much longer wavelengths at LF/MF and significant differences in soil electrical characteristics between LF/MF and HF, the ground systems may be significantly different from what we are accustomed to at HF.

The instructions for an adequate ground system can be stated as:

1) Use at least 50 radials. Most backyards will only have room for 30 to 40-foot radials. Where possible the radials should be somewhat longer than the height of the vertical

2) In the case of a very large top-hat, the radials should extend out to 1.25 times the top-hat radius if possible.

3) When a large number of radials are used the wire size is not important. The wire needs to be strong enough to be installed and survive in its environment.

4) Almost any metal can be used for the radials but the usual choice is insulated copper house wiring because it is usually cheaper than the same wire bare. For an elevated system #17 AWG aluminum electric fence wire can be used. However, lying on the surface or buried, aluminum wire may degrade quickly

5) If the radials are lying on the surface, use lots of staples to keep them close to the ground so mowing or other traffic will not damage them.

6) Use at least one ground stake at the base for safety.

Consider three ground systems with an inductor Q_L of 400: a single 8-foot × ⅝-inch ground rod or stake, 32 10-foot radials and 32 25-foot radials. With the single ground rod the ground loss (R_g) is so large that R_L doesn't matter very much. As soon as we add even the small radial system (32 × 10 feet) the efficiency increases by almost an order of magnitude and expanding the radial lengths to 25 feet yields another factor of ≈3× in efficiency. This is due to reductions in R_g with longer radials.

Increasing the number of radials is very helpful. In fact, we could have gone to 64 radials and still have had some useful improvement over 32. Second, the efficiency improves rapidly up to lengths of 60 to 70 feet before the point of decreasing returns is reached. By 150 feet there isn't much point in making the radials longer. Independent of radial number, that point in this example corresponds to a radial length of approximately 65 to 70 feet which is a bit more than H (50 feet).

Once you have greatly reduced the losses near the base of the antenna, adding more close-in copper doesn't buy much. At some point it's more useful to put the copper further out and reduce more distant losses, which may be smaller but still significant. The difference in break point (in terms of radial number) stems from differences in the field intensities around the two antennas. For the same power, the fields near the base of a short vertical will be much higher than those for the ¼-wave vertical so we need to put more effort into reducing the close-in power losses.

Elevated Ground Systems

In many cases the ground under and near the antenna may not be suitable for a buried radial system. Systems with elevated wires are well known at HF, i.e. ground-plane verticals, but these systems typically use radials with lengths close to $\lambda/4$. For amateur installations this will not be possible but all is not lost. In the early days of radio it was recognized that an elevated system called a "counterpoise" or "capacitive ground," with dimensions significantly smaller than $\lambda/4$, could be very effective.

If you have reasonable heights for the vertical and lots of capacitive top-loading but very restricted room for the ground system, then a counterpoise may be the best option. But we have to be careful in drawing general conclusions. There are many variables: ground characteristics, height of the top of the vertical, height of the bottom of the vertical, the amount of top-loading, the number of wires in the counterpoise, the radius, etc. The choice between buried wire and counterpoise ground systems is not obvious! The considerable mechanical complexity, vulnerability to ice damage and visual impact of a counterpoise may also militate against it. This choice has to be made on a case-by-case basis and will probably require modeling with *NEC4* software.

9.7 BIBLIOGRAPHY

Source material and more extended discussion of topics covered in this chapter can be found in the references given below.

ARRL's Wire Antenna Classics (Newington: ARRL, 1999).

D. Atchley, Jr., "Putting the Quarter-Wave Sloper to Work on 160," *QST*, Jul 1979, pp 19-20.

B. Beezley, "A Gain Antenna for 28 MHz," *QST*, Jul 1994, pp 70.

J. Belrose, "Transmission Line Low Profile Antennas," *QST*, Dec 1975, pp 19-25.

J. Belrose, "Terminated Folded Dipole," Technical Correspondence, *QST*, May 1994, p 88.

J. Belrose, "A Horizontal Loop for 80-Meter DX," *QST*, Aug 2002, pp 30-35.

J. Belrose and D. DeMaw, "The Half-Delta Loop: A Critical Analysis and Practical Deployment," *QST*, Sep 1982, pp 28-32.

L. Braskamp, AA6GL, "*MOBILE*, a Computer Program for Short HF Verticals," *The ARRL Antenna Compendium Vol 4* (Newington: ARRL, 1995), pp 92-96.

G. H. Brown, "The Phase and Magnitude of Earth Currents Near Radio Transmitting Antennas," *Proc. IRE*, Vol 23, No. 2, Feb 1935, pp 168-182.

G. H. Brown, R. F. Lewis and J. Epstein, "Ground Systems as a Factor in Antenna Efficiency," *Proc. IRE*, Vol 25, No. 6, Jun 1937, pp 753-787.

B. Cake, *The Antenna Designer's Notebook* (Newington: ARRL, 2009).

B. Cake, "The 'C Pole' — A Ground Independent Vertical Antenna," *QST*, Apr 2004, pp 37-39.

P. Carr, "A Two Band Half-Square Antenna with Coaxial Feed," *CQ*, Sep 1992, pp 40-45.

P. Carr, "A DX Antenna for 40 Meters," *CQ*, Sep 1994, pp 40-43.

P. Carr, "The N4PC Loop," *CQ*, Dec 1990, pp 11-15.

L.B. Cebik, "Best way (of) Loading the Half-Length 80M Vertical Monopoles – V," various online sources.

L.B. Cebik, "Notes on a Wide-Band 50/75-Ohm Coax Feed System for Low HF Band Dipoles and Vees," 2007, various online sources.

Christman, "Elevated Vertical Antennas for the Low Bands," *The ARRL Antenna Compendium Vol 5* (Newington: ARRL, 1996), pp 11-18.

D. DeMaw, "Additional Notes on the Half Sloper," *QST*, Jul 1979, pp 20-21.

D. DeMaw, L. Aurick, "The Full-Wave Delta Loop at Low Height," *QST*, Oct 1984, pp 24-26.

J. Devoldere, *Low Band DXing — 5th Edition* (Newington: ARRL, 2010).

P. Dodd, *The LF Experimenter's Source Book* (Potters Bar: RSGB, 1996).

A. C. Doty, Jr., J. A. Frey and H. J. Mills, "Efficient Ground Systems for Vertical Antennas," *QST*, Feb 1983, pp 9-12.

S. Ford, "*Low*fing on 1750 Meters," *QST*, Oct 1993, pp 67-68.

R. Fosberg, "Some Notes on Ground Systems for 160 Meters," *QST*, Apr 1965, pp 65-67.

J. Hall, "Off-Center-Loaded Dipole Antennas," *QST*, Sep 1974, pp 28-34.

J. Hallas, "The Fan Dipole as a Wideband and Multiband Antenna Element," *QST*, May 2005, pp 33-35.

J. Hallas, "A Close Look at the Terminated Folded Dipole Antenna," Getting on the Air, *QST*, Sep 2010, pp 51-52.

A. Harbach, "Broad-Band 80-Meter Antenna," *QST*, Dec 1980, pp 36-37.

H. Hawkins, "A Low-Budget, Rotatable 17 Meter Loop," *QST*, Nov 1997, p 35.

J. Heys, *Practical Wire Antennas* (Potters Bar: RSGB, 1989).

G. Hubbell, "Feeding Grounded Towers as Radiators," *QST*, Jun 1960, pp 32-33, 140, 142.

C. Hutchinson and R. D. Straw, *Simple and Fun Antennas for Hams* (Newington: ARRL, 2002).

P. H. Lee, *The Amateur Radio Vertical Antenna Handbook*, 1st edition (Port Washington, NY: Cowan Publishing Corp, 1974).

D. Leeson, "The Story of the Broadband Dipole," *QEX*, Nov/Dec 2018, pp 18-22.

L.D. Lopes, "Designing a Shortened Antenna" *QST*, Oct 2003, pp 28-32.

A. Lopez, "Double-Tuned Impedance Matching," *IEEE Antennas and Propagation Magazine,* Vol. 54, No. 2, April 2012, pp 109-115.

W. Maxwell, "Technical Correspondence: The Double Bazooka Antenna — How Broad Is It?" *QST*, Sep 1976, pp 29-30.

W. Maxwell, "A Revealing Analysis of the Coaxial Antenna," *Ham Radio*, Aug 1976, p 46.

C. J. Michaels, "Some Reflections on Vertical Antennas," *QST*, July 1987, pp 15-19; feedback *QST*, Aug 1987, p 39.

More Wire Antenna Classics (Newington: ARRL, 1999).

L. Moxon, *HF Antennas for All Locations*, 2nd Edition (RSGB, 1993)

I. Poole, *Practical Wire Antennas 2* (Potters Bar: RSGB, 2005).

Prediction of Sky-wave Field Strength at Frequencies Between About 150 and 1700 kHz, ITU Doc 3/14, Radiocommunication Study Groups, Feb 1995.

T. Rappaport and J. Parnell, "Use Your Tower as a Dual-Band, Low-Band DX Antenna," *QST*, May 2019, pp 41-45.

Rashed and Tai, "A New Class of Wire Antennas," 1982 International Symposium Digest, *Antennas and Propagation*, Vol 2, published by IEEE.

T. Russell, "Simple, Effective, Elevated Ground-Plane Antennas," *QST*, June 1994, pp 45-46.

G. Saviers, "Broad-banding a 160 m Vertical Antenna," *QEX*, May/June 2019, pp 9-12.

F. J. Schnell, "The Flagpole Deluxe," *QST*, Mar 1978, pp 29-32.

W. Schultz, "Designing a Vertical Antenna," *QST*, Sep 1978, p 19.

R. Severns, "A Wideband 80-Meter Dipole," *QST*, Jul 1995, pp 27-29.

R. Severns, "A Closer Look at Vertical Antennas With Elevated Ground Systems," *QEX*, Mar/Apr 2012, pp 32-44 and May/Jun 2012, pp 24-33.

R. Severns, "Some Ideas for Short 160 Meter Verticals," *QEX*, May/Jun 2013, pp 35-46

J. Sevick, "The Ground-Image Vertical Antenna," *QST*, Jul 1971, pp 16-19, 22.

J. Sevick, "The W2FMI Ground-Mounted Short Vertical," *QST*, Mar 1973, pp 13-18, 41.

J. Sevick, "The Constant-Impedance Trap Vertical," *QST* , Mar 1974, pp 29-34.

J. Sevick, "Short Ground-Radial Systems for Short Verticals," *QST*, Apr 1978, pp 30-33.

J. Sevick, *Transmission Line Transformers* (Atlanta: Noble Publishing, 1996).

K. Siwiak and R. Quick, "Live Trees Affect Antenna Performance," *QST*, Feb 2018, pp 33-37.

J. Stanford, "Linear-Loaded Short Wire Antennas," *The ARRL Antenna Compendium Vol 5* (Newington: ARRL, 1996), pp 105-107.

Vertical Antenna Classics (Newington: ARRL, 1995)

A. D. Watt, *VLF Radio Engineering* (Pergamon Press, 1967) (out of print).

J. Weigl, *Sloper Antennas* (New York: CQ Communications, 2009).

F. Witt, AI1H, "A Simple Broadband Dipole for 80 Meters," *QST*, Sep 1993, pp 27-30, 76.

TABLE OF CONTENTS

Chapter 10 — Downloadable Supplemental Content

Supplemental Articles

- "A Compact Multiband Dipole" by Zack Lau, W1VT
- "A No Compromise Off-Center Fed Dipole for Four Bands" by Rick Littlefield, K1BQT
- "A Triband Dipole for 30, 17, and 12 Meters" by Zack Lau, W1VT
- "An Effective Multi-Band Aerial of Simple Construction" by Louis Varney, G5RV (Original G5RV article)
- "An Experimental All-Band Non-directional Transmitting Antenna," by G.L. Countryman, W3HH
- "An Improved Multiband Trap Dipole Antenna" by Al Buxton, W8NX
- "Broadband Transmitting Wire Antennas for 160 through 10 Meters" by Floyd Koontz, WA2WVL
- "Cat Whiskers — The Broadband Multi-Loop Antenna" by Jacek Pawlowski, SP3L
- "End-Fed Antennas" by Ward Silver, NØAX
- "HF Discone Antennas"
- "HF Discone Antenna Projects" by W8NWF
- "Nested Loop Antennas" by Scott Davis, N3FJP
- "Revisiting the Double-L" by Don Toman, K2KQ
- "Six Band Loaded Dipole Antenna" by Al Buxton, W8NX
- "The HF Discone Antenna" by John Belrose, VE2CV
- "The J78 Antenna: An Eight-band Off-Center-Fed HF Dipole" by Brian Machesney, K1LI/J75Y
- "The Multimatch Antenna System" by Chester Buchanan, W3DZZ
- "The Open Sleeve Antenna" by Roger Cox, WBØDGF
- "The Open-Sleeve Antenna" from previous editions
- "Two New Multiband Trap Dipoles" by Al Buxton, W8NX
- "Wideband 80 Meter Dipole" by Rudy Severns, N6LF

Chapter 10

Multiband HF Antennas

For operation on a number of bands below 30 MHz, it would be impractical for most amateurs to put up a separate antenna for each band. But this is not necessary — for example, a dipole one half-wavelength long on the lowest frequency band to be used can be operated readily on higher frequencies. In fact, most common antennas can be used on multiple bands through the use of antenna tuners and other techniques. What is usually referred to as a "multiband antenna," however, is one for which a method has been devised that allows the antenna to operate on a number of bands while still offering a good match to a transmission line, usually coaxial cable.

When a single physical antenna is used on different bands, one must be aware that the changing electrical heights and lengths lead to changes in the feed point impedance and the azimuth and the elevation patterns of the antenna as described in the chapters **Antenna Fundamentals** and **Dipoles and Monopoles**. For example, a horizontal wire antenna at an electrical height of $\lambda/2$ on 20 meters is $2\lambda/3$ high on 15 meters and $\lambda/4$ on 40 meters, leading to very different elevation patterns than if the antenna were at the same electrical height on all bands. Similarly, the elevation pattern and feed point impedance of a single vertical antenna will also change dramatically on different bands.

In fact, it is usually more effective to consider the installation as a "multiband antenna system" in which the antenna, feed line, and any impedance matching devices are considered together — as a package. By thinking about the performance of the antenna on different bands you can select a combination of system elements that result in good performance on all bands and not just one.

This chapter describes a number of antennas and antenna systems that are designed to be used on two or more of the HF bands. Separate chapters cover nonresonant **Long-Wire and Traveling Wave Antennas** as well as the popular **HF Yagi and Quad Antennas**. See the **Transmission Line System Techniques** chapter for more information on using feed lines and impedance matching circuits.

Harmonic Radiation from Multiband Antennas

Since a multiband antenna is intentionally designed for operation on a number of different frequencies, any harmonics or spurious emissions with frequencies that happen to coincide with one of the antenna resonant frequencies will be radiated with very little, if any, attenuation. Particular care should be exercised, therefore, to prevent such harmonics from reaching the antenna. While output signals from properly operating commercial equipment are typically quite "clean," they can be misadjusted or defective, or another piece of equipment in the antenna system could be acting to create unwanted signals. As a consequence, amateurs need to remain vigilant about signal quality and harmonic content.

If there is any concern about whether harmonics or spurious emissions are being generated, it is advisable to conduct tests with other nearby amateur stations. If harmonics of the transmitting frequency or spurious emissions can be heard at a distance of, say, a mile or so, more selectivity should be added to the system since a harmonic that is heard locally, even if weak, may be quite strong at a distance because of propagation conditions. In addition, the source of spurious emissions should be identified and the unwanted signals removed.

10.1 SIMPLE WIRE ANTENNAS

10.1.1 RANDOM-WIRE ANTENNAS

The simplest multiband antenna is a random length of wire, attached directly to the output of a transmitter or antenna tuner. Power can be fed to the wire on practically any frequency using one or the other of the methods shown in **Figure 10.1**. If the wire is approximately 67 or 137 feet long (λ/4 or λ/2 on 80 meters) the end impedance will be high on the bands that are harmonics of 80 meters and it can be fed through a tuned circuit, as in **Figure 10.2**. Many antenna tuners have the option to feed an end-fed random wire in this way. Use an SWR meter between the transmitter and the matching network to adjust for minimum SWR. (This is a variation of the End-Fed Half-Wave (EFHW) antenna popular for portable use and discussed later in this chapter and in the **Portable Antennas** chapter.)

It is also possible to use a beam's coaxial feed line as an antenna on HF. Connect the shield and center conductor together at the station end and use them as a random-length wire as in Figure 10.1. The beam at the far end will serve to end-load the wire as a capacitance hat. This technique may turn out to be useful if a primary antenna has been damaged, such as after a natural disaster. Practicing using this technique is therefore good preparation.

The primary disadvantage of all such directly-fed systems is that the antenna system is composed of the random wire plus all of the station equipment enclosures and the station ground system. The point at which the antenna is connected can be thought of as a randomly chosen feed point in an antenna that has one end tied to ground. As such, there is a good chance that you will have "RF hot spots" in your station because of the RF current in the antenna system.

RF voltages within the station can often be minimized by choosing an antenna and ground wire length so that the low feed point impedance at a current maximum occurs at or near the transmitter. A short connection (several feet or less) with heavy wire or strap to a ground rod or metallic water pipe that runs through ground may be sufficient on the lower bands but most ground connections are not short enough to minimize RF voltage by themselves. Regardless of how you address this issue, begin by connecting all equipment enclosures together (bonding) to prevent significant voltages from existing between pieces of equipment. See the *ARRL Handbook's* chapter on **Assembling a Station** for more information on managing the RF in your station.

Using an antenna wire length close to λ/4 (65 feet at 3.6 MHz, 33 feet at 7.1 MHz), or an odd multiple of λ/4 (¾ λ is 195 feet at 3.6 MHz, 100 feet at 7.1 MHz, 50 feet at 14 MHz, etc) may be helpful. The goal is to place the antenna system's connection to the transmitter or antenna tuner at a point of low voltage. Obviously, this can be done for only one band even in the case of harmonically related bands, since the wire length that presents a current maximum at the transmitter will present a voltage maximum at two (or four) times that frequency.

Another possibility is to attach a counterpoise wire to the transmitter or antenna tuner enclosure. The counterpoise length is adjusted so that RF voltage on the station equipment is minimized. The length may or may not be λ/4 at the operating frequency since the impedance at the end of the antenna wire is unknown. Be prepared to experiment with

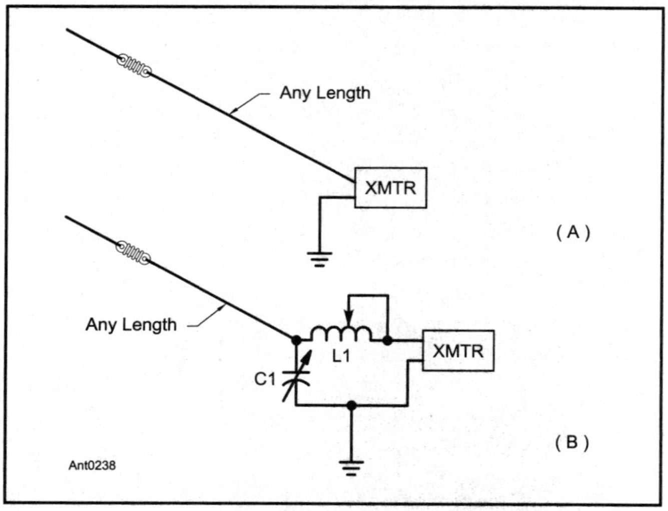

Figure 10.1 — At A, a random-length wire can be driven directly from the pi-network output of a vacuum-tube transmitter. At B, an L network (or antenna tuner) can be used with solid state transmitters that do not have tunable output networks. C1 should have plate spacing sufficient for at least several hundred volts; a maximum capacitance of 100 pF is sufficient if L1 is 20 to 25 µH. A suitable coil would consist of 30 turns of #12 AWG wire, 2½ inches diameter, 6 turns per inch. Bare wire should be used so the tap can be placed as required for loading the transmitter.

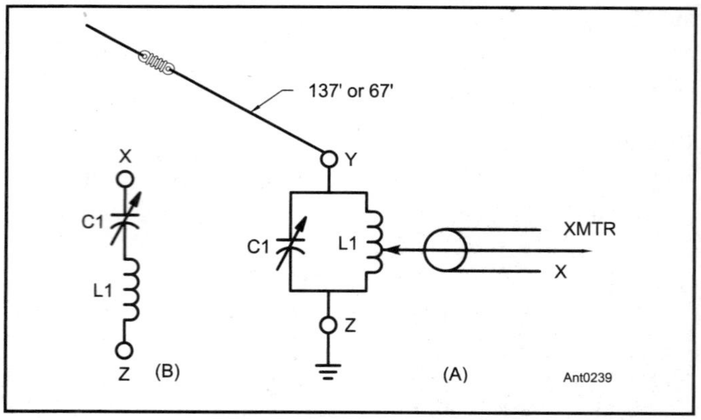

Figure 10.2 — If the antenna length is 135 to 140 feet, a parallel-tuned coupling circuit (A) can be used on each amateur band from 3.5 through 30 MHz, with the possible exception of the 10-, 18- and 24-MHz bands. C1 should be from 500-1000 pF with plate spacing capable of withstanding several hundred volts. L1 should be chosen to resonate with 20-80% of C1's maximum value. If the wire is 67 feet long, series tuning can be used on 3.5 MHz as shown at the left; parallel tuning will be required on 7 MHz and higher frequency bands. The L network shown in Figure 10.1B is also suitable for these antenna lengths.

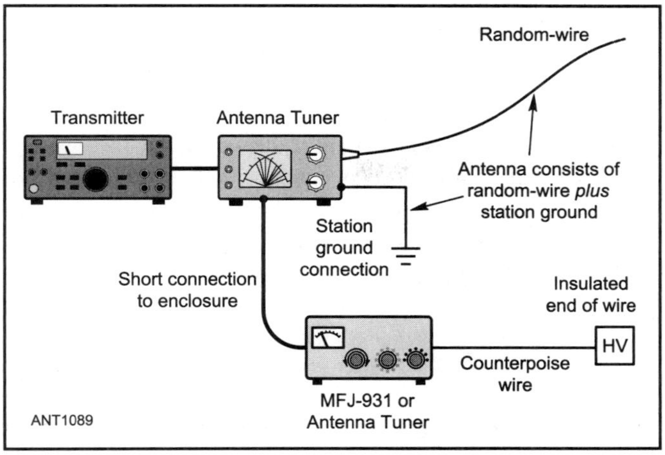

Figure 10.3 — An "artificial ground" can be used to tune a random length of wire to minimize RF voltage on station equipment enclosures.

different lengths. Different wires can be attached at different frequencies.

Another option is to use an "artificial ground" such as the MFJ-931 (**www.mfjenterprises.com**) as in **Figure 10.3** that tunes the counterpoise on different frequencies. It is also possible in many cases to use an ordinary 100-W antenna tuner to accomplish the same thing — tuning the random-length counterpoise to present a low impedance at the transmitter or antenna tuner enclosure.

If you do use a counterpoise, be sure to insulate the unattached end because like all unconnected ends of antennas, there will likely be enough RF voltage to cause an RF burn, particularly at 100 W or higher.

10.1.2 END-FED ANTENNAS

Another common antenna system for multiband operation is the *end-fed Zepp* antenna shown in **Figure 10.4**. The antenna length is $\lambda/2$ long at the lowest operating frequency. (This name came about because the first documented use of this sort of antennas was on the *Zeppelin* airships where the antenna was hung by one end and trailed below the airship.)

An antenna tuner with a balanced output can provide multiband coverage with an end-fed antenna with any length of open-wire feed line, as shown in Figure 10.4. Open-wire or window line with an impedance of 300 to 600 Ω is most often used.

The feed line length can be anything convenient, but odd multiples of $\lambda/4$ will transform the high feed point impedance to a lower value that is likely to be easier to transform to 50 Ω. (See "Tuned Feeders" below.) The asymmetrical placement of the feed line with respect to the antenna often results in common-mode current being picked up by the feed line. This results in radiation from the feed line portion of the system. (See "Feed Line Radiation" below.) *QST's* "Hands-On Radio: Experiment 136 — End-Fed Antennas" (see Bibliography) discusses these issues.

If you have room for only a 67-foot flattop and yet want to operate in the 3.5-MHz band, the two feed line wires can be tied together at the transmitter end and the entire system treated as a random-length wire fed directly, as in Figure 10.1. Steve Yates, AA5TB, has written an extensive article on the end-fed half-wave antenna at **www.aa5tb.com/efha.html**.

As explained in the section below on Feed Line Radiation, it is important to note that although the feed line is attached at one end of the horizontal wire, the radiated signal comes from current flowing on the wire and also as common-mode current on the feed line. That is, the feed line and whatever it is attached to make up part of the antenna system along with the horizontal wire. For a coaxial feed line, the current flows on the outside surface of the shield.

From the standpoint of a radiated signal, the end-fed antenna is not really "end-fed" at all! It is really an off-center fed antenna with one part of the antenna horizontal and the rest of it made up by the feed line and whatever the feed line is connected to in the station. As you might imagine, the resulting radiation pattern is nearly omnidirectional and not very much like a classic dipole. That may be better for a portable station than an antenna with nulls along its axis.

Nevertheless, the end-fed half-wave user should be aware of where the antenna system current is flowing! The radiated signal from common-mode current flowing on a feed line can cause RFI to appliances or electronics near the feed line and the user can experience "RF in the shack" because of the RF current flowing on equipment enclosures and cables. The same precautions about bonding equipment together and using counterpoise wires for random wire antennas in the previous section should also be applied when using "end-fed" antennas.

10.1.3 CENTER-FED ANTENNAS

A center-fed single-wire antenna can be made to accept power and radiate it with high efficiency on any frequency higher than its fundamental resonant frequency and, with a reduction in efficiency and bandwidth, on frequencies as low as one-half the fundamental.

In fact, it is not necessary for an antenna to be a full half-wavelength long at the lowest frequency. An antenna can be considerably shorter than ½ λ, even as short as ¼ λ, and still

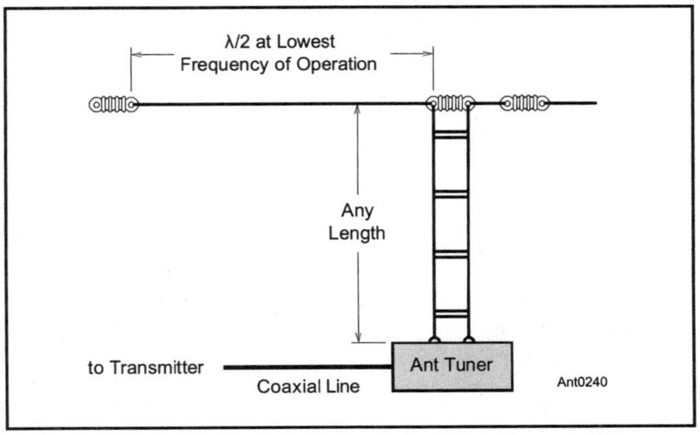

Figure 10.4 — An end-fed Zepp antenna for multiband use.

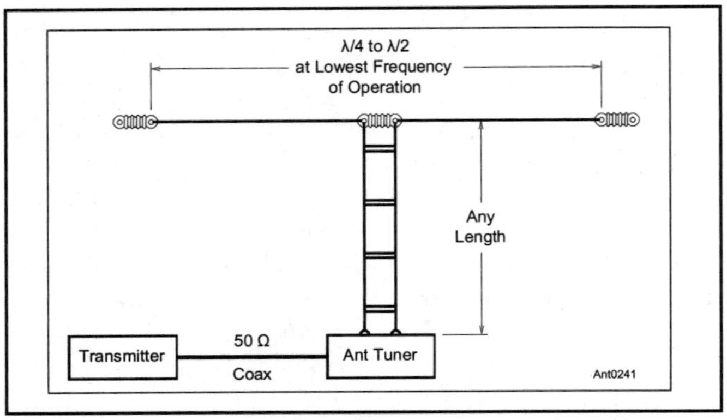

Figure 10.5 — A center-fed antenna system for multiband use.

be a very efficient radiator. The use of such short antennas results in stresses, however, on other parts of the system (for example the antenna tuner and the transmission line) as discussed later on in this section.

The simplest and most flexible (and also least expensive) all-band antennas are those using parallel-wire feed lines to the center of the antenna, as in **Figure 10.5**. Because each half of the flattop is the same length, the feed line currents will be balanced at all frequencies unless, of course, imbalance is introduced by one half of the antenna being closer to ground (or a grounded object) than the other. To maintain balance of the current in each antenna leg and minimize common-mode current on the feed line, the feed line should be run at right angles to the antenna, preferably for a distance of at least λ/4 from the feed point.

Center-feed is not only more desirable than end-feed (described above) because of inherently better balance, but it generally results in a lower SWR on the transmission line, provided a parallel-wire line having a characteristic impedance of 300 to 600 Ω is used. Ladder or window line is satisfactory for all but possibly high power installations (over 500 W), where heavier wire and wider spacing are desirable to handle the larger currents and voltages that may be present at high SWR.

The best type of antenna tuner to use in such an installation is a balanced type designed for coaxial feed line on the input and parallel-wire line on the output. An unbalanced tuner can also be used but because one wire of the output feed line is connected to the enclosure, RF current and voltages are more likely to be present in the station.

Use of a balun at the output of an unbalanced antenna tuner to allow the use of balanced feed line is a common technique. The balun is usually an impedance transformer (voltage balun) with a 4:1 ratio in anticipation of higher impedances on balanced feed lines. This is not always the case as discussed in the chapters on **Transmission Lines** and **Transmission Line System Techniques**. The electrical length of the feed line and SWR at the antenna determine what impedance appears at the transmitter end of the feed line. Expect a wide range of impedance values and be careful not to overstress the balun.

It is not recommended that coaxial feed line be used between the antenna tuner and antenna. At frequencies where the SWR is high, feed line loss in coaxial cable runs of more than 50 feet at HF can quickly become very high. (See the **Transmission Line System Techniques** chapter).

The length of the antenna is not critical, nor is the length of the line. As mentioned earlier, the length of the antenna can be considerably less than λ/2 and still be very effective. If the overall length is at least λ/4 at the lowest frequency, a quite usable system will result. Some experimentation will likely be necessary to find the length that works best at a specific location on the bands required.

Several nonresonant lengths of center-fed doublets have become popular in recent years for their consistent radiation patterns on several bands. For example, L.B. Cebik, W4RNL recommended the following lengths because the pattern remains at peak gain broadside to the antennas:

- 44 feet covers 10, 12, 15, 17, 20, 30, 40 meters
- 66 feet covers 15, 17, 20, 30, 40, 60 meters
- 88 feet covers 20, 30, 40, 60, 80 meters

Cebik's article "My Top Five Backyard Multi-Band Wire HF Antennas" explains why these simple antennas are such good performers (see Bibliography).

The impedance of the antenna varies broadly from band to band, requiring the use of a wide-range tuner, but that is an acceptable tradeoff. Gain drops with frequency but not a great deal below that of a λ/2 dipole. Height above ground also influences the elevation pattern of the antenna as it does for a dipole, so install the antenna as high as you can for best performance at long distances.

Feed Line Radiation

Feed line radiation results when currents in a parallel-wire feed line are not balanced so that the radiation from each wire no longer cancels. This imbalance most commonly occurs when the feed line picks up energy radiated by the antenna on both wires at the same time. This creates *common-mode* current which re-radiates a signal just as an antenna does. (The equivalent situation for coaxial feed line is for the outer surface of the shield to pick up and re-radiate energy.)

Feed lines pick up the antenna's radiated signal when they are not symmetrically oriented with respect to the antenna and its radiated field. For example, a feed line that approaches a dipole at anything other than 90° will couple more strongly to the closer leg of the antenna. The closer the feed line is to one leg, the more energy it will pick up. Feed lines to an end-fed Zepp almost always carry common-mode current because they are connected at one end and not the middle. Common-mode feed line current and techniques for minimizing it are addressed in the chapter **Transmission Line System Techniques**.

It should be emphasized that any radiation from a feed line is not "lost" energy and is not necessarily harmful. Whether or not feed line radiation is important depends entirely on the antenna system being used. For example, feed line radiation is not desirable when a directive array is being used. Such feed line radiation can distort the desired pattern of such an array, producing responses in unwanted directions. In other words, you want radiation only from the directive array, rather than from the directive array and the feed line. If the feed line passes close to appliances or home entertainment equipment, the radiated field can also cause RFI.

On the other hand, in the case of a multiband dipole where general coverage is desired, if the feed line happens to radiate, such energy could actually have a desirable effect. Antenna purists may dispute such a premise, but from a practical standpoint where you are not concerned with a directive pattern, much time and labor can be saved by ignoring possible feed line radiation.

Tuned Feeders

References are often made to "tuned feeders" meaning sections of feed line with a specific electrical length. The lengths act to transform load (antenna feed point) impedances as described in the **Transmission Lines** chapter. The most common application of a tuned feeder is with an end-fed antenna. A feed line that is any number of odd quarter-wavelengths long transforms a high impedance into a low impedance and so can be used to connect a 50-Ω transmitter to a high-impedance end-fed antenna. This only works at frequencies for which the feed line is the required electrical length, thus the term "tuned." Most tuned feeders are constructed from parallel-wire feed line to minimize loss from the high SWR in this application.

Tuned feeders can also create problems due to their length. For example, a feed line some multiple of λ/2 long connected to grounded equipment enclosures at one end also has a low impedance at the other end. That can cause trouble for an end-fed antenna with a high feed point impedance. Resonant feed line lengths (some multiple of λ/4 long) also tend to be effective at picking up energy from the antenna where it creates common-mode currents and re-radiated signals as discussed above.

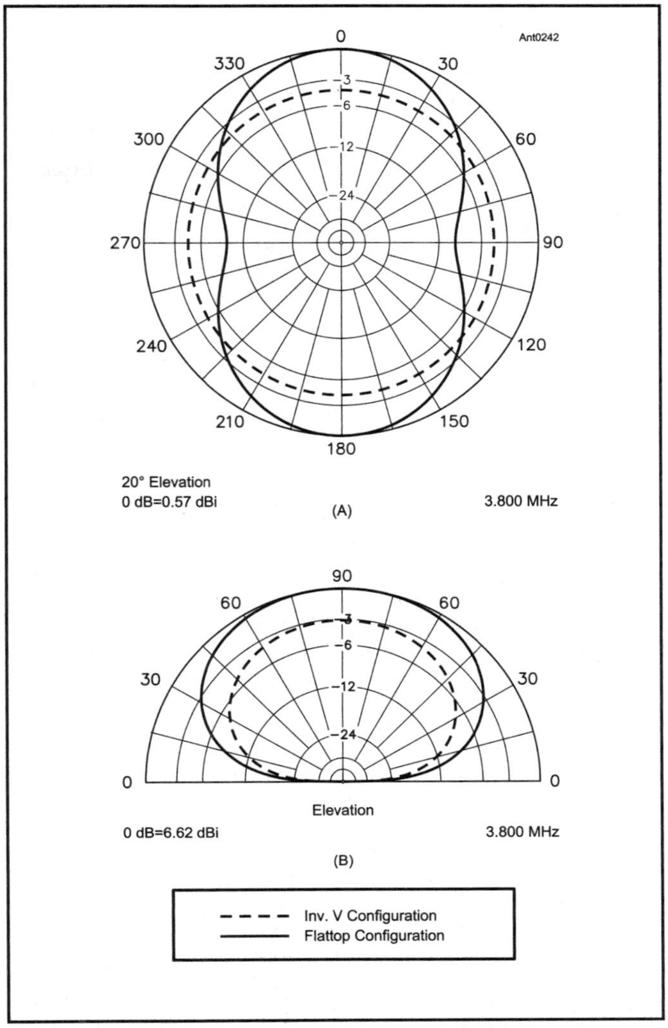

Figure 10.6 — Patterns on 80 meters for 135-foot, center-fed dipole erected as a horizontal flattop dipole at 50 feet, compared with the same dipole installed as an inverted V with the apex at 50 feet and the ends at 10 feet. The azimuth pattern is shown at A, where the dipole wire lies in the 90° to 270° plane. At B, the elevation pattern, the dipole wire comes out of the paper at a right angle. On 80 meters, the patterns are not markedly different for either flattop or inverted V configuration.

10.1.4 THE 135-FOOT, 80 TO 10 METER DIPOLE

As mentioned previously, one of the most versatile antennas around is a simple 80 meter dipole, center-fed with open-wire transmission line and used with an antenna tuner in the station. A 135-foot long dipole hung horizontally between two trees or towers at a height of 50 feet or higher works very well on 80 through 10 meters. Such an antenna system has significant gain at the higher frequencies. The antenna can also be used on 1.8 MHz as a λ/4 antenna with some reduction in efficiency. (See the previous section for non-resonant dipole lengths that work well.)

Flattop or Inverted V Configuration?

There is no denying that the inverted V mounting configuration is very convenient, since it requires only a single support. The flattop configuration, however, where the dipole is mounted horizontally, gives more gain at the higher frequencies. **Figure 10.6** shows the 80 meter azimuth and elevation patterns for two 135-foot long dipoles. The first is mounted as a flattop at a height of 50 feet over flat ground with a conductivity of 5 mS/m and a dielectric constant of 13, typical for average soil. The second dipole uses the same length of wire, with the center apex at 50 feet and the ends drooped down to be suspended 10 feet off the ground. This height is sufficient so that there is no danger to passersby from RF burns.

At 3.8 MHz, the flattop dipole has about 4 dB more peak gain than its drooping cousin. On the other hand, the inverted V configuration gives a pattern that is more omnidirectional than the flattop dipole, which has nulls off the ends of the wire. Omnidirectional coverage may be more important to net operators, for example, than maximum gain.

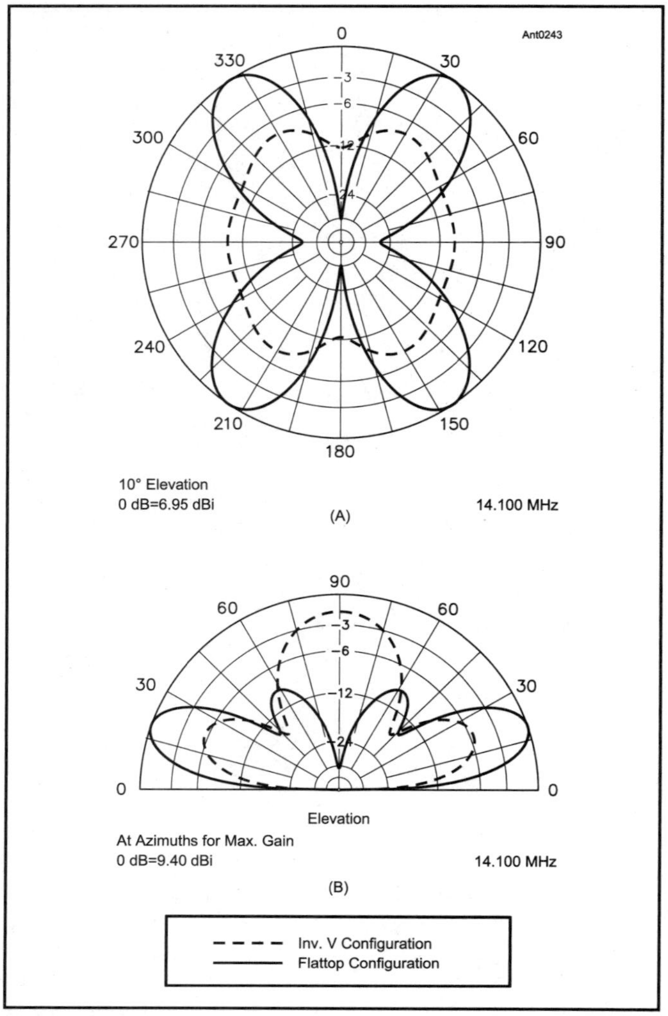

Figure 10.7 — Patterns on 20 meters for two 135-foot dipoles. One is mounted horizontally as a flattop and the other as an inverted V with 120° included angle between the legs. The azimuth pattern is shown in A and the elevation pattern is shown in B. The inverted V has about 6 dB less gain at the peak azimuths, but has a more uniform, almost omnidirectional, azimuthal pattern. In the elevation plane, the inverted V has a large high-angle lobe, making it a somewhat better antenna for local communication, but not quite so good for DX contacts at low elevation angles.

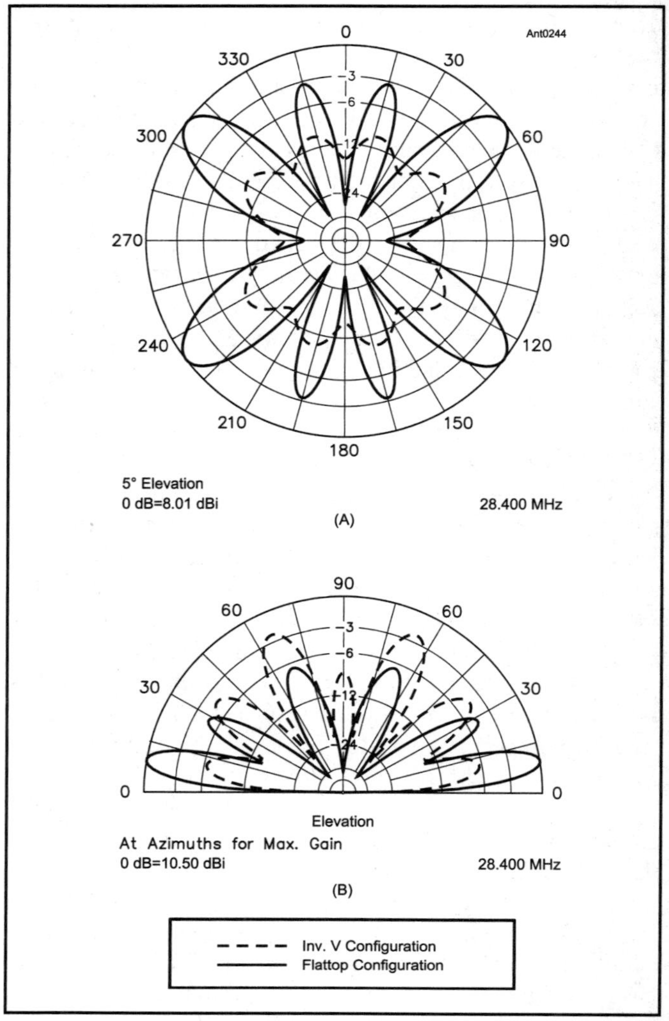

Figure 10.8 — Patterns on 10 meters for same antenna configurations as in Figs 10.6 and 10.7. Once again, the inverted V configuration yields a more omnidirectional pattern, but at the expense of almost 8 dB less gain than the flattop configuration at its strongest lobes.

Figure 10.7 shows the azimuth and elevation patterns for the same two antenna configurations, but this time at 14.2 MHz. The flattop dipole has developed four distinct lobes at a 10° elevation angle, an angle typical for 20 meter skywave communication. The peak elevation angle gain of 9.4 dBi occurs at about 17° for a height of 50 feet above flat ground for the flattop dipole. The inverted V configuration is again nominally more omnidirectional, but the peak gain is down some 6 dB from the flattop.

The antenna's peak is reduced even more at 28.4 MHz for the inverted V configuration. Here the peak gain is down about 8 dB from that produced by the flattop dipole, which exhibits eight lobes at this frequency with a maximum gain of 10.5 dBi at about 7° elevation. See the comparisons in **Figure 10.8**.

Whatever configuration you choose to mount the 135-foot dipole, you will want to feed it with some sort of low-loss open-wire feed line. For example, 450-Ω window line is popular for this application. Be sure to twist the line once or twice per foot to keep it from twisting excessively in the wind. (Do not twist it so much that the wire spacing is reduced.) Make sure also that you provide some mechanical support for the line at the junction with the dipole wires. This will prevent flexing of the transmission-line wire, since excessive flexing will result in breakage. (See the **Antenna Materials and Construction** chapter)

10.1.5 THE G5RV AND RELATED MULTIBAND ANTENNAS

A variation on the center-fed antenna that does not require a lot of space, is simple to construct and low in cost is the G5RV. Designed in England by Louis Varney, G5RV, some years ago, it has become quite popular in the US. (The original article by G5RV in the *RSGB Bulletin* is included with this book's downloadable supplemental information.) The G5RV design is shown in **Figure 10.9**. The antenna may be used from 3.5 through 30 MHz, although the use of an antenna tuner should be expected on any band except 14 MHz as Varney himself recommended. Low SWR with coax feed and no matching network on bands other than 14 MHz probably indicates excessive losses in the coax. In fact, an analysis of the G5RV feed point impedance shows there is no length of balanced line of any characteristic impedance that will transform the terminal impedance to the 50 to 75-Ω range on all bands.

Compared to a standard λ/2 20 meter dipole at 50 feet and a 132-foot long center-fed doublet at 50 feet (also discussed in the next section on Windom-style antennas), on 20 meters the G5RV is within 1 dB of peak gain of either antenna. The G5RV has a four-lobed pattern that is somewhat more omnidirectional than either dipole or doublet. This is somewhat of an advantage for a wire antenna which cannot be rotated. The G5RV patterns for other frequencies are similar to those shown for the 135-foot dipole in the previous section.

The portion of the G5RV antenna shown as horizontal in Figure 10.9 may also be installed in an inverted V dipole arrangement, subject to the same loss of peak gain mentioned above for the 135-foot dipole. Or instead, up to 1/6 of the total length of the antenna at each end may be dropped vertically or semi-vertically, or bent at a convenient angle to the main axis of the antenna, to cut down on the requirements for real estate.

A useful variation on the G5RV theme was designed by Brian Austin, ZS6BKW (now GØGSF — see the Bibliography). It is shown in **Figure 10.10** and has a very similar radiation pattern to the G5RV. It is almost 10 feet shorter than the G5RV and uses a slightly longer length of 450-Ω window line to create the 50-Ω impedance point. The antenna is usable without a tuner in some portion of the 7, 14, 18, 24, and 28 MHz bands. The SWR is high on 3.5 MHz but within range of a tuner.

All of the G5RV/ZS6BKW and other variations that use a section of balanced transmission line to create a 50-Ω point require the use of a 1:1 choke balun as described in the chapter on **Transmission Line System Techniques**. Without the isolation between the balanced and unbalanced feed lines, the coaxial feed line will pick up significant common-mode RF current and allow noise picked up on the coax to enter the feed line.

The weight of the balun should be supported by sturdy construction and strain relief for the parallel conductor feed line. For this antenna, window line using stranded conductors is preferable to copper-plated steel since the repeated flexing will eventually cause the conductors to break. The window line matching section should be oriented at right angles to the top section (or symmetrically in an inverted V configuration) to avoid unbalancing the antenna system which would exacerbate common-mode current problems and distort the pattern unpredictably.

Project: Triband Dipole for 30, 17, and 12 Meters

(This antenna was originally described in the article "A Triband Dipole for 30, 17, and 12 Meters" by Zack Lau, W1VT in the Mar/Apr 2015 issue of *QEX*. A similar design by W1VT for 10, 20, and 40 meters described in the article "A Compact Multiband Dipole" from the March 2016 issue of *QST*. Both articles are available in this chapter's downloadable supplemental information.)

The triband dipole in **Figure 10.11** is a 58-foot doublet made out of #14 THHN solid house wire fed with a 35.5-foot matching section of 600-Ω ladder line having a velocity factor of 0.91. It has modest gain over a dipole on all three of the design bands and SWR at the balun input is approximately 1.5 on 17 meters and 2.4 on 12 meters and 30 meters.

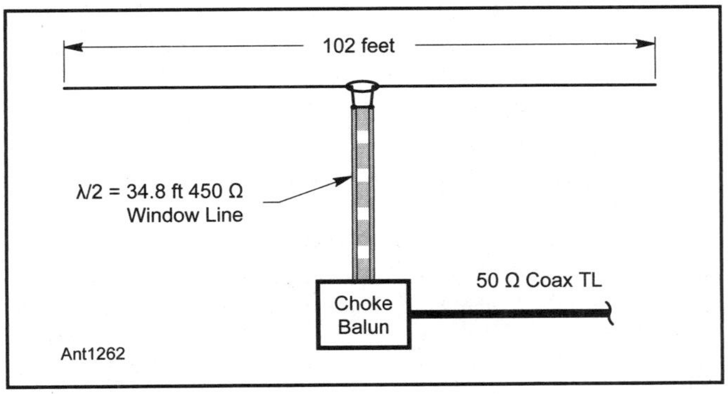

Figure 10.9 — The G5RV multiband antenna covers 3.5 through 30 MHz. It may be fed directly on 14 MHz but its designer recommends a matching network or antenna tuner on other bands.

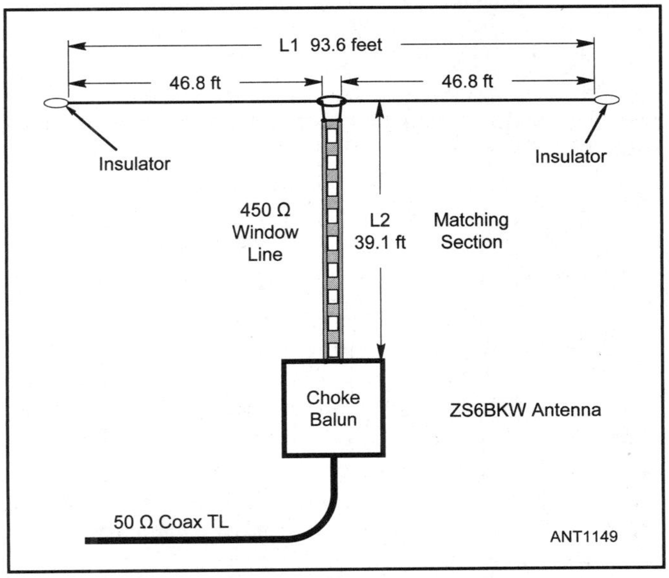

Figure 10.10 — The ZS6BKW multiband antenna is a development of the G5RV. The length of the matching section of feed line is based on a velocity factor of 0.91 (91%). (See text.)

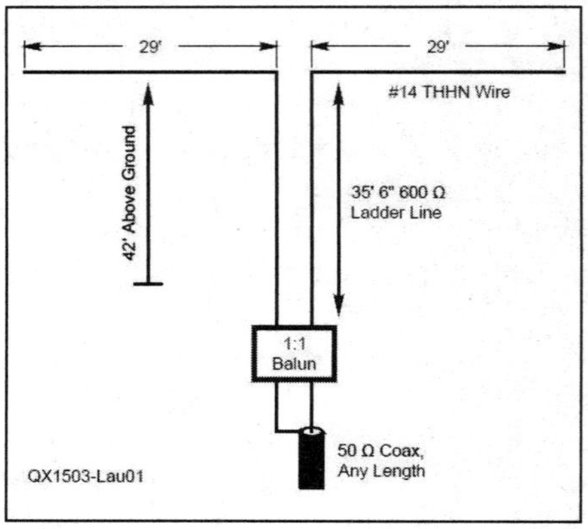

Figure 10.11 — Basic configuration of the triband dipole, consisting of a 58-foot doublet fed with 35.5 feet of 600-Ω open-wire feed line. SWR at the balun input is approximately 1.5:1 on 17 meters and 2.4:1 on 12 meters and 30 meters.

These values of SWR are all easily matched to 1:1 with the auto-tuner built into many transceivers or with an external impedance matching unit.

If the antenna will be installed at a significantly different height, the length of the doublet and the open-wire feed line may have to be adjusted to obtain resonances in all three bands. The length of the 50 Ω cable feed line isn't critical.

The #14 THHN house wire has two layers of insulation: 15 mils of PVC and another 4 mils of nylon. While the nylon typically flakes off in less than a year, the antenna was modeled in *EZNEC* using an insulation thickness of 19 mils and a dielectric constant of 3.5. Changing the insulation thickness to 15 mils doesn't appreciably change the resonance points.

The somewhat low velocity factor of the open-wire line assumes it is constructed using the same insulated wire as the doublet. A spacing of 3 inches is recommended for constructing the 600 Ω open-wire line. If other wire types are used to construct the open-wire line, an accurate approximation for the impedance of air-insulated open-wire line is $Z_0 = 276 \log_{10} (2S/d)$ where S is the center-to-center distance between the conductors and d is the diameter of the conductors in the same units as S. (Z_0 for open-wire line is discussed in detail in the **Transmission Lines** chapter.)

A 1:1 choke balun is required between the open-wire feed line and the coax to prevent the outside of the coax shield from becoming a radiating antenna element and affecting feed point impedance. W1VT recommends 11 turns of RG-58A/U on an FT-140-43 core as working well from 10 to 30 MHz. Other ferrite-core choke designs can be found in the **Transmission Line System Techniques** chapter.

Assuming a height of 42 feet, on 17 meters the antenna has a clean, bidirectional pattern, with maximum gain of 8.9 dBi broadside to the wires, just like a dipole. (All antenna patterns are included in the full article.) On 30 meters, the antenna also has gain broadside to the wires of 6.9 dBi. On 12 meters the antenna has an azimuthal radiation pattern with four main lobes having 8.2 dBi gain, 50° off broadside. The broadside lobes are 3.5 dB weaker than the main lobes.

10.1.6 THE WINDOM AND CAROLINA WINDOM

An antenna that enjoyed popularity in the 1930s and into the 1940s was what we now call the Windom. It was known at the time as a "single-feeder Hertz" antenna, after being described in September 1929 *QST* by Loren G. Windom, W8GZ (see Bibliography).

The Windom antenna, shown in **Figure 10.12**, is fed with a single wire, attached approximately 14% off center. In theory, this location provides a match for the single-wire transmission line, which is driven against an earth ground. Because the single-wire feed line is not inherently well balanced and because it is brought to the operating position, "RF in the shack" is a likely result of using this antenna. For that reason, the true single-feed-wire Windom antenna is rarely used although the name is often given to wires with non-centered feed points as described in the next section.

A recent variation is called the "Carolina Windom," apparently because two of the designers, Edgar Lambert, WA4LVB, and Joe Wright, W4UEB, lived in coastal North Carolina (the third, Jim Wilkie, WY4R, lived in nearby Norfolk, Virginia). One of the interesting parts about the Carolina Windom is that it turns a potential disadvantage — feed line radiation — into a potential advantage.

Figure 10.13 is a diagram of a flattop Carolina Windom, which uses a 50-foot wire joined with an 83-foot wire at the feed point insulator. This resembles the layout shown in Figure 10.12 for the original W8GZ Windom. The "Vertical Radiator" for the Carolina Windom is a 22-foot piece of RG-8X coax, with a "line isolator" (feed line choke) at the bottom end and a 4:1 "matching unit" (impedance transformer) at the top. The system takes advantage of the asymmetry of the horizontal wires to purposely induce current onto the outer shield surface of the vertical coax section. Note that the matching unit is a voltage-type balun transformer, which purposely does not act like a common-mode choke balun. You must use an antenna tuner with this system to

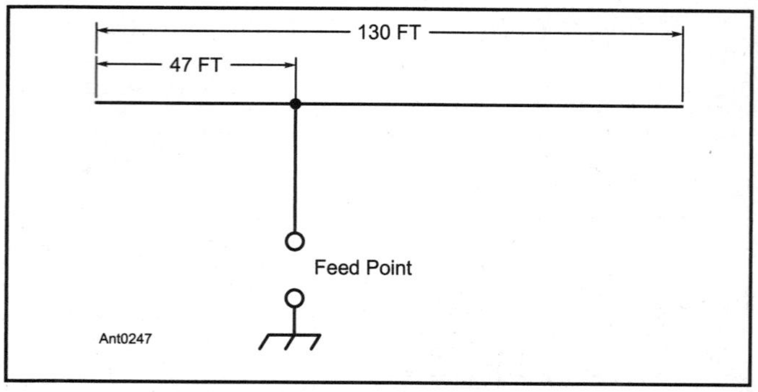

Figure 10.12 — The Windom antenna, cut for a fundamental frequency of 3.75 MHz. The single-wire feed line, connected 14% off center, is brought into the station and the system is fed against ground. The antenna is also effective on its harmonics.

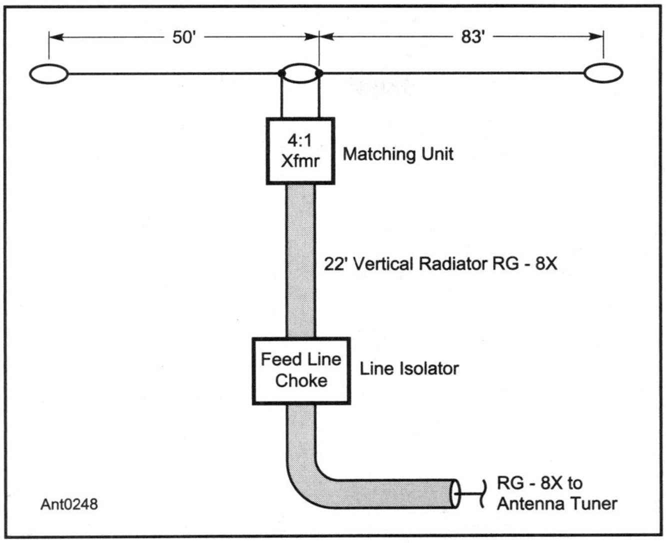

Figure 10.13 — Layout for flattop "Carolina Windom" antenna.

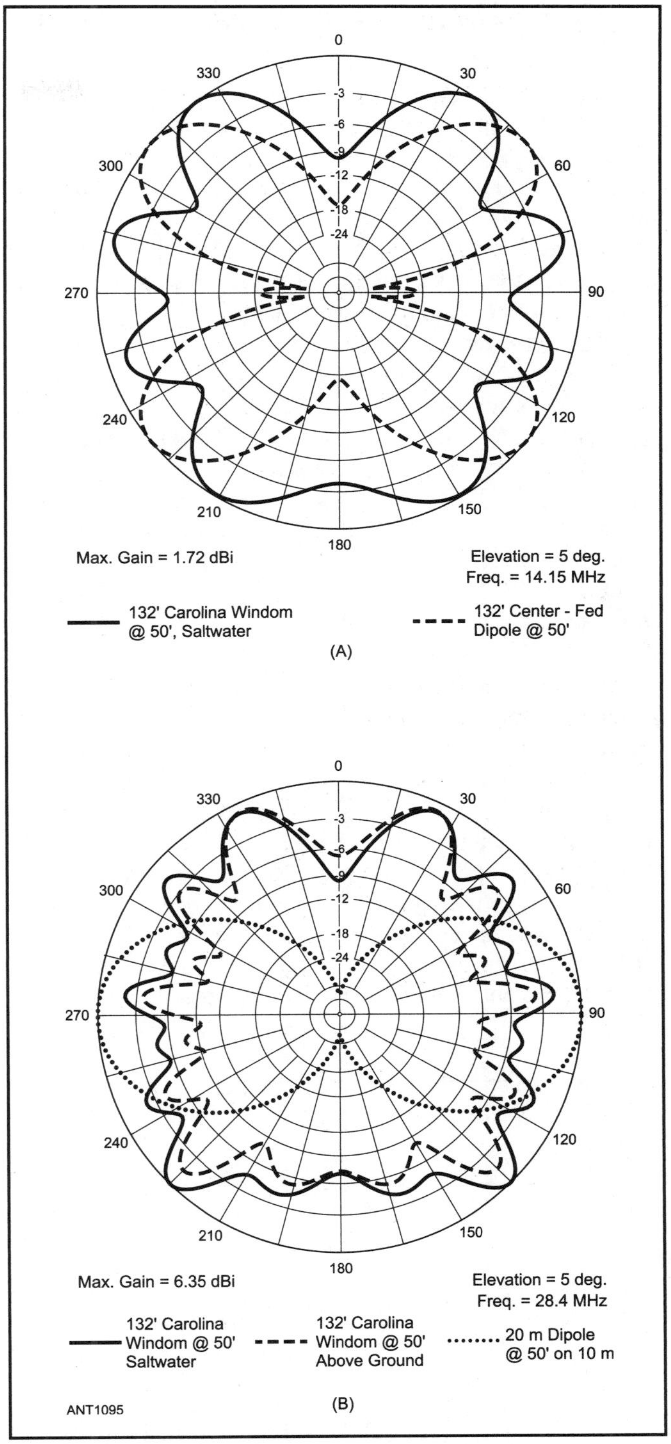

Figure 10.14 — At A, 20 meter azimuth patterns for a 132-foot long off-center fed Carolina Windom and a 132-foot long center-fed flattop dipole on 20 meters, both at a height of 50 feet above saltwater. The response for the Carolina Windom is more omnidirectional because the vertically polarized radiation from the 22-foot long vertical RG-8X coax fills in the deep nulls. At B, 10 meter azimuthal responses for a 132-foot long, 50-foot high Carolina Windom over saltwater (solid line) and over average ground (dashed line), compared to that for a 20 meter half-wave dipole at 50 feet (dotted line).

present a 1:1 SWR to the transmitter on the amateur bands from 80 through 10 meters.

The radiation resulting from current induced onto the 22-foot vertical coax section tends to fill in the deep nulls that would be present if the 132 feet of horizontal wire were center fed. Over saltwater, the vertical radiator can give significant gain at the low elevation angles needed for DX work. Indeed, field reports for the Carolina Windom are most impressive for stations located near or on saltwater. Over average soil the advantage of the additional vertically polarized component is not quite so evident. **Figure 10.14A** compares a 50-foot high Carolina Windom on 14 MHz over saltwater to a 50-foot high, 132-foot long, flattop center-fed dipole. The Carolina Windom has a more omnidirectional azimuthal pattern, a desirable characteristic in a 132-foot long wire antenna that is not normally rotated to favor different directions.

Another advantage of the Carolina Windom over a traditional Windom is that the coax feed line between the transmitter and common-mode choke balun does not radiate, meaning that there will be less "RF in the shack." Since the feed line is not always operating at a low SWR on various ham bands, use the minimum length of feed coax possible to reduce losses in the coax.

Figure 10.14B shows the azimuth responses for a 50-foot high flattop Carolina Windom on 28.4 MHz over saltwater and over average soil. The pattern for a 50-foot high, flattop 20 meter dipole operated on 28.4 MHz is also shown, since this 20 meter dipole can also be used as a multiband antenna, when fed with open-wire transmission line rather than with coax. Again, the Carolina Windom exhibits a more omnidirectional pattern, even if the pattern is somewhat lopsided at the bottom.

10.1.7 OFF-CENTER-FED (OCF) DIPOLES

The usual practice is to feed a λ/2 dipole in the center where the feed point impedance is low and makes a suitable match to coaxial cables. The dipole will accept energy from a feed point anywhere along its length, however, assuming that the source is matched to the higher impedance that is presented away from the center point. (As discussed in the **Dipoles and Monopoles** chapter, if the feed point is moved away from the center of the dipole, the impedance rises because current is dropping while voltage is rising.)

The *off-center-fed* dipole takes advantage of placing the feed point in a location along the dipole at which the impedance is similar on more than one band, generally in the neighborhood of 150-300 Ω. A suitable impedance matching device such as an impedance transformer is then used to reduce the feed point impedance to something closer to 50 Ω. Note that the feed point impedance of the antenna varies with height above ground and so will SWR.

Figure 10.15 shows an off-center-fed or *OCF* dipole. Because it is similar in appearance to the Windom of Figure 10.12, this antenna is often mistakenly called a "Windom," or sometimes a "coax-fed Windom." The two antennas are not the same, since the Windom is driven against an earth ground, while the OCF dipole is fed like a regular dipole — just not at its center. The extreme case of an OCF is the end-fed Zepp where the feed point is moved all the way to the end of the antenna. (See the previous sections.)

The OCF dipole of Figure 10.15, fed ⅓ of its length from one end, may be used on its fundamental and even harmonics. Its free-space antenna-terminal impedance at 3.5, 7 and 14 MHz is on the order of 150 to 200 Ω. At the 6th harmonic, 21 MHz, the antenna is three wavelengths long and fed at a voltage maximum instead of a current maximum. The feed point impedance at this frequency is high, a few thousand ohms, so the antenna is unsuitable for use on this band.

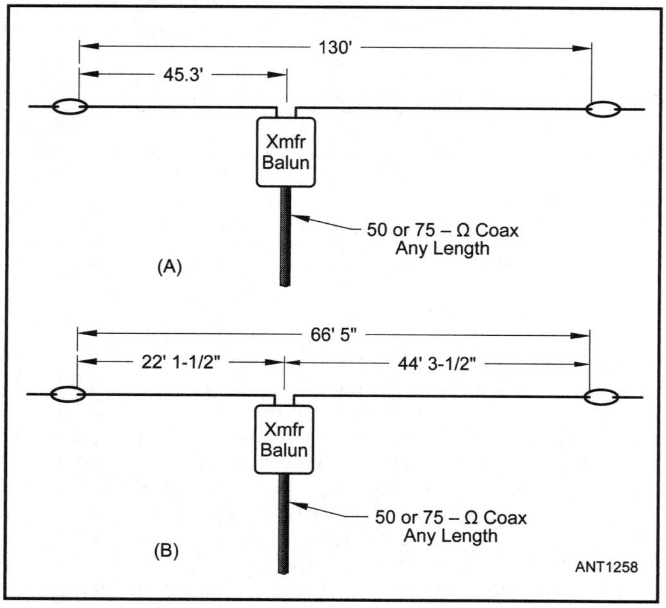

Figure 10.15 — The off-center-fed (OCF) dipole for 3.5, 7 and 14 MHz (A) and for 7, 14, 28, and 50 MHz (B) A 1:4 or 1:6 impedance transformer and choke balun are used at the feed point.

An alternate design that works on 40, 20, 10, and 6 meters is also described in the article "A No Compromise Off-Center Fed Dipole for Four Bands" by Rick Littlefield, K1BQT. An 8-band model that operates on the HF bands from 80 through 10 meters (except 60 meters) is described in the paper "The J78 Antenna: An Eight-band Off-Center-Fed HF Dipole" by Brian Machesney, K1LI/J75Y. Both articles are included in the downloadable supplemental material for this chapter.

All OCF dipole antennas require an impedance transformer at the feed point. A 4:1 or 6:1 ratio typically provides good results. A choke balun on the feed line is also required to reduce coupling between the antenna and feed line, which can affect feed point impedance. Height above ground also affects feed point impedance — be prepared to adjust the dipole length to achieve an acceptable match on the bands to be used.

Balun Requirements

Because the OCF dipole is not fed at the center of the radiator, the feed line is not placed symmetrically with respect to the antenna's radiated field. As a result, common-mode current will flow on the feed line, usually a coaxial cable. How much current flows depends on the impedance of the coaxial cable's outer surface which, in turn, depends on the orientation of the cable, how long it is, height above ground, and so forth. (Some of the common-mode current results from the slightly unequal impedances presented by the OCF legs but most of the shield current is induced by the asymmetric location in the antenna's field.)

Regardless of how the common-mode current is caused to flow on the feed line, it is generally viewed as undesirable and a choke balun is used to increase the impedance of coaxial cable's outer surface. Radiation from the feed line may not be a problem in your installation and may even improve the antenna's radiation pattern by filling in nulls. (See "Feed Line Radiation" above.) In that case, no balun is required. (Choke baluns are discussed in the chapter **Transmission Line System Techniques**.)

10.1.8 MULTIPLE-DIPOLE ANTENNAS

The antenna system shown in **Figure 10.16A** consists of a group of center-fed dipoles, all connected in parallel at the point where the transmission line joins them. Each of the dipole elements is individually constructed to be an electrical λ/2 at different frequencies. This is often referred to as a "fan dipole," although that term is also applied to a dipole constructed as a bow-tie to increase operating bandwidth. (See the section "Broadband Dipoles" in the chapter **Single-Band MF and HF Antennas**.) The general idea is that the feed point impedance of the dipoles far from resonance will be high enough that nearly all of the signal power is radiated by the resonant dipole and not by the nonresonant dipoles.

In theory, the 4-wire antenna of Figure 10.16A can be used with a coaxial feed line on five bands. The four wires are

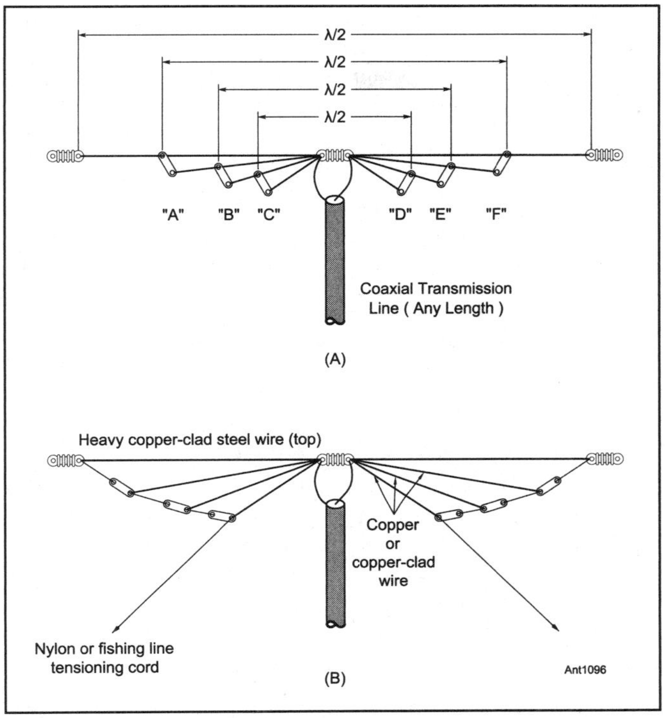

Figure 10.16 — At A, multiband antenna using paralleled dipoles all connected to a common low-impedance transmission line. The half-wave dimensions may be either for the centers of the various bands or selected to fit favorite frequencies in each band. Because of interaction among the various dipoles, the builder should expect to adjust lengths for resonance on each band. B shows a method of constructing the dipole that offers less interaction between the dipoles, making it easier to tune.

prepared as parallel-fed dipoles for 3.5, 7, 14 and 28 MHz. The 7-MHz dipole is intended to be used on its 3rd harmonic for 21-MHz operation to cover a fifth band. However, in practice it has been found difficult to get a good match to coaxial line on all bands.

The λ/2 resonant length of any one dipole in the presence of the others is not the same as for a dipole by itself due to interaction and attempts to optimize all four lengths can become a frustrating procedure. The problem is compounded because the optimum tuning changes in a different antenna environment, so what works for one amateur may not work for another. The builder should start with a single dipole longer than resonance as discussed in the **Dipoles and Monopoles** chapter and be prepared to make repeated adjustments to the dipole lengths as more dipoles are added to the antenna.

Even if a perfect match cannot be obtained on all bands, many amateurs with limited antenna space are willing to accept the mismatch on some bands just so they can operate on those frequencies using a single coax feed line. The fewer dipoles that are used in parallel, the easier it will be to adjust them for the desired performance.

If an attempt is made to model the multi-wire dipole, take extra care to define the feed point construction carefully. As noted in the **Antenna Modeling** chapter, wires that are very close to each other or that join at small angles are hard to model so that the results reflect actual performance.

The multiple-dipole antenna can be fed with parallel-wire feed line and an antenna tuner but that negates the intended advantage of the design over a conventional single-wire nonresonant dipole — the use of a single coaxial feed line. The usual feed method is to use a coaxial feed line and a choke balun at the feed point as described in the chapter **Transmission Line System Techniques**.

The separation between the dipoles for the various frequencies does not seem to be especially critical. One set of wires can be suspended from the next larger set, using insulating spreaders (of the type used for feed line spreaders) to give a separation of a few inches. Users of this antenna often run some of the dipoles at right angles to each other to help reduce interaction. Some operators use inverted V-mounted dipoles as guy wires for the mast that supports the antenna system. The top (and longest) dipole must support the weight of the rest of the antenna plus the feed line, so use heavy wire (copper-clad steel is the strongest) for the top antenna.

While the separation between dipoles does not seem to be especially critical to final performance, it does affect the amount of interaction between them that makes tuning each dipole difficult. A method of construction and tuning reported by Don Butler, N4UJW (**www.hamuniverse.com/multidipole.html**) is shown is Figure 10.16B. For dipoles in the 2-18 MHz range, separating the dipoles at the feed point by at least 5½ inches vertically and at the ends by 38 inches results in a final length closer than ±2% of a single dipole.

An interesting method of construction used successfully by Louis Richard, ON4UF, is shown in **Figure 10.17**. The antenna has four dipoles (for 7, 14, 21 and 28 MHz) constructed from 300-Ω twin lead. A single length of twin lead makes two dipoles. Thus, two lengths, as shown in the sketch, serve to make dipoles for four bands. Be sure to use twin lead with copper-clad steel conductors because all of the weight, including that of the feed line, must be supported by

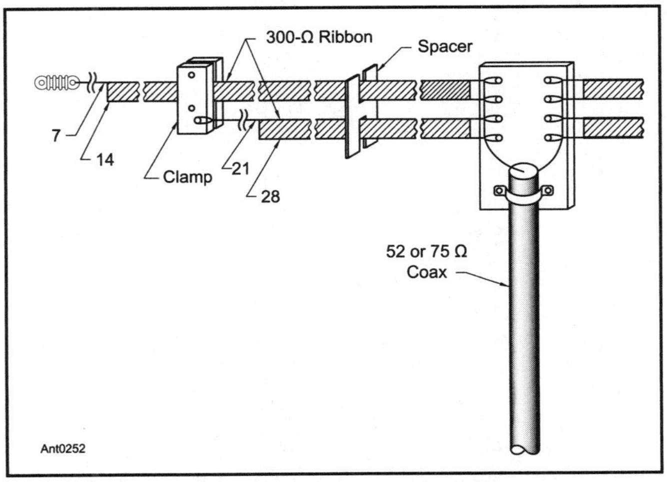

Figure 10.17 — Sketch showing how the twin-lead multiple-dipole antenna system is assembled. The excess wire and insulation are stripped away.

the uppermost wire (450-Ω window line could also be used).

Two pieces of twin lead are first cut to a length suitable for the two halves of the longest dipole. Then one of the conductors in each piece is cut to proper length for the next band higher in frequency. The excess wire and insulation is stripped away. A second pair of lengths is prepared in the same manner, except that the lengths are appropriate for the next two higher frequency bands. (Note the potential for interaction between higher and lower-frequency dipoles that may alter the tuning of previously adjusted dipoles.)

A piece of thick plastic sheet (plexiglass, polycarbonate, or high-density polyethylene) drilled with holes for anchoring each wire serves as the central insulator. The shorter pair of dipoles is suspended the width of the ribbon below the longer pair by clamps also made of poly sheet. Intermediate spacers are made by sawing slots in pieces of plastic sheet so they will fit the ribbon snugly.

The multiple-dipole principle can also be applied to vertical antennas. Parallel or fanned λ/4 elements of wire or tubing can be driven against ground or tuned radials from a common feed point.

Double-L Antenna

The Double-L antenna by Don Toman, K2KQ is a variation of the multi-wire dipole. (**www.yccc.org/Articles/double_l.htm**) Shown in **Figure 10.18**, the antenna is basically a vertical dipole with its ends bent to run horizontally over ground. It can be constructed as a single antenna for one band or a second dipole can be added to use the antenna on two bands.

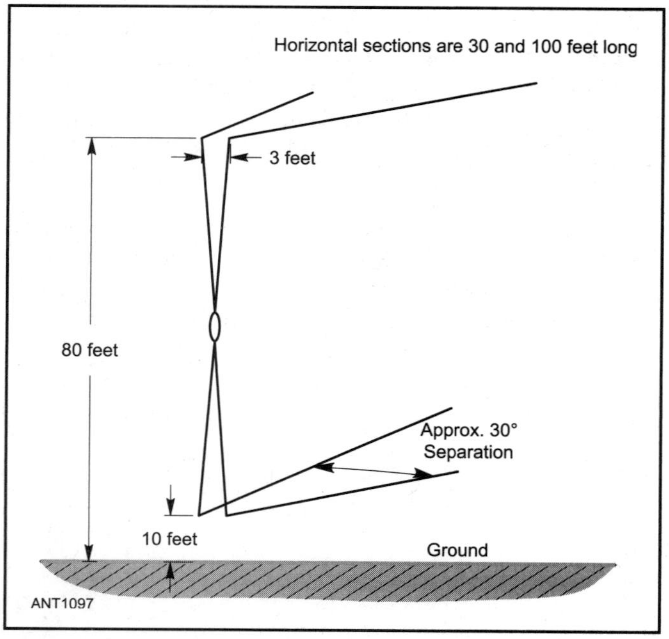

Figure 10.18 — The Double-L antenna by K2KQ is a pair of vertical dipoles with their ends bent to be parallel to the ground. The bottom horizontal wires should be at least 10 feet above ground. For single-band operation, install only a single dipole. The antenna works well as either a single-band or dual-band antenna.

Construction is not critical. The bottom wires should be at least 10 feet above ground and no radial system is required. If you do construct the dual-band version, the vertical wires are connected together at the feed point and separated by about 3 feet where they bend to become horizontal. The two horizontal sections are separated by about 30°. If the antennas are supported by a metal tower, the vertical section should be at least 3 feet from the tower.

The antenna is inherently unbalanced and may be tuned by removing or adding wire to the lower legs without dramatically affecting performance or feed point impedance. The dimensions given result in an SWR minimum near 1.83 MHz and 3.75 MHz.

10.1.9 HORIZONTAL LOOP "SKYWIRE"

A horizontal full-wavelength loop is a very effective omnidirectional antenna for regional communications on its fundamental frequency where its radiation is a maximum at high angles and makes good use of NVIS propagation. The loop is also useful on higher bands where the pattern begins to divide into multiple lobes at lower elevation angles. (Also see Horizontal Loops in the **Loop Antennas** chapter.)

While the feed point impedance might be reasonably low on some bands, using a coax feed line will result in significant losses on others. The best way to feed this versatile antenna is with parallel-wire window or ladder line using an antenna tuner in the station.

The Loop Skywire is shown in **Figure 10.19**. The antenna has one wavelength of wire in its perimeter at the design or fundamental frequency. If you choose to calculate L_{total} in feet, $L_{total} = 1005 / f$ (MHz).

Loop shapes other than a square are possible, but the larger the area enclosed by the loop, the better its performance will be. (A circle encloses the maximum area but this is rarely practical.) The Loop Skywire can also be operated as a vertical antenna with top-hat loading by tying both feed line conductors together at the antenna tuner. This method requires good ground system as described in the previous section on Random-Wire Antennas.

Although the loop can be made for any band or frequency of operation, the following Loop Skywires are good performers.

1.8-MHz Loop Skywire
(1.8-28 MHz loop)
Total loop perimeter: 532 feet
Square side length: 133 feet

3.5-MHz Loop Skywire
(3.5-28 MHz loop and 1.8-MHz vertical)
Total loop perimeter: 272 feet
Square side length: 68 feet

7-MHz Loop Skywire
(7-28 MHz loop and 3.5-MHz vertical)
Total loop perimeter: 142 feet
Square side length: 35.5 feet

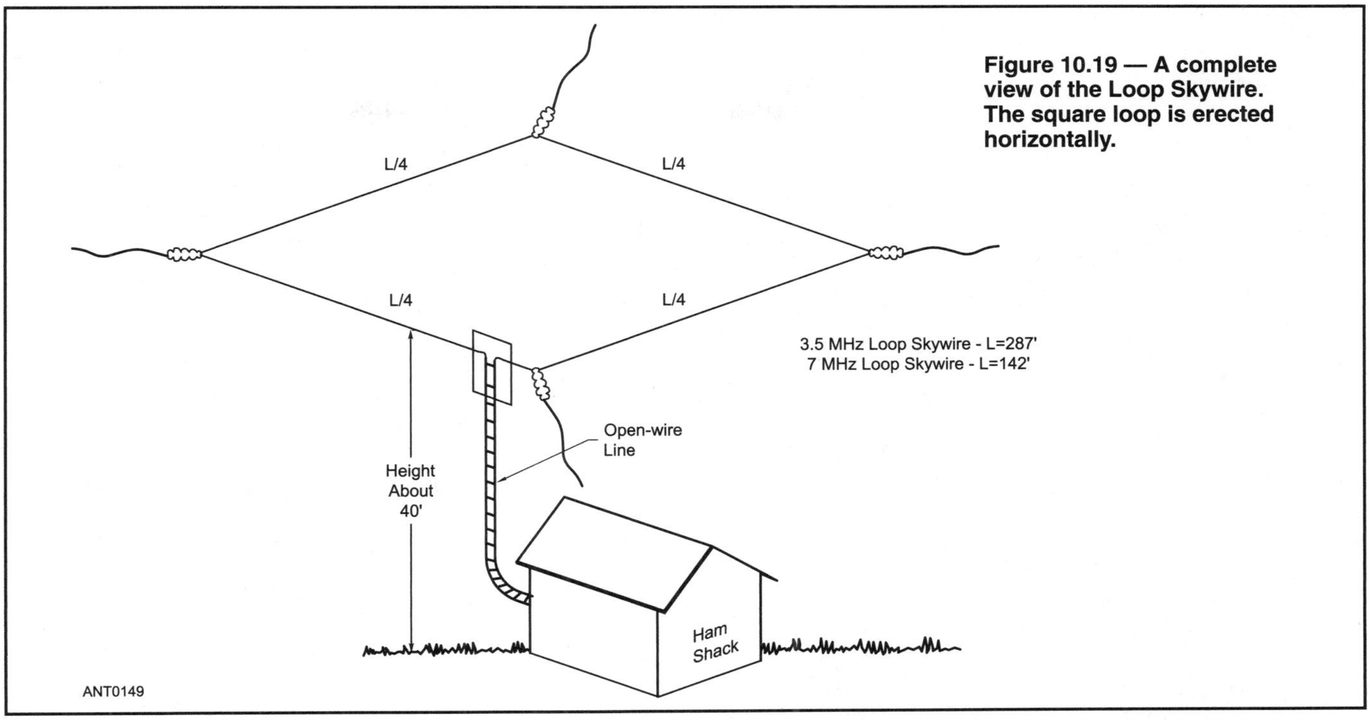

Figure 10.19 — A complete view of the Loop Skywire. The square loop is erected horizontally.

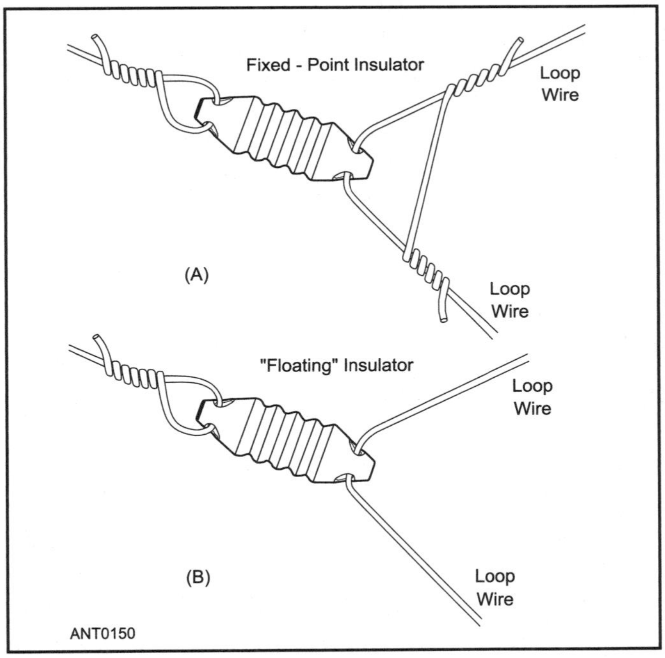

Figure 10.20 — Two methods of installing the insulators at the loop corners.

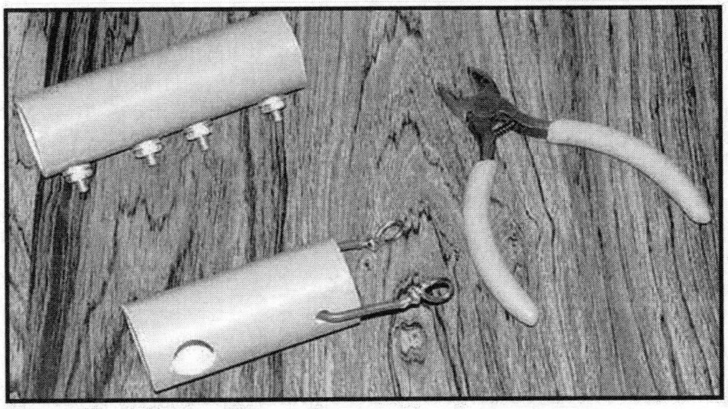

Figure 10.21 — Insulators can also be made from inexpensive PVC pipe. At the top is a feed point insulator for parallel-conductor feed lines. The feed line is attached to the inner terminals and the loop to the output terminals which are jumpered together (jumpers not shown). At the bottom is a corner insulator. The support line is tied through the larger holes and the loop conductors attached to the eyes of the jumper.

The actual total length can vary from the above by a few feet, as the length is not at all critical. Do not worry about tuning and pruning the loop to resonance as it will not make a significant difference in performance.

Bare #14 AWG wire is used in the loop. Copper-clad steel wire is recommended for the 3.5-MHz version. **Figure 10.20** shows the placement of the insulators at the loop corners. Two common methods are used to attach the insulators. Either lock or tie the insulator in place with a loop wire tie, as shown in Figure 10.20A, or leave the insulator free to "float" or slide along the wire, Figure 10.20B. Most loop users float at least two insulators. This allows pulling the slack out of the loop once it is in the air, and eliminates the need to have all the supports exactly placed for equal tension in each leg. Floating two opposite corners is recommended. **Figure 10.21** shows a corner insulator and feed point insulator for parallel-conductor lines made from PVC pipe. Other methods of attaching feed lines can be found in the **Antenna Materials and Construction** chapter.

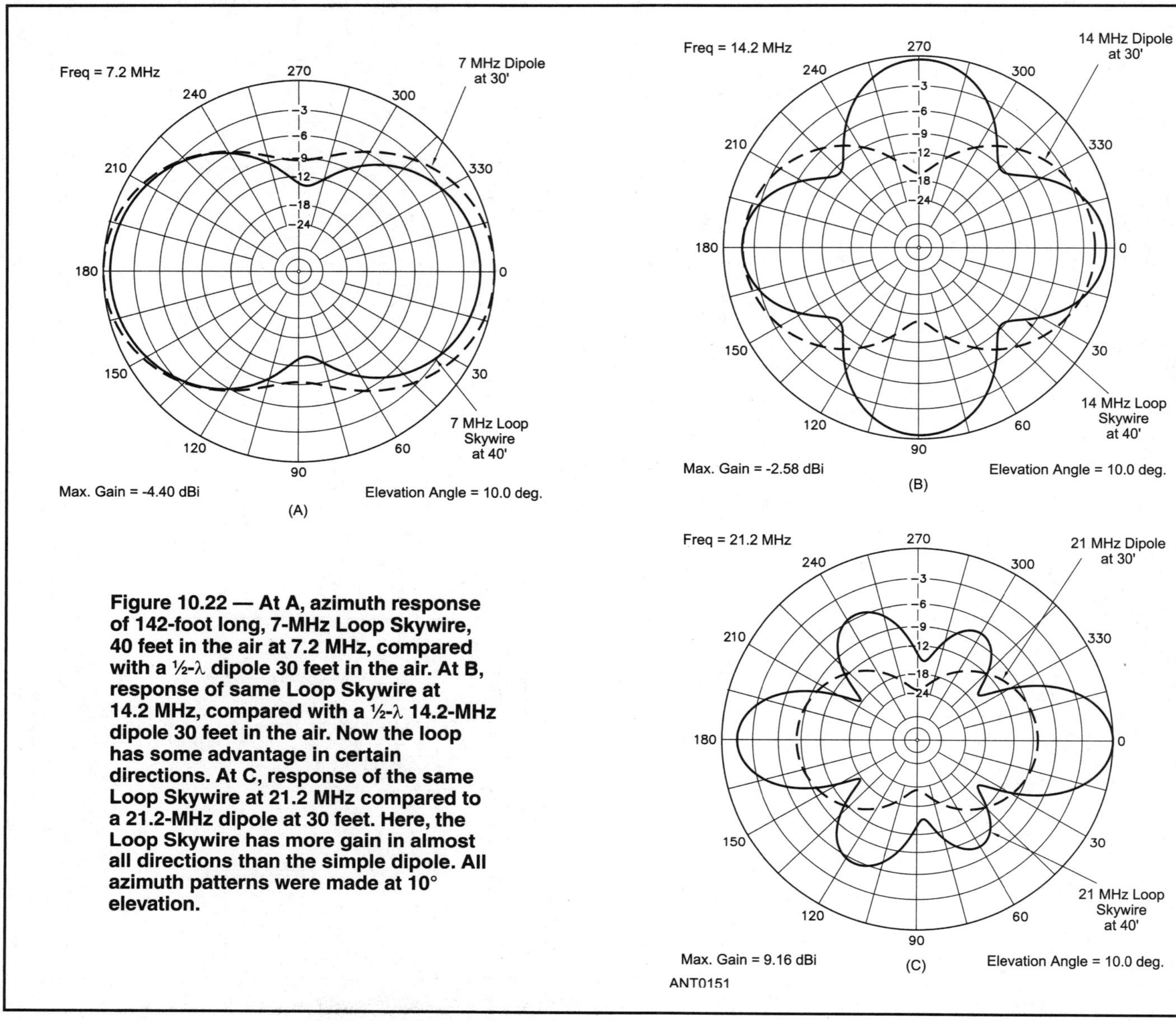

Figure 10.22 — At A, azimuth response of 142-foot long, 7-MHz Loop Skywire, 40 feet in the air at 7.2 MHz, compared with a ½-λ dipole 30 feet in the air. At B, response of same Loop Skywire at 14.2 MHz, compared with a ½-λ 14.2-MHz dipole 30 feet in the air. Now the loop has some advantage in certain directions. At C, response of the same Loop Skywire at 21.2 MHz compared to a 21.2-MHz dipole at 30 feet. Here, the Loop Skywire has more gain in almost all directions than the simple dipole. All azimuth patterns were made at 10° elevation.

The feed point can be positioned anywhere along the loop that you wish. However, most users feed the Skywire at a corner. Placing the feed point a foot or so from one corner allows the feed line to exit more freely and keeps the feed line free of the loop support.

Generally a minimum of four supports is required. If trees are used for supports, then at least two of the ropes or guys used to support the insulators should be counterweighted and allowed to move freely. The feed line corner is almost always tied down, however. Very little tension is needed to support the loop (far less than that for a dipole). Thus, counterweights are light. Several such loops have been constructed with bungee cords tied to three of the four insulators. This eliminates the need for counterweights.

Figure 10.22A shows the azimuth performance on 7.2 MHz of a 142-foot long, 7-MHz Loop Skywire, 40 feet high at an elevation angle of 10°, compared to a regular flattop ½-λ dipole at a height of 30 feet. The loop comes into its own at higher frequencies. Figure 10.22B shows the response at 14.2 MHz, compared again to a ½-λ 14.2-MHz dipole at a height of 30 feet. Now the loop has several lobes that are stronger than the dipole. Figure 10.22C shows the response at 21.2 MHz, compared to a dipole. Now the loop has superior gain compared to the ½-λ dipole at almost any azimuth. In its favored direction on 21.2 MHz, the loop is 8 dB stronger than the dipole.

Recommended height for the antenna is 40 feet or more. Higher is better, especially if you wish to use the loop in the vertical mode. However, successful local and DX operation has been reported in several cases with the antenna at 20 feet.

10.2 TRAP DIPOLES

By using tuned circuits of appropriate design strategically placed in a dipole, the antenna can be made to show what is essentially fundamental resonance at a number of different frequencies. The general principle is illustrated by **Figure 10.23**. The tuned circuits are also referred to as "traps" and so an antenna that uses tuned circuits to change its electrical configuration at different frequencies is called a "trap antenna" or a "trapped antenna."

Even though a trap antenna arrangement is a simple one, an explanation of how a trap antenna works can be elusive. For some designs, traps are resonated in our amateur bands, and for others (especially commercially made antennas) the traps are resonant far outside any amateur band.

A trap in an antenna system can perform either of two functions, depending on whether or not it is resonant at the operating frequency. A familiar case is where the trap is parallel-resonant in an amateur band. For the moment, let us assume that dimension A in Figure 10.23 is 32 feet and that each L/C combination is resonant in the 7-MHz band. Because of its parallel resonance, the trap presents a high impedance at that point in the antenna system. The electrical effect at 7 MHz is that the trap behaves as an open circuit. It serves to separate the outside ends, the B sections, from the inner sections of the antenna. The result is easy to visualize — we now have an antenna system that is resonant in the 7-MHz band. Each 33-foot section (labeled A in the drawing) represents λ/4 with the trap acting as an open circuit. We therefore have a full-size 7-MHz antenna.

The second function of a trap, obtained when the frequency of operation is *not* the resonant frequency of the trap, is one of electrical loading. If the operating frequency is below the trap's resonant frequency, the trap behaves as an inductor; if above, as a capacitor. Inductive loading will electrically lengthen the antenna, and capacitive loading will electrically shorten the antenna.

Let's carry our assumption a bit further and try using the antenna we just considered at 3.5 MHz. With the traps resonant in the 7-MHz band, they will behave as inductors when operation takes place at 3.5 MHz, electrically lengthening the antenna. This means that the total length of sections A and B (plus the length of the inductor) may be something less than a physical λ/4 for resonance at 3.5 MHz. Thus, we have a two-band antenna that is shorter than full size on the lower frequency band. But with the electrical loading provided by the traps, the overall electrical length is λ/2. The total antenna length needed for resonance in the 3.5-MHz band will depend on the L/C ratio of the trap elements.

The key to trap operation away from resonance is its L/C ratio, the ratio of the value of L to the value of C. At resonance, however, within practical limitations the L/C ratio is immaterial as far as electrical operation goes. For example, in the antenna we've been discussing, it would make no difference for 7-MHz operation whether the inductor were 1 μH and the capacitor were 500 pF (the reactances would be just below 45 Ω at 7.1 MHz), or whether the inductor were 5 μH and the capacitor 100 pF (reactances of approximately 224 Ω at 7.1 MHz). But the choice of these values will make a significant difference in the antenna size for resonance at 3.5 MHz. In the first case, where the L/C ratio is 2000, the necessary length of section B of the antenna for resonance at 3.75 MHz would be approximately 28.25 feet. In the second case, where the L/C ratio is 50,000, this length need be only 24.0 feet, a difference of more than 15%.

The above example concerns a two-band antenna with trap resonance at one of the two frequencies of operation. On each of the two bands, each half of the dipole operates as an electrical λ/4. However, the same band coverage can be obtained with a trap resonant at, say, 5 MHz, a frequency quite removed from either amateur band. With proper selection of the L/C ratio and the dimensions for A and B, the trap will act to shorten the antenna electrically at 7 MHz and lengthen it electrically at 3.5 MHz. Thus, an antenna that is intermediate in physical length between being full size on 3.5 MHz and full size on 7 MHz can cover both bands, even though the trap is not resonant at either frequency. Again, the antenna operates with electrical λ/4 sections. Note that such nonresonant traps have less RF current flowing in the trap components, and hence trap losses are less than for resonant traps.

Additional traps may be added in an antenna section to cover three or more bands. Or a judicious choice of dimensions and the L/C ratio may permit operation on three or more bands with just a pair of identical traps in the dipole.

An important point to remember about traps is this. If the operating frequency is below that of trap resonance, the trap behaves as an inductor; if above, as a capacitor. The above discussion is based on dipoles that operate electrically as λ/2 antennas. This is not a requirement, however. Elements may be operated as electrical 3⁄2 λ, or even 5⁄2 λ, and still present a reasonable impedance to a coaxial feed line. In trap antennas covering several HF bands, using electrical lengths that are odd multiples of λ/2 is often done at the higher frequencies.

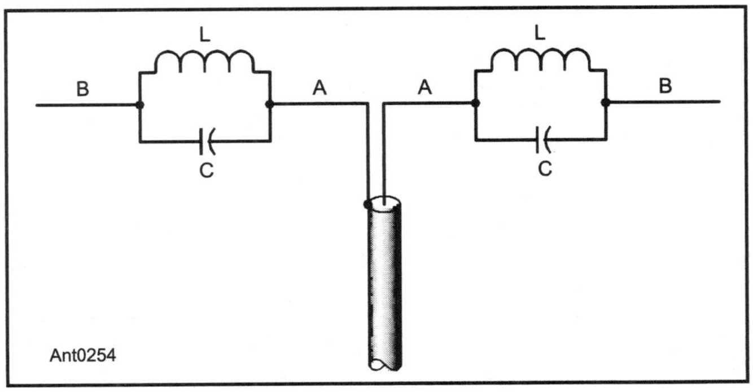

Figure 10.23 — A trap dipole antenna. This antenna may be fed with 50-Ω coaxial line. Depending on the L/C ratio of the trap elements and the lengths chosen for dimensions A and B, the traps may be resonant either in an amateur band or at a frequency far removed from an amateur band for proper two-band antenna operation.

To further aid in understanding trap operation, let's now choose trap L and C components that each have a reactance of 20 Ω at 7 MHz. Inductive reactance is directly proportional to frequency, and capacitive reactance is inversely proportional. When we shift operation to the 3.5-MHz band, the inductive reactance becomes 10 Ω, and the capacitive reactance becomes 40 Ω. At first thought, it may seem that the trap would become capacitive at 3.5 MHz with a higher capacitive reactance, and that the extra capacitive reactance would make the antenna electrically shorter yet. Fortunately, this is not the case. The inductor and the capacitor are connected in parallel with each other.

$$Z = j\frac{X_L X_C}{X_L + X_C} \tag{1}$$

where j indicates a reactive impedance component, rather than resistive. A positive result indicates inductive reactance, and a negative result indicates capacitive. In this 3.5-MHz case, with 40 Ω of capacitive reactance and 10 Ω of inductive, the equivalent series reactance is 13.3 Ω inductive. This inductive loading lengthens the antenna to an electrical λ/2 overall at 3.5 MHz, assuming the B end sections in Figure 10.23 are of the proper length.

With the above reactance values providing resonance at 7 MHz, X_L equals X_C, and the theoretical series equivalent is infinity. This provides the open-switch effect, disconnecting the antenna ends.

At 14 MHz, where X_L = 40 Ω and X_C = 10 Ω, the resultant series equivalent trap reactance is 13.3 Ω capacitive. If the total physical antenna length is slightly longer than 3⁄2 λ at 14 MHz, this trap reactance at 14 MHz can be used to shorten the antenna to an electrical 3⁄2 λ. In this way, three-band operation is obtained for 3.5, 7 and 14 MHz with just one pair of identical traps. The design of such a system is not straightforward, however, because any chosen L/C ratio for a given total length affects the resonant frequency of the antenna on both the 3.5 and 14-MHz bands.

10.2.1 TRAP LOSSES

Since the tuned circuits have some inherent losses, the efficiency of a trap system depends on the unloaded Q values of the tuned circuits. Low-loss (high-Q) coils should be used, and the capacitor losses likewise should be kept as low as possible. With tuned circuits that are good in this respect — comparable with the low-loss components used in transmitter tank circuits, for example — the reduction in efficiency compared with the efficiency of a simple dipole is small, but tuned circuits of low unloaded Q can lose an appreciable portion of the power supplied to the antenna.

The commentary above applies to traps assembled from conventional components. The important function of a trap that is resonant in an amateur band is to provide a high isolating impedance, and this impedance is directly proportional to Q. Unfortunately, high Q restricts the antenna bandwidth, because the traps provide maximum isolation only at trap resonance.

10.2.2 FIVE-BAND W3DZZ TRAP ANTENNA

C. L. Buchanan, W3DZZ, created one of the first trap antennas for the five pre-1979 WARC amateur bands from 3.5 to 30 MHz. Dimensions are given in **Figure 10.24**. Only one set of traps is used, resonant at 7 MHz to isolate the inner (7-MHz) dipole from the outer sections. This causes the overall system to be resonant in the 3.5-MHz band. On 14, 21 and 28 MHz the antenna works on the capacitive-reactance principle just outlined. With a 75-Ω feed line, the SWR with this antenna is under 2:1 throughout the three highest frequency bands, and the SWR is comparable with that obtained with similarly fed simple dipoles on 3.5 and 7 MHz. (The complete article is included with this book's downloadable supplemental information.)

Trap Construction

Traps frequently are built with coaxial aluminum tubes (usually with plastic tubing in-between them for insulation) for the capacitor, with the coil either self-supporting or wound on a form of larger diameter than the tubular capacitor. The coil is then mounted coaxially with the capacitor to form a unit assembly that can be supported at each end by the antenna wires. In another type of trap devised by William J. Lattin, W4JRW (see Bibliography at the end of this chapter), the coil is supported inside an aluminum tube and the trap capacitor is obtained in the form of capacitance between the coil and the outer tube. This type of trap is inherently weatherproof.

A simpler type of trap can be easily assembled from readily available components. A small transmitting-type ceramic "doorknob" capacitor is used, together with a length of commercially available coil material, these being supported by an ordinary ceramic or plastic antenna strain insulator 4¼ inches long. The circuit constants and antenna dimensions differ slightly from those of Figure 10.24, in order to bring the antenna resonance points closer to the centers of the various phone bands. Construction data are given in **Figure 10.25**. If a 10-turn length of inductor is used, a half turn from each end may be used to slip through the anchor holes in the insulator to act as leads.

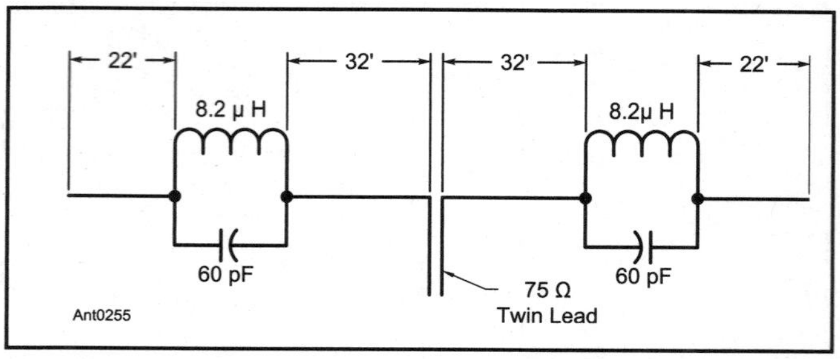

Figure 10.24 — Five-band (3.5, 7, 14, 21 and 28 MHz) trap dipole for operation with 75-Ω feed line at low SWR (C. L. Buchanan, W3DZZ). The balanced (parallel-conductor) line indicated is desirable, but 75-Ω coax can be substituted with a choke balun at the feed point to maintain symmetry. Dimensions given are for resonance (lowest SWR) at 3.75, 7.2, 14.15 and 29.5 MHz. Resonance is very broad on the 21-MHz band, with SWR less than 2:1 throughout the band.

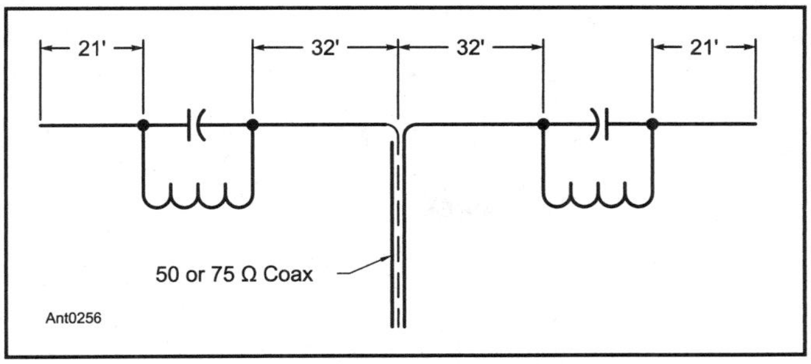

Figure 10.25 — Layout of multiband antenna using traps constructed as shown in Figure 10.26. The capacitors are 100 pF each, transmitting type, 5000-V dc rating (Centralab 850SL-100N). Coils are 9 turns of #12 AWG wire, 2½ inches diameter, 6 turns per inch (B&W 3029) with end turns spread as necessary to resonate the traps to 7.2 MHz. These traps, with the wire dimensions shown, resonate the antenna at approximately the following frequencies on each

The components used in these traps are sufficiently weatherproof in themselves so that no additional weatherproofing has been found necessary. However, if it is desired to protect them from the accumulation of snow or ice, a plastic cover can be made by cutting two discs of plastic slightly larger in diameter than the coil, drilling at the center to pass the antenna wires, and cementing a plastic cylinder on the edges of the discs. The cylinder can be made by wrapping two turns or so of 0.02-inch plastic sheet around the discs, if no suitable ready-made tubing is available. Plastic soft-drink bottles or food jars are easily adaptable for use as impromptu trap covers if protected from solar UV.

For low-power use, John Portune, W6NBC, designed a printed-circuit board trap (see Bibliography). The trap consists of a pair of rectangular spiral inductors, one on each side of the PCB. The inductor traces mirror each other so they exactly overlap. The two traces and the PCB material make up the trap's capacitance. The trap is tuned by moving a jumper along the inductor.

The common FR-4 glass-epoxy PCB material is somewhat lossy with a dissipation factor of 2% but is adequate for intermittent transmitting at 100 W or less. If polyimide or Teflon (PTFE) are available, those materials are a less-lossy dielectric.

10.2.3 W8NX MULTIBAND, COAX-TRAP DIPOLES

Over the last 60 or 70 years, amateurs have used many kinds of multiband antennas to cover the traditional HF bands. The availability of the 30, 17 and 12 meter bands has expanded our need for multiband antenna coverage. This section is based on the August 1994 *QST* article "Two New Multiband Trap Dipoles" by Al Buxton, W8NX. This article and two others by the same author are included with this book's downloadable supplemental information, providing designs for trap dipoles operating on all of the amateur bands below 30 MHz.

Two different antennas are described here. The first covers the traditional 80, 40, 20, 15 and 10 meter bands, and the second covers 80, 40, 17 and 12 meters. Each uses the same type of W8NX trap — connected for different modes of operation — and a pair of short capacitive stubs to enhance coverage. The W8NX coaxial-cable traps have two different modes: a high- and a low-impedance mode. The inner-conductor windings and shield windings of the traps are connected in series for both modes. However, either the low- or high-impedance point can be used as the trap's output terminal. For low-impedance trap operation, only the center conductor turns of the trap windings are used. For high-impedance operation, all turns are used, in the conventional manner for a trap. The short stubs on each antenna are strategically sized and located to permit more flexibility in adjusting the resonant frequencies of the antenna.

80, 40, 20, 15 and 10 meter Dipole

Figure 10.26 shows the configuration of the 80, 40, 20, 15 and 10 meter antenna. The radiating elements are made of #14 AWG stranded copper wire. The element lengths are the wire span lengths in feet. These lengths do not include the lengths of the pigtails at the balun, traps and insulators. The 32.3-foot-long inner 40 meter segments are measured from the eyelet of the input balun to the tension-relief hole in the trap coil form. The 4.9-foot segment length is measured from the tension-relief hole in the trap to the 6-foot stub. The 16.1-foot outer-segment span is measured from the stub to the eyelet of the end insulator.

The coaxial-cable traps are wound on PVC pipe coil forms and use the low-impedance output connection. The stubs are 6-foot lengths of ⅛-inch stiffened aluminum or copper rod hanging perpendicular to the radiating elements. The first inch of their length is bent 90° to permit attachment

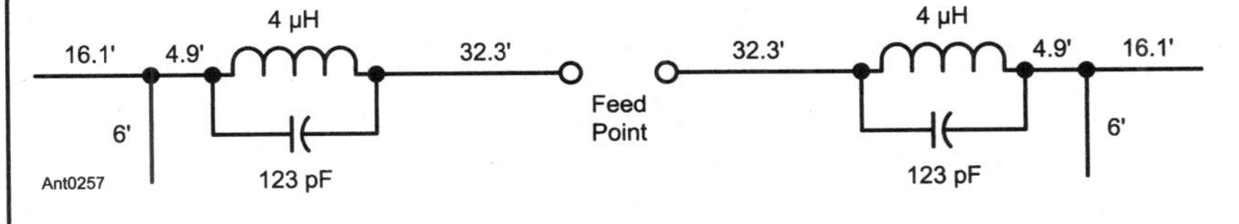

Figure 10.26 — A W8NX multiband dipole for 80, 40, 20, 15 and 10 meters. The values shown (123 pF and 4 µH) for the coaxial-cable traps are for parallel resonance at 7.15 MHz. The low-impedance output of each trap is used for this antenna.

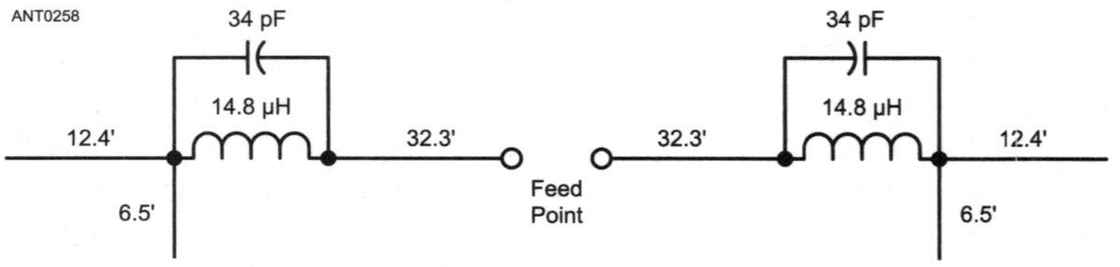

Figure 10.27 — A W8NX multiband dipole for 80, 40, 17 and 12 meters. For this antenna, the high-impedance output is used on each trap. The resonant frequency of the traps is 7.15 MHz.

to the radiating elements by large-diameter copper crimp connectors. Ordinary #14 AWG wire may be used for the stubs, but it has a tendency to curl up and may tangle unless weighed down at the end. You should feed the antenna with 75-Ω coaxial cable using a choke balun.

This antenna may be thought of as a modified W3DZZ antenna due to the addition of the capacitive stubs. The length and location of the stub give the antenna designer two extra degrees of freedom to place the resonant frequencies within the amateur bands. This additional flexibility is particularly helpful to bring the 15 and 10 meter resonant frequencies to more desirable locations in these bands. The actual 10 meter resonant frequency of the original W3DZZ antenna is somewhat above 30 MHz, pretty remote from the more desirable low frequency end of 10 meters.

80, 40, 17 and 12 meter Dipole

Figure 10.27 shows the configuration of the 80, 40, 17 and 12 meter antenna. Notice that the capacitive stubs are attached immediately outboard after the traps and are 6.5 feet long, ½ foot longer than those used in the other antenna. The traps are the same as those of the other antenna, but are connected for the high-impedance parallel-resonant output mode. Since only four bands are covered by this antenna, it is easier to fine tune it to precisely the desired frequency on all bands. The 12.4-foot tips can be pruned to a particular 17 meter frequency with little effect on the 12 meter frequency. The stub lengths can be pruned to a particular 12 meter frequency with little effect on the 17 meter frequency. Both such pruning adjustments slightly alter the 80 meter resonant frequency. However, the bandwidths of the antennas are so broad on 17 and 12 meters that little need for such pruning exists. The 40 meter frequency is nearly independent of adjustments to the capacitive stubs and outer radiating tip elements. Like the first antennas, this dipole is fed with a balun and 75-Ω feed line.

Figure 10.28 shows the schematic diagram of the traps. It explains the difference between the low and high-impedance modes of the traps. Notice that the high-impedance terminal is the output configuration used in most conventional trap applications. The low-impedance connection is made across only the inner conductor turns, corresponding to one-half of the total turns of the trap. This mode steps the trap's impedance down to approximately one-fourth of that of the high-impedance level. This is what allows a single trap design to be used for two different multiband antennas.

Figure 10.29 is a drawing of a cross-section of the coax trap shown through the long axis of the trap. Notice that the traps are conventional coaxial-cable traps, except for the added low-impedance output terminal. The traps are 8¾ close-spaced turns of RG-59 (Belden 8241) on a 2⅜-inch-OD PVC pipe (schedule 40 pipe with a 2-inch ID) coil form. The forms are 4⅛ inches long. Trap resonant frequency is very sensitive to the outer diameter of the coil form, so check it carefully. Unfortunately, not all PVC pipe is made with the same wall thickness. The trap frequencies should be checked with a dip meter and general-coverage receiver and adjusted to within 50 kHz of the 7150 kHz resonant frequency before installation. One inch is left over at each end of the coil forms to allow for the coax feed-through holes and holes for tension-relief attachment of the antenna radiating elements to the traps. Be sure to seal the ends of the trap coax cable to prevent moisture from entering the coaxial cable. (See the discussion on waterproofing in the **Building Antenna Systems and Towers** chapter.)

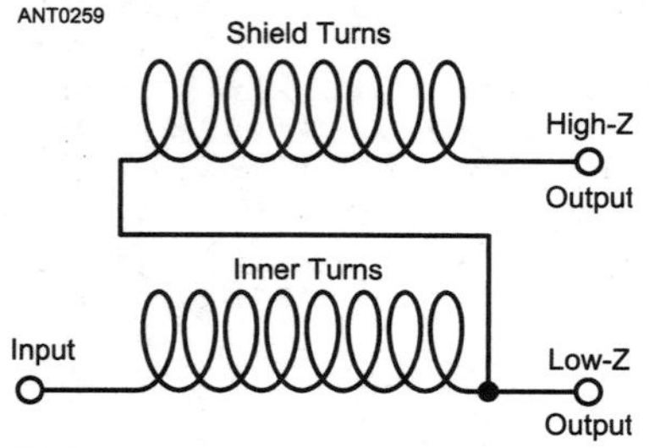

Figure 10.28 — Schematic for the W8NX coaxial-cable trap. RG-59 is wound on a 2⅜-inch OD PVC pipe.

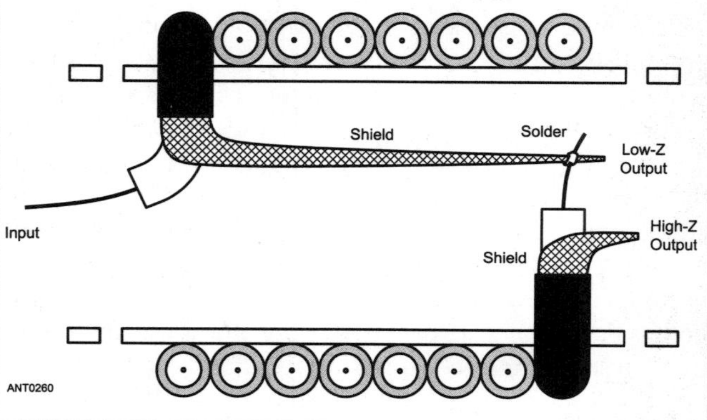

Figure 10.29 — Construction details of the W8NX coaxial-cable trap.

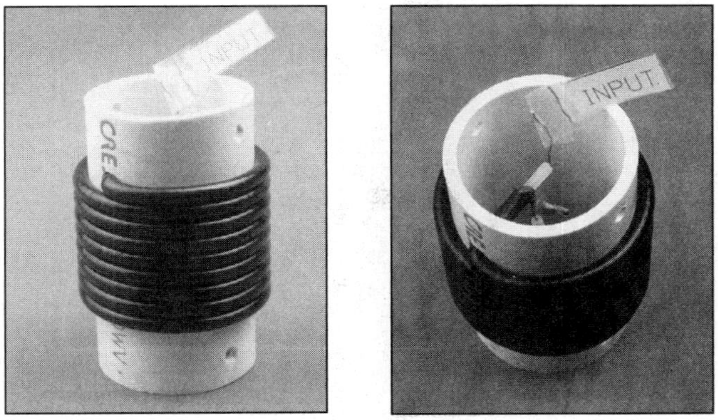

Figure 10.30 — Other views of a W8NX coax-cable trap.

Also, be sure that you connect the 32.3-foot wire element at the start of the inner conductor winding of the trap. This avoids detuning the antenna by the stray capacitance of the coaxial-cable shield. The trap output terminal (which has the shield stray capacitance) should be at the outboard side of the trap. Reversing the input and output terminals of the trap will lower the 40 meter frequency by approximately 50 kHz, but there will be negligible effect on the other bands.

Figure 10.30 shows a coaxial-cable trap. Further details of the trap installation are shown in **Figure 10.31**. This drawing applies specifically to the 80, 40, 20, 15 and 10 meter antenna, which uses the low-impedance trap connections. Notice the lengths of the trap pigtails: 3 to 4 inches at each terminal of the trap. If you use a different arrangement, you must modify the span lengths accordingly. All connections can be made using crimp connectors rather than by soldering. Access to the trap's interior is attained more easily with a crimping tool than with a soldering iron.

Performance

The performance of both antennas has been very satisfactory. W8NX uses the 80, 40, 17 and 12 meter version because it covers 17 and 12 meters. (He has a tribander for 20, 15 and 10 meters.) The radiation pattern on 17 meters is that of a ³⁄₂-wave dipole. On 12 meters, the pattern is that of a ⁵⁄₂-wave dipole. At his location in Akron, Ohio, the antenna runs essentially east and west. It is installed as an inverted V, 40 feet high at the center, with a 120° included angle between the legs. Since the stubs are very short, they radiate little power and make only minor contributions to the radiation patterns. In theory, the pattern has four major lobes on 17 meters, with maxima to the northeast, southeast, southwest and northwest. These provide low-angle radiation into Europe, Africa, South Pacific, Japan and Alaska. A narrow pair of minor broadside lobes provides north and south coverage into Central America, South America and the polar regions.

There are four major lobes on 12 meters, giving nearly end-fire radiation and good low-angle east and west coverage. There are also three pairs of very narrow, nearly broadside, minor lobes on 12 meters, down about 6 dB from the major end-fire lobes. On 80 and 40 meters, the antenna has the usual figure-8 patterns of a half-wave-length dipole.

Both antennas function as electrical half-wave dipoles on 80 and 40 meters with a low SWR. They both function as odd-harmonic current-fed dipoles on their other operating frequencies, with higher, but still acceptable, SWR. The presence of the stubs can either raise or lower the input impedance of the antenna from those of the usual third and fifth harmonic dipoles. Again W8NX recommends that 75-Ω, rather than 50-Ω, feed line be used because of the generally higher input impedances at the harmonic operating frequencies of the antennas.

The SWR curves of both antennas were carefully measured using a 75 to 50-Ω transformer from Palomar Engineers inserted at the junction of the 75-Ω coax feed line and a 50-Ω SWR bridge. The transformer is required for accurate SWR measurement if a 50-Ω SWR bridge is used with a 75-Ω line. Most 50-Ω rigs operate satisfactorily with a 75-Ω line, although this requires different tuning and load settings in the final output stage of a vacuum tube amplifier or antenna tuner. The author uses the 75 to 50-Ω transformer only when making SWR measurements and at low power levels. The transformer is rated for 100 W, and when he runs his 1-kW PEP linear amplifier the transformer is taken out of the line.

Figure 10.32 gives the SWR curves of the 80, 40, 20, 15 and 10 meter antenna. Minimum SWR is nearly 1:1 on 80 meters, 1.5:1 on 40 meters, 1.6:1 on 20 meters, and 1.5:1 on 10 meters. The minimum SWR is slightly below 3:1 on

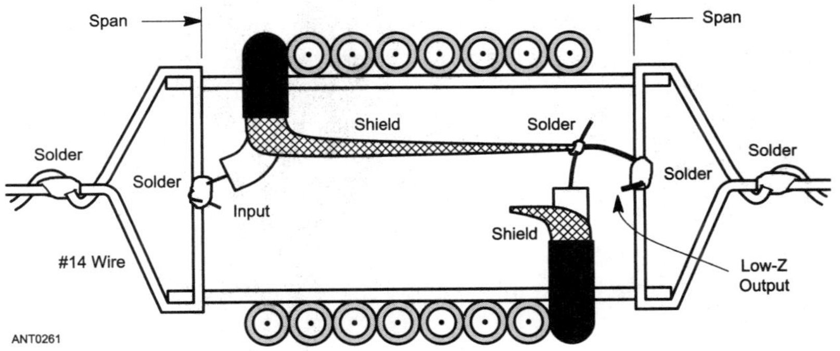

Figure 10.31 — Additional construction details for the W8NX coaxial-cable trap.

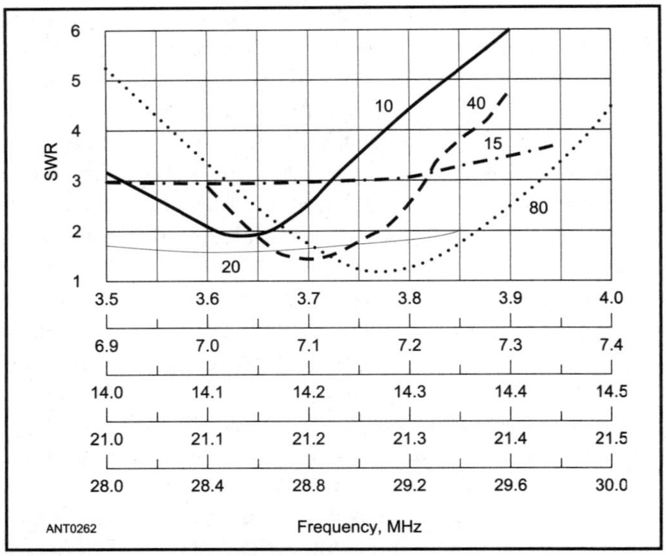

Figure 10.32 — Measured SWR curves for an 80, 40, 20, 15 and 10 meter antenna, installed as an inverted V with 40-ft apex and 120° included angle between legs.

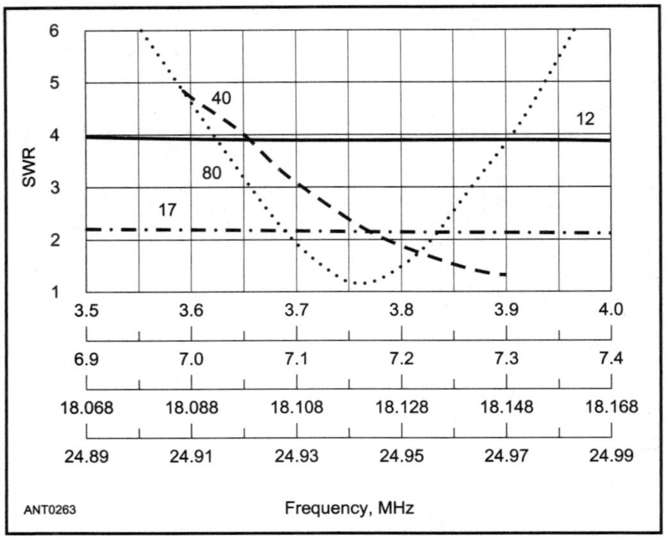

Figure 10.33 — Measured SWR curves for an 80, 40, 17 and 12 meter antenna, installed as an inverted V with 40-ft apex and 120° included angle between legs.

15 meters. On 15 meters, the stub capacitive reactance combines with the inductive reactance of the outer segment of the antenna to produce a resonant rise that raises the antenna input resistance to about 220 Ω, higher than that of the usual 3⁄2-wavelength dipole. An antenna tuner may be required on this band to keep a solid-state final output stage happy under these load conditions.

Figure 10.33 shows the SWR curves of the 80, 40, 17 and 12 meter antenna. Notice the excellent 80 meter performance with a nearly unity minimum SWR in the middle of the band. The performance approaches that of a full-size 80 meter wire dipole. The short stubs and the low-inductance traps shorten the antenna somewhat on 80 meters. Also observe the good 17 meter performance, with the SWR being only a little above 2:1 across the band.

But notice the 12 meter SWR curve of this antenna, which shows 4:1 SWR across the band. The antenna input resistance approaches 300 Ω on this band because the capacitive reactance of the stubs combines with the inductive reactance of the outer antenna segments to give resonant rises in impedance. These are reflected back to the input terminals. These stub-induced resonant impedance rises are similar to those on the other antenna on 15 meters, but are even more pronounced.

High SWR in coaxial cables longer than about 100 feet can lead to high feed line losses as shown in the **Transmission Lines** chapter. If you plan on operating this antenna with an SWR of greater than 3:1, make sure the amount of feed line loss is acceptable.

High voltages in the feed line should not cause too much concern. Even if the SWR is as high as 9:1 *no destructively high voltages will exist on the transmission line*. Recall that transmission-line voltages increase as the square root of the SWR in the line. Thus, 1 kW of RF power in 75-Ω line corresponds to 274 V line voltage for a 1:1 SWR. Raising the SWR to 9:1 merely triples the maximum voltage that the line must withstand to 822 V. This voltage is well below the 3700-V rating of RG-11, or the 1700-V rating of RG-59, the two most popular 75-Ω coax lines. Voltage breakdown in the traps is also very unlikely. As will be pointed out later, the operating power levels of these antennas are limited by RF power dissipation in the traps, not trap voltage breakdown or feed line SWR.

Trap Losses and Power Rating

Table 10.1 presents the results of trap Q measurements and extrapolation by a two-frequency method to higher frequencies above resonance. W8NX employed a Boonton Q meter for the measurements. Extrapolation to higher-frequency bands assumes that trap resistance losses rise with skin effect according to the square root of frequency, and that trap dielectric loses rise directly with frequency. Systematic measurement errors are not increased by frequency extrapolation. However, random measurement errors increase in magnitude with upward frequency extrapolation. Results are believed to be accurate within 4% on 80 and 40 meters, but only within 10 to 15% at 10 meters. Trap Q is shown at both the high- and low-impedance trap terminals. The Q at the low-impedance output terminals is 15 to 20% lower than the Q at the high-impedance output terminals.

W8NX computer-analyzed trap losses for both antennas in free space. Antenna-input resistances at resonance were first calculated, assuming lossless, infinite-Q traps. They were again calculated using the Q values in Table 10.1. The radiation efficiencies were also converted into equivalent trap losses in decibels. **Table 10.2** summarizes the trap-loss analysis for the 80, 40, 20, 15 and 10 meter antenna and **Table 10.3** for the 80, 40, 17 and 12 meter antenna.

The loss analysis shows radiation efficiencies of 90% or more for both antennas on all bands except for the 80, 40, 20,

Table 10.1
Trap Q

Frequency (MHz)	3.8	7.15	14.18	18.1	21.3	24.9	28.6
High Z out (Ω)	101	124	139	165	73	179	186
Low Z out (Ω)	83	103	125	137	44	149	155

Table 10.2
Trap Loss Analysis: 80, 40, 20, 15, 10 meter Antenna

Frequency (MHz)	3.8	7.15	14.18	21.3	28.6
Radiation Efficiency (%)	96.4	70.8	99.4	99.9	100.0
Trap Losses (dB)	0.16	1.5	0.02	0.01	0.003

Table 10.3
Trap Loss Analysis: 80, 40, 17, 12 meter Antenna

Frequency (MHz)	3.8	7.15	18.1	24.9
Radiation Efficiency (%)	89.5	90.5	99.3	99.8
Trap Losses (dB)	0.5	0.4	0.03	0.006

15 and 10 meter antenna when used on 40 meters. Here, the radiation efficiency falls to 70.8%. A 1-kW power level at 90% radiation efficiency corresponds to 50-W dissipation per trap. In W8NX's experience, this is the trap's survival limit for extended key-down operation. SSB power levels of 1 kW PEP would dissipate 25 W or less in each trap. This is well within the dissipation capability of the traps.

When the 80, 40, 20, 15 and 10 meter antenna is operated on 40 meters, the radiation efficiency of 70.8% corresponds to a dissipation of 146 W in each trap when 1 kW is delivered to the antenna. This is sure to burn out the traps — even if sustained for only a short time. Thus, the power should be limited to less than 300 W when this antenna is operated on 40 meters under prolonged key-down conditions such as RTTY. A 50% CW duty cycle would correspond to a 600-W power limit for normal 40 meter CW operation. Likewise, a 50% duty cycle for 40 meter SSB corresponds to a 600-W PEP power limit for the antenna.

The author knows of no analysis where the burnout wattage rating of traps has been rigorously determined. Operating experience seems to be the best way to determine trap burn-out ratings. In his own experience with these antennas, he's had no traps burn out, even though he operated the 80, 40, 20, 15 and 10 meter antenna on the critical 40 meter band using his AL-80A linear amplifier at the 600-W PEP output level. He did not make a continuous, key-down, CW operating test at full power purposely trying to destroy the traps!

Some hams may suggest using a different type of coaxial cable for the traps. The dc resistance of 40.7 Ω per 1000 feet of RG-59 coax seems rather high. However, W8NX has found no coax other than RG-59 that has the necessary inductance-to-capacitance ratio to create the trap characteristic reactance required for the 80, 40, 20, 15 and 10 meter antenna. Conventional traps with wide-spaced, open-air inductors and appropriate fixed-value capacitors could be substituted for the coax traps, but the convenience, weatherproof configuration and ease of fabrication of coaxial-cable traps is hard to beat.

10.3 THE TERMINATED FOLDED DIPOLE

Originally described in June 1949 *QST* by G. L. Countryman, W3HH, the terminated folded dipole (TFD) is often used by amateurs as a wide-band antenna that operates over the HF range without a tuner. (A tilted version is abbreviated as the T2FD. The original article is included with this book's downloadable supplemental information.) The antenna, shown in **Figure 10.34** looks like a folded dipole but acts as a traveling wave antenna. It is generally useful

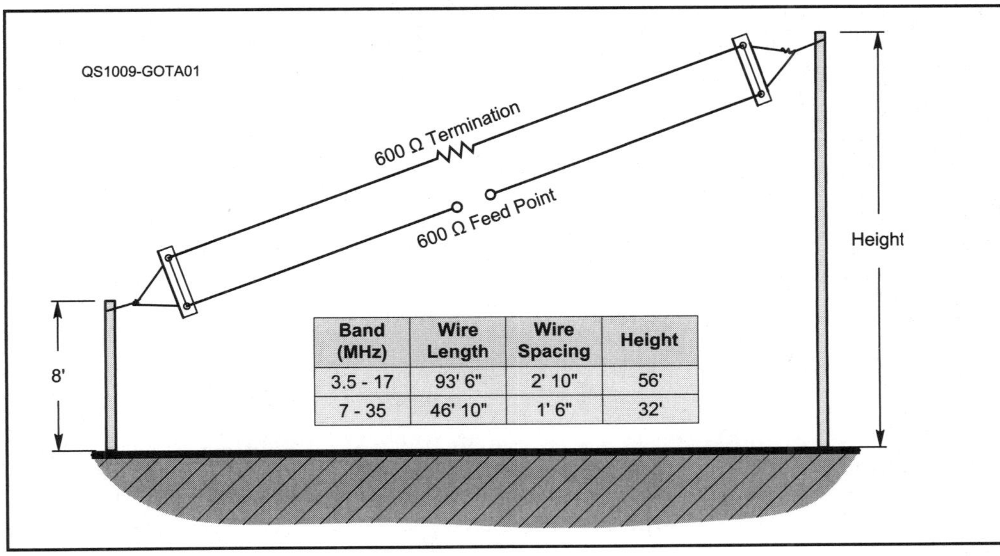

Band (MHz)	Wire Length	Wire Spacing	Height
3.5 - 17	93' 6"	2' 10"	56'
7 - 35	46' 10"	1' 6"	32'

Figure 10.34 — The terminated folded dipole adds a 600-Ω terminating resistor to smooth out the feed point impedance variations over a wide range. The terminating resistor dissipates some of the input power in order to provide a consistent match.

over a 5:1 or 6:1 range with its lower frequency, f_L, used to calculate dimensions.

Two common approximations of the antenna dimensions are used:

Wide-Long:
Length (feet) = 300/f_L (MHz)
Separation (feet) = 10/f_L (MHz) (2)

and

Narrow-Short:
Length (feet) = 200/f_L (MHz)
Separation (feet) = 0.5/f_L (MHz) (3)

The Narrow-Short configuration is closest to commercial models sold today. Figure 10.34 also provides two sets of dimensions for different HF frequency ranges.

The termination resistor directly opposite the feed point acts as a *swamping load* to dampen swings in feed point impedance, particularly toward the lower end of the antenna's range. A value of around 600 Ω is required and must be non-inductive. (The resistance value can vary ±10% and still obtain good results.) The resistor can dissipate an appreciable fraction of the applied power and is usually rated at ⅓ of the transmitter output power. If a single resistor is not available, strings of resistors in series-parallel combinations will work.

The feed point resistance of the antenna requires a 12:1 matching transformer to provide a match to 50-Ω coaxial cable. Designs using an 800-Ω terminating resistor and 16:1 transformer also work well.

The antenna wire chosen must be capable of supporting the antenna's weight, which with the balun and terminating resistor, plus any spacers used to keep the antenna wires separated, can be significantly higher than for a single-wire dipole. A common choice is #12 AWG hard-drawn copper. An analysis by L.B. Cebik, W4RNL, of models of the antennas provides an alternate set of guidelines for the terminating resistor (see Bibliography).

As the operating frequency approaches the lower end of the antenna's range, efficiency and gain will begin to fall off rapidly. An analysis of the TFD by Belrose (see Bibliography) shows that the antenna's gain is approximately 0 dBi over most of its range (see **Figure 10.35A**) and is significantly less effective than a dipole with a tuner by as much as 10 dB (see Figure 10.35B).

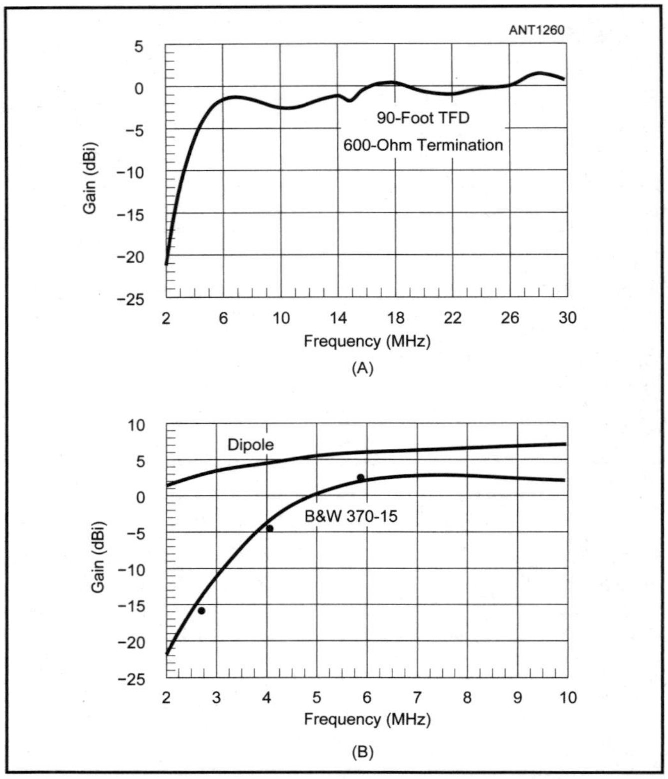

Figure 10.35 — At A, theoretical gain (in dBi) versus frequency for a 90-foot terminated folded dipole (600-Ω termination) in free space. At B, theoretical gain of a dipole and a 90-foot TFD antenna over poor ground (conductivity of 1 mS/m), and measured NVIS gain (the solid circles) for the B&W 370-15 antenna. All antennas were installed

However, at heights of 50 feet or less, the antenna will provide a relatively high-angle, nearly omnidirectional pattern useful for NVIS-like coverage. Tilting the antenna, as described in the original article by W3HH, enhances high-angle radiation even further. This is the TFD's most common application, as a regional coverage antenna over a wide range of HF when only a single, fixed antenna without tuners can be installed, such as for an EOC or station providing temporary public service or disaster relief communications.

10.4 MULTIBAND VERTICAL ANTENNAS

There are two basic types of vertical antennas; either type can be used in multiband configurations. The first is the ground-mounted vertical and the second, the ground plane. These antennas are described in detail in the chapter **Dipoles and Monopoles**.

The efficiency of any ground-mounted vertical depends a great deal on near-field earth losses. As pointed out in the chapter **Effects of Ground**, these near-field losses can be reduced or eliminated with an adequate radial system. Considerable experimentation has been conducted on this subject by Jerry Sevick, W2FMI, and several important results were obtained. It was determined that a radial system consisting of 40 to 50 radials, 0.2 λ long, would reduce the earth losses to about 2 Ω when a λ/4 radiator was being used. These radials should be on the earth's surface, or if buried, placed not more than an inch or so below ground. Otherwise, the RF current would have to travel through the lossy earth before reaching the radials. In a multiband vertical system, the radials should be 0.2 λ long for the lowest band, that is, 55 feet long for 3.5-MHz operation. Any wire size may be used for the radials. The radials should fan out in a circle, radiating from the base of the antenna. A metal plate, such as a piece of sheet copper, can be used at the center connection. Sevick also contributed a great deal of information about short vertical that are much less than λ/4. This subject is covered in the **Single-Band MF and HF Antennas** chapter.

The other common type of vertical is the ground-plane antenna. Normally, this antenna is mounted above ground with the radials fanning out from the base of the antenna. The vertical portion of the antenna is usually an electrical λ/4, as is each of the radials. In this type of antenna, the system of radials acts somewhat like an RF choke, to prevent RF currents from flowing in the supporting structure, so the number of radials is not as important a factor as it is with a ground-mounted vertical system. From a practical standpoint, the customary number of radials is four or five. In a multiband configuration, λ/4 radials are required for each band of operation with the ground-plane antenna.

This is not so with the ground-mounted vertical antenna, where the ground plane is relied upon to provide an image of the radiating section. Note that even quarter-wave-long radials are greatly detuned by their proximity to ground — radial resonance is not necessary or even possible. In the ground-mounted case, so long as the ground-screen radials are approximately 0.2 λ long at the lowest frequency, the length will be more than adequate for the higher frequency bands.

10.4.1 FULL-SIZE VERTICAL ANTENNAS

A vertical antenna should not be longer than about ¾ λ at the highest frequency to be used, however, if low-angle radiation is wanted. You can see why from reviewing the radiation patterns for dipoles in the chapter **Dipoles and Monopoles**. As the antenna lengthens, the pattern breaks up into lobes that are at high elevation angles for a vertical antenna.

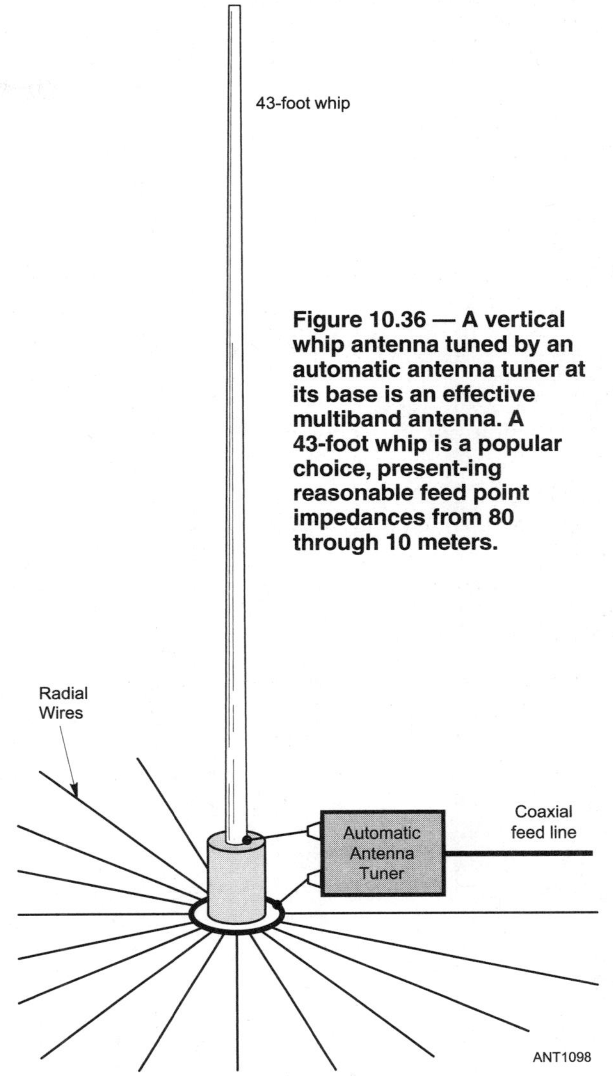

Figure 10.36 — A vertical whip antenna tuned by an automatic antenna tuner at its base is an effective multiband antenna. A 43-foot whip is a popular choice, present-ing reasonable feed point impedances from 80 through 10 meters.

Nevertheless, an antenna that is λ/4 on the lower frequency of operation can still be useful over a 3:1 frequency range or even more if the high-angle radiation can be tolerated. For example, an 80 meter λ/4 vertical around 66 feet high is useful through the 30 meter band and a 25-foot vertical would be useful from about 10 MHz through the 28 MHz band.

The 43-foot vertical monopole shown in **Figure 10.36** has become increasingly popular. While not resonant on any of the amateur bands except 60 meters where it approximates a quarter-wave vertical, with a series inductor at the feed point it has an easily-matched base impedance and is an efficient radiator. In fact, it is very similar to an Extended Double Zepp (EDZ) for 20 meters which is 86 feet long. (See the **Broadside and End-Fire Arrays** chapter for more information on the EDZ.) If the EDZ is cut in half and placed over a ground plane, it becomes a ⅝-λ vertical for 20 meters and the 43-foot monopole results.

While this antenna is not resonant on 20 meters, and by itself has a high SWR, its base impedance is largely capacitive reactance. Adding a simple inductor in series (about 320 Ω of inductive reactance, or 3.6 μH at 14.15 MHz) will reduce SWR to below 2:1. On other bands, the SWR is more extreme.

There are basically two options to feed the antenna on other bands:

• Install a manual or automatic antenna tuner at the antenna base, with switchable loading coils for some bands if needed, and use that arrangement to provide a match to 50 Ω coax. Then run the matched coax to the station with low losses.

• Accept the mismatch and feed mismatched coax to an antenna tuner at the station end. While this is simple, the high SWR creates extra loss in the feed line as explained in the **Transmission Line System Techniques** chapter.

The antenna can also be used on 80 and 160 meters although the high feed point impedance requires special matching techniques. Phil Salas, AD5X, and Steve Masticola, WX2S have designed tunable matching networks for these bands that make the vertical work on all of the HF bands plus the MF band of 160 meters (see Bibliography).

One caveat about this vertical is that on the higher-frequency bands, the radiation pattern breaks up into lobes which radiate a lot of signal at high angles that are not necessarily effective for DX. On 60 through 20 meters, the elevation pattern is similar to that in **Figure 10.37A**. On higher frequency bands, the pattern begins to look more like that in Figure 10.37B. This may be perfectly acceptable, and the antenna's minimal visual impact makes it a feasible choice in many circumstances where a trap vertical or horizontally polarized antenna might not be possible.

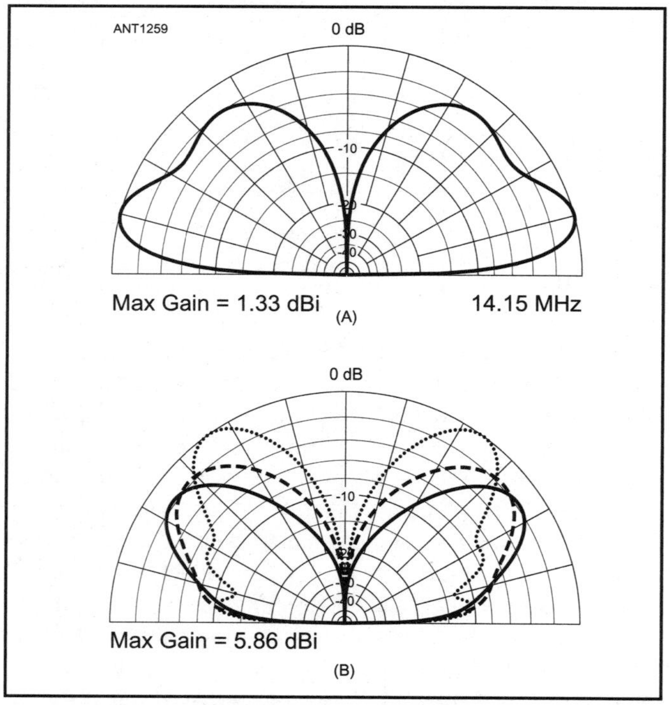

Figure 10.37 — *EZNEC* elevation pattern of ⅝-wavelength ground-mounted monopole on 20 meters over typical ground (A). At B, the same antenna on 17 meters (solid line), 15 meters (dashed line), and 10 meters (dotted line).

10.4.2 TRAP VERTICALS

The trap principle described in Figure 10.23 for center-fed dipoles also can be used for vertical antennas. There are two principal differences. Only one half of the dipole is used, the ground connection taking the place of the missing half, and the feed point impedance is one half the feed point impedance of a dipole. Thus it is in the vicinity of 30 Ω (plus the ground-connection resistance), so 52-Ω cable should be used since it is the commonly available type that comes closest to matching.

Most amateurs prefer to purchase multiband trap verticals because of the mechanical complexities and requirements to be self-supporting. Commercial multiband trap verticals such as the Hustler 4/5/6BTV series and the Hy-Gain AVQ series have been widely used for many years. The Butternut HF-series is another time-tested design with a different approach than traps to multiband design. All of these antenna families provide effective performance as ground-mounted antennas when used with a good radial system.

Verticals advertised as "ground-independent" are intended to be mounted above ground. Models such as the Cushcraft R9 and R6000 and the Hy-Gain AV-680 are end-fed systems that are electrically longer than λ/4 at the frequency of operation. They have a high feed point impedance that is reduced to 50 Ω with a matching network at the base of the antenna. These are particularly useful antennas for temporary stations and when restrictions prevent the installation of ground systems.

Amateurs interested in designing their own trap vertical may find a dual-band antenna a great way to experiment. Antenna modeling software and trap design utilities can be used to capture the antenna's basic elements. Once built, some adjustment fine-tunes the design. For example, Steve Sutterer, AKØM, started with W1JR's ⅜-wavelength vertical design (see the **Single-Band MF and HF Antennas** chapter) and inserted a 20 meter coax trap about 25 feet up from the feed point. Steve designed the trap using VE6YP's online utility at **www.qsl.net/ve6yp/CoaxTrap.html**. Another 25 feet or so of wire above the trap and an auto-tuner at the base resulted in a 50-foot high, tree-supported, wire vertical that works quite well on 80, 40, 30, and 20 meters. If you choose to build this antenna, its final dimensions will depend on the materials you use and the environment in which it is operated — expect to make some adjustments along the way. This kind of simple antenna project is a great way to learn about antenna and trap design.

10.4.3 A FIVE-BAND VERTICAL DIPOLE

This antenna, shown in **Figure 10.38**, is a short version of the 135-foot dipole described earlier, except that it is oriented vertically. The antenna gives good performance on the HF bands from 20 through 10 meters and can be used at

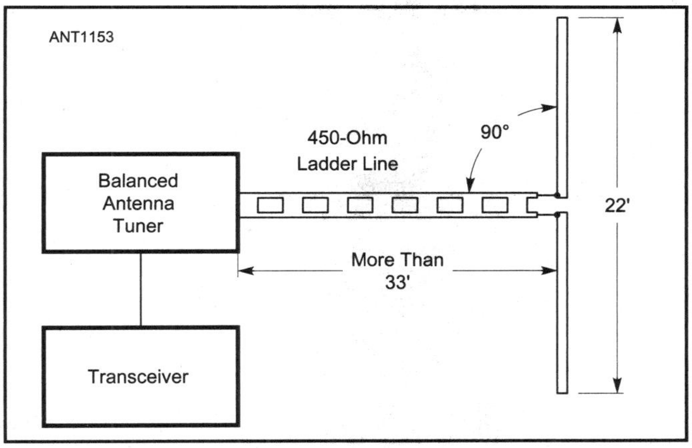

Figure 10.38 — A five-band vertical dipole that covers 20, 17, 15, 12, and 10 meters. The antenna is fed with 450-Ω window line and requires a balanced antenna tuner.

a fixed station or for portable or temporary operation. Like the longer horizontal "flat-top," it is fed with 450-Ω window line and a balanced tuner. The antenna can be installed at an angle as long as the feed line is oriented symmetrically at right angles to the antenna. Feed line lengths of more than 33 feet are recommended to help minimize RF common-mode current on the feed line from coupling to the tuner enclosure.

10.4.4 A FAN VERTICAL

Just like the fan dipole described earlier, the fan vertical shown in **Figure 10.39** connects multiple elements to a single feed point. In the case of the fan vertical, each element is λ/4 long instead of λ/2 and a set of radials is used to provide a ground plane. The same cautions apply regarding interaction between the verticals as for the fan dipoles. Getting a full set tuned on each band can be frustrating! Nevertheless, whether used for a fixed station or for portable operation, being able to use multiple bands with a single feed line is very convenient.

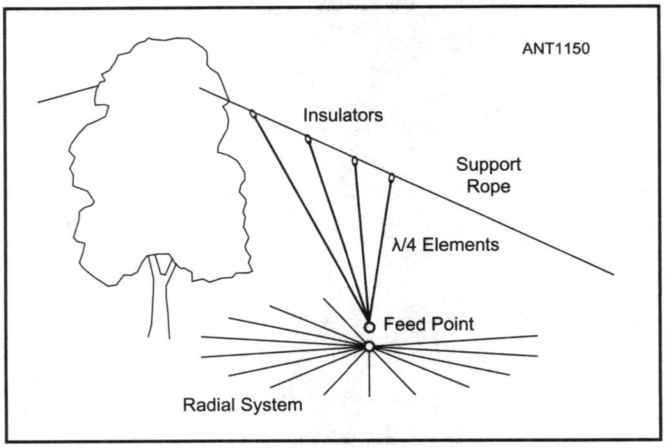

Figure 10.39 — A set of fan verticals. The support must be high enough to clear λ/4 on the lowest frequency band used. At higher frequencies, the shorter elements can be held up with ropes to the support rope as necessary. Radials are required to provide a ground plane.

A similar design was described by Mark Weaver, WB3BJF that places the vertical wires near a tree trunk with radials surrounding the base (see Bibliography).

10.4.5 A DUAL-BAND VERTICAL FOR 80 AND 160

When stationed on Guam, Dave Mueller, N2NL, needed a temporary vertical antenna for contesting on 80 and 160 meters but had only one tall tree to act as a vertical support. Based on the idea of a fan vertical, he used 450-Ω window line as his pair of radiators as shown in **Figure 10.40**.

One of the window line conductors is tuned as an inverted L on 80 meters. Extra wire is then attached to the end of one of the window line conductors and to the point at which the inverted L makes the right-angle bend at the top. These form top loading wires for a 160 meter T or "flat-top" vertical. Thus, one conductor of the window line is made into the inverted L and the other conductor is the top-loaded vertical.

At the feed point, both of the window line conductors are shorted together and connected to the coax center conductor. A set of ground radials is required and connected to the shield of the coax. Tune the 80 meter L first, then adjust the length of the 160 meter top loading wire connected at the bend of the window line — this results in the least interaction during tuning. You will probably have to adjust each of the conductor lengths to get the resonant point of the system to the desired frequencies.

To raise the base impedance of the vertical, a shunt inductor can be used across the feed point. If you have the equipment, measure the feed point impedance to determine the resistive component. The instructions for hairpin matching in the chapter on **Transmission Line System Techniques** provide a chart of required inductive reactances.

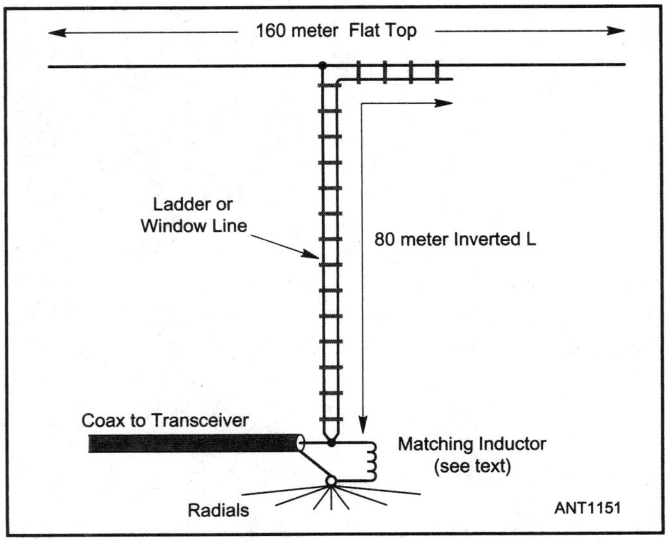

Figure 10.40 — A dual-band vertical for 80 and 160 meters constructed by N2NL/KH2. 450-Ω window line is used to construct an 80 meter inverted L and top loading wires added to create a 160 meter T vertical. A shunt inductor across the base is used to raise the feed point impedance to 50 Ω as described in the text.

Another effective technique is to wind a coil with about 100 Ω of reactance (about 9 µH at 1.8 MHz) and adjust a tap on the coil until a match is obtained. A relay or manual switch can be used to change the tap for different bands or switch the coil in and out of circuit.

10.4.6 HF DISCONE ANTENNAS

The name "discone" is a contraction of the words "disc" and "cone." Although people often describe a discone by its design-center frequency (for example, a "20 meter discone"), discones work very well over a wide frequency range, as much as several octaves. The discone is very popular as a receive antenna for VHF/UHF use, as well, with several commercial versions available along with numerous buildable designs.

The antenna produces a vertically polarized signal at a low-elevation angle and it presents a good match for 50-Ω coax over its operating range. Two excellent articles by Belrose and Stearns (see Bibliography) describe the discone's operation and design. This chapter's downloadable supplemental information includes additional information on the discone and a pair of designs for HF use.

The dimensions of a discone, shown in **Figure 10.41,** are determined by the range of frequencies over which it is to be used. The cone angle, ϕ, is typically around 60° and the height of the discone, L_V, is approximately $\lambda/4$ at the lowest frequency of use. The disc diameter, D, is approximately 0.7 of the cone's maximum width at the bottom.

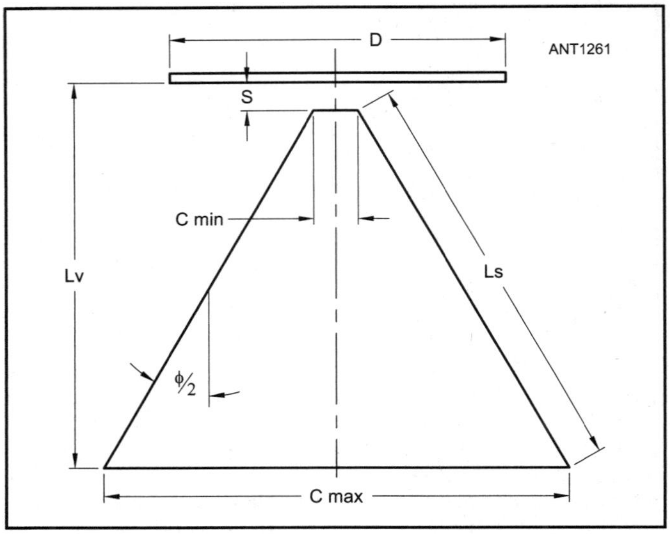

Figure 10.41 — A cross-section sketch of the discone antenna showing the parameters used for design.

One advantage of the discone is that its maximum current area is near the top of the antenna, where it can radiate away from ground clutter, reducing losses. The cone-like skirt of the discone radiates the signal — radiation from the disc on top is minimal. This is because the currents flowing in the skirt wires essentially all go in the same direction, while the currents in the disc elements oppose each other and cancel out.

10.5 THE COUPLED-RESONATOR DIPOLE

A variation of the open-sleeve system above is the coupled-resonator system described by Gary Breed, K9AY, in an article in *The ARRL Antenna Compendium, Vol 5*, entitled "The Coupled-Resonator Principle: A Flexible Method for Multiband Antennas." The following is condensed from that article.

In 1995, *QST* published two antenna designs that use an interesting technique to get multiband coverage in one antenna. Rudy Severns, N6LF, described a wideband 80 and 75 meter dipole using this technique (see the **Single Band MF and HF Antennas** chapter), and Robert Wilson, AL7KK, showed us how to make a three-band vertical. Both of these antennas achieve multi-frequency operation by placing resonant conductors very close to a driven dipole or vertical — with no physical connection.

10.5.1 THE COUPLED-RESONATOR PRINCIPLE

As we all know, nearby conductors can interact with an antenna. Our dipoles, verticals and beams can be affected by nearby power lines, rain gutters, guy wires and other metallic materials. The antennas designed by Severns and Wilson use this interaction intentionally, to combine the resonances of several conductors at a single feed point. While other names have been used, I call the behavior that makes these antennas work the coupled-resonator (C-R) principle.

Take a look at **Figure 10.42**, which illustrates the general idea. Each figure shows the SWR at the feed point of a dipole, over a range of frequencies. When this dipole is all alone, it will have a very low SWR at its half-wave resonant frequency (Figure 10.42A). Next, if we take another wire or tubing conductor and start bringing it close to the dipole, we will see a "bump" in the dipole's SWR at the resonant frequency of this new wire. See Figure 10.42B. We are beginning to the see the effects of interaction between the two conductors. As we bring this new conductor closer, we reach a point where the SWR "bump" has grown to a very deep dip — a low SWR. We now have a good match at both the original dipole's resonant frequency and the frequency of the new conductor, as illustrated in Figure 10.42C.

We can repeat this process for several more conductors at other frequencies to get a dipole with three, four, five, six, or more resonant frequencies. The principle also applies to

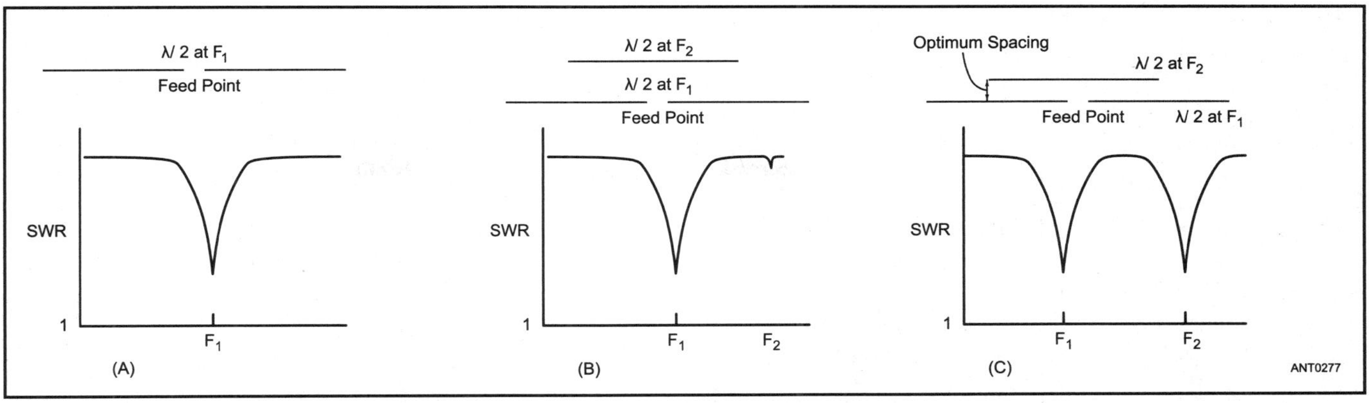

Figure 10.42 — At A, the SWR of a dipole over a wide frequency range. At B, a nearby conductor is just close enough to interact with the dipole. At C, when the second conductor is at the optimum spacing, the combination is matched at both frequencies.

verticals, so any reference to a dipole can be considered to be valid for a vertical, as well.

We can write a definition of the C-R principle this way: *Given a dipole (or vertical) at one frequency and an additional conductor resonant at another frequency, there is an optimum distance between them that results in the resonance of the additional conductor being imposed upon the original dipole, resulting in a low SWR at both resonant frequencies.*

Some History

In the late 1940s, the coaxial sleeve antenna was developed (**Figure 10.43**), covering two frequencies by surrounding a dipole or monopole with a cylindrical tube resonant at the higher of the desired frequencies. In the 1950s, Gonset briefly marketed a two-band antenna based on this design. Other experimenters soon determined that two conductors at the second frequency, placed on either side of the main dipole or monopole, would make a skeleton representation of a cylinder (Figure 10.43B). This is called the *open-sleeve antenna*. Later on, a few antenna developers finally figured out that these extra conductors did not need to be added in pairs, and that a single conductor at each frequency could add the extra resonances (Figure 10.43C). This is the method used by several manufacturers to offer multiband Yagis that only require a single feed line.

This is a perfect example of how science works. A specific idea is discovered, with later developments leading to an underlying general principle. The original coaxial-sleeve configuration is the most specific, being limited to two frequencies and requiring a particular construction method. The open-sleeve antenna is an intermediate step, showing that the sleeve idea is not limited to one configuration.

Finally, we have the coupled-resonator concept, which is the general principle, applicable in many different antenna configurations, for many different frequency combinations. Severns's antenna uses it with a folded dipole, and Wilson uses it with a main vertical that is off-center fed. The author, K9AY used it with conventional dipoles and quarter-wave verticals. Other designers have used the principle more subtly, like putting the first director in a Yagi very close to the driven element, broadening the SWR bandwidth the same way Severns's design does with a dipole.

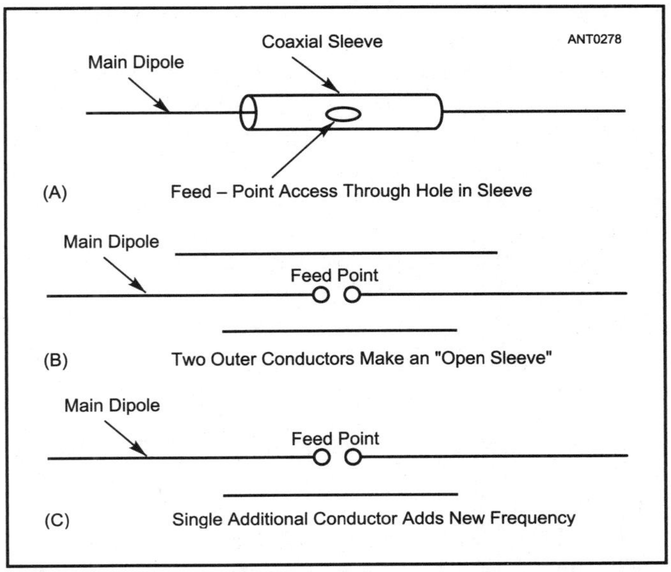

Figure 10.43 — Evolution of coupled-resonator antennas: At A, the *coaxial-sleeve* dipole; at B, the *open-sleeve* dipole; and at C, a *coupled-resonator* dipole, the most universal configuration.

In the past, most open-sleeve or multiple-open-sleeve antennas built with this technique have also been called *open-sleeve* (or *multiple-open-sleeve*) antennas, a term taken from the history of their development. However, the term *sleeve* implies that one conductor must surround another. This is not really a physical or electrical description of the antenna's operation, therefore, K9AY suggests using the term *coupled-resonator*, which is the most accurate description of the general principle.

A Little Math

The interaction that makes the C-R principle work is not random. It behaves in a predictable, regular manner. K9AY derived an equation that shows the relationship between the driven element and the additional resonators for ordinary dipoles and verticals:

$$\frac{\log_{10} d}{\log_{10}(D/4)} = 0.54 \qquad (4)$$

where

d = distance between conductors, measured in wavelengths at the frequency of the chosen additional resonator

D = the diameter of the conductors, also in wavelengths at the frequency of the additional resonator.

Eq 4 assumes they are both the same diameter and that the feed point impedance at both frequencies is the same as a dipole in free space (72 Ω) or a quarter-wave monopole over perfect ground (36 Ω).

The equation only describes the impedance due to the additional resonator. The main dipole element is always part of the antenna, and it may have a fairly low impedance at the additional frequency. This is the case when the frequencies are close together, or when the main element is operating at its third harmonic. At these frequencies, the spacing distance must be adjusted so that the parallel combination of dipole and resonator results in the desired feed point impedance.

K9AY worked out two correction factors, one to cover a range of impedances and another for frequencies close together. These can be included in the basic equation, which is rearranged below to solve for the distance between the conductors:

$$d = 10^{0.54 \log_{10}(D/4)} \times \frac{Z_0 + 35.5}{109} \times \left[1 + e^{-[((((F_2/F_1)-1.1)\times 11.3)+0.1)]}\right] \qquad (5)$$

where

d and D are the same as in Eq 4 above.

Z_0 = the desired feed point impedance at the frequency of the additional resonator (between 20 and 120 Ω). For a vertical, multiply the desired impedance by two to get Z_0. If you want a 50-Ω feed, use 100 Ω for Z_0.

F_1 = the resonant frequency of the main dipole or vertical.

F_2 = the resonant frequency of the additional conductor. The ratio F_2/F_1 is more than 1.1.

e = 2.7183, the base of natural logarithms.

Eq 5 does not directly allow for conductors of unequal diameters, but it can be used as a starting point if you use the diameter of the driven dipole or vertical element for D in the equation.

10.5.2 CHARACTERISTICS OF COUPLED-RESONATOR (C-R) ANTENNAS

Here's the important stuff — what's different about C-R antennas, what are they good for and what are their drawbacks? The key points are:

- Multiband operation without traps, stubs or tuners
- Flexible impedance matching at each frequency

C-R Element Spacing

K9AY's Eq 5 presented in the text does indeed yield a good "first-cut" value for the spacing between coupled-resonator elements. **Figure 10.A** shows the spacing, in inches, plotted against the ratio of frequencies, for two coupled resonator elements with different diameters, again expressed in inches. This is for an upper frequency of 28.4 MHz. Beyond a frequency ratio of about 1.5:1 (28.4:18.1 MHz), the spacing flattens out to a fixed distance between elements for each element diameter. For example, if ½-inch elements are used at 28.4 and 18.1 MHz, the spacing between the elements is about 3.75 inches.

EZNEC verifies Eq 5's computations. Note that a large number of segments are necessary for each element when they are closely spaced from each other, and the segments on the elements must be closely aligned with each other. Be sure to run the Average Gain test, as well as Segmentation tests. The modeler should also be aware that if mutually coupled resonators are placed along a horizontal boom (as they would be on multiband Yagis using coupled resonators), the higher-frequency elements will act like retrograde directors, producing some gain (or lack of gain, depending on the azimuth being investigated).

For example, in the *EZNEC* file **K9AY C-R 28-21-14 MHz 1 In.EZ**, using 1-inch diameter elements spaced 6 inches apart, if the 28-MHz element is placed 6 inches behind the 14-MHz driven element (with the 21-MHz element placed 6 inches ahead), on 28 MHz the system will have a F/B of 2.6 dB, favoring the rearward direction. On 21 MHz, the system will exhibit a F/B of 1.6 dB, favoring the forward direction. Of course, there are systems where gain and F/B due to the C-R configuration may be put to good use, such as the multiband Yagis mentioned above. However, if the elements are spaced above/below the 14-MHz driven element there is no distortion of the dipole patterns.

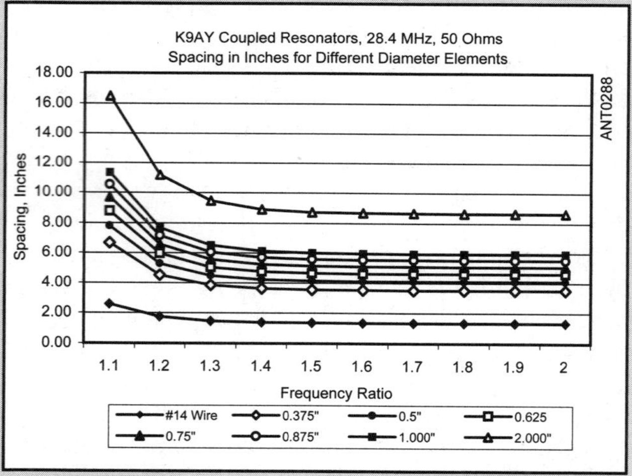

Figure 10.A — Graph of the spacing versus frequency ratio for two Coupled-Resonator elements at 28.4 MHz, for 50-Ω.

• Independent fine-tuning at each frequency (little interaction)
• Easily modeled using *MININEC* or *NEC*-based programs
• Pruning process same as a simple dipole
• Can accommodate many frequencies (seven or more)
• Virtually lossless coupling (high efficiency)
• Requires a separate wire or tubing conductor at each frequency
• Mechanical assembly requires a number of insulated supports
• Narrower bandwidth than equivalent dipole
• Capacitance requires slight lengthening of conductors

To begin with, the most obvious characteristic is that this principle can be used to add multiple resonant frequencies to an ordinary dipole or vertical, using additional conductors that are not physically connected. This gives us three variable factors: (1) the diameter of the conductor, (2) its length, and (3) its position relative to the main element.

Having the freedom to control these factors gives us the advantage of *flexibility*; we have a wide range of control over the impedance at each added frequency. Another advantage is that the behavior at each frequency is quite *independent*, once the basic design is in place. In other words, making fine-tuning adjustments at one frequency doesn't change the resonance or impedance at the other frequencies. A final advantage is *efficiency*. With conductors close together, and with a resonant target conductor, coupling is very efficient. Traps, stubs, and compensating networks found on other multiband antennas all introduce lossy reactive components.

There are two main disadvantages of C-R antennas. The first is the relative *complexity* of construction. Several conductors are needed, installed with some type of insulating spacers. Other multiband antennas have their complexities as well (such as traps that need to be mounted and tuned), but C-R antennas will usually be bulkier. The larger size generally means greater windload, which is a disadvantage to some hams.

The other significant disadvantage is *narrower bandwidth*, particularly at the highest of the operating frequencies. We can partially overcome this problem with large conductors that are naturally broad in bandwidth, and in some cases we might even use an extra conductor to put two resonances in one band. It is interesting to note that the pattern is opposite that of trap antennas. The C-R antenna gets narrower at the highest frequencies of operation, while trap antennas generally have narrowest bandwidth at their lowest frequencies.

There are two special situations that should be noted. First, when the antenna has a resonance near the frequency where the driven dipole is $3/2$ λ long ($3/4$ λ for a vertical), the dipole has a fairly low impedance. The spacing of the C-R element needs to be increased to raise its impedance so that the parallel combination of the main element and C-R element equals the desired impedance (usually 50 Ω). There is also significant antenna current in the part of the main dipole extending beyond the C-R section, contributing to the total radiation pattern. As a result, this particular arrangement radiates as three λ/2 sections in phase, and has about 3 dB gain and a narrower directional pattern compared to a dipole (**Figure 10.44**). This might be an advantage for antennas covering bands with a frequency ratio of about three, such as 3.5 and 10.1 MHz, 7 and 21 MHz, or 144 and 430 MHz.

The other special situation is when we want to add a new frequency very close to the resonant frequency of the main dipole. An antenna for 80 and 75 meters would be an example of this. Again, the driven dipole has a fairly low impedance at the new frequency. Add the fact that coupling is very strong between these similar conductors and we find that a wide spacing is required to make the antenna work. A dipole resonant at 3.5 MHz and another wire resonant at 3.8 MHz will need to be 3 or 4 feet apart, while a 3.5 MHz and 7 MHz combination might only need to be spaced 4 or 5 inches.

Another useful characteristic of C-R antennas is that they are easily and accurately modeled by computer programs based on either *MININEC* or *NEC*, as long as you stay within each program's limitations. For example, Severns points out that *MININEC* does not handle folded dipoles very well, and *NEC* modeling is required. With ease of computer modeling, a precise answer isn't needed for the design equation given above. An approximate solution will provide a starting point that can quickly be adjusted for optimum dimensions.

The added resonators have an effect on the lengths of all conductors, due to the capacitance between the conductors. Capacitance causes antennas to look electrically shorter, so each element needs to be about 1% or 2% longer than a simple dipole at the same frequency. As a rule of thumb,

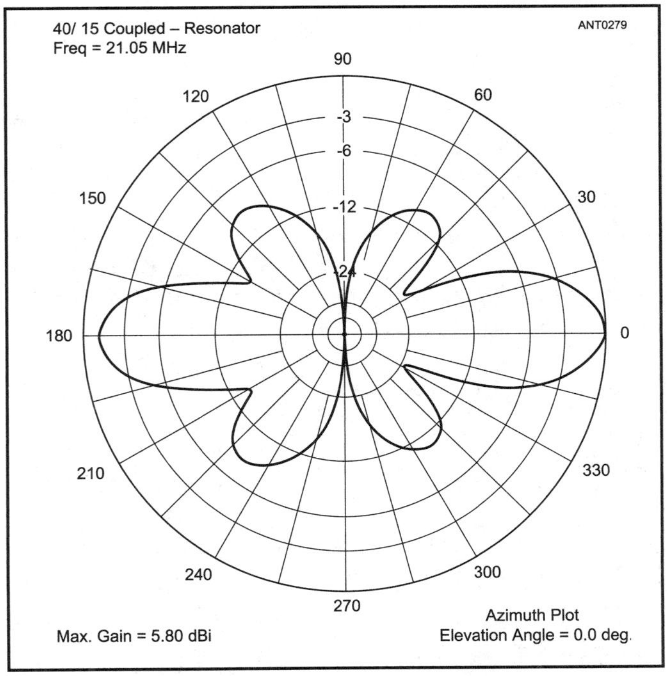

Figure 10.44 — Radiation pattern for the special case of a C-R antenna with the additional resonance at the third harmonic of the main dipole resonant frequency.

use 477/f (in feet) instead of the usual 468/f when calculating dipole length, and 239/f instead of 234/f for a λ/4 vertical.

Summary

The coupled-resonator principle is one more weapon in the antenna designer's arsenal. It's not the perfect method for all multiband antennas, but what the C-R principle offers is an alternative to traps and tuners, in exchange for using more wire or aluminum. Although a C-R antenna requires more complicated construction, its main attraction is in making a multiband antenna that can be built with no compromise in matching or efficiency.

10.5.3 A C-R DIPOLE FOR 30/17/12 METERS

To show how a C-R antenna is designed, let's build a dipole to cover 30, 17 and 12 meters. We'll use #12 AWG wire, which has a diameter of 0.08 inches, and the main dipole will be cut for the 10.1 MHz band. From the equation above, the spacing between the main dipole and the 18-MHz resonator should be 2.4 inches for 72 Ω, or 1.875 inches for 50 Ω. At 24.9 MHz, the spacing to the resonator for that band should be 2.0 inches for 72 Ω, or 1.62 inches for 50 Ω. Of course, this antenna will be installed over real ground, not in free space, so these spacing distances may not be exact. Plugging these numbers into your favorite antenna-modeling program will let you optimize the dimensions for installation at the height you choose.

For those of you who like to work with real antennas, not computer-generated ones, the predicted spacing is accurate enough to build an antenna with minimum trial-and-error. You should use a nice round number just larger than the calculated spacing for 50 Ω. For this antenna, K9AY decided that the right spacing for the desired height would be 2 inches for the 18 MHz resonator and 1.8 inches for the 24.9 MHz resonator. For simplicity of construction, he just used 2 inches for both, figuring that the worst he would get is a 1.2:1 SWR if the numbers were a little bit off. Like all dipoles, the impedance varies with height above ground, but the 2-inch spacing results in an excellent match on the two additional bands, at heights of more than 25 feet.

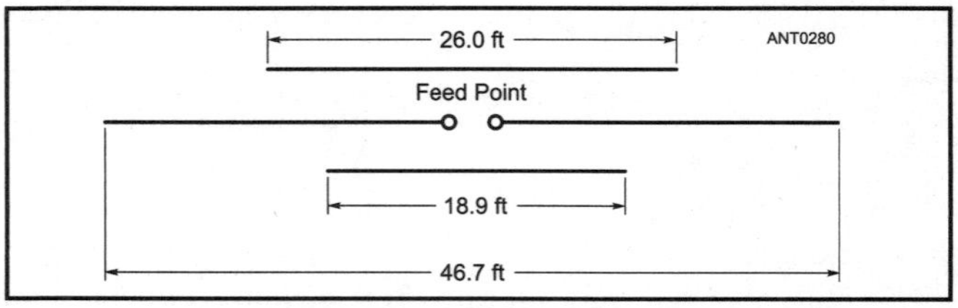

Figure 10.45 — Dimensions of a C-R dipole for the 30, 17 and 12 meter bands.

The final dimensions of the dipole for 10.1, 18.068 and 24.89 MHz are shown in **Figure 10.45**. These are the final pruned lengths for a straight dipole installed at a height of about 40 feet. If you put up the antenna as an inverted V, you will need each wire to be a bit longer. Pruning this type of antenna is just like a dipole — if it's resonant too low in frequency, it's too long and the appropriate wire needs to be shortened. So, you can cut the wires just a little long to start with and easily prune them to resonance.

A final note: if you want to duplicate this antenna design, remember that the 2-inch spacing is just for #12 AWG wire! The required spacing for a C-R antenna is related to the conductor diameter. This same antenna built with #14 AWG wire needs under 1½-inch spacing, while a 1-inch aluminum-tubing version requires about 7-inch spacing.

10.6 LOOP ANTENNAS

A loop antenna one wavelength in circumference on its fundamental frequency is a very effective antenna that is also very tolerant of changes in shape and orientation to fit available space and supports. Loops are effective at harmonics, as well. (Also see the **Loop Antennas** chapter for more information plus several design variations for full-sized quad and delta loops. *Low-Band DXing* by Devoldere (see Bibliography) has an extensive section on loop antennas, as well.

This section presents several examples of loop antennas optimized for use on the fundamental, expecting they can be used on multiple bands with the use of an antenna tuner. In general, these designs can be scaled to work on other bands by multiplying all dimensions by the ratio of the design frequency to the new frequency = f_{design} / f_{new}.

10.6.1 A VERTICALLY POLARIZED QUAD LOOP FOR 7 MHZ

This design is an effective but simple vertical 7 MHz antenna that has a theoretical gain of approximately 1 dB over a dipole. In feet, the overall length of a 1-λ loop is determined from the formula 1005/f (MHz). Hence, for operation at 7.125 MHz the overall wire length will be 141 feet.

Such a loop need not be square, as illustrated in **Figure 10.46**. It can be trapezoidal, rectangular, circular, or some distorted configuration in between those shapes. For best results, however, you should attempt to make the loop as square as possible. The more elongated and narrow the shape, the greater the cancellation of energy in the system, and the less effective it will be. In the extreme case, the antenna loses its identity as a loop and becomes a folded dipole.

You can feed the loop in the center of one of the vertical sides if you want vertical polarization. For horizontal polarization, you feed either of the horizontal sides at the center. Since optimum directivity occurs at right angles to the plane of the loop (or in more simple terms, broadside to the loop), you should hang the loop to radiate the maximum amount in some favored direction.

Figure 10.47A shows the azimuthal response at a takeoff angle of 15°, a typical angle for 40 meter DX, for vertical

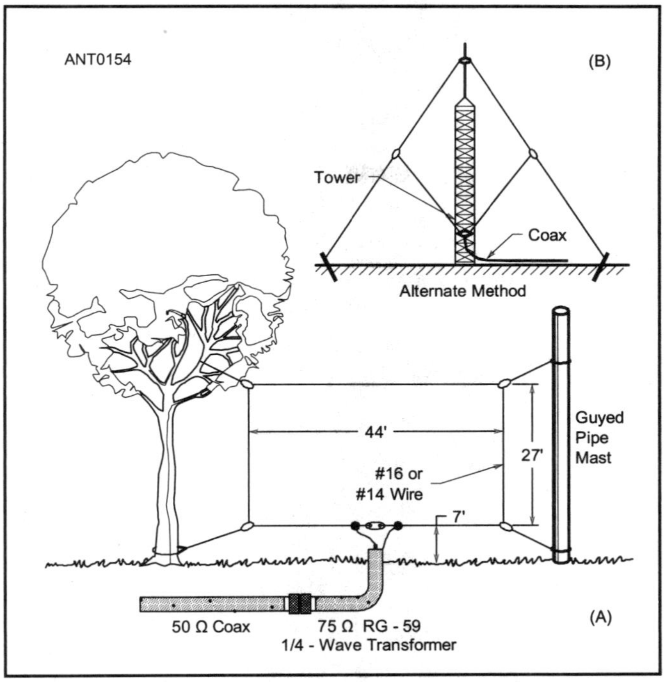

Figure 10.46 — At A, details of the rectangular full-wave loop. The dimensions given are for operation at 7.05 MHz. The height above ground was 7 feet in this instance, although improved performance should result if the builder can install the loop higher above ground without sacrificing length on the vertical sides. At B, illustration how a single supporting structure can be used to hold the loop in a diamond-shaped configuration. Feeding the diamond at the lower tip provides radiation in the horizontal plane. Feeding the system at either side will result in vertical polarization of the radiated signal.

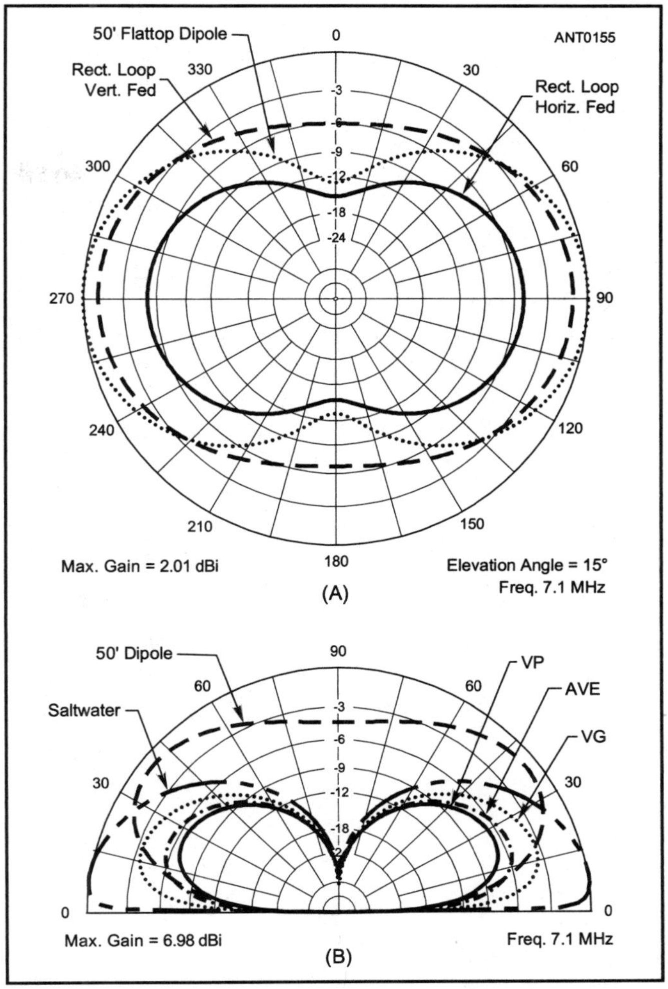

Figure 10.47 — At A, azimuthal plane responses for the vertically and horizontally polarized 7-MHz loop, compared to a flattop 50-foot high dipole, all at a takeoff angle of 15° for DX work. The solid line is for feeding the loop horizontally at the bottom; the dashed line is for feeding the loop vertically at a side, and the dotted line is for a simple flattop horizontal dipole at 50 feet in height. For DX work, the vertically polarized loop is an excellent performer.

and horizontal feed systems over ground with "average" conductivity and dielectric constant. Figure 10.47A includes, for reference, the response of a flattop dipole 50 feet high. For the low elevation angles that favor DX work, the optimal feed point is at the center of one of the vertical wires. Feeding the loop at one of the corners at the bottom gives a compromise result for both local and DX work. The actual impedance is roughly the same at each point: bottom horizontal center, corner or vertical side center.

This same loop antenna in Figure 10.46A fed vertically may be used on the 14 and 21 MHz bands, although its pattern will not be as good as that on its fundamental frequency and you will have to use an open-wire transmission line to feed the loop for multiband use. **Figure 10.48** shows the peak lobe of the loop 14 MHz, at a 45° angle to the plane of the loop, compared to the peak response for a simple half-wave 20 meter dipole, 30 feet high. The gain from a simple flattop dipole, mounted at 30 feet, will be superior to the loop operated on a harmonic frequency.

Just how you erect such a loop will depend on what is available in your backyard. Trees are always handy for supporting loop antennas. A disadvantage to the rectangular loop shown in Figure 10.46A is that two 34-foot high supports are needed, although in many instances a house may be

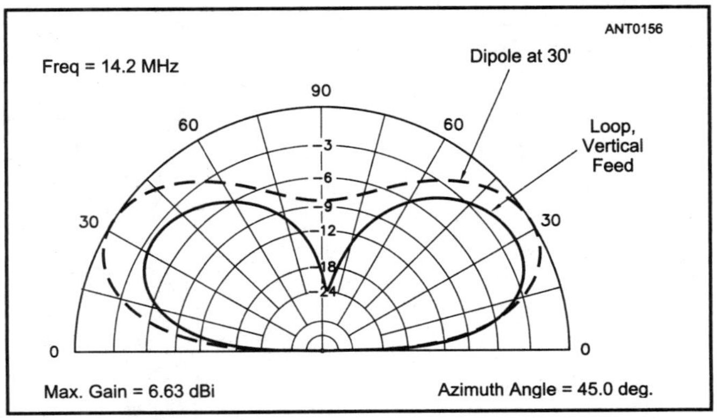

Figure 10.48 — Elevation-plane response of 7-MHz loop used on 14.2 MHz. This is for a feed point at the center of one of the two vertical wires. The dashed line is the response of a flattop 20-meter dipole at 30 feet in height for comparison.

high enough to serve as one of these supports. If you have a tower higher than about 50 feet, Figure 10.46B demonstrates how you can use it to support a diamond-shaped loop for 40 meters. The elevation and azimuthal responses are almost the same for either loop configuration, rectangular- or diamond-shaped.

On 40 meters, the length in feet of the matching transformer section, an electrical ¼ λ of 75-Ω coax cable, is 246 by the operating frequency in MHz, then multiplying that number by the velocity factor of the cable being used. Thus, for operation at 7.125 MHz, 246/7.125 MHz = 34.53 feet. If coax with solid polyethylene insulation is used, a velocity factor of 0.66 must be employed. Foam-polyethylene (FPE) coax has a velocity factor of 0.80. Assuming RG-59 is used, the length of the matching transformer becomes 34.53 (feet) × 0.66 = 22.79 feet, or 22 feet, 9½ inches.

10.6.2 A VERTICALLY POLARIZED DELTA LOOP FOR 14 MHZ

Two common methods of building a delta loop for the 14 MHz band are shown in **Figure 10.49**. (The design is from *Practical Wire Antennas* published by the RSGB.) Both radiate vertically-polarized signals and so ground quality will have an effect on the antenna's efficiency. The total length of

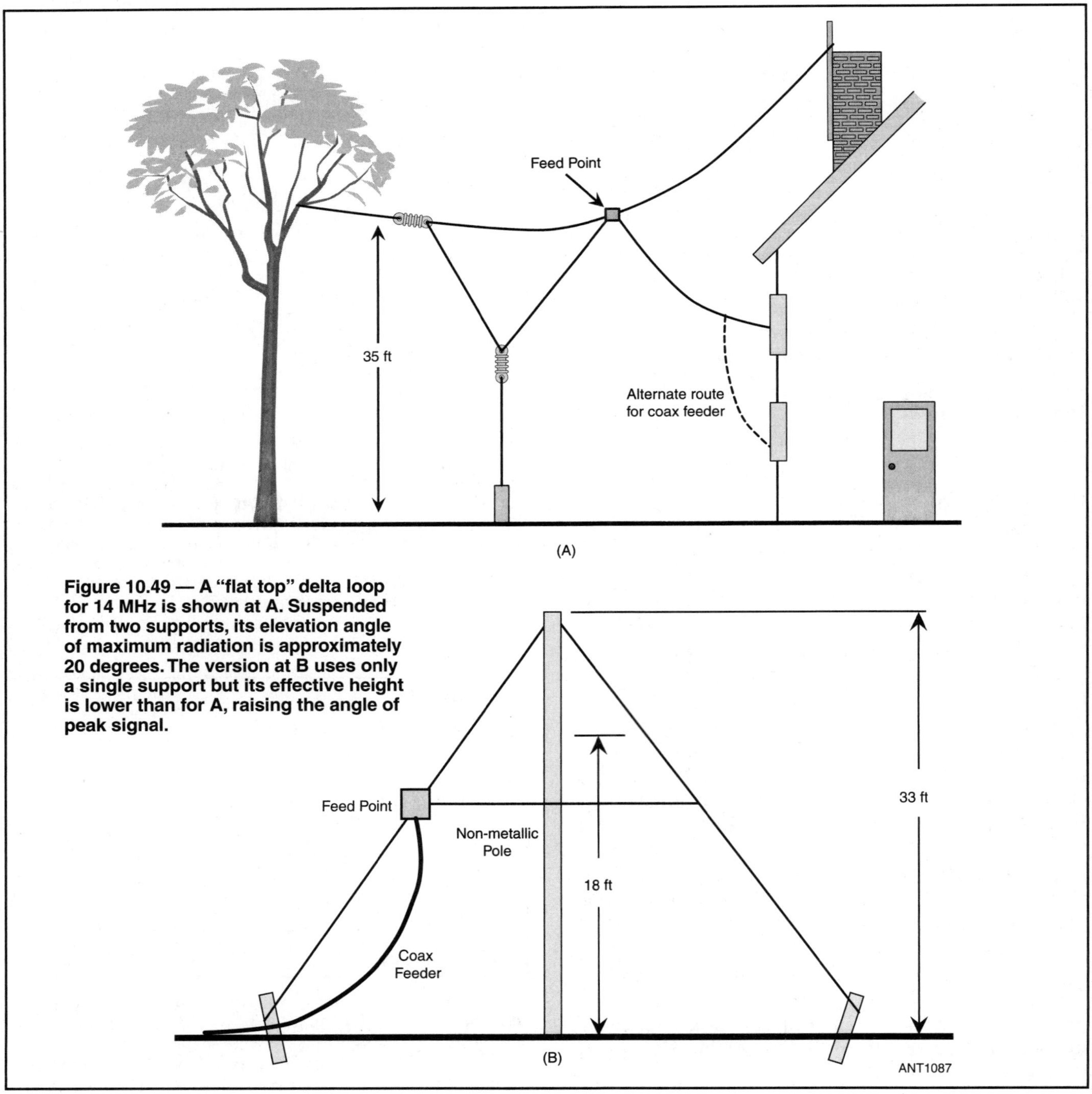

Figure 10.49 — A "flat top" delta loop for 14 MHz is shown at A. Suspended from two supports, its elevation angle of maximum radiation is approximately 20 degrees. The version at B uses only a single support but its effective height is lower than for A, raising the angle of peak signal.

wire in the loop should be approximately 1005/f (MHz) = 71 feet for a resonant frequency of 14.15 MHz. For the optimum pattern, the loop should be equilateral with all three sides about the same length.

The antenna in Figure 10.49A has an effective height of about λ/2. The placement of the feed point at one of the upper corners configures the antenna to provide low-angle radiation for DX operation. The feed line should be suspended so that it runs directly away from the corner of the loop.

Figure 10.49B inverts the delta to use a single supporting mast or the antenna can be suspended from a tree. The effective height of this antenna is much lower than the "flat-top" version in Figure 10.49A and so the elevation angle of maximum radiation will be higher. Nevertheless, the convenience of this configuration makes it a good choice for Field Day and portable operation. The orientation of the feed line is much less important in this configuration — it can simply drop vertically to the ground.

A commercial dipole center insulator with the built-in support point will also work well at the feed point. The antenna can be supported with lightweight fishing line or nylon cord. It is recommended that the lower corner or corners be secured as well to prevent the antenna from moving too much in the wind. Insulators can be installed as in Figure 10.20.

The feed point impedance of both configurations will be 100-150 Ω and a quarter-wave matching section of feed line can be used to match the loop to 50 or 75-Ω feed line. A choke balun should be used at the feed point. (See the **Transmission Line System Techniques** chapter for more information on quarter-wave matching sections and choke baluns.)

10.6.3. TWO-BAND LOOP FOR 30 AND 40 METERS

The following antenna design is from a *QST* Hints and Kinks entry by James Brenner, NT4B, in the May 1989 issue. The version shown in **Figure 10.50** is fed at the apex of a delta loop but can be adapted to a square or quad loop shape.

The original design was derived from "The Mini X-Q Loop" in *All About Cubical Quad Antennas* by Bill Orr, W6SAI (now out of print) which is 1.5 λ in circumference, with an open circuit opposite the feed point. That antenna has approximately 1 dB of additional gain over a 1-λ loop. Since 30 and 40 meters are close to the same 1:1.5 λ ratio, one loop can be converted between 1 λ on 40 meters and 1½ λ on 30 meters with a switch.

A large, ceramic SPST knife switch is installed in the center of the delta loop's bottom leg as shown in Figure 10.50. With the switch open, the loop acts a 1½ λ loop at 10.5 MHz, so 18-inch wires were added to the loop on either side of the switch to lengthen the antenna and lower the resonant frequency to 10.1 MHz. Closing the switch shorts out the wires and the loop becomes a regular 1-λ continuous loop for 40 meters.

Note that there is fairly high voltage present at the switch when transmitting on 30 meters. If a relay is used, be sure the contact spacing is sufficient to avoid arcing or use additional pairs of contacts to increase the overall spacing. (See the discussion of broad-banding 160 meter antennas in the **Single-Band MF and HF Antennas** chapter for suggestions on modifying relays for this application.)

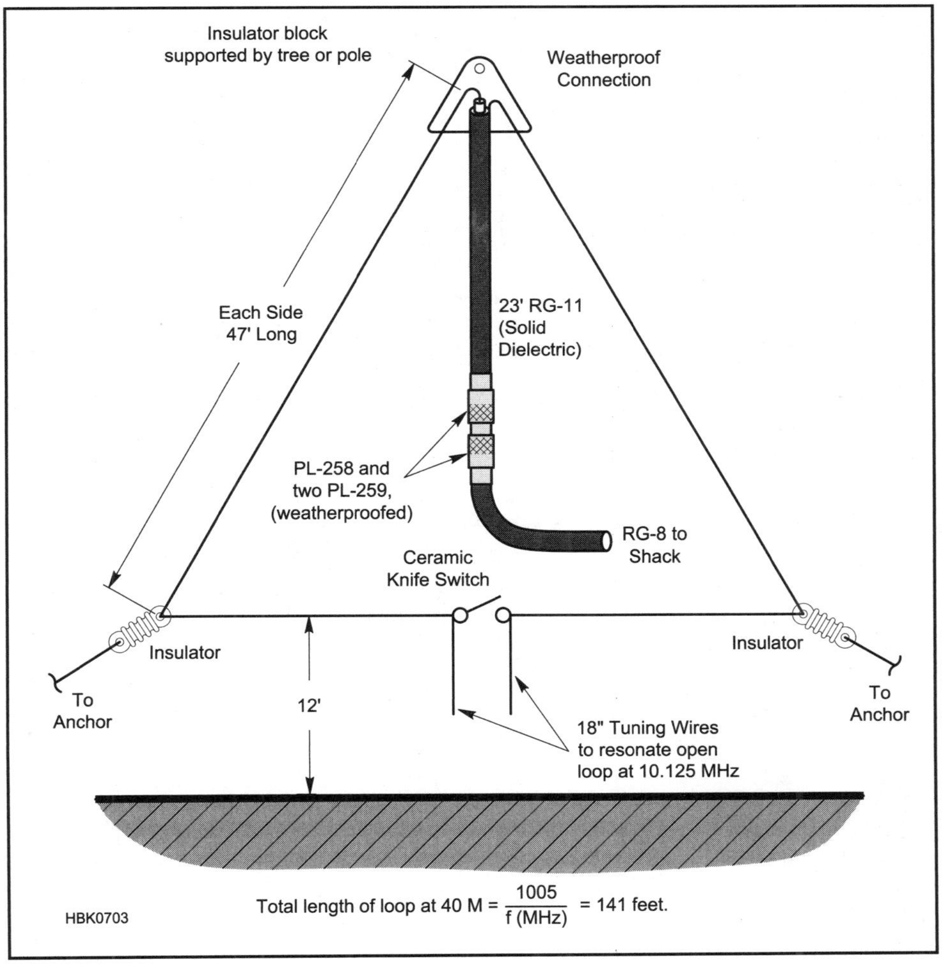

Figure 10.50 — NT4B's 30 and 40 meter loop is fed at the top via a quarter-wave 40 meter matching transformer made of 75 Ω coax. Note the 18-inch tuning wires used to lower the antenna's 30 meter resonance from 10.5 to 10.1 MHz. Adjust the length of these wires to set the 30 meter resonant frequency.

The antenna is fed through a quarter-wave transformer (see the **Transmission Line System Techniques** chapter) of 75-Ω RG-11 coax, approximately 23 feet long. The 40 meter configuration of the loop is reported to have a satisfactory SWR of less than 2:1 on 15 meters. In addition, the 30 meter configuration can be used successfully on 80 meters with the use of an antenna tuner.

10.6.4 NESTED LOOP ANTENNAS FOR MULTIPLE BANDS

The following nested loop array for the 20, 17, 15, 12, and 10 meter bands can be used as a permanent station antenna or for portable operation. The design was originally described in the *QST* article "Nested Loop Antenna" by Scott Davis, N3FJP, which is included with this book's downloadable supplemental information.

The square loops are constructed as in **Figure 10.51** according to the dimensions in **Table 10.4**. The loops hang in the vertical plane in a diamond shape and are fed at the bottom corner to radiate with horizontal polarization. The perimeter, P, of each loop is calculated by dividing 1005 feet by the frequency in MHz.

The PVC pipe horizontal cross support spans between opposite loop corners, and is 1.41 times the largest loop side length, S. Brass screws are used to hold the PVC together. If the horizontal PVC pipe sags excessively, reinforce it with lengths of 1 × 2-inch pressure-treated wood taped to the pipe.

To construct the antenna, start with the largest loop (20 meters). Cut a 70.9-foot piece of wire for the loop perimeter and divide it by 4 to determine the length, S, of each side. Arrange the wire on the PVC structure, temporarily taping it to find where the wire should pass through the PVC pipe. Drill holes through the pipe for the loop wire. After you run the wire through the holes, wrap a bit of electrical tape on each side of the wire next to the pipe to keep the wire from sliding and to give the pipe additional support. Repeat for each band in sequence from large to small loop perimeter.

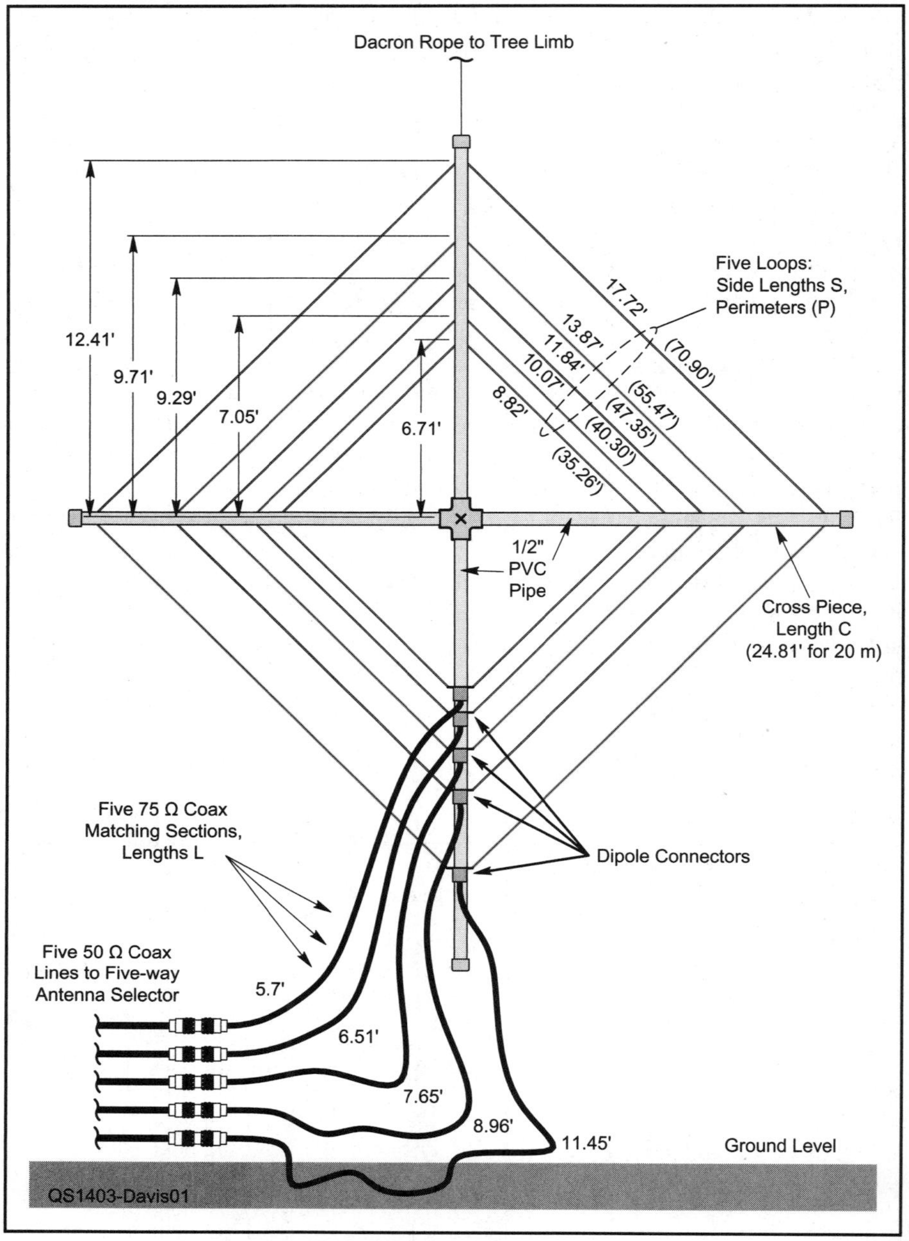

Figure 10.51 — The five-band version of the nested loops with construction notes. See the supplemental article for more construction details and a parts list.

Table 10.4
Nested Loop Antenna Dimensions
75 Ω Matching Section Cable with 0.66 Velocity Factor (VF)

Band	*Freq (MHz)*	*Perimeter, P (ft)*	*Side, S (ft)*	*Cross Support (ft)*	*Distance From Center, D (ft)*	*Length, L of 75 Ω cable (ft)*
20 m	14.175	70.9	17.8	24.8	12.4	11.5
17 m	18.118	55.5	13.9	19.4	9.7	9.0
15 m	21.225	47.4	11.8	16.6	9.3	7.7
12 m	24.940	40.3	10.1	14.1	7.1	6.5
10 m	28.500	35.3	8.8	12.3	6.2	5.7

At the feed point, rather than sliding the wires through the PVC pipe, use brass wood screws into the PVC to secure the ends of the wires. An SO-239 can be installed at this point or pigtails on the feed line can be attached to the loop wire. Be sure to waterproof this connection.

The loop feed point impedance is about 100 Ω, so individual λ/4 matching sections of 75 Ω coax (RG-59 or RG-11) can be used convert the impedance to 50 Ω. Table 10.4 gives the matching section lengths, taking into account velocity factor VF = 0.66 for solid polyethylene coaxial cable. The formula for the matching sections is L = (246 × VF) / f (MHz). A multi-position remote coax switch can be used to use a single feed line to the antenna with the matching sections connected between the loops and the switch.

10.6.5. MULTIBAND "CAT WHISKERS" LOOP FOR 14-30 MHZ

This antenna goes one step farther than the nested multi-loop antenna, combining all of the loops into one composite structure. The design was originally presented in the article "Cat Whiskers — The Broadband Multi-Loop Antenna" by Jacek Pawlowski, SP3L, that is included with this chapter's downloadable supplemental information, including detailed construction drawings.

The antenna in **Figure 10.52** consists of five loops that are all connected together at a single feed point. The path through the various loops having the lowest impedance will carry the most current on the frequency of use. The outer wire forms a 7.4 × 4.5-meter rectangular frame for the inner wires which are soldered to it to form the various loops. The entire structure is held in place by four fiberglass fishing poles mounted on a metal spreader that is held in turn by a metal bracket. A prototype version of the antenna is shown in **Figure 10.53**.

The antenna's feed point impedance varies from 137 Ω to 640 Ω over the whole 14–30 MHz range with attendant SWR changes of 1.83:1 to 2.56:1 when calculated directly at the feed point without a feeder. The SWR is calculated for a 300-Ω impedance because the 6:1 balun in **Figure 10.54** is assumed to be connected between the antenna and the coax feed line.

The balun for the prototype antenna was built with three transformers. T1 is an unun transforming 50 Ω to 75 Ω. Its winding has 10 turns of five enameled #20 AWG wires. Transformers T2 and T3 form a Guanella 4:1 transformer or current balun and ideally should be wound with a pair of wires having a characteristic impedance of 150 Ω. (See the **Transmission Line System Techniques** chapter for paired-wire transmission lines suitable for this application.)

Stranded wires with thick high-voltage isolation were used to construct the transformers. This thicker-than-normal insulation creates wider separation between the wires, which increases their characteristic impedance close to 150 Ω. The T2 and T3 windings also have 10 turns. Three FT-140-61 cores were used. If your transmitter delivers more than approximately 200 W, bigger cores should be used, such as the FT-240-61.

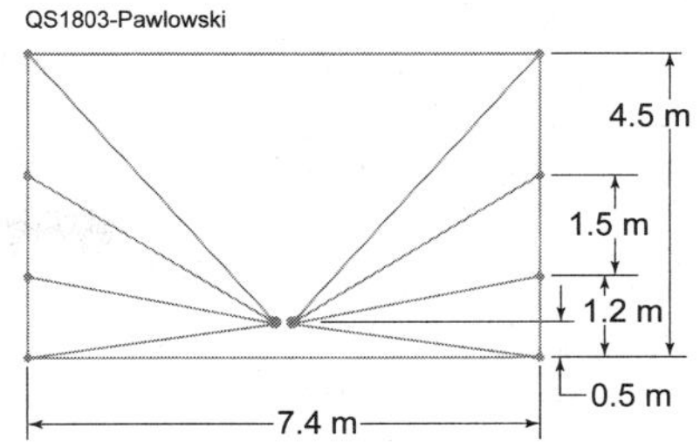

Figure 10.52 — Dimensions for the Cat Whiskers broadband, bi-directional antenna in meters.

Figure 10.53 — Prototype antenna supported by trimmed cross bracket mounted atop a Yaesu G-450C rotator. A plastic box containing the 6:1 balun is mounted behind the cross bracket.

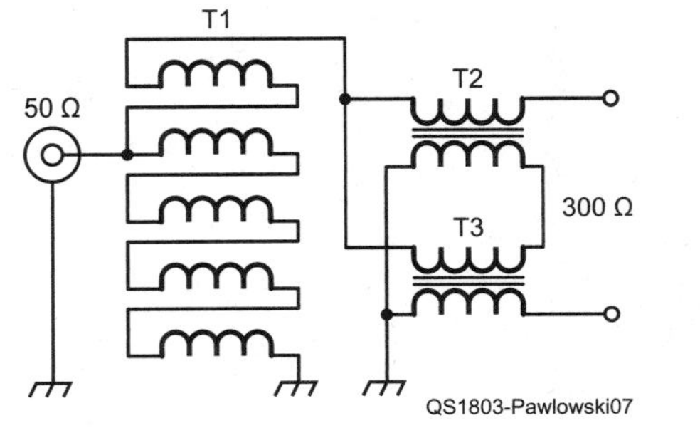

Figure 10.54 — Schematic of 6:1 balun consisting of a 1.5:1 unun (T1) followed by a 4:1 current balun (T2 and T3).

10.9 BIBLIOGRAPHY

Source material and more extended discussion of topics covered in this chapter can be found in the references given below and in the textbooks listed at the end of Chapter 2, **Antenna Fundamentals**.

B. Austin, "An HF Multiband Wire Antenna for Single-Hop Point-to-Point Applications," *Journal of the Institution of Electronics and Radio Engineers*, 57, 1987, pp 167-173.

W. M. Bell, "A Trap Collinear Antenna," *QST*, Aug 1963, pp 30-31.

J. S. Belrose, "The HF Discone Antenna," *QST*, Jul 1975, pp 11-14, 56.

J. Belrose and P. Bouliane, "The Off-Center-Fed Dipole Revisited: A Broadband, Multiband Antenna," *QST*, Aug 1990, pp 28-34.

J. Belrose, "Technical Correspondence: Terminated Folded Dipole," *QST,* May 1994, pp 88-89.

H. J. Berg, "Multiband Operation with Paralleled Dipoles," *QST*, Jul 1956, pp 42-43.

J. T. Bolljahn and J. V. N. Granger, "Omnidirectional VHF and UHF Antennas," *Antenna Engineering Handbook* , H. Jasik, ed. (New York: McGraw-Hill, 1961) pp 27-32 through 27-34.

G. A. Breed, "Multi-Frequency Antenna Technique Uses Closely-Coupled Resonators," *RF Design*, November 1994. US Patent 5,489,914, "Method of Constructing Multiple-Frequency Dipole or Monopole Antenna Elements Using Closely-Coupled Resonators," Gary A. Breed, Feb 6, 1996.

G. H. Brown, "The Phase and Magnitude of Earth Currents Near Radio Transmitting Antennas," *Proc. IRE*, Vol 23, No. 2, Feb 1935, pp 168-182.

G. H. Brown, R. F. Lewis and J. Epstein, "Ground Systems as a Factor in Antenna Efficiency," *Proc. IRE*, Vol 25, No. 6, Jun 1937, pp 753-787.

C. L. Buchanan, "The Multimatch Antenna System," *QST*, Mar 1955. pp 22-23, 155.

L.B. Cebik, "Modeling the T2FD," various online sources.

L.B. Cebik, "Horizontally Oriented, Horizontally Polarized Large Wire Loop Antennas," 29 Mar, 1999, various online sources.

L.B. Cebik, "My Top Five Backyard Multi-Band Wire HF Antennas," various online sources.

S. Davis, "Nested Loop Antennas," *QST*, Mar 2014, pp 40-41.

D. DeMaw, "Lightweight Trap Antennas — Some Thoughts," *QST*, Jun 1983, pp 15-18.

D. DeMaw, "A Closer Look at Horizontal Loop Antennas," *QST*, May 1990, pp 28-29, 35.

W. C. Gann, "A Center-Fed 'Zepp' for 80 and 40," *QST*, May 1966, pp 15-17.

A. Greenberg, "Simple Trap Construction for the Multiband Antenna," *QST*, Oct 1956, pp 18-19, 120.

G. L. Hall, "Trap Antennas," Technical Correspondence, *QST*, Nov 1981, pp 49-50.

J. Hallas, "Getting On the Air: The Terminated Folded Dipole," *QST*, Sep 2010, pp 51-52.

J. Hallas, "The 43 Foot Vertical Monopole — What's the Magic?" *QST*, Jun 2012, pp 30-32.

W. Hayward, "Designing Trap Antennas," Technical Correspondence, *QST*, Aug 1976, p 38.

D. Hollander, "A Big Signal from a Small Lot," *QST*, Apr 1979, pp 32-34.

R. H. Johns, "Dual-Frequency Antenna Traps," *QST*, Nov 1983, pp 27-30.

W. J. Lattin, "Multiband Antennas Using Decoupling Stubs," *QST*, Dec 1960, pp 23-25.

W. J. Lattin, "Antenna Traps of Spiral Delay Line," *QST*, Nov 1972, pp 13-15.

R. Littlefield, "A No Compromise Off-Center Fed Dipole for Four Bands" *QST*, Jun 2008, pp 32-34.

M. A. Logan, "Coaxial-Cable Traps," Technical Correspondence, *QST*, Aug 1985, p 43.

J. R. Mathison, "Inexpensive Traps for Wire Antennas," *QST*, Feb 1977, p 18.

S. Masticola, "An Improved 160/80-Meter Matching Network for Your 43-Foot Vertical," *QST*, Sep 2017, pp 39-41.

L. McCoy, "An Easy-to-Make Coax-Fed Multiband Trap Dipole," *QST*, Dec 1964, pp 28-30.

G. E. O'Neil, "Trapping the Mysteries of Trapped Antennas," *Ham Radio*, Oct 1981, pp 10-16.

W. I. Orr, editor, "The Low-Frequency Discone," *Radio Handbook*, 14th Edition, (Editors and Engineers, 1956), p 369.

J. Pawlowski, "Cat Whiskers — The Broadband Multi-Loop Antenna" *QST*, Mar 2018, pp 40-44.

J. Portune, "Printed Circuit Board Antenna Traps for HF," *QST*, May 2018, pp 30-32.

L. Richard, "Parallel Dipoles of 300-Ohm Ribbon," *QST*, Mar 1957, p 14.

P. Salas, "160 and 80 Meter Matching Network for Your 43 Foot Vertical — Part 1 and Part 2," *QST*, Dec 2009, p 30-32, and Jan 2010, pp 34-35.

W. Sandford, Jr., "A Modest 45-Foot DX Vertical for 160, 80, 40, and 30 Meters," *QST*, Sep 1981, pp 27-31. Also see Feedback, Nov 1981, p 50.

T. H. Schiller, Force 12, US Patent 5,995,061, "No loss, multi-band, adaptable antenna," Nov 30, 1999.

H. Scholle and R. Steins, "Eine Doppel-Windom Antenna fur Acht Bander," *cq-DL*, Sep 1983, p 427. (In English: *QST*, Aug 1990, pp 33-34.)

R. Severns, "A Wideband 80 meter Dipole," *QST*, Jul 1995, pp 27-29.

M. Seybold, "The Low-Frequency Discone," *CQ*, July 1950, p 13.

D. P. Shafer, "Four-Band Dipole with Traps," *QST*, Oct 1958, pp 38-40.

W. Silver, "Hands-On Radio Experiment 136: The End-Fed Antenna," *QST*, May 2014, pp 63-64.

R. C. Sommer, "Optimizing Coaxial-Cable Traps," *QST*, Dec 1984, pp 37-42.

S. Stearns, "All About the Discone Antenna: Antenna of Mysterious Origin and Superb Broadband Performance," *QEX*, Jan/Feb 2007, pp 37-44.

L. Varney, "The G5RV Multiband Antenna . . . Up-to-Date," *The ARRL Antenna Compendium, Vol 1* (Newington: ARRL, 1985), p 86.

M. Weaver, "A Four-Band "Tree" Vertical," *QST*, Nov 1995, pp 69-70.

R. Wilson, "The Offset Multiband Trapless Antenna (OMTA)," *QST*, Oct 1995, pp 30-32. Also see Feedback, Dec 1995, p 79.

S. Yates, "The End-Fed Half-Wave Antenna," **www.aa5tb.com/efha.html**.

TABLE OF CONTENTS

Chapter 11 — Downloadable Supplemental Content

Supplemental Articles

- "A 10 Meter Moxon Beam" by Allen Baker, KG4JJH
- "A 20 Meter Moxon Antenna" by Larry Banks, W1DYJ
- "Construction of W6NL Moxon on Cushcraft XM240" by Dave Leeson, W6NL
- "Having a Field Day with the Moxon Rectangle" by L.B. Cebik, W4RNL
- "Multimatch Antenna System" by Chester Buchanan, W3DZZ

Chapter 11

HF Yagi and Quad Antennas

11.1 YAGI ANTENNAS

Along with the dipole and the quarter-wave vertical, radio amateurs throughout the world make extensive use of the Yagi antenna, more accurately referred to as a Yagi array. Hidetsugu Yagi and Shintaro Uda, two Japanese university professors, invented the Yagi in the 1920s. Uda did much of the developmental work while Yagi introduced the array to the world outside Japan through his writings in English. Although the antenna should properly be called a *Yagi-Uda* array, it is commonly referred to simply as a *Yagi*.

The Yagi is a type of end-fire multielement array as described in the **Multielement Arrays** chapter. At the minimum, it consists of a single *driven element* and a single *parasitic element*. These elements are placed parallel to each other on a supporting boom some distance apart. This arrangement is known as a 2-element Yagi. The parasitic element is termed a *reflector* when it is placed behind the driven element, opposite to the direction of maximum radiation, and is called a *director* when it is placed ahead of the driven element. See **Figure 11.1**. In the VHF and UHF spectrum, Yagis employing 30 or more elements are not uncommon, with a single reflector and multiple directors. See the **VHF and UHF Antenna Systems** chapter for details on VHF and UHF Yagis. Large HF arrays may employ 10 or more elements and will be covered in this chapter.

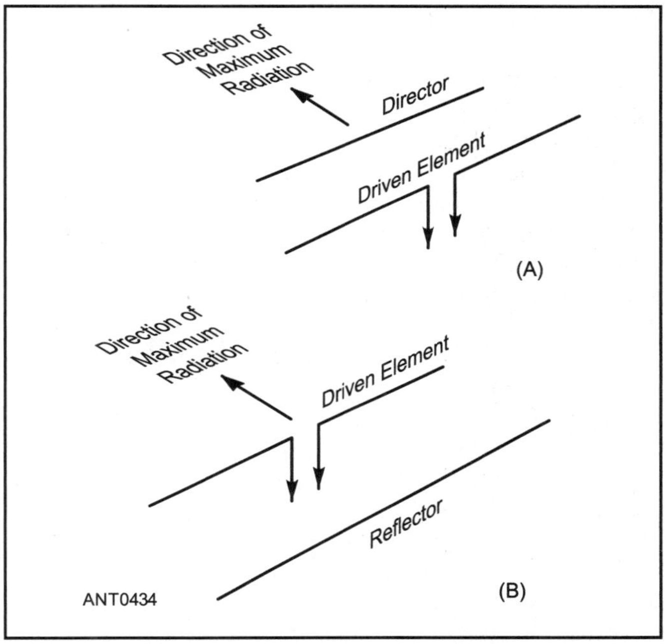

Figure 11.1 — Two-element Yagi systems using a single parasitic element. At A the parasitic element acts as a director, and at B as a reflector. The arrows show the direction in which maximum radiation takes place.

11.1.1 HOW A YAGI WORKS — AN OVERVIEW

The gain and directional pattern of a Yagi array is determined by the relative amplitudes and phases of the currents induced into all the parasitic elements. Unlike directly driven multielement arrays in which the designer must compensate for mutual coupling between elements, proper Yagi operation *relies on* mutual coupling. The current in each parasitic element is determined by its spacing from both the driven element and other parasitic elements, and by the tuning of the element itself. Both length and diameter affect element tuning.

The following discussion is quite over-simplified but serves to illustrate the basic process by which the Yagi antenna creates its radiation pattern. Begin with a dipole driven element resonant at the operating frequency and a single parasitic element configured as a reflector, slightly longer than the driven element. Current in the driven element creates a radiated electromagnetic field (the *direct field*) that induces a current in the parasitic element. That induced current causes a *re-radiated field* just as if the current was caused by a transmitter connected to the element. The re-radiated field combines with the direct field from the driven element to create the antenna's radiation pattern.

Three things determine the phase relationship between the current in the reflector and in the driven element. First, the direct field at the reflector slightly lags the field at the driven element because the direct field must travel from the driven element to the reflector. Second, the induced current is 180° out of phase with the direct field at the location of the reflector. Third, the reflector element is slightly longer than a resonant length and so its self-impedance is inductive, creating additional phase lag in the induced current relative to the direct field.

The combination of phase lags due to the direct field's travel time, the 180° phase inversion for induced current, and the reflector's inductance cause the re-radiated field to partially cancel with the direct field from the driven element along a line from the driven element through the reflector. (Imagine the boom extending beyond the reflector — that is the line being referred to.) This creates the rear null in the Yagi radiation pattern. Similarly, the fields reinforce each other in the opposite direction to the forward direction as shown in Figure 11.1.

The situation is reversed in the case of a director element. The phase lag from travel time and the inversion in the induced current act the same as for the reflector. The director element is slightly shorter than resonant however and so has a capacitive self-impedance, creating a phase lead. The combination results in the fields reinforcing in the forward direction and cancelling in the opposite direction.

Two-element Yagis are useful antennas but even more directivity (gain) can be obtained by adding additional parasitic elements. Additional reflectors are rarely used because field cancellation to the rear of the antenna leaves too little field for them to improve directivity. Thus, multiple directors are used to increase directivity as you will see in practical Yagi designs later in the chapter.

The actual situation is of course far more complicated than this simplistic view of Yagi operation. In a real Yagi, the mutual coupling between all elements must be considered, including between the parasitic elements. This makes determining the optimum spacing and element length for a desired radiation pattern quite involved mathematically and best left to software modeling programs.

11.1.2 YAGI MODELING

For about 50 years amateurs and professionals created Yagi array designs largely by "cut and try" experimental techniques. In the early 1980s, Jim Lawson, W2PV, described in detail for the amateur audience the fundamental mathematics involved in modeling Yagis. His book *Yagi Antenna Design* (now out of print) is highly recommended for serious antenna designers as is his series of articles in *Ham Radio* (see Bibliography). The advent of powerful microcomputers and sophisticated computer antenna modeling software in the mid 1980s revolutionized the field of Yagi design for the radio amateur. In a matter of minutes, a computer can try 100,000 or more different combinations of element lengths and spacings to create a Yagi design tailored to meet a particular set of high-performance parameters. To explore this number of combinations experimentally, a human experimenter would take an unimaginable amount of time and dedication and the process would no doubt suffer from considerable measurement errors. With the computer tools available today, an antenna can be designed, constructed and then put up in the air, with little or no tuning or pruning required.

A very popular modeling program for amateur use is *EZNEC* by Roy Lewallen, W7EL (**www.eznec.com**). *EZNEC* is well-suited to model Yagi antennas. There are several Yagi antenna models included with this book's downloadable supplemental information, and *EZNEC* is discussed in more detail in the **Antenna Modeling** chapter.

The *YW* Modeling Program

Included with this book's downloadable supplemental information, the *YW* modeling program developed by Dean Straw, N6BV, is designed to evaluate monoband Yagi antennas. (*YW* stands for *Yagi for Windows*.) *YW* results compare very closely with Brian Beezley's *YO* or *YA* programs (no longer sold in the amateur market) and with *NEC*-based programs, such as *EZNEC*, *NEC-Win Plus* or *NEC-4*. *YW* is a special-purpose program, designed strictly for monoband Yagis. It has the advantage of running many times more quickly than general-purpose programs such as *NEC* but it has some attendant limitations.

YW evaluations over ground are done over flat "perfect" ground. Mutual impedances between Yagi elements and the ground are not specifically taken into account in *YW*, so calculations for antennas mounted less than approximately λ/8 above ground are likely to be inaccurate. Antennas mounted in the presence of other nearby antennas or mounted very low to the ground are the specialties of method-of-moment programs like *EZNEC*. Despite these caveats, *YW* will get you very close to a final design — one where you can simply cut the elements and expect that your Yagi will work as advertised.

11.2 YAGI PERFORMANCE PARAMETERS

There are three main parameters used to characterize the performance of a particular Yagi — *forward gain*, *pattern* and *drive impedance/SWR*. Another important consideration is mechanical strength. It is very important to recognize that each of the three electrical parameters should be characterized over the frequency band of interest in order to be meaningful. Neither the gain, the SWR nor the pattern measured at a single frequency gives very much insight into the overall performance of a particular Yagi.

Poor designs have even been known to reverse their directionality over a frequency band, while other designs have excessively narrow SWR bandwidths, or gain that peaks excessively in the band. Finally, an antenna's ability to survive the wind and ice conditions expected in one's geographical location is an important consideration in any design. Much of this chapter will be devoted to describing detailed Yagi designs that are optimized for a good balance between gain, pattern and SWR over various amateur bands, and that are designed to survive strong winds and icing.

11.2.1 YAGI GAIN

Like any other antenna, the gain of a Yagi must be stated in comparison to some standard of reference. Designers of phased vertical arrays often state gain referenced to a single, isolated vertical element. See the section on "Phased Array Techniques" in the chapter **Multielement Arrays**.

Many antenna designers prefer to compare gain to that of an *isotropic radiator in free space*. This is a theoretical antenna that radiates equally well in all directions, and by definition, it has a gain of 0 *dBi* (dB isotropic). Many radio amateurs, however, are comfortable using a dipole as a standard reference antenna, mainly because it is *not* a theoretical antenna.

In free space, a dipole does not radiate equally well in all directions — it has a figure-eight azimuth pattern, with deep nulls off the ends of the wire. In its favored directions, a free-space dipole has 2.15 dB gain compared to the isotropic radiator. You may see the term *dBd*, meaning gain referenced to a dipole in free space. Subtract 2.15 dB from gain in dBi to convert to gain in dBd.

Assume for a moment that we take a dipole out of "free space," and place it one wavelength above the ocean, whose saltwater makes an almost perfect ground. At an elevation angle of 15°, where sea water-reflected radiation adds in phase with direct radiation, the dipole has a gain of about 6 dB, compared to its gain when it was in free space, isolated from any reflections. This and other related effects are addressed in the chapter **Effects of Ground**.

It is perfectly legitimate to say that this dipole has a gain of 6 dBd, although the term "dBd" (meaning "dB dipole") makes it sound as though the dipole somehow has gain over itself! Always remember that gain expressed in dBd (or dBi) refers to the *counterpart antenna in free space*. The gain of the dipole over saltwater in this example can be rated at either 6 dBd (over a dipole in free space), or as 8.15 dBi (over an isotropic radiator in free space). Each frame of reference is valid, as long as it is used consistently and clearly. In this chapter we will often switch between Yagis in free space and Yagis over ground. To prevent any confusion, gains will be stated in dBi.

Yagi free-space gain ranges from about 5 dBi for a small 2-element design to about 20 dBi for a 31-element long-boom UHF design. The length of the boom is the main factor determining the gain a Yagi can deliver. Gain as a function of boom length will be discussed in detail after the sections below defining antenna response patterns and SWR characteristics.

11.2.2 RADIATION PATTERN MEASUREMENTS

Figure 11.2 compares the E-plane and H-plane pattern of a 3-element Yagi in free space to those of a dipole and an isotropic radiator. (See the **Antenna Fundamentals** chapter for definitions and conventions associated with measurement of radiation patterns.) These patterns were generated using *NEC-2* modeling software. Figure 11.2A shows that this 3-element Yagi in free space exhibits 7.28 dBi of gain (referenced to isotropic), and has 5.13 dB gain over a free-space dipole. For this particular antenna, the half-power beamwidth is about 66°.

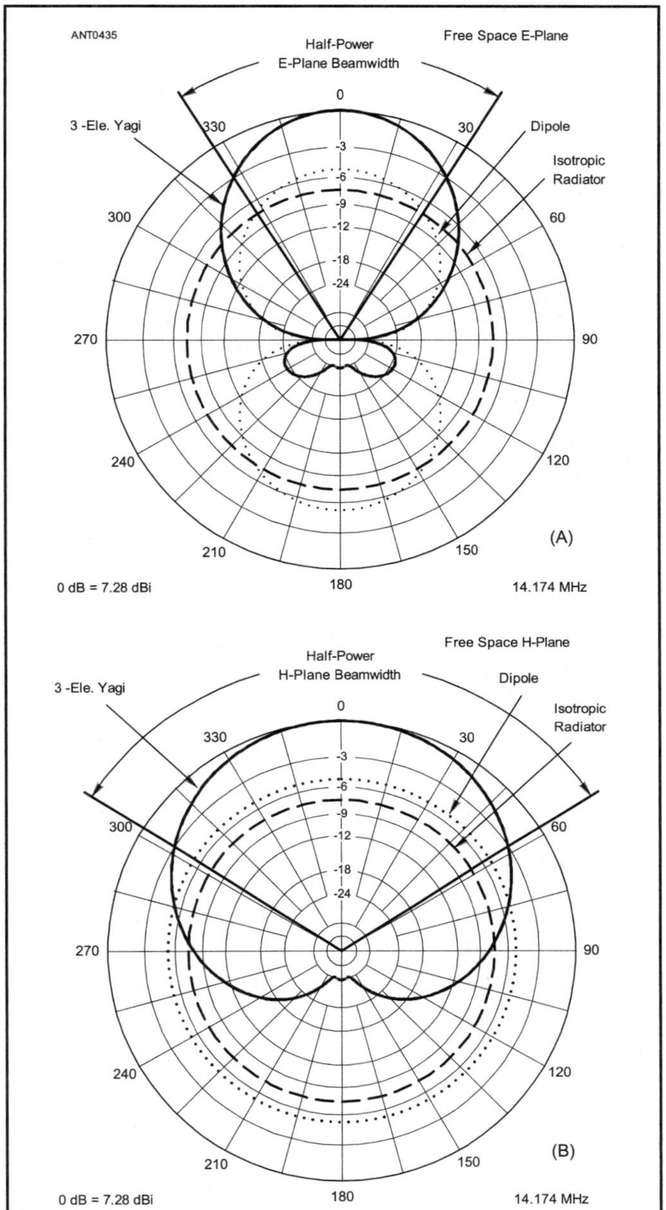

Figure 11.2 — E-Plane (electric field) and H-Plane (magnetic field) response patterns for 3-element 20 meter Yagi in free space. At A the E-Plane pattern for a typical 3-element Yagi is compared with a dipole and an isotropic radiator. At B the H-Plane patterns are compared for the same antennas. The Yagi has an E-Plane half-power beamwidth of 66°, and an H-Plane half-power beamwidth of about 120°. The Yagi has 7.28 dBi (5.13 dBd) of gain. The front-to-back ratio, which compares the response at 0° and at 180°, is about 35 dB for this Yagi. The front-to-rear ratio, which compares the response at 0° to the largest lobe in the rearward 180° arc behind the antenna, is 24 dB, due to the lobes at 120° and 240°.

Front-to-Back Ratio

Again as seen in Figure 11.2A, this antenna's front-to-back ratio is 34 dB comparing response at 180° to that in the forward direction at 0°. (The ratio of the forward response to the averaged response over the entire 180° rearward section is called the *front-to-rear ratio.*) In Figure 11.2A there are two sidelobes, at 120° and at 240°, which are about 24 dB below the peak response at 0°. Since interference can come from any direction, not only directly off the back of an antenna, these kinds of sidelobes limit the ability to discriminate against rearward signals. The term *worst-case front-to-rear ratio* is used to describe the worst-case rearward lobe in the 180°-wide sector behind the antenna's main lobe. In this case, the worst-case front-to-rear ratio is 24 dB.

In the rest of this chapter the worst-case front-to-rear ratio will be used as a performance parameter, and will be abbreviated as "F/R." For a dipole or an isotropic radiator, Figure 11.2A demonstrates that F/R is 0 dB. Figure 11.2B depicts the H-field response for the same 3-element Yagi in free space, again compared to a dipole and an isotropic radiator in free space. Unlike the E-field pattern, the H-field pattern for a Yagi does not have a null at 90°, directly over the top of the Yagi. For this 3-element design, the H-field half-power beamwidth is approximately 120°.

Figure 11.3 compares the azimuth and elevation patterns for a horizontally polarized 6-element 14-MHz Yagi with a 60-foot boom mounted one wavelength over ground to a dipole at the same height. As with any horizontally polarized antenna, the height above ground is the main factor determining the peaks and nulls in the elevation pattern of each antenna. Figure 11.3A shows the E-field pattern, which has now been labeled as the Azimuth pattern. This antenna has a half-power azimuthal beamwidth of about 50°, and at an elevation angle of 12° it exhibits a forward gain of 16.02 dBi, including about 5 dB of ground reflection gain over relatively poor ground, with a dielectric constant of 13 and conductivity of 5 mS/m. In free space this Yagi has a gain of 10.97 dBi.

The H-field elevation response of the 6-element Yagi has a half-power beamwidth of about 60° in free space, but as shown in Figure 11.3B, the first lobe (centered at 12° in elevation) has a half-power beamwidth of only 13° when the antenna is mounted one wavelength over ground. The dipole at the same height has a very slightly larger first-lobe half-power elevation beamwidth of 14°, since its free-space H-field response is omnidirectional.

Note that the free-space H-field directivity of the Yagi suppresses its second lobe over ground (at an elevation angle of about 40°) to 8 dBi, while the dipole's response at its second lobe peak (at about 48°) is at a level of 9 dBi.

The shape of the azimuthal pattern for a Yagi operated over real ground will change slightly as the Yagi is placed closer and closer to ground. Generally, however, the azimuth pattern doesn't depart significantly from the free-space pattern until the antenna is less than 0.5 λ high. This is just over 17 feet high at 28.4 MHz and just below 35 feet at 14.2 MHz — heights that are not difficult to achieve for most amateurs. Some advanced modeling programs can optimize Yagis at the exact installation height.

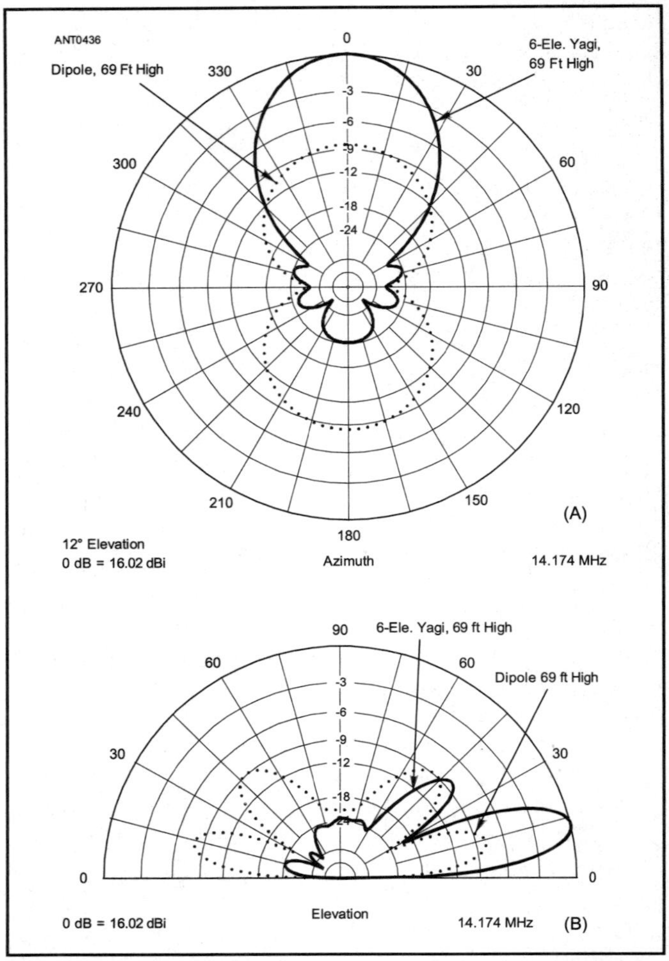

Figure 11.3 — Azimuth pattern for 6-element 20 meter Yagi on 60-foot long boom, mounted 60 feet over ground. At A, the azimuth pattern at 12° elevation angle is shown, compared to a dipole at the same height. Peak gain of the Yagi is 16.04 dBi, or just over 8 dB compared to the dipole. At B, the elevation pattern for the same two antennas is shown. Note that the peak elevation pattern of the Yagi is compressed slightly lower compared to the dipole, even though they are both at the same height over ground. This is most noticeable for the Yagi's second lobe, which peaks at about 40°, while the dipole's second lobe peaks at about 48°. This is due to the greater free-space directionality of the Yagi at higher angles.

11.2.3 FEED POINT IMPEDANCE AND SWR

The impedance at the feed point of the driven element in a Yagi is affected not only by the tuning of the driven element itself, but also by the spacing and tuning of nearby parasitic elements, and to a lesser extent by the presence of ground. In some designs that have been tuned solely for maximum gain, the driven-element impedance can fall to very low levels, sometimes less than 5 Ω. This can lead to excessive losses due to conductor resistance, especially at VHF and UHF. In a Yagi that has been optimized solely for gain, conductor losses are usually compounded by large excursions in impedance levels with relatively small changes in frequency. The SWR can thus change dramatically over a band and can create additional losses in the feed line. **Figure 11.4** illustrates the SWR over the 28 to 28.8 MHz portion of the 10 meter amateur band for a 5-element Yagi on a 24-foot boom, tuned for maximum forward gain at a spot frequency of 28.4 MHz. Its SWR curve is contrasted to that of a Yagi designed for a good compromise of gain, SWR and F/R.

Even professional antenna designers have difficulty accurately measuring forward gain. On the other hand, SWR can easily be measured by professional and amateur alike. Few manufacturers would want to advertise an antenna with the narrow-band SWR curve shown in Figure 11.4!

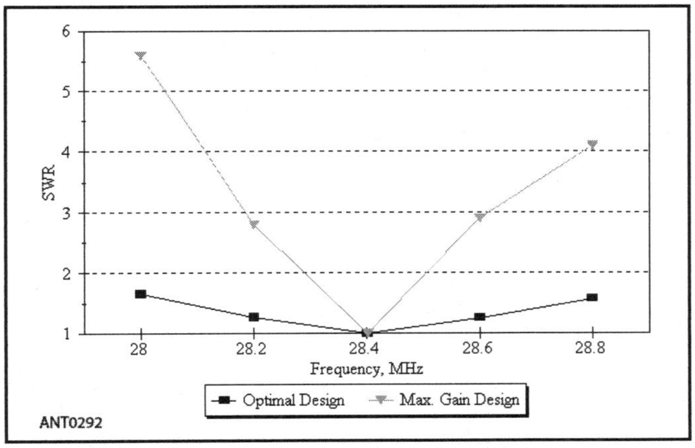

Figure 11.4 — SWR over the 28.0 to 28.8 MHz portion of the 10 meter band for two different 3-element Yagi designs. One is designed strictly for maximum gain, while the second is optimized for F/R pattern and SWR over the frequency band. A Yagi designed only for maximum gain usually suffers from a very narrow SWR bandwidth.

Direct Feed Yagis

By carefully adjusting the position and tuning of the Yagi elements by using modeling software it is possible to create an antenna design for which the feed point impedance is close to 50 Ω and can be fed directly with coaxial cable. The tradeoff is usually a small amount of gain, but such *direct feed* designs are becoming increasingly common with no compromise in performance. Direct feed designs are somewhat more complex mechanically as the driven element must be insulated from the boom. This includes designs that require beta or hairpin matching.

Choke Baluns

The use of a choke or current balun is good practice for any Yagi with a balanced driven element, regardless of feed point impedance. To be sure, many Yagi antennas provide adequate performance without a balun at the feed point but obtaining top performance from the antenna requires decoupling or isolation of the feed line from the antenna. If a choke balun is *not* used, interaction between the outer surface of the coaxial cable shield and the antenna can affect feed point impedance and result in significant common-mode current on the shield. Re-radiation from the common-mode current can fill in the radiation pattern nulls, degrading front-to-side and front-to-back performance. Common-mode current on the feed line can also result in RF-related problems in the station. (See "Common-Mode Transmission Line Currents" in the **Transmission Line System Techniques** chapter.)

11.3 MONOBAND YAGI PERFORMANCE OPTIMIZATION

11.3.1 YAGI DESIGN GOALS

The previous section discussing driven-element impedance and SWR hinted at possible design trade-offs among gain, pattern and SWR, especially when each parameter is considered over a frequency band rather than at a spot frequency. Trade-offs in Yagi design parameters can be a matter of personal taste and operating style. For example, one operator might exclusively operate the CW portions of the HF bands, while another might only be interested in the Phone portions. Another operator may want a good pattern in order to discriminate against signals coming from a particular direction; someone else may want the most forward gain possible, and may not care about responses in other directions.

There are only a few variables available to adjust when one is designing a Yagi to meet certain design goals. The variables are:

1) The physical length of the boom
2) The number of elements on the boom
3) The spacing of each element along the boom
4) The tuning of each element
5) The type of matching network used to feed the array.

For elements that are created from telescoping tubing sections, the lengths of individual sections (called the taper schedule) affects antenna performance as well. Taper schedule is usually varied in order to provide mechanical strength and is not considered a primary electrical design variable.

Extensive computer modeling of Yagis indicates that the parameter that must be compromised most to achieve wide bandwidths for front-to-rear ratio and SWR is forward gain. However, not much gain must be sacrificed for good F/R and SWR coverage, especially on long-boom Yagis. Although 10 and 7-MHz Yagis are not rare, the HF bands from 14 to 30 MHz are where Yagis are most often found, mainly due to the mechanical difficulties involved with making sturdy antennas for lower frequencies. The highest HF band, 28.0 to 29.7 MHz, represents the largest percentage bandwidth of the upper HF bands, at almost 6%. It is difficult to try to optimize in one design the main performance parameters of gain, worst-case F/R ratio and SWR over this large a band. Many commercial designs thus split up their 10 meter designs into antennas covering one of two bands: 28.0 to 28.8 MHz, and 28.8 to 29.7 MHz. For the amateur bands below 10 meters, optimal designs that cover the entire band are more easily achieved.

The performance requirements for Yagis used at VHF and UHF are similar to those of HF Yagis but place more emphasis on reduction of side lobes due to the importance of lowering received noise above 30 MHz. In addition, there are differences in feed point matching and considerations of losses are handled differently. These topics are addressed in the **VHF and UHF Antenna Systems** chapter. The remainder of this chapter will focus on HF designs unless specifically noted otherwise.

11.3.2 GAIN AND BOOM LENGTH

As pointed out earlier, the gain of a Yagi is largely a function of the length of the boom. As the boom is made longer, the maximum gain potential rises. For a given boom length, the number of elements populating that boom can be varied, while still maintaining the antenna's gain, provided of course that the elements are tuned properly. In general, putting more elements on a boom gives the designer added flexibility to achieve desired design goals, especially to broaden the response across a frequency band.

Figure 11.5A is an example illustrating gain versus frequency for three different types of 3-element Yagis on 8-foot booms. The three antennas were designed for the lower end of the 10 meter band, 28.0 to 28.8 MHz, based on the following different design goals:

Antenna 1: Maximum mid-band gain, regardless of F/R or SWR across the band

Antenna 2: SWR less than 2:1 over the frequency band; best compromise gain, with no special consideration for F/R over the band.

Antenna 3: "Optimal" case: F/R greater than 20 dB, SWR less than 2:1 over the frequency band; best compromise gain.

Figure 11.5B shows the F/R over the frequency band for these three designs, and Figure 11.5C shows the SWR curves over the frequency band. Antenna 1, the design that strives strictly for maximum gain, has a poor SWR response over the band, as might be expected after the previous section discussing SWR. The SWR is 10:1 at 28.8 MHz and rises to 22:1 at 29 MHz. At 28 MHz, at the low end of the band, the SWR of the maximum-gain design is more than 6:1. Clearly, designing for maximum gain alone produces an unacceptable design in terms of SWR bandwidth. The F/R for Antenna 1 reaches a high point of about 20 dB at the low-frequency end of the band, but falls to only 3 dB at the high-frequency end.

Antenna 2, designed for the best compromise of gain while the SWR across the band is held to less than 2:1, achieves this goal, but at an average gain sacrifice of 0.7 dB compared to the maximum gain case. The F/R for this design is just under 15 dB over the band. This design is fairly typical of many amateur Yagi designs before the advent of computer modeling and optimization programs. SWR can easily be measured, and experimental optimization for forward gain is a fairly straightforward procedure. By contrast, overall pattern optimization is not a trivial thing to achieve experimentally, particularly for antennas with more than four or five elements.

Antenna 3, designed for an optimum combination of F/R, SWR and gain, compromises forward gain an average of 1.0 dB compared to the maximum gain case, and about 0.4 dB compared to the compromise gain/SWR case. It achieves its design objectives of more than 20 dB F/R over the 28.0 to 28.8 MHz portion of the band, with an SWR less than 2:1 over that range.

Figure 11.6A shows the free-space gain versus frequency for the same three types of designs, but for a bigger 5-element

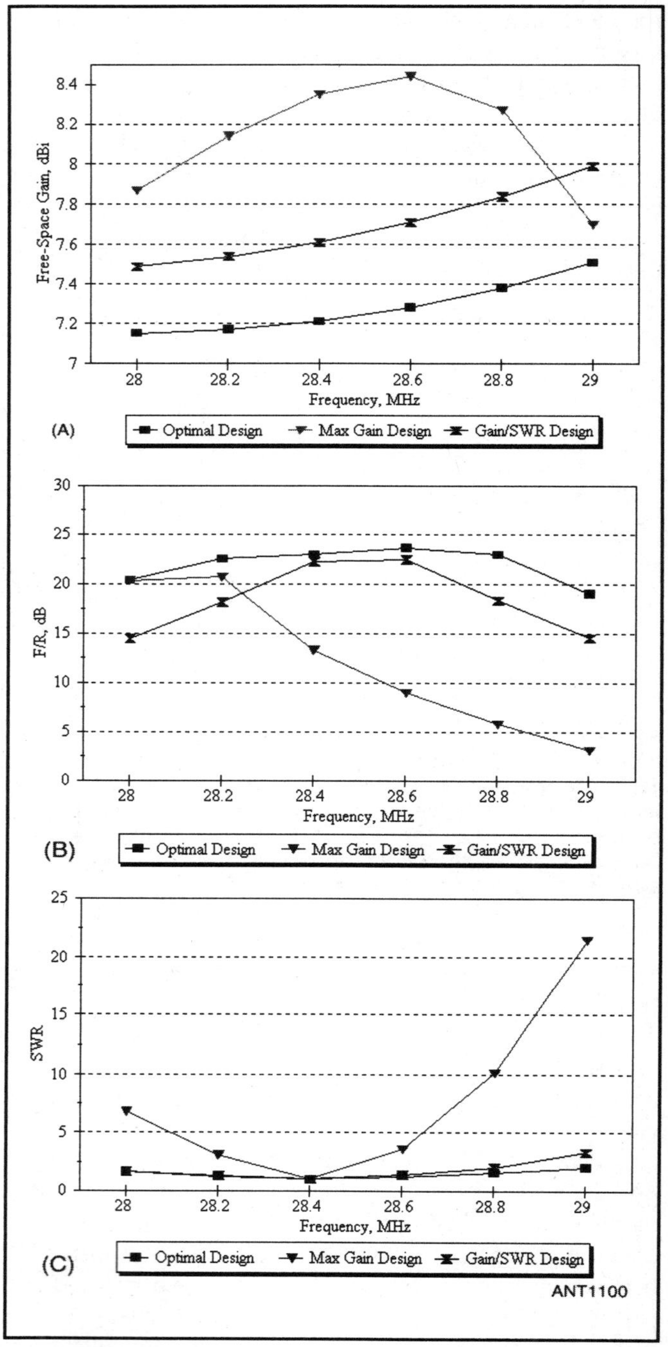

Figure 11.5 — Comparisons of three different 3-element 10 meter Yagi designs using 8-foot booms. At A, gain comparisons are shown. The Yagi designed for the best compromise of gain and SWR sacrifices an average of about 0.5 dB compared to the antenna designed for maximum gain. The Yagi designed for optimal F/R, gain and SWR sacrifices an average of 1.0 dB compared to the maximum-gain case, and about 0.4 dB compared to the compromise gain and SWR case. At B, the front-to-rear ratio is shown for the three different designs. The antenna designed for optimal combination of gain, F/R and SWR maintains a F/R higher than 20 dB across the entire frequency range, while the antenna designed strictly for gain has a F/R of 3 dB at the high end of the band. At C, the three antenna designs are compared for SWR bandwidth. At the high end of the band, the antenna designed strictly for gain has a very high SWR.

10 meter Yagi on a 20-foot boom. Figure 11.6B shows the variation in F/R, and Figure 11.6C shows the SWR curves versus frequency. Once again, the design that concentrates solely on maximum gain has a poor SWR curve over the band, reaching just over 6:1 toward the high end of the band. The difference in gain between the maximum gain case and the optimum design case has narrowed for this size of boom to an average of under 0.5 dB. This comes about because the designer has access to more variables in a 5-element design than he does in a 3-element design, and he can stagger-tune the various elements to spread the response out over the whole band.

Figure 11.7A, **B** and **C** show the same three types of designs, but for a 6-element Yagi on a 36-foot boom. The SWR bandwidth of the antenna designed for maximum gain has improved compared to the previous two shorter-boom examples, but the SWR still rises to more than 4:1 at 28.8 MHz, while the F/R ratio is pretty constant over the band, at a mediocre 11 dB average level. While the antenna designed for gain and SWR does hold the SWR below 2:1 over the band, it also has the same mediocre level of F/R performance as does the maximum-gain design.

The optimized 36-foot boom antenna achieves an excellent F/R of more than 22 dB over the whole 28.0 to 28.8 MHz band. Again, the availability of more elements and more space on the 36-foot long boom gives the designer more flexibility in broad-banding the response over the whole band, while sacrificing only 0.3 dB of gain compared to the maximum-gain design.

Figure 11.8A, **B**, and **C** show the same three types of 10 meter designs, but now for a 60-foot boom, populated with eight elements. With eight elements and a very long boom on which to space them out, the antenna designed solely for maximum gain can achieve a much better SWR response across the band, although the SWR does rise to more than 7:1 at the very high end of the band. The SWR remains less than 2:1 from 28.0 to 28.7 MHz, much better than for shorter-boom, maximum-gain designs. The worst-case F/R ratio is never better than 19 dB, however, and remains around 10 dB over much of the band. The antenna designed for the best compromise gain and SWR loses only about 0.1 dB of gain compared to the maximum-gain design, but does little better in terms of F/R across the band.

Contrasted to these two designs, the antenna optimized for F/R, SWR and gain has an outstanding pattern, exhibiting an F/R of more than 24 dB across the entire band, while keeping the SWR below 2:1 from 28.0 to 28.9 MHz. It must sacrifice an average of only 0.4 dB compared to the maximum gain design at the low end of the band, and actually has more gain than the maximum gain and gain/SWR designs at the high-frequency end of the band.

The conclusion drawn from these and many other detailed comparisons is that designing strictly for maximum mid-band gain yields an inferior design when the antenna is examined over an entire frequency band, especially in terms of SWR. Designing a Yagi for both gain and SWR will yield antennas that have mediocre rearward patterns, but that lose relatively

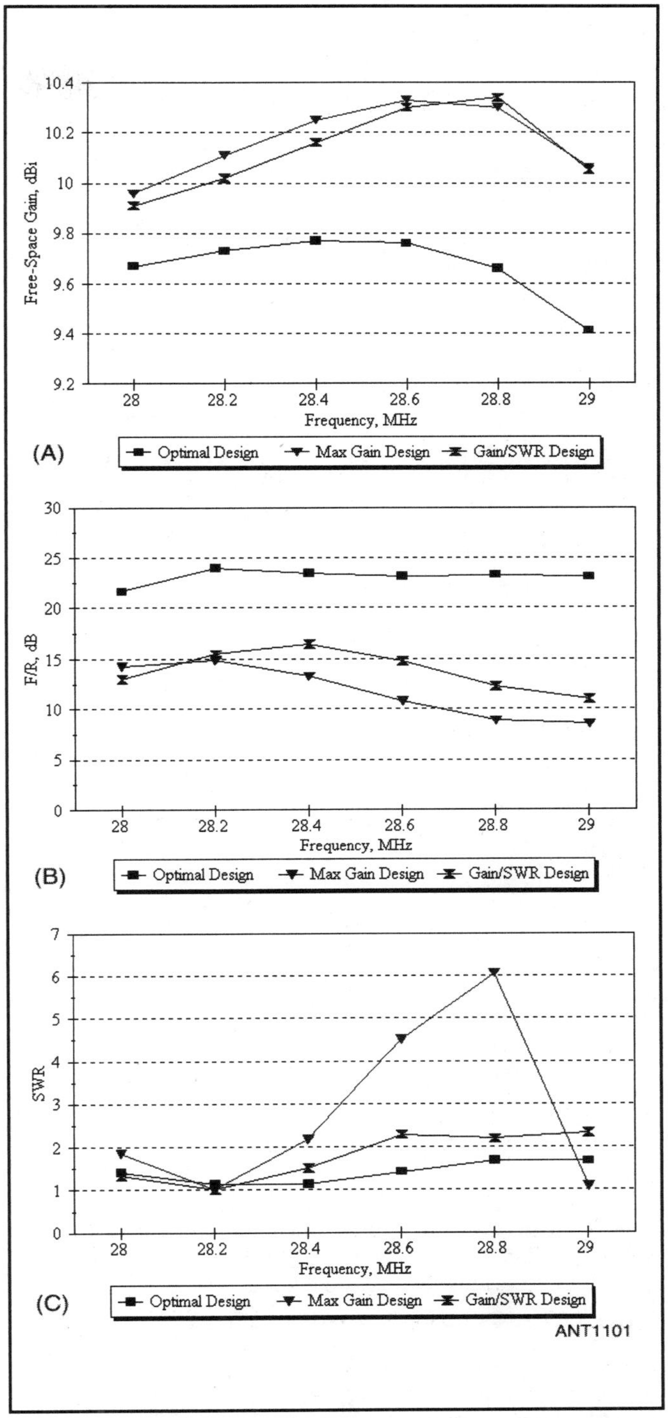

Figure 11.6 — Comparisons of three different designs for 5-element 10 meter Yagis on 20-foot booms. At A, the gain of three different 5-element 10 meter Yagi designs are graphed. The difference in gain between the three antennas narrows because the elements can be stagger-tuned to spread the response out better over the desired frequency band. The average gain reduction for the fully optimized antenna design is about 0.5 dB. At B, the optimal antenna displays better than 22 dB F/R over the band, while the Yagi designed for gain and SWR displays on average 10 dB less F/R throughout the band. At C, the SWR bandwidth is compared for the three Yagis. The antenna designed strictly for forward gain has a poor SWR bandwidth and a high peak SWR of 6:1 at 28.8 MHz.

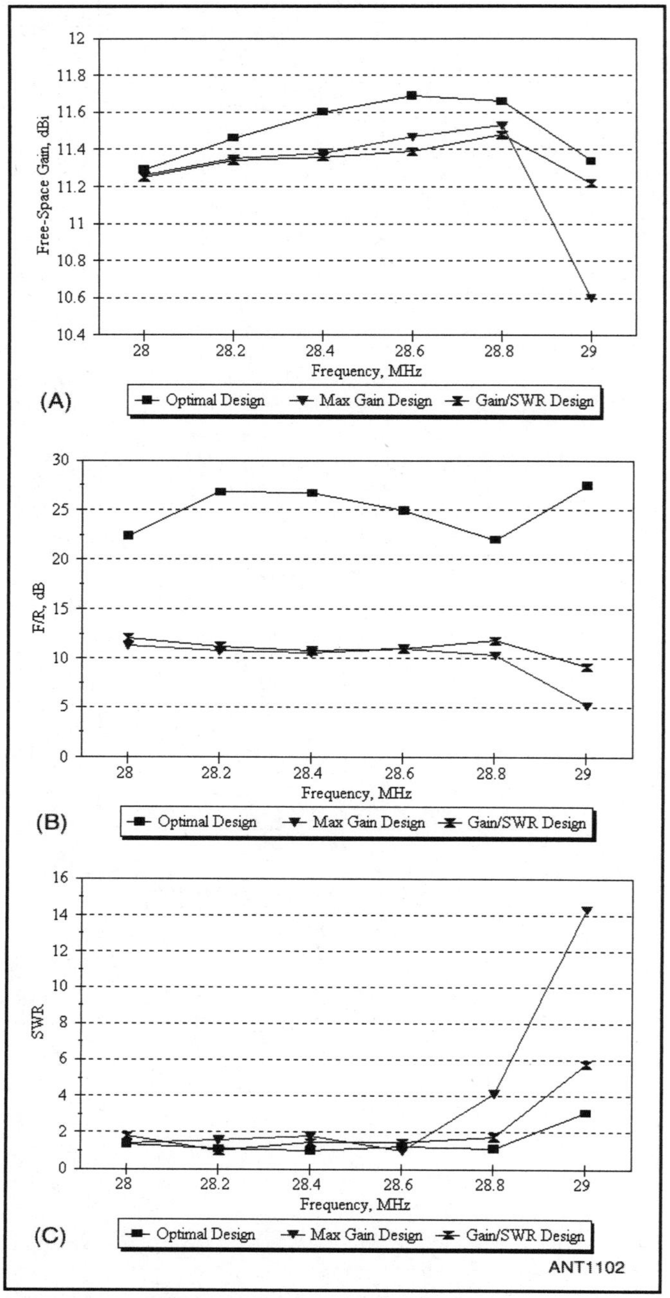

Figure 11.7 — Comparisons of three different 6-element 10 meter Yagi designs on 36-foot booms. At A, gain is shown over the band. With more elements and a longer boom, the tuning can be staggered even more to make the antenna gain more uniform over the band. This narrows the gain differential between the antenna designed strictly for maximum gain and the antenna designed for an optimal combination of F/R, SWR and gain. The average difference in gain is about 0.2 dB throughout the band. At B, the F/R performance over the band is shown for the three antenna designs. The antenna designed for optimal performance maintains an average of almost 15 dB better F/R over the whole band compared to the other designs. At C, the SWR bandwidth is compared. Again, the antenna designed strictly for maximum gain exhibits a high SWR of 4:1 at 28.8 MHz, and rises to more than 14:1 at 29.0 MHz.

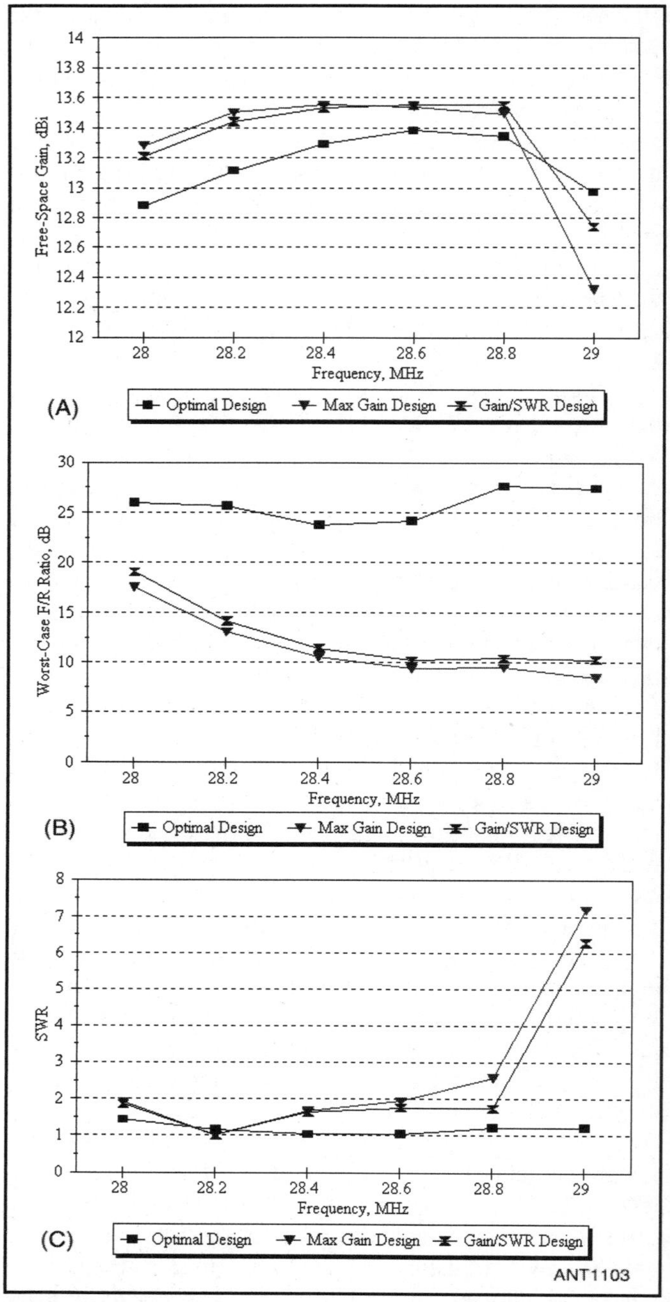

Figure 11.8 — Comparisons of three different 8-element 10 meter Yagi designs using 60-foot booms. At A, gain is shown over the frequency band. With even more freedom to stagger-tune elements and a very long boom on which to place them, the average antenna gain differential over the band is now less than 0.2 dB between the three design cases. At B, an excellent 24 dB F/R for the optimal design is maintained over the whole band, compared to the average of about 12 dB for the other two designs. At C, the SWR differential over the band is narrowed between the three designs, again because there are more variables available to broaden the bandwidth.

little gain compared to the maximum gain case, at least for designs with more than three elements.

However, designing a Yagi for an optimal combination of F/R, SWR and gain results in a loss of gain less than 0.5 dB compared to designs designed only for gain and SWR. **Figure 11.9** summarizes the forward gain achieved for the three different design types versus boom length, as expressed in wavelength.

Except for the 2-element designs, the Yagis described in the rest of this chapter have the following design goals over a desired frequency band:

1) Front-to-rear ratio over the frequency band of more than 20 dB

2) SWR over the frequency band less than 2:1

3) Maximum gain consistent with points 1 and 2 above

Just for fun and to illustrate what an imaginative antenna designer can do with modeling software, **Figure 11.10** shows the gain versus boom length for theoretical 20 meter Yagis that have been designed to meet the three design goals above. The 31-element design for 14 MHz would be wondrous to behold. Sadly, it is unlikely that anyone will build one, considering that the boom would be 724 feet long! However, such a design *does* become practical when scaled to 432 MHz. In fact, a K1FO 22-element and a K1FO 31-element Yagi described in the **VHF and UHF Antenna Systems** chapter are the prototypes for the theoretical 14-MHz long-boom designs.

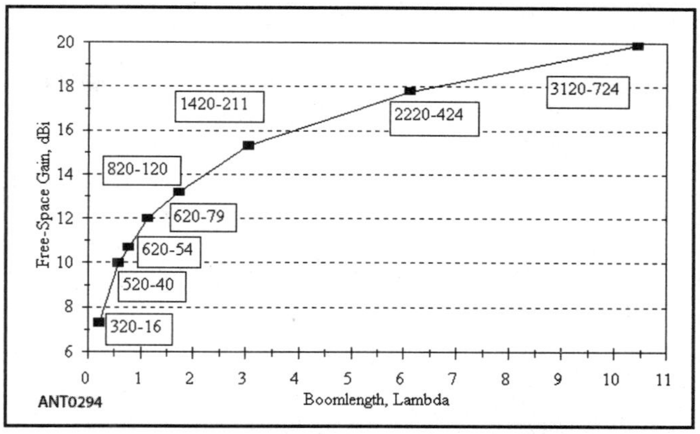

Figure 11.10 — Theoretical gain versus boom length for 20 meter Yagis designed for optimal combination of F/R, SWR and gain across the entire 14.0 to 14.35 MHz band. The theoretical gain approaches 20 dBi for a gigantic 724-foot boom, populated with 31 elements. Such a design on 20 meters is not too practical, of course, but can readily be achieved on a 24-foot boom on 432 MHz.

11.3.3 OPTIMIZED DESIGNS AND ELEMENT SPACING

Two-Element Yagis

Many hams consider a 2-element Yagi to give "the most bang for the buck" among various Yagi designs, particularly for portable operations such as Field Day. A 2-element Yagi has about 4 dB of gain over a simple dipole (sometimes jokingly called a "one-element Yagi") and gives a modest F/R of about 10 dB to help with rejection of interference on receive. By comparison, going from a 2-element to a 3-element Yagi increases the boom length by about 50% and adds another element, a 50% increase in the number of elements — for a gain increase of about 1 dB and another 10 dB in F/R.

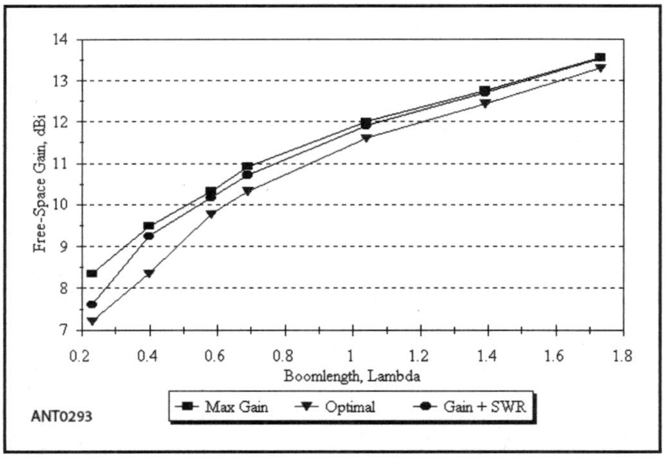

Figure 11.9 — Gain versus boom length for three different 10 meter design goals. The goals are: (1) designed for maximum gain across band, (2) designed for a compromise of gain and SWR, and (3) designed for optimal F/R, SWR and gain across 28.0 to 28.8 MHz portion of 10 meter band. The gain difference is less than 0.5 dB for booms longer than approximately 0.5 λ.

Element Spacing in Larger Yagis

One of the more interesting results of computer modeling and optimization of high-performance Yagis with four or more elements is that a distinct pattern in the element spacings along the boom shows up consistently. This pattern is relatively independent of boom length, once the boom is longer than about 0.3 λ.

The reflector, driven element and first director of these optimal designs are typically bunched rather closely together, occupying together only about 0.15 to 0.20 λ of the boom. This pattern contrasts sharply with older designs, where the amount of boom taken up by the reflector, driven element and first director was typically more than 0.3 λ. **Figure 11.11** shows the element spacings for an optimized 6-element, 36-foot boom, 10 meter design, compared to a W2PV 6-element design with constant spacing of 0.15 λ between all elements.

A problem arises with such a bunching of elements toward the reflector end of the boom — the wind loading of the antenna is not equal along the boom. Unless properly compensated, such new-generation Yagis will act like wind vanes, punishing and often breaking, the rotators trying to turn, or hold, them in the wind. One successful solution to wind-vaning has been to employ "dummy elements" made of PVC pipe. These non-conducting elements — called *torque compensators* — are placed on the boom close to the last director so the wind load is equalized at the mast-to-boom bracket. Flat plates can also be installed on the boom to oppose the turning force from the elements.

Along with an unbalanced wind load, the weight balance

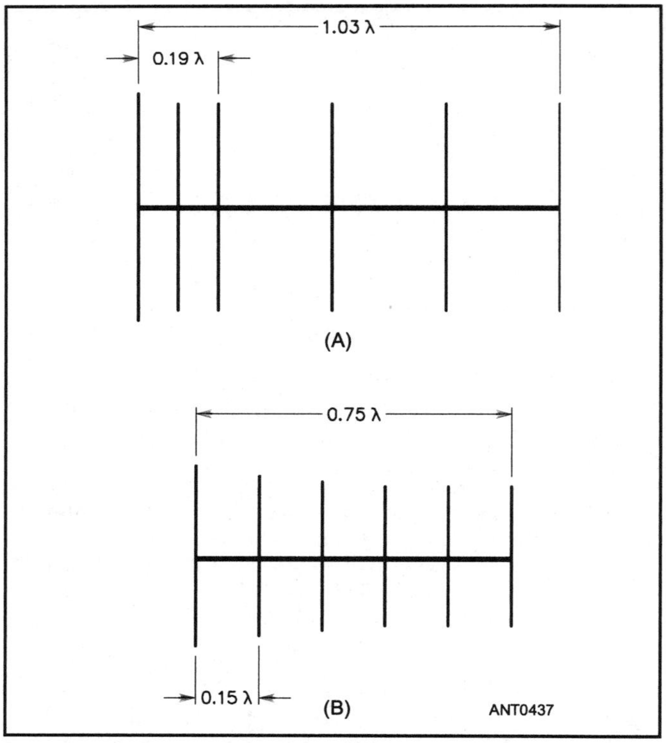

Figure 11.11 — Tapering spacing versus constant element spacing. At A, illustration of how the spacing of the reflector, driven element and first director (over the first 0.19 λ of the boom) of an optimally designed Yagi is bunched together compared to the Yagi at B, which uses constant 0.15 λ spacing between all elements. The optimally designed antenna has more than 22 dB F/R and an SWR less than 1.5:1 over the frequency band 28.0 to 28.8 MHz.

point is likely to be different than wind load balance point. The solution is generally to place a small amount of lead or iron inside one end of the boom in order to balance the antenna weight.

Despite the relatively close spacing of the reflector, driven element and first director, modern optimal Yagi designs are not overly sensitive to small changes in either element length or spacing. In fact, these antennas can be constructed from design tables without excessive concern about close dimensional tolerances. In the HF range up to 30 MHz, building the antennas to the nearest ⅛-inch results in performance remarkably consistent with the computations, without any "tweaking" or fine-tuning when the Yagi is on the tower.

11.3.4 ELEMENT TUNING

Element tuning (or *self-impedance*) is a complex function of the effective electrical length of each element and the effective diameter of the element. In turn, the effective length and diameter of each element is related to the taper schedule (if telescoping aluminum tubing is used, the most common method of construction), the length of each telescoping section, the type and size of mounting bracket used to secure the element to or through the boom, and the size of the Yagi boom itself. Note especially that Yagis constructed using wire elements will perform very differently compared to the same antenna constructed with elements made of telescoping aluminum tubing.

The process by which a modern Yagi is designed usually starts out with the selection of the longest boom possible for a given installation. A suitable number of elements of a given taper schedule are then placed on this boom, and the gain, pattern and SWR are calculated over the entire frequency band of interest to the designer. Once an electrical design is chosen, the designer must then ensure the mechanical integrity of the antenna design. This involves verifying the integrity of the boom and each element in the face of the wind and ice loading expected for a particular location. The chapter **Antenna Materials and Construction** discusses the details of tapered telescoping aluminum elements for the upper HF bands. In addition, the ARRL book *Physical Design of Yagi Antennas*, by Dave Leeson, W6NL, describes the mechanical design process for all portions of a Yagi antenna very thoroughly, and is highly recommended for serious Yagi builders. (This book is now out of print.)

11.4 MONOBAND YAGI DESIGNS

The detailed Yagi design tables that follow are for two taper schedules for HF Yagis covering the 14 through 30-MHz amateur bands. The heavy-duty elements are designed to survive at least 120-mph winds without icing, or 85-mph winds with ¼-inch radial ice. The medium-duty elements are designed to survive winds greater than 80 mph, or 60-mph winds with ¼-inch radial ice.

For 10.1 MHz, the elements shown are capable of surviving 105-mph winds, or 93-mph winds with ¼-inch radial ice. For 7.1 MHz the elements shown can survive 93-mph winds, or 69-mph winds with ¼-inch radial ice. For these two lower frequency bands, the elements and the booms needed are very large and heavy. Mounting, turning and keeping such antennas in the air is not a trivial task.

Each element is mounted above the boom with a heavy rectangular aluminum plate by means of U-bolts with saddles, as shown in **Figure 11.12A**. Stauff clamps (**www.us.stauff.com**) can also be used to hold the elements on the boom as discussed in the VHF, UHF, and Microwave Antennas chapter. This method of element mounting is rugged and stable, and because the element is mounted away from the boom, the amount of element detuning due to the presence of the boom is minimal. The element dimensions given in each table already take into account any element detuning due to the boom-to-element mounting plate. For each element, the length of the tip determines the tuning, since the inner tubes are fixed in diameter and length.

The element-to-boom mounting plates are modeled as a short section of element equivalent to a cylinder with an effective diameter given for each antenna. These dimensions to simulate the effect of the mounting plate are incorporated in the files for the *YW* (*Yagi for Windows*) computer modeling program with this book's downloadable supplemental information.

The second column in each design table shows the spacing of each element relative to the next element in line on the boom, starting at the reflector, which itself is defined as being at the 0.000-inch reference point on the boom. The boom for antennas less than 30 feet long can be constructed of 2-inch OD tubing with 0.065-inch wall thickness. Designs larger than 30 feet long should use 3-inch OD heavy-wall tubing for the boom. Because each boom has extra space at each end, the reflector is actually placed 3 inches from the end of the boom. For example, in the 310-08H.YW design (a 10 meter Yagi with 3 elements on an 8-foot boom), the driven element is placed 36 inches ahead of the reflector, and the director is placed 54 inches ahead of the driven element.

The next columns give the lengths for the variable tips for the heavy-duty and then the medium-duty elements. In the example above for the 310-08H.YW Yagi, the heavy-duty reflector tip, made out of ½-inch OD tubing, sticks out 66.750 inches from the ⅝-inch OD tubing. Note that each telescoping piece of tubing overlaps 3 inches inside the piece into which it fits, so the overall length of ⅛-inch OD tubing is 69.750 inches long for the reflector. The medium-duty reflector tip has 71.875 inches protruding from the ⅝-inch OD tube, and is 74.875 inches long overall. As previously stated, the dimensions are not extremely critical, although measurement accuracy to ⅛ inch is desirable.

The last row in each variable tip column shows the length of one-half of the "dummy element" torque compensator used to correct for uneven wind loading along the boom. This compensator is made from 2.5 inches OD PVC water pipe mounted to an element-to-boom plate like those used for each element. The compensator is mounted 12 inches behind the last director, the first director in the case of the 3-element 310-08H.YW antenna. Note that the heavy-duty elements require a correspondingly longer torque compensator than do the medium-duty elements.

Half Elements

Each design shows the dimensions for *one-half* of each element, mounted on *one side* of the boom. The other half of each element is symmetrical, mounted on the other side of the boom. The use of a tubing sleeve inside the center portion of the element is recommended, so that the element is not crushed by the mounting U-bolts. Unless otherwise noted, each section of tubing is made of 6061-T6 aluminum tubing, with a 0.058-inch wall thickness. This wall thickness ensures that the next standard size of tubing can telescope with it. Each telescoping section is inserted 3 inches into the larger tubing, and is secured by one of the methods shown in the **Antenna Materials and Construction** chapter, which also includes generic half-element designs rated for specific wind- and ice-loading conditions.

Direct Feed Hairpin Match

Each antenna is designed with a driven-element length appropriate for a hairpin or *beta match* network. The driven element's length may require slight readjustment for best match, particularly if a different matching network is used. *Do not change* either the lengths or the telescoping tubing schedule of the parasitic elements — they have been optimized for best performance and will not be affected by tuning of the driven element!

Note that the center of the hairpin is connected to the boom using a grounding lug. The center of the hairpin inductor is electrically neutral and may be connected to the boom for dc grounding and mechanical stability. The hairpin match requires a choke balun, described in the **Transmission Line System Techniques** chapter. Hairpin dimensions are included at the end of each *YW* file and in the following tables.

Figure 11.12B shows the driven element for a 2-element 17 meter Yagi built by Chuck Hutchinson, K8CH. The aluminum tubing on each side of the boom is 1-inch OD, and the two pieces were mechanically joined together with a 3/4-inch OD fiberglass rod insulator. Electrical tape over the insulator protects the fiberglass from UV. Three-inch lengths of 1-inch UV-resistant PVC conduit, split lengthwise, make the grey outer insulators for the driven element. Aluminum plates were obtained commercially. Stainless steel saddle clamps ensure that the elements don't rotate on the boom in heavy winds. Bolts are used to pin the center fiberglass rod to the aluminum tubing, while also providing an electrical connection for the #12 AWG hairpin inductor wire and the feed line coax.

(A)

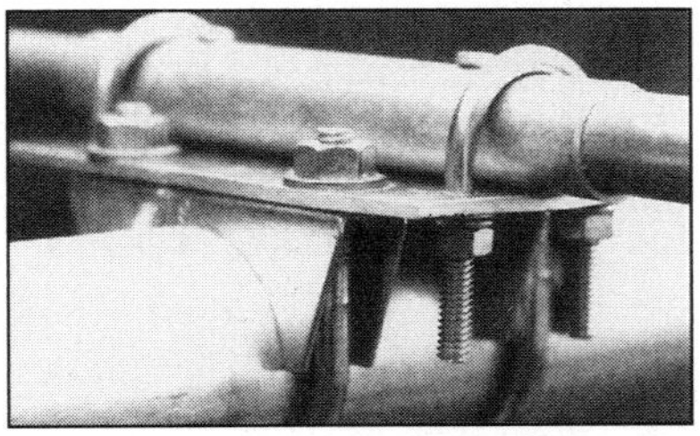

(B)

Figure 11.12 — Typical construction techniques for an HF Yagi. Photo A shows a typical element-to-boom clamp. U-bolts are used to hold the element to the plate and muffler clamps hold the plate to the boom. Photo B shows a hairpin match on a driven element insulated from a mounting plate that is attached to the boom with muffler clamps and saddles. Outdoor-rated gray PVC conduit sleeves insulate the element from the mounting plate. U-bolts hold the element on the plate. The feed line is connected to the two screws to which the hairpin inductor is attached. Note that the hairpin inductor's center point is attached to the boom at an electrically neutral point. All mounting hardware should be galvanized or stainless steel. The latter requires the use of an anti-seize compound to prevent thread galling.

11.4.1 10 METER YAGIS

Figure 11.13 describes the electrical performance of eight optimized 10 meter Yagis with boom lengths between 6 to 60 feet. The end of each boom includes 3 inches of space for the reflector and last-director (or driven element for the 2-element designs) mounting plates. Figure 11.13A shows the free-space gain versus frequency for each antenna; Figure 11.13B shows the front-to-rear ratio, and Figure 11.13C shows the SWR versus frequency. Each antenna with three or more elements was designed to cover the lower half of the 10 meter band from 28.0 to 28.8 MHz, with SWR less than 2:1 and F/R better than 20 dB over that range.

Figure 11.13D shows the taper schedule for two types of 10 meter elements. The heavy-duty design can survive 125-mph winds with no icing, and 88-mph winds with ¼-inch of radial ice. The medium-duty design can handle 96-mph winds with no icing, and 68-mph winds with ¼-inch of radial ice.

The element-to-boom mounting plate for these Yagis is a 0.250-inch thick flat aluminum plate, 4 inches wide by 4 inches long. Each element except for the insulated driven element, is centered on the plate, held by two stainless-steel U-bolts with saddles. Another set of U-bolts with saddles is used to secure the mounting plate to the boom. The mounting plate has an effective diameter of 2.405 inches for the heavy-duty element and 2.310 inches for the medium-duty element. The equivalent length on each side of the boom is 2 inches.

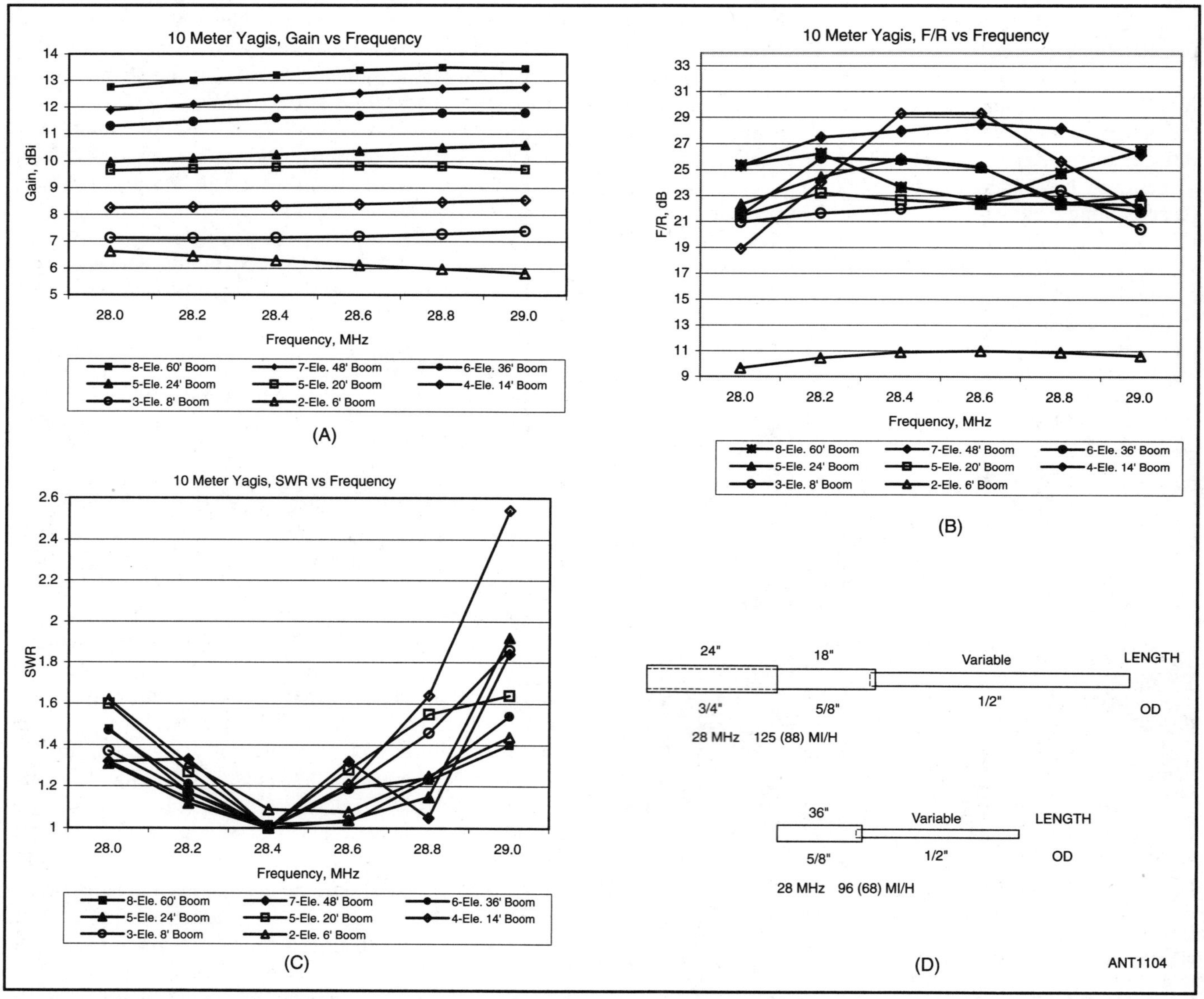

Figure 11.13 — Gain, F/R and SWR performance versus frequency for optimized 10 meter Yagis. At A, gain is shown versus frequency for eight 10 meter Yagis whose booms range from 6 feet to 60 feet long. Except for the 2-element design, these Yagis have been optimized for better than 20 dB F/R and less than 2:1 SWR over the frequency range 28.0 to 28.8 MHz. At B, front-to-rear ratio for these antennas is shown versus frequency, and at C, SWR is shown over the frequency range. At D, the taper schedule is shown for heavy-duty and for medium-duty 10 meter elements. The heavy-duty elements can withstand 125-mph winds without icing, and 88-mph winds with ¼-inch radial ice. The medium-duty elements can survive 96-mph winds without icing, and 68-mph winds with ¼-inch radial ice. The wall thickness for each telescoping section of 6061-T6 aluminum tubing is 0.058 inches, and the overlap at each telescoping junction is 3 inches.

Table 11.1

Optimized 10 meter Yagi Designs

Two-element 10 meter Yagi, 6 foot boom

Element	*Spacing*	*Heavy-Duty Tip*	*Medium-Duty Tip*
File Name		210-06H.YW	210-06M.YW
Reflector	0.000"	66.000"	71.500"
Driven Element	66.000"	57.625"	63.000"

Three-element 10 meter Yagi, 8 foot boom

Element	*Spacing*	*Heavy-Duty Tip*	*Medium-Duty Tip*
File Name		310-08H.YW	310-08M.YW
Reflector	0.000"	66.750"	71.875"
Driven Element	36.000"	57.625"	62.875"
Director 1	54.000"	53.125"	58.500"
Compensator	12" behind Dir. 1	19.000"	18.125"

Four-element 10 meter Yagi, 14 foot boom

Element	*Spacing*	*Heavy-Duty Tip*	*Medium-Duty Tip*
File Name		410-14H.YW	410-14M.YW
Reflector	0.000"	66.000"	72.000"
Driven Element	36.000"	58.625"	63.875"
Director 1	36.000"	57.000"	62.250"
Director 2	90.000"	47.750"	53.125"
Compensator	12" behind Dir. 2	22.000"	20.500"

Five-element 10 meter Yagi, 24 foot boom

Element	*Spacing, inches*	*Heavy-Duty Tip*	*Medium-Duty Tip*
File Name		510-24H.YW	510-24M.YW
Reflector	0.000"	65.625"	70.750"
Driven Element	36.000"	58.000"	63.250"
Director 1	36.000"	57.125"	62.375"
Director 2	99.000"	55.000"	60.250"
Director 3	111.000"	50.750"	56.125"
Compensator	12" behind Dir. 3	28.750"	26.750"

Six-element 10 meter Yagi, 36 foot boom

Element	*Spacing, inches*	*Heavy-Duty Tip*	*Medium-Duty Tip*
File Name		610-36H.YW	610-36M.YW
Reflector	0.000"	66.500"	71.500"
Driven Element	37.000"	58.500"	64.000"
Director 1	43.000"	57.125"	62.375"
Director 2	98.000"	54.875"	60.125"
Director 3	127.000"	53.875"	59.250"
Director 4	121.000"	49.875"	55.250"
Compensator	12" behind Dir. 4	32.000"	29.750"

Seven-element 10 meter Yagi, 48 foot boom

Element	*Spacing, inches*	*Heavy-Duty Tip*	*Medium-Duty Tip*
File Name		710-48H.YW	710-48M.YW
Reflector	0.000"	65.375"	70.500"
Driven Element	37.000"	59.000"	64.250"
Director 1	37.000"	57.500"	62.750"
Director 2	96.000"	54.875"	60.125"
Director 3	130.000"	52.250"	57.625"
Director 4	154.000"	52.625"	58.000"
Director 5	116.000"	49.875"	55.250"
Compensator	12" behind Dir. 5	35.750"	33.750"

Eight-element 10 meter Yagi, 60 foot boom

Element	*Spacing, inches*	*Heavy-Duty Tip*	*Medium-Duty Tip*
File Name		810-60H.YW	810-60M.YW
Reflector	0.000"	65.000"	70.125"
Driven Element	42.000"	58.000"	63.500"
Director 1	37.000"	57.125"	62.375"
Director 2	87.000"	55.375"	60.625"
Director 3	126.000"	53.250"	58.625"
Director 4	141.000"	51.875"	57.250"
Director 5	157.000"	52.500"	57.875"
Director 6	121.000"	50.125"	55.500"
Compensator	12" behind Dir. 6	59.375"	55.125"

These 10 meter Yagi designs are optimized for > 20 dB F/R, and SWR < 2:1 over frequency range from 28.000 to 28.800 MHz, for heavy-duty elements (125 mph wind survival) and for medium-duty (96 mph wind survival).
For coverage from 28.8 to 29.7 MHz, subtract 2.000 inches from end of each element, but leave element spacings the same as shown here. Only element tip dimensions are shown, and all dimensions are inches. See Fig 11.13D for element telescoping tubing schedule. Torque compensator element is made of 2.5" OD PVC water pipe placed 12 inches behind last director. Dimensions shown for compensators is one-half of total length, centered on boom.

11.4.2 12 METER YAGIS

Figure 11.14 describes the electrical performance of seven optimized 12 meter Yagis with boom lengths between 6 to 54 feet. The end of each boom includes 3 inches of space for the reflector and last director (or driven element) mounting plates. The narrow frequency range of the 12 meter band allows the performance to be optimized easily. Figure 11.14A shows the free-space gain versus frequency for each antenna; Figure 11.14B shows the front-to-rear ratio, and Figure 11.14C shows the SWR versus frequency. Each antenna with three or more elements was designed to cover the narrow 12 meter band from 24.89 to 24.99 MHz, with SWR less than 2:1 and F/R better than 20 dB over that range.

Figure 11.14D shows the taper schedule for two types of 12 meter elements. The heavy-duty design can survive 123-mph winds with no icing, and 87-mph winds with ¼ inch of radial ice. The medium-duty design can handle 85-mph winds with no icing, and 61-mph winds with ¼ inch of radial ice.

The element-to-boom mounting plate for these Yagis is a 0.375 inch thick flat aluminum plate, 5 inches wide by 6 inches long. The mounting plate has an effective diameter of 2.945 inches for the heavy-duty element, and 2.857 inches for the medium-duty element. The equivalent length on each side of the boom is 3 inches. As usual, the torque compensator is mounted 12 inches behind the last director.

11.4.3 15 METER YAGIS

Figure 11.15 describes the electrical performance of eight optimized 15 meter Yagis with boom lengths between 6 feet to a spectacular 80 feet. The end of each boom includes 3 inches of space for the reflector and last director (or driven

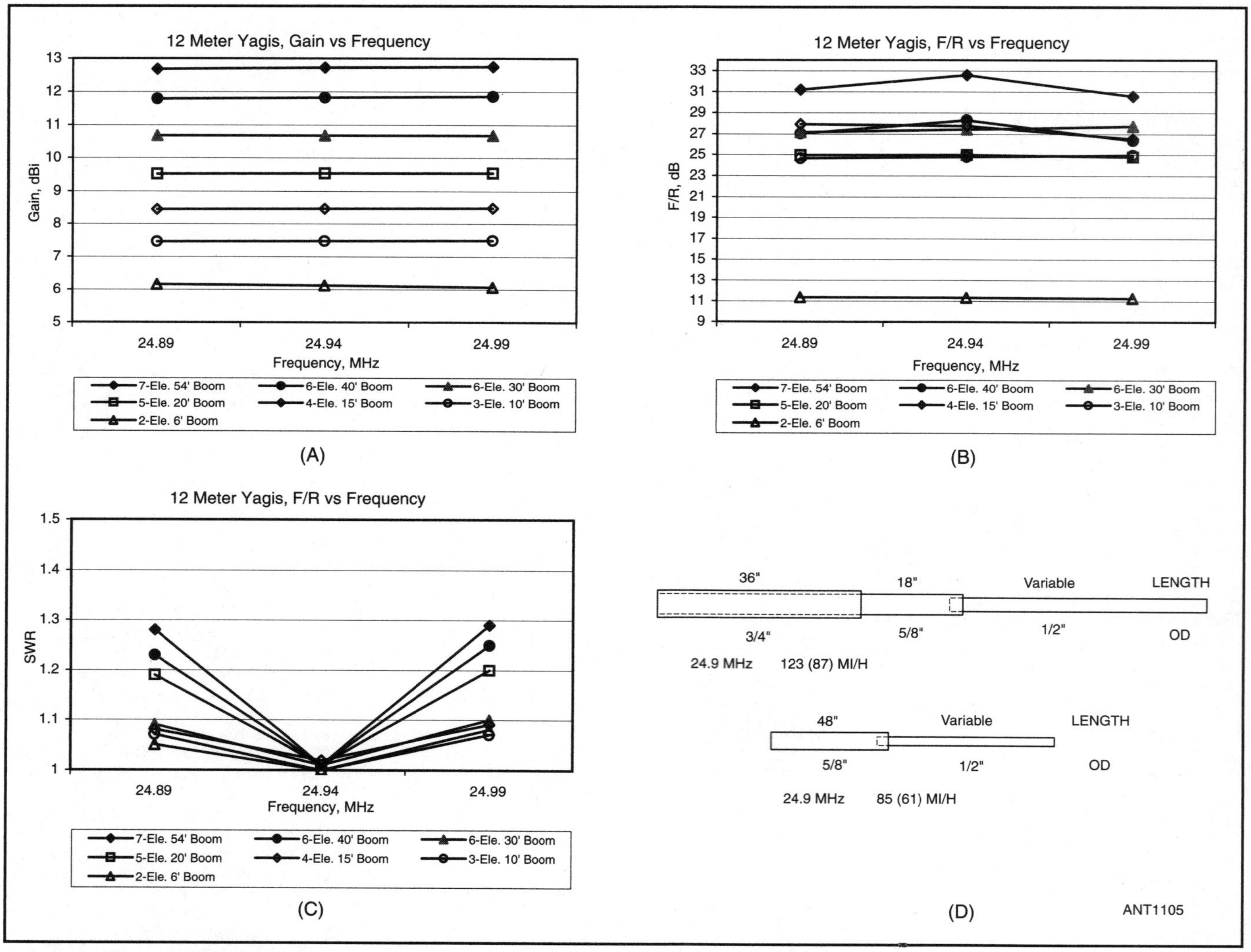

Figure 11.14 — Gain, F/R and SWR performance versus frequency for optimized 12 meter Yagis. At A, gain is shown versus frequency for seven 12 meter Yagis whose booms range from 6 feet to 54 feet long. Except for the 2-element design, these Yagis have been optimized for better than 20 dB F/R and less than 2:1 SWR over the narrow 12 meter band 24.89 to 24.99 MHz. At B, front-to-rear ratio for these antennas is shown versus frequency, and at C, SWR over the frequency range is shown. At D, the taper schedule for heavy-duty and for medium-duty 12 meter elements is shown. The heavy-duty elements can withstand 123-mph winds without icing, and 87-mph winds with ¼-inch radial ice. The medium-duty elements can survive 85-mph winds without icing, and 61-mph winds with ¼-inch radial ice. The wall thickness for each telescoping section of 6061-T6 aluminum tubing is 0.058 inches, and the overlap at each telescoping junction is 3 inches.

Table 11.2

Optimized 12 meter Yagi Designs

Two-element 12 meter Yagi, 6 foot boom

Element	*Spacing*	*Heavy-Duty Tip*	*Medium-Duty Tip*
File Name		212-06H.YW	212-06M.YW
Reflector	0.000"	67.500"	72.500"
Driven Element	66.000"	59.500"	65.000"

Three-element 12 meter Yagi, 10 foot boom

Element	*Spacing, inches*	*Heavy-Duty Tip*	*Medium-Duty Tip*
File Name		312-10H.YW	312-10M.YW
Reflector	0.000"	69.000"	73.875"
Driven Element	40.000"	60.250"	65.250"
Director 1	74.000"	54.000"	59.125"
Compensator	12" behind Dir. 1	13.625"	12.000"

Four-element 12 meter Yagi, 15 foot boom

Element	*Spacing, inches*	*Heavy-Duty Tip*	*Medium-Duty Tip*
File Name		412-15H.YW	412-15M.YW
Reflector	0.000"	66.875"	71.875"
Driven Element	46.000"	61.000"	66.000"
Director 1	46.000"	58.625"	63.750"
Director 2	82.000"	50.875"	56.125"
Compensator	12" behind Dir. 2	16.375"	14.500"

Five-element 12 meter Yagi, 20 foot boom

Element	*Spacing, inches*	*Heavy-Duty Tip*	*Medium-Duty Tip*
File Name		512-20H.YW	512-20M.YW
Reflector	0.000"	69.750"	74.625"
Driven Element	46.000"	62.250"	67.000"
Director 1	46.000"	60.500"	65.500"
Director 2	48.000"	55.500"	60.625"
Director 3	94.000"	54.625"	59.750"
Compensator	12" behind Dir. 3	22.125"	19.625"

Six-element 12 meter Yagi, 30 foot boom

Element	*Spacing, inches*	*Heavy-Duty Tip*	*Medium-Duty Tip*
File Name		612-30H.YW	612-30M.YW
Reflector	0.000"	68.125"	73.000"
Driven Element	46.000"	61.750"	66.750"
Director 1	46.000"	60.250"	65.250"
Director 2	73.000"	52.375"	57.625"
Director 3	75.000"	57.625"	62.750"
Director 4	114.000"	53.625"	58.750"
Compensator	12" behind Dir. 4	30.000"	26.250"

Six-element 12 meter Yagi, 40 foot boom

Element	*Spacing, inches*	*Heavy-Duty Tip*	*Medium-Duty Tip*
File Name		612-40H.YW	612-40M.YW
Reflector	0.000"	67.000"	71.875"
Driven Element	46.000"	60.125"	65.500"
Director 1	46.000"	57.375"	62.500"
Director 2	91.000"	57.375"	62.500"
Director 3	157.000"	57.000"	62.125"
Director 4	134.000"	54.375"	59.500"
Compensator	12" behind Dir. 4	36.500"	31.625"

Seven-element 12 meter Yagi, 54 foot boom

Element	*Spacing, inches*	*Heavy-Duty Tip*	*Medium-Duty Tip*
File Name		712-54H.YW	712-54M.YW
Reflector	0.000"	68.000"	73.000"
Driven Element	46.000"	60.500"	65.500"
Director 1	46.000"	56.750"	61.875"
Director 2	75.000"	58.000"	63.125"
Director 3	161.000"	55.625"	60.750"
Director 4	174.000"	56.000"	61.125"
Director 5	140.000"	53.125"	58.375"
Compensator	12" behind Dir. 5	43.125"	37.500"

These 12 meter Yagi designs were optimized for > 20 dB F/R, and SWR < 2:1 over frequency range from 24.890 to 24.990 MHz, for heavy-duty elements (123 mph wind survival) and for medium-duty (85 mph wind survival). Only element tip dimensions are shown, and all dimensions are inches. See Fig 11.14D for element telescoping tubing schedule. Torque compensator element is made of 2.5" OD PVC water pipe placed 12" behind last director. Dimensions shown for compensators is one-half of total length, centered on boom.

Table 11.3
Optimized 15 meter Yagi Designs

Two-element 15 meter Yagi, 6 foot boom

Element	*Spacing*	*Heavy-Duty Tip*	*Medium-Duty Tip*
File Name		215-06H.YW	215-06M.YW
Reflector	0.000"	62.000"	85.000"
Driven Element	66.000"	51.000"	74.000"

Three-element 15 meter Yagi, 12 foot boom

Element	*Spacing*	*Heavy-Duty Tip*	*Medium-Duty Tip*
File Name		315-12H.YW	315-12M.YW
Reflector	0.000"	62.000"	84.250"
Driven Element	48.000"	51.000"	73.750"
Director 1	92.000"	43.500"	66.750"
Compensator	12" behind Dir. 1	34.750"	37.625"

Four-element 15 meter Yagi, 18 foot boom

Element	*Spacing*	*Heavy-Duty Tip*	*Medium-Duty Tip*
File Name		415-18H.YW	415-18M.YW
Reflector	0.000"	61.000"	83.500"
Driven Element	56.000"	51.500"	74.500"
Director 1	56.000"	48.000"	71.125"
Director 2	98.000"	36.625"	60.250"
Compensator	12" behind Dir. 2	20.875"	18.625"

Five-element 15 meter Yagi, 24 foot boom

Element	*Spacing*	*Heavy-Duty Tip*	*Medium-Duty Tip*
File Name		515-24H.YW	515-24M.YW
Reflector	0.000"	62.000"	84.375"
Driven Element	48.000"	52.375"	75.250"
Director 1	48.000"	47.875"	71.000"
Director 2	52.000"	47.000"	70.125"
Director 3	134.000"	41.000"	64.375"
Compensator	12" behind Dir. 3	40.250"	35.125"

Six-element 15 meter Yagi, 36 foot boom

Element	*Spacing*	*Heavy-Duty Tip*	*Medium-Duty Tip*
File Name		615-36H.YW	615-36M.YW
Reflector	0.000"	61.000"	83.375"
Driven Element	53.000"	52.000"	75.000"
Director 1	56.000"	49.125"	72.125"
Director 2	59.000"	45.125"	68.375"
Director 3	116.000"	47.875"	71.000"
Director 4	142.000"	42.000"	65.375"
Compensator	12" behind Dir. 4	45.500"	39.750"

Seven-element 15 meter Yagi, 48 foot boom

Element	*Spacing*	*Heavy-Duty Tip*	*Medium-Duty Tip*
File Name		615-48H.YW	615-48M.YW
Reflector	0.000"	62.000"	84.000"
Driven Element	48.000"	52.000"	75.000"
Director 1	48.000"	51.250"	74.125"
Director 2	125.000"	48.000"	71.125"
Director 3	190.000"	45.500"	68.750"
Director 4	161.000"	42.000"	65.375"
Compensator	12" behind Dir. 4	51.500"	45.375"

Seven-element 15 meter Yagi, 60 foot boom

Element	*Spacing*	*Heavy-Duty Tip*	*Medium-Duty Tip*
File Name		715-60H.YW	715-60M.YW
Reflector	0.000"	59.750"	82.250"
Driven Element	48.000"	52.000"	75.000"
Director 1	48.000"	52.000"	74.875"
Director 2	93.000"	49.500"	72.500"
Director 3	173.000"	44.125"	67.375"
Director 4	197.000"	45.500"	68.750"
Director 5	155.000"	41.750"	65.125"
Compensator	12" behind Dir. 5	58.500"	51.000"

Eight-element 15 meter Yagi, 80 foot boom

Element	*Spacing*	*Heavy-Duty Tip*	*Medium-Duty Tip*
File Name		815-80H.YW	815-80M.YW
Reflector	0.000"	62.000"	84.000"
Driven Element	56.000"	52.500"	75.500"
Director 1	48.000"	51.500"	74.375"
Director 2	115.000"	48.375"	71.500"
Director 3	164.000"	45.750"	69.000"
Director 4	202.000"	43.125"	66.500"
Director 5	206.000"	44.750"	68.000"
Director 6	163.000"	40.875"	64.250"
Compensator	12" behind Dir. 6	95.000"	83.375"

These 15 meter Yagi designs are optimized for > 20 dB F/R, and SWR < 2:1 over entire frequency range from 21.000 to 21.450 MHz, for heavy-duty elements (124 mph wind survival) and for medium-duty (86 mph wind survival). Only element tip dimensions are shown. See Fig 11.15D for element telescoping tubing schedule. All dimensions are in inches. Torque compensator element is made of 2.5" OD PVC water pipe placed 12" behind last director, and dimensions shown for compensators is one-half of total length, centered on boom.

element) mounting plates. Figure 11.15A shows the free-space gain versus frequency for each antenna; Figure 11.15B shows the worst-case front-to-rear ratio, and Figure 11.15C shows the SWR versus frequency. Each antenna with three or more elements was designed to cover the full 15 meter band from 21.000 to 21.450 MHz, with SWR less than 2:1 and F/R ratio better than 20 dB over that range.

Figure 11.15D shows the taper schedule for two types of 15 meter elements. The heavy-duty design can survive 124-mph winds with no icing, and 90-mph winds with ¼ inch of radial ice. The medium-duty design can handle 86-mph winds with no icing, and 61-mph winds with ¼ inch of radial ice.

The element-to-boom mounting plate for these Yagis is a 0.375-inch thick flat aluminum plate, 5 inches wide by 6 inches long. The mounting plate has an effective diameter of 3.0362 inches for the heavy-duty element, and 2.9447 inches for the medium-duty element. The equivalent length on each side of the boom is 3 inches. As usual, the torque compensator is mounted 12 inches behind the last director.

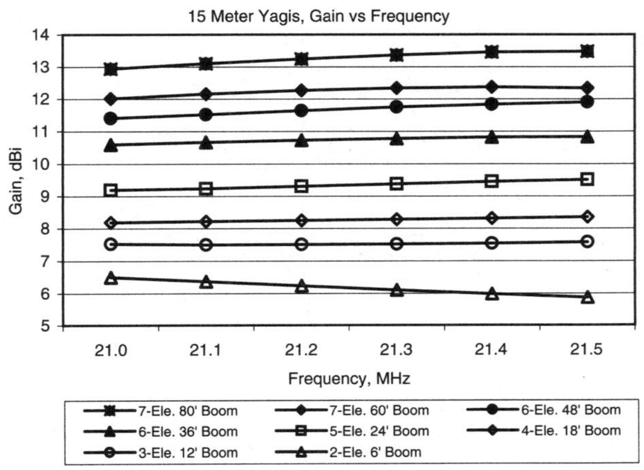

(A)

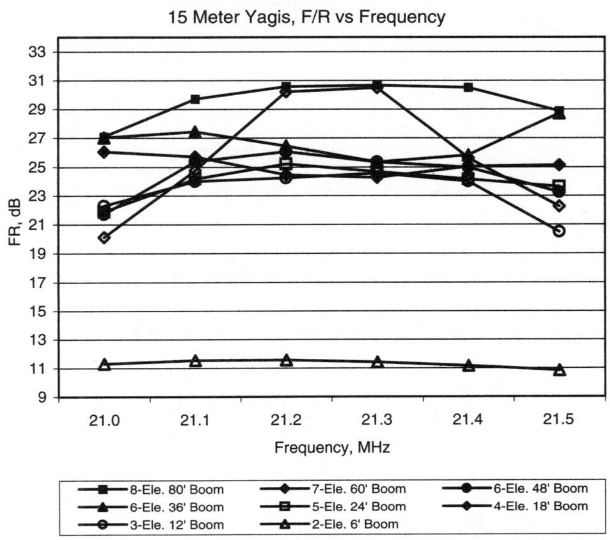

(B)

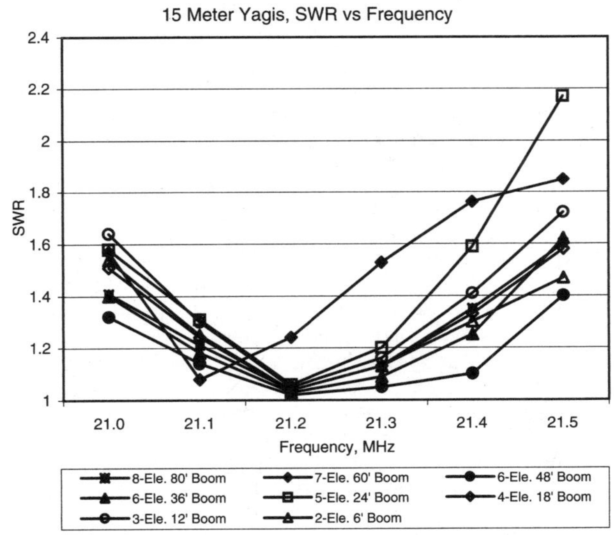

(C)

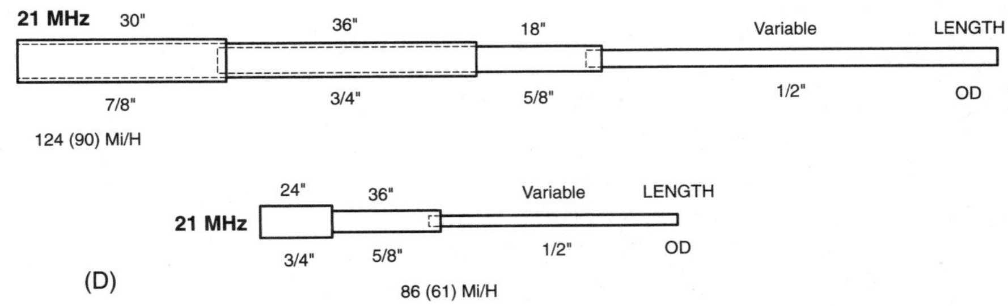

ANT1106

(D)

Figure 11.15 — Gain, F/R and SWR performance versus frequency for optimized 15 meter Yagis. At A, gain versus frequency is shown for eight 15 meter Yagis whose booms range from 6 feet to 80 feet long. Except for the 2-element design, these Yagis have been optimized for better than 20 dB F/R and less than 2:1 SWR over the frequency range 21.0 to 21.45 MHz. At B, front-to-rear ratio for these antennas is shown versus frequency, and at C, SWR over the frequency range is shown. At D, the taper schedule for heavy-duty and for medium-duty 15 meter elements is shown. The heavy-duty elements can withstand 124-mph winds without icing, and 90-mph winds with ¼-inch radial ice. The medium-duty elements can survive 86-mph winds without icing, and 61-mph winds with ¼-inch radial ice. The wall thickness for each telescoping section of 6061-T6 aluminum tubing is 0.058 inches, and the overlap at each telescoping junction is 3 inches.

11.4.4 17 METER YAGIS

Figure 11.16 describes the electrical performance of six optimized 17 meter Yagis with boom lengths between 6 to a heroic 60 feet. As usual, the end of each boom includes 3 inches of space for the reflector and last director (or driven element) mounting plates. Figure 11.16A shows the free-space gain versus frequency for each antenna; Figure 11.16B shows the worst-case front-to-rear ratio, and Figure 11.16C shows the SWR versus frequency. Each antenna with three or more elements was designed to cover the narrow 17 meter band from 18.068 to 18.168 MHz, with SWR less than 2:1 and F/R ratio better than 20 dB over that range.

Figure 11.16D shows the taper schedule for two types of 17 meter elements. The heavy-duty design can survive 123-mph winds with no icing, and 83-mph winds with ¼-inch of radial ice. The medium-duty design can handle 83-mph winds with no icing, and 59-mph winds with ¼ inch of radial ice.

The element-to-boom mounting plate for these Yagis is a 0.375-inch thick flat aluminum plate, 6 inches wide by 8 inches long. The mounting plate has an effective diameter of 3.5122 inches for the heavy-duty element, and 3.3299 inches for the medium-duty element. The equivalent length on each side of the boom is 4 inches. As usual, the torque compensator is mounted 12 inches behind the last director.

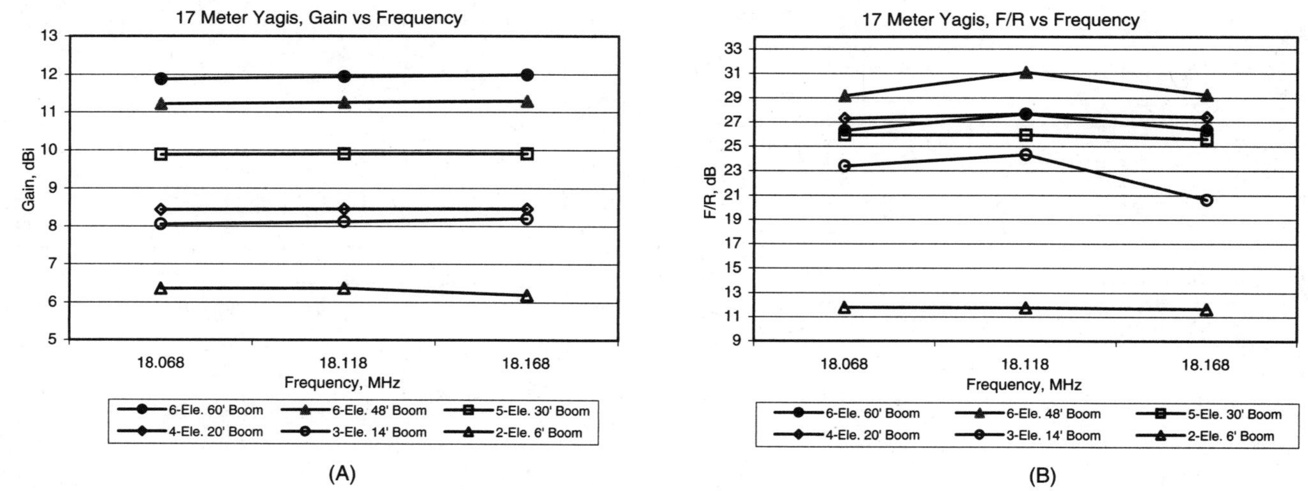

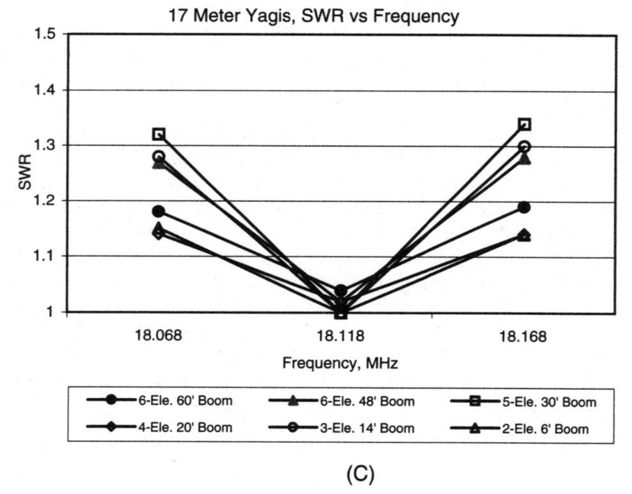

Figure 11.16 — Gain, F/R and SWR performance versus frequency for optimized 17 meter Yagis. At A, gain versus frequency is shown for six 17 meter Yagis whose booms range from 6 feet to 60 feet long. Except for the 2-element design, these Yagis have been optimized for better than 20 dB F/R and less than 2:1 SWR over the narrow 17 meter band 18.068 to 18.168 MHz. At B, front-to-rear ratio for these antennas is shown versus frequency, and at C, SWR over the frequency range is shown. At D, the taper schedule for heavy-duty and for medium-duty 10 meter elements is shown. The heavy-duty elements can withstand 123-mph winds without icing, and 89-mph winds with ¼-inch radial ice. The medium-duty elements can survive 83-mph winds without icing, and 59-mph winds with ¼-inch radial ice. The wall thickness for each telescoping section of 6061-T6 aluminum tubing is 0.058 inches, and the overlap at each telescoping junction is 3 inches.

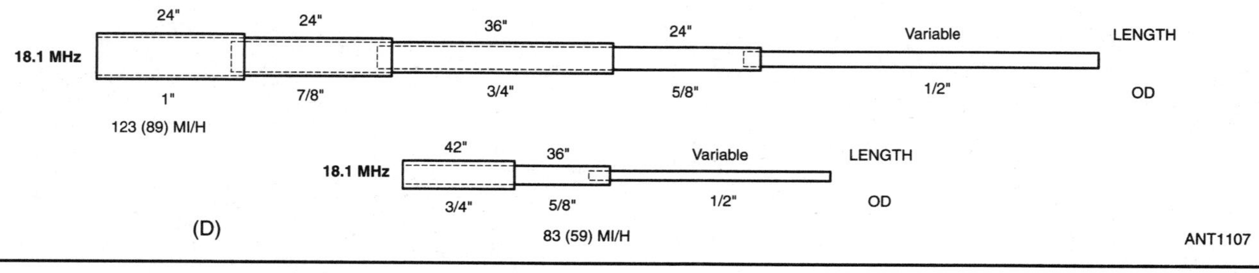

Table 11.4
Optimized 17 meter Yagi Designs

Two-element 17 meter Yagi, 6 foot boom

Element	*Spacing*	*Heavy-Duty Tip*	*Medium-Duty Tip*
File Name		217-06H.YW	217-06M.YW
Reflector	0.000"	61.000"	89.000"
Driven Element	66.000"	48.000"	76.250"

Three-element 17 meter Yagi, 14 foot boom

Element	*Spacing*	*Heavy-Duty Tip*	*Medium-Duty Tip*
File Name		317-14H.YW	317-14M.YW
Reflector	0.000"	61.500"	91.500"
Driven Element	65.000"	52.000"	79.500"
Director 1	97.000"	46.000"	73.000"
	12" behind Dir. 1	12.625"	10.750"

Four-element 17 meter Yagi, 20 foot boom

Element	*Spacing*	*Heavy-Duty Tip*	*Medium-Duty Tip*
File Name		417-20H.YW	417-20M.YW
Reflector	0.000"	61.500"	89.500"
Driven Element	48.000"	54.250"	82.625"
Director 1	48.000"	52.625"	81.125"
Director 2	138.000"	40.500"	69.625"
Compensator	12" behind Dir. 2	42.500"	36.250"

Five-element 17 meter Yagi, 30 foot boom

Element	*Spacing*	*Heavy-Duty Tip*	*Medium-Duty Tip*
File Name		517-30H.YW	517-30M.YW
Reflector	0.000"	61.875"	89.875"
Driven Element	48.000"	52.250"	80.500"
Director 1	52.000"	49.625"	78.250"
Director 2	93.000"	49.875"	78.500"
Director 3	161.000"	43.500"	72.500"
Compensator	12" behind Dir. 3	54.375"	45.875"

Six-element 17 meter Yagi, 48 foot boom

Element	*Spacing*	*Heavy-Duty Tip*	*Medium-Duty Tip*
File Name		617-48H.YW	617-48M.YW
Reflector	0.000"	63.000"	90.250"
Driven Element	52.000"	52.500"	80.500"
Director 1	51.000"	45.500"	74.375"
Director 2	87.000"	47.875"	76.625"
Director 3	204.000"	47.000"	75.875"
Director 4	176.000"	42.000"	71.125"
Compensator	12" behind Dir. 4	68.250"	57.500"

Six-element 17 meter Yagi, 60 foot boom

Element	*Spacing*	*Heavy-Duty Tip*	*Medium-Duty Tip*
File Name		617-60H.YW	617-60M.YW
Reflector	0.000"	61.250"	89.250"
Driven Element	54.000"	54.750"	83.125"
Director 1	54.000"	52.250"	80.750"
Director 2	180.000"	46.000"	74.875"
Director 3	235.000"	44.625"	73.625"
Director 4	191.000"	41.500"	70.625"
Compensator	12" behind Dir. 4	62.875"	53.000"

These 17 meter Yagi designs are optimized for > 20 dB F/R, and SWR < 2:1 over entire frequency range from18.068 to 18.168 MHz, for heavy-duty elements (123 mph wind survival) and for medium-duty (83 mph wind survival). Only element tip dimensions are shown. All dimensions are in inches. Torque compensator element is made of 2.5" OD PVC water pipe placed 12" behind last director, and dimensions shown for compensators is one-half of total length, centered on boom.

11.4.5 20 METER YAGIS

Figure 11.17 describes the electrical performance of eight optimized 20 meter Yagis with boom lengths between 8 to a giant 80 feet. As usual, the end of each boom includes 3 inches of space for the reflector and last director (driven element) mounting plates. Figure 11.17A shows the free-space gain versus frequency for each antenna; Figure 11.17B shows the front-to-rear ratio, and Figure 11.17C shows the SWR versus frequency. Each antenna with three or more elements was designed to cover the complete 20 meter band from 14.000 to 14.350 MHz, with SWR less than 2:1 and F/R ratio better than 20 dB over that range.

Figure 11.17D shows the taper schedule for two types of 20 meter elements. The heavy-duty design can survive 122-mph

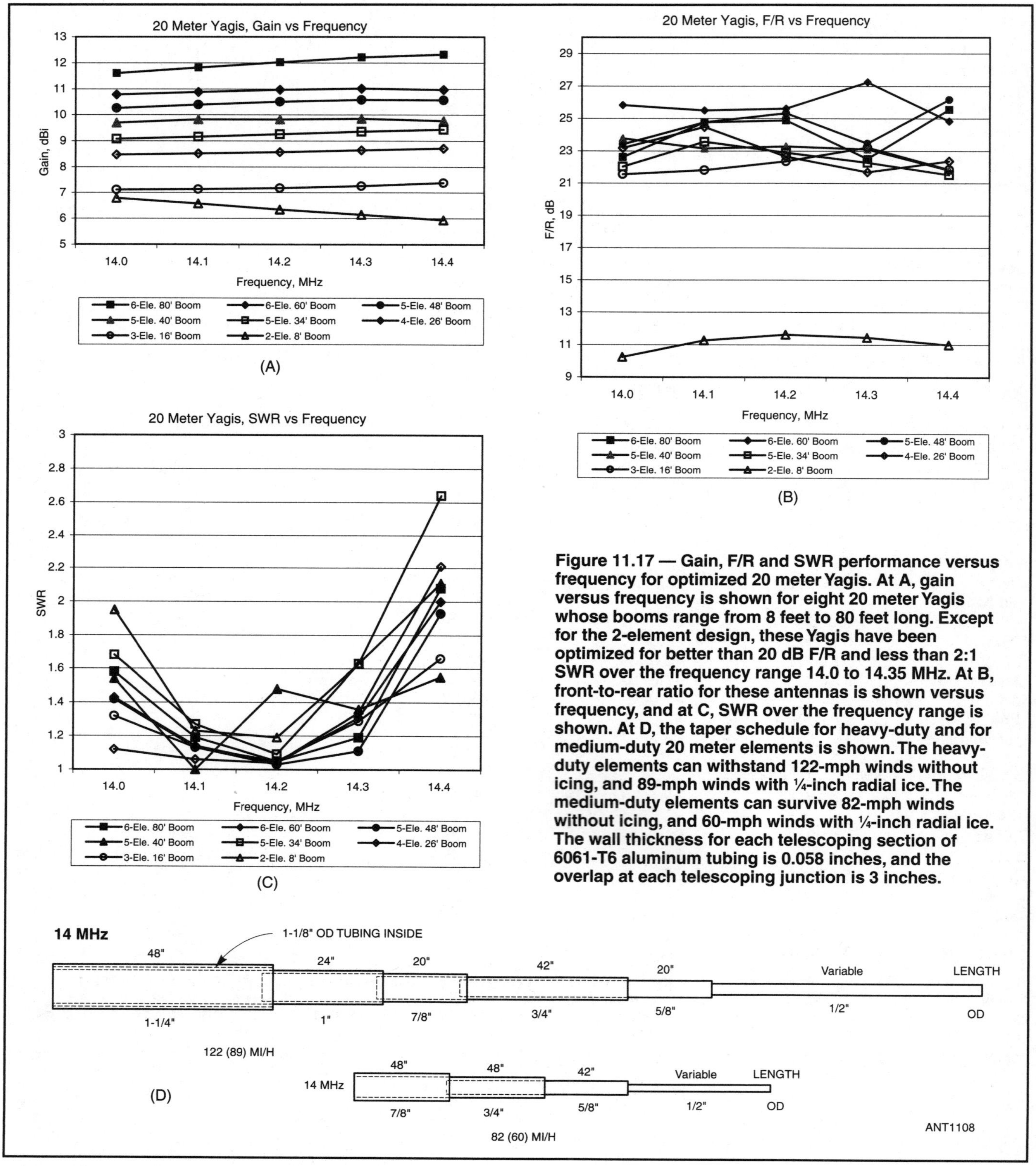

Figure 11.17 — Gain, F/R and SWR performance versus frequency for optimized 20 meter Yagis. At A, gain versus frequency is shown for eight 20 meter Yagis whose booms range from 8 feet to 80 feet long. Except for the 2-element design, these Yagis have been optimized for better than 20 dB F/R and less than 2:1 SWR over the frequency range 14.0 to 14.35 MHz. At B, front-to-rear ratio for these antennas is shown versus frequency, and at C, SWR over the frequency range is shown. At D, the taper schedule for heavy-duty and for medium-duty 20 meter elements is shown. The heavy-duty elements can withstand 122-mph winds without icing, and 89-mph winds with ¼-inch radial ice. The medium-duty elements can survive 82-mph winds without icing, and 60-mph winds with ¼-inch radial ice. The wall thickness for each telescoping section of 6061-T6 aluminum tubing is 0.058 inches, and the overlap at each telescoping junction is 3 inches.

Table 11.5
Optimized 20 meter Yagi Designs

Two-element 20 meter Yagi, 8 foot boom			
Element	*Spacing*	*Heavy-Duty Tip*	*Medium-Duty Tip*
File Name		220-08H.YW	220-08M.YW
Reflector	0.000"	66.000"	80.000"
Driven Element	90.000"	46.000"	59.000"
Three-element 20 meter Yagi, 16 foot boom			
Element	*Spacing*	*Heavy-Duty Tip*	*Medium-Duty Tip*
File Name		320-16H.YW	320-16M.YW
Reflector	0.000"	69.625"	81.625"
Driven Element	80.000"	51.250"	64.500"
Director 1	106.000"	42.625"	56.375"
Compensator	12" behind Dir. 1	33.375"	38.250"
Four-element 20 meter Yagi, 26 foot boom			
Element	*Spacing*	*Heavy-Duty Tip*	*Medium-Duty Tip*
File Name		420-26H.YW	420-26M.YW
Reflector	0.000"	65.625"	78.000"
Driven Element	72.000"	53.375"	65.375"
Director 1	60.000"	51.750"	63.875"
Director 2	174.000"	38.625"	51.500"
Compensator	12" behind Dir. 2	54.250"	44.250"
Five-element 20 meter Yagi, 34 foot boom			
Element	*Spacing*	*Heavy-Duty Tip*	*Medium-Duty Tip*
File Name		520-34H.YW	520-34M.YW
Reflector	0.000"	68.625"	80.750"
Driven Element	72.000"	52.250"	65.500"
Director 1	71.000"	45.875"	59.375"
Director 2	68.000"	45.875"	59.375"
Director 3	191.000"	37.000"	51.000"
Compensator	12" behind Dir. 3	69.250"	56.250"
Five-element 20 meter Yagi, 40 foot boom			
Element	*Spacing*	*Heavy-Duty Tip*	*Medium-Duty Tip*
File Name		520-40H.YW	520-40M.YW
Reflector	0.000"	68.375"	80.500"
Driven Element	72.000"	53.500"	66.625"
Director 1	72.000"	51.500"	64.625"
Director 2	139.000"	48.375"	61.750"
Director 3	191.000"	38.000"	52.000"
Compensator	12" behind Dir. 3	69.750"	56.750"
Five-element 20 meter Yagi, 48 foot boom			
Element	*Spacing*	*Heavy-Duty Tip*	*Medium-Duty Tip*
File Name		520-48H.YW	520-48M.YW
Reflector	0.000"	66.250"	78.500"
Driven Element	72.000"	53.000"	66.000"
Director 1	88.000"	50.500"	63.750"
Director 2	199.000"	47.375"	60.875"
Director 3	211.000"	39.750"	53.625"
Compensator	12" behind Dir. 3	70.325"	57.325"
Six-element 20 meter Yagi, 60 foot boom			
Element	*Spacing*	*Heavy-Duty Tip*	*Medium-Duty Tip*
File Name		620-60H.YW	620-60M.YW
Reflector	0.000"	67.000"	79.250"
Driven Element	84.000"	51.500"	65.000"
Director 1	91.000"	45.125"	58.750"
Director 2	130.000"	41.375"	55.125"
Director 3	210.000"	46.875"	60.375"
Director 4	199.000"	39.125"	53.000"
Compensator	12" behind Dir. 4	72.875"	59.250"
Six-element 20 meter Yagi, 80 foot boom			
Element	*Spacing*	*Heavy-Duty Tip*	*Medium-Duty Tip*
File Name		620-80H.YW	620-80M.YW
Reflector	0.000"	66.125"	78.375"
Driven Element	72.000"	52.375"	65.500"
Director 1	122.000"	49.125"	62.500"
Director 2	229.000"	44.500"	58.125"
Director 3	291.000"	42.625"	56.375"
Director 4	240.000"	38.750"	52.625"
Compensator	12" behind Dir. 4	78.750"	64.125"

These 20 meter Yagi designs are optimized for > 20 dB F/R, and SWR < 2:1 over entire frequency range from 14.000 to 14.350 MHz, for heavy-duty elements (122 mph wind survival) and for medium-duty (82 mph wind survival). Only element tip dimensions are shown. See Fig 11.17 for element telescoping tubing schedule. All dimensions are in inches. Torque compensator element is made of 2.5" OD PVC water pipe placed 12" behind last director, and dimensions shown for compensators is one-half of total length, centered on boom.

winds with no icing, and 89-mph winds with ¼ inch of radial ice. The medium-duty design can handle 82-mph winds with no icing, and 60-mph winds with ¼ inch of radial ice.

The element-to-boom mounting plate for these Yagis is a 0.375-inch thick flat aluminum plate, 6 inches wide by 8 inches long. The mounting plate has an effective diameter of 3.7063 inches for the heavy-duty element, and 3.4194 inches for the medium-duty element. The equivalent length on each side of the boom is 4 inches. As usual, the torque compensator is mounted 12 inches behind the last director.

11.4.6 30 METER YAGIS

Figure 11.18 describes the electrical performance of three optimized 30 meter Yagis with boom lengths between 15 to 34 feet. Because of the size and weight of the elements alone for Yagis on this band, only 2-element and 3-element designs are described. The front-to-rear ratio requirement for the 2-element antenna is relaxed to be greater than 10 dB over the band from 10.100 to 10.150 MHz, while that for the 3-element designs is kept at greater than 20 dB over that frequency range.

As usual, the end of each boom includes 3 inches of space for the reflector and last director mounting plates. Figure 11.18A shows the free-space gain versus frequency for each antenna; Figure 11.18B shows the worst-case front-to-rear ratio, and Figure 11.18C shows the SWR versus frequency.

Figure 11.18D shows the taper schedule for the 30 meter

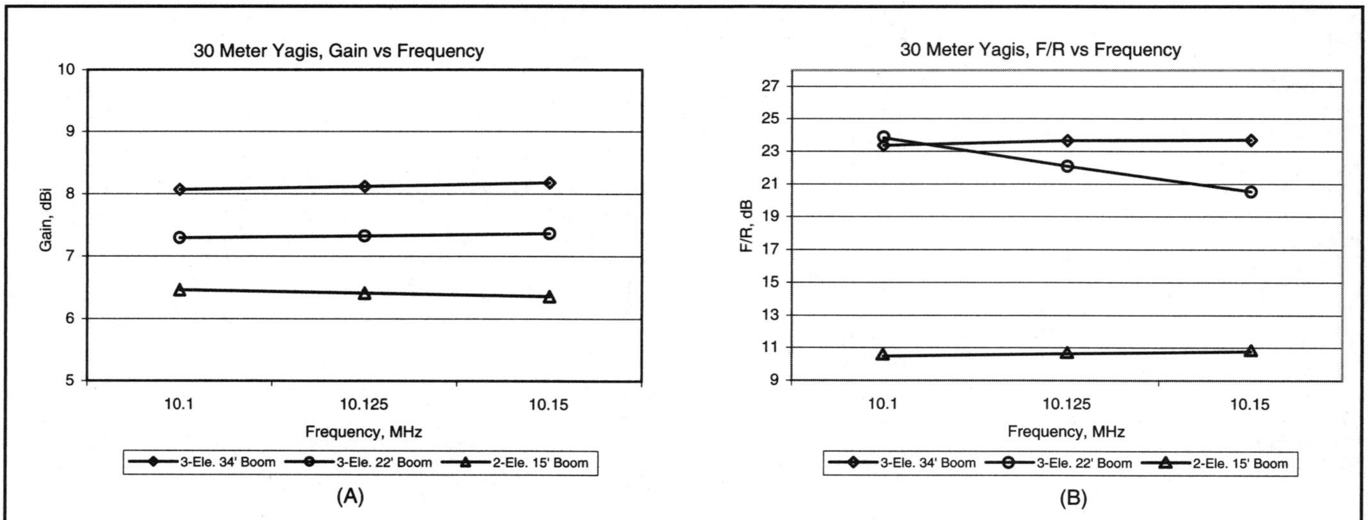

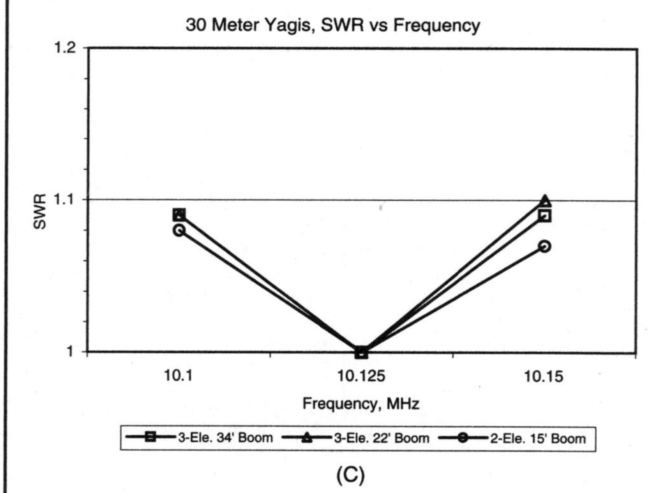

Figure 11.18 — Gain, F/R and SWR performance versus frequency for optimized 30 meter Yagis. At A, gain versus frequency is shown for three 30 meter Yagis whose booms range from 15 feet to 34 feet long, and which have been optimized for better than 10 dB F/R and less than 2:1 SWR over the frequency range 10.1 to 10.15 MHz. At B, front-to-rear ratio for these antennas is shown versus frequency, and at C, SWR over the frequency range is shown. At D, the taper schedule is shown for heavy-duty 30 meter elements, which can withstand 107-mph winds without icing, and 93-mph winds with ¼-inch radial ice. Except for the 2¼-inch and 2-inch sections, which have 0.083 inch thick walls, the wall thickness for the other telescoping sections of 6061-T6 aluminum tubing is 0.058 inches, and the overlap at the 1 inch telescoping junction with the ⅞-inch section is complete. The 2-inch section utilizes two machined aluminum reducers to accommodate the 1-inch tubing.

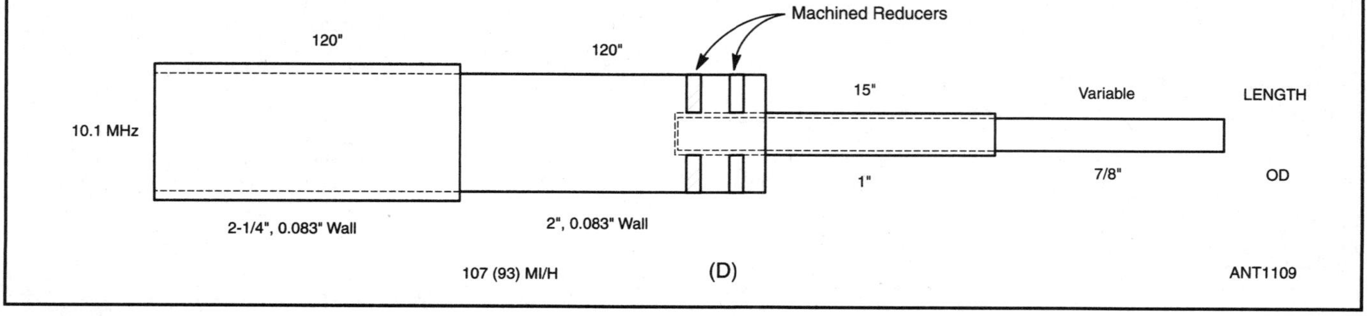

elements. Note that the wall thickness of the first two sections of tubing is 0.083 inches, rather than 0.058 inches. This heavy-duty element design can survive 107-mph winds with no icing, and 93-mph winds with ¼ inch of radial ice.

The element-to-boom mounting plate for these Yagis is a 0.500-inch thick flat aluminum plate, 6 inches wide by 24 inches long. The mounting plate has an effective diameter of 4.684 inches. The equivalent length on each side of the boom is 12 inches. These designs require no torque compensator.

11.4.7 40 METER YAGIS

Figure 11.19 describes the electrical performance of three optimized 40 meter Yagis with boom lengths between 20 to 48 feet. Like the 30 meter antennas, because of the size and weight of the elements for a 40 meter Yagi, only 2-element and 3-element designs are described. The front-to-rear ratio requirement for the 2-element antenna is relaxed to be greater than 10 dB over the band from 7.000 to 7.300 MHz, while the goal for the 3-element designs is 20 dB over the frequency range of 7.000 to 7.200 MHz. It is exceedingly difficult to hold the F/R greater than 20 dB over the entire 40 meter band without sacrificing excessive gain with a 3-element design.

As usual, the end of each boom includes 3 inches of space for the reflector and last director mounting plates. Figure 11.19A shows the free-space gain versus frequency for each antenna;

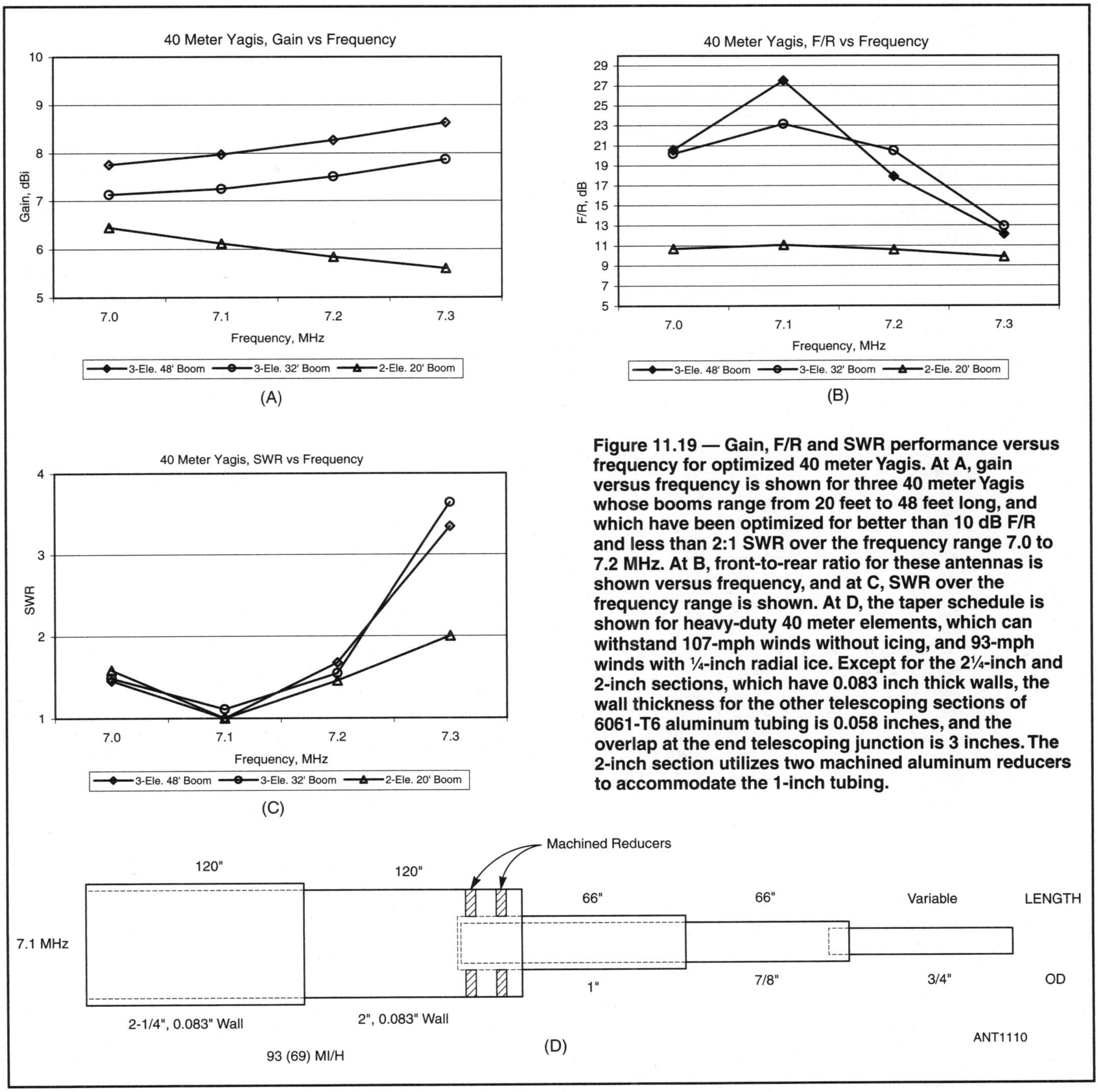

Figure 11.19 — Gain, F/R and SWR performance versus frequency for optimized 40 meter Yagis. At A, gain versus frequency is shown for three 40 meter Yagis whose booms range from 20 feet to 48 feet long, and which have been optimized for better than 10 dB F/R and less than 2:1 SWR over the frequency range 7.0 to 7.2 MHz. At B, front-to-rear ratio for these antennas is shown versus frequency, and at C, SWR over the frequency range is shown. At D, the taper schedule is shown for heavy-duty 40 meter elements, which can withstand 107-mph winds without icing, and 93-mph winds with ¼-inch radial ice. Except for the 2¼-inch and 2-inch sections, which have 0.083 inch thick walls, the wall thickness for the other telescoping sections of 6061-T6 aluminum tubing is 0.058 inches, and the overlap at the end telescoping junction is 3 inches. The 2-inch section utilizes two machined aluminum reducers to accommodate the 1-inch tubing.

Table 11.6
Optimized 30 meter Yagi Designs

Two-element 30 meter Yagi, 15 foot boom

Element	*Spacing*	*Heavy-Duty Tip*
File Name		230-15H.YW
Reflector	0.000"	50.250"
Driven Element	174.000"	14.875"

3-element 30 meter Yagi, 22 foot boom

Element	*Spacing*	*Heavy-Duty Tip*
File Name		330-22H.YW
Reflector	0.000	59.375
Driven Element	135.000	35.000
Director 1	123.000	19.625

Three-element 30 meter Yagi, 34 foot boom

Element	*Spacing*	*Heavy-Duty Tip*
File Name		330-34H.YW
Reflector	0.000"	53.750"
Driven Element	212"	29.000"
Director 1	190"	14.500"

These 30 meter Yagi designs are optimized for > 10 dB F/R, and SWR < 2:1 over entire frequency range from 10.100 to 10.150 MHz for heavy-duty elements (105 mph wind survival). Only element tip dimensions are shown. See Fig 11.18D for element telescoping tubing schedule. All dimensions are in inches. No torque compensator element is required.

Table 11.7
Optimized 40 meter Yagi Designs

Two-element 40 meter Yagi, 20 foot boom

Element	*Spacing*	*Heavy-Duty Tip*
File Name		240-20H.YW
Reflector	0.000"	85.000"
Driven Element	234.000"	35.000"

Three-element 40 meter Yagi, 32 foot boom

Element	*Spacing*	*Heavy-Duty Tip*
File Name		340-32H.YW
Reflector	0.000"	90.750"
Driven Element	196.000"	55.875"
Director 1	182.000"	33.875"

Three-element 40 meter Yagi, 48 foot boom

Element	*Spacing*	*Heavy-Duty Tip*
File Name		340-48H.YW
Reflector	0.000"	81.000"
Driven Element	300.000"	45.000"
Director 1	270.000"	21.000"

These 40 meter Yagi designs are optimized for > 10 dB F/R, and SWR < 2:1 over low-end of frequency range from 7.000 to 7.200 MHz, for heavy-duty elements (95 mph wind survival). Only element tip dimensions are shown. See Fig 11.19D for element telescoping tubing schedule. All dimensions are in inches. No wind torque compensator is required.

Figure 11.19B shows the front-to- rear ratio, and Figure 11.19C shows the SWR versus frequency.

Figure 11.19D shows the taper schedule for the 40 meter elements. Note that the wall thickness of the first two sections of tubing is 0.083 inches, rather than 0.058 inches. This element design can survive 93-mph winds with no icing, and 69-mph winds with ¼ inch of radial ice.

The element-to-boom mounting plate for these Yagis is a 0.500-inch thick flat aluminum plate, 6 inches wide by 24 inches long. The mounting plate has an effective diameter of 4.684 inches. The equivalent length on each side of the boom is 12 inches. These designs require no torque compensator.

11.4.8 MODIFYING MONOBAND HY-GAIN YAGIS

Enterprising amateurs have long used the Hy-Gain "Long John" series of HF monobanders as a source of top-quality aluminum and hardware for customized Yagis. Often-modified older models include the 105BA for 10 meters, the 155BA for 15 meters, and the 204BA and 205BA for 20 meters. Newer Hy-Gain designs, the 105CA, 155CA and 205CA, have been redesigned by computer for better performance.

Hy-Gain antennas have historically had an excellent reputation for superior mechanical design. In the older designs the elements were purposely spaced along the boom to achieve good weight balance at the mast-to-boom bracket, with electrical performance as a secondary goal. Thus, the electrical performance was not necessarily optimal, particularly over an entire amateur band.

Newer Hy-Gain designs are electrically superior to the older ones, but because of the strong concern for weight

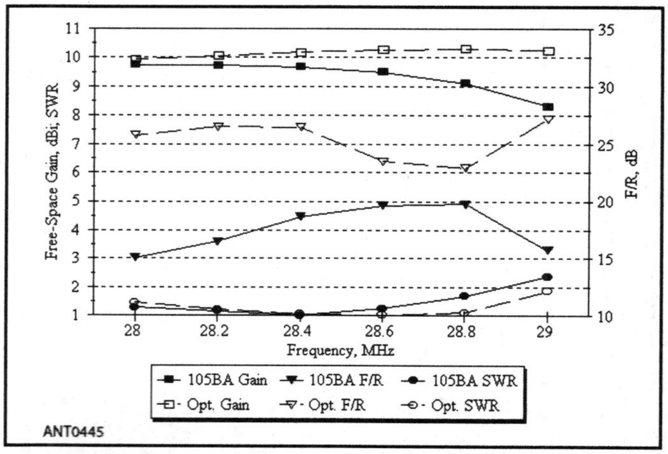

Figure 11.20 — Gain, F/R and SWR over the 28.0 to 28.8 MHz range for original and optimized Yagis using Hy-Gain hardware. Original 105BA design provided excellent weight balance at boom-to-mast bracket, but compromised the electrical performance somewhat because of non-optimum spacing of elements. Optimized design requires wind torque-balancing compensator element, and compensating weight at director end of boom to rebalance weight. The F/R ratio over the frequency range for the optimized design is more than 23 dB. Each element uses the original Hy-Gain taper schedule and element-to-boom clamp, but the length of the tip is changed per Table 11.8.

balance are still not optimal by the definitions used in this chapter. With the addition of wind torque-compensation dummy elements, and with extra lead weights where necessary at the director end of the boom for weight-balance, the electrical performance can be enhanced, using the same proven mechanical parts.

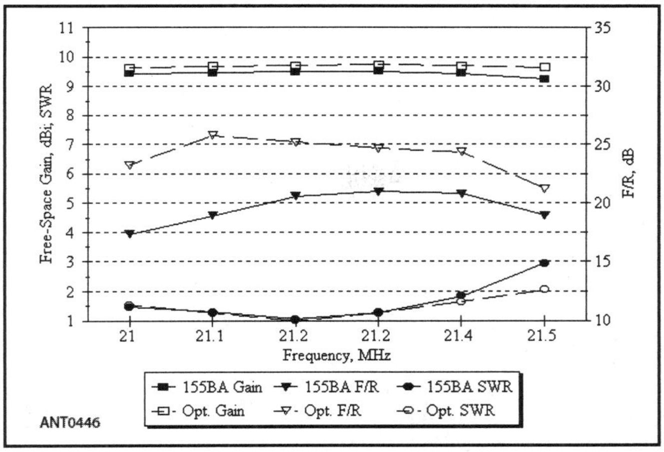

Figure 11.21 — Gain, F/R and SWR over the 21.0 to 21.45 MHz band for original and optimized Yagis using Hy-Gain hardware. Original 155BA design provided excellent weight balance at boom-to-mast bracket, but compromised the electrical performance somewhat because of non-optimum spacing of elements. Optimized design requires wind torque-balancing compensator element, and compensating weight at director end of boom to rebalance weight. The F/R ratio over the frequency range for the optimized design is more than 22 dB. Each element uses the original Hy-Gain taper schedule and element-to-boom clamp, but the length of the tip is changed per Table 11.9.

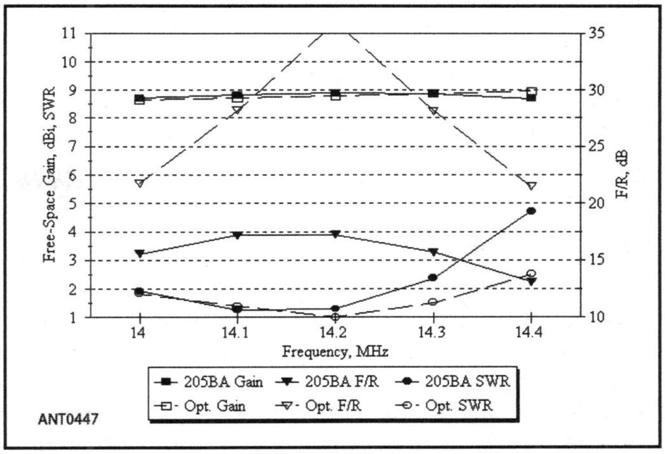

Figure 11.22 — Gain, F/R and SWR over the 14.0 to 14.35 MHz band for original and optimized Yagis using Hy-Gain hardware. Original 205BA design provided good weight balance at boom-to-mast bracket, but compromised the electrical performance because of non-optimum spacing of elements. Optimized design requires wind torque-balancing compensator element, and compensating weight at director end of boom to rebalance weight. The F/R ratio over the frequency range for the optimized design is more than 23 dB, while the original design never went beyond 17 dB of F/R. Each element uses the original Hy-Gain taper schedule and element-to-boom clamp, but the length of the tip is changed per Table 11.10.

Table 11.8
Optimized Hy-Gain 20 meter Yagi Designs

Optimized 204BA, Four-element 20 meter Yagi, 26 foot boom

Element	*Spacing*	*Element Tip*
File Name		BV204CA.YW
Reflector	0.000"	56.000"
Driven Element	85.000"	52.000"
Director 1	72.000"	61.500"
Director 2	149.000"	50.125"

Optimized 205CA, Five-element 20 meter Yagi, 34 foot boom

Element	*Spacing*	*Element Tip*
File Name		BV205CA.YW
Reflector	0.000"	62.625"
Driven Element	72.000"	53.500"
Director 1	72.000"	63.875"
Director 2	74.000"	61.625"
Director 3	190.000"	55.000"

Note that because the HyGain boom-to-element clamps require several inches of boom, the elements can't be mounted exactly at the end of the boom. Since the boom length of 34' is the same as the sum of element spacings, Director 3 cannot have a spacing of 190" and will have to be a few inches less. This does not result in a significant change in the antenna pattern according to designer Dean Straw, N6BV.

Figure 11.20 shows the computed gain, F/R ratio and SWR for a 24-foot boom, 10 meter optimized Yagi (modified 105BA) using Hy-Gain hardware. **Figure 11.21** shows the same for a 26-foot boom 15 meter Yagi (modified 155BA), and **Figure 11.22** shows the same for a 34-foot boom (modified 205BA) 20 meter Yagi. **Tables 11.8** through **11.10** show dimensions for these designs. The original Hy-Gain taper schedule is used for each element. Only the length of the end tip (and the spacing along the boom) is changed for each element.

Table 11.9
Optimized Hy-Gain 15 meter Yagi Designs

Optimized 155BA, Five-element 15 meter Yagi, 26 foot boom

Element	*Spacing*	*Element Tip*
File Name		BV155CA.YW
Reflector	0.000"	64.000"
Driven Element	48.000"	65.500"
Director 1	48.000"	63.875"
Director 2	82.750"	61.625"
Director 3	127.250"	55.000"

Table 11.10
Optimized Hy-Gain 10 meter Yagi Designs

Optimized 105BA, Five-element 10 meter Yagi, 24 foot boom

Element	*Spacing, inches*	*Element Tip*
File Name		BV105CA.YW
Reflector	0.000"	44.250"
Driven Element	40.000"	53.625"
Director 1	40.000"	52.500"
Director 2	89.500"	50.500"
Director 3	112.250"	44.750"

11.5 MULTIBAND YAGIS

So far, this chapter has discussed monoband Yagis — that is, Yagis designed for a single Amateur Radio frequency band. Because hams have operating privileges on more than one band, multiband coverage has always been very desirable.

Interlacing Elements

In the late 1940s, some experimenters tried interlacing Yagi elements for different frequencies on a single boom, mainly to cover the 10 and 20 meter bands (at that time the 15 meter band wasn't yet available to hams). The experimenters discovered that the mutual interactions between different elements tuned to different frequencies are very difficult to handle.

Adjusting a lower-frequency element usually results in interaction with higher-frequency elements near it. In effect, the lower-frequency element acts like a retrograde reflector, throwing off the effectiveness of the higher-frequency directors nearby. Element lengths and the spacing between elements can be changed to improve performance of the higher-frequency Yagi, but the resulting compromise is rarely equal to that of an optimized monoband Yagi. A reasonable compromise for portable operation was developed by VE7CA and is described in the **Portable Antennas** chapter.

Trap Multibanders

Multiband Yagis using a single boom can also be made using traps. Traps allow an element to have multiple resonances. The **Multiband Antennas** chapter provides details on trap designs. The general function is very similar to trap dipoles in which the traps act as open circuits or reactances that change the electrical length of the element at different frequencies.

Commercial vendors have sold trap antennas to hams since the 1950s and surveys show that after simple wire dipoles and multiband verticals, trap triband Yagis are the most popular antennas in the Amateur Radio service.

The originator of the trap tribander was Chester Buchanan, W3DZZ, in his March 1955 *QST* article, "The Multimatch Antenna System." On 10 meters this rather unusual tribander used two reflectors (one dedicated and one with traps) and two directors (one dedicated and one with traps). On 20 and 15 meters three of the five elements were active using traps. The W3DZZ tribander employed 12 traps overall, made with heavy wire and concentric tubular capacitors to hold down losses in the traps. Each trap was individually fine-tuned after construction before mounting it on an element.

Another example of a homemade tribander was the 26-foot boom 7-element 20/15/10 meter design described by Bob Myers, W1XT (ex-W1FBY) in December 1970 *QST*. The W1FBY tribander used only two sets of traps in the driven element, with dedicated reflectors and directors for each frequency band. Again, the traps were quite robust in this design to minimize trap losses, using 7⁄16-inch aluminum tubing for the coils and short pieces of RG-8 coax as high-voltage tuning capacitors.

Relatively few hams actually build tribanders for themselves, mainly because of the mechanical complexity and the close tolerances required for such antennas. The traps themselves must be constructed quite accurately for reproducible results, and they must be carefully weatherproofed for long life in rain, snow, and often polluted or corrosive atmospheres.

Traps, like any lumped-constant circuit, have some amount of loss which can be minimized with careful design. The primary compromise incurred in a trap multiband Yagi is the fixed element spacing on all bands. The usual tribander design is optimized for the middle band while the spacing is a bit too long for the highest band and a bit too short for the lowest band. Nevertheless, trap tribanders provide good performance in a compact package.

Christmas Tree Stacks

Another possible method for achieving multiband coverage using monoband Yagis is to stack them in a "Christmas tree" arrangement as in **Figure 11.23**. For an installation covering 20, 15 and 10 meters, you could mount the 20 meter monobander on the rotating mast just at the top of the tower. Then perhaps 9 feet above that you would mount the 15 meter monobander, followed by the 10 meter monoband Yagi 7 feet further up on the mast. Another configuration would be to place the 10 meter Yagi in between the lower 20 meter and upper 15 meter Yagis. Whatever the arrangement, the antenna in the middle of such a Christmas-tree always suffers the most interaction from the lowest-frequency Yagi.

Dave Leeson, W6NL, mentions that the 10 meter Yagi in a closely stacked Christmas Tree (15 meters at the top, 10 meters in the middle, and 20 meters at the bottom of the rotating mast) loses "substantial gain" because of serious interaction with the 20 meter antenna. (N6BV and K1VR calculated that the free-space gain in the W6NL stack drops to 5 dBi, compared to about 9 dBi with no surrounding antennas.) Monobanders are *definitely not* universally superior to tribanders in multiband installations.

Forward Staggering

Some hams have built multiband Yagis on a common boom, using a technique called *forward staggering*. This means that that most (or all) of the higher-frequency elements are placed in front of any lower-frequency elements — in other words, most of the elements are not interlaced. Richard Fenwick, K5RR, described his triband Yagi design in September 1996 *QEX* magazine. This uses forward-stagger and open-sleeve design techniques and was optimized using several sophisticated modeling programs.

Fenwick's tribander used a 57-foot, 3-inch OD boom to hold 4 elements on 20 meters, 4 elements on 15 meters and

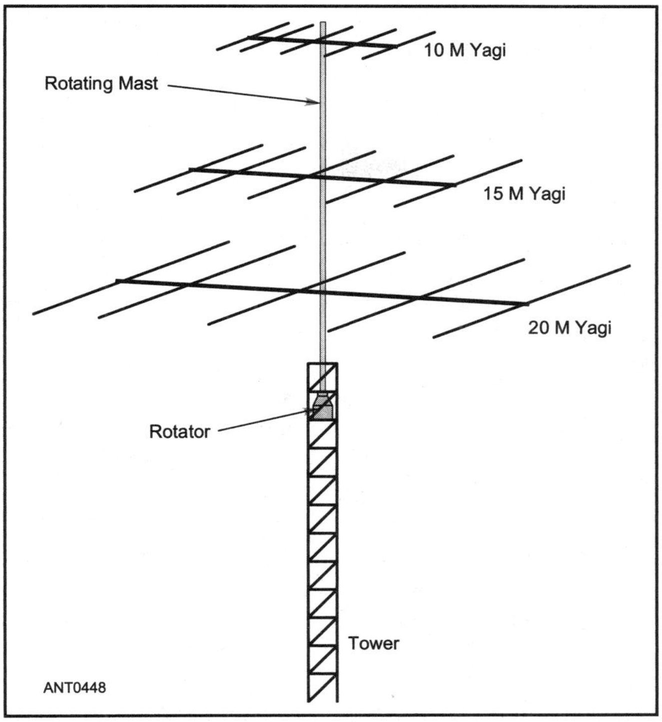

Figure 11.23 — "Christmas Tree" stack of 20/15/10 meter Yagis spaced vertically on a single rotating mast.

5 elements on 10 meters. **Figure 11.24** shows the element placement for the K5RR tribander. Most hams, of course, don't have the real-estate or the large rotator needed to turn such a large, but elegant solution to the interaction problem!

Force 12 C-3 "Multi-Monoband" Triband Yagi

Antenna manufacturer Force 12 used forward-stagger layouts and patented combinations of open- and closed-sleeve drive techniques extensively in their product line of multiband antennas, which they called "multi-monoband Yagis." **Figure 11.25** shows the layout for the popular Force 12 C-3 triband Yagi. The C-3 uses no traps, thereby avoiding any losses due to traps. The C-3 consists of three 2-element Yagis on an 18-foot boom, using full-sized elements designed to withstand high winds. (There is a pair of 10 meter driven elements for coverage of the full band.) Similar multiband Yagis with various band combinations are available from several manufacturers.

The C-3 feed system employs open-sleeves, where the 20 meter driver element is fed with coax through a common-mode current balun and parasitically couples to the closely spaced 15 meter driver and the two 10 meter driven elements to yield a feed point impedances close to 50 Ω on all three bands. Open-sleeve dipoles are discussed in the **Multiband Antennas** chapter.

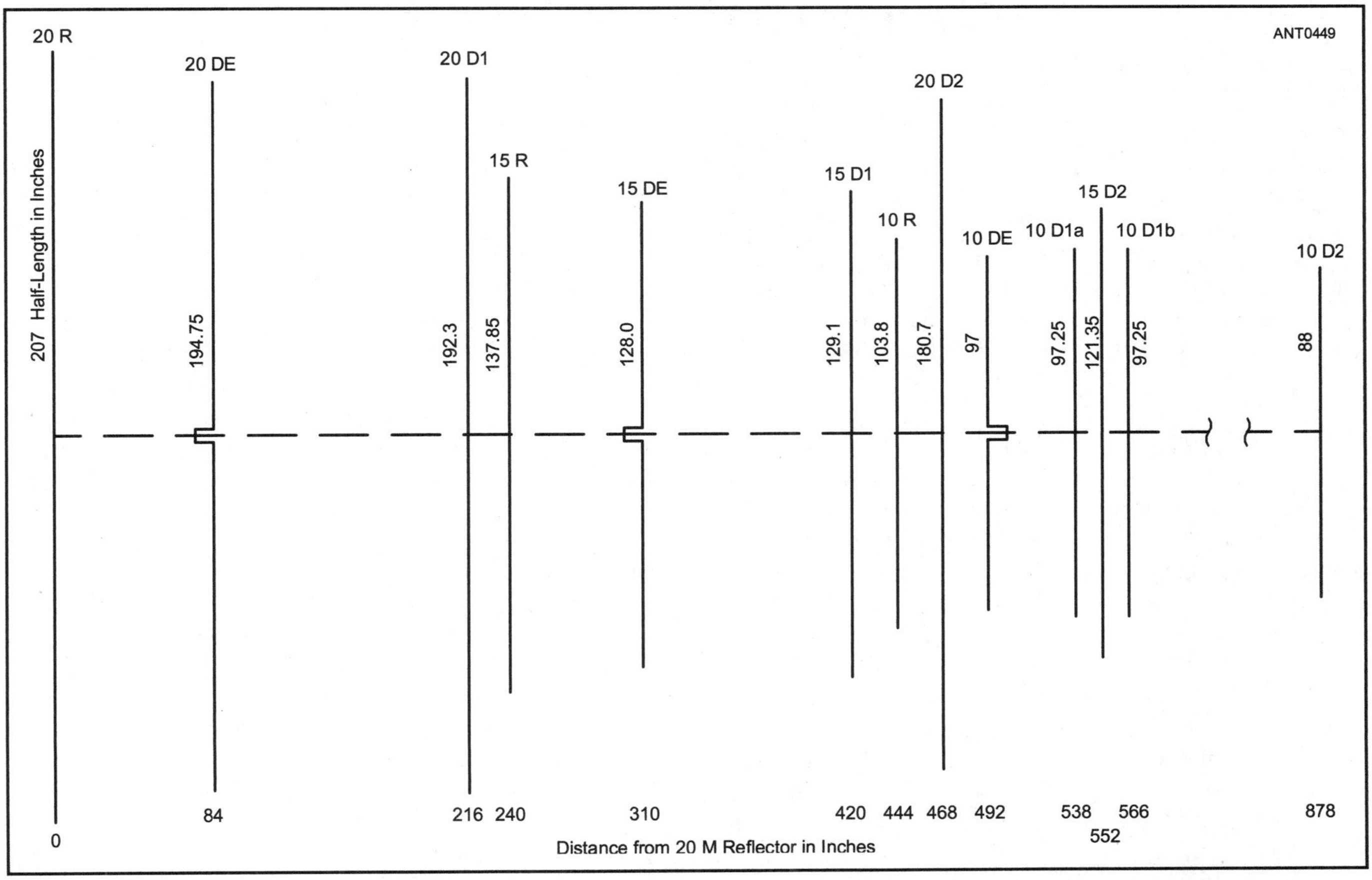

Figure 11.24 — Dimensions of K5RR's trap-less tribander using "forward stagger" and open-sleeve techniques to manage interaction between elements for different frequencies.

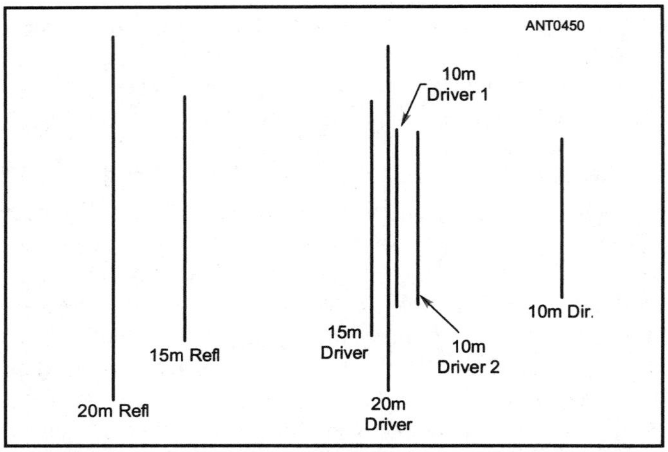

Figure 11.25 — Layout of Force 12 C3 multiband Yagi. Note that the 10 meter (driver/director) portion of the antenna is "forward staggered" ahead of the 15 meter (reflector/driver) portion, which in turn is placed ahead of the 20 meter (reflector/driver) portion. The antenna is fed at the 20 meter driver, which couples parasitically to the 15 meter driver and the two 10 meter drivers.

Note the use of the forward-stagger technique in the C-3, especially on 10 meters. To reduce interaction with the lower-frequency elements behind it, the 10 meter portion of the C-3 is mounted on the boom ahead of all the lower-frequency elements with the main 10 meter parasitic element (#7) acting as a director. The lower-frequency elements behind the 10 meter section act as retrograde reflectors, gaining some improvement of the gain and pattern compared to a monoband 2-element Yagi. A simplified *EZNEC* model of the C-3 is included with this book's downloadable supplemental information.

On 15 meters, the main parasitic element (#2) is a dedicated reflector, but the other elements ahead on the boom act like retrograde directors to improve the gain and pattern somewhat over a typical 2-element Yagi with a reflector. On 20 meters, the C-3 is a 2-element Yagi with a dedicated reflector (#1) at the back end of the boom.

The exact implementation of any Yagi, of course, depends on the way the elements are constructed using telescoping aluminum tubing. The C-3 type of design is no exception.

11.6 SHORTENING YAGI ELEMENTS

Almost any technique that can be used to reduce the physical length of a dipole can also be used to shorten the physical length of a Yagi element. The tradeoffs are additional mechanical complexity and reduced performance with respect to forward gain and SWR bandwidth. As with shortened dipoles and monopoles, placement of the loading structures is critical to obtaining good performance and careful modeling is required. (Caution should be used in modeling wires that are very close to each other, junctions of large-diameter conductors, and other complex mechanical arrangements.)

Linear Loading

The most common size-reducing technique is *linear loading* and it can be applied to Yagis as well as dipoles and verticals. An example of linear loading for a dipole was presented by Lew Gordon, K4VX, in his July 2002 *QST* article. A very similar example of linear loading for a 2-element 20 meter Yagi can be found in a June 1976 *QST* article by Cole Collings, WØYNF.

Linear loading essentially consists of folding the antenna into a zig-zag pattern. Each back-and-forth folded segment radiates very little because the field from each of the folded conductors partially cancels that of the adjacent conductors. Nevertheless, the folding does extend the electrical length of the antenna. The effective length of the folded antenna is somewhat longer than if the section remained unfolded.

The Hy-Gain 402BA 2-element 40 meter Yagi was a popular linearly-loaded antenna with 46-foot elements. A full-size element on 40 meters is approximately 65 feet long, so linear loading provided a substantial reduction in size.

End Loading and Inductor Loading

The technique of adding capacitance hats near the end of an antenna to lower its resonant frequency is most often encountered in vertical ground-plane antennas for the lower HF bands. The technique can also be put to good use on HF Yagis as seen in the Cushcraft (**www.cushcraftamateur.com**) MA5B mini-beam for 20/17/15/12/10 meters. The capacitance hats on this multiband Yagi play a major role in reducing the longest element to a bit over 17 feet long — just over $\lambda/4$ on 20 meters.

The elements of the MA5B also use traps and that also helps reduce length by inserting inductance into the element below the trap's resonant frequency. The Cushcraft XM240 2-element 40 meter Yagi also uses a combination of capacitance hats and coils to reduce element size.

Inductors on large Yagis for 75/80 meters are used similarly to base loading in verticals. The same general concerns apply with the inductance and placement of the coil, as well as losses in the coil.

11.7 THE MOXON RECTANGLE

The Moxon design is becoming increasingly popular on the HF and low VHF bands. Two additional Moxon designs, one for 10 meters and another for 20 meters, are included with this book's downloadable supplemental information.

L.B. Cebik, W4RNL, has written extensively about the *Moxon rectangle*, an antenna invented by Les Moxon, G6XN, derived from a design by VK2ABQ. The Moxon rectangle beam takes less space horizontally than a conventional 2-element Yagi design, yet it offers nearly the same amount of gain and a superior front-to-back ratio. And as an additional benefit, the drive-point impedance is close to 50 Ω, so that it doesn't need a matching section.

For example, rather than a "wingspan" of 17 feet for the reflector in a conventional 2-element 10 meter Yagi, the Moxon rectangle is 13 feet wide, a saving of almost 25%. The Moxon rectangle W4RNL created for *The ARRL Antenna Compendium, Vol 6*, had an SWR less than 2:1 from 28.0 to 29.7 MHz, with a gain over ground of 11 dBi. It had a F/B of 15 dB at 28.0 MHz, more than 20 dB at 28.4 MHz, and 12 dB at 29.7 MHz.

The Moxon rectangle relies on controlling the spacing (hence controlling the coupling) between the ends of the driven element tips and the ends of the reflector tips, which are both bent toward each other. See **Figure 11.26** which shows the general outline for W4RNL's 10 meter aluminum Moxon rectangle. The tips of the elements are kept a fixed distance from each other by PVC spacers. The closed rectangular mechanical assembly gives some rigidity to the design, keeping it stable in the wind. W4RNL described other Moxon rectangle designs using wire elements in June 2000 *QST*.

11.7.1 40 METER MOXON RECTANGLE

Dave Leeson, W6NL, has modified the Cushcraft XM240 2-element 40 meter Yagi to a Moxon Rectangle design shown in **Figure 11.27**. The W6NL Moxon Yagi is a high efficiency design that uses cross elements to provide both loading and the Moxon coupling. The upgrade of the XM240 to the W6NL Moxon consists of replacing the loading coil LCA sections with four new assemblies, each consisting of two new sections and the new tee loading element. The remaining parts are original Cushcraft.

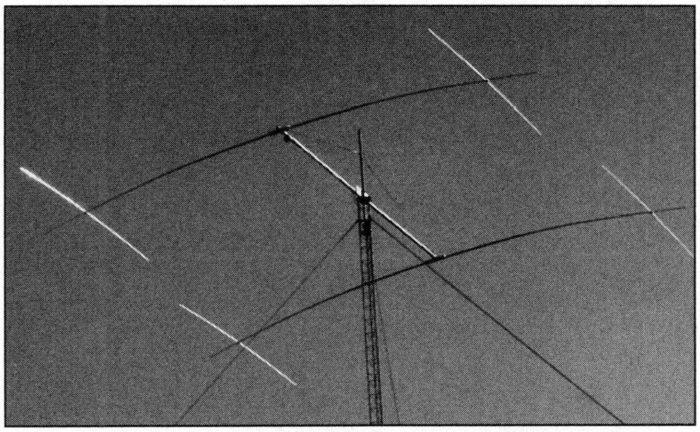

Figure 11.27 — A Cushcraft XM240 2-element 40 meter Yagi is modified by W6NL to become a Moxon Rectangle. The antenna is mechanically strengthened during the modification, as well. (Photo by Dave Leeson, W6NL)

The antenna has a gain of more than 10 dBi (including ground reflections) and a high front-to-back ratio (not specified by the designer). As is usual for Moxon designs, the SWR bandwidth is very good — more than 300 kHz with an SWR of less than 1.5:1.

Modifying the XM240 is described in detail in W6NL's design article, "Construction of W6NL Moxon on Cushcraft XM240," included with this book's downloadable supplemental information The mechanical strength of the antenna is also improved as part of the modification procedure.

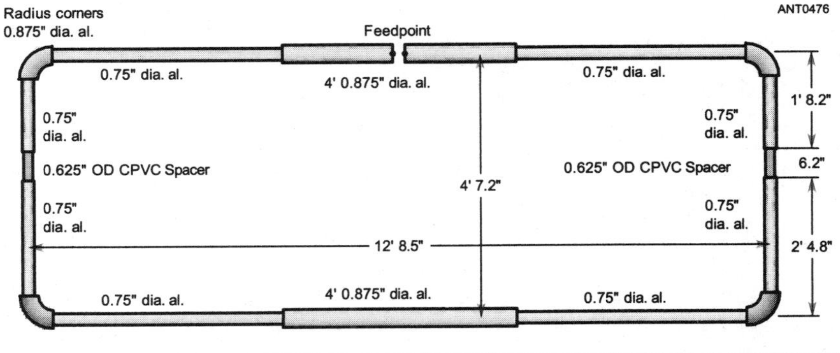

Figure 11.26 — General outline of the 10 meter aluminum Moxon rectangle, showing tubing dimensions.

11.8 QUAD ANTENNAS

The previous section discussed Yagi arrays as systems of approximately half-wave dipole elements that are coupled together mutually. You can also employ other kinds of elements using the same basic principles of analysis. For example, loops of various types may be combined into directive arrays. A popular type of parasitic array using loops is the *quad antenna*, in which loops having a perimeter of about one wavelength are used in much the same way as half-wave dipole elements in the Yagi antenna.

Clarence Moore, W9LZX, created the quad antenna in the early 1940s while he was at the Missionary Radio Station HCJB in Quito, Ecuador. He developed the quad to combat the effects of corona discharge at high altitudes. The problem at HCJB was that their large Yagi was literally destroying itself by melting its own element tips. This occurred due to the huge balls of corona it generated in the thin atmosphere of the high Andes Mountains. Moore reasoned correctly that closed loop elements would generate less high voltage — and hence less corona — than would the high impedances at the ends of a half-wave dipole element.

Figure 11.28 shows the original version of the two-element quad, with a driven element and a parasitic reflector. The square loops may be mounted either with the corners lying on horizontal and vertical lines, as shown at the left, or with two sides horizontal and two vertical (right). The feed points shown for these two cases will result in horizontal polarization, which is commonly used.

Quad designers may want to look up a copy of Bill Orr, W6SAI's *All About Cubical Quads* (now out of print) for a variety of design notes and ideas. Similarly, R. P. Haviland, W4MB's series of quad-related articles in *Ham Radio* and *QEX* are also worth reading. (See Bibliography.)

11.8.1 QUADS VERSUS YAGIS

Since its invention, there has been controversy whether the quad is a better performer than a Yagi. The three main electrical performance parameters of a Yagi are gain, response patterns (front-to-rear ratio, F/R) and feed point impedance/SWR. Proper analysis of a quad also involves checking all these parameters across the entire frequency range over which you intend to use it. Both a quad and a Yagi are classified as "parasitic, end-fire arrays." Modern antenna modeling by computer shows that monoband Yagis and quads with the same boom lengths and optimized for the same performance parameters have gains within about 1 dB of each other, with the quad slightly ahead of the Yagi.

Figure 11.29 plots the three parameters of gain, front-to-rear ratio (F/R) and SWR over the 14.0 to 14.35-MHz band for two representative antennas — a monoband three-element quad and a monoband four-element Yagi. Both of these have 26-foot booms and both are optimized for the best compromise of gain, F/R and SWR across the whole band.

While the quad in Figure 11.29 consistently exhibits about 0.5 dB more gain over the whole band, its F/R pattern toward the rear isn't quite as good as the Yagi's over that span of frequencies. This quad attains a maximum F/R of 25 dB at 14.1 MHz, but it falls to 17 dB at the bottom end of the band and 15 dB at the top. On the other hand, the Yagi's F/R stays consistently above 21 dB across the whole 20 meter band. The quad's SWR rises to just under 3:1 at the top end of the band, but stays below 2:1 from 14.0 to almost 14.3 MHz. The Yagi's SWR remains lower than 1.5:1 over the whole band.

The reason the Yagi in Figure 11.29 has more consistent responses for gain, F/R and SWR across the whole 20 meter band is that it has an additional parasitic element, giving two additional variables to play with — that is, the length of that

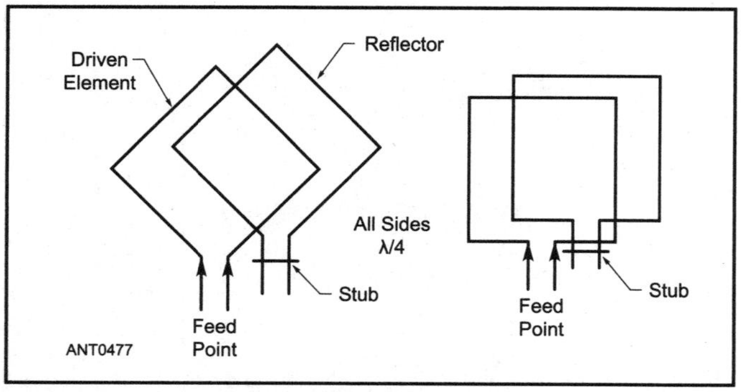

Figure 11.28 — The basic two-element quad antenna, with driven-element loop and reflector loop. The driven loops are electrically one wavelength in circumference (¼ wavelength on a side); the reflectors are slightly longer. Both configurations shown give horizontal polarization. For vertical polarization, the driven element should be fed at one of the side corners in the arrangement at the left, or at the center of a vertical side in the "square" quad at the right.

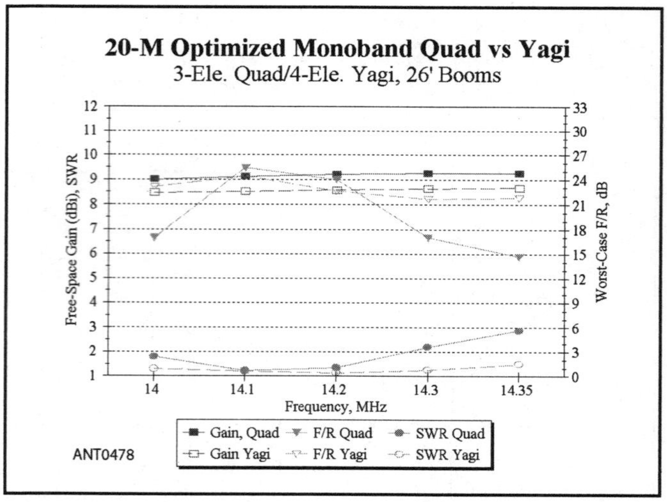

Figure 11.29 — Comparison of gain, F/R and SWR over the 14.0 to 14.35-MHz range for an optimized three-element quad and an optimized three-element Yagi, both on 26-foot booms. The quad exhibits almost 0.5 dB more gain for the same boom length, but doesn't have as good a rearward pattern over the whole frequency range compared to the Yagi. This is evidenced by the F/R curve. The quad's SWR curve is also not quite as flat as the Yagi. The quad's design emphasizes gain more than the other two parameters.

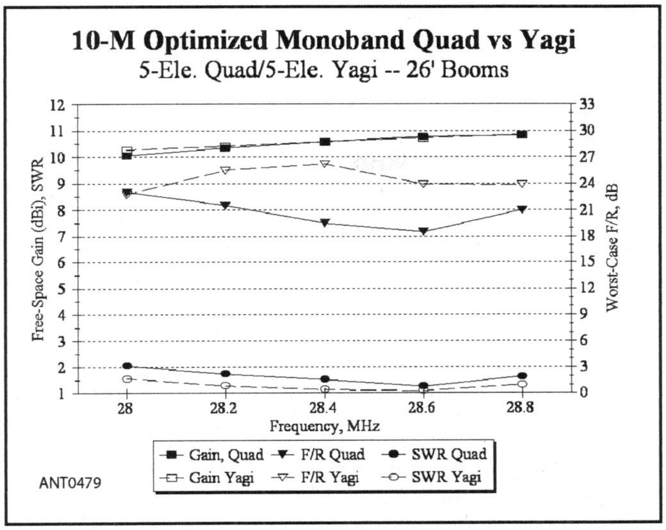

Figure 11.30 — Comparison of gain, F/R and SWR over the 28.0 to 28.8-MHz range for an optimized five-element quad and an optimized five-element Yagi, both on 26-foot booms. The gain advantage of the quad is about 0.25 dB at the low end of the band. The F/R is more peaked in frequency for the quad, however, than the Yagi.

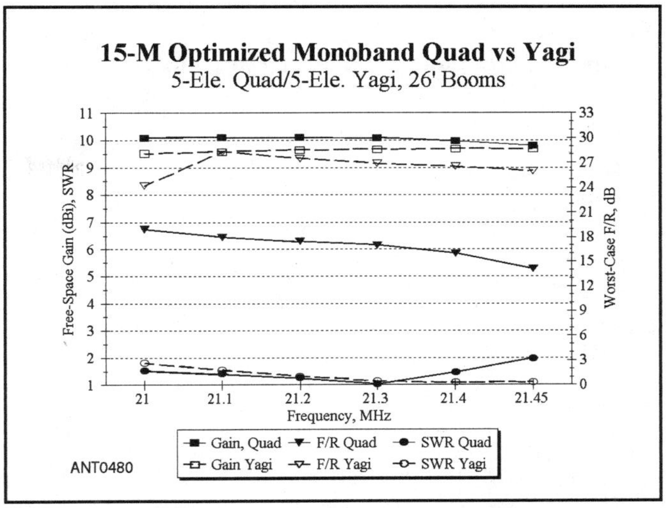

Figure 11.31 — Comparison of gain, F/R and SWR over the 21.0 to 21.45-MHz range for an optimized 5-element quad and optimized 5-element Yagi, both on 26-foot booms. The quad enjoys a gain advantage of about 0.5 dB over most of the band. Its rearward pattern is not as good as the Yagi, which remains higher than 24 dB across the whole range, compared to the quad, which remains in the 16-dB average range.

additional element and the spacing of that element from the others on the boom.

Yagi advocates point out that it is easier to add extra elements to a Yagi, given the mechanical complexities of adding another element to a quad. Extra parasitic elements give a designer more flexibility to tailor all performance parameters over a wide frequency range. Quad designers have historically opted to optimize strictly for gain and, as stated before, they can achieve as much as 1 dB more gain than a Yagi with the same length boom. But in so doing, a quad designer typically has to settle for front-to-rear patterns that are peaked over more narrow frequency ranges. The 20 meter quad plots in Figure 11.29 actually represent an even-handed approach, where the gain is compromised slightly to obtain a more consistent pattern and SWR across the whole band.

Figure 11.30 plots gain, F/R and SWR for two 10 meter monoband designs: a five-element quad and a five-element Yagi, both placed on 26-foot booms. The quad now has the same degrees of freedom as the Yagi, and as a consequence the pattern and SWR are more consistent across the range from 28.0 to 28.8 MHz. The quad's F/R remains above about 18.5 dB from 28.0 to 28.8 MHz. Meanwhile, the Yagi maintains an F/R of greater than 22 dB over the same range, but has almost 0.8 dB less gain compared to the quad at the low end of the band, eventually catching up at the high end of the band. The SWR for the quad is just over 2:1 at the bottom of the band, but remains less than 2:1 up to 28.8 MHz. The SWR on the Yagi remains less than 1.6:1 over the whole band.

Figure 11.31 shows the performance parameters for two 15 meter monoband designs: a five-element quad and a five-element Yagi, both on 26-foot booms. The quad is still the leader in gain, but has a less optimal rearward pattern and

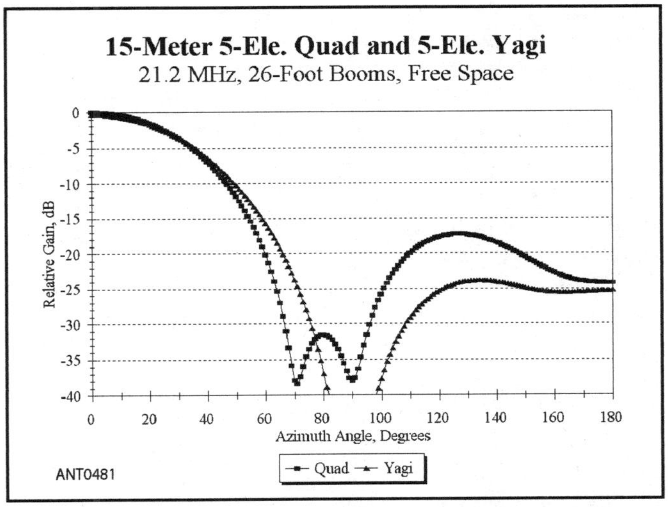

Figure 11.32 — Comparing the pattern of the 15 meter quad and Yagi shown in Figure 11.31. The quad has a slightly narrower frontal beamwidth (it has 0.5 dB more gain than the Yagi), but has higher "rear quartering" sidelobes at about 125° (with a twin sidelobe, not shown, at 235°). These sidelobes limit the worst-case front-to-rear (F/R) to about 17 dB, while the F/B (at 180°, directly at the back of the quad) is more than 24 dB for each antenna.

a somewhat less flat SWR curve than the Yagi. One thing should be noted in Figures 11.29-11.31. The F/R pattern on the Yagi is largely determined by the response at the 180° point, directly in back of the frontal lobe. This point is usually referred to when discussing the "front-to-back ratio."

The quad on the other hand has what a sailor might term "quartering lobes" (referring to the direction back toward

Table 11.11
Dimensions for Optimized Monoband Quads in Figs 11.29, 11.30 and 11.31, on 26-Foot Booms

	14.2 MHz	*21.2 MHz*	*28.4 MHz*
Reflector	73' 9"	49' 6"	37' 3"
R-DE Spacing	17' 8"	7'	6' 4"
Driven Element	71' 8"	47' 6"	35' 9"
DE-D1 Spacing	8' 3"	5'	5' 6"
Director 1	68' 7"	46' 8"	34' 8"
D1-D2 Spacing	—	6' 8"	6' 9"
Director 2	—	46' 10"	35' 2"
D2-D3 Spacing	—	7' 4"	7' 5"
Director 3	—	45' 8"	34' 2"
Feed method	Direct 50 Ω	Direct 50 Ω	Direct 50 Ω

the "quarterdeck" at the stern of a sailing vessel) in the rearward pattern. These quartering lobes are often worse than the response at 180°, directly in back of the main beam. **Figure 11.32** overlays the free-space E-Field responses of the 15 meter quad and Yagi together. At 21.2 MHz, the quad actually has a front-to-back ratio (F/B) of about 24 dB, excellent in anyone's book. The Yagi at 180° has a F/B of about 25 dB, again excellent.

However, at an azimuth angle of about 125° (and at 235° azimuth on the other side of the main lobe) the quad's "quartering lobe" is down only some 17 dB, setting the worst-case F/R at 17 dB also. As explained in the sections on Yagis, the reason F/R is more important than just the F/B is that on receive, signals can come from any direction, not just from directly behind the main beam.

Table 11.11 lists the dimensions for the three computer-optimized monoband quads shown in Figures 11.29, 11.30, and 11.31.

Cubical versus Concentric Quads

First — no quad is truly "cubical" in the sense of the distance between the elements being the same as the side of an element. That would place the elements λ/4 apart which is too widely spaced for good performance. The term "cubical quad" generally applies to multiband quads that maintain the same electrical spacing between elements on each band whereas "concentric quad" refers to a set of elements mounted on the spreaders in one plane, concentric to each other. (The two quad antennas shown in this chapter are concentric quads.)

The cubical quad with its consistent electrical spacing has a very slight performance advantage on the higher frequency bands but requires a special spreader mount at the center of the boom to hold the spreaders in the required tilted configuration. In fact, the boom of a true cubical quad is only inches long since the spreaders meet near the center. The cubical quad's spreaders, being both diagonal and tilted, must be a few percent longer than the planar spreaders of the concentric quad.

Quads Versus Yagis at Low Heights

Another belief held by some quad enthusiasts is that they need not be mounted very high off the ground to give excellent DX performance. Quads are somehow supposed to be greatly superior to a Yagi at the same height above ground. Unfortunately, this is mainly wishful thinking.

Figure 11.33 compares the same two 10 meter antennas as in Figure 11.30, but this time with each one mounted on a 50-foot tower over flat ground, rather than in theoretical free space. The quad does indeed have slightly more gain than a Yagi with the same boom length, as it has in free space. This is evidenced by the very slight compression of the quad's main lobe, but is more obvious when you look at the third lobe, which peaks at about 53° elevation. In effect, the quad squeezes some energy out of its second and third lobes and adds that to the first lobe. However, the difference in gain compared to the Yagi is only 0.8 dB for this particular quad design at a 9° elevation angle. And while it's true that every dB counts, you can also be certain that on the air you wouldn't be able to tell the difference between the two antennas. After all, a 10- to 20-dB variation in the level of signals is pretty common because of fading at HF.

11.8.2 MULTIBAND QUADS

On the other hand, one of the valid reasons quads have remained popular over the years is that antenna homebrewers can build multiband quads far more easily than they can construct multiband Yagis. In effect, all you have to do with a quad is add more wire to the existing support arms. It's not quite as simple as that, of course, but the idea of ready expandability

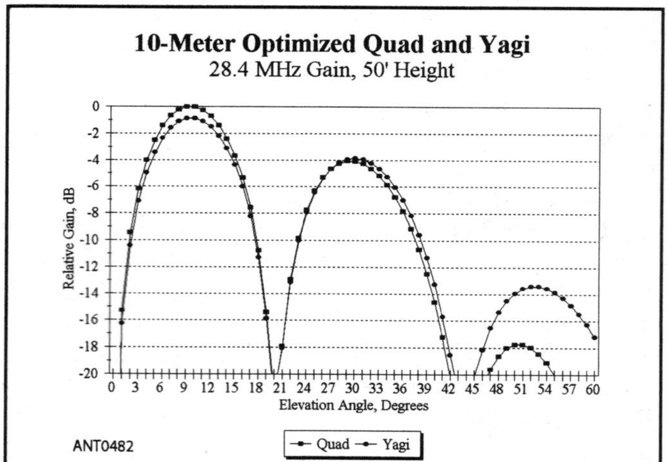

Figure 11.33 — A comparison on 10 meters between an optimized five-element quad and an optimized five-element Yagi, both mounted 50 feet high over flat ground and both employing 26-foot booms. There is no appreciable difference in the peak elevation angle for either antenna. In other words, a quad does not have an appreciable elevation-angle advantage over a Yagi mounted at the same boom height. Note that the quad achieves its slightly higher gain by taking energy from higher-angle lobes and concentrating that energy in the main elevation lobe. This is a process that is similar to what happens with stacked Yagis.

for other bands is very appealing to experimenters.

Like the Yagi, the quad does suffer from interactions between wires of different frequencies, but the degree of interaction between bands is usually less for a quad. The higher-frequency bands are the ones that often suffer most from any interaction, for both Yagis and quads. For example, the 10 and 15 meter bands are usually the ones affected most by nearby 20 meter wires in a triband quad, while the 20 meter elements are not affected by the 10 or 15 meter elements.

Modern computer modeling software can help you counteract at least some of the interaction by allowing you to do virtual "retuning" of the quad on the computer screen — rather than clinging precariously to your tower fiddling with wires. However, the programs (such as *NEC-2* or *EZNEC*) that can model three-dimensional wire antennas such as quads typically run far more slowly than those designed for monoband Yagis (such as *YW* included with this book). This makes optimizing rather tedious, but you use the same considerations for tradeoffs between gain, pattern (F/R) and SWR over the operating bandwidth as you do with monoband Yagis.

11.8.3 BUILDING A QUAD

The parasitic element shown in Figure 11.28 is tuned in much the same way as the parasitic element in a Yagi antenna. That is, the parasitic loop is tuned to a lower frequency than the driven element when the parasitic is to act as a reflector, and to a higher frequency when it is to act as a director. Figure 11.28 shows the parasitic element with an adjustable tuning stub, a convenient method of tuning since the resonant frequency can be changed simply by changing the position of the shorting bar on the stub. In practice, it has been found that the length around the loop should be approximately 3.5% greater than the self-resonant length if the element is a reflector, and about 3.0% shorter than the self-resonant length if the parasitic element is a director. Approximate formulas for the loop lengths in feet are:

$$\text{Driven Element} = \frac{1008}{f_{MHz}}$$

$$\text{Reflector} = \frac{1045}{f_{MHz}}$$

$$\text{Director} = \frac{977}{f_{MHz}}$$

These are valid for quad antennas intended for operation below 30 MHz and using uninsulated #14 AWG stranded copper wire. At VHF, where the ratio of loop circumference to conductor diameter is usually relatively small, the circumference must be increased in comparison to the wavelength. For example, a one-wavelength loop constructed of ¼-inch tubing for 144 MHz should have a circumference about 2% greater than in the above equation for the driven element.

Element spacings on the order of 0.14 to 0.2 free-space wavelengths are generally used. You would employ the smaller spacings for antennas with more than two elements, where the structural support for elements with larger spacings tends to become challenging. The feed point impedances of antennas having element spacings on this order have been found to be in the 40- to 60-Ω range, so the driven element can be fed directly with coaxial cable with only a small mismatch.

For spacings on the order of 0.25 wavelength (physically feasible for two elements, or for several elements at 28 MHz) the impedance more closely approximates the impedance of a driven loop alone — that is, 80 to 100 Ω. The feed methods described in the **Transmission Line System Techniques** chapter can be used, just as in the case of the Yagi.

Feeding the Multiband Quad

There are two approaches to feeding a multiband quad with several driven elements. If the driven elements are all on one set of spreaders the *combined feed* ties all of the elements together at a single feed point. This allows the use of a single feed line but creates a great deal of interaction between harmonically-related elements, reducing gain and F/B dramatically as described by L.B. Cebik in "Feeding the 5-Band Quad" (see Bibliography). Using separate feed lines to each driven element results in much less interaction and preserves the quad's performance.

A compromise that allows the use of a single feed line to the shack but separate feed lines for each element is to use a remote coax switch such as the Ameritron RCS-4 or RCS-8V (**www.ameritron.com**). The coax switch can be mounted on the antenna boom or mast and short feed lines run from the switch to the elements. The editor used just such a configuration for a number of years for a five-band 2-element quad with good results.

The impedance of the multiband quad driven elements varies quite a bit from the free-space value of a single loop. Cebik's article mentioned above shows that the feed point impedance varies from close to 50 Ω on 10 meters (the innermost element) to more than 100 Ω on 20 meters (the outermost element). If multiple feed lines are used, quarter-wave matching sections as described in the **Transmission Line System Techniques** chapter can be used to provide an acceptable SWR.

Mechanical Construction Issues

The most obvious problem related to quad antennas is the ability to build a structurally sound system. If high winds or heavy ice are a normal part of the environment, special precautions are necessary if the antenna is to survive a winter season.

Both multiband quad arrays use fiberglass spreaders. Bamboo is a suitable substitute (if economy is of great importance). However, the additional weight of the bamboo spreaders over fiberglass is an important consideration. A typical 12-foot bamboo pole weighs about 2 pounds; the fiberglass type weighs less than a pound. By multiplying the difference times 8 for a two-element array, times 12 for a three-element antenna, and so on, it quickly becomes apparent that fiberglass is worth the investment if weight is an important factor. Properly treated, bamboo has a useful life of three or four years, while fiberglass life is probably 10 times longer.

One step beyond the conventional fiberglass arm is the pole-vaulting arm. For quads designed to be used on 7 MHz, surplus "rejected" pole-vaulting poles are highly recommended. Their ability to withstand large amounts of bending is very desirable. The cost of these poles is high, and they are difficult to obtain.

Spreader supports (sometimes called *spiders*) described for the multiband quad section below are designed to be less likely to rotate on the boom as a result of wind pressure.

The physical sturdiness of a quad is directly proportional to the quality of the material used and the care with which it is constructed. The size and type of wire selected for use with a quad antenna is important because it will determine the capability of the spreaders to withstand high winds and ice. One of the more common problems confronting the quad owner is that of broken wires. A solid conductor is more apt to break than stranded wire under constant flexing conditions. For this reason, stranded copper wire is recommended. For 14-, 21- or 28-MHz operation, #14 or #12 AWG stranded wire is a good choice. Soldering of the stranded wire at points where flexing is likely to occur should be avoided.

You may connect the wires to the spreader arms in many ways. The simplest method is to drill holes through the fiberglass at the appropriate points on the arms and route the wires through the holes. Some amateurs have experienced cracking of fiberglass poles which might be a result of drilling holes through the material. However, this seems to be the exception rather than the rule.

Soldering a wire loop across the spreader, as shown in the designs below, is recommended. However, you should take care to prevent solder from flowing to the corner point where flexing could break it. A better method is to clamp a piece of plastic tubing to the spreader with a stainless steel hose clamp and run the wire through the tubing. This allows the wire to slide when the antenna flexes.

Every effort must be placed upon proper construction if you want to have freedom from mechanical problems. Hardware must be secure or vibration created by the wind may cause separation of assemblies. Solder joints should be clamped in place to keep them from flexing, which might fracture a connection point.

While a boom diameter of 2 inches is sufficient for smaller quads using two or even three elements for 14, 21 and 28 MHz, when the boom length reaches 20 feet or longer a 3-inch diameter boom is highly recommended. Wind creates two forces on the boom, vertical and horizontal. The vertical load on the boom can be reduced with a guy-wire truss cable. The horizontal forces on the boom are more difficult to relieve, so 3-inch diameter tubing is desirable.

Diamond or Square?

The question of how to orient the spreader arms has been raised many times over the years. Should you mount the loops in a diamond or a square configuration? Should one set of spreaders be horizontal, giving the loop a diamond shape as shown in Figure 11.28 on the left, or should the wire itself be horizontal to the ground (spreaders mounted diagonally in the fashion of an X) as shown at the right in Figure 11.28? From the electrical point of view, there is not enough difference in performance to worry about.

From the mechanical point of view there is no question which version is better. The diamond quad, with the associated horizontal and vertical spreader arms, is capable of holding an ice load much better than a system where no vertical support exists to hold the wire loops upright. Put another way, the vertical poles of a diamond array, if sufficiently strong, will hold the rest of the system erect. When water droplets are accumulating and forming into ice, it is very reassuring to see water running down the wires to a corner and dripping off, rather than just sitting there on the wires and freezing. The wires of a loop (or several loops, in the case of a multiband antenna) help support the horizontal spreaders under a load of ice. A square quad will droop severely under heavy ice conditions because there is nothing to hold it up straight.

Of course, in climates where icing is not a problem, many amateurs point out that they like the aesthetics of the square configuration. There are thousands of square-configuration quads in temperate areas around the world.

Another consideration will enter into your choice of orientation for a quad. You must mount a diamond quad somewhat higher on the mast or tower than for an equivalent square array, just to keep the bottom spreader away from the tower guys when you rotate the antenna.

Getting It Up the Tower

The many elements of a Yagi are hard enough to maneuver around guy wires but the quad's three-dimensional structure can make it a challenge to lift to the top of a tower. If the tower is a crank-up or tilt-over, it is much easier to get a quad mounted on the antenna mast. On a fixed, lattice-style tower with guys, you'll have to carefully work the antenna around each set of guy wires as it is raised. The tram technique described in the **Building Antenna Systems and Towers** chapter is highly recommended as the work to rig the tram pays off with a lot easier lift of the antenna over the guys.

Another technique used by builders of the more common concentric quads it to assemble each set of spreaders and elements separately on the ground and lift them one by one to the top of the tower where they are mounted to the boom one after another. This requires some planning but is a lot easier than lifting the entire assembled antenna, particularly when there are guy wires to contend with.

11.9 TWO MULTIBAND QUAD DESIGNS

This section describes two multiband quad designs. The first is a large triband 20/15/10 meter quad built on a 26-foot boom made of 3-inch irrigation tubing. This antenna has three elements on 20 meters, four elements on 15 meters, and five elements on 10 meters. **Figure 11.34** shows a photograph of the five-element triband quad. This is a *big* antenna!

The second project is a compact two-element triband quad on an 8-foot boom that covers 20, 17, 15, 12 and 10 meters. We call this a "pentaband" quad since it covers five bands. This antenna uses five concentric wire loops mounted on each of the two sets of spreaders. Either antenna may be constructed in a diamond or square configuration.

While the same basic construction techniques are employed for both multiband quads, the scale of the larger triband antenna makes it a far more ambitious undertaking! The large quad requires a strong tower and a rugged rotator. It also requires a fair amount of real estate in order to raise the quad to the top of the tower without getting tangled in trees or other antennas.

11.9.1 A FIVE-ELEMENT, 26-FOOT BOOM TRIBAND QUAD

Five sets of element spreaders are used to support the three elements used on 14 MHz, four elements on 21 MHz and five elements on 28 MHz. We chose to use four elements on 15 meters in this design (rather than the five we could have been employed on this length of boom) because the difference in optimized performance wasn't great enough to warrant the extra complexity of using five elements. The dimensions are listed in **Table 11.12**, and are designed for center frequencies of 14.175, 21.2 and 28.4 MHz.

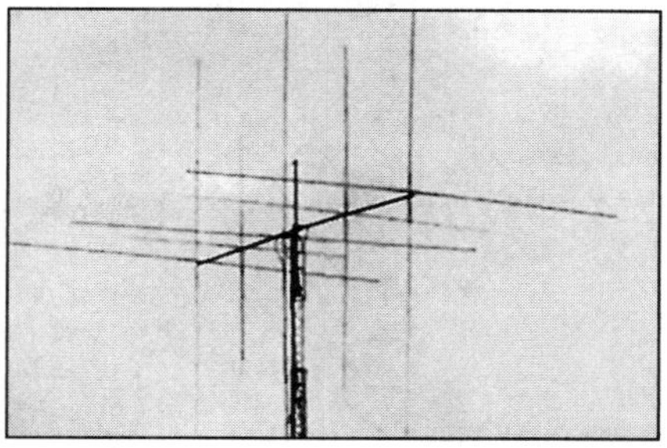

Figure 11.34 — Photo of the three-band, five-element quad antenna.

The spacing between elements has been chosen to provide good compromises in performance consistent with boom length and mechanical construction. You can see that the element spacings for 20 meters are quite different from those for the optimized monoband design. This is because the same set of spreaders is used for all three bands on three out

Table 11.12
Three-Band Five-Element Quad on 26-Foot Boom

	14.15 MHz	*21.2 MHz*	*28.4 MHz*
Reflector	72' 6"	49' 4"	36' 8"
R-DE Spacing	12'	12'	6'
Driven Element	71'	47' 6"	35' 4"
DE-D1 Spacing	14'	7'	6'
Director 1	68' 6"	46' 8"	34' 8"
D1-D2 Spacing	—	14'	7'
Director 2	—	46' 5"	34' 8"
D2-D3 Spacing	—	—	7'
Director 3	—	—	34'
Feed method	Direct 50 Ω	Direct 50 Ω	Direct 50 Ω

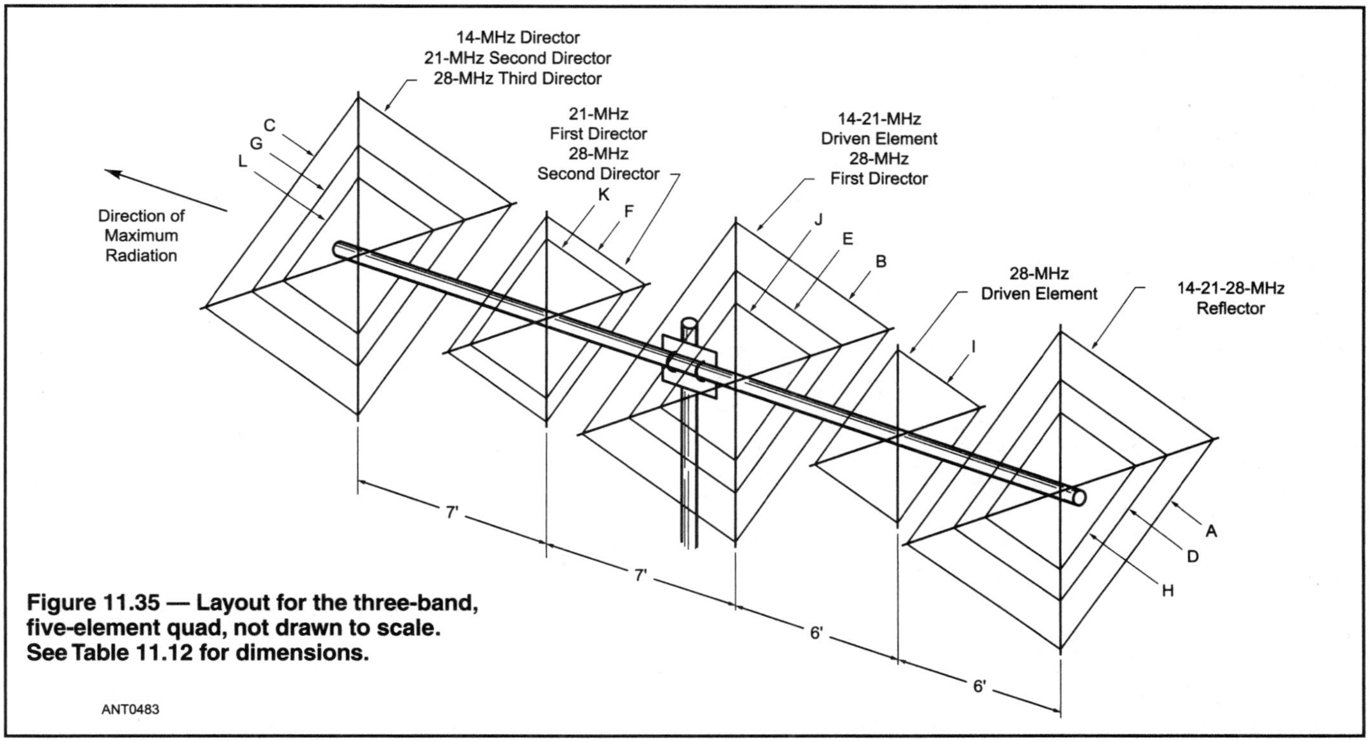

Figure 11.35 — Layout for the three-band, five-element quad, not drawn to scale. See Table 11.12 for dimensions.

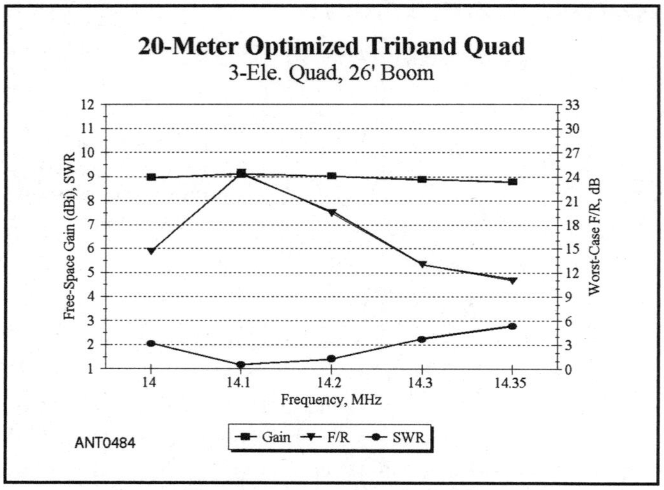

Figure 11.36 — Computed performance of the triband, five-element quad over the 20 meter band. The direct 50-Ω feed system holds the SWR below 2.8: 1 across the whole band. This could be improved with a gamma-match system tuned to 14.1 MHz if the builder really desires a low SWR. The F/R peaks at 14.1 MHz and remains above 10 dB across the whole band.

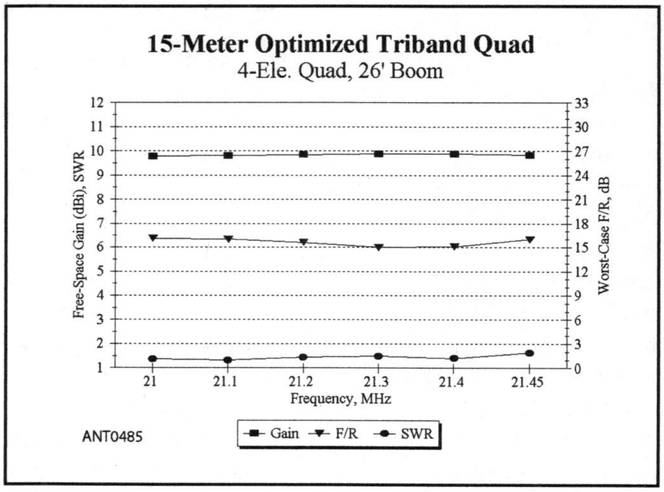

Figure 11.37 — Computed performance of the triband, five-element quad over the 15 meter band. There is some degree of interaction with the 20 meter elements, limiting the worst-case F/R to about 15 dB. The gain and SWR curves are relatively flat across the band.

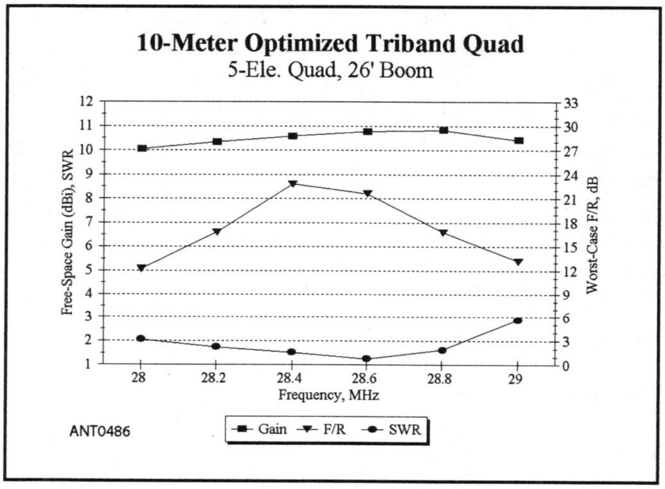

Figure 11.38 — Computed performance of the triband, five-element quad over the 10 meter band. The F/R is higher than 12 dB across the band from 28.0 to 29.0 MHz, but the SWR rises at the top end of the band beyond 2:1. The free-space gain is higher than 10 dBi across the band.

of the five elements, and the higher-frequency bands dictate the spacing because they are more critical.

Each of the parasitic loops is closed (ends soldered together) and requires no tuning. **Figure 11.35** shows the physical layout of the triband quad. **Figure 11.36** plots the computed free-space gain, front-to-rear ratio and SWR response across the 20 meter band. With only a few degrees of freedom in tuning and spacing of the three elements, it is impossible to spread the response out to cover the entire 20 meter band. The compromise design results in a rearward pattern that varies from a worst-case of just under 10 dB at the high end of the band, to a peak F/R of just under 19 dB at 14.2 MHz, in the phone portion of the band. The F/R is about 11 dB at the low end of the band.

The SWR remains under 3:1 for the entire 20 meter band, rising to 2.8:1 at the high end. The feed system for this triband quad consists of three separate 50-Ω coax lines, one per driven element, together with a relay switchbox mounted to the boom so that a single coax can be used back to the operating position. Each feed line uses a ferrite-bead balun to control common-mode currents and preserve the radiation pattern and each coax going to the switchbox is cut to be an electrical three-quarter wavelength on 15 meters. This presents a short at the unused driven elements since modeling indicated that the 15 meter band is adversely affected by the presence of the 20 meter driven element if it is left open-circuited. If you use RG-213 coax, the ¾-λ electrical length of each feed line is 23 feet long at 21.2 MHz. This is sufficient physical length to reach each driven element from the switchbox.

Figure 11.37 shows the free-space response for the 15 meter band. The rearward response is roughly 15 dB across the band. This is a result of the residual interaction between the 20 meter elements on 15 meters, and no further tuning could improve the F/R. Note how flat the SWR curve is. This SWR characteristic is what gives the quad the reputation of being "wideband." A flat SWR curve, however, is not necessarily a good indicator of optimal performance for directional antennas like quads or Yagis, particularly multiband designs where compromises must be made by physical necessity.

Figure 11.38 shows the characteristics of the 10 meter portion of the two-element triband quad. The response favors the low-phone band, with the F/R falling to about 12 dB at the low end of the frequency range and rising to just about 23 dB at 28.4 MHz. The SWR curve is once again relatively flat across the major portion of the band up to 28.8 MHz.

Construction

A 3-foot length of steel angle stock, 1 inch per side, is used to interconnect the pairs of spreader arms. The steel is drilled at the center to accept a muffler clamp of sufficient size to clamp the assembly to the boom. The fiberglass is clamped to the steel angle stock with stainless steel hose clamps, two per pole. Each quad-loop spreader frame consists of two assemblies of the type shown in **Figure 11.39**.

Connecting the wires to the fiberglass is shown in **Figure 11.40**. The model described here has no holes in the spreader arms; the wires are attached to each arm with a few layers of plastic electrical tape and then wrapped approximately 20 times in a crisscross fashion with ⅛-inch diameter nylon string, followed by more electrical tape for UV protection, as shown in **Figure 11.41**.

The wire loops are left open at the bottom of each driven element where the feed line coaxes are attached. All of the parasitic elements are continuous loops of wire; the solder joint is at the base of the diamond.

Although you could run three separate coax cables down to the shack, we suggest that you install a relay box at the

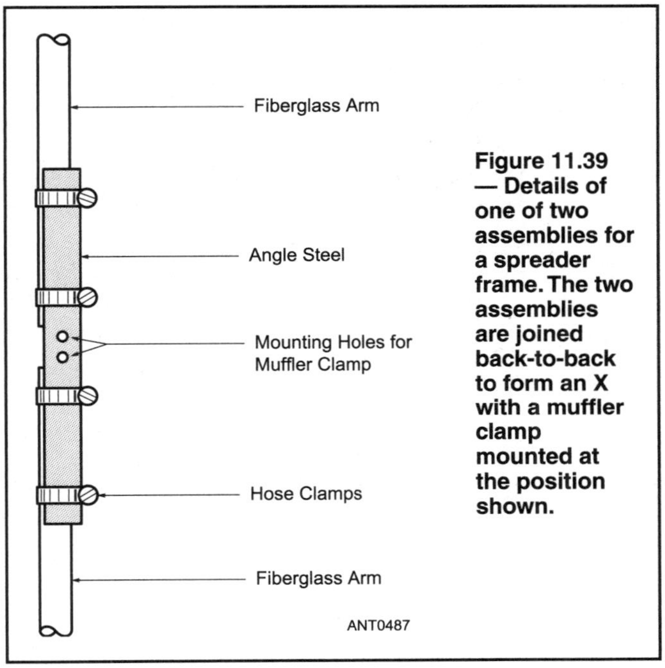

Figure 11.39 — Details of one of two assemblies for a spreader frame. The two assemblies are joined back-to-back to form an X with a muffler clamp mounted at the position shown.

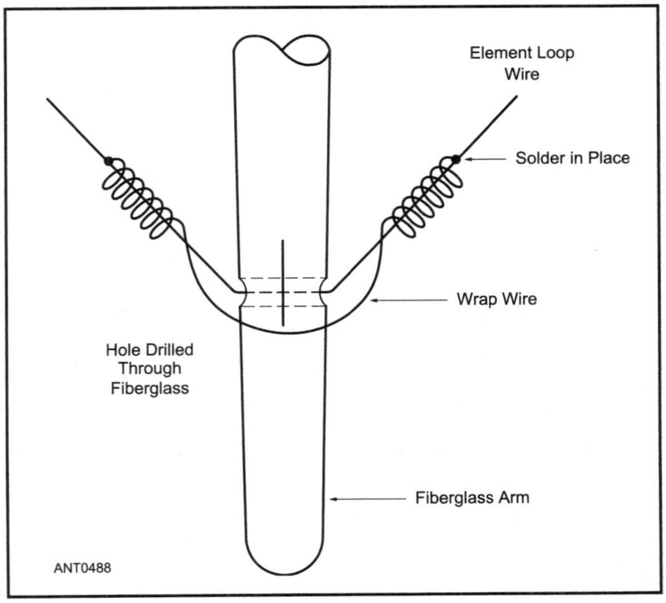

Figure 11.40 — A method of assembling a corner of the wire loop of a quad element to the spreader arm.

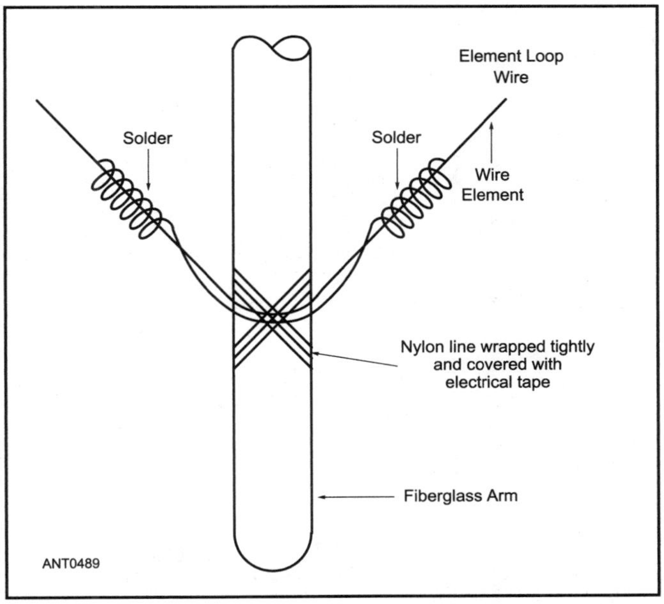

Figure 11.41 — An alternative method of assembling the wire of a quad loop to the spreader arm.

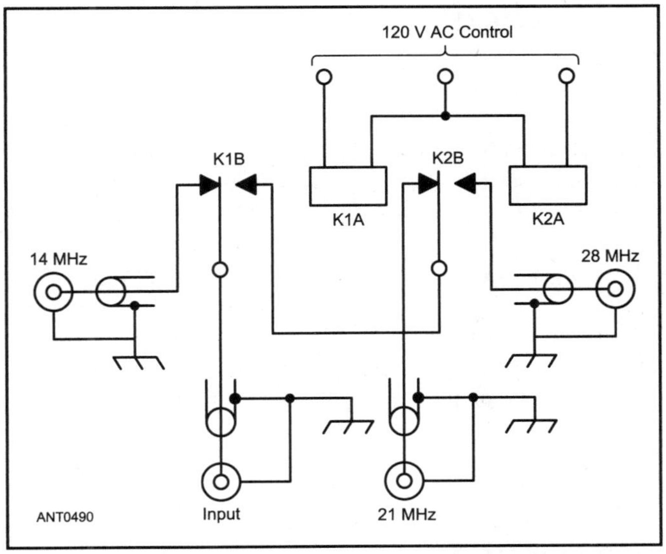

Figure 11.42 — Suitable circuit for relay switching of bands for the three-band quad. A three-wire control cable is required. K1, K2 — any type of relay suitable for RF switching, coaxial type not required (Potter and Brumfield MR11A acceptable; although this type has double-pole contacts, mechanical arrangements of most single-pole relays make them unacceptable for switching of RF).

Figure 11.43 — The relay box is mounted on the boom near the center. Each of the spreader-arm fiberglass poles is attached to steel angle stock with hose clamps.

center of the boom. A three-wire control system may be used to apply power to the proper relay for changing bands. The circuit diagram of a typical configuration is presented in **Figure 11.42** and its installation is shown in **Figure 11.43**.

11.9.2 A TWO-ELEMENT, 8-FOOT BOOM PENTABAND QUAD

This two-element pentaband (20/17/15/12/10 meter) quad uses the same construction techniques as its big brother above. Since only two elements are used, the boom can be less robust for this antenna, at 2 inches diameter rather than 3 inches. Those who like really rugged antennas can still use the 3-inch diameter boom, of course.

This quad is very similar to those sold commercially by vendors such as Cubex who also sell hard-to-find parts for quads such as spreaders and the spiders that mount the spreaders to the boom. Readers may also want to review the article on improving the 2-element quad by Mees (see Bibliography).

Table 11.13 lists the element dimensions for the pentaband quad. The following plots show the performance for each of the five bands covered. The feed system for the pentaband quad uses five, direct 50-Ω coaxes, one to each driven element. These five coaxes are cut to be ¾-λ electrically on 10 meters (17 feet, 2 inches for RG-213 at 28.4 MHz). In this design the 10 meter band is the one most affected by the presence of the other driven elements if they are left un-shorted. The ¾-λ lines open-circuited at the switchbox are long enough physically to reach all elements from a centrally mounted switchbox. This length assumes that the switchbox open-circuits the unused coaxes. If the switchbox short-circuits unused coaxes (as several commercial switchboxes do), then use ½-λ long lines to feed all five driven elements (11 feet, 5 inches for RG-213 at 28.4 MHz).

The SWR curves do not necessarily go down to 1:1 because of this simple, direct feed system. If anyone is bothered by this, of course they can always implement individual matching systems, such as gamma matches. Most amateurs would agree that such a degree of complexity is not warranted. The worst-case SWR is less than 2.3:1 on each band, even with direct feed on 20 meters. With typical lengths of coaxial feed line from the shack to the switchbox at the antenna, say 100 feet of RG-213, the SWR at the transmitter would be less than 2.0:1 on all bands due to losses in the feed line.

Figure 11.44 shows the computed responses for the pentaband quad over the 20 meter band. With only two degrees of freedom (spacing and element tuning) there is not much that can be done to spread the response out over the entire 20 meter band. Nonetheless, the performance over the band is still pretty reasonable for an antenna this small. The F/R pattern peaks at 19 dB at 14.1 MHz and falls to about 10 dB at either end of the band. The free-space gain varies from about 7.5 dBi to just above 6 dBi, comparable to a short-boom

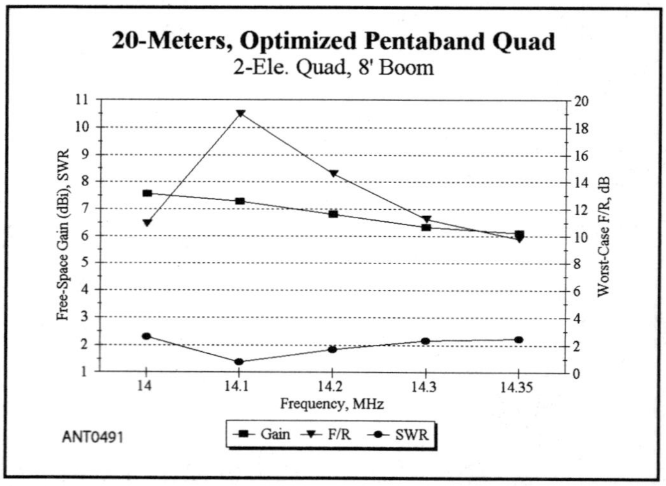

Figure 11.44 — Computed performance of the pentaband two-element quad on 20 meters. With the simple direct-feed system, the SWR rises to about 2.3:1 at the low end of the band. A gamma match can bring the SWR down to 1:1 at 14.1 MHz, if desired.

Table 11.13
Five-Band Two-Element Quad on 8-Foot Boom

	14.2 MHz	*18.1 MHz*	*21 MHz*	*24.9 MHz*	*28.4 MHz*
Reflector	72' 4"	56' 4"	48' 6"	40' 11¼"	37' 5½"
R-DE Spacing	8'	8'	8'	8'	8'
Driven Element	69' 10½"	54' 10½"	46' 7"	39' 10½"	34' 6"

three-element Yagi. The SWR curve remains below 2.3:1 across the band. If you were to employ a gamma match tuned at 14.1 MHz, you could limit the peak SWR to less than 2.0:1, and this would still occur at 14.0 MHz.

On 17 meters, **Figure 11.45** shows that the other elements are affecting 18 MHz, even with element-length optimization. Careful examination of the current induced on the other elements shows that the 20 meter driven element is interacting on 18 MHz, deteriorating the pattern and gain slightly. Even still, the performance on 17 meters is reasonable, especially for a five-band quad on an 8-foot boom.

On 15 meters, the interactions seems to have been contained, as **Figure 11.46** demonstrates. The F/R peaks at 21.1 MHz, at 19 dB and remains better than 12 dB past the top of the band. The SWR curve is low across the whole band.

On 12 meters, the interaction between bands is minor, leading to the good results shown in **Figure 11.47**. The SWR change across this band is quite flat, which isn't surprising given the narrow bandwidth of the 12 meter band.

On 10 meters, the interaction seems to have been tamed well by computer-tuning of the elements. The F/R remains higher than about 14 dB from 28 to 29 MHz. The SWR remains below 2.2:1 up to about 28.8 MHz, while the gain is relatively flat across the band at more than 7.2 dBi in free space. See **Figure 11.48**.

Overall, this pentaband quad is physically compact and yet it provides good performance across all five bands. It is competitive with commercial Log Periodic Dipole Array (LPDA) designs and triband Yagi designs that employ longer booms.

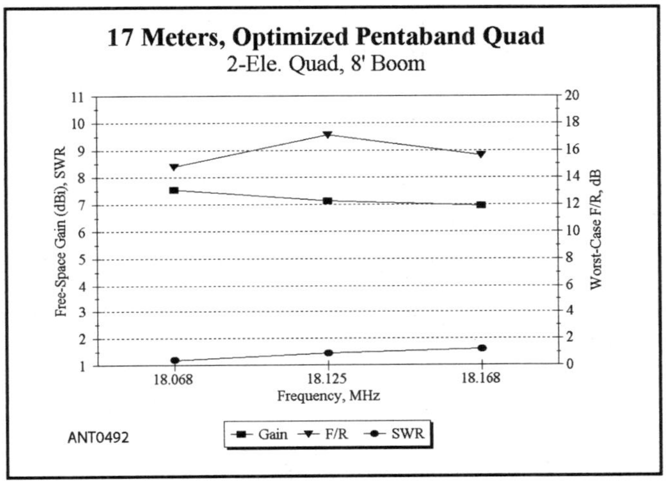

Figure 11.45 — Computed performance of the pentaband two-element quad on 17 meters. There is some interaction with the other elements, but overall the performance is satisfactory on this band.

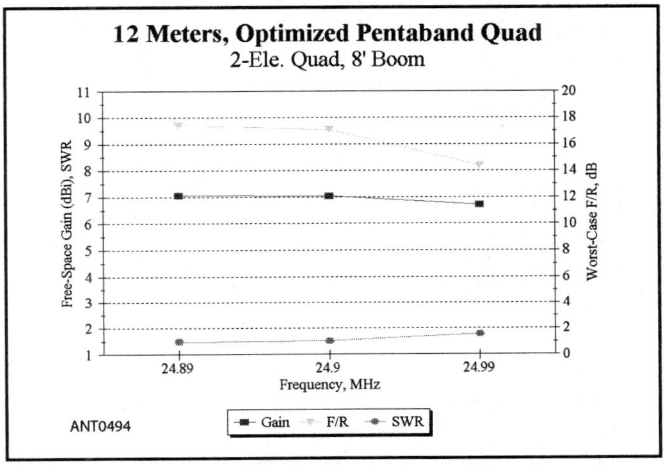

Figure 11.47 — Computed performance of the pentaband two-element quad on 12 meters.

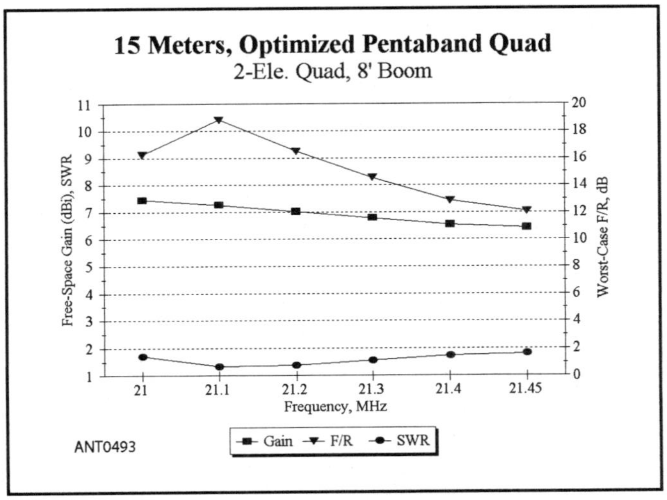

Figure 11.46 — Computed performance of the pentaband two-element quad on 15 meters. The performance is acceptable across the whole band.

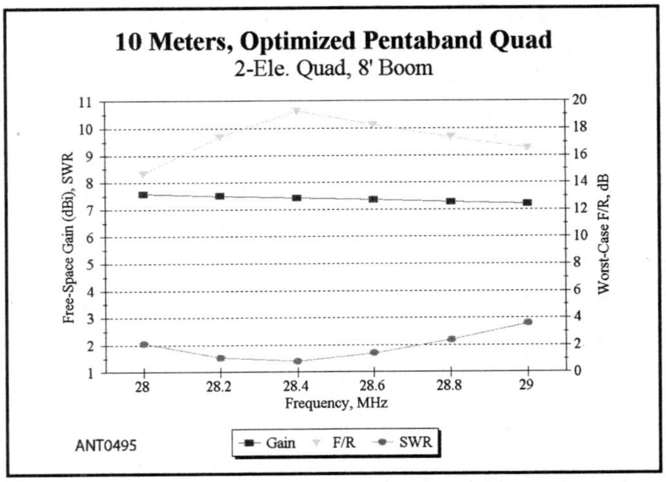

Figure 11.48 — Computed performance of the pentaband two-element quad on 10 meters. The SWR curve is slightly above the target 2:1 at the low end of the band and rises to about 2.2:1 at 28.8 MHz. This unlikely to be a problem, even with rigs with automatic power-reduction due to SWR, since the SWR at the input of a typical coax feed line will be lower than that at the antenna due to losses in the line.

11.10 BIBLIOGRAPHY

Source material and more extended discussions of the topics covered in this chapter can be found in the references given below and in the textbooks listed at the end of the **Antenna Fundamentals** chapter.

ARRL's Yagi Antenna Classics, ARRL, 2001.

C. Buchanan, "The Multimatch Antenna System," *QST*, Mar 1955, pp 22-23, 130.

P. S. Carter, C. W. Hansell and N. E. Lindenblad, "Development of Directive Transmitting Antennas by R.C.A. Communications," *Proc. IRE*, Oct 1931.

L.B. Cebik, "A 2 Element Quad for 17 and 12 Meters Using a Combined Feed," *ARRL Antenna Compendium, Volume 8* (Newington: ARRL, 2010).

L.B. Cebik, "Feeding the 5-Band Quad," *ARRL Antenna Compendium, Volume 7* (Newington: ARRL, 2002).

L.B. Cebik, "Having a Field Day with the Moxon Rectangle," *QST*, Jun 2000, pp 38-42.

C. Cleveland, "More'n One Way to Switch an Antenna," Technical Correspondence, *QST*, Nov 1986, pp 45-46.

C. Collings, "Linearly Loaded 20-Meter Beam," *QST*, Jun 1976, pp 18-19.

D. Cutter, "Simple Switcher," *73*, May 1980.

D. DeMaw, "A Remote Antenna Switcher for HF," *QST*, Jun 1986, pp 24-26.

R. Fenwick, "A High-Performance Triband Beam with No Traps," *QEX*, Sep 1996, pp 3-7.

L. Gordon, "The K4VX Linearly Loaded Dipole for 7 MHz," *QST*, July 2002, pp 40-42.

R. Haviland, "The Quad Antenna: Part 1, General Concepts," *Ham Radio*, May 1988, pp 43-53.

R. Haviland, "The Quad Antenna: Part 2, Circular and Octagonal Shapes," *Ham Radio*, Jun 1988, pp 54-67.

R. Haviland, "The Quad Antenna: Part 3, Circular Loop and Octagonal Arrays," *Ham Radio*, Aug 1988, pp 34-47.

R. Haviland, "The Quad Antenna Revisited, Part 1: Developments in Antenna Analysis," *Communications Quarterly,* Summer 1999, pp 43-73. Also Correction Fall 1999, p 108.

R. Haviland, "The Quad Antenna Revisited, Part 2: The Basic Two-Element Quad," *Communications Quarterly,* Fall 1999, pp 65-85.

R. Haviland, "The Quad Antenna Revisited, Part 3: Multi-Element Quads," *QEX,* Nov/Dec 2000, pp 10-19.

R. Haviland, "The Quad Antenna Revisited, Part 4: Effects of Ground on Quad Loops," *QEX,* Mar/Apr 2001, pp 47-54.

R. Haviland, "The Quad Antenna Revisited, Part 5: Quad Design Variations," *QEX,* Jan/Feb 2002, pp 23-32.

M. G. Knitter, Ed., *Loop Antennas — Design and Theory* (Cambridge, WI: National Radio Club, 1983).

H. Landskov, W7KAR, "Evolution of a Quad Array," *QST*, Mar 1977, pp 32-36.

J. Lawson, *Yagi Antenna Design* (Newington: ARRL, 1986) (out of print)

J. Lawson, "Yagi Antenna Design," *Ham Radio,* Jan 1980, pp 22-27; Feb 1980, pp 19-27; May 1980, pp 18-26; Jun 1980, pp 33-40; Jul 1980, pp 18-31; Sep 1980, pp 37-45; Oct 1980, pp 29-37; Nov 1980, pp 22-34; Dec 1980, pp 30-41.

D. Leeson, *Physical Design of Yagi Antennas* (Newington: ARRL, 1992) (out of print)

J. Lindsay, "Quads and Yagis," *QST*, May 1968, pp 11-19, 150.

D. Mees, "Improving the Cubex Three-Element, Five-Band Quad," *ARRL Antenna Compendium, Volume 6*, (Newington: ARRL, 1999).

R. Myers, "A Wide-Spaced Multielement Tribander," *QST*, Dec 1970, p 33-38.

W. Orr, *All About Cubical Quad Antennas* (Radio Publications, 1970, out of print).

T. Schiller, *Array of Light, 3rd Edition*, **nextgenerationantennas.com**, 2010.

F. E. Terman, *Radio Engineering*, 3rd ed. (New York: McGraw-Hill Book Co, 1947).

R. Welsh, "Yagi: The Man and His Antenna," *QST*, Oct 1993, pp 45-47.

E. M. Williams, "Radiating Characteristics of Short-Wave Loop Aerials," *Proc. IRE*, Oct 1940.

TABLE OF CONTENTS

Chapter 12 — Downloadable Supplemental Content

Supplemental Articles

- "A Dipole Curtain for 15 and 10 Meters" by Mike Loukides, W1JQ
- "Bob Zepp: A Low Band, Low Cost, High Performance Antenna - Parts 1 and 2" by Robert Zavrel, W7SX
- "Curtains for You" by Jim Cain, K1TN (and Feedback)
- "Hands-On Radio Experiment #133 – Extended Double Zepp Antenna" by Ward Silver, NØAX
- "The Extended Double Zepp Revisited" by Jerry Haigwood, W5JH
- "The Extended Lazy H Antenna" by Walter Salmon VK2SA
- "The Multiband Extended Double Zepp and Derivative Designs" by Robert Zavrel, W7SX
- "The N4GG Array" by Hal Kennedy, N4GG
- "The W8JK Antenna: Recap and Update" by John Kraus, W8JK

Chapter 12

Broadside and End-Fire Arrays

12.1 BROADSIDE ARRAYS

Broadside arrays can be made up of collinear or parallel elements or combinations of the two. They can provide performance comparable to rotatable beams at very low cost if the amateur has the necessary supports. This chapter was originally contributed by Rudy Severns, N6LF, and is written from the perspective of using these antennas at HF. Much of the material translates easily to VHF and higher frequencies as well. The reader will find a number of projects for designing and constructing these antennas in the Bibliography and with this book's downloadable supplemental information.

12.1.1 COLLINEAR ARRAYS

Collinear arrays are always operated with the elements in-phase. (If alternate elements in such an array are out-of-phase, the system simply becomes a harmonic type of antenna.) A collinear array is a broadside radiator, the direction of maximum radiation being at right angles to the line of the antenna.

Power Gain

Because of the nature of the mutual impedance between collinear elements, the feed point resistance (compared to a single element, which is ≈73 Ω) is increased as shown in the **Multielement Arrays** chapter. For this reason the power gain does not increase in direct proportion to the number of elements. The gain with two elements, as the spacing between them is varied, is shown by **Figure 12.1**. Although the gain is greatest when the end-to-end spacing is in the region of 0.4 to 0.6 λ, the use of spacings of this order is inconvenient to build and introduces problems in feeding the two elements. As a result, collinear elements are almost always operated with their ends quite close together — in wire antennas, usually with just a strain insulator between.

With very small spacing between the ends of adjacent elements the theoretical power gain of collinear arrays, assuming the use of #12 AWG copper wire, is approximately as follows over a dipole in free space:

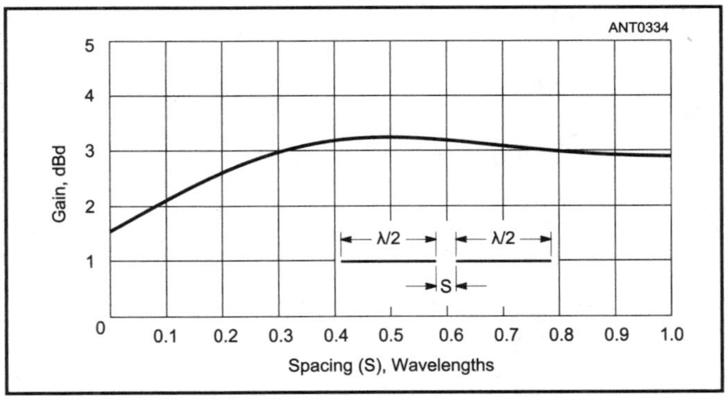

Figure 12.1 — Gain of two collinear λ/2 elements as a function of spacing between the adjacent ends.

2 collinear elements — 1.6 dB
3 collinear elements — 3.1 dB
4 collinear elements — 3.9 dB

More than four elements are rarely used.

Directivity

The directivity of a collinear array, in a plane containing the axis of the array, increases with its length. Small secondary lobes appear in the pattern when more than two elements are used, but the amplitudes of these lobes are low enough so that they are usually not important. In a plane at right angles to the array the directive diagram is a circle, no matter what the number of elements. Collinear operation, therefore, affects only E-plane directivity, the plane containing the antenna.

When a collinear array is mounted with the elements vertical, the antenna radiates equally well in all geographical directions. An array of such stacked collinear elements tends to confine the radiation to low vertical angles. This configuration is common in base station antennas for VHF and UHF and is discussed in the **VHF and UHF Antenna Systems** chapter.

If a collinear array is mounted horizontally, the directive pattern in the vertical plane at right angles to the array is the same as the vertical pattern of a simple λ/2 antenna at the same height as discussed in the chapter **Effects of Ground**.

12.1.2 TWO-ELEMENT ARRAYS

The simplest and most popular collinear array is one using two elements, as shown in **Figure 12.2**. This system is commonly known as two half-waves in phase. The directive pattern in a plane containing the wire axis is shown in **Figure 12.3**, which shows superimposed patterns for a dipole and 2, 3 and 4-element collinear arrays. Depending on the conductor size, height, and similar factors, the impedance at the feed point can be expected to be in the range of 4 to 6 kΩ, for wire antennas. If the elements are made of tubing having a low λ/dia (wavelength to diameter) ratio, values as low as 1 kΩ are representative. The system can be fed through an open-wire tuned line with negligible loss for ordinary line lengths, or a matching section may be used if desired.

A number of arrangements for matching the feed line to this antenna are described in the chapter **Transmission Line System Techniques**. If elements somewhat shorter than λ/2 are used, then additional matching schemes can be employed at the expense of a slight reduction in gain. When the elements are shortened two things happen — the impedance at the feed point drops and the impedance has inductive reactance that can be tuned out with simple series capacitors, as shown in Figure 12.2B.

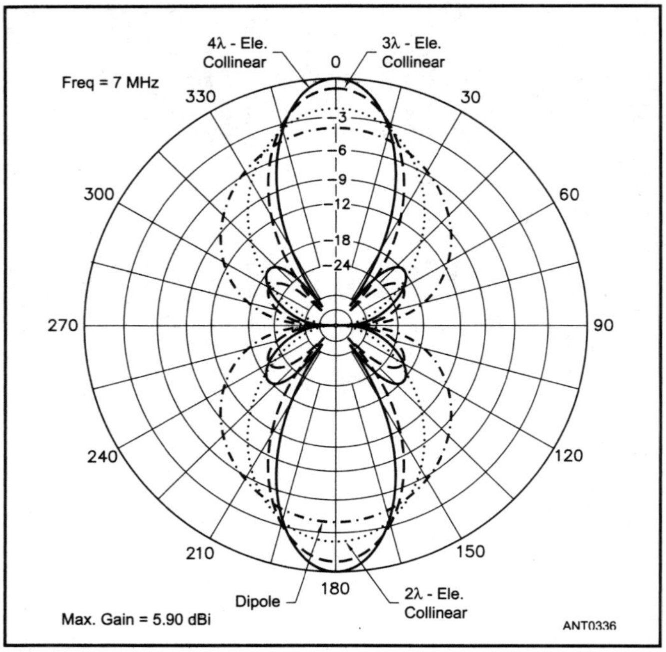

Figure 12.3 — Free-space E-plane directive diagram for dipole, 2, 3 and 4-element collinear arrays. The solid line is a 4-element collinear; the dashed line is for a 3-element collinear; the dotted line is for a 2-element collinear and the dashed-dotted line is for a λ/2 dipole.

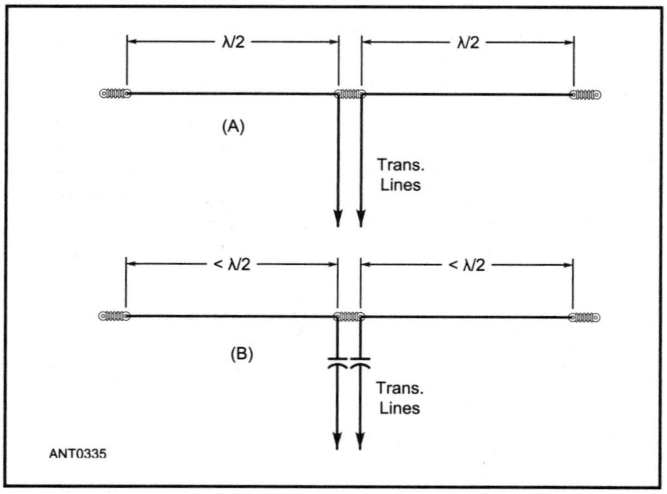

Figure 12.2 — At A, two-element collinear array (two half-waves in phase). The transmission line shown would operate as a tuned line. A matching section can be substituted and a nonresonant line used if desired, as shown at B, where the matching section is two series capacitors.

Note that these capacitors must be suitable for the power level. Small doorknob capacitors, such as those frequently used in power amplifiers, are suitable. By way of an example, if each side of a 40 meter 2-element array is shortened from 67 to 58 feet, the feed point impedance drops from nearly 6000 Ω to about 1012 Ω with an inductive reactance of 1800 Ω. The reactance can be tuned out by inserting 25 pF capacitors at the feed point. The 1012 Ω resistance can be transformed to 200 Ω using a λ/4 matching section made of 450-Ω ladder line and then transformed to 50 Ω with a 4:1 balun. Shortening the array as suggested reduces the gain by about 0.5 dB.

Another scheme that preserves the gain is to use a 450-Ω λ/4 matching section and shorten the antenna only slightly to have a resistance of 4 kΩ. The impedance at the input of the matching section is then near 50 Ω and a simple 1:1 balun can be used. Many other schemes are possible. The free-space E-plane response for a 2-element collinear array is shown in Figure 12.3, compared with the responses for more elaborate collinear arrays described below.

12.1.3 THREE- AND FOUR-ELEMENT ARRAYS

In a long wire the direction of current flow reverses in each λ/2 section. Consequently, collinear elements cannot simply be connected end to end; there must be some means for making the current flow in the same direction in all elements. When more than two collinear elements are used it is necessary to connect phasing stubs between adjacent elements in order to bring the currents in all elements in-phase. In **Figure 12.4A** the direction of current flow is correct in the two left-hand elements because the shorted λ/4 transmission line (*stub*) is connected between them. This stub may be looked upon simply as the alternate λ/2 section of a long-wire antenna folded back on itself to cancel its radiation. In Figure 12.4A the part to the right of the transmission line has a total length of three half wavelengths, the center half wave being folded back to form a λ/4 phase-reversing stub. No data are available on the impedance at the feed point in this arrangement, but various considerations indicate that it should be over 1 kΩ.

An alternative method of feeding three collinear elements is shown in Figure 12.4B. In this case power is applied at the center of the middle element and phase-reversing stubs are used between this element and both of the outer elements. The impedance at the feed point in this case is somewhat over 300 Ω and provides a close match to 300 Ω line. The SWR will be less than 2:1 when 600-Ω line is used. Center feed of this type is somewhat preferable to the arrangement in Figure 12.4A because the system as a whole is balanced. This assures more uniform power distribution among the elements. In Figure 12.4A, the right-hand element is likely to receive somewhat less power than the other two because a portion of the input power is radiated by the middle element before it can reach the element located at the extreme right.

A four-element array is shown in Figure 12.4C. The system is symmetrical when fed between the two center elements as shown. As in the three-element case, no data are available on the impedance at the feed point. However, the SWR with a 600 Ω line should not be much over 2:1.

Figure 12.3 compares the directive patterns of 2, 3 and 4-element arrays. Collinear arrays can be extended to more than four elements. However, the simple 2-element collinear array is the type most frequently used, as it lends itself well to multiband operation. More than two collinear elements are seldom used because more gain can be obtained from other types of arrays.

12.1.4 COLLINEAR ARRAY ADJUSTMENT

In any of the collinear systems described, the lengths of the radiating elements are the same as for λ/2 dipoles. The lengths of the phasing stubs can be found from the equations given in the chapter **Transmission Line System Techniques**

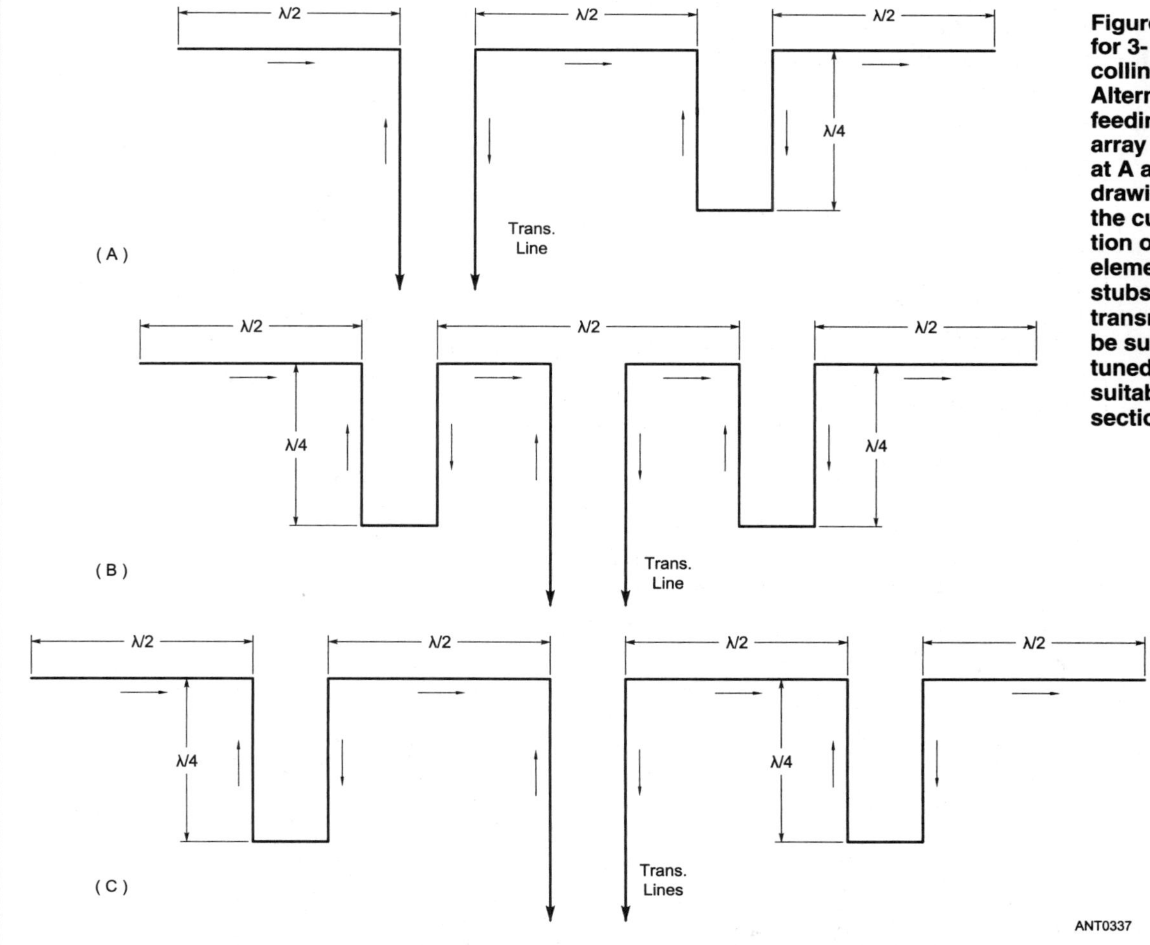

Figure 12.4 — Layouts for 3- and 4-element collinear arrays. Alternative methods of feeding a 3-element array are shown at A and B. These drawings also show the current distribution on the antenna elements and phasing stubs. A matched transmission line can be substituted for the tuned line by using a suitable matching section.

for the type of line used. If the stub is open-wire line (500 to 600 Ω impedance) you may assume a velocity factor of 0.975 in the formula for a λ/4 line. On-site adjustment is, in general, an unnecessary refinement. If desired, however, the following procedure may be used when the system has more than two elements.

Disconnect all stubs and all elements except those directly connected to the transmission line (in the case of a feed such as is shown in Figure 12.4B leave only the center element connected to the line). Adjust the elements to resonance, using the still-connected element. When the proper length is determined, cut all other elements to the same length. Make the phasing stubs slightly long and use a shorting bar to adjust their length. Connect the elements to the stubs and adjust the stubs to resonance, as indicated by maximum current in the shorting bars or by the SWR on the transmission line. If more than three or four elements are used it is best to add elements two at a time (one at each end of the array), resonating the system each time before a new pair is added.

12.1.5 THE EXTENDED DOUBLE ZEPP

One method to obtain higher gain that goes with wider spacing in a simple system of two collinear elements is to make the elements somewhat longer than λ/2. As shown in **Figure 12.5**, this increases the spacing between the two in-phase λ/2 sections at the ends of the wires. The section in the center carries a current of opposite phase, but if this section is short the current will be small; it represents only the outer ends of a λ/2 antenna section. Because of the small current and short length, the radiation from the center is small. The optimum length for each element is 0.64 λ. At greater lengths the system tends to act as a long-wire antenna, and the gain decreases.

This system is known as the *extended double Zepp* or *EDZ*, first described in *QST* in 1938 by Hugo Romander, W2NB. (See the Bibliography.) The gain over a λ/2 dipole is approximately 3 dB, as compared with about 1.6 dB for two collinear λ/2 dipoles. The directional pattern in the plane containing the axis of the antenna is shown in **Figure 12.6**. As in the case of all other collinear arrays, the free-space pattern in the plane at right angles to the antenna elements is the same as that of a λ/2 antenna — circular. The article "The Extended Double Zepp Revisited" by Jerry Haigwood, W5JH from September 2006 *QST* provides dimensions for the EDZ on 40 through 10 meters, along with building tips. (The article is also included with this book's downloadable supplemental information. An analysis of the EDZ and related designs by Zavrel is listed in the Bibliography.)

This antenna is not resonant at the operating frequency so that the feed point impedance is complex (R ± *j*X). A typical example of the variation of the feed point impedance over the band for a 40 meter double-extended Zepp is shown in **Figure 12.7**. This antenna is normally fed with open-wire transmission line to an antenna tuner. This allows the antenna to be used on multiple bands, although SWR may be high on some bands. Impedance at the antenna tuner depends on the antenna's feed point impedance and the length of the feed line.

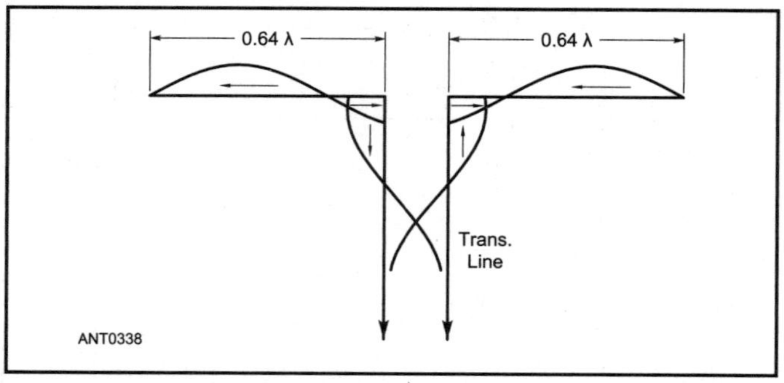

Figure 12.5 — The extended double Zepp. This system gives somewhat more gain than two λ-sized collinear elements.

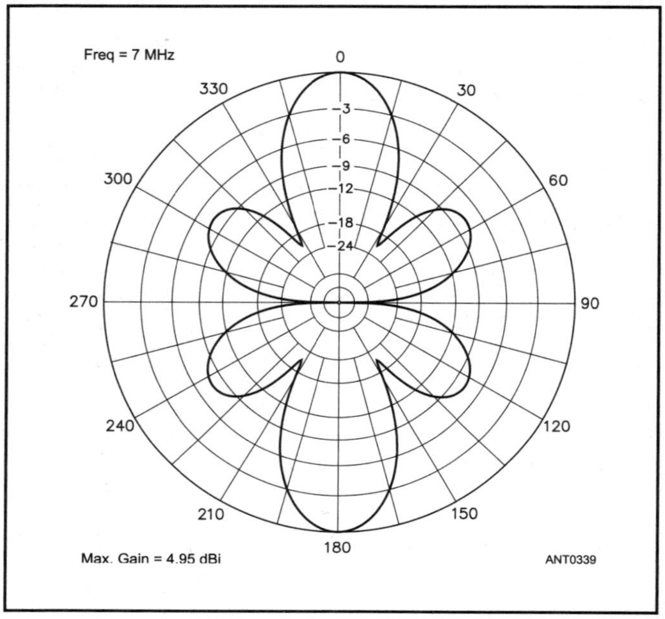

Figure 12.6 — E-plane pattern for the extended double Zepp of Figure 12.5. This is also the horizontal directional pattern when the elements are horizontal. The axis of the elements lies along the 90°-270° line. The free-space array gain is approximately 4.95 dBi.

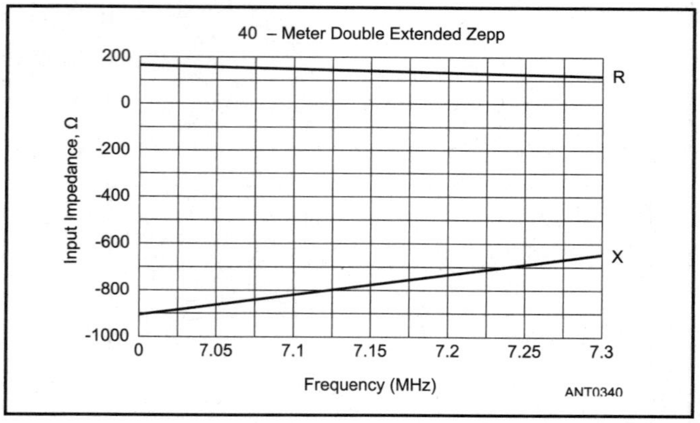

Figure 12.7 — Resistive and reactive feed point impedance of a 40 meter extended double Zepp in free space.

Variations on the Extended Double Zepp

By selecting the right length of feed line, the feed point impedance of the EDZ can be brought close to 50 Ω on the desired band. At that point, a choke balun can be used to create a transition to coaxial feed line. (See the **Transmission Line System Techniques** chapter regarding baluns.) The general design is shown in **Figure 12.8**.

Table 12.1 shows EDZ designs by W5JH including the length of the antenna (L_d) and 450-Ω window line (L_f) that result in approximately 50 Ω impedance at the end of the window line. (Note that the design also includes height above average ground which also affects feed point impedance.) The 50-Ω point is created only on the band shown in the table — SWR will be greatly different on other bands. (The original article by W5JH is provided with this book's downloadable supplemental information.) The exact length of antenna which reproduces these impedances will depend on height above ground and type of ground. Be prepared to adjust antenna length and window line length.

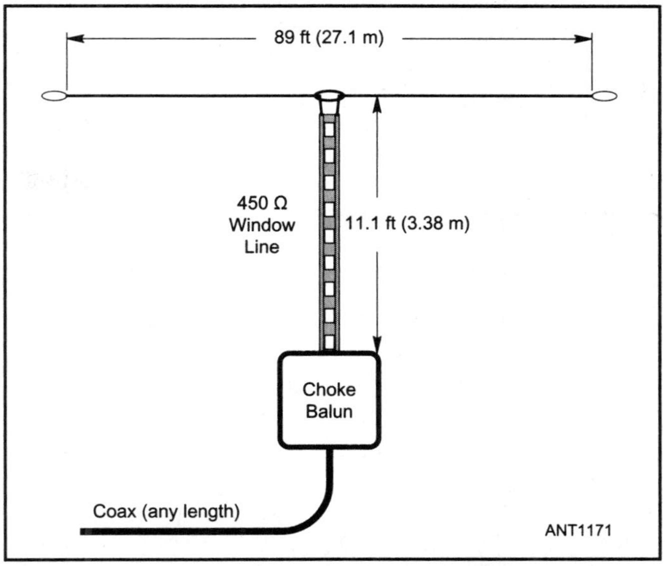

Figure 12.9 — The 20/15 meter EDZ with feed line length specified for low SWR on 20 and 15 meters.

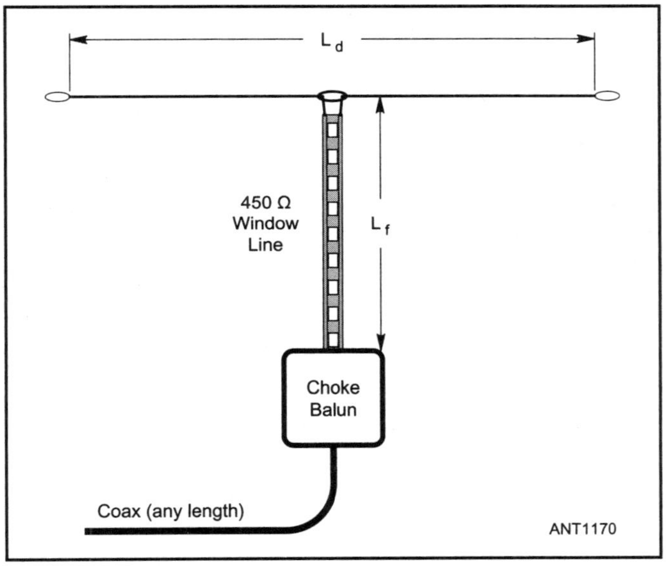

Figure 12.8 — A general design for Extended Double Zepp antennas by W5JH. Values for L_d (doublet length) and L_f (feed line length) are given in Table 12.1.

If it is desired to place the coax transition point farther from the antenna, add an integer number of λ/2 of feed line which will create a 50-Ω impedance at which the transition can be made. The transmission line software *TLW* can be used to calculate physical lengths for a variety of different types of parallel conductor feed lines.

Figure 12.9 is a 20/15 meter variation of the EDZ with low SWR on both bands through careful selection of the length of the 450-Ω feed line section. The pattern for 20 meters shown in **Figure 12.10** is similar to the classic EDZ of Figure 12.6 but because of the extra length on 15 meters, the pattern takes on a clover-leaf shape as shown in **Figure 12.11**. A 74.7-foot section of 450-Ω window line (two λ/2 on 20 meters and 3λ/2 on 15 meters) brings the coax transition point to ground level and SWR is less than 1.5:1on both bands. (The original article, "Hands-On Radio, Experiment #133," is provided with this book's downloadable supplemental information.)

A versatile antenna for 40, 80, and 160 meters, the "Bob

Table 12.1
EDZ Antenna Dimensions for Different Bands

Freq (MHz)	*L_d (ft)*	*Min Height (ft)*	*Antenna Z (Ω)*	*Feed point Z (Ω)*	*L_f (ft)*	*SWR*
7.075	175.2	66	170.5 –*j*976.1	47.10 +*j*0.25	21.65	1.062:1
10.11	122.6	47	163.0 –*j*934.1	47.80 –*j*0.07	14.85	1.046:1
14.175	87.5	34	155.3 –*j*889.6	48.62 –*j*0.36	10.35	1.029:1
18.1	68.5	30	133.4 –*j*848.9	44.63 +*j*0.38	7.92	1.121:1
21.2	58.5	30	132.1 –*j*799.9	47.65 –*j*0.28	6.56	1.050:1
24.9	49.8	30	156.7 –*j*772.3	58.60 –*j*0.10	5.51	1.172:1
28.2	44	30	169.8 –*j*772.4	63.24 +*j*0.26	4.88	1.265:1

L_d is the antenna length, L_f is the length of the matching feed line

Zepp" by Robert Zavrel, W7SX, is shown in **Figure 12.12**. This design uses traps to isolate sections of the antenna at 40 meters where it acts as a true EDZ. The antenna becomes an extended dipole on 80 meters and a two-vertical bidirectional, top-fed array on 160 meters. The antenna was designed for a height of around 110 feet. Significantly higher installation will affect the antenna's feed point impedance. The antenna can be installed at lower heights but the lower vertical sections and horizontal wires will have to be altered. See the original article, provided with this book's downloadable supplemental

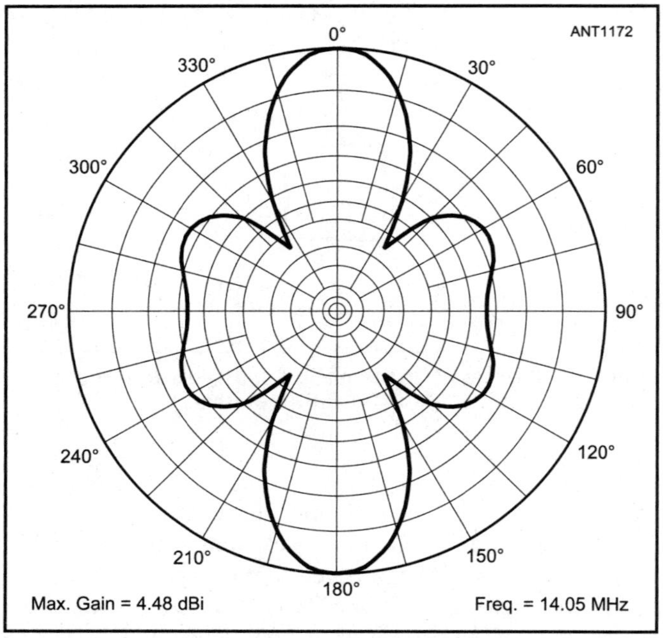

Figure 12.10 — The pattern of the 20/15 meter EDZ on 20 meters.

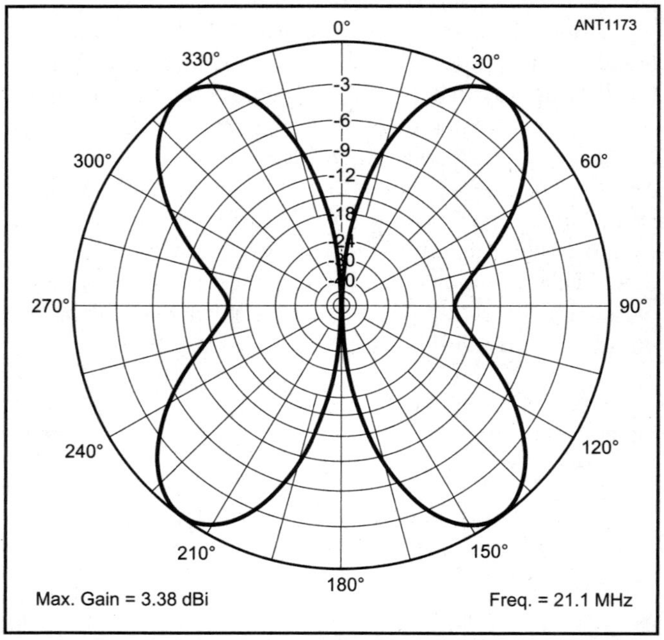

Figure 12.11 — The pattern of the 20/15 meter EDZ on 15 meters.

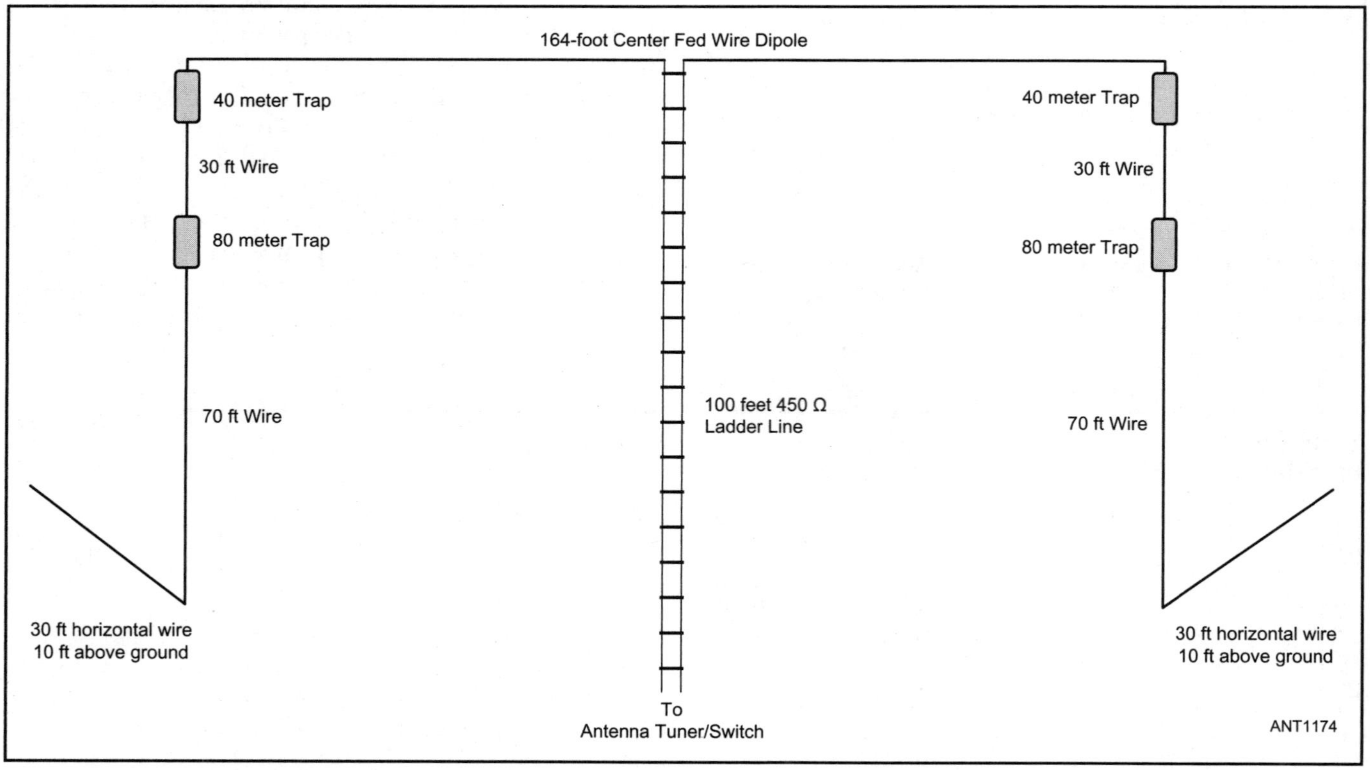

Figure 12.12 — The Bob-Zepp is an EDZ on 40 meters, an extended dipole on 80 meters, and a bi-directional array on 160 meters.

information, for the complete design, including a full-power tuning unit and numerous construction drawings.

12.1.6 THE STERBA CURTAIN

Two collinear arrays can be combined to form the Sterba array, often called the Sterba curtain. An 8-element example of a Sterba array is shown in **Figure 12.13**. The four λ/4 elements joined on the ends are equivalent to two λ/2 elements. The two collinear arrays are spaced λ/2 and the λ/4 phasing lines connected together to provide λ/2 phasing lines. This arrangement has the advantage of increasing the gain for a given length and also increasing the E-plane directivity, which is no longer circular. An additional advantage of this array is that the wire forms a closed loop. For installations where icing is a problem a low voltage dc or low frequency (50 or 60 Hz) ac current can be passed through the wire to heat it for deicing. The heating current is isolated from RF by decoupling chokes. This is standard practice in commercial installations.

The number of sections in a Sterba array can be extended as far as desired but more than four or five are rarely used because of the slow increase in gain with extra elements, the narrow H-plane directivity and the appearance of multiple sidelobes. When fed at the point indicated the impedance is about 600 Ω. The antenna can also be fed at the point marked X. The impedance at this point will be about 1 kΩ. The gain of the 8-element array in Figure 12.13 will be between 7 to 8 dB over a single element. A 10 meter Sterba curtain is described in the article, "Curtains for You," by Jim Cain, K1TN, that is included with this book's downloadable supplemental information.

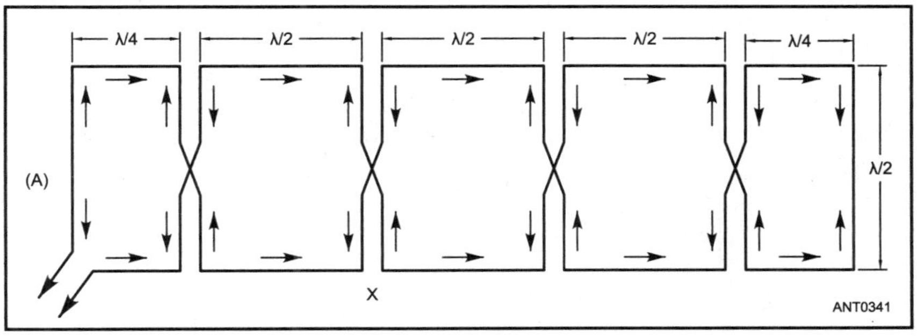

Figure 12.13 — Typical Sterba array, an 8-element version.

12.2 PARALLEL BROADSIDE ARRAYS

To obtain broadside directivity with parallel elements the currents in the elements must all be in-phase. At a distant point lying on a line perpendicular to the axis of the array and also perpendicular to the plane containing the elements, the fields from all elements add up in phase. The situation is similar to four parallel λ/2 dipoles fed together as a broadside array.

Broadside arrays of this type theoretically can have any number of elements. However, practical limitations of construction and available space usually limit the number of broadside parallel elements. These practical aspects of building a dipole curtain are illustrated in the article "A Dipole Curtain for 15 and 10 Meters" by Mike Loukides, W1JQ, in the Aug 2003 *QST* article with this book's downloadable supplemental information.

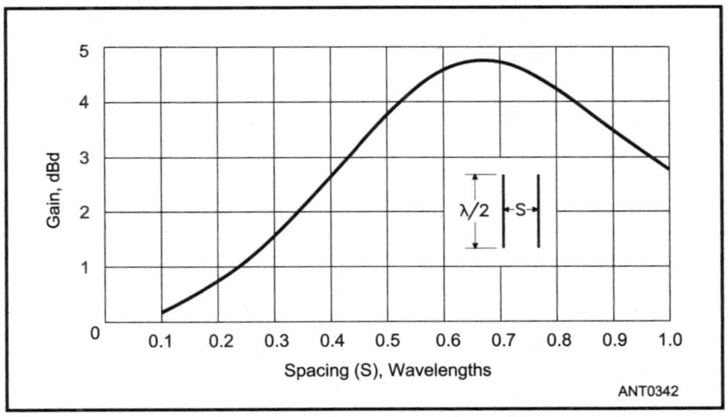

Figure 12.14 — Gain as a function of the spacing between two parallel elements operated in-phase (broadside).

12.2.1 POWER GAIN

The power gain of a parallel-element broadside array depends on the spacing between elements as well as on the number of elements. The way in which the gain of a two-element array varies with spacing is shown in **Figure 12.14**. The greatest gain is obtained when the spacing is in the vicinity of 0.67 λ.

The theoretical gains of broadside arrays having more than two elements are approximately as follows:

No. of Parallel Elements	*dB Gain with λ/2 Spacing*	*dB Gain with 3λ/4 Spacing*
3	5.7	7.2
4	7.1	8.5
5	8.1	9.4
6	8.9	10.4

The elements must, of course, all lie in the same plane and all must be fed in-phase.

12.2.2 DIRECTIVITY

The sharpness of the directive pattern depends on spacing between elements and number of elements. Larger element spacing will sharpen the main lobe, for a given number of elements, up to a point as was shown in Figure 12.1. The two-element array has no minor lobes when the spacing is λ/2, but small minor lobes appear at greater spacings. When three or more elements are used the pattern always has minor lobes.

12.3 OTHER FORMS OF BROADSIDE ARRAYS

For those who have the available room, multielement arrays based on the broadside concept have something to offer. The antennas are large but of simple design and non-critical dimensions; they are also very economical in terms of gain per unit of cost.

Large arrays can often be fed at several different points. However, the pattern symmetry may be sensitive to the choice of feed point within the array. Nonsymmetrical feed points will result in small asymmetries in the pattern but these are not usually of great concern.

Arrays of three and four elements are shown in **Figure 12.15**. In the 3-element array with λ/2 spacing at A, the array is fed at the center. This is the most desirable point in that it tends to keep the power distribution among the elements uniform. However, the transmission line could alternatively be connected at either point B or C of Figure 12.15A, with only slight skewing of the radiation pattern.

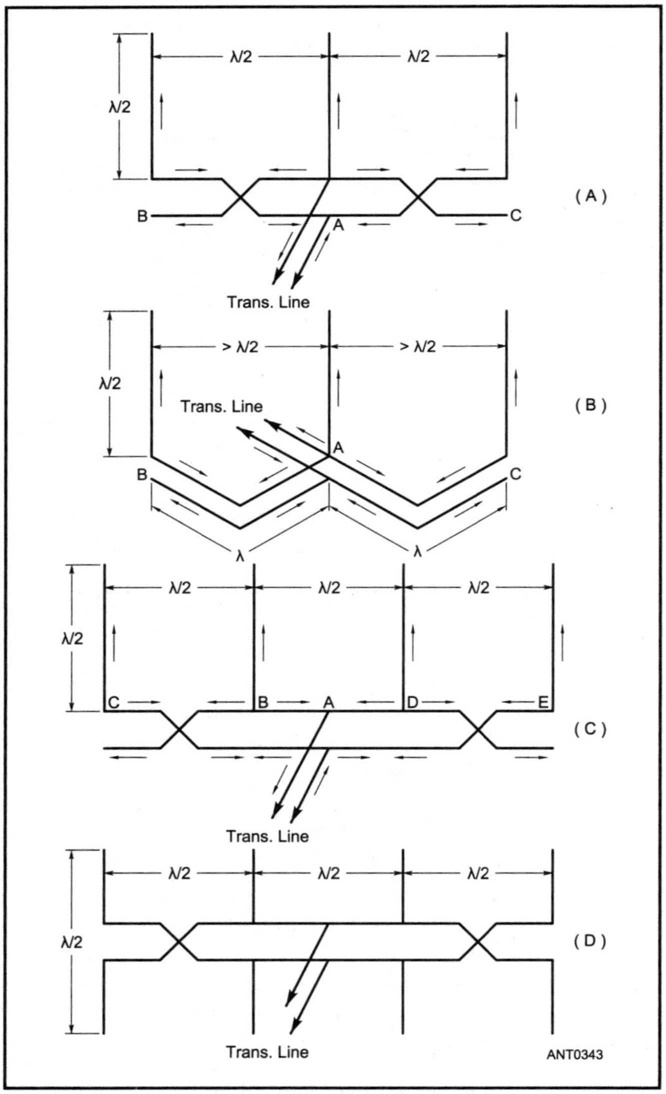

Figure 12.15 — Methods of feeding 3- and 4-element broadside arrays with parallel elements.

When the spacing is greater than λ/2, the phasing lines must be 1 λ long and are not transposed between elements. This is shown Figure 12.15B. With this arrangement, any element spacing up to 1 λ can be used, if the phasing lines can be folded as suggested in the drawing.

The 2-element array at C is fed at the center of the system to make the power distribution among elements as uniform as possible. However, the transmission line could be connected at either point B, C, D or E. In this case the section of phasing line between B and D must be transposed to make the currents flow in the same direction in all elements. The 4-element array at C and the 3-element array at B have approximately the same gain when the element spacing in the array at B is 3λ/4.

An alternative feeding method is shown in Figure 12.15D. This system can also be applied to the 3-element arrays, and will result in better symmetry in any case. It is necessary only to move the phasing line to the center of each element, making connection to both sides of the line instead of one only.

The free-space pattern for a 4-element array with λ/2 spacing is shown in **Figure 12.16**. This is also approximately the pattern for a 3-element array with 3λ/4 spacing.

Larger arrays can be designed and constructed by following the phasing principles shown in the drawings. No accurate figures are available for the impedances at the various feed points indicated in Figure 12.15. You can estimate it to be in the vicinity of 1 kΩ when the feed point is at a junction between the phasing line and a λ/2 element, becoming

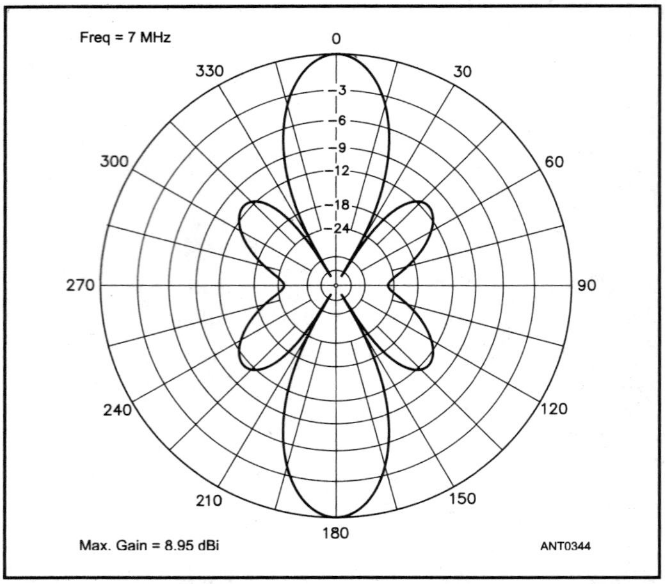

Figure 12.16 — Free-space E-plane pattern of a 4-element broadside array using parallel elements (Figure 12.15). This corresponds to the horizontal directive pattern at low wave angles for a vertically polarized array over ground. The axis of the elements lies along the 90°-270° line.

smaller as the number of elements in the array is increased. When the feed point is midway between end-fed elements as in Figure 12.15C, the feed point impedance of a 4-element array is in the vicinity of 200 to 300 Ω, with 600-Ω open-wire phasing lines. The impedance at the feed point with the antenna shown at D should be about 1.5 kΩ.

12.3.1 NON-UNIFORM ELEMENT CURRENTS

The pattern for a 4-element broadside array shown in Figure 12.16 has substantial sidelobes. This is typical for arrays more than λ/2 wide when equal currents flow in each element. Sidelobe amplitude can be reduced by using non-uniform current distribution among the elements. Many possible current amplitude distributions have been suggested. All of them have reduced current in the outer elements and greater current in the inner elements. This reduces the gain somewhat but can produce a more desirable pattern. One of the common current distributions is called binomial current grading. In this scheme the ratio of element currents is set equal to the coefficients of a polynomial. For example:

$$1x + 1, \Rightarrow 1, 1$$

$$(x+1)^2 = 1x^2 + 2x + 1, \Rightarrow 1, 2, 1$$

$$(x+1)^3 = 1x^3 + 3x^2 + 3x + 1, \Rightarrow 1, 3, 3, 1$$

$$(x+1)^4 = 1x^4 + 4x^3 + 6x^2 + 6x + 1, \Rightarrow 1, 4, 6, 4, 1$$

In a 2-element array the currents are equal, in a 3-element array the current in the center element is twice that in the outer elements, and so on.

12.3.2 HALF-SQUARE ANTENNA

On the low-frequency bands (40, 80 and 160 meters) it becomes increasingly difficult to use λ/2 elements because of their size. The half-square antenna is a 2-element broadside array with λ/4-high vertical elements and λ/2 horizontal spacing. See **Figure 12.17**. The free-space H-plane pattern for this array is shown in **Figure 12.18**. The antenna gives modest (4.2 dBi) but useful gain and has the advantage of only λ/4 height. Like all vertically polarized antennas, real-world performance depends directly on the characteristics of the ground surrounding it.

The half-square can be fed either at the point indicated or at the bottom end of one of the vertical elements using a voltage-feed scheme, such as for the Bobtail curtain described below. The feed point impedance is in the region of 50 Ω when fed at a corner as shown in Figure 12.17. The SWR bandwidth is typically quite narrow as shown in the following design examples.

Variations on the Half-Square Antenna

The following section was originally presented in *The ARRL Antenna Compendium Vol 5*, by Rudy Severns, N6LF.

A simple modification to a standard dipole is to add two λ/4 vertical wires, one at each end, as shown in **Figure 12.19**. This makes a *half-square antenna*. The antenna can be fed at one corner (low-impedance, current fed) or at the lower end of one of the vertical wires (high-impedance, voltage fed). Other feed arrangements are also possible.

The "classical" dimensions for this antenna are λ/2 (131 feet at 3.75 MHz) for the top wire and λ/4 (65.5 feet) for the vertical wires. However, there is nothing sacred

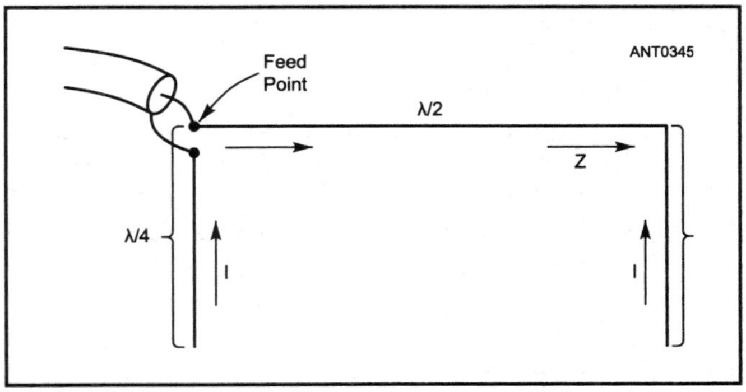

Figure 12.17 — Layout for the half-square antenna.

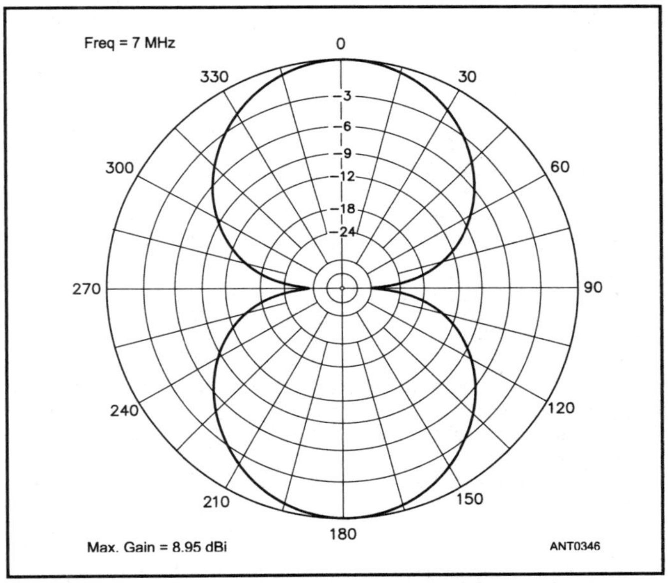

Figure 12.18 — Free-space E-plane directive pattern for the half-square antenna.

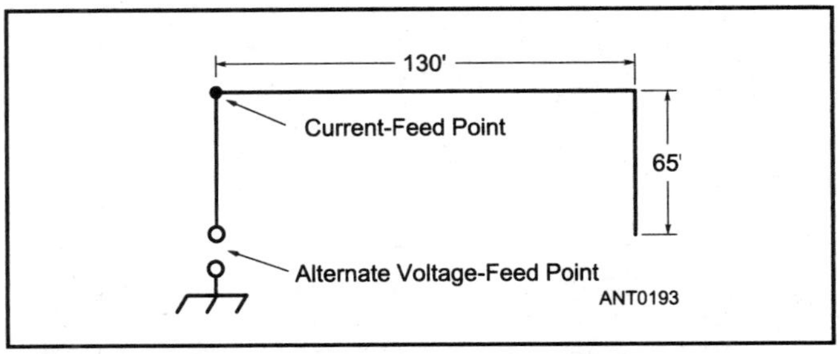

Figure 12.19 — Typical 80 meter half-square, with λ/4-high vertical legs and a λ/2-long horizontal leg. The antenna may be fed at the bottom or at a corner. When fed at a corner, the feed point is a low-impedance, current-feed. When fed at the bottom of one of the wires against a small ground counterpoise, the feed point is a high-impedance, voltage-feed.

about these dimensions! They can vary over a wide range and still obtain nearly the same performance.

This antenna is two λ/4 verticals, spaced λ/2, fed in-phase by the top wire. The current maximums are at the top corners. The theoretical gain over a single vertical is 3.8 dB. An important advantage of this antenna is that it does not require the extensive ground system and feed arrangements that a conventional pair of phased λ/4 verticals would.

Comparison to a Dipole

In the past, one of the things that has turned off potential users of the half-square on 80 and 160 meters is the perceived need for λ/4 vertical sections. This forces the height to be >65 feet on 80 meters and >130 feet on 160 meters. That's not really a problem. If you don't have the height there are several things you can do. For example, just fold the ends in, as shown in **Figure 12.20**. This compromises the performance surprisingly little.

It is helpful to compare the examples given in Figures 12.19 and 12.20 to dipoles at the same height. Two heights, 40 and 80 feet, and average, very good and sea water grounds, were used for this comparison. It is also assumed that the lower end of the vertical wires had to be a minimum of 5 feet above ground.

At 40 feet the half-square is really mangled, with only 35-foot long (≈ λ/8) vertical sections. The elevation-plane comparison between this antenna and a dipole of the same height is shown in **Figure 12.21**. Over average ground the half-square is superior below 32° and at 15° is almost 5 dB better. That is a worthwhile improvement. If you have very good soil conductivity, like parts of the lower Midwest and South, then the half-square will be superior below 38° and at 15° will be nearly 8 dB better. For those fortunate few with saltwater frontal property the advantage at 15° is 11 dB! Notice also that above 35°, the response drops off rapidly. This is great for DX but is not good for local work.

Figure 12.22 shows the azimuthal-plane pattern for the 80 meter half-square antenna in Figure 12.20, but this time compared with the response of a flattop horizontal dipole that is 100 feet high. These comparisons are for average ground and are for an elevation angle of 5°. The message here is that the lower your dipole and the better your ground, the more you have to gain by switching from a dipole to a half-square. The half-square antenna looks like a good bet for DXing.

Changing the Shape of the Half Square

Just how flexible is the shape? There are several common distortions of practical importance. Some have very little effect but a few are fatal to the gain. Suppose you have either more height and less width than called for in the standard version or more width and less height, as shown in **Figure 12.23A**.

The effect on gain from this type of dimensional variation is given in **Table 12.2**. For a top length (L_T) varying between 110 and 150 feet, where the vertical wire lengths (L_V)

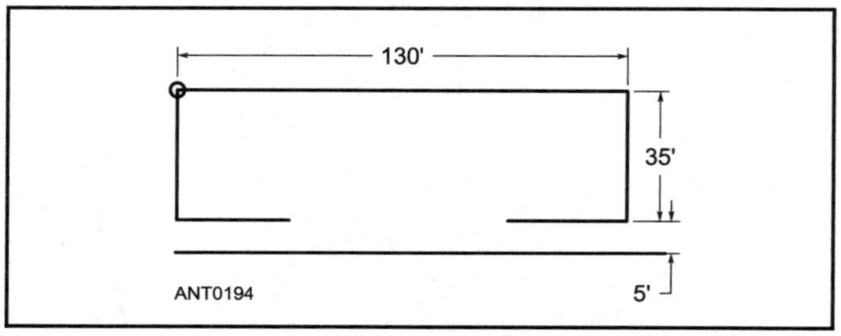

Figure 12.20 — An 80 meter half-square configured for 40-foot high supports. The ends have been bent inward to reresonate the antenna. The performance is compromised surprisingly little.

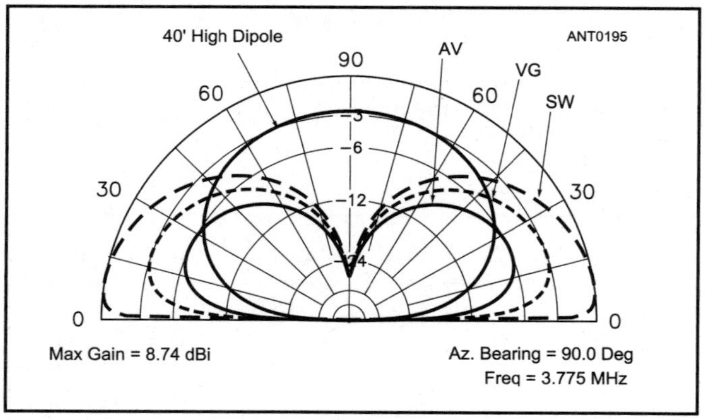

Figure 12.21 — Comparison of 80 meter elevation response of 40-foot high, horizontally polarized dipole over average ground and a 40-foot high, vertically polarized half-square, over three types of ground: average (conductivity σ = 5 mS/m, dielectric constant ε = 13), very good (σ = 30 mS/m, ε = 20) and salt water (σ = 5000 mS/m, ε = 80). The quality of the ground clearly has a profound effect on the low-angle performance of the half-square. Even over average ground, the half-square outperforms the low dipole below about 32°.

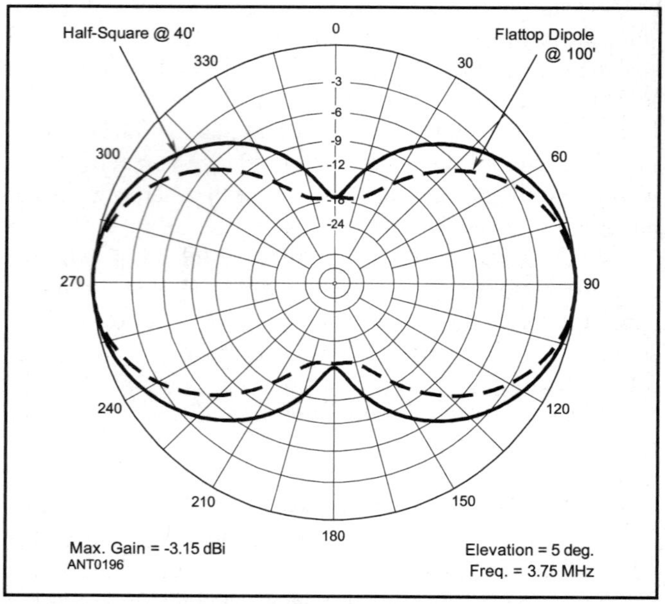

Figure 12.22 — 80 meter azimuth patterns for shortened half-square antenna (solid line) compared with flattop dipole (dashed line) at 100 feet height. Average ground is assumed for these cases.

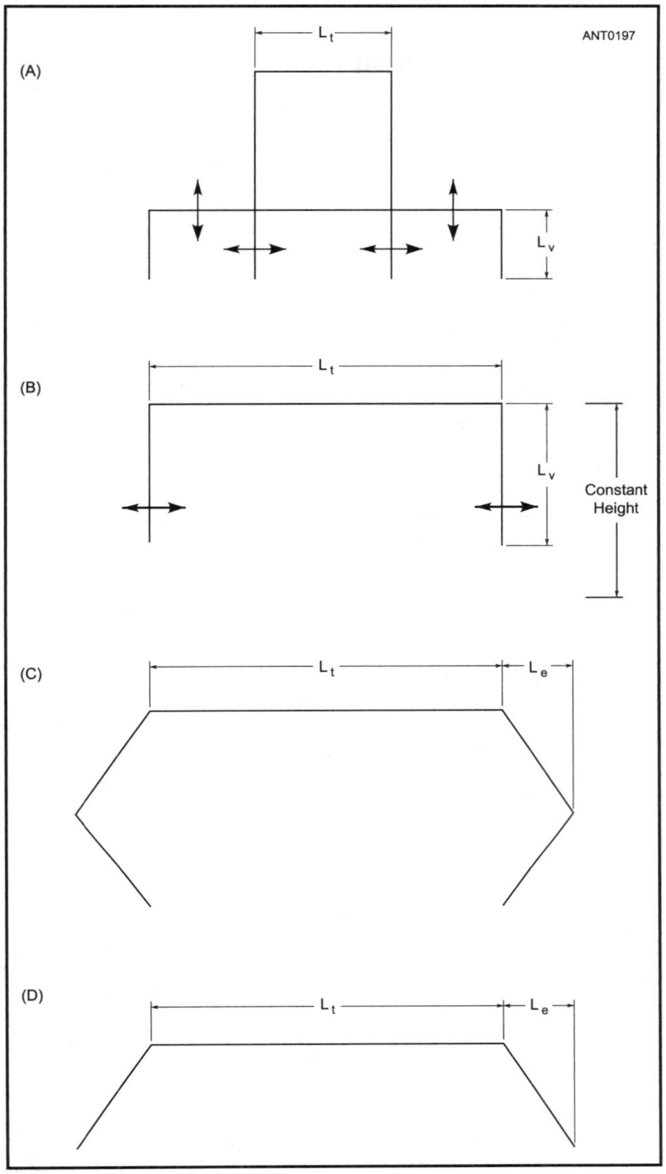

Figure 12.23 — Varying the horizontal and vertical lengths of a half-square. At A, both the horizontal and vertical legs are varied, while keeping the antenna resonant. At B, the height of the horizontal wire is kept constant, while its length and that of the vertical legs is varied to keep the antenna resonant. At C, the length of the horizontal wire is varied and the legs are bent inwards in the shape of "vees." At D, the ends are sloped outward and the length of the flattop portion is varied. All these symmetrical forms of distortion of the basic half-square shape result in small performance losses.

readjusted to resonate the antenna, the gain changes only by 0.6 dB. For a 1-dB change the range of L_T is 100 to 155 feet, a pretty wide range.

Another variation results if we vary the length of the horizontal top wire and readjust the vertical wires for resonance, while keeping the top at a constant height. See Figure 12.23B. Table 12.2 shows the effect of this variation on the peak gain. For a range of L_T = 110 to 145 feet, the gain changes only 0.65 dB.

The effect of bending the ends into a V shape, as shown

Table 12.2
Variation in Gain with Change in Horizontal Length
Vertical Height Readjusted for Resonance (Figure 12.23A)

L_T (feet)	L_V (feet)	Gain (dBi)
100	85.4	2.65
110	79.5	3.15
120	73.7	3.55
130	67.8	3.75
140	61.8	3.65
150	56	3.05
155	53	2.65

Vertical Length Readjusted for Resonance, but Horizontal Wire Kept at Constant Height (Figure 12.23B)

L_T (feet)	L_V (feet)	Gain (dBi)
110	78.7	3.15
120	73.9	3.55
130	68	3.75
140	63	3.35
145	60.7	3.05

Table 12.3
Gain for Half-Square Antenna, Where Ends Are Bent Into V-Shape (see Figure 12.23C)

Height ⇒	H=40 feet	H=40 feet	H=60 feet	H=60 feet
L_T (feet)	L_V (feet)	Gain (dBi)	L_e (feet)	Gain (dBi)
40	57.6	3.25	52.0	2.75
60	51.4	3.75	45.4	3.35
80	45.2	3.95	76.4	3.65
100	38.6	3.75	61.4	3.85
120	31.7	3.05	44.4	3.65
140	—	—	23	3.05

in Figure 12.23C, is given in **Table 12.3**. The bottom of the antenna is kept at a height of 5 feet and the top height (H) is either 40 or 60 feet. Even this gross deformation has only a relatively small effect on the gain. Sloping the ends outward as shown in Figure 12.23D and varying the top length also has only a small effect on the gain. While this is good news because it allows you dimension the antenna to fit different QTHs, not all distortions are so benign.

Suppose the two ends are not of the same height, as illustrated in **Figure 12.24**, where one end of the half-square is 20 feet higher than the other. The elevation-plane radiation pattern for this antenna is shown in **Figure 12.25** compared to a dipole at 50 feet. This type of distortion does affect the pattern. The gain drops somewhat and the zenith null goes away. The nulls off the end of the antenna also go away, so that there is some end-fire radiation. In this example the difference in height is fairly extreme at 20 feet. Small differences of 1 to 5 feet do not affect the pattern seriously.

If the top height is the same at both ends but the length

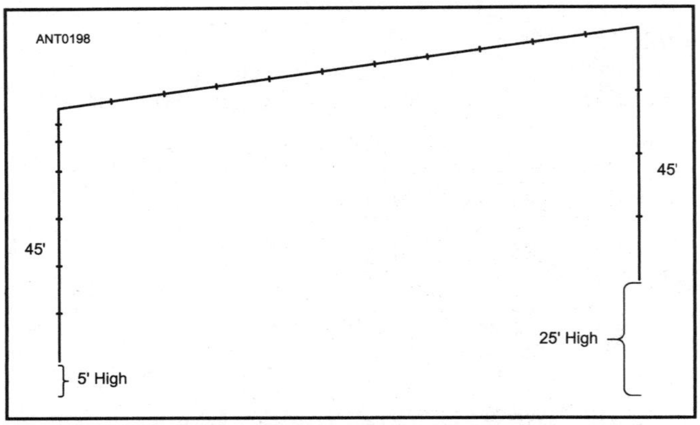

Figure 12.24 — An asymmetrical distortion of the half-square antenna, where the bottom of one leg is purposely made 20 feet higher than the other. This type of distortion does affect the pattern!

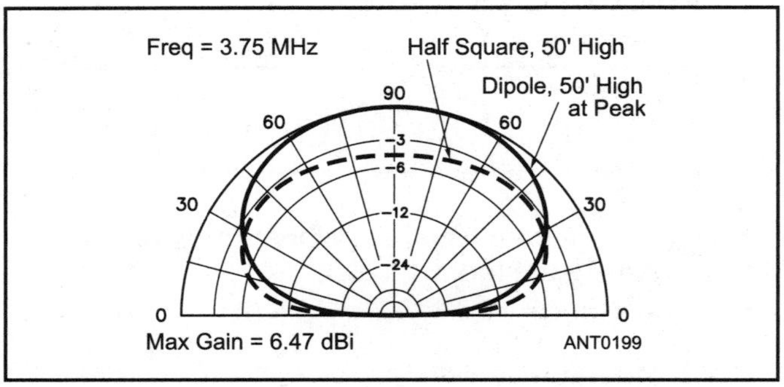

Figure 12.25 — Elevation pattern for the asymmetrical half-square compared with pattern for a 50-foot high dipole. This is over average ground, with a conductivity of 5 mS/m and a dielectric constant of 13. Note that the zenith-angle null has filled in and the peak gain is lower compared to conventional half-square over the same kind of ground.

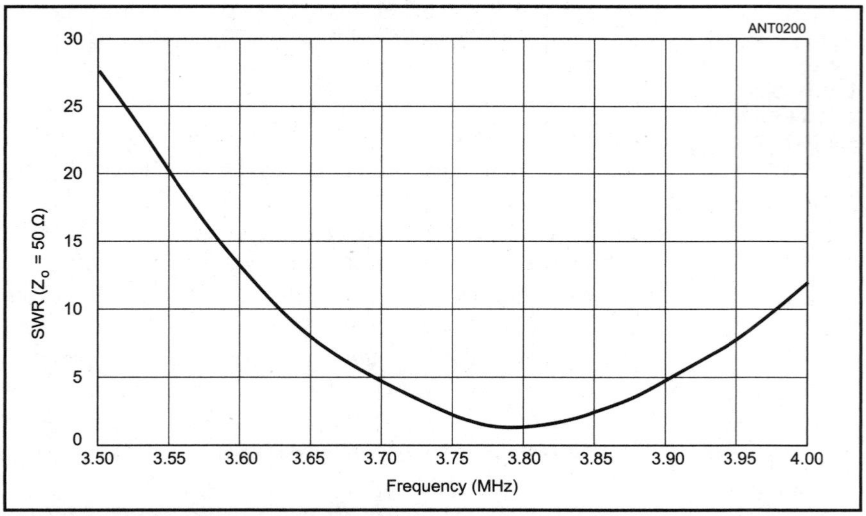

Figure 12.26 — Variation of SWR with frequency for current-fed half-square antenna. The SWR band- width is quite narrow.

of the vertical wires is not the same, then a similar pattern distortion can occur. The antenna is very tolerant of symmetrical distortions but it is much less accepting of asymmetrical distortion.

What if the length of the wires is such that the antenna is not resonant? Depending on the feed arrangement, that may or may not matter. We will look at that issue later on, in the section on patterns versus frequency. The half-square antenna, like the dipole, is very flexible in its proportions.

Half-Square Feed Point Impedance

There are many different ways to feed the half-square. Traditionally the antenna has been fed either at the end of one of the vertical sections, against ground, or at one of the upper corners as shown in Figure 12.19.

For voltage feed at the bottom against ground, the impedance is very high, on the order of several thousand ohms. For current feed at a corner, the impedance is much lower and is usually close to 50 Ω. This is very convenient for direct feed with coax.

The half-square is a relatively high-Q antenna (Q ≈ 17). **Figure 12.26** shows the SWR variation with frequency for this feed arrangement. An 80 meter dipole is not particularly wideband either, but a dipole will have less extreme variation in SWR than the half-square.

Patterns Versus Frequency

Impedance is not the only issue when defining the bandwidth of an antenna. The effect on the radiation pattern of changing frequency is also a concern. For a voltage-fed half-square, the current distribution changes with frequency. For an antenna resonant near 3.75 MHz, the current distribution is nearly symmetrical. However, above and below resonance the current distribution increasingly becomes asymmetrical. In effect, the open end of the antenna is constrained to be a voltage maximum but the feed point can behave less as a voltage point and more like a current maximum. This allows the current distribution to become asymmetrical.

The effect is to reduce the gain by –0.4 dB at 3.5 MHz and by –0.6 dB at 4 MHz. The depth of the zenith null is reduced from –20 dB to –10 dB. The side nulls are also reduced. Note that this is exactly what happened when the antenna was made physically asymmetrical. Whether the asymmetry is due to current distribution or mechanical arrangements, the antenna pattern will suffer.

When current feed at a corner is used, the asymmetry introduced by off-resonance operation is much less, since both ends of the antenna are open circuits and constrained to be voltage maximums. The resulting gain reduction is only –0.1 dB. It is interesting that the sensitivity of the pattern to changing frequency depends on the feed scheme used.

Of more concern for corner feed is the effect of the transmission line. The usual instruction is to simply feed the antenna using coax, with the shield connected to vertical wire and the center conductor to the top wire. Since the shield of the coax is a conductor, more or less parallel with the radiator, and is in the immediate field of the antenna, you might expect the pattern to be seriously distorted by this practice. This arrangement seems to have very little effect on the pattern. The greatest effect is when the feed line length was near a multiple of $\lambda/2$. Such lengths should be avoided.

Of course, you may use a choke balun at the feed point if you desire. This might reduce the coupling to the feed line even further but it doesn't appear to be worth the trouble. In fact, if you use an antenna tuner in the shack to operate away from resonance with a very high SWR on the transmission line, a balun at the feed point would take a beating.

Voltage-Feed at One End of Antenna: Matching Schemes

Several straightforward means are available for narrowband matching. However, broadband matching over the full 80 meter band is much more challenging. Voltage feed with a parallel-resonant circuit and a modest local ground, as shown in **Figure 12.27**, is the traditional matching scheme for this antenna. Matching is achieved by resonating the circuit at the desired frequency and tapping down on the inductor in Figure 12.27A or using a capacitive divider (Figure 12.27B). It is also possible to use a $\lambda/4$ transmission-line matching scheme, as shown in Figure 12.27C.

If the matching network shown in Figure 12.27B is used, typical values for the components would be: L = 15 µH, C1 = 125 pF and C2 = 855 pF. At any single point the SWR can be made very close to 1:1 but the bandwidth for SWR < 2:1 will be very narrow at <100 kHz. Altering the L-C ratio doesn't make very much difference. The half-square antenna has a well-earned reputation for being narrowband.

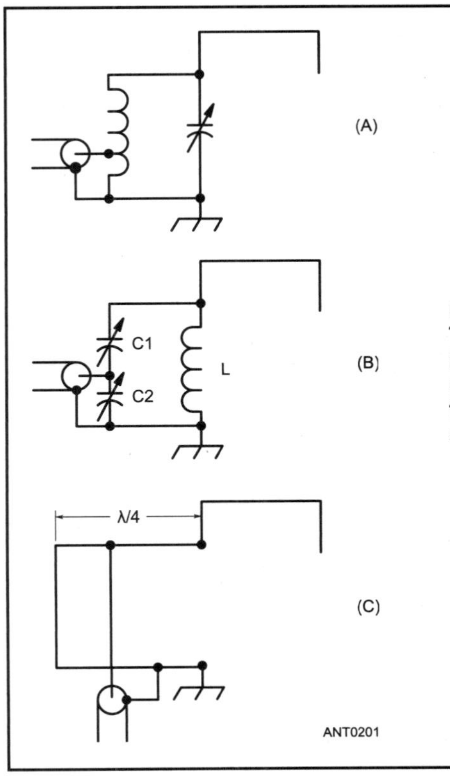

Figure 12.27 — Typical matching networks used for voltage-feeding a half-square antenna.

12.3.3 BOBTAIL CURTAIN

The antenna system in **Figure 12.28**, called a Bobtail curtain, was originally described by Woodrow Smith, W6BCX, in 1948 (see Bibliography for this and other articles on the Bobtail.) It uses the principles of co-phased verticals to produce a broadside, bidirectional pattern providing approximately 5.1 dB of gain over a single $\lambda/4$ element. The antenna performs as three in-phase, top-fed vertical radiators approximately $\lambda/4$ in height and spaced approximately $\lambda/2$. It is most effective for low-angle signals and makes an excellent long-distance antenna for 1.8, 3.5 or 7 MHz.

The three vertical sections are the actual radiating components, but only the center element is fed directly. The two horizontal parts, A, act as phasing lines and contribute very little to the radiation pattern. Because the current in the center element must be divided between the end sections, the current distribution approaches a binomial 1:2:1 ratio. The radiation pattern is shown in **Figure 12.29**.

The vertical elements should be as vertical as possible. The height for the horizontal portion should be slightly greater than B, as shown in Figure 12.28. The tuning network is resonant at the operating frequency. The L/C ratio should be fairly low to provide good loading characteristics. As a starting point, a maximum capacitor value of 75 to 150 pF is recommended, and the inductor value is determined by C and the operating frequency. The network is first tuned to resonance and then the tap point is adjusted for the best match.

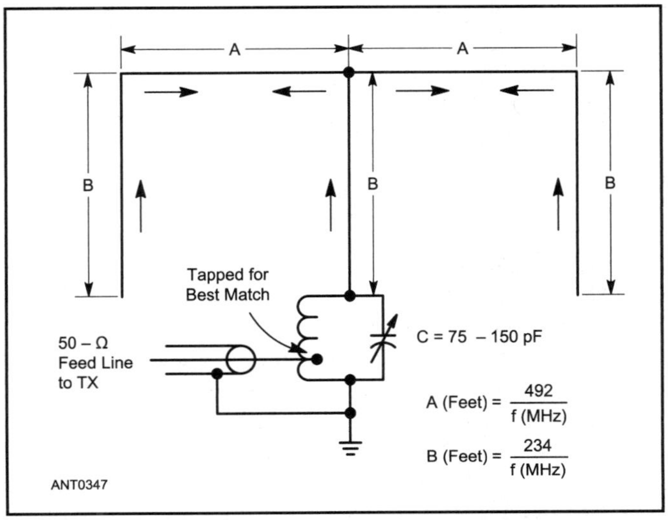

Figure 12.28 — The Bobtail curtain is an excellent low-angle radiator having broadside bidirectional characteristics. Current distribution is represented by the arrows. Dimensions A and B (in feet, for wire antennas) can be determined from the equations.

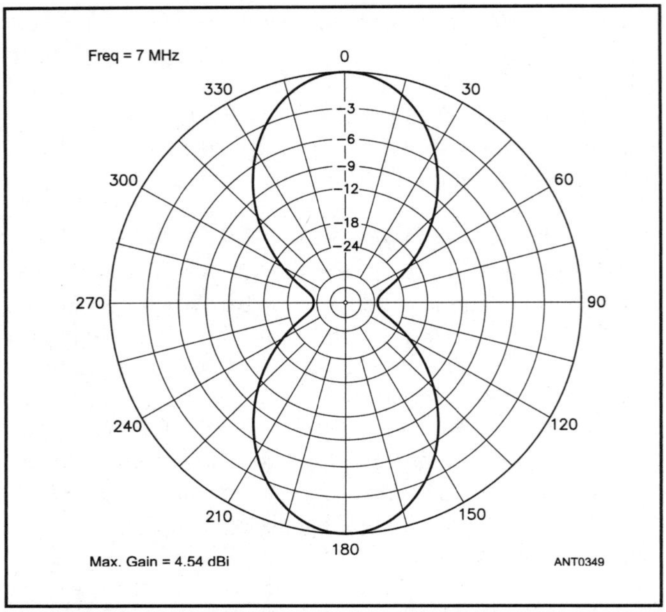

Figure 12.29 — Calculated free-space E-plane directive diagram of the Bobtail curtain shown in Figure 12.28. The array lies along the 90°-270° axis.

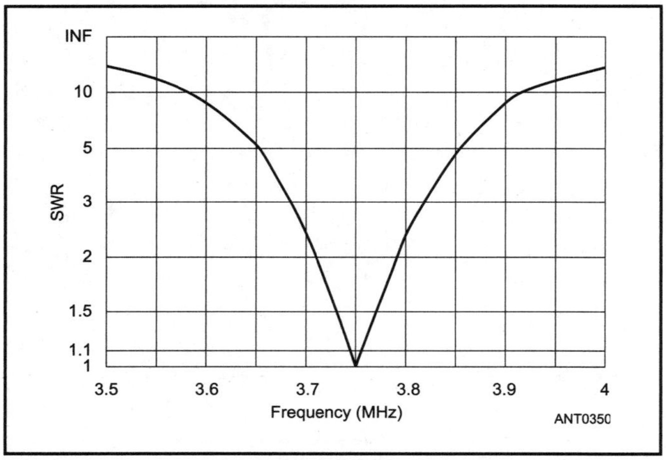

Figure 12.30 — Typical SWR plot for an 80 meter Bobtail curtain in free space. This is a narrow-band antenna.

A slight readjustment of C may be necessary. A link coil consisting of a few turns can also be used to feed the antenna.

A feeling for the matching bandwidth of this antenna can be obtained by looking at a feed point located at the top end of the center element. The impedance at this point will be approximately 32 Ω. An SWR plot (for $Z_0 = 32\ \Omega$) for an 80 meter Bobtail curtain at this feed point is shown in **Figure 12.30**. However, it is not advisable to actually connect a feed line at this point since it would detune the array and alter the pattern. This antenna is relatively narrow band. When fed at the bottom of the center element as shown in Figure 12.28, the SWR can be adjusted to be 1:1 at one frequency but the operating bandwidth for SWR less than 2:1 may be even narrower than Figure 12.30 shows. For 80 meters, where operation is often desired in the CW DX portion (3.510 MHz) and in the phone DX portion (3.790 MHz), it will be necessary to retune the matching network as you change frequency. This can be done by switching a capacitor in or out, manually or remotely with a relay.

While the match bandwidth is quite narrow, the radiation pattern changes more slowly with frequency. **Figure 12.31** shows the variation in the pattern over the entire band (3.5 to 4.0 MHz). As would be expected, the gain increases with frequency because the antenna is larger in terms of wavelengths. The general shape of the pattern, however, is quite stable.

A variation of the Bobtail for multiple bands, the N4GG Array, is described in a July 2002 *QST* article that is included with this book's downloadable supplemental information. The antenna covers multiple bands using parallel wires similarly to a fan dipole and with vertical wires acting as they do in the Bobtail curtain.

12.3.4 THE BRUCE ARRAY

Four variations of the Bruce array are shown in **Figure 12.32**. The Bruce is simply a wire folded so that the vertical sections carry large in-phase currents, while the horizontal sections carry small currents flowing in opposite directions with respect to the center of a section (indicated by dots). The radiation is vertically polarized. The gain is proportional to the length of the array but is somewhat smaller than you can obtain from a broadside array of λ/2 elements of the same length. This is because the radiating portion of the elements is only λ/4.

The Bruce array has a number of advantages:

1) The array is only λ/4 high. This is especially helpful on 80 and 160 meters, where the height of λ/2 supports becomes impractical for most amateurs.

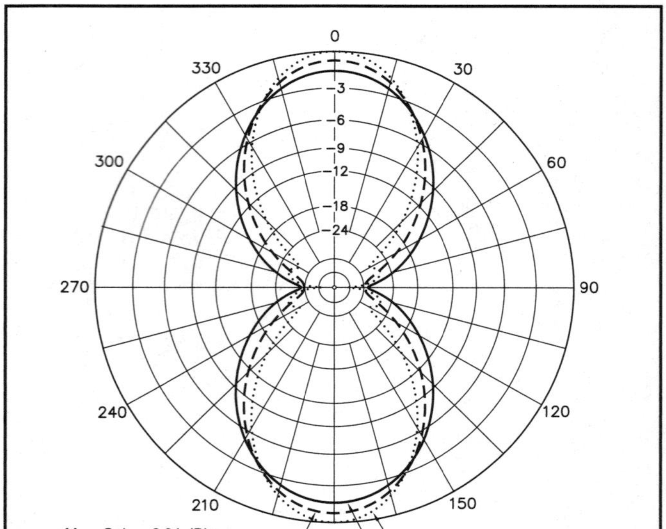

Figure 12.31 — 80 meter Bobtail curtain's free-space E-plane pattern variation over the 80 meter band.

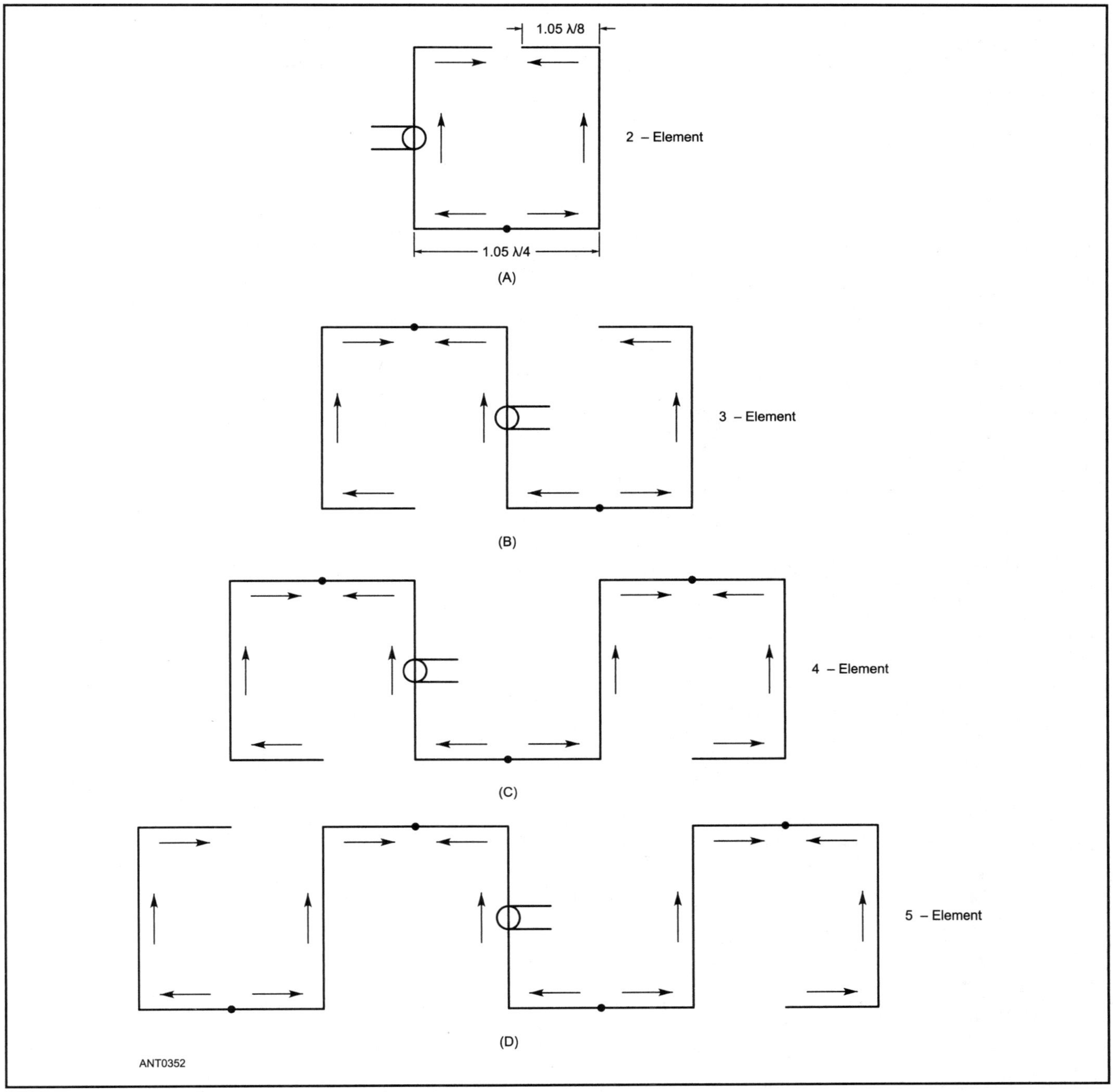

Figure 12.32 — Various Bruce arrays: 2, 3, 4 and 5-element versions.

2) The array is very simple. It is just a single piece of wire folded to form the array.

3) The dimensions of the array are very flexible. Depending on the available distance between supports, any number of elements can be used. The longer the array, the greater the gain.

4) The shape of the array does not have to be exactly 1.05 $\lambda/4$ squares. If the available height is short but the array can be made longer, then shorter vertical sections and longer horizontal sections can be used to maintain gain and resonance. Conversely, if more height is available but width is restricted then longer vertical sections can be used with shorter horizontal sections.

5) The array can be fed at other points more convenient for a particular installation.

6) The antenna is relatively low Q, so that the feed point impedance changes slowly with frequency. This is very helpful on 80 meters, for example, where the antenna can be relatively broadband.

7) The radiation pattern and gain is stable over the width of an amateur band.

Note that the nominal dimensions of the array in

Table 12.4
Bruce Array Length, Impedance and Gain as a Function of Number of Elements

Number Elements	*Gain Over λ/2 Vertical Dipole*	*Gain over λ/4 Ground-Plane*	*Array Length Wavelengths*	*Approx. Feed Z, Ω*
2	1.2 dB	1.9 dB	¼	130
3	2.8 dB	3.6 dB	½	200
4	4.3 dB	5.1 dB	¾	250
5	5.3 dB	6.1 dB	1	300

Figure 12.32 call for section lengths = 1.05 λ/4. The need to use slightly longer elements to achieve resonance is common in large wire arrays. A quad loop behaves in the same manner. This is quite different from wire dipoles, which are typically shortened by 2-5% to achieve resonance.

Figure 12.33 shows the variations in gain and pattern for 2 to 5-element 80 meter Bruce arrays. **Table 12.4** lists the gain over a vertical λ/2 dipole, a 4-radial ground-plane vertical and the size of the array. The gain and impedance parameters listed are for free space. Over real ground the patterns and gain will depend on the height above ground and the ground characteristics. Copper loss using #12 AWG conductors is included.

Worthwhile gain can be obtained from these arrays, especially on 80 and 160 meters, where any gain is hard to come by. The feed point impedance is for the center of a vertical section. From the patterns in Figure 12.33 you can see that sidelobes start to appear as the length of the array is increased beyond 3λ/4. This is typical for arrays using equal currents in the elements.

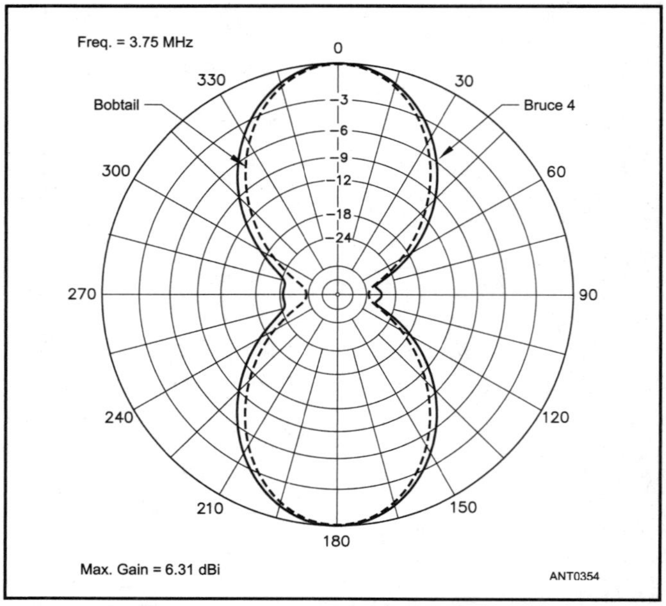

Figure 12.34 — Comparison of free space patterns of a 4-element Bruce array (solid line) and a 3-element Bobtail curtain (dashed line).

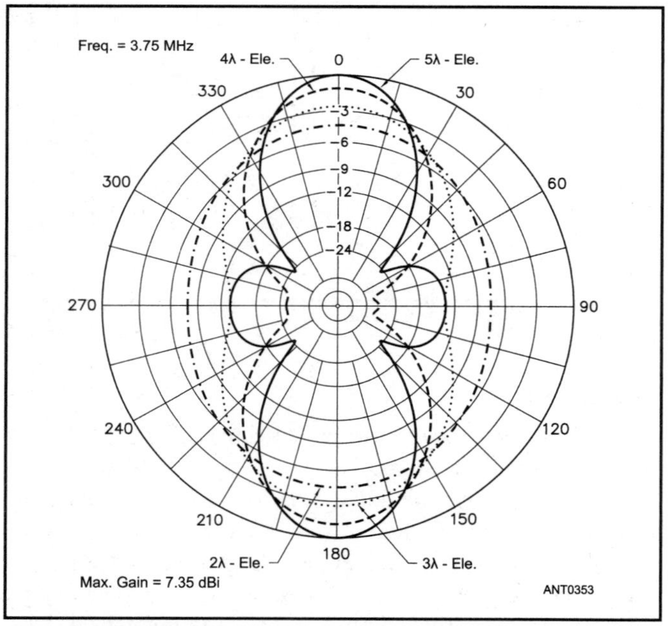

Figure 12.33 — 80 meter free-space E-plane directive patterns for the Bruce arrays shown in Figure 12.32. The 5-element's pattern is a solid line; the 4-element is a dashed line; the 3-element is a dotted line, and the 2-element version is a dashed-dotted line.

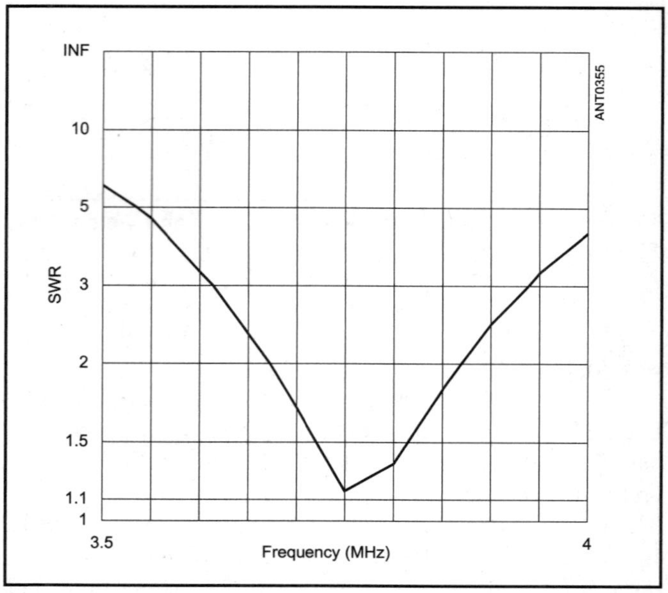

Figure 12.35 — Typical SWR curve for a 4-element 80 meter Bruce array.

It is interesting to compare the Bobtail curtain (Figure 12.28) with a 4-element Bruce array. **Figure 12.34** compares the radiation patterns for these two antennas. Even though the Bruce is shorter (3λ/4) than the Bobtail (1 λ), it has slightly more gain. The matching bandwidth is illustrated by the SWR curve in **Figure 12.35**. The 4-element Bruce has over twice the match bandwidth (200 kHz) than does the Bobtail (75 kHz in Figure 12.30). Part of the gain difference is due to the binomial current distribution — the center element has twice the current as the outer elements in the Bobtail. This reduces the gain slightly so that the 4-element Bruce becomes competitive. This is a good example of using more than the minimum number of elements to improve performance or to reduce size. On 160 meters the 4-element Bruce will be 140 feet shorter than the Bobtail, a significant reduction. If additional space is available for the Bobtail (1 λ) then a 5-element Bruce could be used, with a small increase in gain but also introducing some sidelobes.

The 2-element Bruce and the half-square antennas are both 2-element arrays. However, since the spacing between radiators is greater in the half-square (λ/2) the gain of the half-square is about 1 dB greater. If space is available, the half-square would be a better choice. If there is not room for a half-square then the Bruce, which is only half as long (λ/4), may be a good alternative. The 3-element Bruce, which has the same length (λ/2) as the half-square, has about 0.6 dB more gain than the half-square and will have a wider match bandwidth.

The Bruce antenna can be fed at many different points and in different ways. In addition to the feed points indicated in Figure 12.32, you may connect the feed line at the center of any of the vertical sections. In longer Bruce arrays, feeding at one end will result in some current imbalance among the elements but the resulting pattern distortion is small. Actually, the feed point can be anywhere along a vertical section. One very convenient point is at an outside corner. The feed point impedance will be higher (about 600 Ω). A good match for 450-Ω ladder-line can usually be found somewhere on the vertical section. It is important to recognize that feeding the antenna at a voltage node (dots in Figure 12.32) by breaking the wire and inserting an insulator, completely changes the current distribution. This will be discussed in the section on end-fire arrays.

A Bruce can be fed unbalanced against ground or against a counterpoise as shown in **Figure 12.36**. Because it is a vertically polarized antenna, the better the ground system, the better the performance. As few as two elevated radials can be used as shown in Figure 12.36B, but more radials can also be used to improve the performance, depending on local ground constants. The original development of the Bruce array in the late 1920s used this feed arrangement.

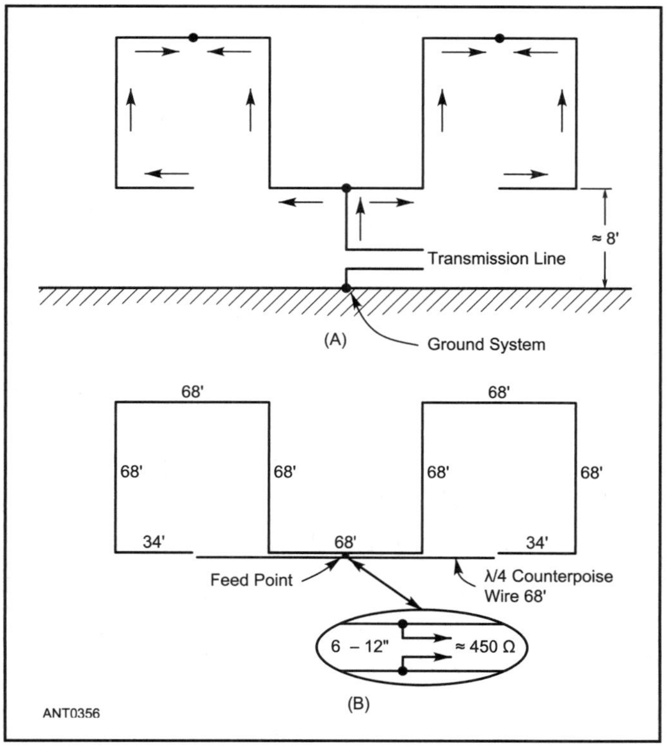

Figure 12.36 — Alternate feed arrangements for the Bruce array. At A, the antenna is driven against a ground system and at B, it uses a two-wire counterpoise.

12.3.5 FOUR-ELEMENT BROADSIDE ARRAY

The 4-element array shown in **Figure 12.37** is commonly known as the Lazy H. It consists of a set of two collinear elements and a set of two parallel elements, all operated in-phase to give broadside directivity. The gain and directivity will depend on the spacing, as in the case of a simple parallel-element broadside array. The spacing may be chosen between the limits shown on the drawing, but spacings below 3λ/8 are

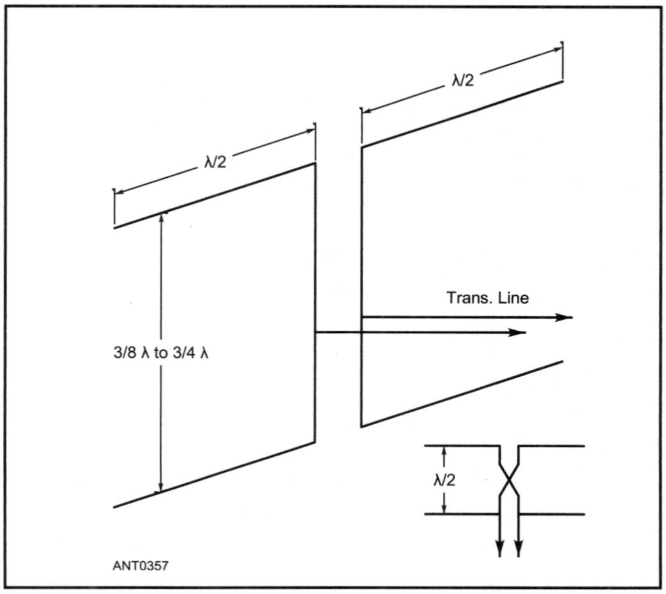

Figure 12.37 — Four-element broadside array ("lazy H") using collinear and parallel elements.

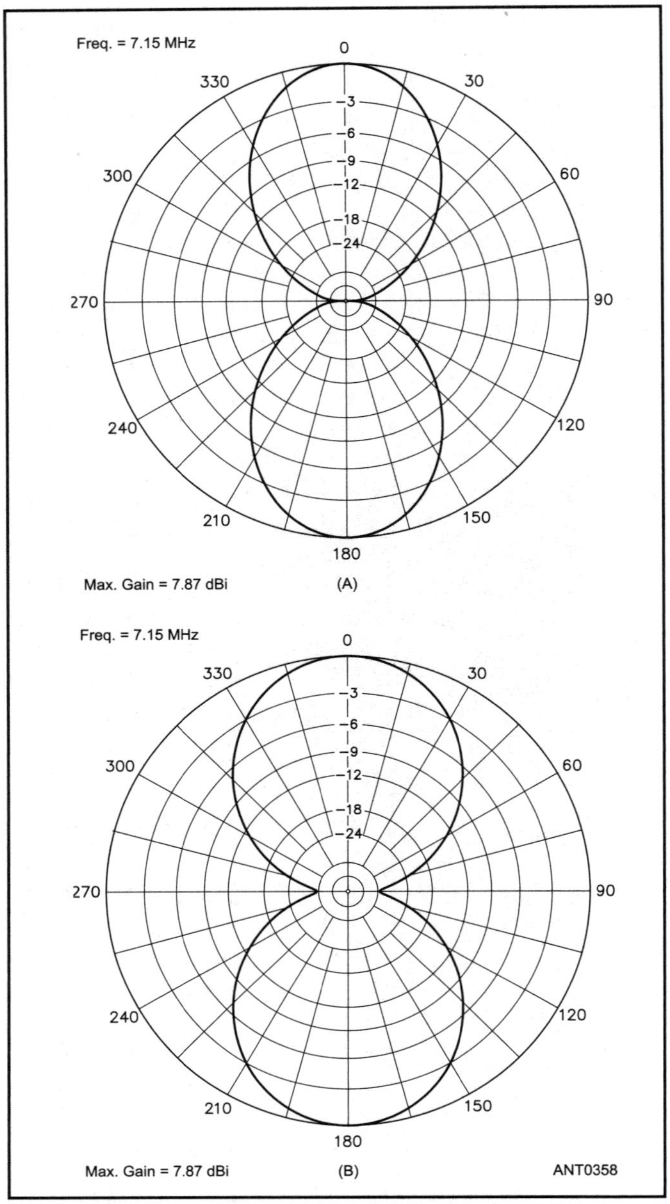

Figure 12.38 — Free-space directive diagrams of the 4-element antenna shown in Figure 12.37. At A is the E-plane pattern. The axis of the elements lies along the 90°-270° line. At B is the free-space H-plane pattern, viewed as if one set of elements is above the other from the ends of the elements.

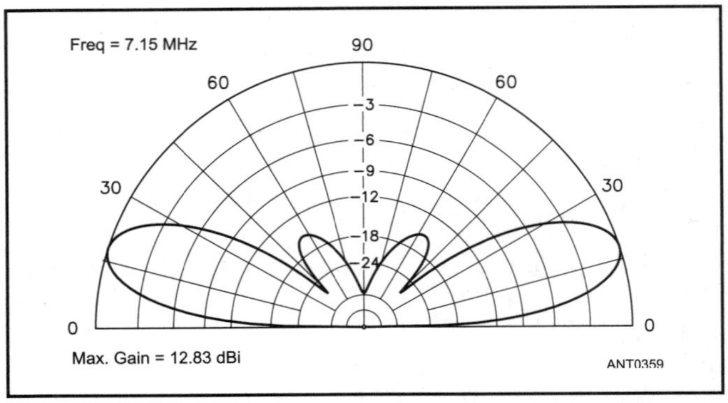

Figure 12.39 — Vertical pattern of the 4-element broadside antenna of Figure 12.37, when mounted with the elements horizontal and the lower set λ/4 above flat ground. Stacked arrays of this type give best results when the lowest elements are at least λ/2 high. The gain is reduced and the wave angle raised if the lowest elements are too close to ground.

not worthwhile because the gain is small. Estimated gains compared to a single element are:

3λ/8 spacing — 4.2 dB
λ/2 spacing — 5.8 dB
5λ/8 spacing — 6.7 dB
3λ/4 spacing — 6.3 dB

Half-wave spacing is generally used. Directive patterns for this spacing are given in **Figures 12.38** and **12.39**. With λ/2 spacing between parallel elements, the impedance at the junction of the phasing line and transmission line is resistive and in the vicinity of 100 Ω. With larger or smaller spacing the impedance at this junction will be reactive as well as resistive. Matching stubs are recommended in cases where a non-resonant line is to be used. They may be calculated and adjusted as described in the **Transmission Line System Techniques** chapter.

The system shown in Figure 12.37 may be used on two bands having a 2-to-1 frequency relationship. It should be designed for the higher of the two frequencies, using 3λ/4 spacing between parallel elements. It will then operate on the lower frequency as a simple broadside array with 3λ/8 spacing.

An alternative method of feeding is shown in the small diagram in Figure 12.37. In this case the elements and the phasing line must be adjusted exactly to an electrical half wavelength. The impedance at the feed point will be resistive and on the order of 2 kΩ.

A variation of this antenna called the "extended Lazy H" makes an effective broadside antenna on its fundamental and several higher bands. It is a good Field Day antenna if the supports are available for the lower elements to be at least λ/4 above the ground. It can be used with a tuner on all HF bands and as a top-loaded vertical by connecting the feed line conductors together and driving it against a ground system. A version for 7, 14, and 21 MHz is described in "The Extended Lazy H Antenna," by Walter Salmon in Oct 1955 *QST* and included with this book's downloadable supplemental information.

12.3.6 THE BI-SQUARE ANTENNA

A development of the lazy H, known as the bi-square antenna, is shown in **Figure 12.40**. The gain of the bi-square is somewhat less than that of the lazy-H, but this array is attractive because it can be supported from a single pole. It has a circumference of 2 λ at the operating frequency, and is horizontally polarized.

The bi-square antenna consists of two 1 λ radiators, fed 180° out-of-phase at the bottom of the array. The radiation resistance is 300 Ω, so it can be fed with either 300- or 600-Ω line. The free space gain of the antenna is about

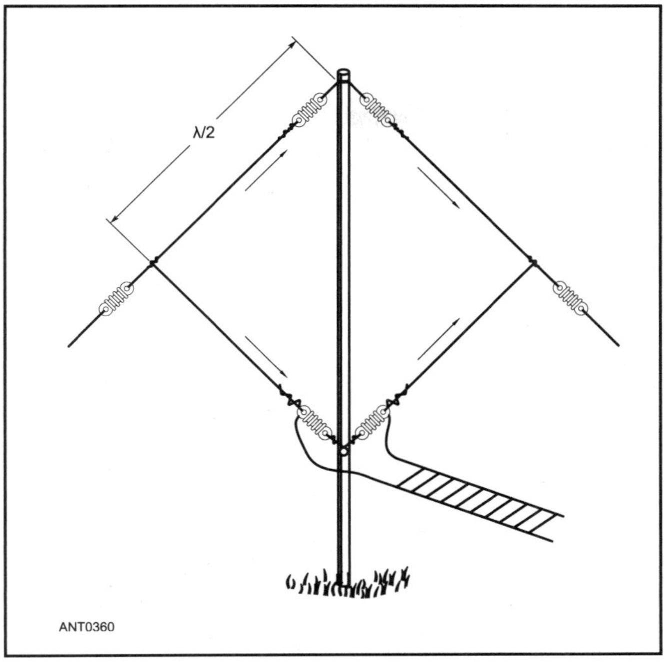

Figure 12.40 — The bi-square array. It has the appearance of a loop, but is not a true loop because the conductor is open at the top. The length of each side, in feet, is 480/f (MHz).

5.8 dBi, which is 3.7 dB more than a single dipole element. Gain may be increased by adding a parasitic reflector or director. Two bi-square arrays can be mounted at right angles and switched to provide omnidirectional coverage. In this way, the antenna wires may be used as part of the guying system for the pole.

Although it resembles a loop antenna, the bi-square is not a true loop because the ends opposite the feed point are open. However, identical construction techniques can be used for the two antenna types. Indeed, with a means of remotely closing the connection at the top for lower frequency operation, the antenna can be operated on two harmonically related bands. As an example, an array with 17 feet per side can be operated as a bi-square at 28 MHz and as a full-wave loop at 14 MHz. For two-band operation in this manner, the side length should favor the higher frequency. The length of a closed loop is not as critical.

12.4 END-FIRE ARRAYS

The term end-fire covers a number of different methods of operation, all having in common the fact that the maximum radiation takes place along the array axis, and that the array consists of a number of parallel elements in one plane. End-fire arrays can be either bidirectional or unidirectional. In the bidirectional type commonly used by amateurs there are only two elements, and these are operated with currents 180° out-of-phase. Even though adjustment tends to be complicated, unidirectional end-fire driven arrays have also seen amateur use, primarily as a pair of phased, ground-mounted λ/4 vertical elements. Extensive discussion of this array is contained in the **Multielement Arrays** chapter.

Horizontally polarized unidirectional end-fire arrays see little amateur use except in log-periodic arrays (described in the **Log-Periodic Dipole Arrays** chapter). Instead, horizontally polarized unidirectional arrays usually have parasitic elements (described in the **HF Yagi and Quad Antennas** chapter) and are called Yagis.

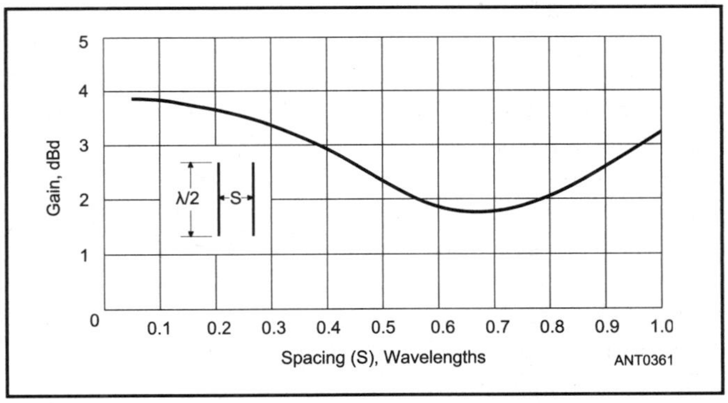

Figure 12.41 — Gain of an end-fire array consisting of two elements fed 180° out-of-phase, as a function of the spacing between elements. Maximum radiation is in the plane of the elements and at right angles to them at spacings up to λ/2, but the direction changes at greater spacings.

12.4.1 TWO-ELEMENT END-FIRE ARRAY

In a 2-element array with equal currents out-of-phase, the gain varies with the spacing between elements as shown in **Figure 12.41**. The maximum gain occurs in the neighborhood of 0.1 λ spacing. Below that the gain drops rapidly due to conductor loss resistance.

The feed point resistance for either element is very low at the spacings giving greatest gain, as shown in the **Multielement Arrays** chapter. The spacings most frequently used are λ/8 and λ/4, at which the resistances of center-fed λ/2 elements are about 9 and 32 Ω, respectively.

The effect of conductor resistance on gain for various spacings is shown in **Figure 12.42**. Because current along the element is not constant (it is approximately sinusoidal), the resistance shown is the equivalent resistance (R_{eq}) inserted at the center of the element to account for the loss distributed along the element.

The equivalent resistance of a λ/2 element is one half the

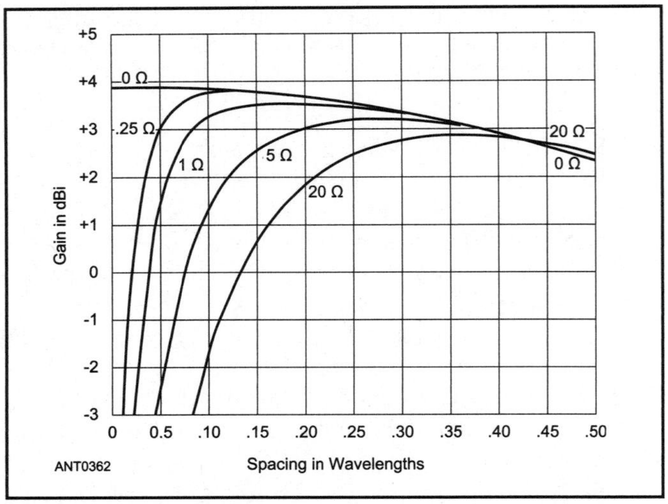

Figure 12.42 — Gain over a single element of two out-of-phase elements in free space as a function of spacing for various loss resistances.

ac resistance (R_{ac}) of the complete element. R_{ac} is usually >> R_{dc} due to skin effect. For example, a 1.84 MHz dipole using #12 AWG copper wire will have the following R_{eq}:

Wire length = 267 feet

$R_{dc} = 0.00159\ [\Omega/\text{foot}] \times 267\ [\text{feet}] = 0.42\ \Omega$

$F_r = R_{ac}/R_{dc} = 10.8$

$R_{eq} = (R_{dc}/2) \times F_r = 2.29\ \Omega$

For a 3.75 MHz dipole made with #12 AWG wire, $R_{eq} = 1.59\ \Omega$. In Figure 12.42, it is clear that end-fire antennas made with #12 AWG or smaller wire will limit the attainable gain because of losses. There is no point in using spacings much less than λ/4 if you use wire elements. If instead you use elements made of aluminum tubing then smaller spacings can be used to increase gain. However, as the spacing is reduced below λ/4 the increase in gain is quite small even with good conductors. Closer spacings give little gain increase but can drastically reduce the operating bandwidth due to the rapidly increasing Q of the array.

Unidirectional End-Fire Arrays

Two parallel elements spaced λ/4 apart and fed equal currents 90° out-of-phase will have a directional pattern in the plane at right angles to the plane of the array. See **Figure 12.43**. The maximum radiation is in the direction of the element in which the current lags. In the opposite direction the fields from the two elements cancel.

When the currents in the elements are neither in-phase nor 180° out-of-phase, the feed point resistances of the elements are not equal. This complicates the problem of feeding equal currents to the elements, as discussed in the **Multielement Arrays** chapter.

More than two elements can be used in a unidirectional end-fire array. The requirement for unidirectivity is that there must be a progressive phase shift in the element currents equal to the spacing, in electrical degrees, between the elements. The amplitudes of the currents in the various elements also must be properly related. This requires binomial current distribution. In the case of three elements, this requires that the current in the center element be twice that in the two outside elements, for 90° (λ/4) spacing and element current phasing. This antenna has an overall length of λ/2. The directive diagram is shown in **Figure 12.44**. The pattern is similar to that

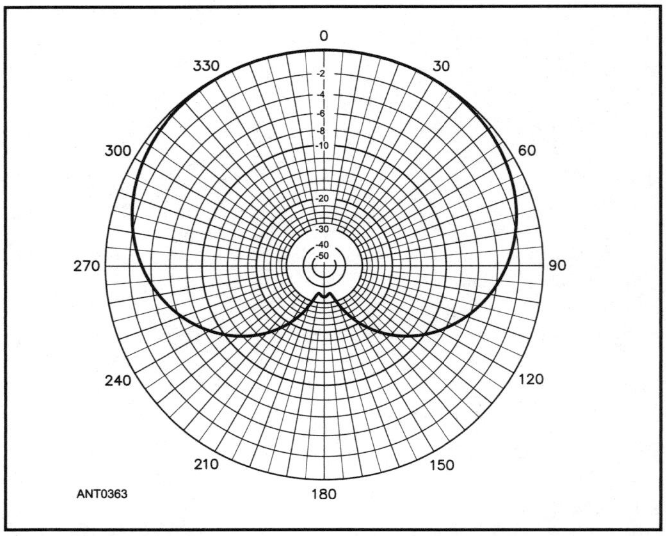

Figure 12.43 — Representative H-plane pattern for a 2-element end-fire array with 90° spacing and phasing. The elements lie along the vertical axis, with the uppermost element the one of lagging phase. Dissimilar current distributions are taken into account.

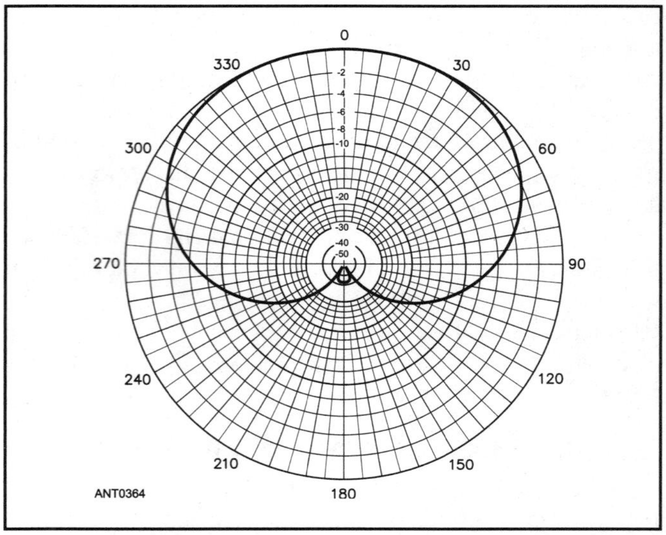

Figure 12.44 — H-plane pattern for a 3-element end-fire array with binomial current distribution (the current in the center element is twice that in each end element). The elements are spaced λ/4 apart along the 0°-180° axis. The center element lags the lower element by 90°, while the upper element lags the lower element by 180° in phase. Dissimilar current distributions are taken into account.

of Figure 12.43, but the 3-element binomial array has greater directivity, evidenced by the narrower half-power beamwidth (146° versus 176°). Its gain is 1.0 dB greater.

12.4.2 THE W8JK ARRAY

John Kraus, W8JK, described his bidirectional flat-top W8JK beam antenna in 1940. See **Figure 12.45**. (His June 1982 *QST* article "The W8JK Recap and Update" is included with this book's downloadable supplemental information.) Two λ/2 elements are spaced λ/8 to λ/4 and driven 180° out-of-phase. The free-space radiation pattern for this antenna, using #12 AWG copper wire, is given in **Figure 12.46**. The pattern is representative of spacings between λ/8 and λ/4 where the gain varies less than 0.5 dB. The gain over a dipole is about 3.3 dB (5.4 dBi referenced to an isotropic radiator), a worthwhile improvement. The feed point impedance (including wire resistance) of each element is about 11 Ω for λ/8 spacing and 33 Ω for λ/4 spacing. The feed point impedance at the center connection will depend on the length and Z_0 of the connecting transmission line.

Kraus gave a number of other variations for end-fire arrays, some of which are shown in **Figure 12.47**. The ones fed at the center (A, C and E) are usually horizontally polarized flat-top beams. The end-fed versions (B, D and F) are usually

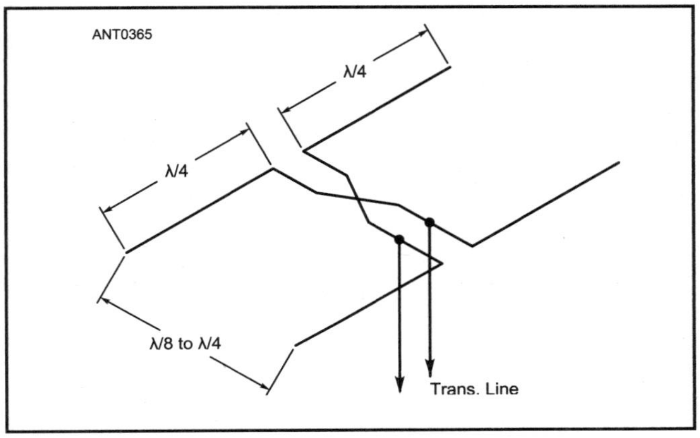

Figure 12.45 — A 2-element W8JK array.

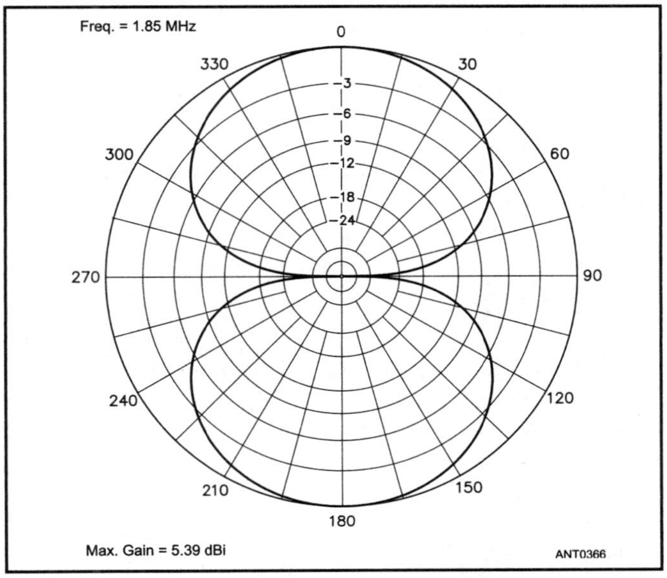

Figure 12.46 — Free-space E-plane pattern for the 2-element W8JK array.

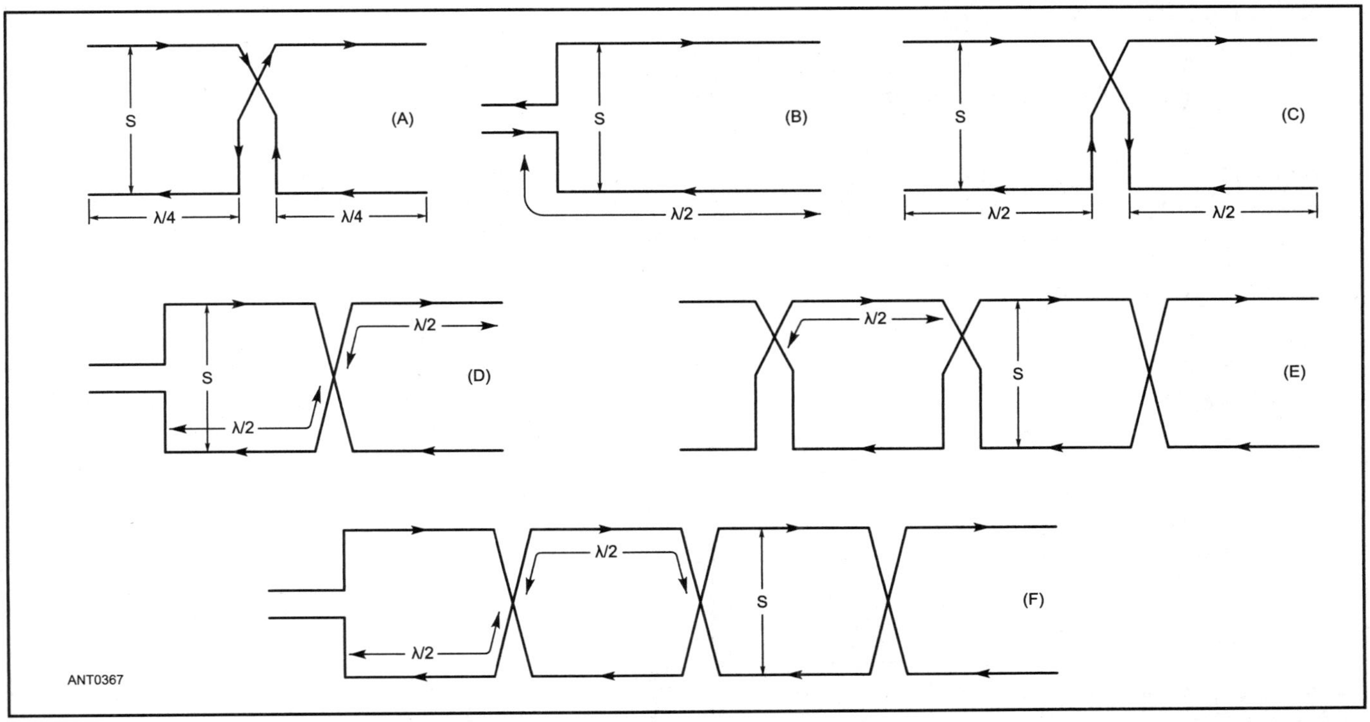

Figure 12.47 — Six other variations of W8JK "flat-top beam" antennas.

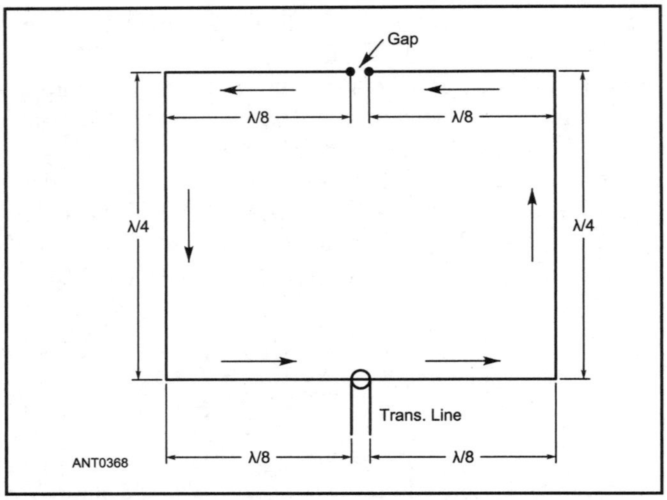

Figure 12.48 — A 2-element end-fire array with reduced height.

vertically polarized, where the feed point can be conveniently near ground.

A practical variation of Figure 12.47B is given in **Figure 12.48**. In this example, the height is limited to λ/4 so the ends can be bent over as shown, producing a 2-element Bruce array. This reduces the gain somewhat but allows much shorter supports, an important consideration on the low bands. If additional height is available, then you can achieve some additional gain. The upper ends can be bent over to fit the available height. The feed point impedance will greater than 1 kΩ.

The article "Building the W8JK" by Suggs (see Bibliography) shows how to build a W8JK beam that covers 20 through 6 meters.

12.4.3 FOUR-ELEMENT END-FIRE AND COLLINEAR ARRAYS

The array shown in **Figure 12.49** combines collinear in-phase elements with parallel out-of-phase elements to give both broadside and end-fire directivity. It is a two-section W8JK. The approximate free-space gain using #12 AWG copper wire is 4.9 dBi with λ/8 spacing and 5.4 dBi with λ/4 spacing. Directive patterns are given in **Figure 12.50** for free space, and in **Figure 12.51** for heights of 1 λ and λ/2 above flat ground.

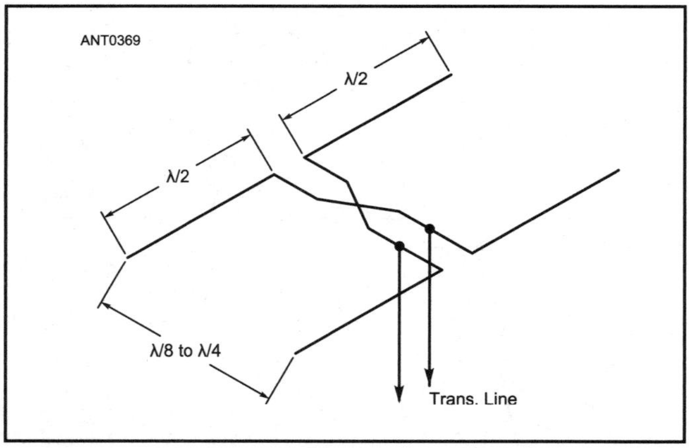

Figure 12.49 — A 4-element array combining collinear broadside elements and parallel end-fire elements, popularly known as a two-section W8JK array.

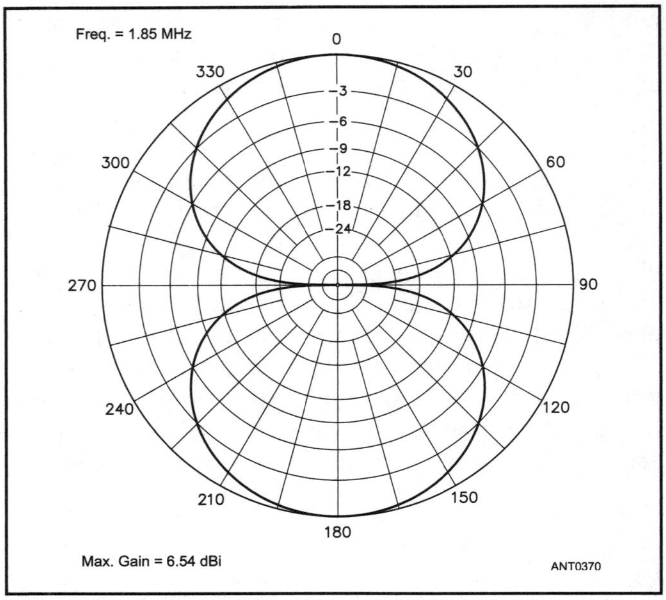

Figure 12.50 — Free-space E-plane pattern for the antenna shown in Figure 12.49, with λ/8 spacing. The elements are parallel to the 90°-270° line in this diagram. Less than a 1° change in half-power beamwidth results when the spacing is changed from λ/8 to λ/4.

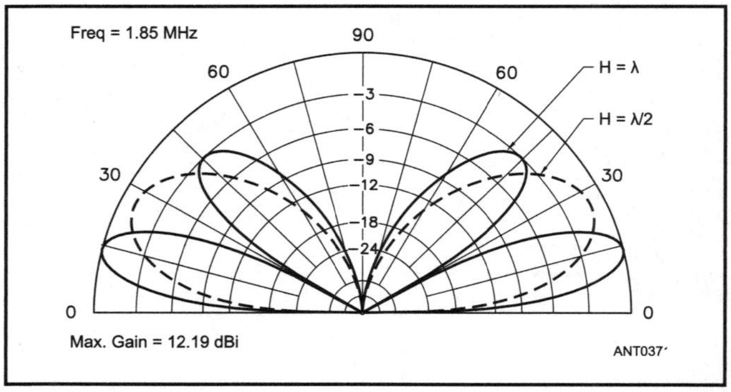

Figure 12.51 — Elevation-plane pattern for the 4-element antenna of Figure 12.49 when mounted horizontally at two heights over flat ground. Solid line = 1 λ high; dashed line = λ/2 high.

The impedance between elements at the point where the phasing line is connected is of the order of several thousand ohms. The SWR with an unmatched line consequently is quite high, and this system should be constructed with open-wire line (500 or 600 Ω) if the line is to be resonant. With λ/4 element spacing the SWR on a 600 Ω line is estimated to be in the vicinity of 3 or 4:1.

To use a matched line, you could connect a closed

stub 3λ/16 long at the transmission-line junction shown in Figure 12.49. The transmission line itself can then be tapped on this matching section at the point resulting in the lowest line SWR. This point can be determined by trial.

This type of antenna can be operated on two bands having a frequency ratio of 2 to 1, if a resonant feed line is used. For example, if you design for 28 MHz with λ/4 spacing between elements, you can also operate on 14 MHz as a simple 2-element end-fire array having λ/8 spacing.

Combination Driven Arrays

You can readily combine broadside, end-fire and collinear elements to increase gain and directivity, and this is in fact usually done when more than two elements are used in an array. Combinations of this type give more gain, in a given amount of space, than plain arrays of the types just described. Since the combinations that can be worked out are almost endless, this section describes only a few of the simpler types.

The accurate calculation of the power gain of a multi-element array requires a knowledge of the mutual impedances between all elements, as discussed in earlier sections. For approximate purposes it is sufficient to assume that each set (collinear, broadside, end-fire) will have the gains as given earlier, and then simply add up the gains for the combination. This neglects the effects of cross-coupling between sets of elements. However, the array configurations are such that the mutual impedances from cross-coupling should be relatively small, particularly when the spacings are λ/4 or more, so the estimated gain should be reasonably close to the actual gain. Alternatively, an antenna modeling program, such as *EZNEC*, can give good estimates of all parameters for a real-world antenna, providing that you take care to model all applicable parameters.

12.4.4 FOUR-ELEMENT DRIVEN ARRAYS

The array shown in **Figure 12.52** combines parallel elements with broadside and end-fire directivity. The smallest array (physically) — 3λ/8 spacing between broadside and λ/8 spacing between end-fire elements — has an estimated gain of 6.5 dBi and the largest — 3λ/4 and λ/4 spacing, respectively — about 8.4 dBi. Typical directive patterns for a λ/4 × λ/2 array are given in **Figures 12.53** and **12.54**.

The impedance at the feed point will not be purely resistive unless the element lengths are correct and the phasing lines are exactly λ/2 long. (This requires somewhat less than λ/2 spacing between broadside elements.) In this case the impedance at the junction is estimated to be over 10 kΩ. With other element spacings the impedance at the junction will be reactive as well as resistive, but in any event the SWR will be quite large. An open-wire line can be used as a resonant line, or a matching section may be used for non-resonant operation.

12.4.5 EIGHT-ELEMENT DRIVEN ARRAYS

The array shown in **Figure 12.55** is a combination of collinear and parallel elements in broadside and end-fire directivity. Common practice in a wire antenna is to use λ/2

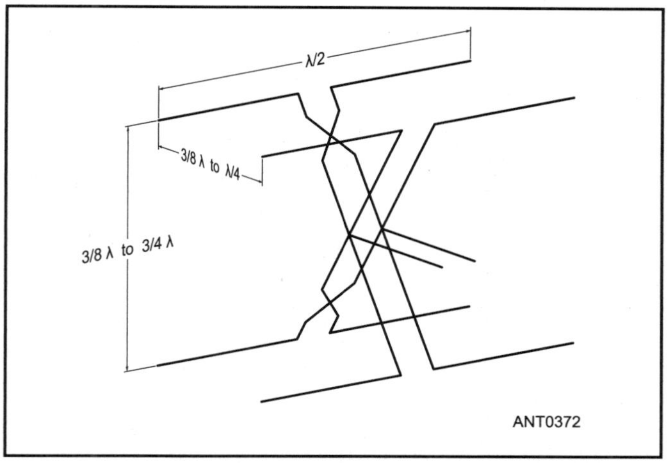

Figure 12.52 — Four-element array combining both broadside and end-fire elements.

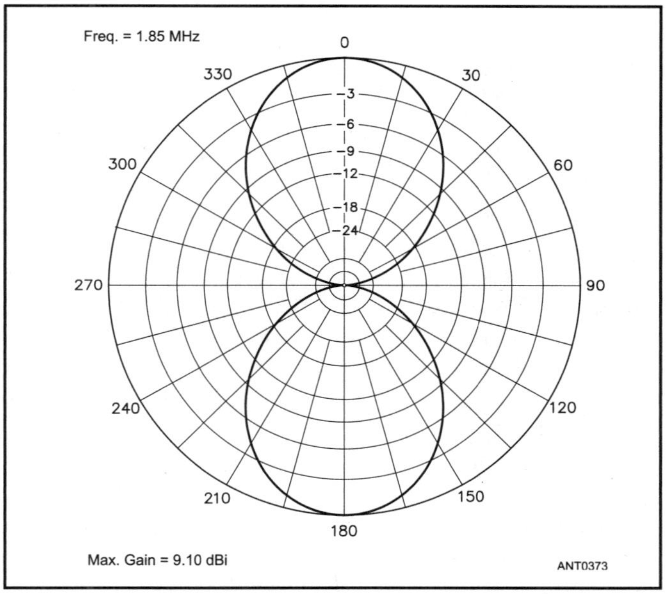

Figure 12.53 — Free-space H-plane pattern of the 4-element antenna shown in Figure 12.52.

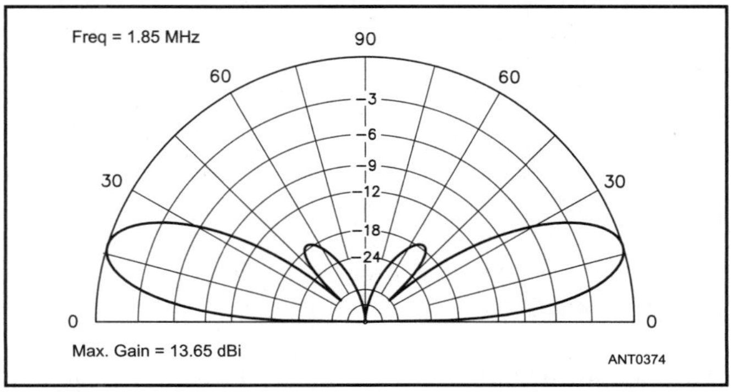

Figure 12.54 — Vertical pattern of the antenna shown in Figure 12.52 at a mean height of 3λ/4 (lowest elements λ/2 above flat ground) when the antenna is horizontally polarized. For optimum gain and low wave angle the mean height should be at least 3λ/4.

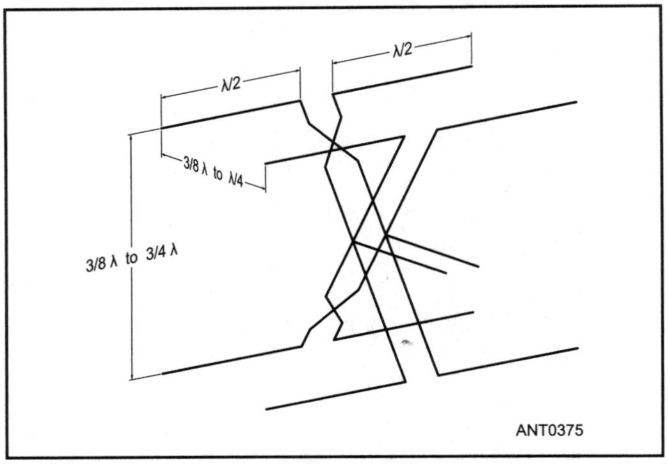

Figure 12.55 — Eight-element driven array combining collinear and parallel elements for broadside and end-fire directivity.

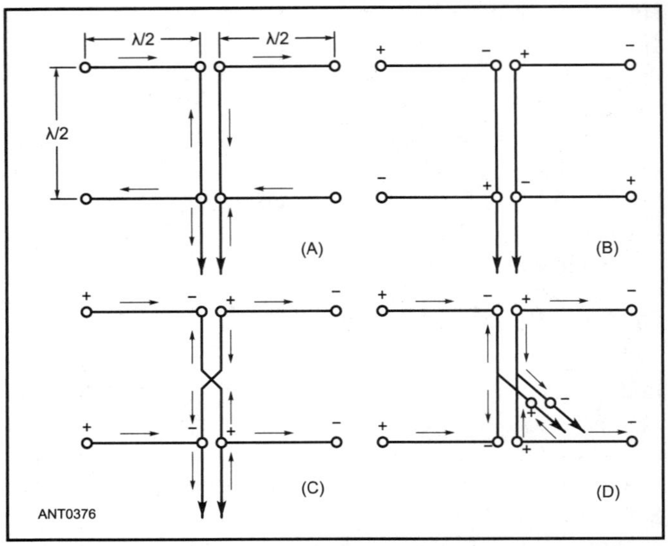

Figure 12.56 — Methods of checking the phase of currents in elements and phasing lines.

spacing for the parallel broadside elements and λ/4 spacing for the end-fire elements. This gives a free-space gain of about 9.1 dBi. Directive patterns for an array using these spacings are similar to those of Figures 12.53 and 12.54, but are somewhat sharper.

The SWR with this arrangement will be high. Matching stubs are recommended for making the lines non-resonant. Their position and length can be determined as described in the chapter **Transmission Line System Techniques**.

This system can be used on two bands related in frequency by a 2-to-1 ratio, providing it is designed for the higher of the two, with 3λ/4 spacing between the parallel broadside elements and λ/4 spacing between the end-fire elements. On the lower frequency it will then operate as a 4-element antenna of the type shown in Figure 12.52, with 3λ/8 broadside spacing and λ/8 end-fire spacing. For two-band operation a resonant transmission line must be used.

12.4.6 PHASING ARROWS IN ARRAY ELEMENTS

In the antenna diagrams of preceding sections, the relative direction of current flow in the various antenna elements and connecting lines was shown by arrows. In laying out any antenna system it is necessary to know that the phasing lines are properly connected; otherwise the antenna may have entirely different characteristics than anticipated. The phasing may be checked either on the basis of current direction or polarity of voltages. There are two rules to remember:

1) In every λ/2 section of wire, starting from an open end, the current directions reverse. In terms of voltage, the polarity reverses at each λ/2 point, starting from an open end.

2) Currents in transmission lines always must flow in opposite directions in adjacent wires. In terms of voltage, polarities always must be opposite.

Examples of the use of current direction and voltage polarity are given at A and B, respectively, in **Figure 12.56**. The λ/2 points in the system are marked by small circles. When current in one section flows toward a circle, the current in the next section must also flow toward it, and vice versa. In the 4-element antenna shown at A, the current in the upper right-hand element cannot flow toward the transmission line because then the current in the right-hand section of the phasing line would have to flow upward and thus would be flowing in the same direction as the current in the left-hand wire. The phasing line would simply act like two wires in parallel in such a case. Of course, all arrows in the drawing could be reversed, and the net effect would be unchanged.

C shows the effect of transposing the phasing line. This transposition reverses the direction of current flow in the lower pair of elements, as compared with A, and thus changes the array from a combination collinear and end-fire arrangement into a collinear-broadside array.

The drawing at D shows what happens when the transmission line is connected at the center of a section of phasing line. Viewed from the main transmission line, the two parts of the phasing line are simply in parallel, so the half wavelength is measured from the antenna element along the upper section of phasing line and thence along the transmission line. The distance from the lower elements is measured in the same way. Obviously, the two sections of phasing line should be the same length. If they are not, the current distribution becomes quite complicated; the element currents are neither in-phase nor 180° out-of-phase, and the elements at opposite ends of the lines do not receive the same current. To change the element current phasing at D into the phasing at A, simply transpose the wires in one section of the phasing line. This reverses the direction of current flow in the antenna elements connected to that section of phasing line.

12.5 BIBLIOGRAPHY

J. Cain, "Curtains for You," *QST*, Oct 1991, pp 26-30. See also Feedback in Dec 1991 *QST*, p 73. This article also appears in *ARRL's Wire Antenna Classics*.

L.B. Cebik, "Some Notes on Two-Element Horizontal Phased Arrays," in four parts, *NCJ*, Nov/Dec 2001, pp 4-10; Jan/Feb 2002, pp 4-9; Mar/Apr 2002, pp 3-8; and May/Jun 2002, pp 3-8.

D. Cooper, "The Bi-Square Array," *Ham Radio*, May 1990, pp 42-44.

J. Haigwood, "The Extended Double Zepp Revisited," *QST*, Sep 2006, pp 35-36.

H. Jasik, *Antenna Engineering Handbook*, 1st ed. (New York: McGraw-Hill, 1961). Later editions are edited by Richard C. Johnson.

H. Kennedy, "The N4GG Array", *QST*, Jul 2002, pp 35-39.

J. D. Kraus, *Antennas*, 2nd ed. (New York: McGraw-Hill Book Co., 1988).

J. D. Kraus, "The W8JK Antenna Recap and Update," *QST*, Jun 1982, pp 11-14.

R. Johnson, *Antenna Engineering Handbook*, 3rd ed. (New York: McGraw-Hill Inc., 1993). This is a later edition of the volume by the same name edited by H. Jasik.

E. A. Laport, *Radio Antenna Engineering* (New York: McGraw-Hill Book Co, 1952).

M. Loukides, "A Dipole Curtain for 15 and 10 Meters," *QST*, Aug 2003, pp 34-38.

H. Romander, "The Extended Double-Zepp Antenna," *QST*, Jun 1938, pp 12-16. This article also appears in *More Wire Antenna Classics*, published by ARRL.

W. Salmon, "The Extended Lazy H Antenna," *QST*, Oct 1955, p 20.

W. Smith, "Bet My Money on a Bobtail Beam," *CQ*, Mar 1948, pp 21-23.

W. Smith, "The Bobtail Curtain and Inverted Ground Plane, Part One," *Ham Radio*, Feb 1983, pp 82-86.

W. Smith, "Bobtail Curtain Follow-Up: Practical DX Signal Gain" *Ham Radio*, Mar 1983, pp 28-30.

D. Suggs, "Building the W8JK Beam," *QST*, Sep 2005, pp 31-35.

R. Zavrel, "The Multiband Extended Double Zepp and Derivative Designs," *QEX*, Jul/Aug 1999, pp 34-40.

R. Zimmerman, "A Simple 50-Ohm Feed for W8JK Beams," *QST*, Jun 1999, pp 41-42, 47. See also Feedback in Jul 1999 *QST*, p 63.

TABLE OF CONTENTS

Chapter 13 — Downloadable Supplemental Content

Supplemental Articles

- "A Four Wire Steerable V Beam for 10 through 40 Meters" by Sam Moore, NX5Z

Chapter 13

Long-Wire and Traveling-Wave Antennas

The power gain and directive characteristics of electrically long wires (that is, wires that are long in terms of wavelength) make them useful for long-distance transmission and reception on the higher frequencies. Long wires can be combined to form antennas of various shapes that increase the gain and directivity over a single wire. The term *long wire*, as used in this chapter, means any such configuration, not just a straight-wire antenna. Techniques for feeding these antennas are discussed in the chapter **Transmission Line System Techniques**. The Beverage antenna is covered in the **Receiving and Direction-Finding Antennas** chapter.

13.1 OVERVIEW

13.1.1 LONG WIRES VERSUS MULTIELEMENT ARRAYS

In general, the gain obtained with long-wire antennas is not as great, when the space available for the antenna is limited, as you can obtain from the multielement phased arrays in or from a parasitic array such as a Yagi or quad. (See the **Multielement Arrays** chapter.) However, the long-wire antenna has advantages of its own that tend to compensate for this deficiency. The construction of long-wire antennas is simple both electrically and mechanically, and there are no especially critical dimensions or adjustments. The long-wire antenna will work well and give satisfactory gain and directivity over a 2-to-1 frequency range. In addition, it will accept power and radiate well on any frequency for which its overall length is not less than about a half wavelength. Since a wire is not electrically long, even at 28 MHz, unless its physical length is equal to at least a half wavelength on 3.5 MHz, any long-wire can be used on all amateur bands that are useful for long-distance communication.

Between two directive antennas having the same theoretical gain, one a multielement array and the other a long-wire antenna, many amateurs have found that the long-wire antenna seems more effective in reception. One possible explanation is that there is a *diversity effect* with a long-wire antenna because it is spread out over a large distance, rather than being concentrated in a small space, as would be the case with a Yagi, for example. This may raise the average level of received energy for ionospheric-propagated signals. Another factor is that long-wire antennas have directive patterns that can be extremely sharp in the horizontal (azimuthal) plane. This is an advantage that other types of multielement arrays do not have, but it can be a double-edged sword too. We'll discuss this aspect in some detail in this chapter.

13.1.2 GENERAL CHARACTERISTICS OF LONG-WIRE ANTENNAS

Whether the long-wire antenna is a single wire running in one direction or is formed into a V-beam, rhombic, or some other configuration, there are certain general principles that apply and some performance features that are common to all types. The first of these is that the power gain of a long-wire antenna as compared with a half-wave dipole is not considerable until the antenna is really long (its length measured in wavelengths rather than in a specific number of feet). The

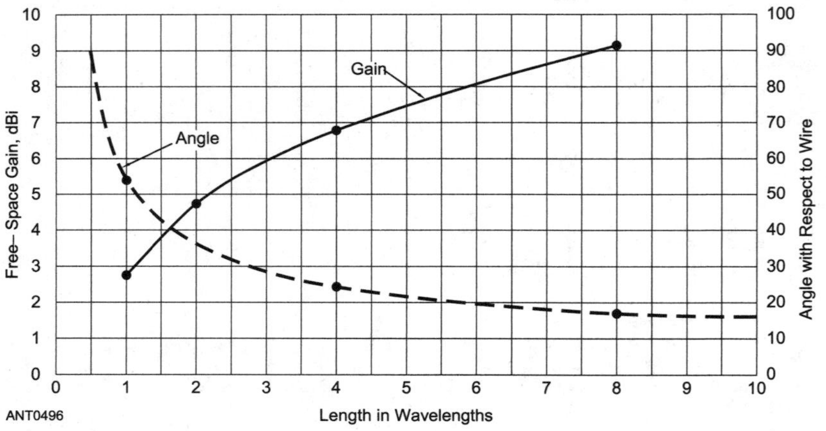

Figure 13.1 — Theoretical gain of a long-wire antenna, in dBi, as a function of wire length. The angle, with respect to the wire, at which the radiation intensity is maximum also is shown.

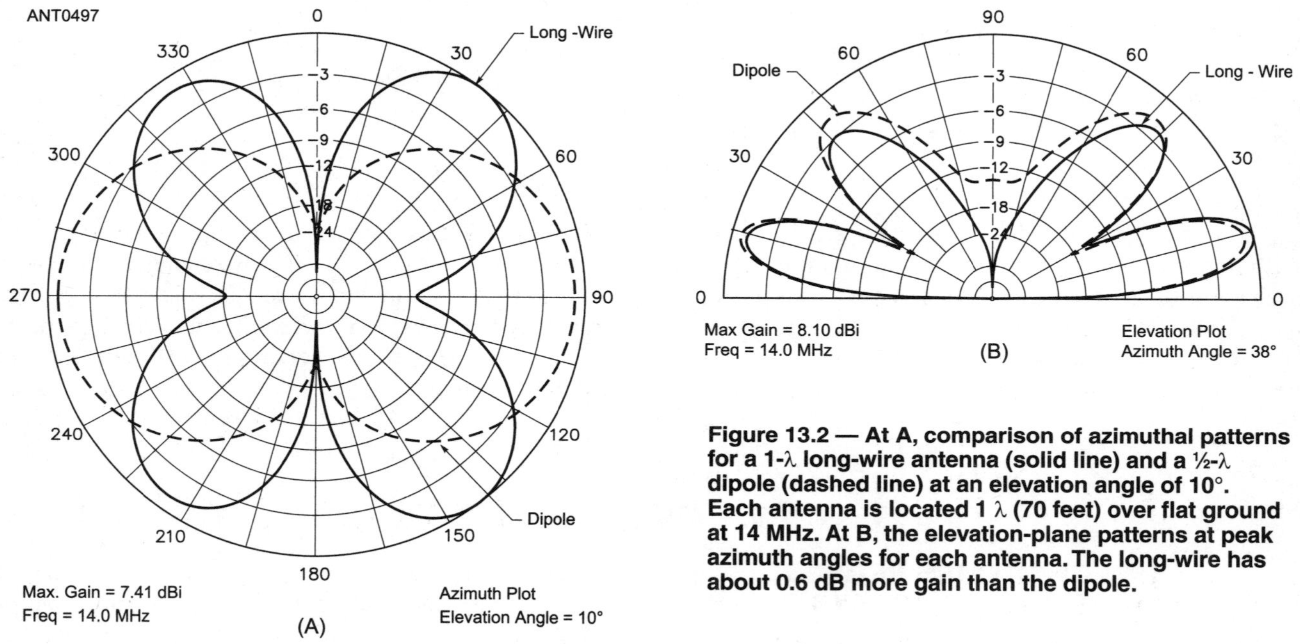

Figure 13.2 — At A, comparison of azimuthal patterns for a 1-λ long-wire antenna (solid line) and a ½-λ dipole (dashed line) at an elevation angle of 10°. Each antenna is located 1 λ (70 feet) over flat ground at 14 MHz. At B, the elevation-plane patterns at peak azimuth angles for each antenna. The long-wire has about 0.6 dB more gain than the dipole.

reason for this is that the fields radiated by elementary lengths of wire along the antenna do not combine, at a distance, in as simple a fashion as the fields from half-wave dipoles used in other types of directive arrays.

There is no point in space, for example, where the distant fields from all points along the wire are exactly in phase (as they are, in the optimum direction, in the case of two or more collinear or broadside dipoles when fed with in-phase currents). Consequently, the field strength at a distance is always less than would be obtained if the same length of wire were cut up into properly phased and separately driven dipoles. As the wire is made longer, the fields combine to form increasingly intense main lobes, but these lobes do not develop appreciably until the wire is several wavelengths long. See **Figure 13.1**.

The longer the antenna, the sharper the lobes become, and since it is really a hollow cone of radiation about the wire in free space, it becomes sharper in both planes. Also, the greater the length, the smaller the angle with the wire at which the maximum radiation lobes occur. There are four main lobes to the directive patterns of long-wire antennas; each makes the same angle with respect to the wire.

Figure 13.2A shows the azimuthal radiation pattern of a 1-λ long-wire antenna, compared with a ½-λ dipole. Both antennas are mounted at the same height of 1 λ above flat ground (70 feet high at 14 MHz, with a wire length of 70 feet) and both patterns are for an elevation angle of 10°, an angle suitable for long-distance communication on 20 meters. The long-wire in Figure 13.2A is oriented in the 270° to 90° direction, while the dipole is aligned at right angles so that its characteristic figure-8 pattern goes left-to-right. The 1-λ long-wire has about 0.6 dB more gain than the dipole, with four main lobes as compared to the two lobes from the dipole.

You can see that the two lobes on the left side of Figure 13.2A are about 1 dB down compared to the two lobes on the right side. This is because the long-wire here is fed at the left-hand end in the computer model. Energy is radiated as a wave travels down the wire and some energy is also lost to ohmic resistance in the wire and the ground. The forward-going wave then reflects from the open-circuit at the right-hand end of the wire and reverses direction, traveling toward the left end, still radiating as it travels. An antenna operating in this way has much the same characteristics as a transmission line that is terminated in an open circuit — that is, it has standing waves on it. Unterminated long-wire antennas are often referred to as standing wave antennas. As the length of a long-wire antenna is increased, a moderate front-to-back ratio results, about 3 dB for very long antennas.

Figure 13.2B shows the elevation-plane pattern for the long-wire and for the dipole. In each case the elevation pattern is at the azimuth of maximum gain — at an angle of 38° with respect to the wire-axis for the long-wire and at 90° for the dipole. The peak elevation for the long-wire is very slightly lower than that for the dipole at the same height above ground, but not by much. In other words, the height above ground is the main determining factor for the shape of the main lobe of a long-wire's elevation pattern, as it is for most horizontally polarized antennas.

The shape of the azimuth and elevation patterns in Figure 13.2 might lead you to believe that the radiation pattern is simple. **Figure 13.3** is a 3-D representation of the pattern from a 1-λ long-wire that is 1 λ high over flat ground. Besides the main low-angle lobes, there are strong lobes at higher angles. Things get even more complicated when the length of the long-wire increases.

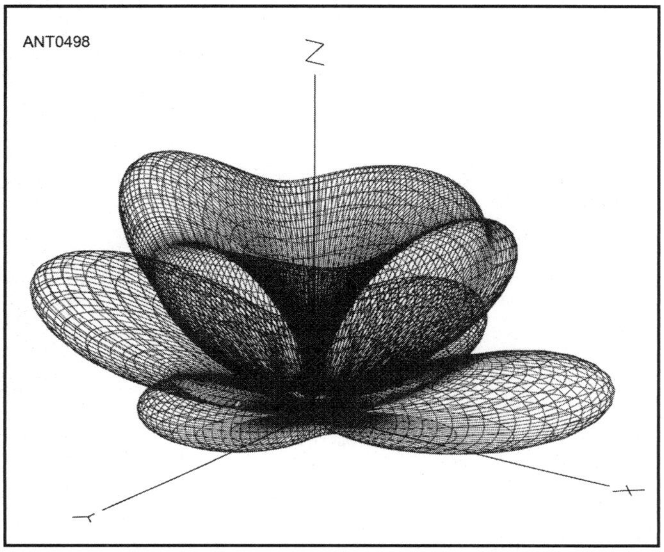

Figure 13.3 — A 3-D representation of the radiation pattern for the 1-λ long-wire shown in Figure 13.2. The pattern is obviously rather complex. It gets even more complicated for wires longer than 1 λ.

Directivity

Because many points along a long wire are carrying currents in different phases (with different current amplitudes as well), the field pattern at a distance becomes more complex as the wire is made longer. This complexity is manifested in a series of minor lobes, the number of which increases with the wire length. The intensity of radiation from the minor lobes is frequently as great as, and sometimes greater than, the radiation from a half-wave dipole. The energy radiated in the minor lobes is not available to improve the gain in the major lobes, which is another reason why a long-wire antenna must be long to give appreciable gain in the desired directions.

Figure 13.4 shows an azimuthal-plane comparison between a 3-λ (209 feet long) long-wire and the comparison ½-λ dipole. The long-wire now has eight minor lobes besides the four main lobes. Note that the angle the main lobes make with respect to the axis of the long-wire (also left-to-right in Figure 13.4) becomes smaller as the length of the long-wire increases. For the 3-λ long-wire, the main lobes occur 28° off the axis of the wire itself.

Other types of simple driven and parasitic arrays do not have minor lobes of any great consequence. For that reason they frequently seem to have much better directivity than long-wire antennas, because their responses in undesired directions are well down from their response in the desired direction. This is the case even if a multielement array and a long-wire antenna have the same peak gain in the favored direction. **Figure 13.5** compares the same 3-λ long-wire with a 4-element Yagi and a ½-λ dipole, again both at the same height as the long-wire. Note that the Yagi has only a single rear lobe, down about 21 dB from its broad main lobe, which

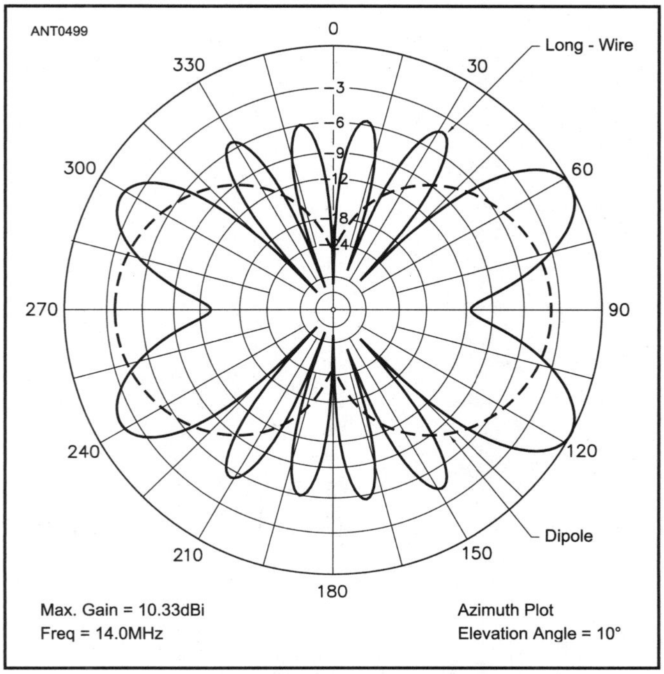

Figure 13.4 — An azimuthal-plane comparison between a 3-λ (209 feet long) long-wire (solid line) and the comparison ½-λ dipole (dashed line) at 70 feet high (1 λ) at 14 MHz.

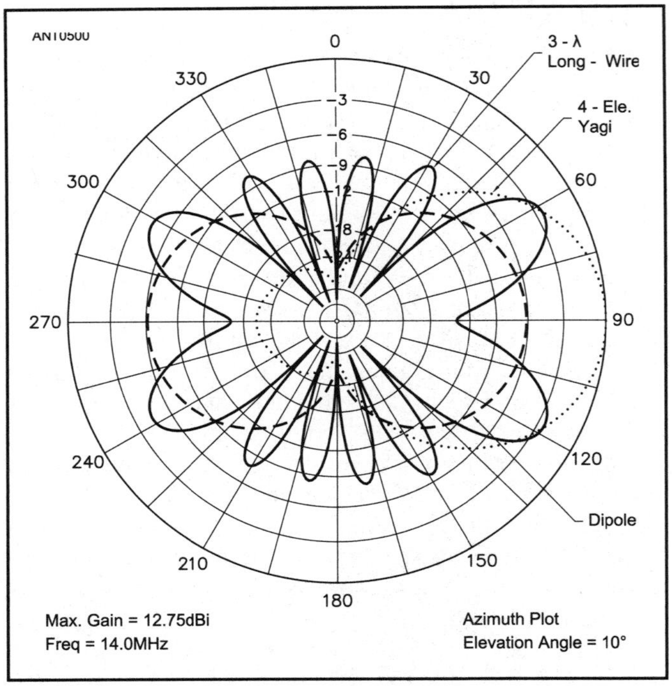

Figure 13.5 — A comparison between the 3-λ long-wire (solid line) in Figure 13.4, a 4-element 20-meter Yagi on a 26-foot boom (dotted line), and a ½-λ dipole (dashed line), again at a height of 70 feet. The main lobes of the long-wire are very narrow compared to the wide frontal lobe of the Yagi. The long-wire exhibits an azimuthal pattern that is more omnidirectional in nature than a Yagi, particularly when the narrow, deep nulls in the long-wire's pattern are filled-in due to irregularities in the terrain under its long span of wire.

has a 3-dB beamwidth of 63°. The 3-dB beamwidth of the long-wire's main lobes (at a 28° angle from the wire axis) is far more narrow, at only 23°.

For amateur work, particularly with directive antennas that cannot be rotated, the minor lobes of a long-wire antenna have some advantages. Although the nulls in the computer model in Figure 13.5 are deeper than 30 dB, they are not so dramatic in actual practice. This is due to irregularities in the terrain that inevitably occur under the span of a long wire. In most directions the long-wire antenna will be as good as a half-wave dipole, and in addition will give high gain in the most favored directions, even though that is over narrow azimuths.

Figure 13.6A compares the azimuth responses for a 5-λ long-wire (350 feet long at 14 MHz) to the same 4-element Yagi and dipole. The long-wire now exhibits 16 minor lobes in addition to its four main lobes. The peaks of these sidelobes are down about 8 dB from the main lobes and they are stronger than the dipole, making this long-wire antenna effectively omnidirectional. Figure 13.6B shows the elevation pattern of the 5-λ long-wire at its most effective azimuth compared to a dipole. Again, the shape of the main lobe is mainly determined by the long-wire's height above ground, since the peak angle is only just a bit lower than the peak angle for the dipole. The long-wire's elevation response breaks up into numerous lobes above the main lobes, just as it does in the azimuth plane.

For the really ambitious, **Figure 13.7** compares the performance for an 8-λ (571 feet) long-wire antenna with a 4-element Yagi and the ½-λ dipole. Again, in actual practice, the nulls would tend to be filled in by terrain irregularities, so a very long antenna like this would be a pretty potent performer.

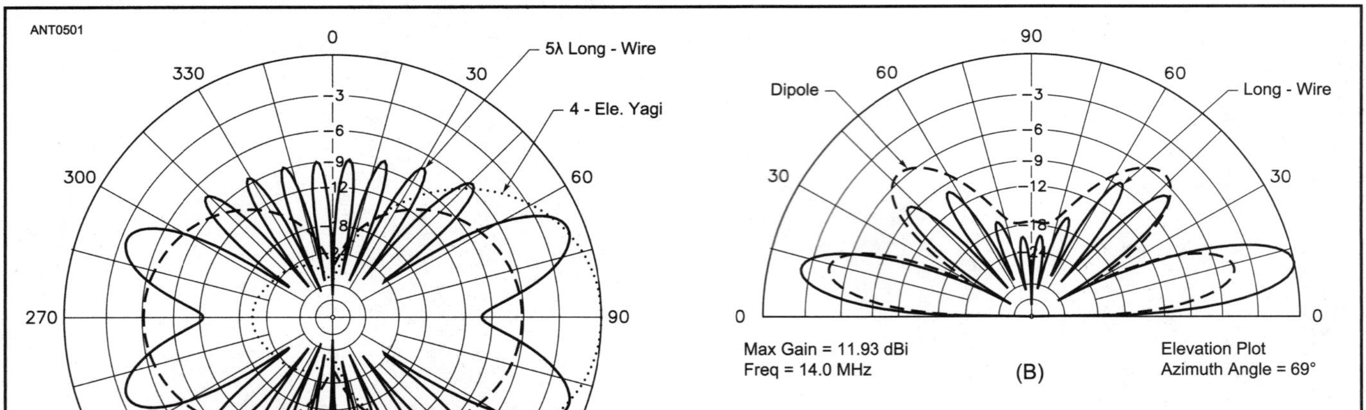

Figure 13.6 — At A, the azimuth responses for a 5-λ long-wire (350 feet long at 14 MHz — solid line) to the same 4-element Yagi (dotted line) and dipole (dashed line) as in Figure 13.5. At B, the elevation-plane responses for the long-wire (solid line) and the dipole (dashed line) by themselves. Note that the elevation angle giving peak gain for each antenna is just about the same. The long-wire achieves gain by compressing mainly the azimuthal response, squeezing the gain into narrow lobes; not so much by squeezing the elevation pattern for gain.

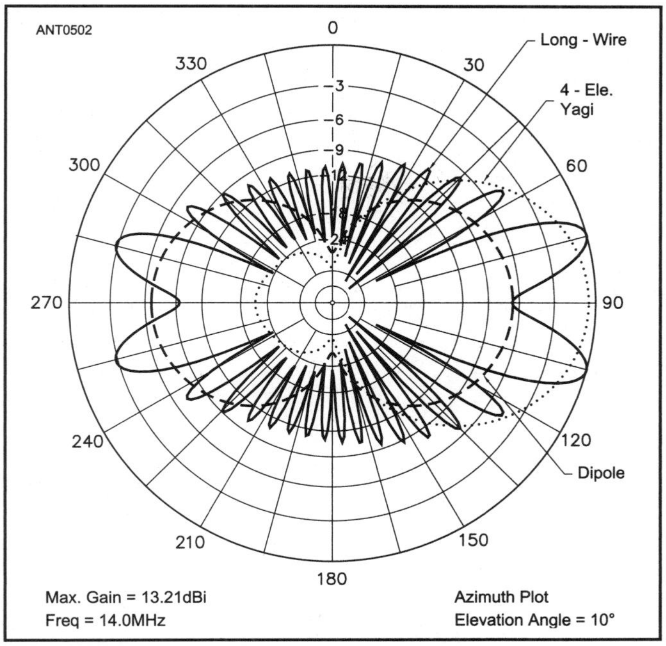

Figure 13.7 — The azimuthal-plane performance for an 8-λ (571 feet) long-wire antenna (solid line), compared with a 4-element Yagi (dotted line) and a ½-λ dipole (dashed line).

Calculating Length

In this chapter, lengths are discussed in terms of wavelengths. Throughout the preceding discussion the frequency in the models was held at 14 MHz. Remember that a long-wire that is 4 λ long at 14 MHz is 8 λ long at 28 MHz.

There is nothing very critical about wire lengths in an antenna system that will work over a frequency range including several amateur bands. The antenna characteristics change very slowly with length, except when the wires are short (around one wavelength, for instance). There is no need to try to establish exact resonance at a particular frequency for proper antenna operation.

The formula for determining the lengths for harmonic wires is:

$$\text{Length (feet)} = \frac{984\,(N - 0.025)}{f\,(\text{MHz})}$$

where N is the antenna length in wavelengths. In cases where precise resonance is desired for some reason (for obtaining a resistive load for a transmission line at a particular frequency, for example) it is best established by trimming the wire length until the standing-wave ratio on the line is minimum.

Tilted Wires

In theory, it is possible to maximize gain from a long-wire antenna by tilting it to favor a desired elevation take-off angle. Unfortunately, the effect of real ground under the antenna negates the possible advantages of tilting, just as it does when a Yagi or other type of parasitic array is tilted from horizontal. You would do better keeping a long-wire antenna horizontal, but raising it higher above ground, to achieve more gain at low takeoff angles.

13.1.3 FEEDING LONG WIRES

A long-wire antenna is normally fed at the end or at a current maximum where feed point impedance is relatively low. Since a current maximum changes to a minimum when the antenna is operated at any even multiple of the frequency for which it is designed, a long-wire antenna will operate as a true long wire on all bands only when it is fed at the end where feed point impedance is always high. It is important to note that for antennas with more than one current maximum (typically 1 λ or longer), the position of the feed point will alter the current distribution on the antenna and that will affect the antenna's radiation pattern. In such cases, modeling will help determine the best place to feed the antenna.

A common method of feeding a long-wire is to use a resonant open-wire line. This system will work on all bands down to the one, if any, at which the antenna is only a half-wave long. Any convenient line length can be used if you match the transmitter to the line's input impedance using an antenna tuner. Using coaxial cable to feed long wires directly can lead to excessive losses if the SWR is high and so open-wire line is the usual choice.

Two arrangements for using nonresonant lines are given in **Figure 13.8**. The one at A is useful for one band only since the matching section must be a quarter-wave long, approximately, unless a different matching section is used for each band. In B, the λ/4 transformer (Q-section) impedance can be designed to match the antenna to the line. You can determine the value of radiation resistance using a modern modeling program or you can actually measure the feed point impedance. Although it will work as designed on only one band, the antenna can be used on other bands by treating the line and matching transformer as a resonant line. In this case, as mentioned earlier, the antenna will not radiate as a true long wire on even multiples of the frequency for which the matching system is designed.

The end-fed arrangement, although the most convenient

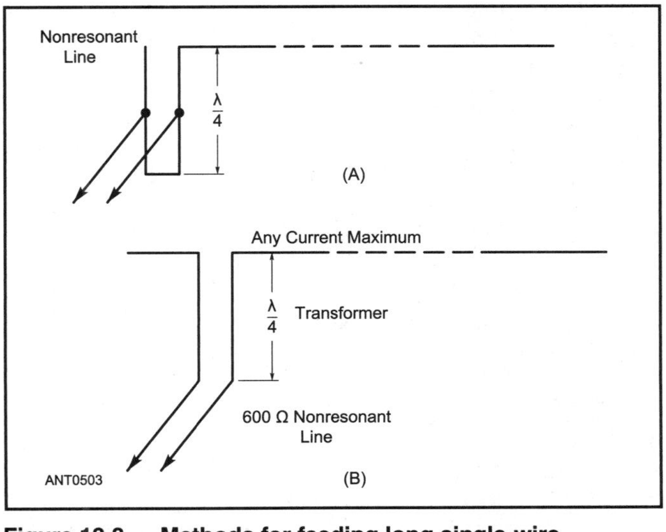

Figure 13.8 — Methods for feeding long single-wire antennas.

when tuned feeders are used, has the disadvantage that there is likely to be a considerable antenna current on the line. In addition, the antenna reactance changes rapidly with frequency. Consequently, when the wire is several wavelengths long, a relatively small change in frequency — a fraction of the width of a band — may require major changes in the adjustment of the antenna tuner. Also, the line becomes unbalanced at all frequencies between those at which the antenna is resonant. This leads to a considerable amount of radiation from the line. The unbalance can be overcome by using multiple long wires in a V or rhombic shape, as described below.

13.2 COMBINATIONS OF LONG WIRES

The directivity and gain of long wires may be increased by using two wires placed in relation to each other such that the fields from both combine to produce the greatest possible field strength at a distant point. The principle is similar to that used in designing multielement arrays.

13.2.1 PARALLEL WIRES

One possible method of using two (or more) long wires is to place them in parallel, with a spacing of ½ λ or so, and feed the two in phase. In the direction of the wires the fields will add in phase. However, the takeoff angle is high directly in the orientation of the wire, and this method will result in rather high-angle radiation even if the wires are several wavelengths long. With a parallel arrangement of this sort the gain should be about 3 dB over a single wire of the same length, at spacings in the vicinity of ½ wavelength.

13.2.2 THE V-BEAM ANTENNA

Instead of using two long wires parallel to each other, they may be placed in the form of a horizontal V, with the included angle between the wires equal to twice the angle made by the main lobes referenced to the wire axis for a single wire of the same physical length. For example, for a leg length of 5 λ, the angle between the legs of a V should be about 42°, twice the angle of 21° of the main lobe referenced to the long-wire's axis. See Figure 13.6A.

The plane directive patterns of the individual wires combine along a line in the plane of the antenna and bisecting the V, where the fields from the individual wires reinforce each other. The sidelobes in the azimuthal pattern are suppressed by about 10 dB, so the pattern becomes essentially bidirectional. See **Figure 13.9**.

The included angle between the legs is not particularly critical. This is fortunate, especially if the same antenna is used on multiple bands, where the electrical length varies directly with frequency. This would normally require different included angles for each band. For multiband V-antennas, a compromise angle is usually chosen to equalize performance. **Figure 13.10** shows the azimuthal pattern for a

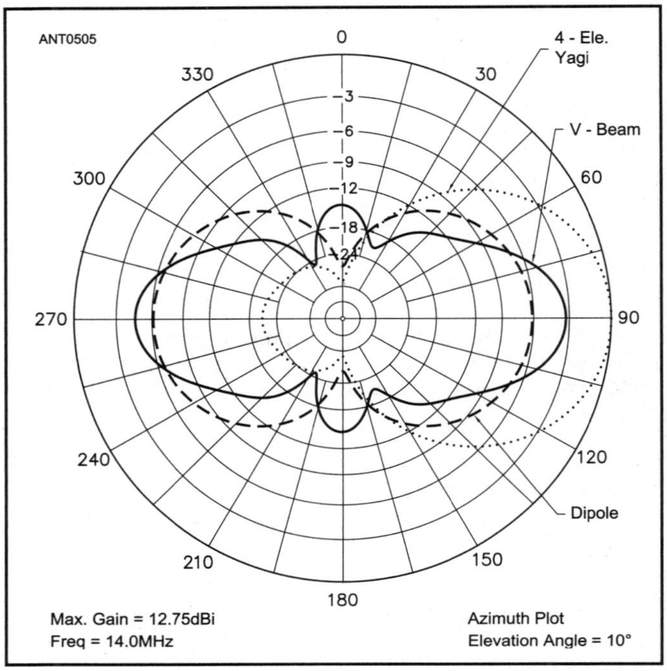

Figure 13.10 — Azimuthal-plane pattern at 10° elevation angle for a 14-MHz V-beam (solid line) with 1-λ legs (68.5 feet long), using an included angle of 75° between the legs. The V-beam is mounted 1 λ above flat ground, and is compared with a ½-λ dipole (dashed line) and a 4-element 20-meter

Figure 13.9 — Two long wires and their respective patterns are shown at the left. If these two wires are combined to form a V with an angle that is twice that of the major lobes of the wires and with the wires excited out of phase, the radiation along the bisector of the V adds and the radiation in the other directions tends to cancel.

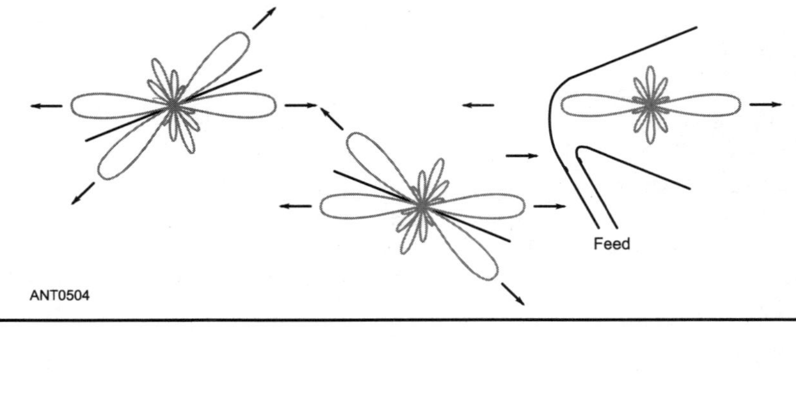

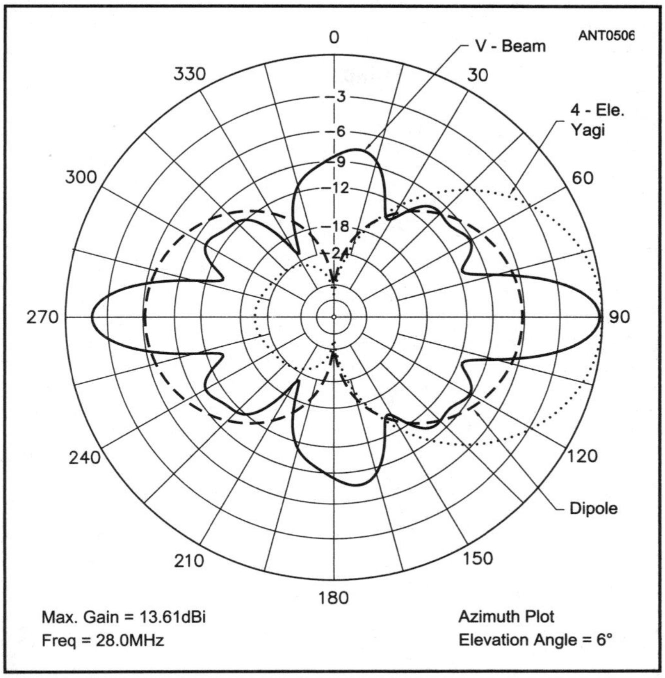

Figure 13.11 — The same V-beam as in Figure 13.10 at 28 MHz (solid line), at an elevation angle of 6°, compared to a 4-element Yagi (dotted line) and a dipole (dashed line). The V-beam's pattern is very narrow, at 18.8° at the 3-dB points, requiring accurate placement of the supports poles to aim the antenna at the desired geographic target.

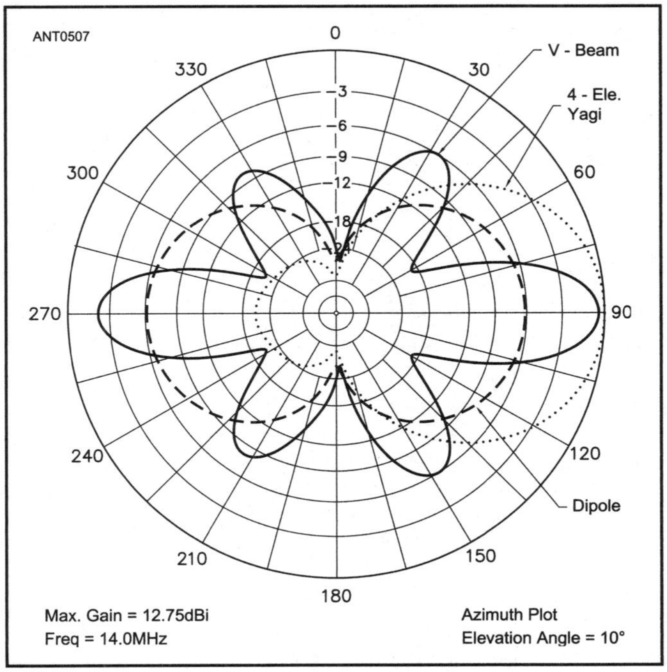

Figure 13.12 — Azimuthal pattern for a V-beam (solid line) with 2-λ legs (137 feet at 14 MHz), with an included angle of 60° between them. The height is 70 feet, or 1 λ, over flat ground. For comparison, the response for a 4-element Yagi (dotted line) and a dipole (dashed line) are shown. The 3-dB beamwidth has decreased to 23.0° .

V-beam with 1-λ legs, with an included angle of 75° between the legs, mounted 1 λ above flat ground. This is for a 10° elevation angle. At 14 MHz the antenna has two 70-foot high, 68.5-foot long legs, separated at their far ends by 83.4 feet. For comparison, the azimuthal patterns for the same 4-element Yagi and ½-λ dipole used previously for the long-wires are overlaid on the same plot. The V has about 2 dB more gain than the dipole but is down some 4 dB compared to the Yagi, as expected for relatively short legs.

Figure 13.11 shows the azimuthal pattern for the same antenna in Figure 13.10, but at 28 MHz and at an elevation angle of 6°. Because the legs are twice as long electrically at 28 MHz, the V-beam has compressed the main lobe into a narrow beam that now has a peak gain equal to the Yagi, but with a 3-dB beamwidth of only 18.8°. Note that you could obtain about 0.7 dB more gain at 14 MHz, with a 1.7-dB degradation of gain at 28 MHz, if you increase the included angle to 90° rather than 75°.

Figure 13.12 shows the azimuthal pattern for a V-beam with 2-λ legs (137 feet at 14 MHz), with an included angle of 60° between them. As usual, the assumed height is 70 feet, or 1 λ at 14 MHz. The peak gain for the V-beam is just about equal to that of the 4-element Yagi, although the 3-dB nose beamwidth is narrow, at 23°. This makes setting up the geometry critical if you want to maximize gain into a particular geographic area. While you might be able to get away with using convenient trees to support such an antenna, it's far more likely that you'll have to use carefully located towers to make sure the beam is aimed where you expect it to be pointed.

For example, in order to cover all of Europe from San Francisco, an antenna must cover from about 11° (to Moscow) to about 46° (to Portugal). This is a range of 35° and signals from the V-beam in Figure 13.12 would be down some 7 dB over this range of angles, assuming the center of the beam is pointed exactly at a heading of 28.5°. The 4-element Yagi on the other hand would cover this range of azimuths more consistently, since its 3-dB beamwidth is 63°.

Figure 13.13 shows the same V-beam as in Figure 13.12, but this time at 28 MHz. The peak gain of the main lobe is now about 1 dB stronger than the 4-element Yagi used as a reference, and the main lobe has two nearby sidelobes that tend to broaden out the azimuthal response. At this frequency the V-beam would cover all of Europe better from San Francisco.

Figure 13.14 shows a V-beam with 3-λ (209 feet at 14 MHz) legs with an included angle of 50° between them. The peak gain is now greater than that of a 4-element Yagi, but the 3-dB beamwidth has been reduced to 17.8°, making aiming the antenna even more critical. **Figure 13.15** shows the same V-beam at 28 MHz. Here again, the main lobe has nearby sidelobes that broaden the effective azimuth to cover a wider area.

Figure 13.16 shows the elevation-plane response for the same 209-foot leg V-beam at 28 MHz (3-λ at 14 MHz), compared to a dipole at the same height of 70 feet. The higher-gain V-beam suppresses higher-angle lobes, essentially

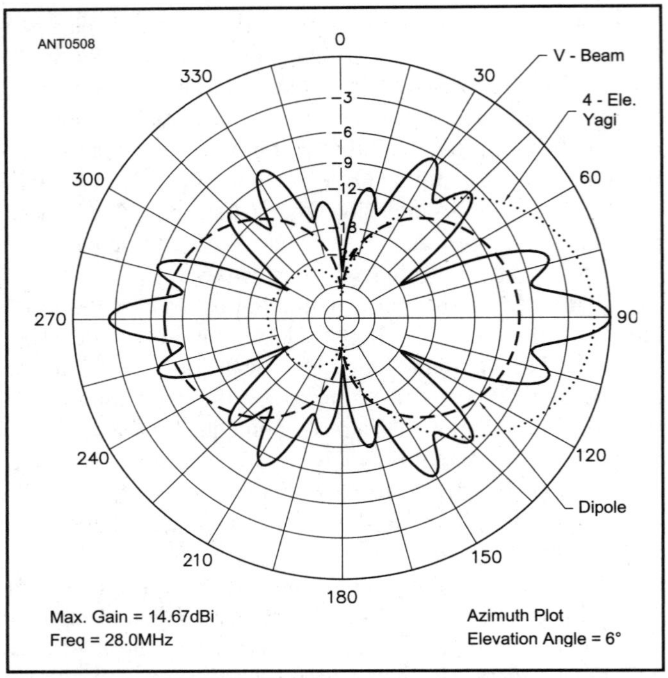

Figure 13.13 — The same 2-λ-per-leg V-beam (solid line) as in Figure 13.12, but at 28 MHz and at a 6° takeoff elevation angle. Two sidelobes have appeared flanking the main lobe, making the effective azimuthal pattern wider at this frequency.

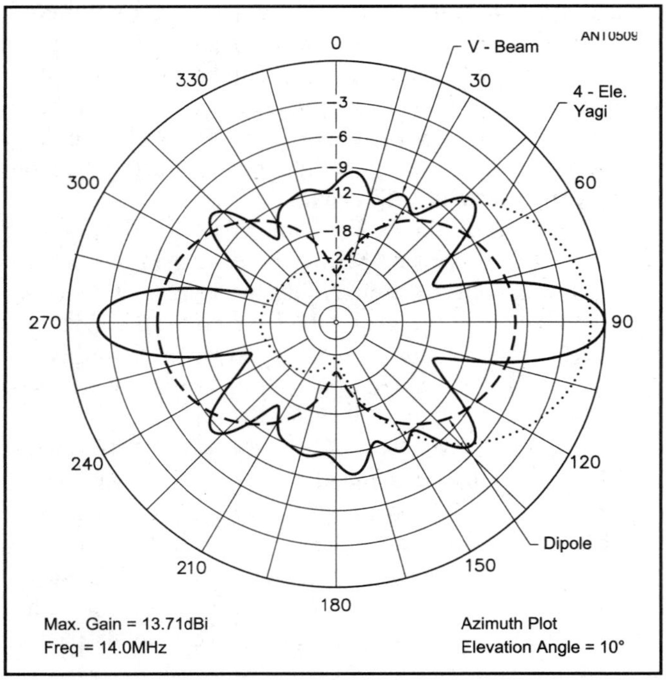

Figure 13.14 — A V-beam (solid line) with 3-λ (209 feet at 14 MHz) legs using an included angle of 50° between them, compared to a 4-element Yagi (dotted line) and a dipole (dashed line). The 3-dB beamwidth has now decreased to 17.8°.

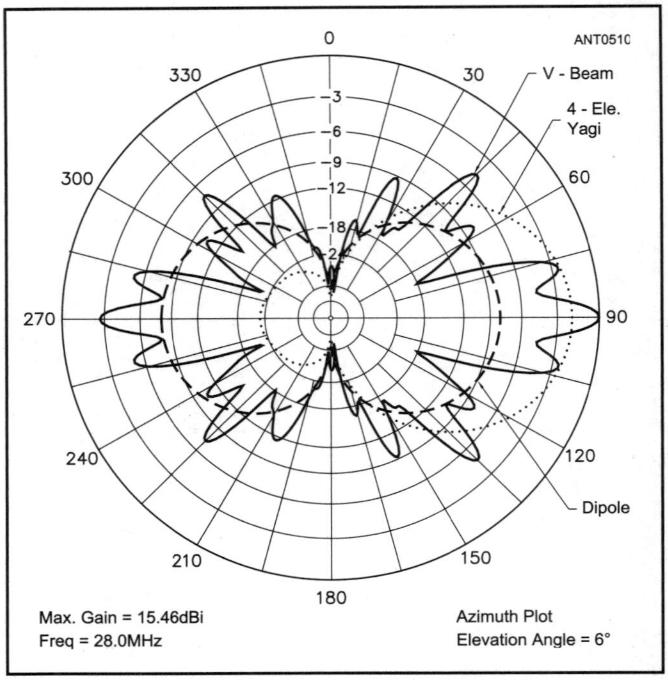

Figure 13.15 — The same 209-foot-per-leg V-beam as Figure 13.14, but at 28 MHz. Again, the two close-in sidelobes tend to spread out the azimuthal response some at 28 MHz.

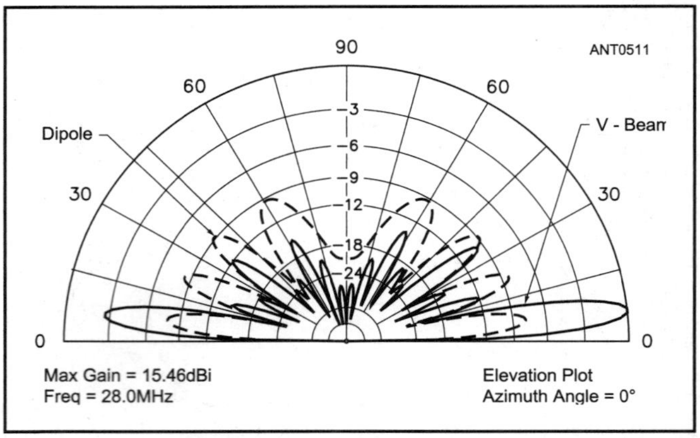

Figure 13.16 — The elevation-plane of the 209-foot-per-leg V-beam (solid line) compared to the dipole (dashed line). Again, the elevation angle for peak gain corresponds well to that of the simple dipole at the same height.

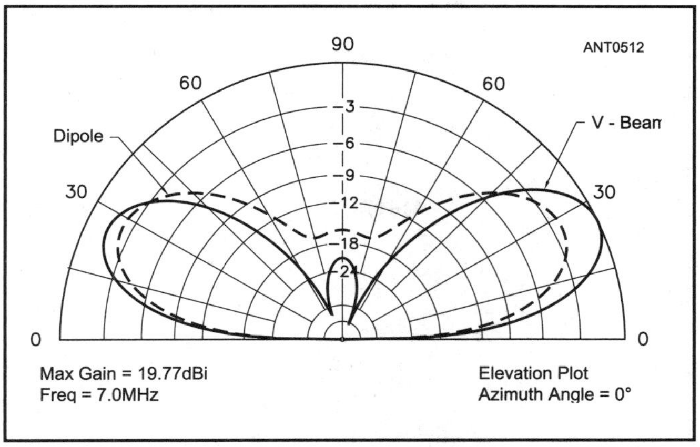

Figure 13.17 — Elevation pattern for the same 209-foot-per-leg V-beam (solid line), at 7 MHz, compared to a 40-meter dipole (dashed line) at the same height of 70 feet.

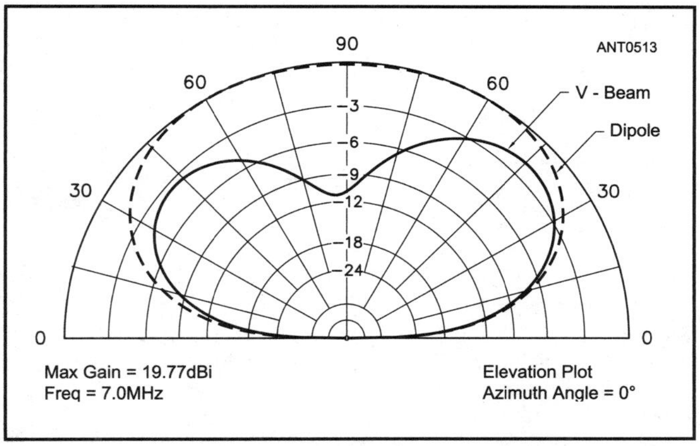

Figure 13.18 — Elevation pattern for the same 209-foot-per-leg V-beam (solid line), at 3.5 MHz, compared to an 80-meter dipole at 70 feet (dashed line).

stealing energy from them and concentrating it in the main beam at 6° elevation.

The same antenna can be used at 3.5 and 7 MHz. The gain will not be large, however, because the legs are not very long at these frequencies. **Figure 13.17** compares the V-beam versus a horizontal ½-λ 40-meter dipole at 70 feet. At low elevation angles there is about 2 dB of advantage on 40 meters. **Figure 13.18** shows the same type of comparison for 80 meters, where the 80 meter dipole is superior at all angles.

Other V Combinations

A gain increase of about 3 dB can be had by stacking two V-beams one above the other, a half wavelength apart, and feeding them with in-phase currents. This will result in a lowered angle of radiation. The bottom V should be at least a quarter wavelength above the ground, and preferably a half wavelength. This arrangement will narrow the elevation pattern and it will also have a narrow azimuthal pattern.

The V antenna can be made unidirectional by using a second V placed an odd multiple of a quarter wavelength in back of the first and exciting the two with a phase difference of 90°. The system will be unidirectional in the direction of the antenna with the lagging current. However, the V reflector is not normally employed by amateurs at low frequencies because it restricts the use to one band and requires a fairly elaborate supporting structure. Stacked Vs with driven reflectors could, however, be built for the 200- to 500-MHz region without much difficulty.

Feeding the V Beam

The V-beam antenna is most conveniently fed with tuned open-wire feeders with an antenna tuner, since this permits multiband operation. Although the length of the wires in a V-beam is not at all critical, it is important that both wires be the same electrical length. If a single band matching solution is desired, probably the most appropriate matching system is that using a stub or quarter-wave matching section.

13.3 THE RESONANT RHOMBIC ANTENNA

The diamond-shaped or rhombic antenna shown in **Figure 13.19** can be looked upon as two acute-angle V-beams placed end-to-end. This arrangement is called a resonant rhombic. The leg lengths of the resonant rhombic must be an integral number of half wavelengths to avoid reactance at its feed point.

The resonant rhombic has two advantages over the simple V-beam. For the same total wire length it gives somewhat greater gain than the V-beam. A rhombic with 3 λ on a leg, for example, has about 1 dB gain over a V antenna with 6 wavelengths on a leg. **Figure 13.20** compares the azimuthal pattern at a 10° elevation for a resonant rhombic with 3 λ legs on 14 MHz, compared to a V-beam with 6 λ legs at the same height of 70 feet. The 3-dB nose beamwidth of the resonant rhombic is only 12.4° wide, but the gain is very high at 16.26 dBi.

The directional pattern of the rhombic is less frequency sensitive than the V when the antenna is used over a wide frequency range. This is because a change in frequency causes the major lobe from one leg to shift in one direction while the lobe from the opposite leg shifts the other way. This automatic compensation keeps the direction the same over a considerable frequency range. The disadvantage of the rhombic as compared with the V-beam is that an additional support is required. Some authors also report success with "half-rhombics" oriented vertically over ground with and without a counterpoise. (See Bibliography entry for Orr.)

The same factors that govern the design of the V-beam apply in the case of the resonant rhombic. The optimal apex angle A in Figure 13.19 is the same as that for a V having an

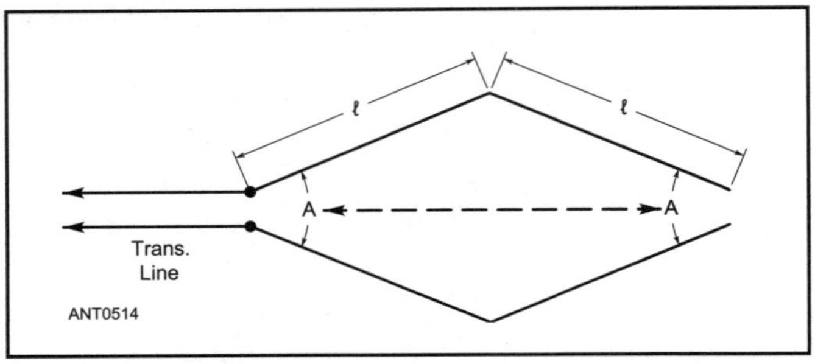

Figure 13.19 — The resonant rhombic or diamond-shaped antenna. All legs are the same length, and opposite angles of the diamond are equal. Length ℓ is an integral number of half wavelengths for resonance.

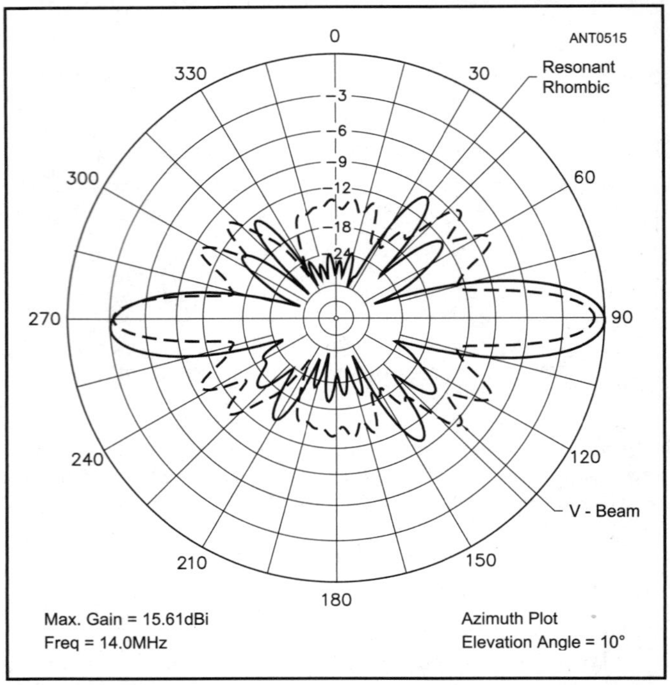

Figure 13.20 — Azimuthal-plane pattern of resonant (unterminated) rhombic (solid line) with 3-λ legs on 14 MHz, at a height of 70 feet above flat ground, compared with a 6-λ per leg V-beam (dashed line) at the same height. Both azimuthal patterns are at a takeoff angle of 10°. The sidelobes for the resonant rhombic are suppressed to a greater degree than those for the V-beam.

equal leg length. The diamond-shaped antenna also can be operated as a terminated antenna, as described later in this chapter, and much of the discussion in that section applies to the resonant rhombic as well.

The resonant rhombic has a bidirectional pattern, with minor lobes in other directions, their number and intensity depending on the leg length. In general, these sidelobes are suppressed better with a resonant rhombic than with a V-beam. When used at frequencies below the VHF region, the rhombic antenna is always mounted with the plane containing the wires horizontal. The polarization in this plane, and also in the perpendicular plane that bisects the rhombic, is horizontal. At 144 MHz and above, the dimensions are such that the antenna can be mounted with the plane containing the wires vertical if vertical polarization is desired.

When the rhombic antenna is to be used on several HF amateur bands, it is advisable to choose the apex angle, A, on the basis of the leg length in wavelengths at 14 MHz. Although the gain on higher frequency bands will not be quite as favorable as if the antenna had been designed for the higher frequencies, the system will still work well at the low angles that are necessary at such frequencies.

The resonant rhombic has lots of gain, but you must not forget that this gain comes from a radiation pattern that is very narrow. This requires careful placement of the supports for the resonant rhombic to cover desired geographic areas. This is definitely not an antenna that allows you to use just any convenient trees as supports!

Even if you cannot place its corners exactly, the rhombic can still give good performance. (See the Bibliography entry for Hallas.) The main lobe broadens and peak gain is lower but the author found it to be a very effective antenna.

The resonant rhombic antenna can be fed in the same way as the V-beam. Resonant feeders are necessary if the antenna is to be used in several amateur bands.

13.4 TERMINATED LONG-WIRE ANTENNAS

All the antenna systems considered so far in this chapter have been based on operation with standing waves of current and voltage along the wire. Although most hams use antenna designs based on using resonant wires, resonance is by no means a necessary condition for the wire to radiate and intercept electromagnetic waves efficiently, as discussed in the **Antenna Fundamentals** chapter. The result of using nonresonant wires is reactance at the feed point, unless the antenna is terminated with a resistive load.

In **Figure 13.21**, suppose that the wire is parallel with the ground (horizontal) and is terminated by a load Z equal to its characteristic impedance, Z_{ANT}. The wire and its image in the ground create a transmission line. The load Z can represent a receiver matched to the line. The *terminating resistor* R is also equal to the Z_{ANT} of the wire. A wave coming from direction X will strike the wire first at its far end and sweep across the wire at some angle until it reaches the end at which Z is connected. In so doing, it will induce voltages in the antenna, and currents will flow as a result. The current flowing toward Z is the useful output of the antenna, while the current flowing backwards toward R will be absorbed in R. The same thing is true of a wave coming from the direction X'. In such an antenna there are no standing waves, because all received power is absorbed at either end.

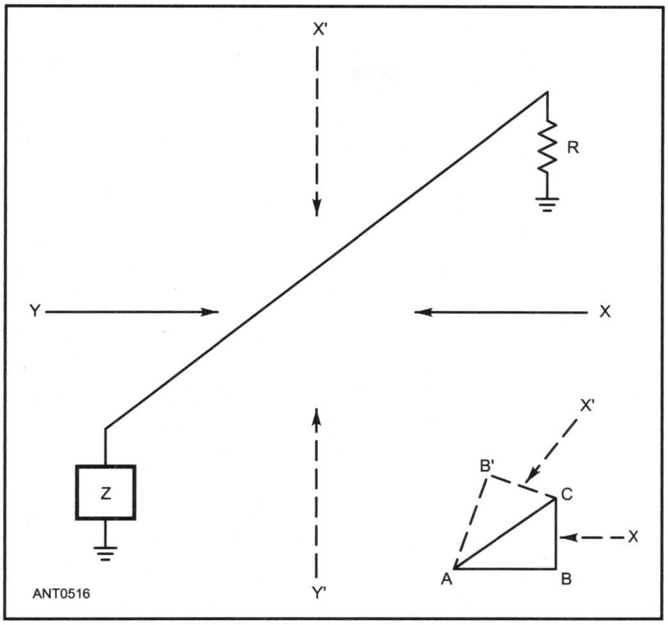

Figure 13.21 — Layout for a terminated long-wire antenna.

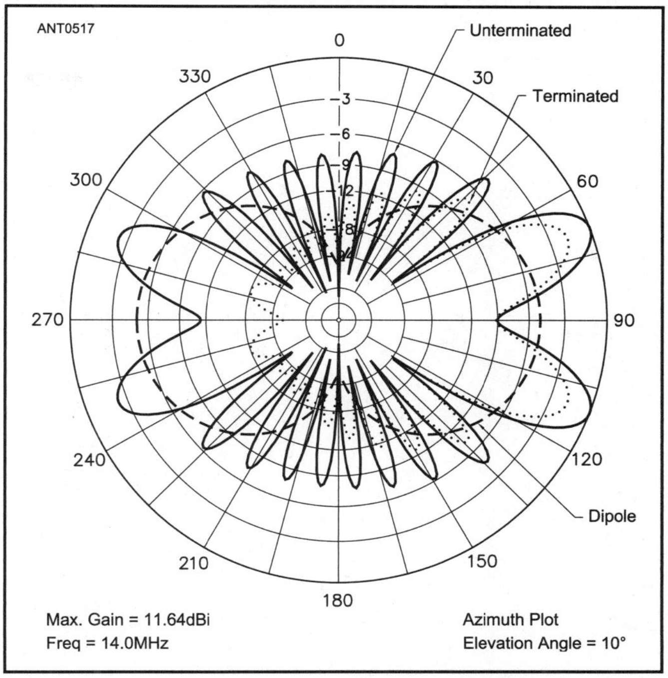

Figure 13.22 — Azimuthal-plane pattern for 5-λ long-wire antenna at 14 MHz and 70 feet above flat ground. The solid line shows the long-wire terminated with 600-Ω to ground, while the dashed line is for the same antenna unterminated. For comparison, the response for a ½-λ dipole is overlaid with the two other patterns. You can see that the terminated long-wire has a good front-to-back pattern, but it loses about 2 dB in forward gain compared to the unterminated long-wire.

The greatest possible power will be delivered to the load Z when the individual currents induced as the wave sweeps across the wire all combine properly on reaching the load. The currents will reach Z in optimum phase when the time required for a current to flow from the far end of the antenna to Z is exactly one-half cycle longer than the time taken by the wave to sweep over the antenna. A half cycle is equivalent to a half wavelength greater than the distance traversed by the wave from the instant it strikes the far end of the antenna to the instant that it reaches the near end. This is shown by the small drawing, where AC represents the antenna, BC is a line perpendicular to the wave direction, and AB is the distance traveled by the wave in sweeping past AC. AB must be one-half wavelength shorter than AC. Similarly, AB' must be the same length as AB for a wave arriving from X'.

A wave arriving at the antenna from the opposite direction Y (or Y'), will similarly result in the largest possible current at the far end. However, since the far end is terminated in R, which is equal to Z, all the power delivered to R by the wave arriving from Y will be absorbed in R. The current traveling to Z will produce a signal in Z in proportion to its amplitude. If the antenna length is such that all the individual currents arrive at Z in such phase as to add up to zero, there will be no current through Z. At other lengths the resultant current may reach appreciable values. The lengths that give zero amplitude are those which are odd multiples of ¼ λ, beginning at ¾ λ. The response from the Y direction is greatest when the antenna is any even multiple of ½ λ long; the higher the multiple, the smaller the response.

Directional Characteristics

Figure 13.22 compares the azimuthal pattern for a 5-λ long 14-MHz long-wire antenna, 70 feet high over flat ground, when it is terminated and when it is unterminated. The rearward pattern when the wire is terminated with a 600 Ω resistor is reduced about 15 dB, with a reduction in gain in the forward direction of about 2 dB.

For a shorter leg length in a terminated long-wire antenna, the reduction in forward gain is larger — more energy is radiated by a longer wire before the forward wave is absorbed in the terminating resistor. The azimuthal patterns for terminated and unterminated V-beams with 2-λ legs are overlaid for comparison in **Figure 13.23**. With these relatively short legs the reduction in forward gain is about 3.5 dB due to the terminations, although the front-to-rear ratio approaches 20 dB for the terminated V-beam. Each leg of this terminated V-beam use a 600-Ω non-inductive resistor to ground. Each resistor would have to dissipate about one-quarter of the transmitter power. For average conductor diameters and heights above ground, the Z_{ANT} of the antenna is of the order of 500 to 600 Ω.

13.4.1 THE TERMINATED RHOMBIC ANTENNA

The highest development of the long-wire antenna is the *terminated rhombic*, shown schematically in **Figure 13.24**. It consists of four conductors joined to form a diamond, or *rhombus*. All sides of the antenna have the same length and the opposite corner angles are equal. The antenna can be

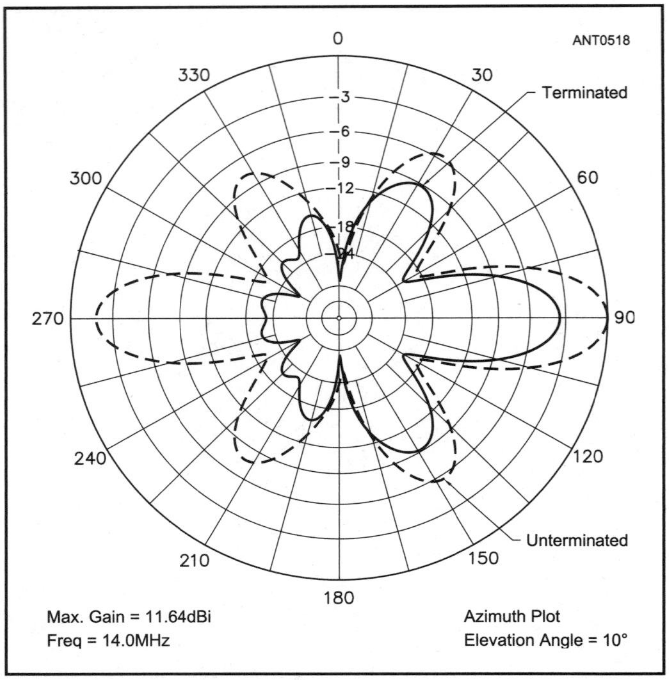

Figure 13.23 — The azimuthal patterns for a shorter-leg V-beam (2-λ legs) when it is terminated (solid line) and unterminated (dashed line). With shorter legs, the terminated V-beam loses about 3.5 dB in forward gain compared to the unterminated version, while suppressing the rearward lobes as much as 20 dB.

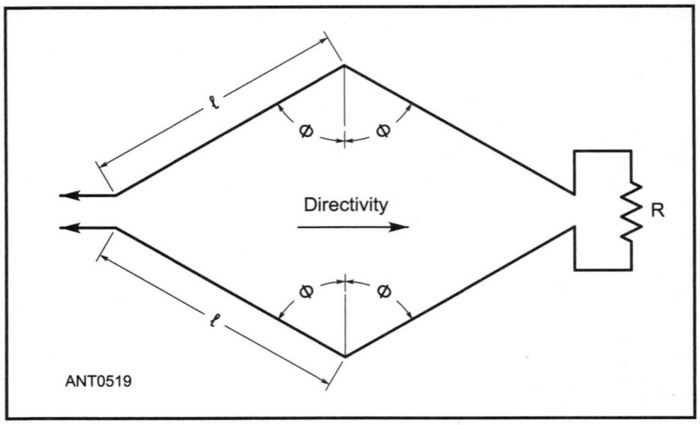

Figure 13.24 — The layout for a terminated rhombic antenna.

considered as being made up of two V antennas placed end to end and terminated by a noninductive resistor to produce a unidirectional pattern. The terminating resistor is connected between the far ends of the two sides, and is made approximately equal to the characteristic impedance of the antenna as a unit. The rhombic may be constructed either horizontally or vertically, but is practically always constructed horizontally at frequencies below 54 MHz, since the pole height required is considerably less. Also, horizontal polarization is equally, if not more, satisfactory at these frequencies over most types of soil.

The basic principle of combining lobes of maximum radiation from the four individual wires constituting the rhombus or diamond is the same in either the terminated type or the resonant type described earlier in this chapter.

Tilt Angle

In dealing with the terminated rhombic, it is a matter of custom to talk about the tilt angle (ϕ in Figure 13.24), rather than the angle of maximum radiation with respect to an individual wire. **Figure 13.25** shows the tilt angle as a function of the antenna leg length. The curve marked "0°" is used for a takeoff elevation angle of 0°; that is, maximum radiation in the plane of the antenna. The other curves show the proper tilt angles to use when aligning the major lobe with a desired takeoff angle. For a 5° takeoff angle, the difference in tilt angle is less than 1° for the range of lengths shown.

The broken curve marked "optimum length"

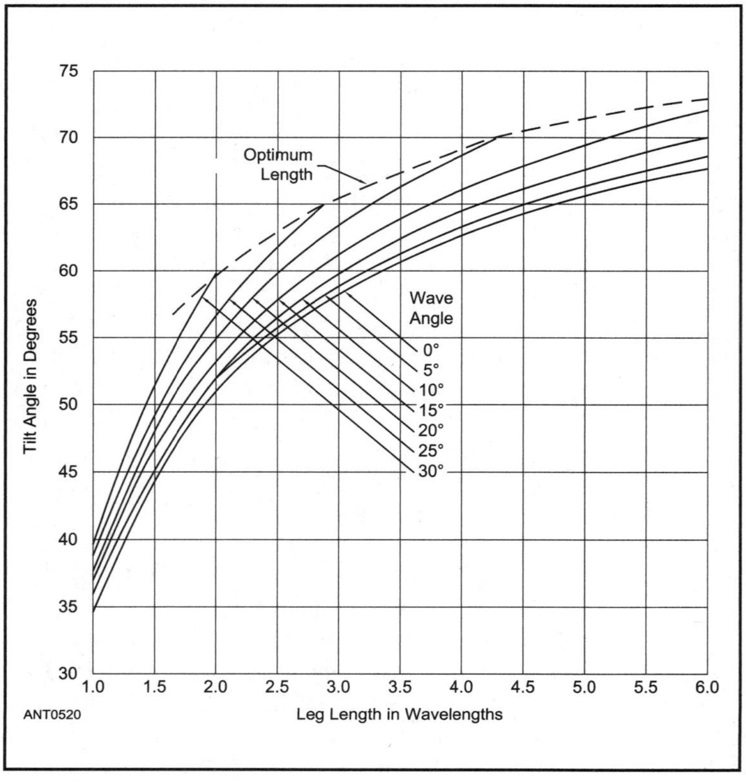

Figure 13.25 — Rhombic-antenna design chart. For any given leg length, the curves show the proper tilt angle to give maximum radiation at the selected takeoff angle. The broken curve marked "optimum length" shows the leg length that gives the maximum possible output at the selected takeoff angle. The optimum length as given by the curves should be multiplied by 0.74 to obtain the leg length for which the takeoff angle and main lobe are aligned.

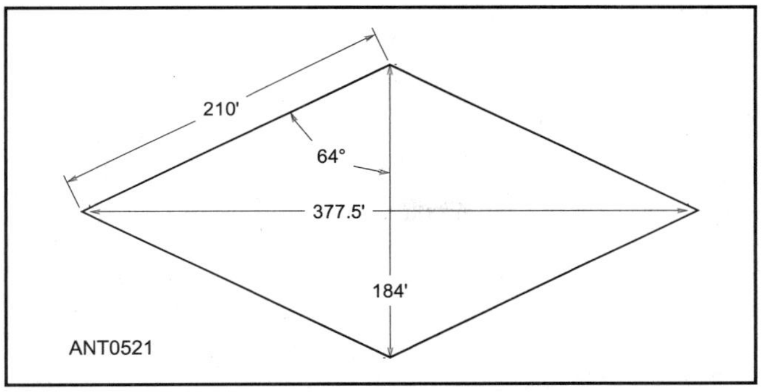

Figure 13.26 — Rhombic antenna dimensions for a compromise design between 14- and 28-MHz requirements, as discussed in the text. The leg length is 6 λ at 28 MHz, 3 λ at 14 MHz.

shows the leg length at which maximum gain is obtained at any given takeoff angle. Increasing the leg length beyond the optimum will result in less gain, and for that reason the curves do not extend beyond the optimum length. Note that the optimum length becomes greater as the desired takeoff angle decreases. Leg lengths over 6 λ are not recommended because the directive pattern becomes so sharp that the antenna performance is highly variable with small changes in the angle, both horizontal and vertical, at which an incoming wave reaches the antenna. Since these angles vary to some extent in ionospheric propagation, it does not pay to attempt to try for too great a degree of directivity.

Multiband Design

When a rhombic antenna is to be used over a considerable frequency range, a compromise must be made in the tilt angle. **Figure 13.26** gives the design dimensions of a suitable compromise for a rhombic that covers the 14 to 30 MHz range well. **Figure 13.27** shows the azimuth and elevation patterns for this antenna at 14 MHz, at a height of 70 feet over flat ground. The comparison antenna in this case is a 4-element Yagi on a 26-foot boom, also 70 feet above flat ground. The rhombic has about 2.2 dB more gain, but its azimuthal pattern is 17.2° wide at the 3 dB points, and only 26° at the –20 dB points! On the other hand, the Yagi has a 3-dB beamwidth of 63°, making it far easier to aim at a distant geographic location. Figure 13.27B shows the elevation-plane patterns for the same antennas above. As usual, the peak angle for either horizontally polarized antenna is determined mainly by the height above ground.

The peak gain of a terminated rhombic is less than that of an unterminated resonant rhombic. For the rhombic of Figure 13.26, the reduction in peak gain is about 1.5 dB. **Figure 13.28** compares the azimuthal patterns for this rhombic with and without an 800-Ω termination.

Figure 13.29 shows the azimuth and elevation patterns for the terminated rhombic of Figure 13.26 when it is operated at 28 MHz. The main lobe becomes very narrow, at 6.9° at the 3-dB points. However, this is partially compensated for by the appearance of two sidelobes each side of the main beam. These tend to spread out the main pattern some. Again, a 4-element Yagi at the same height is used for comparison.

Termination

Although the difference in the gain is relatively small with terminated or unterminated rhombics of comparable design, the terminated antenna has the advantage that over a wide frequency range it presents an essentially resistive and constant load to the transmitter. In a sense, the power

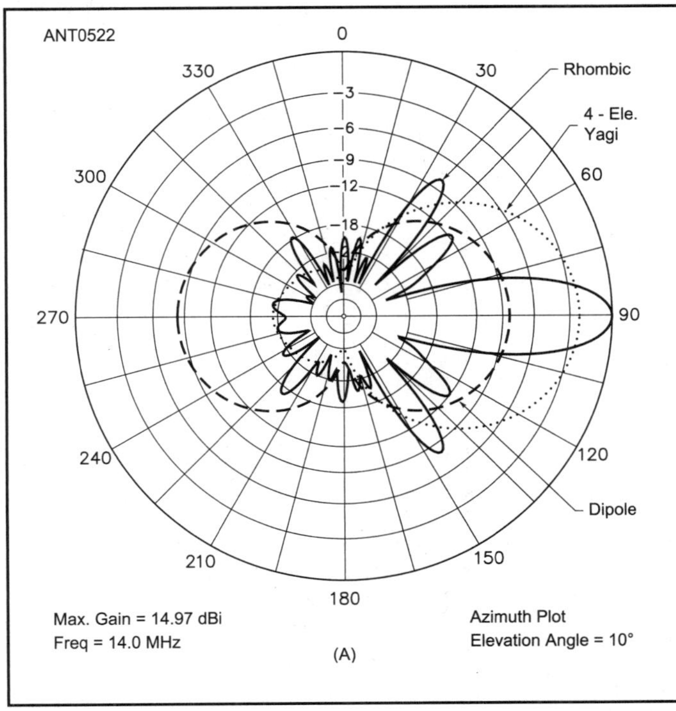

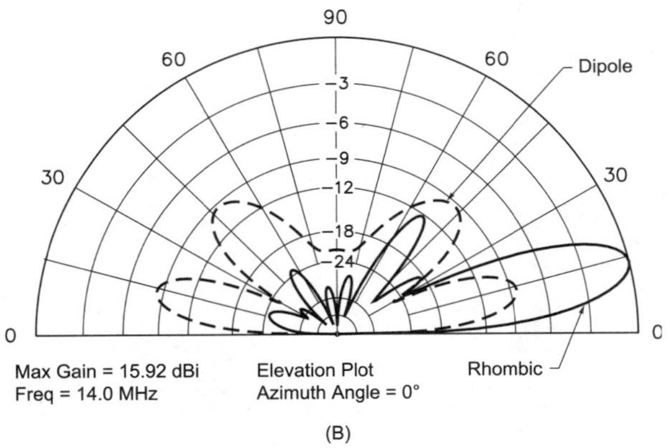

Figure 13.27 — At left, azimuthal pattern for 3-λ (at 14 MHz) terminated rhombic (solid line) shown in Figure 13.26, compared with 4-element 20-meter Yagi (dotted line) on a 26-foot boom and a 20-meter dipole (dashed line). All antennas are mounted 70 feet (1 λ) above flat ground. The rearward pattern of the terminated rhombic is good and the forward gain exceeds that of the Yagi, but the frontal lobe is very narrow. Above, elevation-plane pattern of terminated rhombic compared to that of a simple dipole at the same height.

dissipated in the terminating resistor can be considered power that would have been radiated in the other direction had the resistor not been there. Therefore, the fact that some of the power (about one-third) is used up in heating the resistor does not mean that much actual loss in the desired direction.

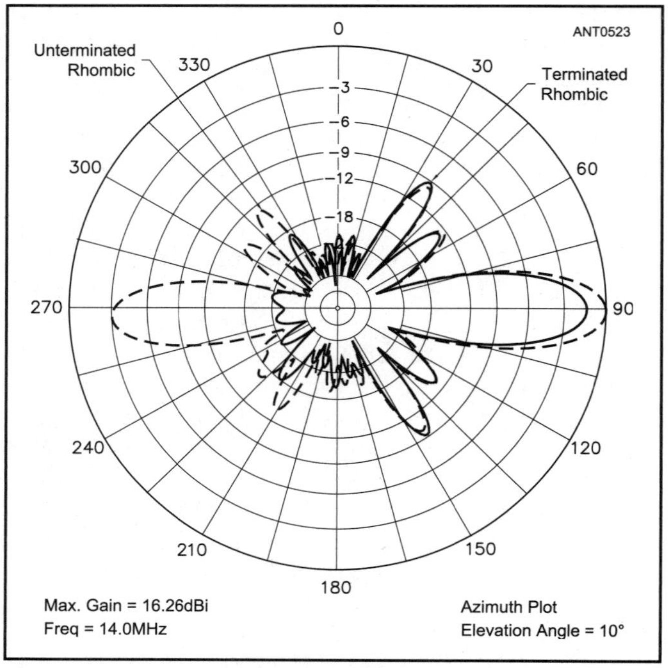

Figure 13.28 — Comparison of azimuthal patterns for terminated (solid line) and unterminated (dashed line) rhombic antennas, using same dimensions as Figure 13.26 at a frequency of 14 MHz. The gain tradeoff is about 1.5 dB in return for the superior rearward pattern of the terminated antenna.

The characteristic impedance of an ordinary rhombic antenna, looking into the input end, is in the order of 700 to 800 Ω when properly terminated in a resistance at the far end. The terminating resistance required to bring about the matching condition usually is slightly higher than the input impedance because of the loss of energy through radiation by the time the far end is reached. The correct value usually will be found to be of the order of 800 Ω, and should be determined experimentally if the flattest possible antenna is desired. However, for average work a noninductive resistance of 800 Ω can be used with the assurance that the operation will not be far from optimum.

The terminating resistor must be practically a pure resistance at the operating frequencies; that is, its inductance and capacitance should be negligible. Ordinary wire-wound resistors are not suitable because they have far too much inductance and distributed capacitance. Small carbon resistors have satisfactory electrical characteristics but will not dissipate more than a few watts and so cannot be used, except when the transmitter power does not exceed 10 or 20 watts or when the antenna is to be used for reception only. The special resistors designed either for use as dummy antennas or for terminating rhombic antennas should be used in other cases. To allow a factor of safety, the total rated power dissipation of the resistor or resistors should be equal to half the power output of the transmitter.

To reduce the effects of stray capacitance it is desirable to use several units, say three, in series even when one alone will safely dissipate the power. The two end units should be identical and each should have one fourth to one third the total resistance, with the center unit making up the difference. The units should be installed in a weatherproof housing at the end of the antenna to protect them and to permit mounting

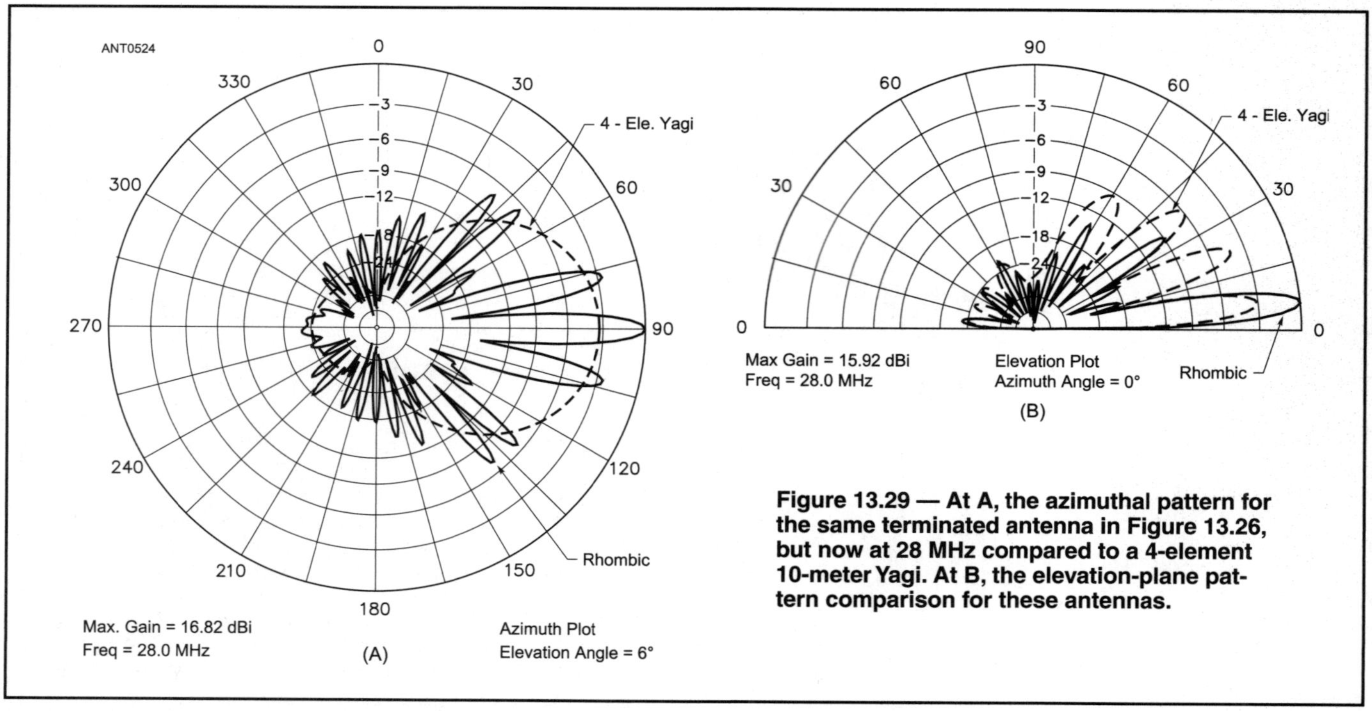

Figure 13.29 — At A, the azimuthal pattern for the same terminated antenna in Figure 13.26, but now at 28 MHz compared to a 4-element 10-meter Yagi. At B, the elevation-plane pattern comparison for these antennas.

without mechanical strain. The connecting leads should be short so that little extraneous inductance is introduced.

Alternatively, the terminating resistance may be placed at the end of an 800-Ω line connected to the end of the antenna. This will permit placing the resistors and their housing at a point convenient for adjustment rather than at the top of the pole. Resistance wire may be used for this line, so that a portion of the power will be dissipated before it reaches the resistive termination, thus permitting the use of lower wattage lumped resistors.

If the rhombic is to be used on a single-band, Hallas (see the Bibliography) presents an interesting method of using an antenna tuner and a more common 50-Ω dummy load to create a "tunable load" that can be adjusted for the best performance.

Multi-Wire Rhombics

The input impedance of a rhombic antenna constructed as in Figure 13.26 is not quite constant as the frequency is varied. This is because the varying separation between the wires causes the characteristic impedance of the antenna to vary along its length. The variation in Z_{ANT} can be minimized by a conductor arrangement that increases the capacitance per unit length in proportion to the separation between the wires.

The method of accomplishing this is shown in **Figure 13.30**. Three conductors are used, joined together at the ends but with increasing separation as the junction between legs is approached. For HF work the spacing between the wires at the center is 3 to 4 feet, which is similar to that used in commercial installations using legs several wavelengths long. Since all three wires should have the same length, the top and bottom wires should be slightly farther from the support than the middle wire. Using three wires in this way reduces the Z_{ANT} of the antenna to approximately 600 Ω, thus providing a better match for practical open-wire line, in addition to smoothing out the impedance variation over the frequency range.

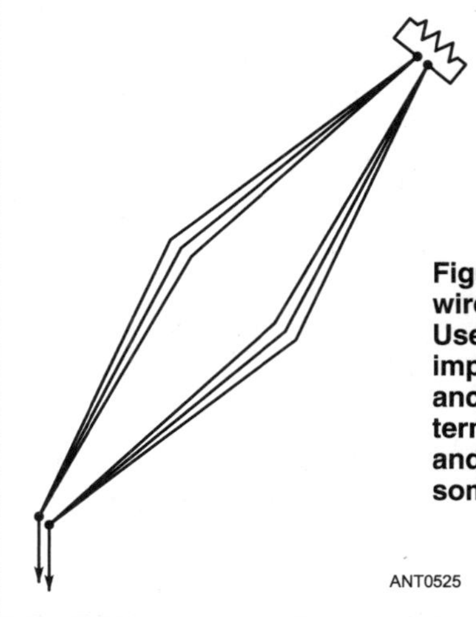

Figure 13.30 — Three-wire rhombic antenna. Use of multiple wires improves the impedance characteristic of a terminated rhombic and increases the gain somewhat.

A similar effect (although not quite as favorable) is obtained by using two wires instead of three. The 3-wire system has been found to increase the gain of the antenna by about 1 dB over that of a single-conductor version.

Front-to-Back Ratio

It is theoretically possible to obtain an infinite front-to-back ratio with a terminated rhombic antenna, and in practice very large values can be had. However, when the antenna is terminated in its characteristic impedance, the infinite front-to-back ratio can be obtained only at frequencies for which the leg length is an odd multiple of a quarter wavelength. The front-to-back ratio is smallest at frequencies for which the leg length is a multiple of a half wavelength.

When the leg length is not an odd multiple of a quarter-wave at the frequency under consideration, the front-to-back ratio can be made very high by decreasing the value of terminating resistance slightly. This permits a small reflection from the far end of the antenna, which cancels out the residual response at the input end. With large antennas, the front-to-back ratio may be made very large over the whole frequency range by experimental adjustment of the terminating resistance. Modification of the terminating resistance can result in a splitting of the back null into two nulls, one on either side of a small lobe in the back direction. Changes in the value of terminating resistance thus permit steering the back null over a small horizontal range so that signals coming from a particular spot not exactly to the rear of the antenna may be minimized.

Methods of Feed

If the broad frequency characteristic of the terminated rhombic antenna is to be utilized fully, the feeder system must be similarly broadbanded. Open-wire transmission line of the same characteristic impedance as that shown at the antenna input terminals (approximately 700 to 800 Ω) may be used. Data for the construction of such lines is given in the chapter on **Transmission Lines**. While the usual matching stub can be used to provide an impedance transformation to more satisfactory line impedances, this limits the operation of the antenna to a comparatively narrow range of frequencies centering about that for which the stub is adjusted. Probably a more satisfactory arrangement would be to use a coaxial transmission line and a broadband transformer balun at the antenna feed point.

13.5 PROJECT: FOUR-WIRE STEERABLE V BEAM FOR 10 THROUGH 40 METERS

A simple arrangement of four wires can be used to work multiple bands and have antenna gain in different directions without using a rotator. A version of this antenna was described in *QST* (see Bibliography entry for Colvin) and is included in ARRL's *Wire Antenna Classics*. That version had wires 584 feet long. In this version, built by Sam Moore, NX5Z, each wire is only 106 feet long. Many DX stations have had great success with this type of antenna.

Antenna Characteristics

An unterminated V beam gain pattern is bidirectional with two main gain lobes 180° apart if the leg lengths are at least a wavelength long. In **Figure 13.31**, a long wire antenna at the left is shown to have a gain pattern of four major lobes. Another long wire antenna positioned 45° from the first is also shown. If these are combined to form a V, it has the gain pattern as shown to the right in Figure 13.31.

In this design, four 106 foot wires are spaced at 45°. The length of the wire is not as important as that they all be the same length. The author installed his V beam with the apex and relay control box at a height of 40 feet with the wire ends 10 feet off the ground in a sloping V configuration. This V beam's gain approximates that of a three element Yagi on 10, 12, 15 and 17 meters and is within a few dB on 20 meters. The antenna provides useful operation on 30 and 40 meters, with essentially an omnidirectional pattern on 40. The beam direction is controlled by simply switching two switches in the station.

This antenna may also be built with wire lengths as short as 60 feet to more easily fit on a city lot. There will be a small decrease in gain. The V beam gain increases with the length of the wires. The longer the wires, the greater the gain. As the wire lengthens, however, the beamwidth narrows. The gains and beamwidths of 106 and 60 foot versions are shown in **Table 13.1**, based on *EZNEC* analysis. (*EZNEC* modeling software is discussed in the **Antenna Modeling** chapter.) As a reference, the typical two element Yagi has 6 to 7 dBi gain while a three element Yagi can be expected to have a 7.5 to 8.1 dBi gain, depending on design, especially boom length.

The azimuth pattern looking down on a V beam is shown in **Figure 13.32**. If the height of the V beam is less than ½ wavelength, the gain pattern will distort and make the antenna more omnidirectional.

To reduce the gain lobe to the rear of the V beam you can terminate the wire ends with a resistor. An unterminated version has gain in both directions. If terminated, the antenna would need eight wires instead of four to have gain in all directions.

Since this antenna may be used for multiband operation, the gain waveform changes somewhat depending on the frequency of operation. The higher the frequency, the greater the gain, since the frequency to wire length ratio changes. For example, if your V beam is 1 wavelength long at 20 meters, it is 2 wavelengths long at 10 meters, thus causing greater gain and narrower beamwidth as shown in Table 13.1. While essentially bidirectional on the upper bands, there is a 1 to 2 dB front to back ratio, with the maximum signal to the open end of the V. The beamwidth shown in Table 13.1 is of the front beam, with the rear beam

Table 13.1
Gain and Beamwidth of the V Beam on Each Band

Frequency (MHz)	*Gain at 106' (dBi)*	*3 dB Beamwidth at 106' (°)*	*Gain at 60' (dBi)*	*3 dB Beamwidth at 60' (°)*
7.15	1.9*	Omnidirectional	2.4*	Omnidirectional
10.12	3.6	133	3.7*	Omnidirectional
14.15	6.7	71	4.1	137
18.11	8.5	42	4.1	136
21.2	9.1	33	6.0	63
24.93	9.7	28	6.1	61
28.3	10.7	23	7.3	40

*Essentially omnidirectional with maximum gain nearly perpendicular to the wire bisector.

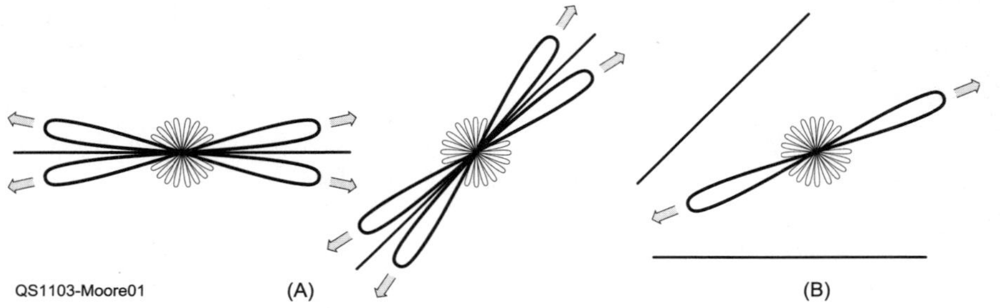

Figure 13.31 — The azimuth patterns of two long wire antennas are shown at (A). If the two are combined in phase to form a V, the resulting pattern is shown at (B).

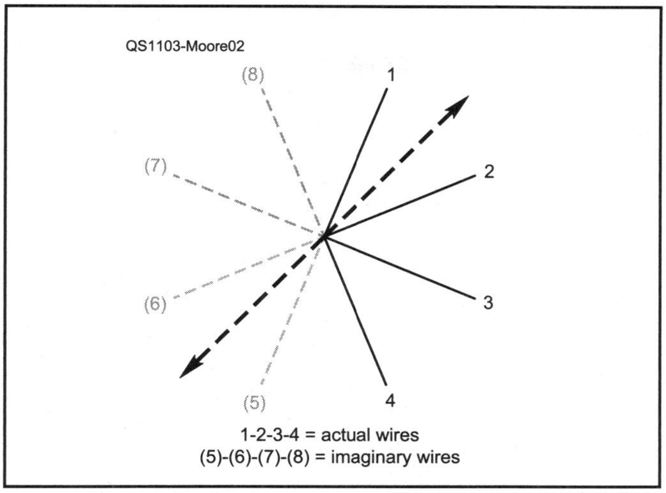

Figure 13.32 — The selectable azimuth looking down on the V beam. The arrow shows directions of maximum radiation with wires 1 and 2 connected.

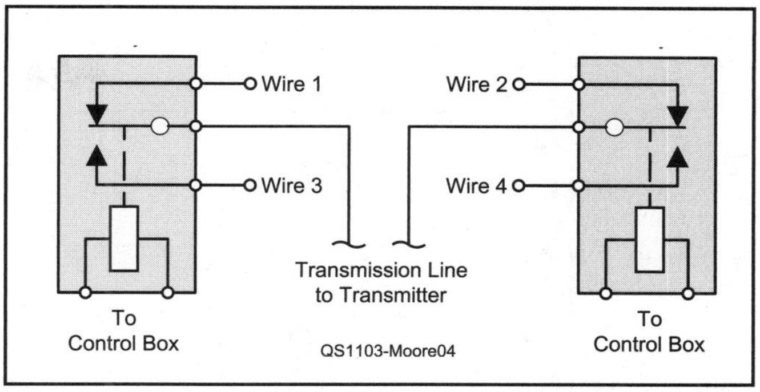

Figure 13.34 — Schematic diagram of the relay box used to remotely select the V beam wires.

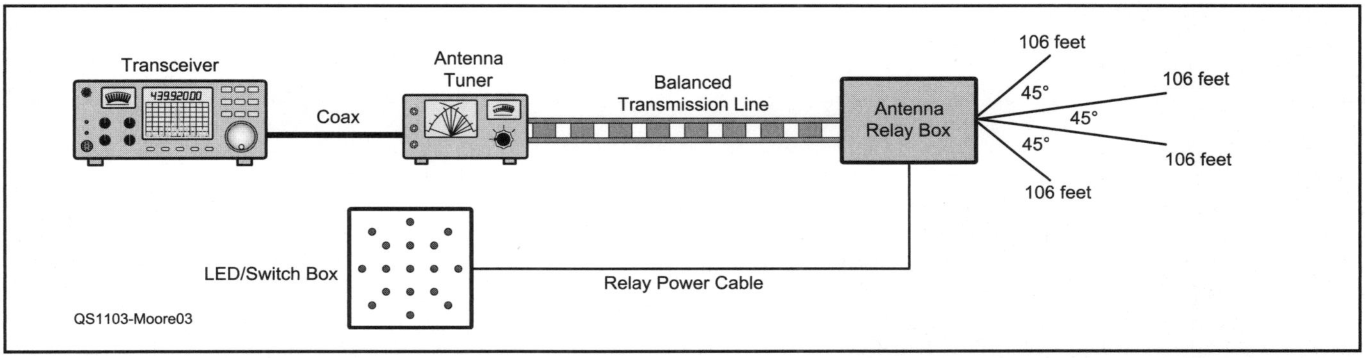

Figure 13.33 — The block diagram of the V beam system. The antenna tuner must be able to accept balanced transmission line and a built-in or external 4:1 balun is necessary.

generally somewhat narrower. A horizontal, rather than sloping, V beam will be more symmetrical.

The block diagram of the V beam system is shown in **Figure 13.33**. The antenna tuner must be able to accept balanced transmission line and a built in or external 4:1 balun is necessary. The author made a homebrew air core external 4:1 balun using 1 inch PVC pipe and used a small automatic antenna tuner.

Controls and Indicators

The LED switch box supplies power to the relays in the antenna relay box at the center of the V beam via a three wire cable such as three wire electrical zip cord. Smaller wires would work.

The relay box schematic is shown in **Figure 13.34**. Only two switches are needed to power relays 1 and 2. Relay 1 switches between wire 1 and 3 and relay 2 switches between wire 2 and 4. Note that wire 4 is used in combination with wire 1 instead of (imaginary) wire 5. This obtuse angle yields

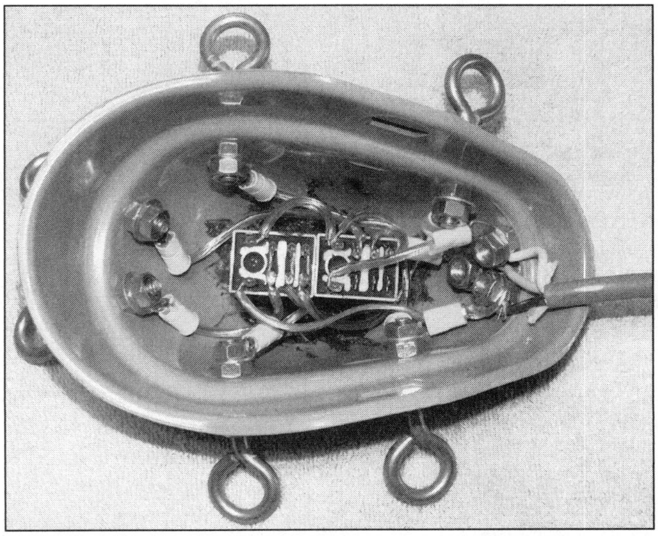

Figure 13.35 — Relay box assembled in a power entry PVC cover.

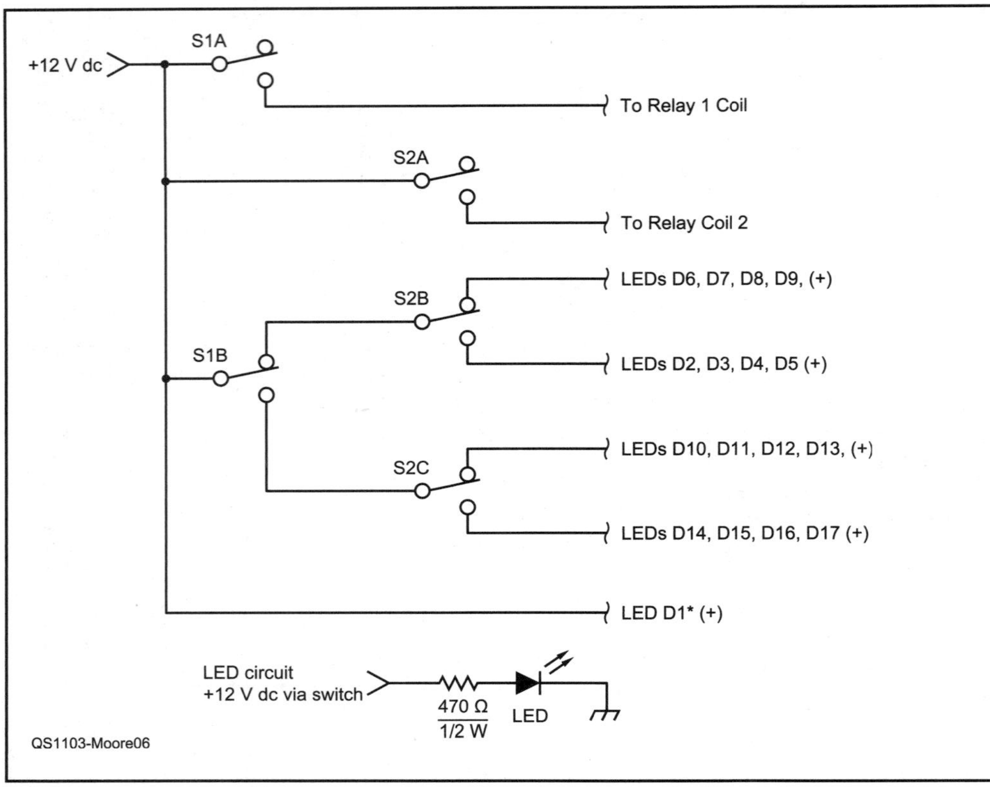

Figure 13.36 — Schematic diagram of the relay power switches and the 17 LEDs used as direction indicators.

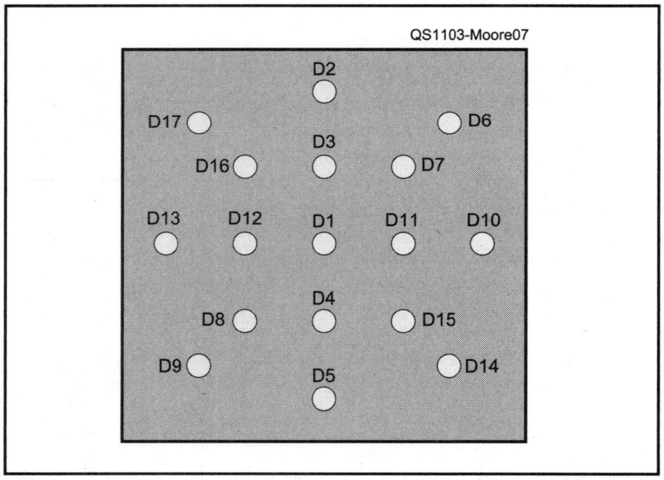

Figure 13.37 — Top view of the indicator panel showing LED placement.

Figure 13.38 — The V beams are supported by a mast and a standard PVC power-entry cover. Relays are used to switch between the beams and are controlled through a separate control cable.

the about same gain and waveform as wire 4 to 5 would have offered, without having to string another wire. **Figure 13.35** shows an assembled relay box in a power entry PVC cover.

The schematic in **Figure 13.36** shows the relay power switches and the 17 LED connections. LED and relay common connections go to a 12 V return. A top view of the LEDs is shown in **Figure 13.37**. The LED switch box illuminated LEDs indicate the direction of greatest gain. Note LED 1 is always on, since it's used in all directions. The other 4 LEDs in a particular row, in a bingo board pattern, are connected and supplied with +12 V dc via switch 1 or 2, depending on wires chosen. Use a 3-pole switch for S2, or use two closely spaced DPDT switches and switch them at the same time.

The assembled control head is mounted as shown in **Figure 13.38**. Total cost is around $50, not counting the balun and balanced transmission line. For the four wires, the author used electric fence wire, which accepted solder surprisingly well. You can buy a ¼ mile roll of electric fence wire inexpensively at agricultural supply stores. You may also have a few necessary parts in your junk box.

13.6 BIBLIOGRAPHY

Source material and more extended discussion of topics covered in this chapter can be found in the references given below.

E. Bruce, "Developments in Short-Wave Directive Antennas," *Proc IRE*, Aug 1931.

E. Bruce, A. C. Beck and L. R. Lowry, "Horizontal Rhombic Antennas," *Proc IRE*, Jan 1935.

P. S. Carter, C. W. Hansel and N. E. Lindenblad, "Development of Directive Transmitting Antennas by R.C.A. Communications," *Proc IRE*, Oct 1931.

L. Colvin, DL4ZC (W6KG), "Multiple V Beams," *QST*, Aug 1956.

J. Devoldere, *ON4UN's Low-Band DXing* 5th ed, ARRL, 2010.

J. Hallas, W1ZR, "Achieving Near Perfection with the Imperfect Rhombic," *QST*, Nov 2004, pp 28-32.

A. E. Harper, *Rhombic Antenna Design* (New York: D. Van Nostrand Co, Inc).

E. A. Laport, "Design Data for Horizontal Rhombic Antennas," *RCA Review*, Mar 1952.

G. M. Miller, *Modern Electronic Communication* (Englewood Cliffs, NJ: Prentice Hall, 1983).

S. Moore, NX5Z, "A Four Wire Steerable V Beam for 10 through 40 Meters," *QST*, Mar 2011, pp 30-33.

J. H. Mullaney, Capt., W4HGU, "The Half-Rhombic Antenna," *QST*, Jan 1946, pp 28-31.

M. Orr, AA2PE, "The Tilted Half-Rhombic Antenna," *Antenna Compendium, Vol 4*, ARRL, 1999, pp 5-10 through 5-13.

F. E. Terman, *Radio Engineering*, Second Edition (New York: McGraw-Hill, 1937).

TABLE OF CONTENTS

Chapter 14 — Downloadable Supplemental Content

Supplemental Articles

Chapter 14

HF Antenna System Design

This chapter combines information from previous editions into a condensed discussion of HF antenna system design. An amateur just beginning to build an HF station may be more interested in trying out different types of antennas and gaining experience with selecting, building and installing them. Later on, as experience is gained and specific goals are formed, the process of system design becomes important.

No single book can provide a step-by-step procedure for designing antenna systems — there are too many different needs and operating styles. What can be done, however, is to give an overview of the process by which system-level issues are identified and dealt with. Tools such as propagation prediction and antenna modeling software will be discussed from the antenna system perspective. Methods of using antennas to meet certain goals, such as stacking Yagis and using near vertical incidence skywave propagation (NVIS), will be covered.

By thinking about your "antenna farm" as a system — whether a single antenna in a tree or a multiple-tower contest station — you will be able to make better use of your time and materials and have more success on the air.

We will begin with an overview of the system design process and how to approach it. The next step is a section covering the use of propagation prediction tools as a means of assessing the coverage of an antenna system. Then the effects of local terrain on antenna system planning and performance are covered. The final sections address the use of vertical stacks of Yagi antennas to control elevation angle.

14.1 SYSTEM DESIGN BASICS

The most important time spent in putting together an antenna system is the time spent in planning. Later in this chapter the section on Local Terrain will present steps needed to evaluate how your local terrain can affect HF communications. You will need to compare the patterns resulting from your own terrain to the statistically relevant elevation angles needed for coverage of various geographic areas. (The elevation-angle statistics were discussed in the **Radio Wave Propagation** chapter and are located with this book's downloadable supplemental information, as is the terrain-assessment program *HFTA*.)

The implicit assumptions in using propagation data and terrain analysis are (1) that you know where you want to talk to, and (2) that you'd like the most effective system possible. At the start of such a theoretical analysis, cost is no object. Practical matters, like cost or the desires of your spouse, can come later! After all, you're just checking out all the possibilities. If nothing else, you will use the methodology in this chapter to evaluate any property you are considering buying so that you can build your "dream station."

By using the techniques and tools available in this book, you can rationally and logically plan an antenna system that will be best suited for your own particular conditions. Now, however, you have to get practical. Thinking through and planning the installation can save a lot of time, money and frustration.

One often overlooked part of successful antenna system design (and station design, too) is the keeping of a station notebook. Make sure you save and organize the various computer files and documents associated with your system design. Being able to revisit the steps leading to a decision — successful or unsuccessful — is very important. Important data from measurements or tests should always be clearly labeled and stored so that you can find it later. Think of each page or file as a brick in the grand structure you are building. No one ever regrets having kept good records!

While no one can tell you the exact steps you should take in developing your own master plan, this section, prepared originally by Chuck Hutchinson, K8CH, should help you with some ideas.

14.1.1 DESIRES AND LIMITATIONS

Begin planning by spelling out your communications desires and the limitations placed on them. Engineers call these "requirements" and "constraints" — all successful projects begin with clearly understanding and recording them. What bands are you interested in? Who (or where) do you want to talk to? When do you operate? How much time and money are you willing to spend on an antenna system? What physical limitations affect your master plan?

From the answers to the above questions, begin to formulate goals — short, intermediate and long range. Be realistic about those goals. Remember that there are three station effectiveness factors that are under your control. These are: operator skill, equipment in the shack, and the antenna system. There is no substitute for developing operating skills. Some tradeoffs are possible between shack equipment and antennas. For example, a high-power amplifier can compensate for a less than optimum antenna but only for transmitted signals. By contrast, a better antenna has advantages for receiving as well as for transmitting.

Consider your limitations. Are there regulatory restrictions on antennas in your community? Are there any deed restrictions or covenants that apply to your property? Do other factors (finances, family considerations, other interests, and so forth) limit the type or height of antennas that you can erect? All of these factors must be investigated because they play a major role determining the type of antennas you erect.

Chances are that you won't be able to immediately do all you desire. Think about how you can budget your resources over a period of time. Your resources are your money, your time available to work, materials you may have on hand, friends that are willing to help, etc. One way to budget is to concentrate your initial efforts on a given band or two. If your major interest is in chasing DX, you might want to start with a very good antenna for the 14-MHz band. A simple multiband antenna could initially serve for other frequencies. Later you can add better antennas for those other bands.

14.1.2 SITE PLANNING

A map of your property or proposed antenna site can be of great help as you begin to consider alternative antennas.

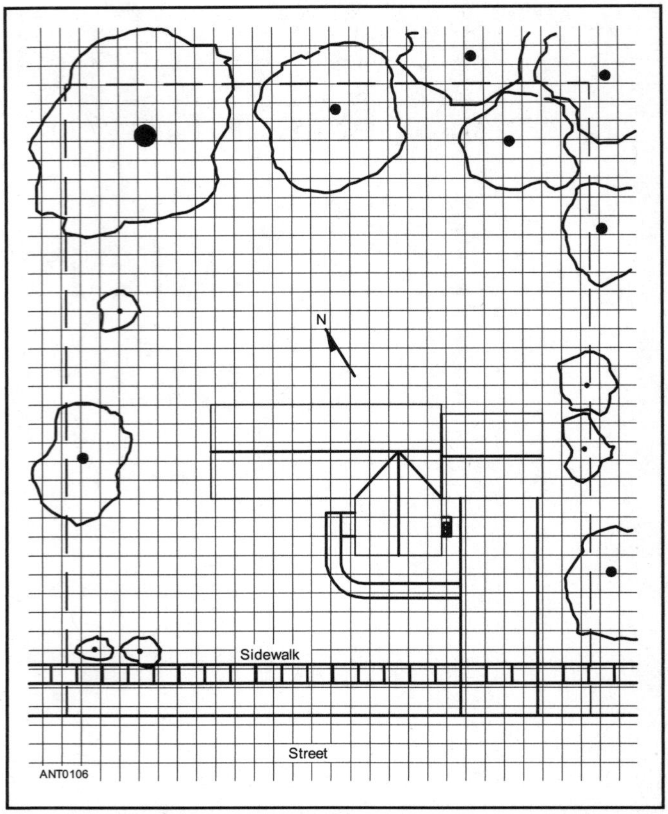

Figure 14.1 — A site map such this one is a useful tool for planning your antenna installation.

You'll need to know the size and location of buildings, trees and other major objects in the area. Be sure to note compass directions on your map. Graph or quadrille paper (or a simple CAD program) can be very useful for this purpose. See **Figure 14.1** for an example. It's a good idea to make a few photocopies of your site map so you can mark on the copies as you work on your plans. If you create a master map with CAD software, you can create and save lots of alternatives for comparisons and evaluations.

Use your map to plan antenna layouts and locations of any supporting towers or masts. If your plan calls for more than one tower or mast, think about using them as supports for wire antennas. As you work on a layout, be sure to think in three dimensions even though the map shows only two.

Be sensitive to your neighbors. A 70-foot guyed tower in the front yard of a house in a residential neighborhood is not a good idea (and probably won't comply with local ordinances!). You probably will want to locate that tower in the back yard.

Be sure to include restrictions and hazards on the map. For example, you may have set-back requirements from property lines for any structure on your property, such as a tower. You may not be allowed to intrude on neighboring "air space" with antenna elements. Power lines and other hazards such as buried utilities should be on your map, as well. It's just as important to identify where antennas can't go as where they can.

As discussed in the **Building Antenna Systems and**

Towers chapter, consider access needs when laying out your system. If you will be putting up towers, consider how a backhoe or concrete truck can get to the location of the tower base. You'll need to allow space for towers that fold over or that are tipped up for installation, too.

14.1.3 INITIAL ANALYSIS

Use the information in this chapter, antenna modeling software and propagation evaluation tools to analyze antenna patterns in both horizontal and vertical planes toward geographic areas of interest. Consider the azimuthal pattern of fixed antennas. You'll want to orient any fixed antennas to favor the directions of greatest interest to you.

Use antenna modeling tools to help you evaluate what type of antenna might be suitable to your own particular style of operating. Do you want a Yagi with a lot of rejection of received signals from the rear? Let's say that terrain analysis shows that you need an antenna at least 50 feet high. Do you really need a steel tower, or would a simple dipole in the trees serve your communication needs just fine? How about a vertical in your backyard? Would that be inconspicuous enough to suit your neighbors and your own family, yet still get you on the air?

If you want to work DX, you'll want antennas that radiate energy at low as well as intermediate angles. An antenna pattern is greatly affected by the presence of ground and by the local topography of the ground. Therefore, be sure to consider what effect ground will have on the antenna pattern at the height you are considering. A 70-foot high antenna is approximately ½, 1, 1½ and 2 wavelengths high on 7, 14, 21 and 28 MHz respectively. Those heights are useful for long-distance communications. The same 70-foot height represents only $\lambda/4$ at 3.5 MHz, however. Most of the radiated energy from a dipole at that height would be concentrated straight up. This condition is not great for long-distance communication, but can still be useful for some DX work and excellent for short-range communications.

Lower antenna heights can be useful for certain types of communications — see the section on NVIS communications later in this chapter, for example. However, for most amateur operation it is generally true that "the higher, the better" as far as communications effectiveness is concerned. This general rule of thumb, of course, should be tempered by an exact analysis of your local terrain. Being located at the top of a steep hill can mean that you can use lower tower heights to achieve good coverage.

There may be cases where it is not possible to install low-frequency dipoles $\lambda/4$ or more above the ground. A vertical antenna with many radials is a good choice for long-distance communications. You may want to install both a dipole and a vertical for the 3.5- or 7-MHz bands. On the 1.8-MHz band, unless extremely tall supports are available, a vertical antenna is likely to be the most useful for DXing. You can then choose the antenna that performs best for a given set of conditions. A low dipole will generally work better for shorter-range communications, while the vertical will generally be the better performer over longer distances.

The performance of ground-mounted monopole antennas depends strongly on a system of ground radials and the characteristics of the ground. Be sure to review this book's chapter **The Effects of Ground** when considering how and where to install the antenna. In particular, Al Christman, K3LC's article on maximizing the effectiveness of ground radials for a fixed amount of wire makes good economic sense for practical system builders.

14.1.4 BUILDING A SYSTEM PLAN

At this point, you will enter a repeated sequence of "design-model-adjust" as you evaluate the plan. You should start with modeling and then compare the results to those "desires" you wrote down at the beginning. With each round of modeling and comparison, your antenna system will be improved.

As you refine your system design, you can also build the long-term plan for construction of the antenna system. Chances are that you can divide the actual construction of your system into a series of phases or steps. By keeping the long-range plan in mind you will be able to make better decisions at every step of the way toward achieving your goals!

Say, for example, that you have lots of room and that your long-range plan calls for a pair of towers, one 100-feet high, and the other 70-feet high, to support monoband Yagi antennas. The towers will also support a horizontal 3.5-MHz dipole, for DX work. On your map you've located them so the 80 meter dipole will be broadside to Europe. You decide to build the 70-foot tower with a triband beam and 80 and 40 meter inverted-V dipoles to begin the project.

In your master plan you design the guys, anchors and all hardware for the 70-foot tower to support the load of stacked 4-element 10 and 15 meter monobanders Yagis. So you make sure you buy a heavy-duty rotator and the stout mast needed for the monoband antennas later because you have a long-range plan for them. Thus you avoid having to buy, and then sell, a medium-duty rotator and lighter weight tower materials later on when you upgrade the station. You could have saved money in the long run by putting up a monoband beam for your favorite band, but you decided that for now it is more important to have a beam on 14, 21 and 28 MHz, so you choose a commercial triband Yagi.

The second step of your plan calls for installing the second tower and stacking a 2-element 40 meter and a 4-element 20 meter monoband Yagi on it. You also plan to replace the tribander on the 70-foot tower with stacked 4-element 10 and 15 meter monoband Yagis. Although this is still a "dream system" you can now apply some of the modeling techniques discussed earlier in this chapter to determine the overall system performance.

14.1.5 MODELING INTERACTIONS

In this next step of analysis we're going to assume that you have sufficient real estate to separate the 70- and 100-foot towers by 150 feet so that you can easily support an 80 meter dipole between them. We'll also assume that you want the 80 meter dipole to have its maximum response

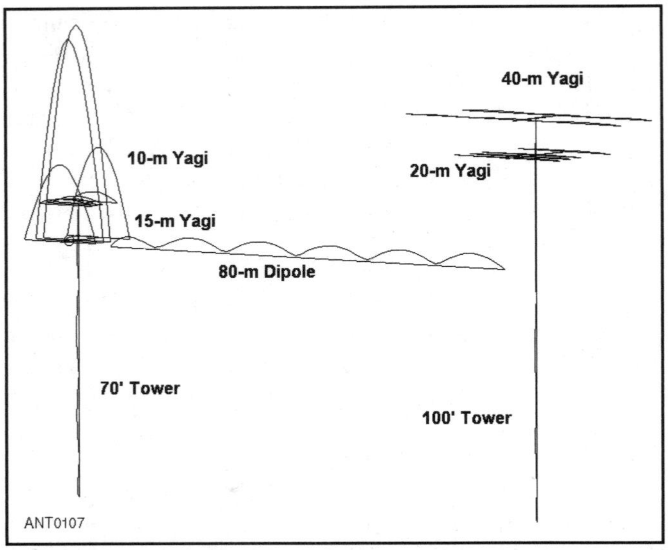

Figure 14.2 — Layout for two-tower antenna system, at 70 and 100 feet high and 150 feet apart. The 70-foot tower has a 4-element 10 meter Yagi at 80 feet on a 10-foot rotating mast and a 4-element 15 meter Yagi at 70 feet. An 80 meter dipole goes from the 70-foot tower to the 100-foot tower, which holds a 2-element 40 meter Yagi at 110 feet and a 4-element 20 meter Yagi at 100 feet. In this figure all the rotatable Yagis are facing the direction of Europe and the currents on the 15 meter Yagi are shown. Note the significant amount of current induced on the nearby 80 meter dipole that will cause a re-radiated signal!

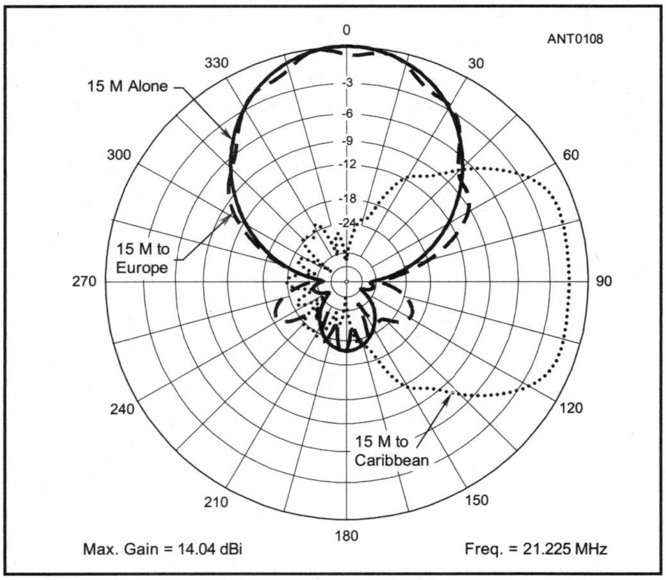

Figure 14.3 — An overlay of azimuth patterns. The solid line is the radiation pattern for the 15 meter Yagi all by itself. The dashed line is the pattern for the 15 meter Yagi, as affected by all the other antennas. The dotted line is the pattern for the 15 meter Yagi when it is pointed toward the Caribbean, with the Yagis on the 100-foot tower pointed toward the 70-foot tower. The peak response of the 15 meter Yagi has dropped by about 1.5 dB.

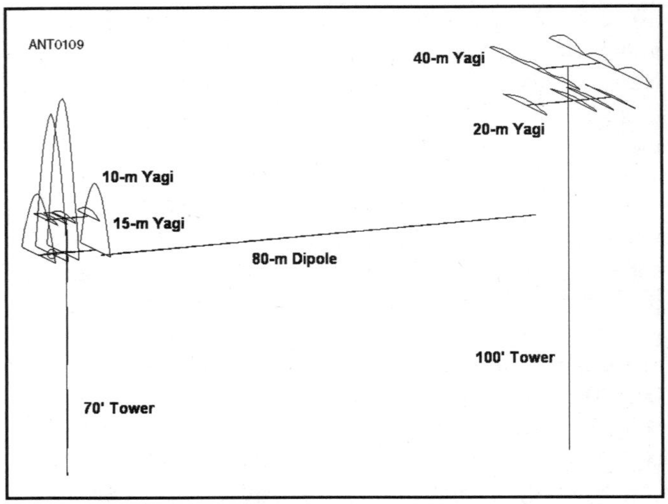

Figure 14.4 — The layout and 15 meter currents when the Yagis on the 100-foot tower are pointed toward the 70-foot tower. The 15 meter Yagi has been rotated to face the direction of the 100-foot tower (toward the Caribbean).

at a heading of 45° into Europe from your location in Newington, Connecticut. The dipole will also have a lobe facing 225° toward the USA and New Zealand, making it a good antenna for both domestic contacts and DX work. Note that it is important to model interactions for the full system even if you don't plan on building all of it right away. This helps avoid "mid-course corrections."

Let's examine the interactions that occur between the rotatable Yagis for 10, 15, 20 and 40 meters. See **Figure 14.2**, which purposely exaggerates the magnitude of the currents on the 4-element 15 meter Yagi mounted at 70 feet. Here, both sets of Yagis have been rotated so that they are pointing into Europe. There is a small amount of current radiated onto the 10 meter antenna but virtually no current is radiated onto the 40 and 20 meter Yagis. This is good.

However, significant current is picked up by the 80 meter dipole. This undesired current and the subsequent reradiated signal affects the radiation pattern of the 15 meter antenna, as shown in **Figure 14.3**, which overlays the pattern of the 4-element 15 meter Yagi by itself with that of the Yagi interacting with the other antennas. You can see "ripples" in the azimuthal response of the 15 meter Yagi due to the effects of the 80 meter dipole's re-radiation. The magnitude of the ripples is about 1 dB at worst, so they don't seriously affect the forward pattern (into Europe), but the rearward lobes are degraded somewhat, to just below 20 dB.

Figure 14.3 also shows the worst-case situation for the 15 meter Yagi. Here, the 15 and 10 meter stack has been turned clockwise 90°, facing the Caribbean, while the 40 and 20 meter Yagis on the 100-foot tower have been turned counter-clockwise 90° (in the direction of Japan) to face the 70-foot tower holding the 10/15 meter Yagis. You can see the layout and the currents in **Figure 14.4**. Now the 40 and 20 meter Yagis re-radiate some 15 meter energy and reduce the maximum gain by about 1.5 dB. Note that in this direction

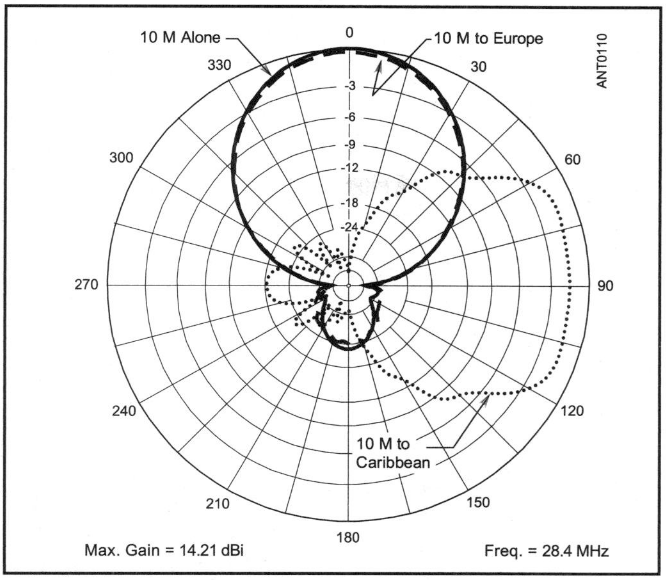

Figure 14.5 — The radiation patterns for the 10 meter Yagi. The solid line is the 10 meter Yagi by itself. The dashed line is for the same Yagi, with all other antenna interactions. The dotted line shows the worst-case pattern, with the stacked Yagis on the 100-foot tower facing the 70-foot tower and the 10 meter Yagi pointed toward the Caribbean. Again, the peak response of the 10 meter Yagi has dropped about 1.5 dB in the worst-case situation.

the 80 meter dipole no longer has 15 meter energy radiated onto it by the 15 meter Yagi.

The shape of the patterns will change depending on whether you specify "current" or "voltage" sources in the models for the other antennas, since this effectively opens up or shorts the feed points at the other antennas so far as 15 meter energy is concerned. In practice, this means that the interaction between antennas will vary somewhat depending on the length of the feed lines going to each antenna and whether each feed line is open-circuited or short-circuited when it is not in use.

You can now see that interactions between various antennas pointing in different directions can be significant in a real-world antenna system. In general, higher frequency antennas are affected by re-radiation from lower-frequency antennas, rather than the other way around. Thus the presence of a 10 or 15 meter stack does not affect the 20 meter Yagi at all.

Modeling can also help determine the minimum stacking distance required between monoband Yagis on the same rotating mast. In this case, stacking the 10 and 15 meter monobanders 10 feet apart holds down interaction between them so that the pattern and gain of the 10 meter Yagi are not impacted adversely. **Figure 14.5** demonstrates this in the European direction, where the patterns for the 10 meter beam by itself looks very clean compared to the same Yagi separated by 10 feet from the 15 meter Yagi below it. The worst-case situation is pointing toward the Caribbean, when the 40 and 20 meter stack is facing the 70-foot tower. This drops the 10 meter gain down about 1.5 dB from maximum, indicating significant interaction is occurring.

In this situation you might find it best to place the 70-foot tower in the direction closest to the Caribbean if this direction is very important to you. Doing so will, however, cause the pattern in the direction of the Far East to be affected on 10 and 15 meters. You have the modeling tools necessary to evaluate various configurations to achieve whatever is most important to you.

14.1.6 COMPROMISES

Because of limitations, most amateurs are never able to build their dream antenna system. This means that some compromises must be made. Do not, under any circumstances, compromise the safety of an antenna installation. Follow the manufacturer's recommendations for tower assembly, installation and accessories. Make sure that all hardware is being used within its ratings. (The ARRL document "Antenna Height and Communications Effectiveness" by Dean Straw, N6BV, and Jerry Hall, K1TD, may be of use in dealing with local regulatory agencies. It is available for downloading at **www.arrl.org/files/file/antplnr.pdf**.)

Guyed towers are frequently used by radio amateurs because they cost less than more complicated unguyed or freestanding towers with similar ratings. (See the chapter **Building Antenna Systems and Towers** for more information.) Guyed towers are fine for those who can climb or those with a friend who is willing to climb. But you may want to consider an antenna tower that folds over or one that cranks up (and down). Some towers crank up (and down) and fold over too. See **Figure 14.6**. That makes for convenient access to antennas for adjustments and maintenance without climbing. Crank-up towers also offer another advantage. They allow antennas to be lowered during periods of no operation, for aesthetic reasons, or during periods of high winds.

A well-designed monoband Yagi should outperform a multiband Yagi. In a monoband design the best adjustments can be made for gain, front-to-rear ratio (F/R) and matching, but only for a single band. In a multiband design, there are always tradeoffs in these properties for the ability to operate on more than one band. Nevertheless, a multiband antenna has many advantages over two or more single band antennas. A multiband antenna requires less heavy-duty hardware, requires only one feed line, takes up less space and it costs less.

Apartment dwellers face much greater limitations in their choice of antennas. For most, the possibility of a tower is only a dream. (One enterprising ham made arrangements to purchase a top-floor condominium from a developer. The arrangements were made before construction began, and the plans were altered to include a roof-top tower installation.) For apartment and condominium dwellers, the situation is still far from hopeless. The chapters **Stealth and Limited Space Antennas** and **Portable Antennas** present ideas for consideration.

14.1.7 SYSTEM DESIGN EXAMPLES

You can plan according to the preceding sections to put together modest or very large antenna systems. The process may sound intimidating but the hardest part is usually just

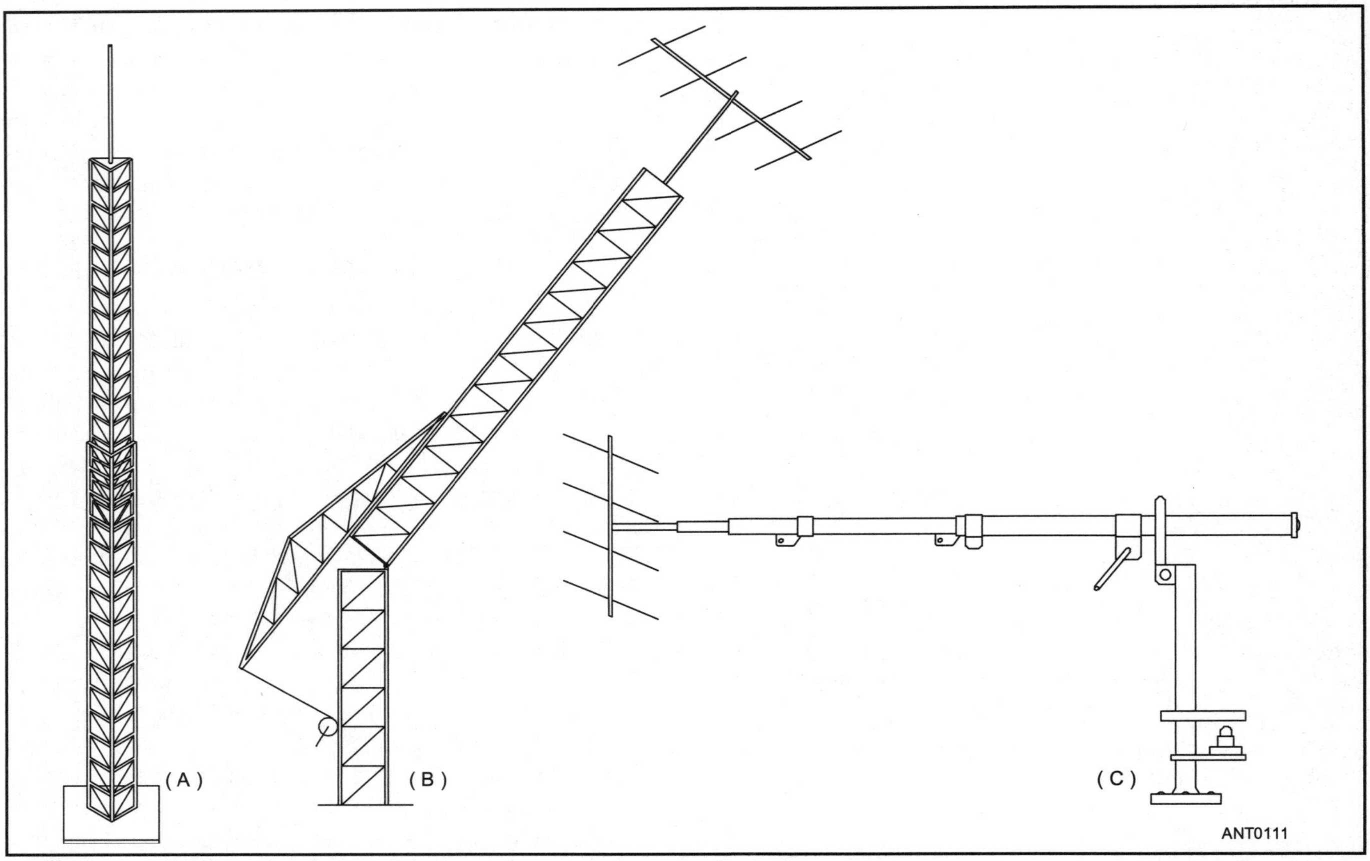

Figure 14.6 — Alternatives to a guyed tower are shown here. At A, the crank-up tower permits working on antennas at reduced height. It also allows antennas to be lowered during periods of no operation. Motor-driven versions are available. The fold-over tower at B and the combination at C permit working on antennas at ground level.

getting started! At this point, some simple examples might be instructive and encourage you to start planning.

Antenna System Example #1

What might a ham put together for antennas when he or she wants to try a little of everything, and has a modest budget? Let's suppose that the goals are (1) low cost, (2) no tower, (3) coverage of all HF bands and the repeater portion of one VHF band and (4) the possibility of working some DX.

After studying the pages of this book, the station owner decides to first put up a 135-foot center-fed antenna. High trees in the back yard will serve as supports to about 50 feet. This antenna will cover all the HF bands by using a balanced feeder and an antenna tuner. It should be good for DX contacts on 10 MHz and above and will probably work okay for DX contacts on the lower bands. However, her plan calls for a ground-mounted vertical and radial system for 3.5 and 7 MHz to enhance the DX possibilities on those bands. For VHF, a chimney-mounted vertical is included.

Antenna System Example #2

A licensed couple has bigger ambitions. Goals for their station are (1) a good setup for DX on 14, 21 and 28 MHz, (2) moderate cost, (3) one tower, (4) ability to work some DX on 1.8, 3.5 and 7 MHz, and (5) no need to cover the CW portion of the bands.

After considering the options, the couple decides to install a 65-foot guyed tower. A large commercial triband Yagi will be mounted on top of the tower. The center of a trap dipole tuned for the phone portion of the 3.5- and 7-MHz bands will be supported by a wooden yardarm installed at the 60-foot level of the tower, with ends drooping down to form an inverted-V. An inverted-L for 1.8 MHz starts near ground level and goes up to a similar yardarm on the opposite side of the tower. The horizontal portion of the inverted L runs away from the tower at right angles to the trap dipole. Later, the husband will experiment with sloping antennas for 3.5 MHz. If those experiments are not successful, a $\lambda/4$ vertical will be used on that band.

14.1.8 EMPIRICAL TESTING

Part of system design is "closing the loop" and evaluating the performance of what you have designed. If the performance is as expected, that validates your planning and design approach. If the performance isn't as expected, find out why and use that as a learning experience to improve your skills.

Unfortunately, many amateurs do not know how to evaluate performance scientifically or compare one antenna with another. Typically, they will put up one antenna and try it out on the air to see how it "gets out" in comparison with a previous antenna. This is obviously a very poor evaluation method because there is no way to know if the better or worse

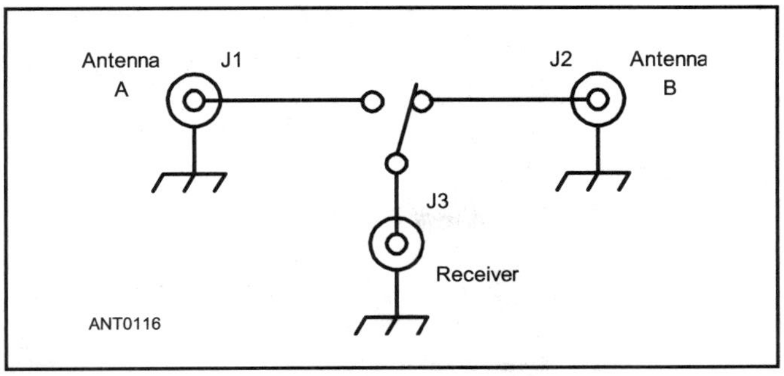

Figure 14.7 — When antennas are compared on fading signals, the time delay involved in disconnecting and reconnecting coaxial cables is too long for accurate measurements. A simple slide switch will do well for switching coaxial lines at HF. The four components can be mounted in a tin can or any small metal box. Leads should be short and direct. J1 through J3 are coaxial connectors.

reports are caused by changing band conditions, different S meter characteristics or any of several other factors that could influence the reports received.

Many times the difference between two antennas or between two different locations for identical antennas amounts to only a few decibels, a difference that is hard to discern unless instantaneous switching between the two is possible. Those few decibels are not important under strong signal conditions, of course, but when the going gets rough a few dB can make the difference between solid copy and no possibility of real communication.

Very little in the way of test equipment is needed for casual antenna evaluation, other than a communications receiver. You can even do a qualitative comparison by ear, if you can switch antennas instantaneously. Differences of less than 2 dB, however, are still hard to discern. The same is true of S meter readings. Signal strength differences of less than a decibel are usually difficult to see. If you want to measure that last fraction of a decibel, you should use a good ac voltmeter at the receiver audio output (with the AGC turned off).

In order to compare two antennas, switching the coaxial transmission line from one to the other is necessary. No elaborate coaxial switch is needed; even a simple double-throw toggle or slide switch will provide more than 40 dB of isolation at HF. See **Figure 14.7**. Switching by means of manually connecting and disconnecting coaxial lines is not recommended because that takes too long. Fading can cause signal-strength changes during the changeover interval.

Whatever difference shows up in the strength of the received signal will be the difference in performance between the two antennas in the direction of that signal. For this test to be valid, both antennas must have nearly the same feed point impedance, a condition that is reasonably well met if the SWR is below 2:1 on both antennas.

On ionospheric propagated signals (sky wave) there will be constant fading, and for a valid comparison it will be necessary to take an average of the difference between the two antennas. Occasionally, the inferior antenna will deliver a stronger signal to the receiver, but in the long run the law of averages will put the better antenna ahead.

Of course with a ground-wave signal, such as that from a station across town, there will be no fading problems. A ground-wave signal will enable the operator to properly evaluate the antenna under test in the direction of the source. The results will be valid for ionospheric-propagated signals at low elevation angles in that direction. On 28 MHz, all sky-wave signals arrive and leave at low angles. But on the lower bands, particularly 3.5 and 7 MHz, we often use signals propagated at high elevation angles, almost up to the zenith. For these angles a ground-wave test between local stations may not provide a proper evaluation of the antenna, and use of sky wave signals becomes necessary.

14.2 PROPAGATION AND COVERAGE

The section "Elevation Angles for HF Communication" in the **Radio Wave Propagation** chapter is an excellent introduction to the use of propagation prediction software such as *IONCAP* and *VOACAP* to assess the coverage of an HF antenna at different frequencies for a wide range of solar conditions. This book's downloadable supplemental information includes a set of elevation angle statistics derived from these tools that you can use when designing your antenna system. The author of that elevation angle data and the editor of this book's previous edition, Dean Straw, N6BV, compiled a new and expanded set of data that is available from Radioware (**www.radio-ware.com**) at reasonable cost. The data set has been expanded to more than 240 locations around the world in all 40 CQ zones and covers the five primary HF amateur bands (80 through 10 meters) for 24 hours at six levels of solar activity. These tables show signal strength in S units for easier use by amateurs.

As you plan your antenna system, it is strongly recommended that you become familiar with at least one propagation prediction tool and undertake a study of propagation at your location to the areas of the world with which you want to communicate. Two descriptions of using propagation information are presented as examples of how understanding propagation can inform your antenna system design choices.

14.2.1 ELEVATION ANGLES FOR LOW-BAND DXING

In the chapter **Effects of Ground**, the importance was noted of matching the elevation response of your antennas as closely as possible to the range of elevation angles needed for communication with desired geographic areas. **Figure 14.8** shows the statistical 40 meter elevation angles needed over the entire 11-year solar cycle to cover the path from Boston, Massachusetts, to all of Europe. These angles range from 1° (at 9.6% of the time when the 40 meter band is open to Europe) to 28° (at 0.3% of the time). Creating an antenna

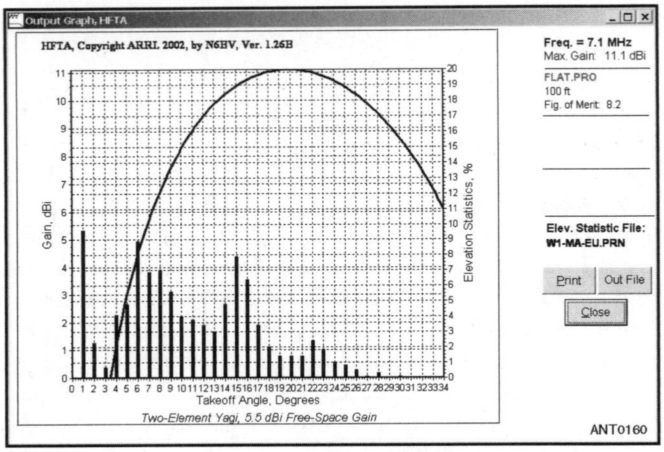

Figure 14.8 — Screen capture from HFTA (HF Terrain Assessment) program showing elevation response for 100-foot high dipole over flat ground on 7.1 MHz, with bar-graph overlay of the statistical elevation angles needed over the whole 11-year solar cycle from New England (Boston) to all of Europe. Even a 100-foot high antenna cannot cover all the necessary angles.

system that concentrates the radiated energy at these low elevation angles is crucial to work DX on the bands below 10 MHz.

Figure 14.8 also overlays the elevation pattern response of a 100-foot high flattop dipole on the elevation-angle statistics, illustrating that even at this height the coverage is hardly optimum to cover all the necessary elevation angles. While Figure 14.8 is dramatic in its own right, the data can be viewed in another way that emphasizes even more the importance of low elevation angles. **Figure 14.9** plots the *cumulative distribution function*, the total percentage of time 40 meters is open from Boston to Europe, at or below each elevation angle. For example, Figure 14.9 says that 40 meters is open to Europe from Boston 50% of the time at an elevation angle of 9° or less. The band is open 90% of the time at an elevation angle of 19° or less.

Figure 14.10 plots the 40 meter elevation-angle data for six major geographic areas around the world from Boston. In general, the overall range of elevation angles for far-distant locations is smaller, and the angles are lower than for closer-in areas. For example, from Boston to southern Asia (India), 50% of the time the takeoff angles are 4° or less. On the path to Japan from Boston, the takeoff angles is less than or equal to 6° about 70% of the time. These are low angles indeed.

Figure 14.11 shows similar data for the 40 meter band from San Francisco, California, to the rest of the world. The path to southern Africa from the US West Coast is a very long-distance path, open some 65% of the time it is open at angles of 2° or less! The 40 meter path to Japan involves takeoff angles of 10° or less more than 50% of the time. If you are fortunate enough to have a 100-foot high flattop dipole for 40 meters, at a takeoff angle of 10° the response would be down about 3 dB from its peak level at 20°. At an elevation angle of 5° the response would be about 8 dB down from peak. You can see why the California stations located on mountain tops do best on 40 meters for DXing.

Figure 14.12 shows the same percentage-of-time data for the 80 meter band from Boston to the world. Into Europe from Boston, the 80 meter elevation angle is 13° or less more than 50% of the time. Into Japan from Boston, 90% of the time the band is open is at a takeoff angle of 13° or less. (Note

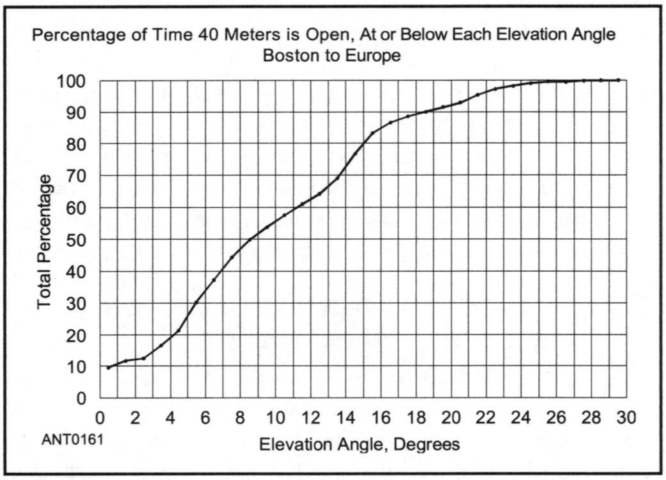

Figure 14.9 — Another way of looking at the elevation statistics from Figure 14.8. This shows the percentage of time the 40 meter band is open, at or below each elevation angle, on the path from Boston to Europe. For example, the band is open 50% of the time at an angle of 9° or lower. It is open 90% of the time at an angle of 19° or lower.

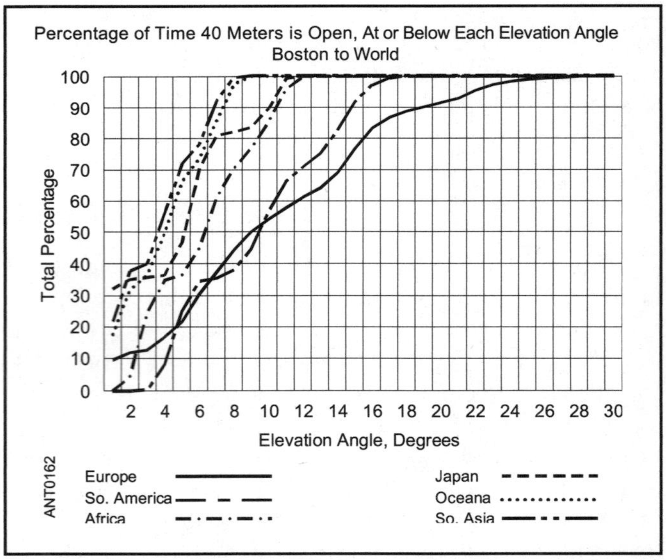

Figure 14.10 — The percentage of time the 40 meter band is open, at or below each elevation angle, for various DX paths from Boston: to Europe, South America, southern Africa, Japan, Oceania and south Asia. The angles are predominantly quite low. For example, on the path from Boston to Japan, 90% of the time when the 40 meter band is open, it is open at elevation angles less than or equal to 10°. Achieving good performance at these low takeoff angles requires very high horizontally polarized antennas, or efficient vertically polarized antennas.

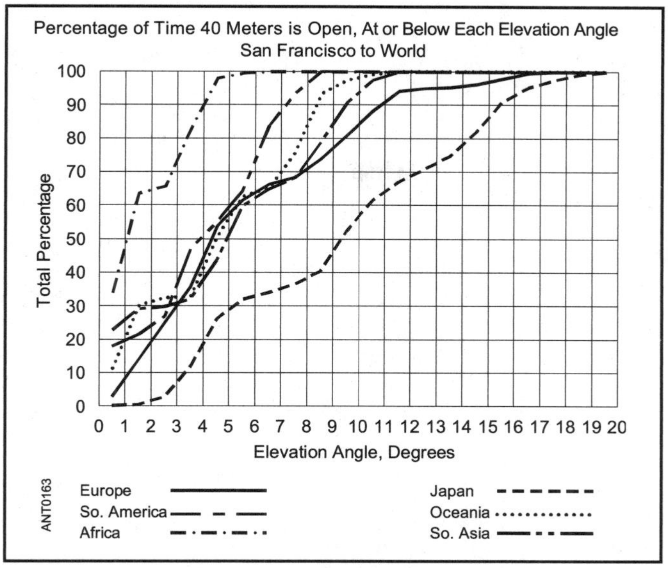

Figure 14.11 — The 40 meter statistics from the West Coast: from San Francisco to the rest of the DX world. Here, 90% of the time the path to Europe is open, it is at takeoff angles less than or equal to 11°. No wonder the hams living on mountain tops do best into Europe from the West Coast.

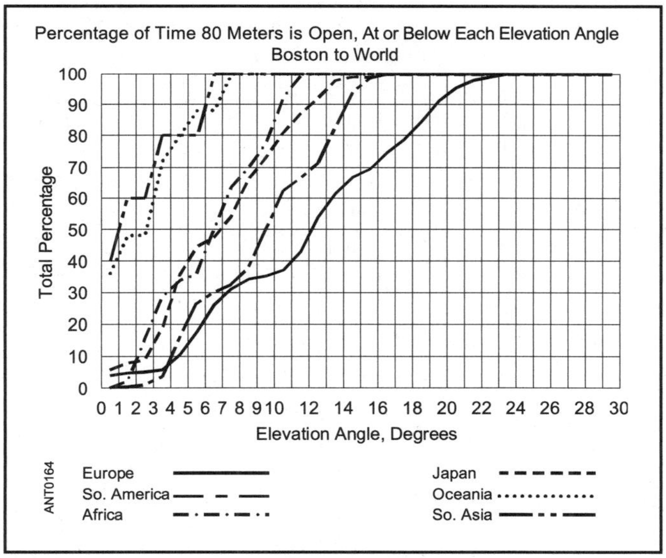

Figure 14.12 — The situation on 80 meters from Boston to the rest of the DX world. Into Europe, 90% of the time the elevation angle is less than or equal to 20°. Into Japan from Boston, 90% of the time the angle is less than or equal to 12°.

that these elevation statistics are computed for "undisturbed" ionospheric conditions. There are times when the incoming angles are affected by geomagnetic storms, and generally speaking the elevation angles rise under these conditions.)

Figure 14.13 shows the 80 meter data from San Francisco to the world. Low elevation angles dominate in this graph and high horizontal antennas would be necessary to optimal coverage. In fact, 50% of the time for all paths, the elevation angle is less than 10°.

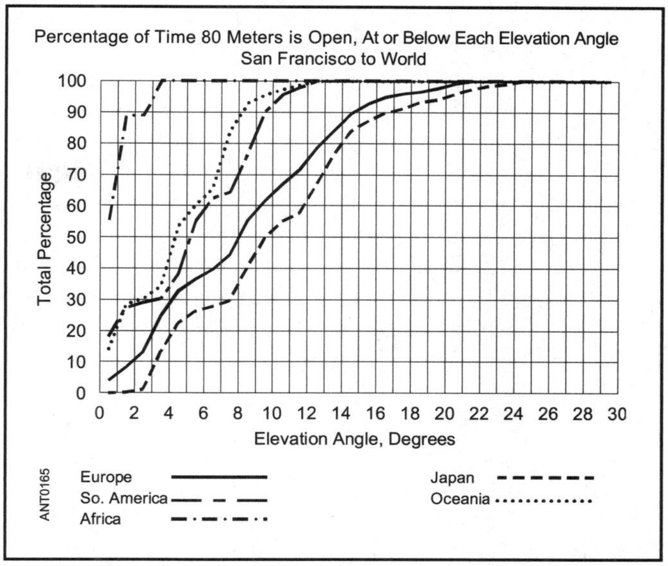

Figure 14.13 — From San Francisco to the rest of the world on 80 meters: 90% of the time on the path to Japan, the takeoff angle is less than or equal to 17°; 50% of the time the angle is less than or equal to 10°; 25% of the time the angle is less than or equal to 6°. A horizontally polarized antenna would have to be 600 feet above flat ground to be optimum at 6°!

14.2.2 NVIS COMMUNICATION

Not all hams are interested in working stations thousands of miles from them. Traffic handlers and rag chewers may, in fact, only be interested in *nearby* communications — perhaps out to 600 miles from their location. In such cases, the low elevation angles needed for effective DXing may be completely ineffective in providing the required short-range coverage.

For example, a ham in Boston may want to talk with his brother-in-law in Cleveland, Ohio, a path that is just over 550 miles away. Or an operator in Buffalo, New York, may be the net control station (NCS) for a regional net involving the states of New York and New Jersey. She needs to cover distances up to about 300 miles away.

Depending on the time of day, the most appropriate ham frequencies needed for nearby communications are the 40 and 80/75 meter bands, with 160 meters also a possibility during the night hours, particularly during low portions of the sunspot cycle. The elevation angles involved in such nearby distances are usually high, even almost directly overhead for distances beyond ground-wave coverage (which may be as short as a few miles on 40 meters). For example, the distance between the Massachusetts cities of Boston and Worcester is about 40 miles. On 40 meters, 40 miles is beyond ground-wave coverage. So you will need sky-wave signals that use the ionosphere to communicate between these two cities, where the elevation angle is 83° — very nearly straight up.

Hams using vertical antennas for communications with nearby stations may well find that their signals will be below the noise level typical on the lower bands, especially if they aren't running maximum legal power. Such relatively short-range paths involve what is called *NVIS*, "Near Vertical Incidence Skywave," a fancy name for HF communication systems covering nearby geographic areas. The US military discusses NVIS out to about 500 miles, encompassing the territory a brigade might cover. Elevation angles needed to cover distances from 0 to 500 miles range from about 40° to 90°. This also covers the circumstances involved in amateur communications, particularly in emergency situations. (An Internet group on NVIS, **groups.yahoo.com/neo/groups/NVIS/info**, focuses on antenna designs and techniques for NVIS communication.)

For the interested reader, a study of the use of NVIS communication is presented in "Near Vertical Incidence Skywave Propagation: Elevation Angles and Optimum Antenna Height for Horizontal Dipole Antennas" in the February 2015 issue of *IEEE Antennas and Propagation Magazine* by Ben Witvliet, PA5BW, and other researchers.

The following section is adapted from the article "What's the Deal About NVIS?" by Dean Straw, N6BV, that appeared in December 2005 *QST*. This article used an example of a hypothetical earthquake in San Francisco to analyze HF emergency communication requirements.

Table 14.1
Average Elevation Angles for Target Destinations from San Francisco

Location	*Distance (Miles)*	*Average Elevation Angle (Degrees)*
San Jose, CA	43	80
Sacramento, CA	75	78
Fresno, CA	160	63
Reno, NV	185	60
Los Angeles	350	44
San Diego	450	42
Portland, OR	530	30
Denver, CO	950	18
Dallas, TX	1500	8

Ham Radio Response in Natural Disasters

One of San Francisco's somewhat less endearing nicknames is "the city that waits to die." When the *Big Earthquake* does come, you can be assured that all the cell phones and the land-line telephones will be totally jammed, making calling in or out of the San Francisco Bay Area virtually impossible. The same thing occurred in Manhattan on September 11, 2001. The Internet will also be severely affected throughout northern California because of its trunking via the facilities of the telephone network. Commercial electricity will be out in wide areas because power lines will be down.

If the repeaters on the hills around the San Francisco Bay Area haven't been damaged by the shaking itself, there will be some ham VHF/UHF voice coverage in the intermediate area, at least until the backup batteries run down. But connecting to the dysfunctional telephone system will be difficult at best through amateur repeaters.

With little or no telephone coverage, an obvious need for ham radio communications to aid disaster relief would be from San Francisco to Sacramento, the state capital. Sacramento is 75 miles northeast of the Bay Area, well outside VHF/UHF coverage, so amateur HF will be required on this radio circuit. On-the-ground communications directly between emergency personnel (including the armed-forces personnel who will be brought into the rescue and rebuilding effort) will often be difficult on VHF/UHF since San Francisco is a hilly place. So HF will probably be needed even for short distance, operator-to-operator or operator-to-communications center work. Throughout the city, portable HF stations will have to be quickly set up and staffed to provide such communications.

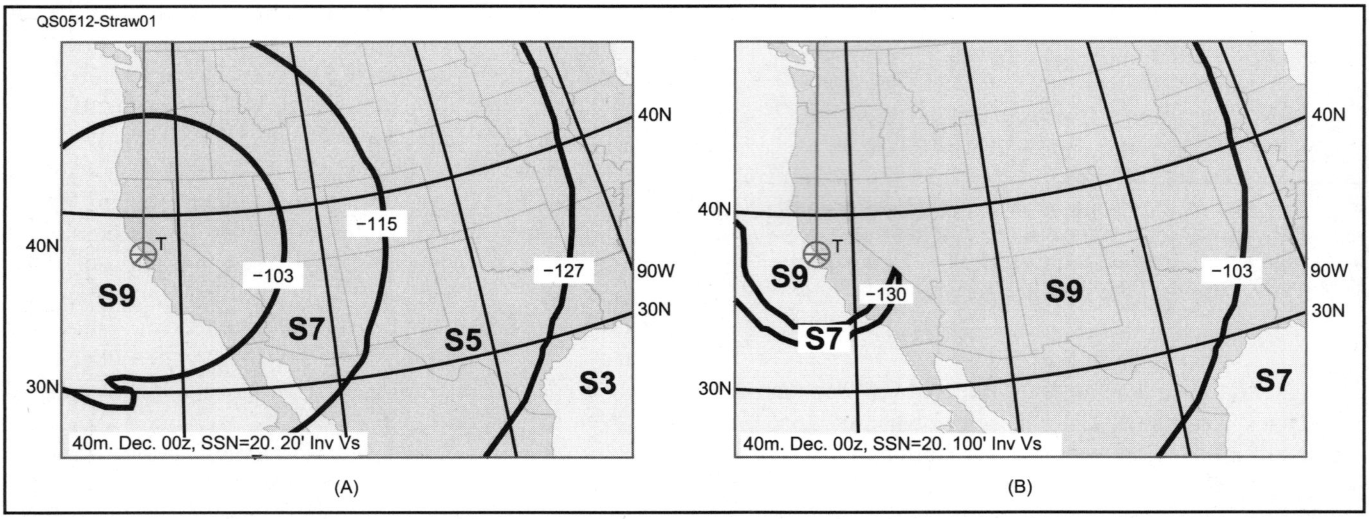

Figure 14.14 — At A, Predicted 40 meter geographic coverage plot for a 100 W transmitter in December at 0000 UTC (near sunset), for a SSN (Smoothed Sunspot Number) of 20. The antennas used are 20-foot-high inverted V dipoles. At B, 40 meter coverage for same date and time, but for 100-foot-high flattop dipoles. Most of California is well covered with S9 signals in both cases, but there is more susceptibility in the higher dipole case to thunderstorm crashes coming from outside California, for example from Arizona or even Texas. Such noise can interfere with communications inside California.

Hams used to half jokingly call short range HF communications on 40 and 80 meters "cloud warming." This is an apt description, because the takeoff angles needed to launch HF signals up into the ionosphere and then down again to a nearby station are almost directly upward. **Table 14.1** lists the distance and takeoff angles from San Francisco to various cities around the western part of the USA. The distance between San Francisco and Sacramento is about 75 miles, and the optimum takeoff angle is about 78°. Launching such a high-angle signal is best done using horizontally polarized antennas mounted relatively close to the ground, such as low dipoles.

Geographic Coverage for NVIS

Figure 14.14A shows the geographic area coverage around San Francisco for a 100-W station on 7.2 MHz using an inverted V dipole. The center of this antenna is 20 feet above flat ground and the ends are 8 feet high. An actual implementation of such an antenna could be as an 80 meter inverted V, fed in parallel with a 40 meter inverted V dipole at a 90° angle. See **Figure 14.15**. The 8-foot height puts the ends high enough to prevent RF burns to humans (or most animals). The low height of the antenna above ground means that the azimuthal pattern is omnidirectional for high elevation angles.

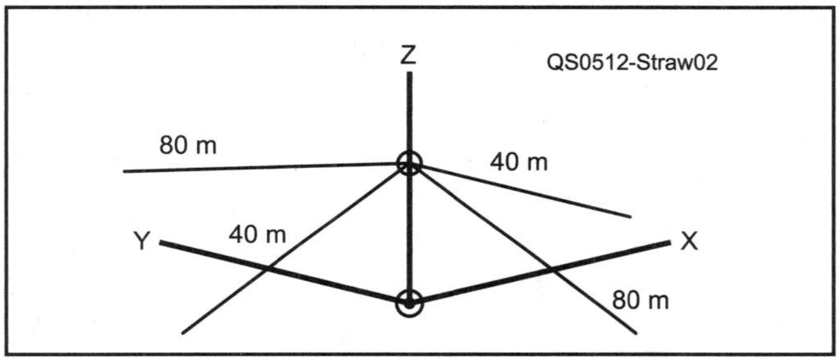

Figure 14.15 — Layout for two band inverted V dipoles for 40 and 80 meters. The two dipoles are fed together at the center and are laid out at right angles to each other to minimize interaction between them. Each end of both dipoles is kept 8 feet above ground for personal safety.

Figure 14.14 was generated using the *VOAAREA* program, part of the *VOACAP* propagation-prediction suite, for the month of December. This was for 0000 UTC, close to sundown, for a low period of solar activity (Smoothed Sunspot Number, SSN of 20). The receiving stations were also assumed to be using identical inverted-V dipoles.

You can see that almost the whole state of California is covered with S9 signals, minus only a thin slice of land near the Mexican border in the southeast portion of the state, where the signal drops to S7. Signals from Texas are predicted to be only S5 or less in strength. Signals (or thunderstorm static) coming from, say, Louisiana would be several S units weaker than signals from central Texas.

Now take a look at Figure 14.14B. Here, the date, time and solar conditions remain the same, but now the antennas are 100-foot high flattop dipoles. California is still blanketed with S9 signals, save for an interesting crescent-shaped slice near Los Angeles, where the signal drops down to S7. Close investigation of this intriguing drop in signal strength reveals that the necessary elevation angle, 44°, from San Francisco to this part of southern California falls in the first null of the 100-foot high antenna's elevation pattern. See **Figure 14.16**, which shows the elevation patterns for five 40 meter antennas at different heights. In the null at a 44° takeoff angle, the 100-foot high dipole is just about equal to a 2-foot high dipole. We'll discuss 2-foot high dipoles in more detail later.

For most of California, the problem with 100-foot high 40 meter antennas is that interfering signals from Texas, Colorado or Washington State will *also* be S9 in San Francisco. So will static crashes coming from thunderstorms

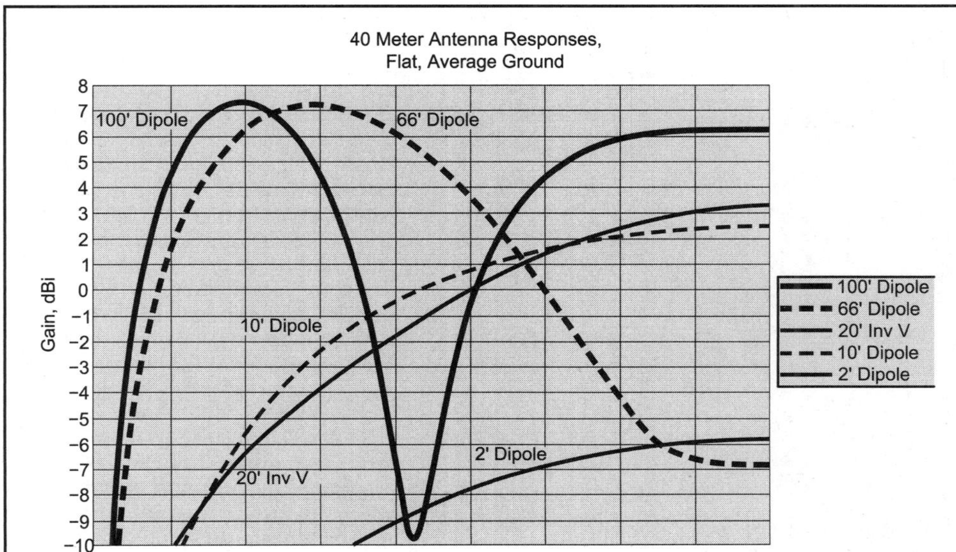

Figure 14.16 — Elevation plots for different 40 meter antennas above flat ground with average ground characteristics (5 mS/m conductivity and dielectric constant of 13). The 10-foot-high flattop dipole and the 20 foot-high inverted V dipoles both have close to the same characteristics. Note that there is a null in the response of the 100-foot-high flattop dipole at a 42° elevation angle. The gain there is roughly that of a 2 foot-high dipole!

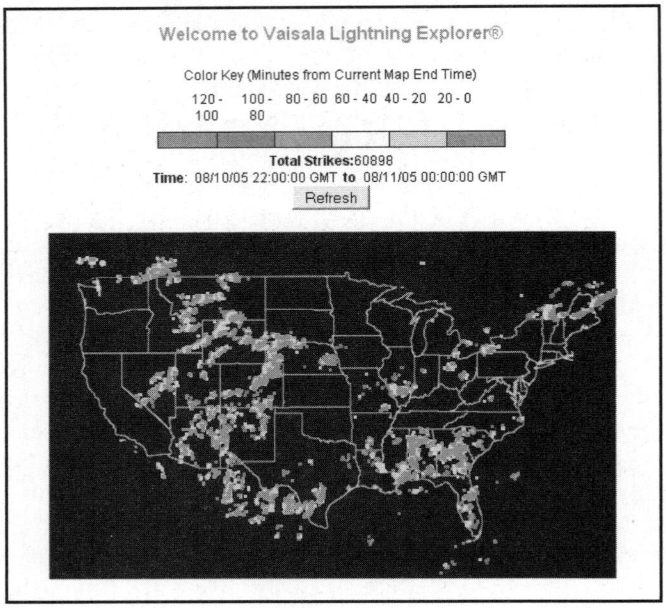

Figure 14.17 — The distribution of lightning strikes across the USA for August 10, 2005 from 2200 to 0000 UTC, in the afternoon California time. There are lots of lightning strikes in the US during the summer — 60,898 of them in this two-hour period! (Courtesy Vaisala Lightning Explorer.)

all over the West and much of the Gulf Coast. See **Figure 14.17**, which shows a typical distribution of thunderstorms across the US in the late afternoon, California time, in mid-August. There certainly are a lot of thunderstorms raging around the country in the summer.

The signal-to-noise and signal-to-interference ratios for a 20-foot high inverted V dipole will be superior for medium-range distances, say out to 500 miles from the center, compared to a 100-foot high antenna. The 20-foot high antenna can discriminate against medium-angle thunderstorm noise in the late afternoon coming from the Arizona desert, although it wouldn't help much for thunderstorms in the Sierra Nevada in central Nevada, which are arriving in San Francisco at high angles, along with the desired NVIS signals.

This is the essence of what NVIS means. NVIS exploits the difference in elevation pattern responses of low horizontally polarized antennas compared to higher horizontal antennas, or even verticals. Over the years, many hams have been lead to believe that higher is always better. This is not quite so true for consistent coverage of medium or short distance signals!

If NVIS only involved putting up a low horizontally polarized antenna on 40 meters the story would end here. However, real cloud warming is more complicated. It also involves the intelligent choice of more than just one operating frequency to achieve reliable all day, all-night communications coverage.

Figure 14.18 shows the signal strength predicted using *VOACAP* for the 350-mile path from San Francisco to Los Angeles for the month of December for a period of low solar activity (SSN of 20). The antennas used in this case are 10-foot high dipoles, just for some variety. These act almost like 20-foot high Inverted V dipoles. December at a low SSN was chosen as a worst-case scenario because the *winter solstice* occurs on December 21. This is the day that has the fewest hours of daylight in the year. (Contrast this with the *summer solstice*, on June 21, which has the most hours of daylight in the year.) Note that the upper signal limit in Figure 14.18 is "S10" — a fictitious quantity that allows easier graphing. S10 is equivalent to S9+, or at least S9+10 dB.

The 40 meter curve in Figure 14.18 shows that the MUF (maximum usable frequency) actually drops below the 7.2 MHz amateur band after sunset. The signal becomes

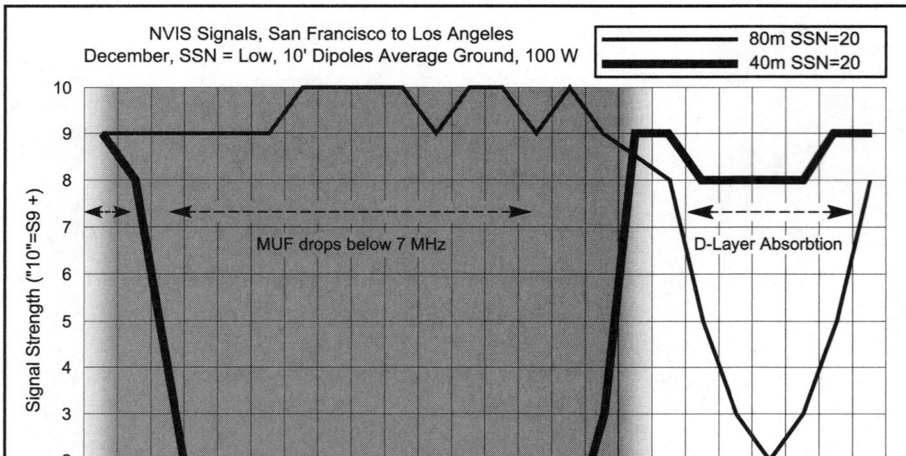

Figure 14.18 — VOACAP calculations for a 350 mile path from San Francisco to Los Angeles, using 10 foot-high flattop dipoles. This plot shows the signal strength in S units ("S10" = S9+10) for a worst-case month/SSN combination — winter solstice, in December, for a low level of solar activity (SSN = 20). The 40 meter signal drops to a very low level during the night because the MUF drops well below 7.2 MHz. The 80 meter signal drops in the afternoon because of D-layer absorption. For 24-hour communications on this path, the rule of thumb is to select 40 meters during the day and 80 meters during the night.

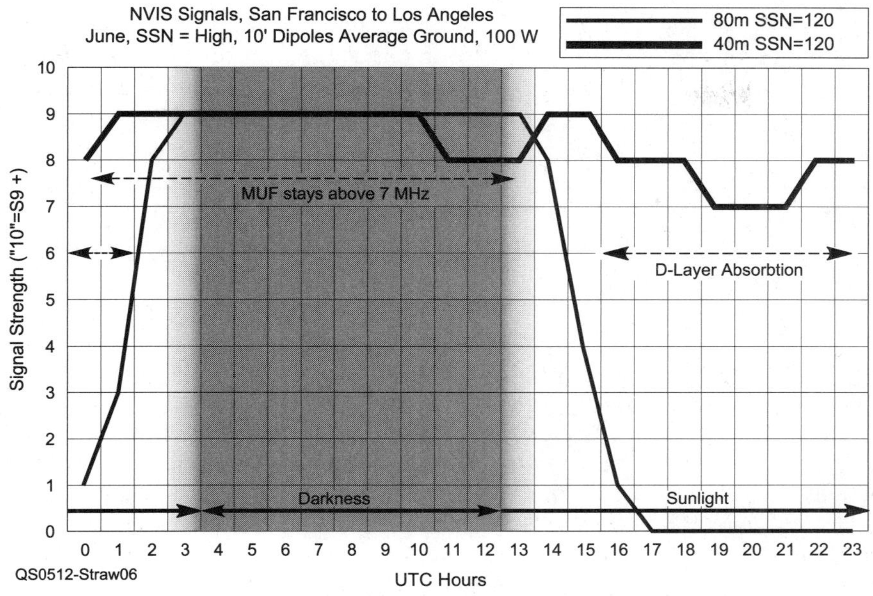

Figure 14.19 — Signal strengths for the San Francisco to Los Angeles path for a worst-case month/SSN combination — summer solstice, in June, for a high level of solar activity (SSN = 120). Now 80 meters drops out more dramatically during the daylight hours, due to increased D-layer absorption. At this high level of solar activity, 40 meters remains open 24 hours with reasonable signal levels. However, the NVIS rule-of-thumb still holds: Use 40 meters during the day; 80 meters at night.

quite weak for about 14 hours during the night, from about 0300 to 1700 UTC. In a period of low solar activity the 40 meter band thus becomes strictly a *daytime band* on this medium-distance path.

The 80 meter curve in Figure 14.18 shows strong signals after dusk, through the night and up until about an hour after sunrise. After sunrise, 80 meters starts to suffer absorption in the D layer of the ionosphere and hence the signal strength drops. Here, 80 meters is a true *nighttime band.*

Let's see what happens from San Francisco to Los Angeles during a period of high solar activity (SSN of 120) during the summer solstice in June. **Figure 14.19** shows that 40 meters now stays open all hours of the day due to the greater number of hours of sunlight in June and because the ionosphere becomes more highly ionized by higher solar activity. Meanwhile, 80 meters still remains a nighttime band during these conditions on this path.

Now, let's look at a shorter-distance path — our 75-mile emergency communications path from San Francisco to Sacramento. We'll again use June during the summer solstice, at a high level of solar activity (SSN of 120) because this represents another worst-case scenario. **Figure 14.20** shows that 40 meters remains open on this path all day, dropping to a lower signal level just before sunrise. At sunrise, the MUF drops close to 7.2 MHz. 80 meters is still mainly a nighttime band to Sacramento, even though it does

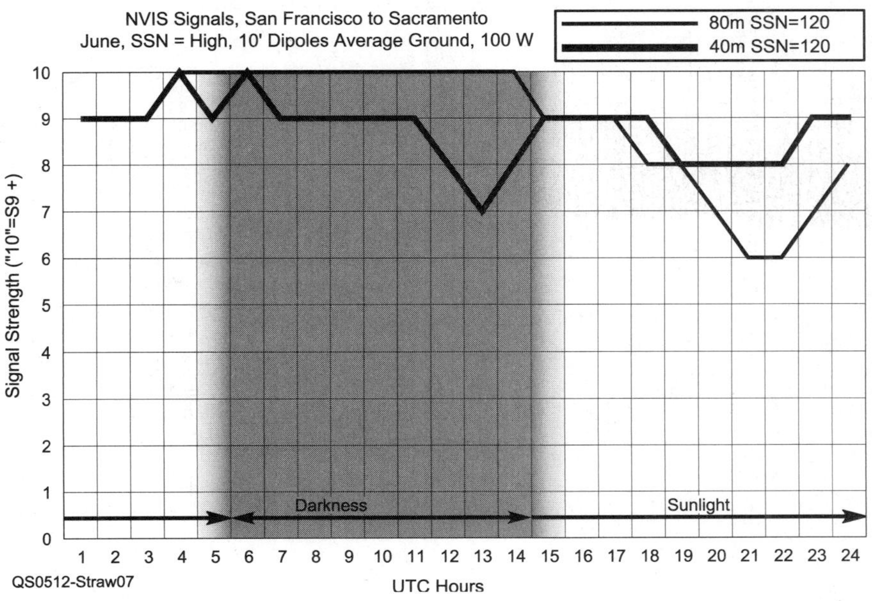

Figure 14.20 — Signal strengths for a 75 mile path — San Francisco to Sacramento. This is for June and SSN = 120. Either band could be used successfully over the full 24-hour period because signal levels are always higher than S6. But the simple NVIS rule-of-thumb still holds: Use 40 meters during the day; 80 meters at night. This simplifies giving instructions to operators unaccustomed to the use of HF.

yield workable signal levels even during the daylight hours. However, 40 meters is better from 1200 to 0400 UTC, so 40 would be still the right daytime band for this path during the day.

Choosing the Right NVIS Frequency

You can see that a pattern is developing here for efficient NVIS short/medium-distance communications out to 500 miles:

- You should pick a frequency on 40 meters during the day.
- You should pick a frequency on 80 meters during the night.
- You should choose an antenna that emphasizes moderate to high elevation angles, from 40° to almost directly overhead at 90°.

"What about 60 meters?" you might ask. The characteristics on 60 meters fall in between 40 and 80 meters, although it resembles 40 meters more closely. With characteristics close to that of 40, but with only five channels available and a 50-W power limit, the 60 meter band is of low utility for serious NVIS use.

What about 160 meters? For 100-W level radios, even at the worst-case month or during low solar activity, the critical frequency doesn't fall below 3.8 MHz often enough to destroy the ability to communicate, even for short distances. That is a relief, considering that installing a 160 meter half-wave dipole involves a 255-foot wingspan, and it would need to be elevated at least 30 feet in the center. A short loaded vertical such as a 160 meter mobile whip would have poor response at the high elevation angles needed for NVIS. You could probably put a monster 160 meter horizontal dipole up at a permanent location, but hauling such a thing around in the field would not be an easy task.

NVIS Strategy

You could pose the question about whether NVIS is an operating *mode* or whether it is actually an operating *strategy*. We maintain that NVIS is a strategy. It involves choosing both appropriate frequencies and then appropriate antennas for those frequencies. Figure 14.20 does show that on short-distance paths, such as between San Francisco and Sacramento, you could stay on 80 meters all day and night. But if you have to give a single rule-of-thumb to operators who are not very experienced at operating HF, we would tell them to operate on the higher frequency band during the day and on the lower frequency band at night.

Antenna Height for NVIS

Some NVIS aficionados have advocated placing dipoles only a few feet over ground, something akin to saying, "If low is good for NVIS, then lower must be even better." Now we are not claiming that a very low antenna *won't* work in specific instances — for example, covering a small state such as Rhode Island or even just the San Francisco Bay Area.

It certainly is convenient to mount a 40 meter dipole on some 2-foot high red traffic cones! You should be very skeptical, however, about the ability of such antennas to cover all of a large state, such as California or Texas, especially on 80 meters. **Figure 14.21** shows the computed elevation responses for a number of 80 meter antennas, including a 2-foot-high dipole. (In addition, ground losses increase dramatically as the antenna height is reduced. Mounting an antenna lower than 10 feet above ground is not recommended for safety reasons, as well — *Ed.*)

Figure 14.22B shows the 80 meter geographic coverage plot for 2-foot-high flattop dipoles, compared with the plot in Figure 14.22A for 20-foot-high inverted V dipoles on both ends of the path. The 2-foot-high dipoles produce about two S-units less signal across all of California than the 20-foot-high inverted V dipoles, at 0300 UTC in December, with an SSN of 20. The reason is that a low dipole will suffer more losses in the ground under it.

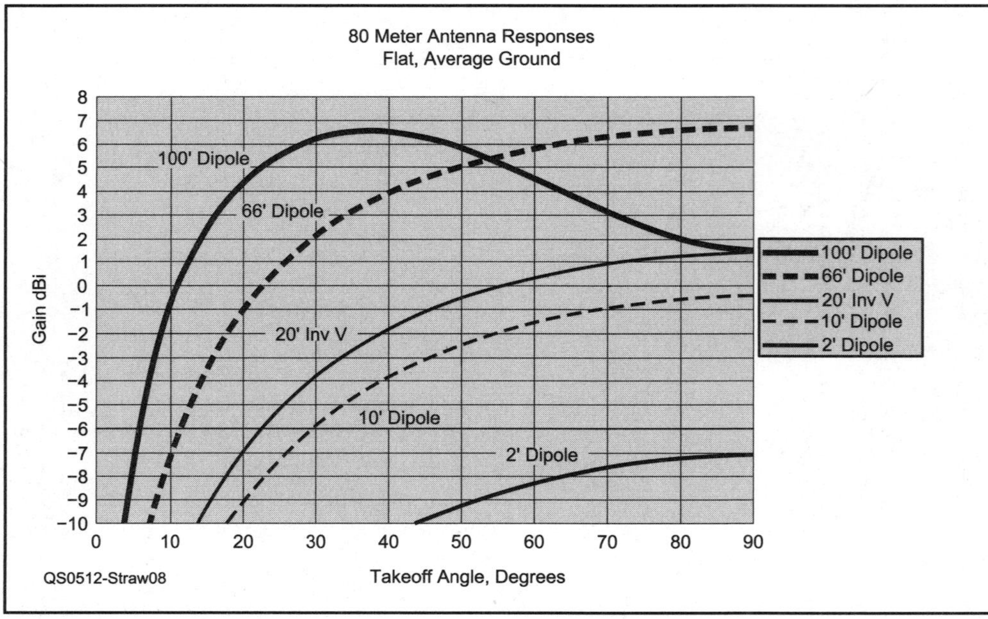

Figure 14.21 — Elevation response patterns for 80 meter antennas over average soil. The shapes track each other rather well, remaining parallel for heights from 2 to 66 feet over flat ground. The 2 foot dipole is substantially down, about 9 dB, from the 20 foot inverted V dipole at all angles.

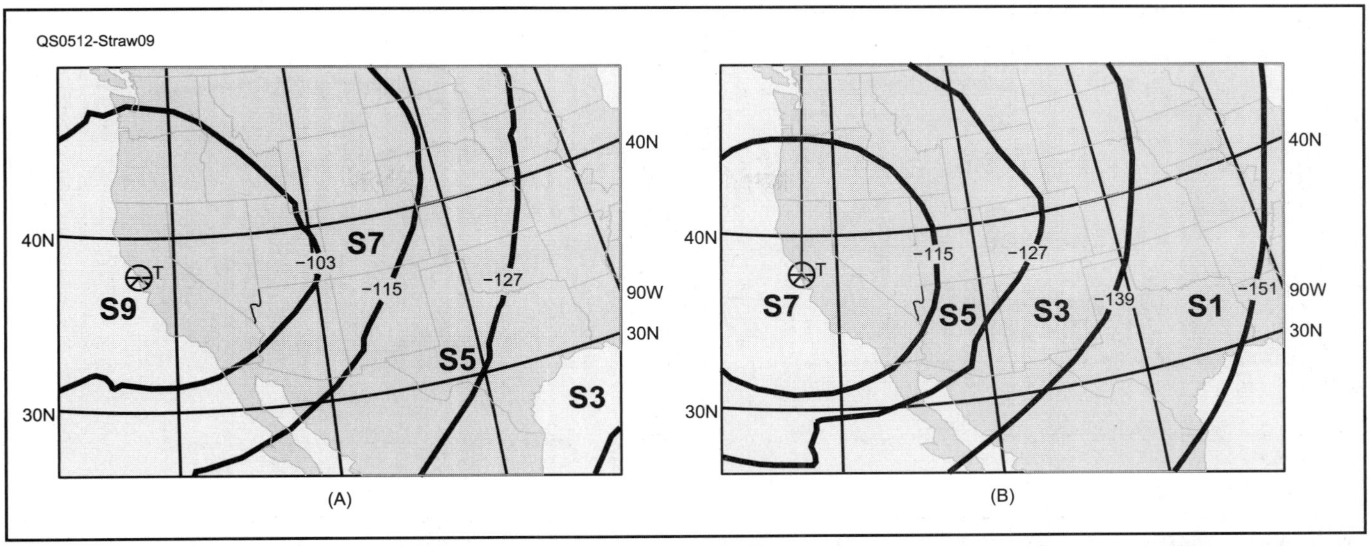

Figure 14.22 — Geographic coverage plots for December, SSN = 20, 0300 UTC. At A, antennas are 20-foot-high inverted V dipoles over Average soil. At B, antennas are 2-foot-high flattop dipoles over Average soil. The response for the 2-foot-high antennas is down about 2 S Units, 8 to 12 dB for a typical communications receiver.

The differential between California signals and possible interfering signals from, say, New Mexico, is predicted to be four S-units, the same as it is for the higher inverted V dipole at 20 feet. Thus there is no real advantage in terms of signal-to-interference ratio or signal-to-noise ratio (for thunderstorm static crashes) for either height. This is because the shape of all the response curves in Figure 14.21 below 20 feet essentially track each other in parallel.

However, the lower the antenna, the lower the transmitted signal strength. Physics remain physics. And if you are in an emergency situation operating on batteries, you could reduce power from 100 W to 10 W with a 20-foot high inverted-V antenna and still maintain the same signal strength as a 2-foot high dipole at 100 W.

Low NVIS Antennas and Local Power Line Noise

Some advocates of really low antennas have stated that the received noise is much lower than that received from higher antennas, and this therefore leads to better signal-to-noise ratios (SNR). How much this is true depends on the source of the noise. If the noise comes from distant thunderstorms, then the SNR advantage going to a 2-foot antenna from a 20-foot-high one is insignificant, as Figure 14.22 indicates.

If noise is from an arcing insulator on a HV power line half a mile away, that noise will arrive at the antenna as a ground-wave signal. We calculate that the 2-foot antenna receives 4.4 dB less noise by ground-wave than a 20-foot-high inverted V dipole. However, at an incoming elevation angle of 45° — suitable for a signal going from Los Angeles to San Francisco — the signal would be down 7.1 dB on the low dipole compared to the higher antenna. The net loss in SNR for the 2-foot-high dipole is thus 7.1– 4.4 or 2.7 dB. Close, but no cigar. Summarizing about really low NVIS antennas:

- A 2-foot-high dipole yields weaker signals, but without an SNR advantage compared to its more elevated brethren.
- A 2-foot-high dipole is a lot easier to trip over at night. We would call this a "knee biter."
- You (and your dog) can easily get RF burns from an antenna that is only 2 feet off the ground.

This is not a winning strategy to make friends or QSOs, it seems. But still, a really low dipole may serve your short-range communication needs just fine. But remember, that just as "higher is better" isn't universally true for NVIS (or even longer range) applications, "lower is better" isn't a panacea either.

Elevation Angles for Moderate Distances on 75/80 Meters

Figure 14.23 shows the elevation angles statistics for a 75 meter, 550-mile path from Boston to Cleveland, together with overlays of the elevation patterns for several different types of antennas. These elevation statistics cover all parts of the 11-year solar cycle for this path. The responses for the popular G5RV antenna (see the **Multiband Antennas** chapter) are shown for two different heights above flat ground: 50 and 100 feet. An 80 meter half-wave sloper ("full sloper") and an 80 meter ground-plane antenna are also shown. All antenna patterns are for "average ground" constants of 5 mS/m conductivity and a dielectric constant of 13.

At the statistically most significant takeoff angles around 50°, the two horizontally polarized G5RV antennas are about equal. At the second-highest elevation peak near 30°, the 100-foot G5RV has about a 4-dB advantage over its lower counterpart. The full sloper has comparable performance to the 100-foot high G5RV from 1° to about 20° and then gradually rises to its peak at angles higher than 70°. The full sloper is superior to the 50-foot horizontal G5RV at low takeoff elevation angles. The 80 meter ground plane has a deep null directly overhead. At an elevation angle of 70° it is down

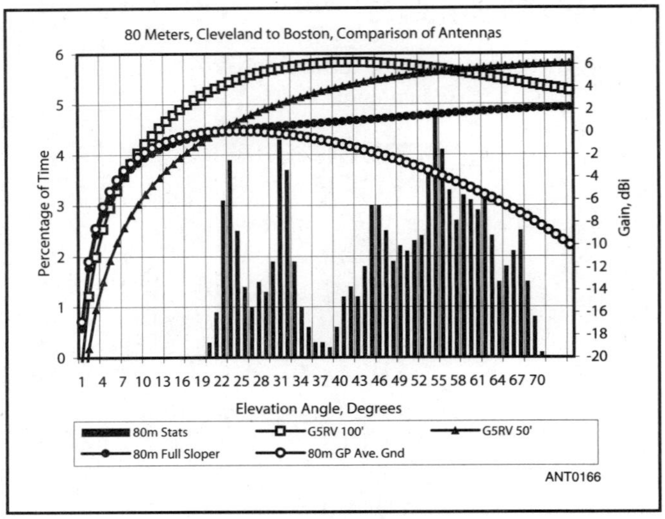

Figure 14.23 — 80/75 meter elevation statistics for all portions of the 11-year solar cycle for the path from Cleveland, Ohio, to Boston, Massachusetts, together with the elevation responses for four different multiband antennas. The 100-foot high horizontally polarized G5RV performs well over the entire range of necessary takeoff elevation angles.

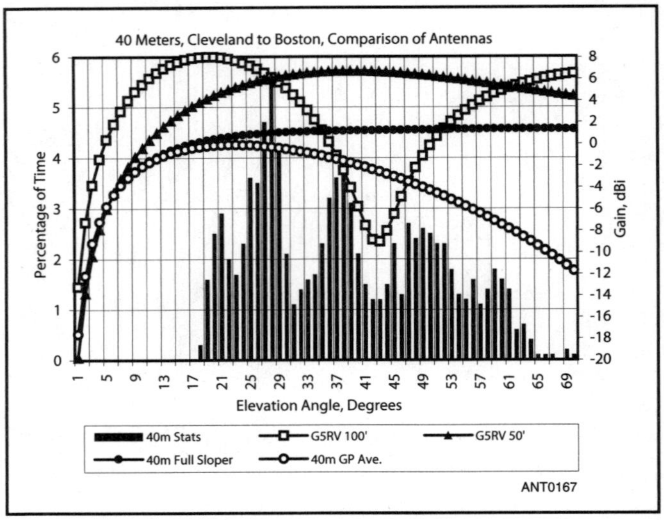

Figure 14.24 — 40 meter elevation statistics for the Cleveland to Boston path, together with elevation patterns for four antennas. Here, the 100-foot high horizontally polarized G5RV would have a null in the middle of the range of elevation angles needed for consistent performance on this path. For multiband use on this path to relatively nearby stations, the 50-foot high horizontal antenna would be a better choice than the 100-foot high antenna.

some 16 dB compared to the 50-foot high horizontal G5RV.

The advantage of antennas suitable for high-angle radiation was vividly demonstrated during a 75 meter QSO one fall evening between N6BV/1 in southern New Hampshire and W1WEF in central Connecticut. This involved a distance of about 100 miles and W1WEF was using his Four Square vertical array. Although W1WEF's signal was S9 on the Four Square, N6BV/1 suggested an experiment. Instead of connecting the so-called "dump power" connector on his Comtek ACB-4 hybrid phasing coupler to a 50-Ω dummy load (the normal configuration), W1WEF switched the dump power to his 100-foot high 80 meter horizontal dipole. W1WEF's signal came up more than 20 dB! The approximately 100-W of power that would otherwise be "wasted" in the dummy load was converted to useful signal.

Elevation Angles for Moderate Distances on 40 Meters

Figure 14.24 shows the situation for the 40 meter band, from Boston to Cleveland, together with the same antennas used for 80 meters in Figure14.23. Note that the 100-foot high horizontally polarized G5RV has about a 16-dB null at an elevation angle of 43°. This doesn't affect things for low elevation angles, but it certainly has a profound effect on signals arriving between about 30° to 60°, especially when compared to the 50-foot high horizontal G5RV. The 40 meter full sloper beats out the high horizontal antenna from about 35° to 50°. And the ground plane is obviously not the antenna of choice for this moderate-range path from Boston to Cleveland, although it is still a good performer on longer-distance paths, with their low takeoff angles.

A 100-foot high multiband dipole is about ⅜-λ high on 75/80 meters. It is an excellent antenna for general-purpose local and DXing operation. But the same dipole used on 40 meters becomes ¾-λ high. At that height, the nulls in its elevation pattern give large holes in coverage for nearby 40 meter contacts. Many operators have found that a 40- to 50-foot high dipole on 40 meters gives them far superior performance for close-in QSOs, when compared to a high dipole, or even a high 2-element 40 meter Yagi.

NVIS Summary

The use of NVIS strategies to cover close-in and intermediate distance communications within about 600 miles involves the intelligent choice of low HF frequencies. As a rule-of-thumb for ham band NVIS, 40 meters is recommended for use during the day; 80 meters during the night.

NVIS involves the choice of antennas suitable for this strategy. Horizontally polarized dual-band 80 and 40 meter flattop dipoles that are mounted higher than about 10 feet high will work adequately for portable operations. Dual-band 80 and 40 meter inverted V dipoles supported 20 feet above the ground at the center can also work well in portable operations.

Single-band 40 meter flattop antennas about 30 feet high and 80 meter flattop antennas about 60 feet high can do a good job for fixed locations.

14.3 EFFECTS OF LOCAL TERRAIN

The following material is condensed from an article by R. Dean Straw, N6BV, in July 1995 *QEX* magazine and updated for this edition. *HFTA* (HF Terrain Assessment) and supporting data files are included with this book's downloadable supplemental information. *HFTA* is the latest version of the *YT* program included with earlier editions of *The ARRL Antenna Book*.

Prior to the introduction of this material, the last major study that appeared in the amateur literature on the subject of local terrain as it affects DX operation appeared in four *QST* "How's DX" columns, by Clarke Greene, K1JX, from October 1980 to January 1981. Greene's work was an update of a landmark series of 1966 *QST* articles entitled "Station Design for DX," by Paul Rockwell, W3AFM. The long-range profiles of several prominent, indeed legendary, stations in Rockwell's articles are fascinating: W3CRA, W4KFC and W6AM. (The articles by Rockwell are included with this book's downloadable supplemental information.)

14.3.1 CHOOSING A QTH FOR DX

The subject of how to choose a QTH for working DX has fascinated hams since the beginning of amateur operations. No doubt, Marconi probably spent a lot of time wandering around Newfoundland looking for a great radio QTH before making the first transatlantic transmission. Putting together a high-performance HF station for contesting or DXing has always followed some pretty simple rules. First, you need the perfect QTH, preferably on a rural mountaintop or at least on top of a hill. Even better yet, you need a mountaintop surrounded by seawater! Then, after you have found your dream QTH, you put up the biggest antennas you possibly can, on the highest towers you can afford. Then you work all sorts of DX — sunspots willing, of course.

The only trouble with this straightforward formula for success is that it doesn't always work. Hams fortunate enough to be located on mountain tops with really spectacular drop-offs often find that their highest antennas don't do very well, especially on 15 or 10 meters, but often even on 20 meters. When they compare their signals with nearby locals in the flatlands, they sometimes (but not always) come out on the losing end, especially when sunspot activity is high.

On the other hand, when the sunspots drop into the cellar, the high antennas on the mountaintop are usually the ones crunching the pileups — but again, not always. So, the really ambitious contest aficionados, the guys with lots of resources and infinite enthusiasm, have resorted to putting up antennas at all possible heights, on a multitude of towers.

There is a more scientific way to figure out where and how high to put your antennas to optimize your signal during all parts of the 11-year solar cycle. We advocate the system approach to HF antenna system design, in which you need to know the following:

1) The range of elevation angles necessary to get from point A to point B

2) The elevation patterns for various types and configurations of antennas

3) The effect of local terrain on elevation patterns for horizontally polarized antennas.

14.3.2 REQUIRED RANGE OF ELEVATION ANGLES

Up until 1994, *The ARRL Antenna Book* contained only a limited amount of information about the elevation angles needed for communication throughout the world. In the 1974 edition, Table 1-1 in the Wave Propagation chapter was captioned: "Measured vertical angles of arrival of signals from England at receiving location in New Jersey."

What the caption didn't say was that Table 1-1 was derived from measurements made during 1934 by Bell Labs. The highest frequency data seemed pretty shaky, considering that 1934 was the low point of Cycle 17. Neither was this data applicable to any other path, other than the one from New Jersey to England. Nonetheless, many amateurs located throughout the US tried to use the sparse information in Table 1-1 as the only rational data they had for determining how high to mount their antennas. (If they lived on hills, they made estimates of the effect of the terrain, assuming that the hill was adequately represented by a long, unbroken slope. More on this later.)

In 1993 ARRL HQ embarked on a major project to tabulate the range of elevation angles from all regions of the US to important DX QTHs around the world. This was accomplished by running many thousands of computations using the *IONCAP* computer program. *IONCAP* has been under development for more than 40 years by various agencies of the US government and is considered the standard of comparison for propagation programs by many agencies, including the Voice of America, Radio Free Europe, and more than 100 foreign governments throughout the world. *IONCAP* is a real pain in the neck to use, but it is the standard of comparison.

The calculations were done for all levels of solar activity, for all months of the year, and for all 24 hours of the day. The results were gathered into some very large databases, from which special custom-written software extracted detailed statistics. The results appeared in summary form in Tables 4 through 13 printed in Chapter 23, Radio Wave Propagation, of the 17th Edition and in more detail on the diskette included with that book. (More statistical data is included with this book's downloadable supplemental information. The author has also made available an expanded set of data through Radioware.)

Figure 14.25 shows the full range of elevation angles (represented as vertical bars) for the 20 meter path from New England (centered on Newington, Connecticut) to all of Europe. This is for all openings, in all months, over the entire 11-year solar cycle. The most likely elevation angle occurs at 5° for about 13% of the times when the 20 meter band is open to Europe from New England. The band is open from 4° to 6° a total of about 34% of the times the band is open. There is a secondary peak between 10° to 12°, occurring for a total of about 25% of the times the band is open.

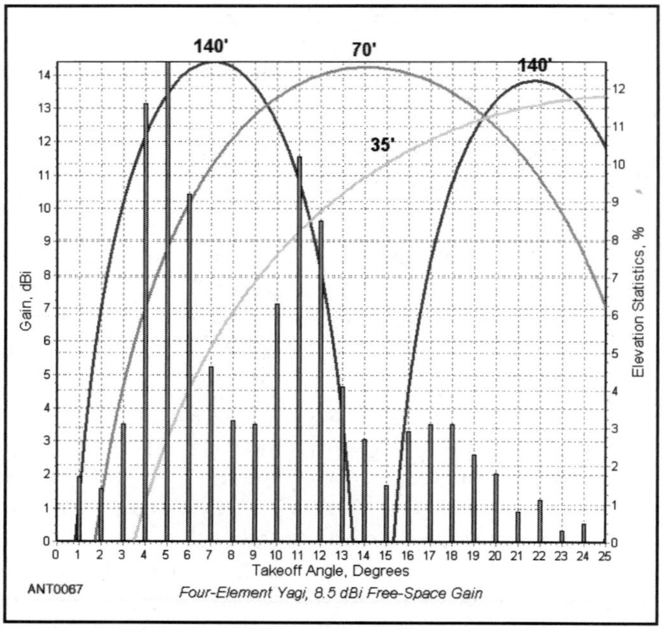

Figure 14.25 — Graph showing 20 meter percentage of all openings from New England to Europe versus elevation angles, together with overlay of elevation patterns over flat ground for three 20 meter antenna systems. The most statistically likely angle at which the band will be open is 5°, although at any particular hour, day, month and year, the actual angle will likely be different. Note the deep null exhibited by the 140-foot high antenna centered at 14°.

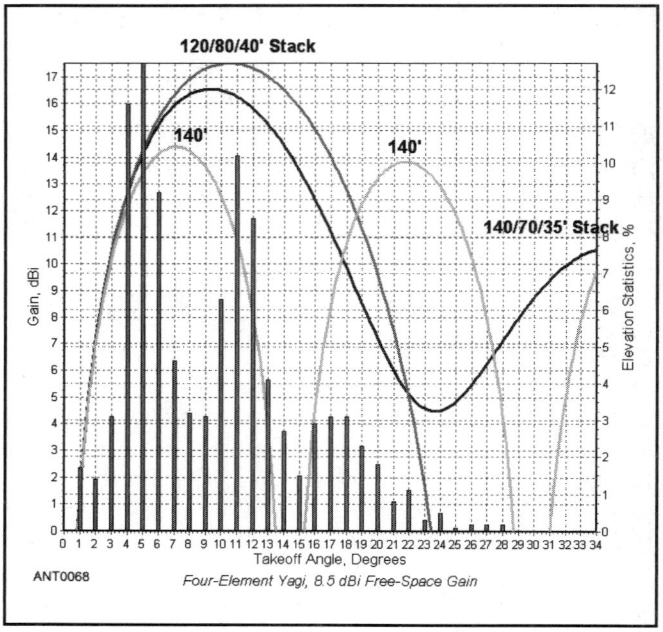

Figure 14.26 — Graph showing results of stacking antennas at different heights on the same tower to cover a wider range of elevation angles, in this case for the path from Connecticut (W1) to all of Europe on 20 meters. The optimized stack at 120/80/40 feet covers the needed range of elevation angles better than the stack at 140/70/35 feet or the single Yagi at 140 feet.

Overlaid on Figure 14.25 along with the elevation-angle statistics are the elevation-plane responses for three different horizontally polarized Yagi beams, all over flat ground. The first is mounted 140 feet high, 2 λ in terms of wavelength. The second Yagi is mounted 70 feet high (at 1 λ) and the third is 35 feet (0.5 λ). The 140-foot high antenna has a deep null at 15°, but it also has the highest response (13.4 dBi) of the three at the statistical peak elevation angle of 5°. However, at 12° — where the band is open some 9% of the time — the 140-foot high Yagi is down 4 dB compared to the 70-foot antenna.

The 70-foot high Yagi arguably covers the overall range best, since it has no disastrous nulls in the 1° to 25° range, where most of the action is occurring on 20 meters. At 5°, however, its response is only 8.8 dBi, 4.6 dB down from the 140-foot high antenna at that angle. The 35-foot antenna peaks above 26° in elevation angle, and is down some 10.4 dB compared to the 140-foot antenna at 5°. Obviously, no single antenna covers the complete range of elevation angles needed.

Note that the highest Yagi has a strong *second lobe* peaking at 22°. Let's say that you could select between two antennas, one at 140 and one at 70 feet, and that the incoming angle for a particular distant station is 22°. You might be fooled into thinking that the incoming angle is around 6°, favoring the first peak of the higher antenna, when in truth the angle is relatively high. The 70-foot antenna's response would be lower at 22° than the higher one, but only because the 140-foot antenna is operating on its second lobe. (What would clinch a determination of the correct incoming angle — 6° or 22° — would be the response of the 35-foot high Yagi, which would be close to its peak at 22°, while it would be very far down at 6°.)

Now, we must emphasize that these elevation angles are *statistical entities* — in other words, just because 5° is the "statistically most likely angle" for the 20 meter path from New England to Europe doesn't mean that the band will be open at 11° at any particular hour, on a particular day, in a particular month, in any particular year. In fact, however, experience agrees with the *IONCAP* computations: the 20 meter path to Europe usually opens at a low angle in the New England morning hours, rising to about 11° during the afternoon, when the signals remain strongest throughout the afternoon until the evening in New England.

What would happen if we were to feed all three Yagis at 140, 70 and 35 feet in-phase as a stack? **Figure 14.26** shows this situation, along with a more highly optimized stack at 120, 80 and 40 feet that better covers the overall range of elevation angles from Connecticut to Europe.

Now see **Figure 14.27**, which uses the same 120/80/40-foot stack of 20 meter antennas as in Figure 14.26, but this time from Seattle, Washington, to Europe. For comparison, the response of a single 4-element Yagi at 100 feet over flat ground is also shown in Figure 14.27. Just because 5° is the statistically most prevalent angle (occurring some 13% of the

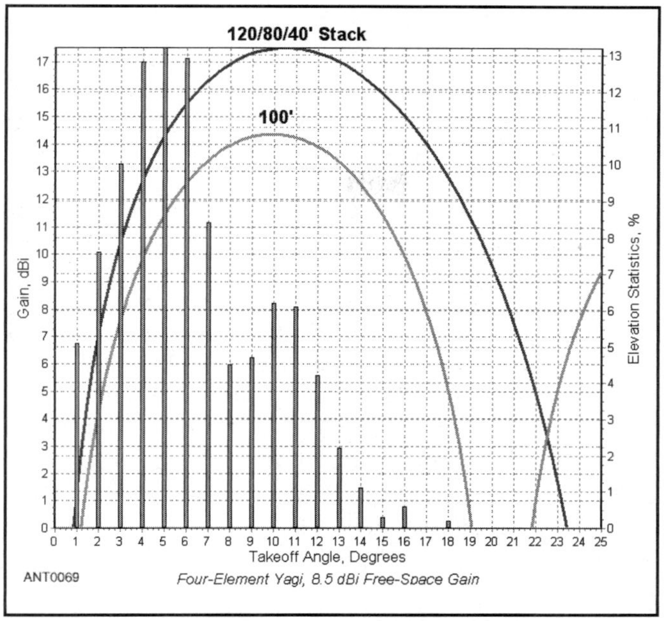

Figure 14.27 — Graph showing 20 meter percentage of all openings, this time from Seattle, WA, to Europe, together with an overlay of elevation patterns over flat ground for two 20 meter antenna systems. The statistically most likely angle on this path is 5°, occurring about 13% of the time when the band is actually open. Higher antennas predominate on this low-angle path.

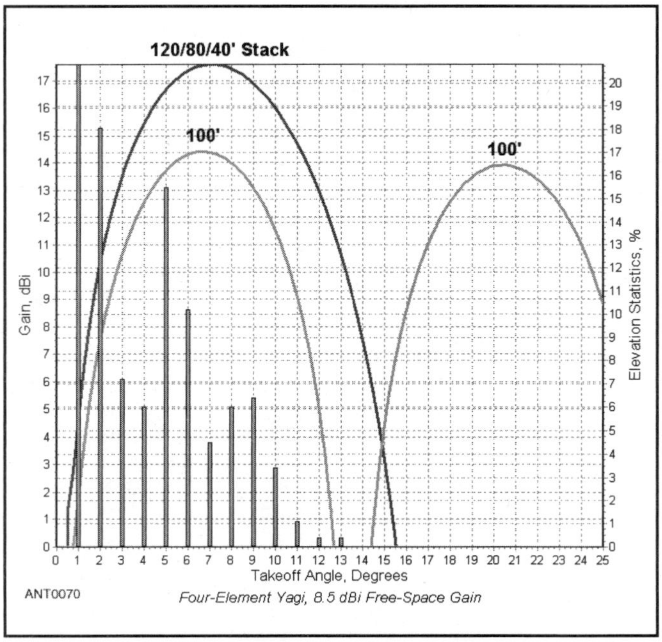

Figure 14.28 — Graph showing 15 meter percentage of all openings from Chicago to Southern Africa, together with overlay of elevation patterns over flat ground for two 15 meter antenna systems. On this long-distance, low-angle path, higher antennas are again most effective.

time) from Seattle to Europe on 20 meters, this doesn't mean that the actual angle *at any particular moment in time* might not be 10°, or even 2°. The statistics for W7 to Europe say that 5° is the most likely angle, but 20 meter signals from Europe arrive at angles ranging from 1° to 18°. Note that this range of angles is quite a bit less than from W1 to Europe, which is much closer geographically to Europe than is the Pacific Northwest coast of the US. If you design an antenna system to cover all possible angles needed to talk to Europe from Seattle (or from Seattle to Europe) on 20 meters, you would need to cover the full range from 1° to 18° equally well.

Similarly, if you wish to cover the full range of elevation angles from Chicago to Southern Africa on 15 meters, you would need to cover 1° to 13°, even though the most statistically likely signals arrive at 1°, for 21% of the time when that the band is open for that path. See **Figure 14.28**.

It is important to recognize that Figures 14.25 through 14.28 are for flat ground. When the antennas are mounted over irregular local terrain, things get much more complicated. First, however, we'll discuss general-purpose antenna modeling programs as they try to model real terrain.

14.3.3 DRAWBACKS OF COMPUTER MODELS OVER REAL TERRAIN

Modern general-purpose antenna modeling programs such as *NEC* or *MININEC* (or their commercially upgraded equivalents, such as *NEC-Win Plus* and *EZNEC*) can accurately model almost any type of antenna commonly used by radio amateurs. In addition, there are specialized programs specifically designed to model Yagis efficiently, such as *YW* (Yagi for *Windows*, included with this book's downloadable supplemental information). These programs however are all unable to model antennas accurately over anything other than *purely flat ground.*

While both *NEC* and *MININEC* can simulate irregular ground terrain, they do so in a decidedly crude manner, employing step-like concentric rings of height around an antenna. The documentation for *NEC* and *MININEC* both clearly state that diffraction off these steps is not modeled. Common experience among serious modelers is that the warnings in the manuals are worth heeding.

Although you can analyze and even optimize antenna designs using free-space or flat-earth ground models, it is *diffraction* that makes the real world a very, very complicated place. This should be clarified — diffraction is hard, even tortuous, to analyze properly, but it makes analysis of real world results far more believable than a flat-world reflection model does.

14.3.4 RAY-TRACING OVER UNEVEN LOCAL TERRAIN

The Ray-Tracing Technique

First, let's look at a simple ray-tracing procedure involving only horizontally polarized reflections, with no diffractions. From a specified height on the tower, an antenna shoots "rays" (just as though they were bullets) in 0.25° increments from +35° above the horizon to –35° below the horizon. Each ray is traced over the foreground terrain to see if it hits the ground at any point on its travels in the direction of interest. If it does hit the ground, the ray is reflected following the classical law of reflection. That is, the outgoing angle equals the incoming angle, reflected through the normal to the slope of the surface. Once the rays exit into the ionosphere, the individual contributions are vector-summed to create the overall far-field elevation pattern.

The next step in terrain modeling involves adding *diffractions* as well as reflections. At the Dayton antenna forum in 1994, Jim Breakall, WA3FET, gave a fascinating and tantalizing lecture on the effect of foreground terrain. Later Breakall, Dick Adler, K3CXZ, Joel Young and a group of other researchers published an extremely interesting paper entitled "The Modeling and Measurement of HF Antenna Skywave Radiation Patterns in Irregular Terrain" in the July 1994 *IEEE Transactions on Antennas and Propagation*. They described in rather general terms the modifications they made to the *NEC-BSC* program. They showed how the addition of a ray-tracing reflection and diffraction model to the simplistic stair-stepped reflection model in regular *NEC* gave far more realistic results. For validation, they compared actual pattern measurements made on a site in Utah (with an overflying helicopter) to computed patterns made using the modified *NEC* software. However, because the US Navy funded this work the software remained for a long time a military secret.

Thumbnail History of the Uniform Theory of Diffraction

It is instructive to look briefly at the history of how *Geometric Optics* (GO) evolved (and still continues to evolve) into the *Uniform Theory of Diffraction* (UTD). The following is summarized from the historical overview in one book found to be particularly useful and comprehensive on the subject of UTD: *Introduction to the Uniform Geometrical Theory of Diffraction*, by McNamara, Pistorius, and Malherbe.

Many years before the time of Christ, the ancient Greeks studied optics. Euclid is credited with deriving the law of reflection about 300 BC. Other Greeks, such as Ptolemy, were also fascinated with optical phenomena. In the 1600s, a Dutchman named Snell finally figured out the law of refraction, resulting in *Snell's law*. By the early 1800s, the basic world of classical optics was pretty well described from a mathematical point of view, based on the work of a number of individuals.

As its name implies, classical geometric optical theory deals strictly with geometric shapes. Of course, the importance of geometry in optics shouldn't be minimized — after all, we wouldn't have eyeglasses without geometric optics. Mathematical analysis of shapes utilizes a methodology that traces the paths of straight-line *rays* of light. (Note that the paths of rays can also be likened to the straight-line paths of particles.) In classical geometric optics, however, there is no mention of three important quantities: phase, intensity and polarization. Indeed, without phase, intensity or polarization, there is no way to deal properly with the phenomenon of *interference*, or its cousin, *diffraction*. These phenomena require theories that deal with *waves* rather than rays.

Wave theory has also been around for a long time, although not as long as geometry. Workers like Hooke and Grimaldi had recorded their observations of interference and diffraction in the mid 1600s. Huygens had used elements of wave theory in the late 1600s to help explain refraction. By the late 1800s, the work of Lord Rayleigh, Sommerfeld, Fresnel, Maxwell and many others led to the full mathematic characterization of all electromagnetic phenomena, light included.

Unfortunately, ray theory doesn't work for many problems, at least ray theory in the classical optical form. The real world is a lot more jagged, pointy and fuzzy in shape than can be described in a totally rigorous mathematic fashion. Some properties of the real world are most easily explained on the micro level using electrons and protons as conceptual objects, while other macro phenomena (like resonance, for example) are more easily explained in terms of waves. To get a handle on a typical real-world physical situation, a combination of classical ray theory and wave theory was needed.

The breakthrough in the combination of classical

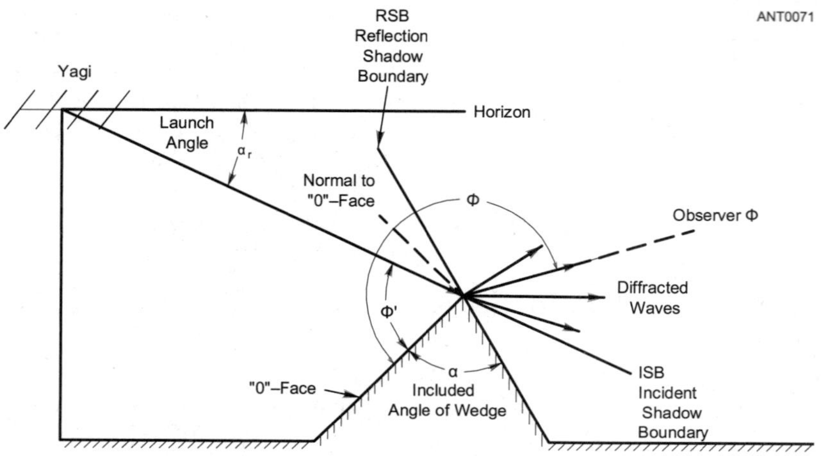

Figure 14.29 — Diagram showing diffraction mechanism of ray launched at angle α_r below the horizon at a diffraction wedge, whose included angle is α. Referenced to the incident face (the o-face as it is called in UTD terminology), the incoming angle is ϕ' (phi prime). The wedge creates an infinite number of diffracted waves. Shown is one whose angle referenced to the o-face is ϕ, the so-called observation angle in UTD terminology.

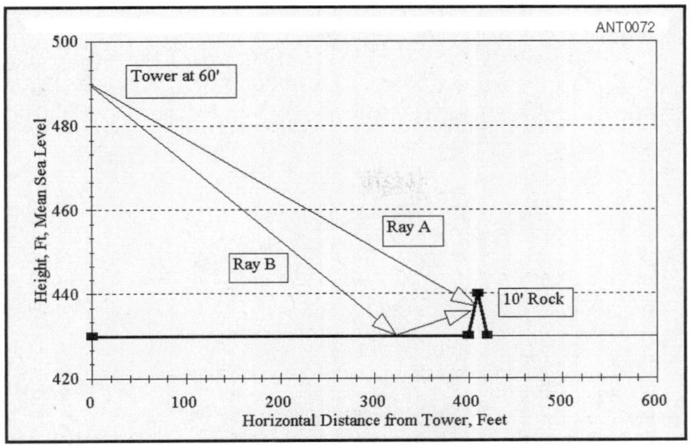

Figure 14.30 — Hypothetical terrain exhibiting so-called "10-foot rock effect." The terrain is flat from the tower base out to 400 feet, where a 10-foot high rock is placed. Note that this forms a diffraction wedge, but that it also blocks direct waves trying to shoot through it to the flat surface beyond, as shown by Ray A. Ray B reflects off the flat surface before it reaches the 10-foot rock, but it is blocked by the rock from proceeding further. A simple Geometric Optics (GO) analysis of this terrain without taking diffraction into account will result in the elevation response shown in Figure 14.31.

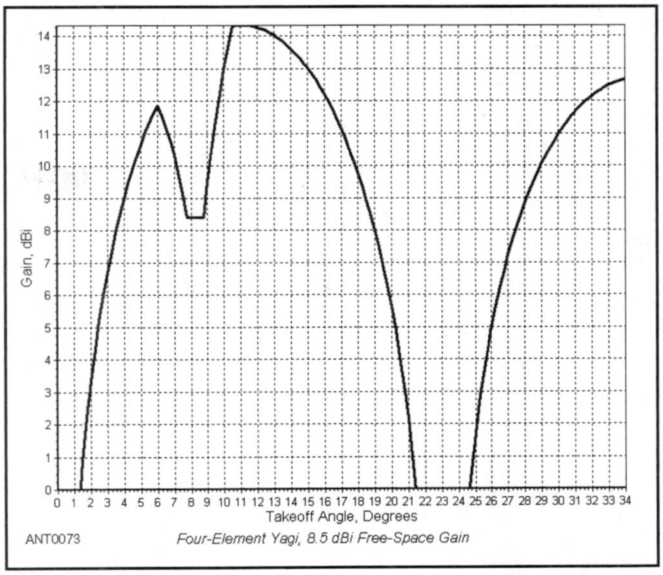

Figure 14.31 — Elevation response for rays launched at terrain in Figure 14.30 from a height of 60 feet using a 4-element Yagi. This was computed using a simple Geometrical Optics (GO) reflection-only analysis. Note the hole in the response between 6° to 10° in elevation. It is not reasonable for a 10-foot high rock to create such a disturbance at 21 MHz!

geometric optics and wave concepts came from J. B. Keller of Bell Labs in 1953, although he published his work in the early 1960s. In the very simplest of terms, Keller introduced the notion that shooting a ray at a diffraction *wedge* causes wave interference at the tip, with an infinite number of diffracted waves emanating from the diffraction point. Each diffracted wave can be considered to be a point source radiator at the place of generation, the diffraction point. Thereafter, the paths of individual waves can be traced as though they were individual classical optic rays again. What Keller came up with was a reasonable mathematical description of what happens at the tip of the diffraction wedge.

Figure 14.29 is a picture of a simple diffraction wedge, with an incoming ray launched at an angle of α_r, referenced to the horizon, impinging on it. The diffraction wedge here is considered to be perfectly conducting, and hence impenetrable by the ray. The wedge generates an infinite number of diffracted waves, going in all directions not blocked by the wedge itself. The amplitudes and phases of the diffracted waves are determined by the interaction at the wedge tip, and this in turn is governed by the various angles associated with the wedge. Shown in Figure 14.29 are the included angle α of the wedge, the angle ϕ' of the incoming ray (referenced to the incoming surface of the wedge), and the observed angle ϕ of one of the outgoing diffracted waves, also referenced to the wedge surface.

The so-called *shadow boundaries* are also shown in Figure 14.29. The Reflection-Shadow Boundary (RSB) is the angle beyond which no further reflections can take place for a given incoming angle. The Incident-Shadow Boundary (ISB) is that angle beyond which the wedge's face blocks any incident rays from illuminating the observation point.

Keller derived the amplitude and phase terms by comparing the classical Geometric Optics (GO) solution with the exact mathematical solution calculated by Sommerfeld for a particular case where the boundary conditions were well known — an infinitely long, perfectly conducting wedge illuminated by a plane wave. Simply speaking, whatever was left over had to be diffraction terms. Keller combined these diffraction terms with GO terms to yield the total field everywhere.

Keller's new theory became known as the *Geometric Theory of Diffraction* (abbreviated henceforth as GTD). The beauty of GTD was that in the regions where classical GO predicted zero fields, the GTD "filled in the blanks," so to speak. For example, see **Figure 14.30**, showing the terrain for a hypothetical case, where a 60-foot high 4-element 15 meter Yagi illuminates a wide, perfectly flat piece of ground. A 10-foot high rock has been placed 400 feet away from the tower base in the direction of outgoing rays. **Figure 14.31** shows the elevation pattern predicted using reflection-only GO techniques. Due to blockage of the direct wave (A) trying to shoot past the 10-foot high rock, and due to blockage of (B) reflections from the flat ground in front of the rock by the rock, there is a *hole* in the smooth elevation pattern.

Now, doesn't it defy common sense to imagine that a single 10-foot high rock will really have such an effect on a 15 meter signal? Keller's GTD took diffraction effects into account to show that waves do indeed sneak past and over the rock to fill in the pattern. The whole GTD scheme is very clever indeed.

However, GTD wasn't perfect. Keller's GTD predicts some big spikes in the pattern, even though the overall shape of the elevation pattern is much closer to reality than a simple GO reflection analysis would indicate. The region right at the RSB and ISB shadow boundaries is where problems are found. The GO terms go to zero at these points because of blockage by the wedge, while Keller's diffraction terms tend to go to infinity at these very spots. In mathematical terms this is referred to as a *caustic problem*. Nevertheless, despite these nasty problems at the ISB and RSB, the GTD provided a remarkably better solution to diffraction problems than did classical GO.

In the early 1970s, a group at Ohio State University under R. G. Kouyoumjian and P. H. Pathak did some pivotal work to resolve this caustic problem, introducing what amounts to a clever "fudge factor" to compensate for the tendency of the diffraction terms at the shadow boundaries to go to infinity. They introduced what is known as a *transition function*, using a form of Fresnel integral. Most importantly, the Ohio State researchers also created several *FORTRAN* computer programs to compute the amplitude and phase of diffraction components. Now computer hackers could get to work!

The ARRL program that finally resulted is called *HFTA*, standing for "HF Terrain Assessment," written by Dean Straw, N6BV. (An earlier DOS version of *HFTA* was known as *YT*, standing for "Yagi Terrain.") As the name suggests, *HFTA* analyzes the effect of local terrain on HF propagation through the ionosphere. It is designed for horizontally polarized Yagis at various heights, although it will model the effects of a simple flattop dipole also. The accurate appraisal of the effect of terrain on vertically polarized signals is a far more complex problem than for horizontally polarized waves, and *HFTA* doesn't do verticals. (*HFTA* is included with this book's downloadable supplemental information.)

There are a set of help files available with *HFTA* that will be invaluable for first-time users. In addition the tutorial, "A Beginner's Guide to *HFTA* High Frequency Terrain Assessment" by John White, VA7JW is available online at **www.orcadxcc.org/content/VA7JW_HFTA_Manual.pdf**.

14.3.5 SIMULATION EXAMPLES

We want to focus first on some simple results, to show that the computations do make some sense by presenting some simulations over simple terrains. We've already described the "10-foot rock at 400 feet" situation, and showed where a simple GO reflection analysis is inadequate to the task without taking diffraction effects into account.

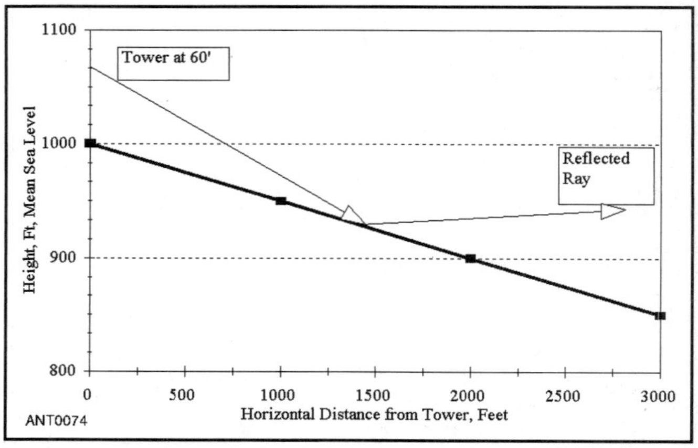

Figure 14.32 — A long, gentle downward-sloping terrain. This terrain has no explicit diffraction points and can be analyzed using simple GO reflection techniques.

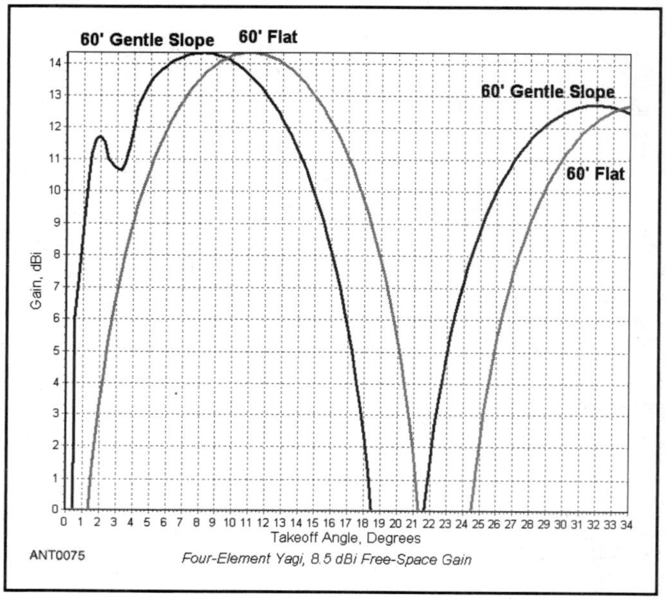

Figure 14.33 — Elevation response for terrain shown in Figure 14.32, using a 4-element 15 meter Yagi, 60 feet high. Note that the shape of the response is essentially shifted toward the left, toward lower elevation angles, by the angle of the sloping ground. For reference, the response for an identical Yagi placed over flat ground is also shown.

Simple Terrain Examples

Now look at the simple case shown in **Figure 14.32**, where a very long, continuous down-slope from the tower base is shown. Note that the scales used for the X- and Y-axes are different: the Y-axis changes 300 feet in height (from 800 to 1100 feet), while the X-axis goes from 0 to 3000 feet. This exaggerates the apparent steepness of the downward slope, which is actually a rather gentle slope, at $\tan^{-1}(1000 - 850) / (3000 - 0) = -2.86°$. In other words, the terrain falls 150 feet in height over a range of 3000 feet from the base of the tower.

Figure 14.33 shows the computed elevation response for this terrain profile, for a 4-element horizontally polarized Yagi on a 60-foot tower. The response is compared to that of an identical Yagi placed 60 feet above flat ground. Compared to the "flatland" antenna, the hilltop antenna has an elevation response shifted over by almost 3° toward the lower elevation angles. In fact, this shift is directly due to the –2.86° slope of the hill. Reflections off the slope are tilted by the slope. In this situation there is a single diffraction at the bottom of the gentle slope at 3000 feet, where the program assumes that the terrain becomes flat.

Look at **Figure 14.34**, which shows another simple terrain profile, called a "Hill-Valley" scenario. Here, the 60-foot high tower stands on the edge of a gentle hill overlooking a long valley. Once again the slope of the hill is exaggerated by

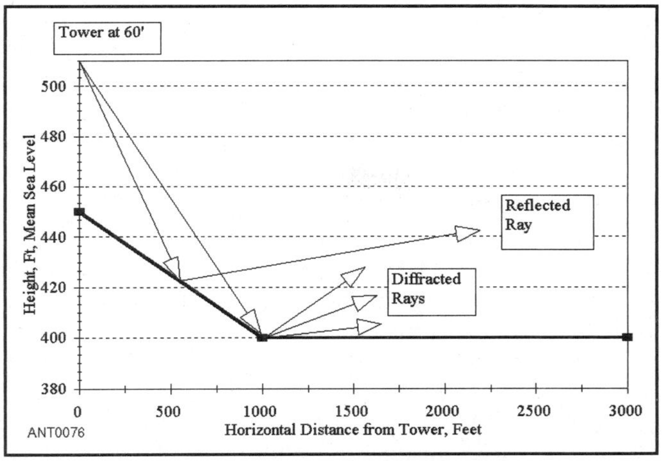

Figure 14.34 — "Hill-Valley" terrain, with reflected and diffracted rays.

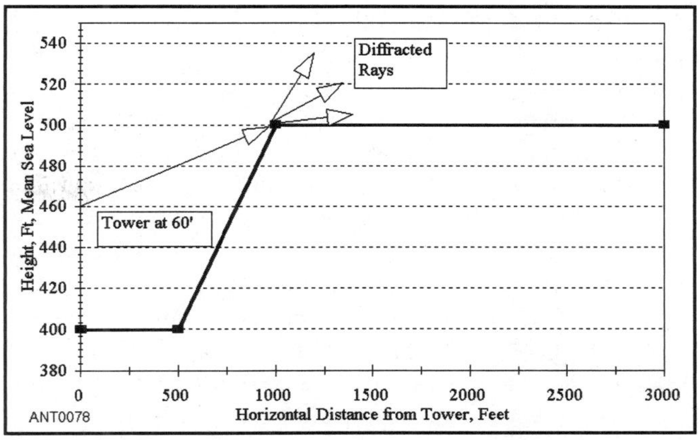

Figure 14.36 — "Hill-Ahead" terrain, shown with diffracted rays created by illumination of the edge of the plateau at the top of the hill.

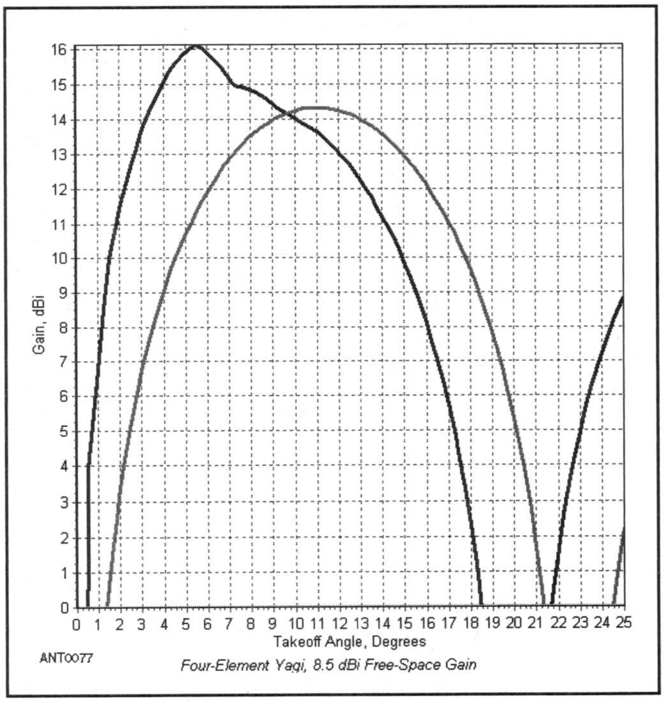

Figure 14.35 — Elevation response computed by HFTA program for single 4-element 15 meter Yagi at 60 feet above "Hill-Valley" terrain shown in Figure 14.34. Note that the slope has caused the response in general to be shifted toward lower elevation angles. At 5° elevation, the diffraction components add up to increase the gain slightly above the amount a GO-only analysis would indicate.

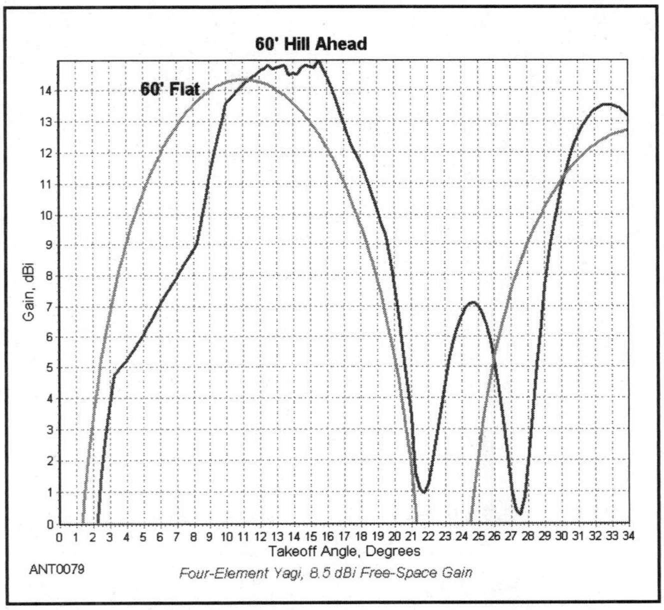

Figure 14.37 — Elevation response computed by HFTA for "Hill-Ahead" terrain shown in Figure 14.36. Now the hill blocks direct rays and also precludes possibility of any constructive reflections. Above 10°, diffraction components add up together with direct rays to create the response shown.

the different X and Y-axes. **Figure 14.35** shows the computed elevation response at 21.2 MHz for a 4-element Yagi on a 60-foot high tower at the edge of the slope.

Once again, the pattern is overlaid with that of an identical 60-foot-high Yagi over flat ground. Compared to the flatland antenna, the hilltop antenna's response above 9° in elevation is shifted by almost 3° toward the lower elevation angles. Again, this is due to reflections off the downward slope. From 1° to 9°, the hilltop pattern is enhanced even more compared to the flatland antenna, this time by diffraction occurring at the bottom of the hill.

Now let's see what happens when there is a hill ahead in the direction of interest. **Figure 14.36** depicts such a situation, labeled "Hill-Ahead." Here, at a height of 400 feet above mean sea level, the land is flat in front of the tower, out to a distance 500 feet, where the hill begins. The hill then rises 100 feet over the range 500 to 1000 feet away from the tower base. After that, the terrain is a plateau, at a constant 500 feet elevation.

Figure 14.37 shows the computed elevation pattern for a 4-element 21-MHz Yagi 60-feet high on the tower, compared again with an overlay for an identical 60-foot high antenna over flat ground. The hill blocks low-angle waves directly radiated from the antenna from 0° to 2.3°. In addition, waves that would normally be reflected from the ground, and that would normally add in phase from about 2.3° to 12°, are blocked by the hill also. Thus the signal at 8° is down almost 5 dB from the signal over flat ground, all due to the effect of the hill. Diffracted waves start kicking in once the direct wave rises enough above the horizon to illuminate the top edge of the hill. These diffracted waves tend to augment elevation angles above about 12°, which reflected waves can't reach.

Is there is any hope for someone in such a lousy QTH for DXing? **Figure 14.38** shows the elevation response for a truly heroic solution. This involves a stack of four 4-element Yagis, mounted at 120, 90, 60 and 30 feet on the tower. Now, the total gain at low angles is just about comparable to that from a single 4-element Yagi mounted over flat ground. Where there's a ham, there is a way!

At 5° elevation, four diffraction components add up (there are zero reflection components) to achieve the far-field pattern. This seems reasonable, because each of the four antennas is illuminating the diffraction point separately and we know that none of the four antennas can *see over* the hill directly to produce a reflection at a low launch angle.

At an elevation angle of 5°, 15 meter signals arrive from Europe to New England about 13% of the total time when the band is actually open. We can look at this another way. For about two-thirds of the times when the band is open on this path, the incoming angle is between 3° to 12°. For about one-third of the time, signals arrive above 10°, where the "heroic" four-stack is really beginning to come into its own.

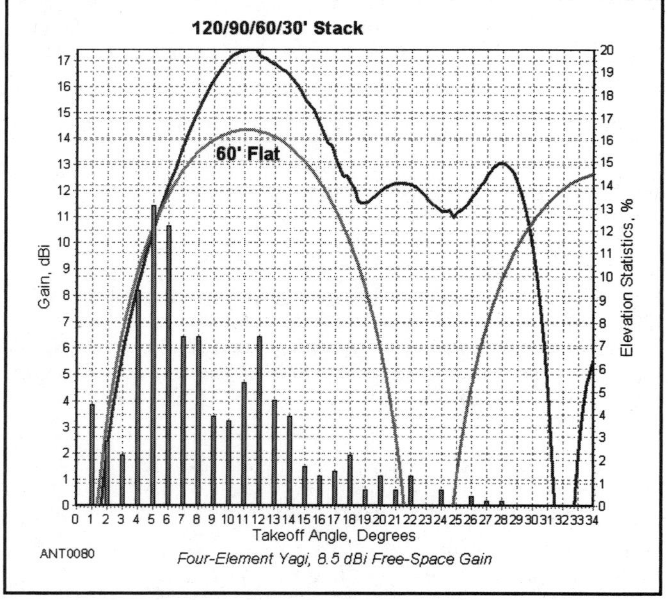

Figure 14.38 — Elevation response of "heroic effort" to surmount the difficulties imposed by hill in Figure 14.36. This effort involves a stack of four 4-element Yagis in a stack starting at 120 feet and spaced at 30-foot increments on the tower. The response is roughly equivalent to a single 4-element Yagi at 60 feet above flat ground, hence the characterization as being a "heroic effort." The elevation-angle statistics from New England to Europe are overlaid on the graph for reference.

Complex Terrain Example

The results for simple terrains look reasonable; let's try a more complicated real-world situation. **Figure 14.39** shows the terrain from the New Hampshire N6BV/1 QTH toward Japan. The terrain was complex, with 52 different points *HFTA* identifies as diffraction points. **Figure 14.40** shows a labeled *HFTA* output for three different types of antennas on 20 meters: a stack at 120 and 60 feet, the 120-foot antenna by itself, and then a 120/60-foot stack over flat ground, for reference. The elevation-angle statistics for New England to Japan are overlaid on the graph also, making for a very complicated looking picture — it is a *lot* easier to decipher the lines on the color monitor, by the way, than on a black-and-white printer.

Comparison of the same 120/60-foot stacks over irregular terrain and flat ground is useful to show where the terrain itself is affecting the elevation response. The flatland stack has more gain in the region of 3° to 7° than the same stack over the N6BV/1 local terrain toward Japan. On the other hand, the N6BV/1 local terrain boosts signals in the range of 8° to about 12°. This demonstrates the conservation of energy — you may gain a stronger signal at certain elevation angles, but you will lose gain at others. In this case, the N6BV/1 station always felt "weak" toward Japan on 20 meters, because the dominant angles are low.

Examination of the detailed data output from *HFTA* shows that at an elevation angle of 5°, there are 6159 diffraction components. There are many, many signals bouncing around off the terrain on their trip to Japan! Note that because

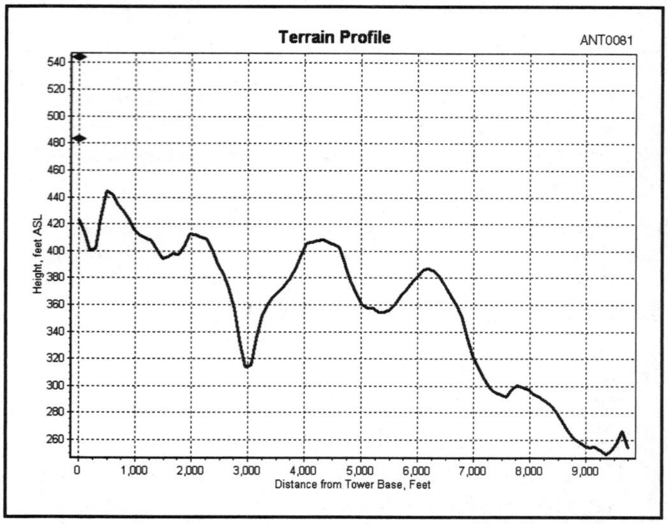

Figure 14.39 — Terrain of N6BV/1 in Windham, NH, toward Japan. HFTA identifies 52 different points where diffraction can occur.

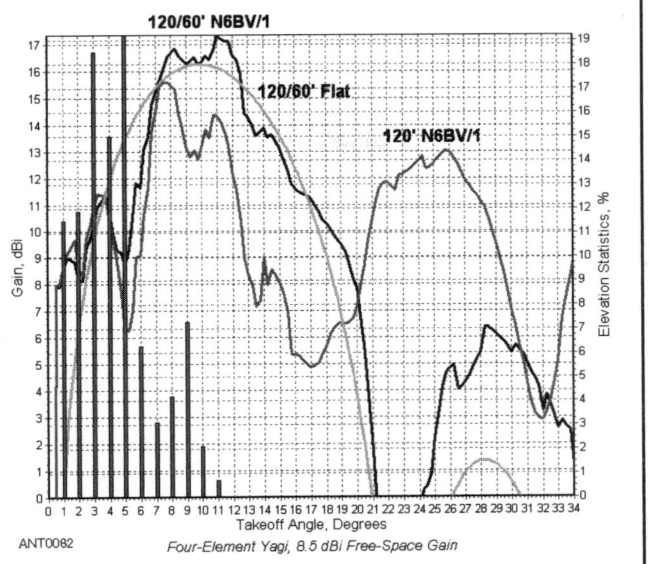

Figure 14.40 — Elevation responses computed by HFTA for N6BV/1 terrain shown in Figure 14.39, for a stack of two 4-element 20 meter Yagis at 120 and 60 feet, together with the response for a single Yagi at 120 feet and a 120/60-foot stack over flat ground for reference. Due to the response, many diffraction and reflection components is quite complicated!

of blockage of some parts of the terrain, the 60-foot high Yagi cannot illuminate all the diffraction points, while the higher 120-foot Yagi is able to see these diffraction points.

It is fascinating to reflect on the thought that received signals coming down from the ionosphere to the receiver are having encounters with the terrain, but from the opposite direction. It's not surprising, given these kinds of interactions, that transmitting and receiving might not be totally reciprocal.

The 120/60-foot stack in Figure 14.40 achieves its peak gain of 17.3 dBi at 11° elevation, where it is about 3 dB stronger than the single Yagi at 120 feet. It maintains this 3-dB advantage over most of the range of incoming signals from Japan. This difference in performance between the stack and each antenna by itself was observed many times on the air. Much of the time when comparisons are being made, however, the small differences in signal are difficult to measure meaningfully, especially when the fading varies signals by 20 dB or so during a typical QSO. It should be noted that the stack usually exhibited less fading compared to each antenna by itself.

14.3.6 USING *HFTA*

Manually Generating a Terrain Profile

The *HFTA* program uses two distinct algorithms to generate the far-field elevation pattern. The first is a simple reflection-only Geometric Optics (GO) algorithm. The second is the diffraction algorithm using the Uniform Theory of Diffraction (UTD). These algorithms work with a digitized representation of the terrain profile for a single azimuthal direction — for example, toward Japan or toward Europe.

You can generate a terrain file manually using a topographic map and a ruler or a pair of dividers. The HFTA.PDF file (accessed by clicking on the HELP button) and included with this book's downloadable supplemental information gives complete instructions on how to create a terrain file manually (or automatically). The manual process is simple enough in concept. Mark on your US Geological Survey 7.5-minute map the exact location of your tower. You will find 7.5-minute maps available from some local sources, such as large hardware stores, but the main contact point is the U.S. Geological Survey (**nationalmap.gov**). Many countries outside the USA have topographic charts also. Most are calibrated in meters. To use these with *HFTA*, you will have to convert meters to feet by multiplying meters by 3.28 or else inserting a single line at the very beginning of the disk file, saying "meters" for *HFTA* to recognize meters automatically.

Mark off a pencil line from the tower base, in the azimuthal direction of interest, perhaps 45° from New England to Europe, or 335° to Japan. Then measure the distance from the tower base to each height contour crossed by the pencil line. Enter the data at each distance/height into an ASCII computer file, whose filename extension is "PRO," standing for *profile*.

Figure 14.41 shows a portion of the USGS paper map for the N6BV/1 QTH in Windham, NH, along with lines scribed in several directions toward various parts of Europe and the Far East. Note that the elevation heights of the intermediate contour lines are labeled manually in pencil in order to make sense of things. It is very easy to get confused unless you do this!

The terrain model used by *HFTA* assumes that the terrain is represented by flat *plates* connecting the elevation points in the *.PRO file with straight lines. The model is two dimensional, meaning that range and elevation are the only data for a particular azimuth. In effect, *HFTA* assumes that the width of a terrain plate is wide relative to its length. Obviously, the world is three-dimensional. If your shot in a particular direction involves aiming your Yagi down a canyon with steep walls, then it's pretty likely that your actual elevation pattern will be different from what *HFTA* tells you. The signals must careen horizontally from wall to wall, in addition to being affected by the height changes of the terrain. *HFTA* isn't designed to do canyons.

To get a true 3-D picture of the full effects of terrain, a terrain model would have to show azimuth, along with range and elevation, point-by-point for about two miles in every direction around the base of the tower. After you go through the pain of creating a profile for a single azimuth, you'll appreciate the immensity of the process if you were to try to create a full 360° 3D profile manually.

Generating HFTA Data Using the K6TU Data Service

Stu Phillips, K6TU, has greatly simplified the process of obtaining terrain elevation data for use with *HFTA* by automating the complete process on **www.k6tu.net**. The

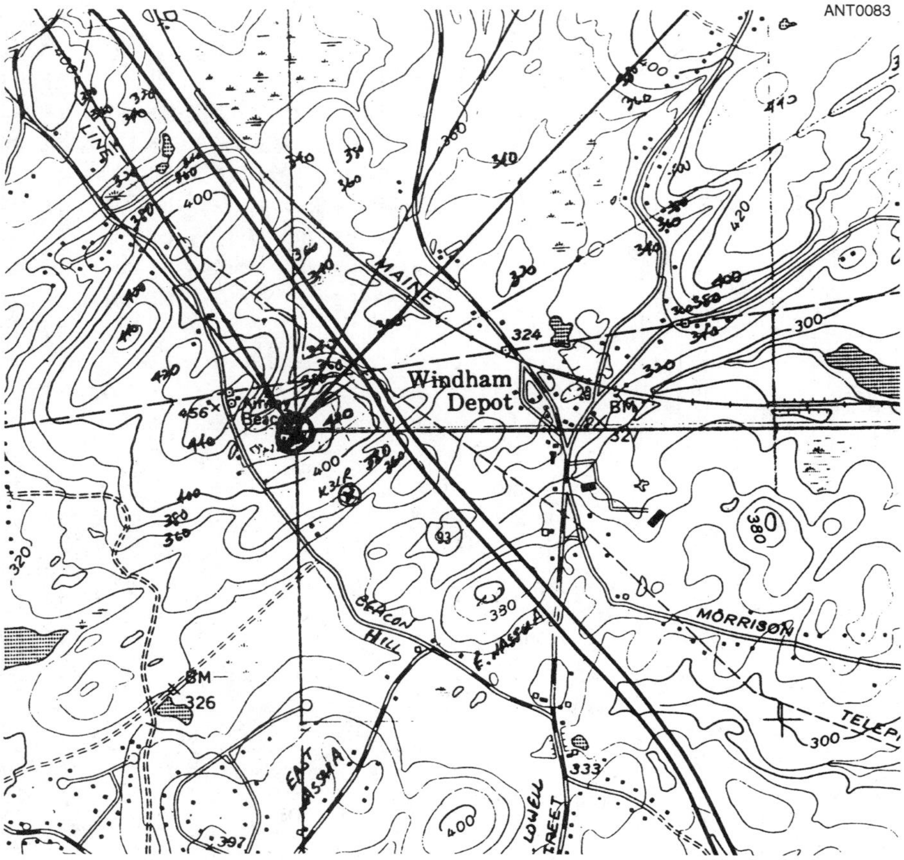

Figure 14.41 — A portion of USGS 7.5-minute topographic map, showing N6BV/1 QTH, together with marks in direction of Europe and Japan from tower base. Note that the elevation contours were marked by hand to help eliminate confusion. This required a magnifying glass and a steady hand!

service is available at no charge to any registered user. The signup process is free and gives ongoing access to both the propagation prediction services of the site as well as generating terrain profiles. K6TU obtained the complete 0.5 Tbyte database from USGS. For non-US locations, the service uses the Shuttle Radar Topography Mission dataset.

From the home page's Main Menu (at upper left), select HF TERRAIN ANALYSIS. A page describing the *HFTA* program and how to use the terrain profile service will be displayed. When you are ready to generate a profile for your location, click NEW in the NAVIGATION menu at the upper right then TERRAIN PROFILE REQUEST on the next page displayed (see **Figure 14.42**). The data entry form will be displayed with the following information to be supplied by you:

- Name of the profile, such as "W1AW Tower 1 Terrain Profile"
- Latitude to six decimal degrees (41.714511)
- Longitude to six decimal degrees (-72.727325)

The easiest way to obtain the location lat/lon to this precision is to use an online mapping service, such as *Google Maps* (**maps.google.com**). Select the satellite view, then zoom in to the highest resolution view of your location. Click once on the exact location for which you want to generate a profile. The lat/lon position of the location will display in a small label window. Click on the lat/lon data values and a window will appear at the upper left giving lat/lon in both decimal and degree-minute-second format. Highlight and copy the latitude value then paste it into the data service's LATITUDE window. Do the same for the longitude value.

With both the latitude and longitude data entered, click SAVE and then GENERATE PROFILE on the following page. The service will send you an email when the file of data has been created containing the URL where the file is saved. After you click on the URL and see the [filename}.zip file, right-click on the filename and save it. You can then extract all 360 PRO files into a folder with the name you selected for the profile. To use the data, follow the instructions that come with *HFTA* and select the appropriate PRO file.

K6TU also offers a downloadable *HFTASweep* program to generate gain tables. (It has been tested on Windows 7, 8, and 10.) As explained on the K6TU website, *HFTASweep* is a program "wrapper" for *HFTA*. It runs *HFTA* 90 times programmatically to model a *horizontally* polarized antenna over the actual terrain around your location. The program captures the results for each azimuth direction (four different azimuth angles at a time) and at the end, builds a *VOACAP* type 13 antenna model as a file called **antenna.13**.

The **antenna.13** file is a table containing the gain of the modeled antenna over actual terrain for all radiation angles from 0 to 34 degrees (the maximum radiation angle considered

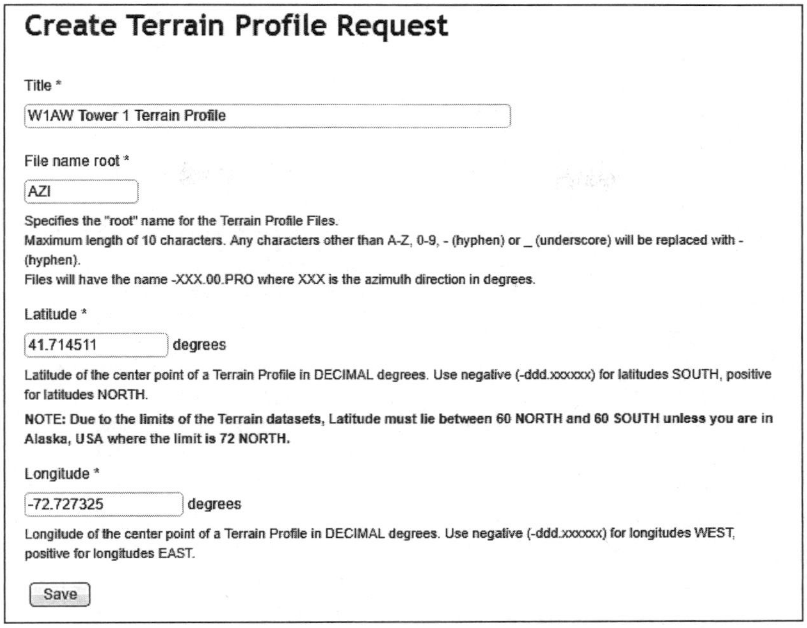

Figure 14.42 — The location data entry screen for one of the towers at W1AW. Google Maps (maps.google.com) was used to obtain the lat/lon location data as described in the text.

by *HFTA*). The remaining elevation angles simply contain the same data for angles 35 through 90 as the data shows for 34 degrees. This is a reasonable simplification for horizontal antennas that are at least a quarter wavelength or more above ground level.

Algorithm for Ray-Tracing the Terrain

Once a terrain profile is created, there are a number of mechanisms that *HFTA* takes into account as a ray travels over that terrain:

1) Classical ray reflection, with Fresnel ground coefficients.

2) Direct diffraction, where a diffraction point is illuminated directly by an antenna, with no intervening terrain features blocking the direct illumination.

3) When a diffracted ray is subsequently reflected off the terrain.

4) When a reflected ray encounters a diffraction point and causes another series of diffracted rays to be generated.

5) When a diffracted ray hits another diffraction point, generating another whole series of diffractions.

Certain unusual, bowl-shaped terrain profiles, with sheer vertical faces, can conceivably cause signals to reflect or diffract in a backward direction, only to be reflected back again in the forward direction by the sheer-walled terrain to the rear. *HFTA* does not accommodate these interactions, mainly because to do so would increase the computation time too much. It only evaluates terrain in the forward direction along one azimuth of interest.

Figure 14.43 shows a portion of an *HFTA* screen capture in the direction toward Europe from the N6BV/1 location in New Hampshire on 21.2 MHz. It compares the results for a 90/60/30-foot stack of TH7DX tribanders to the same stack over flat land, and to a single antenna at 70 feet over flat ground. The 70-foot single antenna represents a pretty typical station on 15 meters. The terrain produces excellent gain at lower elevation angles compared to the same stack over flat ground. The stack is very close to or superior to the single 70-foot high Yagi at all useful elevation angles. Terrain can indeed exhibit a profound effect on the launch of signals into the ionosphere — for good or for bad.

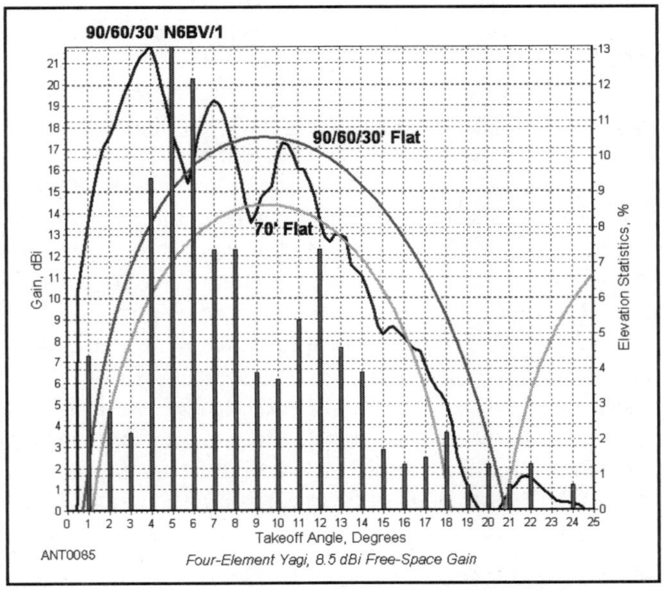

Figure 14.43 — The 21-MHz elevation response for a stack of three TH7DX Yagis mounted on a single tower at 90/60/30 feet, at the N6BV/1 QTH for a 45° azimuth toward Europe. The terrain focuses the energy at low elevation angles compared to the same stack over flat ground. This illustrates once again the conservation of energy: Energy squeezed down into low elevation angles is stolen from other, higher, angles.

HFTA's Internal Antenna Model

The operator selects the antenna used inside *HFTA* to be anything from a dipole to an 8-element Yagi. The default assumes a simple cosine-squared mathematic response, equivalent to a 4-element Yagi in free space. *HFTA* traces rays only in the forward direction from the tower along the azimuth of interest. This keeps the algorithms reasonably simple and saves computing time.

HFTA considers each antenna in a stack as a separate *point source*. The simulation begins to fall apart if a traveling wave type of antenna like a rhombic is used, particularly if the terrain changes under the antenna — that is, the ground is not flat under the entire antenna. For a typical Yagi, even a long-boom one, the point-source assumption is reasonable. The internal antenna model also assumes that the Yagi is horizontally polarized. *HFTA* does not do vertically polarized antennas, as discussed previously. The documentation for *HFTA* also cautions the user to work with practical spacings between stacked Yagis — 0.5 λ or more because *HFTA* doesn't explicitly model mutual coupling between Yagis in a stack.

HFTA compares well with the measurements for the horizontal antennas described earlier by Jim Breakall, WA3FET, using a helicopter in Utah. Breakall's measurements were done with a 15-foot high horizontal dipole.

More About *HFTA* Frequency Coverage

HFTA can be used on frequencies higher than the HF bands, although the graphical resolution is only 0.25°. The patterns above about 100 MHz thus look rather grainy. The UTD is a *high-frequency-asymptotic* solution, so in theory the results become more realistic as the frequency is raised. Keep in mind too that *HFTA* is designed to model launch angles for skywave propagation modes, including E- and F-layer, and even Sporadic-E. Since by definition the ionospheric launch angles include only those above the horizon, direct line-of-sight UHF modes involving negative launch angles are not considered in *HFTA*.

See the HFTA.PDF documentation file for further details on the operation of *HFTA*. This file, as well as sample terrain profiles for some *big-gun* stations, is included with this book's downloadable supplemental information.

14.4 STACKING YAGIS AND SWITCHING SYSTEMS

The preceding sections illustrate the importance of controlling the elevation angle of an antenna's radiation pattern at HF. In addition, the wide variations also illustrate that a single antenna, no matter how much gain it produces, at a single height is often inadequate in maintaining effective communications over the desired path. For example, during a DX band opening on the upper HF bands the initial signals usually appear at very low elevation angles. Later, as the opening strengthens and spreads, signals at higher elevation angles are the strongest. Finally, as the band closes to that area, signals will again be the strongest at low angles. Being able to select the right elevation angle at the right time is important to sustained success in DXing or contest operation.

In HF amateur stations, the most common arrangement to control elevation angle is a vertical stack of identical Yagis on a single tower. This arrangement is commonly called a *vertical stack*. At VHF and UHF, amateurs sometimes employ collinear stacks, where identical Yagis are stacked side-by-side at the same height. This arrangement is called a *horizontal stack*, and is not usually found at HF, because of the severe mechanical difficulties involved with large, rotatable side-by-side arrays. In addition, whereas on HF a primary goal is being able

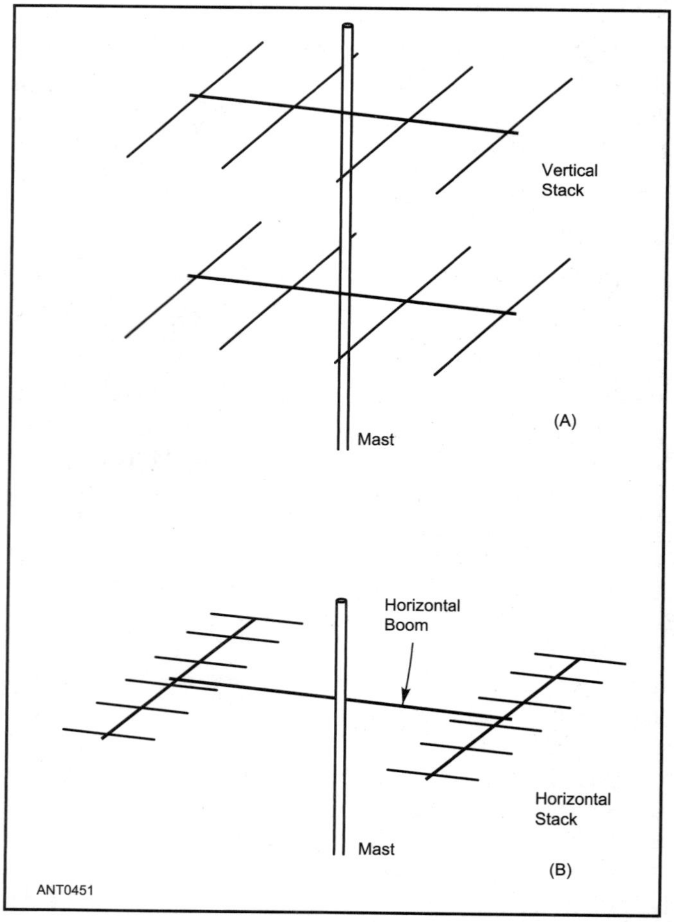

Figure 14.44 — Stacking arrangements. At A, two Yagis are stacked vertically (broadside) on the same mast. At B, two Yagis are stacked horizontally (collinear) side-by-side. At HF the vertical stack is more common because of mechanical difficulties involved with large HF antennas stacked side-by-side, whereas at VHF and UHF the horizontal stack is common.

to control the elevation angle of the radiation pattern for the optimum ionospheric path, on VHF and UHF it is more important to narrow the azimuthal width of the array's main lobe and minimize side lobes to improve the signal-to-noise ratio of very weak signals on both ends of the path.

Figure 14.44 illustrates the two different stacking arrangements. In either case, the individual Yagis making up the stack are generally fed in phase. There are times, however, when individual antennas in a stacked array are purposely fed out of phase in order to emphasize a particular elevation pattern. See the **Repeater Antenna Systems** chapter for such a case where elevation pattern steering is implemented for a repeater station.

Let's look at the reasons hams stack Yagis:

- For more gain
- For a wider elevation footprint in a target geographical area
- For azimuthal diversity — two or more directions at once
- For less fading
- For less precipitation static

14.4.1 STACKS AND GAIN

Figure 14.45 compares the elevation responses for three antenna systems of 4-element 15 meter Yagis. The response for the single Yagi at a height of 120 feet peaks at an elevation of about 5°, with a second peak at 17° and a third at 29°. When operated by itself, the 60-foot high Yagi has its first peak at about 11° and its second peak beyond 34°.

The basic principle of a vertically stacked HF array is that it takes energy from higher-angle lobes and concentrates that energy into the main elevation lobe. The main lobe of the 120/60-foot stack peaks about 7° and is about 2 dB stronger than either the 60- or 120-foot antenna by itself. The shape of the left-hand side of the stack's main lobe is determined mainly by the 120-foot antenna's response. The right-hand side of the stack's main lobe is "stretched" rightward (toward higher angles) mainly by the 60-foot Yagi, while the shape follows the curve of the 120-foot Yagi.

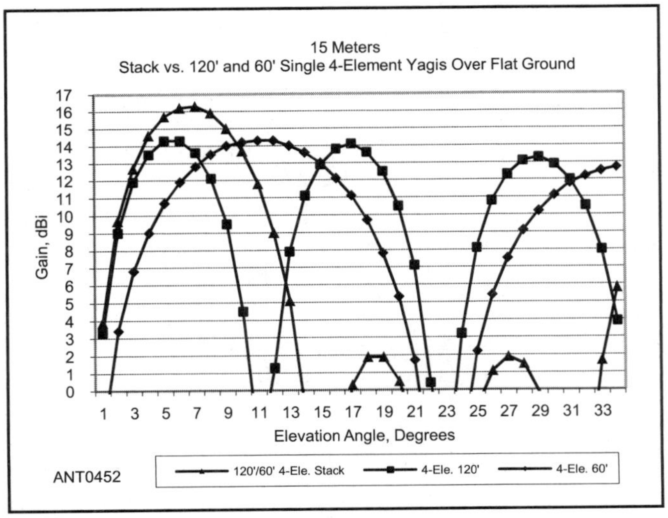

Figure 14.45 — Comparison of elevation patterns on 15 meters for a stack of 4-element Yagis at 120 and 60 feet and individual Yagis at those two heights. The shape of the stack's response is determined mainly by that of the top antenna.

Look at the second and third lobes of the stack, which appear about 18° and 27°. These are about 14 dB down from the stack's peak gain, showing that energy has indeed been extracted from them. By contrast, look at the levels of the second and third lobes for the individual Yagis at 60 and 120 feet. These higher-angle lobes are almost as strong as the first lobes.

The stack squeezes higher-angle energy into its main elevation lobe, while maintaining the frontal lobe azimuth pattern of a single Yagi. This is the reason why many state-of-the-art contest stations are stacking arrays of relatively short-boom antennas, rather than stacking long-boom, higher-gain Yagis. A long-boom HF Yagi narrows the azimuthal pattern (and the elevation pattern too), making pointing the antenna more critical and making it more difficult to spread a signal over a wide azimuthal area, such as all of Europe and Asiatic Russia at one time.

14.4.2 STACKS AND WIDE ELEVATION COVERAGE

Detailed studies using sophisticated computer models of the ionosphere have revealed that coverage of a wide range of elevation angles is necessary to ensure consistent DX or contest coverage on the HF bands. These studies have been conducted over all phases of the 11-year solar cycle, and for numerous transmitting and receiving QTHs throughout the world.

The chapter **Radio Wave Propagation** covers these studies in more detail, and this book's downloadable supplemental information includes a huge number of elevation-angle statistical tables for locations all around the world. The *HFTA* (HF Terrain Assessment) program included with this book's downloadable supplemental information can not only compute antenna elevation patterns over irregular local terrain, but it can compare them directly to the elevation-angle statistics for a particular target geographic area.

A 10 Meter Example

Figure 14.46 shows the 10 meter elevation-angle statistics for the New England path from Boston, Massachusetts, to all of the continent of Europe. The statistics are overlaid with the computed elevation response for three individual 4-element Yagis, at three heights: 90, 60 and 30 feet above flat ground. In terms of wavelength, these heights are 2.60 λ, 1.73 λ and 0.86 λ high.

You can see that the 90-foot high Yagi covers the lower elevation angles best, but it has a large null in its response centered at about 11°. This null puts a big hole in the coverage for some 22% of all the times the 10 meter band is open to Europe. At those angles where the 90-foot Yagi exhibits a null, the 60-foot Yagi would be effective, and so would the 30-foot Yagi. If that is the only antenna you have, the 90-foot high Yagi would be too high for good coverage of Europe from New England.

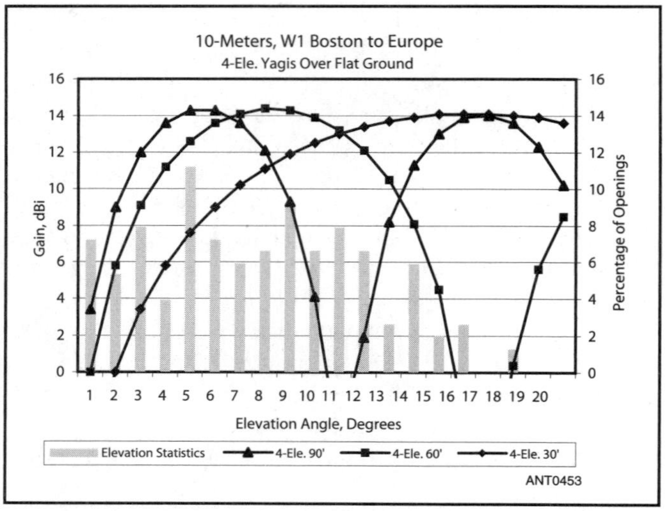

Figure 14.46 — Comparison of elevation patterns and elevation-angle statistics for individual 10-meter TH7DX tribanders mounted over flat ground aiming from New England to Europe. No single antenna can cover the wide range of angles needed — from 1° to 18°.

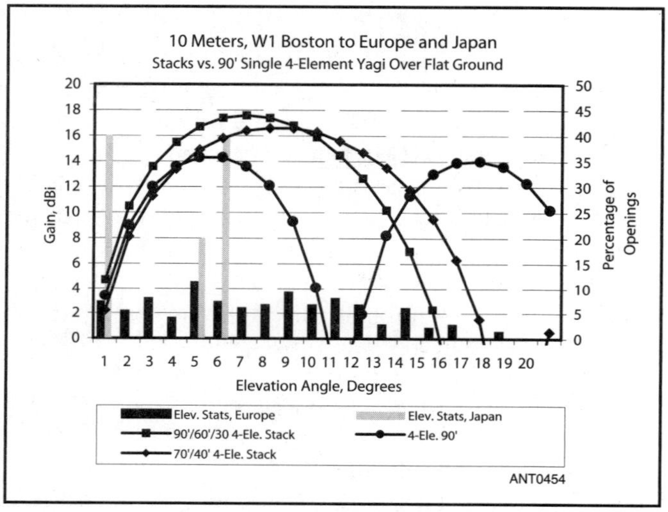

Figure 14.47 — Combinations of 4-element Yagis over flat ground. The elevation-angle statistics into Japan from New England (Boston) are represented by the black vertical bars, while the grey vertical bars represent the elevation-angle statistics to Europe. The 90/60/30-foot stack has the best elevation footprint into Japan, although the 70/40-foot stack performs well also.

The peak statistical elevation angle into Europe is 5°, and this occurs about 11% of all the times the 10 meter band is open to Europe from Boston. At an elevation of 5° the 30-foot high Yagi would be down almost 7 dB compared to the 90-foot high Yagi, but at 11° the 90-foot Yagi would be more than 22 dB down from the 30-foot Yagi. There is no single height at which one Yagi can optimally cover all the necessary elevation angles, especially to a large geographic area such as Europe — although the 60-foot high antenna is arguably the best compromise for a single height. To cover all the possibilities to Europe, however, you need a 10 meter antenna system that can cover equally well the entire range of elevation angles from 1° to 18°.

Figure 14.47 compares elevation-angle statistics for two 10 meter paths from New England to Europe and to Japan. The elevation angles needed for communications with the Far East are very low. Overlaid on Figure 14.47 for comparison are the elevation responses over flat ground for three different antenna systems, using identical 4-element Yagis:

- Three Yagis, stacked at 90, 60 and 30 feet
- Two Yagis, stacked at 70 and 40 feet
- One Yagi at 90 feet.

The best coverage of all the necessary angles on 10 meters to Europe is with the stack of three Yagis at 90/60/30 feet. The two-Yagi stack at 70 and 40 feet comes in a close second to Europe, and for elevation angles higher than about 9° the 70/40-foot stack is actually superior to the 90/60/30-foot stack.

Both of the stacks illustrated here give a wider *elevation footprint* than any single antenna, so that all the angles can be covered automatically without having to switch from higher to lower antennas manually. This is perhaps the major benefit of using stacks, but not the only one, as we'll see.

To Japan, the necessary range of elevation angles is considerably smaller than that needed to a larger geographic target area like Europe. The 90/60/30-foot stack is still best on the basis of having higher gain at low angles, although the two-Yagi stack at 70 and 40 feet is a good choice too. Note that the single 90-foot high Yagi's performance is very close to the 70/40-foot stack of two Yagis at low angles, but the two-Yagi stack is superior to the single 90-foot antenna for angles higher than about 5° on 10 meters.

A 15 Meter Example

The situation is similar on 15 meters from New England to Europe. On 15 meters, the range of angles needed to fully cover Europe is 1° to 28°. This large range of angles makes covering all the angles even more challenging. Ken Wolff, K1EA, a devoted contest operator and the author of the famous *CT* contest logging program, put it very clearly when he wrote in the bulletin for the Yankee Clipper Contest Club:

"Suppose you have 15 meter Yagis at 120 feet and 60 feet, but can feed only one at a time. A 15 meter beam at 120 feet has its first maximum at roughly 5° and the first minimum at 10°. The Yagi at 60 feet has a maximum at 10° and a minimum at 2°. At daybreak, the band is just opening, signals are arriving at 3° or less and the high Yagi outperforms the low one by 5-10 dB. Late in the morning, western Europeans are arriving at angles of 10° or more, while UA6 is still arriving at 4-5°. Western Europe can be 20-30 dB louder on the low antenna than the high! What to do? Stack 'em!"

Figure 14.48 illustrates K1EA's scenario, showing the elevation statistics to Europe from Massachusetts and the elevation responses for a 120- and a 60-foot high, 4-element Yagi, both over flat ground, together with the response for both antennas operated as a vertical stack. The half-power beamwidth of the stack's main lobe is 6.9°, while that for the

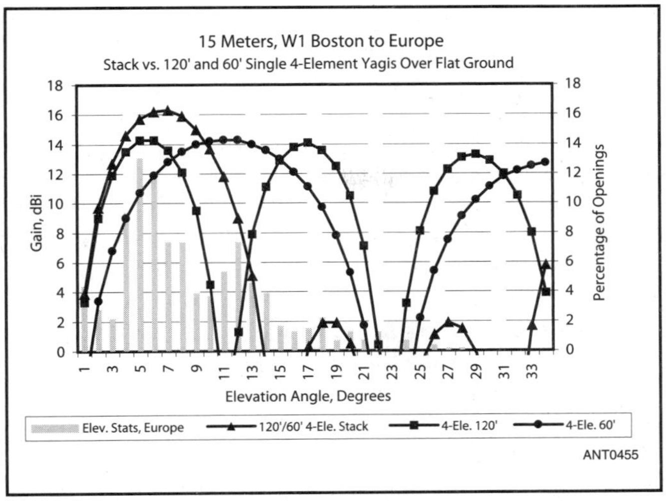

Figure 14.48 — Comparison of elevation patterns for K1EA's illustration about 15 meter Yagis mounted over flat ground, with elevation-angle statistics to Europe added. The stack at 120 and 60 feet yields a better footprint over the range of 3° to 11° at its half-power points, better than either antenna by itself.

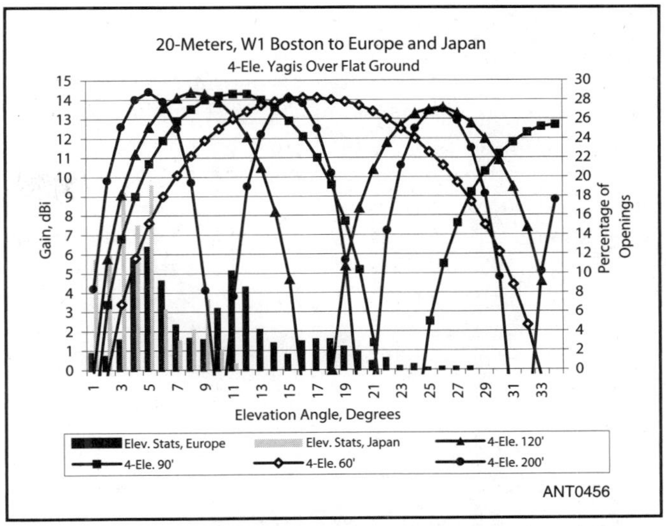

Figure 14.49 — Comparison of elevation patterns for individual 20 meter Yagis over flat ground, compared with the range of elevation angles needed on this band from New England to Europe (gray bars) and to Japan (black bars). For fun, the response of a 200-foot high Yagi is included — this antenna is far too high to cover the needed range of angles to Europe because of its deep nulls at critical angles, like 10°. But the 200 footer is great into Japan!

120-foot antenna by itself is 5.5° and that for the 60-foot antenna by itself is 11.1°. The half-power beamwidth numbers by themselves can be deceiving, mainly because the stack starts out with a higher gain. A more meaningful observation is that the stack has equal to or more gain than either of the two individual antennas from 1° to about 10°.

Is such a stack of 15 meter Yagis at 120 and 60 feet optimal for the New England to Europe path? No, it isn't, as we'll explore later, but the stack is clearly better than either antenna by itself for the scenario K1EA outlined above.

A 20 Meter Example

Take a look now at **Figure 14.49**, which overlays elevation-angle statistics for Europe (gray vertical bars) and Japan (black vertical bars) from Boston on 20 meters, plus the elevation responses for four different sets of antennas mounted over flat ground. Just for emphasis, the highest antenna is a 200-foot high 4-element Yagi. It is clearly too high for complete coverage of all the needed angles into Europe. A number of New England operators have verified that this is true — a really high Yagi will open the 20 meter band to Europe in the morning and may shut it down in the afternoon, but during the middle of the day the high antenna gets soundly beaten by lower antennas.

To Japan, however, from New England the range of angles needed narrows considerably on 20 meters, from 1° to only 11°. For these angles, the 200-foot Yagi is the best antenna to work Japan from New England on 20 meters.

This is true provided that the antenna is aiming out over flat ground. The actual, generally irregular, terrain in various directions can profoundly modify the takeoff angles favored by an antenna system, particularly on steep hills. There will be more discussion on this important topic later on.

14.4.3 ELIMINATING DEEP NULLS

Now, let's look closely at some other 20 meter antennas in Figure 14.46, the ones at 120 and 60 feet. At an elevation angle of 8° the difference in elevation response between the 60- and 120-foot high Yagis is just over 3 dB. Can you really notice a change of 3 dB on the air? Signals on the HF bands often rise and fall quickly due to fading, so differences of 2 or 3 dB are difficult to discern. Consequently, the difference between a Yagi at 120 feet and one at 60 feet may be difficult to detect at elevation angles covered well by both antennas. But a *deep null* in the elevation response is very noticeable.

Back in 1990, when Dean Straw, N6BV, put up his 120-foot tower in Windham, New Hampshire, his first operational antenna was a 5-element triband Yagi, with 3 elements on 40 and 4 elements on both 20 and 15 meters. Just as the sun was going down on a late August day Straw finished connecting the feed line in the shack. The antenna seemed to be playing like it should, with a good SWR curve and a good pattern when it was rotated. So N6BV/1 called a nearby friend, John Dorr, K1AR, on the telephone and asked him to get on the air to make some signal comparisons on 20 meters into Europe.

Straw was shocked that every European they worked that evening said his signal was several S units weaker than K1AR's. Dorr was using a 4-element 20 meter monobander at 90 feet, which at first glance should have been comparable to Straw's 4-element antenna at 120 feet. But N6BV really shouldn't have been so shocked — in New England, the elevation angles from Europe late in the day on 20 meters are almost always higher than 11°, and that is true for the entire solar cycle.

The N6BV/1 station was located on a small hill, while

K1AR was located on flat terrain toward Europe. The elevation response for N6BV/1's 120-foot high Yagi fell right into a deep null at 11°. This was later confirmed many times in the following eight years that the N6BV/1 station was operational. During the early morning opening on 20 meters into Europe, the top antenna was always very close to or equal to the stack of three TH7DX tribanders at 90/60/30 feet on the same tower. But in the afternoon the top antenna was *always* decidedly worse than the stack, so much so that Straw often wondered whether something had gone wrong with the top antenna!

So what's the moral to this short tale? It's simple: *The gain you can achieve, while useful, is not so important as the deep nulls you can avoid by using a stack.*

14.4.4 STACKING DISTANCES BETWEEN YAGIS

So far, we've examined stacks as a means of achieving more gain over an individual Yagi, while also matching the antenna system's response to the range of elevation angles needed for particular propagation paths. Most importantly, we seek to avoid nulls in the elevation response. Earlier we asked whether a 120/60-foot stack was optimal for the path from New England to Europe on 15 meters. Let's examine how the stacking distance between individual antennas affects the performance of a stack.

Figure 14.50 shows overlays of various combinations of 15 meter Yagis. Just for reference, a plot for a single 60-foot high Yagi is also included. Let's start by looking at the most widely spaced stack in the group: the 120/30-foot stack. Here, the spacing is obviously too large, since the second lobe is actually stronger than the first lobe. In terms of wavelength, the 90-foot spacing between antennas in this stack is 1.94 λ, a large spacing indeed.

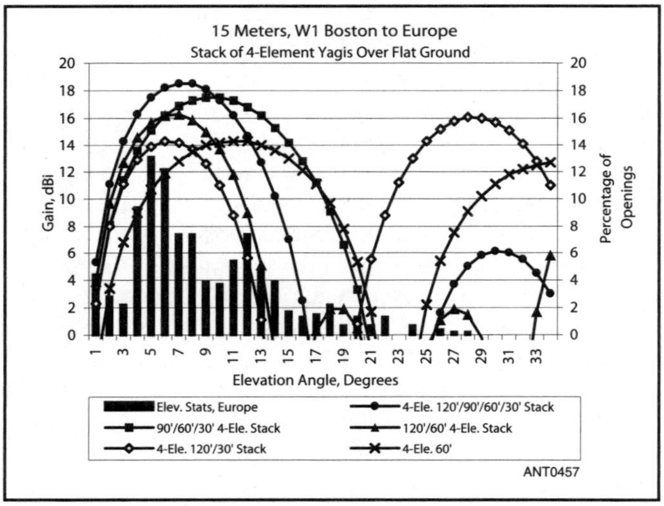

Figure 14.50 — Various stacks toward Europe from New England for 15 meters. The stack at 120 and 30 feet is clearly suboptimal, since the second lobe is higher than the first lobe. The 120/60-foot stack is better in this regard, but is still not as good a performer as the 90/60/30-foot stack. It's debatable whether going to four Yagis in the 120/90/60/30-foot stack is a good idea because it drops below the performance of the 90/60/30-foot stack at about 10° in elevation. The exact distance between practical HF Yagis is not critical to obtain the benefits of stacking. For a stack of tribanders at 90, 60 and 30 feet, the distance in wavelengths between individual antennas is 0.87 λ at 28.5 MHz, 0.65 λ at 21.2 MHz, and 0.43 λ at 14.2 MHz.

There is a great deal of folklore and superstition among amateurs about stacking distances for HF arrays. For years, high-performance stacked Yagi arrays have been used for weak-signal DXing on the VHF and UHF bands. The most extreme example of weak-signal work is EME work (Earth-Moon-Earth, also called *moonbounce*) because of the huge path losses incurred on the way to and from the Moon. The most successful arrays used for moonbounce have low sidelobe levels and very narrow frontal lobes that give huge amounts of gain. The low sidelobes help minimize received noise, since the receive levels for signals that do manage to bounce off the Moon and return to Earth are exceedingly weak.

But HF operation is different from moonbounce in that rigorously trying to minimize high-angle lobes is far less crucial at HF, where we've already shown that the main goal is to achieve gain over a wide elevation-plane footprint without any disastrous nulls in the pattern. The gain gradually increases as spacing in terms of wavelength is increased between individual Yagis in a stack, and then decreases slowly once the spacing is greater than about 1.0 λ. The difference in gain between spacings of 0.5 λ to 1.0 λ for a stack of typical HF Yagis amounts to only a fraction of a decibel. Stacking distances on the order of 0.6 λ to 0.75 λ give best gain commensurate with good patterns.

While the stack at 120/60 feet in Figure 14.50 doesn't have the second-lobe-stronger problem the 120/30-foot stack has — 60 feet between antennas is 1.29 λ, again outside the normal range of HF stack spacings. As a consequence, the 120/60-foot stack doesn't cover the range of elevation angles as well as it could, and is inferior to both the 90/60/30-foot stack and the 120/90/60/30-foot stack. The 120/60-foot two-Yagi stack needs at least one more antenna placed in-between to spread out the elevation-range coverage and to provide more gain.

It could be debated, but the 90/60/30-foot stack seems optimal for coverage of all the angles into Europe from New England on 15 meters. Note that the 30-foot spacing between Yagis is 0.65 λ on 21.2 MHz, right in the middle of the range of typical stack spacings.

Switching Out Yagis in the Stack

Still, the extra gain that is available at low elevation angles from a 120/90/60/30-foot high, four-Yagi stack in Figure 14.50 is alluring. For those statistically possible, but less likely, occasions when the elevation angle is higher than about 12°, it would be advantageous to switch out the top 120-foot Yagi and operate with only the lower three Yagis in a stack. (This also allows the top antenna to be rotated in another direction, an aspect we'll explore later.) There are even times when the incoming angles are really high and when the

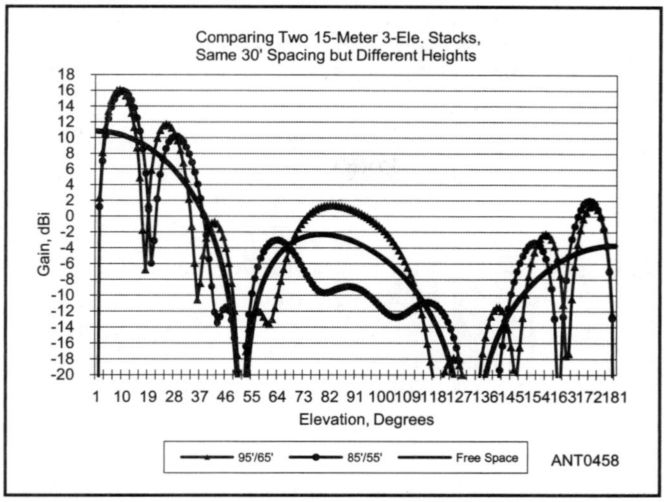

Figure 14.51 — Rectangular plot comparing two 15-meter stacks of 3-element Yagis — each antenna is spaced 30 feet from its partner, but at different heights. The lobes are a complicated function of the antenna height, not the spacing, since that remains constant.

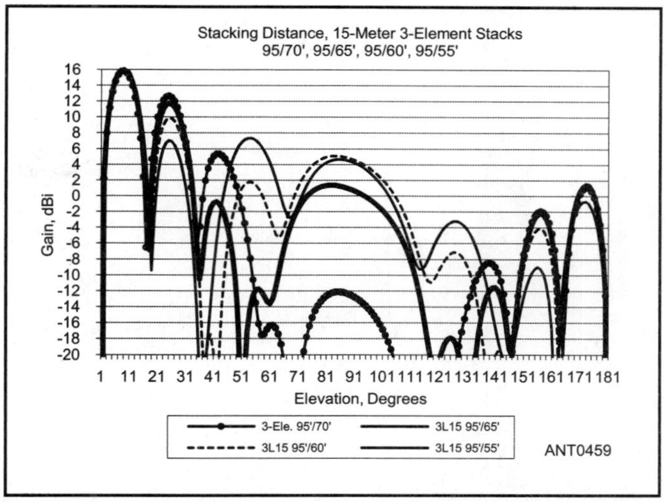

Figure 14.52 — Four spacing scenarios for two 3-element 15-meter Yagis. Things get very complicated. The optimal spacing in terms of stacking gain is 30 feet, which is 0.65 λ. The near-overhead lobes turn out to be ugly looking, but unimportant for skywave propagation.

top two antennas might be switched out to create a 60/30-foot stack. Later in this chapter we'll present circuitry for such stack switching.

Stacking Distance and Lobes at HF

Let's look a little more closely at how a stack achieves gain and a wide elevation footprint. **Figure 14.51** shows a rectangular X-Y graph of the elevation response from 0° to 180° for two 3-element 15 meter Yagis (with 12-foot booms) spaced 30 feet apart (0.65 λ at 21.2 MHz), but mounted at two different heights: 95/65 and 85/55 feet. The rectangular plot gives more resolution than is possible on a polar plot. Note that the heights shown represent typical stacking heights on 15 meters — there's nothing magic about these choices. The free-space H-Plane pattern for the 30-foot spaced stack is also shown for reference.

The worst-case overhead elevation lobe, which ranges from about 60° to 120° in elevation (±30° from straight overhead at 90°), is about 14.7 dB down for the 95/65-foot stack. The overhead lobe peaks broadly at an elevation angle of about 82°. The overhead lobe for the lower 85/55-foot stack occurs at an elevation of about 64°, where it is 19 dB down.

The F/B for both 3-element sets of heights is about 15 dB, well down from the excellent 32 dB F/B for each Yagi by itself. The degradation of F/B is mainly due to mutual coupling to its neighbor in the stack.

The ground-reflection pattern in effect "modulates" the free-space pattern of the individual Yagi, but in a complex and not always intuitive manner. This is quite evident for the 85/55-foot stack at near-overhead angles. In this region things become complicated indeed, because the fourth and fifth lobes due to ground reflections are interacting with the free-space pattern of the stack.

Because the spacing remains constant at 30 feet for these pairs of antennas, however, the main determinant for the upper-elevation angle lobes is the distance of the horizontally polarized antennas above the ground, not the spacing between them.

Changing the Stack Spacing

Figure 14.52 demonstrates just how complicated things get for four different spacing scenarios. Here, the lower Yagi in the stack is moved down in 5-foot increments from the 95/70 feet level, to 95/65, 95/60 and 95/55 feet. The closest spacing, 25 feet in the 95/70-foot stack, yields nominally the "cleanest" pattern in the overhead region from 60° to 120°. The worst-case overhead lobe for the 95/70-foot stack is down 28 dB from peak. The F/B is again about 15 dB.

The worst case overhead lobe for the widest spacing, 40 feet in the 95/55-foot stack, is about 11 dB down from peak. The F/B has increased marginally, but is still only about 16 dB. It is difficult to pinpoint directly whether the spacing or the height above ground is the major determinant for the various lobe amplitudes for the 3-element stack. We'll soon look closely at whether the overhead lobe is important or not for HF work.

Longer Boom Length and Stack Spacing

Figure 14.53 shows the same type overlay of elevation plots, but this time for two 7-element 15 meter Yagis on gigantic 64-foot booms. These Yagis are also spaced 30 feet apart (0.65 λ at 21.2 MHz), mounted at the same four sets of heights in Figure 14.52. As you'd expect, the free-space elevation pattern for a stacked pair of 7-element Yagis on 64-foot booms is narrower than that for a stacked pair of 3-element Yagis on 12-foot booms. The intrinsic F/B of the longer Yagi is also better than the F/B of the shorter antenna. As a result, all lobes beyond the main lobe of the stacked 7-element pair are lower for both sets of heights than their 3-element counterparts. The worst-case overhead lobe for the

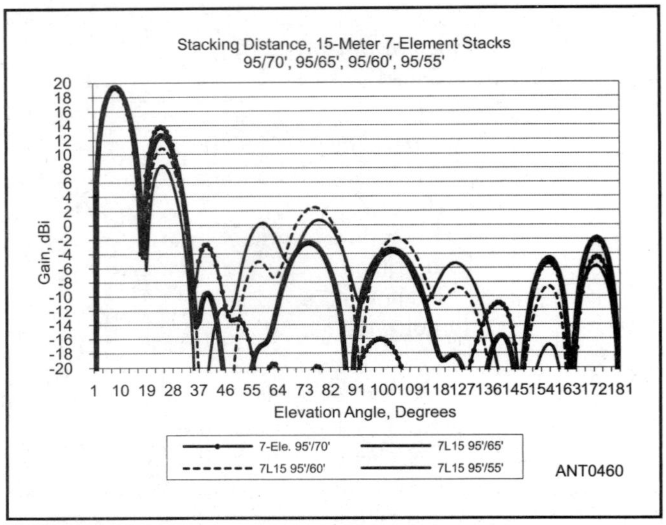

Figure 14.53 — Four spacing scenarios for two large 7-element 15-meter Yagis (on 64-foot booms). Again, a 0.65-λ spacing (30 feet) provides the most stacking gain.

7-element 95/65-foot pair is about 22 dB down at 76° and the F/B at 172° is greater than 21 dB for all four sets of heights.

Table 14.2 summarizes the main performance characteristics for four sets of stacked Yagis. The first entry for each boom length is for the Yagi by itself at a height of 95 feet. Stacked configurations are next listed in order of gain. The column labeled "Worst lobe, dB re Peak" is the amplitude of the second lobe due to ground reflections, and the elevation angle of that second lobe is listed as well.

Besides the 3- and 7-element designs discussed above, we've also added 4- and 5-element designs in Table 14.2. Over the range of stacking distances between 20 and 40 feet on 15 meters (0.43 λ to 0.86 λ), the peak gain for the 3-element stacks changes less than 0.75 dB, with the 30-foot spacing exhibiting the highest gain. The differences between peak gains versus stacking distance become smaller as the boom length increases. For example, for the 64-foot boom Yagi, the gain varies 19.39 – 19.08 = 0.31 dB for stack spacings from 20 to 40 feet.

In other words, changing the spacing from 20 to 40 feet (0.43 λ to 0.86 λ) doesn't change the gain significantly for boom lengths from 12 to 64 feet (0.26 λ to 1.38 λ). From the point of view of gain, the vertical spacing between individual antennas in an HF stack is not critical.

The worst-case lobes (generally speaking, the second lobe due to ground reflections) are highest for a Yagi operated by itself. After all, a single Yagi doesn't benefit from the redistribution of energy from higher-angle lobes into the main lobe that a stack gives. Thus, the 3-element, 12-foot boom Yagi by itself at 95 feet would have a second lobe at 21° that is only 0.9 dB down from the main lobe, while the stack of two such antennas with 30-foot (0.65 λ) spacing at 95/65 feet would have a second lobe down 4.5 dB. As the spacing between antennas in a vertical stack increases, the second lobe is suppressed more, up to 8.7 dB with 40-foot (0.86 λ) spacing.

Since the free-space elevation pattern for a 3-element Yagi is wider than that for a 7-element Yagi, the second lobe due to ground reflection will be somewhat reduced. This is true for all longer-boom antennas operating by themselves over ground. Used in stacks, the second lobe's amplitude will vary depending on spacing between antennas, but they range only about 6 dB.

The front-to-back ratio will also tend to increase with longer boom lengths on a properly designed Yagi. Table 14.2 shows that the F/B is somewhat better for

Table 14.2
Example, Spacing Between 15-Meter Yagis

Antenna	*Peak Gain (dBi)*	*Worst Lobe (dB re Peak)*	*Worst Lobe Angle (°)*	*F/B (dB)*	*Overhead Lobe (dB re Peak)*
3 Elements, 12 Foot Boom					
By itself 95'	13.2	–0.9	21	28.8	–17.5
95'/65' (Δ 30')	16.08	–4.5	25	14.9	–14.7
95'/60' (Δ 35')	16.01	–6.2	24	15.1	–10.9
95'/70' (Δ 25')	15.81	–3.2	24	14.8	–28
95'/55' (Δ 40')	15.71	–8.7	24	16.4	–11
95'/75' (Δ 20')	15.34	–2.3	23	16.3	–17.2
4 Elements, 18 Foot Boom					
By itself 95'	13.92	–1	21	28.3	–20.4
95'/65' (Δ 30')	16.63	–4.5	23	18.5	–17.3
95'/60' (Δ 35')	16.6	–6.2	24	18.2	–13.1
95'/55' (Δ 40')	16.36	–8.7	24	19.8	–13.2
95'/70' (Δ 25')	16.36	–3.3	24	20.4	–31.8
95'/75' (Δ 20')	15.92	–2.5	23	25.9	–19
5 Elements, 23 Foot Boom					
By itself 95'	14.26	–1.1	21	27.9	–22.3
95'/65' (Δ 30')	16.86	–4.6	24	20.8	–19
95'/60' (Δ 35')	16.86	–6.3	24	20.7	–14.4
95'/55' (Δ 40')	16.67	–8.8	24	23.5	–14.4
95'/70' (Δ 25')	16.59	–3.4	24	24.9	–34.4
95'/75' (Δ 20')	16.18	–2.6	23	34.3	–20.2
7 Elements, 64 Foot Boom					
By itself 95'	17.93	–2.2	21	28.9	–17.1
95'/65' (Δ 30')	19.39	–6.9	24.3	21.4	–21.9
95'/60' (Δ 35')	19.38	–8.6	24	21.4	–16.9
95'/55' (Δ 40')	19.29	–10.9	24	25.0	–18.6
95'/70' (Δ 25')	19.26	–5.5	23	24	–35.3
95'/75' (Δ 20')	19.08	–4.6	23	27	–23.4

closer spacings between antennas in a stack, a rather non-intuitive result, considering that the mutual coupling should be greater for closer antennas. For example, the 5-element Yagi stack with 20-foot spacing has a exceptional F/B of 34.3 dB, compared to a F/B of 21.4 dB with the 30-foot spacing distance that gives nominally the most gain. High values of F/B, however, rarely hold over a wide frequency range because of the very critical phasing relationships necessary to get a deep null, so the difference between 34.3 and 21.4 dB would rarely be noticeable in practice.

The near-overhead lobe structure (between 60° to 120° in elevation) tends also to be lower for smaller stack spacings — for all boom lengths — peaking in this example at a spacing of 25 feet for the boom lengths considered here. Since the peak gain actually occurs with smaller spacing between Yagis in this 7-element stack, even relatively large and messy looking overhead lobes are not subtracting from the stacking gain. In the next section we'll now examine whether this overhead lobe is important or not.

Stacking Distances for Multiband Yagis

By definition, a stack of multiband Yagis (such as a "tribander" covering 20/15/10 meters) has a constant vertical spacing between antennas in terms of feet or meters, but not in terms of wavelength. Tribanders are no different than monobanders in terms of optimal spacing between individual antennas. Again, the difference in gain between spacings of 0.5 λ and 1.0 λ for a stack of triband Yagis amounts to only a fraction of a decibel. Furthermore, the main practical constraint that limits choice of stacking distances between any kind of Yagis, multiband or monoband, is the spacing between guy wire sets on the tower itself.

Summary — Stacking Distances

In short, let us summarize that there is nothing magical about stacking distances for practical HF Yagis — a good rule-of-thumb is a stacking distance of 0.65 λ. This is 23 feet on 10 meters, 30 feet on 15 meters and 45 feet on 20 meters for monoband stacks. Practically speaking, however, you've only got limited places where you can mount antennas on the tower — mainly where guy wires allow you to place them. This is especially applicable if you wish to rotate lower antennas on the tower, where you must clear the guys from above the antenna.

14.4.5 RADIATION OUTSIDE THE MAIN LOBE

The Importance of Higher-Angle Lobes

We've already shown that the exact spacing between HF Yagis is not critical for stacking gain. Further, the heights (and hence spacing) of the individual Yagis in a stack interact in a complicated fashion to determine higher-angle lobes.

Let's examine the relevance of such higher-angle lobes for stacked HF Yagis, this time in terms of interference reduction on receive. As the **Radio Wave Propagation** chapter points out, few DX signals arrive at elevation angles greater than about 30°. In fact, DX signals only propagate at elevation angles in the range from 1° to 30° on all the bands where operators might reasonably expect to stack Yagis — nominally from 7 to 29.7 MHz.

You should remember that the definition of the *critical frequency* for HF propagation is the highest frequency for which a wave launched directly overhead at 90° elevation is reflected back down to Earth, rather than being lost into outer space. The maximum critical frequency for extremely high levels of solar flux is about 15 MHz. In other words, high overhead angles do not propagate signals on the upper HF bands.

However, some domestic signals do arrive at relatively high elevation angles. Let's look at some scenarios where higher angles might be encountered and how the elevation patterns of typical HF stacks affect these signals. Let's examine a situation where a medium-range interfering station is on the same heading as a more distant target station.

We'll examine a typical scenario involving stations in Atlanta, Boston and Paris. The heading from Atlanta to Paris is 49°, the same heading as Atlanta to Boston. In other words, the Atlanta station would have to transmit over (and listen through) a Boston station for communication with Paris. The distance between Atlanta and Boston is about 940 miles, while the distance from Atlanta to Paris is about 4350 miles. Ground wave signals obviously cannot travel either of these distances at 21 MHz (ground wave coverage is less than about 10 miles at this frequency), and so the propagation between Atlanta to Boston and Atlanta to Paris will be entirely by means of the ionosphere.

Let's evaluate the situation on 15 meters in the month of October. We'll assume a smoothed sunspot number (SSN) of 100 and that each station puts 1500 W of power into theoretical isotropic antennas that have +10 dBi of gain at all elevation and azimuth angles. [We use such theoretical isotropic antennas because they make it easier to work in *VOACAP*. We will factor in real-world stacks later.] *VOACAP* predicts that the signal from Boston will be S9 + 8 dB in Atlanta at 1400 UTC, arriving at an elevation angle of 21.3° on a single F2 hop. This elevation angle is higher than commonly encountered angles for DX signals, but it is still far away from near-overhead angles.

The signal from Paris into Atlanta is predicted to be about S6 for the same theoretical isotropic antennas, at an incoming elevation angle of 6.4° on three F2 hops. The S6 level validates the rule-of-thumb that each extra hop loses approximately 10 dB of signal strength, assuming that each S unit is about 4 dB, typical for modern receivers.

Now look at **Figure 14.54**, which shows the response for a stack of 3-element Yagis at 90/60/30 feet over flat ground, along with the response for a similar stack of 7-element Yagis. Again, we'll assume that all three stations are using such 3-element 90/60/30-foot stacks. The stations in Atlanta and Boston point their stacks into Europe and the Parisian station points his stack toward the USA. The gain of the Atlanta array at 6.4° into Paris will be about 16 dBi, or 6 dB more than the isotropic array with its +10 dBi of gain selected for use in

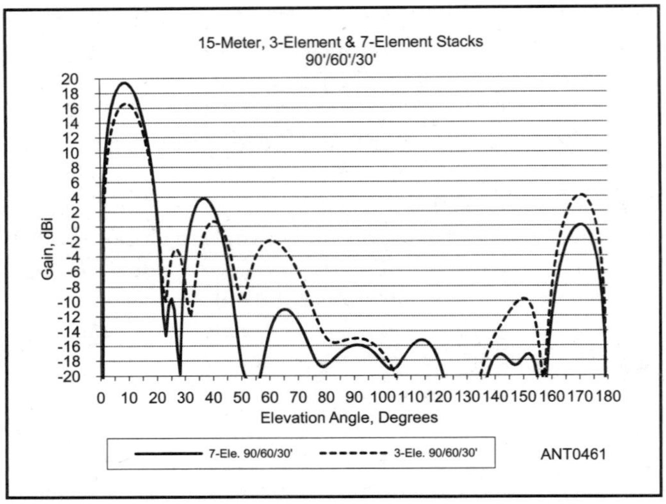

Figure 14.54 — Stacks of three 3-element and 7-element Yagis on 15 meters at 90/60/30 feet heights. The F/B for the 7-element stack is superior to the 3-element stack mainly because the F/B is intrinsically better for the long-boom design.

VOACAP. Similarly, the French station's transmitted signal will enjoy a 6 dB gain advantage over the isotropic array used in the *VOACAP* calculation, and thus the French signal into Atlanta will now be S6 + 12 dB, or about S9.

By comparison, the interfering signal from Boston into Atlanta will be reduced by the rearward pattern of his array, which will launch a signal at 180° – 21.3° = 158.7° in elevation at the single F2 mode from Boston to Atlanta. From Figure 14.51, the Boston station's gain at this rearward elevation is going to drop from the isotropic's +10 dBi of gain down to –11 dBi, a drop of 21 dB. The signal into the Atlanta receiver will also be reduced by the pattern of the Atlanta array on receive, which has a gain of about 0 dBi at 21.3°, compared to the isotropic's +10 dBi gain at 6.4°, a net drop of 10 dB.

Thus, the Boston station's signal will drop by about 21 + 10 = 31 dB, bringing the interfering signal from Boston, which would be S9 + 8 dB for isotropic antennas, down to about S3 due to the combined effects of the arrays. This is a very significant reduction in interference. But you will note that the reduction has nothing to do with the near-overhead lobes, dealing as it does with the trailing edge of the main lobe and the F/B lobe.

Higher Elevation Angles

Now let's evaluate a station that is even closer to Boston, say a station in Philadelphia. The heading from Philadelphia to Paris is 53° and the distance is 3220 miles. On the same day in October as above, *VOACAP* predicts a signal strength of S8 from Paris to Philadelphia, at a 2.7° elevation angle on two F2 hops. Again, the *VOACAP* computations assume isotropic antennas with +10 dBi gain at all three stations. The gain of the 3-element stacks at both ends of the circuit at 2.7° is also about +10 dBi, so the signal level from Paris to Philadelphia would be S8 with the 3-element stacks.

Now *VOACAP* computes the elevation angle from Philadelphia to Boston as 56.3°, on one F_2 hop launched at an azimuth of 53°, well within the azimuthal beamwidth of the stack. *VOACAP* says the predicted signal strength for isotropic antennas with +10 dBi of gain is less than S1!

What's happening here? Boston and Philadelphia are within the "skip" region on 21 MHz and signals are skipping right over Boston from Philadelphia (and vice versa). Actual signals would be much weaker than they would be with theoretical isotropic antennas because of the actual patterns of the transmitting and receiving stacks. At an elevation angle of 56.3° the receiving stack would have a gain of –10 dBi, while at an elevation of 180° – 56.3° = 123.7° the transmitting stack would be down to –10 dBi as well. The net reduction for the stacks compared to isotropics with +10 dBi gain each would be 40 dB, putting the interfering signal well into the receiver noise.

You can safely say that near-overhead angles don't enter into the picture, simply because signals at intermediate distances are in the ionospheric skip zone and interfering signals are very weak in that zone already.

Even in situations where having a poor front-to-back ratio might be beneficial — because it alerts stations tuning across your signal that you are occupying that frequency — the ionosphere doesn't cooperate for intermediate-distance signals that are in the skip zone. Often two stations may be on the same frequency without either knowing that the other is there.

Ground Wave and Stacks

What happens, you might wonder, for ground-wave signals? Let's look at a situation where the interfering station is in the same direction as the desired target, but is only 5 miles away. Unfortunately, his signal is S9 + 50 dB. Even reducing the level by 30 dB, a huge number, is still going to make his signal 20 dB stronger than signals from your desired target location! There is not much you can do about ground-wave signals and fretting about optimizing stack heights to discriminate against local signals is generally futile.

14.4.6 REAL-WORLD TERRAIN AND STACKS

So far, the stacking examples shown have been for flat ground. Things can become a lot more complicated when you deal with real-world irregular terrains! **Figure 14.55** shows the *HFTA*-computed 20 meter elevation responses toward Europe (at an azimuth of 45°) for three antennas at the N6BV/1 location in Windham, New Hampshire. Overlaid as a bar graph are the elevation-angle statistics for the path to all of Europe from New England (Massachusetts). The stack at 90/60/30 feet clearly covers all the angles needed best at 14 MHz. The N6BV/1 120-foot Yagi has a severe null in the region from about 7° to about 20°, with the deepest part of that null occurring at about 13° and is roughly comparable to the 90/60/30-foot stack between 2° to 7°.

In practice, the 120-foot Yagi was indeed comparable to the stack during morning openings to Europe on 20 meters, when the elevation angles are typically about 5°. In the New England afternoon, when the elevation angles typically rise

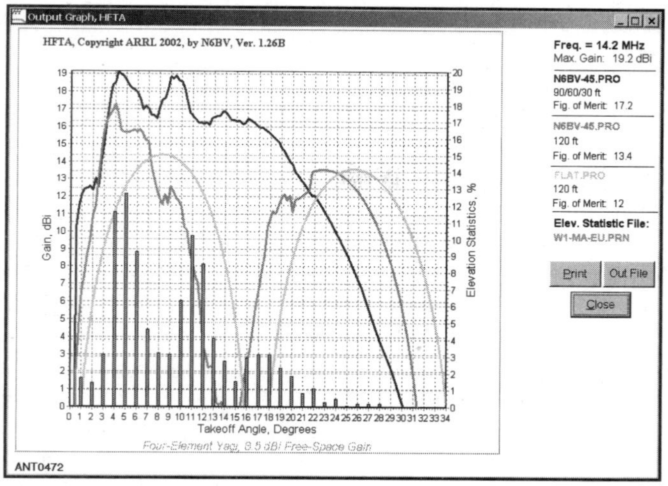

Figure 14.55 — *HFTA* screen shot showing how complicated things become when real-world irregular terrain is analyzed. This is the 20-meter elevation pattern for the N6BV/1 station location in Windham, NH, for the 90/60/30-foot stack of tri-band TH7DX Yagis and a 4-element Yagi at 120 feet on the same tower. For comparison, the response of a 120-foot Yagi over flat ground is also included.

to about 11°, the 120-foot Yagi was always distinctly inferior to the stack.

For reference, the response of a single 120-foot high Yagi over flat ground is also shown. Note that the N6BV 120-foot high Yagi has about 3 dB more gain at a 5° takeoff angle than does its flatland counterpart. This additional gain is due to the focusing effects of the local terrain, which had about a 3° downward slope toward Europe.

Figure 14.56 shows the *HFTA*-computed 15 meter elevation responses toward Europe for the 90/60/30-foot stack at 90/60/30 feet at N6BV/1, compared to the same 120-foot high Yagi and a 90/60/30-foot stack, but this time over flat ground. Again, the N6BV/1 terrain toward Europe has a significant effect on the gain of the stack compared to that of an identical stack over flat ground. In fact, the peak gain of 20.1 dBi at a 4° elevation angle is close to moon-bounce levels.

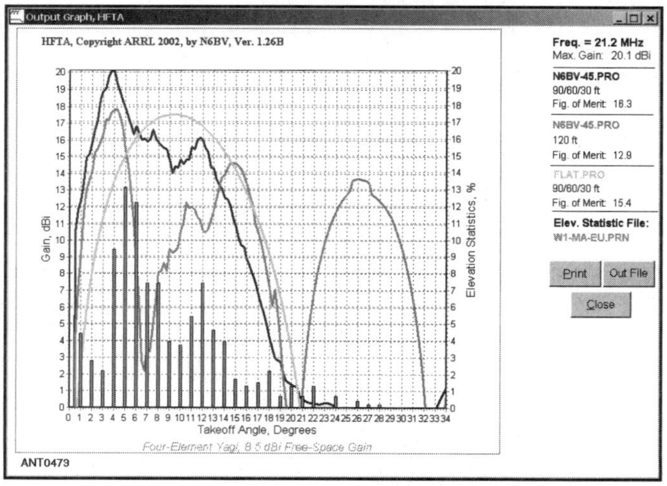

Figure 14.56 — *HFTA* screen shot showing the 15-meter elevation pattern for the N6BV/1 station location in Windham, NH, for the 90/60/30-foot stack of triband TH7DX Yagis and a 4-element Yagi at 120 feet on the same tower. For comparison, the response of a 120-foot Yagi over flat ground is also included.

Optimizing Over Local Terrain

There are only a small number of possibilities to optimize an installation over local terrain:

- Change the antenna height(s) above ground.
- Stack two (or more) Yagis.
- Change the spacing between stacked Yagis.
- Move the tower back from a cliff (or a hill).
- BIP/BOP (Both In Phase/Both Out of Phase).

The *HFTA* program included with this book's down-

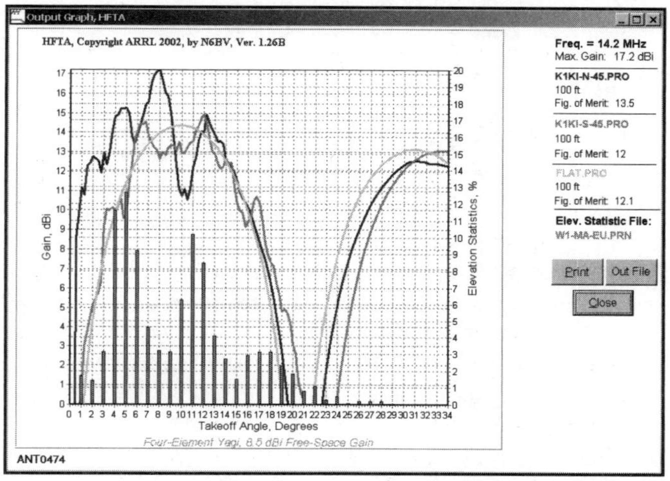

Figure 14.57 — *HFTA* screen shot showing the 20-meter elevation pattern for K1KI's North and South towers, with 100-foot high 4-element Yagis pointing into Europe at an azimuth of 45°. The responses are surprisingly different for two towers separated by only 600 feet.

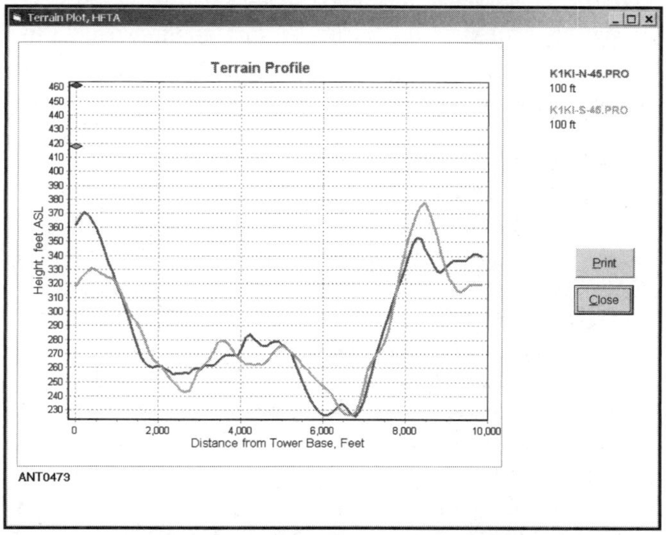

Figure 14.58 — K1KI's terrain profiles for the North and South towers at an azimuth of 45° into Europe.

loadable supplemental information can be used, together with Digital Elevation Model (DEM) topographic data available on the Internet, to evaluate all these options.

It is sometimes very surprising to compare elevation responses for different towers located at various points on the same property, particularly when that property is located in the mountains. **Figure 14.57** shows the computed elevation responses for three 100-foot high 14-MHz Yagis over three terrains toward Europe: from the North tower at K1KI's location in West Suffield, Connecticut, from the South tower at K1KI, and over flat ground. The elevation response from the South tower follows that over flat ground well, while the response from the North tower is quite a bit stronger at low elevation angles — about 1.5 dB on average, as the Figure of Merit shows from *HFTA*.

Figure 14.58 shows the reason why this happens — the terrain from the North tower slopes down quickly toward Europe, while the terrain from the South tower goes out almost 900 feet before starting to fall off. These two towers are about 600 feet apart.

14.4.7 STACKING TRIBANDERS

Enterprising amateurs have built stacked tribander arrays even with full recognition that they are compromise antennas when compared one-on-one against monoband Yagis. Bob Mitchell, N5RM, is a prominent example, with his so-called "TH28DX" array of four TH7DX tribanders on a 145-foot-high rotating tower. Mitchell employed a rather complex system of relay-selected tuned networks to choose either the upper stacked pair, the lower stacked pair or all four antennas in stack. Others in Texas have also had good results with their tribander stacks. Contester Tom Owens, K7RI, has very successfully used a pair of stacked KT-36XA tribanders for years.

A major reason why tribanders were used is that over the years both amateurs have had good results using TH6DXX or TH7DX antennas. They are ruggedly built, mechanically and electrically, and their 24-foot long booms are long enough to produce significant gain, despite trap-loss compromises. Trap losses estimated at approximately 0.5 dB are not high enough to be of serious concern. A long-boom tribander like the TH6DXX or TH7DX also has enough space to employ elements dedicated to different bands, so the compromises in element spacing usually found on short-boom 3 or 4-element tribanders can be avoided.

Another factor in favor of tribanders is the serious interaction that can result from stacking monoband antennas closely together on one mast in a Christmas Tree configuration. N6BV's worst experience was with the ambitious 10 through 40 meter Christmas Tree at W6OWQ in the early 1980s. This installation used a Tri-Ex SkyNeedle tubular crank-up tower with a rotating 10-foot-long heavy-wall mast. The antenna suffering the greatest degradation was the 5-element 15 meter Yagi, sandwiched 5 feet below the 5-element 10 meter Yagi at the top of the mast, and 5 feet above the full-sized 3-element 40 meter Yagi, which also had five 20 meter elements interlaced on its 50-foot boom.

The front-to-back ratio on 15 meters was at best about 12 dB, down from the 25+ dB measured with the bottom 40/20 meter Yagi removed. No amount of fiddling with element spacing, element tuning or even orientation of the 15 meter boom with respect to the other booms (at 90° or 180°, for example) improved its performance. Further, the 20 meter elements had to be lengthened by almost a foot *on each end of each element* in order to compensate for the effect of the interlaced 40 meter elements. It was a lucky thing that the tower was a motorized crank-up, because it went up and down hundreds of times as various experiments were attempted!

Interaction due to close proximity to other antennas in a short Christmas Tree can definitely destroy carefully optimized patterns of individual Yagis. Nowadays, such interaction can be modeled using a computer program such as *EZNEC* or *NEC*. A gain reduction of as much as 2 to 3 dB can easily result due to close vertical spacing of monobanders, compared to the gain of a single monoband antenna mounted in the clear. Curiously enough, at times such a reduction in gain can be found even when the front-to-back ratio is not drastically degraded, or when the front-to-back occasionally is actually *improved*.

If you plan on stacking monoband Yagis — for example, putting 15 and 20 meter Yagis on a single tower, do make sure you model the system to see if any interactions occur. You may be quite surprised.

Finally, triband antennas make for less mechanical complexity than do an equivalent number of monobanders. There were five Yagis on the N6BV/1 tower, yielding gain from 40 to 10 meters, as opposed to using 12 or 13 monobanders on the tower.

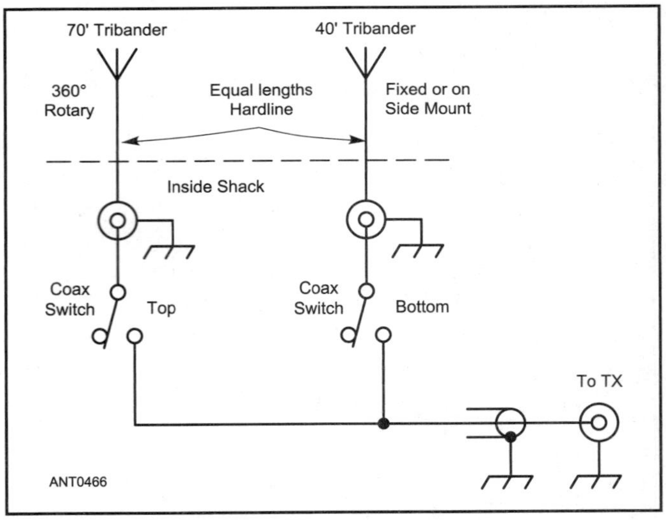

Figure 14.59 — Simple feed system for 70/40-foot stack of tribanders. Each tribander is fed with equal lengths of 0.5-inch 75-Ω Hardline cables (with equal lengths of flexible coax at the antenna to allow rotation), and can be selected singly or in parallel at the operator's position in the shack. Again, no special provision is made in this system to equal SWR for any of the combinations.

Simple Tribander Stacks

All this discussion of large stacks of many antennas is simply out of the question for most amateurs. However, many hams already have a tribander on top of a moderately tall tower, typically at a height of about 70 feet. It is not terribly difficult to add another, identical tribander at about the 40-foot level on such a tower. The second tribander can be pointed in a fixed direction of particular interest (such as Europe or Japan), or it can be rotated around the tower on a side mount or a Ring Rotor. If guy wires get in the way of rotation, the antenna can usually be arranged so that it is fixed in a single direction.

Insulate the guy wires at intervals to ensure that they don't shroud the lower antenna electrically. A simple feed system consists of equal-length runs of surplus ½-inch 75-Ω hardline (or more expensive 50-Ω hardline, if you are really obsessed by SWR) from the shack up the tower to each antenna. Each tribander is connected to its respective hardline feeder by means of an equal length of flexible coaxial cable, with a ferrite choke balun, so that the antenna can be rotated.

Down in the shack, the two runs of hardline can simply be switched in and out of parallel to select the upper antenna only, the lower antenna only, or the two antennas as a stack. See **Figure 14.59**. Any impedance differences can be handled as stated previously, simply by retuning the linear amplifier, or by means of the internal antenna tuner (included in most modern transceivers) when the transceiver is run barefoot. The extra performance experienced in such a system will be far greater than the extra decibel or two that modeling calculates.

14.4.8 STACKING DISSIMILAR YAGIS

So far we have been discussing vertical stacks of identical Yagis. Less commonly, hams have successfully stacked dissimilar Yagis. For example, consider a case where two 5-element 10 meter Yagis are placed 46 and 25 feet above flat ground, with a 7-element 10 meter Yagi at 68 feet on the same tower. See **Figure 14.60**, which is a schematic of the layout for this stack. Note that the driven element for the top 7-element Yagi is well behind the vertical plane of the driven elements for the two 5-element Yagis. This offset distance must be compensated for with a phase shift in the drive system for the top Yagi.

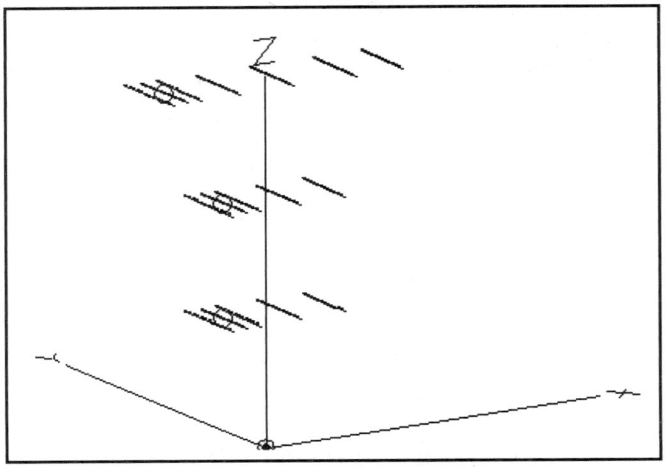

Figure 14.60 — Stacking dissimilar Yagis. In this case a 7-element 10-meter Yagi is stacked over two 5-element Yagis. Note the displacement of the 7-element Yagi's driven element compared to the position of the two 5-element Yagis. This leads to an undesired phase shift for the higher antenna.

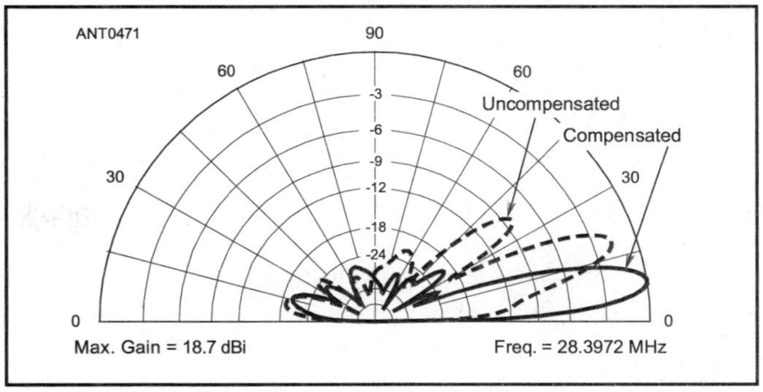

Figure 14.61 — Comparison of elevation responses for 7/5/5-element 10-meter stacks, with and without compensation for driven-element offset.

Figure 14.61 shows the elevation-pattern responses for uncompensated (equal-length feed lines) and the compensated (additional 150° of phase shift to top Yagi) stacks. These patterns were computed using *EZNEC*. Not only is about 1.7 dB of maximum gain lost, but the peak elevation angle is shifted upward by 11° from the optimal takeoff angle of 8° — where some 10 dB of gain is also lost. Without compensation, this is a severe distortion of the stack's elevation pattern.

For RG-213 coax, the extra length needed to provide an additional 150° of phase shift = 150°/360° λ = 0.417 λ = 9.53 feet at 28.4 MHz. This was computed using the program *TLW* (Transmission Line for *Windows*) included with this book's downloadable supplemental information.

It is not always possible to compensate for dissimilar Yagis in a stack with a simple length of extra coax, so you should be sure to model such combinations to make sure that they work properly. A safe alternative, of course, is to stack only identical Yagis, feeding all of them with equal lengths of coax to ensure in-phase operation.

14.4.9 THE WXØB APPROACH TO STACK SWITCHING

Earlier we mentioned how useful it would be to switch various antennas in or out of a stack, depending on the elevation angles that need to be emphasized at that moment. Jay Terleski, WXØB, of Array Solutions (**www.arraysolutions.com**) has designed switchable matching systems, called *StackMatches*, for stacks of monoband or multiband Yagis. This has become the standard method of switching for stacks of Yagi antennas, whether monoband or triband. (A description of two other systems used by N6BV/1 and K1VR is included with this book's downloadable supplemental information.)

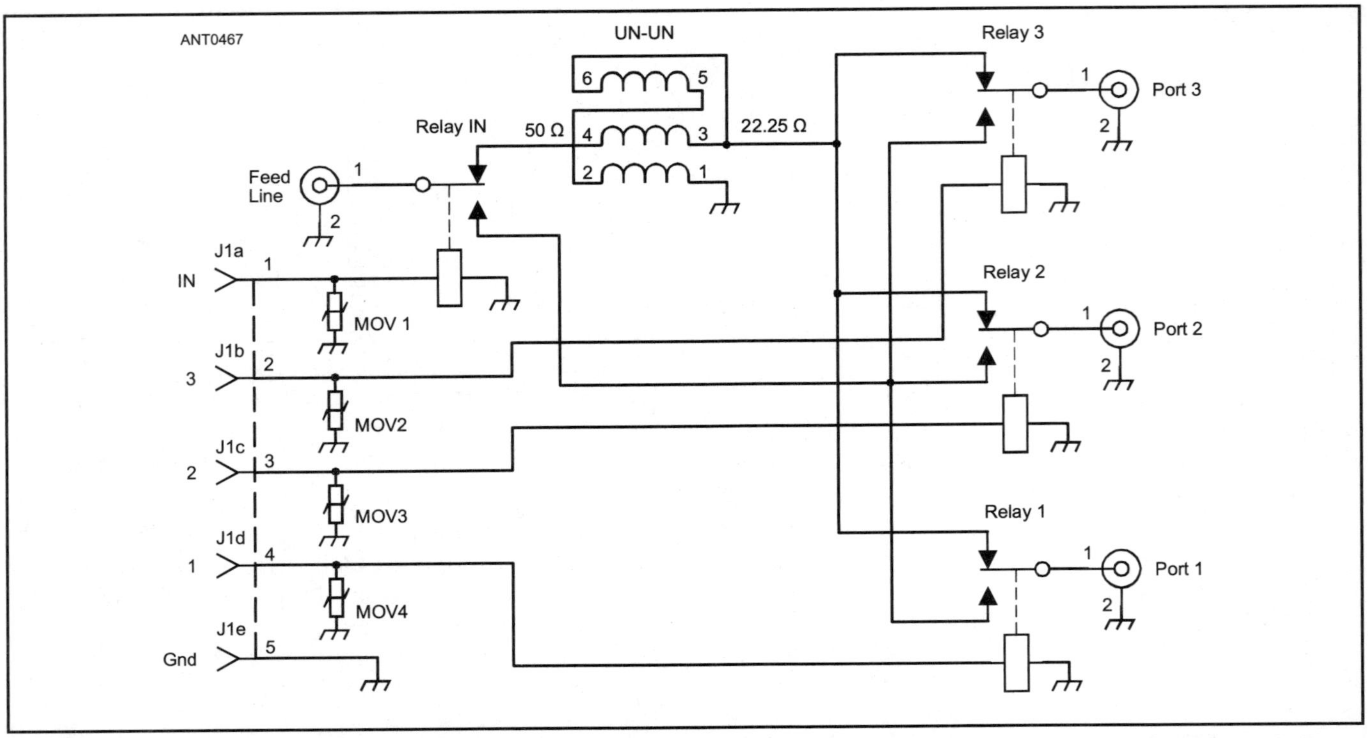

Figure 14.62 — Schematic of WXØB's StackMatch 2000 switchbox, which uses a broadband transmission line transformer using trifilar #12 enamel-insulated wires. (*Courtesy Array Solutions.*)

The StackMatch uses a 50-Ω to 22.25-Ω broadband transmission-line transformer to match combinations of up to three Yagis in a stack. See **Figure 14.62** for a schematic of the StackMatch. For selection of any 50-Ω Yagi by itself, no matching transformer is needed and Relay IN routes RF directly to the common bus going to Relay 1, 2 and 3. For selection of two Yagis together the parallel impedance is 50/2 = 25 Ω and Relay IN routes RF to the matching transformer. The SWR is 25/22.25 = 1.1:1. For three Yagis used together, the parallel impedance is 50/3 = 16.67 Ω, and the SWR is 22.25/16.67 = 1.3:1.

The broadband transformer consists of four trifilar turns of #12 enamel-insulated wire wound on a Ferrite Corporation FT-240 2.4-inch OD core made of #61 material (μ = 125). WXØB uses 10-A relays enclosed in plastic cases to do the RF switching, selected by a control box at the operating position. (10-A relays can theoretically handle 10 $A^2 \times 50\ \Omega$ = 5000 W.) **Figure 14.63** shows a photo of the transmission-line transformer and StackMaster PCB.

The control/indicator box uses a diode matrix to switch various combinations of antennas in/out of the stack. Three LEDs lined up vertically on the front panel indicate which antennas in a stack are selected.

14.4.10 TRANSMISSION LINE STACK MATCHING BY K1EA

As a complement to the transformer-based system of Array Solutions, the approach taken by Ken Wolff, K1EA, to stack switching uses only lengths of feed line. Ken relied on the current-forcing effect of a ¼-λ length of feed line and of

Figure 14.63 — Inside view of StackMatch. (*Photo courtesy Array Solutions.*)

combining parallel lengths of feed line for impedance transformation. Whether or not you replicate this system, the technique — originally published in the December 1989 issue of the Yankee Clipper Contest Club's *Scuttlebutt* newsletter — can be applied in many different antenna system designs.

The technique works best based on four rules:

1) The antennas are physically identical.

2) The feed line is identical — use cable off the same spool.

3) Use choke baluns to block common-mode RF current

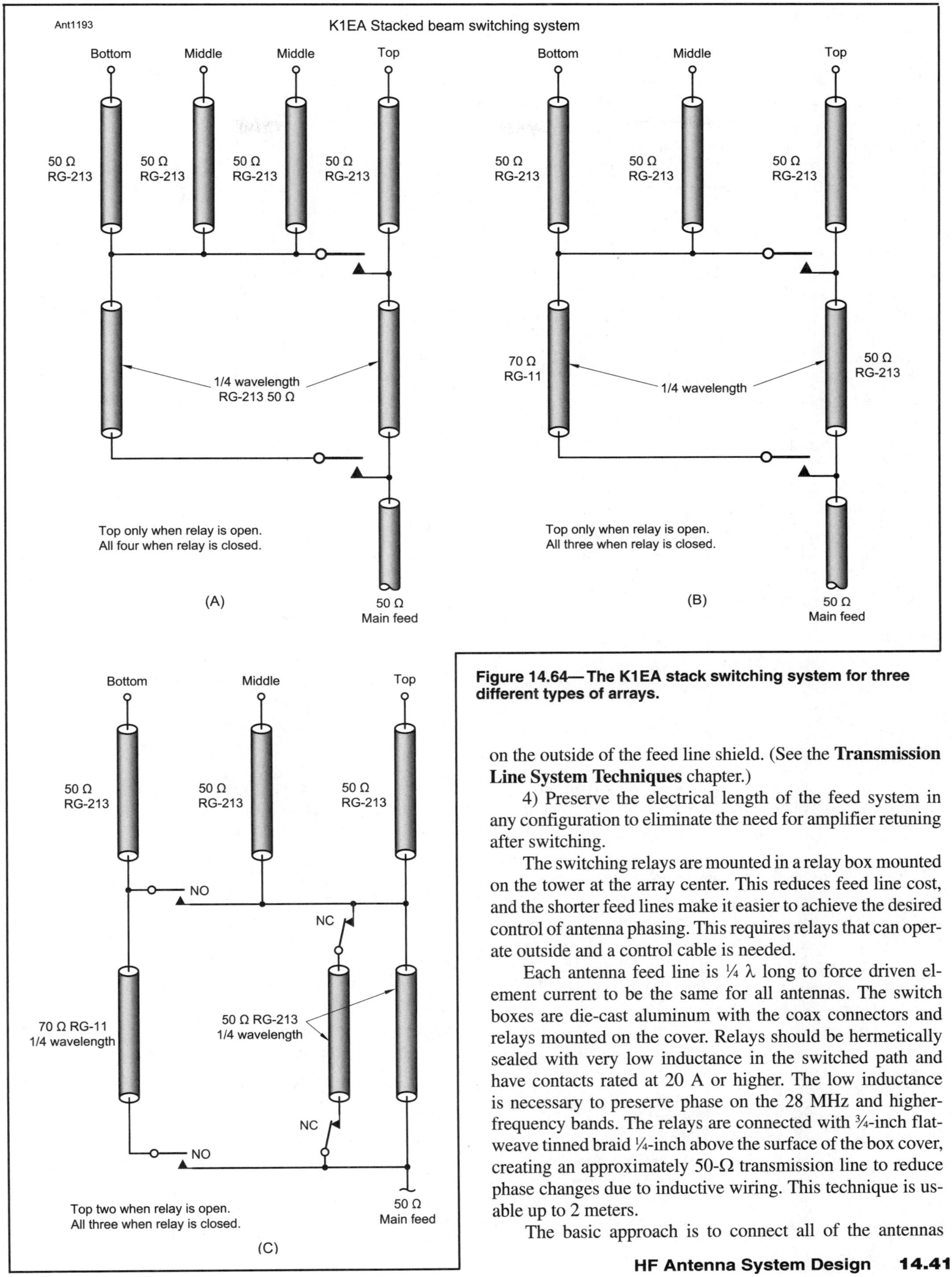

Figure 14.64—The K1EA stack switching system for three different types of arrays.

on the outside of the feed line shield. (See the **Transmission Line System Techniques** chapter.)

4) Preserve the electrical length of the feed system in any configuration to eliminate the need for amplifier retuning after switching.

The switching relays are mounted in a relay box mounted on the tower at the array center. This reduces feed line cost, and the shorter feed lines make it easier to achieve the desired control of antenna phasing. This requires relays that can operate outside and a control cable is needed.

Each antenna feed line is ¼ λ long to force driven element current to be the same for all antennas. The switch boxes are die-cast aluminum with the coax connectors and relays mounted on the cover. Relays should be hermetically sealed with very low inductance in the switched path and have contacts rated at 20 A or higher. The low inductance is necessary to preserve phase on the 28 MHz and higher-frequency bands. The relays are connected with ¾-inch flat-weave tinned braid ¼-inch above the surface of the box cover, creating an approximately 50-Ω transmission line to reduce phase changes due to inductive wiring. This technique is usable up to 2 meters.

The basic approach is to connect all of the antennas

in parallel, creating a low impedance, then transforming that impedance to 50 Ω with a ¼-λ transmission line transformer. (See "Quarter-Wave Transformers" in the chapter on **Transmission Line System Techniques**.) Coaxial cables of different impedances (50 and 70 Ω) are combined in parallel to produce low-impedance feed lines. For example, two 50-Ω lines in parallel create a 25-Ω line, and a 50-Ω line in parallel with a 70-Ω line creates a 29.3-Ω cable. For the impedance transformer section, the formula is:

$$Z_{NEW} = (Z_{LINE} \times Z_{LINE}) / Z_{OLD}$$

Some examples of this technique are shown in **Figure 14.64**. For example, the system with three 50-Ω antennas in parallel labeled "Top only or all three" (Figure 14.64B) creates a 50/3 = 16.7 Ω impedance. The 70-Ω and 50-Ω lines in parallel create a 29.2-Ω line. Using the transformation formula, the resulting impedance is (29.2 × 29.2) / 16.7 = 51 Ω which is a very close match to 50 Ω. Similarly, the four-stack (Figure 14.64A) antennas in parallel are 12.5 Ω and the two 50-Ω lines in parallel create a 25-Ω line, resulting in 50 Ω exactly.

Similarly, six 50-Ω antennas in parallel (8.33 Ω) are matched with 20.6-Ω line made of two 70-Ω lines in parallel with one 50-Ω line, creating (20.6 × 20.6) / 8.33 = 50.9 Ω impedance. Five 50-Ω antennas in parallel create 10 Ω which is matched by a 23.3-Ω section of three 70-Ω lines in parallel, creating (23.3 × 23.3) / 10 = 54.4 Ω. The possibilities are endless: switch the antennas to be driven so they are in parallel, then switch in combinations of 50 and 70-Ω lines to match the resulting impedance to 50 Ω.

Figure 14.65 — 3D representation of the pattern for two 4-element 15-meter Yagis, with the top antenna at 95 and the bottom at 65 feet, but pointed in the opposite direction.

14.4.11 MISCELLANEOUS TOPICS

Stacks and Fading

The following is derived from an article by Fred Hopengarten, K1VR, and Dean Straw, N6BV, in a February 1994 *QST* article. Using stacked Hy-Gain TH7DXs or TH6DXXs at their respective stations, they have solicited a number of reports from stations, mainly in Europe, to compare various combinations of antennas in stacks and as single antennas. The peak gain of the stack is usually just a little bit higher than that for the best of the single antennas, which is not surprising. Even a large stack has no more than about 6 dB of gain over a single Yagi at a height favoring the prevailing elevation angle. Fading on the European path can easily be 20 dB or more, so it is very confusing to try to make definitive comparisons. They have noticed over many tests that the stacks are much less susceptible to fading compared to single Yagis. Even within the confines of a typical SSB bandwidth, frequency-selective fading occasionally causes the tonal quality of a voice to change on both receive and transmit, often dramatically becoming fuller on the stacks, and tinnier on the single antennas. This doesn't happen all the time, but is often seen. They have also observed often that the depth of a fade is less, and the period of fading is longer, on the stacks compared to single antennas.

Exactly *why* stacks exhibit less fading is a fascinating subject, for which there exist a number of speculative ideas, but little hard evidence. Some maintain that stacks outperform single antennas because they can afford *space diversity* effects, where by virtue of the difference in physical placement one antenna will randomly pick up signals that another one in another physical location might not hear.

This is difficult to argue with, and equally difficult to prove scientifically. A more plausible explanation about why stacked Yagis exhibit superior fading performance is that their narrower frontal elevation lobes can discriminate against undesired propagation modes. Even when band conditions favor, for example, a very low 3° elevation angle on 10 or 15 meters from New England to Western Europe, there are signals, albeit weaker ones, that arrive at higher elevation angles. These higher-angle signals have traveled longer distances on their journey through the ionosphere, and thus their signal levels and their phase angles are different from the signals traversing the primary propagation mode. When combined with the dominant mode, the net effect is that there is both destructive and constructive fading. If the elevation response of a stacked antenna can discriminate against signals arriving at higher elevation angles, then in theory the fading will be reduced. Suffice it to say: In practice, stacks do reduce fading.

Stacks and Precipitation Static

The top antenna in a stack is often much more affected by rain or snow precipitation static than is the lower antenna. N6BV and K1VR have observed this phenomenon, where signals on the lower antenna by itself are perfectly readable, while S9+ rain static is rendering reception impossible on the higher antenna or on the stack. This means that the ability

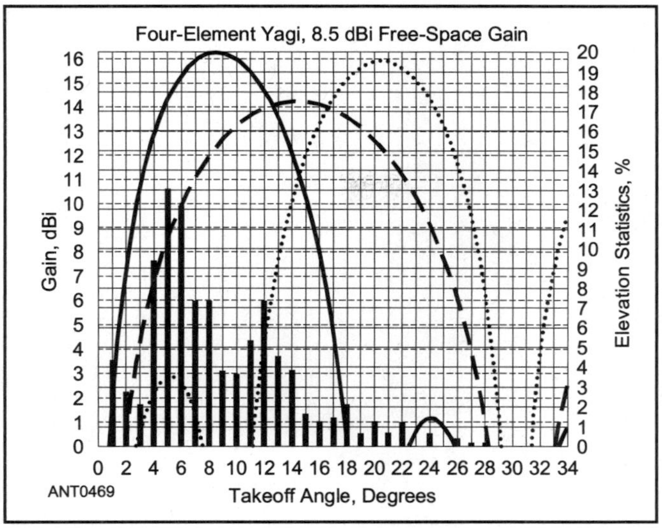

Figure 14.66 — *HFTA* screen shot of "BIP/BOP" operation of two 4-element 15-meter Yagis at 93 and 46 feet above flat ground. The elevation response in BOP (both out-of-phase) operation is shifted higher, peaking at about 21°, compared to the BIP (both in-phase) operation where the peak is at 8°. The dashed line is response of single Yagi at 46 feet.

to select individual antennas in a stack can sometimes be extremely important for reasons unrelated to elevation angle.

Stacks and Azimuthal Diversity

Azimuthal diversity is a term coined to describe the situation where one of the antennas in a stack is purposely pointed in a direction different from the main direction of the stack. During most of the time in a DX contest from the East Coast, the lower antennas in a stack are pointed into Europe, while the top antenna is often rotated toward the Caribbean or Japan. In a stack of three identical Yagis, the first-order effect of pointing one antenna in a different direction is that one-third of the transmitter power is diverted from the main target area. This means that the peak gain is reduced by 1.8 dB, not a very large amount considering that signals are often 10 to 20 dB over S9 anyway when the band is open from New England to Europe.

Figure 14.65 shows the 3D pattern of a pair of 4-element Yagis fed in-phase at 95 and 65 feet, but where the lower antenna has been rotated 180° to fire in the –X direction. The backwards lobe peaks at a higher elevation angle because the antenna doing the radiating in this direction is lower on the tower. The forward lobe peaks at a lower angle because its main radiator is higher.

"BIP/BOP" Operation

The contraction "BIP" means "both in-phase," while "BOP" means "both out-of-phase." BIP/BOP refer to stacks containing two Yagis, although the term is commonly used for stacks containing more than two Yagis. In theory, feeding a stack with the antennas out-of-phase will shift the elevation response higher than in-phase feeding.

Figure 14.66 shows a rectangular plot comparing BIP/BOP operation of two 3-element 15 meter Yagis at heights of 2 λ and 1 λ (93 and 46 feet) over flat ground. The BOP pattern is the higher-angle lobe and the two lobes cross over about 14°. The maximum amplitude of the BOP stack's gain is about ½ dB less than the BIP pair. For reference, the pattern of a single 46-foot high Yagi is overlaid on the pattern for the stacks.

The most common method for feeding one Yagi 180° out-of-phase is to include an extra electrical half wavelength of feed line coax going to one of the antennas. This method obviously works on a single frequency band and thus is not applicable to stacks of multiband Yagis, such as tribanders. For such multiband stacks, feeding only the lower antenna(s) — by switching out higher antenna(s) in the stack — is a practical method for achieving better coverage at medium or high elevation angles.

Notes

The ARRL

ANTENNA BOOK

FOR RADIO COMMUNICATIONS

24th EDITION

Volume 1: Antenna Fundamentals — Ch. 1-8

Volume 2: Antennas for LF/MF/HF— Ch. 9-14

▶ **Volume 3: Antennas for VHF through Microwave and Specialty Antennas — Ch. 15-22**

Volume 4: Transmission Lines and Building Antenna Systems, and Index — Ch. 23-28

Editor
H. Ward Silver, NØAX

Contributing Editors
Steven R. Ford, WB8IMY
Mark J. Wilson, K1RO

Editorial Assistant
Maty Weinberg, KB1EIB

Production
Michelle Bloom, WB1ENT
Sue Fagan, KB1OKW
— Cover Art
Jodi Morin, KA1JPA
David F. Pingree, N1NAS

Contributors to the 24th Edition
Alan Applegate, KØBG
Gary Breed, K9AY
Jim Brown, K9YC
Glen Brown, W6GJB
David Conn, VE3KL
Remco den Besten, PA3FYM
Wyatt Dirks, ACØRA
James Duffey, KK6MC
Darryl Holman, WW7D
Justin Johnson, GØKSC
Matt Kastigar, N9ES
Steve Kostro, N2CEI
Sean Kutzko, KX9X
Carl Luetzelschwab, K9LA
Brian Machesney, K1LI
Paul Marsh, MØEYT
Tino Pavic, VK3EGN
Stu Phillips, K6TU
Tom Planer, KJ9P
Gilles Renucci, VA2EW
Ulrich Rohde, N1UL
Rick Rosen, K1DS
Rudy Severns, N6LF
Corey Shields, KB9JHU
Kai Siwiak, KE4PT
Andrea Slack, K2EZ
Steve Stearns, K6OIK
Steve Sutterer, AKØM
John Thompson, K3MD
Paul Wade, W1GHZ
Mike Willis, GØMJW
Ken Wolff, K1EA
Grant Zehr, AA9LC

Published by:
ARRL The national association for AMATEUR RADIO®
225 Main Street, Newington, CT 06111-1400 USA
www.arrl.org

Printed in the USA

ISBN: 978-1-62595-111-3 Softcover
978-1-62595-114-4 Four-Volume Boxed Set

Kindle eBook Editions
ISBN: 978-1-62595-115-1 — Volume 1
ISBN: 978-1-62595-116-8 — Volume 2
ISBN: 978-1-62595-118-2 — Volume 3
ISBN: 978-1-62595-119-9 — Volume 4

Twenty-Fourth Edition
First Printing

Contents

A more detailed Table of Contents is included at the beginning of each chapter.

VOLUME 1
ANTENNA FUNDAMENTALS

VOLUME 2
ANTENNAS FOR LF/MF/HF

VOLUME 3
ANTENNAS FOR VHF THROUGH MICROWAVE AND SPECIALTY ANTENNAS

VOLUME 4
TRANSMISSION LINES AND BUILDING ANTENNAS SYSTEMS, AND INDEX

TABLE OF CONTENTS

Chapter 15 — Downloadable Supplemental Content

Supplemental Articles

- "2 x 3 = 6" by L.B. Cebik, W4RNL
- "A 6 Meter Moxon Antenna" by Allen Baker, KG4JJH
- "A 902-MHz Loop Yagi Antenna" by Don Hilliard, WØPW
- "A Short Boom, Wideband 3 Element Yagi for 6 Meters" by L.B. Cebik, W4RNL
- "A VHF/UHF Discone Antenna" by Bob Patterson, K5DZE
- "An Optimum Design for 432 MHz Yagis — Parts 1 and 2" by Steve Powlishen, K1FO
- "An Ultra-Light Yagi for Transatlantic and Other Extreme DX" by Fred Archibald, VE1FA, including the EZNEC model
- "Building a Medium-Gain, Wide-Band, 2 Meter Yagi" by L.B. Cebik, W4RNL
- "C Band TVRO Dishes" convert provided file to PDF
- "Development and Real World Replication of Modern Yagi Antennas (III) — Manual Optimisation of Multiple Yagi Arrays" by Justin Johnson, GØKSC
- "High-Performance 'Self-Matched' Yagi Antennas" by Justin Johnson, GØKSC
- "High-Performance Yagis for 144, 222 and 432 MHz" by Steve Powlishen, K1FO
- "LPDA for 2 Meters Plus" by L.B. Cebik, W4RNL
- "Making the LFA Loop" by Justin Johnson, GØKSC
- "Microwavelengths — Microwave Transmission Lines" by Paul Wade, W1GHZ
- "RF — A Small 70-cm Yagi" by Zack Lau, W1VT
- "The Helical Antenna — Description and Design" by David Conn, VE3KL
- "Three-Band Log-Periodic Antenna" by Robert Heslin, K7RTY/2
- "Using LPDA TV Antennas for the VHF Ham Bands" by John Stanley, K4ERO
- "V-Shaped Elements versus Straight Elements" by John Stanley, K4ERO

Support Files

- Model files and sample radiation patterns for Yagi designs by Justin Johnson, GØKSC (require *EZNEC PRO/4* to reproduce the gain and other performance specifications listed)

Chapter 15

VHF, UHF and Microwave Antennas

A good antenna system is one of the most valuable assets available to the VHF/UHF/microwave enthusiast. Compared to an antenna of lesser quality, an antenna that is well designed, is built of good quality materials, and is well maintained, will increase transmitting range, enhance reception of weak signals and reduce interference problems. The work itself building antennas is by no means the least attractive part of the job. Even with high-gain antennas, experimentation is greatly simplified at and above VHF because the antennas are a physically manageable size. Setting up a home antenna range is within the means of most amateurs, and much can be learned about the nature and adjustment of antennas. No large investment in test equipment is necessary.

Antenna design at VHF and higher frequencies has seen much innovation since the advent of cellular telephony and wireless data. The twin frontiers of miniaturization and higher frequencies have driven much research into novel forms for the antennas themselves and the associated feed line and matching structures.

Amateurs will benefit from technology developed to support consumer microwave equipment now operating at 75 GHz (vehicle navigation) and millimeter-wave technology for 5G wireless systems. There are many opportunities for amateur innovation in circuit and antenna design at microwave frequencies because of the excellent tools available to them at low cost, including modeling and simulation software.

The article "Antenna Technologies for the Future" by Patrick Hindle in the January 2018 issue of *Microwave Journal* explores 3D-printed antennas, metamaterials, fractal antenna structures, and other innovations. (The article is available online with free registration at **www.microwavejournal.com/articles/29572-antenna-technologies-for-the-future**.) Amateurs would do well to pay close attention to these interesting developments!

15.1 DESIGN FACTORS AT AND ABOVE VHF

The fundamental principles of antenna systems are the same at VHF and UHF as at HF. There is no magic dividing line at 50 MHz that suddenly changes the way antenna system components operate. However, factors that may be insignificant at HF must be taken into account at higher frequencies as the wavelength of the signals drops, dielectric loss increases, and skin depth shrinks. Similarly, techniques that may be impractical at HF such as dishes and long-boom Yagis with 20 elements can be put to work at VHF and higher frequencies. Instead of repeating the theory presented in other chapters, this section will identify areas that must be treated differently than at HF and give guidelines for how to approach the problem.

As on HF, the first step in choosing the right antenna is figuring out what you want it to do. Most VHF/UHF falls into one of two categories — weak-signal and local or regional repeater communication. Weak-signal operating on CW, SSB, and increasingly various digital modes, benefits from horizontally polarized, rotatable antennas with narrow beamwidths and minimum sidelobes. Satellite operation on CW and SSB goes farther and adds elevation control and circular polarization to the list. FM repeater and simplex operation uses vertical polarization for both directional and omnidirectional antennas. Simple ground-plane and low-gain omnidirectional antennas are common.

Just the polarization issue alone can have a dramatic effect as an antenna cross-polarized to an incoming signal receives up to 20 dB less signal than if the antenna and signal polarization are the same. Similarly, a narrow-beamwidth rotatable antenna can be a poor choice if the goal is to use several nearby repeaters that are located in different directions from the station. As a result, it is not uncommon for an amateur station to include both types — a horizontally polarized beam and a vertically polarized omnidirectional antenna — for VHF and UHF operation.

Gain

At VHF and UHF, it is possible to build Yagi antennas with very high gain — 15 to 20 dBi — on a physically manageable boom. Such antennas then can be combined in arrays of two, four, six, eight or more antennas. These arrays are attractive for EME, tropospheric scatter or other weak-signal communications modes where the path loss is very high.

Collinear antennas such as Franklin arrays become much more manageable at and above 2 meters with gains of 6 to 12 dBi in a single, vertical package similar in size to a 10 meter ground plane antenna. The collinear dipole array is very popular as a repeater antenna (see the **Repeater Antenna Systems** article in the downloadable supplemental information) with potential gains of up to 9 dBd for eight dipole arrays as described by Belrose. (See Bibliography.)

Reflectors, horns and dishes offer even higher gains (and narrower patterns) at UHF and microwave frequencies. A medium-sized dish can develop up to 30 dBi gain at 10 GHz, for example, turning 1 W of power into an EIRP of 1 kW!

Radiation Patterns

Antenna radiation can be made omnidirectional, bidirectional, practically unidirectional, or anything between these configurations. A VHF net operator may find an omnidirectional system almost a necessity, but it may be a poor choice otherwise. Noise pickup and other interference problems are greater with such omnidirectional antennas, and omnidirectional antennas having some gain are especially bad in these respects. Maximum gain and low radiation angle are usually prime interests of the weak-signal DX aspirant. A clean pattern, with lowest possible pickup and radiation off the sides and back, may be important in high-activity areas, or where the noise level is high.

Frequency Response

The ability to use an entire VHF band may be important in some types of operation. Modern Yagis can achieve performance over a remarkably wide frequency range, providing that the boom length is long enough and enough elements are used to populate the boom. Modern Yagi designs in fact are competitive with directly driven collinear arrays of similar size and complexity. The primary performance parameters of gain, front-to-rear ratio and SWR can be optimized over all the VHF or UHF amateur bands readily, with the exception of the full 6 meter band from 50.0 to 54.0 MHz, which is an 8% wide bandwidth. A Yagi can be easily designed to cover any 2 MHz portion of the 6 meter band with superb performance.

Height Gain

In general, higher is better in VHF and UHF antenna installations. Raising the antenna over nearby obstructions may make dramatic improvements in coverage. Within reason, greater height is almost always worth its cost, but height gain (see the **Radio Wave Propagation** chapter) must be balanced against increased transmission line loss. This loss can be considerable, and it increases with frequency. The best available line may not be very good if the run is long in terms of wavelengths. Line loss considerations as discussed in the **Transmission Lines** chapter are important in antenna planning.

Conference Proceedings and Presentations Online

Don't forget that more and more microwave and VHF/UHF conferences post papers and presentation videos online. Instead of having to order a printed book, you can now download a PDF or watch and listen to the presenter discuss the subject. YouTube is the most popular platform for videos. Just enter the conference name into the search window. Search engines will easily find conference proceedings, as well.

Physical Size

A given antenna design for 432 MHz has the same gain as the same design for 144 MHz, but being only one third as large intercepts only one-ninth as much energy in receiving. In other words, the antenna has less pickup efficiency at 432 MHz. To be equal in communication effectiveness, the 432-MHz array should be at least equal in *size* to the 144-MHz antenna, which requires roughly three times as many elements. With all the extra difficulties involved in using the higher frequencies effectively, it is best to keep antennas as large as possible for these bands.

Polarization

Whether to position antenna elements vertically or horizontally has been widely debated since early VHF pioneering days. Tests have shown little evidence about which polarization sense is most desirable. On long propagation paths there is no consistent advantage either way. Shorter paths tend to yield higher signal levels with horizontally polarized antennas over some kinds of terrain. Man-made noise, especially ignition interference, also tends to be lower with horizontal antennas. These factors make horizontal polarization somewhat more desirable for weak-signal communications. On the other hand, vertically polarized antennas are much simpler to use in omnidirectional systems and in mobile operation. Circular polarization is commonly used for satellite and EME communication with antenna systems that can switch between right-hand and left-hand orientation.

Vertical polarization was widely used in early VHF operation, but horizontal polarization gained favor when directional arrays started to become widely used. The widespread use of FM and repeaters, particularly in the VHF/UHF bands, has tipped the balance in favor of vertical antennas in mobile and repeater use. Horizontal polarization predominates in other communication on 50 MHz and higher frequencies. An additional loss of up to 20 dB can be expected when cross-polarized antennas are used over direct paths.

15.2 BASIC ANTENNAS FOR VHF AND UHF

Local operation with mobile stations and handheld radios requires an antenna with wide coverage capabilities and a generally omnidirectional pattern. Most mobile operation uses FM and the polarization used with this mode is generally vertical. Some simple vertical systems for fixed or base station use are described below. Additional material on antennas of this type is presented in the **Mobile VHF and UHF Antennas** chapter.

15.2.1 GROUND-PLANES AND DIPOLES

For the FM operator living in the primary coverage area of a repeater, the ease of construction and low cost of a ¼ λ ground-plane antenna make it an ideal choice. Three different types of construction are detailed in the following section; the choice of construction method depends upon the materials at hand and the desired style of antenna mounting. (Note that while UHF connectors are not generally recommended for use on the upper VHF bands and at UHF, they will work fine as a base for ground-plane antennas. It is their uncontrolled impedance above 100 MHz that causes problems in transmission lines but as part of an antenna, their impedance is accounted for when trimming the antenna for minimum SWR.)

The 144-MHz model shown in **Figure 15.1** uses a flat piece of sheet aluminum, to which radials are connected with machine screws. A 45° bend is made in each of the

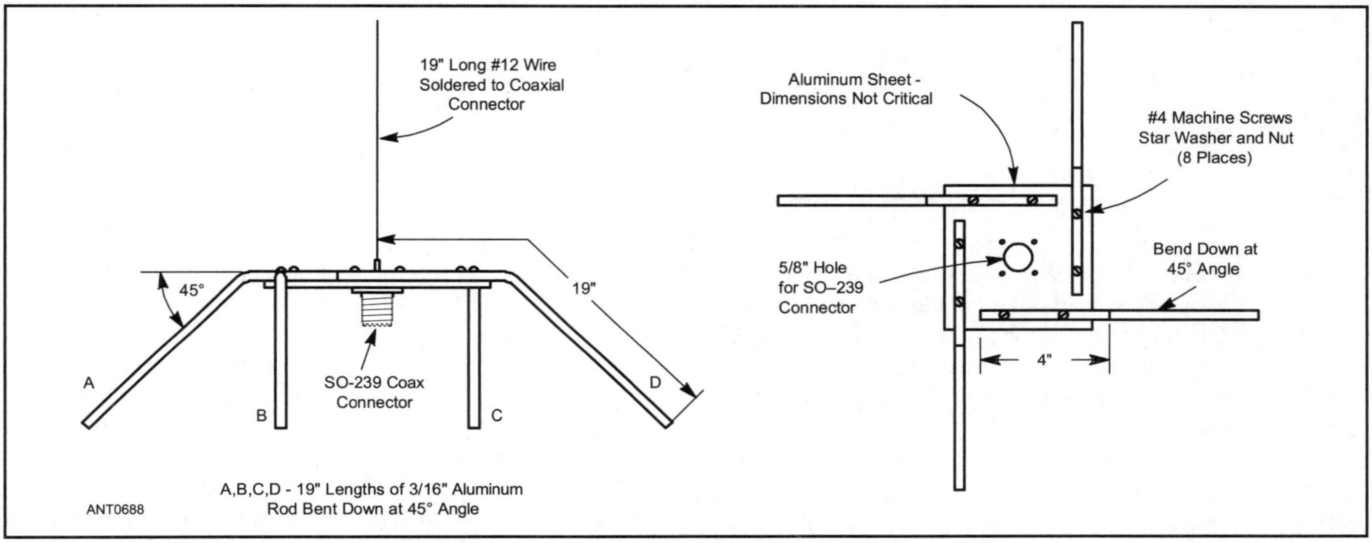

Figure 15.1 — These drawings illustrate the dimensions for the 144-MHz ground-plane antenna. The radials are bent down at a 45° angle.

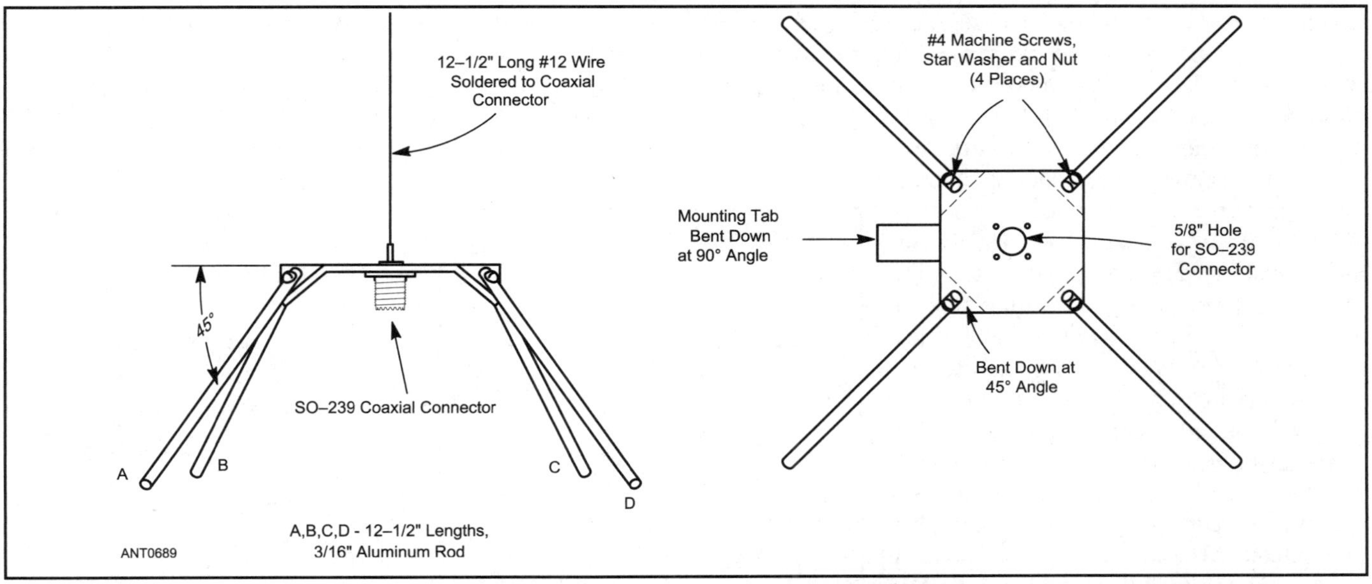

Figure 15.2 — Dimensional information for the 222-MHz ground-plane antenna. Lengths for A, B, C and D are the total distances measured from the center of the SO-239 connector. The corners of the aluminum plate are bent down at a 45° angle rather than bending the aluminum rod as in the 144-MHz model. Either method is suitable for these antennas.

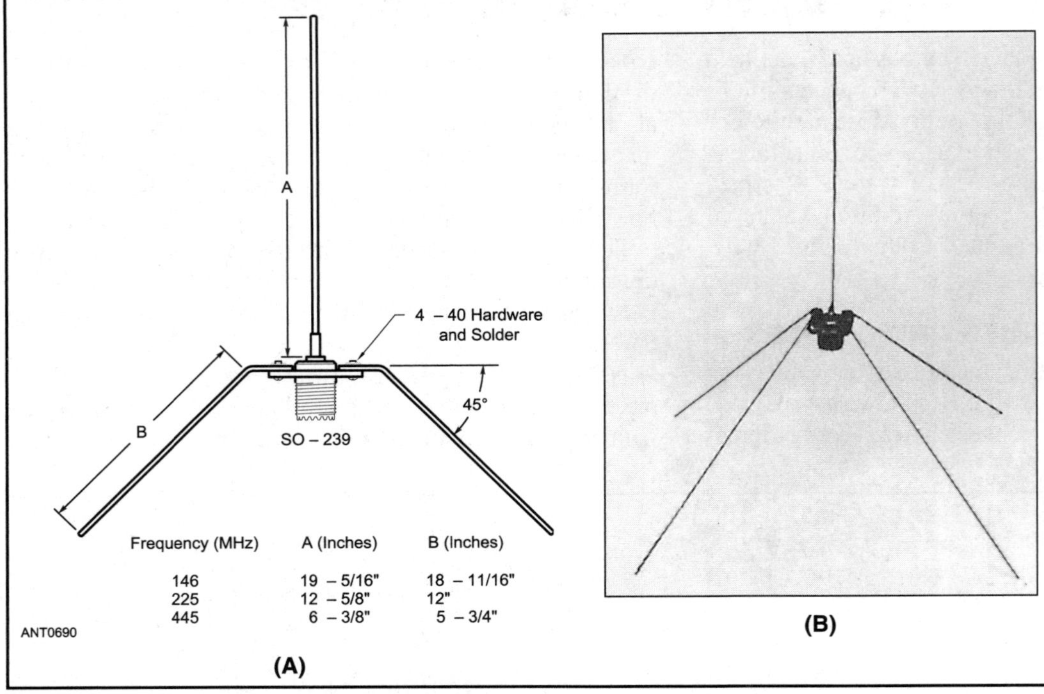

Figure 15.3 — Simple ground-plane antenna dimensions for the 144-, 222- and 440-MHz bands. (A) The vertical element and radials are 3/32- or 1/16-inch brass welding rod. Although 3/32-inch rod is preferred for the 144-MHz antenna, #10 or #12 AWG copper wire can also be used. The photograph (B) shows a 440-MHz ground-plane constructed using only an SO-239 connector, #4-40 hardware and 1/16-inch brass welding rod.

radials. This bend can be made with an ordinary bench vise. An SO-239 chassis connector is mounted at the center of the aluminum plate with the threaded part of the connector facing down. The vertical portion of the antenna is made of #12 AWG copper wire soldered directly to the center pin of the SO-239 connector.

The 222-MHz version, **Figure 15.2**, uses a slightly different technique for mounting and sloping the radials. In this case the corners of the aluminum plate are bent down at a 45° angle with respect to the remainder of the plate. The four radials are held to the plate with machine screws, lock washers and nuts. A mounting tab is included in the design of this antenna as part of the aluminum base. A compression type of hose clamp could be used to secure the antenna to a mast. As with the 144-MHz version, the vertical portion of the antenna is soldered directly to the SO-239 connector.

A very simple method of construction, shown in **Figure 15.3**, requires nothing more than an SO-239 connector and some #4-40 hardware. A small loop formed at the inside end of each radial is used to attach the radial directly to the mounting holes of the coaxial connector. After the radial is fastened to the SO-239 with #4-40 hardware, a large soldering iron or propane torch is used to solder the radial and the mounting hardware to the coaxial connector. The radials are bent to a 45° angle and the vertical portion is soldered to the center pin to complete the antenna. The antenna can be mounted by passing the feed line through a mast of ¾-inch ID plastic or aluminum tubing. A compression hose clamp can be used to secure the PL-259 connector, attached to the feed line, in the end of the mast. Dimensions for the 144-, 222- and 440-MHz bands are given in Figure 15.3.

Dipole antennas are used frequently above the HF bands because horizontally polarized gain antennas are fairly small and easy to construct. Nevertheless, a rotatable dipole is very inexpensive and can be used for weak-signal operating when a beam isn't practical. A dipole may actually be better than a beam when a very broad pattern is needed, such as for meteor scatter when the direction of propagation isn't known until a station is heard.

The rotatable dipole shown in **Figure 15.4** can be made of copper or aluminum tube or rod. The mounting plate can be made of almost any non-conductive plastic material such as thick plastic kitchen cutting boards. The simplicity of the antenna lends itself to experimenting or scrounging. (This design is from the ARRL book *Magic Band Antennas for Ham*

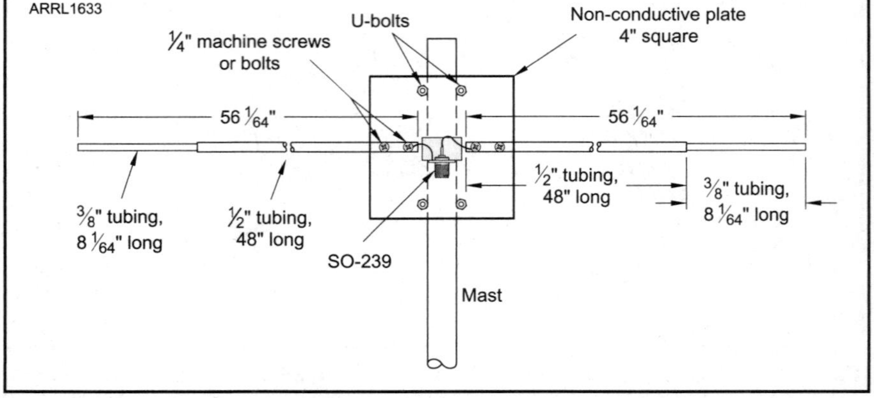

Figure 15.4 — Dimensions for a simple rotatable 6 meter dipole.

Radio by Bruce Walker, N3JO — see the Bibliography.)

If these antennas are to be permanently mounted outside, waterproof the antenna by applying a small amount of sealant around the areas of the center pin of the connector to prevent the entry of water into the connector and coax line. The coax connector should be waterproofed as well. Techniques and materials for waterproofing are described in the **Building Antenna Systems and Towers** chapter.

15.2.2 THE J-POLE ANTENNA

The J-Pole is a half-wave antenna that is end-fed at its bottom. Since the radiator is longer than that of a ¼-wave ground-plane antenna, the vertical lobe is compressed down toward the horizon and it has about 1.5 dB of gain compared to the ground-plane configuration. The stub-matching section used to transform the high impedance at the end of a half-wave antenna to 50 Ω is shorted at the bottom, making the antenna look like the letter "J," and giving the antenna its name.

Rigid copper tubing, fittings and assorted hardware can be used to make a rugged J-pole antenna for the VHF bands through 440 MHz. (A flexible "roll-up" J-pole is described in the **Mobile and Portable Antennas** chapter.) When copper tubing is used, the entire assembly can be soldered together, ensuring electrical integrity, and making the whole antenna weatherproof. A general-purpose set of dimensions for the J-pole is provided in **Figure 15.5** along with a table of dimensions for 53 MHz, 146 MHz, 223 MHz, and 440 MHz. MHz. The dimensions assume ½-inch copper pipe is used to construct the antenna. The 53-MHz version is somewhat large for this construction method and the 440 MHz version a little small. Note that the inside dimensions of the matching section are between the outside surfaces of the tubing, not center-to-center. For placing the feed point, start with the feed point approximately as high above the bottom of the matching section as the tubing spacing.

The J-Pole can be fed directly from 50-Ω coax through a choke balun. A choke balun can be made by coiling the feed line or by using ferrite beads or cores as described in the **Transmission Line System Techniques** chapter. If the balun is not used, the outer surface of the coaxial cable will become part of the antenna, making tuning difficult and highly dependent on cable placement. In addition, radiation from the current flowing on the feed line can distort the pattern of the antenna, leading to poor performance by breaking up the low-elevation main lobe expected from this design.

There are many J-pole designs available online and in the ARRL's online archive of *QST* articles at **www.arrl.org**. One of the more popular variants is known as the "Copper Cactus" (see Bibliography) and has been adapted to dual- and tri-band designs.

Construction

No special hardware or machined parts are used in this antenna, nor are insulating materials needed. If mounted on a metal mast the antenna is grounded, as well. The following 2 meter J-pole design came from an article by Michael Hood, KD8JB, in *The ARRL Antenna Compendium, Vol. 4*.

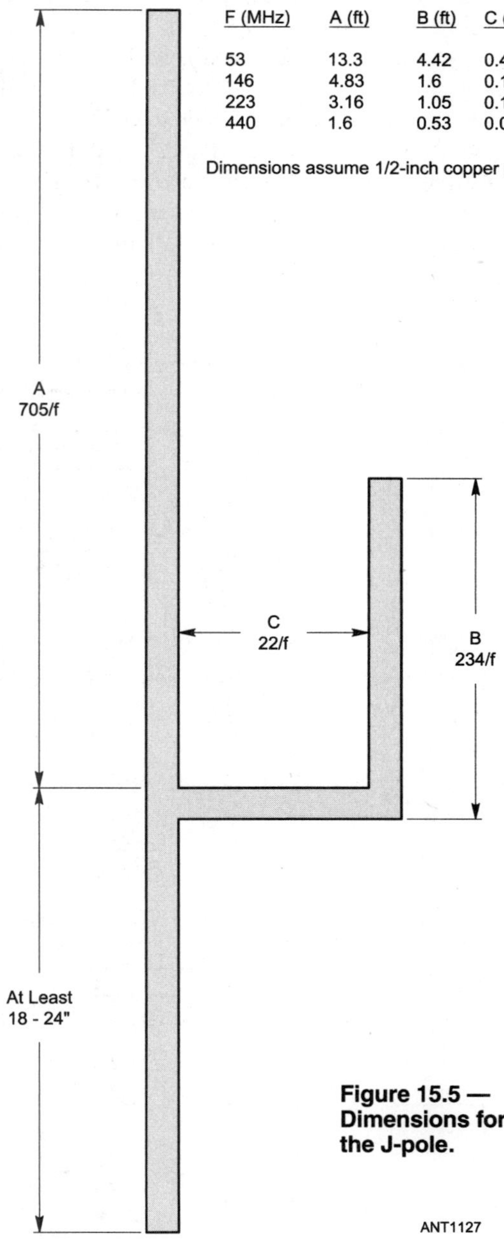

F (MHz)	A (ft)	B (ft)	C (ft)
53	13.3	4.42	0.42
146	4.83	1.6	0.15
223	3.16	1.05	0.10
440	1.6	0.53	0.05

Dimensions assume 1/2-inch copper pipe.

Figure 15.5 — Dimensions for the J-pole.

Copper and brass is used exclusively in this antenna. These metals get along together, so dissimilar metal corrosion is eliminated. Both metals solder well, too. See **Figure 15.6**. Cut the copper tubing to the lengths indicated. Item 9 is a 1¼-inch nipple cut from the 20-inch length of ½-inch tubing. This leaves 18¾ inches for the ¼-λ matching stub. Item 10 is a 3¼-inch long nipple cut from the 60-inch length of ¾-inch tubing. The ¾-wave element should measure 56¾ inches long. Remove burrs from the ends of the tubing after cutting, and clean the mating surfaces with sandpaper, steel wool or emery cloth.

After cleaning, apply a very thin coat of flux to the mating elements and assemble the tubing, elbow, tee, end caps and stubs. Solder the assembled parts with a propane torch and rosin-core solder. Wipe off excess solder with a damp cloth, being careful not to burn yourself. The copper tubing will hold heat for a long time after you've finished soldering. After soldering, set the assembly aside to cool.

Flatten one each of the ½-inch and ¾-inch pipe clamps. Drill a hole in the flattened clamp as shown in Figure 15.6A. Assemble the clamps and cut off the excess metal from the flattened clamp using the unmodified clamp as a template. Disassemble the clamps.

Assemble the ½-inch clamp around the ¼-wave element and secure with two of the screws, washers, and nuts as shown in Figure 15.6B. Do the same with the ¾-inch clamp around the ¾-wave element. Initially set the clamps to a spot about 4 inches above the bottom of the "J" on their respective elements. Tighten the clamps only finger tight, since you'll need to move them when tuning.

Tuning

Before tuning, mount the antenna vertically, about 5 to

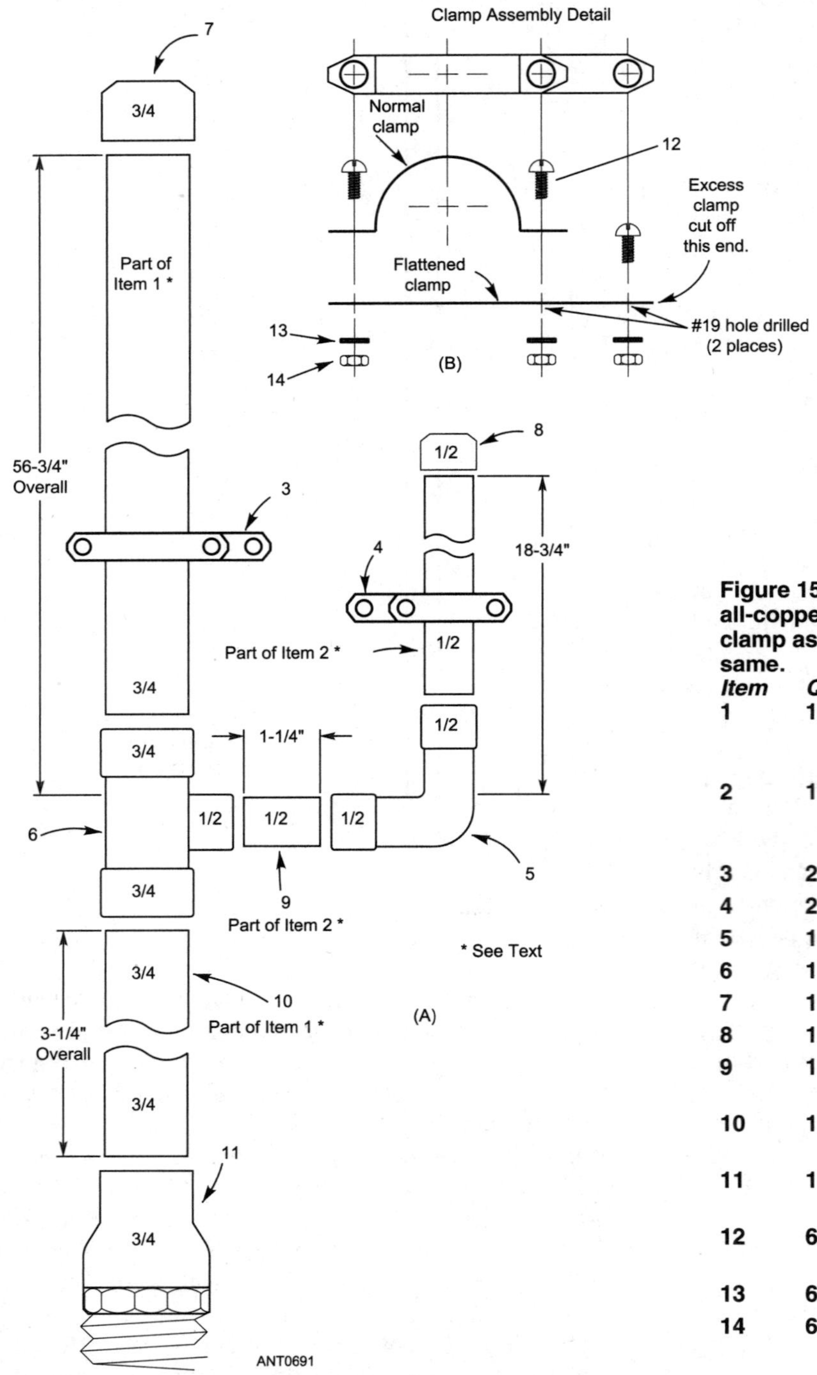

Figure 15.6 — At A, exploded assembly diagram of all-copper J-Pole antenna for 2 meters. At B, detail of clamp assemblies. Both clamp assemblies are the same.

Item	*Qty*	*Part or Material Name*
1	1	¾-inch × 10 foot length of rigid copper tubing (enough for 2 antennas, 60 inches per antenna)
2	1	½-inch × 10 ft length of rigid copper tubing (enough for 6 antennas, 20 inches per antenna)
3	2	¾-inch copper pipe clamps
4	2	½-inch copper pipe clamps
5	1	½-inch copper elbow
6	1	¾ × ½-inch copper tee
7	1	¾-inch copper end cap
8	1	½-inch copper end cap
9	1	½ × 1¼-inch copper nipple (Make from item 2. See text)
10	1	¾ × 3¼-inch copper nipple (Make from item 1. See text)
11	1	Your choice of coupling to mast fitting (¾ × 1 inch NPT used at KD8JB)
12	6	#8-32 × ½-inch brass machine screws (round, pan, or binder head)
13	6	#8 brass flat washers
14	6	#8-32 brass hex nuts

10 feet from the ground. A short TV mast on a tripod works well for this purpose. When tuning VHF antennas, keep in mind that they are sensitive to nearby objects — such as your body. Attach the feed line to the clamps on the antenna, and make sure all the nuts and screws are at least finger tight. It really doesn't matter to which element (¾-wave element or stub) you attach the coaxial center lead. KD8JB has done it both ways with no variation in performance. Tune the antenna by moving the two feed point clamps equal distances a small amount each time until the SWR is a minimum at the desired frequency. The SWR will be close to 1:1. (Stand clear of the antenna when measuring the SWR and include the choke balun in the feed line when making measurements.)

Final Assembly

The final assembly of the antenna will determine its long-term survivability. Perform the following steps with care. After adjusting the clamps for minimum SWR, mark the clamp positions with a pencil and then remove the feed line and clamps. Apply a very thin coating of flux to the inside of the clamp and the corresponding surface of the antenna element where the clamp attaches. Install the clamps and tighten the clamp screws.

Solder the feed line clamps where they are attached to the antenna elements. Now, apply a small amount of solder around the screw heads and nuts where they contact the clamps. Don't get solder on the screw threads! Clean away excess flux with a noncorrosive solvent. After final assembly and erecting/mounting the antenna in the desired location, attach the feed line and secure with the remaining washer and nut. Weatherproof this joint as described in the **Building Antenna Systems and Towers** chapter.

15.2.3 COLLINEAR AND CURTAIN ARRAYS

The information given earlier in this chapter pertains mainly to parasitic arrays, but the collinear array is worthy of consideration in VHF/UHF operation. Two types of collinear arrays are commonly used by amateurs; the *transposed-coaxial array* and the *collinear dipole array.*

Collinear arrays tend to be tolerant of construction tolerances, making them easy to build and adjust for VHF and UHF applications. The use of many collinear driven elements

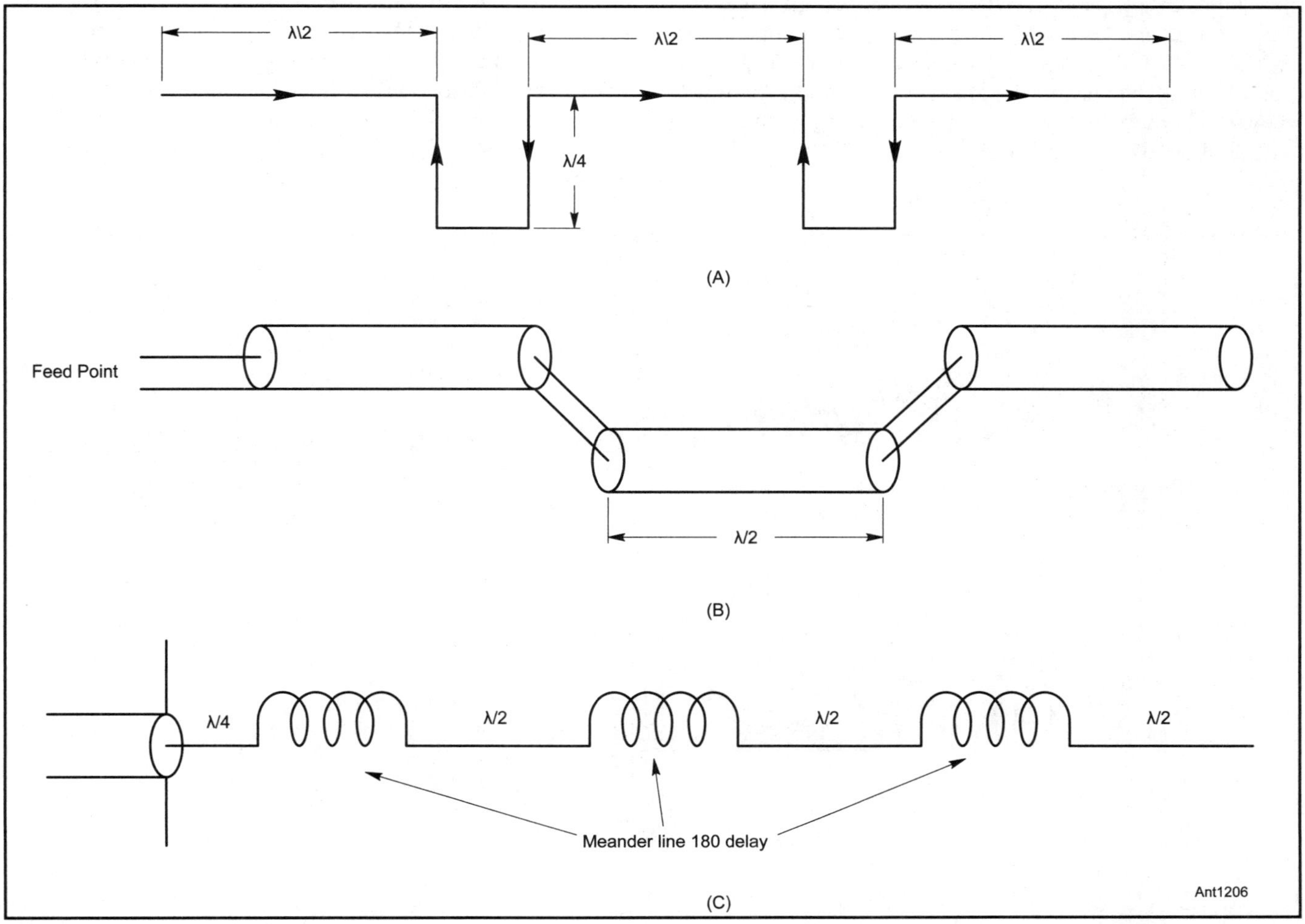

Figure 15.7 — The most popular collinear array is the Franklin array of half-wave dipoles (A) oriented vertically for an omnidirectional pattern. B shows the usual construction of transposed half-wavelength sections of coaxial cable for use at VHF and UHF. An alternative design (C) uses meander lines to create the 180° phase reversal.

was once popular in very large phased arrays, such as those required in moonbounce (EME) communications, but computer-optimized Yagi arrays have largely replaced them. A collinear array of four dipoles is a popular repeater antenna as described in the Repeater Antenna Systems article included with this book's downloadable content.

Collinear Transposed-Coax Arrays

The most popular collinear array is the omnidirectional array of half-wave dipoles constructed of transposed sections of coaxial cable as shown in **Figure 15.7**. The original array of this type is the Franklin array shown in Figure 15.7A. The phase-reversing stubs allow multiple half-wave sections to operate in phase, creating gain at right angles to the antenna. An example of this array is the popular Cushcraft Ringo Ranger series of omnidirectional VHF and UHF antennas.

While the phasing stubs make the Franklin array inconvenient for vertical stacking of more than two elements, a derivative of this array uses transposed sections of coaxial cable as in Figure 15.7B. The phasing stub is created by the inside of each coaxial section. The outer surface of the coaxial shield forms the radiating element. The resulting antenna can be enclosed in a PVC or fiberglass tube, such as the Comet GP-series of VHF/UHF omnidirectional antennas. Numerous examples of this design are available online. An article by WA6SVT in *73* magazine was the initial description of these antennas in the amateur literature. (See **www.repeater-builder.com/antenna/wa6svt.html** and this chapter's Bibliography — see the entries for Collis and Belrose.) Gains claimed for this antenna may be optimistic (**www.owenduffy.net/antenna/WA6SVT/index.htm**) but the basic design is quite serviceable.

Another method of creating the phase reversal between radiating sections is the *meander line* shown in Figure 15.7C. The meander line is a coil of wire that forms a delay line of 180 degrees. The pitch (turns per unit length) and overall length are the important characteristics of the meander line. There are several designs for meander line collinear arrays online such as from WA3AYW at **www.hamuniverse.com/wb3aywcollinear.html**.

The practical limit for gain in this type of array is about 10 dBi. A choke balun or other method of decoupling such as a set of λ/4 radials is required at the feed point of the array to prevent current from being induced on the outer surface of the coaxial feed line. Feed line current would both upset the radiation pattern, reducing gain, and affect the feed point impedance in unpredictable ways.

Collinear Omnidirectional Array for 70 cm

Figure 15.8 shows the basic construction of a transposed-coax array for the 70 cm band with dimensions in millimeters for accuracy. The λ/4 whip at the end of the array is optional. The gain of this array is approximately 9 dBi (slightly less without the whip). The original design of this antenna is credited to the Radio Amateur Society of Norwich (**www.rason.org**). More information is available via the "Projects" page of the RASON website.

The physical length of each λ/2 section of coax must

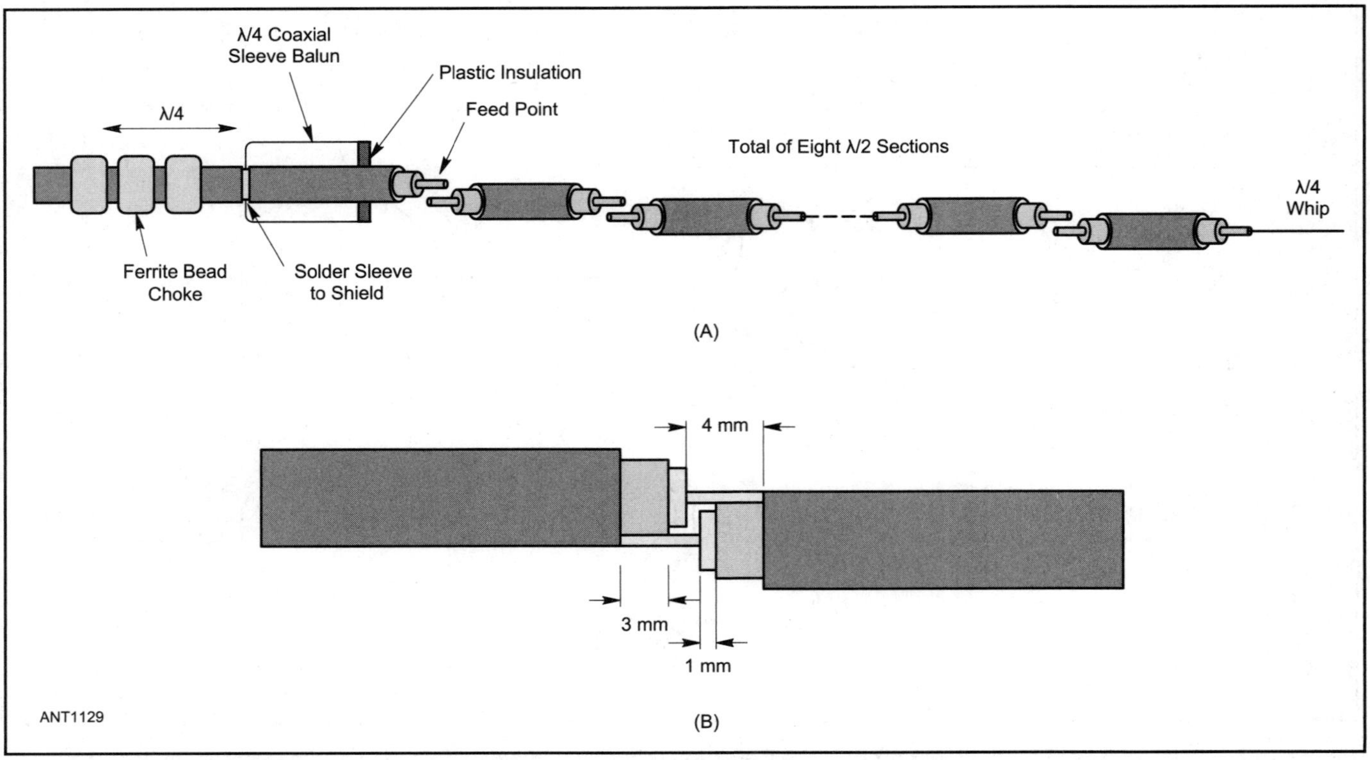

Figure 15.8 — Basic construction of a transposed-coax array for the 70 cm band. Dimensions are given in millimeters for accuracy.

account for the velocity factor of the cable which should be measured accurately before cutting any cable. Once the physical length of λ/2 has been determined, add 8 mm to allow for creating the 4 mm connecting surfaces on each end. For a VF = 0.66, the λ/2 sections should be 223 mm long plus 8 mm for a total of 231 mm. RG-58, RG-8, RG-8X or RG-213 can be used for this antenna. Do not remove the outer jacket from the cable other than at the connecting ends as this will allow the individual braid strands to loosen, reducing the shield's effectiveness as a continuous conductor.

Use a 169 mm segment of #16 AWG copper wire for the top whip section. A λ/4 coaxial sleeve balun is attached at the feed point of the antenna. (See the **Transmission Line System Techniques** chapter.) The balun is made from copper tubing that is soldered to the shield of the feed line using strips of brass or copper shim. If ⅝-inch tubing is used, the length should be 160 mm. The feed line should be centered in the balun tubing by using small pieces of plastic inserted between the coax jacket and the tubing's inner surface. Approximately λ/4 beyond the end of the balun's closed end add an additional choke balun of three type #43 ferrite beads (choose the ID to fit the feed line coax). The entire antenna should be enclosed in a length of PVC or fiberglass tubing to protect it from the weather. If necessary for mechanical stability, support the antenna sections with a length of wooden dowel or plastic rod, secured with electrical tape.

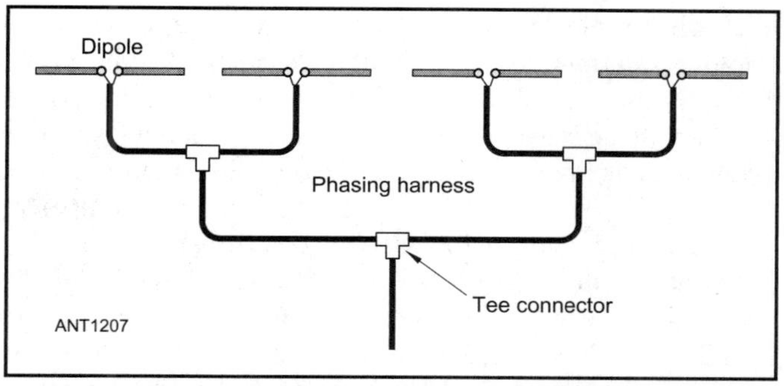

Figure 15.9 — A four-dipole collinear array fed with a phasing harness so that all of the dipoles are in-phase. Most commercial models use folded dipoles.

Collinear Dipole Array

The vertical four-dipole collinear array in **Figure 15.9** is a very common repeater antenna, giving an omnidirectional pattern. Gain can be from 3 to 7.5 dBd depending on the dipoles vertical spacing and whether all of the dipoles are mounted on the same side of the supporting mast. Arrays of two to eight dipoles are practical. (See the **Repeater Antenna Systems** article in the downloadable supplemental information.)

KG4JJH has published a very detailed article on the design and construction of 2-element and 4-element arrays for 2 meters using single-conductor dipole elements (available from **www.kg4jjh.com**). Most commercial versions use folded dipoles so that all antenna elements can be maintained at dc ground.

The phasing lines used to connect the individual dipoles must be of the correct length within a few electrical degrees in order to present a 50 Ω impedance to the main feed line. Individual phasing line segments may be of 50, 75, or some other impedance so be careful when repairing or replacing a phasing line or harness so that the antenna's radiation pattern and feed point impedance are correct.

Dipole Curtain Arrays

Collinear dipole arrays were popular in the past because of simplicity, before computer modeling of antennas. Modern optimized Yagi-Uda antennas offer higher performance in terms of gain, cost, size, weight, and wind loading. Still, there are possibly applications where collinear arrays might be useful. Strictly speaking, the antennas discussed here are broadside arrays and not true collinear arrays since the antennas are not aligned along a single line. Nevertheless, they are often referred to as collinear arrays and included here for convenient reference.

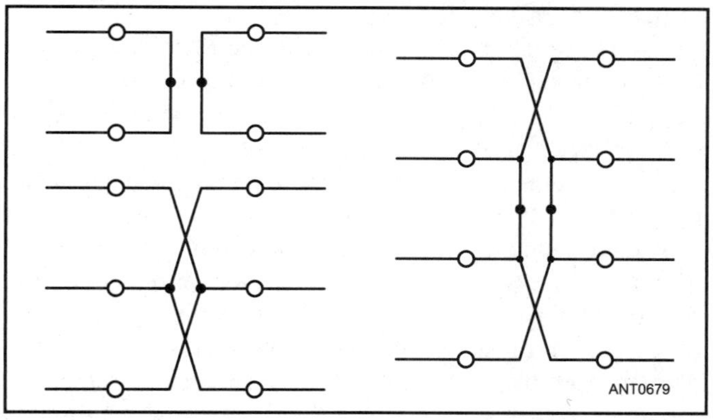

Figure 15.10 — Element arrangements for 8-, 12- and 16-element collinear arrays. Elements are λ/2 long and spaced λ/2. Parasitic reflectors, omitted here for clarity, are 5% longer and 0.2 λ behind the driven elements. Feed points are indicated by black dots. Open circles show recommended support points. The elements can run through wood or metal booms, without insulation, if supported at their centers in this way. Insulators at the element ends (points of high RF voltage) detune and unbalance the system.

Bidirectional curtain arrays of four, six and eight half waves in phase are shown in **Figure 15.10**. Usually reflector elements are added, normally at about 0.2 λ behind each driven element, for more gain and a unidirectional pattern. Such parasitic elements are omitted from the sketch in the interest of clarity.

The feed point impedance of two half waves in phase is high, typically 1000 Ω or more. When they are combined in parallel and parasitic elements are added, the feed impedance is low enough for direct connection to open wire line or twin-lead, connected at the points indicated by black dots. With coaxial line and a balun, it is suggested that the universal stub match (see the **VHF-UHF Antenna System Design** chapter) be used at the feed point. All elements should be mounted at their electrical centers, as indicated by open circles in Figure 15.10. The framework can be metal or insulating material. The metal supporting structure is entirely behind the plane of the reflector elements. Sheet-metal clamps can be cut from scraps of aluminum for this kind of assembly. Collinear elements of this type should be mounted at their centers (where the RF voltage is a minimum), rather than at their ends, where the voltage is high and insulation losses and detuning can be harmful.

Collinear arrays of 32, 48, 64 and even 128 elements can give outstanding performance. Any collinear array should be fed at the center of the system, to ensure balanced current distribution. This is very important in large arrays, where sets of six or eight driven elements are treated as "sub arrays," and are fed through a balanced harness. The sections of the harness are resonant lengths, usually of open wire line. The 48-element collinear array for 432 MHz in **Figure 15.11** illustrates this principle.

A reflecting plane, which may be sheet metal, wire mesh, or even closely spaced elements of tubing or wire, can be used in place of parasitic reflectors. To be effective, the plane reflector must extend on all sides to at least ¼ λ beyond the area occupied by the driven elements. The plane reflector provides high F/B ratio, a clean pattern, and somewhat more gain than parasitic elements, but large physical size limits it to use above 420 MHz. An interesting space-saving possibility lies in using a single plane reflector with elements for two different bands mounted on opposite sides. Reflector spacing from the driven element is not critical — about 0.2 λ is common.

Wideband 23 cm Collinear Array

This design for a wideband beam by F5JIO is taken from the RSGB publication *Antennas for VHF and Above*. In the development of the antenna F5JIO consulted *Rothammel*, the German antenna reference text which gives the following guidelines for the reflector plane:

- For the best F/B ratio, the reflector should extend at least half a wavelength beyond the perimeter of the curtain on all sides.
- If made of wire or mesh instead of solid sheet metal to reduce wind loading surface area, the wire pitch should be 0.1 λ or less.
- A reflector plane spaced ⅝ λ behind the radiator adds a maximum gain of up to 7 dB, but a spacing of 0.1 to 0.3 λ provides a better F/B ratio.
- If spaced at least 0.3 λ behind the curtain, the reflector plane does not affect the feed point impedance of the array.

Details for the matching of the antenna can be seen in **Figure 15.12**. With the antenna dimensions given, the feed point impedance of each dipole pair is approximately 600 Ω balanced. There are three pairs in parallel which divides this impedance by three to give 200 Ω, and a 4:1 coaxial balun transforms this to provide an excellent match to 50-Ω coax which is unbalanced. Note that as each dipole is supported at its voltage node, the insulators need to be of good quality.

The construction of the antenna is fairly straightforward, although reasonable care and precision are required. Being a 23 cm band antenna, it is quite small and therefore wind loading is not normally a problem and this makes a solid reflector feasible. This then means that the plate used as the reflector can be used as the support for the other components. During construction it is necessary to bend the phasing rods slightly so that they do not touch at the cross-over points. Then, for weather protection, a plastic food container can used as a radome. This can be used as the RF absorption appears to be negligible and it is much cheaper than a Teflon equivalent.

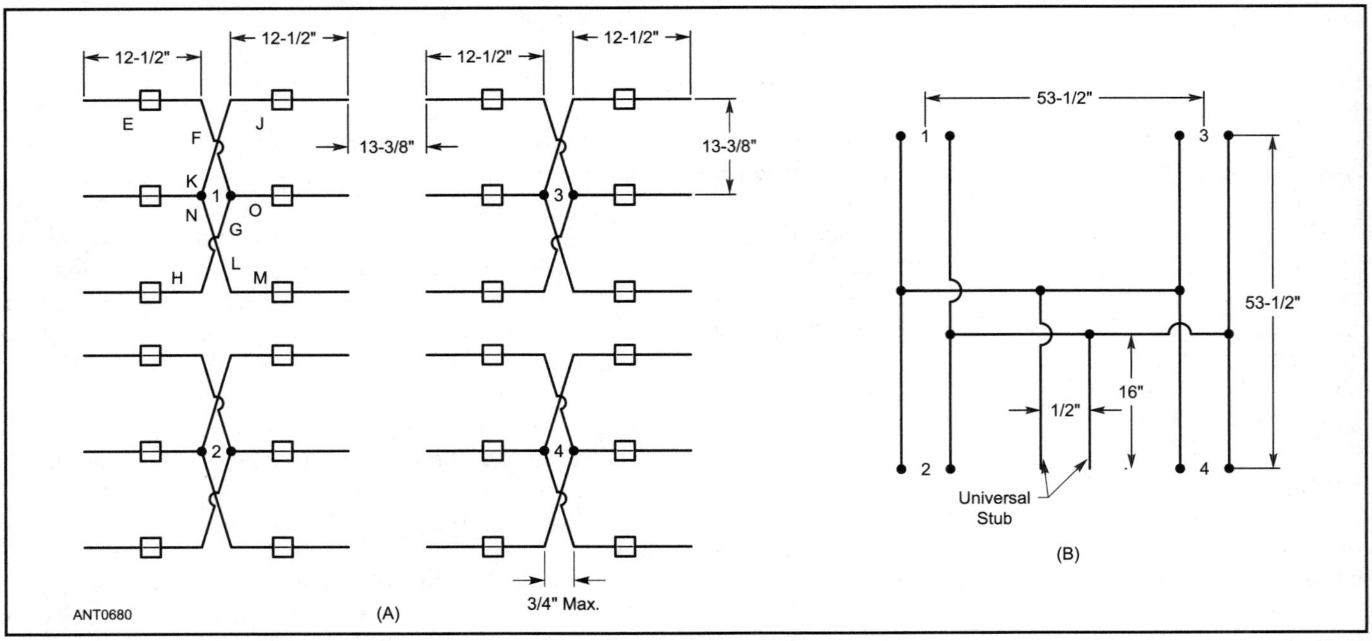

Figure 15.13 — Large collinear arrays should be fed as sets of no more than eight driven elements each, interconnected by phasing lines. This 48-element array for 432 MHz (A) is treated as if it were four 12-element collinear antennas. Reflector elements are omitted for clarity. The phasing harness is shown at B. Squares represent supporting insulators.

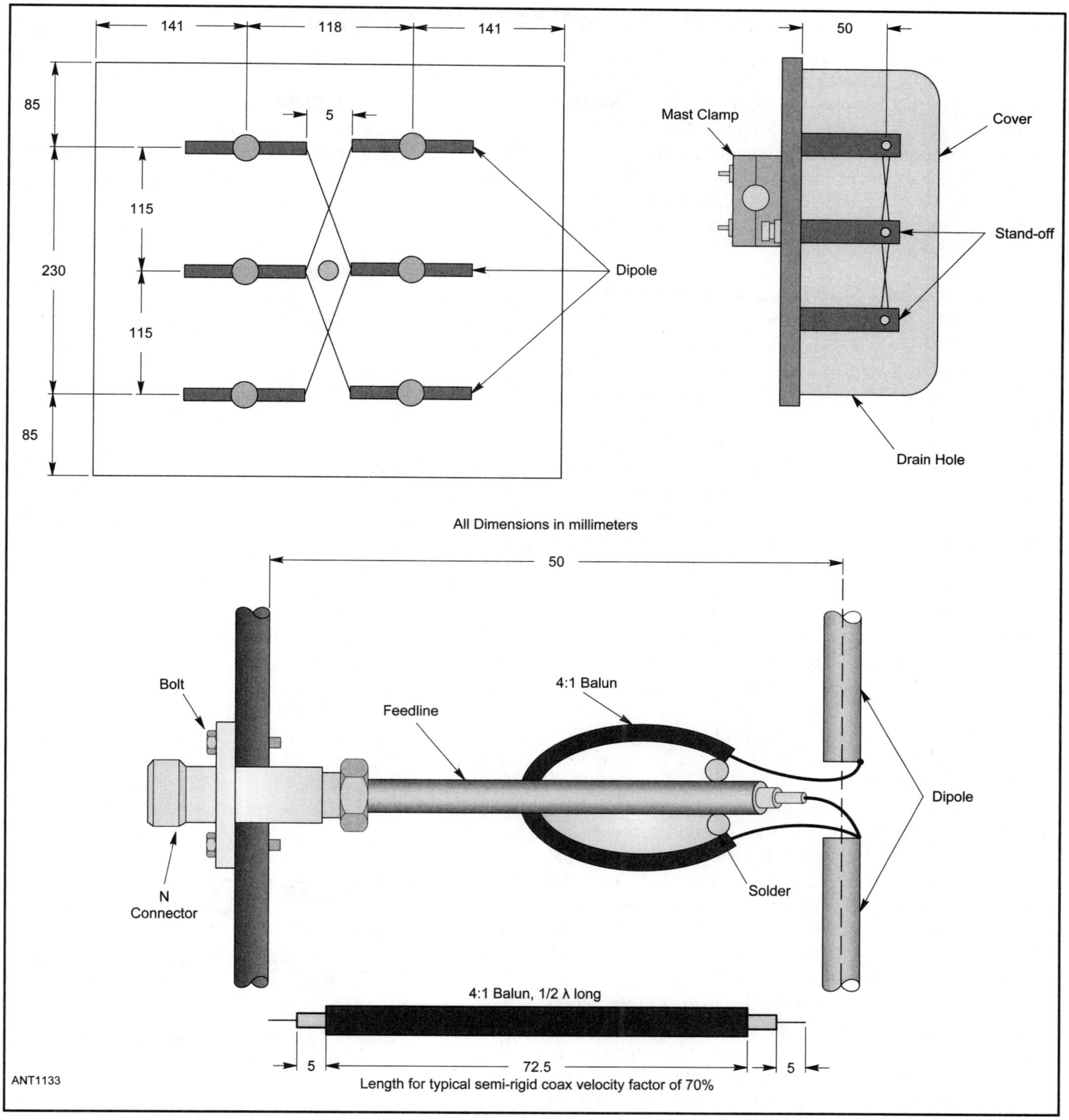

Figure 15.12 — Details of the F5JIO 23 cm collinear array.

Parts list
Reflector — 400 mm × 400 mm (340 mm min), 2.5 mm thick aluminum sheet
Standoffs — Teflon or PVC, 60 mm L × 20 mm D (qty 6)
Dipoles — brass, silver plated (opt), 108 mm L × 6 mm D (qty 6)
Phasing rods — Wire, silver plated (opt), 2 mm D (qty 4)
Connector — N-type receptacle
Feed line — semi-rigid coax 50-Ω approx 4 mm D, UT-141 typical
Balun — same type as feed line, 92.5 mm L or ½ λ
Bolt — M3 × 8 mm, stainless steel (qty 4)
Cover — plastic food container
Mast clamp from TV antenna

15.3 YAGIS AND QUADS AT VHF AND UHF

Without doubt, the Yagi is king of home-station VHF and UHF antennas for weak-signal operating and for long-distance repeater and simplex operation. Today's best designs are computer optimized. The **HF Yagi and Quad Antennas** chapter describes the parameters associated with Yagi antennas. Due to the shorter wavelengths above 50 MHz, high-performance designs that would be impractical at HF are easily achievable at VHF and UHF. A variety of designs are presented for 50 through 432 MHz.

15.3.1 CONSTRUCTING VHF AND UHF YAGIS

Before discussing materials, it is important to note that high-performance, especially at and above 144 MHz, requires that design specifications be followed very closely. Measurement or machining errors that can be ignored at HF become more significant at short wavelengths. The antenna designs in this chapter are fairly tolerant of deviations in the final assembly dimensions from those specified by the model and in the dimension tables. Good performance will be obtained using standard building practices and paying attention to details. However, accurate assembly is required if maximum performance is required or to duplicate the modeled performance.

Materials

Normally, aluminum tubing or rod is used for Yagi elements. Brass tubing is also used and has the additional advantage of being solderable. Hard-drawn copper wire can also be used on Yagis above 420 MHz. Resistive losses are inversely proportional to the square of the element diameter and the square root of its conductivity.

Element diameters of less than 3⁄16 inch or 4 mm should not be used on any band. The size should be chosen for reasonable strength. Half-inch diameter elements are the minimum suitable for 50 MHz (use a tempered alloy) and should be used at 144 MHz. One-quarter to three-sixteenths inch elements are acceptable for higher frequencies. Steel, including stainless steel and unprotected brass or copper wire, should not be used for elements.

When developing a Yagi at VHF and up, it is important to make the driven elements adjustable. This allows the builder to compensate for minor variations in feed line attachments and slight variations in element placement. See the note regarding connections in the section on Feed Point Construction below.

Boom material may be aluminum tubing, either square or round. High-strength aluminum alloys such as 6061-T6 or 6063-T651 offer the best strength-to-weight advantages. If the original design uses a metal boom, use the same size and shape metal boom when you duplicate it. Larger or smaller conductive booms may require an adjustment in element length. If the design calls for a wood boom, use a nonconductive material. Fiberglass tubes or poles are also good for booms but may need painting for UV protection.

Wood is popular for temporary or portable antennas, such as those in the section Cheap Yagis by WA5VJB elsewhere in this chapter. Suitable sizes of lumber include 1 × 3 (up to 15 feet long), 1 × 2 or 3⁄4 × 1 1⁄4 pine molding stock, or even strips of 1⁄2-inch exterior plywood for very short antennas. The wood should be well seasoned and free from knots. Clear pine, spruce and Douglas fir are often used. The wood should be well treated to avoid water absorption and warping. If varnished well, wood can outlast aluminum in salt air and marine environments.

Insulated and Non-insulated Elements

Elements may be mounted insulated or non-insulated, above or through the boom. Insulating the elements from the boom reduces interaction between the elements and boom which becomes increasingly important in high-performance designs.

Non-insulated elements as in **Figure 15.13** are mechanically convenient and are at dc ground, assuming the boom of the antenna is also grounded. Two muffler clamps hold each aluminum plate to the boom, and two U bolts fasten each element to the plate, which is 0.25 inch thick and 4 × 4 inches square. Stainless steel is the best choice for hardware, but galvanized hardware can be substituted. Automotive muffler clamps do not work well in this application because they are not galvanized and quickly rust once exposed to the weather.

Computer modeling can apply a correction for the connection of the element with the boom — make sure you account for that interaction when designing the antenna as it is significant at VHF and higher frequencies! (Correction tables are available on the DG7YBN and YU7EF websites referenced in the sidebar later in this chapter.)

Insulated elements can be mounted on shoulder insulators and run through the boom as in **Figure 15.14**. The

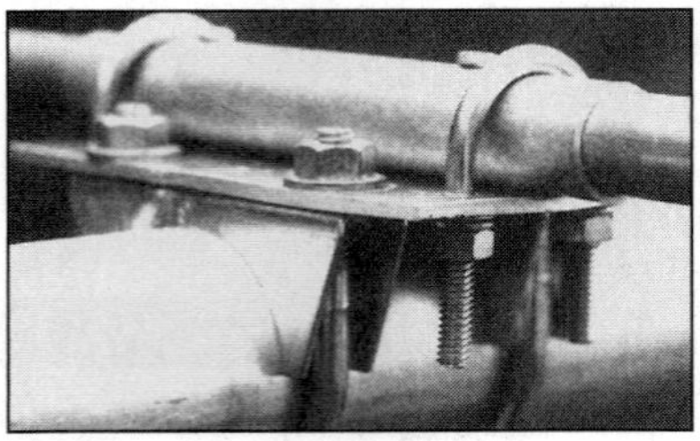

Figure 15.13 — The element to boom clamp. U bolts are used to hold the element to the plate, and 2-inch galvanized muffler clamps hold the plates to the boom.

Figure 15.14 — Insulated elements up to 3⁄8 inch in diameter can be mounted through the boom using plastic insulators. Stainless-steel push-nut retaining rings hold the element in place.

stainless-steel element retainers are usually referred to as push-on retainers or "pushnuts" such as those made by Auveco Products (**www.auveco.com**). The insulating shoulder washers should be UV-resistant Teflon or Delrin, such as are available from Unicorp (**www.unicorpinc.com**). Directive Systems & Engineering (**www.directivesystems.com**) can supply small quantities of both parts.

Mounting non-insulated elements through a metal boom is the least desirable method unless the elements are welded in place. The Yagi elements will oscillate, even in moderate winds. Over several years this element oscillation will work open the boom holes or loosen connecting hardware. This will allow the elements to move in the boom, creating noise (in the receiver) when the wind blows, as the element contact changes. (Rope or string inside the element helps damp this movement.) Eventually the element-to-boom junction will corrode (aluminum oxide is a good insulator). This loss of electrical contact between the boom and element will reduce the boom's effect and change the resonant frequency of the Yagi.

One of the most popular construction methods for insulated elements is to mount the elements through the boom using insulating shoulder washers. This method is lightweight and durable. Its main disadvantage is difficult disassembly, making this method impractical for portable antennas.

Stauff clamps (**www.us.stauff.com**) can be used to hold the elements on the boom as shown in **Figure 15.15**. These clamps are relatively new to US antenna builders but solve several problems with the traditional plate-and-U-bolt construction and are rated for industrial and outdoor use. The clamps for reflector and director elements are typically mounted directly to the boom. Various brackets and supports are also available from Stauff. Be sure to use clamps with polypropylene (PP) insulation at VHF and above as other plastics exhibit excessive loss.

If a conductive boom is used, element lengths must be corrected for the mounting method used. The amount of correction is dependent upon the boom diameter in wavelengths. (A change in boom diameter also requires element length adjustment.) See **Figure 15.16** for an example of the effect of element mounting. Elements mounted through the boom and not insulated require the greatest correction. Mounting on top of the boom or through the boom on insulated shoulder washers requires about half of the through-the-boom correction. When using a model or design plans for a Yagi, be sure to note whether the elements are in contact with a conductive boom and whether corrections are incorporated into the model and design.

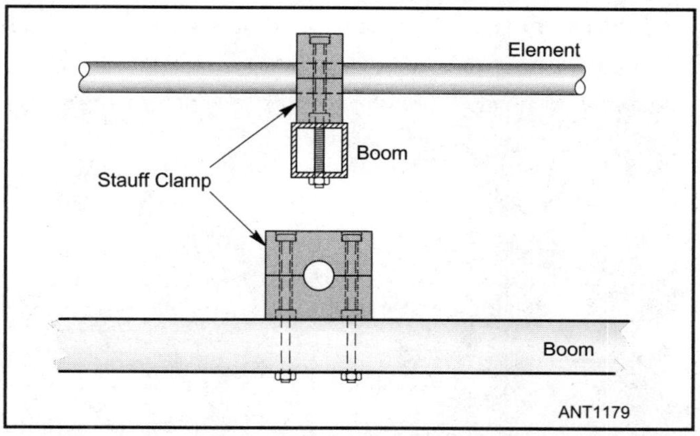

Figure 15.15 — Using a Stauff clamp to mount an insulated element on a square boom.

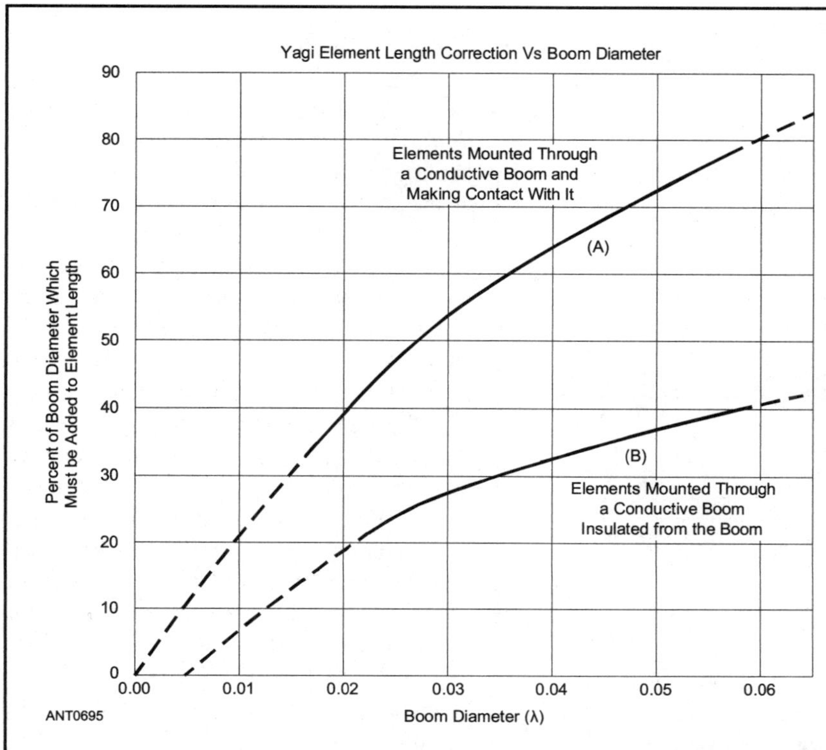

Figure 15.16 — Typical Yagi element correction vs boom diameter. Curve A is for elements mounted through a round or square conductive boom, with the elements in mechanical contact with the boom. Curve B is for insulated elements mounted through a conductive boom, and for elements mounted on top of a conductive boom (elements make electrical contact with the boom). The patterns were corrected to computer simulations to determine Yagi tuning. The amount of element correction is not affected by element diameter. This graph is an example of typical element length corrections and should not be applied in all circumstances.

Feed Point Construction

The following applies especially to high-performance antennas at VHF and above. Modeling software assumes that at the antenna feed point, the coax stops and the driven element starts and there are no wires or pigtails or connectors between them. This means that when an antenna is built from a software model, the driven element will need to be shorter than the model suggests when built, in order to account for the connections that will indeed need to exist between the coax and the antenna feed point in the real world.

RF does not wait until it arrives at the element itself to radiate. At the exact point at which the coax cable is no longer coaxial, the radiating element begins and this includes any wires or pigtails. It is for this reason that a driven element must usually be a bit shorter than modeled, assuming that the antenna is built correctly and any correction factors have been appropriately applied. Additionally, this highlights the fact that tail length should be reduced to an absolute minimum and more T shaped across the feed point as in **Figure 15.17** rather than Y-shaped in order for the software model can be replicated as closely as possible. Similar considerations apply to the use of connectors. The higher the frequency, the more relevant this rule becomes.

Leads from a feed line or balun to the feed point (or coax pigtails) should be as short as possible and spread apart parallel to the driven element. Once no longer inside the coaxial cable, the leads form part of the driven element and if they are excessively long it will affect antenna performance.

Weatherproofing a coax pigtail can be a challenge, especially for VHF/UHF antennas where the length of the connections must be short. John Portune, W6NBC, designed a 3D-printed housing for these pigtails that makes the job easier. The March 2019 *QST* article, "3D-Printed Coax-to-Wire Connection Blocks" is included in the downloadable supplemental information for the chapter **Building Antenna Systems and Towers** and is listed in this chapter's Bibliography.

Figure 15.17 — A close-up of the feed line connection showing proper technique for creating and attaching coaxial cable to a driven element. The configuration should be as close to T-shaped as possible and in line with the element to avoid affecting performance at VHF and higher frequencies.

Choke Baluns for VHF/UHF Yagis

A choke balun should be used at the feed point to prevent interaction between the antenna and the feed line shield's outer surface. Alternately, resonant transmission line baluns are commonly used at VHF and UHF. See the **Transmission Line System Techniques** chapter for design and construction information on choke and transmission line baluns. At VHF and UHF, the most consistent performance from bead baluns requires using an appropriate ferrite mix such as #43 or #61.

If a choke balun at the feed point is used, feed line length between the balun and the feed point should be as short as possible to limit interaction between the feed line's outer surface and the antenna.

Gamma Match for 6 Meter Yagis

The drawing in **Figure 15.18** shows a gamma match design in the ARRL book *Magic Band Antennas for Ham Radio* by Bruce Walker, N3JO. (See the Bibliography.) The full article goes into some detail about the construction but the basic idea is well-illustrated here. Be sure to use anti-oxidation compound for all metal-to-metal connections, including the sheet metal screws holding the bracket to the driven element. For additional support of the gamma match, UV-resistant cable ties can be used.

Tune the gamma match by adjusting the position of the shorting strap connecting the driven element and ⅜-inch tubing. If the minimum obtainable SWR remains too high, shorten the length of the driven element by ½ inch and readjust the strap. If minimum SWR has decreased, continue to shorten the driven element and adjust the strap position. If minimum SWR has increased, the driven element needs to be lengthened, instead.

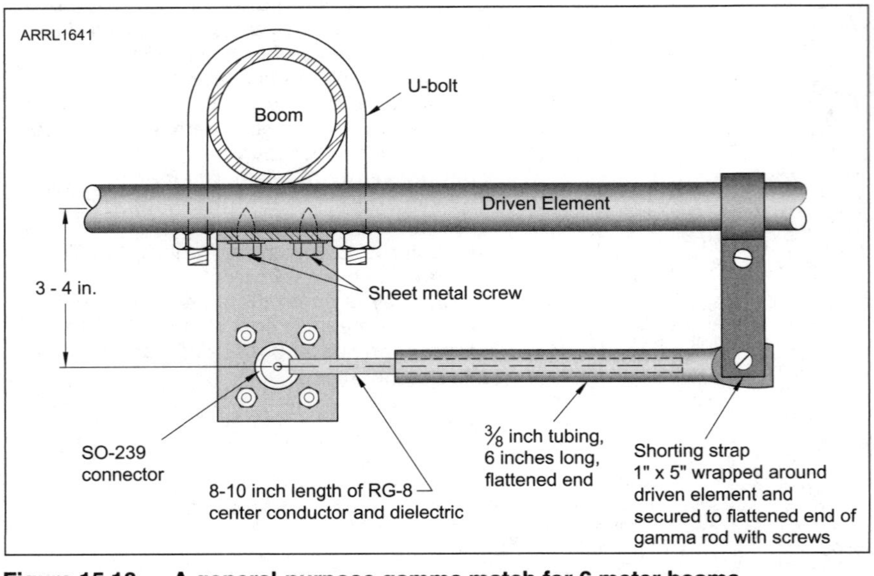

Figure 15.18 — A general-purpose gamma match for 6 meter beams.

15.3.2 YAGIS FOR 50 MHZ

Boom length often proves to be the deciding factor when one selects a Yagi design. **Table 15.1** shows three 6 meter Yagis designed for convenient boom lengths (6, 12 and 22 feet). The 3-element, 6-foot boom design has 8.0 dBi gain in free space; the 12 foot boom, 5-element version has 10.1 dBi gain, and the 22-foot, 7 element Yagi has a gain of 11.3 dBi. All antennas exhibit better than 22 dB front-to-rear ratio and cover 50 to 51 MHz with better than 1.7:1 SWR. A high-performance OWL (Optimized Wideband Low Impedance) design for 50 MHz by Justin Johnson, GØKSC, is included in the High-Performance Yagi Design section of this chapter.

A beam designed for FM operation higher in the band is described by the August 2007 *QST* article "A Short Boom, Wideband 3 Element Yagi for 6 Meters," by L.B. Cebik, W4RNL. Cebik describes two additional 3-element Yagis for 6 meters — one optimized for gain and F/B and the other optimized for bandwidth — in the February 2000 *QST* article, "2 x 3 = 6." Both articles are included with this book's downloadable supplemental information.

Half-element lengths and spacings are given in the table. Elements can be mounted to the boom as shown in Figure 15.13. Please note that the element lengths shown in Table 15.1 are half the overall element lengths. See the **Antenna Materials and Construction** chapter for practical details of telescoping aluminum elements.

The driven element is mounted to the boom on a Bakelite or G-10 fiberglass plate of similar dimension to the other mounting plates. A 12-inch piece of Plexiglas rod is inserted into the driven element halves. The Plexiglas allows the use of a single clamp on each side of the element and also seals the center of the elements against moisture. Self-tapping screws are used for electrical connection to the driven element.

Refer to **Figure 15.19** for driven-element and hairpin match details. A bracket made from a piece of aluminum is

Table 15.1
Optimized 6 Meter Yagi Designs
(Lengths are for half elements)

	Spacing Between Elements (inches)	*Seg1 OD Length (inches)*	*Seg2 OD Length (inches)*	*Midband Gain F/R*
306-06				
OD		0.750	0.625	
Refl.	0	36	23.500	7.9 dBi
D.E.	24	36	16.000	27.2 dB
Dir. 1	42	36	15.500	
506-12				
OD		0.750	0.625	
Refl.	0	36	24.000	10.1 dBi
D.E.	24	36	17.125	24.7 dB
Dir. 1	12	36	19.375	
Dir. 2	44	36	18.250	
Dir. 3	58	36	15.375	
706-22				
OD		0.750	0.625	
Refl.	0	36	25.000	11.3 dBi
D.E.	27	36	17.250	29.9 dB
Dir. 1	16	36	18.500	
Dir. 2	51	36	15.375	
Dir. 3	54	36	15.875	
Dir. 4	53	36	16.500	
Dir. 5	58	36	12.500	

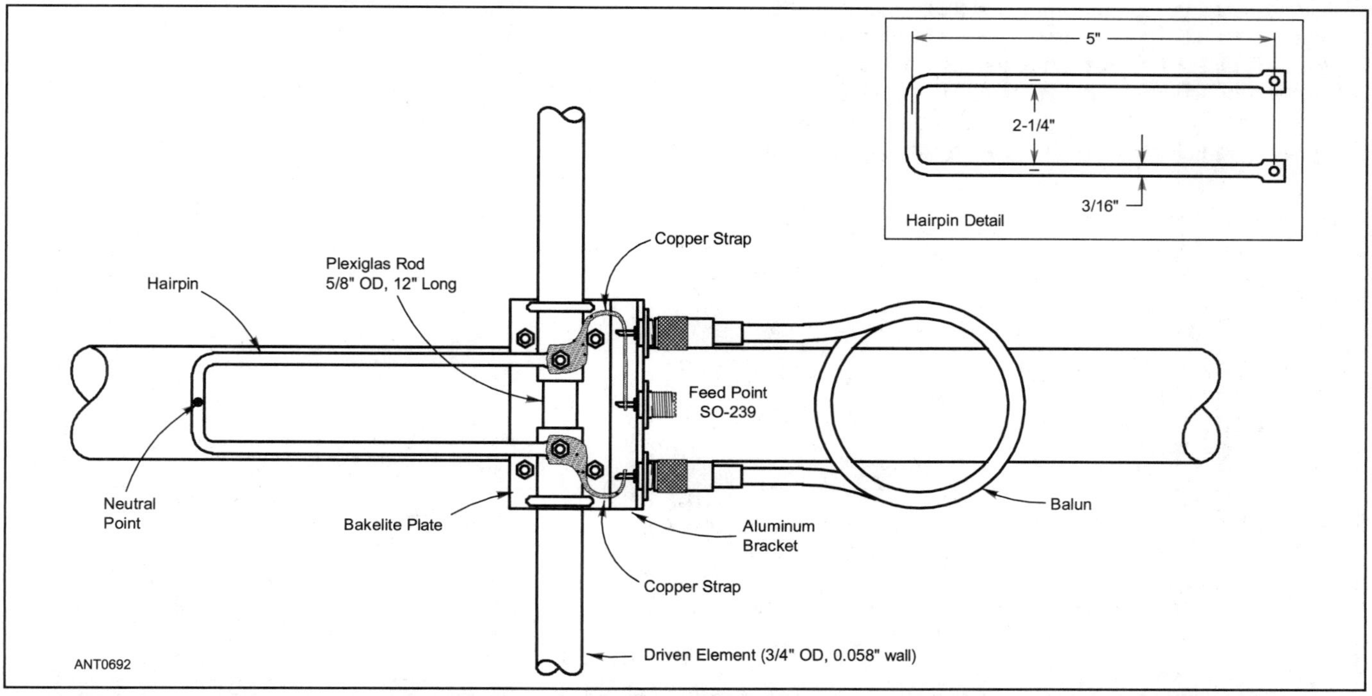

Figure 15.19 — This shows how the driven element and feed system are attached to the boom. The phasing line is coiled and taped to the boom. The center of the hairpin loop may be connected to the boom electrically and mechanically if desired. Phasing-line lengths:
For cable with 0.80 velocity factor — 7 ft, 10⅜ inches
For cable with 0.66 velocity factor — 6 ft, 5¾ inches

used to mount the three SO-239 connectors to the driven element plate. A 4:1 transmission line balun connects the two element halves, transforming the 200 Ω resistance at the hairpin match to 50 Ω at the center connector. Note that the electrical length of the balun is λ/2, but the physical length will be shorter due to the velocity factor of the particular coaxial cable used. The hairpin is connected directly across the element halves. The exact center of the hairpin is electrically neutral and should be fastened to the boom. This has the advantage of placing the driven element at dc ground potential.

The hairpin match requires no adjustment as such. However, you may have to change the length of the driven element slightly to obtain the best match in your preferred portion of the band. Changing the driven-element length will not adversely affect antenna performance. *Do not adjust the lengths or spacings of the other elements — they are optimized already.* If you decide to use a gamma match, add 3 inches to each side of the driven element lengths given in the table for all antennas.

Moxon Rectangles

The Moxon Rectangle is a two-element parasitic beam

Meteor Scatter: How Much Antenna is Too Much?

Can an antenna be too big or have too much gain? Perhaps surprisingly, in some circumstances the answer is a definite "Yes."

High gain means narrow beamwidth. Even supposing that a sharp beam can be directed just as desired, you may sometimes want your transmitter to illuminate a larger range of directions, or to receive signals with reasonable gain over a larger range. Such situations can exist even for point-to-point communication — for example, when station A tries to work station B, at a known location some 800 to 1200 km away, on a VHF band using meteor scatter.

The most probable path geometries for random meteor scatter are offset by angles of about 8° to 16° either side of the great circle path. Smaller offsets apply to the longest paths, on the order of 2200 to 2400 km; paths less than 1000 km have optimum offsets near the high end of the range. The largest number of meteor-scatter reflections will occur when stations A and B use antenna beamwidths that overlap throughout most of the potentially useful scattering volume. This implies beamwidths at least twice the offset angle: around 32° for 800 km paths, or 16° for the longest feasible paths. Of course, antennas with higher gain and narrower beams may yield stronger signals, when they produce any at all; but for efficient completion of their desired contact, A and B may be interested in getting *more* meteor reflections, rather than *stronger* ones.

A Yagi antenna with 30° beamwidth has boom length of about 3 wavelengths and gain of 13 dBd. Three wavelengths at 50 MHz is nearly 60 feet, so few if any amateur antennas for this band are likely to be "too large" for effective meteor-scatter use. At 144 MHz, however, Yagis of 5 wavelengths and more are quite practical. Their beamwidths will be significantly less than 30°, so they will be sub-optimal for meteor-scatter contacts at moderate distances.

Real-world amateur meteor scatter experience confirms the picture outlined above. For meteor scatter out to 1600 km on the 2 meter band, an optimized 10 to 12 element Yagi (length 1.8 to 2.5 λ) is probably close to the optimum antenna. Takeoff angles for meteor scatter are no more than about 15°, so a vertical stack of two such Yagis (which would have the same beamwidth in azimuth) would be even better. Horizontal stacking of a pair, or a 2 × 2 box of four such Yagis, would work well beyond about 1600 km, but would be sub-optimal at shorter distances. On the longest feasible meteor-scatter paths, beyond about 1800 km, the rule-of-thumb once again becomes "bigger is better." Note that for these long paths the optimum takeoff angle has fallen to less than 3°, so antenna height in excess of 5 λ (about 35 feet at 144 MHz) is also important. — *Joe Taylor, K1JT*

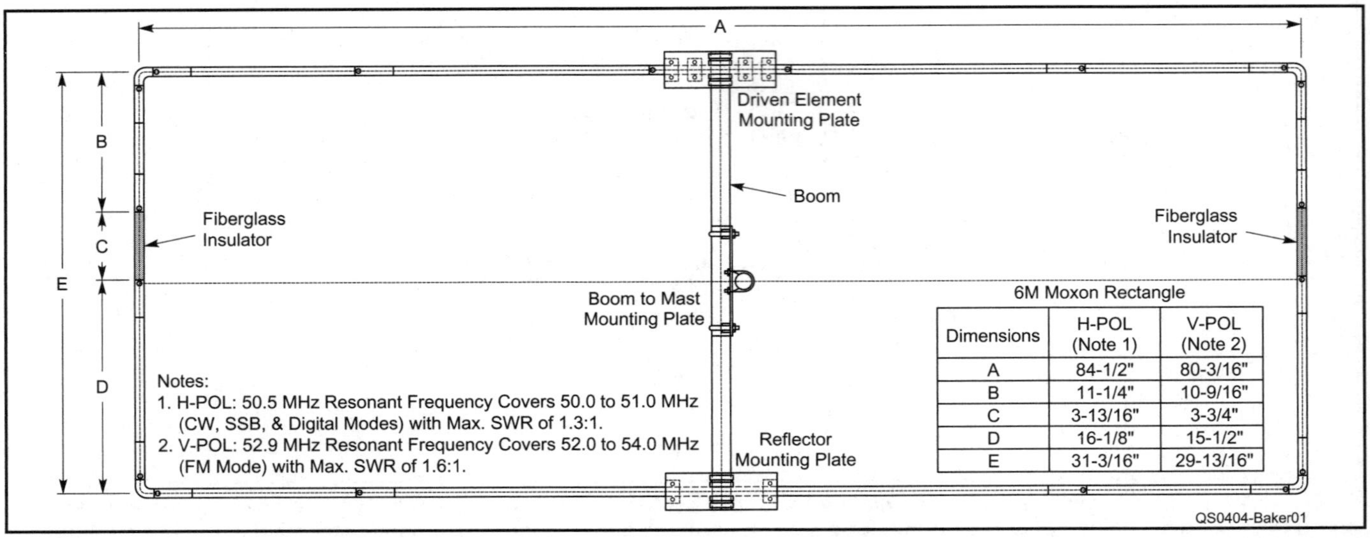

6M Moxon Rectangle

Dimensions	H-POL (Note 1)	V-POL (Note 2)
A	84-1/2"	80-3/16"
B	11-1/4"	10-9/16"
C	3-13/16"	3-3/4"
D	16-1/8"	15-1/2"
E	31-3/16"	29-13/16"

Figure 15.20 — Basic construction dimensions for the 6 Meter Moxon rectangle antenna. The two sets of dimensions are for use at different frequencies — see text for details.

similar to a Yagi with a director and reflector elements. The element tips are bent back toward each other, resulting in a two-element beam about 70 percent as wide as a regular two-element Yagi. The Moxon has almost as much gain as a two-element Yagi but a much better front-to-back ratio. Because of its reduced size, the Moxon is popular on HF and 6 meters. Moxon designs for the higher frequency bands are also available. (See the Bibliography entries for Cebik for more articles about the Moxon and the chapter **HF Yagi and Quad Antennas** for HF Moxon antennas.)

The most popular VHF band for "Moxons" is 6 meters, with many designs mechanically sturdy enough to be used as a mobile antenna for roving and portable operation. The "stressed" Moxon has a flexible support structure that keeps its thin elements under tension for extra stability and light weight, making it a popular antenna for roving. PAR Electronics (**www.parelectronics.com**) makes a commercial version.

The 6 meter Moxon design in **Figure 15.20** is from the *QST* article "A 6 Meter Moxon Antenna," by Allen Baker, KG4JJH. (See the Bibliography and the downloadable supplemental information for the complete construction article.) The antenna can be mounted either horizontally or vertically and two sets of dimensions are provided: one for operation from 50 to 51 MHz and the second for 52 to 54 MHz. The design uses aluminum tubing and channel for strength. Final weight is 8½ pounds, light enough for portable or rover use.

15.3.3 UTILITY YAGIS FOR 144 MHZ AND 432 MHZ

There are many applications for Yagis on 144 MHz that do not require high gain or tightly-controlled pattern. In fact, for casual operating, a beamwidth that is too narrow can actually prevent a station from hearing weak signals not in the main lobe of the antenna. For meteor scatter and other applications (see the sidebar, "Meteor Scatter: How Much Antenna is Too Much?") where the opening comes from an unknown azimuth, a wider beamwidth is preferred. Rover and portable stations often find the lighter weight and shorter boom length of the smaller antennas easier to handle.

Utility Yagi for 144 MHz

The following material is a summary of the design presented by L.B. Cebik, W4RNL in the December 2004 *QST* article "Building a Medium-Gain, Wide-Band, 2 Meter Yagi." (The complete article is included with this book's downloadable supplemental information.)

The 6-element Yagi presented here is a derivative of the "optimized wideband antenna" (OWA) designs developed for HF use by NW3Z and WA3FET. **Figure 15.21** shows the general structure of the beam and **Figure 15.22** gives the free-space E-plane pattern. If mounted with the elements horizontal, the E-plane pattern would be the azimuthal pattern.

Oversimplifying the design somewhat, the reflector and first director largely set the feed point impedance. The next two directors contribute to setting the operating bandwidth. The final director sets the gain.

Designed using *NEC-4*, the antenna's six elements are arranged on a 56-inch boom **Table 15.2** gives the specific

Table 15.2
2 Meter OWA Yagi Dimensions
(Lengths are for full elements)

Element	*Element Length (inches)*	*Spacing from Reflector (inches)*	*Element Diameter (inches)*
Reflector	40.52	—	3⁄16
Driven Ele.	39.70	10.13	½
Director 1	37.36	14.32	3⁄16
Director 2	36.32	25.93	3⁄16
Director 3	36.32	37.28	3⁄16
Director 4	34.96	54.22	3⁄16

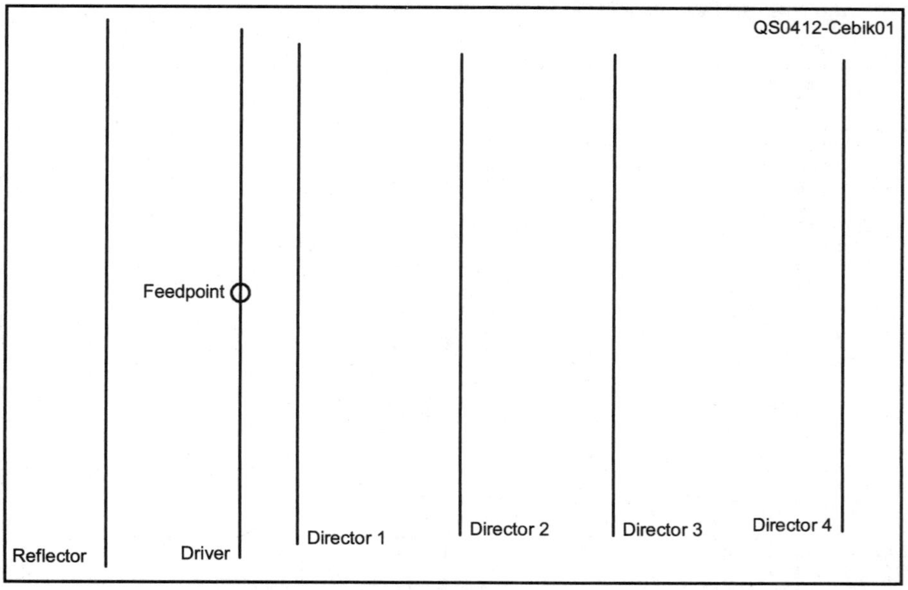

Figure 15.21 — The general structure of the 2 meter, 6-element OWA Yagi. See Table 15.2 for dimensions.

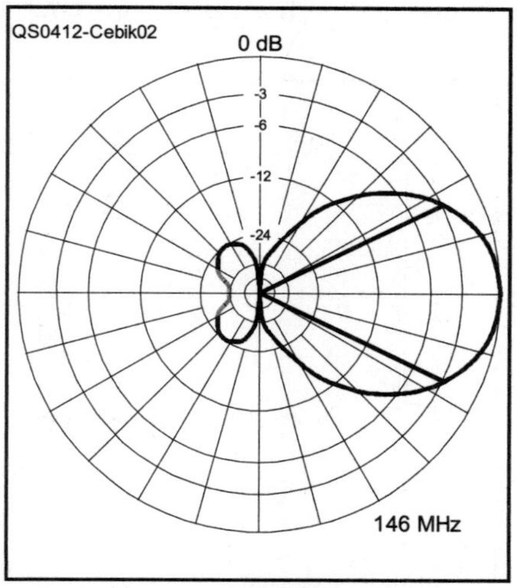

Figure 15.22 — E-plane (horizontal azimuth) pattern of the 2 meter, 6-element OWA Yagi in free space at mid-band — 146 MHz. The antenna exhibits a gain of about 10.2 dBi, consistent across the 2 meter band.

dimension for the antenna. The parasitic elements are all 3⁄16-inch aluminum rod while the driver uses ½-inch aluminum tubing for reasons of construction. Dimensions for the beam with an alternate driver or the use of ⅛-inch elements is given in the original article.

The OWA design provides about 10.2 dBi of free-space gain with better than 20 dB F/B across the entire 2 meter band. The horizontal beamwidth is considerably wider if the beam is mounted with the elements vertical for use on FM.

One significant feature of the OWA design is its direct 50-Ω feed point impedance that requires no matching network. Of course, a common-mode choke balun (see the **Transmission Line System Techniques** chapter) is desirable. The SWR as shown in **Figure 15.23** is very flat across the band and never exceeds 1.3:1. The SWR and pattern consistency together create a very useful utility antenna for 2 meters.

Utility Yagi for 432 MHz

The following design was developed by Zack Lau, W1VT and described in his "RF" column "A Small 70-cm Yagi" in the July/August 2001 *QEX*. The complete article is included with this book's downloadable supplemental information.

This six-element Yagi was designed for a wide bandwidth — in gain, F/B and SWR. Its gain was measured at 8.5 dBd during the 1995 Eastern States VHF/UHF Conference — with little gain variation between 417 and 446 MHz. The SWR is almost as broad, with better than 1.4:1 SWR between 422 and 446 MHz. The measured gain and return loss curves are shown in **Figure 15.24**. The short 30-inch boom is small enough to fit in the trunk of a compact sedan, perfect for portable or emergency operation. The F/B bandwidth is also very good, with over 20 dB of F/B between 424 and 450 MHz, according to a *Yagi Analyzer* computer model.

Even if you only intend to use this antenna for 432-MHz SSB or 436-MHz satellite operation, the extra bandwidth is useful when it rains. Heavy rain causes antenna elements to resonate lower in frequency. This is much worse if the antenna is tweaked for maximum gain. Yagis typically have a low-pass gain response. The gain falls off rapidly past the maximum-gain point. Thus, while the maximum gain is around 442 MHz, the gain is significantly lower at 457 MHz, while only a little bit lower at 427 MHz.

The optimized design is shown in **Figure 15.25** and the element lengths and placement are given in **Table 15.3**. The element lengths are adjusted to work with a particular boom

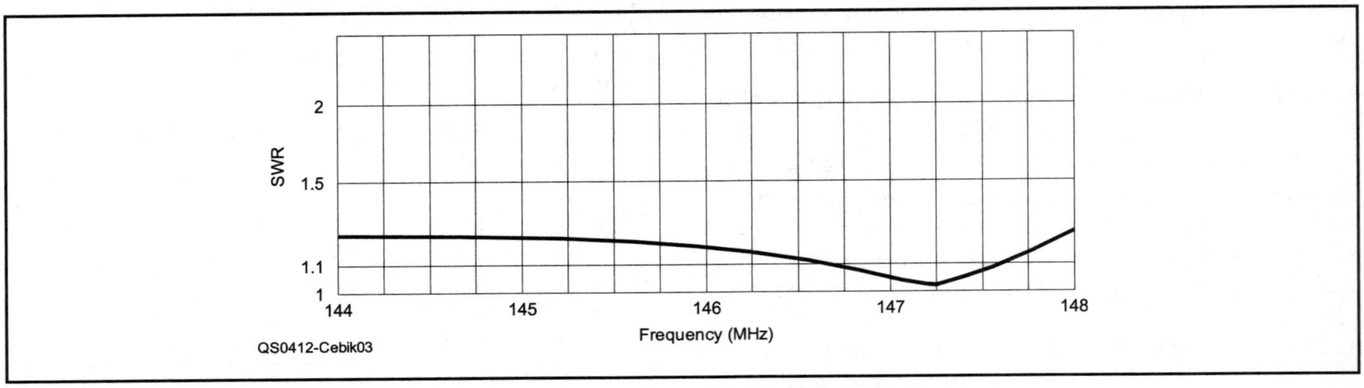

Figure 15.23 — The SWR for the OWA 2 meter Yagi from 144 to 148 MHz as modeled by *NEC-4*.

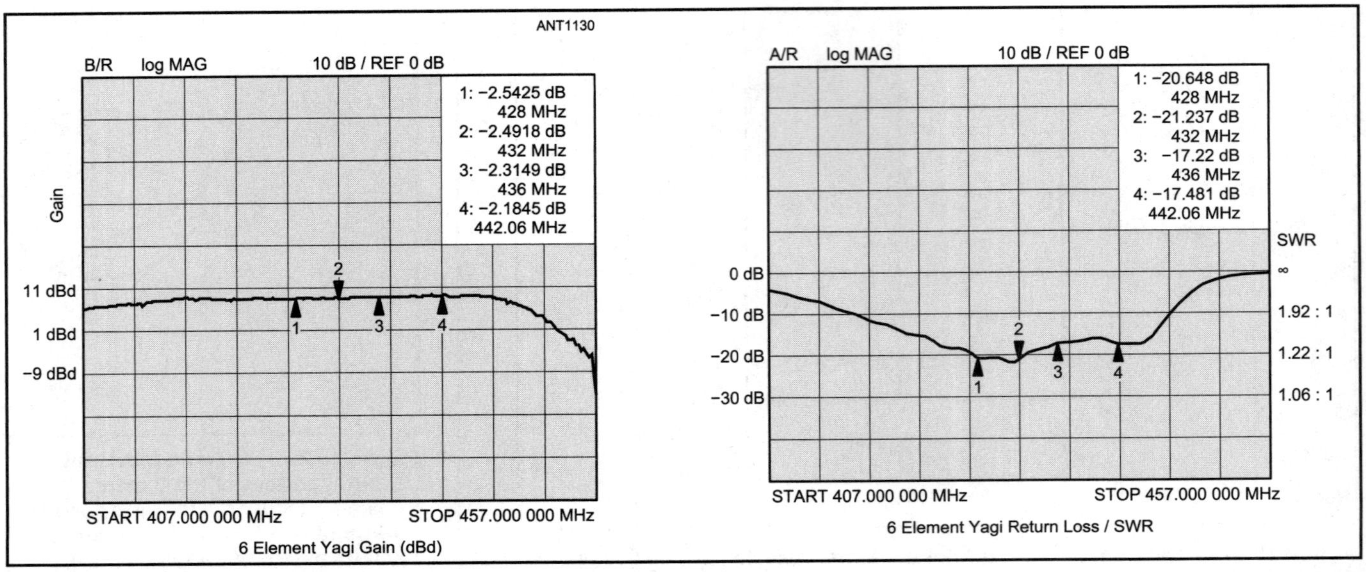

Figure 15.24 — Gain and SWR measurements for the 70 cm Yagi.

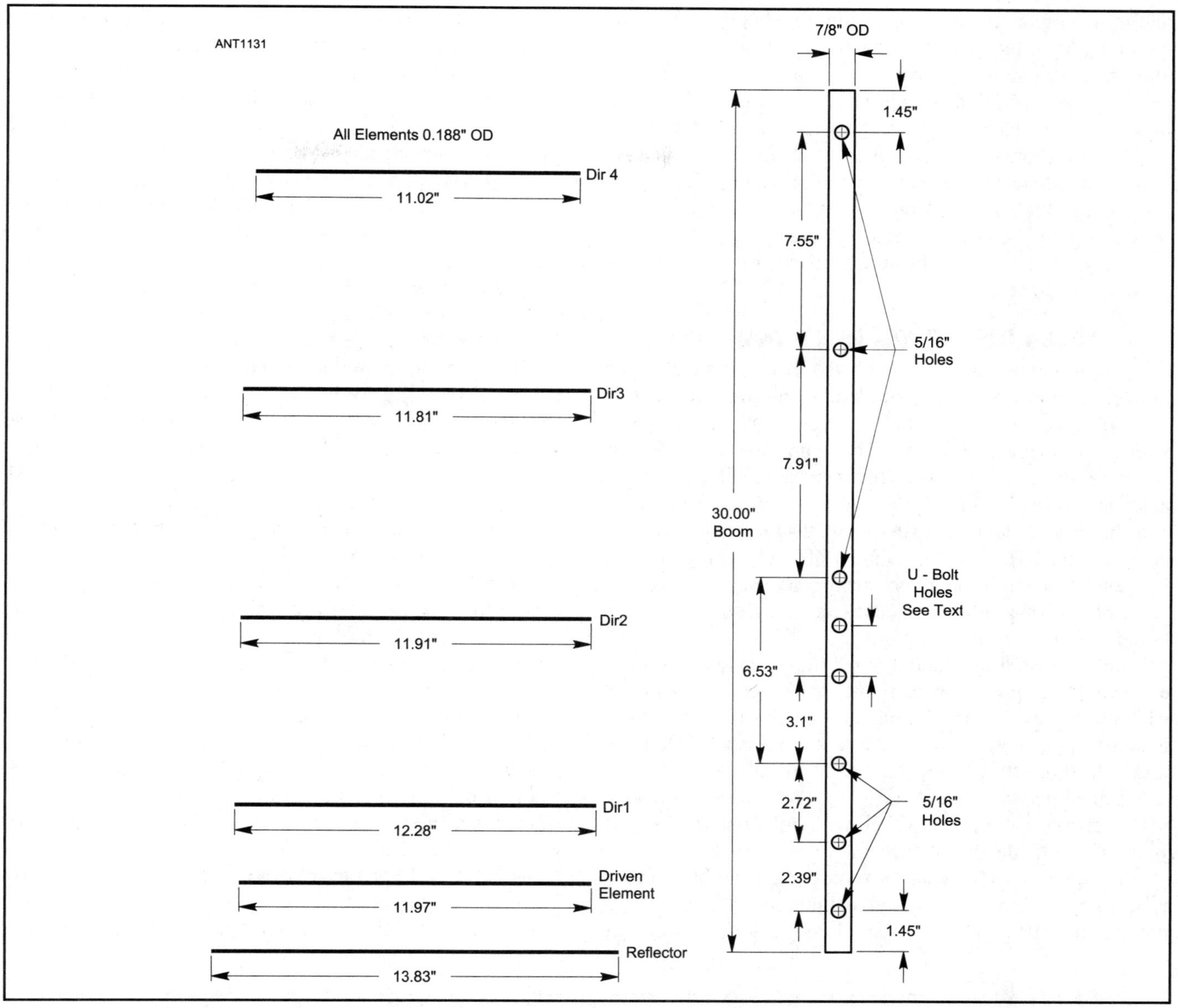

Figure 15.25 — Rough scale drawing of the 70 cm Yagi boom and elements.

Table 15.3
432-MHz Yagi Dimensions

	Spacing Between Ele. (inches)	*Spacing from Reflector (inches)*	*Full Element Length (inches)*
Reflector	0	—	13.832
Driven Ele.	2.394	2.394	11.968
Dir. 1	2.715	5.109	12.284
Dir. 2	6.528	11.637	11.908
Dir. 3	7.907	19.544	11.810
Dir. 4	7.546	27.09	11.01

and mounting arrangement. Changing the boom or element mounting may require adjusting the element lengths. The antenna uses a simple T-match, as simpler gamma matches have a poor reputation on this band. A T-matched Yagi is more likely to have a symmetrical radiation pattern. The feed system shown in the complete article included with this book's downloadable supplemental information is a copy of that used in the K2RIW Yagi. A half-wave balun made out of semi-rigid UT-141 coax steps up the impedance to 200 Ω. Similarly, the T match steps up the impedance of the driven element to 200 Ω.

15.3.4 CHEAP YAGIS BY WA5VJB

The following material is adapted from an online paper by Kent Britain, WA5VJB, entitled "Controlled Impedance 'Cheap' Antennas." The paper is available from **www.wa5vjb.com/references.html**. The simplified feed uses the structure of the antenna itself for impedance matching. The antennas were designed with *YagiMax*, tweaked in *NEC*, and the driven elements experimentally determined on the antenna range. The result is a family of Yagis with good performance that can be built very inexpensively.

Construction of the antennas is straightforward. The boom is ¾-inch square, or ½-inch by ¾-inch wood. To install an element, drill a hole through the boom and insert the element. A drop of cyanoacrylate "super glue," epoxy, or silicone adhesive is used to hold the elements in place. There is no boom-to-mast plate — drill holes in the boom and use a U-bolt to attach it to the mast! The life of the antenna is determined by what you coat it with. The author had a 902-MHz version in the air varnished with polyurethane for two years with little deterioration.

The parasitic elements on prototypes have been made from silicon-bronze welding rod, aluminum rod, brass hobby tubing, and #10 or #12 AWG solid copper ground wire. So that you can solder to the driven element, use the welding rod, hobby tubing or copper wire. The driven element is folded at one end with its ends inserted through the boom.

Figure 15.26 shows the basic plan for the antenna and labels the dimensions that are given in the table for each band. All table dimensions are given in inches.

Figure 15.27 shows how the driven element is constructed for each antenna. Trim the free end of the driven element to tune it for minimum SWR at the desired frequency. **Figure 15.28** shows how to attach coaxial cable to the feed point. Sliding a quarter-wave sleeve along the coax had little effect, so there's not much RF on the outside of the coax. You may use a ferrite bead choke balun if you like, but these antennas are designed for minimum expense!

144 MHz Yagi: While others have reported good luck with 16-element long-boom wood antennas, six elements was about the maximum for most rovers. The design is peaked at 144.2 MHz, but performance is still good at 146.5 MHz. All parasitic elements are made from ³⁄₁₆-inch aluminum rod and the driven element is made from ⅛-inch rod. Lengths and spacings are given in **Table 15.4**.

222 MHz Yagi: This antenna is peaked at 222.1 MHz, but performance has barely changed at 223.5 MHz. You can drill the mounting holes to mount it with the elements horizontal or vertical. All parasitic elements are made from ³⁄₁₆-inch aluminum rod and the driven element is made from ⅛-inch rod. Lengths and spacings are given in Table 15.4.

432 MHz Yagi: At this band the antenna is getting very practical and easy to build. All parasitic elements are made from ⅛-inch diameter rod and the driven element is made from #10 AWG solid copper wire. Lengths and spacings are given in **Table 15.5**.

435 MHz Yagi for AMSAT: Ed Krome, K9EK, provided help and motivation for these antennas. A high front-to-back ratio (F/B) was a major design consideration of all

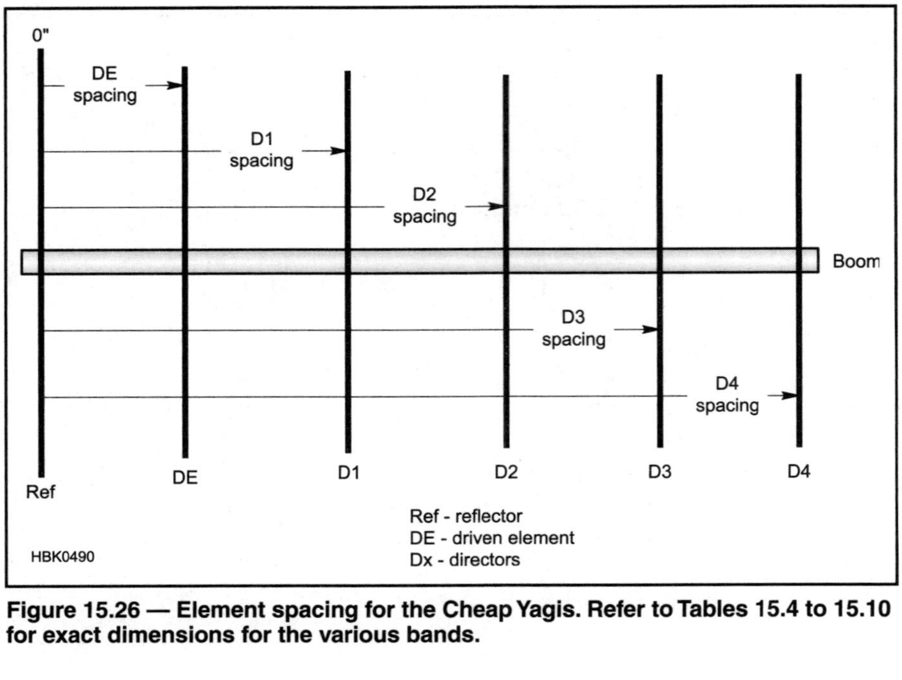

Figure 15.26 — Element spacing for the Cheap Yagis. Refer to Tables 15.4 to 15.10 for exact dimensions for the various bands.

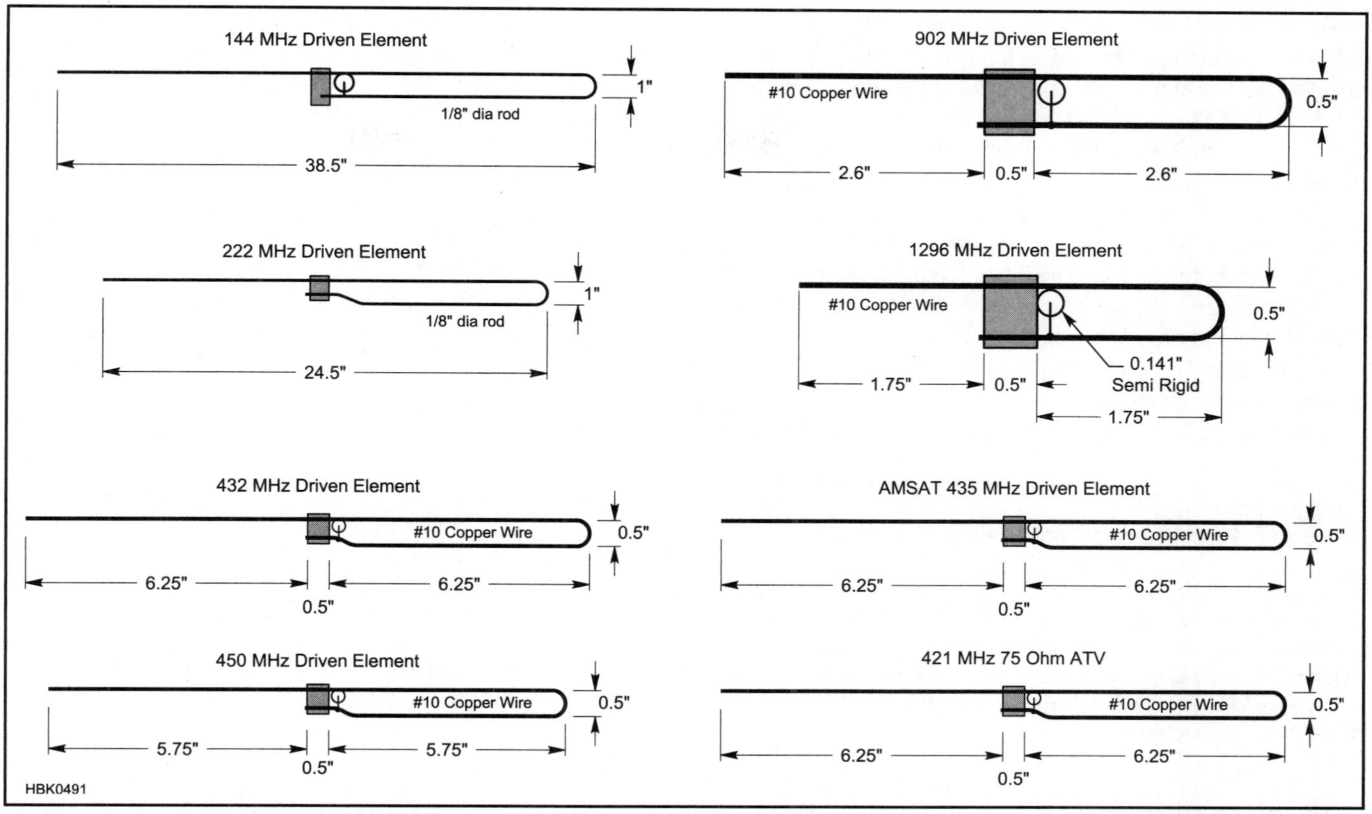

Figure 15.27 — Driven element dimensions for the Cheap Yagis. Attaching the coax shield to the center of the driven element is appropriate because that is the lowest impedance point of the element.

Table 15.4
WA5VJB 144 and 222 MHz Yagi Dimensions
144 MHz Yagi

		Ref	*DE*	*D1*	*D2*	*D3*	*D4*
3-element	Length	41.0	—	37.0			
	Spacing	0	8.5	20.0			
4-element	Length	41.0	—	37.5	33.0		
	Spacing	0	8.5	19.25	40.5		
6-element	Length	40.5	—	37.5	36.5	36.5	32.75
	Spacing	0	7.5	16.5	34.0	52.0	70.0

222 MHz Yagi

		Ref	*DE*	*D1*	*D2*	*D3*	*D4*
3-element	Length	26.0	—	23.75			
	Spacing	0	5.5	13.5			
4-element	Length	26.25	—	24.1	22.0		
	Spacing	0	5.0	11.75	23.5		
6-element	Length	26.25	—	24.1	23.5	23.5	21.0
	Spacing	0	5.0	10.75	22.0	33.75	45.5

Dimensions in inches.

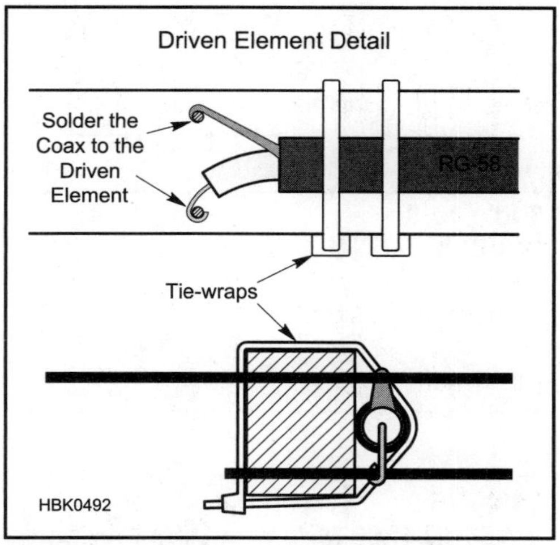

Figure 15.28 — Construction details and feed line attachment for the Cheap Yagi driven element.

Table 15.5
WA5VJB 432 MHz Yagi Dimensions

		Ref	*DE*	*D1*	*D2*	*D3*	*D4*	*D5*	*D6*	*D7*	*D8*	*D9*
6-element	Length	13.5	—	12.5	12.0	12.0	11.0					
	Spacing	0	2.5	5.5	11.25	17.5	24.0					
8-element	Length	13.5	—	12.5	12.0	12.0	12.0	12.0	11.25			
	Spacing	0	2.5	5.5	11.25	17.5	24.0	30.75	38.0			
11-element	Length	13.5	—	12.5	12.0	12.0	12.0	12.0	12.0	11.75	11.75	11.0
	Spacing	0	2.5	5.5	11.25	17.5	24.0	30.75	38.0	45.5	53.0	59.5

Dimensions in inches.

versions. The model predicts 30 dB F/B for the six-element and over 40 dB for the others. For gain, *NEC* predicts 11.2 dBi for the six-element, 12.6 dBi for the eight-element, and 13.5 dBi for the 10-element, and 13.8 dBi for the 11-element.

Using ¾-inch square wood for the boom makes it easy to build two antennas on the same boom for cross-polarization. Offset the two antennas 6½ inch along the boom and feed them in-phase for circular polarization, or just use one for portable operations. All parasitic elements are made from ⅛-inch diameter rod and the driven element is made from #10 AWG solid copper wire. Lengths and spacings are given in **Table 15.6**. The same element spacing is used for all four versions of the antenna.

450 MHz Yagi for FM: this six-element Yagi is a good, cheap antenna to get a newcomer into a repeater or make a simplex-FM QSO during a contest. Aluminum ground wire, typically ⅛-inch diameter, was used in the prototype for all the elements except the driven element, which is made from #10 AWG solid copper wire. Other ⅛-inch diameter material could be used. Lengths and spacings are given in **Table 15.7**.

902 MHz Yagi: The 2.5-ft length has proven very practical. All parasitic elements are made from ⅛-inch-diameter rod and the driven element is made from #10 AWG solid copper wire. Lengths and spacings are given in **Table 15.8**.

1296 MHz Yagi: This antenna is the veteran of several "Grid-peditions" and has measured 13.5 dBi on the Central States VHF Society antenna range. Dimensions must be followed with great care. The driven element is small enough to

Table 15.6
WA5VJB 435 MHz Yagi Dimensions

		Ref	*DE*	*D1*	*D2*	*D3*	*D4*	*D5*	*D6*	*D7*	*D8*	*D9*
6-element	Length	13.4	—	12.4	12.0	12.0	11.0					
8-element	Length	13.4	—	12.4	12.0	12.0	12.0	12.0	11.1			
10-element	Length	13.4	—	12.4	12.0	12.0	12.0	12.0	11.75	11.75	11.1	
11-element	Length	13.4	—	12.4	12.0	12.0	12.0	12.0	11.75	11.75	11.75	11.1
	Spacing	0	2.5	5.5	11.25	17.5	24.0	30.5	37.75	45.0	52.0	59.5

Dimensions in inches.

Table 15.7
WA5VJB 450 MHz Yagi Dimensions

		Ref	*DE*	*D1*	*D2*	*D3*	*D4*
6-element	Length	13.0	—	12.1	11.75	11.75	10.75
	Spacing	0	2.5	5.5	11.0	18.0	28.5

Dimensions in inches.

Table 15.8
WA5VJB 902 MHz Yagi Dimensions

		Ref	*DE*	*D1*	*D2*	*D3*	*D4*	*D5*	*D6*	*D7*	*D8*
10-element	Length	6.2	—	5.6	5.5	5.5	5.4	5.3	5.2	5.1	5.1
	Spacing	0	2.4	3.9	5.8	9.0	12.4	17.4	22.4	27.6	33.0

Dimensions in inches.

Table 15.9
WA5VJB 1296 MHz Yagi Dimensions

		Ref	*DE*	*D1*	*D2*	*D3*	*D4*	*D5*	*D6*	*D7*	*D8*
10-element	Length	4.3	—	3.9	3.8	3.75	3.75	3.65	3.6	3.6	3.5
	Spacing	0	1.7	2.8	4.0	6.3	8.7	12.2	15.6	19.3	23.0

Dimensions in inches.

Table 15.10
WA5VJB 421.25 MHz 75-Ω Yagi Dimensions

		Ref	*DE*	*D1*	*D2*	*D3*	*D4*	*D5*	*D6*	*D7*	*D8*	*D9*
6-element	Length	14.0	—	12.5	12.25	12.25	11.0					
9-element	Length	14.0	—	12.5	12.25	12.25	12.0	12.0	11.25			
11-element	Length	14.0	—	12.5	12.25	12.25	12.0	12.0	12.0	11.75	11.75	11.5
	Spacing	0	3.0	6.5	12.25	17.75	24.5	30.5	36.0	43.0	50.25	57.25

Dimensions in inches.

allow 0.141-inch semi-rigid coax to be used. The prototype antennas use ⅛-inch silicon-bronze welding rod for the elements, but any ⅛-inch-diameter material can be used. The driven element is made from #10 AWG solid copper wire. Lengths and spacings are given in **Table 15.9**.

421.25 MHz 75-Ω Yagi for ATV: 421 MHz vestigial sideband video is popular in North Texas for receiving the FM video input repeaters. These antennas are made for 421 MHz use and the driven element is designed for 75 Ω. RG-59 or an F adapter to RG-6 can be directly connected to a cable-TV converter or cable-ready TV on channel 57. All parasitic elements are made from ⅛-inch diameter rod and the driven element is made from #10 AWG solid copper wire. Lengths and spacings are given in **Table 15.10**. The same spacing is used for all versions.

15.3.5 HIGH-PERFORMANCE YAGI DESIGN

This section was primarily updated and extended by Justin Johnson, GØKSC, based on his articles in *DUBUS* and from material on his website at **www.g0ksc.co.uk**. In addition to the summarized information here, several articles by Justin are included with this book's downloadable supplemental information. The supplemental information also includes the classic Yagi designs by Steve Powlishen, K1FO, featured in several recent editions of this book. For those who wish to construct antennas based on DL6WU's work, a family of designs is available at the article referenced in the Bibliography.

The treatment of high-performance Yagi design in this edition takes advantage of high-precision modeling developed over the past few years to achieve better control of antenna pattern through manual and automatic optimization. In addition, construction techniques that can have a significant effect on performance across a band and susceptibility to noise pickup are discussed.

New techniques pioneered by YU7EF, DG7YBN, UA9TC, RA3AQ, and others (see the sidebar Yagi Designs Online for web URLs) have contributed to the development of Yagis optimized for wideband (flat) performance, consideration of elevation plane lobes, self-matching radiating elements, close-spaced "driver cell" (first three elements), and other key performance indicators, particularly gain/noise temperature performance as described in the sidebar Gain/Noise Temperature (G/T). It should be understood that not all of the antenna designs found online take into account the entire set of considerations in the following discussion while being optimized.

Building on the current state of computer-optimized antenna design, this section details some additional attributes that contribute to the "ideal" Yagi. In addition, reasons are presented and discussed as to why Yagis for UHF and microwave bands sometimes do not perform at the level predicted by software models.

On a philosophical note, recent advances in modeling and optimization of antenna performance have led to some exciting new advances, all pioneered by amateurs. The combination of sophisticated design tools, inexpensive materials, and the manageable weight and size for Yagis above 50 MHz, make it possible for any amateur so inclined to construct their own state of the art antennas.

Yagi Designs Online

Many designers have been creating high-performance Yagis for EME and VHF+ contesting. Here are a few of the active designers websites:

DG7YBN — **dg7ybn.de/index.htm**
DK7ZB — **www.qsl.net/d/dk7zb**
GØKSC — **www.g0ksc.co.uk**
G4CQM — **g4cqm.www.idnet.com**
UA9TC — **www.vhfdx.ru/faylyi/view-details/shemyi-i-opisaniya/ant-ua9tc**
YU7EF — **www.yu7ef.com**
YU7XL— **www.qslnet.de/member/yu7xl**
DUBUS Magazine — **www.dubus.org**

Gain/Noise Temperature (G/T)

This parameter is a figure of merit for evaluating the antenna's ability to receive weak signals. That ability is particularly important at VHF/UHF/microwave where signals can be very weak, such as for EME operation and in contests. G represents the antenna gain in dB and T_a is the equivalent noise temperature of the antenna in degrees Kelvin. (See T. Milligan, *Modern Antenna Design, 2nd Edition,* IEEE Press, p. 32.)

For the purposes of this discussion:

$$G/T = (G + 2.15) - (10 \log T_a)$$

where more positive values indicate better performance. T_a includes noise received from all directions including side lobes.

An alternative calculation of G/T for the entire receiving system includes the noise produced by the antenna and receiving system, which includes the feed line, any preamplifiers, and the receiver itself.

Optimizing G/T is similar to optimizing signal-to-noise ratio (SNR) in that the goal is optimizing the quality of the received signal and not necessarily absolute signal level or noise level.

G/T may be calculated directly from the Far Field radiation pattern tables produced by *EZNEC* or *4nec2* by using *TANT*, a DOS utility program developed by Sinisa Miloskjovic, YU1NT, originally for use in developing EME antenna systems. It imports the far field data from the file and computes G/T in 5-degree increments from elevation angles of 0 to 90 degrees. *TANT* may be downloaded at **www.dg7ybn.de/Ant_Temp/Ant_Temp.htm#TANT** with instructions for use and sample input and output files.

It is important to note that while this is a good method of comparison between antennas, it is intended for use in EME systems and the calculations are performed assuming an antenna elevation fixed at 30°. With any given set of Yagis pointed at the horizon or at elevation angles greater than 30° very different comparative results may be seen.

High-Performance At and Above 144 MHz

At 144 MHz and above, most high-performance operation requires Yagi antennas two or more wavelengths in length. Before computer-based optimization became practical for amateurs, a boom length of 2 wavelengths was the point at which classic Yagi performance started to fall apart in terms of gain per boom length, bandwidth, and pattern quality. Careful optimization techniques have extended the range of high-performance Yagi designs considerably beyond the 2-wavelength limit. This is discussed in the sections Optimization and Bandwidth followed by Optimizing to Minimize Real-World Noise.

The Classic Design Approach

As described in previous editions of this book, classic high-performance Yagi design approaches start with closely spaced directors. The spacings gradually increase until a constant spacing of about 0.4 λ is reached. Conversely, the director lengths start out longest with the first director and decrease in length in a decreasing rate of change until they are virtually constant in length. This method of construction results in a wide gain bandwidth. A bandwidth of 7% of the center frequency at the –1 dB forward-gain points is typical for these Yagis even when they are longer than 10 λ. The driven-element impedance also changes moderately with boom length.

The actual rate of change in element lengths is determined by the diameter of the elements (in wavelengths). The spacings can be optimized for an individual boom length or chosen as a best compromise for most boom lengths.

Measurements and computer analysis by both amateurs and professionals indicates that given an optimum classic design, doubling a Yagi's boom length will result in a maximum theoretical gain increase of about 2.6 dB. (This value is not exact and varies with optimization technique and element construction.) In practice, the real gain increase may be less because of escalating resistive losses and the greater possibility of construction error. **Figure 15.29** shows the maximum theoretically possible gain per boom length expressed in decibels, referenced to an isotropic radiator. The actual number of directors does not play an important part in determining the gain vs boom length as long as a reasonable number of directors are used. The use of more directors per boom length will normally give a wider gain bandwidth, but a point exists where too many directors will adversely affect all performance aspects.

While short antennas (< 1.5 λ) may show increased gain with the use of quad or loop elements, long Yagis (> 2 λ) will not exhibit measurably greater forward gain or pattern integrity with loop-type elements. Similarly, loops used as driven elements and reflectors will not significantly change the properties of a long log-taper Yagi. Multiple-dipole driven-element assemblies will also not result in any significant gain increase per given boom length when compared to single-dipole feeds.

Once a long-Yagi director string is properly tuned, the reflector becomes relatively non-critical. Reflector spacings between 0.15 λ and 0.2 λ are preferred. The spacing can be chosen for best pattern and driven element impedance. Multiple-reflector arrangements will not significantly increase the forward gain of a Yagi which has its directors properly optimized for forward gain.

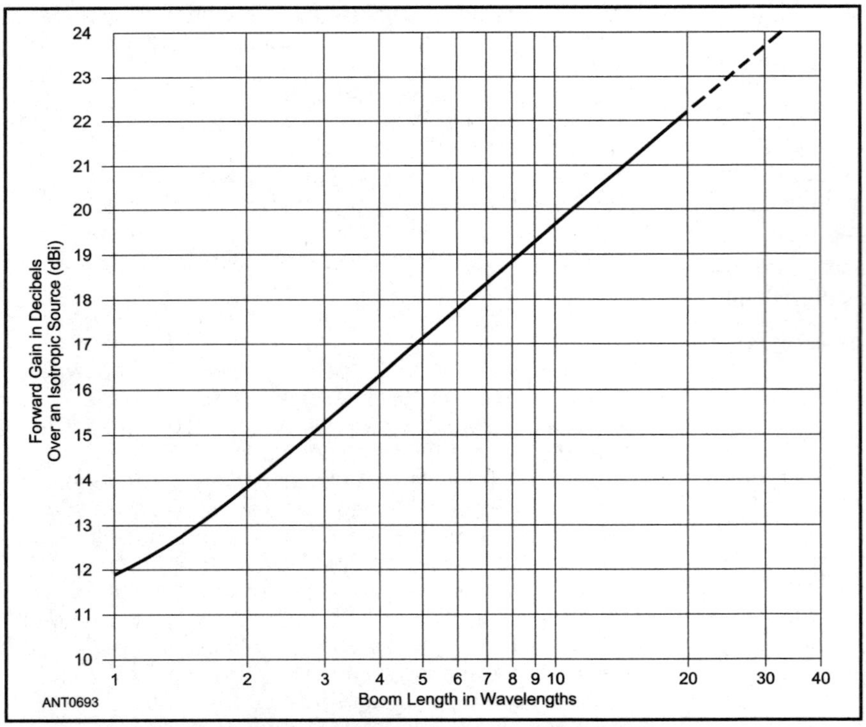

Figure 15.29 — This chart shows maximum gain per boom length for optimally designed long Yagi antennas using the classic design approach.

Bent-Element Yagis

By bending elements in the most active part of the Yagi (the reflector, driven element, and first director) a variety of improvements can be made to antenna performance with a variety of additional construction complexity.

UA9TC first experimented with bending the reflector in a right angle at the ends, similar to the Moxon designs, resulting in improved bandwidth and less noise pickup but gain was reduced. GØKSC then changed the design to bend the tips of the driven element back toward the reflector. (OP-DES designs)

Another early experimenter was K6STI who developed designs with V-shaped driven elements to raise the feed point impedance. (The V opens rearward toward the reflector.) A five-element version of this design for FM broadcast has been published at **www.ham-radio.com/k6sti/five.htm**. This approach was extended by DG7YBN and others.

LFA Yagis

The LFA Yagi (Loop Fed Array) replaces the bent tips of the driven element with an extended folded-dipole type feed laid flat on the boom. Thus, both sides of the driven loop are in line with the parasitic elements, rather than extending above or below the boom. Unlike a traditional folded dipole driven element, the feed point of the LFA design is in line with the boom and all elements as shown in **Figure 15.30** with the feed point toward the front of the antenna.

The LFA design leads to a symmetrical pattern in both the E and H planes. However, this mechanical arrangement adds certain construction complications. With all elements in line, the feed point lies at the boom, centered on its axis. Workable construction options include using a metallic boom, although for optimum long-term performance the elements must be welded to the boom. Insulated elements passing through a metallic boom are another option, but this practice can lead to eddy currents in the boom, detuning the antenna and causing deterioration of both pattern and system temperature. With these problems in mind, a hollow fiberglass boom is recommended.

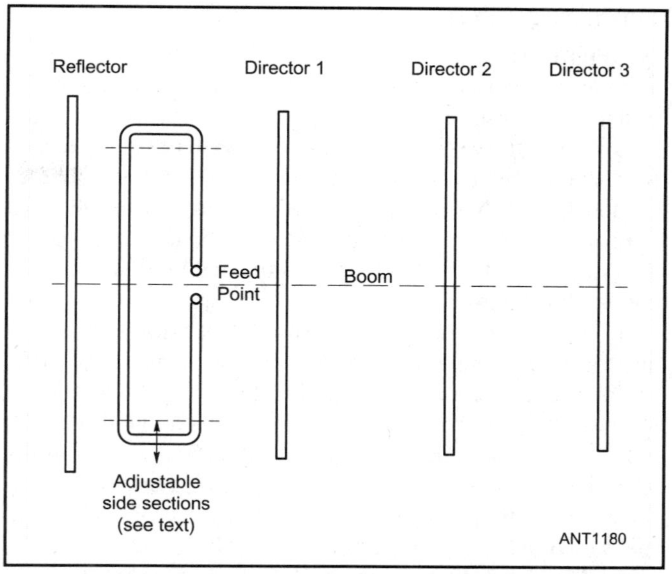

Figure 15.30 — Typical construction for an LFA Yagi with the loop driven element laying along the boom in the same plane as the elements.

OWA, OWL, and OWM Yagis

Optimized Wideband Low Impedance (OWL) Yagis are a modification of the Optimized Wideband Array (OWA) Yagi designs developed by WA3FET and NW3Z (**www.naic.edu/~angel/kp4ao/ham/owa.html**). The OWA Yagi has a feed point impedance of 50 Ω for direct feed and wide bandwidth but as a tradeoff has lower peak gain and F/B. A benefit of the OWA design at VHF and higher frequencies is that the OWA design is less sensitive to small impedance shifts from weather or interaction with surrounding objects such as trees, buildings, and most importantly, other antennas.

The OWL Yagi has a conventional, split-dipole driven element, is designed to have a 12.5 Ω feed point impedance, and can be easily matched to 50 Ω with a $\lambda/4$ section of 25 Ω transmission line made from two parallel sections of 50 Ω coax. (See the **Transmission Lines** and **Transmission Line System Techniques** chapters for information on coaxial impedance transformers.) This enables good performance over a wider bandwidth than was previously available.

An alternate implementation of the OWL is to use a folded dipole for the driven element. This conveys the benefits of closed-loop feed systems, including that the feed point impedance is transformed to 50 Ω for direct connection to feed lines. This is the type of driven element used in the 144 MHz OWL designs later in this chapter.

The OWM (Optimized Wideband Medium Impedance) Yagi is designed for 28 Ω feed point impedance. This impedance can be matched to 50 Ω with a $\lambda/4$ section of 37.5 Ω transmission line made from two parallel sections of 75 Ω coax or a matching device can be used. (See the section on 144 MHz and 222 MHz Yagis for more information on building these coaxial cable transformer sections.)

Self-Matched Yagis

"Self-matched" Yagis are those that have the driven element constructed in such a way as to increase the impedance to 50 Ω for direct connection to 50 Ω feed lines. Rearranging the driven element can include bending the element, using folded dipoles as in the OWL designs in this chapter, or using a loop as for the Loop-Fed Array (LFA).

There are a number of advantages of doing so, not the least of which is that the Yagi can be modeled, optimized and viewed exactly as it will be built with no additional structure (matching device) being added outside the model during the build-phase. This added structure and connections, including the feed line, can and do affect and change performance parameters in the real world. At the same time, direct feed can reduce the susceptibility to man-made noise and drastically increase the power levels of that can fed to the antenna system without problems.

VE7BQH Antenna Performance Tables

Similar to the Sherwood Engineering receiver performance tables (**www.sherweng.com/table.html**) that show dynamic range and other performance metrics for popular transceivers, Lionel Edwards, VE7BQH, has compiled the performance data of a large number of antennas for 50, 144, and 432 MHz. (a.k.a. – the VH List) The tables are maintained online at **www.dxmaps.com/VE7BQH.html** and are also available as downloadable spreadsheet files from **www.bigskyspaces.com/w7gj/6mTable.htm**.

Optimizing and Bandwidth

Figure 15.31 shows a graph of gain versus (F/R – F/B) in a "typical" Yagi with a single point (frequency) of optimization that is focused on maximum gain within the optimization parameter setup. (F/R is the ratio of forward to gain averaged over the entire rear-ward hemisphere — the "rear bubble" — and F/B is the ratio of forward gain to that at the exact opposite direction to the main lobe.) This is not a real plot of any Yagi and is very much exaggerated in order that the point can be illustrated.

The problem with optimizing metrics at a single frequency and to single parameters is the potential impact on real-world performance in changing conditions and from variations in materials used to build these antennas which could result in a shift of performance (and ultimately G/T) away from the specified frequency toward the band edges. For example, as the center of frequency on the VH list (the list of antennas in the VE7BQH Antenna Performance Tables, see sidebar) is 144.1 MHz and the bandwidth of each antenna is measured between 144 MHz and 145 MHz, the potential issue of the antenna's performance shifting within or even outside of its operating range is plain to see in Figure 15.31.

Often, the presented usable bandwidth is simply specified as the frequencies between which SWR is below a certain threshold (1.5:1 for example) rather than an average of all performance parameters over a given range. When correctly optimized, a good Yagi will have characteristics similar to a bandpass filter (BPF) in terms of performance with stable and consistent performance up to several hundred kHz (at VHF) or several MHz (at UHF) on either side of its center frequency. It's not just a nice flat SWR curve over a good range — gain and F/R will remain fairly constant, too.

What stands out clearly in Figure 15.31 is the best F/B (and/or F/R) and best forward gain are typically at opposite ends of the bandwidth of the antenna. Gain is highest at the top of this bandwidth (naturally) because of the increasing boom length (in terms of λ). F/B and F/R drop off very quickly in the same direction, usually because the Yagi is too long for the number of elements the modeler has selected for this given boom length, or the modeler has optimized for an exceedingly long boom length. In that case the Yagi cannot be optimized for a balance of gain and F/B (F/R) across the desired range. This "ski sloping" of performance parameters in opposite directions is very common and often the reason why gain and F/B figures are quoted as being "peak gain, peak F/B."

In Figure 15.31, the vertical line denotes the performance of this hypothetical antenna at 144.1 MHz and the corresponding gain and F/B results. Shifting frequency up and down just 50 kHz or so will show very different gain – F/B combinations which will result in a large variation in antenna temperature and G/T as well. Furthermore, it is important to note how close the center of operation (144.1 MHz) is to the band edge. Taking into account the desired BPF-type characteristics, the center of activity for any 144 MHz Yagi should more likely be focused around 144.300 MHz if modes other than just EME will be practiced by the end user. It would not take too much for narrower-band antennas to move well out of their peak performance characteristic range in real-world conditions (wet weather, ice, other antennas close by, and so on) if they were optimized between 144 and 145 MHz and were being used at 144.100 MHz. While the focus of the VH list is G/T performance at 144.1 MHz for EME applications, the comparison of G/T at three points (perhaps 144.0, 144.1 and 144.2 MHz) may give a much more accurate indication as to what the user might expect for day-to-day or contest use.

Because performance tends to fall off toward the edge of an antenna's design bandwidth, optimizing should be performed with 144.300 MHz, for example, as the true center of operation with a guided bandwidth of 500 kHz either side of that point (143.800 to 144.800 MHz). Doing this ensures very constant performance either side of the center frequency rather than perhaps experiencing the typical tail-off of performance at the band edges as discussed above. This leads to less impressive table values across 144-145 MHz but a more stable design to be used in varying weather conditions. An antenna which yields the most consistent results across a range centered on the most likely frequencies of use is likely to be the most stable for day to day use and/or use in extreme environments and not just for EME applications either!

Optimizing to Minimize Real-World Noise

The collection and pick-up of real world noise is dependent on the lack of side lobes in the elevation (El) plane. If lobes in the El plane are prominent and down-facing, regardless of how quiet a location is believed to be, higher levels of noise will be received in certain directions (direction of the shack and/or house, for example) than if any such lobes were more highly suppressed. When measuring and comparing G/T, rear-facing lobes in back of the 90°-270° line are what are considered for calculation and measurement. (See the sidebar Gain/Noise Temperature (G/T).) However, real-world operation by hams requires us to pay equal consideration to more forward and down facing lobes in this plane. At this point optimization starts to become more complicated — generally speaking, optimizing on one band then scaling to another will not show the same improvements in performance.

Different considerations and attributes must be taken into account during the design phase when switching from

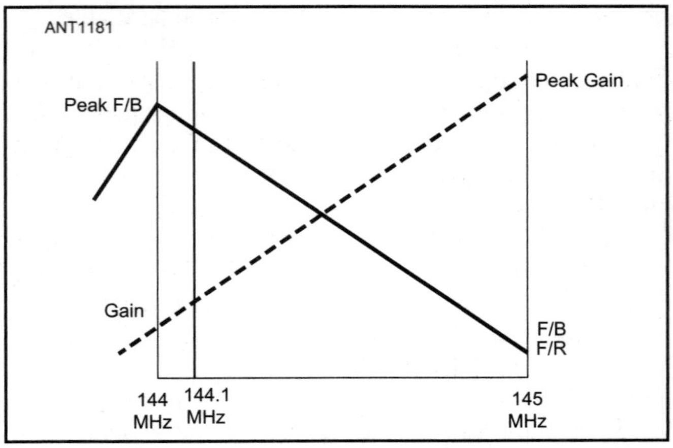

Figure 15.31 — Hypothetical performance of a typical Yagi across the 2 meter weak-signal band.

designing a Yagi on one band and then looking to repeat the results on another band. Quiet Yagis are very much band-specific — note that what is being discussed here is relevant only when optimizing on 144 MHz.

Take a look at **Figure 15.32** and the design considerations taken in order to not just show a good G/T figure (assume G/T is based on T_a unless noted otherwise), but to also reduce the likelihood of man-made noise pick-up to an absolute minimum from beneath the antenna within its near-field. This particular antenna used a closed-loop driven element to allow direct-feed (50 Ω feed point impedance) and lower noise pickup.

Within Figure 15.32 are two bars marked T1 and T2. T1 shows a sharp taper from the back towards the front. This level of taper right at the back of the antenna and forward is important to ensure good G/T results as tighter suppression from the 90° line backward will yield much better results. However, to continue this level of taper for the first side lobes would be disastrous for near-field noise pick-up. From having very wide side lobes in the azimuth (Az) plane (not much more than 12 dB below the main lobe) additional noise sources could be detected and interfere with signals in the desired capture direction from noise sources either side of center. The ability for this antenna to hear weak signals (real-world) would be greatly reduced by having what in effect would be three forward lobes in both planes, all receiving whatever was beneath or either side of the antenna. It is for this reason that an amount of suppression has been applied to the first lobe to arrive at the best compromise between the overall size of the "rear bubble" and outright forward gain.

The challenge is to achieve the best from the antenna in terms of performance while at the same time, keeping the El pattern as clean as possible. During optimization, GØKSC uses a maximum limit or "marker" for side lobes. Basically, this is a parameter that can be controlled during software optimization that is not so easily achieved when optimizing manually. Some software packages allow the starting point at which F/R is measured (normally 90°) to be moved forward towards the forward lobe. The advantage of so doing is this starting point can be moved forward until it covers the angle from the forward lobe where forward lobes would start to increase in size. While this sounds simple, in practice, getting excellent results take a lot of time and work.

Antennas of typical length up to around six elements tend not to produce side lobes of any consequence, at least not in the Az plane. For weak signal and EME work, the desire is to have much longer antennas than six elements and normally they would have booms of multiple wavelengths. If uncontrolled, the natural course of gain-focused optimization would see very large side lobes at large angles away from the center of the forward lobe upon optimization completion. Simply moving the starting point (within software) further forward than the point of these lobes will result in two side-effects: First, a reduction in forward gain and the second, a "blown" rear bubble with odd small lobes or spikes that cause F/R to be much worse than the starting point.

As the boom gets longer, the forward lobe becomes narrower and in-turn, the side lobes get closer to one another either side of the main forward lobe but exactly how close they sit to the main lobe can be controlled, to a point.

In order to achieve the best overall gain results and to ensure the rear bubble can be minimized, an antenna is best optimized (assuming computer optimization now) with F/B parameters being set just behind the Az side lobe position as in **Figure 5.33**. For example, if the side lobes on a subject antenna are at 50°, the F/B point would be set at 55°. The

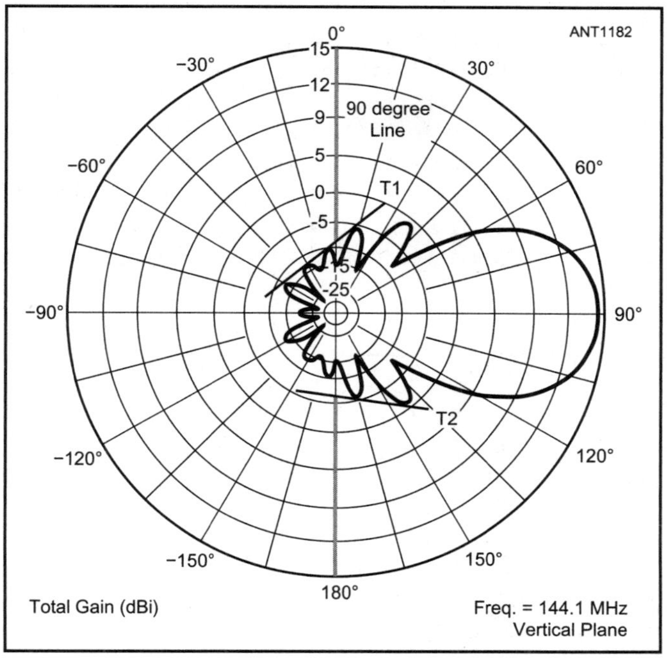

Figure 15.32 — Elevation plot of a 9 element Yagi showing the side lobe taper both in the rear hemisphere (T1) and between the rear hemisphere and the main lobe (T2).

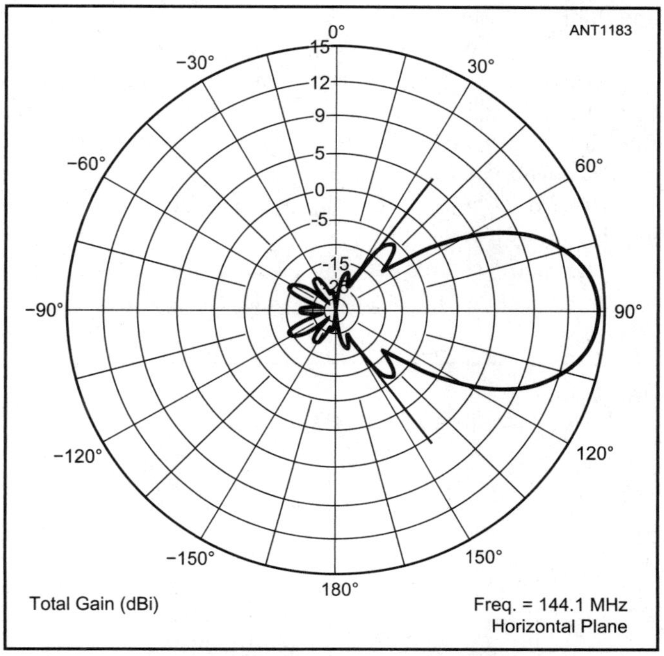

Figure 15.33 — Same elevation plot as in Figure 15.41 showing where optimization limits can be placed to move side lobes closer to the main lobe. This helps minimize pickup of noise from nearby sources.

antenna can then be optimized for bandwidth and gain several times until no further improvements can be made. (At 144 MHz and higher, optimization should be performed in 1° increments.)

At this point, move the optimization point from 55° to 54° and re-optimize then 53° then 52° and so on. Improvements should be seen in terms of gain and bandwidth by doing this method of controlling the elevation lobes in addition to (hopefully) pushing the side lobes closer to the main lobes resulting in less significance or negative consequences. (For best results, computer optimization/controlling of side lobes should only be done in the El plane, so doing will see the Az lobes kept in-check automatically. The same does not happen in reverse should you optimize in the Az plane.)

Each time the optimization results should be saved individually as there will become a point where the gain starts to drop and the rear bubble starts to "blow" (rear lobes growing quickly with further changes). At this point you know you are trying to compress the side lobes too tightly and you should go back to your last improvement optimization for your best usable result. The whole optimization process is much more detailed than the explanation given in these few lines but at least now an understanding of the levels of attention and time taken to optimize this antenna can be perhaps much more appreciated.

High-Performance LFA and OWL VHF/UHF Yagi Designs

The antenna designs by GØKSC and listed in **Table 15.11** are new designs not previously published or made available as products. Justin is a primary designer of HF, VHF, and UHF antennas for InnovAntennas (**www.innovantennas.com**). He has published a number of articles featuring innovative and high-performance antennas, including discussions of what makes a design successful, issues for competitive and high-performance antennas, and helpful information on the construction details for these designs. Model files and sample radiation patterns for all of the Yagis are available with this book's downloadable supplemental information but require *EZNEC PRO/4* to reproduce the gain and other performance specifications listed.

The Stauff clamps (**www.us.stauff.com**) recommended for these designs are industrial pipe clamps designed for rugged, outdoor service. The standard series part numbers (DIN 3015, Part 1) in **Table 15.12** are sufficiently rated for these designs. Stauff clamps are easiest to use with booms of square tubing although adapters for round booms are available.

Table 15.12
Stauff Clamps

Standard Series (DIN 3015-1)

¼ in elements:	106,4APP (1 per element)
½ in loop:	212,7PP (3 per loop - 1 for DE1, 2 for DE2)
Angled weld plate	WSP 1A U W1 (2 per loop at DE2)

-PP part numbers are polypropylene material
(replace with –AL for aluminum)
Available from **www.us.stauff.com**

Constructing the Loop Driven Element

The loop driven element may be unfamiliar. GØKSC has created a detailed description of the construction process at **www.g0ksc.co.uk/intro-lfa/making-the-lfa-loop.html** which is also available as a PDF file included with this book's downloadable supplemental information. The following set of instructions are summarized from that document.

Figure 15.30 shows the orientation of the loop on the boom with the feed point located on the forward side. **Figure 15.34** shows the overall construction and adjustment of the LFA Yagi's loop driven element. LFA driven elements are constructed with straight sections (DE1 and DE2, parallel to the other elements) and side sections of slightly smaller diameter that are adjustable "trombone-style" by sliding in and out of the straight sections. This allows SWR to be adjusted without a separate impedance-matching structure and to compensate for feed point construction variations.

Once the SWR is satisfactory, the sliding sections are secured to the straight sections with a stainless-steel screw (be sure to use anti-corrosion compound), an aluminum rivet, or a hose clamp (the straight section would require a short slot to allow compression by the clamp). The screw and rivet are convenient but have limited contact area. Spot welding the tubing sections together also works very well. If brass tubing is used, the sliding and fixed sections should be soldered together.

Table 15.11
High-Performance LFA and OWL Yagis

Freq (MHz)	*No. Elements*	*Boom Length*	*Peak Gain) (dBi)*	*Peak F/B (dB)*	*E-plane Beamwidth (degrees)*	*H-plane Beamwidth (degrees)*
50	4	12' 8" (3.86 m)	10.6	31.9	42	67
144	9	17' 3" (5.26 m)	14.8	24.7	34	37
144	14	32' 4" (9.86 m)	17.0	33.0	27	29
222	10	11' 5" (3.48 m)	14.5	34.6	37	41
222	19	29' 2" (8.88 m)	18.1	39.7	24	25
432	10	6' 7" (2.01 m)	14.5	25.6	36	40
432	20	17' 0" (5.18 m)	18.6	37.0	23	24

Note: All parameters are free-space

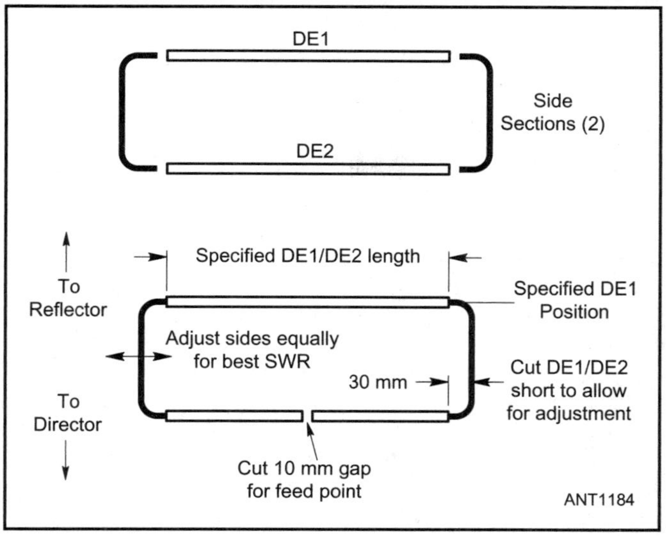

Figure 15.34 — Construction of the LFA loop driven-element showing the sliding end sections and how loop dimensions are measured.

The tubing for DE1 and DE2 should be cut 50 mm short of the model's full dipole length in the tables. Measure 30 mm from the end of the remaining straight ½ inch section to the inside of the loop end as in the figure. This additional width provides a correction for the radius at the corners of the loop. The additional 5 mm of width remains fairly constant on all bands since the radius becomes more like a 90° bend at lower frequencies as modeled. (This assumes use of the same bending tool to create all bends.) Absolute accuracy here is not essential; this is a starting point from where the antenna is adjusted for best SWR.

After cutting and deburring the loop's straight sections, cut the side section tubing such that it has approximately 80 mm of extra length beyond the difference between the DE1 and DE2 positions. For example, if the positions of DE1 and DE2 are 0.128 m and 0.235 m, respectively, cut the side section tubing to be (0.235 – 0.128) + 0.080 = 0.107 + 0.080 = 0.187 m long. Use an automotive brake line bending tool (see the PDF instructions for photographs) to bend approximately 40 mm of the section length at a right angle. Insert the bent section into either the DE1 section. Bend the other end of the side section tubing so that the DE2 section is 0.107 m from DE1. Repeat for the remaining side section.

Cut the DE2 section to leave a feed point gap of approximately 10 mm. To support the loop at the feed point (see **Figure 15.35A**), insert a short section of fiberglass, polycarbonate, or Teflon rod approximately 25 mm longer than the gap on each side. Drill through the element and supporting rod. Use stainless steel #8 hardware to hold the element and supporting rod together and create attachment points for the feed line. Use Stauff clamps with angled mounting plates as in Figure 15.35 to support the feed point assembly.

Note that the exact center of the loop driven element opposite the feed point is at an RF-neutral point and can be connected directly to the boom by using an aluminum clamp. (Substitute –AL for –PP in the Stauff clamp part number or fabricate your own mounting bracket.) Doing so will place the driven element at dc ground for static protection and it will also cause the driven element impedance to increase rapidly away from the design frequency.

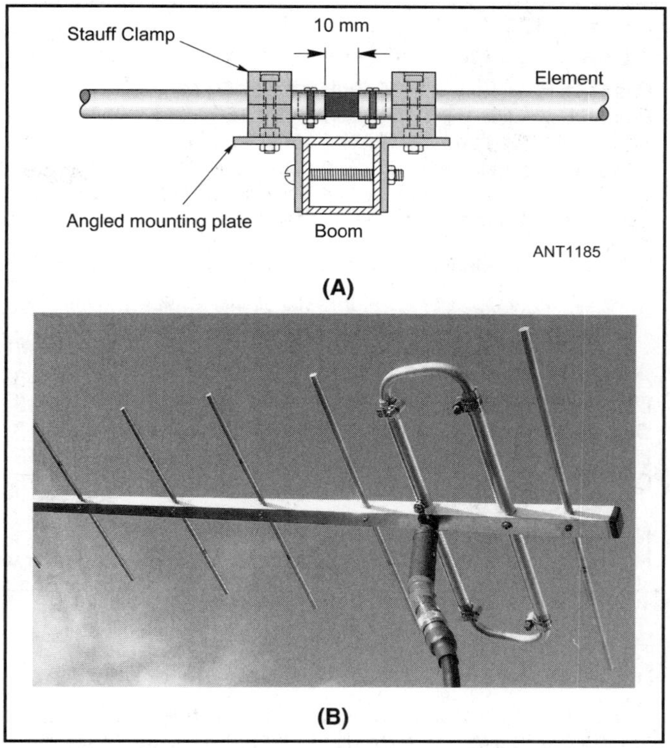

Figure 15.35 — Figure A illustrates mounting the driven element feed point on a square boom using Stauff clamps and angled mounting plate. At B, the driven element loop is mounted using through-the-boom construction.

In Figure 15.35B, the driven element loop for a 10-element 432 MHz LFA Yagi is shown with a through-the-boom construction option that eliminates the need for extra clamps with the smaller driven element.

Following construction, temporarily mount the beam at least 1 wavelength above ground or pointed at the sky with the reflector at least ½ wavelength above ground, Adjust each of the loop sliding sections in equal increments starting from a symmetrical position until SWR is satisfactory. Following adjustment, secure the sliding sections to the fixed sections as described above.

50 MHz LFA Yagi

The 4-element design in **Table 15.13** is an illustration of what can be achieved by careful optimization on a fairly short boom (12 feet 8 inches). The design is well suited for stacking and can be handled by small rotators. It is ideal for portable and rover station use as well as at a home station.

The reflector and both directors have three segments of tubing per half-element — one center segment and a pair of segments on each half-element. The driven element loop's DE1 and DE2 section both have two segments per half-element. Element lengths assume a conductive boom with insulated elements.

Table 15.13
4-element 50 MHz LFA Yagi

Peak Gain:	10.6 dBi @ 50.150 MHz
Peak F/B:	31.9 dB @ 50.150 MHz
Beamwidth (E-plane):	42 dB @ 50.150 MHz
Beamwidth (H-plane):	67 dB @ 50.150 MHz
SWR:	Below 1.3.1 from 50 MHz to 50.400 MHz

Note: All parameters are free-space

Half-element dimensions and placement (lengths are for half elements)

	Element	*----Section 1 (Middle)----*		*---------Section 2---------*		*--------Section 3--------*	
	Position (m)	*OD (in/mm)*	*Length (m)*	*OD (in/mm)*	*Length (m)*	*OD (in/mm)*	*Length (m)*
Reflector	0.030 (1)	⅝ / 16	0.415	½ / 13	0.315	⅜ / 10	0.788
DE1 (loop)	0.694	⅝ / 16	0.415	½ / 13	0.84 (2)		
DE2 (loop)	1.157	⅝ / 16	0.415	½ / 13	0.84 (2)		
D1	2.213	⅝ / 16	0.415	½ / 13	0.315	⅜ / 10	0.674
D2	3.963	⅝ / 16	0.415	½ / 13	0.84	⅜ / 10	0.610

Note 1— End of boom is zero (0) reference.
Note 2 — The ends of DE1 and DE2 are connected together with ⅜ inch / 10 mm tube.

144 MHz OWL Yagis

Common dimensions and notes for the high-performance 144, 222, and 432 MHz Yagis are listed in **Table 15.14**. Two designs are presented in this section — a 9-element in **Table 15.15** and a 14-element antenna in **Table 15.16**. Performance is specified at 144.2 MHz. The E-plane pattern for the 14-element antenna is shown in **Figure 15.36**.

Element lengths assume a conductive 1.25 inch square boom with insulated elements. If a non-conductive boom is used, subtract 1 mm from all element lengths. If a 1.5 inch square conductive boom is used, add 1 mm to all element lengths.

A folded-dipole driven element is used on both antennas. Construction is similar to that of the LFA loop driven-element. Two methods of mounting the driven element are shown in **Figure 15.37**. The feed point's insulating rod is mounted through a short mounting section of boom material which is, in turn, attached to the top of the main boom. The feed point thus straddles the mounting section — be sure to minimize coax-to-feed point leads lengths.

As with the LFA driven element, the point on the folded dipole directly opposite the feed point is a neutral point at RF and can be attached directly to the boom as shown in the figure's front view. The same caution applies regarding rapid impedance change away from the design frequency. An insulating support such as a Stauff clamp can be used, as well.

The boom is assumed to be made from 1.25 inch square tubing. If a ¾ inch square boom is used, an under-boom support will be required as in **Figure 15.38**. Alternatively, boom guying could also be used.

222 MHz LFA Yagis

Two designs are presented in this section — a 10-element in **Table 15.17** and a 19-element antenna in **Table 15.18**. Performance is specified at 222.1 MHz. The E-plane pattern for the 19-element antenna is shown in **Figure 15.39**.

Table 15.14
Common Dimensions and Notes for the High-Performance 144, 222, and 432 MHz Yagis

Boom is 1.25" square aluminum unless otherwise specified
Element diameter is ¼" unless otherwise specified
DE1, DE2 diameter ½" (sliding sections are ⅜" diameter)

Note 1– End of boom is zero (0) reference.
Note 2 – DE1 position dimension is the centerline of the rear-most loop tubing
Note 3 – DE1 and DE2 width are the outside edge of the loop.

Table 15.15
9-element 144 MHz OWL Yagi

Gain:	14.8 dBi
SWR:	Less than 1.1:1
F/B:	24.7 dB
Beamwidth (E-plane):	34 degrees
Beamwidth (H-plane):	37 degrees

Performance specified at 144.2 MHz
Note: All parameters are free-space

Element	*Element Position (m)*	*Half-Element Length (m)*	*Element Length (m)*
REF	0.030	0.514	1.028
DE (Note)	0.1625	0.4765	0.953
DIR1	0.453	0.4705	0.941
DIR2	1.009	0.455	0.910
DIR3	1.7275	0.444	0.888
DIR4	2.533	0.437	0.874
DIR5	3.358	0.432	0.864
DIR6	4.222	0.427	0.854
DIR7	4.9685	0.429	0.858

Note: All elements are ½" diameter
Note: DE is 0.953 m wide and 0.026 m high, measured on outside edges

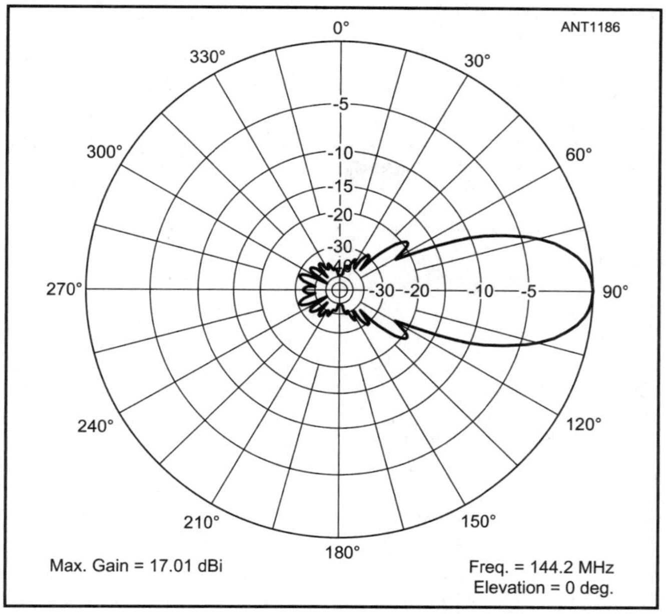

Figure 15.36— E-plane pattern, 14-element 144 MHz LFA Yagi.

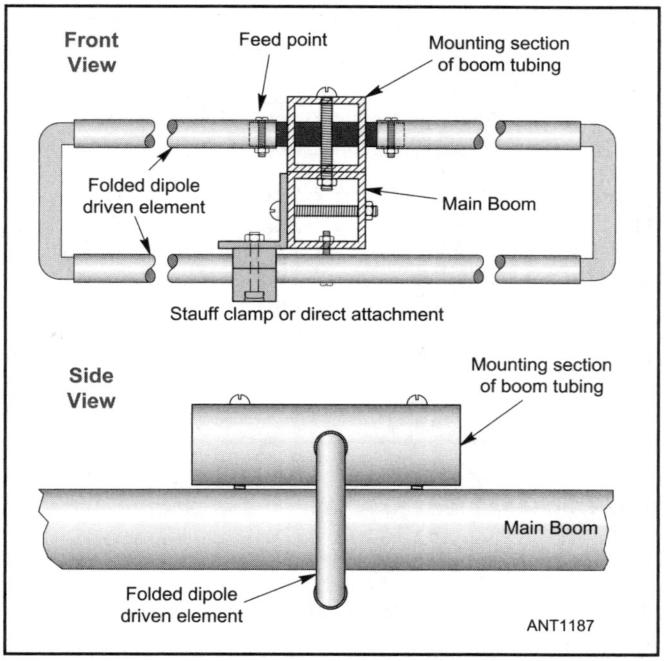

Figure 15.37 — Construction and mounting of an OWL Yagi's loop driven-element. The plane of the loop is perpendicular to the boom.

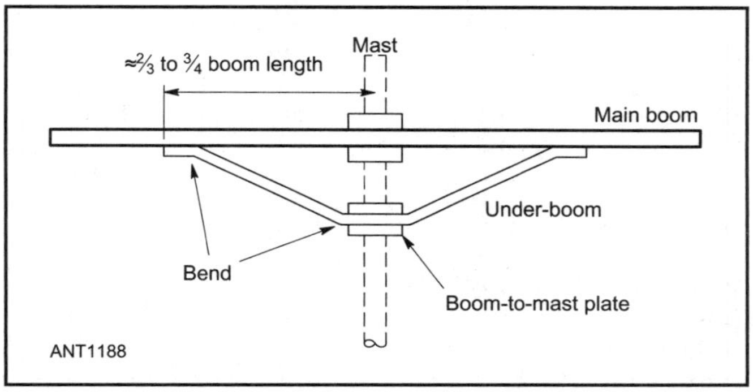

Table 15.16
14-element 144 MHz OWL Yagi

Gain:	17.0 dBi
SWR:	Less than 1.1:1
F/B:	33.0 dB
Beamwidth (E-plane):	27 degrees
Beamwidth (H-plane):	29 degrees

Performance specified at 144.2 MHz
Note: All parameters are free-space

Element	*Element Position (m)*	*Half-Element Length (m)*	*Element Length (m)*
REF	0.030	0.5115	1.023
DE (Note)	0.253	0.469	0.938
DIR1	0.5785	0.4805	0.961
DIR2	1.156	0.4665	0.933
DIR3	1.8525	0.457	0.914
DIR4	2.686	0.4495	0.899
DIR5	3.526	0.4435	0.887
DIR6	4.4265	0.4395	0.879
DIR7	5.3365	0.436	0.872
DIR8	6.254	0.433	0.866
DIR9	7.1735	0.4295	0.859
DIR10	8.108	0.425	0.850
DIR11	9.060	0.416	0.832
DIR12	9.8625	0.427	0.854

Note: All elements are ½" diameter
Note: DE is 0.948 m wide and 0.026 m high, measured on outside edges

Table 15.17
10-element 222 MHz LFA Yagi

Gain:	14.5 dBi
SWR:	Less than 1.1:1
F/B:	34.6 dB
Beamwidth (E-plane):	37 degrees
Beamwidth (H-plane):	41 degrees

Performance specified at 222.1 MHz
Note: All parameters are free-space

Element	*Element Position (m)*	*Half-Element Length (m)*	*Element Length (m)*
REF	0.030	0.3315	0.6630
DE1 (loop)	0.128	0.233	0.566
DE2 (loop)	0.235	0.233	0.233
DIR1	0.390	0.3075	0.6150
DIR2	0.626	0.292	0.584
DIR4	1.316	0.289	0.578
DIR5	1.819	0.2835	0.567
DIR6	2.358	0.277	0.554
DIR7	2.939	0.2675	0.535
DIR8	3.455	0.2645	0.529

Figure 15.38 — Use of an under-boom to support the long-boom Yagis. The same material is used for both the boom and under-boom. Alternatively, boom guying can be employed.

See the notes on constructing the LFA driven element above. The 19-element antenna will require boom guying or an under-boom as in Figure 15.38.

Element lengths assume a conductive boom with insulated elements. If a non-conductive boom is used, subtract 1 mm from all element lengths.

432 MHz LFA Yagis

Two designs are presented in this section — a 10-element broadband LFA in **Table 15.19** and a 20-element antenna in **Table 15.20**. Performance is specified at 432.1 MHz.

The broadband 10-element design provides a flat, low SWR across a 6 MHz bandwidth as shown in **Figure 15.40**. The broad-banded nature of this antenna makes it more accepting of measurement variations in both boom and element lengths.

The 20-element design is optimized for use in stacked arrays, allowing some forward side lobes to appear in exchange for a highly suppressed rear bubble. The forward side lobes are kept close to the main lobe, however, and elevation plane lobes are highly suppressed, as well. As a result, when stacked with the correct separation, no odd "spike-lobes" should appear and the pattern should remain clear. E- and H-plane patterns for the 20-element antenna are shown in **Figures 15.41** and **15.42**.

See the notes on constructing the LFA driven element above. All element lengths are based on a metal boom. If a non-conducting boom, such as fiberglass, is used, subtract 1.5 mm from all element lengths.

Both antennas can be constructed using Stauff clamps and a 1.25 inch square boom as for the 144 and 222 MHz Yagis.

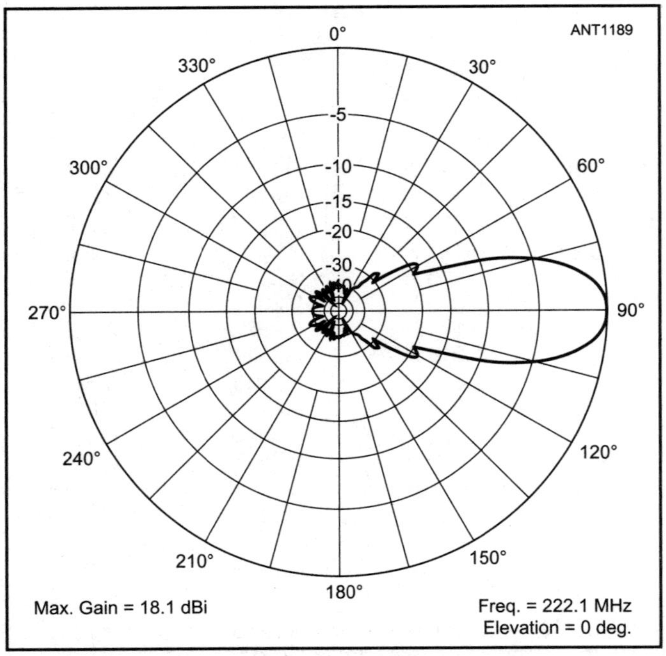

Figure 15.39 — E-plane pattern, 19-element 222 MHz LFA Yagi.

For the 10-element antenna, a much lighter version (3 lbs versus 6 lbs) with less wind load can be constructed using a ¾ inch square boom and mounting the elements through the boom, secured by a stainless steel screw. The loop driven element is also mounted through the boom, requiring a wider

Table 15.18
19-element 222 MHz LFA Yagi

Peak Gain: 18.1 dBi
SWR: Less than 1.1:1
F/B: 39.7 dB
Beamwidth (E-plane): 24 degrees
Beamwidth (H-plane): 25 degrees
Performance specified at 222.1 MHz
Note: All parameters are free-space

Element	*Element Position (m)*	*Half-Element Length (m)*	*Element Length (m)*
REF	0.030	0.3325	0.665
DE1 (loop)	0.145	0.285	0.570
DE2 (loop)	0.251	0.285	0.285
DIR1	0.411	0.3095	0.619
DIR2	0.676	0.288	0.576
DIR3	0.902	0.2945	0.589
DIR4	1.320	0.2925	0.585
DIR5	1.836	0.2885	0.577
DIR6	2.380	0.285	0.570
DIR7	2.946	0.282	0.564
DIR8	3.536	0.280	0.560
DIR9	4.123	0.2775	0.555
DIR10	4.725	0.2755	0.551
DIR11	5.330	0.273	0.546
DIR12	5.940	0.2715	0.543
DIR13	6.5415	0.2705	0.541
DIR14	7.1385	0.2685	0.537
DIR15	7.7255	0.266	0.532
DIR16	8.3105	0.2545	0.509
DIR17	8.8545	0.2505	0.501

Table 15.19
10-element 432 MHz LFA Yagi

Peak Gain: 14.5 dBi
SWR: Less than 1.1:1
F/B: 25.6 dB
Beamwidth (E-plane): 36 degrees
Beamwidth (H-plane): 40 degrees
Performance specified at 432.1 MHz
Note: All parameters are free-space

Element	*Element Position (m)*	*Half-Element Length (m)*	*Element Length (m)*
REF	0.030	0.1685	0.337
DE1 (loop)	0.078	0.150	0.300
DE2 (loop)	0.1495	0.150	0.300
DIR1	0.212	0.157	0.314
DIR2	0.3425	0.150	0.300
DIR3	0.494	0.146	0.292
DIR4	0.6845	0.1445	0.289
DIR5	0.9215	0.143	0.286
DIR6	1.1785	0.1405	0.281
DIR7	1.470	0.1365	0.273
DIR8	1.716	0.1355	0.271

feed point gap. The non-conductive rod is extended through the boom as shown in Figure 15.35B. The lighter version of the antenna can be mounted to the mast using a single U-bolt through the boom.

For the 20-element antenna, boom guys are required if the 1.25 inch square boom and Stauff clamps are used for construction. If the ¾ inch square boom technique is used, an under-boom is required as in Figure 15.38.

15.3.6 QUAGI ANTENNAS

At higher frequencies, especially 420 MHz and above, Yagi arrays using dipole driven elements can be difficult to feed and match, unless special care is taken to keep the feed point impedance relatively high by proper element spacing and tuning. The cubical quad described earlier overcomes the feed problems to some extent. When many parasitic elements are used, however, the loops are not nearly as convenient to assemble and tune as are straight cylindrical ones used in conventional Yagis. The *Quagi*, designed and popularized by Wayne Overbeck, N6NB, is an antenna having a full-wave

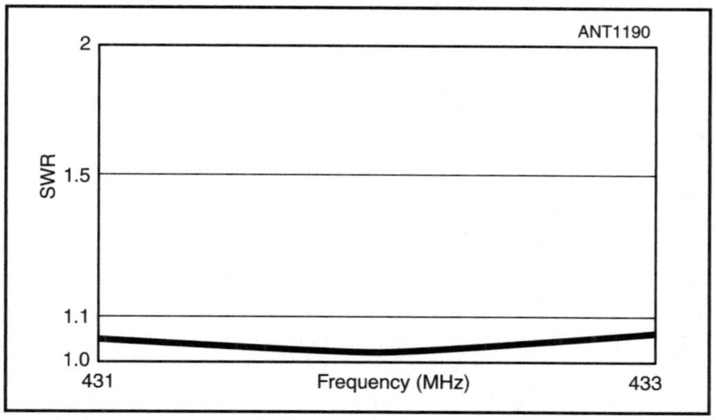

Figure 15.40 — SWR versus frequency, 10-element 432 MHz LFA Yagi.

Table 15.20
20-element 432 MHz LFA Yagi

Peak Gain:	18.6 dBi
SWR:	Less than 1.1:1
F/B:	37.0 dB
Beamwidth (E-plane):	23 degrees
Beamwidth (H-plane):	24 degrees

Performance specified at 432.1 MHz
Note: All parameters are free-space

Element	*Element Position (m)*	*Half-Element Length (m)*	*Element Length (m)*
REF	0.030	0.167	0.334
DE1 (loop)	0.117	0.153	0.306
DE2 (loop)	0.189	0.153	0.306
DIR1	0.2445	0.15775	0.3155
DIR2	0.4015	0.151	0.302
DIR3	0.556	0.14525	0.2905
DIR4	0.7305	0.14425	0.2885
DIR5	0.959	0.14325	0.2865
DIR6	1.2275	0.14125	0.2825
DIR7	1.5135	0.1395	0.2790
DIR8	1.814	0.138	0.276
DIR9	2.120	0.1365	0.273
DIR10	2.4315	0.13525	0.2705
DIR11	2.750	0.13425	0.2685
DIR12	3.0655	0.13425	0.2685
DIR13	3.378	0.135	0.270
DIR14	3.682	0.13525	0.2705
DIR15	3.982	0.13425	0.2685
DIR16	4.2835	0.13075	0.2615
DIR17	4.598	0.12425	0.2485
DIR18	4.879	0.120	0.240

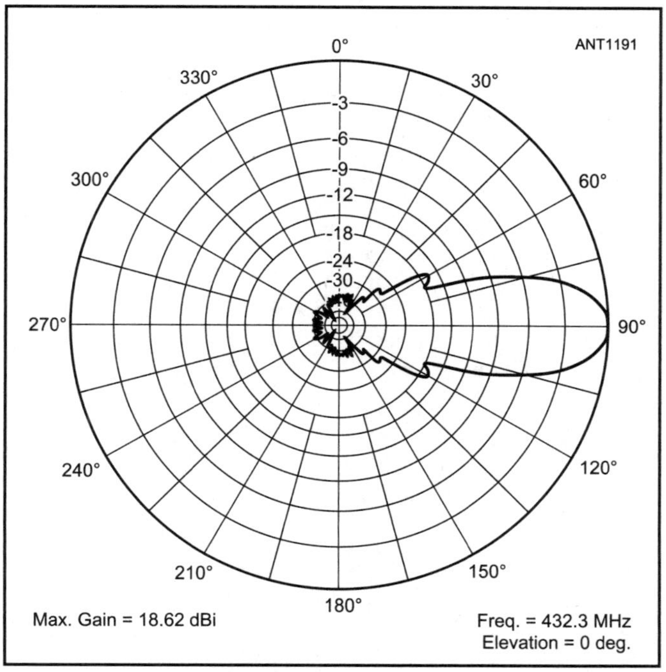

Figure 15.41 — E-plane pattern, 20-element 432 MHz LFA Yagi.

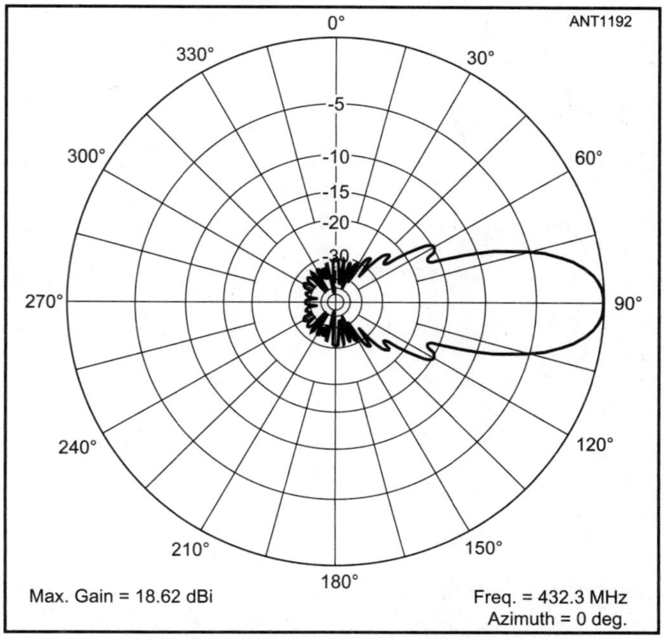

Figure 15.42 — H-plane pattern, 20-element 432 MHz LFA Yagi.

loop driven element and reflector, and Yagi type straight rod directors. Information was first published on this antenna in 1977. (See Bibliography.)

Quagi Construction

There are a few tricks to Quagi building, but nothing very difficult or complicated is involved. **Table 15.21** and **Table 15.22** give the dimensions for Quagis for various frequencies up to 446 MHz.

For the designs of Tables 15.21 and 15.22, the boom is wood or any other nonconductor (such as, fiberglass or Plexiglas). If a metal boom is used, a new design and new element lengths will be required. See the information on materials in the previous section on Yagi Construction. The 144-MHz version is usually built on a 14 foot, 1 × 3 inch boom, with the boom tapered to 1 inch at both ends. At 222 MHz the boom is under 10 feet long, requiring 1 × 2 or (preferably) ¾ × 1¼ inch pine molding stock. At 432 MHz, except for long-boom versions, the boom should be ½ inch thick or less.

The quad elements are supported at the current maxima (the top and bottom, the latter beside the feed point) with Plexiglas or small strips of wood. See **Figure 15.43**. The quad elements are made of #12 AWG copper wire, commonly used in house wiring. Some builders may elect to use #10 AWG wire on 144 MHz and #14 AWG wire on 432 MHz, although this changes the resonant frequency slightly. Solder a type N connector (an SO-239 is often used at 144 MHz) at the midpoint of the driven element bottom side, and close the reflector loop.

The directors are mounted through the boom. They can be made of almost any metal rod or wire of about ⅛-inch diameter. Welding rod or aluminum clothesline wire works well if straight. (The designer uses ⅛-inch stainless-steel rod obtained from an aircraft surplus store.)

A TV type U bolt mounts the antenna on a mast. A single machine screw, washers and a nut are used to secure the spreaders to the boom so the antenna can be quickly "flattened" for travel. In permanent installations two screws are recommended.

Based on the experiences of Quagi builders, the following hints are offered. First, remember that at 432 MHz even a ⅛-inch measurement error results in performance deterioration. Cut the loops and elements as carefully as possible.

Table 15.22
432-MHz, 15-Element, Long Boom Quagi Construction Data

Element Lengths (Inches)	*Interelement Spacing (Inches)*
R — 28	R-DE — 7
DE — 26⅝	DE-D1 — 5¼
D1 — 11¾	D1-D2 — 11
D2 — 11¹¹⁄₁₆	D2-D3 — 5⅞
D3 — 11⅝	D3-D4 — 8¾
D4 — 11⁹⁄₁₆	D4-D5 — 8¾
D5 — 11½	D5-D6 — 8¾
D6 — 11⁷⁄₁₆	D6-D7 — 12
D7 — 11⅜	D7-D8 — 12
D8 — 11⁵⁄₁₆	D8-D9 — 11¼
D9 — 11⁵⁄₁₆	D9-D10 — 11½
D10 — 11¼	D10-D11 — 9⁹⁄₁₆
D11 — 11³⁄₁₆	D11-D12 — 12⅝
D12 — 11⅛	D12-D13 — 13¾
D13 — 11¹⁄₁₆	

Boom: 1 × 2 inch × 12-ft Douglas fir, tapered to ⅝ inch at both ends.
Driven element: #12 AWG TW copper wire loop in square configuration, fed at bottom center with type N connector and 52-Ω coax.
Reflector: #12 AWG TW copper wire loop, closed at bottom.
Directors: ⅛ inch rod passing through boom.

Table 15.21
Dimensions, Eight-Element Quagi

Element Lengths	*144.5 MHz*	*147 MHz*	*Frequency 222 MHz*	*432 MHz*	*446 MHz*
Reflector[1]	86⅝"	85"	56⅜"	28"	27⅛"
Driven[2]	82"	80"	53½"	26⅝"	25⅞"
Directors	35¹⁵⁄₁₆" to 35" in ³⁄₁₆" steps	35⁵⁄₁₆" to 34⅜" in ³⁄₁₆" steps	23⅜" to 23¾" in ⅛" steps	11¾" to 11⁷⁄₁₆" in ¹⁄₁₆" steps	11⅜" to 11¹⁄₁₆" in ¹⁄₁₆" steps
Spacing					
R-DE	21"	20½"	13⅝"	7"	6.8"
DE-D1	15¾"	15⅜"	10¼"	5¼"	5.1"
D1-D2	33"	32½"	21½"	11"	10.7"
D2-D3	17½"	17⅛"	11⅜"	5.85"	5.68"
D3-D4	26.1"	25⅝"	17"	8.73"	8.46"
D4-D5	26.1"	25⅝"	17"	8.73"	8.46"
D5-D6	26.1"	25⅝"	17"	8.73"	8.46"
Stacking Distance Between Bays					
	11'	10' 10"	7' 1½"	3'7"	3' 5 ⅝"

[1]All #12 AWG TW (electrical) wire, closed loops.
[2]All #12 AWG TW wire loops, fed at bottom.

Figure 15.43 — A close-up view of the feed method used on a 432-MHz Quagi. This arrangement produces a low SWR and gain in excess of 13 dBi with a 4-ft 10-inch boom! The same basic arrangement is used on lower frequencies, but wood may be substituted for the Plexiglas spreaders. The boom is ½-inch exterior plywood.

No precision tools are needed, but accuracy is necessary. Also make sure to get the elements in the right order. The longest director goes closest to the driven element.

Finally, remember that a balanced antenna is being fed with an unbalanced line. Every balun the designer tried introduced more trouble in terms of losses than the feed imbalance caused. Some builders have tightly coiled several turns of the feed line near the feed point to limit line radiation. In any case, the feed line should be kept at right angles to the antenna. Run it from the driven element directly to the supporting mast and then up or down perpendicularly for best results.

A Quagi for 1296 MHz

This Quagi is designed for the 1296-MHz band, where good performance is extremely difficult to obtain from homemade conventional Yagis. **Figure 15.44** shows the construction and **Table 15.23** gives the design information for antennas with 10, 15 and 25 elements.

At 1296 MHz, even slight variations in design or building materials can cause substantial changes in performance. The 1296 MHz antennas described here work every time — but only if the same materials are used and the antennas are built *exactly* as described. This is not to discourage experimentation, but if modifications to these 1296-MHz antenna designs are contemplated, consider building one antenna as described here, so a reference is available against which variations can be compared.

The Quagis (and the cubical quad) are built on ¼-inch thick Plexiglas booms. The driven element and reflector (and also the directors in the case of the cubical quad) are made of insulated #18 AWG solid copper bell wire, available at hardware and electrical supply stores. Other types and sizes of wire work equally well, but the dimensions vary with the wire diameter. Even removing the insulation usually necessitates changing the loop lengths.

Quad loops are approximately square (**Figure 15.45**), although the shape is relatively uncritical. The element lengths, however, *are* critical. At 1296 MHz, variations of 1⁄16 inch alter the performance measurably, and a ⅛ inch departure can cost several decibels of gain. The loop lengths given are *gross* lengths. Cut the wire to these lengths and then solder the two ends together. There is a ⅛-inch overlap where the two ends of the reflector (and director) loops are joined, as shown in Figure 15.45.

The driven element is the most important of all. The #18 AWG wire loop is soldered to a standard UG-290 chassis-mount BNC connector as shown in the photographs. This exact type of connector must be used to ensure uniformity in construction. Any substitution may alter the driven element

Figure 15.44 — A view of the 10-element version of the 1296-MHz Quagi. It is mounted on a 30-inch Plexiglas boom with a 3 × 3-inch square of Plexiglas to support the driven element and reflector. Note how the driven element is attached to a standard UG-290 BNC connector. The elements are held in place with silicone sealing compound.

Table 15.23
Dimensions, 1296-MHz Quagi Antennas

Note: All lengths are gross lengths. See text and photos for construction technique and recommended overlap at loop junctions. All loops are made of #18 AWG solid-covered copper bell wire. The Yagi type directors are 1⁄16-inch brass brazing rod. See text for a discussion of director taper.
Feed: Direct with 52-Ω coaxial cable to UG-290 connector at driven element; run coax symmetrically to mast at rear of antenna.
Boom: 1¼-inch thick Plexiglas, 30 inches long for 10-element quad or Quagi and 48 inches long for 15-element Quagi; 84 inches. for 25-element Quagi.

10-Element Quagi for 1296 MHz

Element	*Length (Inches)*	*Construction*	*Element*	*Interelement Spacing (inches)*
Reflector	9.5625	Loop	R-DE	2.375
Driven	9.25	Loop	DE-D1	2.0
Director 1	3.91	Brass rod	D1-D2	3.67
Director 2	3.88	Brass rod	D2-D3	1.96
Director 3	3.86	Brass rod	D3-D4	2.92
Director 4	3.83	Brass rod	D4-D5	2.92
Director 5	3.80	Brass rod	D5-D6	2.92
Director 6	3.78	Brass rod	D6-D7	4.75
Director 7	3.75	Brass rod	D7-D8	3.94
Director 8	3.72	Brass rod		

15-Element Quagi for 1296 MHz

The first 10 elements are the same lengths as above, but the spacing from D6 to D7 is 4.0 inches; D7 to D8 is also 4.0 inches.

Director 9	3.70	D8-D9	3.75
Director 10	3.67	D9-D10	3.83
Director 11	3.64	D10-D11	3.06
Director 12	3.62	D11-D12	4.125
Director 13	3.59	D12-D13	4.58

25-Element Quagi for 1296 MHz

The first 15 elements use the same element lengths and spacings as the 15-element model. The additional directors are evenly spaced at 3.0-inch intervals and taper in length successively by 0.02 inch per element. Thus, D23 is 3.39 inches.

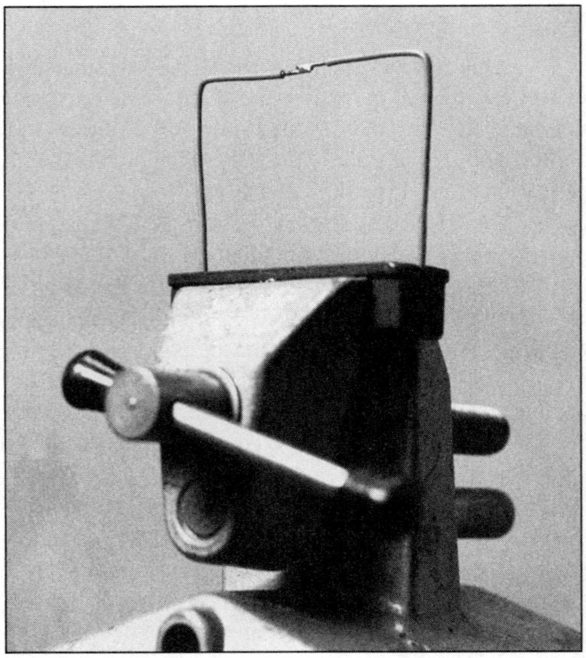

Figure 15.45 — These photos show the construction method used for the 1296-MHz quad type parasitic elements. The two ends of the #18 AWG bell wire are brought together with an overlap of ⅛ inch and soldered.

electrical length. One end of the 9¼ inch driven loop is pushed as far as it can go into the center pin, and is soldered in that position. The loop is then shaped and threaded through small holes drilled in the Plexiglas support. Finally, the other end is fed into one of the four mounting holes on the BNC connector and soldered. In most cases, the best SWR is obtained if the end of the wire just passes through the hole so it is flush with the opposite side of the connector flange.

15.3.7 LOOP YAGIS

The loop Yagi fits into the quad family of antennas, as each element is a closed loop with a length of approximately 1 λ. Several versions are described, so the builder can choose the boom length and frequency coverage desired for the task at hand. Mike Walters, G3JVL, brought the original loop-Yagi design to the amateur community in the 1970s in the out-of-print RSGB *VHF/UHF Manual*. Since then, many versions have been developed with different loop and boom dimensions. G3JVL's *Loopquad* software is available online at **g3jvl.com/programPages/loopQuad.php** to design loop Yagis. Along with the 1296-MHz version described below construction articles for a 902-MHz and 2304-MHz are included with this book's downloadable supplemental information.

A Loop Yagi for 1296 MHz

Described here are loop Yagis for the 1296-MHz band designed by Chip Angle, N6CA. Three sets of dimensions are given. Good performance can be expected if the dimensions are carefully followed. Check all dimensions before cutting or drilling anything. The 1296-MHz version is intended for weak-signal operation, while the 1270-MHz version is optimized for FM and mode L satellite operation. The 1283-MHz antenna provides acceptable performance from 1280 to 1300 MHz.

These antennas have been built on 6- and 12-foot booms. Results of gain tests at VHF conferences and by individuals around the country show the gain of the 6-foot model to be about 18 dBi, while the 12-foot version provides about 20.5 dBi. Swept measurements indicate that gain is about 2 dB down from maximum gain at ±30 MHz from the design frequency. The SWR, however, deteriorates within a few megahertz on the low side of the design center frequency.

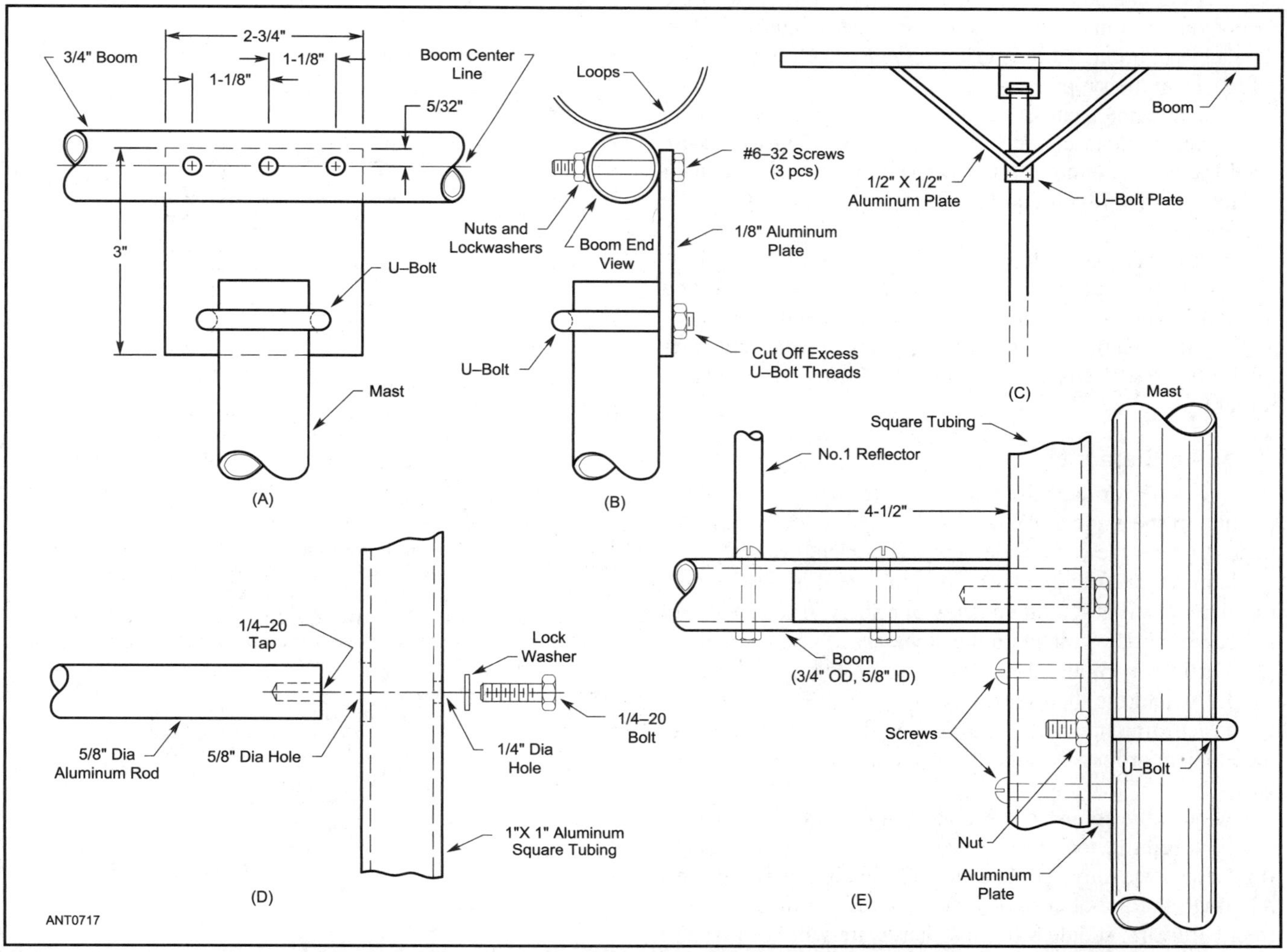

Figure 15.46 — Loop Yagi boom-to-mast plate details are given at A. At B, the mounting of the antenna to the mast is detailed. A boom support for long antennas is shown at C. The arrangement shown in D and E may be used to rear-mount antennas up to 6 or 7 ft long.

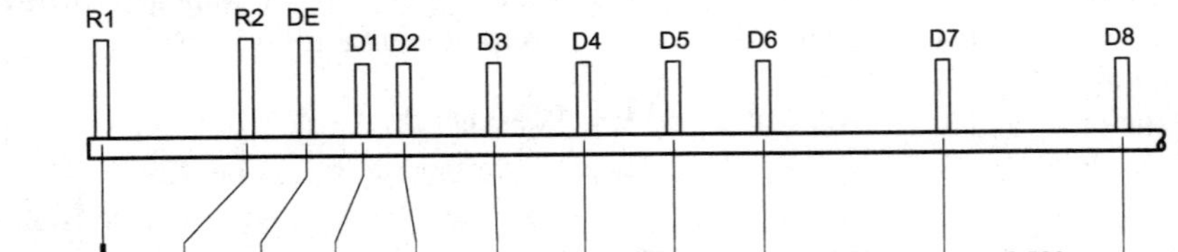

Freq										
1296	3.050	1.180	1.120	0.830	1.780	1.780	1.780	1.780	3.560	3.560
1283	3.090	1.193	1.135	0.841	1.804	1.804	1.804	1.804	3.607	3.607
1270	3.122	1.202	1.146	0.850	1.822	1.822	1.822	1.822	3.644	3.644

Element Spacing (inches)

Spacing remains constant for all elements from D6 up

ANT0718

Figure 15.47 — Boom drilling dimensions. These dimensions must be carefully followed and the same materials used if performance is to be optimum. Element spacings are the same for all directors after D6 — use as many as necessary to fill the boom.

The Boom

The dimensions given here apply only to a ¾-inch OD boom. If a different boom size is used, the dimensions must be scaled accordingly. Many hardware stores carry aluminum tubing in 6- and 8-foot lengths, and that tubing is suitable for a short Yagi. If a 12-foot antenna is planned, find a piece of more rugged boom material, such as 6061-T6 grade aluminum. Do not use anodized tubing. The 12-foot antenna must have additional boom support to minimize boom sag. The 6-foot version can be rear mounted. For rear mounting, allow 4½ inches of boom behind the last reflector to eliminate SWR effects from the support.

The antenna is attached to the mast with a gusset plate. This plate mounts at the boom center. See **Figure 15.46**. Drill the plate mounting holes perpendicular to the element mounting holes (assuming the antenna polarization is to be horizontal).

Elements are mounted to the boom with no. 4-40 machine screws, so a series of no. 33 (0.113 inch) holes must be drilled along the center of the boom to accommodate this hardware. **Figure 15.47** shows the element spacings for different parts of the band. Dimensions should be followed as closely as possible.

Parasitic Elements

The reflectors and directors are cut from 0.032-inch thick aluminum sheet and are ¼ inch wide. **Figure 15.48** indicates the lengths for the various elements. These lengths apply only to elements cut from the specified material. For best results, the element strips should be cut with a shear. If the edges are left sharp, birds won't sit on the elements.

Drill the mounting holes as shown in Figure 15.48 after carefully marking their locations. After the holes are drilled, form each strap into a circle. This is easily done by wrapping the element around a round form. (A small juice can works well.)

Mount the loops to the boom with no. 4-40 × 1-inch machine screws, lock washers and nuts. See **Figure 15.49**. It is best to use only stainless steel or plated-brass hardware. Although the initial cost is higher than for ordinary plated-steel hardware, stainless or brass hardware will not rust and need replacement after a few years. Unless the antenna is painted, the hardware will definitely deteriorate.

Driven Element

The driven element is cut from 0.032-inch copper sheet and is ¼ inch wide. Drill three holes in the strap as detailed in Figure 15.47. Trim the ends as shown and form the strap into a loop similar to the other elements. This antenna is like a quad; if the loop is fed at the top or bottom, it is horizontally polarized.

Driven element mounting details are shown in **Figure 15.50**. A mounting fixture is made from a ¼-20 × 1¼ inch

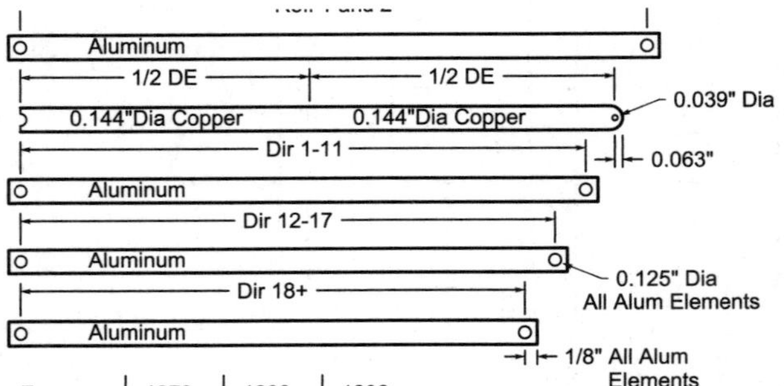

Freq	1270	1283	1296
Refl 1,2	9.929	9.829	9.700
1/2 DE	4.752	4.704	4.643
Dir 1–11	8.445	8.359	8.250
Dir 12–17	8.189	8.106	8.000
Dir 18+	7.882	7.802	7.700

Element Lengths (Inches) (Hole to Hole)

These Dimensions Apply Only to:
0.250" Element Width
0.0325" Element Thickness
0.750" Diameter Boom

NOTE: All Dimensions are in Inches

ANT0719

Figure 15.48 — Parasitic elements for the loop Yagi are made from aluminum sheet, the driven element from copper sheet. The dimensions given are for ¼-inch wide by 0.0325-inch thick elements only. Lengths specified are hole to hole distances; the holes are located ⅛ inch from each element end.

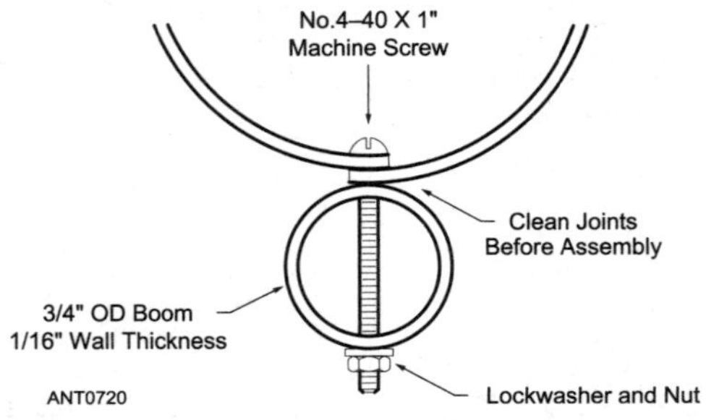

Figure 15.49 — Element-to-boom mounting details.

brass bolt. File the bolt head to a thickness of ⅛ inch. Bore a 0.144-inch (no. 27 drill) hole lengthwise through the center of the bolt. A piece of 0.141 inch semi-rigid hardline (UT-141 or equivalent) mounts through this hole and is soldered to the driven loop feed point. The point at which the UT-141 passes through the copper loop and brass mounting fixture should be left unsoldered at this time to allow for matching adjustments when the antenna is completed, although the range of adjustment is not very large.

The UT-141 can be any convenient length. Attach the connector of your choice (preferably type N). Use a short piece of low-loss RG-8 size cable (or ½-inch Hardline) for the run down the boom and mast to the main feed line. For best results, the main feed line should be the lowest loss 50-Ω cable obtainable. Good ⅞-inch hardline has 1.5 dB of loss per 100 feet and virtually eliminates the need for remote mounting of the transmit converter or amplifier.

Tuning the Driven Element

If the antenna is built carefully to the dimensions given, the SWR should be close to 1:1. Just to be sure, check the SWR if you have access to test equipment. Be sure the signal source is clean, however; wattmeters respond to "dirty" signals and can give erroneous readings. If problems are encountered, recheck all dimensions. If they look good, a minor improvement may be realized by changing the shape of the driven element. Slight bending of reflector 2 may also improve the SWR. When the desired match has been obtained, solder the point where the UT-141 jacket passes through the loop and brass bolt.

15.3.8 QUADS FOR VHF

The quad antenna can be built with inexpensive materials, yet its performance is comparable to other arrays of its size. Adjustment for resonance and impedance matching can be accomplished readily.

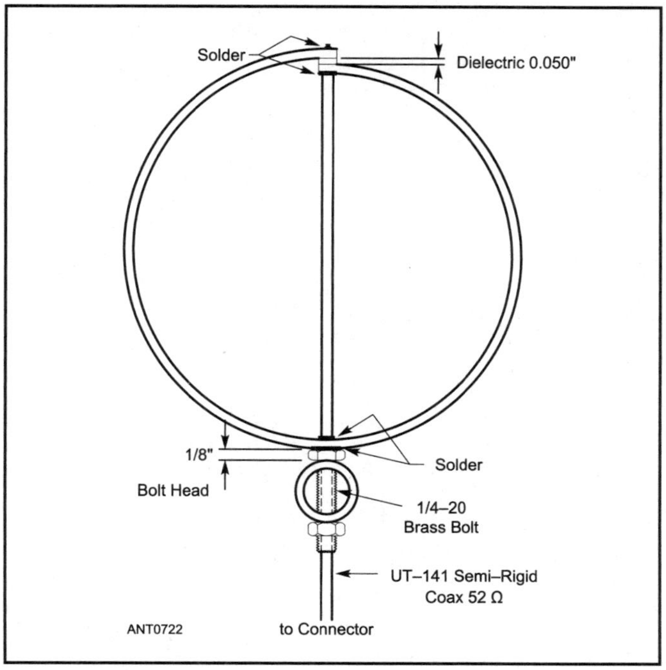

Figure 15.50 — Driven-element details. See Figure 15.57 and the text for additional information.

Quads can be stacked horizontally and vertically to provide high gain, without sharply limiting frequency response. Quads can be mounted side by side or one above the other, or both, in the same general way as other beam antennas. Sets of driven elements can also be mounted in front of a screen reflector. The recommended spacing between adjacent element sides is ½ λ. Phasing and feed methods are similar to those employed with other antennas described in this chapter.

Parasitic elements ahead of the driven element work in a manner similar to those in a Yagi array. Closed loops can be used for directors by making them 5% shorter than the driven element. Spacings are similar to those for conventional Yagis. In an experimental model the reflector was spaced 0.25 λ and the director 0.15 λ. A square array using four 3-element bays worked extremely well.

Because of the small size of the quad at VHF and UHF, many of the mechanical issues associated with HF quads are no longer significant. PVC pipe, fiberglass rod, and wood are all acceptable materials for booms and spreaders.

Quad antennas are best suited for the 6 meter and 2 meter bands. They are very popular for portable and backpacking operation. A quad design for 144 MHz is presented below. See the **Portable Antennas** chapter for a 2-element, 6 meter quad design.

A 144-MHz 4-Element Quad

Element spacing for quad antennas found in the literature ranges from 0.14 λ to 0.25 λ. Factors such as the number of elements in the array and the parameters to be optimized (F/B ratio, forward gain, bandwidth, etc), determine the optimum element spacing within this range. The 4-element quad antenna described here was designed for portable use, so a compromise between these factors was chosen. This antenna, pictured in **Figure 15.51**, was designed and built by Philip D'Agostino, W1KSC.

Based on several experimentally determined correction factors related to the frequency of operation and the wire size, optimum design dimensions were found to be as follows.

$$\text{Reflector length (ft)} = 1046.8/f_{MHz} \quad (1)$$

$$\text{Driven element length (ft)} = 985.5/f_{MHz} \quad (2)$$

$$\text{Directors (ft)} = 937.3/f_{MHz} \quad (3)$$

Cutting the loops for 146 MHz provides satisfactory performance across the entire 144-MHz band.

Materials

The quad was designed for quick and easy assembly and disassembly, as illustrated in **Figure 15.52**. Wood (clear trim pine) was chosen as the principal building material because of its light weight, low cost and ready availability. Pine is used for the boom and element supporting arms. Round wood clothes closet poles comprise the mast material. Strips connecting the mast sections are made of heavier pine trim. (See the previous section on Yagi Construction for more information about wood boom material.) Elements are made of #8 AWG aluminum wire. Plexiglas is used to support the feed point. **Table 15.24** lists the hardware and other parts needed to duplicate the quad.

Construction

The elements of the quad are assembled first. The mounting holes in the boom should be drilled to accommodate 1½ inch #8 hardware. Measure and mark the locations where the holes are to be drilled in the element spreaders, **Figure 15.53**. Drill the holes in the spreaders just large enough to accept the #8 AWG wire elements. It is important to drill all the holes straight so the elements line up when the antenna is assembled.

Construction of the wire elements is easiest if the directors are made first. A handy jig for bending the elements can be made from a piece of 2 × 3-inch wood cut to the side length of the directors. It is best to start with about 82 inches of wire for each director. The excess can be cut off when the elements are completed. (The total length of each director is 77 inches.) Two bends should initially be made so the directors can be slipped into the spreaders before the remaining corners are bent. See **Figure 15.54**. Electrician's copper-wire clamps can be used to join the wires after the final bends are made, and they facilitate adjustment of element length. The reflector is made the same way as the directors, but the total length is 86 inches.

Figure 15.51 — The 4-element 144-MHz portable quad, assembled and ready for operation. Sections of clothes closet poles joined with pine strips make up the mast. (W1MPO photo)

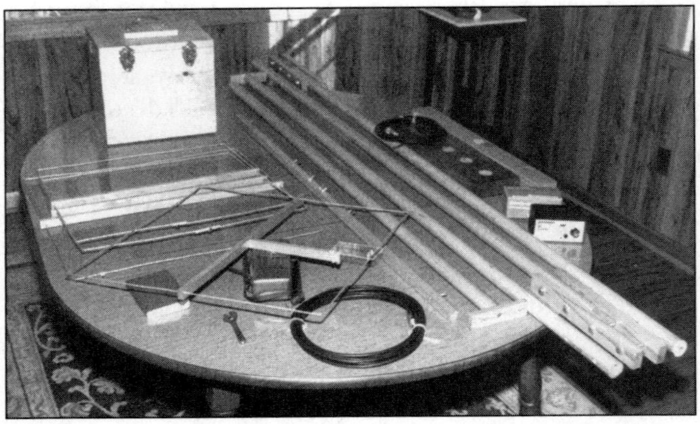

Figure 15.52 — The complete portable quad, broken down for travel. Visible in the foreground is the driven element. The pine box in the background is a carrying case for equipment and accessories. A hole in the lid accepts the mast, so the box doubles as a base for a short mast during portable operation. (W1MPO photo)

Table 15.24
Parts List for the 144 MHz 4-element Quad

Boom: ¾ × ¾ × 48-inch pine
Driven element support (spreader): ½ × ¾ × 21¼ inch pine
Driven element feed point strut: ½ × ¾ × 7½ inch pine
Reflector support (spreader): ½ × ¾ × 22½ inch pine
Director supports (spreaders): ½ × ¾ × 20¼ inch pine, 2 req'd
Mast brackets: ¾ × 1½ × 12 inch heavy pine trim, 4 req'd
Boom to mast bracket: ½ × 1⅝ × 5 inch pine
Element wire: Aluminum ground wire (Radio Shack no. 15-035)
Wire clamps: ¼ inch electrician's copper or zinc plated steel clamps, 3 req'd

Boom hardware:
- 6 no. 8-32 × 1½ inch stainless steel machine screws
- 6 no. 8-32 stainless steel wing nuts
- 12 no. 8 stainless steel washers

Mast hardware:
- 8 hex bolts, ¼-20 × 3½ inch
- 8 hex nuts, ¼-20
- 16 flat washers

Mast material: 1$\frac{5}{16}$ inch × 6 ft wood clothes closet poles, 3 req'd
Feed point support plate: 3½ × 2½ inch Plexiglas sheet
Wood preparation materials: Sandpaper, clear polyurethane, wax
Feed line: 52-Ω RG-8 or RG-58 cable
Feed line terminals: Solder lugs for no. 8 or larger hardware, 2 req'd
Miscellaneous hardware: 4 small machine screws, nuts, washers; 2 flat-head wood screws

The driven element, total length 81 inches, requires special attention, as the feed attachment point needs to be adequately supported. An extra hole is drilled in the driven element spreader to support the feed point strut, as shown in **Figure 15.55**. A Plexiglas plate is used at the feed point to support the feed point hardware and the feed line. The feed point support strut should be epoxied to the spreader, and a wood screw used for extra mechanical strength.

For vertical polarization, locate the feed point in the center of one side of the driven element, as shown in Figure 15.55. Although this arrangement places the spreader supports at voltage maxima points on the four loop conductors, D'Agostino reports no adverse effects during operation. However, if the antenna is to be left exposed to the weather, the builder may wish to modify the design to provide support for the loops at current maxima points, such as shown in Figure 15.55. (The element of Figure 15.55 should be rotated 90° for horizontal polarization.)

Orient the driven element spreader so that it mounts properly on the boom when the antenna is assembled. Bend the driven element the same way as the reflector and directors, but do not leave any overlap at the feed point. The ends of the wires should be ¾ inch apart where they mount on the Plexiglas plate. Leave enough excess that small loops can be bent in the wire for attachment to the coaxial feed line with stainless steel hardware.

Drill the boom as shown in **Figure 15.56**. It is a good idea to use hardware with wing nuts to secure the element spreaders to the boom. After the boom is drilled, clean all the wood parts with denatured alcohol, sand them, and give them two coats of glossy polyurethane. After the polyurethane dries, wax all the wooden parts.

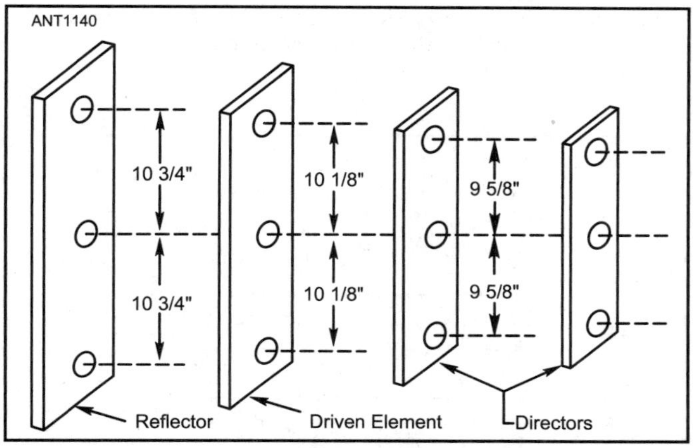

Figure 15.53 — Dimensions for the pine element spreaders for the 144-MHz 4-element quad.

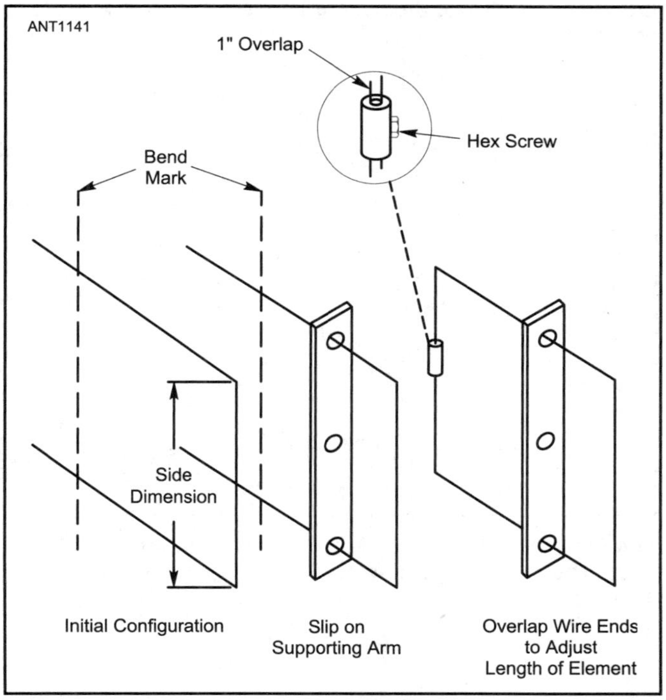

Figure 15.54 — Illustration showing how the aluminum element wires are bent. The adjustment clamp and its location are also shown.

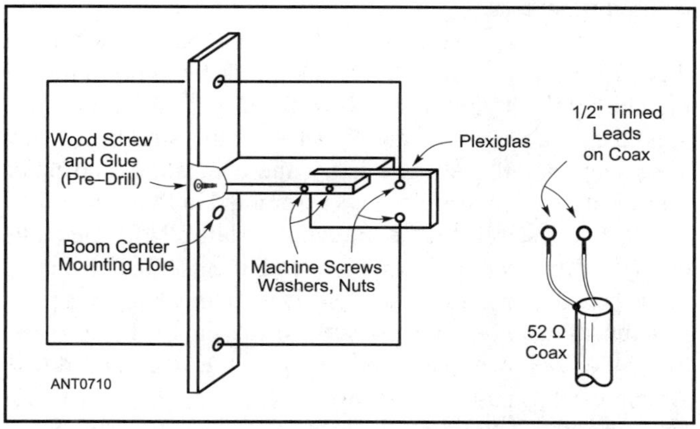

Figure 15.55 — Layout of the driven element of the 144-MHz quad. The leads of the coaxial cable should be stripped to ½ inch and solder lugs attached for easy connection and disconnection. See text regarding impedance at loop support points.

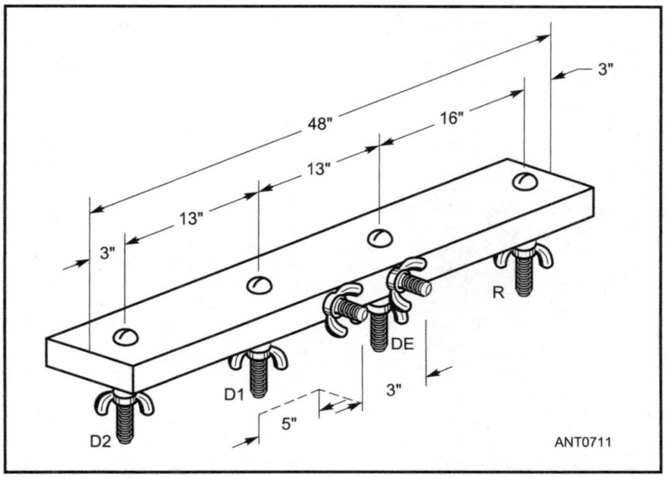

Figure 15.56 — Detail of the boom showing hole center locations and boom to mast connection points.

The boom to mast attachment is made next. Square the ends of a 6-foot section of clothes closet pole (a miter box is useful for this). Drill the center holes in both the boom attachment piece and one end of the mast section (**Figure 15.57**). Make certain that the mast hole is smaller than the flat-head screw to be used to ensure a snug fit. Accurately drill the holes for attachment to the boom as shown in Figure 15.57.

Countersink the hole for the flat-head screw to provide a smooth surface for attachment to the boom. Apply epoxy cement to the surfaces and screw the boom attachment piece securely to the mast section. One 6 foot mast is used for attachment to the other mast sections.

Two additional 6-foot mast sections are prepared next. This brings the total mast height to 18 feet. It is important to square the ends of each pole so the mast stands straight when assembled. Mast-section connectors are made of pine as shown in **Figure 15.58**. Using 3½ × ¼-inch hex bolts, washers and nuts, sections may be attached as needed, for a total height of 6, 12 or 18 feet. Drill the holes in two connectors at a time. This ensures good alignment of the holes. A drill press is ideal for this job, but with care a hand drill can be used if necessary.

Line up two mast sections end to end, being careful that they are perfectly straight. Use the predrilled connectors to maintain pole straightness, and drill through the poles, one at a time. If good alignment is maintained, a straight 18-foot mast section can be made. Label the connectors and poles immediately so they are always assembled in the same order.

When assembling the antenna, install all the elements on the boom before attaching the feed line. Connect the coax to the screw connections on the driven element support plate and run the cable along the strut to the boom. From there, the cable should be routed directly to the mast and down. Assemble the mast sections to the desired height. The antenna provides good performance, and has a reasonable SWR curve over the entire 144 MHz band (**Figure 15.59**).

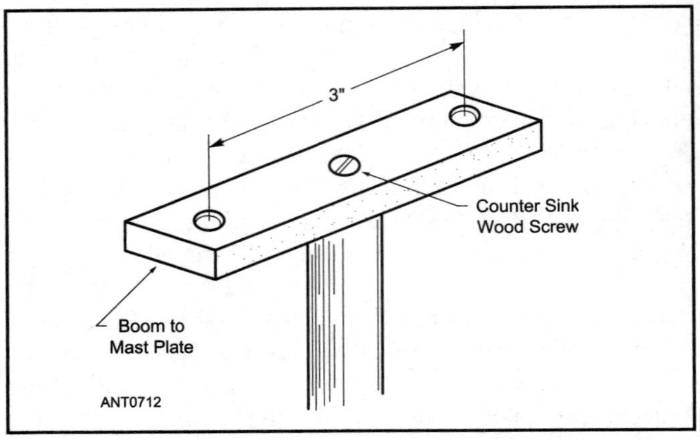

Figure 15.57 — Boom to mast plate for the 144-MHz quad. The screw hole in the center of the plate should be countersunk so the wood screw attaching it to the mast does not interfere with the fit of the boom.

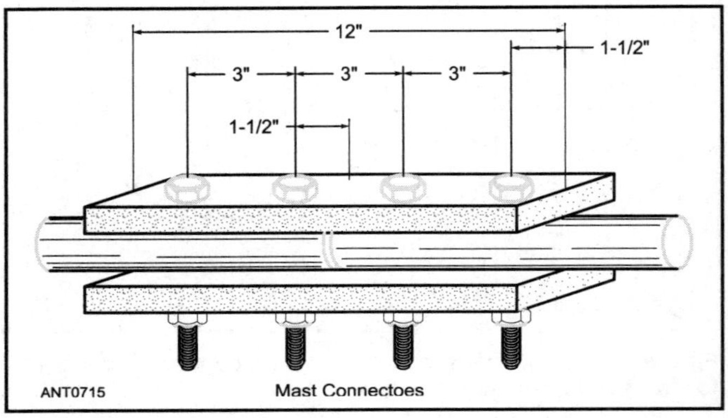

Figure 15.58 — Mast coupling connector details for the portable quad. The plates should be drilled two at a time to ensure the holes line up.

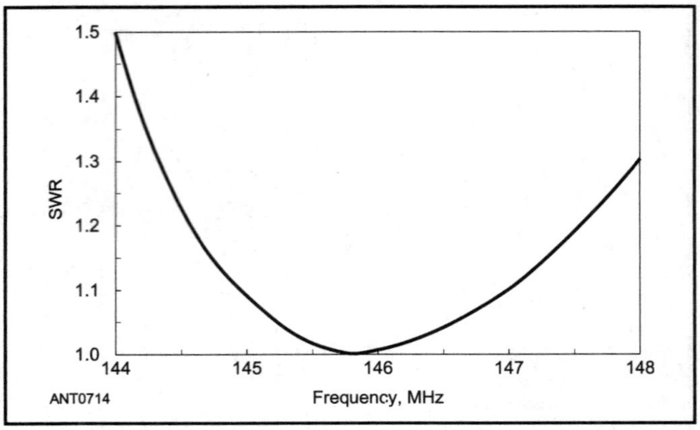

Figure 15.59 — Typical SWR curve for the 144-MHz portable quad. The large wire diameter and the quad design provide excellent bandwidth.

15.4. LOG-PERIODIC AND DISCONE ANTENNAS

Log-periodic antennas designed for use on single VHF or UHF bands have largely been displaced by Yagi designs that can be used across an entire band. The shorter wavelengths at VHF and above make "heavily filled" designs practical that can cover wide frequency ranges. (The design of log-periodic antennas was presented in the **Log-Periodic Dipole Arrays** chapter. See also the short article "V-Shaped Elements versus Straight Elements" by K4ERO with this book's downloadable supplemental information.)

Operation on several bands with a single antenna makes the log-periodic antenna a popular choice for the amateur with limited antenna options. An example of such a design is the Tennadyne T-28 shown in **Figure 15.60**. This antenna

Figure 15.60 — The Tennadyne T-28 covers 50-1300 MHz with boom length of 12 feet.

Figure 15.61 — Outline and sketch of the dimensions for the 2 meter Plus log-periodic antenna covering 130 to 170 MHz.

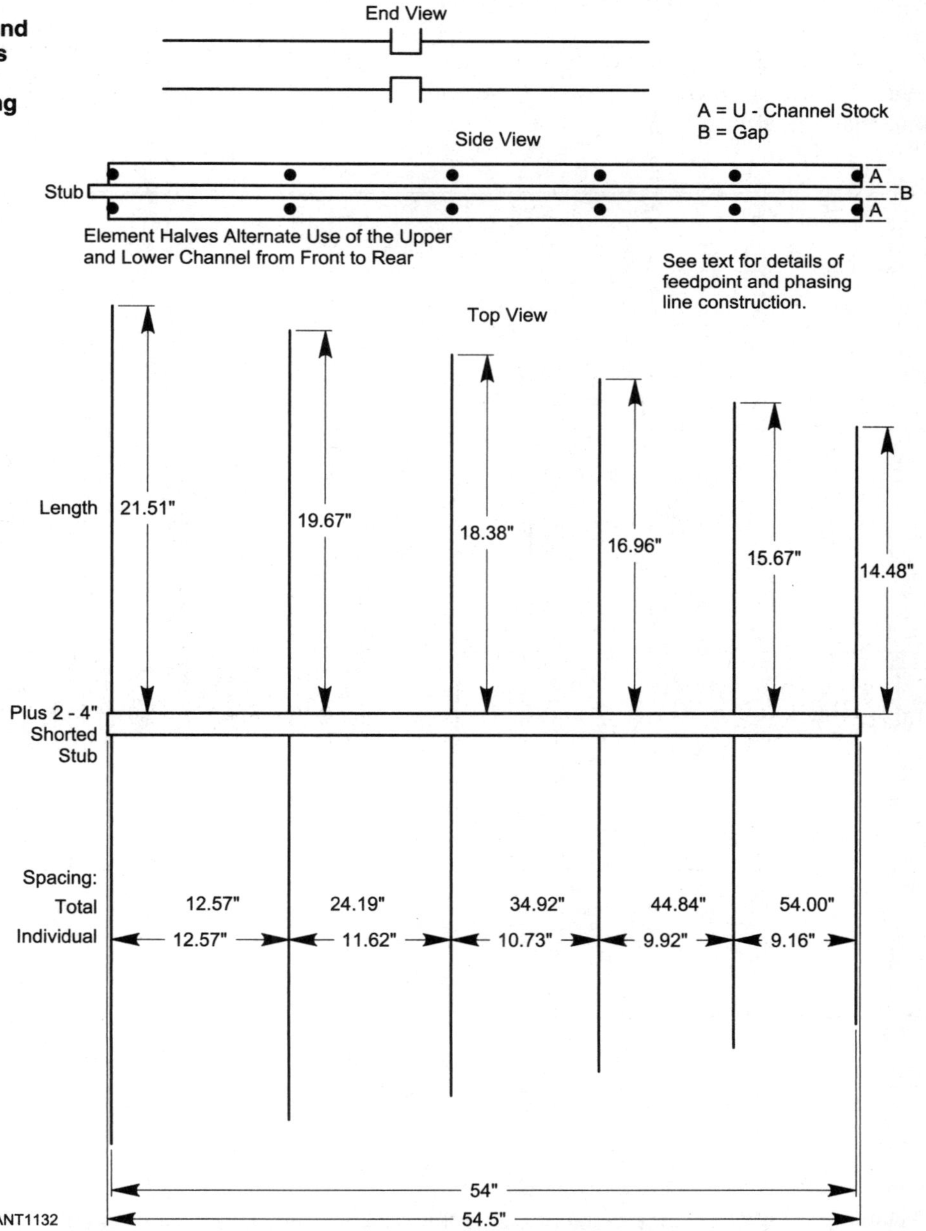

covers 50 to 1300 MHz with a boom length of only 12 feet. In addition, the antenna looks very much like a TV-receive antenna, attracting much less attention than a stack of monoband Yagis for the same frequency range!

Two VHF log-periodic designs are presented by reprints of *QST* articles included with this book's downloadable supplemental information. The first is a single-band design covering 2 meters, "An LPDA for 2 Meter Plus," by L.B. Cebik, W4RNL. The antenna, described in **Figure 15.61**, covers 130-170 MHz and can be used for listening to air band and public safety channels along with transmit and receive operation across 2 meters.

The second design is a three-band log-periodic covering the 144, 222, and 432 MHz bands, "A Three-Band Log-Periodic Antenna," by Robert Heslin, K7RTY, from June 1963 *QST*. This antenna is shown in **Figure 15.62**. The design is based on the same principles used today and the antenna is similar to that of commercial models covering the same frequency range.

The wideband discone antenna is a very popular omnidirectional antenna for scanner use at VHF and above with numerous commercial models available. (Discone design is discussed in the **Multiband HF Antennas** chapter.) Discones for VHF and UHF coverage are fairly simple to build, such as the design shown in **Figure 15.63** from the May 2003 *QST* article, "A VHF/UHF Discone Antenna," by Bob Patterson, K5DZE. The antenna is constructed from wire-mesh hardware cloth but sheet metal or heavy screen can be used. As the author mentions in the article, even aluminum foil on cardboard worked fine as an indoor receive antenna!

Yes, That's a TV Antenna!

If you have noticed the similarities between TV-receive antennas and the log-periodic antennas that cover the amateur VHF and lower UHF bands, you are not alone! In an article included on this book's downloadable supplemental information, John Stanley, K4ERO, shows how to modify a mid-sized log-periodic originally designed for receiving TV broadcasts into a stealthy, yet effective ham antenna covering 50 through 222 MHz. For hams limited to TV-antennas only, this might be a good solution to getting on at least a few of the ham bands and you can answer truthfully when asked about your new "TV antenna"!

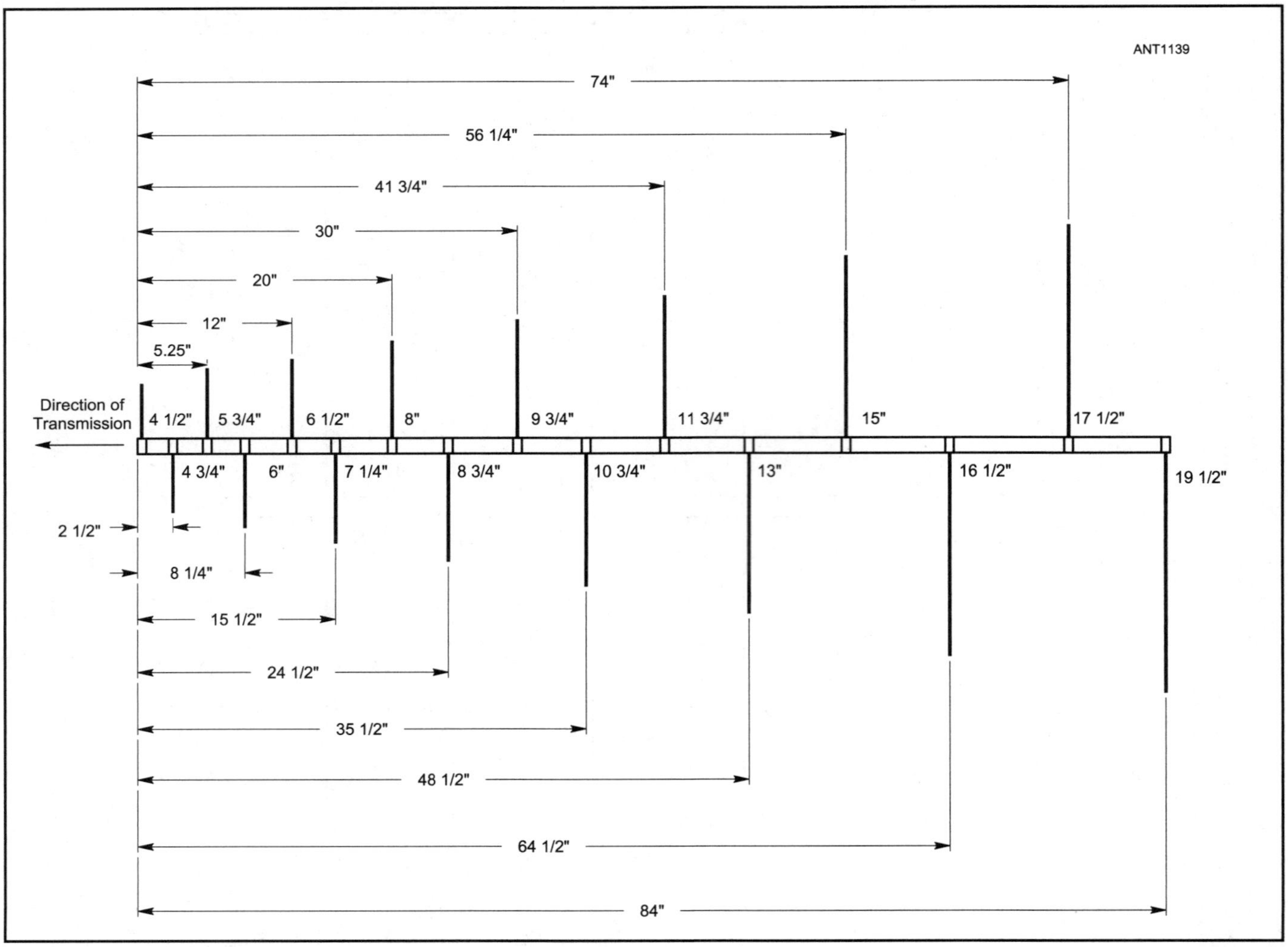

Figure 15.62 — Outline and sketch of the dimensions for the log-periodic antenna covering the 144, 222, and 432 MHz bands.

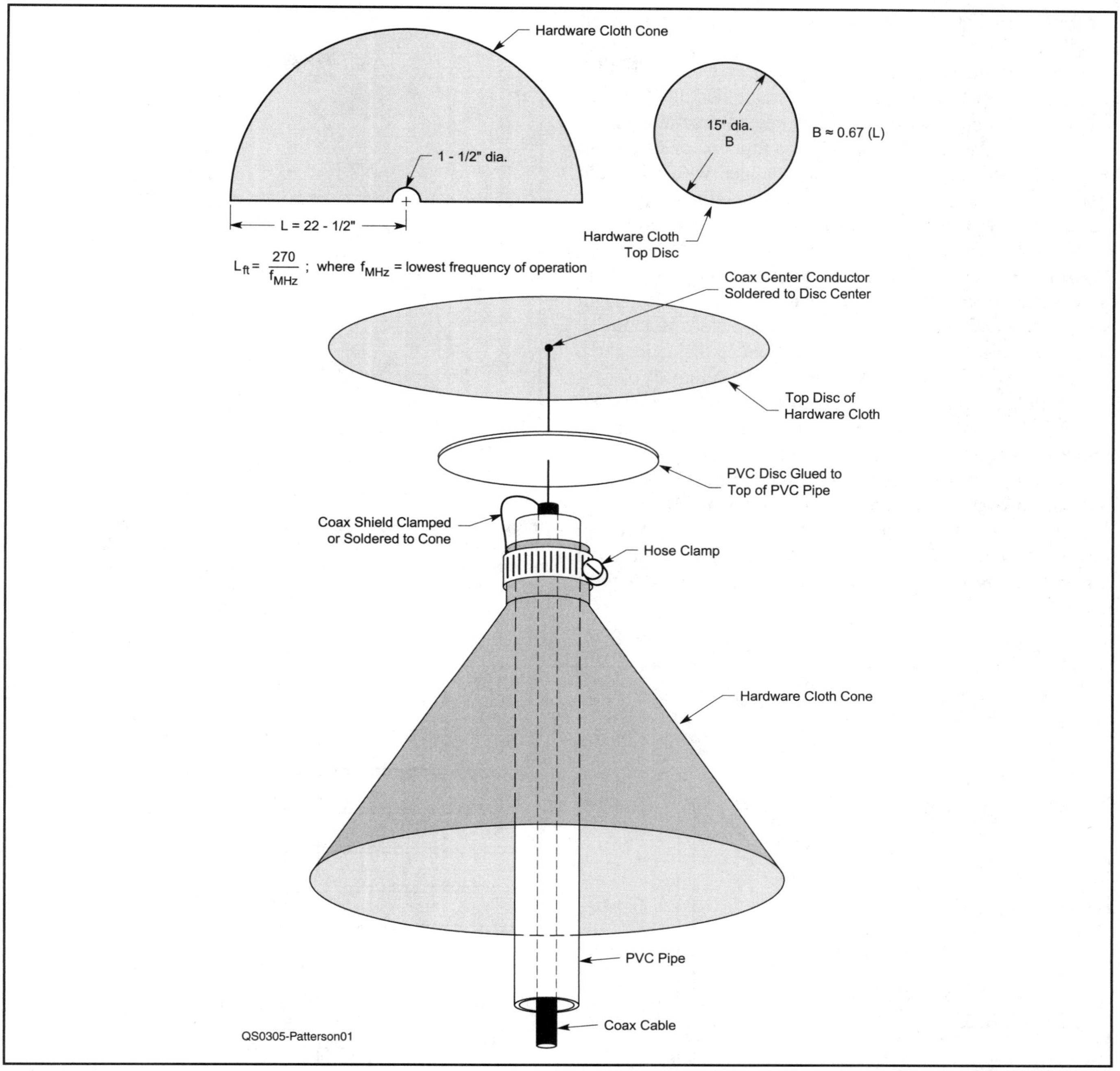

Figure 15.63 — Construction details for a VHF/UHF discone antenna. The largest dimension of the discone is determined by the lowest frequency of use.

15.5 REFLECTOR ANTENNAS

When a single driven element is used, the reflector screen may be bent to form an angle, giving an improvement in the radiation pattern and gain. At 222 and 420 MHz its size assumes practical proportions, and at 902 MHz and higher, practical reflectors can approach ideal dimensions (very large in terms of wavelengths), resulting in more gain and sharper patterns. The corner can be used at 144 MHz, though usually at much less than optimum size. For a given aperture, the reflector does not equal a parabola in gain, but it is simple to construct, broadband, and offers gains from about 9 to 14 dBi, depending on the angle and size. This section was written by Paul M. Wilson, W4HHK.

15.5.1 CORNER REFLECTORS

The corner angle can be 90, 60 or 45°, but the side length must be increased as the angle is narrowed. For a 90° corner, the driven element spacing can be anything from 0.25 to 0.7 λ, 0.35 to 0.75 λ for 60°, and 0.5 to 0.8 λ for 45°. In each case the gain variation over the range of spacings given is about 1.5 dB. Because the spacing is not very critical to gain, it may be varied for impedance-matching purposes. Closer spacings yield lower feed point impedances, but a folded dipole radiator could be used to raise this to a more convenient level.

Radiation resistance is shown as a function of spacing in **Figure 15.64**. The maximum gain obtained with minimum spacing is the primary mode (the one generally used at 144, 222 and 432 MHz to maintain reasonable side lengths). A 90° corner, for example, should have a minimum side length (S, **Figure 15.65**) equal to twice the dipole spacing, or 1 λ long for 0.5-λ spacing. A side length greater than 2 λ is ideal. Gain with a 60° or 90° corner reflector with 1-λ sides is about 10 dB. A 60° corner with 2-λ sides has about 13 dBi gain, and a 45° corner with 3-λ sides has about 14 dBi gain.

Reflector length (L, Figure 15.65) should be a minimum of 0.6 λ. Less than that spacing causes radiation to increase to the sides and rear, and decreases gain.

Spacing between reflector rods (G, Figure 15.65) should not exceed 0.06 λ for best results. A spacing of 0.06 λ results in a rear lobe that is about 6% of the forward lobe (down 12 dB). A small mesh screen or solid sheet is preferable at the higher frequencies to obtain maximum efficiency and highest

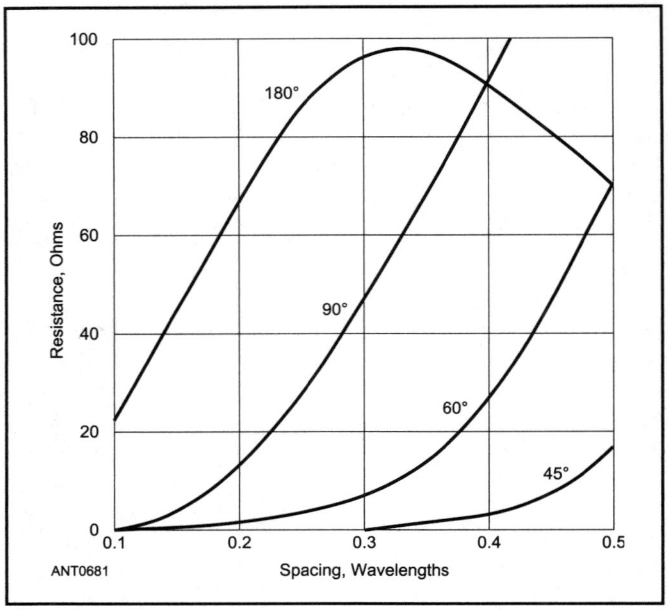

Figure 15.64 — Radiation resistance of the driven element in a corner reflector array for corner angles of 180° (flat sheet), 90°, 60° and 45° as a function of spacing D, as shown in Figure 15.65.

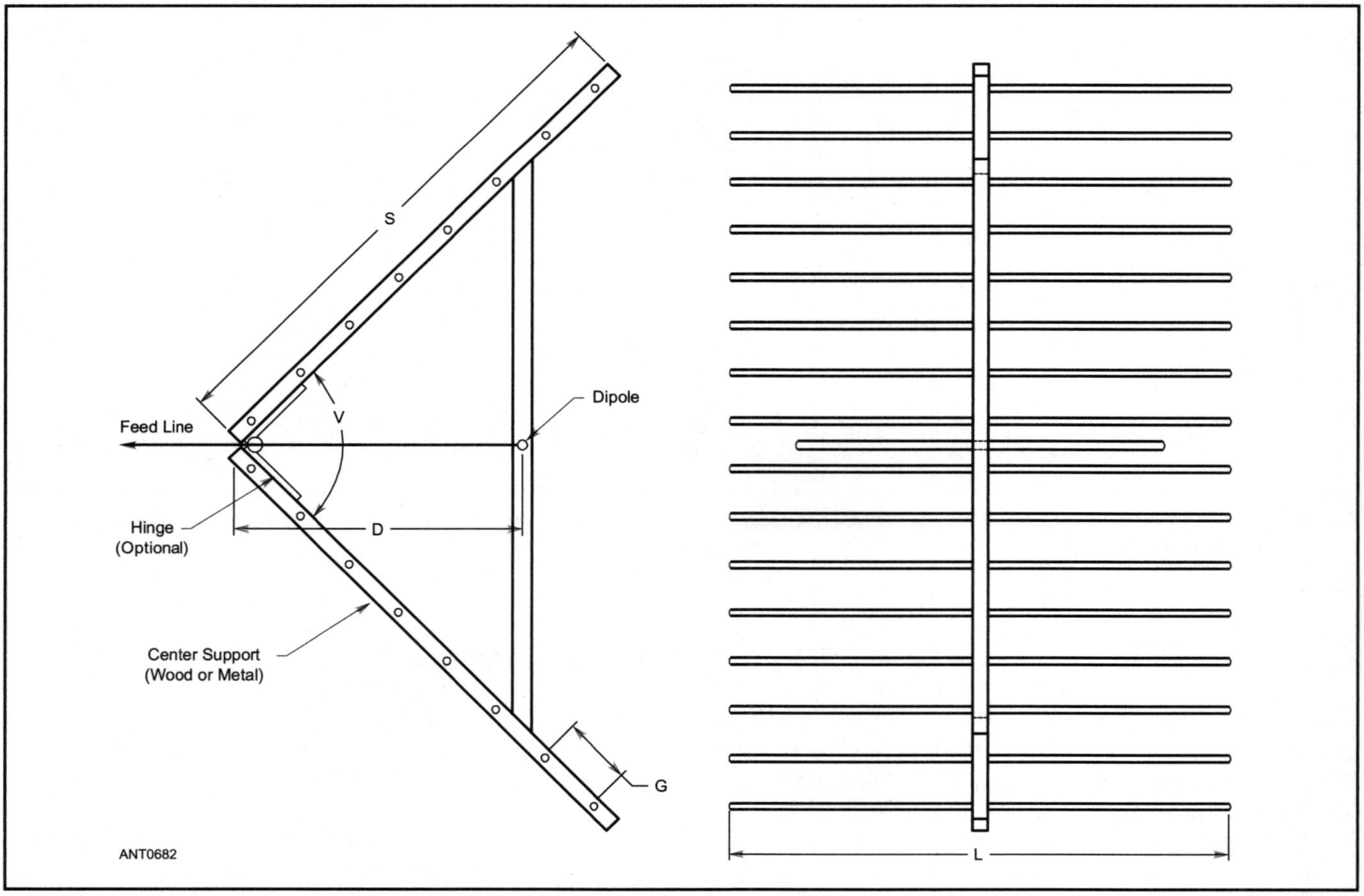

Figure 15.65 — Construction of a corner reflector array. The frame can be wood or metal. Reflector elements are stiff wire or tubing. Dimensions for several bands are given in Table 15.25. Reflector element spacing, G, is the maximum that should be used for the frequency; closer spacings are optional. The hinge permits folding for portable use.

F/B ratio, and to simplify construction. A spacing of 0.06 λ at 1296 MHz, for example, requires mounting reflector rods about every ½ inch along the sides. Rods or spines may be used to reduce wind loading. The support used for mounting the reflector rods may be of insulating or conductive material. Rods or mesh weave should be parallel to the radiator.

A suggested arrangement for a corner reflector is shown in Figure 15.65. The frame may be made of wood or metal, with a hinge at the corner to facilitate portable operation or assembly atop a tower. A hinged corner is also useful in experimenting with different angles. **Table 15.25** gives the principal dimensions for corner reflector arrays for 144 to 2300 MHz. The arrays for 144, 222 and 420 MHz have side lengths of twice to four times the driven element spacing. The 915 MHz corner reflectors use side lengths of three times the element spacing, 1296 MHz corners use side lengths of

Table 15.25
Dimensions of Corner Reflector Arrays for VHF and UHF

Freq (MHz)	*Side Length, S (inches)*	*Dipole to Vertex, D (inches)*	*Reflector Length, L (inches)*	*Reflector Spacing, G (inches)*	*Corner Angle, Vo*	*Radiation Resistance (Ω)*
144*	65	27½	48	7¾	90	70
144	80	40	48	4	90	150
222*	42	18	30	5	90	70
222	52	25	30	3	90	150
222	100	25	30	Screen	60	70
420	27	8¾	16¼	2⅝	90	70
420	54	13½	16¼	Screen	60	70
915	20	6½	25¾	0.65	90	70
915	51	16¾	25¾	Screen	60	65
915	78	25¾	25¾	Screen	45	70
1296	18	4½	27½	½	90	70
1296	48	11¾	27½	Screen	60	65
1296	72	18¼	27½	Screen	45	70
2304	15½	2½	20½	¼	90	70
2304	40	6¾	20½	Screen	60	65
2304	61	10¼	20½	Screen	45	70

*Side length and number of reflector elements somewhat below optimum — slight reduction in gain.

Notes:

915 MHz
Wavelength is 12.9 inches
Side length S is 3 × D, dipole to vertex distance
Reflector length L is 2.0 λ
Reflector spacing G is 0.05 λ

1296 MHz
Wavelength is 9.11 inches
Side length S is 4 × D, dipole to vertex distance
Reflector length L is 3.0 λ
Reflector spacing G is 0.05 λ

2304 MHz
Wavelength is 5.12 inches
Side length S is 6 × D, dipole to vertex distance
Reflector length L is 4.0 λ
Reflector spacing G is 0.05 λ

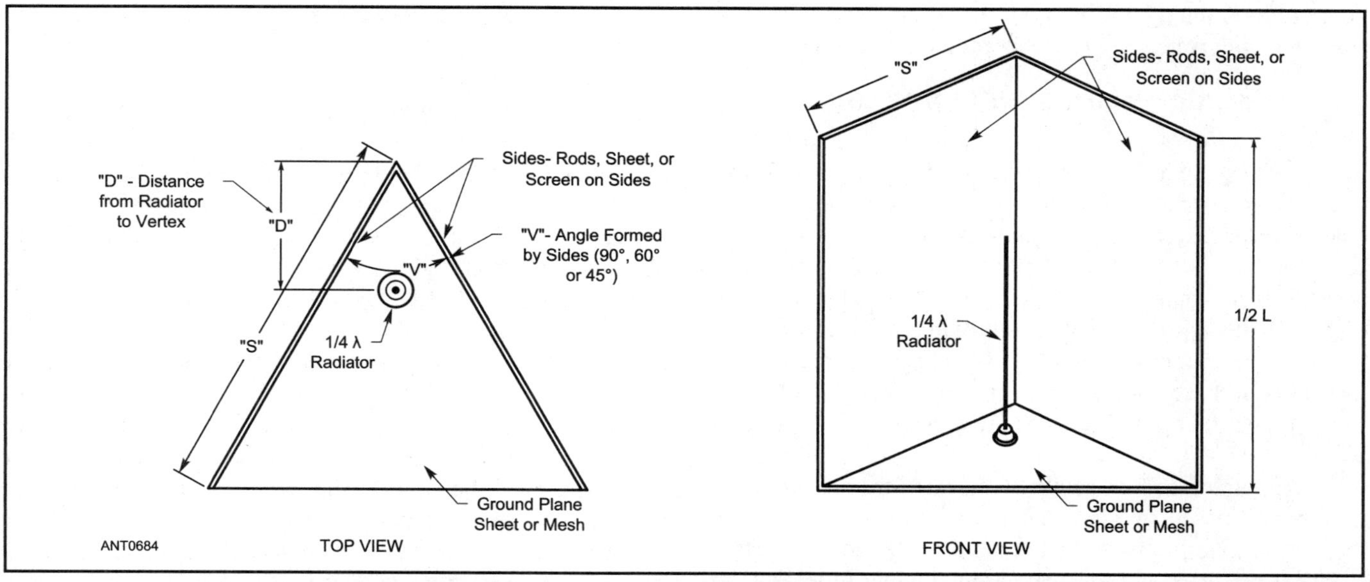

Figure 15.66 — A ground-plane corner reflector antenna for vertical polarization, such as FM communications or packet radio. The dimension ½ L in the front view refers to data in Table 15.25.

four times the spacing, and 2304 MHz corners employ side lengths of six times the spacing. Reflector lengths of 2, 3, and 4 wavelengths are used on the 915, 1296 and 2304 MHz reflectors, respectively. A 4 × 6 λ reflector closely approximates a sheet of infinite dimensions.

A corner reflector may be used for several bands, or for UHF television reception, as well as amateur UHF operation. For operation on more than one frequency, side length and reflector length should be selected for the lowest frequency, and reflector spacing for the highest frequency. The type of driven element plays a part in determining bandwidth, as does the spacing to the corner. A fat cylindrical element (small λ/dia ratio) or triangular dipole (bow tie) gives more bandwidth than a thin driven element. Wider spacings between driven element and corner give greater bandwidths. A small increase in gain can be obtained for any corner reflector by mounting collinear elements in a reflector of sufficient size, but the simple feed of a dipole is lost if more than two elements are used.

A dipole radiator is usually employed with a corner reflector. This requires a balun between the coaxial line and the balanced feed point impedance of the antenna. Baluns are easily constructed of coaxial line on the lower VHF bands, but become more difficult at the higher frequencies. This problem may be overcome by using a ground-plane corner reflector, which can be used for vertical polarization. A ground-plane corner with monopole driven element is shown in **Figure 15.66**. The corner reflector and a ¼ λ radiator are mounted on the ground plane, permitting direct connection to a coaxial line if the proper spacing is used. The effective aperture is reduced, but at the higher frequencies, second- or third-mode radiator spacing and larger reflectors can be employed to obtain more gain and offset the loss in effective aperture. A J antenna could be used to maintain the aperture area and provide a match to a coaxial line.

For vertical polarization operation, four 90° corner reflectors built back-to-back (with common reflectors) could be used for scanning 360° of horizon with modest gain. Feed line switching could be used to select the desired sector.

15.5.2 TROUGH REFLECTORS

To reduce the overall dimensions of a large corner reflector the vertex can be cut off and replaced with a plane reflector. Such an arrangement is known as a *trough reflector*. See **Figure 15.67**. Performance similar to that of the large corner reflector can thereby be had, provided that the dimensions of S and T as shown in Figure 15.67 do not exceed the limits indicated in the figure. This antenna provides performance very similar to the corner reflector, and presents fewer mechanical problems because the plane center portion is relatively easy to mount on the mast. The sides are considerably shorter, as well.

The gain of both corner reflectors and trough reflectors may be increased by stacking two or more and arranging them to radiate in phase, or alternatively by adding further collinear dipoles (fed in phase) within a wider reflector. Not more than two or three radiating units should be used, because the great virtue of the simple feeder arrangement would then be lost.

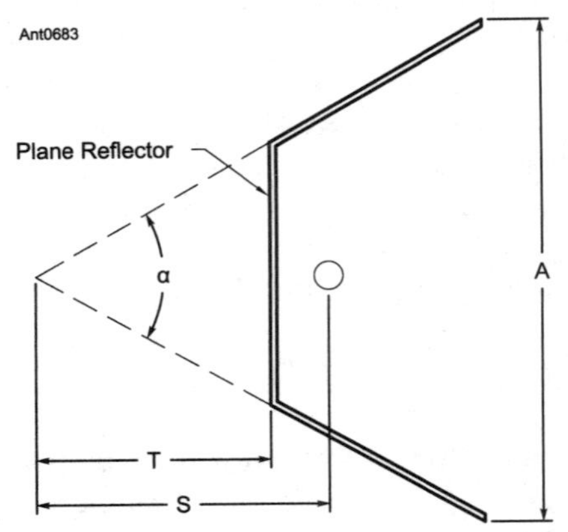

Angle α	*Value of S for maximum gain*	*Gain*	*Value of T*
90°	1.5 λ	13.5 dB	1λ - 1.25 λ
60°	1.75 λ	15 dB	1.0 λ
45°	2.0 λ	16 dB	1.9 λ

Figure 15.67 — The trough reflector. This is a useful modification of the corner reflector. The vertex has been cut off and replaced by a simple plane section. The tabulated data shows the gain obtainable for greater values of S than those covered in Table 15.25, assuming that the reflector is of adequate size.

Trough Reflectors for 432 and 1296 MHz

Dimensions are given in **Figure 15.68** for 432- and 1296-MHz trough reflectors. The gain to be expected is 16 dBi and 15 dBi, respectively. A very convenient arrangement, especially for portable operation, is to use a metal hinge at each angle of the reflector. This permits the reflector to be folded flat for transit. It also permits experiments to be carried out with different apex angles.

A housing is required at the dipole center to prevent the entry of moisture and, in the case of the 432-MHz antenna, to support the dipole elements. The dipole may be moved in and out of the reflector to get either minimum SWR or, if this cannot be measured, maximum gain. If a two-stub tuner or other matching device is used, the dipole may be placed to give optimum gain and the matching device adjusted to give optimum match. In the case of the 1296-MHz antenna, the dipole length can be adjusted by means of the brass screws at the ends of the elements. Locking nuts are essential.

The reflector should be made of sheet aluminum for 1296 MHz, but can be constructed of wire mesh (with one set of mesh wires parallel to the dipole) for 432 MHz. To increase the gain by 3 dB, a pair of these arrays can be stacked so the reflectors are barely separated (to prevent the formation of a slot radiator by the edges). The radiating dipoles must then be fed in phase, and suitable feeding and matching must be arranged. A two-stub tuner can be used for matching either a single- or double-reflector system.

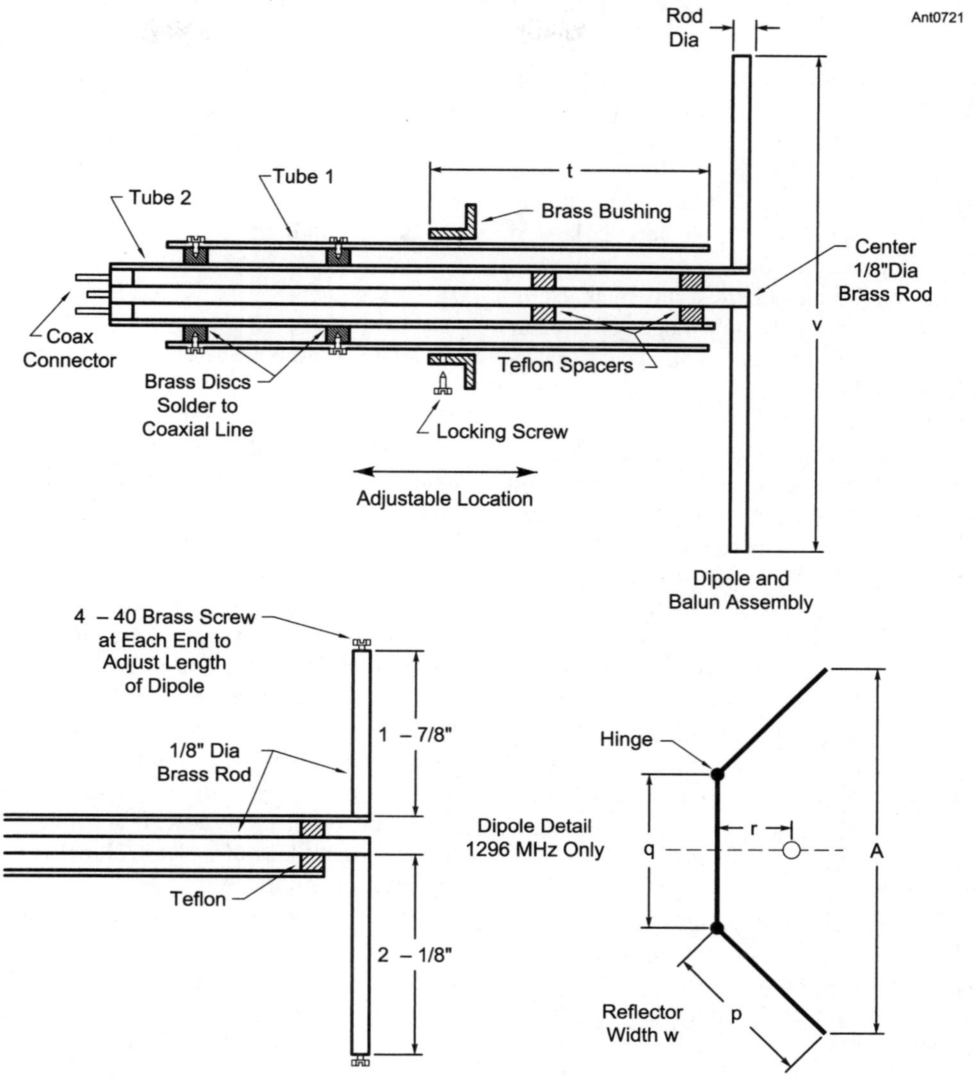

Dimensions in Inches

Band	A	p	q	r	w	t	u	v	Tube 1 Brass or Copper	Tube 2 Brass or Copper	Gain
432	120	100	50	7–1/2	60	6–1/2	1/4	12–3/4	1–1/2" ID 1/16" Wall	5/8" OD 1/16" Wall	16 dBi
1296	45	36	9–1/2	2–1/2	20	2–1/8	1/8	4–1/4	3/4" ID	3/8" OD 20 s.w.g.	15 dBi

Figure 15.68— Practical construction information for trough reflector antennas for 432 and 1296 MHz.

15.6 HELICAL ANTENNAS

Probably the most common amateur use of the helical antenna is in satellite communications, where the spinning of the satellite antenna system (relative to the Earth) and the effects of *Faraday rotation* cause the polarization of the satellite signal to be unpredictable. Using a linearly polarized antenna in this situation can result in deep fading, but with the helical antenna (which responds equally to linearly polarized signals), fading is essentially eliminated.

This same characteristic makes helical antennas useful in polarization-diversity systems. The advantages of circular polarization have been demonstrated on VHF voice schedules over non-optical paths, in cases where linearly polarized beams did not perform satisfactorily.

Another use for the helical antenna is the transmission of color ATV signals. Many beam antennas (when adjusted for maximum gain) have far less bandwidth than the required 6 MHz, or lack uniform gain over this frequency range. The result is significant distortion of the transmitted and received signals, affecting color reproduction and other features. This problem becomes more aggravated over non-optical paths.

The helix exhibits maximum gain (within 1 dB) across a range of more than 20 MHz anywhere above 420 MHz. Not only does the helix give high gain over an entire amateur band, but it also allows operation on FM, SSB and CW without the need for separate vertically and horizontally polarized antennas.

Helical Antenna Basics

The helical antenna is an unusual specimen in the antenna world, in that its physical configuration gives a hint to its electrical performance. A helix looks like a large air-wound coil with one of its ends fed against a ground plane, as shown in **Figure 15.69**. (Also see the article "The Helical Antenna — Description and Design" by VE3KL in this book's downloadable supplemental information.)

The ground plane is a screen of 0.8 to 1.1 λ diameter (or on a side for a square ground plane). The circumference (C_λ) of the coil form must be between 0.75 and 1.33 λ for the antenna to radiate in the axial mode. The coil should have at least three turns to radiate in this mode. The ratio of the spacing between turns (in wavelengths), S_λ to C_λ, should be in the range of 0.2126 to 0.2867. This ratio range results from the requirement that the pitch angle, α, of the helix be between 12° and 16°, where:

$$\alpha = \arctan \frac{S_\lambda}{C_\lambda} \qquad (4)$$

These constraints result in a single main lobe along the axis of the coil.

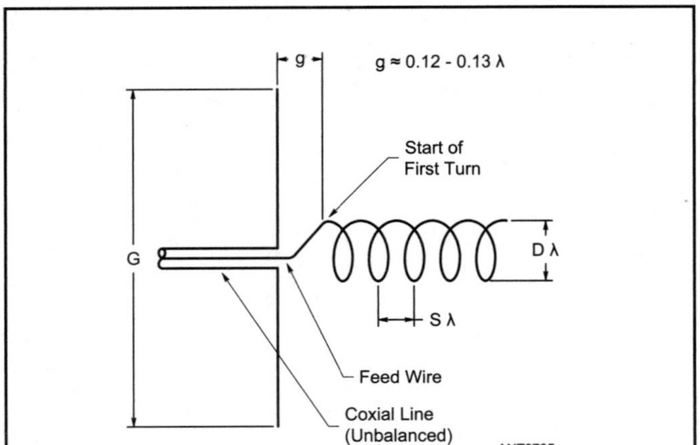

Figure 15.69 — The basic helical antenna and design parameters.

A helix with a C_λ of 1 λ has a wave propagating from one end of the coil (at the ground plane), corresponding to an instantaneous dipole "across" the helix. The electrical rotation of this dipole produces circularly polarized radiation. Because the wave is moving along the helix conductor at nearly the speed of light, the rotation of the electrical dipole is at a very high rate, and true circular polarization results.

Regarding the type of circular polarization, in simple terms the IEEE definition is that when viewing the antenna from the feed point end, a clockwise winding results in RHCP, and a counterclockwise winding results in LHCP. This is important, because when two stations use helical antennas over a nonreflective path, both must use antennas with the same polarization sense. If antennas of opposite sense are used, a signal loss of at least 20 dB results from the cross-polarization alone.

As mentioned previously, circularly polarized antennas can be used in communication with any linearly polarized antenna (horizontal or vertical), because circularly polarized antennas respond equally to all linearly polarized signals. The gain of a helix appears 3 dB less than the theoretical gain in this case, because the linearly polarized antenna does not respond to linearly polarized signal components orthogonal to it.

The response of a helix to all polarizations is indicated by a term called *axial ratio*, also known as *circularity*. Axial ratio is the ratio of amplitude of the polarization that gives maximum response to the amplitude of the polarization that gives minimum response. An ideal circularly polarized antenna has an axial ratio of 1.0. A well-designed practical helix exhibits an axial ratio of 1.0 to 1.1. The axial ratio of a helix is:

$$AR = \frac{2n+1}{2n} \qquad (5)$$

where

AR = axial ratio

n = the number of turns in the helix

Axial ratio can be measured in two ways. The first is to excite the helix and use a linearly polarized antenna with an amplitude detector to measure the axial ratio directly. This is done by rotating the linearly polarized antenna in a plane perpendicular to the axis of the helix and comparing the maximum and minimum amplitude values. The ratio of maximum to minimum is the axial ratio.

The impedance of the helix is easily predicted. The terminal impedance of a helix is unbalanced, and is defined by:

$$Z = 140 \times C_l \qquad (6)$$

where Z is the impedance of the helix in ohms.

The gain of a helical antenna is determined by its physical characteristics. Gain can be calculated from:

$$\text{Gain (dBi)} = 11.8 + 10 \log (C_l^2 n S_\lambda) \qquad (7)$$

In practice, helical antennas do not deliver the gain in Eq 7 for antennas with turns count greater than about twelve. This will be discussed further regarding practical antennas.

The beamwidth of the helical antenna (in degrees) at the half-power points is:

$$BW = \frac{52}{C_\lambda \sqrt{nS_\lambda}} \qquad (8)$$

The diameter of the helical antenna conductor should be between 0.006 and 0.05 λ but smaller diameters have been used successfully at 144 MHz. The previously noted diameter of the ground plane (0.8 to 1.1 λ) should not be exceeded if you desire a clean radiation pattern. As the ground plane size is increased, the sidelobe levels also increase. The ground plane need not be solid; it can be in the form of a spoked wheel or a frame covered with hardware cloth or screen. Cupped ground planes have also been used according to Kraus. (See the Bibliography.)

50-Ω Helix Feed

Joe Cadwallader, K6ZMW, presented this feed method in June 1981 *QST*. (See Bibliography) Terminate the helix in an N connector mounted on the ground screen at the periphery of the helix. See **Figure 15.70**. Connect the helix conductor to the N connector as close to the ground screen as possible (**Figure 15.71**). Then adjust the first quarter turn of the helix to a close spacing from the reflector.

This modification goes a long way toward curing a deficiency of the helix — the 140-Ω nominal feed point impedance. The traditional λ/4 matching section has proved difficult to fabricate and maintain. But if the helix is fed at the periphery, the first quarter turn of the helix conductor (leaving the N connector) acts much like a transmission line — a single conductor over a perfectly conducting ground plane. The impedance of such a transmission line is:

$$Z_0 = 138 \log \frac{4h}{d} \qquad (9)$$

where

Z_0 = line impedance in ohms

h = height of the center of the conductor above the ground plane

d = conductor diameter (in the same units as h).

The impedance of the helix is 140 Ω a turn or two away from the feed point. But as the helix conductor curves down toward the feed connector (and the ground plane), h gets smaller, so the impedance decreases. The 140-Ω nominal impedance of the helix is transformed to a lower value. For any particular conductor diameter, an optimum height can be found that will produce a feed point impedance equal to 50 Ω. The height should be kept very small, and the diameter should be large. Apply power to the helix and measure the SWR at the operating frequency. Adjust the height for an optimum match.

Typically, the conductor diameter may not be large enough to yield a 50-Ω match at practical (small) values of h. In this case, a strip of thin brass shim stock or flashing copper can be soldered to the first quarter-turn of the helix conductor (**Figure 15.72**). This effectively increases the conductor

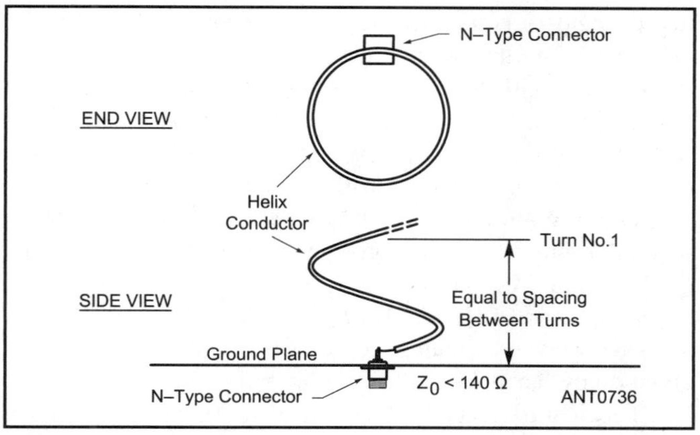

Figure 15.70 — End view and side view of peripherally fed helix.

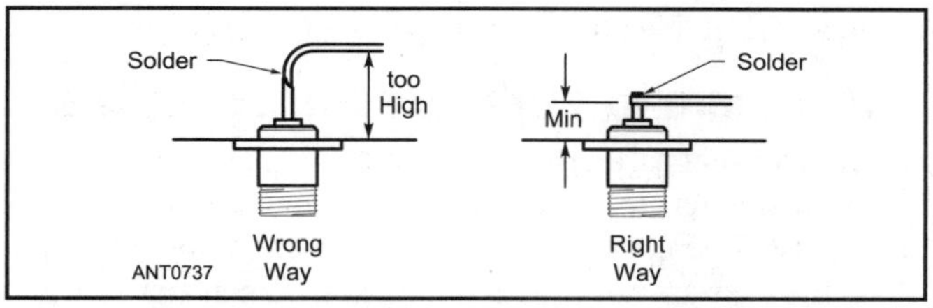

Figure 15.71— Wrong and right ways to attach a helix to a type N connector for 50-Ω feed.

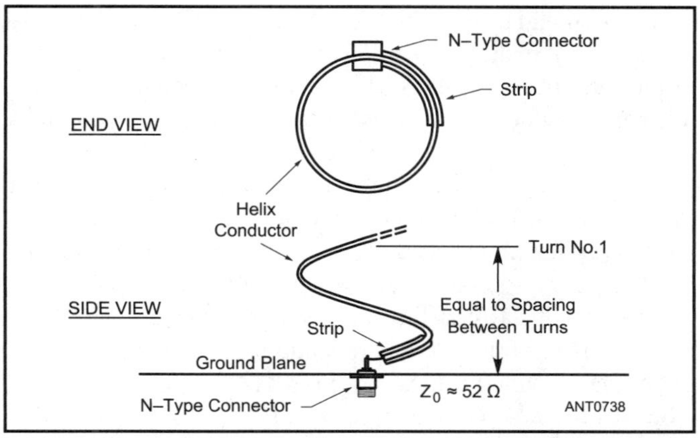

Figure 15.72 — End view and side view of peripherally fed helix with metal strip added to improve transformer action.

diameter, causing the impedance to decrease further yet. The edges of this strip can be slit every ½ inch or so, and the strip bent up or down (toward or away from the ground plane) to tune the line for an optimum match.

This approach yields a perfect match to nearly any coax. The usually wide bandwidth of the helix (70% for less than 2:1 SWR) will be reduced slightly (to about 40%) for the same conditions. This reduction is not enough to be of any consequence for most amateur work. The improvements in performance, ease of assembly and adjustment are well worth the effort in making the helix more practical to build and tune.

15.7 MICROWAVE ANTENNAS

The domain of amateur microwaves begins at 902 MHz and includes all higher frequency bands. (The 10 GHz and higher bands are also referred to as mm-wave bands.) The short wavelength of microwaves enables a wide range of interesting designs quite different from the antennas based on discrete linear and loop elements popular at lower frequencies. At microwaves, surfaces and shapes are used in ways that are impractical at longer wavelengths.

This section of the book has been extensively updated by Paul Wade, W1GHZ, a prolific designer and author of the *QST* column, Microwavelengths. Paul has also published the excellent online *W1GHZ Microwave Antenna Book* and his website, **www.w1ghz.org**, contains a wealth of information about many facets of microwave operating and building.

The RSGB texts listed in the Bibliography provide a more complete treatment of amateur microwave antennas. A number of horn and dish designs, including conversion of surplus offset-feed satellite TV receive dishes are presented in the RSGB publication *Antennas for VHF and Above*.

15.7.1 MICROWAVE ANTENNA CAVEATS

Many antenna construction practices that are common on lower frequencies cannot be used at microwave frequencies. This is the most important reason why all who venture to microwaves are not equally successful. When a proven antenna design is used, copy it exactly; don't change *anything*.

Do not allow the mast to pass through the elements, as is common on antennas for lower frequencies. Avoid any unnecessary metal around the antenna: ¼ λ at 1296 MHz is only a little over 2 inches. Cut all U-bolts and mounting hardware to the minimum length needed so that no resonant or near-resonant conductors are present to couple to the antenna's field.

After antenna performance, feed line loss is the next most important aspect of antenna system design. Mount the antennas to keep feed line losses to an absolute minimum. Antenna height is less important than keeping the line losses low.

Use the best feed line you can get. As an example of why this is important, here are some realistic measurements of common coaxial cables at 1296 MHz (loss per 100 feet):

- RG-8, 213, 214 coaxial cable: 11 dB
- ½ inch foam/copper hardline: 4 dB
- ⅞ inch foam/copper hardline: 1.5 dB

Preamps should be mounted at the antenna wherever practical and only connectors designed for frequency of operation should be used.

3D-Printing and CNC Techniques for Microwaves

Amateurs have long been limited to using surplus microwave components or building relatively simple antenna designs because special machining or construction techniques, particularly at 10 GHz and higher frequencies, are beyond most amateur shops. This situation is changing as 3D-printing and CNC machining equipment has become affordable. Amateurs can not only replicate commercial designs but can implement custom designs with subtle and precise aspects. Expect to see more of these techniques in design and construction articles in the amateur literature!

RF Safety for Waveguides, Horns and Dishes

Never look into the open end of a waveguide when power is applied, or stand directly in front of a dish while transmitting. Tests and adjustments in these areas should be done while receiving or at extremely low levels of transmitter power (less than 0.1 watt). The FCC has set a limit of 10 mW/cm^2 averaged over a 6-minute period as the safe maximum. Other authorities believe even lower levels should be used. Destructive thermal heating of body tissue results from excessive exposure. This heating effect is especially dangerous to the eyes. The accepted safe level of 10 mW/cm^2 is reached in the near field of a parabolic antenna if the level at $2D^2/\lambda$ is 0.242 mW/cm^2. The equation for power density at the far-field boundary is

$$\text{Power Density} = \frac{137.8P}{D^2} \text{ mW / cm}^2$$

where

P = average power in kilowatts
D = antenna diameter in feet
λ = wavelength in feet

15.7.2 WAVEGUIDES

Above 2 GHz, coaxial cable is a losing proposition for communications operation. Fortunately, at this frequency the wavelength is short enough to allow practical, efficient energy transfer by an entirely different means. A *waveguide* is a conducting tube through which energy is transmitted in the form of electromagnetic waves. The tube is not considered as carrying a current in the same sense that the wires of a two-conductor line do, but rather as a *boundary* that confines the waves in the enclosed space. Skin effect prevents any electromagnetic effects from being evident outside the guide. The energy is injected at one end, either through capacitive or inductive coupling or by radiation, and is removed from the other end in a like manner. Waveguide merely confines the energy of the fields, which are propagated through it to the receiving end by means of reflections against its inner walls.

Evolution of Waveguide

Suppose an open-wire line is used to carry UHF or microwave energy from a generator to a load. Imagine the transmission line is supported with quarter-wave stubs, shorted at the far end. The open end of such a stub presents an infinite impedance to the transmission line, provided that the shorted stub is non-reactive. Thus, the stub acts as an insulating support. Since the stubs act as an open-circuit, an infinite number of them may be connected in parallel without affecting the open-wire line.

Because the shorting link has finite length it also has some inductance. This inductance can be minimized by making the RF current flow on the surface of a plate rather than through a thin wire. If the plate is large enough, it will prevent the magnetic lines of force from encircling the RF current.

The transmission line may be supported from the top as well as the bottom and when infinitely many supports are added, they form the walls of a waveguide at its *cutoff frequency*. **Figure 15.73** illustrates how a rectangular waveguide evolves from a two-wire parallel transmission line.

Waveguide Operation

As a signal propagates along a waveguide, the metal walls contain the electric and magnetic fields. We'll concentrate on the electric field here, because the dominant mode of propagation for waveguide is called TE or *Transverse Electric*. **Figure 15.74** shows how the electric and magnetic fields are oriented for the TE_{10} mode. (See the discussion on waveguide modes below.) The electric field intensity in the rectangular waveguide, which is oriented parallel to the shorter side walls. The electric field is strongest in the center and must be zero at the side walls, since the walls are short circuits. This is the reason for the E-plane and H-plane terminology in Figure 15.74D.

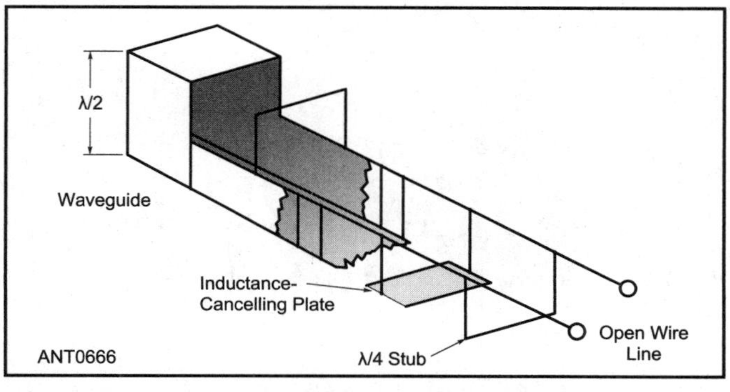

Figure 15.73 — At its cutoff frequency a rectangular waveguide can be thought of as a parallel two-conductor transmission line supported from top and bottom by an infinite number of ¼-wavelength stubs.

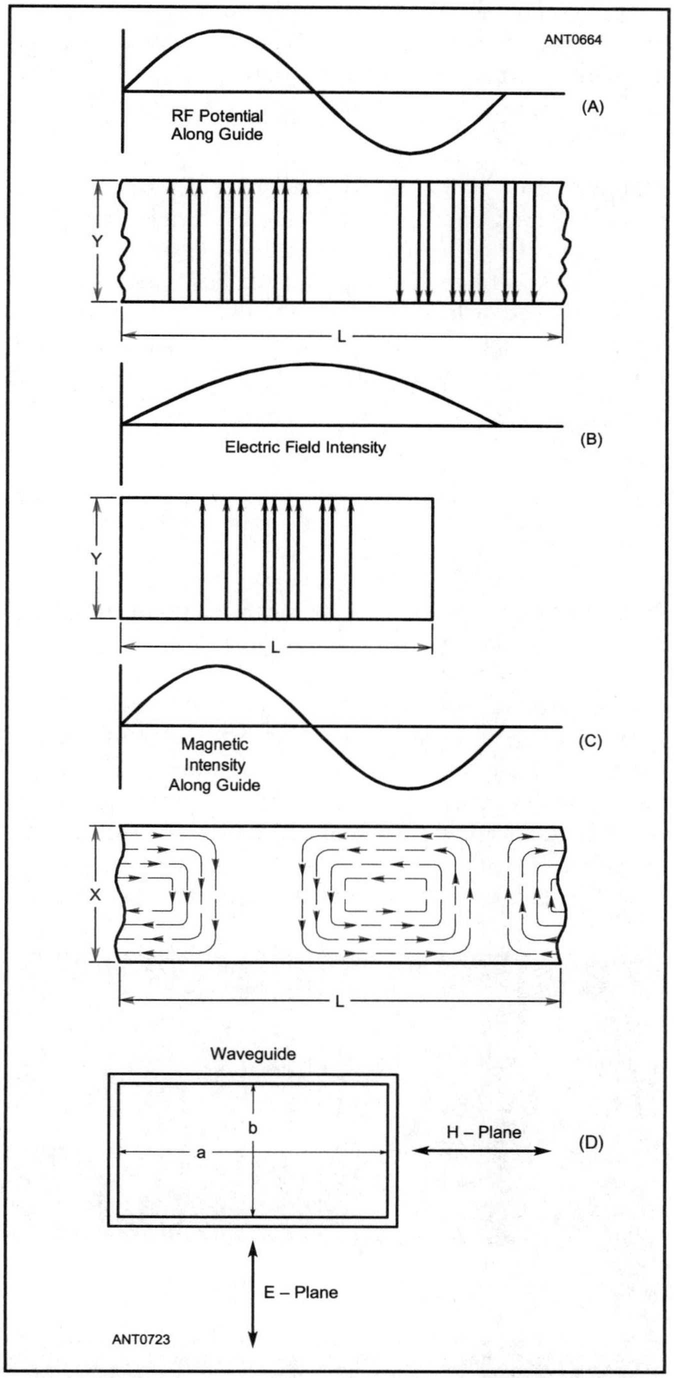

Figure 15.74 — Field distribution in a rectangular waveguide. The TE_{10} mode of propagation is depicted.

The field strength distribution is half of a sine wave at the operating frequency, and propagates down the waveguide as if it were bouncing off the side walls. For this to work, the width of the waveguide must be at least one-half the wavelength of the propagating signal. At lower frequencies with longer wavelengths, the field cannot be zero at both walls so these signals will not propagate in the waveguide.

Waveguide Dimensions

Cutoff and Upper Frequencies

The minimum frequency of operation for a waveguide is that at which the waveguide width, a, is ½ wavelength. This is called the waveguide's *cutoff frequency*, f_c.

$$f_c = c/2a$$

where c = the speed of light in free space, 2.9979 × 10^8 meters per second, and a is the waveguide's larger dimention

A wavelength in the waveguide, λ_g, is longer than a wavelength in free space, λ_0. This implies a velocity faster than the speed of light. But only the *phase velocity* exceeds the speed of light — energy cannot travel faster. The waveguide wavelength varies with frequency as a function of the cutoff frequency:

$$\lambda_g = \frac{\lambda_0}{\sqrt{1-\left(\frac{\lambda_0}{\lambda_c}\right)^2}} \qquad (10)$$

Near the cutoff frequency, λ_g is much longer than the free-space wavelength λ_0, becoming closer to λ_0 as frequency increases.

Waveguide operating frequencies are usually well above the cutoff frequency — near (and below) the cutoff frequency, losses increase and the guide wavelength changes rapidly with frequency causing dispersion of the transmitted waveform. This is why a waveguide makes an excellent high-pass filter.

The height of a rectangular waveguide, between top and bottom walls, determines both the upper frequency limit and the characteristic impedance. The upper limit is the frequency at which the waveguide height is ½ λ — above this frequency, the electric field may change orientation and other modes may propagate.

Waveguide Dimensions

In a rectangular guide the critical dimension is X in Figure 15.74. This dimension must be more than ½ λ at the lowest frequency to be transmitted. In practice, the Y dimension usually is made about equal to ½ X to avoid the possibility of operation in other than the dominant mode.

Cross-sectional shapes other than a rectangle can be used, the most important being the circular pipe. Much the same considerations apply as in the rectangular case.

Wavelength dimensions for rectangular and circular guides are given in **Table 15.26**, where X is the width of a rectangular guide and r is the radius of a circular guide. All figures apply to the dominant mode.

Characteristic Impedance

The characteristic impedance is usually much higher than 50 ohms and is calculated for TE modes using this formula:

$$Z_0 = 377\left(\frac{\lambda_g}{\lambda_0}\right)\left(\frac{2b}{a}\right) \qquad (11)$$

where *a* and *b* are the large and small dimensions, respectively, of the rectangular waveguide. 377 Ω is the approximate impedance of free space.

For example, at 10 GHz, WR90 waveguide is often used.

Table 15.26
Waveguide Operating Dimensions in Wavelengths

	Rectangular	*Circular*
Cutoff wavelength	*2X*	*3.41r*
Longest wavelength transmitted with little attenuation	1.6X	3.2r
Shortest wavelength before next mode becomes possible	1.1X	2.8r

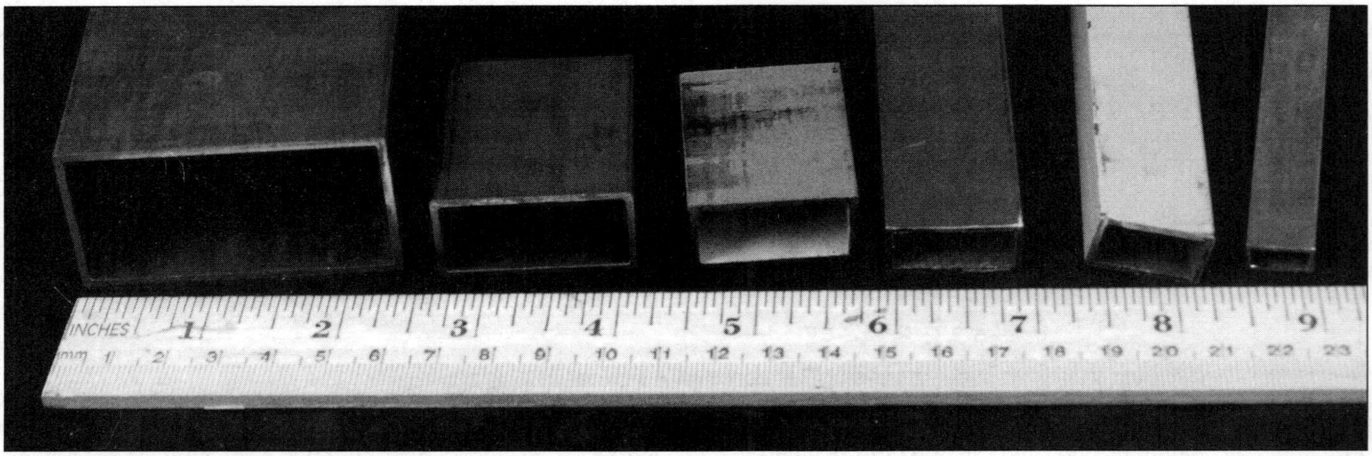

Figure 15.75 — Typical waveguide sizes from WR229 on the left to WR42 on the right.

The width is 0.9 inches, or 22.86 mm, and the height is 0.4 inches, or 10.16 mm. The cutoff frequency is 6.56 GHz, but the recommended operating frequency range is 8 to 12.4 GHz. At 10.368 GHz, the free space wavelength is l_0 = 28.915 mm, the guide wavelength is l_g = 37.33 mm and the characteristic impedance is Z_0 = 433 ohms. Several common waveguides are pictured in cross-section in **Figure 15.75**.

For circular waveguide, the cutoff wavelength is λ_c = 1.706 x diameter and the characteristic impedance is

$$Z_0 = 377\left(\frac{\lambda_g}{\lambda_0}\right) \quad (12)$$

Waveguide Modes

The operating mode described above is for the dominant mode, TE_{10} (or TE_{11} in circular waveguide). This is the lowest frequency mode at which a given waveguide will operate, and is the preferred mode for waveguide transmission.

If there is no upper limit to the frequency to be transmitted, there are an infinite number of ways exist in which the fields can arrange themselves in a guide. Each field configuration is a mode. All modes may be separated into two general groups. One group, designated TM (*Transverse Magnetic*), has the magnetic field entirely crosswise to the direction of propagation, but has a component of electric field in the propagation direction. The other group, designated TE (*Transverse Electric*) has the electric field entirely crosswise to the direction of propagation, but has a component of magnetic field in the direction of propagation. TM waves are sometimes called E-waves in older references and TE waves are sometimes called H-waves. The TM and TE designations are preferred, however. The particular mode of transmission is identified by the group letters followed by subscript numbers; for example TE_{11}, TM_{11} and so on. The number of possible modes increases with frequency for a given size of guide.

Higher-order modes are useful in certain applications, for instance, in multi-mode feed horns, where the additional modes can shape the radiation pattern, special high-power waveguides, and in certain cavity filters.

Waveguide Coupling

Energy may be introduced into or extracted from a waveguide or resonator by means of either the electric or magnetic field. One type of adapter, shown in **Figure 15.76**, is a probe like a monopole antenna in the center of a wide wall of the waveguide. The probe in Figure 15.76A is simply a short extension of the inner conductor of the coaxial line, oriented so that it is parallel to the electric lines of force. If the probe were very thin and had no capacitance or inductance, it would be ¼ λ long and spaced ¼ λ from a short-circuit — the closed end of the waveguide. Actual dimensions compensate for the probe inductance and capacitance.

The loop shown in Figure 15.76B is arranged so that it encloses some of the magnetic lines of force. The point at which maximum coupling is obtained depends upon the mode of propagation in the guide or cavity. Coupling is maximum when the coupling device is in the most intense field.

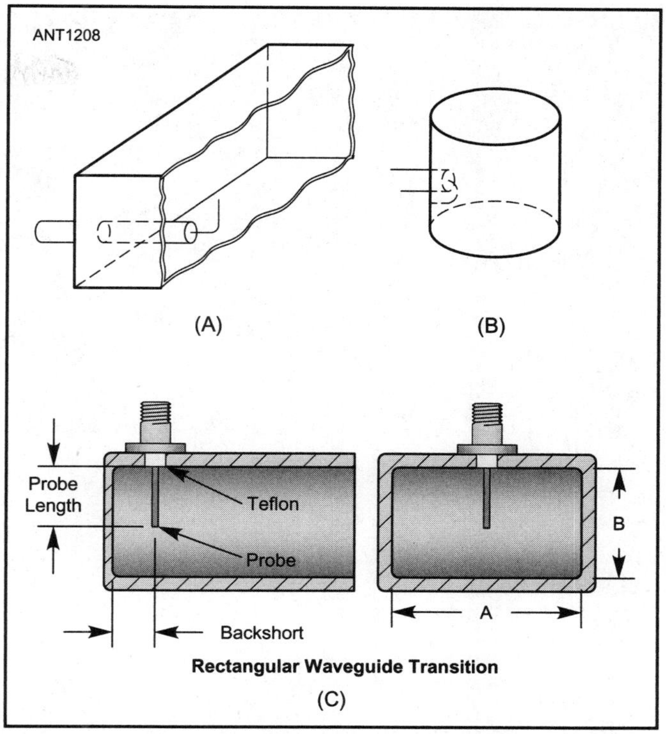

Figure 15.76 — Parts A and B shows methods of coupling coaxial line to waveguide and resonators. At C is a sketch of rectangular waveguide to coax transition, showing dimensions.

Coupling can be varied by turning the probe or loop through a 90° angle. When the probe is perpendicular to the electric lines the coupling is minimum. Similarly, when the plane of the loop is parallel to the magnetic lines the coupling is minimum.

Waveguide Termination

If a waveguide is not terminated in its characteristic impedance, there will be an elevated SWR on the line like any other transmission line. A typical termination is a horn antenna, which flares out from the end of the waveguide to match the waveguide's characteristic impedance to the impedance of free space, 377 Ω.

Waveguide connections are made by bolting their flanges together firmly. Several flanges are shown in **Figure 15.77**. There are two types of flanges, *flat flanges* and *choke flanges*, which have a groove around the waveguide. The groove acts like a shorted stub that presents a high impedance to the RF energy to prevent leakage. Choke flanges should be mated with flat flanges, but two flat flanges may be mated together.

Waveguides of two different sizes may be mated, but there should be a transition between them since different waveguide sizes have different Z_0. Just as in coaxial lines, impedance discontinuities such as at a transition will cause reflections.

Practical Waveguides

Standard waveguide sizes dating to World War II are

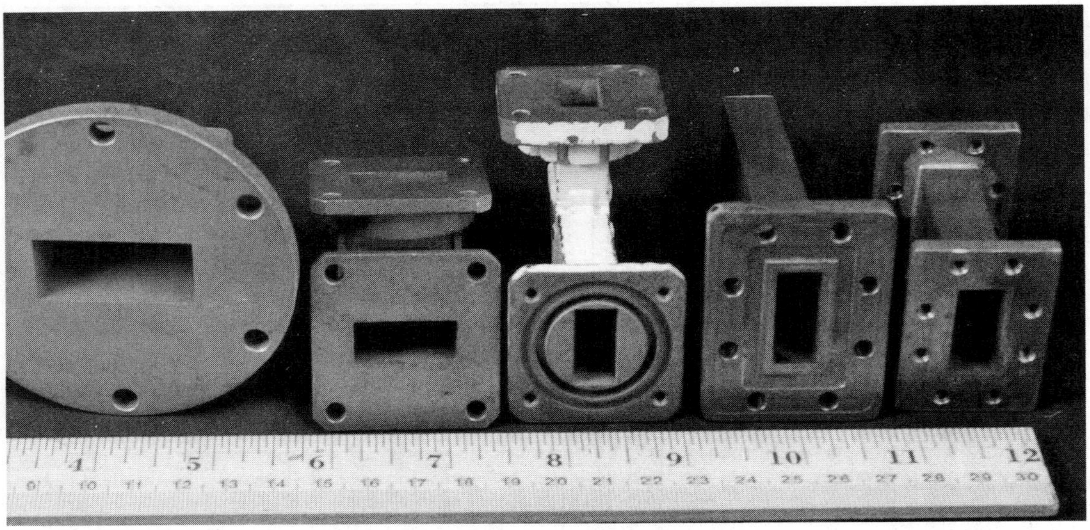

Figure 15.77 — Several typical waveguide flanges used for joining sections of waveguide. The deep grooves in choke flanges (see center flange) place a high-impedance in the path of any RF leakage out of the flange.

Table 15.27
Waveguide Dimensions and Coax Transitions

Waveguide	*Dimensions (mm)*	*Freq Range (GHz)*	*Freq (GHz)*	*Probe Diam. (mm)*	*Probe Length (mm)*	*Backshort (mm)*	*Bandwidth*
WR42	10.668×4.318	18-26.5	24.192	1.27	2.413	2.489	>17%
WR75	19.05×9.525	10.0-15	10.368	1.27	5.49	5.26	14%
WR90	22.86×10.16	8.2-12.4	10.368	1.27	5.89	5.46	7%
WR112	28.24×12.62	7.05-10	10.368	1.27	6.5	6.6	15%
WR112			5.76	1.27	8.8	9.8	7%
WR137	35.85×15.80	5.85-8.2	5.76	1.27	10.5	8.5	10%
WR159	40.39×20.19	4.9-7.05	5.76	1.27	11.17	10.0	11%
WR187	47.55×22.15	3.95-5.85	5.76	2.36	11.3	11.0	16%
WR187			3.456	2.36	14.5	18.0	5%
WR229	58.17×29.08	3.3-4.9	3.456	1.27	18.2	15.0	8%
WR229			3.456	2.36	17.4	15.06	11%
WR229			3.456	3.175	17	15.6	11%
WR229			3.456	4.76	16.2	16.2	14%
WR229			3.456	6.35	15.5	16.75	17%
WR284	72.14×34.04	2.6-3.95	3.456	6.35	17.5	17.8	27%
WR284			2.304	6.35	20	28	9%
WR340	86.36 43.18	2.2-3.2	2.304	6.35	25	23	11%

still in use today. The standard designator is WR*xx*, where *xx* is the wide inside dimension in hundredths of an inch; for instance, WR90, often used at 10 GHz, has a wide dimension of 90 hundredths of an inch, or 0.9 inches. There are no standards for circular waveguide, so common copper plumbing is often used — ¾ inch tubing works well at 10 GHz. Practical dimensions for standard waveguides at amateur microwave calling frequencies are shown in **Table 15.27**.

Table 15.27 includes dimensions for the waveguide sizes likely to be encountered in microwave work; while a waveguide would work very well at lower frequencies, it would be very large — one meter wide for the 2-meter band! The recommended frequency range for each type is also shown in the table. For narrowband amateur work, we can stretch the frequency range a bit to take advantage of available waveguide — some of the waveguide sizes are usable on more than one band. Many smaller size guides are used at mm-wave frequencies.

Losses in waveguide are very low, much less than coaxial transmission line, but not negligible at the higher frequencies. For example, WR90 loss is approximately 10 dB per 100 feet at 10 GHz. Power handling is not a problem; even the smallest waveguide is rated at far more than the amateur power limit.

Where the waveguide has to change direction, special fittings called *bends* are used, shown in **Figure 15.78**. These are constructed so that impedance discontinuities from the change in direction are minimized.

Waveguide transmission lines used outdoors will suffer from internal water condensation, like any closed metal container with temperature variations. Even a short length used in a portable station can collect condensation. Commercial installations often pressurize the waveguide with dry air. Otherwise, a drain hole should be provided at the lowest point of a run.

Figure 15.78 — Special sections called bends make right- and 45° angles to avoid introducing impedance discontinuities where the waveguide has to change direction.

15.7.3 HORN ANTENNAS

Horn antennas are an excellent choice for microwaves — they work well, are easy to build, and are almost foolproof. A horn antenna is the ideal choice for a rover station. It offers moderate gain in a small, rugged package with no adjustments needed, and has a wide enough beam to be easily pointed under adverse conditions. Larger horn antennas can provide higher gain, even enough for EME operation. For horns intended as feed horns for dishes and lenses, beam angle and phase center are more important than horn gain.

Horn Design

An antenna may be considered as a transformer from the impedance of a transmission line to the impedance of free space, 377 Ω. A common microwave transmission line is waveguide, a hollow tube carrying an electromagnetic wave. If one dimension of the tube is greater than one-half wavelength, then the wave can propagate through the waveguide with extremely low loss. If the end of a waveguide is simply left open, the wave will radiate out from the open end.

Practical waveguides have the larger dimension greater than one-half wavelength, to allow wave propagation, but smaller than one wavelength, to suppress higher-order modes which can interfere with low-loss transmission. Thus, the aperture of an open-ended waveguide is less than a wavelength, which does not provide much gain.

For more gain, a larger aperture is desirable, but a larger waveguide is not. However, if the waveguide size is slowly expanded, or tapered, into a larger aperture, then more gain is achieved while preventing undesired modes from reaching the waveguide. In common rectangular waveguide, the taper creates a familiar *pyramidal horn*, sketched in **Figure 15.79**. Horns come in many sizes, like those shown in the photograph, **Figure 15.80**. In cylindrical waveguide, a funnel-like taper is called a *conical horn*. The larger conical horn for 2304 MHz shown in Figure 15.80 was made by pop-riveting aluminum flashing to a coffee can. (See the article "How To Build A Tin Can Waveguide WiFi Antenna" by Gregory Rehm at **www.turnpoint.net/wireless/cantennahowto.html**. The

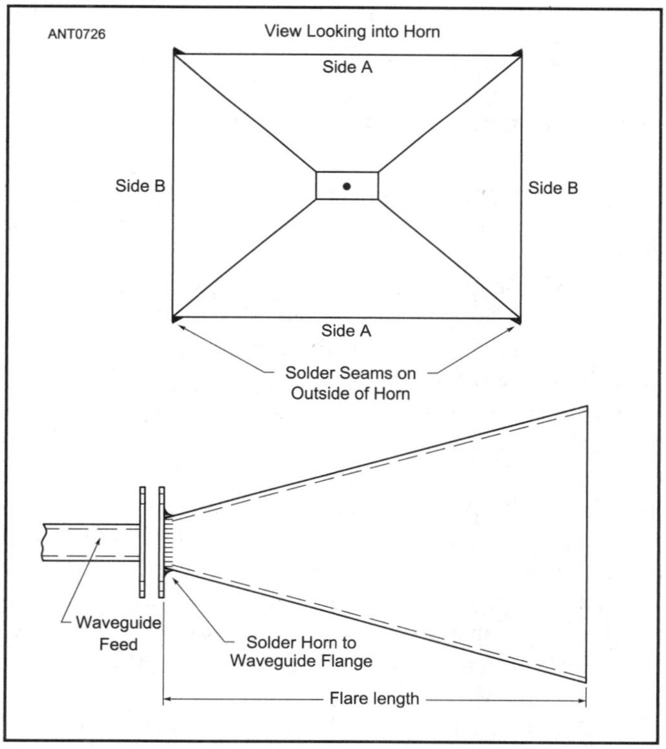

Figure 15.79 — Typical pyramidal horn. These assembly instructions are for the 10 GHz horn project shown in Figure 15.86.

Figure 15.80 — An assortment of horn antennas.

Table 15.28
Pyramidal Horn Dimensions

Gain (dB)	*Flare Length (λ)*	*A (H-plane) (λ)*	*B (E-plane) (λ)*
10	0.08	1.48	1.09
13	0.6	2.09	1.55
16	1.7	2.95	2.18
19	4	4.16	3.08
22	8.7	5.88	4.36
25	18.3	8.31	6.15

webpage includes a calculator for usable frequencies based on can diameter along with connector and coupling probe dimensions.)

To achieve maximum gain for a given aperture size, the taper must be long enough so that the phase of the wave is nearly constant across the aperture. An optimum horn is one that provides a specified gain with the least material; several definitions are available. The **Table 15.28** uses approximate dimensions from a set of tables by Cozzens to design pyramidal horn antennas with gains from 10 to 25 dB. (see Bibliography) Higher gains are possible, but the length of the horn increases much faster than the gain, so very high gain horns tend to be unwieldy.

The dimensions in Table 15.28 are in wavelengths, so they are applicable to any frequency. Horns are very forgiving, so the dimensions are not critical — small differences will result in a very small gain difference.

The radiation pattern of a horn antenna can be tailored for special purposes; for instance, a broad azimuth pattern with a narrow vertical pattern might be useful to cover a broad sector without needing rotation. In *Antennas* (see Bibliography) Kraus gives the following approximations for beamwidth in degrees and dBd gain (with respect to a dipole):

$$E_{plane} = \frac{56}{A_{e\lambda}} \text{ degrees} \qquad (13A)$$

$$H_{plane} = \frac{67}{A_{h\lambda}} \text{ degrees} \qquad (13B)$$

and for gain

$$G \cong 10 \log_{10} (4.5\, A_{e\lambda}\, A_{h\lambda}) \text{ dB over dipole} \qquad (14)$$

where $A_{e\lambda}$ is the aperture dimension in wavelengths in the E-plane and $A_{h\lambda}$ is the aperture in wavelengths dimension in the H-plane. Horns shorter than the optimum horns will have less gain than this equation.

Horn Construction

If you are fortunate enough to find a suitable surplus horn, then this section is unnecessary. Otherwise, you may want to homebrew one. Horn fabrication is quite simple, so we can homebrew them as needed, for primary antennas with moderate gain or as feeds for higher gain dishes and lenses. Performance of the finished horn almost always matches predictions, with no tuning adjustments required. The horns are broadband and dimensions are not critical.

Small horns may be constructed from sheet metal, from raw PC board material, or even machined from solid metal for extremely high microwave frequencies. (See sidebar on 3D-printing of microwave antennas.) Larger horns have been made from mesh screening and from foil-coated Styrofoam insulation.

A recent construction technique is 3D-printed horns. The printed plastic is transparent to RF, so the horn must be metalized. Glenn Robb, KS4VA, and Michelle Thompson, W5NYV, have worked to perfect the techniques. Some of Glenn's horn antennas are shown in **Figure 15.81**. See the "Microwavelengths" column in the January 2019 issue of *QST* for details.

Figure 15.82 is a template for a nominal 14 dB horn for 5760 MHz. **Figure 15.83** is another template example, a nominal 18 dB horn for 10,368 MHz. You can try it by making a photocopy of the template and folding it to see how easy it is to make a horn. It's almost as easy with thin copper. Flashing copper works well — the copper is taped to a template, cut

Figure 15.81 — 3D-printed horns before and after metalization.

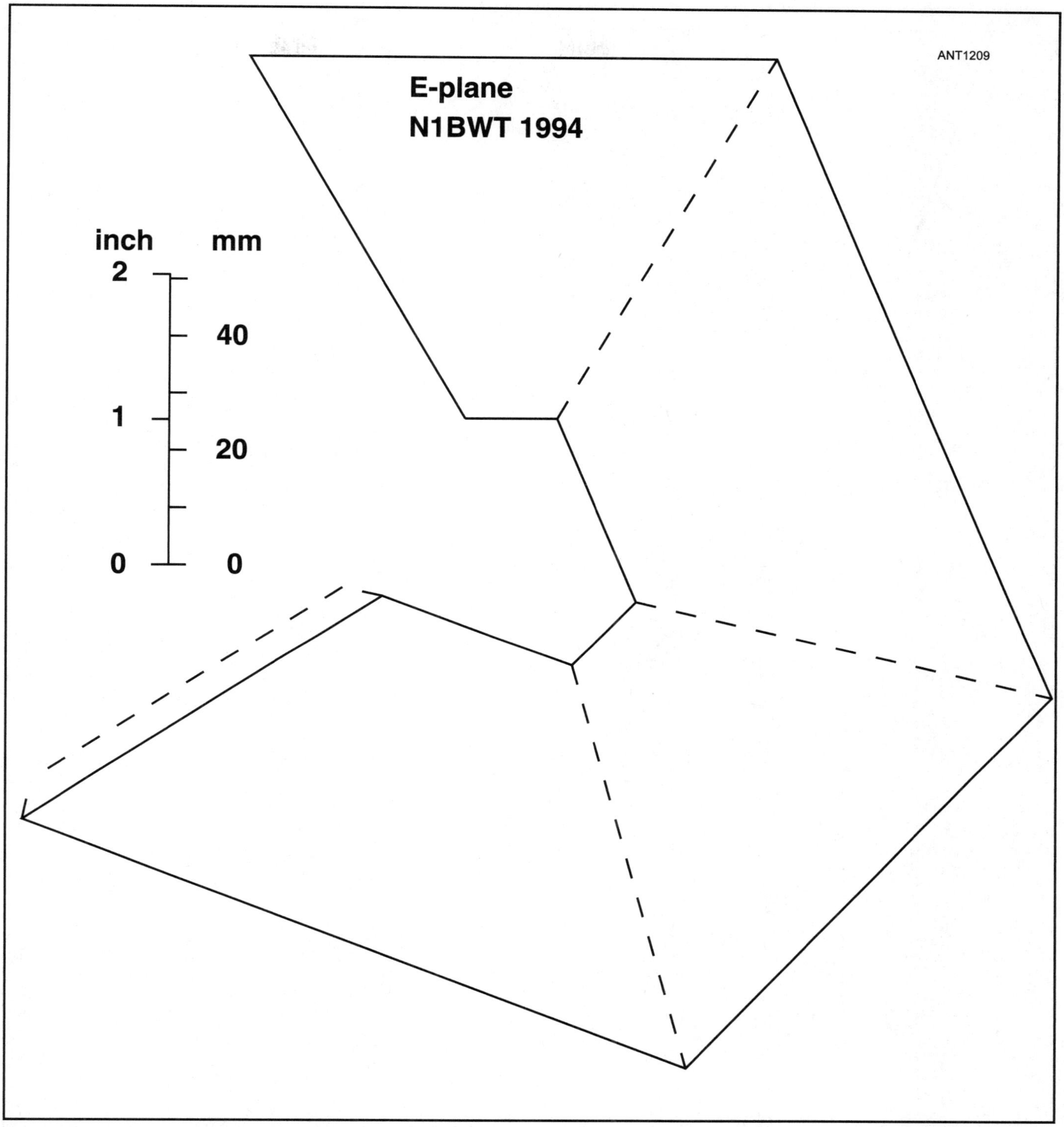

Figure 15.82 — Template for 13.84 dBi horn for 5760 MHz.

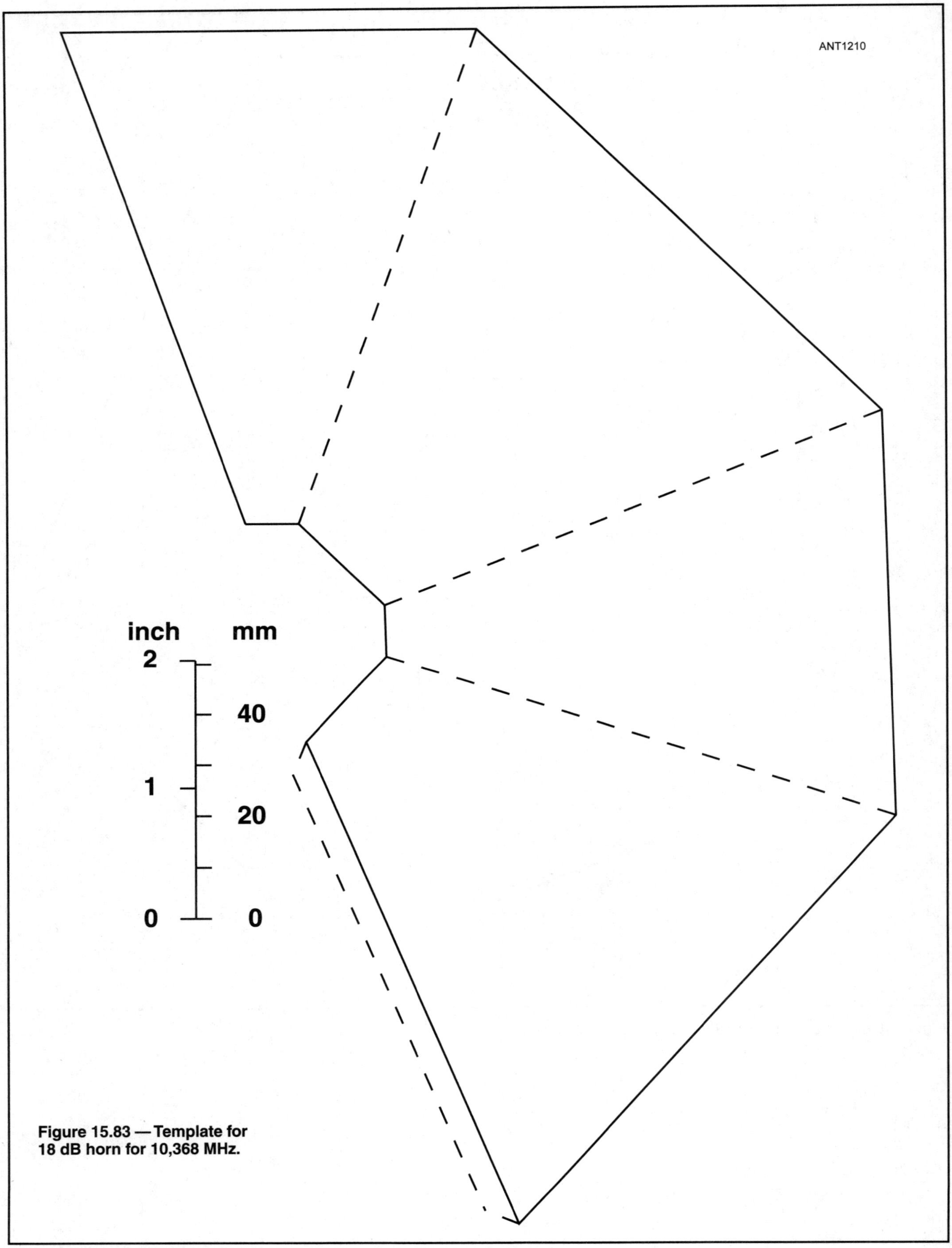

Figure 15.83 — Template for 18 dB horn for 10,368 MHz.

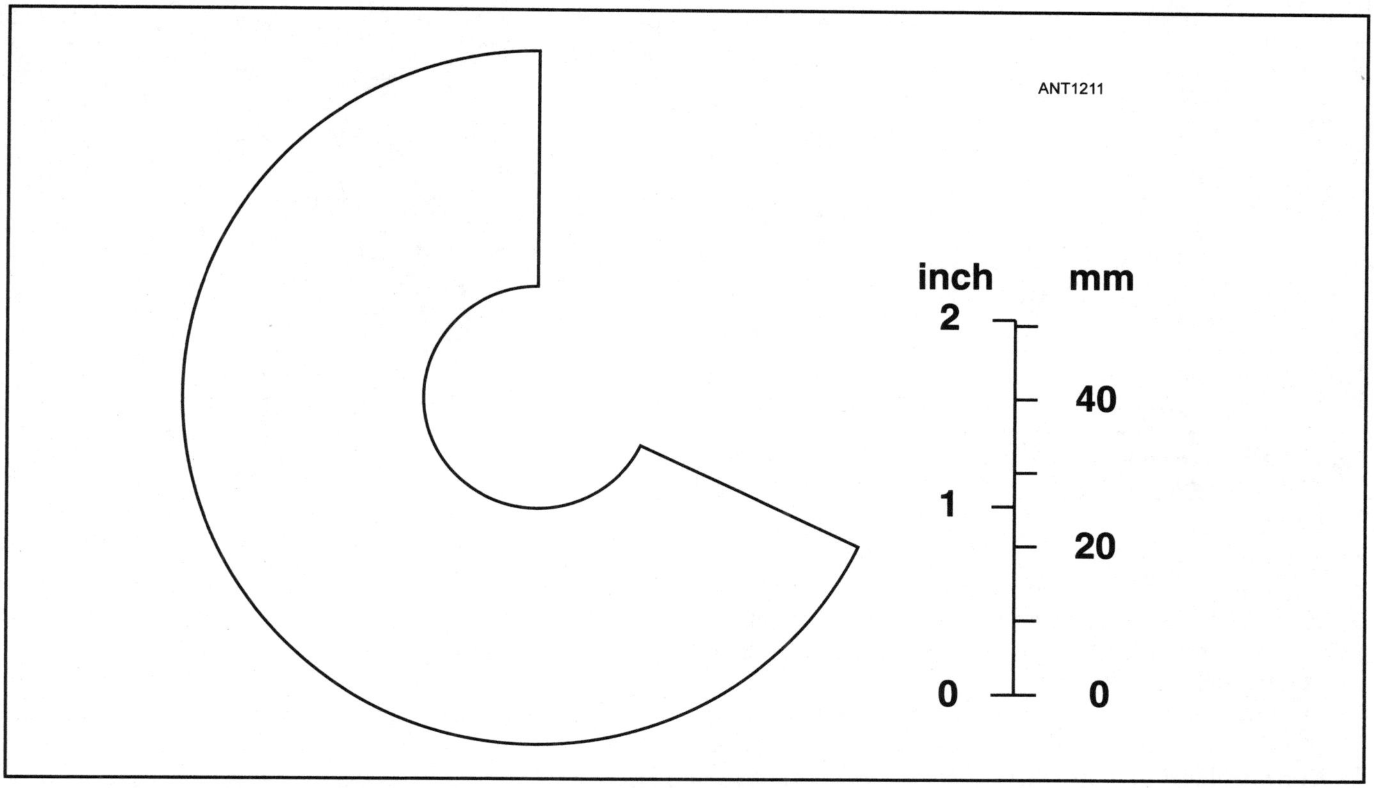

Figure 15.84 — Template for 14 dBi conical horn for 10,368 MHz.

out with tin snips, folded into a horn, and soldered to a bit of waveguide. If real waveguide is not available, another bit of copper can be folded into a homebrew waveguide. A homebrew waveguide to coax transition can be fabricated — see the preceding section on waveguides for dimensions. Waveguide flanges are not necessary, as the horn may be soldered directly to the waveguide or transition. Printed circuit board material also works well, with copper foil on one or both sides — only the inside needs to be soldered together.

Circular horns are also easy to make. **Figure 15.84** is a template for a conical horn with about 14 dB of gain at 10,368 MHz. Use the template as a guide to cut metal sheet. Then the ends are joined to make a funnel, and the smaller end attached to a circular waveguide. Copper water pipe is good for 10 GHz and 5760 MHz but heavy and expensive for lower frequencies. Ordinary tin cans make usable circular waveguide, and the horn can be aluminum flashing, with everything held together with pop rivets or screws. (See the earlier reference to Cantennas.)

Surplus horns may be found in many shapes and sizes; for instance, on satellite TV antennas and various WiFi devices. The key is the input waveguide size — if the diameter or large rectangular dimension is greater than 0.6 λ and less than 1 λ, the horn will work as an antenna, so it is worth a try.

A Horn Antenna for 10 GHz

The horn antenna is the easiest antenna for the beginner on 10 GHz to construct. It can be made out of readily available flat sheet brass. Because it is inherently a broadband structure, minor constructional errors can be tolerated. The one drawback is that horn antennas become physically cumbersome at gains over about 25 dBi, but for most line-of-sight operation this much gain is rarely necessary. This antenna was designed by Bob Atkins, KA1GT, and appeared in *QST* for April and May 1987.

There are many varieties of horn antennas. If the waveguide is flared out only in the H-plane, the horn is called an H-plane sectoral horn. Similarly, if the flare is only in the E-plane, an E-plane sectoral horn results. If the flare is in both planes, the antenna is called a pyramidal horn.

For a horn of any given aperture, directivity (gain along the axis) is maximum when the field distribution across the aperture is uniform in magnitude and phase. When the fields are not uniform, sidelobes that reduce the directivity of the antenna are formed. To obtain a uniform distribution, the horn should be as long as possible with minimum flare angle. From a practical point of view, however, the horn should be as short as possible, so there is an obvious conflict between performance and convenience.

Figure 15.85 illustrates this problem. For a given flare angle and a given side length, there is a path-length difference from the apex of the horn to the center of the aperture (L), and from the apex of the horn to the edge of the aperture (L′). This causes a phase difference in the field across the aperture, which in turn causes formation of sidelobes, degrading directivity (gain along the axis) of the antenna. If L is large this difference is small, and the field is almost uniform. As L decreases however, the phase difference increases

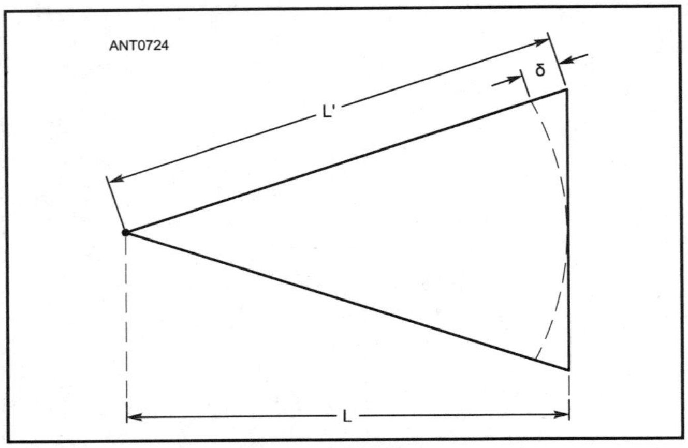

Figure 15.85 —The path-length (phase) difference between the center and edge of a horn antenna is δ.

Figure 15.86 — This pyramidal horn has 18.5 dBi gain at 10 GHz. Construction details are given in the text.

and directivity suffers. An optimum (shortest possible) horn is constructed so that this phase difference is the maximum allowable before sidelobes become excessive and axial gain markedly decreases.

The magnitude of this permissible phase difference is different for E-plane and H-plane horns. For the E-plane horn, the field intensity is quite constant across the aperture. For the H-plane horn, the field tapers to zero at the edge. Consequently, the phase difference at the edge of the aperture in the E-plane horn is more critical and should be held to less than 90° (¼ λ). In an H-plane horn, the allowable phase difference is 144° (0.4 λ). If the aperture of a pyramidal horn exceeds one wavelength in both planes, the E-plane and H-plane patterns are essentially independent and can be analyzed separately.

The usual direction for orienting the waveguide feed is with the broad face horizontal, giving vertical polarization. If this is the case, the H-plane sectoral horn has a narrow horizontal beamwidth and a very wide vertical beamwidth. This is not a very useful beam pattern for most amateur applications. The E-plane sectoral horn has a narrow vertical beamwidth and a wide horizontal beamwidth. Such a radiation pattern could be useful in a beacon system where wide coverage is desired.

The most useful form of the horn for general applications is the optimum pyramidal horn. In this configuration the two beamwidths are almost the same. The E-plane (vertical) beamwidth is slightly less than the H-plane (horizontal), and also has greater sidelobe intensity.

Building the Antenna

A 10-GHz pyramidal horn with 18.5 dBi gain is shown in **Figure 15.86**. The first design parameter is usually the required gain, or the maximum antenna size. These are of course related, and the relationships can be approximated by the following:

$$L = \text{H-plane length } (\lambda) = 0.0654 \times \text{gain} \quad (15)$$

$$A = \text{H-plane aperture } (\lambda) = 0.0443 \times \text{gain} \quad (16)$$

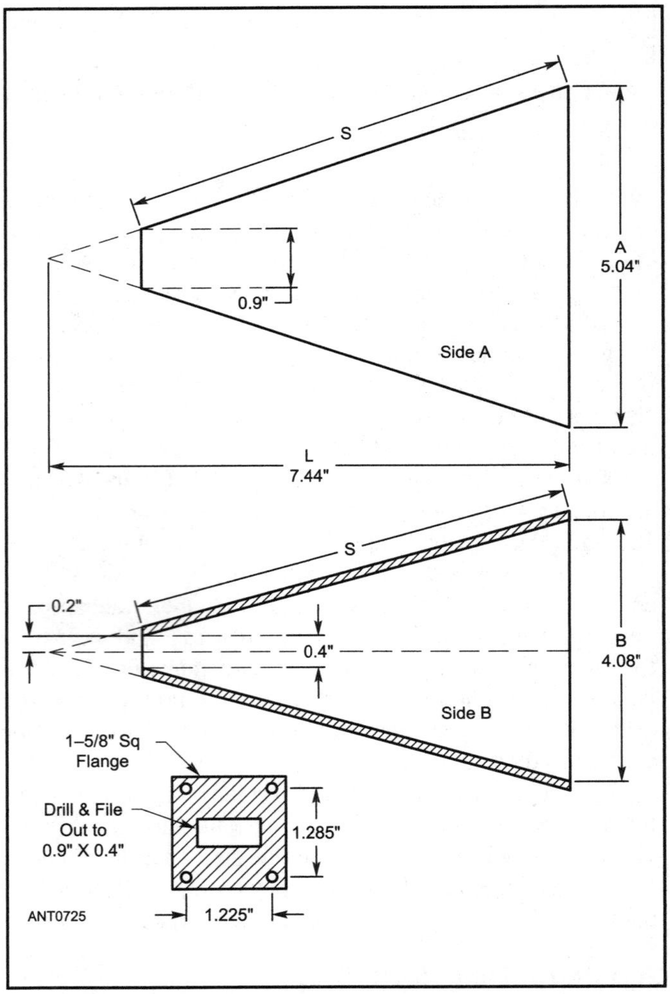

Figure 15.7 — Dimensions of the brass pieces used to make the 10-GHz horn antenna. Construction requires two of each of the triangular pieces (side A and side B).

B = E-plane aperture (λ) = 0.81 A (17)

where gain is expressed as a *ratio*; 20 dBi gain = 100, and L, A and B are dimensions shown in **Figure 15.87.**

From these equations, the dimensions for a 20-dBi gain horn for 10.368 GHz can be determined. One wavelength at 10.368 GHz is 1.138 inches. The length (L) of such a horn is 0.0654 × 100 = 6.54 λ. At 10.368 GHz, this is 7.44 inches. The corresponding H-plane aperture (A) is 4.43 λ (5.04 inches), and the E-plane aperture (B), 4.08 inches.

The easiest way to make such a horn is to cut pieces from brass sheet stock and solder them together. Figure 15.87 shows the dimensions of the triangular pieces for the sides and a square piece for the waveguide flange. (A standard commercial waveguide flange could also be used.) Because the E-plane and H-plane apertures are different, the horn opening is not square. Sheet thickness is unimportant; 0.02 to 0.03 inch works well. Brass sheet is often available from hardware or hobby shops.

Note that the triangular pieces are trimmed at the apex to fit the waveguide aperture (0.9 × 0.4 inch). This necessitates that the length, from base to apex, of the smaller triangle (side B) is shorter than that of the larger (side A). Note that the length, S, of the two different sides of the horn must be the same if the horn is to fit together! For such a simple looking object, getting the parts to fit together properly requires careful fabrication.

The dimensions of the sides can be calculated with simple geometry, but it is easier to draw out templates on a sheet of cardboard first. The templates can be used to build a mock antenna to make sure everything fits together properly before cutting the sheet brass.

First, mark out the larger triangle (side A) on cardboard. Determine at what point its width is 0.9 inch and draw a line parallel to the base as shown in Figure 15.87. Measure the length of the side S; this is also the length of the sides of the smaller (side B) pieces.

Mark out the shape of the smaller pieces by first drawing a line of length B and then constructing a second line of length S. One end of line S is an end of line B, and the other is 0.2 inch above a line perpendicular to the center of line B as shown in Figure 15.86. (This procedure is much more easily followed than described.) These smaller pieces are made slightly oversize (shaded area in Figure 15.87) so you can construct the horn with solder seams on the outside of the horn during assembly.

Cut out two cardboard pieces for side A and two for side B and tape them together in the shape of the horn. The aperture at the waveguide end should measure 0.9 × 0.4 inch and the aperture at the other end should measure 5.04 × 4.08 inches.

If these dimensions are correct, use the cardboard templates to mark out pieces of brass sheet. The brass sheet should be cut with a bench shear if one is available, because scissors type shears tend to bend the metal. Jig the pieces together and solder them on the *outside* of the seams. It is important to keep both solder and rosin from contaminating the inside of the horn; they can absorb RF and reduce gain at these frequencies.

Assemble as shown in Figure 15.79. When the horn is completed, it can be soldered to a standard waveguide flange, or one cut out of sheet metal as shown in Figure 15.87. The transition between the flange and the horn must be smooth. This antenna provides an excellent performance-to-cost ratio (about 20 dBi gain for about five dollars in parts).

15.7.4 PARABOLIC DISH ANTENNAS

Parabolic dish antennas can provide extremely high gains at microwave frequencies. A 2-foot dish at 10 GHz can provide more than 30 dB of gain. The gain is only limited by the size of the parabolic reflector; a number of hams have dishes larger than 20 feet, and occasionally a much larger commercial dish is made available for amateur operation. For example, the 1000-foot dish Arecibo dish in Puerto Rico has been operational on 432 MHz EME on a few occasions. High gains are only achievable if the antennas are properly implemented and dishes have more critical dimensions than horns and lenses. The fundamental parameters are explained here using pictures and graphics as an aid to understanding the critical areas and how to deal with them.

New commercial dishes are expensive, but surplus ones can often be purchased at low cost. Some amateurs build theirs, while others modify satellite TV dishes or even circular metal snow sleds for the amateur bands. **Figure 15.88** shows a dish using a homemade coffee-can feed described below.

Alternatives

Bear in mind that the narrow beamwidth of a dish may actually make contacts more difficult, particularly in windy conditions. It is often easier to complete a contact for all but

Figure 15.88 — Coffee-can 2304 MHz feed described in text and Figure 15.85 mounted on a 4-foot dish.

the longest paths with smaller, easier to point antennas, such as horns and flat panel antennas. As an extreme example, Rex Moncur, VK7MO, has made 10 GHz EME contacts with a horn antenna — DX doesn't get any farther than that.[1]

For a rover station, a reasonable size horn might be a good compromise with adequate gain and moderate beamwidth for easy aiming. I often use the 17.5 dBi Gunnplexer horn, with a 12-inch lens ready to place in front of it when signals are marginal.

Aiming

A quality compass and a way of accurately aligning a dish antenna to it are essential for successful operation. Narrow beamwidth and frequency uncertainty can make searching for weak signals frustrating and time-consuming. A heavy tripod with setting circles is a good start; hang a heavy object like a portable station operating battery from the center of the tripod and it will be more stable, especially in the wind. Calibrate your headings by locating a station with a known beam heading rather than by eyeballing the dish heading; small mechanical tolerances can easily shift the beam a few degrees from the apparent *boresight* (the line along which the dish is aimed).

Dish Antenna Design

A dish antenna works the same way as a reflecting optical telescope. Electromagnetic waves, either light or radio, arrive as parallel rays (or planar wavefronts) from a distant source and are reflected by a parabolic mirror to a common point, called the *focus*. When a ray of light reflects from a mirror or flat surface, the angle of the path leaving (angle of reflection) is the same as the angle of the path arriving (angle of incidence). If the mirror is a flat surface, then two rays of light leave in parallel paths; however, if the mirror is curved, two parallel incident rays leave at different angles. If the curve is parabolic ($y = ax^2$) then all the reflected rays meet at one point, as shown in **Figure 15.89**. A dish is a *parabola of rotation*, a parabolic curve rotated around an axis which passes through the focus and the center of the curve.

A transmitting antenna reverses the path: The light or radio wave originates from a point source at the focus and is reflected into a beam of rays parallel to the axis of the parabola, as shown in Figure 15.89.

There are two basic types of parabolic dishes: *prime-focus* dishes, the classic shape, and *offset-fed* dishes, like the popular small satellite TV dishes. While almost all offset-fed dishes that you are likely to find have the same basic geometry, prime-focus dishes come in various configurations, from very deep dishes to shallow ones. They are characterized by the *f/D ratio*, the ratio of focal length of the parabola to its diameter. Deep dishes (such as a soup bowl) have a small f/D, less than about 0.35, while shallow dishes (such as a dinner plate) have larger a f/D and thus a larger focal length for a given diameter. All dishes with the same f/D have the same geometry, regardless of size, which simplifies antenna system design.

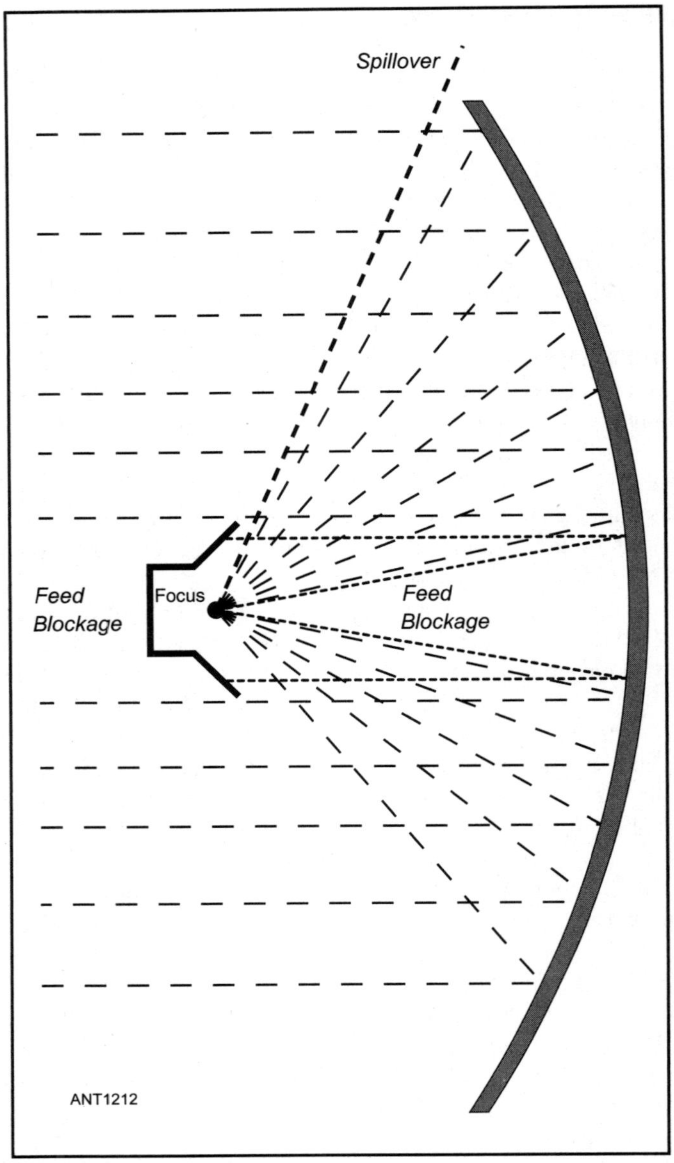

Figure 15.89 — Geometry of parabolic dish antenna.

Illuminating the Dish

Some of the difficulties found in real antennas are easier to understand when considering a transmitting antenna but are also present in receiving antennas, since antennas are reciprocal. One difficulty is finding a point source, since any antenna, even a half-wave dipole at 10 GHz, is much bigger than a point. (A point source is equivalent to the *isotropic radiator* used as a reference for specifying gain.) Even if we were able to find a point source, it would radiate equally in all directions, so the energy that was not radiated toward the reflector would be wasted. The energy radiated from the focus toward the reflector illuminates the reflector, just as a light bulb would. What we are looking for is a point source that illuminates only the reflector, without any spillover missing the reflector or aimed away from the dish entirely.

Aperture, Gain, and Efficiency

The aperture, A, of a dish antenna is the area of the reflector as seen by a passing radio wave:

$$A = \pi r^2$$

where r is the radius, half of the dish diameter.

If the dish antenna is replaced with a much larger one, the greater aperture of the larger dish captures much more of the passing radio wave, so larger dish has more gain than the smaller one. From a little geometry, we find that the gain is proportional to the aperture area.

The gain of a dish with reference to an isotropic radiator is calculated as:

$$G_{dB} = 10\log_{10}\left(\eta\frac{4\pi}{\lambda^2}A\right) \quad (18)$$

where η is the efficiency of the antenna.

How much efficiency should be expected? References suggest that 55% is reasonable and 70 to 80% is possible with very good feeds. These values are possible with large dishes, > 25 λ in diameter, but many amateur dishes are relatively small. Realizing an efficiency greater than 50% is difficult for small dishes, and efficiency decreases further for diameters less than 10 λ.

See **Table 15.29** for parabolic antenna gain for the bands 420 MHz through 10 GHz and diameters of 2 to 30 feet.

A close approximation of beamwidth may be found from

$$\psi = \frac{70\lambda}{D} \quad (19)$$

where

ψ = beamwidth in degrees at half-power points (3 dB down)

D = dish diameter in feet

λ = wavelength in feet

Practical Dish Antennas

Feed Patterns

The parabolic dish antenna was first described with a point source at the focus so that energy would radiate with uniform magnitude and phase in all directions. The problem is that energy not radiated toward the reflector is wasted. What is desired is a feed antenna that only radiates toward the reflector and has a phase pattern that appears to radiate from a single point.

We have already seen that efficiency is a measure of how well the aperture is used. If the whole reflector is illuminated, then we should be using the whole aperture. Perhaps the feed pattern should be as shown in **Figure 15.90**, with uniform feed illumination across the reflector. Looking more closely at the parabolic surface, the focus is farther from the edge of the reflector than from the center. Since radiated power diminishes with the square of the distance (inverse-square law), less energy is arriving at the edge of the reflector than at the center; this is commonly called *space attenuation* or *space taper*. In order to compensate, more power must be provided to the edge of the dish than in the center. This is done by adjusting the feed pattern as shown in **Figure 15.91** in order to have constant illumination over the surface of the reflector.

Simple feed antennas, like a circular horn (coffee-can feed) used by many hams, have a $\cos^n(\theta)$ pattern like the idealized pattern shown in **Figure 15.92. Figure 15.93** superimposes the ideal pattern on our desired pattern; there is too much energy in the center, not enough at the edges, and some

Table 15.29
Gain, Parabolic Antennas*

	Dish Diameter (Feet)						
Frequency	*2*	*4*	*6*	*10*	*15*	*20*	*30*
420 MHz	6.0	12.0	15.5	20.0	23.5	26.0	29.5
902	12.5	18.5	22.0	26.5	30.0	32.5	36.0
1215	15.0	21.0	24.5	29.0	32.5	35.0	38.5
2300	20.5	26.5	30.0	34.5	38.0	40.5	44.0
3300	24.0	30.0	33.5	37.5	41.5	43.5	47.5
5650	28.5	34.5	38.0	42.5	46.0	48.5	52.0
10 GHz	33.5	39.5	43.0	47.5	51.0	53.5	57.0

*Gain over an isotropic antenna (subtract 2.1 dB for gain over a dipole antenna). Reflector efficiency of 55% assumed.

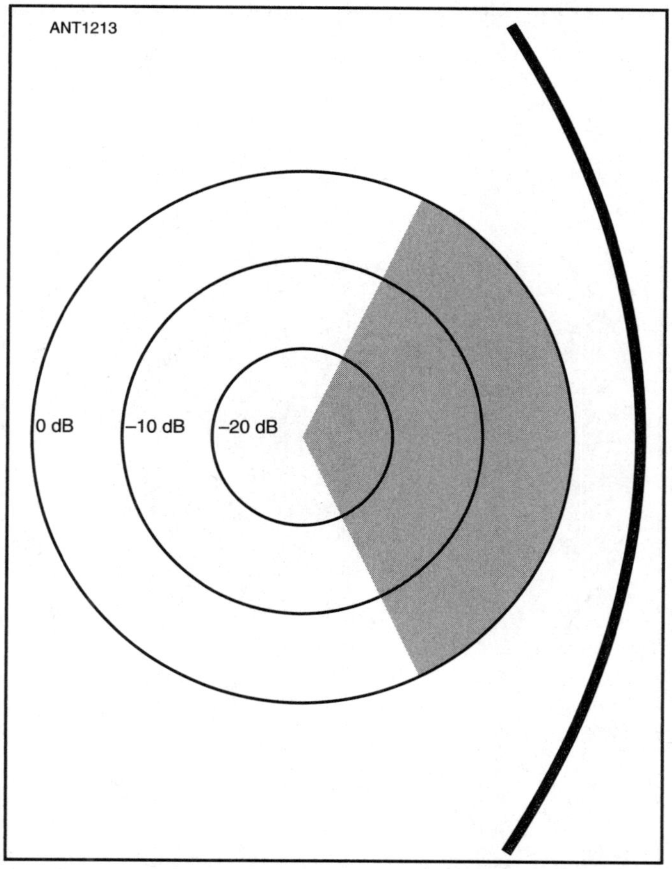

Figure 15.90 — Parabolic dish antenna with uniform feed illumination.

misses the reflector entirely. The missing energy at the edges is called *illumination loss* and the energy that misses the reflector is called *spillover loss*. The more energy we have at the edge, the more spillover we have, but if we reduce spillover, then the outer part of the dish is not well illuminated and is not contributing to the gain. Therefore, simple horn feeds are not ideal for dish feeds (although they are useful). In order to have very efficient dish illumination we need to increase energy near the edge of the dish and have the energy drop off very quickly beyond the edge.

Edge Taper

Almost all feed horns will provide less energy at the edge of dish than at the center, as in Figure 15.92. The difference in power at the edge is referred to as the *edge taper*. With different feed horns, edge taper can be varied. Different edge tapers produce different amounts of illumination loss and spillover loss, as shown in **Figure 15.94**: a small edge taper results in larger spillover loss, while a large edge taper reduces the spillover loss at the expense of increased illumination loss.

Plotting these losses versus the energy at the edge of the dish in **Figure 15.95**, we find that the total efficiency of a dish antenna peaks with an illumination taper, like Figure 15.94, so that the energy at the edge is about 10 dB lower than the energy at the center. This is often referred to as 10 dB edge

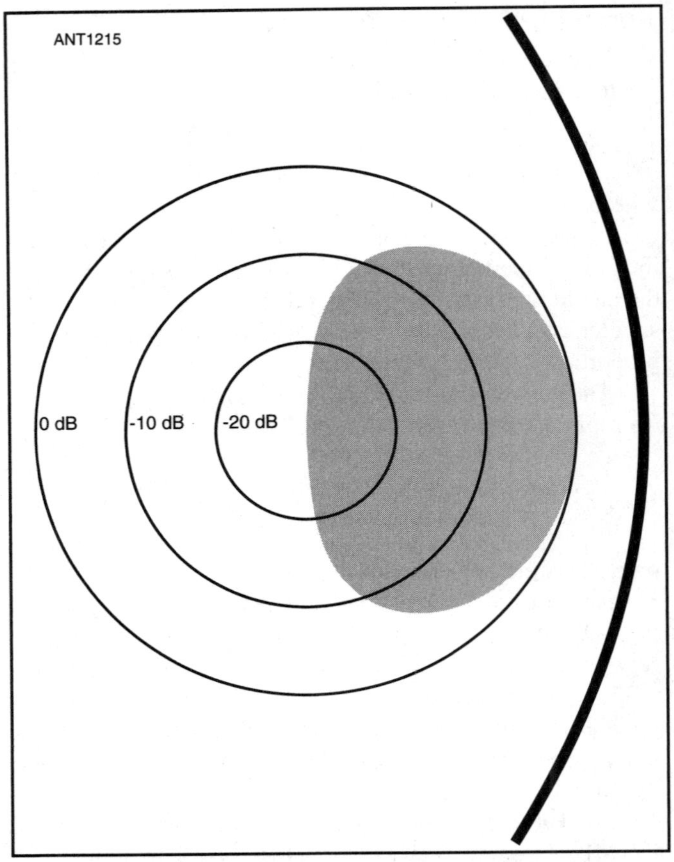

Figure 15.92 — Parabolic dish antenna with typical feed horn illumination.

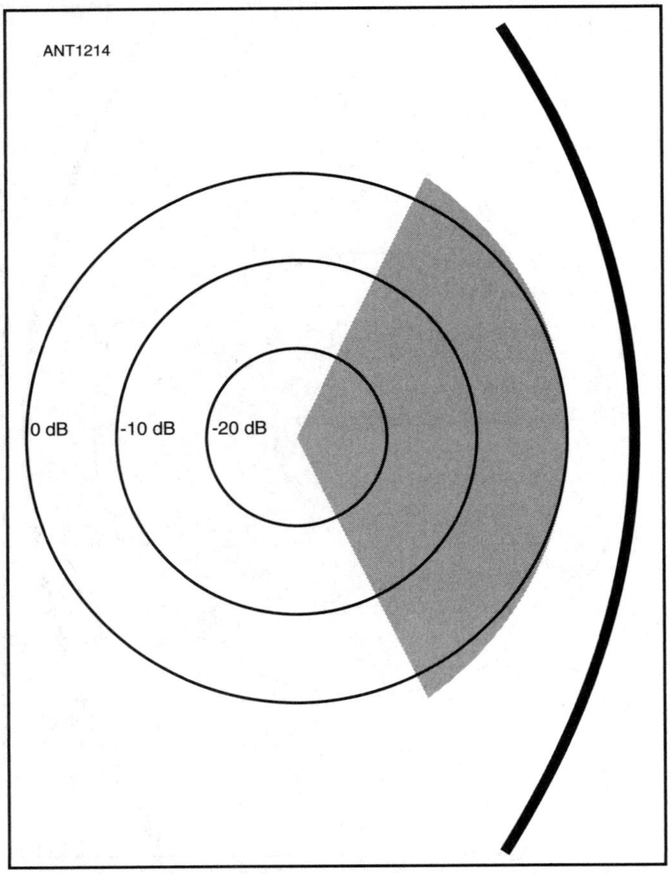

Figure 15.91 — Desired dish illumination - uniform reflector illumination.

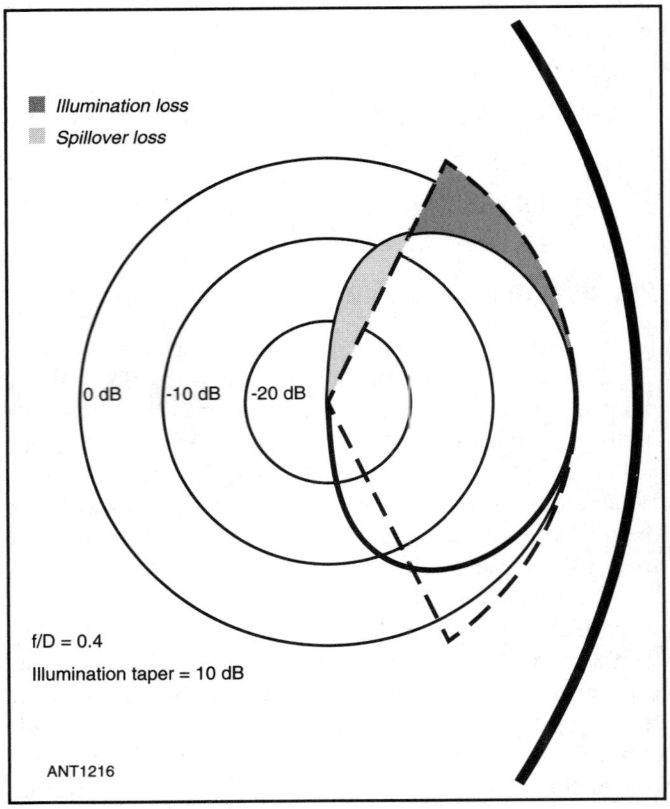

Figure 15.93 — Typical vs. desired dish illumination.

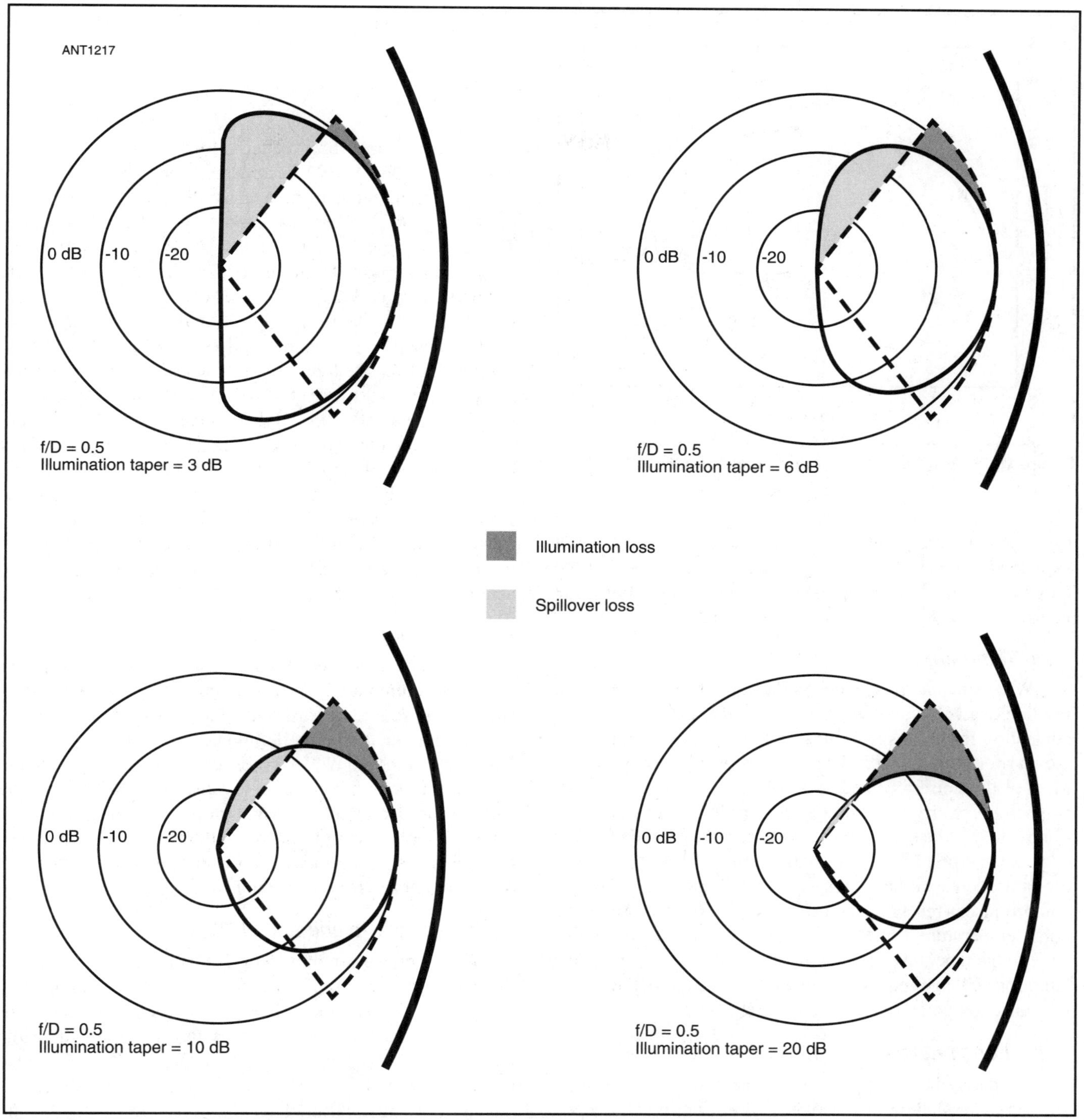

Figure 15.94 — Dish illumination with various illumination tapers.

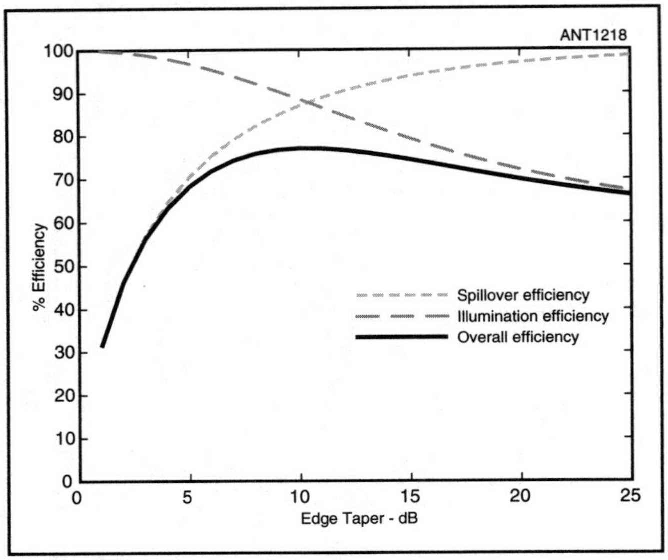

Figure 15.95 — Efficiency vs. edge taper for a dish.

taper or edge illumination — often recommended but not explained. However, some high-efficiency feeds shape the radiation pattern for maximum dish performance. For these feeds, the best edge taper may not be 10 dB.

Gain/Temperature (G/T)

When an antenna is receiving a signal from space, like a satellite or EME signal, there is very little background noise emanating from the sky compared to the noise generated by the warm (300° K) earth during terrestrial communications. Most of the noise received by an antenna pointed at the sky is *earth noise* arriving through feed spillover. As we saw in Figure 15.94, the spillover can be reduced by increasing the edge taper, while Figure 15.95 shows the efficiency, and thus the gain, decreasing slowly as edge taper is increased. The best compromise is reached when *G/T*, the ratio of gain to antenna noise temperature, is maximized. This typically occurs with a larger edge taper than for maximum gain. The optimum edge taper for G/T is a function of receiver noise temperature and sky noise temperature at any given frequency.

Focal Length and f/D Ratio

All parabolic dishes have the same parabolic curvature, but some are shallow dishes while others are much deeper, more like a bowl. They are just different parts of a parabola which extends to infinity. A convenient way to describe how much of the parabola is used is the *f*/D ratio, the ratio of the *focal length*, f, to the diameter, D, of the dish. All dishes with the same f/D ratio require the same feed geometry, in proportion to the diameter of the dish. The figures so far have depicted one arbitrary f/D: **Figure 15.96** shows the relative geometries for commonly used f/D ratios, typically from 0.25 to 0.65, with the desired and idealized feed patterns for each.

To calculate the focal length and f/D ratio of a dish, measure the diameter of the dish and the depth, d, in the center of the dish. This may need to be an approximation for some dishes, due to holes or flat areas in the center. The focal length is calculated as:

$$f = \frac{D^2}{16d} \qquad (20)$$

Notice the feed horn patterns for the various f/D ratios in Figure 15.96. As f/D becomes smaller, the feed pattern to illuminate it becomes broader so different feed horns are needed to properly illuminate dishes with different f/D ratios. The feed horn pattern must be matched to the reflector's f/D. Dishes with larger f/D ratios need a feed horn with a moderate beamwidth, while a dish with an f/D of 0.25 has its focus level with the edge of the dish and the subtended angle that must be illuminated is 180 degrees. Also, the edge of the dish is twice as far from the focus as the center of the dish, so the desired pattern would have to be 6 dB stronger (according to the inverse-square law) at the edge as in the center. This is an extremely difficult feed pattern to generate, and consequently, it is almost impossible to efficiently illuminate a dish this deep.

Given a choice, a reflector with a large f/D (0.5 to 0.6) would be preferable. As described earlier, dishes with small f/D are hard to illuminate efficiently, and are more sensitive to focal length errors. On the other hand, a dish that is available for the right price is always a good starting point!

Phase Center

A well-designed feed for a dish or lens has a single *phase center*, so illuminating radiation appears to emanate from a single point source, at least in the feed's main beam which is the part of the pattern that illuminates the dish or lens. Away from the main beam, the phase center may move around and appear at multiple points because stray reflections and surface currents affect the radiation pattern. Also, the phase center will move with frequency, adding difficulty to broadband feed design. Fortunately, amateur microwave operation only uses narrow frequency ranges.

Symmetry of E-plane and H-Plane

On paper, we can only depict radiation in one plane. For a simple antenna with linear polarization, like a dipole, this is all we really care about. A dish, however, is three-dimensional, so it must be fed uniformly in all planes. The usual plane for linear polarization is the E-plane, while the plane perpendicular to it is the H-plane. Unfortunately, most antennas not only have different radiation patterns in the E- and H- planes but also have different phase centers in each plane, so both phase centers cannot be at the focus. A good feed antenna has the same phase center in both E- and H- planes and all other planes.

Focal Length Error

The most critical dimension in a dish antenna is the focal length — the axial distance from the feed to the center of the dish. **Figure 15.97** shows the loss as the feed horn is moved closer and farther from the focus for various f/D dishes with uniform illumination; the tapered illumination used in practice will not have nulls as deep as these curves. It is clear that

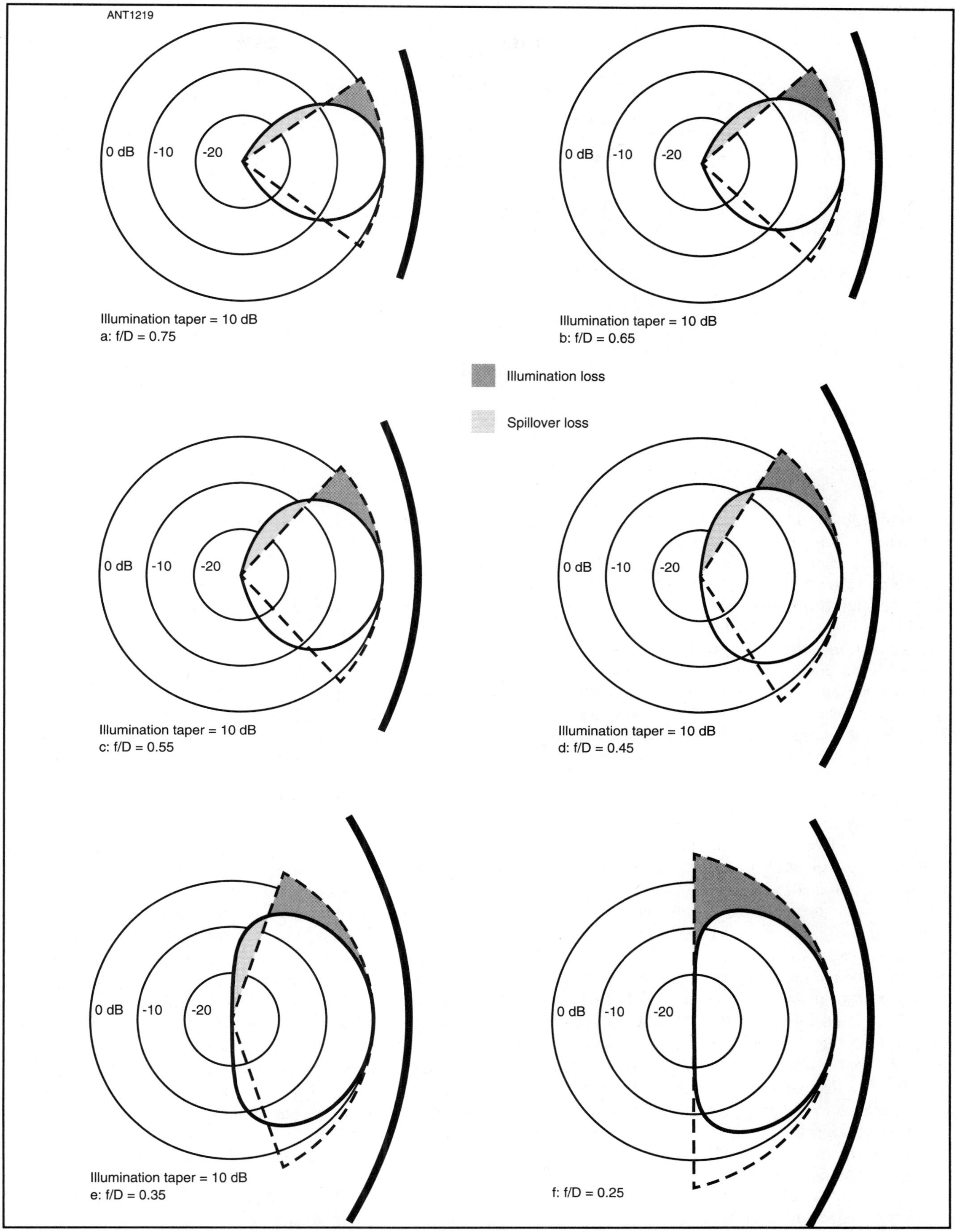

Figure 15.96 — Dish illumination for various f/D ratios.

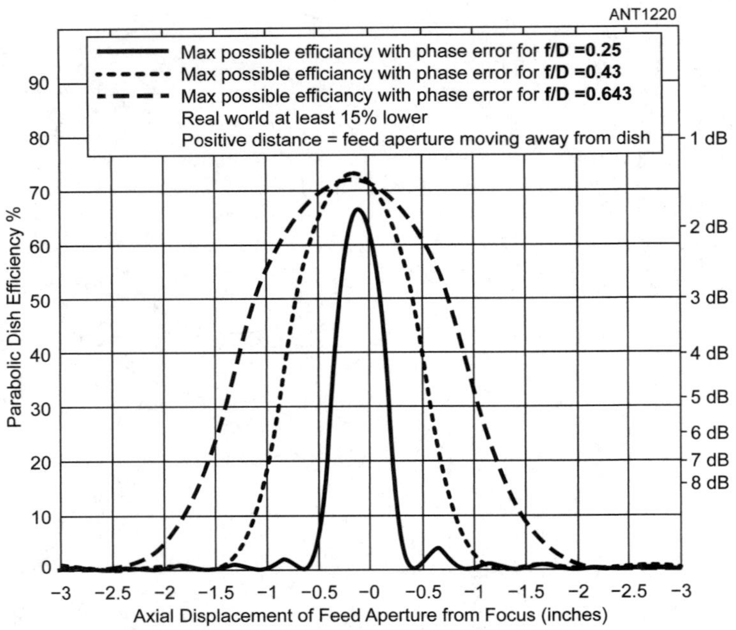

Figure 15.97 — Maximum efficiency versus phase error.

dishes with small f/D are much more sensitive to focal length error. Remember that a wavelength at 10 GHz is just over an inch! Lateral errors in feed horn position are far less serious; small errors have little effect on gain, but do result in shifting the beam slightly off boresight.

Notice that the focal length error in Figure 15.97 is in *wavelengths*, independent of the dish size. A 1/4-wavelength error in focal length produces the same loss for a 150-foot dish as for a 2-foot dish, and a 1/4-wavelength at 10 GHz is just over 1/4 inch. Another implication is that multiband feeds should be optimized for the highest band, since they will be less critical at lower bands with longer wavelengths.

Total Efficiency

We want high efficiency because a dish has the same size, wind loading, and narrow beamwidth regardless of efficiency — we should get as much performance as possible for these operational difficulties.

The major factors affecting aperture efficiency are illumination taper and spillover, but there are several other factors that can significantly reduce efficiency. Because the feed horn and its supporting structures are in the beam of the dish, part of the radiation is blocked or deflected. A real feed horn also has sidelobes, so part of its radiation is in undesired directions and thus wasted. Finally, no reflector is a perfect parabola, so the focusing of the beam is not perfect. The result is quite a list of contributions to total efficiency:

- Illumination taper
- Spillover loss
- Asymmetries in E- and H-Planes
- Focal point error
- Feed horn sidelobes
- Blockage by the feed horn
- Blockage by supporting structures
- Imperfections in parabolic surface.
- Feed line loss

The most critical are:

Focal point error — the phase center of the feed must be at the focal point of the parabolic reflector. Errors here can add up to many dB.

Feed illumination — the feed must efficiently illuminate the reflector. The difference between a good feed and a poor one can be a few dB.

Everything else is a matter of good engineering practice. Shortcuts might only cost a few tenths of a dB, but a few of them can add up.

Practical Feed Systems

An optimum feed would approximate the desired feed pattern for the f/D of the parabolic reflector in both planes and have the same phase center in both planes.

The feed aperture is located at the focal point of the dish and aimed at the center of the reflector. The feed mounts should permit adjustment of the aperture either side of the focal point and should present a minimum of blockage to the reflector. Correct distance to the dish center places the focal point about 1 inch inside the feed aperture. The use of a non-metallic support minimizes blockage. PVC pipe, fiberglass and Plexiglas are commonly used materials. A simple test by placing a material in a microwave oven reveals if it is satisfactory up to 2450 MHz. PVC pipe has tested satisfactorily and appears to work well at 2300 MHz. A simple, clean looking mount for a 4-foot dish with 18 inches focal length, for example, can be made by mounting a length of 4-inch PVC pipe using a PVC flange at the center of the dish. At 2304 MHz the circular feed is approximately 4 inches ID, making a snug fit with the PVC pipe. Precautions should be taken to keep rain and small birds from entering the feed.

Circular Feed

One of the simplest feed horns for a prime-focus dish is a plain cylindrical waveguide. (Rectangular waveguide feeds can also be used, but dish illumination is not as uniform as with round guide feeds.) A circular feed can be made of copper, brass, aluminum, or even tin cans. The circular feed must be within a proper diameter range for the frequency being used. This feed operates in the circular waveguide's dominant TE mode. The guide must be large enough to pass the mode with no attenuation, but smaller than the diameter that permits the next higher mode to propagate. To support the desirable mode in circular waveguide, the cutoff frequency, F_c, is given by

$$f_c\,(TE_{11}) = \frac{6917.26}{d\text{ (inches)}} \qquad (21)$$

where

f_c = cutoff frequency in MHz for mode
d = waveguide inner diameter

Circular waveguide will support the mode having a cutoff frequency

$$f_c\,(TM_{01}) = \frac{9034.85}{d\text{ (inches)}} \qquad (22)$$

The wavelength in a waveguide always exceeds the free-space wavelength and is called guide wavelength, λ_g. It is related to the cutoff frequency and operating frequency by the equation

$$\lambda_g = \frac{11802.85}{\sqrt{f_0^{\,2} - f_C^{\,2}}} \qquad (23)$$

where

λ_g = guide wavelength, inches
f_0 = operating frequency, MHz
f_C = waveguide cutoff frequency, MHz

An inside diameter range of about 0.66 to 0.76 λ is suggested. The lower frequency limit (longer dimension) is dictated by proximity to the cutoff frequency. The higher frequency limit (shorter dimension) is dictated by higher order waves. See **Table 15.30** for recommended inside diameter dimensions for the 902 MHz to 10 GHz amateur bands.

The probe that excites the waveguide and makes the transition from coaxial cable to waveguide is ¼ λ long and spaced from the closed end of the guide by ¼ guide wavelength. The length of the feed should be 2 to 3 guide wavelengths. The latter is preferred if a second probe is to be mounted for polarization change or for *polaplexer* operation where duplex communication (simultaneous transmission and reception) is possible because of the isolation between two properly located and oriented probes. The second probe for polarization switching or polaplexer operation should be spaced ¾ guide wavelength from the closed end and mounted at right angles to the first probe. (A polaplexer is a polarization-based diplexer antenna, or antenna feed, which supports two simultaneous inputs or outputs that are independent and isolated from each other by use of orthogonal (at right angles) linear polarization. (See the article by Munn listed in the Bibliography.)

Table 15.31 gives the subtended angle at focus for dish f/D ratios from 0.2 to 1.0. A dish, for example, with a typical f/D of 0.4 requires a 10-dB beamwidth of 130°. A circular waveguide feed with a diameter of approximately 0.7 λ provides nearly optimum illumination, but does not uniformly illuminate the reflector in both the magnetic (TM) and electric (TE) planes. **Figure 15.98** shows data for plotting radiation patterns from circular guides. The waveguide feed aperture can be modified to change the beamwidth.

At 1296 and 2304 MHz, coffee cans are roughly the right diameter, roughly 0.71 λ, and have been frequently used as a feed horn. These simple feeds work reasonably well, but the performance can be significantly improved by adding a choke ring which shapes the feed radiation pattern for better dish illumination. A sketch is shown in **Figure 15.99**.

A version of the choke ring popularized by Barry Malowanchuk, VE4MA, has a choke depth, C, of ½ λ and choke diameter, B, of one λ greater than the horn diameter, A. However, the dimensions which offer best performance are a choke depth of 0.45 λ and a choke width of 1.2 λ greater than the horn diameter. The choke position may be adjusted to optimize the horn projection for different f/D — the horn projection should be larger for small f/D. The phase center of these feeds is very close to the center of the aperture of the central horn. Patch antennas have also been used as

Table 15.30
Circular Waveguide Dish Feeds

Freq. (MHz)	*Inside Diameter Circular Waveguide Range (inches)*
915	8.52-9.84
1296	6.02-6.94
2304	3.39-3.91
3400	2.29-2.65
5800	1.34-1.55
10,250	0.76-0.88

Table 15.31
f/D Versus Subtended Angle at Focus of a Parabolic Reflector Antenna

f/D	*Subtended Angle (Deg.)*	*f/D*	*Subtended Angle (Deg.)*
0.20	203	0.65	80
0.25	181	0.70	75
0.30	161	0.75	69
0.35	145	0.80	64
0.40	130	0.85	60
0.45	117	0.90	57
0.50	106	0.95	55
0.55	97	1.00	52
0.60	88		

Taken from graph "f/D vs Subtended Angle at Focus," page 170 of the 1966 *Microwave Engineers' Handbook and Buyers Guide*. Graph courtesy of K. S. Kelleher, Aero Geo Astro Corp, Alexandria, Virginia

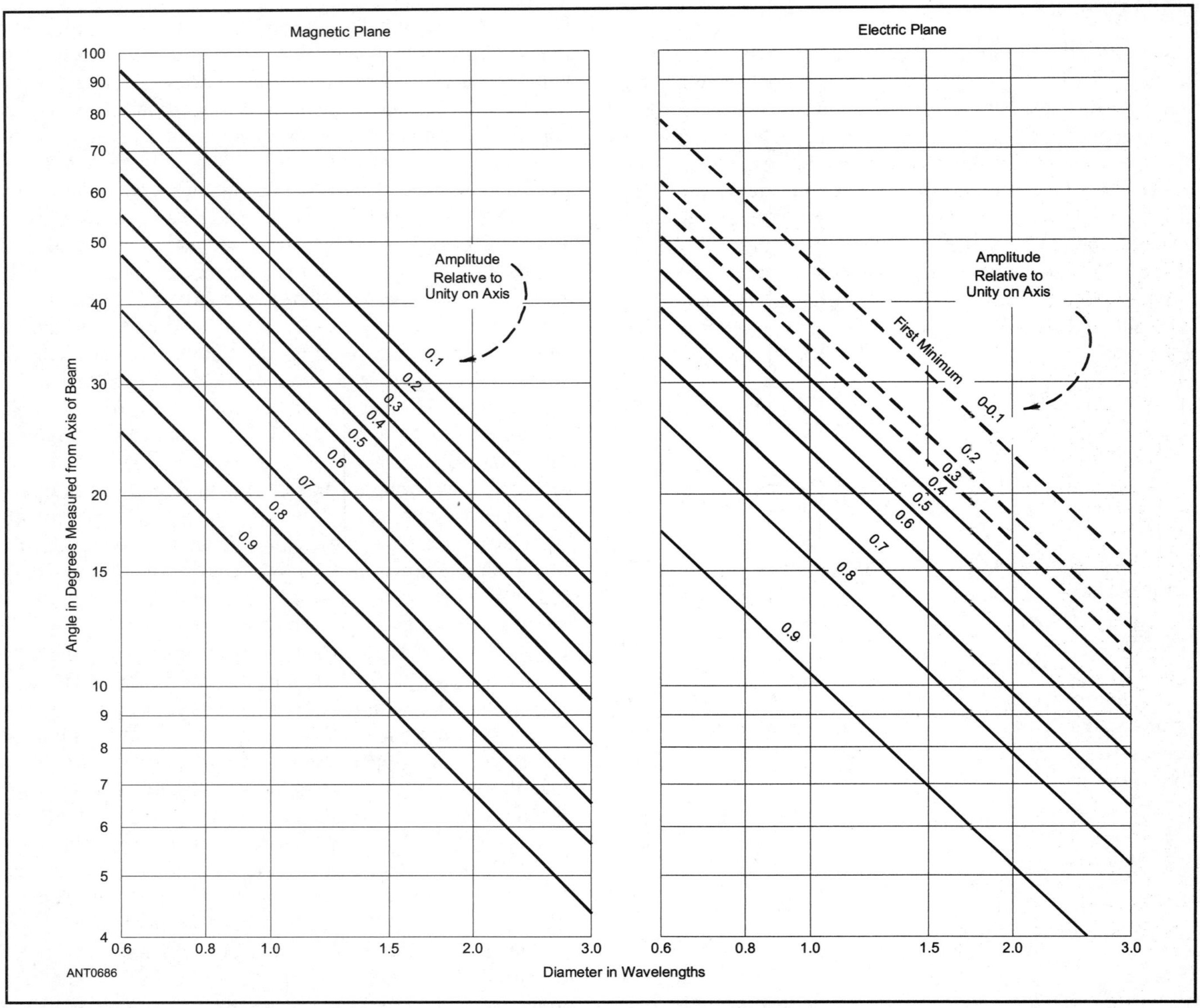

Figure 15.98 — This graph can be used in conjunction with Table 15.31 for selecting the proper diameter waveguide to illuminate a parabolic reflector.

feeds for dishes. (See examples in the **Antennas for Space Communication** chapter.)

Mechanical support

There are two critical mechanical problems: mounting the feed horn to the dish, and mounting the dish to a tripod. Most small dishes have no backing structure, so the thin aluminum surface is easily deformed. Larry Filby, K1LPS, discovered that some cast-aluminum frying pans have a rolled edge that sits nicely on the back of a dish: Mirro is one suitable brand. This is a good use for an old frying pan with worn-out non-stick coating. Drill and tap a few holes in the edge of the old pan, screw the dish to it, and you have a solid backing. A solid piece of angle iron or aluminum attaches the bottom of the frying pan to the top of a tripod.

The mounting structure for the feed horn is in the RF field of view, so we must minimize its blockage. We do this by using non-conductive materials and by mounting the support struts diagonally so they aren't in the plane of the polarization. Fiberglass is a good material; plant stakes or bicycle flags are good sources. Using four rather than three struts is recommended — if they are all the same length, then the feed will be centered. The base of the struts should be attached to the backing structure or edge of the frying pan; the thin dish surface is not mechanically strong.

The feed horn is in the center of the beam, also blocking part of the beam and reducing gain and efficiency. If the electronics are placed near the feed horn, they may add additional blockage, while placing the electronics behind the dish requires lossy feed line. A good compromise is to place an LNA at the feed horn for best G/T, while the transmit signal suffers feed line loss.

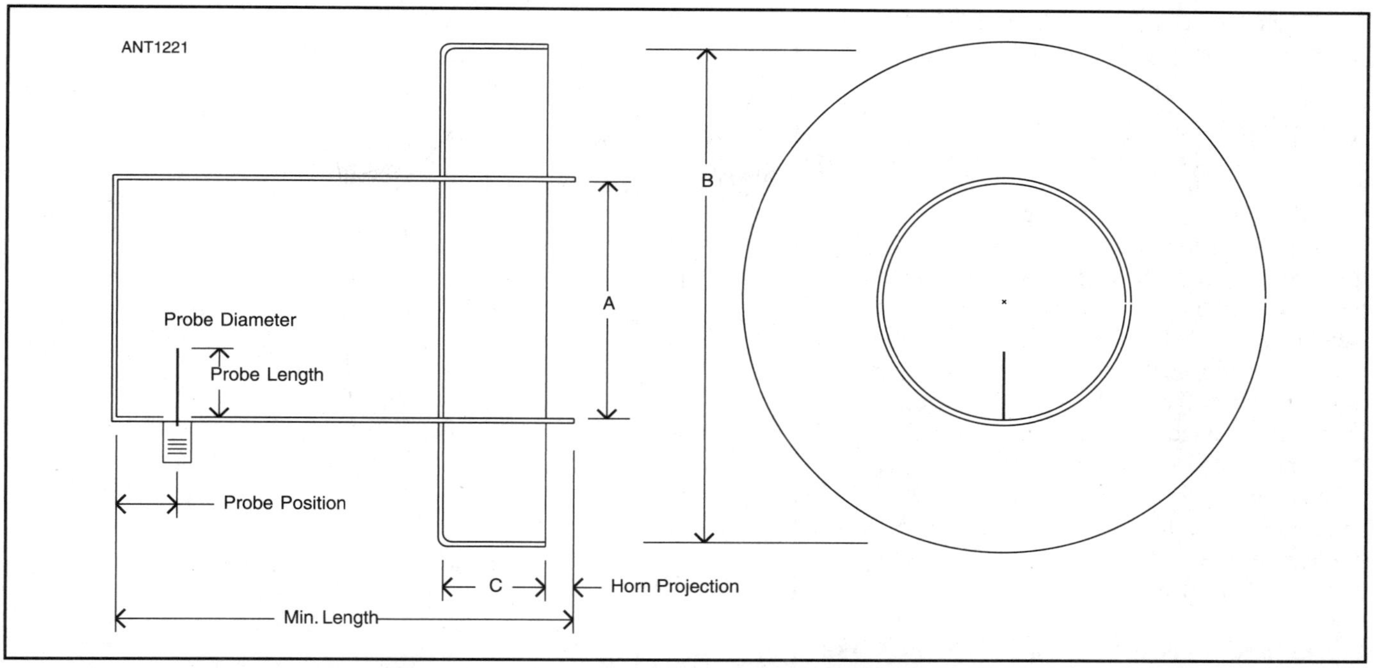

Figure 15.99 — A choke ring mounted on a circular feed to improve dish illumination.

There is also a mechanical problem. Prime-focus dishes are mounted and supported from the rear, resulting in an unbalanced structure with all the weight on one side. Small dishes may be balanced by the weight of the electronics on the back. Larger dishes may require a counterweight.

Offset Parabolic Dishes

An offset-fed dish has some advantages. The major advantage is that the feed horn is not in the beam of the antenna, so that the whole reflector is utilized and efficiency is higher. Equipment may also be placed out of the beam but close to the feed horn for minimum feed line loss. But setting up an offset-fed dish is much less obvious: where is the focus, where to point the feed horn, and how to aim the antenna?

Almost all offset dishes, especially the ubiquitous small satellite-TV dishes, use a geometry shown in **Figure 15.100** where the oval reflector projects as a circle looking along the beam from the front, so the effective diameter, D, equals the width of the oval. The bottom of the offset dish is the vertex of a full parabola, so that the vertex, focus and the beam are still in line. This simplifies the required calculations. (For a more complete treatment, see "Microwavelengths" in the April 2018 issue of *QST*.)

Focal length, f, is calculated from the height and width of the reflector using Legon's equation:

$$f = \frac{width^3}{16 \times depth \times height} \qquad (24)$$

The resulting f/D is about 0.6 for most common offset dishes.

The feed horn is placed with its phase center at the focus,

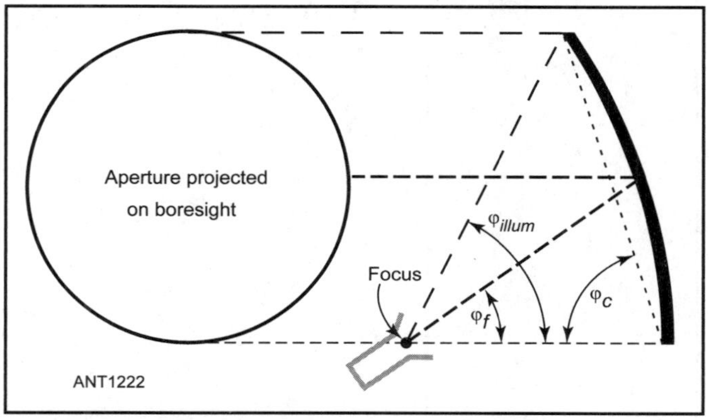

Figure 15.100 — Common offset parabolic dish antenna.

and aimed so that the reflector is evenly illuminated. Note in Figure 15.100 that the focus is closer to the bottom of the dish than to the top — the feed must be aimed slightly higher than the center of the dish to compensate. The feed is aimed up toward the dish by the feed angle:

$$\varphi_f = 2\tan^{-1}\left(\frac{1}{4 \times {}^{f}\!/\!_{d}}\right)$$

about 40° for common offset dishes.

The offset reflector is then tilted forward by the tilt angle φ_c to aim the beam on the horizon:

$$\varphi_c = \tan^{-1}\left(\frac{4f}{D}\right)$$

about 67° for common offset dishes.

Then the feed horn must illuminate the whole reflector, a subtended angle of:

$$\varphi_o = 2\tan^{-1}\left(\frac{1}{2 \times f/d}\right)$$

about 80° for common offset dishes.

The focal point of an offset dish is the most important dimension, but the location is not obvious. If you find one with the original feed assembly, it should be close to your calculations. Otherwise, the focal point is separated from the bottom edge of the dish by the focal length, and from the top edge by a distance = D/sin φ_o.

The feed horn should be chosen to properly illuminate the f/D of the reflector, about 0.6 for common offset dishes. The aiming angle for the feed is less critical — aiming a little above the center will work fine.

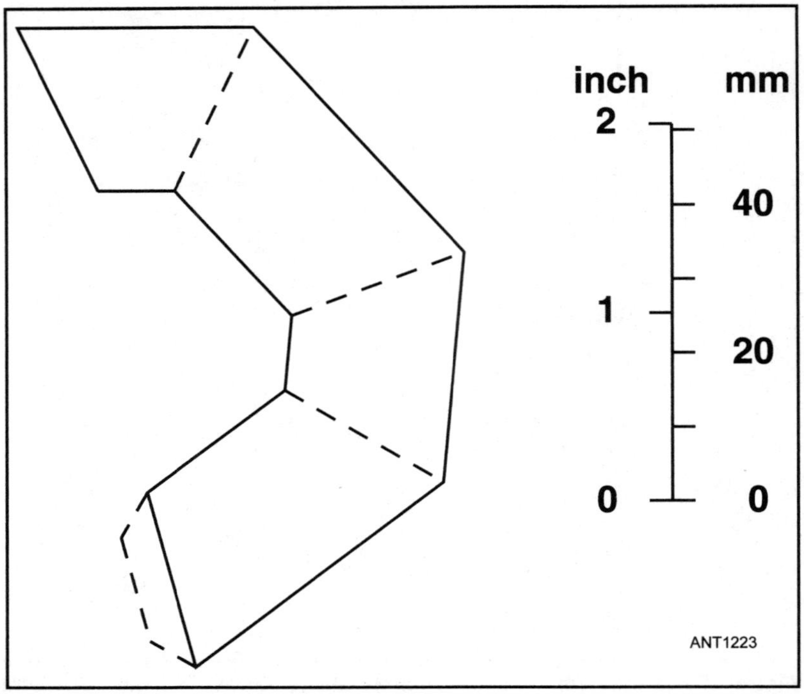

Figure 15.101 — Feed horn template for RCA DSS offset dish and WR-90 waveguide at 10.368 GHz.

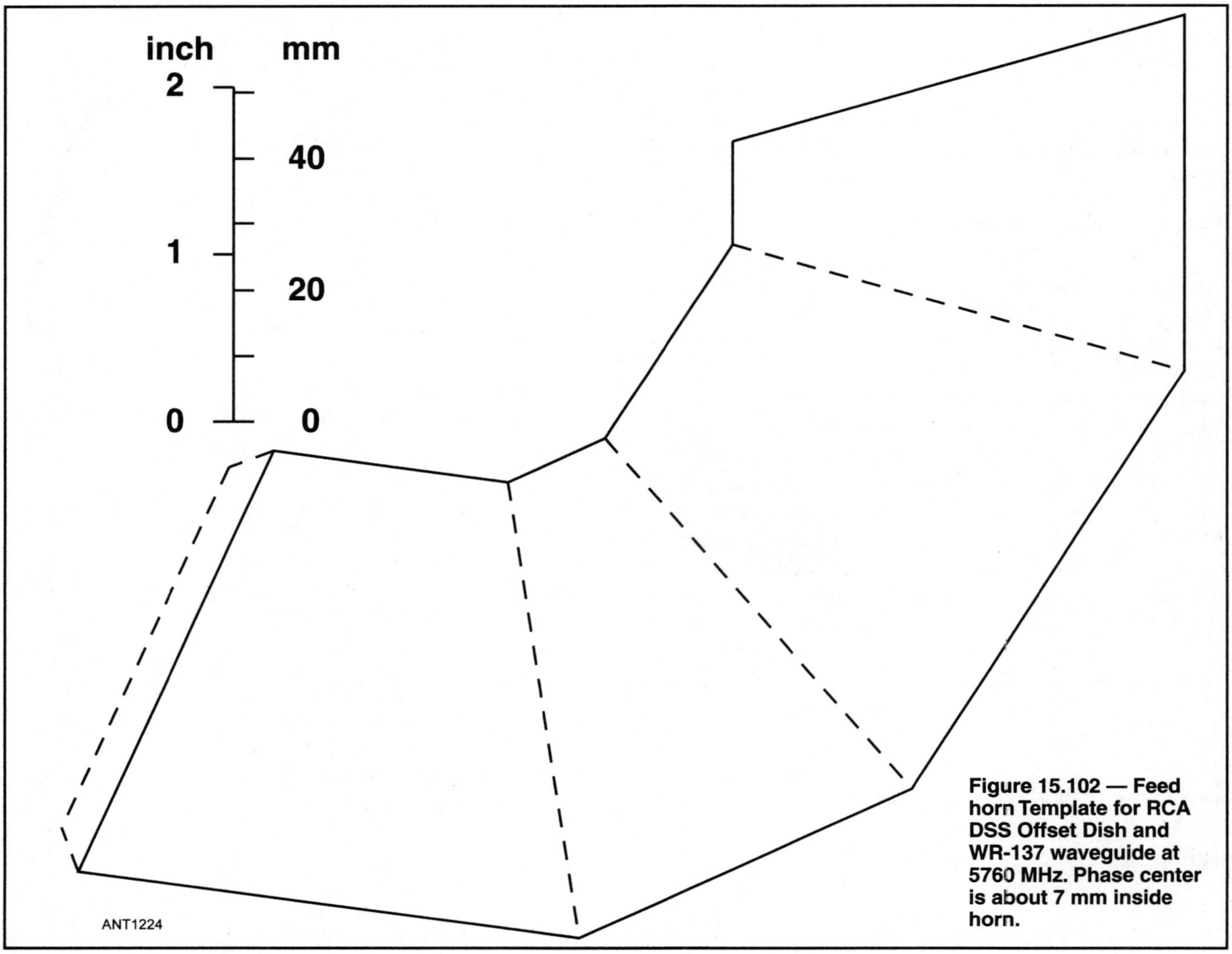

Figure 15.102 — Feed horn Template for RCA DSS Offset Dish and WR-137 waveguide at 5760 MHz. Phase center is about 7 mm inside horn.

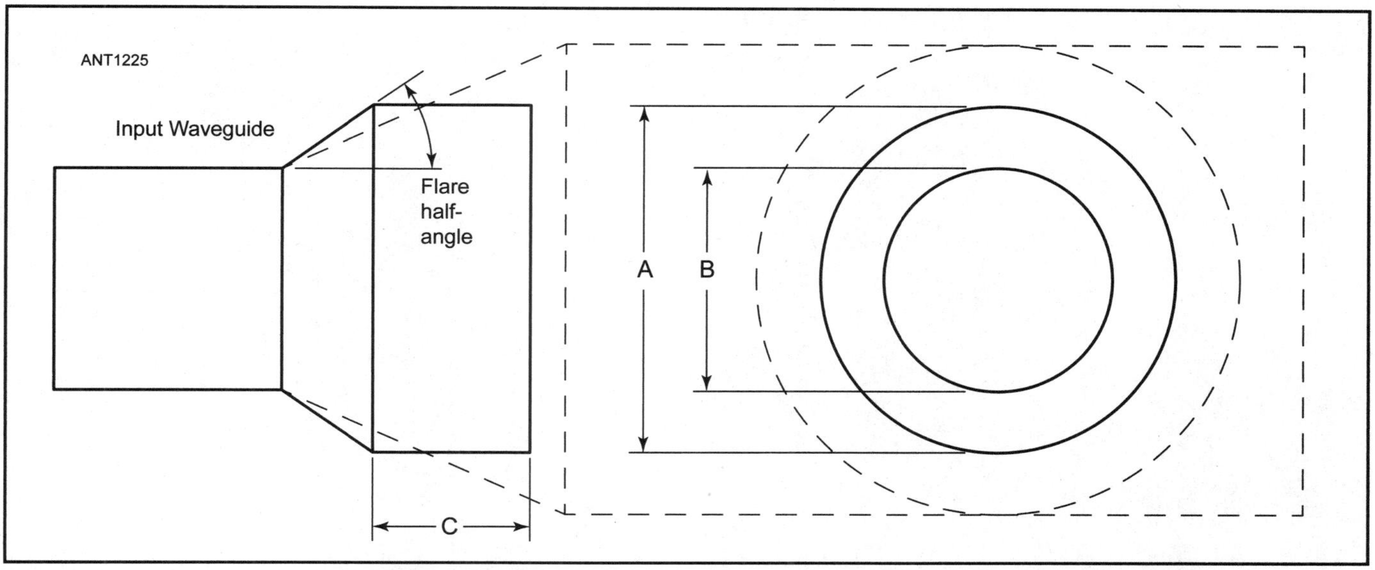

Figure 15.103 — The W2IMU dual-mode feed horn. See Table 15.32 for dimensions.

Feed Horns for Offset Dish

The subtended angle that the feed horn must illuminate is narrower for offset dishes, which suggests that a higher gain antenna is required. A simple rectangular horn may be designed to provide equal beamwidths in the E- and H- planes with a common center.

Figure 15.101 is a template for a 10 GHz feed horn using WR-90 waveguide; the phase center is about 6 mm inside the horn aperture, centered in the horn. **Figure 15.102** is a template for a 5.76 GHz horn using WR-137 waveguide, with phase center about 6mm inside the horn aperture. Both are suitable for the ubiquitous small satellite TV dishes.

A higher performance feed horn is the dual-mode horn, invented and patented by Dick Turrin, W2IMU. In the sketch of **Figure 15.103**, the conical section of the horn generates a second waveguide mode which cancels currents in the rim of the horn and thus reduces unwanted sidelobes. The dimensions shown in **Table 15.32** are fairly critical.

Table 15.32
Dimensions of Two Dual-Mode Feeds and the Original W2IMU Feed
Dimensions shown in wavelengths may be scaled to anyfrequency

f/D	*Flare*	*B = Aperture Diam.*	*C = Output Length*
0.55	30	1.31 l	1.31 l
0.7	27.4	1.63 l	2.8 l
0.8	24.9	1.79 l	3.52 l

Practical Considerations for Offset Dishes

Small errors in an offset-fed dish result in a beam which is tilted slightly up or down, are easily compensated for by tilting the antenna elevation. The final elevation angle should be found by peaking on a distant signal. I put a bubble level on my dishes at the approximate angle for a horizontal beam angle.

Offset dishes also have mechanical problems. Ideally, the electronics are placed under the feed horn, with short feed line and out of the beam. However, this puts all the weight at the end of the feed support, as shown in **Figure 15.104A**. If the reflector is mounted from the rear, as most are, a sturdy tripod is required even for a small dish. Another choice is to mount the offset dish on top of the electronics, as in Figure 15.104B. A wooden wedge holds the dish at the required tilt angle.

With any dish, it is desirable to have some elevation adjustment, since microwave signals can bend due to atmospheric effects. Distant (beyond line-of-sight) signals often peak at a few degrees of elevation, and occasionally below the horizon.

For portable operation, always calibrate azimuth and elevation on a signal at each setup. Bouncing around in a vehicle tends to shift adjustments and even distort parabolic reflectors slightly, so aiming by eye might be off. If you are lucky enough to have a beacon available, calibration is easier and more accurate.

Table 15.33
Scaling for the Vivaldi Antenna Template

Opening	*Low End Frequency Response*
40 mm	10 GHz
75 mm	5 GHz
150 mm	2 GHz
200 mm	1 GHz

15.7.5 VIVALDI ANTENNAS

The following material is reprinted from the RSGB publication *Microwave Know-How.* (See Bibliography.) The Vivaldi antenna in **Figure 15.105** is an exponential antenna from the same family as V-beams and Rhombics (see the

(A)

Figure 15.104 — Mounting the electronics under the feed horn (A) places most of the assembly weight to the rear, requiring a heavy-duty tripod. Mounting the dish over the electronics (B) requires more feed line but is more balanced.

(B)

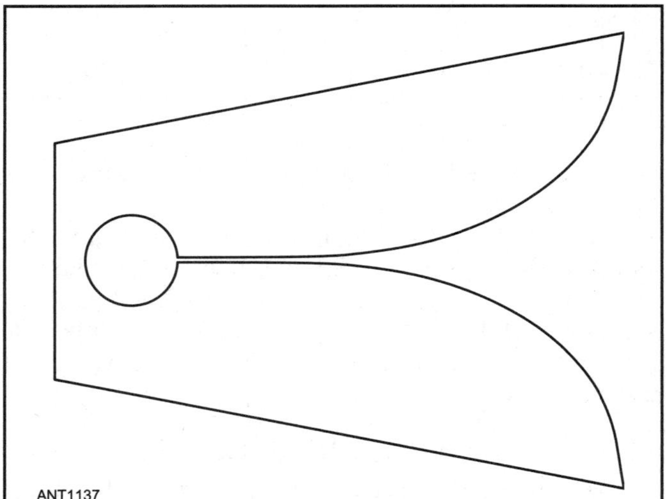

Figure 15.105 — The template for a Vivaldi antenna. Scale as shown in Table 15.33.

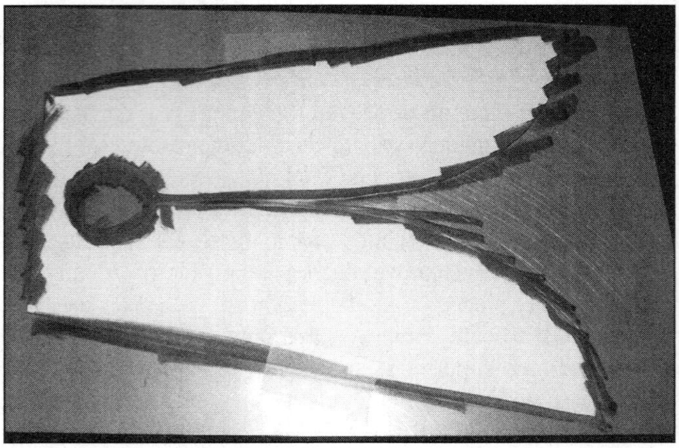

Figure 15.106 — Marking out a Vivaldi antenna using the template placed on your chosen material.

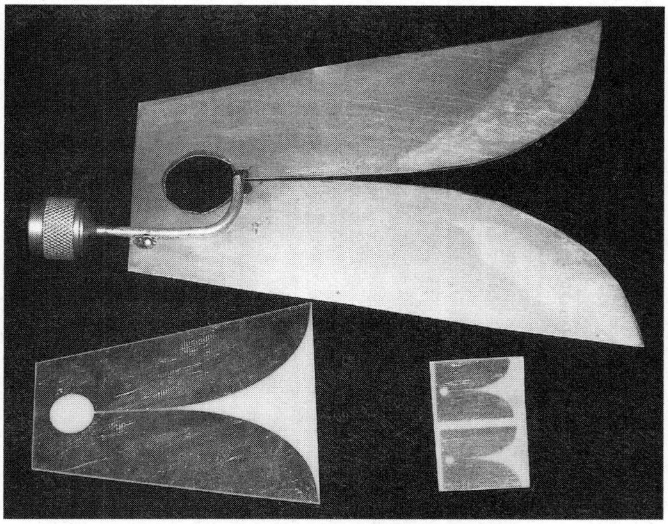

Figure 15.107 — A complete Vivaldi antenna.

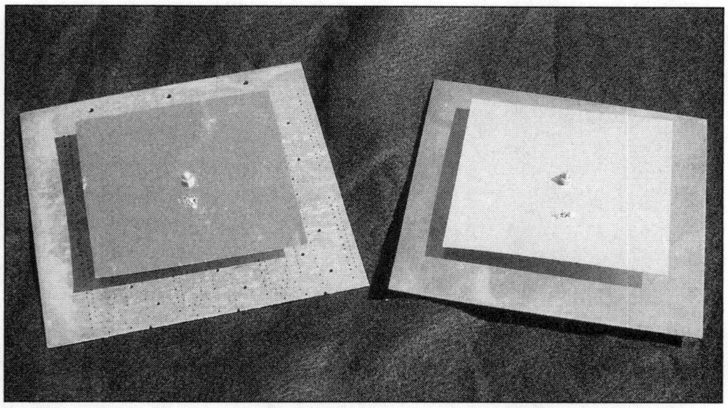

Figure 15.108 — Two patch antennas for the 23 cm band. The patch on the left is constructed from sheet metal and the one on the right from PCB material.

Long-Wire and Traveling-Wave Antennas chapter). They have exceptionally wide bandwidth. The lowest frequency is determined by the width of the opening.

The higher frequency of operation is determined by how accurately the slot is formed. As an example, the 75 mm PCB version has an excellent return loss from 5 GHz to 18 GHz and is usable from 2 GHz. (See **www.wa5vjb.com/pcb-pdfs/10-25GHzSweep.pdf** for additional construction information.)

All versions start with the template shown in Figure 15.105. Place the template on a photocopy machine and enlarge or reduce to the desired frequency range as shown in **Table 15.33**. Cut out the template and mark your material as shown in **Figure 15.106**. Thin brass, tin plate, or PC board material have all been used.

Cut out the antenna using sharp scissors or a band saw. The feed line shield should be soldered to one side of the slot and the center conductor to the other side as close to the circle as possible. (See **Figure 15.107**.) Both semi-rigid and Teflon braided coax types can be used.

Vivaldi antennas make excellent test antennas for use with a test instruments or can be used as dish feeds over several bands. The phase center of the Vivaldi does move back and forth in the narrow region of the slot, but when the dish is focused at the highest frequency of planned use, the lower bands will be very close. Mount the narrow area of the slot at the focus of the dish.

15.7.6 PATCH ANTENNAS

The following material is adapted from the RSGB publication *Microwave Know-How.* (See Bibliography for additional articles by Kraus and Krug.) Patch antennas (also called *microstrip antennas*) are a good example of how an antenna's shape is used at microwave frequencies in ways not possible at 70 cm and longer wavelengths. Patch antennas become practical at and above the 902 MHz band and are very common in commercial microwave applications such as GPS reception, wireless telephony, and wireless data links. As more amateurs investigate operation at microwave frequencies, the patch antenna should receive more attention. A comprehensive tutorial on microstrip antennas is available from *Microwaves & RF* magazine. (See the Bibliography entry for Puglia.)

The patch, an example of which is shown in **Figure 15.108**, consists of a radiating surface mounted over a ground plane although there are many variations of the basic design. The patch is approximately $\lambda/2$ on a side for a square patch. Patch antenna gain is on the order of 7 to 9 dBi.

Some patches are constructed of double-sided PCB material with the patch etched on one side and the unetched side acting as the ground plane. The shape of the patch is such that when excited by a signal, the resulting currents form patterns that create a useful radiation pattern. It works the same as an arrangement of discrete elements. The closest electrical analogy is that the square patch acts similarly to a pair of slot antennas fed in phase and approximately $\lambda/2$ apart.

Since the impedance of the patch is high at the edges where current is low (just as in a linear element), the feed point is usually close to the center of the patch. Placement of the feed point determines the feed point impedance and also influences the pattern of current on the surface of the patch. An alternate method of feeding the patch is to create a 50-Ω microstrip or stripline transmission line from a location with a 50-Ω impedance to the edge of the structure where a feed line can be attached.

It is not necessary for the patch to be rectangular in shape and could conveniently be round or polygon shaped. A rectangular patch with its opposite corners cut off will produce circular polarization.

Flat-Panel Patch Array Antennas

Flat panel antennas are arrays of printed antennas which can provide good gain in a compact package. A version for 24 GHz is shown in **Figure 15.109**, with 256 printed patch antennas. Compare this with the collinear dipole arrays discussed earlier in this chapter — the printed array is groups of four patches combined with a tree of printed transmission lines. An array like this can provide very good gain, which we

Figure 15.109 — An array of printed patch antennas for 24 GHz.

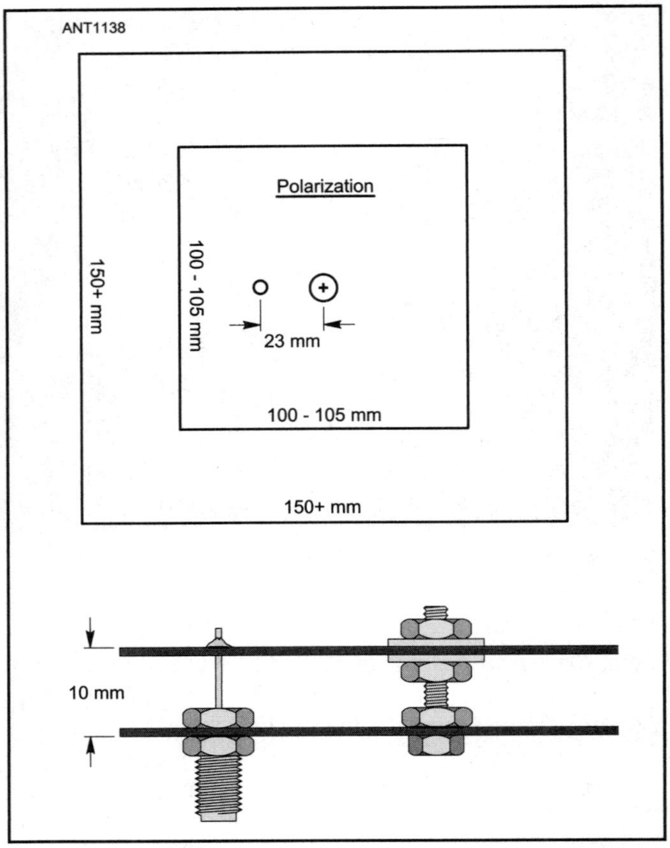

Figure 15.110 — Dimensions for the 23 cm patch antenna. The size of the patch determines the frequency range of the antenna (see text). The orientation of the feed point determines the antenna's polarization.

can estimate from the aperture area of the array.

A printed antenna like this can be economically produced in large quantities, but would be very expensive to make only a single antenna. A significant amount of engineering is required. A dense array like this has significant mutual coupling between adjacent antenna elements, which must be compensated -- notice that the combining lines are not all identical. And for low loss, the array is printed on an expensive Teflon-based dielectric.

Fortunately, flat panel antennas have been mass-produced for a number of applications, and can often be found at reasonable prices on online auction sites. These are usually intended for outdoor use, so they are packaged with a weatherproof cover. Look for versions that are close to or include the desired microwave ham band. Just be wary of the advertised gains — a better estimate can be made from the aperture area of the array.

A Patch Antenna for 23 cm

This simple patch antenna for the middle range of the 23 cm band was designed by Kent Britain, WA5VJB. The antenna works for use as a dish feed as well as for point-to-point communication such as for D-STAR, ATV, or satellite contacts.

The antenna can be made from almost any sheet metal. The base can be made from sheet aluminum, brass, copper, or PCB material. It is probably easier to assemble if the patch is made from something that can be soldered. Figure 15.95 shows two patches. The one on the right is made from PCB material and the one on the left from galvanized sheet steel. **Figure 15.110** shows the dimensions for the 23 cm band patch.

Figure 15.111 — An illustration showing how the patch is mounted above the ground plane using the center screw and, in this case, the SMA connector.

Since the very center of the patch is electrically neutral, similar to the center of a dipole, you can use a metal screw to support the patch over the conductive plate or ground plane. This provides a dc ground for the antenna and dissipates any static charge. A #4 or #6 brass or similar screw can be used. The diameter of the screw is not important but the height at which it holds the patch above the ground plane is. Adjust the height of the patch above the ground plane for the best impedance match. If swept frequency measurements are not possible, adjustment at a single frequency is acceptable.

Coaxial feed line is attached to the patch 23 mm from the mounting screw as shown in Figure 15.110 and **Figure 15.111**. The orientation of the line from the feed point to the center of the patch determines the antenna's polarization. If the antenna is placed with the feed point below the center, the antenna will be vertically polarized.

An SMA connector is used for this design, but coax can be soldered directly to the patch. The center conductor attaches to the patch and the shield to the ground plane. Ground plane size is not critical and 150 mm × 150 mm or larger will work well.

The typical patch will have a bandwidth of 50 MHz at this frequency. To use the 1240-1280 MHz portion of the band, increase the patch to 105 mm × 105 mm. For 1280-1325 MHz reduce the patch size to 100 mm × 100 mm.

15.7.7 PERISCOPE ANTENNA SYSTEMS

One problem common to all who use microwaves is that of mounting an antenna at the maximum possible height while trying to minimize feed line losses. The higher the frequency, the more severe this problem becomes, as feeder losses increase with frequency. Because parabolic dish reflectors are most often used on the higher bands, there is also the difficulty of waterproofing feeds (particularly waveguide feeds). Inaccessibility of the dish is also a problem when changing bands. Unless the tower is climbed every time and the feed changed, there must be a feed for each band mounted on the dish. One way around these problems is to use a periscope antenna system (sometimes called a "flyswatter antenna").

The material in this section was prepared by Bob Atkins, KA1GT, and appeared in *QST* for January and February 1984. **Figure 15.112** shows a schematic representation of a periscope antenna system. A plane reflector is mounted at the top of a rotating tower at an angle of 45°. This reflector can be elliptical with a major to minor axis ratio of 1.41, or rectangular. At the base of the tower is mounted a dish or other type of antenna such as a Yagi, pointing straight up. The advantage of such a system is that the feed antenna can be changed and worked on easily. Additionally, with a correct choice of reflector size, dish size, and dish to reflector spacing, feed losses can be made small, increasing the effective system gain. In fact, for some particular system configurations, the gain of the overall system can be greater than that of the feed antenna alone.

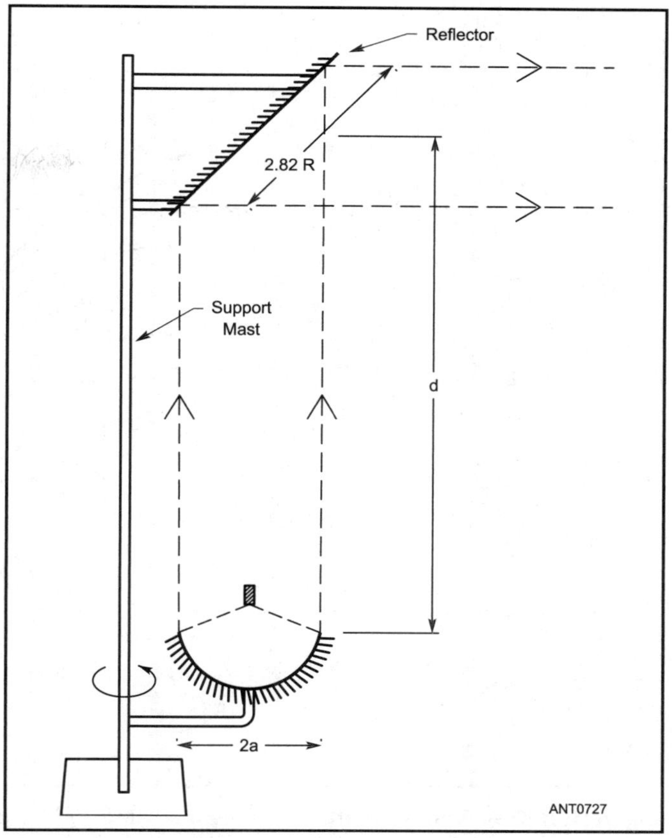

Figure 15.112 — The basic periscope antenna. This design makes it easy to adjust the feed antenna.

Gain of a Periscope System

Figure 15.113 shows the relationship between the effective gain of the antenna system and the distance between the reflector and feed antenna for an elliptical reflector. At first sight, it is not at all obvious how the antenna system can have a higher gain than the feed alone. The reason lies in the fact that, depending on the feed to reflector spacing, the reflector may be in the near field (Fresnel) region of the antenna, the far field (Fraunhöffer) region, or the transition region between the two.

In the far field region, the gain is proportional to the reflector area and inversely proportional to the distance between the feed and reflector. In the near field region, seemingly strange things can happen, such as decreasing gain with decreasing feed to reflector separation. The reason for this gain decrease is that, although the reflector is intercepting more of the energy radiated by the feed, it does not all contribute in phase at a distant point, and so the gain decreases.

In practice, rectangular reflectors are more common than elliptical. A rectangular reflector with sides equal in length to the major and minor axes of the ellipse will, in fact, normally give a slight gain increase. In the far field region, the gain will be proportional to the area of the reflector. To use

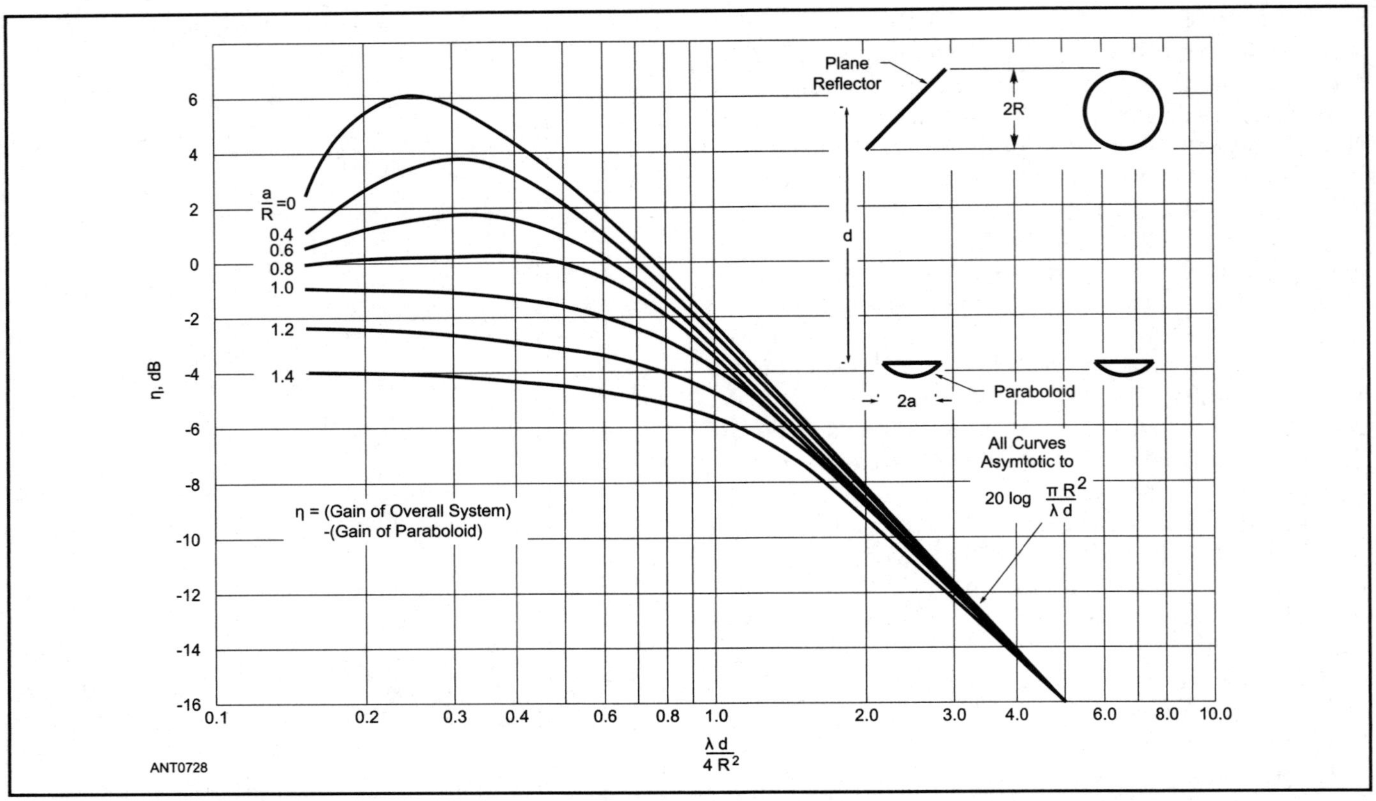

Figure 15.113 — Gain of a periscope antenna using a plane elliptical reflector (after Jasik — see Bibliography).

Figure 15.113 with a rectangular reflector, R^2 may be replaced by A / π, where A is the projected area of the reflector. The antenna pattern depends in a complicated way on the system parameters (spacing and size of the elements), but **Table 15.34** gives an approximation of what to expect. R is the radius of the projected circular area of the elliptical reflector (equal to the minor axis radius), and b is the length of the side of the projected square area of the rectangular reflector (equal to the length of the short side of the rectangle).

For those wishing a rigorous mathematical analysis of this type of antenna system, several references are given in the Bibliography at the end of this chapter.

Table 15.34
Radiation Patterns of Periscope Antenna Systems

	Elliptical Reflector	*Rectangular Reflector*
3-dB beamwidth, degrees	60 λ/2R	52 λ/b
6-dB beamwidth, degrees	82 λ/2R	68 λ/b
First minimum, degrees from axis	73 λ/2R	58 λ/b
First maximum, degrees from axis	95 λ/2R	84 λ/b
Second minimum, degrees from axis	130 λ/2R	116 λ/b
Second maximum, degrees from axis	156 λ/2R	142 λ/b
Third minimum, degrees from axis	185 λ/2R	174 λ/b

Mechanical Considerations

There are some problems with the physical construction of a periscope antenna system. Since the antenna gain of a microwave system is high and, hence, its beamwidth narrow, the reflector must be accurately aligned. If the reflector does not produce a beam that is horizontal, the useful gain of the system will be reduced. From the geometry of the system, an angular misalignment of the reflector of X degrees in the vertical plane will result in an angular misalignment of 2X degrees in the vertical alignment of the antenna system pattern. Thus, for a dish pointing straight up (the usual case), the reflector must be at an angle of 45° to the vertical and should not fluctuate from factors such as wind loading.

The reflector itself should be flat to better than ¹⁄₁₀ λ for the frequency in use. It may be made of mesh, provided that the holes in the mesh are also less than ¹⁄₁₀ λ in diameter. A second problem is getting the support mast to rotate about a truly vertical axis. If the mast is not vertical, the resulting beam will swing up and down from the horizontal as the system is rotated, and the effective gain at the horizon will fluctuate. Despite these problems, amateurs have used periscope antennas successfully on the bands through 10 GHz. Periscope antennas are used frequently in commercial service, though usually for point-to-point transmission. Such a commercial system is shown in **Figure 15.114**.

Circular polarization is not often used for terrestrial

Figure 15.114 — Commercial periscope antennas, such as this one, are often used for point-to-point communication.

operation, but if it is used with a periscope system there is an important point to remember. The circularity sense changes when the signal is reflected. Thus, for right hand circularity with a periscope antenna system, the feed arrangement on the ground should produce left hand circularity. It should also be mentioned that it is possible (though more difficult for amateurs) to construct a periscope antenna system using a parabolically curved reflector. The antenna system can then be regarded as an offset fed parabola. More gain is available from such a system at the added complexity of constructing a parabolically curved reflector, accurate to 1/10 λ.

15.7.8 OMNIDIRECTIONAL MICROWAVE ANTENNAS

Omnidirectional antennas are ideal for microwave beacons and handy for test antennas. If you are lucky enough to have enough local microwave stations then an omni might be good for a mobile or station antenna or even for a microwave repeater.

A real omnidirectional antenna would radiate in all directions in a sphere, but hams use the term loosely for an antenna that radiates in all azimuth directions — there is little point in radiating into the sky. Coincidentally, it is easier to make this sort of antenna than a true omnidirectional one.

A complication for microwaves is that horizontal polarization is normally used on the air. The vertical whips used by VHF mobiles have 360° azimuth coverage by their nature but with vertical polarization. To achieve the same coverage with horizontal polarization takes a bit more work.

Waveguide Slot Antenna

One type of antenna that can radiate horizontal polarization with a broad azimuth pattern is a *slot antenna.* A slot in an infinite metal plane is the dual of a dipole — a vertical slot has a radiation pattern identical to a horizontal dipole of the same size in free space. Infinite planes are as hard to find as free space but we can make a working antenna with slots in a metal sheet.

A waveguide slot antenna, pictured in **Figure 115**, has an array of λ/2 slots cut in the broad wall of a waveguide which acts as the transmission line feeding them. A vertical slot behaves like a horizontal dipole. Thus, the slots act like a vertical array of dipoles and the array provides more gain.

If the slots are spaced an electrical half-wavelength apart along the transmission line, their impedances all appear in parallel. The impedance of a slot is controlled by the distance each slot is displaced from the center line of the waveguide. If we add identical slots on the other face of the waveguide, the result is a broad radiation pattern in both directions, a cloverleaf pattern with a few dB variation, resulting in an approximately omnidirectional antenna with horizontal polarization and gain. To make the radiation pattern more uniform, some implementations have added metal wings to the narrow sides of the waveguide.

The electrical wavelength in a waveguide is longer than a wavelength in free space, so the slot spacing must be more than one-half wavelength in free space, complicating the calculations. Choosing the right combination of slot length, spacing, and displacement results in a well-matched antenna with an omnidirectional radiation pattern; a spreadsheet at **www.w1ghz.org/software/slotantenna.xls** calculates these dimensions. (The author acknowledges the help of Dan Welch, W6DFW in validating the calculations by making some very accurate slot antennas on a CNC machine in order to fine-tune the dimensions.) Figure 15.115 is a 10 GHz version made by Dan — the tuning screws aren't needed when the dimensions are right.

For those who do not have access to a manual or CNC milling machine, microwave slot antennas can also be made

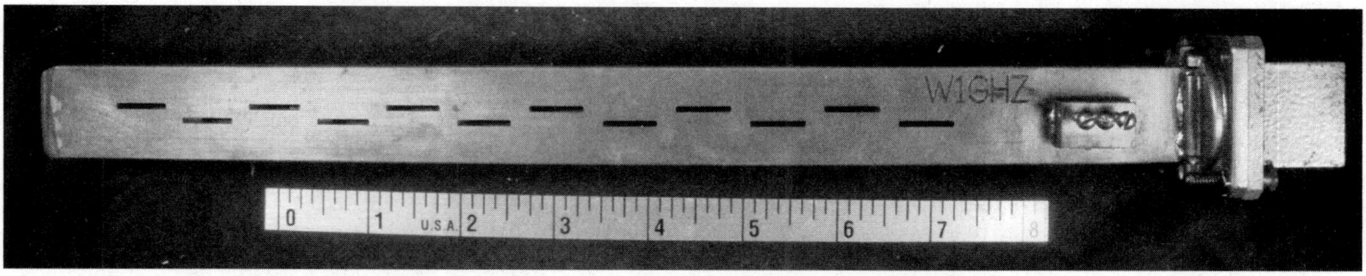

Figure 15.115 — 24-slot waveguide slot antenna for 10 GHz made by Dan Welch, W6DFW.

Figure 15.116 — A waveguide slot for 1296 MHz and its maker, Rene Barbeau, VE2UG.

by hand. Donn Baker, WA2VOI, makes slot antennas for 10 GHz by scribing the slot pattern on the waveguide, drilling a row of holes, and filing out to the scribe lines. Hams have made these antennas for microwave bands from 1296 MHz to 24 GHz — Rene Barbeau, VE2UG, made the 1296 MHz waveguide slot antenna shown in **Figure 15.116**. He used ordinary rectangular aluminum tubing with dimensions not too different than commercial waveguide dimensions and made the slots with drills and files.

Alford Slot Antenna

The Alford Slot is frequently confused with the waveguide slot antenna but is a much different antenna. It is a single long slot cut lengthwise in a round tube. It is based on a 1947 paper, "Long Slot Antennas," by Andrew Alford (available from **www.w1ghz.org/antbook/Long_Slot_Antennas_Alford.pdf**). Rob Swinbank, MØDTS, made the 2.4 GHz version shown in **Figure 15.117**.

A long slot has more gain than a simple λ/2 antenna. The electrical wavelength in the slot, like the waveguide, is longer than a wavelength in free space, so that currents in the long slot do not have the phase reversals that create many lobes in a long dipole. The slot wavelength is controlled mainly by the inner diameter of the tube. Alford suggests a slot 2 λ long in a tube with an inner diameter of 0.14 λ. This is approximately 32 mm at 1296 MHz, about the size of a mast, so a thinwall mast could also be a sturdy antenna.

The slot is fed in the center by a balanced transmission line connected to the sides of the slot, with the transmission line travelling inside the tube along the wall opposite the slot. According to Alford, a typical impedance is 250 Ω. A half-wave balun of semi-rigid coax could make a reasonable match to 50 Ω coax.

Like the waveguide slot antenna, wings may be added along the slot to make the radiation pattern more uniform. These also affect the slot impedance, so they can also improve matching. Both types of slot antenna may be stacked for higher gain.

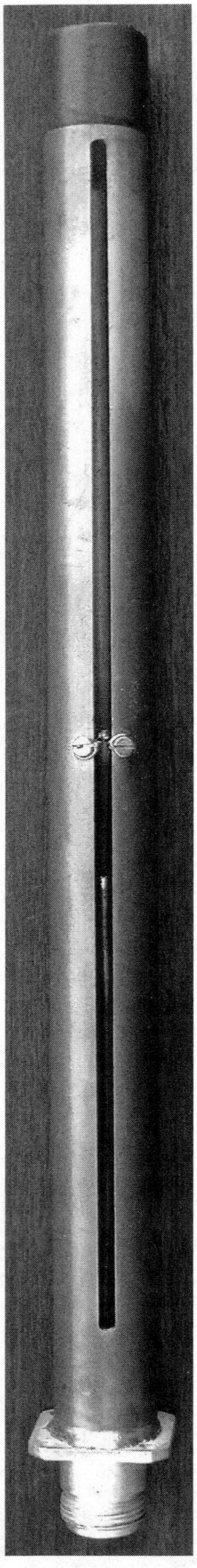

Figure 15.117 — An Alford slot antenna for 2.4 GHz made by Rob Swinbank, MØDTS.

Discone Antenna

All the omnidirectional antennas discussed so far are fairly narrowband. This is fine for one microwave ham band but a separate antenna is needed for each band. If vertical polarization is acceptable, the discone antenna is extremely broadband with up to a 10:1 frequency range. **Figure 15.118** shows one made by Don Twombly, W1FKF, for frequencies above 3 GHz. The antenna is made up of a disc, connected at the center to the center conductor of the coax feed line and a cone, connected to the end of the coax outer conductor and surrounding it. The cone length is ¼ λ at the lowest frequency and the disc diameter is 0.7 times the cone length; the cone angle is roughly 30 degrees but not critical. Building one on semi-rigid coax, as Don did, makes a good support for a small microwave version.

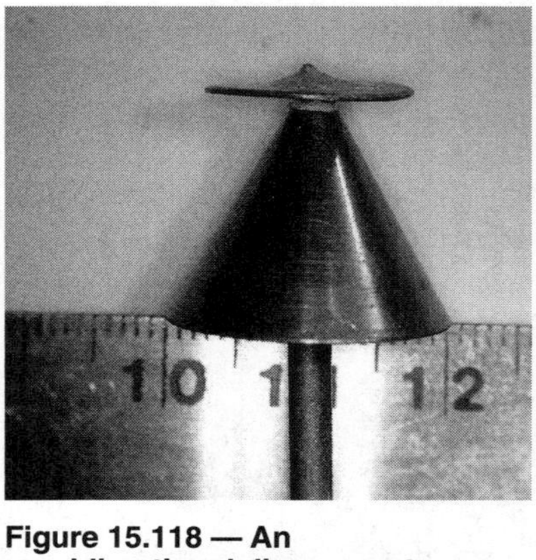

Figure 15.118 — An omnidirectional discone antenna for frequencies above 3 GHz made by Don Twombly, W1FKF.

15.8 BIBLIOGRAPHY

Source material and more extended discussion of topics covered in this chapter can be found in the references given below and in the textbooks listed at the end of the **Antenna Fundamentals** chapter.

RSGB Books

Antennas for VHF and Above (Potters Bar: RSGB, 2008).

International Microwave Handbook (Potters Bar: RSGB, 2008).

Microwave Know-How for the Radio Amateur (Potters Bar: RSGB, 2010).

Radio Communication Handbook, 10th ed. (Potters Bar: RSGB, 2009).

Other Publications

B. Atkins, "Periscope Antenna Systems," The New Frontier, *QST*, Jan 1984, p 70 and Feb 1984, p 68.

B. Atkins, "Horn Antennas for 10 GHz," The New Frontier, *QST*, Apr 1987, p 80 and May 1987, p 63.

B. Atkins, "The New Frontier: Loop Yagi for 2304 MHz," *QST*, Sep 1981, p 76.

A. Baker, "A 6 Meter Moxon Antenna," *QST*, Apr 2004, pp 64-69.

R. Bancroft, *Microstrip and Printed Antenna Design (2nd Edition)* (Raleigh, NC: SciTech Publishing, 2009)

J. Belrose, "Technical Correspondence: Gain of Vertical Collinear Antennas," *QST*, Oct 1982, pp 40-41.

J. Belrose, "Gain of Vertical Collinear Antennas," *QST*, Oct 1982, pp 40-41.

J. Cadwallader, "Easy 50-Ohm Feed For A Helix," *QST*, June 1981, pp 28-29.

L.B. Cebik, "A Short Boom, Wideband 3 Element Yagi for 6 Meters," *QST*, Aug 2007, pp 41-45.

L.B. Cebik, "2X3=6," *QST*, Feb 2000, p 34-36.

L.B. Cebik, "Building a Medium-Gain, Wide-Band, 2 Meter Yagi," *QST*, Dec 2004, pp 33-37.

L.B. Cebik, "Notes on the OWA Yagi," *QEX*, Jul/Aug 2002, pp 22-34.

L.B. Cebik, "An LPDA for 2 Meters Plus," *QST*, Oct 2001, pp 42-46.

L.B. Cebik, "VK2ABQ Squares and Moxon Rectangles," *Modeling and Understanding Small Beams*, various online sources.

L.B. Cebik, "The Moxon Rectangle: A Review," various online sources.

M. Collis, "Omni-Gain Vertical Collinear for VHF and UHF," *73*, Aug 1990.

D. Conn, "The Helical Antenna — Description and Design," *TCA*, Jan/Feb 2006.

D. Cozzens, "Tables Ease Horn Design," *Microwaves*, March 1966, pp. 37-39.

J. Drexler, "An Experimental Study of a Microwave Periscope," *Proc. IRE*, Correspondence, Vol 42, Jun 1954, p 1022.

D. Evans and G. Jessop, *VHF-UHF Manual*, 3rd ed. (London: RSGB), 1976.

N. Foot, "WA9HUV 12 foot Dish for 432 and 1296 MHz," The World Above 50 Mc., *QST*, Jun 1971, pp 98-101, 107.

N. Foot, "Cylindrical Feed Horn for Parabolic Reflectors," *Ham Radio*, May 1976, pp 16-20.

G. Gobau, "Single-Conductor Surface-Wave Transmission Lines," *Proc. IRE*, Vol 39, Jun 1951, pp 619-624; also see *Journal of Applied Physics*, Vol 21 (1950), pp 1119-1128.

R. E. Greenquist and A. J. Orlando, "An Analysis of Passive Reflector Antenna Systems," *Proc. IRE*, Vol 42, Jul 1954, pp 1173-1178.

G. A. Hatherell, "Putting the G Line to Work," *QST*, Jun 1974, pp 11-15, 152, 154, 156.

R. Heslin, "Three-Band Log Periodic Antenna," *QST*, Jun 1963, pp 50-52.

D. L. Hilliard, "A 902 MHz Loop Yagi Antenna," *QST*, Nov 1985, pp 30-32.

G. Hoch, "Extremely Long Yagi antennas," *VHF Communications Magazine*, Mar 1982, pp 131-138.

G. Hoch, "More Gain from Yagi Antennas," *VHF Communications Magazine*, Apr 1997, pp 204-211.

W. C. Jakes, Jr., "A Theoretical Study of an Antenna-Reflector Problem," *Proc. IRE*, Vol 41, Feb 1953, pp 272-274.

H. Jasik, *Antenna Engineering Handbook*, 2nd ed. (New York: McGraw-Hill, 1984).

J. Johnson, "An intro to OWL yagis," **www.g0ksc.co.uk**

J. Johnson, "Making the OWL Match," **www.g0ksc.co.uk**

J. Johnson, "The OWL Folded Dipole," **www.g0ksc.co.uk**

R. T. Knadle, "UHF Antenna Ratiometry," *QST*, Feb 1976, pp 22-25.

J. Kraus, *Antennas, Second Edition*, McGraw Hill, 1988.

G. Kraus, "Modern Patch Antenna Design," *VHF Communications Magazine*, Jan 2001, pp 49-63.

F. Krug, "Micro-Stripline Antennas," *VHF Communications Magazine,* Apr 1985, pp 194-207.

Z. Lau, "RF: A Small 70-cm Yagi," *QEX*, Jul 2001, p 55.

T. Moreno, *Microwave Transmission Design Data* (New York: McGraw-Hill, 1948).

E. Munn, "The Polaplexer Revisited," **www.ham-radio.com/sbms/sd/ppxrdsgn.htm**.

W. Overbeck, "The VHF Quagi," *QST*, Apr 1977, pp 11-14.

W. Overbeck, "The Long-Boom Quagi," *QST*, Feb 1978, pp 20-21.

W. Overbeck, "Reproducible Quagi Antennas for 1296 MHz," *QST*, Aug 1981, pp 11-15.

J. Post, "The Copper Cactus," *73*, Feb 1992, p 9.

K. Puglia, "A Brief Tutorial on Microstrip Antennas, Parts 1 through 4," *Microwaves & RF*, Nov and Dec 2018, Jan and Feb 2019.

S. Powlishen, "An Optimum Design for 432 MHz Yagis — Parts 1 and 2," *QST*, Dec 1987, pp 20-24, and Jan 1988, pp 24-30.

J. Reisert, "VHF/UHF World: Designing and Building Loop Yagis," *Ham Radio*, Sep 1985, pp 56-62.

G. Southworth, *Principles and Applications of Waveguide Transmission* (New York: D. Van Nostrand Co, 1950).

P. P. Viezbicke, "Yagi Antenna Design," *NBS Technical Note 688* (U. S. Dept. of Commerce/National Bureau of Standards, Boulder, CO), Dec 1976.

D. Vilardi, "Easily Constructed Antennas for 1296 MHz," *QST*, Jun 1969, pp 47-49.

D. Vilardi, "Simple and Efficient Feed for Parabolic Antennas," *QST*, Mar 1973, pp 42-44.

P. Wade, "Parabolic Antennas," *QST*, Apr 2018, pp 57-58.

P. Wade, "From a Parabolic Dish to an Antenna," *QST*, Oct 2018, pp 60-61.

P. Wade, "Omnidirectional Microwave Antennas," *QST*, Oct 2016, pp 56-57.

B. Walker, *Magic Band Antennas for Ham Radio*, (Newington: ARRL, 2018).

Williams, "Understanding Microwave Radiolink Antennas," *Mobile Radio Technology*, Apr 1990, pp 36-58.

TABLE OF CONTENTS

Chapter 16 — Downloadable Supplemental Content

Supplemental Articles

- ⅝-Wavelength Whips for 2 Meters and 222 MHz
- "6-Meter Halo Antenna for DXing" by Jerry Clement, VE6AB
- "A 6m Hex Beam for the Rover" by Darryl Holman, WW7D
- "A 6 Meter Halo" by Paul Danzer, N1II
- "A New Spin on the Big Wheel" by L.B. Cebik, W4RNL and Bob Cerreto, WA1FXT
- "A Simple 2 Meter Bicycle-Motorcycle Mobile Antenna" by John Allen, AA1EP
- "A Two Band Halo for V.H.F. Mobile" by Ed Tilton, W1HDQ
- "A VHF UHF 3 Band Mobile Antenna" by J.L. Harris, WD4KGD
- "Bicycle-Mobile Antennas" by Steve Cerwin, WA5FRF and Eric Juhre, KØKJ
- "Introduction to Roving" by Ward Silver, NØAX
- "Omnidirectional 6 Meter Loop" by Bruce Walker, N3JO
- "Six Meters from Your Easy Chair" by Dick Stroud, W9SR
- "The DBJ-2: A Portable VHF-UHF Roll-up J-pole Antenna for Public Service" by Edison Fong, WB6IQN
- "The VHF-UHF Contest Rover Experience — Parts 1 and 2" by Greg Jurrens, K5GJ

Chapter 16

VHF and UHF Mobile and Rover Antennas

Mobile antennas used by amateurs on the VHF and UHF bands usually support one of two applications; FM repeaters for local communication and weak-signal "roving" for competitions and activation of rare locations. The first half of the chapter, updated previously by Alan Applegate, KØBG, presents popular types of mobile antennas for VHF and UHF and discusses issues regarding mounting style and installation technique. The second half discusses the antennas and antenna systems used by rovers, including installation. This material is based on contributions from several experienced rover station builders who are identified in the text.

16.1 ANTENNAS FOR VHF-UHF FM

16.1.1 ANTENNAS FOR HANDHELD TRANSCEIVERS

For frequencies above 30 MHz, most mobile installations permit the use of a full-size antenna but for handheld radios smaller, loaded antennas are used. Antennas designed for use with VHF/UHF handheld FM transceivers can also be considered mobile antennas, even flexible "rubber duck" antennas consisting of a spiral winding of flexible wire in a flexible enclosure.

Pictured in **Figure 16.1** is a telescoping full-size quarter-wave antenna for 2 meters and beside it a flexible antenna for the same band. The flexible antenna is a helically wound radiator made of stiff copper wire enclosed in a protective covering. The inductance of the helical windings provides electrical loading for the antenna. This avoids the problems of a lengthier, cumbersome antenna attached to a handheld radio while sacrificing some efficiency and bandwidth compared to the full-size antenna. The compact flexible antenna withstands the normal rigors of portable use much better than would a full-size antenna. For these antennas, survivability over long use outweighs electrical efficiency.

The use of a full-size antenna will greatly improve the performance of handheld transceivers. By using a coaxial adapter, the transceiver can be connected directly to the feed line of mobile antennas such as those described in the following sections. This allows much more effective use of a handheld transceiver in a vehicle. A mobile antenna can also be installed on top of a metal appliance at home for improved operation. For example, a mag mount antenna on top of a refrigerator or file cabinet is a popular way of improving local coverage of a handheld radio.

SMA connectors have become quite popular on hand-

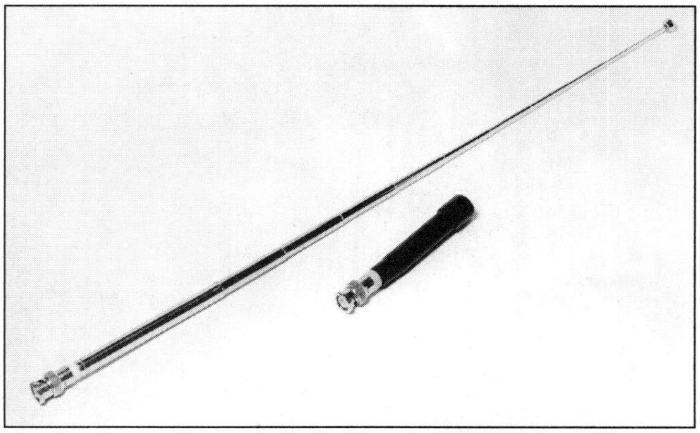

Figure 16.1 — A telescoping ¼-wavelength antenna and a flexible "rubber duck" antenna, both designed for use on 2 meters. The telescoping antenna is approximately 19 inches long when extended, while the flexible antenna is only 3½ inches long. The flexible antenna is a helically wound radiator used because of its mechanical strength.

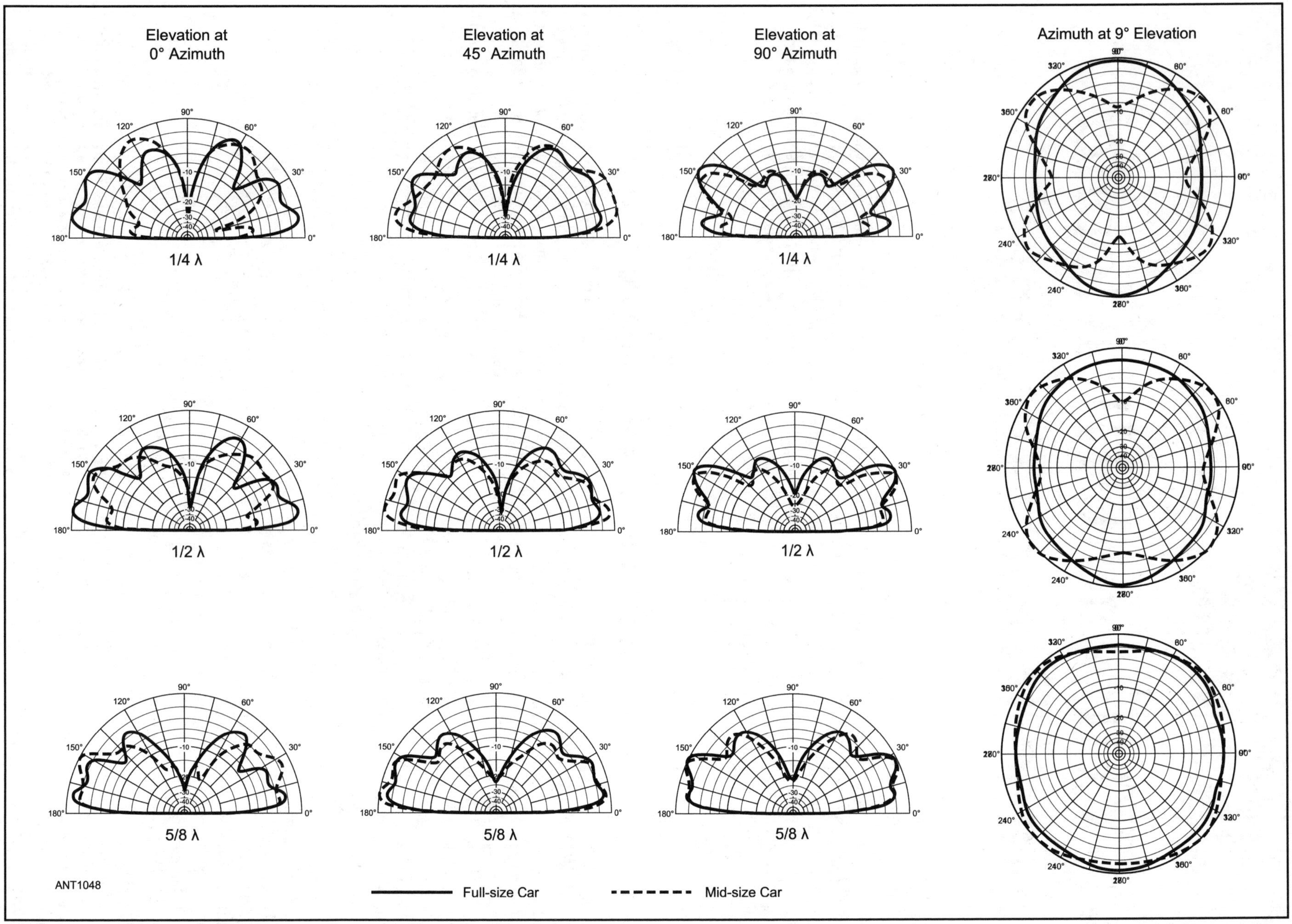

Figure 16.2 — Elevation and azimuth patterns showing the comparison for full and mid-sized cars for the three most popular VHF mobile antennas. (From "VHF Mobile Antenna Performance — The Other Half of the Story" by Dan Richardson, K6MHE.)

held radios, particularly the "reverse SMA." (See the section "Other RF Connectors" in the **Transmission Lines** chapter.) Adapters from SMA to larger connector families such as UHF can put a lot of stress on the smaller SMA. This can damage the SMA connector's attachments to the transceiver's internal circuit board. To avoid this stress a flexible cable with an SMA connector on one end and the desired RF connector on the other can be used.

16.1.2 MOBILE WHIPS

At VHF and UHF, mobile antennas are often full-size whips (meaning ¼- to ½-wavelength long) and simple collinear arrays that provide extra gain on the higher frequency bands. There is always great debate about the best antenna for urban and/or suburban FM use. Which antenna to select depends on many factors — mounting style, mechanical characteristics, local terrain — and can't be based solely on advertised gain. Mobile antennas come in ¼-, ½-, ⅝-λ, and even in collinear styles where several elements are stacked atop one another.

It has been established that in general, ¼-λ vertical antennas for mobile repeater work are not as effective as ⅝-λ verticals. With a ⅝-λ antenna, more of the transmitted signal is directed at a low vertical angle, toward the horizon, offering a gain of about 1 dB over the ¼-λ vertical. However, in areas where the repeater is located nearby on a very high hill or a mountain top, the ¼-λ antenna will usually offer more reliable performance because it radiates more power at higher vertical angles.

Dan Richardson, K6MHE, has done extensive work on mobile VHF antennas, including modeling the various types, and how mounting location affects their radiation patterns. **Figure 16.2** shows representative azimuth patterns for roof mounted antennas. (The complete article is posted on his website **k6mhe.com/files/mobile_vhf_ant.pdf**.) The radiation patterns of antennas mounted on a trunk lid would be different from those depicted in the chart. Where — and how — the antenna is mounted would determine the actual pattern. Radiation pattern distortion aside, proper trunk lid mounting is a good alternative to roof mounting, especially when garage door clearance is an issue.

As can be seen from the patterns, there really isn't much difference between the radiation patterns of a ¼-, ½-, or ⅝-λ antenna. In fact, the vehicle in question and the antenna's mounting location affect the pattern more than the style! Since most mobile VHF and UHF operation is via FM repeaters, where the difference in height between the mobile and the repeater can be a major consideration, a ¼-λ antenna with more radiation at higher vertical angles can be a better choice.

Single-band whips are inexpensive and give excellent performance with proper mounting. If more gain and multi-band use is required, the dual-band collinear that operates on both 2 meters and 70 cm is very popular. The Larsen NMO2/70BK shown in **Figure 16.3** is a typical example. Electrically it is a center-loaded ½-λ on 2 meters with gain identical to a ¼-λ ground-plane. On 70 cm it is a 2-element

Antenna Types for SSB and CW on VHF/UHF

Operating SSB and CW on 6 and 2 meters and 70 cm offers some exciting prospects for all license classes. While communications on the VHF bands are often considered line-of-site, propagation *beyond* line-of-site is common as discussed in the **Propagation of Radio Waves** chapter. This is especially true when using a "weak signal" mode such as SSB or CW, but there's a catch.

FM communications utilize vertically polarized antennas. Vertical polarization can be used for SSB but depending on the propagation path, signal strength via a vertically-polarized mobile antenna can have a 20+ dB disadvantage compared to a horizontally-polarized antenna.

Fortunately, horizontally-polarized antennas are of manageable size on the VHF bands, although they are not as simple to construct as vertically polarized whips. Dipoles and small beams present too much wind resistance to withstand the normal mobile environment. The usual solution is a loop antenna.

Figure 16.A shows an M² Antenna Systems (**www.m2inc.com**) horizontally polarized 6 meter loop called a *halo* (for circular versions) or *squalo* (if square as shown). Equivalent antennas for 2 meters and 70 cm are common. Although this particular design is square, they're still called loops and have a roughly omnidirectional pattern. The "Big Wheel" design is another option. Projects for both types of antennas are provided in the projects section.

Modern mobile SSB/CW transceivers usually output 100 W PEP on 6 meters and at least 50 W PEP on 2 meters and 70 cm. Under good band conditions, using horizontally-polarized antennas, *beyond* line-of-sight distances can exceed 200 miles even without any sky-wave or tropospheric scatter present!

Figure 16.A — A squalo (square halo) is a popular horizontally polarized VHF/UHF mobile antenna.

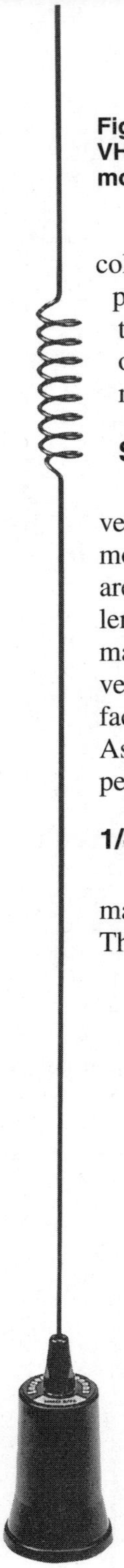

Figure 16.3 — A common style of dual-band VHF/UHF mobile whip antenna. (Larsen model NMO2/70BK)

collinear with a few dB gain over a ¼-λ groundplane. Other models are available which operate on three and even four bands. Antennas covering three or four bands are heavier and require sturdier mounting.

Six Meter Mobile Whips

Antennas for 6 meter FM operation are larger versions of those for 2 meters and often use the same mounts. However, their ground plane requirements are more significant because of the longer wavelength. If radials are used, they should be approximately λ/4 in length — about 53 inches. If used on a vehicle, center the antenna on the largest metal surface available, such as the roof or middle of the trunk. As a bonus, a 2 meter ⅝-λ whip antenna will also perform well as a λ/4 whip on 6 meters.

1/4-Wavelength Whips for VHF and UHF

The ¼-wavelength vertical whip is simple to make and can be made for nearly any type of mount. The preferred stainless-steel wire or rod is available from two-way radio shops and CB antenna dealers. Cut the whip to length using a grinding wheel or score it with a file and break it — use eye protection! Any type of wire can be used in a pinch. Coat hangers, copper wire from home wiring cable, galvanized fence wire — all have been successfully used to replace broken or missing whips. Being able to repair or substitute for a broken antenna is a skill any amateur can learn for flexibility and resiliency during emergency situations.

Table 16.1 shows the approximate lengths for λ/4 whips in the VHF and UHF amateur bands based on a 3/32-inch diameter whip. Thinner whips will be slightly longer and thicker whips slightly shorter. Be sure to include the antenna base in the total length of the antenna. If the base holds the whip with a set screw, cut the whip approximately 5% long and adjust for best SWR before making a final trim to length.

Table 16.1
¼-Wavelength Whip Lengths

Frequency (MHz)	*Length (inches)*
53	53
146	19 3/16
222	12 5/8
440	6
902	2 7/16

To Drill Or Not To Drill?

The decision to drill holes in sheet metal to mount antennas can be hotly debated. While no-hole mounts can be used satisfactorily, it is best to look at both sides of the issue.

One common reason given not to drill is if the vehicle in question is leased, but that doesn't preclude a drilled hole. If it did, there wouldn't be any leased commercial vehicles. What lease agreements specify is body damage such as from an accident or mistreatment. Properly installed NMO mounts, for example, are often acceptable.

Drilled holes and waterproof mounts also minimize common-mode current on the coaxial feed line that could interfere with or receive RFI from on-board computers and electrical devices. Aside from the hole itself, a permanent mount also minimizes damage to the finish.

16.2 MOUNTS FOR WHIP ANTENNAS

VHF and UHF antennas are much smaller and lighter than HF antennas, making mounting quite a bit easier. Some permanent mounts require drilling holes in the vehicle, while others use a hood or trunk lid seam so screw holes don't show. Still others clamp around the outside of a trunk or door edge. For temporary installations, magnetic base mounts are available. For best performance, VHF and UHF antennas should be permanently affixed to the vehicle.

The roof of a vehicle is an inviting place to mount a VHF or UHF antenna as this maximizes performance, but a few precautions need to be followed. First, it is not uncommon for side air bags to be mounted within the headliner area with control wiring running through the roof support pillars. Further, the roof is supported by cross bracing to meet rollover standards. These braces must be avoided. A repair manual for the vehicle in question is a good resource in avoiding installation problems and finding the manufacturer's preferred routes for coaxial and control cables.

The type of mount is also a concern when roof mounting, as the mount must be securely waterproof. If you're unsure about drilling holes in your vehicle (see the sidebar "To Drill Or Not to Drill?"), use the services of a local two-way radio service or vehicle entertainment system installation company.

The center of the trunk lid is a second-best location but care must be taken to assure the antenna doesn't interfere with the opening of the trunk. With the trunk fully open, place the antenna at the desired mounting location to check clearance. Don't forget to include the height of the mount itself and account for vibration of the antenna and trunk lid. Whatever mount is used, care must be taken to assure clearance of the coax cable and control leads if present.

If the antenna's overall length is too great, overhead clearance becomes a problem. While lightly touching the garage door or carport top may be acceptable, if the antenna is long enough to drag the inner surface of the door or roof, you run the chance of catching the antenna between garage door panels or getting it stuck in a rafter. This will damage the antenna and often the vehicle. In these cases, you're much better off with a shorter ¼-λ antenna.

NMO — New Motorola Mount

The recommended antenna mount for VHF and UHF antennas is the NMO (from "New Motorola") as it is waterproof even when the antenna is removed. A permanent NMO mount (see **Figure 16.4**) usually requires a ¾-inch hole. Antennas with an NMO base have an integral O-ring or washer to seal the internal surfaces against water.

SO-239 Mount

Some VHF antennas mounts have a modified SO-239 chassis coax connector with the mating PL-259 forming the base of the antenna. The standard connector type allows you to connect a coaxial cable to the antenna mount, if desired. Most SO-239 mounts *are not* waterproof, especially when the antenna is removed, and shouldn't be used for through-hole body mounting and should be capped when not in use.

Stud Mount

While popular at HF, the stud mount is less common at VHF and UHF. Larsen and other manufacturers offer mounts with a male 5⁄16-24 stud. Detachable whips are then available for all VHF and UHF bands.

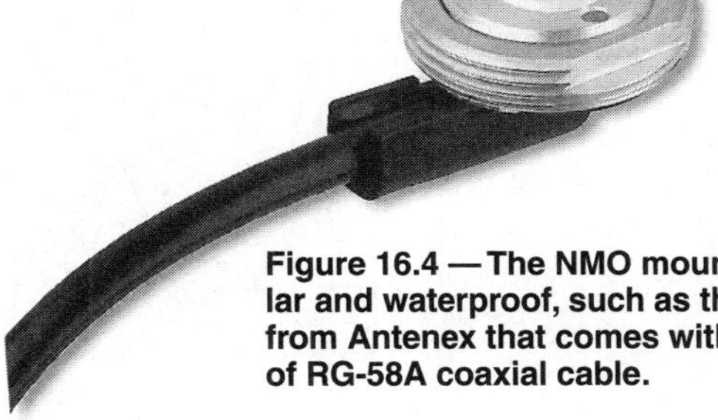

Figure 16.4 — The NMO mount is popular and waterproof, such as this MB8 from Antenex that comes with 17 feet of RG-58A coaxial cable.

Figure 16.5 — This angle bracket mounts to the vehicle body with three sheet metal screws and is drilled to accept a standard NMO mount.

Angle Brackets

Angle brackets are generally attached by three or more sheet metal screws. Properly secured, they work well for lightweight antennas but routing coax through weather seals can be troublesome.

Angle brackets come in about a dozen different styles. The one shown in **Figure 16.5** is pre-drilled for an NMO mount. The brackets are often well-suited for installation along the hood and trunk seams.

Modern vehicles have very little clearance between the body structure and the various doors and hatches. Be sure to check clearance before you actually attach the bracket. Some vehicles may require specially bent or extended brackets as well.

Clip or Lip Mounts

There are a variety of mounts designed to clamp on the edge or "lip" of a trunk, hood, or hatch. Set screws are used to secure the mount to the lip and provide the requisite grounding of the mount. The set screws both secure the mount and make a connection to the sheet metal through the body paint. **Figure 16.6A** shows a typical "hatchback" style adjustable mount with an NMO base and **Figure 16.6B** is a close-up showing the set screws holding the mount to the vehicle body.

All modern vehicles are dipped in a zinc compound before final assembly and painting. When exposed to air, zinc rapidly oxidizes but in this case the oxidation is a good thing! When a piece of road debris nicks the paint down to the zinc layer, it quickly oxidizes, and protects the base metal underneath. Do not remove this zinc coating to bare metal! This removes the protective coating, allowing the underlying steel to rust and creates an intermittent connection.

The coax must often make sharp bends around the lip of the trunk or hood. Because clearance is minimal many lip mounts come preassembled with about 10 feet of miniature, low-loss coax with a connector. While feed line loss isn't much of a concern for HF mobile antennas, it can be significant at UHF where loss is much higher. Low-loss cable such as RG-400 can be used, if necessary.

All lip mounts bring the coax cable into the trunk or passenger cabin through the weather seal, potentially

(B)

(A)

Figure 16.6 — (A) shows an adjustable lip mount made by Diamond. (B) is a close-up of the mount showing the set screws that hold the mount to the vehicle and make an electrical connection to the vehicle.

allowing water to enter. Running the cable under the seal as in Figure 16.6 is often an option. Take care to dress the cables and seals to direct water toward a drain hole or other exit.

Glass Mounts

"Through-glass" or "on-glass" mounts such as the Larsen KG2/70CXPL use adhesive to hold the base of the antenna and cable fitting to opposite sides of a window, relying on metal foil surfaces to create a capacitor and pass VHF/UHF signals. The mount must be clear of window heating strips and cannot be used on tinted (passivated) glass that contains colloidal-sized metallic particles to provide protection from harmful UVA and UVB rays. Antenna performance is somewhat of a compromise because of the lack of a ground-plane but allows a permanent mount without holes, clamps, or magnets.

The outside surface of the coaxial feed line also becomes part of an on-glass antenna because there is no ground-plane, creating a path for common mode current. This allows the coax to both radiate and pick up noise in the vehicle interior.

Luggage Rack Mounts

The biggest issue with using luggage racks as an antenna mount is excessive ground loss. Most luggage racks consist of plastics, composites, and insulated metal beams electrically isolated from the vehicle's metal body. As such, they rarely provide a good ground-plane for the antenna and routing the feed line through door or window weather seals can create leaks. Like on-glass antenna mounts, luggage rack mounting is a compromise for when a permanent mount is not possible

Magnet Mounts

Mag (magnet) mounts are very popular for VHF and UHF operation. They rely on capacitance to make their electrical connection to the vehicle ground plane, so common-mode current on the feed line shield can become a problem. Nevertheless, mag mounts do deliver acceptable performance at VHF and UHF.

Mag mounts are available with the antenna and feed line attached as in **Figure 16.7** or as the mount by itself. There are mag mounts for any of the popular antenna bases — NMO, stud mount, and SO-239. A spare dual-band mag mount, a set of VHF and UHF whips, and several coax connector adapters are a valuable addition to your emergency response capabilities.

Figure 16.7 — A typical dual-band VHF/UHF mag mount with an integral antenna and feed line.

Be wary of the fine grit that can work its way under the magnet and scratch the paint. If you do use a mag mount for long periods of time, remove it and clean the magnet surface occasionally. For temporary installations, a plastic sandwich bag around the magnet protects the finish against grit while still maintaining a solid attachment.

Specialty Brackets and Adapters

Because there are so many variations in vehicles there are many different types of brackets for mounting antennas. One of the most common is the three-way mirror mount in **Figure 16.8** that is sold by many companies. This particular version is drilled to pass the shoulder insulator of the SO-239 to ⅜-24 threaded stud-mount adapter shown in the

Figure 16.8 — The mirror-mount style of clamp-on bracket. This particular bracket is drilled for an SO-239 to ⅜-24 stud mount. The bracket can be mounted on vertical or horizontal struts.

foreground. You can find a wide variety of brackets at hamfest flea markets, from vendors of antenna accessories, online from manufacturers and distributors, and at truck stops and CB shops.

The performance of the antenna depends on the size of what the bracket is attached to. Most mirrors mounts are just barely big enough to act as a counterpoise at UHF but if they are securely mounted to a metal vehicle body, performance will be acceptable. The radiation pattern of the antenna will rarely be omnidirectional due to the off-center antenna placement.

Adapters are also available that convert mounts such as the NMO to other types of bases and connectors, such as the various stud mounts and SO-239 connector. This allows your antenna mount to accommodate other types of antennas but generally increases the length of the antenna by an inch or so, lowering the antenna's resonant frequency. A few mount adapters should be included in your mobile equipment kit.

16.3 PROJECT: BICYCLE MOBILE ANTENNAS FOR VHF AND UHF

Operating while mobile from a bicycle is increasingly popular for recreation or during commuting to work. (The Bicycle Mobile Hams of America website, **www.bmhahams.org**, has a lot of information about operating from your bike.) Being able to radiate an effective signal is straightforward but requires a slightly different approach to conventional mobile operation. For starters, most bicycles and accessories are not made of steel, so mag-mount antennas cannot be used. The frame of the bicycle is mostly oriented vertically so the conventional horizontal ground plane is not available. And of course, personal safety is of paramount importance on a bicycle. This project and the articles included in this book's downloadable supplemental content provide some examples of effective antennas and mounting techniques you can use on your bike.

Unlike the conventional λ/4 ground-plane, the vertical

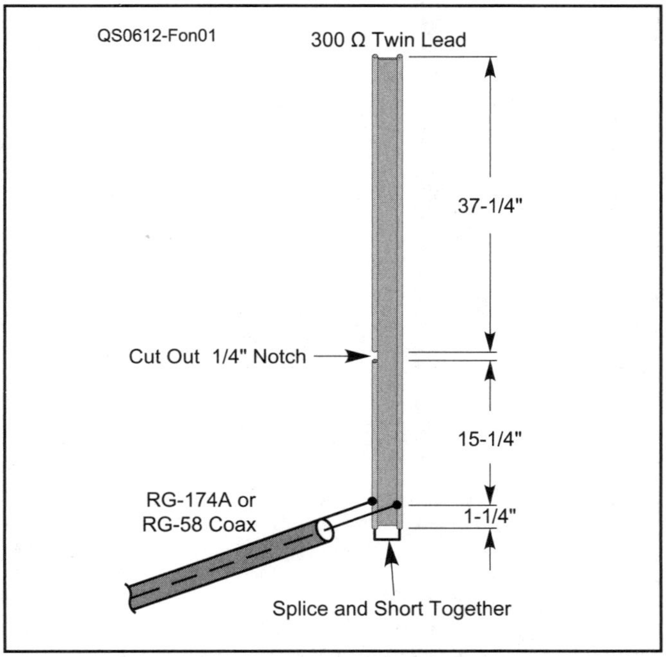

Figure 16.9 — A 2 meter flexible J-pole antenna. Any 50 Ω coaxial cable can be used. RG-58 or RG-8X is recommended for bicycle or other mobile use.

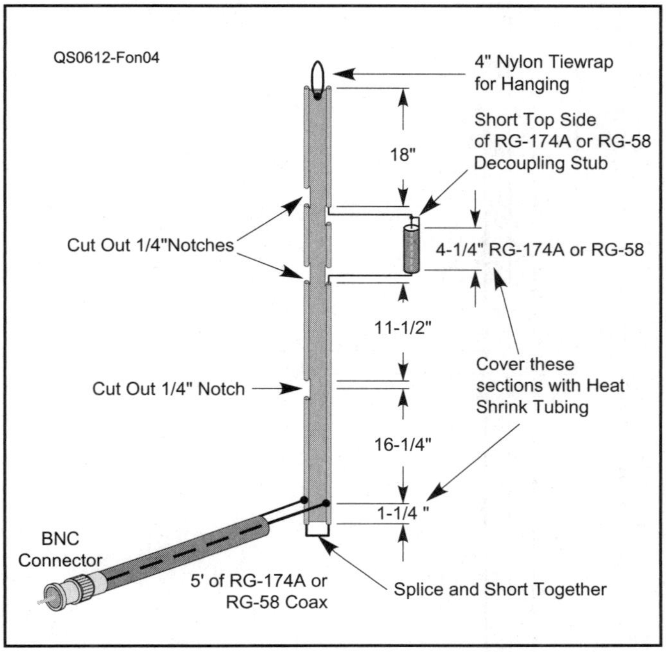

Figure 16.10 — The 2 meter/70 cm J-pole version. See the construction article included with this book's supplemental content for information about tuning the antenna and attaching the feed line.

dipole or J-pole do not use the bicycle frame as part of the antenna. While simple to construct, the main challenge is to support the antennas on the bicycle without adding a lot of weight. A common accessory provides the solution — a bicycle safety flag. Safety flags lift a high-visibility pennant on a slim fiberglass tube that mounts to the bike using a pressed-steel axle mount. Lightweight antennas can be attached to the fiberglass tube and a feed line run along the frame to the transceiver.

The J-pole shown here is a flexible "roll-up" design by Edison Fong, WB6IQN, originally published in March 2007 *QST* as the DBJ-2. **Figure 16.9** shows the initial 2 meter antenna design. RG-174A coax can be used as in the original design which was optimized for weight. Less lossy RG-58 or RG-8X coax would be a better choice if more weight is not a problem. The antenna in **Figure 16.10** works on both 2 meters and 70 cm. Both antennas are discussed in detail, including more construction and tuning details, in the article provided with this book's downloadable supplemental content.

An alternate antenna shown in **Figure 16.11** is a vertical dipole based on the design by Charles Lofgren, W6JJZ, "The Bike 'n Hike Special" described in *QST's* Hints and Kinks. The antenna consists of a 39-inch radiating $\lambda/2$ whip of #14 or #16 AWG wire and an RG-58 coaxial tuning stub attached to the feed line ¼ λ below the radiating whip. The shorted stub adds some inductive reactance at a low impedance point in the feed line to raise the impedance to 50 Ω. From that point, any length of 50 Ω feed line to the transceiver can be used. (See the section "Matching Stubs" in the **Transmission Line System Techniques** chapter for information about how the shorted stub tunes the antenna system.)

The length of the stub depends on the velocity factor (VF) of the coaxial cable being used. Solid polyethylene dielectric coax has a VF of 0.66 (66%), while foam dielectric cable is typically 0.80 (80%). Check the velocity factor of your cable using an antenna analyzer or consult the table of coax characteristics in the chapter on **Transmission Lines**.

The stub should be 1.6 inches long for VF 66% cable and 2.0 inches long for VF 80% cable. Begin with the stub about ⅜ inch too long so that it can be trimmed to length after instal-

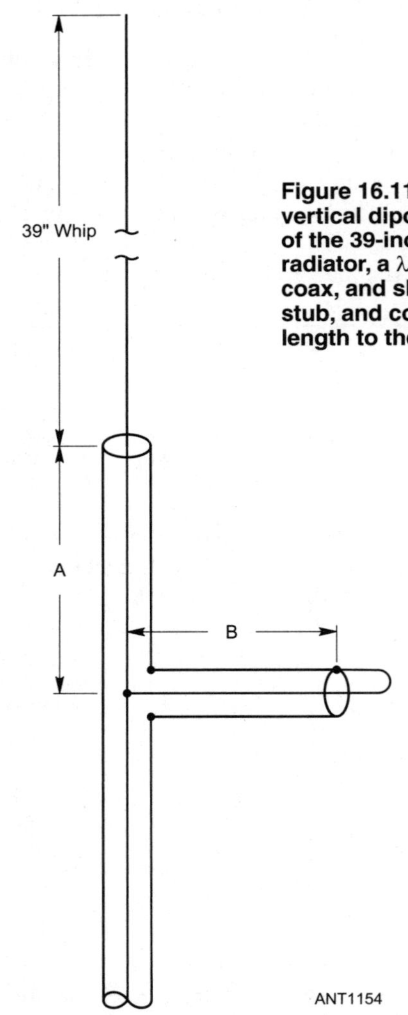

Figure 16.11 — The vertical dipole consists of the 39-inch vertical radiator, a $\lambda/4$ section of coax, and shorted tuning stub, and coax of any length to the transceiver.

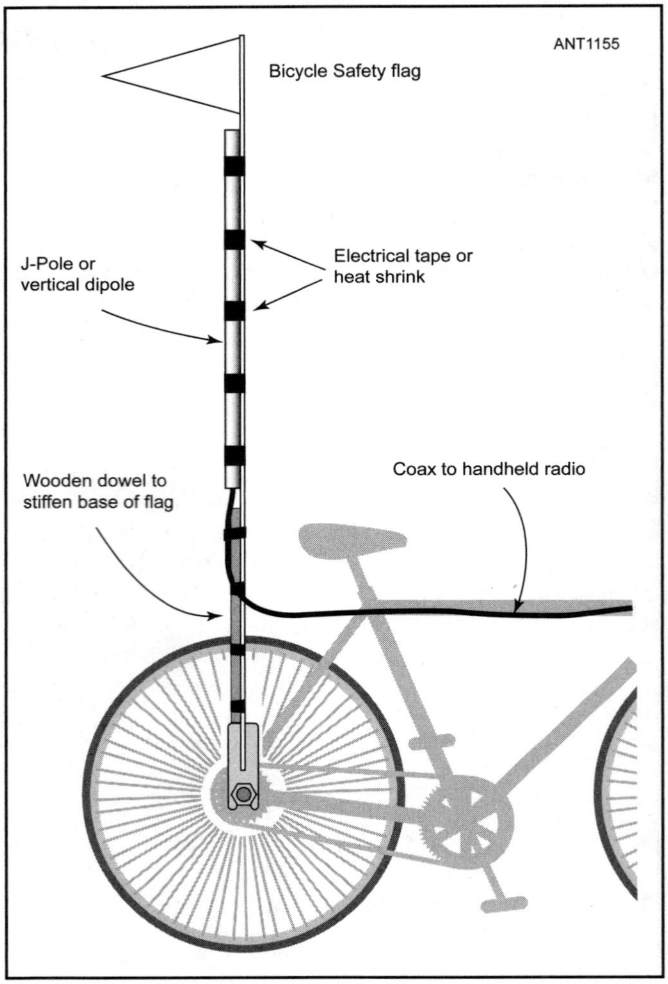

Figure 16.12 — Either the J-pole or vertical dipole can be attached to the fiberglass tube supporting a rear-axle mounted bicycle safety flag. Use tape or heat-shrink tubing to secure the antenna to the fiberglass. A wooden dowel can be used to stiffen the tube if necessary.

lation. Note that the length of the stub includes the short piece of center conductor that connects to the main feed line center conductor. Approximately ¼ inch is enough center conductor and braid to attach the stub to the main feed line. Leave approximately ½ inch of dielectric and a small bit of center conductor exposed on the other end to adjust the stub length.

To attach the stub to the coax feed line, remove about 1 inch of jacket from the main feed line. Using sharp wire cutters, cut through the braid without damaging the dielectric and push it toward the jacket. Use a sharp knife to expose a short section of the center conductor. Solder the stub's center conductor to the main feed line center conductor and insulate it with liquid electrical tape or heat-resistant glue. Slide the main feed line's braid back toward the stub attachment point. Solder the braid of the main feed line and stub. Weatherproof the stub attachment point with more liquid electrical tape and a wrap of good-quality electrical tape.

At the other end of the stub, twist the braid and center conductor of the stub together but don't solder them. Mount the antenna in the clear (at least several feet above the ground and away from any metallic objects). Use an SWR meter or antenna analyzer to adjust the length of the stub to give minimum SWR at the desired frequency. Since the stub is intentionally too long, adjustment consists of untwisting the braid and center conductor, removing a small amount of dielectric, twisting the braid and center conductor together again, and re-measuring. When the stub is at the desired length, solder the braid and center conductor together and seal the stub with heat shrink or tape.

Secure the completed antenna to the safety flag's fiberglass tube with heat shrink tubing or wraps of tape as shown in **Figure 16.12**. If the assembly needs additional support, a length of wooden dowel can be taped to the fiberglass for additional rigidity. If the assembly vibrates or rubs against the frame or a rack, a length of plastic hose can be used to protect the antenna.

16.4 PROJECT: BIG WHEEL FOR TWO METERS

The following section is an overview of the construction project, "A New Spin on the Big Wheel" by L. B. Cebik, W4RNL, and Bob Cerreto, WA1FXT, in the March 2008 issue of *QST*. The complete article detailing the design's history, evolution, and critical elements is included with this book's downloadable supplemental content with all construction details and drawings.

Most attempts to develop a horizontally polarized omnidirectional (HPOD) 2 meter antenna have sought to minimize the antenna's size. Shapes such as circles (halos), squares and rectangles usually result in the need for either hypercritical dimensions or difficult matching conditions — or both. By turning to more conventional full size structures using three dipoles, we can reduce the number of critical parameters and ease the process of replicating the antennas in a home workshop. In fact, we shall describe two versions of the same basic antenna. One is a triangle of three dipoles that folds into a flat package, suitable for easy transport to a hilltop. The other is a circle of three dipoles suitable for mobile operation that requires somewhat less space but needs greater precision in construction. Both antennas share a common feed system and display broadband characteristics that ease the builder's task.

The Three Dipole Design

The center and right outlines in **Figure 16.13** show the basic triangular and circular forms that emerged from the original design at left. Note that the current magnitude curves place the feed points of the dipoles at high current, relatively low impedance positions.

Both forms are very broadband in virtually every operating parameter once the builder gets the dimensions correct. The triangle, with a wider separation between the dipole end tips, is less critical with respect to dimensions, but requires more space. The circular version, with tighter coupling between dipole tips, requires more careful construction, but results in a more compact structure. In fact, for the same performance, the circular three-dipole antenna is smaller than the original big wheel.

The far-field performance of the three-dipole HPODs and the big wheel are virtually identical. Therefore, the data in

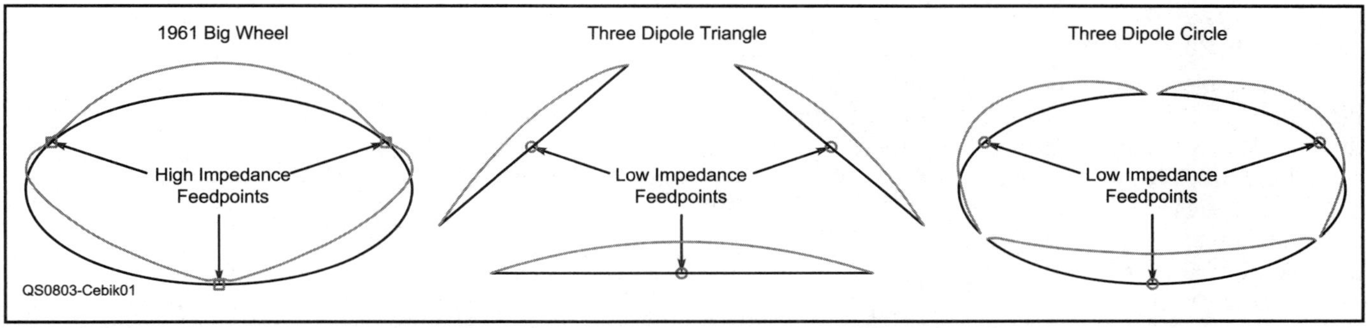

Figure 16.13 — Relative current magnitudes on three different three element HPOD antennas.

Figure 16.14 applies equally to all three designs. At a height of 20 feet above average ground, the three elements in all of the designs provide an average gain in the lowest lobe of about 7.2 dBi. The azimuth pattern is as close to circular as is possible with fewer than four elements. The gain variation for the worst case was less than 0.3 dB.

The modeled SWR curve applies to both of the three-dipole models. Because the dipoles of the final designs present feed point impedance close to 50 Ω, we may use standard coaxial cable of virtually any length to reach the hub without changing the impedance significantly. Matched to a 50-Ω main feed point at the hub junction, the SWR curve is very flat and in the model shown in the graph, the SWR is acceptable (well under 2:1) for at least 8 MHz in the 2 meter range. Moreover, the circularity of the pattern and the gain are virtually constant across the entire 2 meter band. Even though the antenna is likely to see service only in the first MHz of the band, the broadband characteristics ease the difficulty of successfully building a version at home.

To obtain a 50-Ω main feed point impedance, the three-dipole arrays use a somewhat nonstandard arrangement at the hub. Both of our three-dipole designs use a series connection of the lines with the source. The resulting hub impedance is close to 150 Ω, and any stray reactances become very small portions of the impedance magnitude. Therefore, a simple λ/4 matching section can handle the impedance transformation to the 50-Ω region.

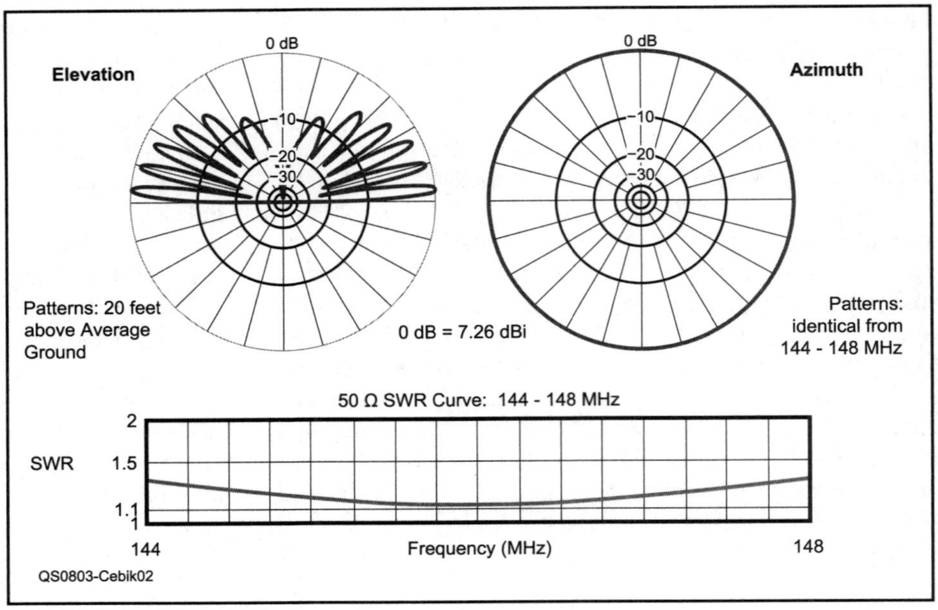

Figure 16.14 — Representative elevation and azimuth patterns and 50-Ω SWR curve for a three-dipole HPOD antenna using either a triangular or a circular shape at 20 feet above average ground. The patterns of the original big wheel are virtually identical in shape and strength.

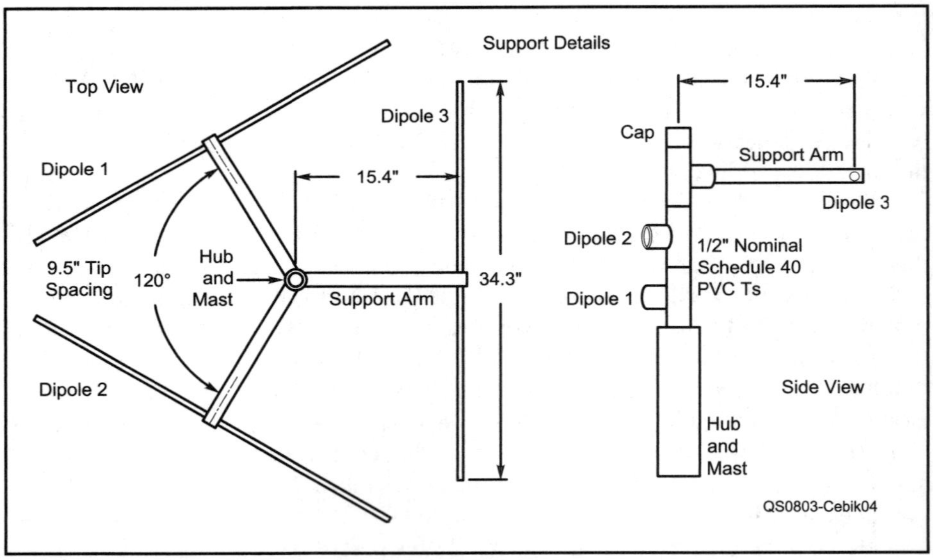

Figure 16.15 — Some details of the support structure used for the three-dipole 2 meter triangle.

The Three-Dipole Triangle

Each dipole is broadside to a direction 120° from the adjacent dipoles. The goal is to find dimensions that will achieve this goal plus provide a workable feed point impedance at each dipole. The prototype constructed to test the basic model of this arrangement used ½-inch diameter aluminum tubing as a light

Table 16.2
Dimensions for a Three-Dipole 2 Meter Triangle

Design Frequency (MHz)	*Element Diameter (inches)*	*Radius to Feed Point (inches)*	*Dipole Length (inches)*	*Tip-to-tip Spacing (inches)*
146	0.5	15.4	34.3	9.5
146	0.375	15.3	34.7	9.15
144.5	0.5	15.6	34.7	9.6
144.5	0.375	15.5	35.1	9.25

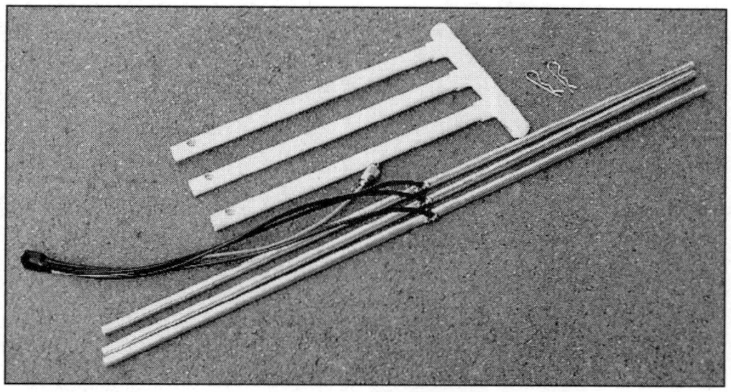

Figure 16.16 — The triangle HPOD disassembled for transport.

Figure 16.17 — The circular HPOD suitable for mobile use.

but sturdy material. Each dipole used a 2-inch length of 0.375-inch diameter fiberglass rod as a center insulator. The dipole halves are held in place with #6 stainless steel sheet metal screws. The gap should be as small as is feasible, ⅛ to ¼ inch. These same screws fasten the ends of the coax cable to the element with a stainless steel washer to prevent electrolysis between the aluminum element and the copper wires. For ease of disassembly in portable operation, the prototype used lugs under the screws.

Table 16.2 lists some dimensions for both 0.5- and 0.375-inch aluminum tubing, perhaps the two most likely materials for this project. For the triangle, 146 MHz was used as the design frequency because the performance and the SWR do not significantly change across the band. This center-design frequency also provided a good view of the antenna's broadband properties. However, the table also lists dimensions that are usable if the builder wishes to place the performance center of the antenna at 144.5 MHz. The prototype used the half-inch-diameter material and the 146 MHz dimensions for that material.

Note the length of the dipole. It is about 3.3 inches shorter than an independent dipole composed of the same material. The resonant impedance (50 Ω) is lower than the usual value for a standard dipole of about 70 Ω. The three dipoles in the triangle do interact by virtue of both the proximity of their feed points and the closeness of their tips. The dimensions of the triangle are therefore quite critical to successful operation of the array as designed. However, in the triangular form, they are not finicky, and cutting errors of ⅛ to ¼ inch will not materially affect performance.

In fact, the relatively relaxed conditions for the triangle prompted the particular design that emerged. The prototype may be useful for field or hilltop service, since the support structure and the elements and their cable come apart and store in a flat package for transport. **Figure 16.15** provides a few of the support structure details and **Figure 16.16** shows the antenna disassembled for transport.

For a permanent installation or for mobile use, you may prefer a circle of three dipoles as shown in **Figure 16.17**. The circle has no loose dipole ends and is more compact than the triangle. Indeed, it is aesthetically more pleasing. However, such pleasure comes at a cost. The construction and adjustment of the elements are somewhat more critical, although completely manageable.

16.5 HALO FOR SIX METERS

The following section is based on the construction project "Omnidirectional 6-Meter Loop" from the book *Magic Band Antennas for Ham Radio* by Bruce Walker, N3JO (see Bibliography). The full article is included in this book's downloadable supplemental information as are two other articles, "A 6 Meter Halo" by Paul Danzer, N1II and "6-Meter Halo Antenna for DXing" by Jerry Clement, VE6AB. One of these versions will be a good addition to your mobile station, depending on your resources. VE6AB's halo is shown mounted on a mobile mast in **Figure 16.18**.

You may also enjoy reading two additional construction articles also included in the downloadable supplement; "Six Meters from your Easy Chair," by Dick Stroud, W9SR in the January 2002 issue of *QST* and one of the original halo articles, "A Two-Band Halo for V.H.F. Mobile," by Ed Tilton, W1HDQ, in the September 1958 issue of *QST*.

The halo (or "squalo" if the loop is square rather than round — see **Figure 16.19**) satisfies several key elements for an inexpensive 6 meter antenna: omnidirectional, horizontal polarization, no exotic components or materials, easy to adjust. With care, the construction should be robust enough for mobile use. Use an anti-oxidation compound such as Noalox or Penetrox for all unsoldered metal-to-metal connections to avoid corrosion.

The halo is basically a half-wave dipole bent into a circle and fed with a gamma match. **Figure 16.20** shows the basic design and typical dimensions for the Omnidirectional 6 Meter Loop by Bruce Walker, N3JO. **Figure 16.21** shows the dimensions of the plate holding the ends of the main antenna together, the feed point connector, and the mast

Figure 16.18 — A 6 meter halo antenna can be used as a mobile antenna if carefully constructed. The antenna shown here was designed and built by Jerry Clement, VE6AB.

Figure 16.19 — The "squalo" is the square version of the halo antenna. This one is available from Cushcraft.

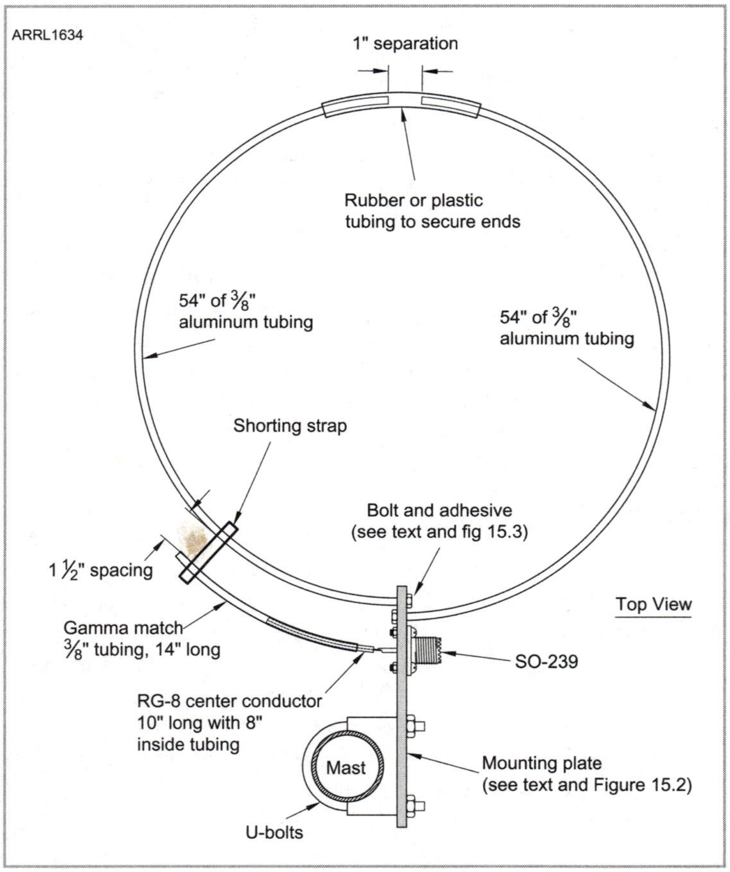

Figure 16.20 — Dimensions of N3JO's omnidirectional 6 meter loop.

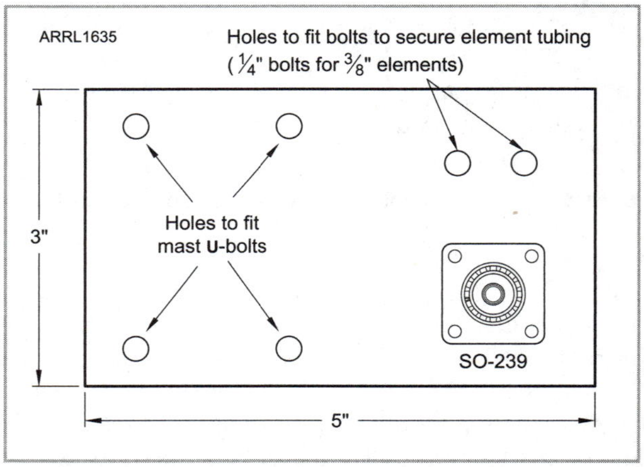

Figure 16.21 — Mounting plate details and dimensions.

mounting holes. The resonant frequency is quite sensitive to tip-to-tip spacing at the ends of the dipole but should initially be in the range of 50 to 52 MHz without requiring critical measurements or assembly. Feed point impedance is adjusted using the gamma match.

Similar to the gamma match design in the **VHF, UHF and Microwave Antennas** chapter, the assembly shown in **Figure 16.22** is made from a 14-inch piece of the ⅜-inch tubing used for the main antenna. The gamma match tube should be curved to follow the main halo ring. Spacing between the main antenna and the gamma match tube is 1½ inch. The gamma match is adjusted by moving the strap back and forth. This should be done with the antenna well off the ground and away from any other conductive surfaces.

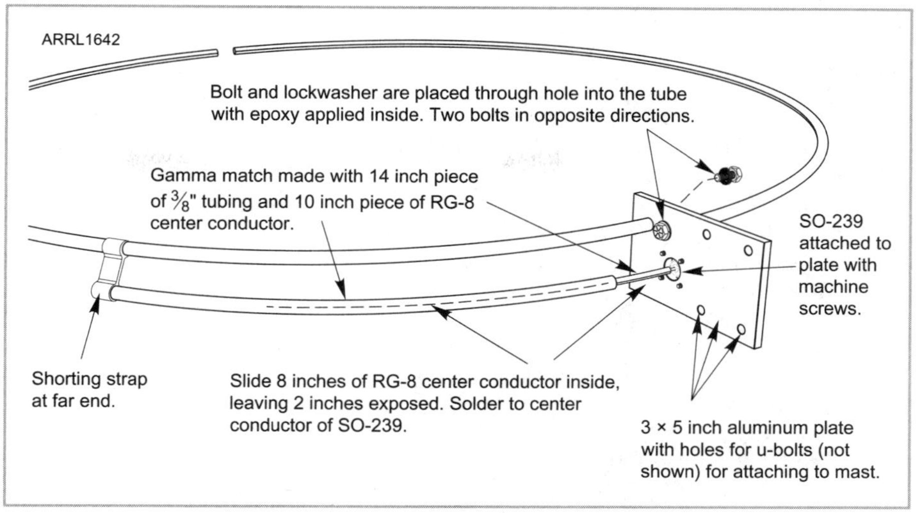

Figure 16.22 — The halo matching section details.

16.6 ROVER ANTENNA SYSTEMS

Roving is a big part of VHF+ contesting and getting more popular all the time. The basic idea is to activate grid squares that are the contest multipliers. Rover stations can either operate in nearly continuous motion or can drive to and operate from a few advantageous locations. Rover antennas are of the same type used at fixed stations but mounted on masts or racks attached to or carried by vehicles.

Because the stations move, often operating at highway speeds, roving places extra requirements on antennas and mounting hardware. A top-tier rover station may also have antennas for as many bands as a fixed station. This makes for many station design and building challenges.

This section discusses some of those challenges and how different rover stations approach the problem. Thanks to contributors Andrea Slack, K2EZ; Wyatt Dirks, ACØRA; Steve Kostro, N2CEI; Rich Rosen, K1DS; Jim Duffey, KK6MC; and Darryl Holman, WW7D who shared some of their tips. You can also get a lot of good ideas from looking at the ARRL Soapbox web pages for after-contest reports. (**www.arrl.org/soapbox**) Two articles on roving are included in the downloadable supplemental information, as well.

16.6.1 ROVER ANTENNA SELECTION

As you can see in **Table 16.3**, there are two primary antenna designs on the VHF/UHF "low bands" of 6 meters through 70 cm: halos and Yagis. The Moxon rectangle is also popular on 6 meters. For these bands, the antennas are large enough to be limited by vehicle overhang laws. On higher frequency bands, straight-element and loop-element Yagis dominate. Beginning at 5.6 GHz, dishes become practical for a mobile station.

Six Meters

Ideally, a 6 meter antenna should be at least one wavelength (about 20 feet) above the ground. If the band is open, height is less critical. Three-element Yagis are popular but may have to be stowed when the vehicle is moving due to mechanical concerns or size limits. For 2-element Yagis, the Moxon rectangle is becoming popular, particularly the SM-50 "stressed Moxon" design in **Figure 16.23** manufactured by PAR Electronics which is only 84 × 31 inches (see **www.parelectronics.com/stress-moxon.php**).

Figure 16.23 — The stressed Moxon SM-50 by PAR Electronics is a Moxon rectangle designed with the forward element under tension. The resulting lightweight construction is robust under rover conditions.

Table 16.3
Examples of Rover Antennas

Band	*Antenna*	*Notes*
6 meters/50 MHz	3-element Yagi	6-feet long to meet overhang limits
	Halo	
	Stressed Moxon	
	Hex beam	Rotatable in motion
2 meters/144 MHz	7-element Yagi	Below 6m Yagi on mast
	Stacked halos	
	8-element "Cheap Yagi"	
	4-element "Cheap Yagi"	Rotatable in motion
1¼ meters/222 MHz	10-element Yagi	With 70cm Yagi on cross-boom
	Stacked halos	
	8-foot Yagi	
	10-element "Cheap Yagi"	
	6-element "Cheap Yagi"	Rotatable in motion
70 cm/432 MHz	15-element Yagi	With 1¼ m Yagi on cross-boom
	Stacked halos	
	8-foot Yagi	
	12-element LFA Yagi	Passive elements mounted with single screw for easy replacement
	8-element "Cheap Yagi"	Rotatable in motion
33 cm/902 MHz	6-foot loop Yagi	Single or on H-frame
	8-foot Yagi	
	33-element loop Yagi	12-foot boom
	10-element "Cheap Yagi"	Rotatable in motion, incl on vert pol for FM
23 cm/1.2 GHz	6-foot loop Yagi	Single or on H-frame
	8-foot Yagi	
	24-element loop Yagi	6-foot boom
	10-element "Cheap Yagi"	Rotatable in motion, incl on vert pol for FM
13 cm/2.3 GHz	6-foot loop Yagi	Single or on H-frame
	45-element loop Yagi	7-foot boom
	18-element Yagi	Rotatable in motion, commercial WiFi Yagi
3.4 GHz	6-foot loop Yagi	On H-frame
	45-element loop Yagi	4.5-foot boom
5.6 GHz	2-foot dish	Not mounted on vehicle
	0.9-m dish	Dual-band with 10 GHz
10 GHz	20-inch dish	Homebrew feedhorn
	2-foot dish	Not mounted on vehicle
	0.9-m dish	Dual-band with 5.6 GHz

"Cheap Yagis" refers to designs by WA5VJB at **www.wa5vjb.com/yagi-pdf/cheapyagi.pdf**

6-Meter Hex Beam by WW7D

Another 6 meter antenna that takes well to the open road is the 2-element hex beam. With no free element ends to oscillate in the wind, similar to a stressed Moxon, there is less mechanical vibration. The overall footprint is smaller than a Yagi, as well. Darryl Holman, WW7D, provides construction details of his 6 meter hex beam in the article "A 6m Hex Beam for the Rover" that is included in the downloadable supplemental information. The article also includes several good photos of his vehicle-mounted antenna mast.

Halos, including stacks of multiple halos, are popular on 6 meters, as well. A number of stations use one or two halos in motion, then switch to higher-gain beams when at a stationary operating location.

2 Meters through 70 cm

For contacts within populated areas, 2 meters can be the most popular band. For all three of these bands, a modest-size horizontally polarized beam with a fairly wide pattern is best. This allows a rover to make contacts quickly across a wide area. If the route will not be in a populated area, a longer beam works better although its beamwidth is smaller. Halos for local/regional coverage and a longer-boom Yagi is a good combination.

Resources for Roving

While this book has a lot of good information about antenna systems for rovers, there is a lot to learn. The best resource for learning about effective roving is other rovers, and the best place to find other rovers is a contest club. There are many contest clubs such as the Society of Midwest Contesters (**www.w9smc.com**), and some specialize in VHF+ contesting, such as the Packrats (**www.packratvhf.com**) in Pennsylvania and New Jersey and the Pacific Northwest VHF Society (**www.pnwvhfs.org**). You can join most clubs even if you don't live in their neighborhood and many post their newsletters and other articles online. You will be sure to find useful information about roving and rover stations there. You can find contest clubs by using the ARRL's Find-A-Club service (**www.arrl.org/find-a-club**) and entering "contest" in the search window.

FM Antennas

Making FM QSOs is an important part of rover strategy, so be sure to include a set of vertically polarized antennas in your rover antenna system. If you are close to an urban or suburban area, whips will do fine. (Remember that a ⅝-wave 2 meter whip will work on 6 meters, too.) Farther out, a small beam oriented for vertical polarization is required.

902-1296-2304-3456 MHz

Loop Yagis are the usual antennas used by rovers on these bands. The antennas should be mounted with the loops facing downward to limit damage when passing under tree limbs. It's easy to straighten out damaged loops by removing them from the boom and using a rolling pin to roll them back into shape. Repair one loop at a time to maintain their proper order on the boom. Versions with 6-foot booms are usually adequate, especially if the rover is in an advantageous location. "Loopers" can be mounted on a single cross boom or in an H-frame array. The long boom models may need additional stabilization to keep them aligned with the other antennas and each other.

5-10-24 GHz

Small dishes are best on these bands, although some rovers have used horns over shorter distances. A 2-foot diameter dish with a dual feed for 5 and 10 GHz is popular. Dual-feed designs by W1GHZ are available for 10 GHz and 24 GHz. These bands usually require transverters which should be mounted in a waterproof box behind the dish to minimize feed line losses. The rover should be able to carefully aim the dish in both azimuth and elevation because the beamwidth of these dishes can be as little as 2–3 degrees.

16.6.2 HALOS AS ROVER ANTENNAS

The halo's lack of directionality is sometimes an advantage and sometimes a disadvantage. It is an advantage when moving because there is no aiming required. Omnidirectional patterns also make it easier to find stations on the band. This is important in populated areas when operators are moving to different frequencies and the rover has to find them quickly.

A disadvantage (along with lower signal strength in the main lobe) is that in lower-activity areas such it is common to stay on or near the calling frequency and rely on antenna directivity to provide isolation from other stations. A rover operating with halos in those areas is at a disadvantage because multiple stations would be received at the same time while they could use the beams to reduce interference.

Stacking halos with $\lambda/2$ separation produces 3 dB of gain over a single halo by narrowing the vertical beamwidth. While the required height is not very practical on 6 meters, on 2 meters through 70 cm halos can be stacked even in motion. In practice the narrower vertical beamwidth aims the peak radiation closer to the horizon so the perceived improvement is a bit higher. Two 6 meter halos can be stacked on an extendable mast, so that when the mast is collapsed, both halos are close together and function like a single halo. A stationary operating location, the mast can be extended to yield the extra gain.

Finally, halos are simple antennas and, if well-built, robust. Should damage occur, the halo can often be bent back into shape. The halo is also easy to tune. When every on-the-road or at-the-site minute counts, survivability and simplicity of tuning are key attributes.

Halos on Third Harmonics

Some 2 meter halos will also operate on 70 cm, the third harmonic, with gain broadside to the plane of the halo. (This is straight up if the halo is horizontal.) Oriented vertically with the feed point at the bottom, this type of halo has a bidirectional pattern broadside to the antenna at low angles and nulls in the plane of the halo. Beamwidth is around of 120 degrees. Mounting two halos vertically and at right-angles to each other creates a switchable forward-rearward or side-to-side pattern. This is a handy compromise between omnidirectional and small beam antennas. Not all halos will operate with acceptable SWR on the 3rd harmonic and some experimenting is required.

16.6.3 ROVER ANTENNA SUPPORTS

There are many ways to get your antennas in the air. The easiest is a telescoping mast like a painter's pole or fiberglass mast with locking-sections. A drive-on base can be simple — a piece of lumber with a pipe flange having a short, threaded pipe stub attached. The mount in **Figure 16.24** used by Jim Wilson, K5ND, is all-wood design. Roll a tire onto the mount, add the mast, secure it to the vehicle's body or roof rack, and up go the antennas. If you have a trailer hitch, U-bolts can clamp a telescoping mast or painter's pole to a hitch-mount bike rack as in **Figure 16.25**.

Trailer-hitch mounted masts as in **Figure 16.26** are practical and sturdy. Tripods mounted in the bed of a pickup truck

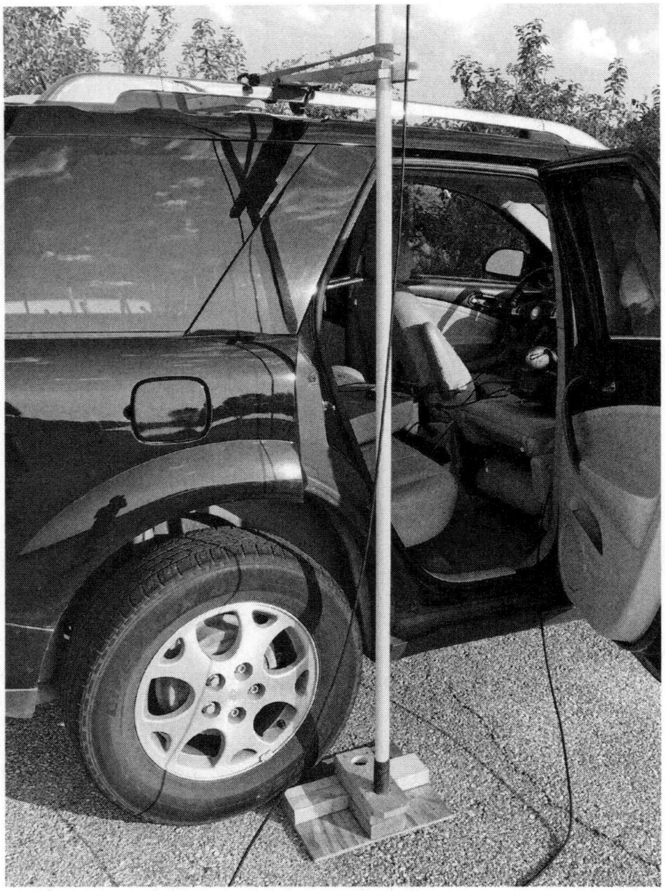

Figure 16.24 — A simple "drive-on" mount for a painter's pole or other inexpensive mast. A strut attached to K5ND's vehicle roof rack secures the mast at about head height.

Figure 16.25 — A trailer-hitch bike rack can serve as a sturdy mount for an extendable mast such as this aluminum telescoping pole on NØAX's car. The mast can be attached to the bike rack with U-bolts or brackets.

can support large arrays (**Figure 16.27**) as can custom racks that mount on vehicle roof racks (**Figure 16.28**). The exact design will depend on your vehicle and whether you want to operate in motion or "shoot and scoot" style, stopping at a series of operating sites. If the mast will be exposed while driving, a "bend-over" capability on the mount is a good idea to avoid mast damage if there is a collision with something overhead.

Many rovers have found that a simple system of raising the antennas once an operation spot has been reached is the most efficient. Some rovers have been fortunate enough to acquire vans or trucks with powered telescoping masts. Others have used manual telescoping masts, military surplus mechanical crank elevated masts, or cantilevered masts that can be laid down for travel and raised when on site. Additional roof racks or custom frames are usually required for large masts and antenna arrays. Having all the antennas attached to the mast and the coaxial cables connected makes for a quick set-up on site. The easier and quicker it is to set up and tear down, the more effective on-site time will be.

Rotating Rover Antennas

Using a regular fixed-station antenna rotator requires the use of an inverter to supply the 120 V ac from a vehicle's dc power system. Inverters are not expensive but if you prefer all-dc operation, the Yaesu G-800 series of rotators operates from 13.8 V dc. To speed up rotation, some operators use a 12 V to 24 V converter to power the rotator, with much faster rotation as a result.

The ever-popular "Armstrong" manual rotator is an option as well but it is hard for a single operator to peak up a weak signal when trying to rotate an antenna. Some operators use the vehicle itself as the rotator with antennas fixed on their mounts. Another option is to have large, high-gain antennas for use with the vehicle stopped and a low-gain set for use while in motion.

Antenna Height and Width Limits

There are a few different maximum heights that tractor-trailers may have, but the most common limit is 13 feet 6 inches. Antennas are not as rigid as truck bodies, and many places don't actively trim the smaller branches because the trucks simply push them aside without damage. Roving with antennas at the maximum height limit is likely to result in antenna damage. Heights under 12 feet are more reasonable.

The maximum allowed vehicle width is 8 feet (96 inches), which includes anything attached to the vehicle such as antennas. (Trailers can be up to 102 inches wide.) Yagis

Figure 16.26 — Heavier trailer-hitch masts can support several antennas. This mast for KK6MC's rover is supported by a strut attached to the roof rack.

can be trimmed to boom lengths of approximately 6 feet. Mounting points for such an antenna must be in the center of the boom instead of at a wind or weight balance point. Remember to account for turning radius which can be quite a bit longer than boom length for lower-frequency antennas. Fixed-mounted Yagis, or those rotated only when stopped, can be much longer.

16.6.4 MISCELLANEOUS ROVER NOTES

For what it is worth, I have 4 to 5 mpg worth of antenna. I used to get 19 to 20 mpg highway but now get 15 mpg on the highway. — *K2EZ*

I prefer wood booms to aluminum booms. Wood doesn't fatigue like metal does and this can become important when driving at highway speeds, where the antennas may be oscillating for hours in the air stream. I also drive down many Forest Service roads with low-hanging foliage, so the antennas do get rather beat up. The wooden antennas booms don't bend, but occasionally break. Wood booms are much easier to replace than metal booms. — *WW7D*

Keep coax runs short and use the best low-loss, flexible coax available. Test all cables each time before hitting the

Figure 16.27— A roof-top tripod for TV antennas is mounted in WØZF's pickup truck on a wooden frame bolted to the bed. This also makes installing a rotator easy and even large arrays can be supported at highway speeds.

Figure 16.28 — N6NB's 11-band (6 meters through 24 GHz) mobile antenna farm is mounted on a frame attached to the vehicle's roof rack.

road as center pins can wander and cables can break. — *K1DS*

Getting your feed lines into the car needn't require any holes. KK6MC uses a "pool noodle" slit down one side on a window and around the vehicle frame (see **Figure 16.29**). Run the cables inside and raise the window until the foam compresses around them.

Remember that the rover is usually the little station being sought by the bigger fixed stations, so having an adequate signal is usually OK and that bigger antennas can be unwieldy and less productive. — *K1DS*

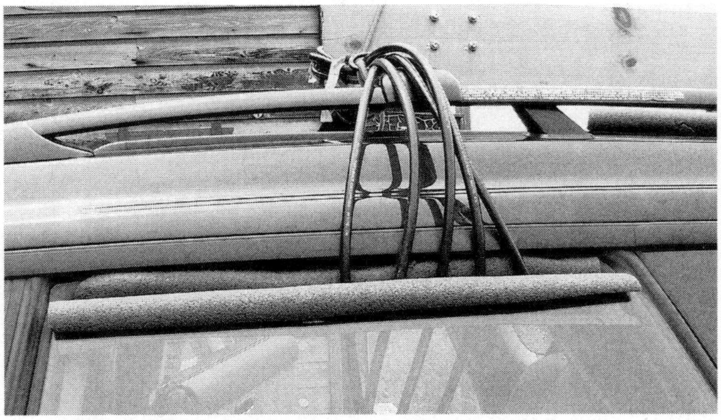

Figure 16.29 — An inexpensive "pool noodle" makes a coax-friendly window seal for getting feed lines into and out of KK6MC's vehicle. Slit the foam along one side, slide it over the window, and raise the window until the foam seats around the cables.

Figure 16.30 — N2CEI and K4SME mounted everything on the trailer, including the station in the heavy-duty toolbox. The trailer-mounted towers can handle substantial antennas with ease.

16.7 REFERENCES AND BIBLIOGRAPHY

J. Allen, "Simple 2 Meter Bicycle-Motorcycle Mobile Antennas," *QST*, Aug 1995, pp 69-70.

S. Cerwin and E. Juhre, "Bicycle-Mobile Antennas," *QST*, Mar 1993, pp 52-53.

J. Clement, "6-Meter Halo Antenna for DXing," *QST*, Feb 2017, pp 30-33.

P. Danzer, "A 6 Meter Halo," *QST*, Sep 2004, pp 37-39.

E. Fong, "The DBJ-2: A Portable VHF-UHF Roll-up J-pole Antenna for Public Service," *ARRL Antenna Compendium*, Vol. 8, pp 155-157.

B. Walker, *Magic Band Antennas for Amateur Radio* (Newington: ARRL 2019)

TABLE OF CONTENTS

Chapter 17 —
Downloadable Supplemental Content

Supplemental Articles

- "A 12-Foot Stressed Parabolic Dish" by Richard Knadle, K2RIW
- "A Parasitic Lindenblad Antenna for 70 cm" by Anthony Monteiro, AA2TX
- "A Portable Helix for 435 MHz" by Jim McKim, WØCY
- "A Simple Fixed Antenna for VHF/UHF Satellite Work" by L.B. Cebik, W4RNL
- "An EZ-Lindenblad Antenna for 2 Meters" by Anthony Monteiro, AA2TX
- "Build a 2-Meter Quadrifilar Helix Antenna" by David Finell, N7LRY
- Converted C-Band TVRO Dishes PDF
- "Double-Cross Antenna – A NOAA Satellite Downlink Antenna" by Gerald Martes, KD6JDJ
- "EME with Adaptive Polarization at 432 MHz" by Joe Taylor, K1JT, and Justin Johnson, GØKSC
- "Inexpensive Broadband Preamp for Satellite Work" by Mark Spencer, WA8SME
- "L Band Helix Antenna Array" by Clare Fowler, VE3NPC
- "Quadrifilar Helix As a 2 Meter Base Station Antenna" by John Portune, W6NBC
- "Simple Dual-Band Dish Feed for Es'hail-2 QO-100" by Mike Willis, GØMJW; Remco den Besten, PA3FYM; and Paul Marsh, MØEYT
- Space Communications Antenna Examples PDF
- "The W3KH Quadrifilar Helix" by Eugene Ruperto, W3KH (plus two Feedback items)
- "The Two Meter EZ Lindenblad Revisited," by Tom Planer, KJ9P and Grant Zehr, AA9LC
- "Two-Meter Eggbeater" by Les Kramer, WA2PTS and Dave Thornburg, WA2KZV
- "Work OSCAR 40 With Cardboard-Box Antennas" by Anthony Monteiro, AA2TX
- "WRAPS: A Portable Satellite Antenna Positioning System" by Mark Spencer, WA8SME
- "WRAPS Rotator Enhancements Add a Second Beam and Circular Polarization" by Mark Spencer, WA8SME

Chapter 17

Antennas for Space Communications

When we consider amateur space communications, we usually think about two basic modes: satellite and Earth-Moon-Earth (EME — also referred to as *moonbounce*). Both modes communicate using one of the Earth's satellites — our natural satellite (the moon) or one of a variety of man-made satellites. The distances involved and the motion of the targets place special requirements on antennas for both types of communications as discussed in this chapter. (Antennas for meteor scatter modes are covered in the **VHF and UHF Antenna Systems** chapter.)

Because of technological advances, particularly regarding new digital modes that allow communications with extremely weak signals, the traditional distinction between antenna systems for satellite communications and for EME communications has become blurred. Thus, this chapter has been rearranged by antenna type and then specific requirements for each type of operation are discussed.

Material in this chapter has been contributed by several authors. Dick Jansson, KD1K, developed satellite-related topics while the EME material is largely the work of Dave Hallidy, K2DH and Joe Taylor, K1JT. Wherever possible, designs referenced or illustrated in the text are also listed in the Bibliography. For additional information on constructing antennas, feeds and equipment techniques for use at microwave frequencies, see the AMSAT website (**www.amsat.org**) and the ARRL and RSGB books listed in the Bibliography. All of these resources provide a wealth of information for the experimenter.

17.1 SPACE COMMUNICATION ANTENNA SYSTEMS

There are two main differences between the moon and man-made satellites in orbits closer to the Earth. The first is one of distance. The moon is about 250,000 miles from Earth, while man-made satellites in highly elliptical orbits can be as far as 52,000 miles away. This 5:1 difference in distance makes a huge difference in the signals that arrive at the satellite, since transmission loss varies as the square of the distance. In other words, the signal arriving at the moon is 20 dB weaker than that arriving at a geosynchronous satellite 25,000 miles high, due to distance alone.

The second difference between the moon and a man-made satellite is that the moon is a *passive reflector* — and not a very good one at that, since it has a craggy and rather irregular surface, at least when compared to a flat mirror-like surface that would make an ideal reflector. Signals scattered by the moon's irregular surface are thus weaker than those for better reflecting surfaces. By comparison, a man-made satellite is an *active* system, where the satellite receives the signal coming from Earth, amplifies it and then retransmits the signal (usually at a different frequency) using a high-gain antenna. Think of a satellite as an ideal reflector, with gain.

The net result of these differences between a man-made satellite and the Earth's natural satellite is that moonbounce (EME) operation challenges the station builder considerably more than satellite operation, particularly in the area of antennas. Successful EME requires higher transmitting power and receiver sensitivity, along with sophisticated computer software for digital modes or an excellent operator capable of pulling weak analog signals out of the noise.

There are areas of commonality between satellite and EME antenna requirements, of course. Both require consideration of the effects of polarization and elevation angle, along with the azimuth directions of transmitted and received signals. High-performance Yagi arrays or helical antenna systems designed for satellite operation will likely suffice to make EME contacts using digital modes such as those of the

Receiving NOAA Satellite Signals

US National Oceanographic and Atmospheric Administration (NOAA) polar orbiting weather satellites (POES) transmit data for production of gray-scale images of the ground below them. Data is transmitted at 137 MHz frequency used by the NOAA satellites and can be received twice a day. There are many free programs available to decode the data and produce images. The article "Double-Cross — A NOAA Satellite Downlink Antenna" included with this book's downloadable supplemental information describes a fixed antenna shown in the photo designed for the 137 MHz frequency and can receive signals from any other satellite in that band. The SatNOGS system described in this chapter's section on Antenna Position Control can also be used to receive weather satellite data automatically.

Figure 17.A — The Double Cross antenna is made from four dipoles. [Gerald Martes, KD6JDJ]

WSJT software suite (**www.physics.princeton.edu/pulsar/K1JT**). Dish antennas, such as those converted from commercial C-band (4 to 8 GHz range) TVRO (television, receive only) service will certainly suffice for both types of communication.

This chapter will first explore antennas suitable for satellite operations and then describe the antennas needed for EME work.

17.1.1 ANTENNA SYSTEMS FOR SATELLITES

Amateur satellites provide links from 2 meters and up and these provide opportunities to use antennas of many types — from the very simple to the pretty complex. Antenna design and construction requirements for use with amateur satellites vary from low-gain antennas for low-Earth-orbit (LEO) satellites to higher-gain antennas for the high-altitude elliptical-orbit satellites (HEO). The AMSAT website (**www.amsat.org**) is a good general resource for antenna and transceiver design, operating information and satellite parameters. See the AMSAT website's Station and Operating Hints page for antenna designs for satellite operations and other useful accessories and station components.

Contacts can be made via FM LEO satellites with a basic dual-band VHF/UHF FM transceiver. Some amateurs manage to work the FM birds with hand-held radios and a multi-element directional antenna such as the popular Arrow Antenna shown in **Figure 17.1A**. Of course, this means they must aim their antennas at the satellites, even as they cross overhead. It is best to hold the antenna and manually aim it instead of using a tripod. This allows you to rotate the antenna to compensate for polarization shift in the ionosphere and from satellite tumbling. This reduces fading and improves contact quality and speed. A diplexer, shown in Figure 17.1B allows a single radio to use different

(A)

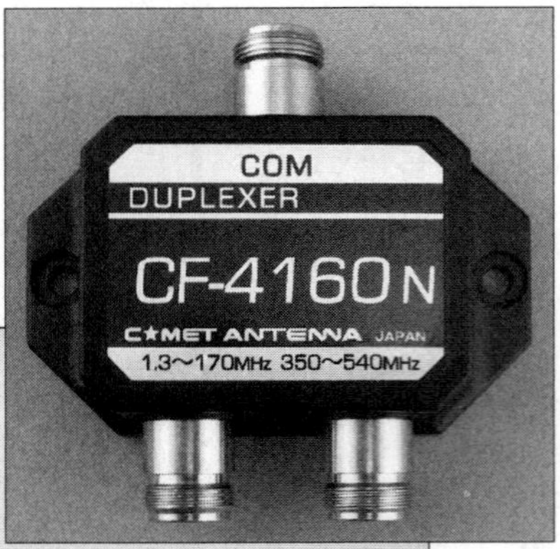

(B)

Figure 17.1 — A dual-band handheld and a lightweight Arrow Antenna (A) can be used to make contacts through FM repeater satellites such as SO-50, AO-91, AO-91 and others. When used in an open location free of foliage, the antenna provides enough gain to work the satellites, even close to the horizon. A diplexer (B) allows a single dual-band radio to use the 2 meter and 70 cm sections separately. These units are available from manufacturers of dual-band hand-held and mobile radios. [Photo (A) courtesy Keith Baker, KB1SF]

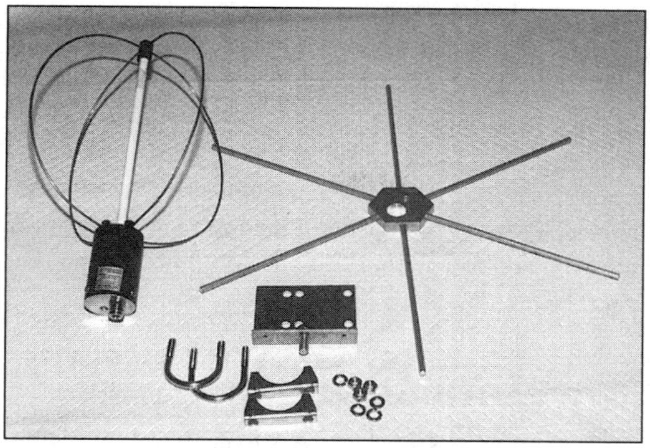

Figure 17.2 — Eggbeater antennas are popular for base station LEO satellite operations. This M² EB-432 eggbeater antenna for 70 cm is small enough to put in an attic. Antenna gain pattern is helped with the radials placed below the antenna.

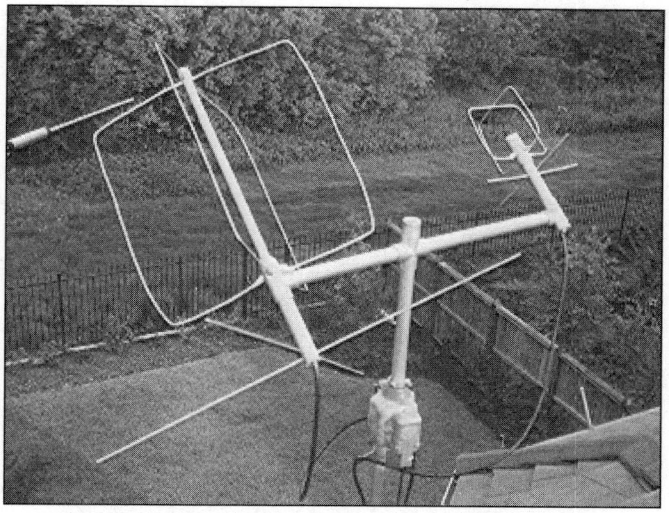

Figure 17.5 — Jerry Brown, K5OE, uses his Texas Potato Masher antennas to work LEO satellites.

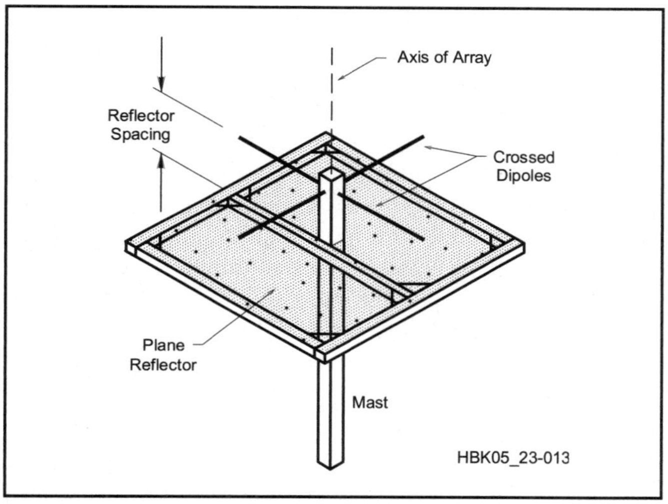

Figure 17.3 — The Turnstile Over Reflector antenna has served well for LEO satellite service for a number of years.

antennas on each band, such as on 2 meters and 70 cm.

Omnidirectional fixed antennas that do not track a satellite are a home station option for starting out of if using rotators is not possible or practical. The M² Enterprises EB-144 and EB-432 Eggbeater antennas shown in **Figure 17.2** are a commercial option. The turnstile-over-reflector antenna has been around for a long time, as shown in **Figure 17.3**. L.B. Cebik, W4RNL, described a fixed satellite antenna system that uses crossed-Moxon antennas to produce a circularly polarized, hemispherical pattern. This system is described in the article "A Simple Fixed Antenna for VHF/UHF Satellite Work" included with this book's downloadable supplemental information and is shown in **Figure 17.4**.

For even better performance, at the modest cost of a single, simple TV antenna rotator, check out the fixed-elevation *Texas Potato Masher* antenna by Gerald Brown, K5OE, shown in **Figure 17.5.** This antenna provides a dual-band solution for medium-gain directional antennas for LEO satellites. This is a considerable improvement over omnidirectional antennas and does not require an elevation rotator for good performance. If an az-el rotator is available (see az-el rotator projects at the end of this chapter) reflecting screens can be added to the Moxon-pair antennas of W4RNL for even better performance.

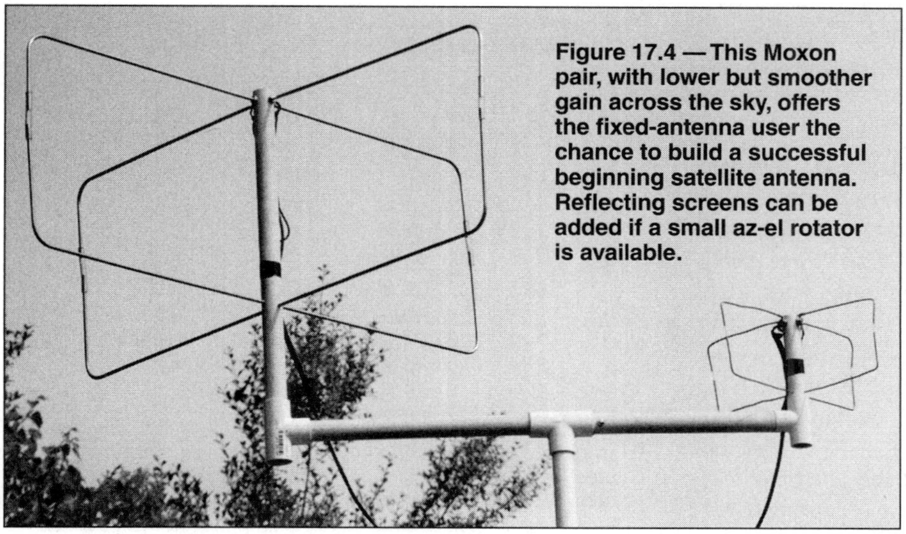

Figure 17.4 — This Moxon pair, with lower but smoother gain across the sky, offers the fixed-antenna user the chance to build a successful beginning satellite antenna. Reflecting screens can be added if a small az-el rotator is available.

A step up from a rotatable fixed-elevation antenna is a pair of short Yagi antennas similar to the handheld Arrow in Figure 17.1. A 3-element Yagi on 2 meters and a 4-7 element Yagi on 70 cm will work quite well with a broad enough pattern that elevation control is not required. A fixed elevation of 25 to 30 degrees will work reasonably well. Inexpensive Yagi designs by WA5VJB

Table 17.1
Amateur Satellite Band Designations

10 meters (29 MHz): H
2 meters (145 MHz): V
70 cm (435 MHz): U
23 cm (1260 MHz): L
13 cm (2.4 GHz): S
5 cm (5.6 GHz): C
3 cm (10 GHz): X

for satellite operation are online at **www.wa5vjb.com**.

There was still one early LEO satellite operating on the 10 meter band as of early 2019. The 1974 AO-7 spontaneously recovered from a battery failure and can be used whenever its solar panels are illuminated. Its 10 meter downlink covers 29.3 to 29.5 MHz. Low-gain antennas for 10 meters, such as dipoles, are used to receive the signal from this satellite.

High Earth Orbit (HEO) satellites such as the Phase 3 platforms launched in the 1980s are no longer operational. AMSAT's GOLF (Greater Orbit, Larger Footprint) program will place satellites into 500 to 600 km orbits that require somewhat higher gain antennas and transmit/receive ability. For these satellites, a set of higher-gain Yagi antennas will be required for VHF and UHF links (See the Yagi Arrays section of this chapter.) Satellites also use S-band (2.4 GHz) and X-band (10 GHz) frequencies (see **Table 17.1**), such as the QO-100, the Es'hail-2/P4-A geosynchronous platform serving most of ITU Region 1. (See **amsat-dl.org/p4-a-nb-transponder-bandplan-and-operating-guidelines**.) Similar platforms are under development, such as the "five-and-dime" architectures using C-band (5 GHz) and X-band. The GOLF series of satellites referenced in the previous paragraph may include some microwave capabilities, as well. Advantages of microwave systems include:

- Good performance with physically small downlink antennas.
- Availability of good quality receive converters and transmitting modules.
- Availability of preamps at reasonable prices.

A number of people advocate S-band operation, including Bill McCaa, KØRZ, who led the team that designed and built the AO-13 S-band transponder and James Miller, G3RUH, who operated one of the AO-40 command stations. Ed Krome, K9EK, and James Miller have published a number of articles detailing construction of preamps, downconverters and antennas for S band. (See **Table 17.1** for a list of the satellite band designations used throughout this chapter.)

Preamplifiers and Feed Lines

Preamplifiers are available from Advanced Receiver Research, High Sierra Microwave, SSB Electronic, and other vendors. The WA5VJB preamp design "cookbook" (**www.wa5vjb.com/references/preamp-Cookbook.pdf**) has a number of tips and circuits for building your own preamp. An inexpensive broadband preamp suitable for receiving telemetry by WA8SME is described in the article "Inexpensive Broadband Preamp for Satellite Work" included in this book's downloadable supplemental information and is available for purchase from AMSAT.

Preamps will need to be mounted at the antennas and their manufacturers will have the appropriate mounting hardware and enclosures available. Preamps are generally not needed for hand-held antennas since the feed line length is very short.

When installing a fixed station satellite antenna, pay attention to feed line quality and loss. LMR-240 is a good choice for satellite antennas, especially on 70 cm. For long feed lines, consider using hardline between the station and the antenna support with a flexible line making the connection to rotating antennas.

17.1.2 ANTENNA SYSTEMS FOR EARTH-MOON-EARTH (EME)

The antenna is arguably the most important element in determining an EME station's capability. It is not accidental that the baseline station requirements outlined in **Table 17.2** use Yagi arrays on the VHF bands and parabolic dishes at 1296 MHz and above. One of these two antenna types is almost always the best choice for EME.

The gains of some nominal antennas of each type are illustrated graphically in **Figure 17.6**, which helps to show why Yagis are nearly always the best choice for EME on the VHF bands. They are light, easy to build and have relatively low wind resistance. Stacks of four Yagis are small enough that they can be mounted on towers for sky coverage free of nearby obstructions. Larger arrays of 8, 16 or even more Yagis are possible, although the complexity and losses in phasing lines and power dividers then become important considerations, especially at higher frequencies. Long Yagis are narrowband antennas, usable on just a single band.

We usually think of the linear polarization of a transmitted signal as being "horizontal" or "vertical." Of course, on the spherical Earth these concepts have meaning only locally. As seen from the moon, widely separated horizontal antennas may have very different orientations (see **Figure 17.7**). Therefore, in the absence of Faraday rotation an EME signal transmitted with horizontal polarization by station A will have its linear polarization misaligned at stations B and C by angles known as the spatial polarization offset. (Faraday rota-

Table 17.2
Typical Antenna and Power Requirements for CW EME

For use with JT65 or other encoded digital modes, subtract approximately 10 dB of gain or power.

Freq (MHz)	*Ant Type*[1]	*G (dBi)*	*HPBW (deg)*	*TxPwr (W)*
50	4×12 m	19.7	18.8	1200
144	4×6 m	21.0	15.4	500
432	4×6 m	25.0	10.5	250
1296	3 m	29.5	5.5	160
2304	3 m	34.5	3.1	60
3456	2 m	34.8	3.0	120
5760	2 m	39.2	1.8	60
10368	2 m	44.3	1.0	25

[1]Example antennas for 50, 144 and 432 MHz are Yagi arrays with stated lengths; those for 1296 MHz and higher are parabolic dishes of specified diameter.

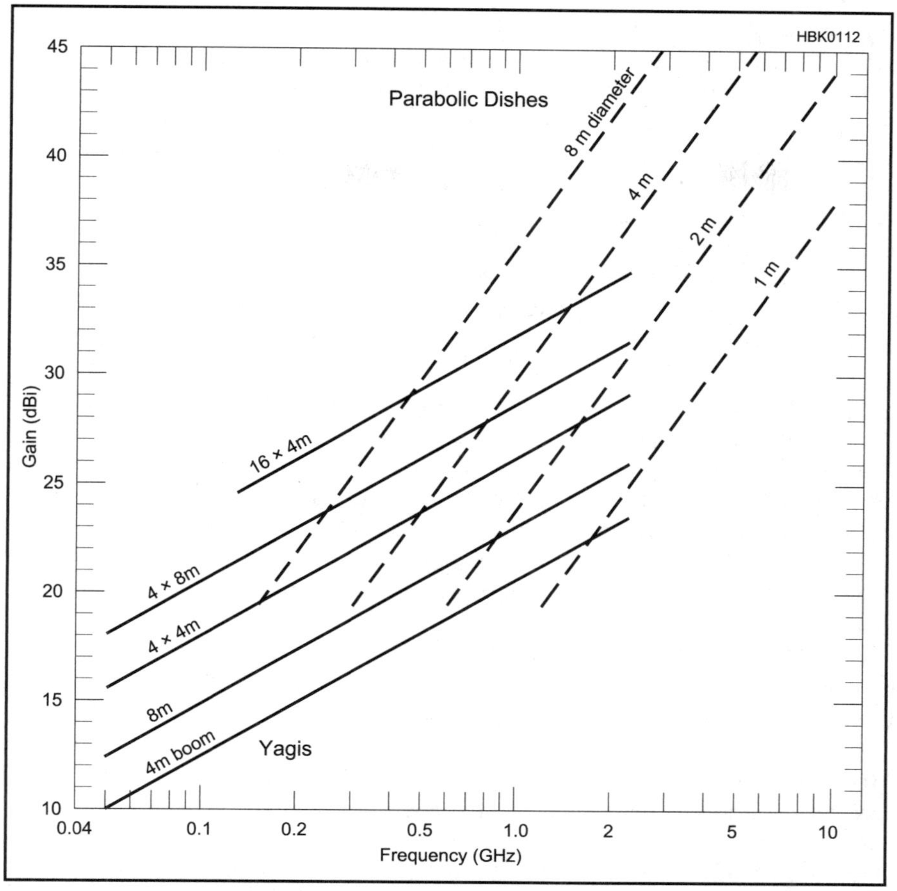

Figure 17.6 — Representative gains of practical Yagi antennas, arrays of Yagis and parabolic dishes as a function of frequency. Yagi arrays make the most cost-effective and convenient antennas for EME on the VHF bands, while parabolic dishes are generally the best choice above 1 GHz.

tion is a rotation of the polarization of radio waves when the waves travel through the ionosphere, in the presence of the Earth's magnetic field.) In Figure 17.7 the signal from A arrives with vertical polarization at B and at 45° to the horizon at C. Suppose C is trying to work A and $q_s = 45°$ is the spatial polarization offset from A to C. The return signal from C to A will be offset in the opposite direction, that is, by an amount $-q_s = -45°$. The Faraday rotation angle θ_F, on the other hand, has the same sign for transmission in both directions. Thus the net polarization shift from A to C is $\theta_F + q_s$, while that from C to A is $\theta_F - q_s$. If θ_F is close to any of the values ±45°, ±135°, ±225°, …, then one of the net polarization shifts is nearly 90° while the other is close to 0°. The result for stations with fixed linear polarization will be apparent one-way propagation: for example, A can copy C, but C cannot copy A.

Obviously no two-way contact can be made under these conditions, so the operators must wait for more favorable circumstances or else implement some form of polarization control or polarization diversity. One cost-effective solution is to mount two full sets of Yagi elements at right angles on the same boom. Arrays of such cross-polarized or "Xpol" Yagis make especially attractive EME antennas on the VHF and lower UHF bands because they offer a flexible solution to the linear polarization misalignment problem. As an example, **Figure 17.8** shows the

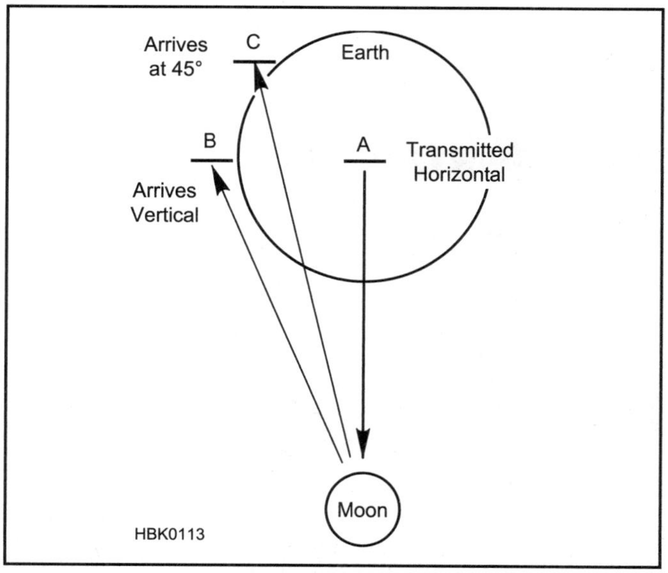

Figure 17.7 — The spherical Earth creates spatial polarization offsets for well-separated stations with horizon-oriented linear polarization. Here, a signal transmitted horizontally at A arrived with vertical polarization at B and midway between horizontal and vertical at C. When combined with Faraday rotation, offsets close to 45° can lead to apparent one-way propagation. See text for details.

Figure 17.8 — Array of four 10-element, dual-polarization 144-MHz Yagis at KL7UW. Alaskan frost makes the horizontal and vertical elements stand out clearly. A pair of loop Yagis for 1296 MHz can be seen inside the 2 meter array.

4 × 10 element, dual-polarization EME array at KL7UW. This antenna and a 160-W solid-state amplifier have accounted for hundreds of EME contacts with the state of Alaska on 2 meters.

At 1296 MHz and above, gains of 30 dBi and more can be achieved with parabolic dishes of modest size. As a result, these antennas are almost always the best choice on these bands. Their structure does not depend on any radio frequency resonances, so in many ways dishes are less critical to build than Yagis. Element lengths in high-gain Yagis must be accurate to better than 0.005 λ, while the reflecting surface of a dish need be accurate only to about 0.1 λ.

A parabolic antenna has a single feed point, so there are no losses in phasing lines or power splitters. You can use a dish on several bands by swapping feeds, and with suitable feed designs you can produce either linear or circular polarization, including dual polarizations. A very attractive and convenient option is to transmit in one sense of circular polarization and receive in the opposite sense. Transmitting in right-hand circular and receiving in left-hand circular has become the standard for EME at 1296 and 2304 MHz, and will probably become the standard on higher bands as well. More information about circular polarization is presented later in this chapter.

As made clear in Figure 17.6, the 432 MHz band lies in a transition region where both Yagis and parabolic dishes have attractive features. Either four long Yagis or a 6 meter dish can produce enough gain (about 25 dBi) to let you work many other EME stations on this band. Many linear-polarization systems are already in use — for good reason, since most amateur use of this band is for terrestrial communication — so converting everyone to circular polarization is impractical. Therefore, schemes have been devised to physically rotate dish feeds and even whole Yagi arrays to cope with the resulting polarization alignment problems. Another scheme is to use a dual-polarization dish feed or dual-polarization Yagis, as described above and increasingly used on 144 MHz. This approach has not yet gained wide popularity on 432 MHz, however.

Antenna Pattern

A clean pattern with good suppression of side and rear lobes is important for all EME antennas — especially at 432 MHz and above, where excessive noise pickup through sidelobes can significantly increase the system noise temperature, T_S. For Yagi arrays you should use modern, computer optimized designs that maximize G/T_S, the ratio of forward gain to system noise temperature. Be sure to pay attention to maintaining a clean pattern when stacking multiple antennas. First sidelobes within 10-15° of the main beam may not be a major problem, because their solid angle is small and they will look mostly at cold sky when EME conditions are favorable. Side and rear lobes farther from the main beam should be suppressed as much as possible, however. Remember that even close-in sidelobes will degrade your receiving performance at low elevations.

For parabolic dishes, G/T_S is optimized by using a feed with somewhat larger taper in illumination at the edge of the dish than would yield the highest forward gain. Best forward gain is generally obtained with edge taper around −10 dB, while best G/T_S occurs around −15 dB. Edge taper of −12 dB is usually a good compromise. Some good reproducible designs for dish feeds are described or referenced later in this chapter.

17.2 CIRCULARLY POLARIZED ANTENNAS

Linearly polarized antennas are horizontal or vertical in terms of the antenna's position relative to the surface of the Earth, a reference that loses its meaning in space. (See the **Antenna Fundamentals** chapter for a discussion on polarization.) If spacecraft antennas used linear polarization, ground stations would not be able to maintain polarization alignment with the spacecraft because of its changing orientation. Thus the ideal antenna for random satellite signal polarization is one with *circular polarization* or *CP*.

Circular polarization is simply linear polarization with a direction that continually rotates as it travels through space as in **Figure 17.9**. The direction of polarization can be imagined as the second hand of a watch that is moving forward with the wave such that the second hand makes one complete revolution per wavelength traveled. The second hand represents the *instantaneous polarization* of the signal.

Figure 17.5 shows a pair of Yagi antennas mounted on

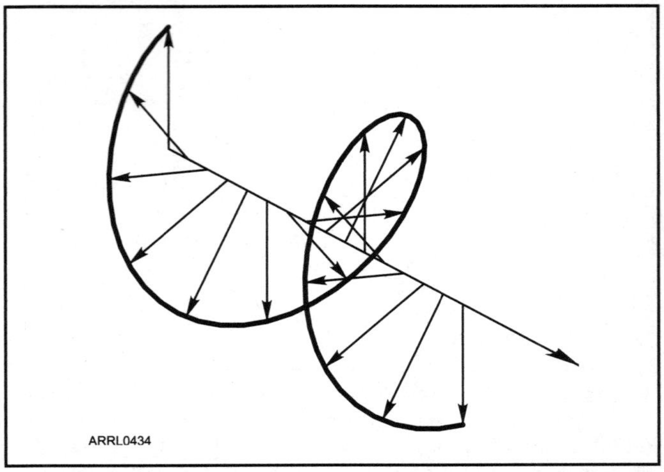

Figure 17.9 — The polarization of a circularly polarized wavefront rotates around its central axis, either clockwise (right-hand or RHCP) or counterclockwise (left-hand or LHCP).

each boom to provide circular polarization. (See the **VHF, UHF, and Microwave Antennas** chapter for detailed information on Yagi antennas.) There are several commonly used antennas with circular polarization described in the following sections.

Polarization Sense

Polarization *sense* is a critical factor, especially in EME and satellite work. The IEEE standard uses the term "clockwise circular polarization" for a *receding* wave (one traveling away from the observer). Amateur technology follows the IEEE standard, calling clockwise polarization for a receding wave as *right-hand circular polarization* or *RHCP*. This means that the second hand of the watch traveling with the receding wave is revolving clockwise. A wave for which polarization rotates in the opposition direction is *left-hand circular polarization* or *LHCP*.

When making satellite contacts using a circularly polarized antenna, it is often convenient to have the capability of switching polarization sense. This is because the sense of the received signal from some of the LEO satellites reverses when the satellite passes its nearest point to you. If the received signal has right-hand circular polarization as the satellite approaches, it may have left-hand circular polarization as the satellite recedes. A sense reversal occurs in EME communications as well, because of the phase reversal of the signal as it is reflected from the lunar surface. A signal transmitted with RHCP will be returned to the Earth with LHCP. Similarly, the polarization is reversed as it is reflected from a dish antenna so that to transmit an RHCP signal, the feed antenna for the dish needs to be LHCP.

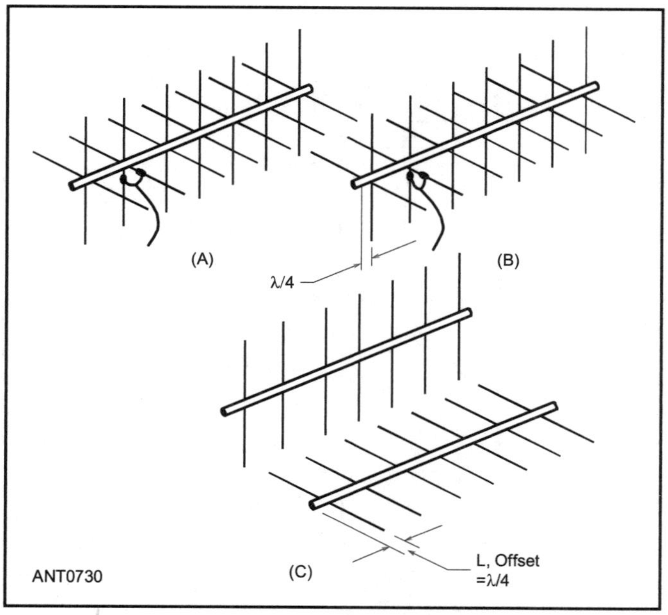

Figure 17.10 — Evolution of the circularly polarized Yagi. The simplest form of crossed Yagi, A, is made to radiate circularly by feeding the two driven elements 90° out of phase. Antenna B has the driven elements fed in phase, but has the elements of one bay mounted ¼ λ forward from those of the other. Antenna C offers elliptical (circular) polarization using separate booms. The elements in one set are perpendicular to those of the other and are ¼ λ forward from those of the other.

17.2.1 CROSSED LINEAR ELEMENTS

Dipoles radiate linearly polarized signals and the polarization direction depends on the orientation of the antenna. If two dipoles are arranged as horizontal and vertical dipoles, and the two outputs are combined with the correct phase difference (90°), a circularly polarized wave results. Because the electric fields are identical in magnitude, the power from the transmitter will be divided equally between the two fields. Another way of looking at this is to consider the power as being divided between the two antennas — hence the gain of each is decreased by 3 dB when taken alone in the plane of its orientation.

A 90° phase shift must exist between the two antennas and the simplest way to obtain this shift is to use two feed lines to a *coplanar pair* of crossed-Yagi antennas in which the elements lie approximately in the same plane, as shown in **Figure 17.10A**. One feed line section is ¼ λ longer than the other, as shown in Figure 17.10. These separate feed lines are then connected in parallel with a common transmission line to the transmitter or receiver. An example is shown in **Figure 17.11** and **Figure 17.12**. Assuming negligible coupling between the crossed antennas, the impedance presented to the common transmission line by the parallel combination is one half that of either section alone. (This is not true when there is mutual coupling between the antennas, as in phased arrays.)

This creates some difficulties for the antenna builder. With this phasing-line method, any mismatch at one antenna

Figure 17.11 — This VHF crossed Yagi design by KH6IJ (Jan 1973 *QST*) illustrates the co-planar, fixed-circularity Yagi.

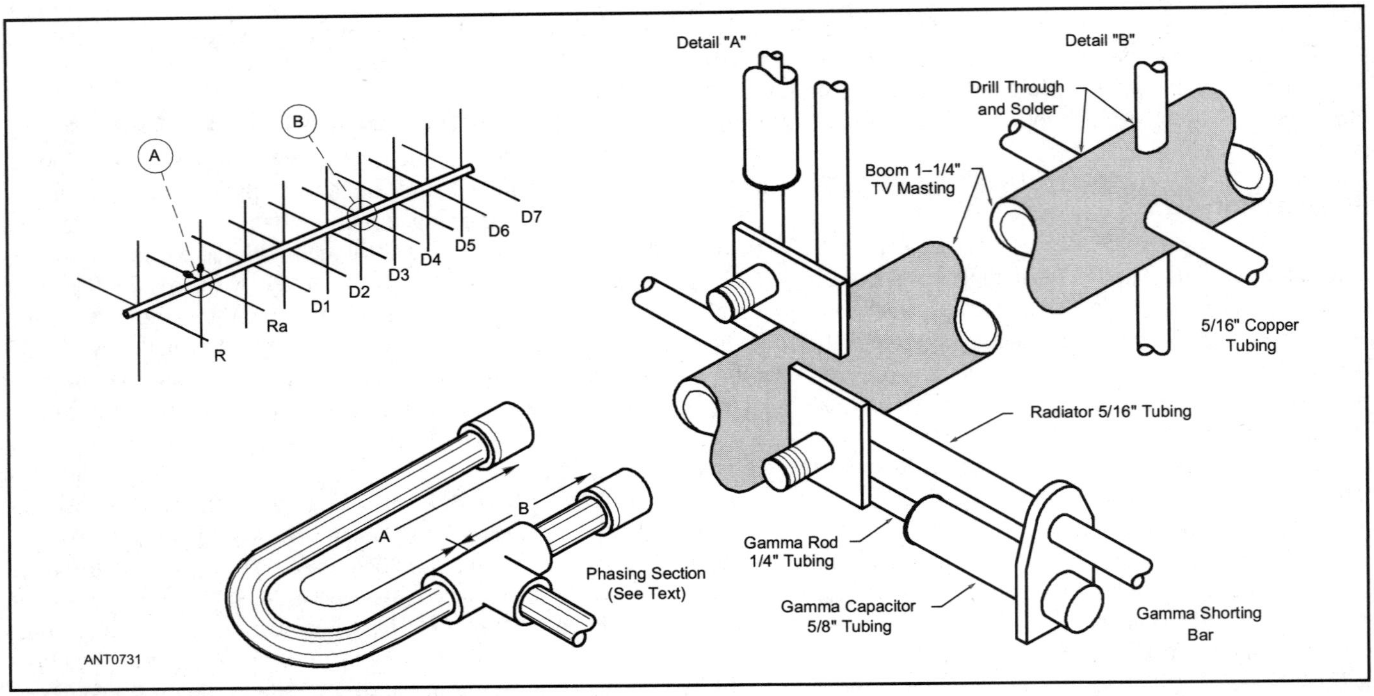

Figure 17.12 — Construction details of a co-planar crossed-Yagi antenna.

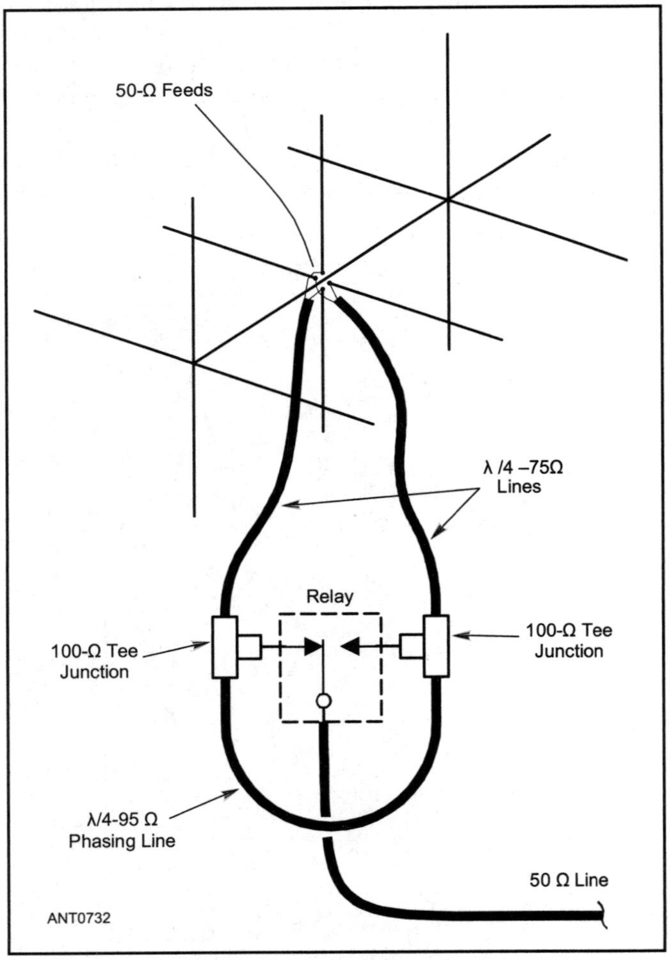

Figure 17.13 — Co-planar crossed Yagi, circularly polarized antenna with switchable polarization phasing harness.

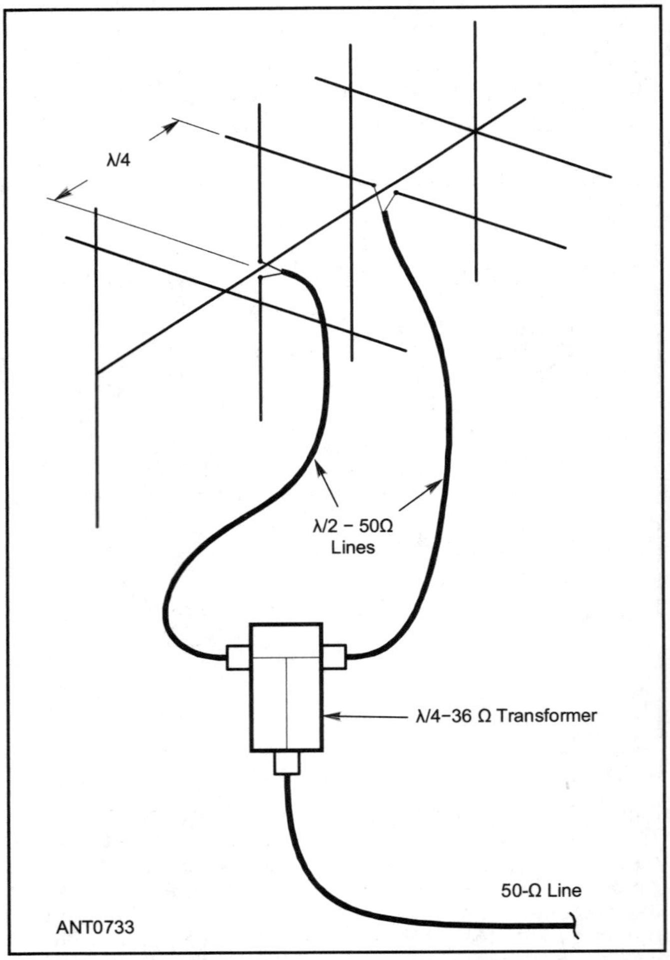

Figure 17.14 — Offset crossed-Yagi circularly polarized antenna-phasing harness with fixed polarization.

will be magnified by the extra ¼ λ of transmission line. This upsets the current balance between the two antennas, resulting in a loss of polarization circularity. Another factor to consider is the attenuation of the cables used in the harness, along with the connectors. Good low-loss coaxial line should be used with Type N or BNC connectors. A practical construction method for implementing a RHCP/LHCP coplanar switched system is shown in **Figure 17.13**.

Another method to obtain circular polarization is to use equal-length feed lines and place one antenna ¼ λ ahead of the other. This offset pair of Yagi-crossed antennas is shown in Figure 17.10B. The advantage of equal-length feed lines is that identical load impedances will be presented to the common feeder, as shown in **Figure 17.14**, which shows a fixed circularity-sense feed. To obtain a switchable-sense feed with the offset Yagi pair, you can use a configuration as in **Figure 17.15**, although you must compensate for the extra phase shift added by the relay and connectors.

Figure 17.10C diagrams a popular method of mounting two separate off-the-shelf Yagis at right angles to each other. The two Yagis may be physically offset by ¼ λ and fed in parallel, as shown in Figure 17.10C, or they may be mounted with no offset and fed 90° out of phase. Neither of these arrangements on two separate booms produces true circular polarization. Instead, *elliptical* polarization results from such a system, an example of which is shown in **Figure 17.16**.

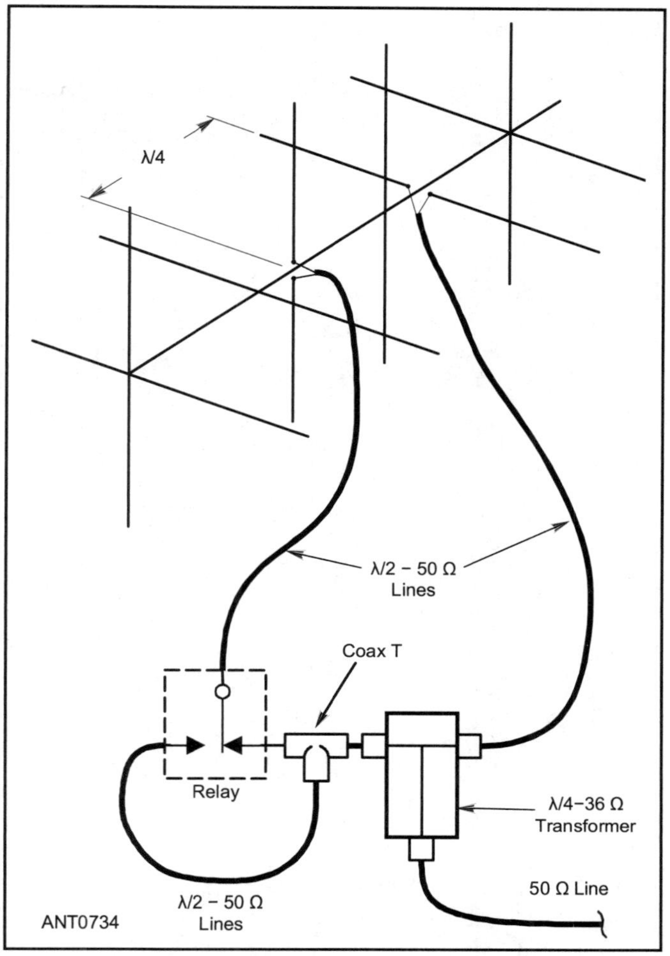

Figure 17.15 — Offset crossed-Yagi circularly polarized antenna-phasing harness with switchable polarization.

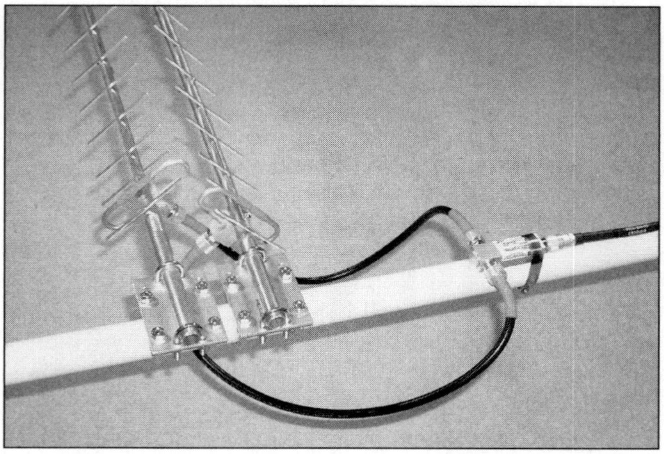

Figure 17.16 — An example of offset crossed-Yagi circularly polarized antennas with fixed polarization. This example is a pair of M2 23CMM22EZA antennas for 1296 MHz, mounted on an elevation boom.

17.2.2 THE EGGBEATER ANTENNA

The eggbeater antenna shown in Figure 17.2 is a popular design named after the old-fashioned kitchen utensil it resembles. The antenna is composed of two full-wave loops of rigid wire or metal tubing. Each of the two loops has an impedance of 100 Ω, and when coupled in parallel they offer an ideal 50-Ω impedance for coaxial feed lines. The loops are fed 90° out of phase with each other and this creates a circularly polarized pattern.

An eggbeater may also use one or more parasitic reflector elements beneath the loops to focus more of the radiation pattern upward. This effect makes it a "gain" antenna, but that gain is at the expense of low-elevation reception. Toward the horizon an eggbeater is actually horizontally polarized. As the pattern rises in elevation, it becomes more and more right-hand circularly polarized. Experience has shown that eggbeaters seem to perform best when reflector elements are installed just below the loops.

Eggbeaters can be built relatively easily, but commercial models such as the one shown in Figure 17.2 are available. The spherical shape of the eggbeater creates a fairly compact antenna when space is an issue, which is another reason why it is an attractive design. (See this book's downloadable supplemental information.)

17.2.3 THE TURNSTILE ANTENNA

The basic turnstile antenna in Figure 17.3 consists of two horizontal half-wave dipoles mounted at right angles to each other (arranged like the letter "X") in the same horizontal plane with a reflector screen beneath. When these two anten-

(A)

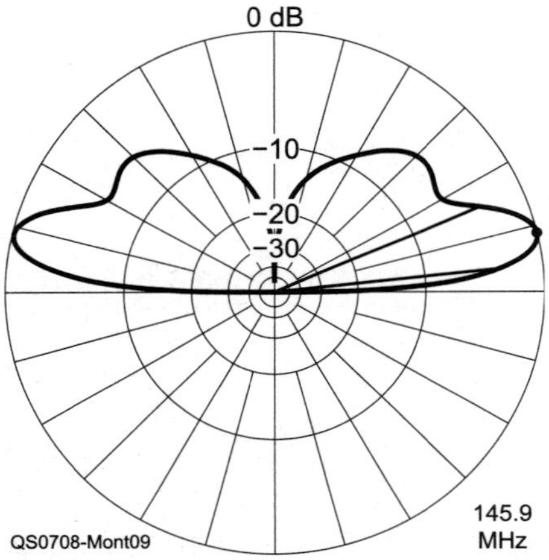

(B)

Figure 17.17 — The Lindenblad antenna in A has circular polarization and an omnidirectional azimuthal pattern as shown in B. [Anthony Montero, AA2TX, photo]

nas are excited with equal currents 90° out of phase, their typical figure-eight patterns merge to produce a nearly circular pattern. (See this book's downloadable supplemental information.)

To get the radiation pattern in the upward direction for space communications, the turnstile antenna needs a reflector underneath. For a broad pattern it is best to maintain a distance of ⅜ λ at the operating frequency between the reflector and the turnstile. Homemade turnstile reflectors often use metal window-screen material that you can pick up at many hardware stores. (Make sure it is a metal, not plastic, screen material.)

Like their cousins the eggbeaters, turnstiles are relatively easy to build. In fact, building one may be your only choice since turnstiles are rarely available off the shelf.

17.2.4 THE LINDENBLAD ANTENNA

The Lindenblad antenna shown in **Figure 17.17A** is constructed from linear elements, is circularly polarized, and has an omnidirectional radiation pattern. With most of its gain at low elevation angles as shown in Figure 17.17B, it is ideal for accessing Low-Earth-Orbit (LEO) satellites. Because it is omnidirectional, it does not need to be pointed at a satellite, eliminating the need for an azimuth/elevation (az/el) rotator system. This makes the Lindenblad especially useful for portable or temporary satellite operations. It is also a good general purpose antenna for a home station because its circular polarization is compatible with the linearly polarized antennas used for FM/repeater and SSB/CW operation. Two complete construction articles for Lindenblad antennas are included with this book's downloadable supplemental information. An improved version of the AA2TX design, "The Two Meter EZ Lindenblad Revisited," by KJ9P and AA9LC is included in the downloadable supplemental information and is listed in the Bibliography for Planer and Zehr.

17.2.5 THE QUADRIFILAR HELIX (QFH)

Designed for spacecraft use in the early days of space exploration, the *quadrifilar helix* (QFH) antenna (also called the quadrifilar helicoidal antenna) has not gained much popularity on the ham bands. Yet, as a general-purpose base-station antenna, such as the 2 meter version in **Figure 17.18**, it's hard to beat. The pattern is almost omnidirectional in both planes, like the mythical *isotropic* radiator, receiving nearly to the horizon. No matter what direction signals come from, or whether the polarization is vertical or horizontal, the QFH receives them. It's good for overhead satellites, such as the International Space Station, for horizontally polarized 2 meter SSB simplex stations on the horizon, and also for vertically polarized mobile and repeater stations. It isn't a gain antenna — no true omni can be. The primary benefit of a QFH is the coverage afforded by its pattern.

The QFH is often used by hams for receiving weather satellite pictures from the 137 MHz NOAA automatic picture transmitting (APT) satellites in low polar orbit. Its omnidirectional and circular polarization characteristics accommodate the constantly changing direction and polarization of the APT satellite signals. Several have been built for this service. Three of these weather birds still fly by every day — NOAA 15, 17, 18 and 19. (Pictures of these satellites are available at **w6nbc.com**.)

The QFH can be envisioned as follows: Take two vertical full wavelength rectangular loops with open feed points *at the top*. Now place them on the same vertical axis, but with one loop rotated 90° horizontally so that they are in quadrature. Also, you need to make one loop slightly larger than the other. This creates a phase shift at the feed point to compensate for the physical rotation of the loops. Next, twist both loops horizontally a quarter turn into helices. Finally connect the feed points in parallel to create a quadrifilar helix antenna.

Figure 17.18 — W6NBC's Quadrifilar Helix base station antenna [John Portune, W6NBC, photo]

The curious egg-beater-like configuration of the QFH has useful characteristics — an almost perfectly spherical radiation pattern as well as circular polarization throughout the pattern. This version is right-handed. For left, twist the loops in the opposite direction. For the general purpose 2 meter base station antenna, the twist direction does not matter. And yes, there is a small loss working linear polarized signals (vertical or horizontal) with a circularly polarized antenna, but it is quite acceptable. Commercial broadcast antennas often use this very technique to accommodate both mobile (vertical) as well as home antennas (horizontal).

After experimenting ham style with square loops and tall versus thin rectangular ones, and the small size difference between the two loops as well as the amount of twist, it has been concluded that the QFH is a dimensionally tolerant design. The performance changed little with all these variations.

The antenna shown in Figure 17.18 is described in the complete construction article by John Portune, W6NBC, included with this book's downloadable supplemental information along with another QFH construction article by Eugene Ruperto, W3KH.

Figure 17.19 — A 16-turn S-band helical antenna. This is about the maximum length of any practical helix. Note the SSB UEK2000 downconverter mounted behind the reflector of the antenna. [Dick Jansson, KD1K, photo]

Figure 17.20 — A pair of helical antennas for service on 2 meters and 70 cm. The 2 meter helical antenna is not small! [Dick Jansson, KD1K, photo]

17.2.6 HELICAL ANTENNAS

The axial-mode helical antenna was introduced by Dr John Kraus, W8JK, in the 1940s. **Figures 17.19** and **17.20** show examples of S-band (2400-MHz), V-band (145-MHz), and U-band (435-MHz) helical antennas, all constructed by KD1K for satellite service. (See the **VHF, UHF, and Microwave Antennas** chapter for design and construction information on the helix antenna.)

This antenna has two characteristics that make it especially interesting and useful in many applications. First, the helix is circularly polarized with a fixed polarization sense determined by its configuration. The polarization rotates about the axis of the antenna.

The second interesting property of the helical antenna is its predictable pattern, gain and impedance characteristics over a wide frequency range. This is one of the few antennas with both broad bandwidth and high gain. The benefit of this property is that, when used for narrowband applications, the helical antenna is very forgiving of mechanical inaccuracies.

Figure 17.21 shows the modeled gain of 5-, 10-, and 15-turn helix antennas with varying circumferences in terms of wavelength. (See the Bibliography entry for Cebik.) The

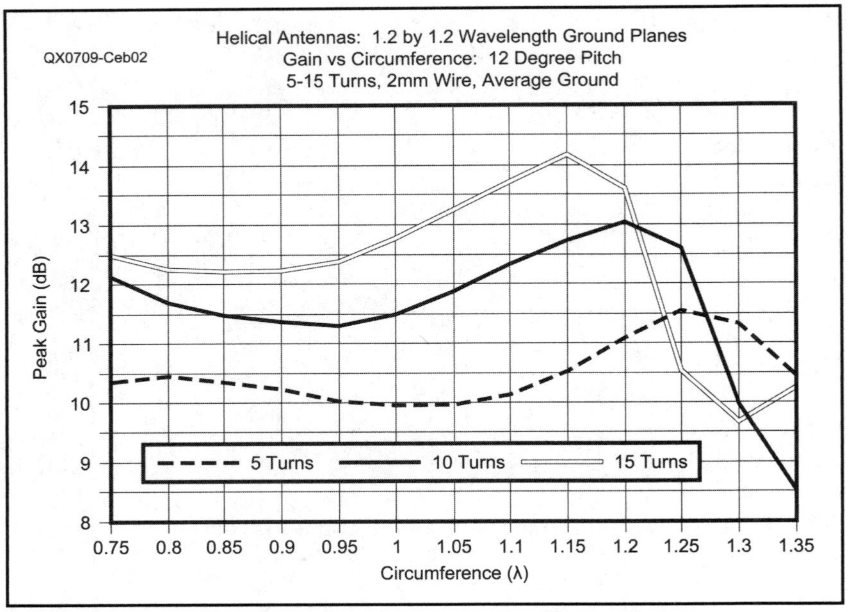

Figure 17.21 — Modeled gain of 5, 10, and 15-turn helices over ground planes 1.2 per side.

ground plane is a wire grid, 1.2 λ on a side and 1 λ above average ground. The wire used for the helix is 2 mm in diameter.

The peak gain of the helices is about 11.7, 13.0, and 14.2 dBi for the 5, 10 and 15-turn antennas, respectively. Note that the gain increases almost linearly with the increase in the number of turns. This is an important fact to keep in mind when comparing axial-mode helices with alternatives to them as circularly (or nearly circularly) polarized antennas.

An axial-mode helical antenna rarely yields perfect circular polarization. Instead, it yields *elliptical polarization*, with a major and a minor axis and a tilt angle. The antennas approach perfect circularity most closely along the axis of the helix. The modeled antennas here improve their circularity with increased length. More pertinent to amateur use is the fact that an axial-mode helix does not produce a perfect single-lobe pattern. **Figure 17.22** shows the total field patterns of the 5, 10 and 15 turn helices over an elevated ground screen. In each case, we can see a considerable collection of side lobes. Each model uses the circumference that produces the best gain, but that circumference does not yield the lowest level of side lobes. Reducing the circumference produces lower gain (from 1 to 2 dB, depending upon the length of the helix), but results in a cleaner pattern. Circumferences below about 0.85 λ rarely have any sidelobes at all through the 15-turn design shown here.

As well, there are remnants of opposite direction polarization within the total field of the axial-mode helix. **Figure 17.23** shows the dominant right-hand polarized component of a 15-turn helix over a ground-screen elevated above average ground. The left-hand component is down by 25 dB, with some of the lower lobes being composed mainly of left-hand components. All of these facets of axial-mode helix performance have a bearing on the sensitivity of such antennas to off-axis signals, whether at high or low angles relative to the axis that marks the centerline of the helix. How much side lobe and oppositely polarized lobe suppression is enough, of course, you must determine based on your application and your local circumstances. Given the low signal levels associated with space communication, reducing off-axis noise is an important consideration in selecting and designing antennas.

Portable Helix for 435 MHz

Helical antennas for 435 MHz are excellent uplinks for U-band satellite communications. The true circular polarization afforded by the helix minimizes signal *spin fading* that is so common in these applications. The antenna shown in **Figure 17.24** fills the need for an effective portable uplink antenna for OSCAR operation. Speedy assembly and disassembly and light weight are among the benefits of this array. This antenna was designed by Jim McKim, WØCY.

Although the helix is about the most tolerant of any antenna in terms of dimensions, the dimensions given here should be followed as closely as possible. Most of the materials specified are available in any well supplied do-it-yourself

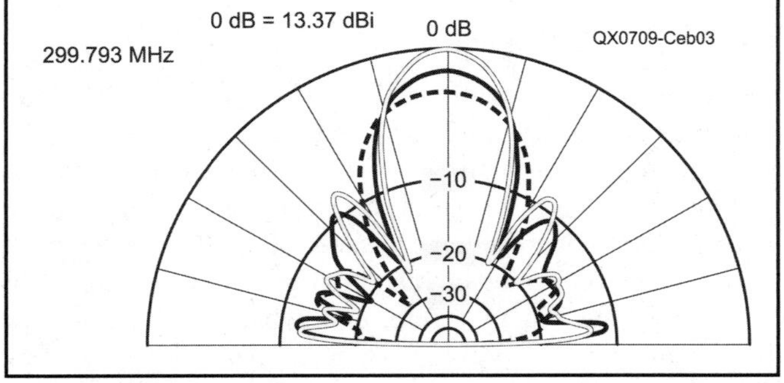

Figure 17.22 — Comparative elevation patterns of 5, 10, and 15-turn helices over ground planes 1.2 λ per side.

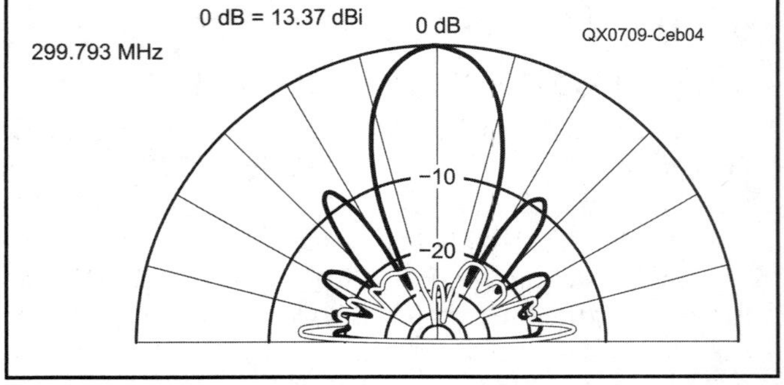

Figure 17.23 — Right-hand and left-hand polarized components of the elevation pattern of a 15-turn helix over a ground plane 1.2 λ per side.

Figure 17.24 — The portable 435-MHz helix assembled and ready for operation. (WØCY photo)

hardware or building supply store.

The portable helix consists of eight turns of ¼-inch soft-copper tubing spaced around a 1-inch fiberglass tube or maple dowel rod 4 feet, 7 inches long. Surplus solid aluminum shield hardline can be used instead of the copper tubing if necessary. The turns of the helix are supported by 5-inch lengths of ¼-inch maple dowel mounted through the 1-inch rod in the center of the antenna. For further details, a complete parts list, and construction information see this book's downloadable supplemental information.

Helix Array for L Band (23 cm)

A four-element array of 27-turn helixes is described in the presentation "L Band Helix Antenna Array" by Clare Fowler, VE3NPC, provided with this book's downloadable supplemental information. While originally designed for use with HEO satellites, the array is also suitable for EME operation, particularly using digital modes. Each antenna has a calculated gain of 19 dBi and the array has an estimated actual gain of 23 dB.

17.3 YAGI ARRAYS

The Yagis in this section are typical of the high-performance designs used for terrestrial communications. For satellite or EME operation, they are often combined into arrays of 2, 4, 8 or even more antennas with both azimuth and elevation position control. Designs of such Yagis can be found in the **VHF and UHF Antenna Systems** chapter or commercial models are available.

17.3.1 ARRAYS FOR SATELLITES

It is not necessary to use a high-gain Yagi array to access an LEO satellite except possibly when it is very near the horizon. Reliable operation via the HEO satellites, however, requires more gain and Yagi arrays are very popular from VHF through 1.2 and 2.4 GHz.

Figure 17.25 shows the satellite antennas at KD1K. The Yagi antennas are used for the U- and L-band uplinks and the V-band downlink, while the S-band dish antenna is for downlink. These satellite antennas are tower mounted at 63 feet (19 meters) to avoid pointing into the many nearby trees and suffering from the resulting "green attenuation." Of course, satellite antennas do not always need to be mounted high on a tower if dense foliage is not a problem. If satellite antennas are mounted lower, feed line length and losses can reduced.

Another benefit, however, to tower mounting of satellite antennas is that they can be used for terrestrial ham communications and contests. The fact that the antennas are set up for circular polarization (CP) does not really degrade these other operating activities.

Experience has clearly shown the advantages of using RHCP antennas for both the uplink and downlink communications. The antennas shown in Figure 17.25 are a single-boom RHCP Yagi antenna for U band, a pair of closely spaced Yagi antennas phased for RHCP for L band (see Figure 17.16), and a helix-fed offset dish antenna for S band described below. The antenna gain requirements for U band can easily be met with the gain of a 30-element crossed Yagi. Antennas of this size have boom lengths of 4 to 4.5 wavelengths. The enterprising amateur can build a Yagi antenna

Figure 17.25 — Details of KD1K's tower cluster of satellite antennas including a home-brew elevation rotator. Top to bottom: M2 436-CP30, a CP U-band antenna; two M2 23CM22EZA antennas in a CP array for L band; "FABStar" dish antenna with helix feed for S band; M2 2M-CP22, a CP V-band antenna (only partially shown.) To left of dish antenna is a NEMA 4 weatherproof equipment box with an internal 40-W L-band amplifier, and also hosts externally mounted preamplifiers. (KD1K photo)

from one of several references but most of us prefer to purchase well-tested antennas from commercial sources. In the past, KLM (now out of business) had offered a 40-element CP Yagi for U-band satellite service, and many of these are still in satisfactory use today.

U-band uplink requirements have clearly demonstrated the need for gain of 16 to 17 dBic RHCP, with an RF power of less than 50 W PEP at the antenna (≈ 2500 WPEP EIRP with a RHCP antenna) depending upon the *squint angle*. The squint angle is the angle at which the main axis of the satellite is pointed away from your antenna on the ground. If the squint angle is less than half of the half-power beamwidth, the ground station will be within the spacecraft antenna's nominal beamwidth. dBic means the gain of a circularly polarized antenna with respect to that of an isotropic antenna with the same polarization characteristic.

A gain of 16 to 17 (dB isotropic-circular) RHCP can be obtained from a 30-element crossed Yagi — good news, considering that the satellite may be over 60,000 km (37,000 miles) from your station. Success on U-band uplinks is easier than those for L band at squint angles wider than 20°. At squint angles less than 10°, U-band uplink operation can even be done with 1-5 W power outputs to a RHCP antenna (≈ 200 W PEP EIRP with RHCP). These lower levels mean that smaller antennas can be used. In practice, these uplinks will produce downlink signals that are 10 to 15 dB above the noise floor, or S7 signals over an S3 noise floor. The beacon will give a downlink S9 signal for these same conditions.

Figure 17.26 — Domenico, I8CVS, has this cluster of satellite antennas. Left to right: array of 4 × 23-element Yagi horizontally polarized for L band; 1.2-meter dish with 3-turn helix feed for S band; 15-turn RHCP helical antenna for U band; 60-cm dish for X band. All microwave preamplifiers and power amplifiers are homebrew and are mounted on this antenna cluster. (I8CVS photo)

Experience with L-band uplinks has demonstrated that 40 W PEP delivered to an antenna with a gain of ≈ 19 dBic (3000 W PEP EIRP with RHCP) is needed for operations at the highest altitudes and with squint angles ≈ 15°. The compact L-band antenna arrangement with two 22-element antennas in a RHCP array shown in Figure 17.16 is an example of such an antenna system.

Using the L-band uplink for HEO operations instead of the U-band uplink allows the use of Yagi antennas that are more manageable since their size for a given gain is only one third of those for U-band. With L band there is a narrower difference between using a dish antenna and a Yagi, since a 21- to 22-dBic dish antenna would be only about 1.2 meters (4 feet) in diameter. However, some of us may not have such "real estate" available on our towers and may seek the lower wind-loading solution offered by Yagis. Long-boom rod-element Yagi, or loop-Yagi antennas are commercially offered by M^2 and DEM, although this band is about the highest for practical Yagis. The example shown in Figure 17.16 is a pair of rod-element Yagi antennas from M^2 in a CP arrangement with a gain of 18 to 19 dBic.

Other amateurs have successful HEO experience with different arrangements. **Figure 17.26** shows I8CVS's 4 × 23 element linear array for a 1270 MHz, a 1.2 meter solid dish for 2400 MHz, a 15 turn helical antenna for 435 MHz, and a 60 cm dish for 10,451 MHz This arrangement clearly shows the advantage and accessibility of having a roof-mounted antenna.

17.3.2 ARRAYS FOR EME

Several types of antennas for 2 meters and 70 cm are popular among EME enthusiasts. Perhaps the most popular antenna for 144-MHz operation is an array of either 4 or 8 long-boom (14 to 15 dBi gain) Yagis. The 4-Yagi array provides approximately 20 dB gain, and an 8-Yagi array gives an approximate 3 dB increase over the 4-antenna array. **Figure 17.27** shows the computed response at a 30° tilt above the horizon for a stack of four 14-element 2-meter Yagis, each with a boom length of 3.1 λ (22 feet). At 432 MHz, EME enthusiasts often use 8 or 16 long-boom Yagis in an array as seen in Figure 17.8 previously. However, recent advances in Yagi design as described in the **VHF and UHF Antenna Systems** chapter make smaller arrays of high-performance antennas a satisfactory alternative.

The main disadvantage of Yagi arrays is that the polarization plane of the individual Yagis cannot be conveniently changed. One way around this is to use cross-polarized Yagis and a relay switching system to select the desired polarization, as described in the previous section. This represents a considerable increase in system complexity to select the

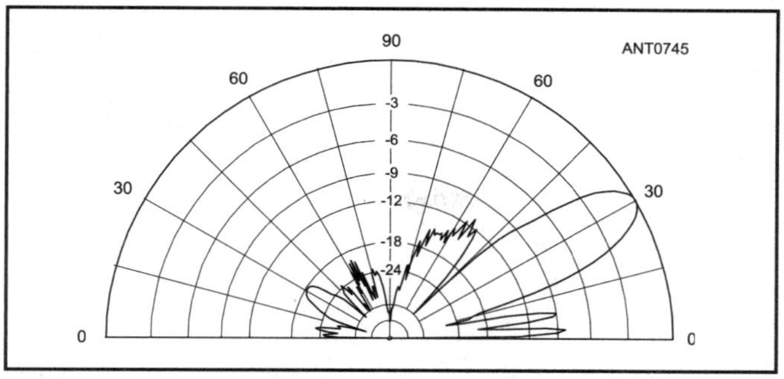

Figure 17.27 — ***EZNEC Pro*** **elevation pattern for four 14-element 2 meter Yagis (3.6-λ boom lengths) at an elevation angle of 30° above the horizon. The computed system gain is 21.5 dBi, suitable for 2 meter EME. This assumes that the phasing system is made of open-wire transmission lines so that feed line losses can be kept below 0.25 dB.**

Figure 17.28 — Four-Yagi dual-polarization 432 MHz array at the Princeton University station, W2PU. The Yagis are rear-mounted; boom length is 3.5 meters, and stacking distance is 1.2 meters in each direction. (Photo courtesy Joe Taylor, K1JT)

desired polarization. Some amateurs have gone so far as to build complicated mechanical systems to allow constant polarization adjustment of all the Yagis in a large array.

Polarization shift of EME signals at 144 MHz is fairly rapid, and the added complexity of a relay-controlled cross-polarized antenna system or a mechanical polarization adjustment scheme is probably not worth the effort. At 432 MHz, however, where the polarization shifts at a much slower rate, an adjustable polarization system does offer a definite advantage over a fixed one. An example of a 70 cm Yagi array with switchable-polarization is shown in **Figure 17.28** and described in the article "EME with Adaptive Polarization at 432 MHz" by Joe Taylor, K1JT, and Justin Johnson, GØKSC (available with this book's downloadable supplemental information).

Although not as popular as Yagis, *Quagi* antennas (made from both quad and Yagi elements) are sometimes used for EME work. Slightly more gain per unit boom length is possible as compared to the conventional Yagi, at the expense of some robustness. Additional information on the Quagi is presented in the **VHF and UHF Antenna Systems** chapter.

The collinear array is an older type of antenna for EME work. A 40-element collinear array has approximately the same frontal area as an array of four Yagis, but produces approximately 1 to 2 dB less gain. One attraction to a collinear array is that the depth dimension is considerably less than the long-boom Yagis. An 80-element collinear is marginal for EME communications, providing approximately 19 dB gain. As with Yagi and Quagi antennas, the collinear cannot be adjusted easily for polarity changes. From a construction standpoint, there is little difference in complexity and material costs between the collinear and Yagi arrays.

17.4 PARABOLIC REFLECTOR (DISH) ANTENNAS

Very few antennas evoke as much interest among UHF amateurs as the parabolic dish, and for good reason. First, the parabola and its cousins — Cassegrain, hog horn and Gregorian — are probably the ultimate in high-gain antennas. One of the highest-gain antennas in the world (148 dB) is a parabola. This is the 200-inch Mt. Palomar telescope. (The very short wavelength of light rays causes such a high gain to be realizable.)

Second, the efficiency of the parabola does not change as size increases. With Yagis and collinear arrays, the losses in the phasing harness increase as the array size increases. The corresponding component of the parabola is lossless air between the feed horn and the reflecting surface. If there are a few surface errors, the efficiency of the system stays constant regardless of antenna size. (See the **VHF, UHF, and Microwave Antennas** chapter for design and construction information on dish antennas.)

The major problems associated with parabolic dish antennas are mechanical ones. For example, a dish of about 16 feet in diameter is the minimum size required for successful analog EME operation on 432 MHz. With wind and ice loading, structures of this size place a real strain on the mounting and positioning system. Extremely rugged mounts are required for large dish antennas, especially when used in windy locations. **Figure 17.29** shows the impressive 7-meter diameter dish built by David Wardley, ZL1BJQ. A smaller dish used for 1296 MHz operation is shown in **Figure 17.30**.

If extreme weather can be avoided, a much lighter dish can be used. For example, Dick Knadel, K2RIW, designed the lightweight 12-foot stressed parabolic dish shown in **Figure 17.31** for portable use. It can be used on 432 through 5760 MHz and when disassembled, transportable by car. (The full construction article is available in the downloadable supplemental information.)

Figure 17.29 — ZL1BJQ's homemade 7-meter (23-foot) parabolic dish, just prior to adding ½-inch wire mesh. (Photo courtesy ZL1BJQ)

Figure 17.30 — This 3-meter TVRO dish with aluminum frame and mesh surface was outfitted for 1296 MHz EME as a joint effort by VA7MM and VE7CNF. The dual circular polarization feed is a VE4MA/W2IMU design.

Figure 17.31 — A 12-foot stressed parabolic dish set up for satellite signals near 2280 MHz. A preamplifier is shown taped below the feed horn. The dish was designed by K2RIW, standing at the right. The complete *QST* construction article from 1972 is available with this book's downloadable supplemental information.

Several aspects of parabolic dish antennas make the extra mechanical problems worth the trouble, however. For example, the dish antenna is inherently broadband, and may be used on several different amateur bands by simply changing the feed. An antenna that is suitable for 432 MHz work will most likely be usable on several of the higher amateur bands too. Increased gain is available as the frequency of operation is increased.

Another advantage of a dish is the flexibility of the feed system. The polarization of the feed, and therefore the polarization of the antenna, can be changed with little difficulty. It is a relatively easy matter to devise a system to rotate the feed remotely from the shack to change polarization. Because polarization changes can account for as much as 30 dB of signal attenuation, the rotatable feed can make the difference between consistent communications and no communications at all.

17.4.1 SHF EME CHALLENGES FOR DISHES

The challenges met when successfully building a station for EME at 900 MHz to 5.7 GHz only become more significant on the SHF bands at 10 GHz and above. Absolute attention to detail is the primary requirement, and this extends to every aspect of the EME antenna system. The dish surface is probably the most difficult problem to solve. As was discussed earlier, shape and accuracy of the reflector contribute directly to the overall gain of the antenna.

But where slight errors in construction can be tolerated at the lower frequencies, the same cannot be said at millimeter wavelengths. Those who have attempted EME on 10 and 24 GHz have discovered that the weight of the dish reflector itself will distort its shape enough to lower the gain to the point where echoes are degraded. Stiffening structures at the back of such dishes are often found necessary.

Pointing accuracy is also paramount. A 16-foot dish at 10 GHz has a beamwidth about equal to the diameter of the moon — 0.5°. This means that the echo degradation due to the moon's movement away from where the dish is pointed is almost immediate, and autotracking systems become more of a necessity than a luxury. At these frequencies, most amateurs actually peak their antennas on moon noise — the black-body radiation from the moon that becomes the dominant source of noise in space.

At these frequencies, the elevation of the moon above the horizon also plays a role in the ability to communicate since tropospheric absorption due to water vapor is greatest at low elevation angles (the signal must pass through a greater portion of the troposphere than when the moon is highly elevated). It is beyond the abilities of most amateurs to construct their own dishes for these frequencies, so surplus dishes for Ku-band (12 GHz) satellite TV (typically 3 meters in diameter) are usually employed, as are high-performance dishes designed for millimeter-wave radar and point-to-point communications at 23 and 38 GHz.

17.4.2 DISH ANTENNAS FOR SATELLITES

Dish antennas are not required for satellite operation except in the case of HEO or geosynchronous satellites operating with microwave up or down-links. At lower frequencies, Yagi arrays are the more practical choice.

A 1.2-meter L-band dish antenna and 40 W of RF power (6100 W PEP EIRP with RHCP) can also provide a superb uplink for squint angles even up to 25°. A dish antenna can have a practical gain of about 21 to 22 dBic. These uplinks will provide the user a downlink that is 10 to 18 dB above the transponder noise floor. In more practical terms, these are S7 to 8 signals over an S3 transponder noise floor, making for very comfortable "armchair" copy.

KD1K shows in **Figure 17.32** what can be done with a 1.2 meter dish antenna kit for HEO operations. **Figure 17.33** shows a WØLMD 8-foot TVRO dish with patch feed, az/el mount, a U-band Yagi, and an L-band helical antenna.

Other hams have also taken advantage of surplus dishes. **Figure 17.34** shows modified MMDS dishes, by K5GNA, and **Figure 17.35**, by K5OE, both using helix feeds.

One very popular spun-aluminum dish antenna in HEO use has been the G3RUH-ON6UG 60-cm unit with its S-band patch feed shown in **Figure 17.36**. With a gain of 21 dBic it provides a 2.5 dB sun noise signal. Surplus dishes have not been the only source of antennas for HEO operations — even cardboard boxes lined with aluminum foil will work as shown in **Figure 17.37**! (This interesting antenna was the subject of the March 2003 *QST* article "Work OSCAR 40 with Cardboard-Box Antennas!" by AA2TX which is included with this book's downloadable supplemental information.)

A dual-band satellite provides special challenges to the single-dish station. For example, the new Es'hail-2/QO-100 geosynchronous satellite operates on 2.4 GHz and 10 GHz. A traditional double feed would be bulky and reduce gain due to its size, blocking some of the signals. Mike Willis GØMJW, Remco den Besten PA3FYM, and Paul Marsh MØEYT

Figure 17.32 — KD1K's completed HEO antenna system mounted to the tower and ready to go. The 40 W, 23 cm amplifier is in the box below the KG6IAL 1.2 meter dish. [Dick Jansson, KD1K, photo]

Figure 17.33 — WØLMD created this 8-foot dish with patch feed for S band for working HEO satellites. On the left is a helical antenna for L band and on the right is a 2 × 9-element offset-feed Yagi for U band. A homebrew az/el mount is provided.

responded by designing a dual-band antenna feed that combines a patch antenna on 2.4 GHz and a waveguide feed on 10 GHz. Their article, "Simple dual band dish feed for Es'hail-2 / QO-100," is included in the downloadable supplemental information for this book.

Figure 17.34 — K5GNA's "circularized" mesh modification of an MMDS dish antenna with a helix-CP feed and preamp. The dish modification reduces the spillover loss by making the antenna fully circular. [Gerald Brown, K5OE, photo]

Figure 17.35 — Mesh modification of an MMDS dish antenna by K5OE, with a helix-CP feed and preamplifier by Down-East Microwave mounted directly to the helix feed point. [Gerald Brown, K5OE, photo]

Figure 17.36 — G3RUH's 60-cm spun-aluminum dish with CP-patch feed is available as a kit. This antenna has been popular with HEO operators all over the world.

Figure 17.37 — The completed high-performance corner-reflector uplink antenna for U band. Note how the box corners hold the reflectors and dipole feed in place. The rear legs set the antenna elevation to 20° — this gives good coverage at the design latitude but will need modification for other stations.

17.5 ANTENNA POSITION CONTROL

EME and satellite antennas have high gain and narrow main beams that must be properly aimed in two coordinates. Although polar mounts (one axis parallel to the Earth's axis) have sometimes been used, by far the most popular mounting scheme today is the elevation-over-azimuth or az/el mount. Readily available computer software can provide azimuth and elevation coordinates for the moon, and a small computer can also control antenna positioning motors to automate the whole pointing system.

For mechanical reasons it is desirable to place the antenna's center of gravity close to the intersection of the vertical (azimuth) and horizontal (elevation) axes. On the other hand, the mounting structure must not interfere with critical active regions of the antenna. Stacked Yagis are generally mounted so that metallic supporting members are perpendicular to the radiating elements or located at midpoints where the effective apertures of separate Yagis meet. Feed lines and conducting support members must not lie in the active planes containing Yagi elements, unless they run wholly along the boom. For dual-polarization Yagis, feed lines should be routed toward the rear of each Yagi and any mid-boom support members must be nonconducting. For space communications there is nothing magical about using horizontal and vertical for the two orthogonal polarizations, and there are some advantages to mounting cross-Yagis with elements in the "X" rather than "+" orientation.

Parabolic dishes are usually mounted from behind, with counterweights extending rearward to relieve torque imbalance on the elevation axis. Jack-screw actuators designed for positioning TVRO dishes can be readily adapted for elevation control. Standard heavy-duty antenna rotators can be used for azimuth positioning of dishes up to about 3 meters in size. Larger dishes may require heavier, one-of-a-kind designs for pointing control.

17.5.1 POSITION CONTROLLERS

Operators through the years have employed many methods for the control of their antenna positions, ranging from true *armstrong* manual positioning, to manual operation of the powered antenna azimuth and elevation rotators, to fully automated computer control of the rotators. While computer control of the rotators is not essential, operation is greatly eased with their use. (See also the section on Rotators in the chapter **Building Antenna Systems and Towers**.)

A standalone controller translates computer antenna-position information into controller commands with an understanding of antenna-position limits. AMSAT-NA has developed the LVB Tracker by G6LVB (**www.g6lvb.com**) shown in **Figure 17.38** that can be obtained in several different forms of kits or completely assembled from AMSAT. This tracker uses an internal PIC microcontroller that uses a 10-bit ADC encoder for rotator position feedback, resulting in sub-degree precision for both elevation and azimuth. Yaesu (**www.yaesu.com**) also sells the GS-232 computer control interface that can be used for tracking with their G-5500 az/el rotator system.

Other position readout and control options are available. For many years ham operators have employed synchros, or *selsyns*, for their position readouts. These are specialized transformers, using principles developed over sixty years ago and employed in such devices as surplus "radio compass" steering systems for aircraft. While the position readout of these devices can be quite precise, in general they only provide a visual position indication, one that is not easily adapted to computer control. I8CVS employs such a system at his station and he uses a weighted arm on the elevation synchro to provide a constant reference to the Earth's gravity vector.

The more up-to-date, computer-friendly position readout methods used these days are usually based on precision potentiometers or digital position encoders. **Figure 17.39** shows a variety of digital encoders employed by WØLMD. He notes that such systems, while providing a very high precision of angular position, they are not absolute systems and that once calibrated, they must be continually powered so they do not lose their calibration. Precision potentiometers, on the other hand, provide an absolute position reference, but with a precision that is limited to the quality of the potentiometer, typically 0.5% (0.45° in elevation and 1.80° in azimuth) to 1.0%. So the choices have their individual limits, unless a lot of money is spent for very precise commercial systems.

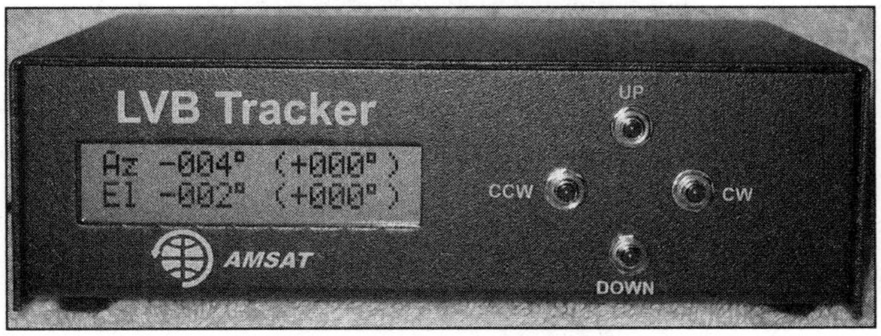

Figure 17.38 — AMSAT-NA LVB Tracker Box assembly.

Figure 17.39 — WØLMD has experimented with highly precise optical encoders for his antenna position systems. See text. [Robert Suding, WØLMD photo]

17.5.2 ELEVATION CONTROL

Satellite antennas need to have elevation control to point up to the sky. This is the "el" part of az/el control of satellite antennas. Generally, elevation booms for CP satellite antennas need to be nonconducting so that the boom does not affect the radiation pattern of the antenna. In the example shown next, the elevation boom One possibility that provides extra mounting strength is to make the center section is a piece of heavy pipe (for greater strength) with fiberglass extensions for the antennas. For smaller installations, a continuous piece of fiberglass-epoxy boom can be placed directly through the elevation rotator.

Elevation boom motion needs to be powered and one solution by KD1K, shown in **Figure 17.40**, uses a surplus jackscrew drive mechanism. I8CVS has also built his own robust elevation mechanism. (See **Figure 17.41**.) Note in each of these applications the methods used to provide bearings for the elevation mechanism. In KD1K's case, the elevation axis is a piece of heavy-duty 1½-inch pipe, ($1\frac{15}{16}$-inch OD) and large 2 inch journal bearings are used for the motion. I8CVS uses a very large hinge to allow this motion.

Robust commercial solutions for az/el rotators have given operators good service over the years. See **Figure 17.42**. Manufacturers such as Yaesu and M² (**www.m2inc.com**) are among these suppliers. AlfaSpid (**www.alfaradio.ca**) also manufactures an az/el rotator.

Figure 17.41 — I8CVS's homebrew elevation mechanism using a very large, industrial hinge as the pivot and a jackscrew drive.

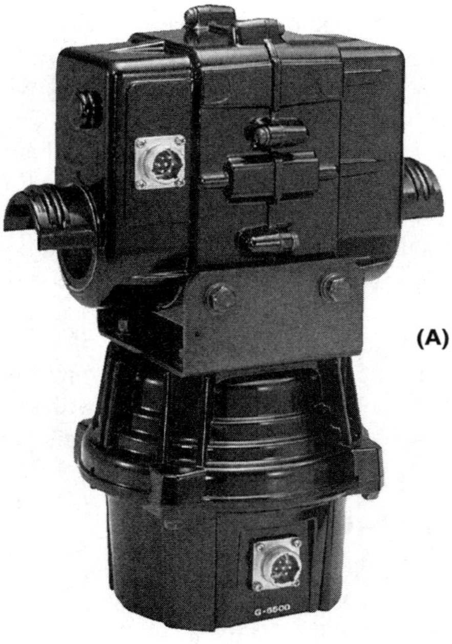

(A)

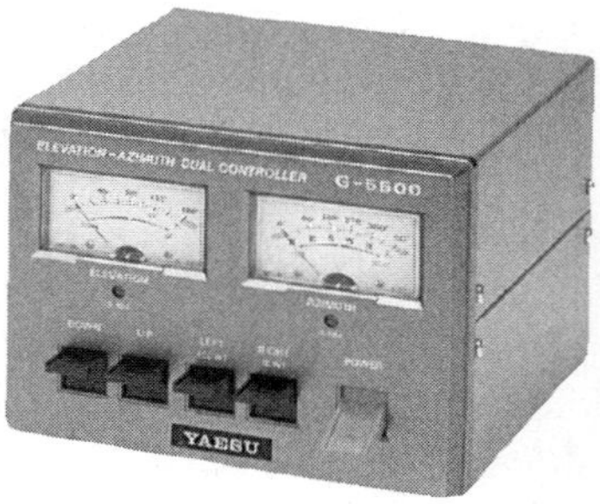

(B)

Figure 17.42 — At A, the Yaesu G5500 az/el antenna-rotator mounting system and control box are. At B is the az/el rotator made by Alfa Radio.

Figure 17.40 — KD1K's homebrew elevation rotator drive using a surplus-store drive screw mechanism. Note also the large journal bearing supporting the elevation axis pipe shaft. [Dick Jansson, KD1K, photo]

Don't forget to provide a rotator loop of coax to allow your antenna to rotate properly in both planes and to allow water to drip off. Also, make sure you position the loop so that it doesn't snag on anything as the antenna rotates throughout its range of motion.

17.5.3 WRAPS: A PORTABLE SATELLITE ANTENNA POSITIONING SYSTEM

This design was originally published as an article of the same name by Mark Spencer, WA8SME, in the January 2014 issue of *QST*. The full article is included with this book's downloadable supplemental information and shows all construction details and references.

Design

WRAPS is a portable, battery operated satellite antenna rotator system using commercial, off-the-shelf (COTS) parts. It can be built using simple hand tools with a minimum of machine work. This rotator system should be an affordable alternative to the industry standard — the Yaesu G-5500 system — which is an excellent and proven rotator for base station operations. It is a limited-duty rotator intended for small handheld Arrow and Elk class satellite antennas, and can be used to receive Fox satellite signals.

The positioning system is powered by a 12 V battery such as a small sealed UPS battery. The cost of parts, including all the associated cabling and computer interfaces, is approximately $275, compared with about $1300 for the G-5500 system. This design includes a USB interface that works with *SatPC32* and other satellite tracking software packages running the EASYCOM protocol. WRAPS is designed for lightweight antennas only, and is not intended to handle large antenna arrays. It is not weatherproof, nor designed for continuous unattended operation.

Figure 17.43 shows a block diagram of the WRAPS circuitry. The heart of the WRAPS circuit is a PIC microcontroller that:

- Receives positioning commands from the satellite tracking program which runs on the personal computer (PC)
- Translates those commands into rotator positions (analog to digital converter values).
- Reads the current rotator positions and determines if a position change is required, and if so, in which direction.
- Commands the motors ("MOT" in the figure) to turn in the proper direction.
- Monitors the motors as they move.
- Stops the motors when they reach the commanded position.
- Waits for the next position update.

The motors are controlled through the individual H-bridge circuits using a pulse width modulation (PWM)

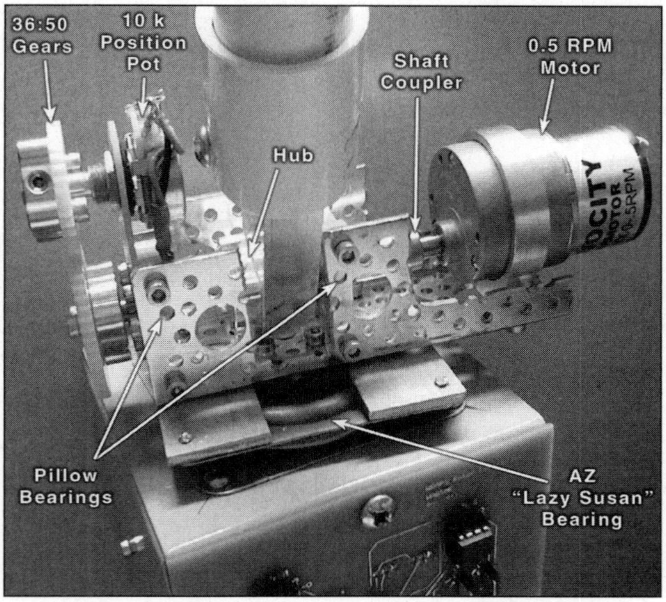

Figure 17.44 — The elevation (el) positioning assembly. [Mark Spencer, WA8SME]

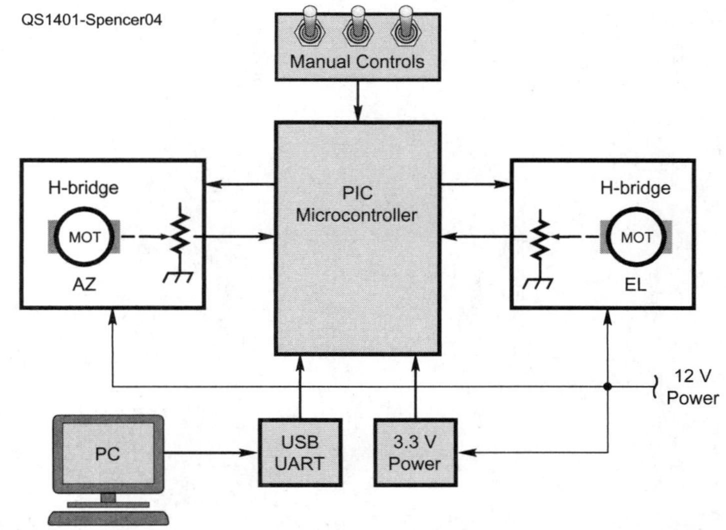

Figure 17.43 — The WRAPS antenna positioning system block diagram.

Figure 17.45 — The azimuth (az) positioning assembly. [Mark Spencer, WA8SME]

produced by the PIC microcontroller to set the motor speed.

WRAPS makes use of precision parts manufactured for the robotics community. **Figure 17.44** illustrates the elevation (el) part of the rotator. The el rotator uses a geared 0.5 rpm dc motor that provides excellent torque at an affordable price. Construction is similar to an "erector set" project. There are a couple of cutouts required in the aluminum channel chassis of the el rotator. These cuts are easy to make with a hand hacksaw, and the rough edges can be cleaned up with a metal file. Eleven holes must be drilled in the rotator chassis box along with some hacksaw, drill, and tap work on two metal brackets made from home improvement store aluminum stock supplies. Finally, a few PVC pipe fitting parts require some drilling. The az rotator is a 1 rpm motor mounted inside the rotator body enclosure along with the associated position potentiometer as seen in **Figure 17.45**.

The azimuth and elevation rotator positions are determined by the wiper positions of wire-wound potentiometers that are connected to the motors by a pair of 36:50 ratio gears. Make the brackets for accurately mounting the potentiometers from circuit board material.

The microcontroller program is written in the C programming language. Position switches allow you to manually position the rotator motors. A calibration (CAL) button switch allows adjustments in the firmware if the system gets out of calibration. The rotator is set to 0 degrees az and 0 degrees el, press the CAL button, and that location is stored in the PIC microcontroller program. Then, set the rotator to 359 degrees az and 90 degrees el, press the CAL button to store the other stop position in the PIC program.

17.5.4 SatNOGS

SatNOGS stands for Satellite Network Of Ground Stations (**satnogs.org** and **wiki.satnogs.org**) and is a project associated with the Libre Space Foundation (**libre.space**). SatNOGS stations are used to build an open-source global network of automated satellite ground stations. Originally designed to automate the process of collecting satellite telemetry data, the innovative project won the Hackaday Prize for 2014. All the information you need to build a SatNOGS system is available on the project website, including an online community of users for support and assistance with building and operating the station.

As part of the project, an azimuth-elevation position control system (i.e. – an az-el rotator) was developed that could be made of 3D-printed parts. (3D-printing design files are

(A)

(B)

Figure 17.46 — The SatNOGS antenna system of Corey Shields, KB9JHU, is shown in photo A. The internal construction of the az-el rotator including the 3D-printed gears and other components is shown in photo B. [Photo B courtesy of Comzeradd and the SatNOGS wiki]

available on the SatNOGS website.) The control hardware is sufficiently strong to manage a circularly-polarized Yagi or helix antennas on the uplink and downlink band. The control software also supports commercial az-el rotators, such as the Yaesu G-5500.

The SatNOGS antenna system of Corey Shields, KB9JHU is shown in **Figure 17.46A**. Figure 17.46A shows the az-el rotator mounted on a small tripod designed for TV antennas. The antenna booms and element-to-boom clamps are also 3D-printed. Figure 17.46B shows the inside of the az-el rotator with the 3D-printed gears and other mechanical parts, along with the microprocessor controllers for the motors. A complete set of instructions for assembling the rotator showing all of the parts is available at **satnogs.dozuki.com/Guide/SatNOGS+Rotator+v3+Mechanical+Assembly/7?lang=en**.

The SatNOGS ground station was primarily designed for receive-only telemetry collection but the system can also be used for two-way communication. If the satellite orbital elements are available, the SatNOGS system will automatically track the satellite while you operate. Building and maintaining a telemetry collection system would be an excellent club project, particularly at the secondary or university level.

17.6 BIBLIOGRAPHY

ARRL and RSGB Books

ARRL UHF/Microwave Projects (CD or book), ARRL (out of print).

ARRL UHF/Microwave Experimenter's Manual, ARRL (out of print).

International Microwave Handbook — 2nd Edition, RSGB.

Microwave Know How, RSGB.

Microwave Projects, Vol. 1 and Vol. 2, RSGB.

Other Publications

G. Brown, "A Helix Feed for Surplus MMDS, Antennas," *Proceedings of the 2001AMSAT-NA Symposium*, Oct 2001, pp 89-94.

G. Brown, "A K-Band Receiver for AO-40," *Proceedings of the 2002 AMSAT-NA Space Symposium*, Oct 2002.

G. Brown, "Build This No-Tune Dual-Band Feed for Mode L/S," *The AMSAT Journal*, Vol 26, No 1, Jan/Feb 2003.

G. Brown, "Dual-Band Dish Feeds for 13/23 cm," *Proceedings of the 2002AMSAT-NA Symposium*, Oct 2002, pp 123-131.

G. Brown, "The Texas Potato Masher: A Medium-Gain Directional Satellite Antenna For LEOs," *The AMSAT Journal*, Vol 22, No. 1, Jan/Feb 1999.

LB. Cebik, "The Axial Mode Helical Antenna," *QEX*, Sep/Oct 2007, pp 51-56.

D. DeMaw, "The Basic Helical Beam," *QST*, Nov 1965, pp 20-25, 170.

N. Foot, "Cylindrical Feed horn for Parabolic Reflectors," *Ham Radio*, May 1976, pp 16-20.

D. Hallidy, "Microwave EME Using a Ten-Foot TVRO Antenna," *The ARRL UHF/Microwave Projects Manual, Vol 2* (Newington: ARRL, 1997) pp 10-9 to 10-13. (out of print).

D. Jansson, "Product Review: M^2 23CM22EZA 1.2 GHz Antenna," *QST*, Sep 2002, pp 59-61.

H. Jasik, *Antenna Engineering Handbook*, 1st ed. (New York: McGraw-Hill, 1961).

M. Kingery, "Setting Up for AO-40 L-Band Uplink," *The AMSAT Journal*, May/Jun 2002, pp 14-16.

R. Knadle, "A Twelve-Foot Stressed Parabolic Dish," *QST*, Aug 1972, pp 16-22.

J. Koehler, "An Inexpensive Az-El Rotator System", *QST*, Dec 1998, pp 42-46.

J. Kraus, *Antennas* (New York: McGraw-Hill Book Company, 1988). See "The Helical Antenna," Chapter 7.

J. Kraus, *Antennas* (New York: McGraw-Hill Book Company, 1988). See "Patch or Microstrip Antennas," pp 745-749.

J. D. Kraus, "A 50-Ohm Input Impedance for Helical Beam Antenna," *IEEE Transactions on Antennas and Propagation*, Nov 1977, p 913.

E. Krome, "Development of a Portable Mode S Ground Station." *The AMSAT Journal*, Vol 16, No. 6, Nov/Dec 1993, pp 25-28.

E. Krome, "S band Reception: Building the DEM Converter and Preamp Kits," *The AMSAT Journal*, Vol 16, No. 2, Mar/Apr 1993, pp 4-6.

E. Krome, *Mode S: The Book*, pp 96, 109.

E. Krome, "Mode S: Plug and Play!," *The AMSAT Journal*, Vol 14, No. 1, Jan 1991, pp 21-23, 25.

H. Long, "My Shack Configuration — Spring 2002" (see **www.g6lvb.com/g6lvb_shack_spring_2002.htm**).

W. McCaa, "Hints on Using the AMSAT-OSCAR 13 Mode S Transponder," *The AMSAT Journal*, Vol 13, No. 1, Mar 1990, pp 21-22.

A. MacAllister, "Field Day 2002," *73 Amateur Radio Today*, Sep 2002, pp 48-52.

B. Malowanchuk, "Use of Small TVRO Dishes for EME," *Proceedings of the 21st Conference of The Central States VHF Society, 1987*, pp 68-77.

B. Malowanchuk, "Selection of An Optimum Dish Feed," *Proceedings of the 23rd Conference of The Central States VHF Society, 1989*, pp 35-43.

J. Miller, "Mode S — Tomorrow's Downlink?," *The AMSAT Journal*, Vol 15, No. 4, Sep/Oct 1992, pp 14-15.

J. Miller, "'Patch' Feed For S-Band Dish Antennas"(see **www.jrmiller.demon.co.uk/products/patch.html**).

J. Miller, "A 60-cm S-Band Dish Antenna," *The AMSAT Journal*, Vol 16 No. 2, Mar/Apr 1993, pp 7-9.

J. Miller, "Small is Best," *The AMSAT Journal*, Vol 16, No. 4, Jul/Aug 1993, p 12.

A. Monteiro, "Work OSCAR 40 with Cardboard-box Antennas!," *QST*, Mar 2003, pp 57-62.

A. Monteiro, "An EZ-Lindenblad Antenna for 2 Meters," *QST*, Aug 2007, pp 37-40.

A. Monteiro, "A Parasitic Lindenblad Antenna for 70 cm," *QST*, Feb 2010, p 46.

Orban Microwave, "The Basics of Patch Antennas," (see **www.orbanmicrowave.com/technical-articles**).

T. Planer and G. Zehr, "The Two Meter EZ Lindenblad Revisited," *AMSAT Journal*, Nov/Dec 2018, pp 22-28.

J. Portune, "The Quadrifilar Helix as a 2 Meter Base Station Antenna," *QST*, Oct 2009, pp 30-32.

E. Ruperto, "The W3KH Quadrifilar Helix Antenna," *QST*, Aug 1996, pp 30-34. See also "Feedback", Jun 1999 *QST*, p 78 and Sep 1999 *QST*, p 80.

M. Seguin, "OSCAR 40 on 24 GHz", *QST*, Dec 2002, pp 55-56.

R. Seydler, "Modifications of the AIDC 3731 Downconverters."

D. Thiel and S. Smith, *Switched Parasitic Antennas for Cellular Communications*, (Artech House, 2002). See Chapter 3, "Patch Antennas," pp 79-96.

G. Tillitson, "The Polarization Diplexer — A Polaplexer," *Ham Radio*, Mar 1977, pp 40-43.

D. Thornburg and L. Kramer, "The Two-Meter Eggbeater," *QST*, April 1971, pp 44-46.

D. Vilardi, "Simple and Efficient Feed for Parabolic Antennas," *QST*, Mar 1973, pp 42-44.

P. Wade, *Online Microwave Antenna Handbook*, 1998-2004. See "Chapter 4, Parabolic Dish Antennas," **www.w1ghz.org/antbook/contents.htm**.

T. Zibrat, "2.4 GHz Patch Design," (see **www.qsl.net/k3tz**).

TABLE OF CONTENTS

Chapter 18 — Downloadable Supplemental Content

Supplemental Articles

- "A 70-cm Power Divider" by Zack Lau, W1VT
- "Feeding Open-Wire Line at VHF and UHF" by Zack Lau, W1VT
- "Rewinding Relays for 12 V Operation," by Paul Wade, W1GHZ
- "Increasing Side Suppression by Using Loop-Fed Directional Antennas" by Justin Johnson, GØKSC

Chapter 18

VHF, UHF and Microwave Antenna Systems

As for HF antenna systems, there are many items at VHF, UHF, and microwave frequencies that affect how the overall antenna system works. Techniques and devices or design elements that apply to operating at VHF and above are dealt with in greater detail here.

It is recommended that you begin by reading the System Design Basics section of the **HF Antenna System Design** chapter since many of the issues discussed there apply equally at higher frequencies. Contest clubs, particularly VHF+ contest clubs, are another source of excellent information on antenna system design. You can find these clubs by using the ARRL's Find-A-Club service at **www.arrl.org/find-a-club**.

The material has been collected from various ARRL publications, including other chapters of this book's earlier editions. The *QST* column "Microwavelengths," by Paul Wade, W1GHZ, is another source, covering many important microwave topics. Justin Johnson, GØKSC, contributed the downloadable article describing his experiments and discoveries in pattern control by using loop- and quad-fed beams.

18.1 TRANSMISSION LINES AND DEVICES

Transmission line principles are covered in detail in the **Transmission Lines** chapter. As at HF, RF is carried principally via coaxial cables at VHF/UHF although parallel-wire transmission lines (window line or twin-lead) are used on the VHF and low UHF bands. Microstrip and other PC board transmission lines are increasingly common at UHF and above. At 10 GHz and higher frequencies, waveguide becomes feasible for amateur use. At VHF and higher frequencies, the primary consideration for transmission lines is loss, which increases dramatically with frequency.

While not in widespread use at VHF/UHF today, properly built parallel-wire line can operate with very low loss in VHF and UHF installations. A total line loss under 2 dB per 100 feet at 432 MHz can easily be obtained. A line made of #12 AWG wire, spaced ¾ inch or more with Teflon spreaders and run essentially straight from antenna to station, can be better than anything but the most expensive coax. Such line can be home-made or purchased at a fraction of the cost of coaxial cables, with comparable loss characteristics. Careful attention must be paid to efficient impedance matching if the benefits of this system are to be realized. A similar system for 144 MHz can easily provide a line loss under 1 dB. (See the article "Feeding Open-Wire Line at VHF and UHF" in the downloadable supplemental information.)

Small coax such as RG-58 or RG-59 should never be used in VHF operation if the length of the run is more than a few feet. Lines of ½-inch diameter (RG-213 or RG-11) work fairly well at 50 MHz, and are acceptable for 144-MHz runs of 50 feet or less. These lines are somewhat better if they employ foam instead of ordinary PE dielectric material but still very lossy. Updated designs for low-loss flexible coax, such as Belden 9913 and the LMR-series and various equivalents, are better choices for longer run. Although designed for use in receive-only cable and satellite TV systems, RG-6 in its various shielding configurations is also useable at VHF and above but only at low power (100 W and lower) because of the lightweight conductors and use of F connectors.

Aluminum-jacket *hardline* coaxial cables with large inner conductors and foam insulation (dielectric) are well worth their cost. Another form of hardline known by its trade name of Heliax has a corrugated outer jacket. Some types of Heliax use foam dielectric, while others are air-insulated with the center conductor supported by a helical plastic strip.

Hardline can sometimes be obtained for free from local

cable TV operators as "end runs" — pieces at the end of a roll. A common CATV cable is ½-inch OD 75-Ω hardline. Matched-line loss for this cable is about 1.0 dB/100 feet at 146 MHz and 2.0 dB/100 feet at 432 MHz. Also available from CATV companies is the ¾-inch 75-Ω hardline, sometimes with a black self-healing hard plastic covering. This line has 0.8 dB of loss per 100 feet at 146 MHz, and 1.6 dB loss per 100 feet at 432 MHz. There will be small additional losses for either line if 75-to-50-Ω transformers are used at each end. The **Transmission Line System Techniques** chapter describes synchronous transmission line transformers for converting between 50- and 75-Ω lines on a single band. Hardline must not be bent too sharply, because it will kink.

Commercial connectors for hardline are more expensive than for flexible cable but provide reliable connections with full waterproofing. They are often available at very reasonable prices via online sites including adapters to UHF and other connector types. Enterprising amateurs have homebrewed low-cost connectors. If they are properly waterproofed, connectors and hardline can last almost indefinitely. See the **Transmission Lines** chapter for details on hardline connectors.

Beware of any "bargains" in coax for VHF or UHF use. Feed line loss can be compensated to some extent by increasing transmitter power, but once lost, a weak signal can never be recovered in the receiver.

Effects of weather on transmission lines should not be ignored. Well-constructed open-wire line works optimally in nearly any weather, and it stands up well. The best grades of coax are completely impervious to weather — they can be run underground, fastened to metal towers without insulation and bent into any convenient position with no adverse effects on performance.

18.1.1 PC TRANSMISSION LINES

PC board material can be used to create a transmission line. There are several variations in which the PC trace forms one of the conductors and ground plane layers form the other. These are summarized in **Figure 18.1,** where e_r is the dielectric constant of the PC board material. (FR4 fire retardant glass-epoxy is the most common material at and above VHF.)

Microstrip (Figure 18.1A) is the most common of the PC transmission lines, consisting of an isolated trace above a ground plane.

Stripline (Figure 18.1B) is also common in multilayer boards with the PC trace embedded in the PC board material and centered between two ground plane layers.

Offset stripline (not shown) is a variation of stripline in which the PC trace is not centered between the ground plane layers.

Coplanar waveguide (Figure 18.1C) is feasible at microwave frequencies.

In microstrip and stripline the RF energy is mostly (but not completely) confined to the region between the large surface of the PC trace and the ground plane. Current is spread across the surface of the PC trace at a depth determined by the *skin effect*. (See the *ARRL Handbook* for more information on skin effect.)

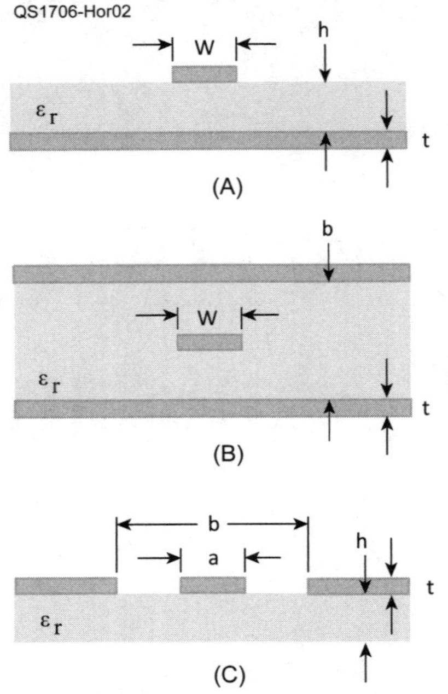

Figure 18.1 — Types of PC transmission line: microstrip (A), stripline (B), and coplanar waveguide (C). Dimensions shown are used by online calculators to determine the line's characteristic impedance. The PCB material's relative permittivity is e_r.

In contrast, the RF energy in coplanar waveguide is contained between the edges of the PC trace and the edges of the adjacent ground plane. The middle surfaces of the PC trace carry little, if any, current. This increases resistive losses because the current is concentrated in a smaller region but the waves travel mostly in air and so have lower losses. This becomes an important tradeoff at microwave frequencies.

Since most designs work with 50-Ω impedances, combinations of common copper foil thicknesses, trace widths, and board layer thicknesses have been calculated to produce 50 Ω. Several are shown in **Table 18.1**. For the interested reader, see Wadell's book that is listed in the Reference section of this chapter. The free program *AppCAD* (**www.hp.woodshot.com**) can handle many PC transmission line design calculations, along with S parameters and balun calculations.

With high-volume commercial and consumer electronics operating at microwave frequencies, connectors for PC transmission lines have become widely available. See the **Transmission Line** chapter's table of connector styles for possible candidates. These small connectors cannot handle a lot of power but are adequate for receiving and low-power transmitting applications. Adaptors and adaptor cables are available to convert these connectors to the more common SMA, UHF, BNC, N, and other styles used by amateurs.

18.1.2 MICROWAVE SWITCHES AND RELAYS

Unless a transmitter's power is very low, we must protect the receiver from the transmitter. If we can keep the leakage

Table 18.1
50-Ω Transmission Line Dimensions

Type of Line	*Dielectric (er)*	*Layer Thickness in mils (mm)*	*Center Conductor in mils (mm)*	*Gap*	*Characteristic Impedance (Ω)*
Microstrip	Prepreg (3.8)	6 (0.152)	11.5 (0.292)	N/A	50.3
		10 (0.254)	20 (0.508)		50.0
Stripline	FR4 (4.5)	12 (0.305)	3.7 (0.094)	N/A	50.0
Coplanar WG	Prepreg (3.8)	6 (0.152)	14 (0.35)	20 (0.50)	49.7

Information from Maxim Integrated, Tutorial 5100 (**www.maximintegrated.com/en/app-notes/index.mvp/id/5100**)

power reaching the receiver front end to a maximum of perhaps 1 mW (0 dBm), it should be safe as long as the receiver amplifier is not powered. Otherwise, the preamplifier could be damaged or could amplify the leakage enough to damage the next stage or mixer.

One way to protect the receiver front end from the transmitted signal is to use separate antennas, far enough apart to attenuate the transmit signal. This could also enable full-duplex operation if so desired, perhaps for a data or repeater link. We must also take care that the antennas are never pointed directly at each other — a precaution we must also take when multiple operators converge on a portable location, or when we operate on multiple bands with separate antennas for different bands.

For higher-performance stations, an RF switch is needed. At HF and VHF, ordinary relays are often adequate for modest powers levels, but they are unsatisfactory for microwaves. Coaxial relays for microwave operation are designed to have low VSWR and good isolation, often shorting out the unconnected terminal to improve isolation. As frequency increases, isolation usually decreases and VSWR gets worse, so each relay has a maximum useful frequency.

Good microwave switches and relays are expensive, but common as surplus items. **Figure 18.2** shows a good selection of surplus coaxial relays; generally, the larger ones are suitable for higher power levels while the smaller ones often work up to 10 GHz. A few coaxial relays will work up to 24 GHz.

An unused relay is preferred, since some used ones are less reliable — one contact may not make a consistent low-resistance connection. If a relay is used or specifications cannot be located, some testing with a power meter will show whether it makes reliable contact and has adequate isolation.

Many surplus relays operate with a coil voltage in the 24 to 28 V range. If only 12 V is applied to the coil, some will exhibit an audible "click" but only operate partway, not completing the switching operation to make contact. Higher voltage is needed to operate reliably. Circuits and kits are available to enable relay operation from a 12 V battery for portable operation. An alternative is to rewind the relay coil to operate from 12 V directly. (The article "Rewinding Relays for 12 V Operation" is available in the downloadable supplemental information.)

For a 1 W transmitter (+30 dBm), at least 30 dB of isolation is needed to keep the leakage under 0 dBm; for 10 W (+40 dBm), 40 dB isolation is required. At 10 GHz, few stations run much higher power and small SMA relays can't handle much higher power. The alternative is a waveguide switch.

Waveguide Switches

Waveguide switches contain curved sections of waveguide that are moved to connect different ports; most are symmetrical with four ports — the fourth terminates the disconnected transmitter or receiver. Isolation is usually very good, but not perfect, especially at high powers. Waveguide switches like those in **Figure 18.3** are used at 10 GHz and higher bands. The largest one is for WR-187, covering 3.95 to 5.85 GHz with cutoff at 3.16 GHz, so it might work at 3456 as well as 5760 MHz. These lower frequency switches are

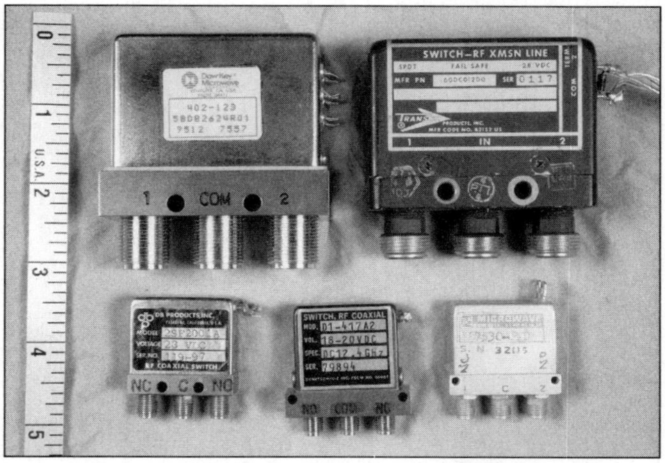

Figure 18.2 — Microwave coaxial relays with Type-N and SMA connectors.

Figure 18.3 — Waveguide switches for WR-75 (10 GHz), WR-42 (24 GHz) and Wr-189 (5760 MHz).

large, heavy and probably unnecessary except at very high power levels.

A caution about power handling: The coaxial relays have delicate gold contacts, which are easily damaged by "hot-switching" — switching while RF power is present. Even 1 W can quickly damage the small relays. Waveguide switches can also be damaged by hot-switching. Use a sequencer to make sure that the relay or switch operates and the preamp power is off before transmit power output is enabled.

Transfer Switches

The transfer switch in **Figures 18.4** and **18.5** allow you to connect a load a termination to both transmitter and receiver so that neither is left open or shorted, except during the instant of switching. The action can be visualized by thinking of the switch as a bridge rectifier. Actuation of the blade pairs forms conducting paths in similar manner to the conduction states of a bridge during alternate half-cycles of ac. Figure 18.4 shows the Dow-Key 412-series as an example of this switch.

The isolation in a transfer switch is, by necessity, 6 dB less than in the corresponding 402-series switch (both types

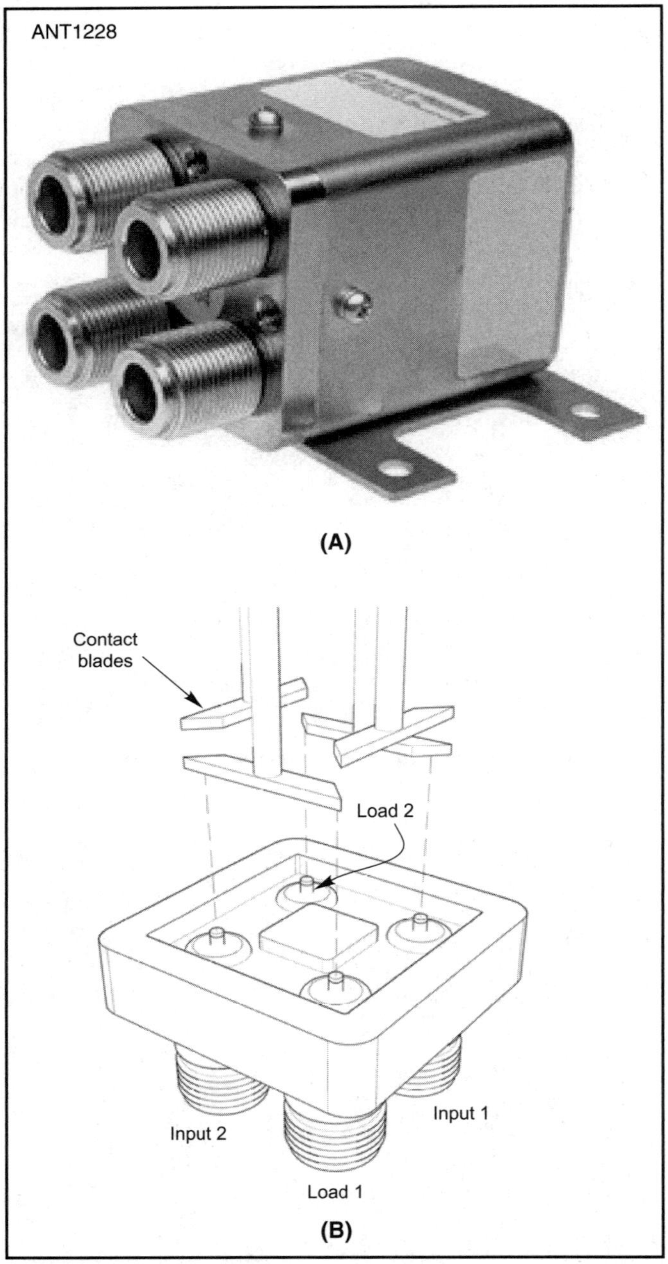

Figure 18.4 — A Dow-Key 412-series microwave transfer switch (A), with an interior view (B). The parallel blade pairs move simultaneously (see text).

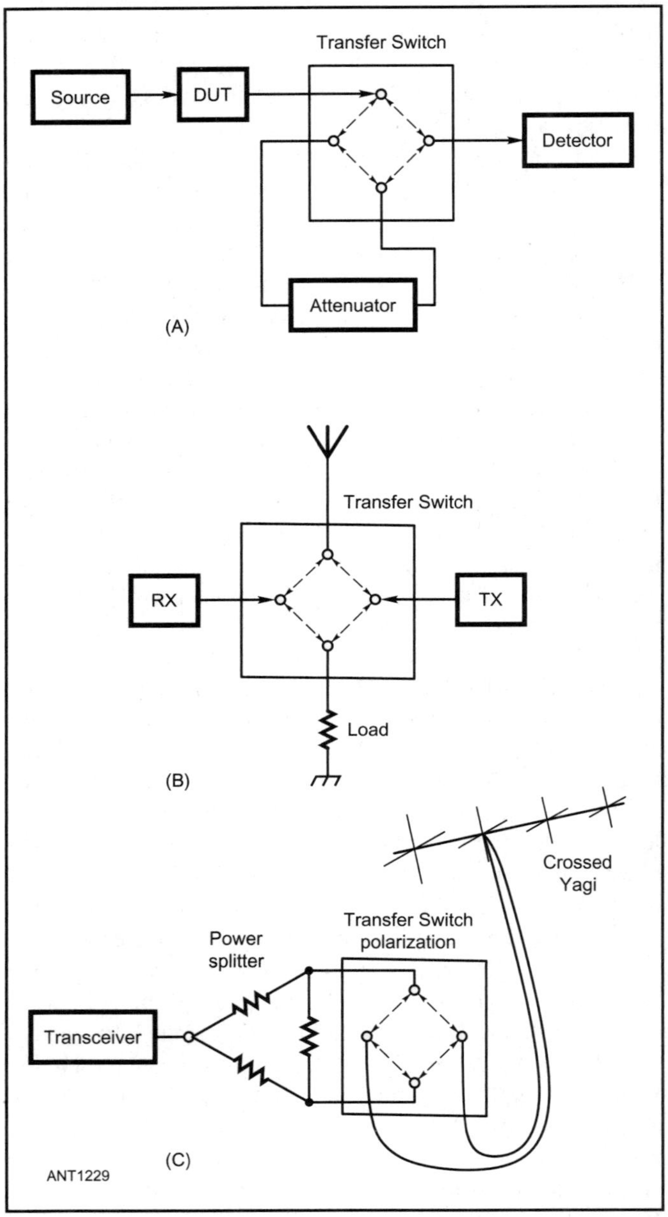

Figure 18.5 — Three circuits for application of 412-series switches: Circuit A inserts or bypasses an attenuator. Circuit B grounds the receiver input during transmission and the transmitter output during reception for weak-signal work. In circuit C, the switch selects the sense of a circularly polarized antenna. One of the transmission lines from the power splitter to the transfer switch should be λ/4 longer that the other.

of switches are common as surplus and used equipment), since there are two leakage paths rather than one. But you would have to use solid-shield cable for the leak to be noticeable. Figure 18.5 shows some typical applications of a transfer switch.

18.1.3 CIRCULATORS AND ISOLATORS

The RF switch protects the receiver, but what protects the transmitter? Microwave power amplifier devices are less forgiving than the 811 tubes in an HF amplifier, and more expensive. High VSWR is the usual culprit for failures. There might be a problem with the feed line, or forgetting to connect the antenna at a portable setup.

One solution is a microwave device called a *circulator*, which can prevent reflected power from getting back to the transmitter. A typical circulator, like the round one on the left in **Figure 18.6**, has three ports and a circular arrow on the side; power only flows in the direction of the arrow. Power from the transmitter goes in to Port "T" and comes out Port "A," going to the antenna. Reflected power comes back into Port "A" and comes out Port "R." If Port "R" is terminated in a 50 Ω load, then all the reflected power is absorbed and none flows back to Port "T," so the transmitter is always happy. More commonly, the ports are numbered 1, 2, 3, with power flowing in that order. An isolator is a circulator with an integral load on the third port, so only two connectors are available, input (1) and output (2).

A circulator contains disks of a special ferrite material with strong magnets on each side, so that the ferrite is in a strong magnetic field. Figure 18.6 shows an open unit on the right; a stripline transmission line between the disks connects the three ports. According to Pozar (see the Bibliography), the ferrite disks form a resonant cavity. The magnetic field creates two resonant modes, which add at the adjacent port in one direction and cancel in the other direction. Also described are waveguide *isolators*, which operate somewhat differently.

Although a circulator is resonant, most are fairly broadband, with usable performance over a frequency range of an octave or more. Some isolators and circulators are shown in **Figure 18.7**; smaller ones are for higher frequencies, as one would expect if they are resonant devices. Typical performance would be greater than 20 dB of isolation with less than 1 dB of insertion loss and VSWR less than 1.3 over the operating range. Some amateurs have experimented with additional small magnets to adjust performance; the operating frequency range does not change, but isolation and loss can be optimized for an amateur band within the operating range. Since they are magnetic devices, they should be kept away from other magnets and from iron or steel — use brass or stainless screws for mounting.

The power-handling capability of an isolator is usually limited by the size of the internal load, while a circulator may have a larger external load. If the isolator is protecting an amplifier, a temperature sensor attached to the load could be used to warn of excessive reflected power and shut down the transmitter before anything is damaged.

Isolators and circulators have other important uses. Since

Figure 18.6 — Circulator on left has arrow showing one-way RF transmission. Isolator on right opened to show the internal construction.

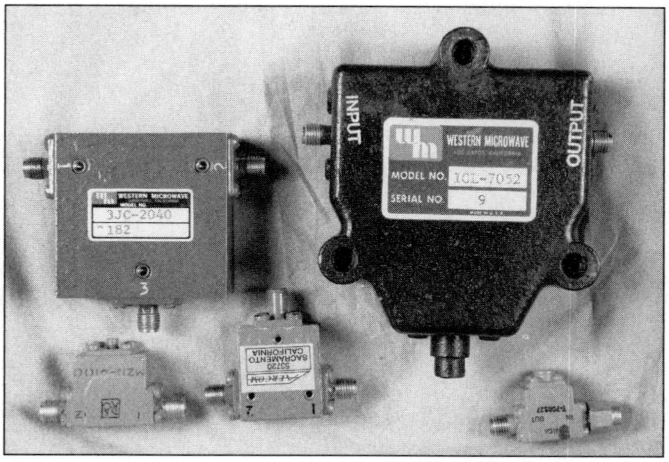

Figure 18.7 — Typical isolators and circulators. Largest is for 1296 MHz. Circulator marked "3JC-2040" indicates that it covers 2.0 to 4.0 GHz. Small isolators all work at 10 GHz.

they provide a good termination not only at the operating frequency but also at low frequencies where amplifying devices may have excessive potential gain, they help to maintain stability if placed between stages, or ahead of potentially unstable preamps. Circulators may also be used to separate signals going in different directions, for instance, using a common mixer for both transmit and receive.

These devices can also be fairly expensive, but are common as surplus. Units with unknown specifications can be very cheap — comparing sizes with known units can help to guess the frequency range. Many surplus assemblies contain isolators that can be salvaged — I've found good isolators in otherwise useless and unwanted microwave assemblies.

18.1.4 POWER DIVIDERS

Power dividers are most often used in place of coaxial synchronous transmission line transformers on the 432 MHz and higher frequency bands. (See the **Transmission Line System Techniques** chapter.) The power dividers shown here use the same principles but in a compact package more suitable to UHF and microwave use.

These dividers are built from 1-inch OD square tubing. Type-N receptacles fit on the outside perfectly. Brass or aluminum are good for the sleeve, but copper should be used for the center conductor. Silver coating the center conductor isn't really necessary, perhaps saving 0.1 dB on 23 cm. Plastic plugs can be used for the open ends of the divider, but a ventilation hole should be provided to keep water from condensation from accumulating.

The characteristic impedance of a coaxial line with square outer conductor is

$$Z = 138 \log\left(1.08 \frac{D}{d}\right) \qquad (1)$$

where

D = inner width of the outer sleeve

d = the OD of the inner conductor

Assuming D is ⅞ inch, a 35.4-Ω section transforming 50 Ω to 25 Ω would have a ½-inch-OD inner conductor.

For higher transformation ratios (4, 6 and 8-way dividers), λ/2 T sections should be used because of the greater bandwidth (and because one cannot put six connectors around a four-side coaxial line). The six-way transformer uses a 40.8-Ω line to match three 50-Ω ports in parallel to 100 Ω on either side of the center connector. If D is again ⅞ inch, the center conductor for the six-way unit is 7⁄16-inch OD.

For other configurations, see **Figure 18.8**. The length of the inner conductor must be exactly λ/4 or λ/2 end-to-end; the same goes for the center-to-center spacing of the connectors. Make the sleeve long enough to receive the end plugs. It should be noted that if wideband performance is not a must, dividers can be used in the third-harmonic mode. A 70-cm T divider, suspended in the radiator plane of four or six 23-cm Yagis will make an excellent feed with very short coaxial lines.

Designs for 144, 220, and 903 MHz are available at **home.teleport.com/~oldaker/power_dividers.htm.** A 50-Ω quarter-wave, four-port power splitter design is also available on the web page.

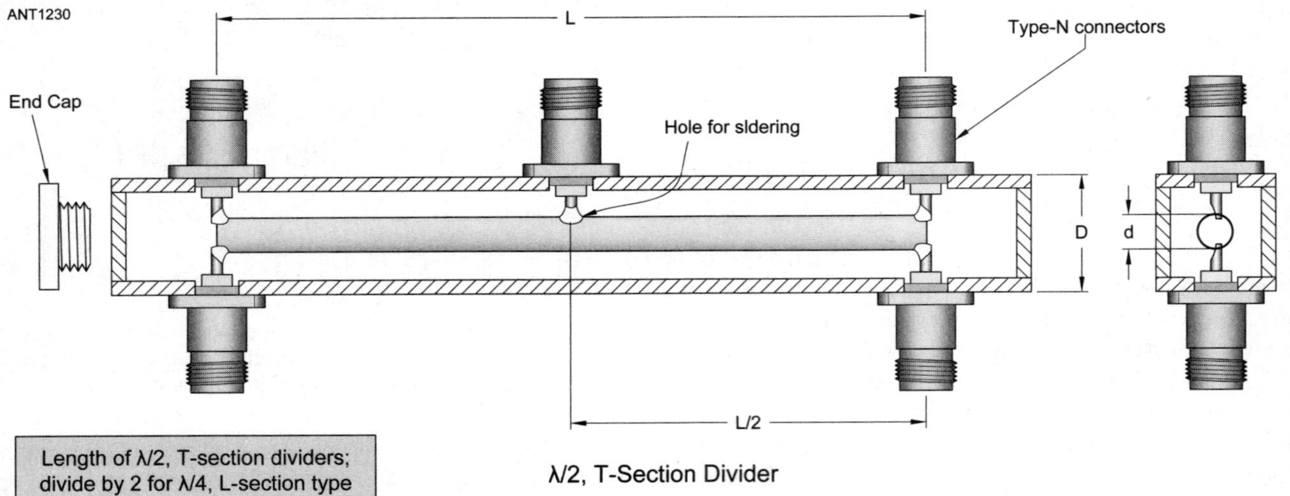

Length of λ/2, T-section dividers; divide by 2 for λ/4, L-section type		
f (MHz)	L (mm)	L (inches)
432	347	13-13/16
1296	116	4-9/16
2304	65	2-9/16

Division Ratio	λ/4 L Section		λ/2 L Section	
	Z	D/d	Z	D/d
2 : 1	35.4 Ω	1.67	70.7 Ω	2.98
3 : 1	28.9 Ω	1.50		
4 : 1	25.0 Ω	1.40	50.0 Ω	2.13
6: 1			40.8 Ω	1.83
8 : 1			35.4 Ω	1.67

Table is only valid for 50-Ω systems

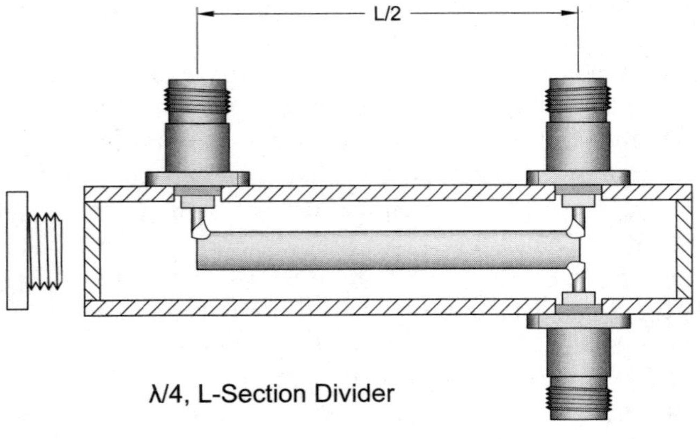

Figure 18.8 — Construction details of coaxial power dividers (see text).

18.2 IMPEDANCE MATCHING

Impedance matching is covered in detail in the **Transmission Line System Techniques** chapter. While advances in modeling have resulted in more designs featuring 50-Ω feed point impedances for direct connection of coaxial feed lines, impedance matching is still an important technique in antenna system design. The various technical aspects of impedance matching are similar at HF and above 50 MHz but the electrical size of the various components can be a primary factor in the choice of methods. Only the matching devices used in practical construction examples later in this chapter are discussed in detail here. This should not rule out consideration of other methods, however.

Impedance matching at the antenna takes on more importance at VHF and UHF because of feed line loss. At HF, the moderate additional feed line loss caused by an impedance mismatch at the antenna can be tolerated and the impedance matched to 50 Ω at the transmitter with an antenna tuner. At VHF and above, with feed line loss much higher, even moderate SWR can result in unacceptable additional losses. Thus, impedance matching is usually done at the antenna so that the minimum matched-line loss is obtained. For that reason, antenna tuners are not usually employed on the bands above 50 MHz.

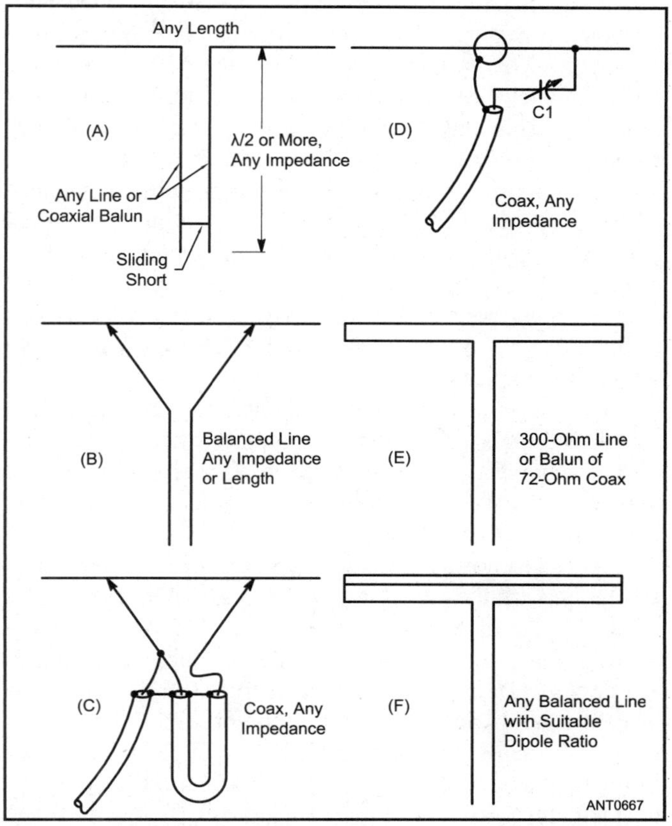

Figure 18.9 — Matching methods commonly used at VHF. The universal stub, A, combines tuning and matching. The adjustable short on the stub and the points of connection of the transmission line are adjusted for minimum reflected power on the line. In the delta match, B and C, the line is fanned out and connected to the dipole at the point of optimum impedance match. Impedances need not be known in A, B or C. The gamma match, D, is for direct connection of coax. C1 tunes out inductance in the arm. A folded dipole of uniform conductor size, E, steps up antenna impedance by a factor of four. Using a larger conductor in the unbroken portion of the folded dipole, F, gives higher orders of impedance transformation.

18.2.1 UNIVERSAL STUB

As its name *universal stub* implies, the double-adjustment stub of **Figure 18.9A** is useful for many matching purposes. The stub length is varied to resonate the system and the transmission line attachment point is varied until the transmission line and stub impedances are equal. In practice this involves moving both the sliding short and the point of line connection for zero reflected power, as indicated on an SWR bridge connected in the line.

The universal stub allows for tuning out any small reactance present in the driven part of the system. It permits matching the antenna to the line without knowledge of the actual impedances involved. The position of the short yielding the best match gives some indication of the amount of reactance present. With little or no reactive component to be tuned out, the stub must be approximately λ/2 from the load toward the short.

The stub should be made of stiff bare wire or rod, spaced no more than 1/20 λ apart. Preferably it should be mounted rigidly, on insulators. Once the position of the short is determined, the center of the short can be grounded, if desired, and the portion of the stub no longer needed can be removed.

It is not necessary that the stub be connected directly to the driven element. It can be made part of a parallel-wire line as a device to match coaxial cable to the line. The stub can be connected to the lower end of a delta match or placed at the feed point of a phased array. Examples of these uses are given later.

18.2.2 DELTA MATCH

Probably the most basic impedance matching device is the *delta match*, fanned ends of a parallel-wire line tapped onto a λ/2 antenna at the point of the most-efficient power transfer. This is shown in Figure 18.9B. Both the side length and the points of connection either side of the center of the element must be adjusted for minimum reflected power on the line, but as with the universal stub, you needn't know the impedances. The delta match makes no provision for tuning out reactance, so the universal stub is often used as a termination for it.

At one time, the delta match was thought to be inferior for VHF applications because of its tendency to radiate if improperly adjusted. The delta has come back into favor now that accurate methods are available for measuring the effects of matching. It is very handy for phasing multiple-bay arrays with open-wire lines, and its dimensions in this use are not particularly critical. It should be checked out carefully in applications like that of Figure 18.9C, where no tuning device is used.

18.2.3 GAMMA AND T MATCHES

An application of the same principle allowing direct connection of coax is the *gamma match*, Figure 18.9D. Because center of a λ/2 dipole is at an RF voltage neutral point, the outer conductor of the coax is connected to the element at this point. This may also be the junction with a metallic or wooden boom. The inner conductor, carrying the RF current, is tapped out on the element at the matching point. Inductance of the arm is tuned out by means of C1, resulting in electrical balance. Both the point of contact with the element and the setting of the capacitor are adjusted for zero reflected power, with a bridge connected in the coaxial line. (Also see the Gamma Match section of the **VHF, UHF and Microwave Antennas** chapter.)

The capacitance can be varied until the required value is found, and the variable capacitor replaced with a fixed unit of that value. C1 can be mounted in a waterproof box. The maximum required value should be about 100 pF for 50 MHz and 35 to 50 pF for 144 MHz.

The capacitor and arm can be combined in one coaxial assembly, with the arm connected to the driven element by means of a sliding clamp and the inner end of the arm sliding inside a sleeve connected to the center conductor of the coax. An assembly of this type can be constructed from concentric pieces of tubing, insulated by a plastic or heat-shrink sleeve. RF voltage across the capacitor is low when the match is adjusted properly, so with a good dielectric, insulation presents no great problem. The initial adjustment should be made with low power. A clean, permanent high-conductivity bond between arm and element is important, since the RF current is high at this point.

Because it is inherently somewhat unbalanced, the gamma match can sometimes introduce pattern distortion, particularly on long-boom, highly directive Yagi arrays. The *T-match*, essentially two gamma matches in series creating a balanced feed system, has become popular for this reason. A coaxial balun like that shown in **Figure 18.10** is used from the 200-Ω balanced T-match to the unbalanced 50-Ω coaxial line going to the transmitter. See the K1FO Yagi designs in the **VHF, UHF and Microwave Antennas** chapter for details on practical use of a T-match. A ferrite bead choke balun as described in the **Transmission Line System Techniques** chapter can be used with a gamma match to decouple the outer surface of the feed line.

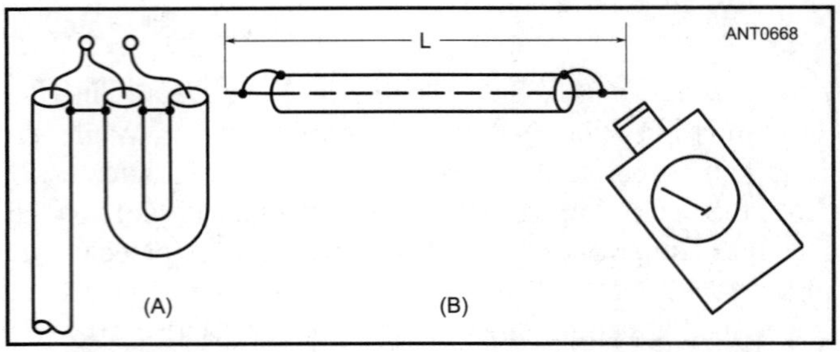

Figure 18.10 — Conversion from unbalanced coax to a balanced load can be done with a 1/2-λ, coaxial balun at A. Electrical length of the looped section should be checked with a dip meter, with the ends shorted, as at B, or with an antenna analyzer. The 1/2-λ balun gives a 4:1 impedance step-up.

18.2.4 FOLDED DIPOLE

As described in the **Dipoles and Monopoles** chapter, if a single conductor of uniform size is folded to make a λ/2 dipole as shown in Figure 18.9E, the impedance is stepped up four times. Such a folded dipole can be fed directly with 300-Ω line with no appreciable mismatch. If a 4:1 balun is used, the antenna can be fed with 75-Ω coaxial cable. (See balun information presented below.) Higher step-up impedance transformation can be obtained if the unbroken portion is made larger in cross-section than the fed portion, as shown in Figure 18.9F.

18.2.5 BETA OR HAIRPIN MATCH

The feed point resistance of most multielement Yagi arrays is less than 50 Ω. If the driven element is split and fed at the center, it may be shortened from its resonant length to add capacitive reactance at the feed point. Then, shunting the feed point with a wire loop resembling a *hairpin* causes a step-up of the feed point resistance. The beta or hairpin match (described in the **Transmission Line System Techniques** chapter) is used together with a 4:1 coaxial balun in some of the 50 MHz antennas described later in this chapter.

18.3 BALUNS

Baluns, circuits and transmission line structures that transfer power while isolating balanced and unbalanced systems are discussed in the **Transmission Line System Techniques** chapter for use at HF and VHF/UHF. An example of a balun made from flexible coax is shown in Figure 18.10A. The looped portion is an electrical λ/2. The physical length depends on the velocity factor of the line used, so it is important to check its resonant frequency as shown in Figure 18.10B. The two ends are shorted, and the loop at one end is coupled to a dip meter coil. This type of balun gives an impedance step-up of 4:1 (typically 50 to 200 Ω, or 75 to 300 Ω).

1:1 coaxial baluns with no impedance transformation are shown in **Figure 18.11**. The coaxial sleeve, open at the top and connected to the outer conductor of the line at the lower end (A) is the preferred type. At B, a conductor of approximately the same size as the line is used with the outer conductor to form a λ/4 stub. Another piece of coax, using only the outer conductor, will serve this purpose. This is known as a Pawsey stub or Pawsey balun. Both baluns are intended to present a high impedance to any RF current that might otherwise flow on the outer surface of the coax shield. Other types of baluns are covered in the **Transmission Line System Techniques** chapter.

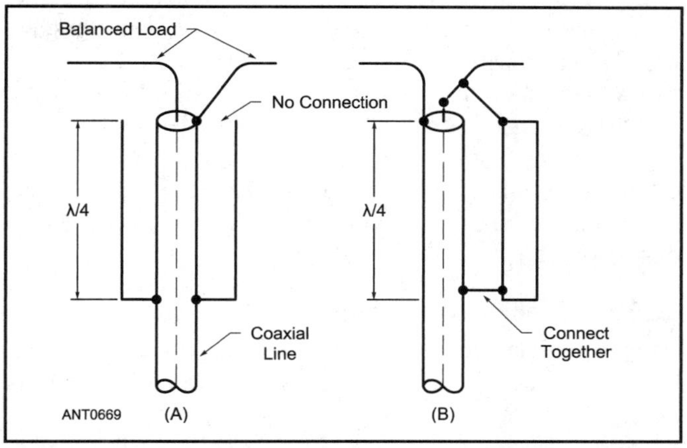

Figure 18.11 — The balun conversion function, with no impedance transformation, can be accomplished with 1/4-λ lines, open at the top and connected to the coax outer conductor at the bottom. The coaxial sleeve at A is preferred.

Ferrite bead choke or current baluns become less attractive at VHF and higher frequencies due to the properties of the ferrite material. However, bead-type choke baluns using type #43 and #61 material can be effective at 50 MHz and even 144 MHz. For 144 MHz and higher frequency bands, coiled-coaxial or resonant transmission line baluns are the usual choice.

18.4 STACKING YAGIS

Where suitable provision can be made for supporting them, two Yagis mounted one above the other and fed in phase can provide better performance than one long Yagi with the same theoretical or measured gain. The pair occupies a much smaller turning space for the same gain, and their wider elevation (El) coverage can provide excellent results. The wide azimuth (Az) coverage for a vertical stack often results in QSOs that might be missed with a single narrow-beam long-boom Yagi pointed in a different direction. On long ionospheric paths, a stacked pair occasionally may show an *apparent* gain much greater than the measured 2 to 3 dB of stacking gain. (See also the extensive section on stacking Yagis in the **HF Antenna System Design** chapter.)

The fundamentals of Yagi stacking are laid out by Ian White, GM3SEK, in the VHF/UHF Long Yagi Workshop section of his website (**www.ifwtech.co.uk/g3sek/index.htm**). The goal is to separate the antennas just enough that their capture areas (or *effective aperture*) do not overlap. This allows each antenna to fully contribute to the overall performance without creating additional sidelobes. The capture area of the Yagi can be thought of as an ellipse centered on the elements of the antenna.

Assuming horizontally-polarized Yagis, as stacking distance increases beyond optimum, the El pattern sidelobes will increase. This narrows the main lobe and more noise to be received from outside the main beam of the antenna. Stacking distances narrower than optimum ("under-stacking") allow a tradeoff between less gain and smaller vertical sidelobes. The tradeoff of a small amount of gain in order to gain improvements in reduced noise may be worthwhile.

It should be noted that vertical stacking of horizontally-polarized Yagis (H-plane stacking) does not narrow the Az beamwidth, only the El beamwidth. Horizontal stacking of the same antennas (E-plane stacking) narrows the Az beamwidth but not the El beamwidth. To narrow both beamwidths requires stacking in both the E- and H-planes, usually implemented as a four-antenna "H-frame" array.

Optimum vertical spacing for Yagis with booms longer than 1 λ or more is about 1 λ (984/50.1 = 19.64 feet), but this may be too much for many builders of 50-MHz antennas to handle. Worthwhile results for 50-MHz stacks can be obtained with as little as ½ λ (10 feet), but ⅝ λ (12 feet) is markedly better. The difference between 12 and 20 feet, however, may not be worth the added structural problems involved in the wider spacing, at least at 50 MHz. The closer spacings give lower measured gain, but the antenna patterns are cleaner in both azimuth and elevation than with 1 λ spacing. Extra gain with wider spacings is usually the objective on 144 MHz and higher-frequency bands, where the structural problems are not as severe.

Yagis can also be stacked in the same plane (collinear elements) for sharper Az directivity. A spacing of ⅝ λ between the ends of the inner elements yields approximately the maximum gain within the main lobe of the array.

DL6WU Stacking Formula

For antennas on the same band and assuming "long-boom" antennas, a formula developed by DL6WU gives excellent results that are close to optimum.

$$D = \lambda / (2 \times \sin(B/2)) \quad (2)$$

where

D = the stacking distance

λ = the wavelength (D and λ must be in the same units)

B = the –3 dB beamwidth of the antenna.

For vertical stacking distance use the antenna's El beamwidth and for horizontal stacking distance, use the Az beamwidth. (A calculator for the DL6WU formula is available online at **dg7ybn.de/Stacking/6WU_online_calc.htm**.)

The formula is approximate. For E-plane stacking (in the plane of the elements) the antennas should have a boom length greater than 0.7 λ and for H-plane stacking, a boom length greater than 2 λ. It is safest to restrict the formula's use to Yagis of at least 2 λ boom length.

If individual antennas of a stacked array are properly designed, they look like non-inductive resistors to the phasing system that connects them. The impedances involved can thus be treated the same as resistances in parallel.

Three sets of stacked dipoles are shown in **Figure 18.12**. Whether these are merely dipoles or the driven elements of Yagi arrays makes no difference for the purpose of these examples. Two 300-Ω antennas at A are 1 λ apart, resulting in a paralleled feed point impedance of 150 Ω at the center. (It actually slightly less than 150 Ω because of coupling between bays, but this can be neglected for illustrative purposes.) This value remains the same regardless of the impedance of the phasing line. Thus, any convenient line can be used for phasing, as long as the *electrical* length of each line is the same.

The velocity factor of the line must be taken into account as well. As with coax, this is subject to so much variation that it is important to make a resonance check on the actual line used. The method for doing this is shown in Figure 18.10B. A ½-λ line is resonant both open and shorted, but the shorted condition (both ends) is usually the more convenient test condition.

The impedance transforming property of a ¼-λ line section can be used in combination matching and phasing lines, as shown in Figure 18.12B and C. At B, two bays spaced ½ λ apart are phased and matched by a 400-Ω line, acting as a double-Q section, so that a 300-Ω main transmission line is matched to two 300-Ω bays. The two halves of this phasing line could also be ¾-λ or 5⁄4-λ long, if such lengths serve a useful mechanical purpose. (An example is the stacking of two Yagis where the desirable spacing is more than ½ λ.)

A double-Q section of coaxial line is illustrated in Figure 18.12C. This is useful for feeding stacked bays that were designed for 50-Ω feed. A spacing of ⅝ λ is useful for small Yagis, and this is the equivalent of a full electrical wavelength of solid-dielectric coax such as RG-11.

If one phasing line is electrically ¼ λ and ¾ λ on the other, the connection to one driven element should be reversed with respect to the other to keep the RF currents in the elements in phase — the gamma match is located on opposite sides of the driven elements in Figure 18.12C. If the number of ¼ λ lengths is the same on either side of the feed point, the two connections should be in the same position, and not reversed. Practically speaking however, you can ensure proper phasing by using exactly equal lengths of line from the same roll of coax. This ensures that the velocity factor for each line is identical.

One marked advantage of coaxial phasing lines is that they can be wrapped around the vertical support, taped or grounded to it, or arranged in any way that is mechanically

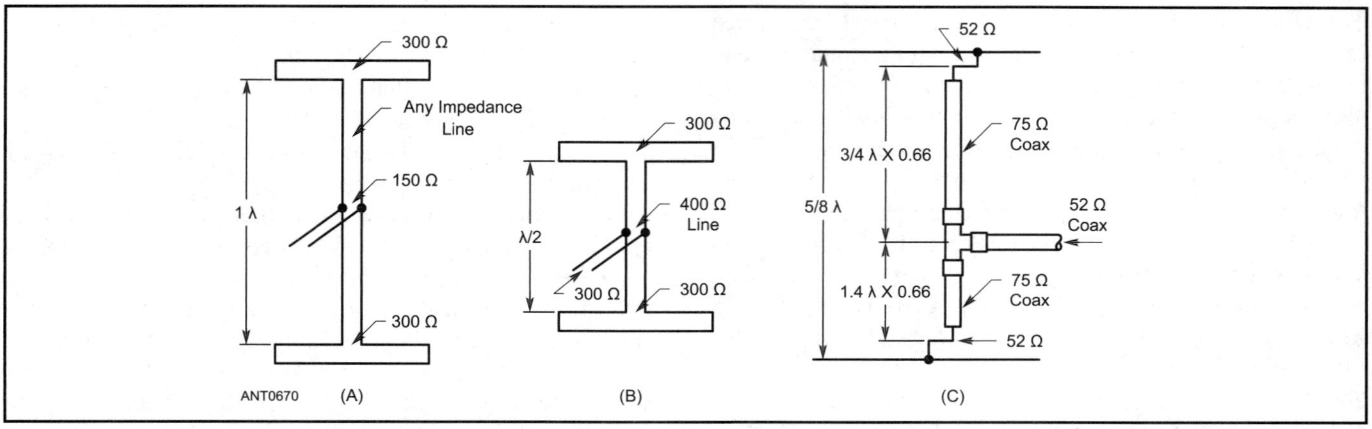

Figure 18.12 — Three methods of feeding stacked VHF arrays. A and B are for bays having balanced driven elements, where a balanced phasing line is desired. Array C has an all-coaxial matching and phasing system. If the lower section is also ¾ λ no transposition of line connections is needed.

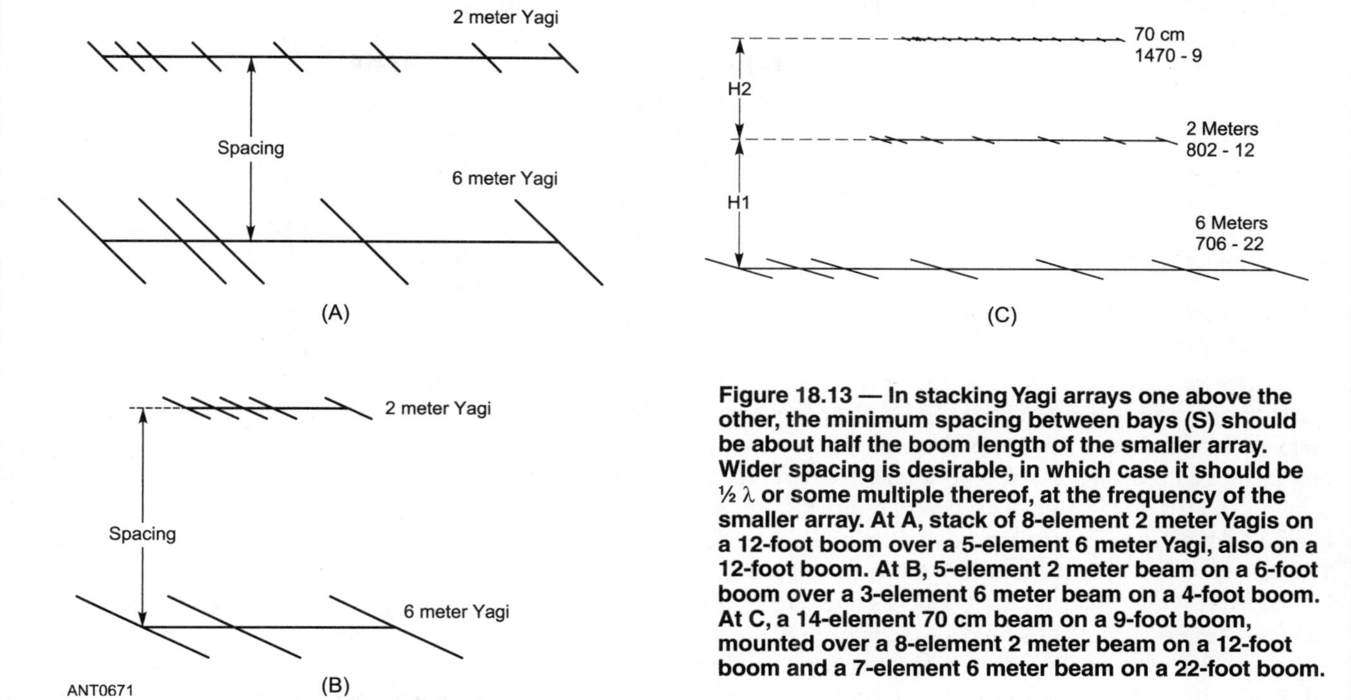

Figure 18.13 — In stacking Yagi arrays one above the other, the minimum spacing between bays (S) should be about half the boom length of the smaller array. Wider spacing is desirable, in which case it should be ½ λ or some multiple thereof, at the frequency of the smaller array. At A, stack of 8-element 2 meter Yagis on a 12-foot boom over a 5-element 6 meter Yagi, also on a 12-foot boom. At B, 5-element 2 meter beam on a 6-foot boom over a 3-element 6 meter beam on a 4-foot boom. At C, a 14-element 70 cm beam on a 9-foot boom, mounted over a 8-element 2 meter beam on a 12-foot boom and a 7-element 6 meter beam on a 22-foot boom.

convenient. The spacing between bays can be set at the most desirable value, and the phasing lines placed anywhere necessary.

18.4.1 STACKING YAGIS FOR DIFFERENT FREQUENCIES

In stacking horizontal Yagis one above the other on a single rotating support, certain considerations apply when the bays are for different bands. As a very general rule of thumb, the minimum desirable spacing is half the boom length of the higher frequency Yagi although computer modeling or manufacturer recommendations for equivalent antennas give better results.

For example, assume the stacked two-band array of **Figure 18.13A** is for 50 and 144 MHz. This vertical arrangement is commonly referred to as a Christmas tree because it resembles one. The 50 MHz Yagi has 5 elements on a 12-foot boom. It tends to look like "ground" to the 8-element 144 MHz Yagi on a 12-foot boom directly above it.

The exact Yagi designs for the examples used in this section are located in the downloadable supplemental information accompanying this book. They may be evaluated as monoband Yagis using the *YW* (*Yagi for Windows*) program also supplied. In each case the bottom Yagi in the stack (at the top of the tower) is assumed to be 20 feet high.

The tables of antenna performance by VE7BQH (see the **VHF, UHF and Microwave Antennas** chapter) also include recommend stacking distances. Comparable antennas can be used as approximations for a homebuilt or unlisted antenna. For antennas on different bands, separate the antennas by at least one-half the recommended stacking distance for the higher-frequency antenna.

SWR Change in a Multi-Frequency Stack

Modern computer modeling programs reveal that while the feed point SWR can indeed be affected from nearby lower-frequency antennas, by far the greatest degradation is in the forward gain and rearward pattern of the higher-frequency Yagi when the booms are closely spaced. In fact, the SWR curve is usually not affected enough to make it a good diagnostic indicator of interaction between the two Yagis.

Figure 18.14 shows an overlay of the SWR curves across the 2 meter band for four configurations: an 8-element

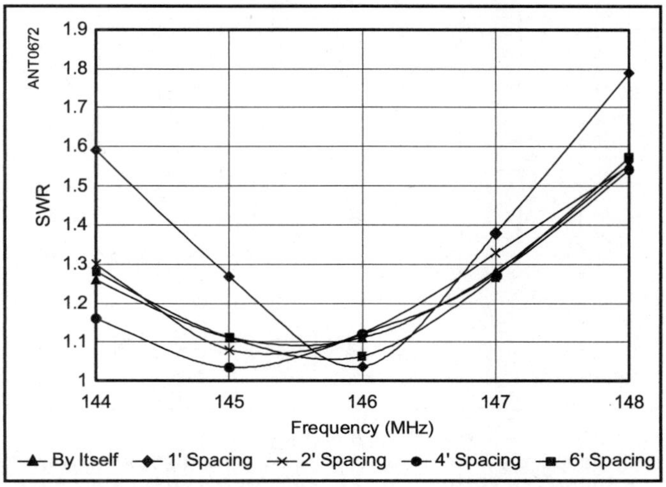

Figure 18.14 — SWR curves for different boom spacing between 8-element 2 meter Yagi on 12-foot boom, over a 5-element 6 meter Yagi on a 12-foot boom. For spacings greater than 1 foot between the booms, differences between the SWR curves are difficult to discern.

2 meter Yagi by itself, and then over a 5-element 6 meter Yagi with spacings between the booms of 1, 2, 4 and 6 feet. The SWR curves are similar — it would be difficult to see any difference between these configurations using typical amateur SWR indicators for anything but the very closest (1-foot) spacing. For example, the SWR curve for the 2-foot spacing case is virtually indistinguishable from that of the Yagi by itself, while the forward gain has dropped more than 0.6 dB because of interactions with the 6 meter Yagi below it.

Gain and Pattern Degradation Due to Stacking

Figure 18.15 shows four overlaid rectangular plots of the azimuth response from 0° to 180° for the 8-element 2 meter Yagi described above, spaced 1, 2, 4 and 6 feet over a 5-element 6 meter beam. The rectangular presentation gives more detail than a polar plot. The most closely spaced configuration (with 1-foot spacing between the booms) shows the largest degradation in the forward gain, a drop of 1.7 dB. The worst-case front-to-rear ratio for the 6-foot spacing is 29.0 dB, while it is 36.4 dB for the 1-foot spacing — actually better than the F/R for the 8-element 2 meter Yagi by itself. Performance change due to the nearby presence of other Yagis can be enormously complicated (and sometimes is not intuitive as well).

What happens when a different kind of 6 meter Yagi is mounted below the 8-element 2 meter Yagi? **Figure 18.16** compares the change in forward gain and the worst-case F/R performance as a function of spacing between the booms for two varieties of 6 meter Yagis: the 5-element design on a 12-foot boom and a 7-element Yagi on a 22-foot boom. The spacing of "0 feet" represents the 8-element 2 meter Yagi when it is used alone, with no other antenna nearby. This sets the reference expectations for gain and F/R.

The most severe degradation occurs for the 1-foot spacing, as you might imagine, for both the 12 and 22-foot boom lengths. Over the 5-element 6 meter Yagi, the 2 meter gain doesn't recover to the reference level of the 8-element 2 meter beam by itself until the spacing is greater than 9 feet. However, the gain is within 0.25 dB of the reference level for spacings of 3 feet or more. Interestingly, the F/R is higher than that of the 2 meter antenna by itself for the 1, 2 and 5-foot spacings and for spacings greater than 11 feet. The 2 meter F/R in the presence of the 12-foot 5-element 6 meter Yagi remains above 20 dB for spacings beyond 1 feet.

Overall, the 2 meter beam performs reasonably well for spacings of 3 feet or more over the 5-element 6 meter Yagi. Put another way, the 2 meter beam's performance is degraded only slightly for boom spacings greater than 3 feet. A spacing of 3 feet is less than the old rule of thumb that the minimum spacing between booms be greater than one-half the boom length of the higher-frequency Yagi, which in this case is 6 feet long.

For the 7-element 6 meter Yagi, the 2 meter gain recovers to the reference level for spacings beyond 7 feet, but the F/R is degraded below the reference level for all spacings shown in Figure 18.16. If we use a gain reduction criterion of less than 0.25 dB and a 20-dB F/R level as the minimum acceptable level, then the spacing must be 5 feet or more over the larger 6 meter Yagi. Again, this is less than the rule of thumb that the minimum spacing between booms be greater than one-half the boom length of the higher-frequency Yagi.

Now, let's try a smaller setup of 2 and 6 meter Yagis stacked vertically in a Christmas-tree configuration to see if the rule of thumb for spacing the booms still holds. **Figure 18.17** shows the performance curves versus boom spacing for a 5-element 2 meter Yagi on a 4-foot boom stacked over a

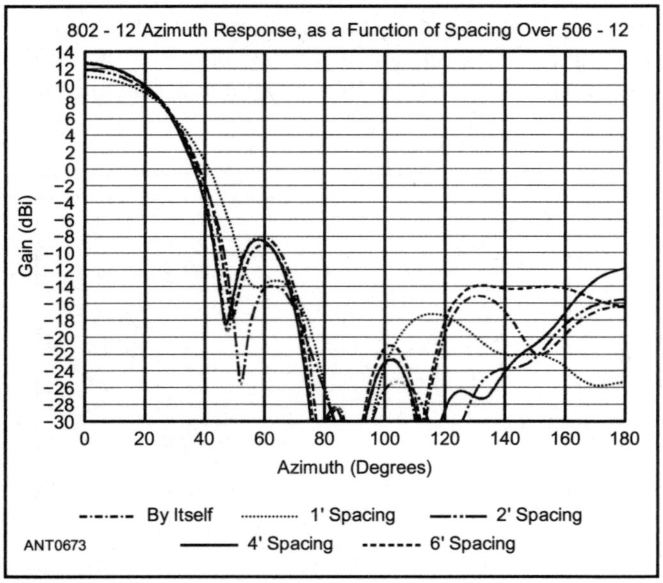

Figure 18.15 — Plots of the 8-element 2 meter Yagi's azimuth response from 0° to 180° for spacing distances from 1 to 6 feet. The sidelobe at about 60° varies about 6 dB over the range of boom spacings, while the shape of worst-case F/R curve varies considerably due to interactions with the lower 6 meter beam. The gain for the 1-foot spacing is degraded by more than 3 dB compared to the 2 meter antenna by itself.

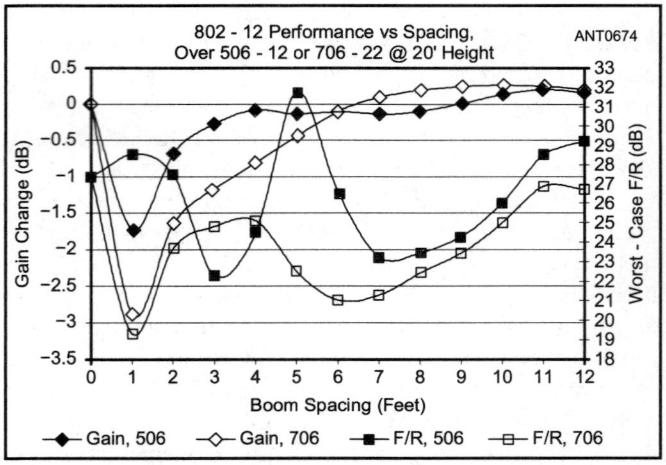

Figure 18.16 — Plot of 8-element 2 meter Yagi's gain and worst-case F/R as a function of distance over two types of 6 meter beams, one on a 12-foot boom and the other on a 22-foot boom. Beyond a spacing of about 5 feet the performance is degraded a minimal amount.

3-element 6 meter Yagi on a 6-foot boom. Again, the 1-foot spacing produces a substantial gain reduction of about 1.3 dB compared to the reference gain when the 2 meter Yagi is used by itself. Beyond a boom spacing of 3 feet the 2 meter gain drops less than 0.25 dB from the reference level of the 2 meter Yagi by itself and the F/R remains above about 20 dB. In this example, the simple rule of thumb that the minimum spacing between booms be greater than half the boom length (half of 4 feet) of the higher-frequency Yagi does not hold up. However, the same minimum spacing of 3 feet we found for the larger 2 meter Yagi remains true. Three feet spacing is almost 0.5 λ between the booms at the higher frequency.

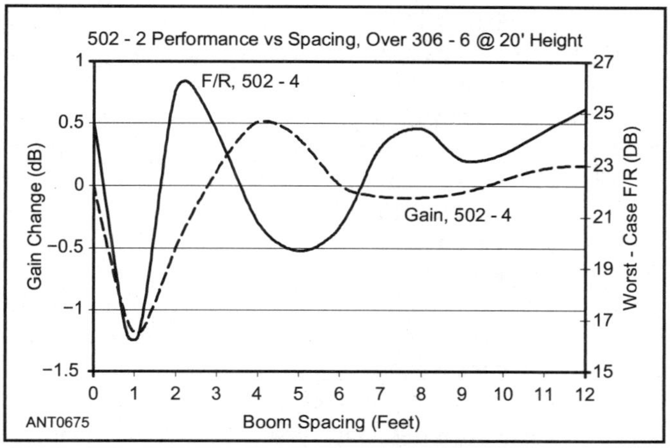

Figure 18.17 — Plot of gain and worst-case F/R of a 5-element 2 meter Yagi on a 4-foot boom as a function of distance over a 3-element 6 meter beam on a 6-foot boom. Beyond a spacing of about 3 feet the performance is degraded a minimal amount.

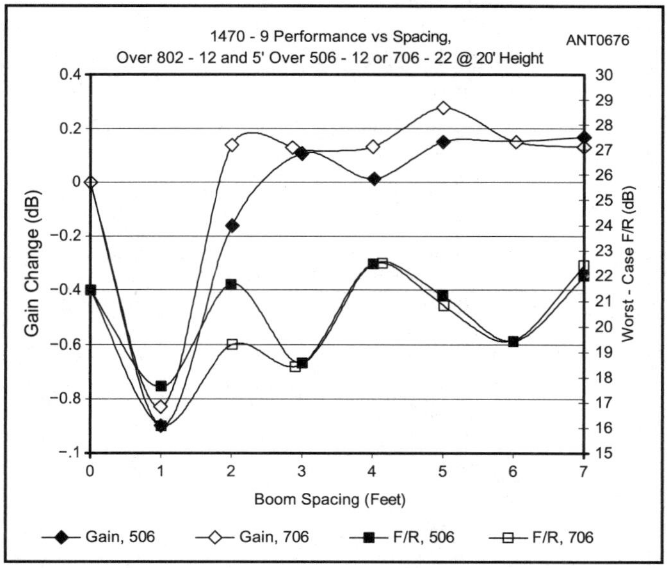

Figure 18.18 — Performance of a 14-element 70 cm Yagi on a 9-foot boom, mounted a variable distance over an 8-element 2 meter Yagi on a 12-foot boom, which is mounted 5 feet above either a 5-element 6 meter Yagi on a 12-foot boom or a 7-element 6 meter Yagi on a 22-foot boom. Beyond a spacing of about 4 feet, the performance of the 70 cm beam is degraded a minimal amount.

Adding a 70 cm Yagi to the Christmas Tree

Let's get more ambitious and set up a larger VHF/UHF Christmas tree, with a 14-element 70 cm Yagi on a 9-foot boom at the top, mounted 5 feet over an 8-element 2 meter Yagi on a 12-foot boom. At the bottom of the stack (at the top of the tower) is either the 5-element 6 meter beam on a 12-foot boom, or a 7-element 6 meter beam on a 22-foot boom. See Figure 18.13C. As before, we will vary the spacing between the 70 cm Yagi and the 2 meter Yagi below it to assess the interactions that degrade the 70 cm performance.

Figure 18.18 compares the change in gain and F/R curves as a function of boom spacings between the 70 cm and 2 meter Yagis for the two different 6 meter Yagis (with a fixed distance of 5 feet between the 2 meter and 6 meter Yagis). In this example, the 70 cm Yagi was designed to be an intrinsic 50-Ω feed, where the F/R has been compromised to some extent. Still, the F/R is greater than 20 dB when the 70 cm Yagi is used by itself.

For spacings greater than 4 feet between the 70 cm and 2 meter booms, the 70 cm gain is equal to or even slightly greater than that of the 70 cm antenna by itself. The increase of gain indicates that the elevation pattern of the 70 cm antenna is slightly compressed by the presence of the other Yagis below it. The F/R stays above at 19.5 dB for spacings greater than or equal to 4 feet. This falls just below our desired lower limit of 20 dB, but it is highly doubtful that anyone would notice this 0.5-dB drop in actual operation. A spacing of 4 feet between booms falls under the rule of thumb that the minimum spacing be at least half the boom length of the higher-frequency Yagi, which in this case is 9 feet.

What should be obvious in this discussion is that you should model the exact configuration you plan to build to avoid unnecessary performance degradation.

18.4.2 STACKING SAME-FREQUENCY YAGIS

This subject has been examined in some detail in the **HF Antenna System Design** chapter. The same basic principles hold at VHF and UHF as they do on HF. That is, the gain increases gradually with increasing spacing between the booms, and then falls off gradually past a certain spacing distance.

At HF, you should avoid nulls in the antenna's elevation response — so that you can cover all the angles needed for geographic areas of interest. At VHF/UHF, propagation is usually at low elevation angles for most propagation modes, and signals are often extremely weak. Thus, achieving maximum gain is the most common design objective for a VHF/UHF stack. Of secondary importance is the cleanliness of the beam pattern, to discriminate against interference and noise sources.

Six meter sporadic-E can sometimes occur at high elevation angles, especially if the E_s cloud is overhead, or nearly overhead. Since sporadic-E is exactly that, sporadic, it's not a good design practice to try to cover a wide range of elevation angles, as you must often do at HF to cover large geographic areas. On 6 meters, you can change to high-angle coverage when necessary. For example, you might switch to a separate Yagi mounted at a low height, or you might provide means to feed stacked antennas out-of-phase. **Figure 18.19** shows an *HFTA* (*HF Terrain Assessment*) plot of two 5-element 6 meter Yagis, fed either in-phase or out-of-phase to cover a much wider range of elevation angles than the in-phase stack alone.

Figure 18.20A shows the change in gain for four 2 meter stacked designs, as a function of the spacing in wavelengths between the booms. The 3-element Yagi is mounted on a 2-foot boom (occupying 0.28 λ of that boom). The 5-element Yagi is on a 4-foot boom (0.51 λ of the boom), while the 8-element Yagi is on a 12-foot boom (1.72 λ of boom). The biggest antenna in the group has 16 elements, on a 27-foot boom (4.0 λ of boom). This range of boom lengths pretty much covers the practical range of antennas used by hams.

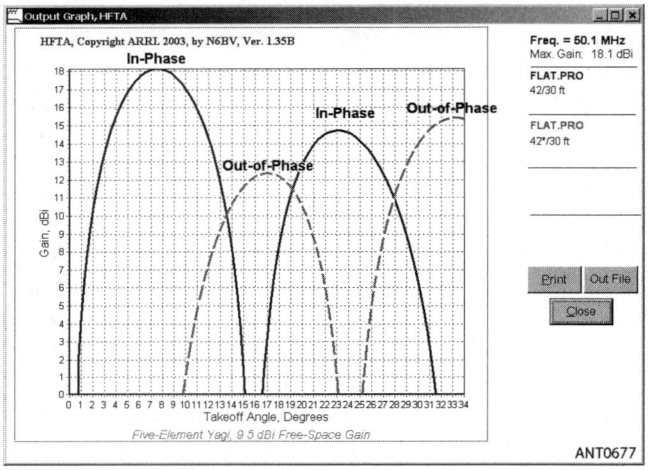

Figure 18.19 — *HFTA* comparison plots of the elevation responses for two 5-element 6 meter Yagis mounted at 42 and 30 feet above flat ground, when they are fed in-phase and out-of-phase. By switching the phasing (adding a half-wavelength of coax to one of the antennas), the elevation angle can be controlled to enhance performance when a sporadic-E cloud is nearly overhead.

The stack of two 3-element Yagis peaks at 3.2 dB of additional gain over a single Yagi for 0.75 λ spacing between the booms. Further increases in spacing see the gain change gradually drop off. Figure 18.20B shows the worst-case F/R of the four stacks, again as a function of boom length. The F/R of a single 3-element Yagi is just over 24 dB, but in the presence of the second 3-element Yagi in the stack, the F/R of the pair oscillates between 15 to 26 dB, finally remaining consistently over the desired 20-dB level for spacings greater than about 1.7 λ, where the gain has fallen about 0.6 dB from the peak possible gain. A boom spacing of 1.7 λ at 146 MHz is 11.5 feet. Thus, you must compromise in choosing the boom spacing between achieving maximum gain and the best pattern.

The increase in gain of the stack of two 5-element Yagis peaks at a spacing of about 1 λ (6.7 feet), where the F/R is an excellent 25 dB. Having more elements on a particular length of boom aids in holding a more consistent F/R in the presence of the second antenna.

The gain increase for the bigger stack of 8-element Yagis peaks at a spacing of about 1.5 λ (10.1 feet), where the F/R is more than 27 dB. The 16-element Yagi's gain increase is 2.6 dB for a spacing of about 2.25 λ (15.2 feet), where the F/R remains close to 25 dB. The stacking distance of 15.2 feet for an antenna with a 27-foot long boom may be a real challenge physically, requiring a very sturdy rotating mast to withstand wind pressures without bending.

These examples show that the exact spacing between booms is not overly critical, since the gain varies relatively slowly around the peak. Figure 18.20A shows that the boom spacing needed to achieve peak gain from a stack increases when higher-gain (longer-boom) individual antennas are used in that stack. It also shows that the increase in maximum gain from stacking decreases for long-boom antennas. Figure 18.20B shows that beyond boom spacings of about 1 λ, the F/R pattern holds well for Yagi designs with booms longer than about 0.5 λ, which is about 4 feet at 146 MHz.

The plots in Figure 18.20 are representative of typical

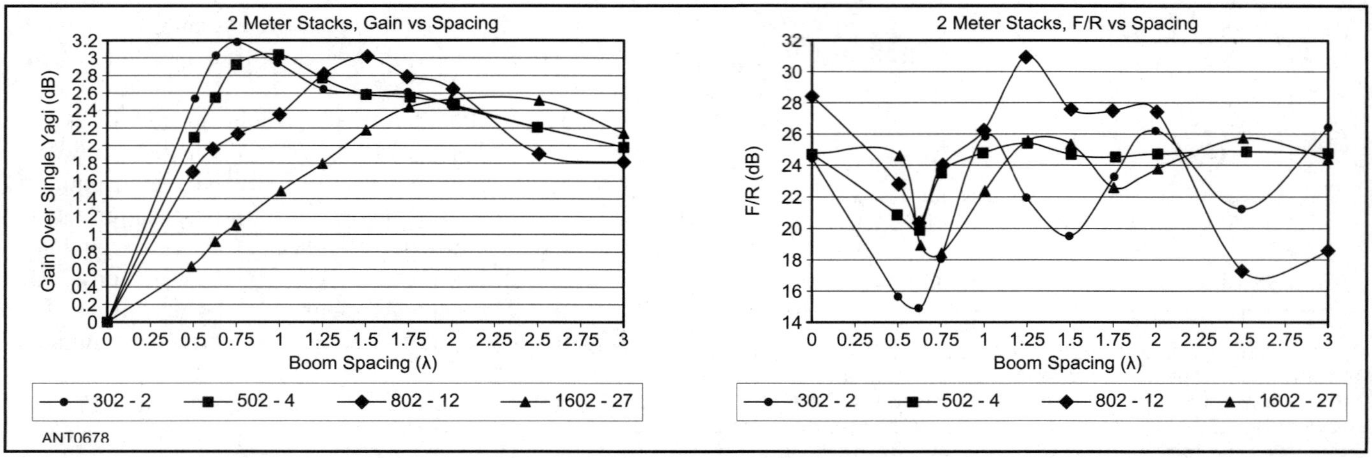

Figure 18.20 — Performance of two different 2 meter Yagis (5 elements on 4-foot boom and 8 elements on 12-foot boom) fed in-phase, as a function of spacing between the booms. Note that the distance is measured in wavelengths.

modern Yagis. You could simply implement these designs as is, and you'll achieve good results. However, we recommend that you model any specific stack you design, just to make sure. Since the boom spacings are displayed in terms of wavelength, you can extend the results for 2 meters to other bands, provided that you use properly scaled Yagi designs to the other bands too.

You can even tweak the element dimensions and spacings of each Yagi used in a stack to optimize the rearward pattern for a particular stacking distance. This strategy can work out well at VHF/UHF, where stacks are often configured for best gain (and pattern) and are "hard-wired" with fixed lengths of feed lines permanently joined together at the junctions.

This is in contrast to the situation at HF (and even on 6 meters). The HF operator usually wants flexibility to select individual Yagis (or combinations of Yagis) from the stack, to match the array's takeoff angle with ionospheric propagation conditions. The designer of a flexible HF stack thus usually doesn't try to redo the element lengths and spacings of the Yagis to optimize a particular stack.

Optimizing Yagi Stacks at VHF and Above

Starting with the DL6WU stacking formula discussed at the beginning of this section, further optimization of stacking distances is required in order to achieve the cleanest, tightest symmetrical patterns, maximizing front to rear (F/R) and front to back (F/B), and eliminating any "spike" lobes appearing in the elevation or azimuth patterns.

For a detailed discussion of the issues involved at this level of optimization, see the article "Development and Real World Replication of Modern Yagi Antennas (III) — Manual Optimisation of Multiple Yagi Arrays" by Justin Johnson, GØKSC, available in the downloadable supplemental information. It is important to note that this optimization described in the article is not being carried out for absolute best sky temperature and/or G/T although the results prove not to be too far away from optimum in these areas.

18.4.3 STACKING STACKS OF DIFFERENT-FREQUENCY YAGIS

The investment in a tower is usually substantial, and most hams want to put as many antennas as possible on a tower, provided that interaction between the antennas can be held to a reasonable level. Really ambitious weak-signal VHF/UHF enthusiasts may want "stacked stacks" — sets of stacked Yagis that cover different bands. For example, a VHF contester might want a stack of two 8-element 2 meter Yagis mounted on the same rotating mast as a stack of two 5-element 6 meter Yagis. Let's assume that the boom length of the 8-element 2 meter Yagis is 12 feet (1.78 λ). We'll assume a boom length of 12 feet (0.61 λ) for the 5-element 6 meter Yagis.

From Figure 18.20, we find the stacking distance between the 8-element 2 meter beams for peak gain and good pattern is 1.5 λ, or 10 feet, but adequate performance can be had for a boom spacing of 0.75 λ, which is 5 feet on 2 meters.

The boom spacing for two 5-element 6 meter beams is 1 λ for peak stacking gain, but a compromise of 0.625 λ (12 feet) still yields an acceptable gain increase of 2 dB over a single Yagi. The overall height of the rotating mast sticking out of the top of the tower is thus set by the 0.625 λ stacking distance on 6 meters, at 12 feet. In-between the 6 meter Yagis at the bottom and top of the rotating mast we will mount the 2 meter Yagi stack. With only 12 feet available on the mast, the spacing for symmetric placement of the two 2 meter Yagis in-between the 6 meter Yagis dictates a distance of only 4 feet between the 2 meter beams. This is less than optimal.

The performance of the 2 meter stack in this "stack within a stack" is affected by the close spacing, but the interactions are not disastrous. The stacking gain is 1.62 dB more than the gain for a single 8-element 2 meter Yagi and the F/R remains above 20 dB across the 2 meter band.

On 6 meters, the stacking gain for two 5-element 6 meter Yagis spaced 12 feet apart is 2.2 dB more than the gain of a single Yagi, while the F/R pattern remains about 20 dB over the weak-signal portion of the 6 meter band. As described in the **HF Antenna System Design** chapter, stacking gives more advantages than merely a gain increase, and 6 meter propagation does require coverage of a range of elevation angles because much of the time ionospheric modes are involved.

Increasing the length of the rotating mast to 18 feet sticking out of the top of the tower will increase performance, particularly on 2 meters. The stacking gain on 6 meters will increase to 2.3 dB while the F/R decreases to 18.5 dB, modest changes both. The 18-foot mast allows the 2 meter Yagis to be spaced 6 feet from each other and 6 feet away from both top and bottom 6 meter antennas. The stacking gain goes to 2.14 dB and the F/R approaches 27 dB in the weak-signal portion of the 2 meter band.

Whether the modest increase in stacking gain is worth the cost and mechanical complexity of stacking two 2 meter Yagis between a stack of 6 meter Yagis is a choice left to the operator. Certainly the cost and weight of a rotating mast that is 20 feet long (18 feet out of the top of the tower and 2 feet down inside the tower), a mast that must be sturdy enough to support the antennas in high winds without bending, should give pause to even the most enthusiastic 6 meter weak-signal operator.

Noise Rejection Using Stacked Quads

ARRL Antenna Book contributor Justin Johnson, GØKSC, has written a short article describing his experimental results as to how very high front-to-side ratios can be achieved with a pair of stacked quads. By changing the feed points of the quads from the traditionally symmetric arrangement, useful improvements in the radiation pattern were achieved. The article is available in this chapter's downloadable supplemental information package.

18.5 WEATHERPROOFING RELAYS AND PREAMPLIFIERS

For stations with switchable-polarization antennas, experience with exposed switching relays and preamplifiers mounted on antennas have shown that they are prone to failure caused by a mechanism known as *diurnal pumping*. Often these relays are covered with a plastic case, and the seam between the case and PC board is sealed with a silicone sealant. Preamps may also have a gasket seal for the cover, while the connectors can easily leak air. None of these methods create a true hermetic seal and as a result the day/night temperature swings pump air and moisture in and out of the relay or preamp case. Under the right conditions of temperature and humidity, moisture from the air will condense inside the case when the outside air cools down. Condensed water builds up inside the case, promoting extensive corrosion and unwanted electrical conduction, seriously degrading component performance in a short time.

A solution for those antennas with "sealed" plastic relays is to avoid problems by making the modifications shown in **Figure 18.21**. Relocate the 4:1 balun as shown and place a clear polystyrene plastic refrigerator container over the relay. Notch the container edges for the driven element and the boom so the container will sit down over the relay, sheltering it from the elements. Bond the container in place with a few dabs of silicone adhesive sealant. (Be sure to use sealers that do not release acetic acid during curing — see the **Antenna Materials and Construction** chapter.) An example for the protective cover for an S-band preamp can be seen in the discussion on feeds for parabolic antennas in the **VHF, UHF and Microwave Antennas** chapter.

For both relay and preamp cases, carefully drill a 3⁄32-inch hole through the low side of the case to provide the needed vent. The added cover keeps rainwater off the relay and preamp, and the holes will prevent any buildup of condensation inside the relay case. Relays and preamplifiers so treated have remained clean and operational over periods of years without problems.

A commercial NEMA 4 equipment box, detailed in **Figure 18.22** (shown inverted), is used to protect the 23 cm power amplifier and its power supply, as well as a multitude of electrical connections. This steel box is very weather resistant, with an exceptionally good epoxy finish, but it is not sealed and so it will not trap moisture to be condensed with temperature changes.

Be sure to use a box with at least a NEMA 3 rating for rainwater and dust protection. The NEMA 4 rating provides a little better protection than the NEMA 3 rating. Using a weather-rated equipment enclosure is very well worth the expense. As you can see, the box also provides some pretty good flanges to mount the mast-mounted preamplifiers for three bands. This box is an elegant solution for the simple need of rain shelter for your equipment. See **Figure 18.23**.

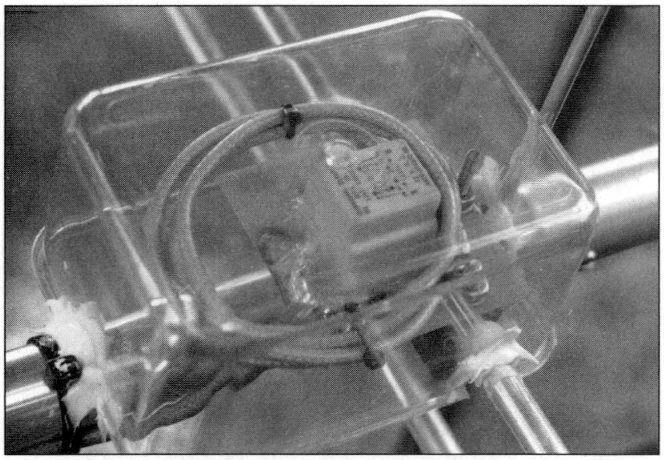

Figure 18.21 — KLM 2M-22C antenna CP switching relay with relocated balun. The protective cover is needed for rain protection, be sure to use a polystyrene kitchen box (see text).

Figure 18.22 — A NEMA 4 box is used to shelter the L-band electronics and power supply. The box flanges are convenient for mounting preamplifiers. The box is shown inverted since it is on a tilt-over tower.

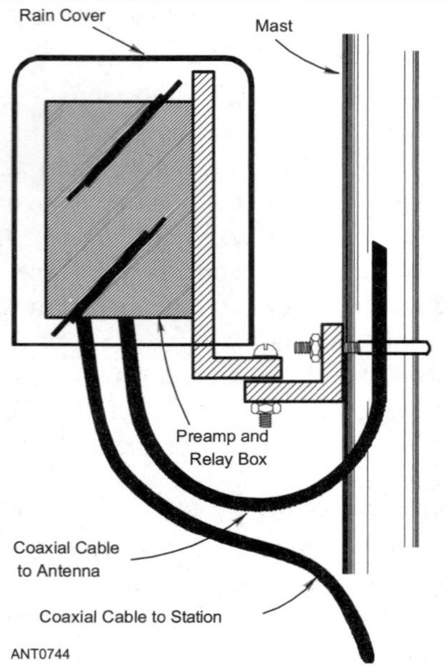

Figure 18.23 — Protection for tower-mounted equipment need not be elaborate. Be sure to dress the cables as shown so that water drips off the cable jacket before it reaches the enclosure. One hazard for such open-bottom enclosures is that of animals gnawing on the cable insulation. Flying insects also like to build their houses in these enclosures.

18.6 REFERENCES AND BIBLIOGRAPHY

A. Barnes, *International Microwave Handbook*, 2nd Ed., RSGB, 2008.

H. Jasik, *Antenna Engineering Handbook*, 2nd Ed. (New York: McGraw-Hill, 1984).

H.W. Johnson and M. Graham, *High Speed Digital Design* (Prentice Hall, 1993).

Microwaves 101, **www.microvaves101.com**.

M. Pozar, *Microwave Engineering*, 2nd Ed., Wiley, 1998, pp 537-543.

J. Reisert, "VHF/UHF World," *Ham Radio* column.

P. Wade, "Microwavelengths," *QST* column.

B. Wadell, *Transmission Line Design Handbook*, ISBN: 0-89006-436-9.

Z. Lau, "RF: A 70-cm Power Divider," *QEX*, Jul/Aug 1999, pp 56-58.

Z. Lau, "RF: Feeding Open-Wire Line at VHF and UHF," *QEX*, Jan/Feb 2000, pp 59-63.

The ARRL UHF/Microwave Experimenter's Manual (Newington: ARRL, 2006). (This book is out of print.)

TABLE OF CONTENTS

Chapter 19 — Downloadable Supplemental Content

Supplemental Articles

- "6 Meter 4 Element Portable Yagi" by Zack Lau, W1VT (plus separate element design drawing)
- "A 6-Meter Portable Yagi Antenna" by Scott McCann, W3MEO
- "A One Person, Safe, Portable and Easy to Erect Antenna Mast" by Bob Dixon, W8ERD
- "A Portable 2-Element Triband Yagi" by Markus Hansen, VE7CA
- "A Portable End-Fed Half-Wave Antenna for 80 Meters" by Rick Littlefield, K1BQT
- "A Portable Inverted V Antenna" by Joseph Littlepage, WE5Y
- "A Simple and Portable HF Vertical Travel Antenna" by Phil Salas, AD5X
- "A Simple HF-Portable Antenna" by Phil Salas, AD5X
- "A Small, Portable Dipole for Field Use" by Ron Herring, W7HD
- "A Super Duper Five Band Portable Antenna" by Clarke Cooper, K8BP
- "A Two-Element Yagi for 18 MHz" by Martin Hedman, SMØDTK
- "An Off Center End Fed Dipole for Portable Operation on 40 to 6 Meters" by Kai Siwiak, KE4PT
- "Compact 40 Meter HF Loop for Your Recreational Vehicle" by John Portune, W6NBC
- "Fishing for DX with a Five Band Portable Antenna" by Barry Strickland, AB4QL
- "Getting the Antenna Aloft" by Stuart Thomas, KB1HQS
- Ladder Mast and PVRC Mount
- "The Black Widow — A Portable 15 Meter Beam" by Allen Baker, KG4JJH
- "The Ultimate Portable HF Vertical Antenna" by Phil Salas, AD5X
- "The W4SSY Spudgun" by Byron Black, W4SSY
- "Three-Element Portable 6 Meter Yagi" by Markus Hansen, VE7CA
- "Tuning Electrically Short Antennas for Field Operation" by Ulrich Rohde, N1UL, and Kai Siwiak, KE4PT
- "Zip Cord Antennas and Feed Lines for Portable Applications" by William Parmley, KR8L

Chapter 19

Portable Antennas

Portable operation is usually taken to mean a temporary operating site away from a fixed station location. Field Day is probably the best-known such example and so a casual search through the literature will find literally dozens of "Field Day Special" antennas intended to provide coast-to-coast coverage on the HF bands and some directivity on the VHF/UHF bands. "Hilltopping" operation is also very popular on the VHF/UHF bands during contests. You will also find stations operating portable while camping or RVing or hiking and special event stations are often using temporary antennas as well. A number of awards programs call for operating from summits, parks, islands, lighthouses, castles, and other temporary locations. Emergency communications or "emcomm" operation during local and regional communication emergencies also requires portable antennas.

With portable operation becoming increasingly popular, antennas for temporary operation are receiving a lot of interest. As of early 2019, a count on the **www.eham.net** review forum — Antennas: HF Portable (not mobile) — shows 201 different portable antennas! They must be designed to be easily packed and stored, transported, unpacked and erected — usually by a single person. They should be able to radiate and receive effectively in a variety of installation environments and they should be robust enough to be used again and again. With such a wide range of operating needs, it should not be a surprise that antennas designated as "portable" come in a wide variety of sizes and shapes for use on any amateur frequency. Similarly, "transport" can mean anything from a backpack to a truck.

Bearing this range of uses in mind, this chapter describes antennas that are designed for portability. However, many of these antennas can also be used in more permanent installations, particularly where a "low profile" antenna is needed as discussed in the **Stealth and Limited Space Antennas** chapter. The antennas in the **Mobile and Maritime HF Antennas** chapter can often be employed as portable antennas, too, so there is overlap between the three applications. Often, the only meaningful difference is the mounting of the antenna or how it is supported! As you read these chapters, envision how each antenna might be adapted to other uses. The goal of this chapter is not necessarily for you to reproduce a design exactly but to give you examples of how other amateurs have satisfied their operating needs in ways you might find useful as well.

Portable operating has captured the imagination of amateurs for decades with far too many innovative antenna designs to be summarized in this chapter. The ARRL publishes several books on the subject which include numerous antenna and station designs. Current selections include *Portable Antenna Classics* and *Portable Operating for Amateur Radio* by Stuart Thomas, KB1HQS, along with the more general *HF Dipoles for Amateur Radio.* (See the Bibliography.) You'll find many designs you can use or adapt for the type of operating you prefer.

19.1 HORIZONTAL ANTENNAS

The most common horizontal wire antenna used for portable operation is the $\lambda/2$ dipole or inverted-V, followed by an end-fed dipole or Zepp. These typically require some kind of support 10 feet or more high — such as a tree or one of the portable masts described later in this chapter. If trees are used, some means of getting the support lines over a branch is also required.

Some types of operation such as backpacking place a premium on minimizing weight of the entire antenna system — antenna, feed line, antenna tuner and supporting lines. For this type of antenna system, some extra loss or operation on a single band is an acceptable tradeoff.

Another solution often used when the operation will be of short duration or if frequent stops along a route will be made is to use a pair of loaded mobile whips in a dipole configuration. These antennas can be mounted on a short mast and tripod. Setting up and taking down these antennas is quick and is completely independent of any other support.

19.1.1 ZIP-CORD ANTENNAS AND FEED LINES

Previous editions of this book included a section on the use of common zip cord (used for ac power cords) for antennas and feed lines. That information was based on a March 1979 *QST* article by Jerry Hall, K1TD and it has been updated according to the March 2009 *QST* article by William Parmley, KR8L. (See the Bibliography.)

A lighter weight style of zip cord (#22 AWG speaker wire) was used compared to the heavier ac power zip cord in the original article. **Tables 19.1** and **19.2** give the measured values for velocity factor and loss in dB/100 feet. The characteristic impedance was estimated to be 150 Ω, somewhat higher than the 105 Ω for ac power cord. Performance of the lighter zip cord appears to be intermediate between the miniature RG-174 coaxial cable (light, but lossy) and RG-58 (less lossy, but heavier). This may be a good trade-off for your application. Given the wide variations in quality and materials used for zip cord, loss and characteristic impedance should be measured with an antenna analyzer before committing to a particular type of line.

The antenna's "center insulator" is made using the electrician's knot shown in **Figure 19.1** — a handy knot to use whenever zip cord is used. The dipole length is calculated as described in the **Dipoles and Monopoles** chapter. At the end of the dipole, extra wire folded back on itself to make a loop for attachment to a support line.

If a low SWR at the transmitter is important, the feed line length can be cut to some multiple of λ/2 using the measured velocity factor. This causes the dipole's feed point impedance to be replicated at the opposite end of the feed line, regardless of the line's characteristic impedance. (See the **Transmission Lines** chapter for an explanation.)

At the transmitter end of the feed line, unzip the wire a couple of inches and attach a banana plug to one side and an alligator clip to the other. The banana plug fits perfectly in the center conductor of a transceiver's SO-239 coax connector, while the alligator clip makes a convenient way to attach to the transceiver's ground connection (as shown in **Figure 19.2**). At low power or QRP levels, the connection did not present any problems.

After building antennas and feed lines for 30, 20, and 17 meters, the antennas were installed in an inverted-V configuration with the apex at about 20 feet. This was done using either a telescoping fishing pole, or by tossing a line over a tree branch and pulling the dipole up with that. The ends of the dipole were brought down to 6 to 8 feet off the ground and tied off with nylon line that was then tied to tent stakes.

The dipole was pruned to resonance by changing the fold point at the end. The extra wire was left in place and was not trimmed off. The 20 meter and 17 meter antennas were also tested as indoor dipoles by attaching the apex to a ceiling lamp and taping the ends to the walls with masking tape. In

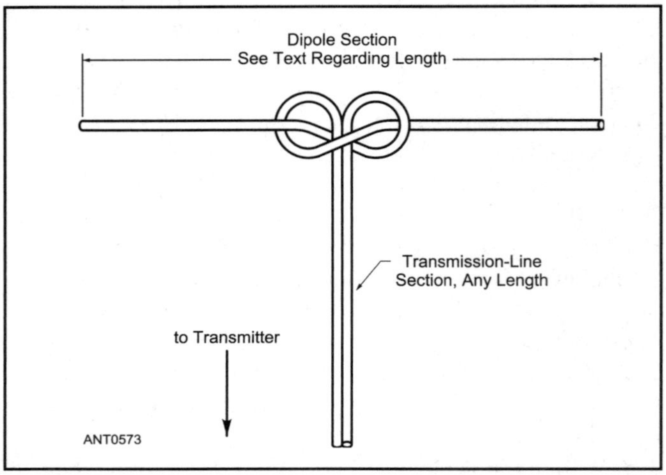

Figure 19.1 — The electrician's knot, often used inside lamp bases and appliances in lieu of a plastic grip, can also serve to prevent the feed line section of a zip-cord antenna from unzipping itself under the tension of dipole suspension. To tie the knot, first use the right-hand conductor to form a loop, passing the wire behind the un-separated zip cord and off to the left. Then pass the left-hand wire of the pair behind the wire extending off to the left, in front of the un-separated pair, and thread it through the loop already formed. Adjust the knot for symmetry while pulling on the two dipole wires.

Figure 19.2 — Rear of radio showing banana plug and clip lead connections.

Table 19.1
Measured Velocity Factor of #22 AWG Zip Cord

Frequency (MHz)	*Velocity Factor (VF)*
3.31	0.68
6.75	0.69
13.67	0.70
27.77	0.71

Table 19.2
Calculated Attenuation of #22 AWG Zip Cord Compared to Small Coax, dB/100 feet

Frequency (MHz)	*Zip Cord #22 AWG*	*RG-174*	*RG-58*
3.31	0.97	2.7	0.8
6.75	1.48	3.3	1.2
13.67	2.39	4.0	1.6
27.77	3.41	5.3	2.4

this configuration they were easily tuned to resonance.

Once the antenna was tuned to resonance it was possible to adjust and optimize the feed point impedance by changing both the horizontal and vertical angles between the two legs. For the author's outdoor installation the best match was obtained with the dipole legs arranged at a horizontal (azimuthal) angle of between 90 and 120°. For indoor applications the feed point impedance was found to be adjustable by changing the amount of droop in the legs, proximity to walls or floors, and the angle between the legs.

As should always be done with parallel-wire feeders, keep the feed line clear of other objects and equidistant from both legs of the dipole to the maximum extent practical.

19.1.2 END-FED HALF-WAVE

The EFHW (End-Fed Half-Wave) antenna has become popular with portable operators because of its mechanical simplicity. The antenna is a half-wavelength dipole fed at one end. (See the End-fed Zepp section of the **Single-Band MF and HF Antennas** chapter.) As such, it will radiate no better than an ordinary center-fed dipole which is likely to be a more effective antenna if the necessary supports are available.

The high feed point impedance requires either tuned feeders or an impedance matching network as shown here. The highly unbalanced configuration of the antenna usually results in significant common-mode current on the antenna feed line which radiates as part of the antenna. The common-mode current can also cause RFI to the station equipment and at higher power levels, RF "hot spots." Tuning of the impedance matching network can be very sensitive, as well.

The configuration shown in the full article by K1BQT addresses some of the antenna's shortcomings and is intended for use as a portable antenna for regional communication using NVIS propagation. (See "A Portable End-Fed Half-Wave Antenna for 80 Meters" in the downloadable supplemental information.) First, the impedance matching network shown in **Figure 19.3** uses a transformer that helps break the feed line's common-mode current path. This reduces the sensitivity of the antenna tuning to the feed line and station equipment orientation and also helps minimize the RF hot spots. Next, the tuning network is mounted directly on a ground rod which also tends to stabilize the tuning settings. A short 3 to 4-foot ground rod may be sufficient but could be augmented by a counterpoise wire that serves to extend the antenna somewhat and can help with impedance matching in some circumstances. Counterpoise wires cut to λ/8 and λ/4 would be good to include as part of the antenna package.

As for any half-wave dipole, maximum radiation occurs from current on the antenna's midsection. That means it is important to raise the center as high as possible. Since the antenna is likely to be installed so that one end is close to ground level and the other may be close to foliage, insulated wire is recommended.

The parallel-tuned LC network is a good choice to convert the antenna's feed point impedance of up to several thousand ohms down to the 50 Ω impedance of coax feed lines. Once set, the operating bandwidth will be approximately 100 kHz and can be adjusted to cover the entire 3.5–4 MHz band.

The EFHW can pose a safety hazard at higher power levels due to the high voltage points at the ends of the wire that may be accessible to people. In response, limiting power to 100 W or less is prudent. Any point of the antenna close to the ground, particularly the feed point, should be made inaccessible to curious people or pets.

19.1.3 PORTABLE INVERTED V ANTENNA

The antenna shown in **Figure 19.4** is a strong, lightweight, rotatable portable system that is constructed of inexpensive and readily available materials. (See the Bibliography entry for Joseph Littlepage, WE5Y.) The apex of the antenna can be raised or lowered to any convenient height. The antenna is light enough for limited backpacking and can be used for emergency communications and Field Day. Since it is easy to raise and lower, it might also be a good choice for a stealth antenna where permanent antennas may not be used.

A telescoping pushup pole is used as a support mast. A portable antenna tripod is used to support the pushup pole. The basic construction of the antenna is described in **Figure 19.5**. The feed line and wire elements are brought together at an angle of at least 90°. Two 10-foot telescoping fishing poles are used as spreaders. A ¾-inch PVC cross sliding on the central support mast is used to mount the fishing poles (see the full article with the downloadable supplemental content for construction details).

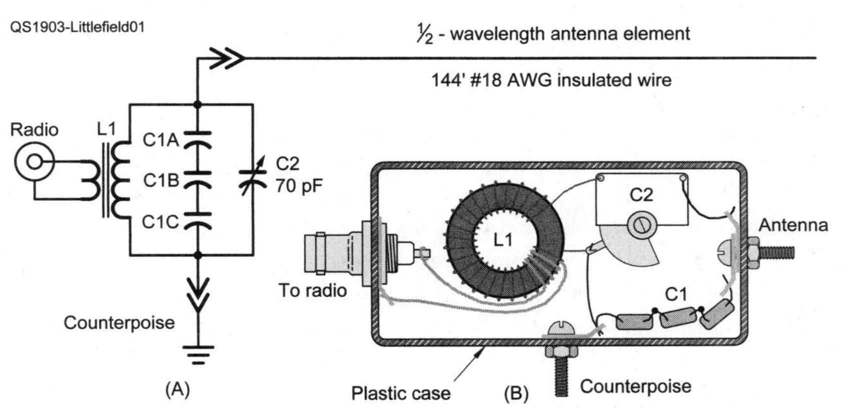

Figure 19.3 —At A, the matching network schematic. At B, the component layout. The network can be mounted directly on a ground rod using heavy wire or strap connected to the Counterpoise terminal. For construction details, see the original article included with this book's downloadable supplemental information.

Figure 19.4 — The portable inverted-V antenna is built using a lightweight fiberglass support mast and two fishing poles. No additional supports are required and the antenna can be moved and rotated by hand.

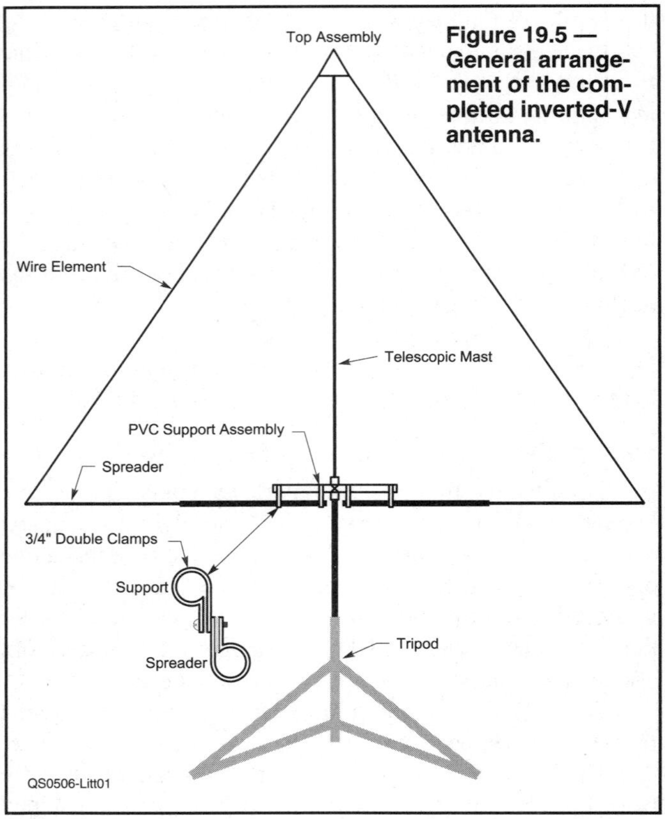

Figure 19.5 — General arrangement of the completed inverted-V antenna.

Table 19.3
Wire Half-Element Lengths for Portable Inverted V Antenna

Band (Meters)	*Design Frequency (MHz)*	*Length*
20	14.175	16 feet, 6½ inches
17	18.1	12 feet, 11½ inches
15	21.175	11 feet, ⅝ inches
12	24.94	9 feet, 4⅝ inches
10	28.4	8 feet, 2⅞ inches

Lengths for the elements on the 20 through 10 meter bands are given in **Table 19.3**. Final measurement and adjustment can be made with an antenna analyzer or SWR bridge.

To set up the antenna, attach the antenna feed point to the top of the mast. The author found the top section of his mast too weak to support the antenna and leaves it telescoped into the next section for additional strength. The mast is then raised section by section and the feed line secured to the mast as it rises.

Figure 19.6 — A commercial mast-mountable insulator from Buddipole (www.buddipole.com) that accommodates whips and wire elements in a variety of configurations.

19.1.4 PORTABLE WHIP DIPOLES

This project describes an antenna that is typical of the style that uses a pair of mobile whip antennas to create a loaded dipole. The design was originally published in the May 2003 issue of *QST* by Ron Herring, W7HD. This style of antenna can be adapted to any band for which mobile whips are available. The low height of the dipole makes this antenna useful for NVIS operation in support of emergency communications, as described in the January 2005 *QST* article by Robert Hollister, N7INK. (Both articles are included with this book's downloadable supplemental information.)

Brackets for mounting mobile whips in a dipole configuration are available from commercial vendors, such as that shown in **Figure 19.6**. Any whip antenna that uses ⅜-24 threads can be used. The article by W7HD includes instructions for making your own bracket, as well. With a collection of whips, the antenna can be used on any band for which mobile whips are available. A set of wire elements can also be attached making the system quite versatile.

The mast for the antenna needs only be strong enough to hold the antenna securely above head height, 8 to 10 feet. The author used a wooden pole. Push-up paint poles or TV mast sections would also work well.

The antenna shown in **Figure 19.7** is similar to the dipole made from mobile whips but uses telescoping whip sections attached to a fixed-length center section. The center section is made from copper and PVC plumbing parts. A small loading coil connects the center section to the whip on the lower bands. The design was originally published by Clarke Cooper, K8BP in the May 2007 issue of *QST* (see Bibliography).

The telescoping whips are 10 feet long when fully extended (see **Figure 19.8**). A table of lengths for each band

Figure 19.7 — This portable dipole uses a fixed center section and extendable telescoping whips to adjust the resonant frequency.

Figure 19.8 — One side of the antenna with the telescoped whip attached.

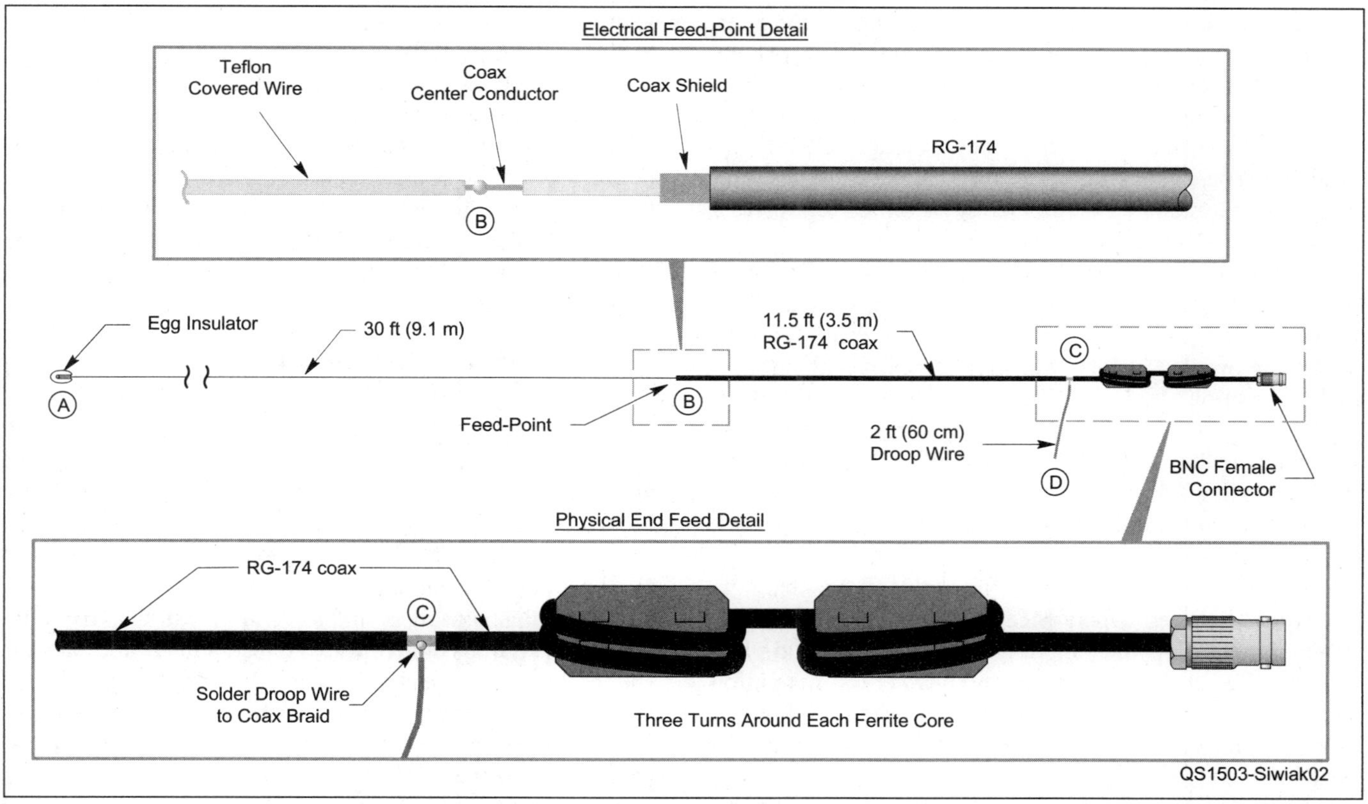

Figure 19.9 — The OCEF dipole detail shows the radiating portions A-D, details of the electrical feed point, and the common mode chokes at the physical feed end. See the full article with this book's downloadable supplemental information for dimensions and a parts list.

allows the operator to quickly adjust the antenna for the desired frequency. The antenna has been tested on 20 through 10 meters and should be useable on 6 meters with a shorter whip. By using loading coils with more turns, operation on 30 and 40 meters may be possible, as well. (The author used MFJ Enterprises MFJ-1954 telescoping whips, which are no longer available, but other telescoping whips may be used.)

As with the previous antenna, the support mast is not a critical part of the assembly, only needing to be high enough to hold the antenna above head level. The author uses a folding portable flood light base to hold the mast.

19.1.5 OFF-CENTER END FED (OCEF) DIPOLE FOR 40 TO 6 METERS

In this project's design, Kai Siwiak, KE4PT, describes a dipole antenna that is physically connected to the feed line at one end of the main antenna wire. Electrically, though, it is off-center fed including the desired section of the feed line's shield and an additional "droop" wire, becoming the "OCEF" dipole. The antenna is designed to roll up into a compact and convenient package for travel. (The full article is available with this book's downloadable supplemental information.)

As shown in **Figure 19.9**, the OCEF consists of two dipole legs and an optional droop wire. For the far-end portion, use 30 feet of Teflon insulated #20 AWG stranded copper wire, beginning at the egg insulator at A. The wire is then soldered to the center conductor of miniature RG-174 coax, forming the physical feed point at B. The second radiating section is the outer shield of the 11.5 feet long section of RG-174 coax extending from the electrical feed point to the ferrite chokes at C.

A 2-foot droop wire can be attached at C to extend the lower frequency range of the antenna and lower the impedance of the antenna near the chokes. This combination of lengths results in impedances that are relatively easy for the antenna tuning unit to match on the ham bands, even though the antenna is not self-resonant in any of the ham bands.

The OCEF can be held away from a vertical structure with a nonconductive fishing pole or other support in either a horizontal or vertical orientation. Alternately, the antenna can be tied to a support structure such as a tree and stretched out back toward the operating position. In either arrangement, the antenna tuning unit should be able to create a 50-Ω match on any band from 40 to 6 meters. If 80 meter operation is desired and the ATU will not create the required match, additional lengths of wire can be clipped onto the droop wire until a match can be obtained. This extra piece of wire must be removed to operate on the higher bands, however.

The OCEF dipole allows all sorts of portable operation, but pay attention to RF exposure — with 50 W of RF input power, the minimum safe distance rises from about 1 foot on 80 meters to 10 feet on 10 and 6 meters.

19.2 VERTICAL ANTENNAS

Somewhat simpler than the horizontal dipole, the many variations of the vertical ground-plane antenna are very common in portable operating. Vertical antennas have even been built into walking sticks for "pedestrian mobile," an increasingly popular activity with the many excellent QRP radios available. You can even operate from a hotel using a simple whip antenna mounted on a balcony or railing and using a tuner. (See the Bibliography entry for McCoy.)

A growing number of amateurs are using PRC-type backpack military surplus radios with built-in vertical whips with excellent results. (See **hfpack.com** for more information.) The article "Tuning Electrically Short Antennas for Field Operation" by Ulrich Rohde, N1UL, and Kai Siwiak, KE4PT, discusses matching the impedance of "manpack" style whip antennas at HF. It is included in the downloadable supplemental information and in the Bibliography.

Vertical antennas can be ground-mounted if they are self-supporting or only need a single line to be hung from a tree or other suitable support. The tradeoff for that simplicity is a greater dependence on the quality of ground system making up the "missing half" of a ground-plane antenna. (See the **Effects of Ground** chapter for more information.) Providing a reasonable ground system will reduce losses and improve the performance of the portable antenna system.

Vertical dipoles are also good performers in a portable set-up. These antennas are discussed in the **Single-Band MF and HF Antennas** chapter. If a typical dipole is mounted vertically, it is a challenge to extend the feed line at right angles to the dipole. The usual configuration is for the feed line to run at a downward angle away from the antenna, creating an asymmetric configuration that results in common-mode current on the coax shield's outer surface. This may not be a problem, but to block the current a choke balun at the feed point is a popular solution. (See the **Transmission Line System Techniques** chapter.) Designs that use the coax shield as one element of the dipole are also presented in the material on vertical dipoles.

19.2.1 TREE-MOUNTED HF GROUND-PLANE ANTENNA

A tree-mounted, vertically polarized antenna does not cost much, is inconspicuous, and it works. This antenna was described by Chuck Hutchinson, K8CH in *QST* for September 1984 (see Bibliography). In addition, losses in the ground are reduced by the antenna's counterpoise radials and raising it off the ground.

The antenna itself is simple, as shown in **Figure 19.10**. A piece of RG-58 cable runs to the feed point of the antenna, and is attached to a center insulator. Two radials are soldered to the coax braid at this point. Another piece of wire forms the vertical element. The top of the vertical section is suspended from a tree limb or other convenient support, and in turn supports the rest of the antenna.

All three wires of the antenna are $\lambda/4$ long as discussed in the **Dipoles and Monopoles** chapter. This generally limits

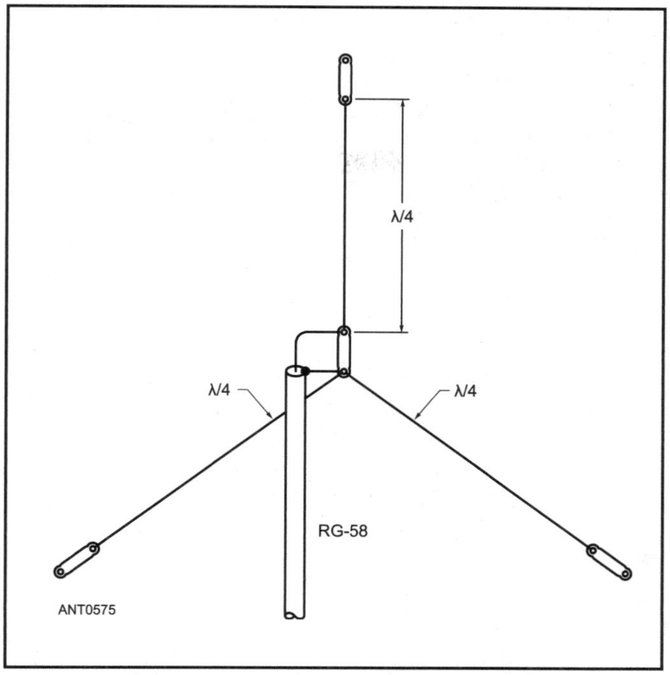

Figure 19.10— Dimensions and construction of the tree-mounted ground-plane antenna from K8CH. The outside ends of the two radial wires are tied off to stakes or other convenient points.

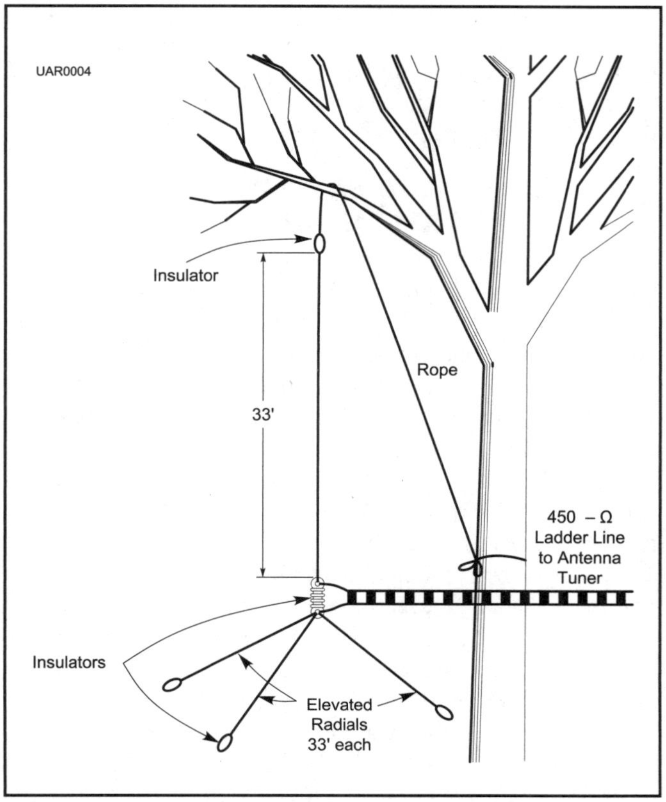

Figure 19.11 — A tree-mounted ground-plane antenna that is resonant on 40 meters but can be used on all HF bands with a tuner.

the usefulness of the antenna for portable operation to 7 MHz and higher bands, as temporary supports higher than 35 or 40 feet are difficult to come by.

The outside surface of the coaxial cable shield will couple to the antenna and may carry substantial common-mode current. This re-radiates a signal just as the antenna does and is generally not a problem unless the current disrupts operation of the transmitter. To reduce common-mode currents on the feed line, use a choke balun as described in the chapter **Transmission Line System Techniques**.

The tree-suspended vertical can also be used for fixed station installations to make an invisible antenna. Shallow trenches can be slit for burying the coax feeder and the radial wires. The radiator itself is difficult to see unless you are standing right next to the tree.

A similar antenna in **Figure 19.11** by Al Brogdon, W1AB, is cut for resonance on the 40 meter band but is fed with 450 Ω window line (see Bibliography). With a tuner, this antenna can be used on all HF bands, including 160 meters according to the author. Like the single-band version, there will be significant common-mode current on the feed line due to the unbalanced configuration. This may require chokes on coax from the tuner or a λ/4 counterpoise wire to manage RF hot spots or RFI in a portable station.

19.2.2 HF VERTICAL TRAVEL ANTENNA

This vertical antenna designed by Phil Salas, AD5X, from July 2005 *QST*, is intended for easy packing and transport, breaking down into several mast sections, a center-loading coil, a short telescoping whip, and a small base support. The total antenna is about 16 feet high when assembled and can be used on 60 through 10 meters. (See the Bibliography for both of the author's articles on this antenna design.)

Figure 19.12 shows the assembled antenna and **Figure 19.13** shows author holding the complete set of disassembled antenna parts, none of which is more than 20 inches long. The antenna uses a ground system of at least six #22 AWG insulated

Figure 19.12 — The complete antenna set up in AD5X's front yard. Total height is about 16 feet.

Figure 19.13 — Phil, AD5X, holding the complete unassembled antenna.

radials. As the author notes, almost any gauge wire can be used, insulated or not, and more radials will improve operation. If the antenna can be mounted on metal structures such as a chain-link fence, even lower ground losses can be obtained.

The antenna is designed for easy assembly and disassembly but do not neglect to make solid, soldered connections for the spade lugs that connect the various radials and jumpers. In small antennas, resistive losses can consume an appreciable amount of signal power.

Guying is required in a strong breeze and the author uses three lengths of light nylon cord to stabilize the antenna. Fishing line would also work well. An adapter is described that will allow the antenna to be mounted on a standard ⅜-24 mobile mount for use while at rest. The antenna is not strong enough for use while moving.

19.2.3 MULTI-SECTION MULTI-BAND HF DIPOLE

This antenna is a simple dipole but with insulators separating each leg into multiple sections. At each insulator, a jumper with an alligator can short out the insulator to extend the antenna. This design by Phil Salas, AD5X, cover 20-10 meters but the design can be reworked for any combination of bands. (The original article, "A Simple HF-Portable Antenna" is included in this book's downloadable supplemental information.)

The basic antenna is a full-size 20 meter dipole with a conventional center insulator. Insulators are inserted to make the individual sections that can be added to the centermost element. **Figure 19.14** shows a typical insulator with the alligator clip attached. Since this antenna is intended for low power operating, the insulators can be easily made from nylon rod or PVC pipe but any insulating material will work.

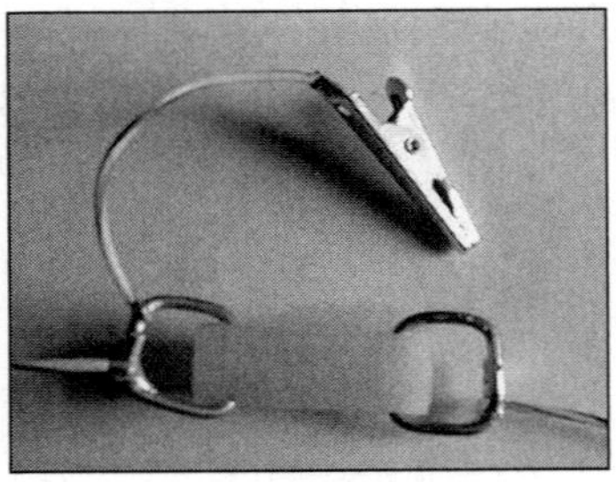

Figure 19.14 — For the multi-band dipole, antenna length and resonant frequency are changed by using alligator clips to short out insulators.

Start by building the section for the highest frequency band you want to use. Then add a section of wire and another insulator on each side for the next lowest band. Use the clip to short circuit the insulator and connect the new section. Adjust the new section's length to present a minimum SWR at the desired frequency. Add additional sections until the lowest frequency configuration is reached.

The author's original design for 20 through 10 meters is as follows with the lengths referring to the sections added on each side:

10 meters:	8 feet 3 inches
12–10 meters:	10 inches
15–12 meters:	1 foot 4 inches
17–15 meters:	1 foot 8 inches
20–17 meters:	3 feet 9 inches

Each side thus has a total length of 15 feet, 10 inches and the full antenna is 31 feet 8 inches long. The design can be extended to 6 meters as the highest band by starting with the 6 meter section in the middle. On the lower frequency end, the dipole can be extended as far as you wish and is practical for your circumstances.

19.2.4 FIVE-BAND PORTABLE VERTICAL ANTENNA

This multi-band vertical antenna project uses five quarter-wave vertical monopoles in parallel, using a common ground screen of 16 radials. This allows multi-band operation without requiring an antenna tuner. (The entire article is included with this book's downloadable supplemental information.)

The antenna, shown schematically in **Figure 19.15A**, consists of four quarter-wave elements attached to spreader rods and the longest, 20 meter element wrapped around the central support. Each antenna is terminated in a banana plug that is attached to a feed point ring on the mast. Each of the 16 radials is 17 feet long and attached to a similar ring at the bottom of the antenna. Remember that the length of the connection from the radial attachment ring to the feed point RF connector also counts as part of the antenna and should not be changed after tuning.

Tuning consists of beginning with the 10 meter element. Trim about ½ of the total length needed to bring the element to resonance. This is in recognition of the interactive tuning process. Move to the 12 meter element and repeat, then the 15 meter element and so forth. Continue to tune each element in sequence until the SWR is acceptable on all bands.

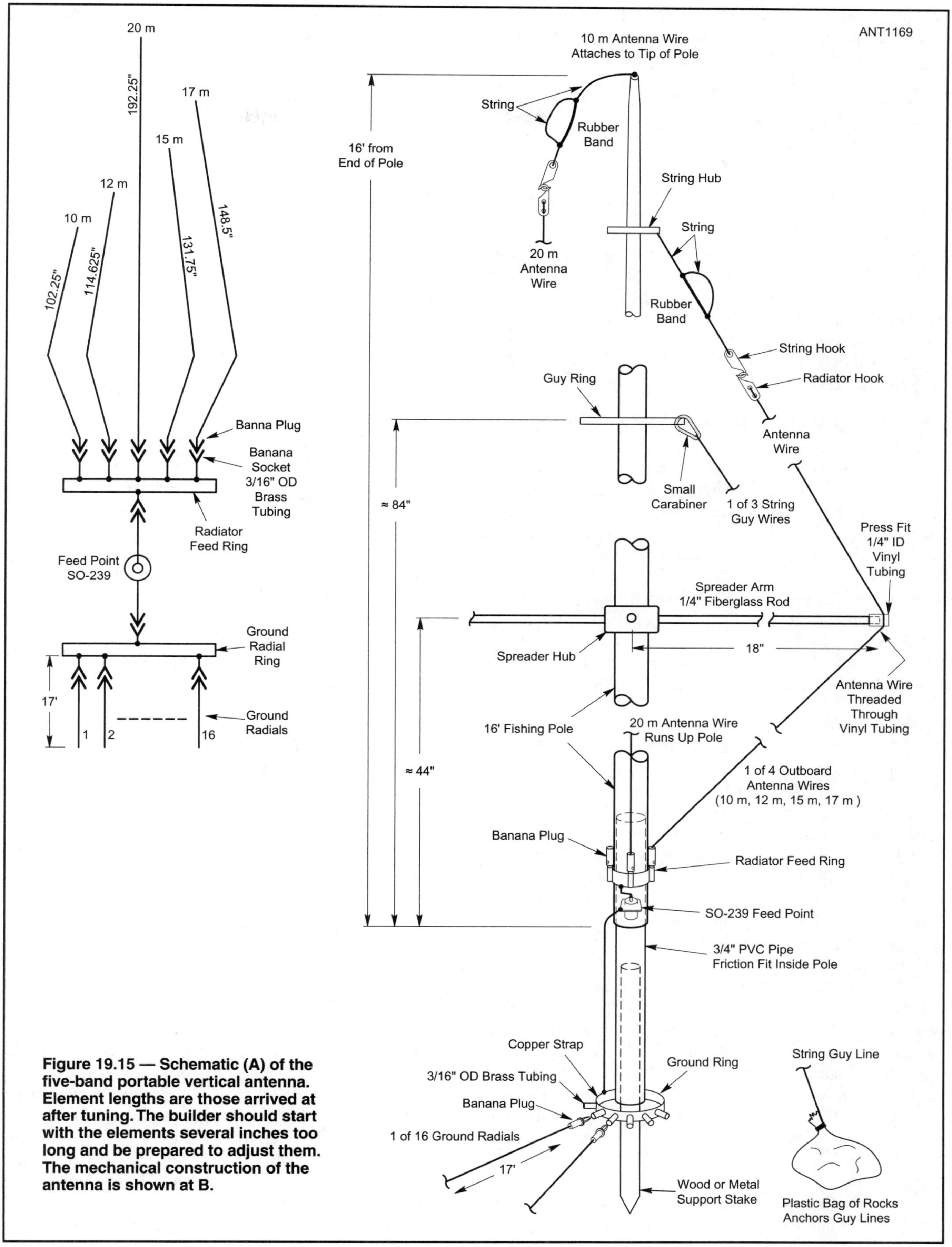

Figure 19.15 — Schematic (A) of the five-band portable vertical antenna. Element lengths are those arrived at after tuning. The builder should start with the elements several inches too long and be prepared to adjust them. The mechanical construction of the antenna is shown at B.

Mechanically, the antenna is assembled on a portable fiberglass fishing rod, 16 feet long. A ground stake and PVC pipe provide the base support. A triangular guy attachment point slides down over the top of the pole until it rests on the top of a middle section. (Guying may not be required if the base support stake and pipe are sufficiently sturdy.

As with all portable antennas, RF exposure can be an issue as RF power begins to exceed QRP levels. Keep people away from the base of the antenna both to minimize exposure and to keep them from tripping over the radials! The edge of the radial field is a good point at which to establish a "safety perimeter" both for electrical and mechanical security!

19.3 BEAM ANTENNAS

Simple horizontal and vertical antennas are light and easy to use for portable operating but having some gain and directivity in the field is very nice. While a full-size triband Yagi or quad is probably out of the question for most portable operations, smaller antennas can still provide good performance at low cost and with relative simplicity of installation. This is particularly true on the higher frequency HF bands and the VHF bands.

19.3.1 PORTABLE 6 METER BEAMS

The 6 meter band lends itself well to portable operation: the wavelength is short enough that full-size antenna elements aren't heavy and don't require special mechanical assemblies. At the same time, long distance propagation from sporadic-E and other modes is common, particularly in the summer months. As a result there are quite a few 6 meter antenna designs to choose from! The Bibliography and downloadable supplemental information contain plenty of additional articles beyond the two presented here. The recent ARRL publication *Magic Band Antennas for Ham Radio* contains numerous antenna designs as does the website of Martin Steyer, DK7ZB (**www.qsl.net/dk7zb**).

Two-Element Quad

The quad antenna was originally described by Markus Hansen, VE7CA, in *The ARRL Antenna Compendium, Vol 5*. After years of HF operation, he became enthusiastic about VHF/UHF operation when he got on 6 meters and discovered the joys of driving to high mountain peaks to operate. Not only does an antenna have to be portable for this kind of operation, it must be easily assembled and disassembled, just in case you have to move quickly to a better location. An article describing a three-element 6 meter Yagi by VE7CA is also provided with this book's downloadable supplemental information.

The distance between the driven and the reflector elements was selected so that the intrinsic feed point impedance was 50 Ω without using a gamma match. (A gamma match does not hold up well to travel and repeated assembly and disassembly.) **Figure 19.16** shows the dimensions for the boom and the boom-to-mast bracket. The boom is made from a 27-¼-inch length of 2 × 2. Use whatever material is available in your area, but lightweight wood is preferred, so clear cedar or pine is ideal. The boom-to-mast bracket is made from ¼-inch fir plywood.

The spreaders are ½-inch dowels. Fiberglass would be ideal but it is not always available locally. Sleeves of plastic pipe over the ends of the spreaders insulate the wire from the spreaders. Elements are made from #14 AWG hard-drawn stranded bare copper wire. Do not use insulated wire unless you are willing to experimentally determine the element lengths, because the insulation detunes each element slightly. The final circumference of the reflector element is 249 inches and of the driven element is 236-⅝ inches from the points where the feed line is attached.

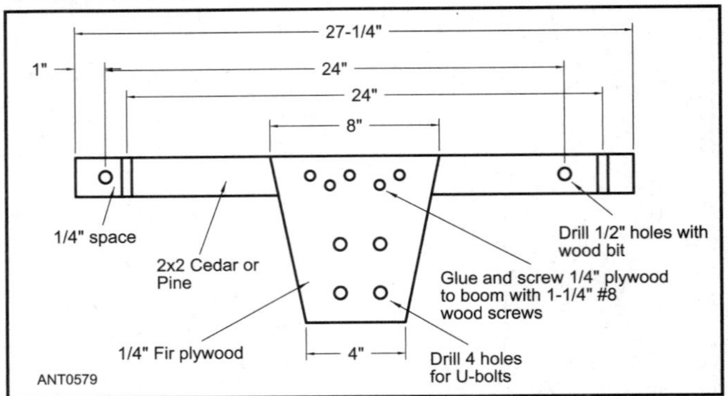

Figure 19.16 — Dimensions for the boom-to-mast bracket of the 2-element 6 meter quad.

The author used RG-58 feed line as it is lightweight. The length required for a portable installation is typically not very long, maybe 20 feet, so the loss in the small cable is not excessive. Near the feed point, coil the coax into six turns with an inside diameter of two inches to choke off RF currents flowing on the outside of the coax shield.

Two U-bolts are used to attach the boom-to-mast bracket to the mast. When the quad is raised, the shape of the loop is commonly known as a diamond configuration and the feed point at the bottom produces horizontally polarization. The mast consists of two six-foot lengths of doweling joined together with a two-foot length of PVC plastic pipe, held together with wood screws.

Four-Element Yagi

Six meters is a great band for home built Yagis. The elements are reasonably small, but not so small that building tolerances are critical. With careful construction and detailed instructions, it is certainly feasible to build no-tune Yagis up to 432 MHz as the author, Zack Lau, W1VT, shows here. (The full article, including detailed construction information, is included with this book's downloadable supplemental information.)

Element construction is shown in **Figure 19.17**. Only a

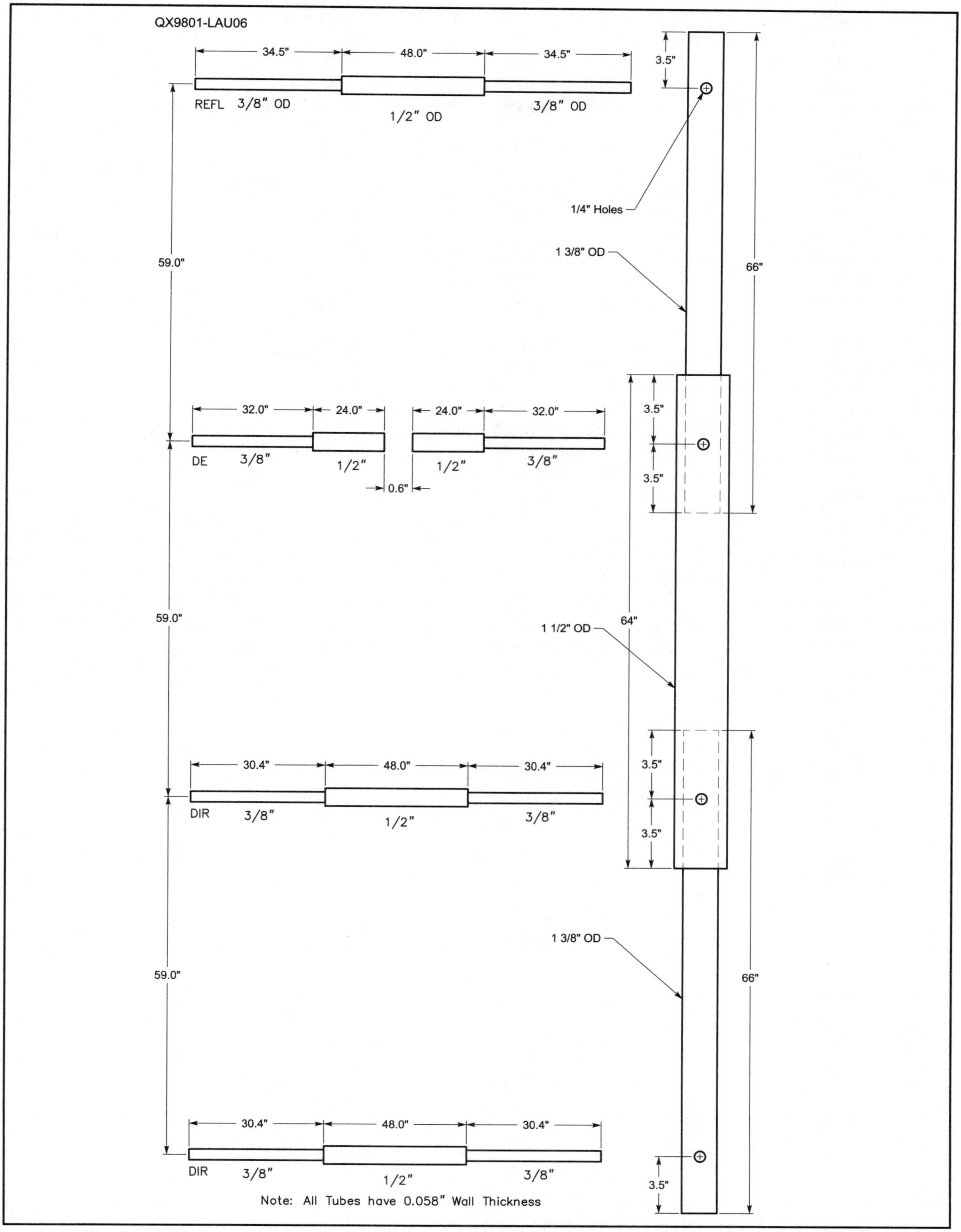

Figure 19.17 — Element construction for the 6 Meter 4 Element Portable Yagi.

few elements are needed for portable work — more elements mean more assembly/disassembly. An extra element allows the beam to work well over a wider bandwidth with more elements, while keeping the boom length constant. Extra bandwidth helps the antenna to work well despite the effects of rain.

The design is taken from Lawson's *Yagi Antenna Design* because it has good gain and pattern for just four elements. (See the Bibliography of the **HF Yagi and Quad Antennas** chapter) The antenna has 10.6 dBi of free-space gain with the unwanted lobes suppressed by 20 dB — a reasonably clean pattern. At typical portable operating heights of 11 to 16 feet, the antenna shows less than 2:1 SWR over the bottom 400 kHz of 6 meters with the minimum SWR close to the edge of the band.

To simplify the electrical design, insulated, telescoping elements of aluminum tubing are used, spaced ¼ inch above the boom. This makes the boom interaction minimal, so it isn't necessary to factor in a boom correction. Lexan mounting plates for the boom and elements were used for strength and UV resistance. Oak blocks were used to attach the elements to the mounting plates. The author fabricated custom element clamps, but regular worm-screw hose clamps would also work.

19.3.2 2-ELEMENT 20/15/10 METER TRIBAND YAGI

This portable HF wire Yagi was described by Markus Hansen, VE7CA, in November 2001 *QST* and in *The ARRL Antenna Compendium, Vol 7*. The need was for a 2-element wire Yagi for 20/15/10 meters that could be easily transported by car. The basic concept comprises three individual dipole driven elements, one each for 20, 15 and for 10 meters tied to a common feed point, plus three separate reflector elements. (See **Figure 19.18**.) The elements are strung between two 7-foot- long, 2 × 2-inch wood spreaders.

A feed point impedance was achieved on each band that allowed the use of a single setting for the shorting bar on a hairpin match. The result was a very acceptable match over the lower portions of each band. The hairpin match is one of the easiest matching systems to make. It is easy to adjust and since wire is the only ingredient, it can be coiled up with the rest of the antenna when the antenna is disassembled. The feed point impedance of the Yagi with a reflector element spaced 0.1 λ behind the driven element typically produces a resistance around 20 Ω. By shortening the driven element from its resonant length, capacitive reactance is added to the feed point resistance. This can be cancelled by shunting the feed point with an inductor in the shape of a wire loop resembling a hairpin. This causes a step up of the 20-Ω feed point resistance to 50 Ω.

Figure 19.19 shows the hairpin match and the common-mode choke balun for the 10/15/20-meter triband wire Yagi. The coax drops straight down from the center insulator and is attached to the center of the hairpin shorting bar. Make a choke balun by coiling the coax in 8 turns with a diameter of about 4 inches. This balun will choke off RF flowing along the outside of the coax shield that would otherwise distort the radiation pattern of the antenna. The center of the shorting bar is at a neutral potential, so there is no harm in mechanically attaching the coax feed line at that point.

Using #14 AWG wire allows all the Yagi antennas

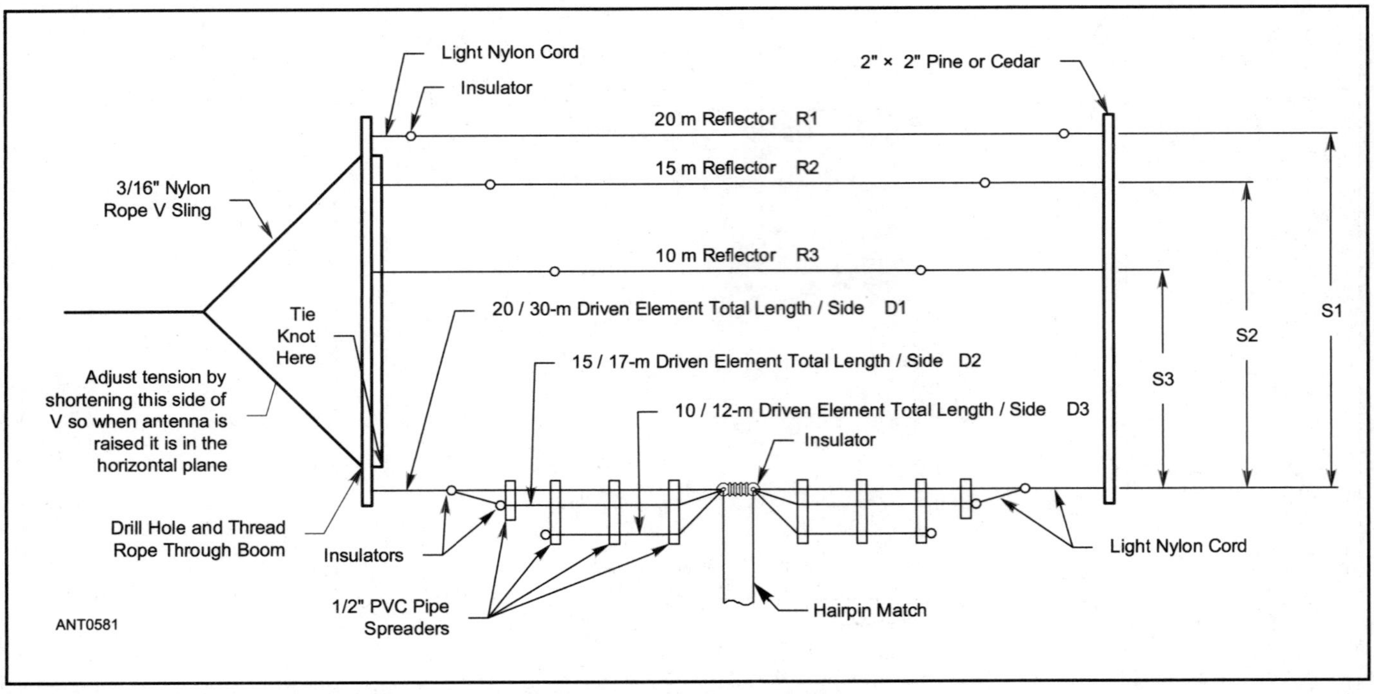

Figure 19.18 — Dimensions for VE7CA's 2-element 10/15/10 meter triband Yagi.

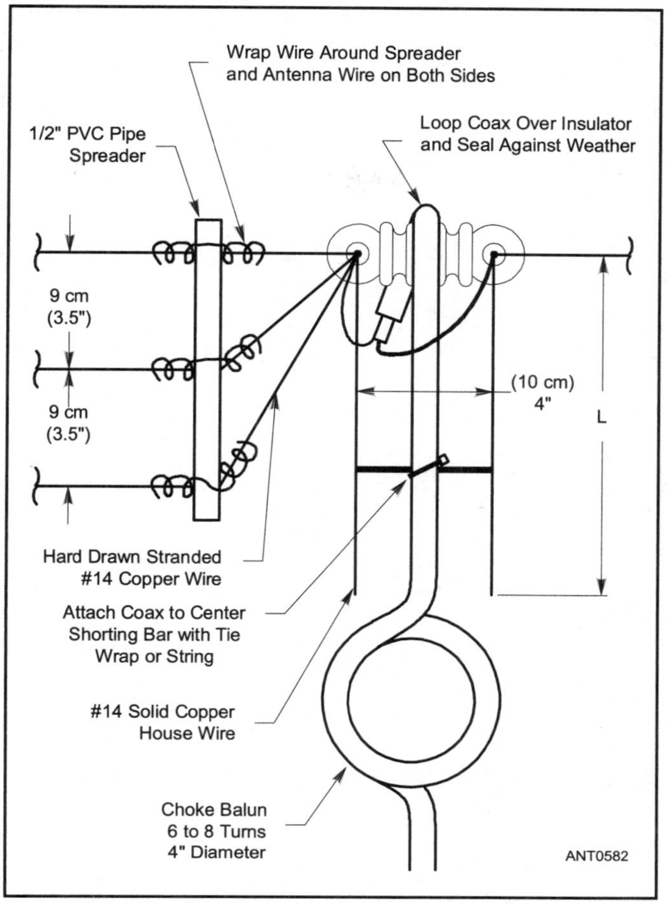

Figure 19.19 — Details of the feed point for the 20/15/10 meter triband Yagi.

Figure 19.20 — The completed 15 meter beam mounted on a painter's pole mast.

referenced in this article to be used at the maximum power levels allowed in North America. The only limiting factor is the power handling capability of the feed line. However, even RG-58 should work for the relatively short length from the feed point down to ground level where you can change to RG-8 or some other higher-power, lower-loss coaxial cable.

19.3.3 15 METER AND 17 METER BEAMS

The 2-element Moxon Rectangle (see the chapter **HF Yagi and Quad Antennas** for a description of the Moxon Rectangle) is often used for single-band Yagis because it reduces the overall element length. In this design, dubbed the "Black Widow" by Allen Baker, KG4JJH, a wire Moxon Rectangle is suspended between fiberglass fishing poles.

The completed antenna is shown in **Figure 19.20**. The fishing poles are mounted on a central hub and the wires stretched between their tips under tension. **Figure 19.21** presents a mechanical drawing of the antenna showing the antenna's basic construction.

The modeled performance of the antenna gives a gain of 9 dBi when mounted at 15 feet above ground and 10.5 dBi at 23 feet. The assembled antenna produced an SWR of 1.2:1 to 1.3:1 across the entire 15 meter band.

The 17 meter band is another popular band for portable operation at this point in the sunspot cycle. As propagation improves, it will provide some excellent openings throughout the daylight hours. The 2-element beam shown in **Figure 19.22** is constructed similarly to the Black Widow and was designed by Martin Hedman, SMØDTK. Gain is approximately 11 dBi across the band. The article "Two-Element Yagi for 18 MHz" is included with this book's downloadable supplemental information.

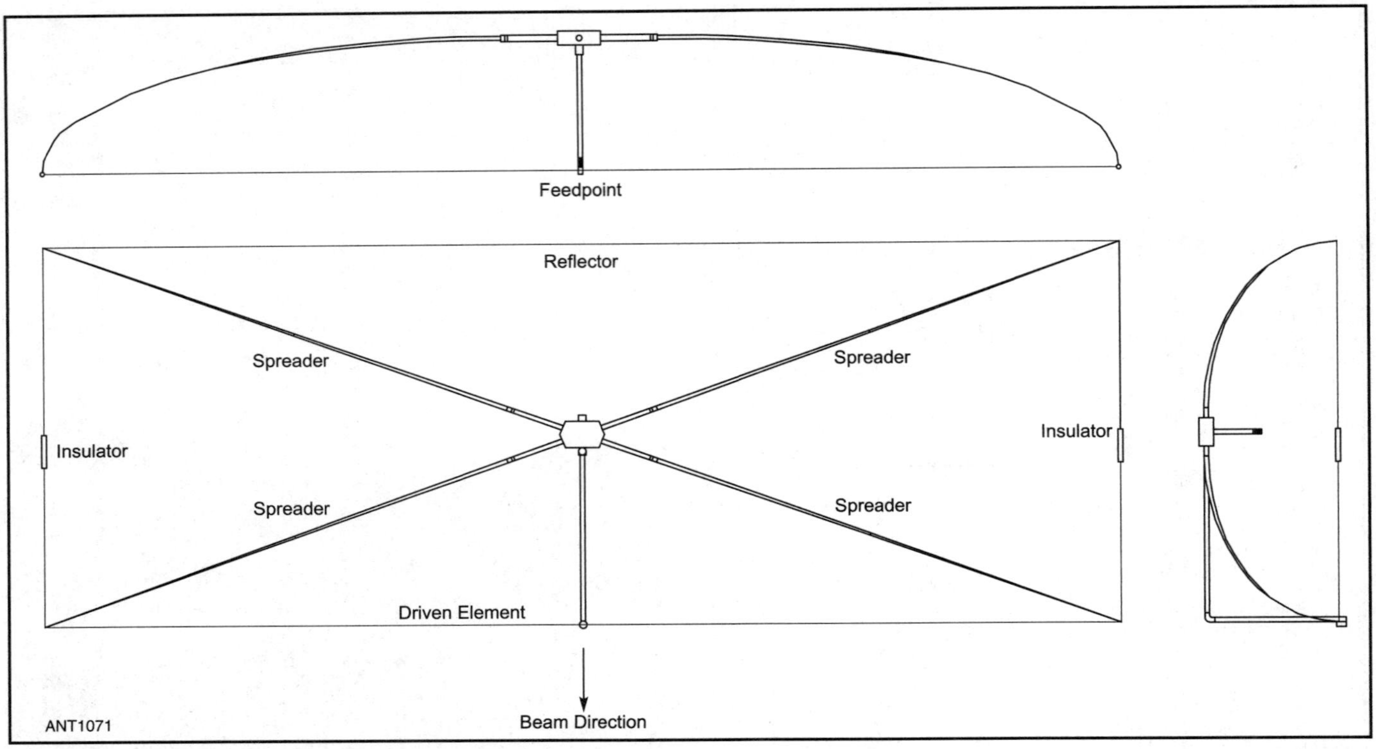

Figure 19.21 — An overview of the antenna and its components. Side drawings show the approximate final bend of the fishing poles with the wire elements attached.

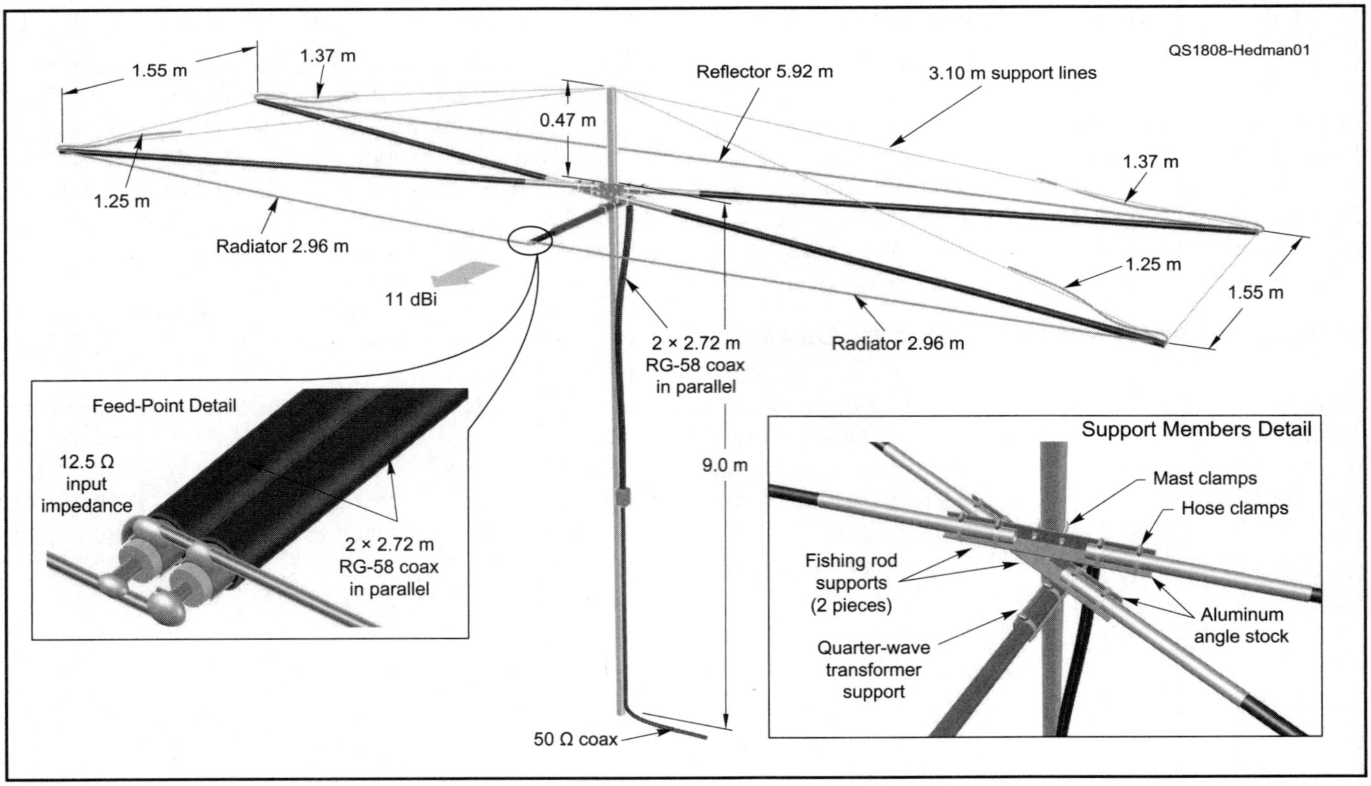

Figure 19.22 — Fishing rods form the structure of this 2-element, 17 meter Yagi. Non-conductive lines keep the antenna under tension. A short mast extension provides the tie-point for supporting lines.

19.4 PORTABLE MASTS AND SUPPORTS

Any of several schemes can be employed to support an antenna during portable operation. For HF antennas made of wire, probably the most common support is a conveniently located tree at the operating site. (See the **Building Antenna Systems and Towers** chapter.) Temporary, lightweight masts are also used such as the increasingly popular extendable fiberglass and aluminum models that reach up to 80 feet in height. An aluminum extension ladder, properly guyed, can serve as a mast for Field Day operation as described in the article included with this book's downloadable supplemental information. A trip to the hardware store will also turn up several other candidates, such as painter's pole and other extendable handles.

Supporting tubular masts is usually done with guys of nylon cord or fishing line. This is fairly straightforward but requires at least three guy points and can be difficult for the usual one-person operation. (See the **Building Antenna Systems and Towers** chapter for more information on guying.) Other possibilities include using concrete- or sand-filled buckets as shown in **Figure 19.23**. SOTAbeams has produced an excellent YouTube video, "Erecting a SOTAbeams HF Dipole" (**www.youtube.com/watch?v=RI6IRgQLokk**) showing how to safely put up and guy a telescoping pole holding an inverted V.

Two of the more popular designs for vehicle-based portable operating are the "drive-on mount" and the trailer hitch mount. **Figure 19.24A** illustrates the basic drive-on concept. A flange, wood block, or pipe stub is attached to a sturdy

Figure 19.23 — A five-gallon plastic bucket filled with sand and rocks weighs from 40 to 60 pounds and makes a solid base for a fiberglass mast.

(A)

(B)

Figure 19.24 — Two examples of drive-on mounts for portable masts. At A, a fiberglass mast base is secured by the mount and additional support is provided by a strut attached to the roof rack of K5ND's vehicle. B shows a heavy-duty welded metal mount made by W3ATB that holds a mast upright on its own. [Photos courtesy Jim Wilson, K5ND, and Tim Carter, W3ATB]

Figure 19.25 — K5ACL's welded mast mount attaches to a conventional trailer hitch receiver. [Courtesy Johnny Twist, K5ACL]

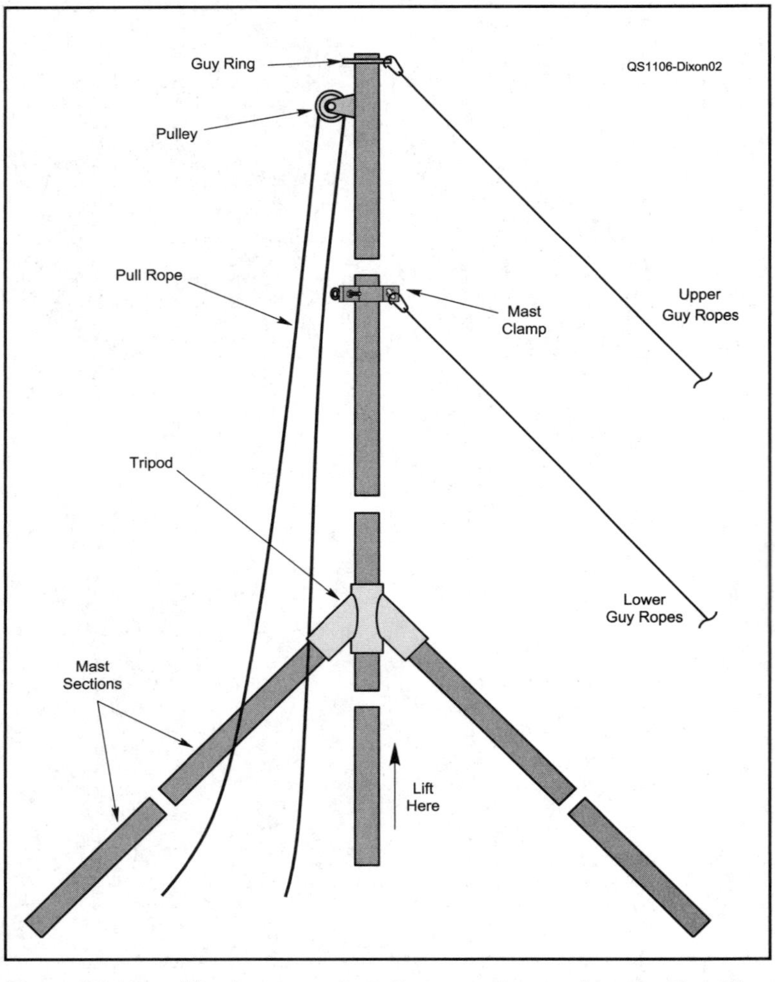

Figure 19.26 — Aluminum mast sections can be combined with a tripod center section to create a mast up to 40 feet high.

board or plank. The board is placed on the ground and the vehicle is driven on to it, securing the base of the mount. The mast can be secured to a vehicle roof rack for extra support. A welded metal version is shown in Figure 19.24B. **Figure 19.25** shows a trailer hitch mount in which the mast is held upright by a vertical tube welded to a conventional trailer hitch bar. Commercial versions are available from several vendors and the FGHM64 from M2 Antennas (**www.m2inc.com**) includes a telescoping 24-foot mast. Masts constructed of separate aluminum or fiberglass sections are also widely available new or as military surplus. The June 2011 *QST* article by Bob Dixon, W8ERD, shows how to use a mast tripod to construct a sturdy mast rising to 40 feet. **Figure 19.26** is a drawing of how the various pieces go together, including guying lines. Since the mast is assembled from the bottom, piece by piece, it is much easier to erect than a mast which must be pulled up from horizontal or lifted and placed in a base.

19.4.1 GETTING THE ANTENNA ALOFT

Finally, there is the issue of getting the antenna over a supporting structure or tree. Assuming that it's not safe to climb to the support point, you'll have to throw or launch a light line over it and pull up the heavier support rope. (An excerpt from *Portable Operating for Amateur Radio* by Stuart Thomas, KB1HQS, discusses this problem — you can find it in the downloadable supplemental information.)

You have several choices, starting with using whatever is at hand that is heavy enough to pull the light line back down to the ground but not so heavy as to not be able to throw sufficiently high. All kinds of things have been used to get antennas into trees — water bottles, rocks, tools (and some are still in there). Professional arborists face this issue all the time and use *throw bags* to get their lines into trees.

If throwing is not an option, the next step is usually a tennis ball launcher for exercising dogs (available at pet stores) or a slingshot and fishing reel, such as the EZ-Hang (**www.ezhang.com**). These work up to heights of about 100 feet. If more height is needed, "spud guns" that use compressed air or hair spray as a propellant can put lines tied to tennis balls over really tall trees. (See the article "The W4SSY Spudgun" in the Bibliography and the downloadable supplemental information.) Some have begun using drones to carry lines over trees, as well.

With any launching device, *think before you shoot*. If a line attached to a projectile snags or doesn't pay out freely, the projectile can snap back with full force. The projectile might not go where you intend, so be sure no innocent bystanders are down-range. Be aware of any power lines in the area, such as behind or even in a tree. If you overshoot, what might the projectile hit or travel over? If the wind is blowing, what happens if the projectile drifts off-line? Think things through and avoid hazards.

19.5 BIBLIOGRAPHY

A. Baker, "The Black Widow — A Portable 15 Meter Beam," *QST*, May 2003, pp 35-39.

A. Brogdon, *Low Profile Amateur Radio*, (Newington: ARRL, 2006) This book is out of print but used copies are available.

B. Black, "The W4SSY Spudgun," *QST*, Mar 2009, pp 67-69.

L.B. Cebik, "Two Hilltoppers for 10 Meters," *ARRL Antenna Compendium, Vol 6* (Newington: ARRL, 1999).

C. Cooper, "Super Duper Five Band Portable Antenna," *QST*, May 2007, pp 34-36.

R. J. Decesari, "A Portable Quad for 2 Meters," *QST*, Oct 1980, pp 26-28 and "Portable Quad for 2 Meters, Part 2," Technical Correspondence, *QST*, Jun 1981, pp 39-40.

D. DeMaw, "A Traveling Ham's Trap Vertical," *QST*, Oct 1980, pp 28-31.

R. Dixon, "A One Person, Safe, Portable and Easy to Erect Antenna Mast," *QST*, Jun 2011, pp 30-32.

D. Fisher, "Supporting Portable Antennas Without Guy Wires," *QST*, May 2011, pp 30-31.

J. Hall, "Zip-Cord Antennas — Do They Work?," *QST*, Mar 1979, pp 31-32.

M. Hansen, "A Portable 2-Element Triband Yagi," *QST*, Nov 2001, pp 35-37.

M. Hansen, "Some More VE7CA 2-Element Portable Yagis," *The ARRL Antenna Compendium, Vol 7,* (Newington: ARRL, 2002), p 183.

M. Hedman, "A Two-Element Yagi for 18 MHz," *QST*, Aug 2018, pp 38-40.

R. Herring, "A Small, Portable Dipole for Field Use," *QST*, May 2003, pp 33-34.

HF Dipole Antennas for Amateur Radio (Newington: ARRL, 2019)

R. Hollister, "A Portable NVIS Antenna," *QST*, Jan 2005, pp 56-58.

C. Hutchinson, "A Tree-Mounted 30-Meter Ground-Plane Antenna," *QST*, Sep 1984, pp 16-18.

R. Johns, "A Ground-Coupled Portable Antenna," *QST*, Jan 2001, pp 28-32.

J. Littlepage, "A Portable Inverted V Antenna," *QST*, Jun 2005, pp 36-39.

L. McCoy, "A Windowsill Semivertical," *QST*, Jun 1967, pp 42-44.

W. Parmley, "Zip Cord Antennas and Feed Lines for Portable Applications," *QST*, Mar 2009, pp 34-36.

Portable Antenna Classics (Newington: ARRL, 2015).

J. Portune, "Compact 40 Meter HF Loop for Your Recreational Vehicle," *QST*, Mar 2007, pp 41-43.

U. Rohde and K. Siwiak, "Tuning Electrically Short Antennas for Field Operation" Microwave Journal, May 2019, pp 104-124.

P. Salas, "A Simple and Portable HF Vertical Travel Antenna," *QST*, Jul 2002, pp 28-31.

P. Salas, "The Ultimate Portable HF Vertical Antenna," *QST*, Jul 2005, p 28-34.

C. W. Schecter, "A Deluxe RV 5-Band Antenna," *QST*, Oct 1980, pp 38-40.

K. Siwiak, "An Off Center End Fed Dipole for Portable Operation on 40 to 6 Meters," *QST*, Mar 2015, pp 44-46.

B. Strickland, "Fishing for DX with a Five Band Portable Antenna," *QST*, May 2014, pp 36-41.

S. Thomas, KB1HQS, *Portable Operating for Amateur Radio* (Newington: ARRL, 2018).

R. Victor, "The Miracle Whip: A Multiband QRP Antenna," *QST*, Jul 2001, pp 32-35.

P. Voorhees, "A Portable Antenna Mast and Support for Your RV," *QST*, Sep 2010, pp 34-35.

TABLE OF CONTENTS

Chapter 20 — Supplemental Downloadable Content

Supplemental Articles

- “A Compact Loop Antenna for 30 through 12 Meters” by Robert Capon, WA3ULH
- “A Disguised Flagpole Antenna” by Albert Parker, N4AQ
- “A 6-Meter Moxon Antenna” by Allen Baker, KG4JJH
- “An All-Band Attic Antenna” by Kai Siwiak, KE4PT
- “An Antenna Idea for Restricted Communities” by Cristian Paun, WV6N
- “Apartment Dweller Slinky Jr Antenna” by Arthur Peterson, W7CZB
- “Better Results with Indoor Antennas” by Fred Brown, W6HPH
- “Honey, I Shrunk the Antenna!” by Rod Newkirk, W9BRD
- “Small High-Efficiency Loop Antennas” by Ted Hart, W5QJR
- “Short Antennas for the Lower Frequencies — Parts 1 and 2” by Yardley Beers, WØJF
- “Stealth 6-Meter Wire Beam” by Bruce Walker, N3JO
- Tuning Capacitors for Transmitting Loops
- “Using LPDA TV Antennas for the VHF Ham Bands” by John Stanley, K4ERO

Chapter 20

Stealth and Limited Space Antennas

The biggest challenge facing many hams today is putting up an effective antenna. Many homes come with severe restrictions or even prohibitions on external antennas of any sort. Apartment and condominium dwellers have even more limiting circumstances. The traveling ham faces a new set of challenges at every stop. Yet many persevere and have rewarding experiences in Amateur Radio without big towers and high wires. The secret? According to Steve Ford, WB8IMY, author of the ARRL's *Small Antennas for Small Spaces*, it's "using the best antenna possible for a given circumstance." That may be a wire in an attic or dangling from a high-rise window but you can get on the air and make lots of contacts. Enjoyable hamming — even DXing — is very achievable without the traditional "aluminum farm" and that is the focus of this chapter.

Much of the material in this chapter is collected from WB8IMY's book mentioned above, Al Brogdon, W1AB's *Low Profile Amateur Radio*, and Steve Nichols, GØKYA's RSGB book *Stealth Antennas*. In addition, several projects from the pages of *QST* and other sources are provided. It is not expected that you will be able to exactly duplicate these designs. Use them as a starting point, adapting to your circumstances, and learn to adjust and work with the resources available. You may also find the **Portable Antennas** chapter interesting reading.

The goal of presenting this collection of antenna designs is to inspire imagination and innovation on the part of the reader. As you review these antennas, think about how you might apply the same styles and approaches to your station. Perhaps these antennas will answer the question, "Would antenna X work in my situation?" Give your imagination free reign!

Once you have selected a design, be prepared to experiment and adjust. The *antenna analyzer* described in the **Antenna and Transmission Line Measurement** chapter is an invaluable tool for this type of antenna building.

20.1 INSTALLATION SAFETY

Why start with a discussion of safety? Because your antennas will likely be a lot closer to power wiring and power lines than the traditional dipole in the trees. In addition, you and your family and possibly your neighbors will be a lot closer to the antenna than if it is installed outside and well above the ground. The *ARRL Handbook* contains additional information on electrical and RF safety and grounding.

20.1.1 ELECTRICAL SAFETY

Before installing or even designing an antenna, check the area around your home and property for power lines, including the household voltage "service drops" to your house. Don't mistake a power line for a cable TV or telephone line. Working on building roofs or lowering wires and cables over the edge of a building or out a window can place you or a wire or cable in contact with hazardous, even lethal, voltages. Here are some rules to live by:

• Keep all objects — including masts, poles, ladders, tools, and antennas far away from power lines at all times. If in doubt — stop. You can be electrocuted if you are touching anything even a little bit conductive that comes in contact with a power line. High voltage electricity does not need much conductivity to create hazardous currents.

• Antennas and masts should never be closer than 10 feet to a power line or your electrical service wiring.

• If you are moving an antenna or taking one down, look for new power lines that may have been installed or rerouted since the antenna was first put in place.

• Never assume that any power line is insulated — any contact may be lethal.

• Don't rely on fiberglass or wooden poles to act as insulators.

• Know first aid for electrical shock and don't work alone if possible.

Installing indoor and otherwise stealthy antennas invariably means drilling holes through and driving fasteners into walls and ceilings. Before drilling or hammering or driving, be sure that you are not about to come in contact with an electrical wire or a water or gas pipe. If you are in doubt, stop and get professional help. The cost and small delay are minor compared to that of a fire or leak. Remember that detectors designed to find metal piping or conduits will not find plastic pipe.

20.1.2 PERSONAL SAFETY

You may have seen comedy sketches where someone puts a foot through the ceiling but it isn't very funny when it's your or your friend's ceiling! Take steps to be sure that you are working safely and not placing yourself in a risky position. When working in unusual spaces in, around, or on top of your home, someone else should be at home in case you become stuck or fall.

When working in an attic or crawl space, make sure you have adequate lighting. If you plan on working in these areas frequently, consider installing permanent lighting. At any rate, an ac or battery operated "trouble light" with an LED bulb will provide plenty of light. Carry a strong flashlight with fresh batteries since it is inevitable that you'll be working in the shadows at some point. A head-mounted LED lamp works well.

Do not attempt to walk on attic joists as they make poor footing, leading to the aforementioned ceiling damage and possible injury. Use boards placed across the joists to support your weight. Again, if you expect to be working in the attic regularly, permanently install boards or plywood sheets.

Glass wool insulation is an irritant as the fibers break off and can stick in skin or be inhaled. Wear gloves, long-sleeve shirts and pants when working around insulation. If the insulation is loose (not in batts or rolls) wear a face mask. A face mask is also a good idea in crawl spaces to avoid inhaling rodent or insect droppings, dust or mold spores.

If you are working on a pitched roof, consider using a safety harness sturdily anchored to a tie point or chimney. Review basic climbing safety techniques and equipment in the chapter **Building Antenna Systems and Towers**.

20.1.3 RF SAFETY

It is a good assumption that the antennas in this chapter will be installed fairly close to people. As such, you should consider the potential effects of your transmitted signal and are required to evaluate your station for RF exposure.

The evaluation procedure — required of all FCC-licensed amateurs — isn't as involved as you might think. No test equipment is required and no paperwork must be submitted to the FCC although you need to log your evaluation results and keep them at your station. An RF safety evaluation amounts to entering some values into an online calculator to determine whether your station is in compliance — it's that simple.

Figure 20.1 shows the RF Power Density calculator created by Paul Evans, VP9KF at **hintlink.com/power_density.htm**. For many of the antennas in this chapter, you can assume the gain is 0 dB. If you use a directional antenna, be sure to use the maximum gain figure and be aware of where the antenna is likely to be pointed.

The calculator mentions *controlled* and *uncontrolled* environments. These terms refer to whether people know RF is present and can take steps to control their exposure. (The **Antenna Fundamentals** chapter defines these terms and includes a large section on RF exposure and RF safety. Another resource is the ARRL RF Exposure web page at **www.arrl.org/rf-exposure**.) Assuming other people live in your home and nearby, the uncontrolled environment should be used. Even so, you will probably find that in most cases your station is in full compliance when transmitting with 100 W or less and for separations of approximately 10 feet. You will find that you must be running a fair amount of power at VHF or UHF and be fairly close to the antenna to exceed the RF level for compliance. As you use the calculator, print the screen images to create your evaluation record.

Amateurs using small transmitting loops should also be cautious about RF exposure from high field strengths near the antenna. The antenna's high Q means that a lot of energy is present near the antenna, even at low power. A table of safe distances is provided in the **Loop Antennas** chapter section on Small Transmitting Loops.

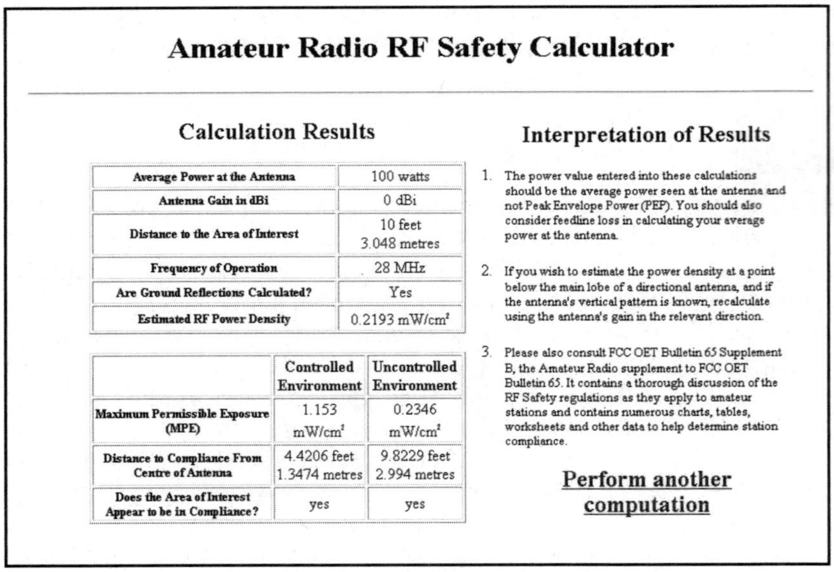
Amateur Radio RF Safety Calculator

Calculation Results

Average Power at the Antenna	100 watts
Antenna Gain in dBi	0 dBi
Distance to the Area of Interest	10 feet 3.048 metres
Frequency of Operation	28 MHz
Are Ground Reflections Calculated?	Yes
Estimated RF Power Density	0.2193 mW/cm²

	Controlled Environment	Uncontrolled Environment
Maximum Permissible Exposure (MPE)	1.153 mW/cm²	0.2346 mW/cm²
Distance to Compliance From Centre of Antenna	4.4206 feet 1.3474 metres	9.8229 feet 2.994 metres
Does the Area of Interest Appear to be in Compliance?	yes	yes

Interpretation of Results

1. The power value entered into these calculations should be the average power seen at the antenna and not Peak Envelope Power (PEP). You should also consider feedline loss in calculating your average power at the antenna.
2. If you wish to estimate the power density at a point below the main lobe of a directional antenna, and if the antenna's vertical pattern is known, recalculate using the antenna's gain in the relevant direction.
3. Please also consult FCC OET Bulletin 65 Supplement B, the Amateur Radio supplement to FCC OET Bulletin 65. It contains a thorough discussion of the RF Safety regulations as they apply to amateur stations and contains numerous charts, tables, worksheets and other data to help determine station compliance.

Perform another computation

Figure 20.1 — The RF Power Density calculator created by Paul Evans, VP9KF, at hintlink.com/power_density.htm.

20.2 LOCATIONS FOR ANTENNAS

If you live in an apartment or condominium, do you have an attic space overhead? If so, find the access door. It is often hidden away in a closet or utility room. With a ladder or step-stool, grab a flashlight, open the hatch and take a look around. If you can easily (and safely) climb into the attic, go ahead and take some measurements. How much height is available? How much horizontal length? What does the insulation look like? Is it blown-in material or paper-backed batts or do you see sections of insulation with reflective metallic backing? Metallic-backed insulation acts as a shield and rules out such spaces for antennas. The same concern applies to metal buildings or buildings with metal siding or roofing.

As a test, take a portable radio into the space and try to receive signals. If you have a "world-band" shortwave radio, this is a great use for it. Start outside the space by tuning in a signal near a frequency at which you will want to operate. Then enter the space with the radio operating. If the signals stay the same level or get louder, an antenna will probably work well in the space. If the signal levels drop, the space will probably not work well for whatever reason. For VHF/UHF operation, a hand-held radio can be used in the same way.

If you don't have an attic, check out the inside of the apartment. Are there any rooms that might accommodate an antenna secured to the ceiling? If so, how much space is available? If you are considering VHF/UHF antennas, don't neglect the windows, especially if you live above the ground floor or have multiple floor levels. If the windows have metal screens, can they be removed? It is quite possible to be successful in pointing directional VHF/UHF antennas through windows.

Even apartment and condominium dwellers should examine the property for nearby trees. Depending on how restrictive the landlord or condo association might be, trees provide excellent opportunities for discreet long-wire antennas.

If you live in a house, your antenna location options expand considerably. Take a walk around the yard and make some measurements. Look for convenient supports such as trees and note their distances from each other and your house. Make a simple map from your measurements for planning.

Don't neglect the roof of your home. A chimney can support small VHF antennas but is not designed to handle the stresses of larger antennas. You may wish to consider a roof tripod such as are available for large TV antennas. (See the **Building Antenna Systems and Towers** chapter for examples.)

It cannot be over-emphasized that you will likely need to be inventive to a degree not required of the traditional outdoor antenna builder. Browse websites, read magazine articles and books, and ask other club members about their experiences. The more information you have, the more likely it is that you'll be able to find an acceptable solution for your particular situation with a little experimentation.

20.3 RF INTERFERENCE

Because your antenna is likely to be close to your living quarters, it will also be close to the many electronic devices in use today, including appliances and security systems. Realistically, you should expect some interference when operating at (or above) the 100-W level. You will probably also experience interference *from* these devices and systems. *The ARRL RFI Book* is an excellent resource to help you deal with interference as is the *ARRL Handbook*.

Nevertheless, many interference issues are quite manageable. Perhaps you can operate with low power. Keep the antennas as far as possible from your electronics and those of your neighbors. Learn how the radiation patterns of your antennas might be used to direct your strongest signal away from them. Study how to apply ferrite chokes to keep your signal out of electronics and vice versa — Jim Brown, K9YC has written an on-line tutorial (see Bibliography) about the use of ferrites to fight RFI.

Be especially aware that indoor antennas often couple very strongly to nearby or adjacent power wiring, telephone and network cables, security system wiring, etc. The best solution is to avoid placing antennas in close proximity to other wiring. If that is not possible, be prepared to mitigate interference with chokes and other measures such as the "Resonant Breaker" described in "Better Results with Indoor Antennas" by Fred Brown, W6HPH, included with this book's downloadable supplemental information.

Another option is to use modes that concentrate your power into narrow bandwidths, allowing you to communicate with a minimum amount of power. For example, CW, PSK31 or PSK63, and the various *WJST* modes such as FT8 pack the entire signal into a bandwidth of less than 100 Hz. In addition, PSK and *WJST* modes are *constant-power* modes and do not cause clicks and thumps and garbled voice in equipment receiving the signal unintentionally. In fact, PSK and *WSJT* modes are used by many hams with antenna restrictions to make contacts around the world at powers of just a few watts.

20.4 INDOOR ANTENNAS

20.4.1 INDOOR HF WIRE ANTENNAS

The basic antennas presented in the chapters **Dipoles and Monopoles** and **Loop Antennas** can be adapted to many styles of installation. Most of them are quite forgiving of being bent and folded although you will have to make adjustments from the full-size antenna to achieve resonance at the frequency you want. Remember that the more an antenna is folded or coiled, the less efficient it becomes because the radiation from the different parts of the antenna tend to cancel out. Keep as much of the antenna in a straight line as you can.

The common $\lambda/2$ dipole in **Figure 20.2** is a very tolerant antenna. At 14 MHz, it is approximately 33 feet long and can be bent to fit many different rooms, under a roof line or eaves, in a hallway, etc. Very thin wire can be used at low power such as #28 AWG stranded hook-up wire that comes in a number of colors to blend in with the surrounding material. You can use adhesive tape or hooks to hold it against the wall or ceiling. **Figure 20.3** shows a multiband antenna fed with ladder line. You can also use the clear 300-Ω twinlead sold for use with FM radio antennas.

Loop antennas can also be used as long as they are not too much smaller than one wavelength. (Very small transmitting loops are covered later in this chapter.) **Figure 20.4A** shows how a loop extended around a ceiling can be fed with low-loss ladder line or twin-lead on multiple bands. Making the loop as large as possible allows it to be effective on the lowest possible frequencies. A loop can also be installed in an attic as described in the section below. Another option is to install a loop around the edges of a roof line as shown in Figure 20.4B and described in the article "160 to 6 Meter Hidden Antenna" by Bruce Walker, N3JO, in his book *Magic Band Antennas for Ham Radio* (see the Bibliography).

Attics and upper-story bedrooms under peaked roofs can make a good home for inverted-V style antennas. Support the feed point at or near the peak of the roof and run the legs down the roof joists or to the floor joists. A dual-band inverted-V can be installed with the pairs of legs connected in parallel and run at right angles to each other. Inverted-V wire Yagi antennas for 20 meters and higher frequency bands can also be made if the attic has a desirable orientation.

If you are working in an attic-type space, the simplest

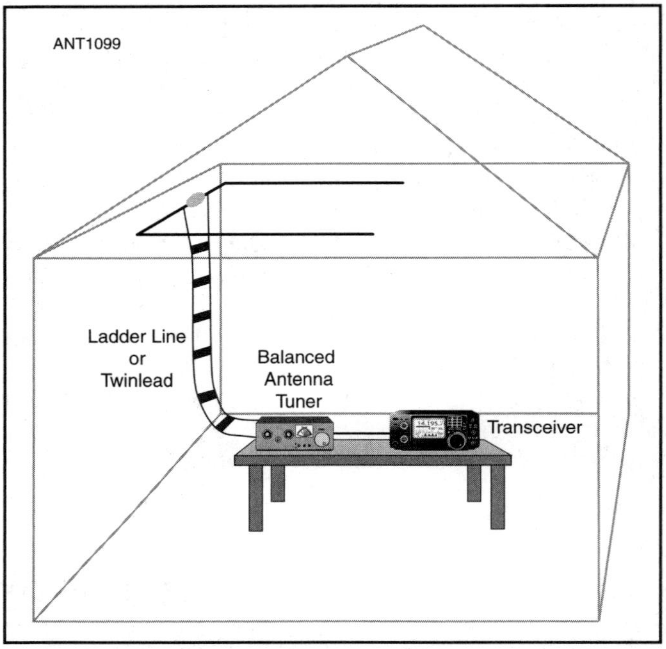

Figure 20.3 — A multiband ceiling dipole fed with ladder line or twinlead. Unlike a tuned dipole, the length isn't critical. As a rule of thumb, make each leg of the dipole as long as the space allows and make sure both legs are of equal length.

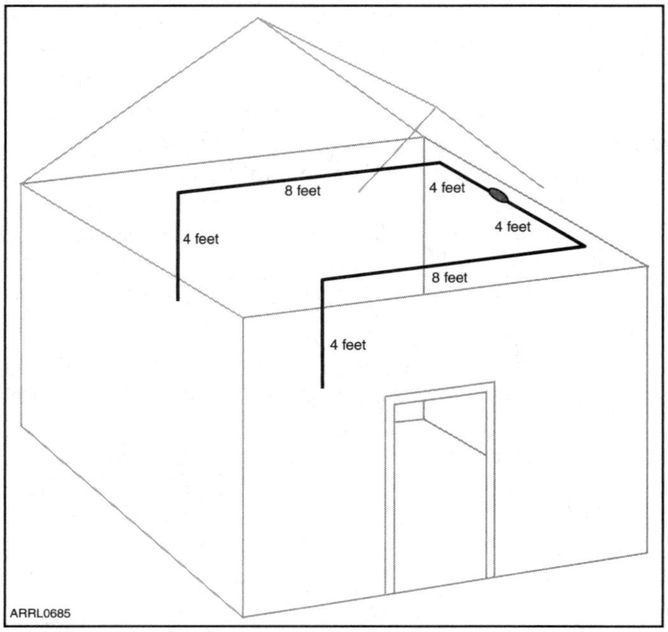

Figure 20.2 — A dipole antenna for the 20 meter band can fit into a small room with a bit of folding.

The Slinky Antenna

If folding an antenna reduces its effectiveness, what about coiling it? This is just what happens when a Slinky™ toy is used as the antenna element! The Slinky Antenna was first described in an Oct 1974 *QST* article by W7ZCB (see Bibliography and this book's downloadable supplemental information). As you might imagine, the antenna is nothing more than a dipole made out of two metal Slinky toys and stretched out until resonance is reached. W7ZCB was able to use his version on 80, 40, and 20 meters. It has been reported that the standard Slinky's quarter-wave resonance occurs on 40 meters when stretched to about 7.5 feet, so a full half-wave dipole would be about 15 feet long. This is well within the space available in a good-sized room. If you try this antenna, be sure to get a metal version as there are plastic models, as well.

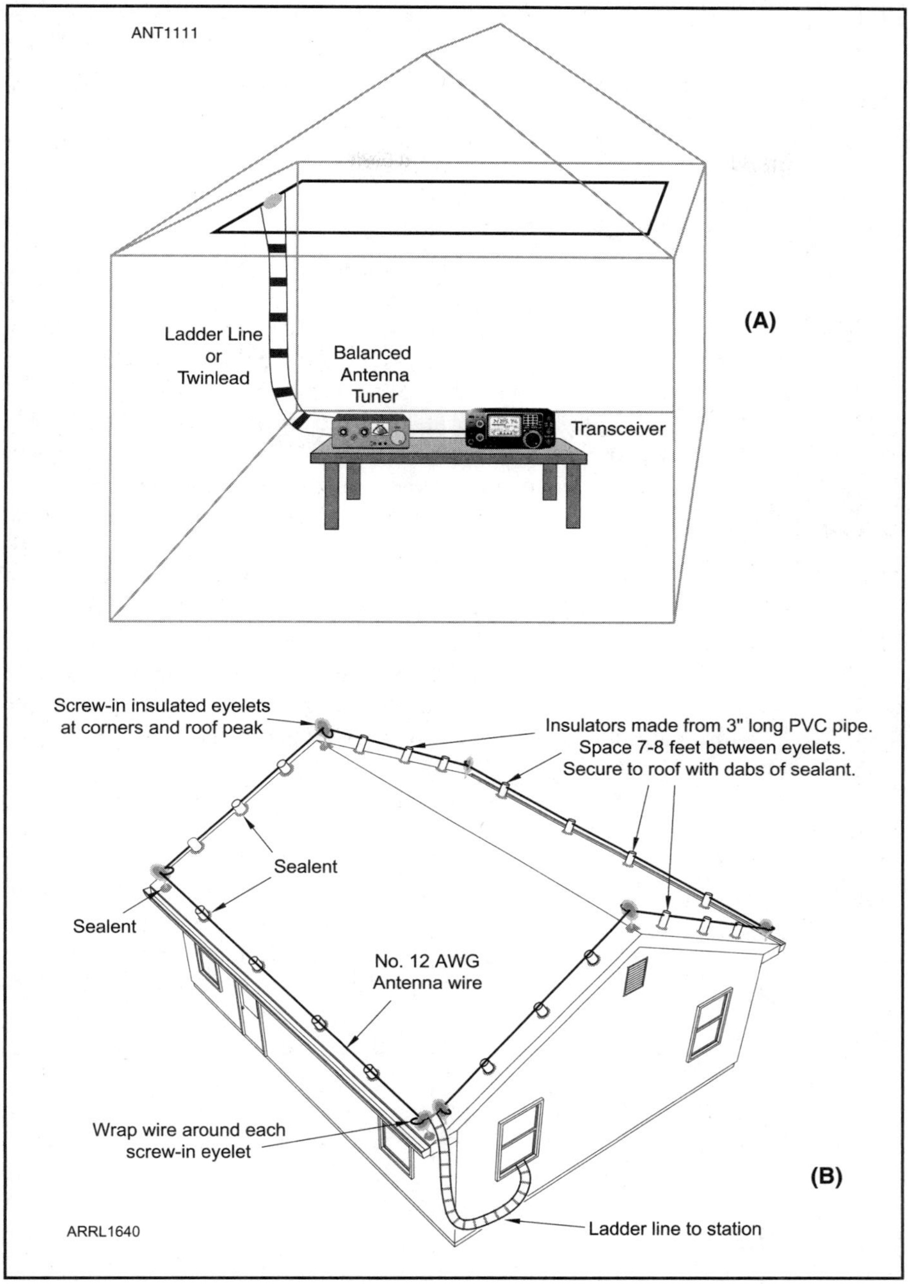

Figure 20.4 — A loop installed around the ceiling of a room at A can be fed with balanced feed line and a tuner for multiband operation. A similar option is to run the loop around the edges of a roof as at B using small standoff insulators.

way to hold wire against wooden trusses and joists is a plastic coaxial cable clip of the sort used for cable TV wiring. Avoid attaching bare or enameled wire directly against wood. PVC-insulated wire can be carefully stapled directly to wood supports.

To get the feed line from the attic to your transmitter, you may be able to find the cap for an internal wall and drill a hole in it for the feed line to drop down between wall studs. You can then install an "old work" electrical box and an appropriate plastic cover plate for a professional-quality installation. Do not run feed line through the same hole as ac wiring or in conduit carrying ac wiring as that is an unsafe practice as well as increasing the probability of RF interference.

An Indoor Stealth Loop

Ted Phelps, W8TP, wrote an article in *The ARRL Antenna Compendium Vol 7* describing his attic-mounted wire loop antenna, fed with an automatic antenna tuner. The full article is included with this book's downloadable supplemental information.

Figure 20.5 shows the final dimensions of the loop hidden the attic of his condo. The antenna is a single-turn rectangular loop, erected in a north-south vertical plane and made from nearly 78 feet of #6 AWG stranded, aircraft primary wire in a PVC jacket, held taut at the lower corners and supported by a pulley and guy rope at each upper corner. The antenna will provide a mix of vertical and horizontal polarization on the different bands, covering many directions at a wide range of vertical angles.

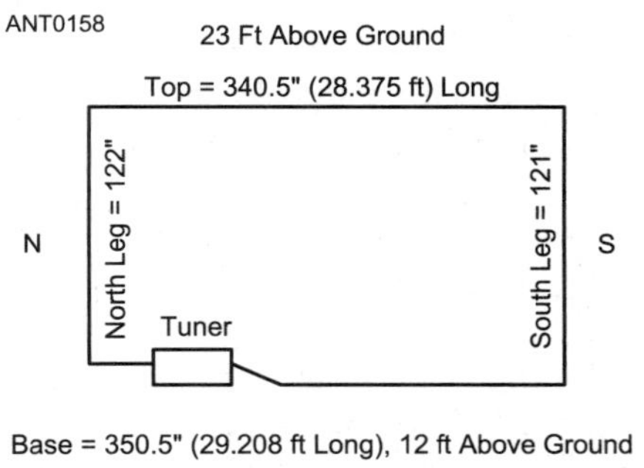

Figure 20.5 — Diagram showing layout of W8TP's indoor hidden loop antenna.

Compact Loops

Rod Newkirk, W9BRD, contributed several designs for multi-turn and tuned loops that can be used on the HF bands. His *QST* article, "Honey, I Shrunk the Antenna!" presented several variations that are suitable for installing in an attic or garage and can also be used for portable operation. (This article is included with this book's downloadable supplemental information.)

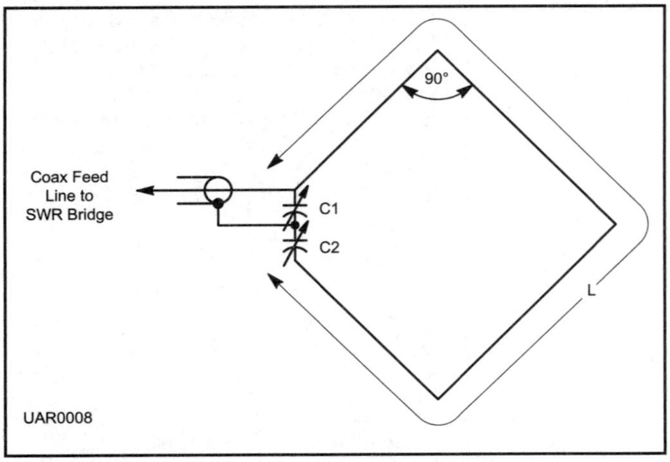

Figure 20.6 — W9BRD's compact loop antenna. L is somewhat shorter than λ/4 (25 feet for 7 MHz). C1 and C2 are both 300 pF broadcast receiving variable capacitors. The loop can be any shape with a large area.

Figure 20.6 shows a single-turn tuned W9BRD loop that is designed for 40 meters (see the Bibliography entry for Brogdon, *Low Profile Amateur Radio*). The circumference L should be somewhat shorter than λ/4, about 25 feet for 7 MHz. C1 and C2 are 300 pF must be frequently re-turned since the bandwidth of the loop is about 50 kHz. At power levels of up to 100 W, broadcast-style 365 pF variable capacitors can be used.

To use the loop on the next highest frequency band of 30 meters, insert a third capacitor in series with the loop, opposite the feed point. To use the loop at 14 MHz or higher-frequency bands, you'll have to re-scale the length of the loop accordingly. Smaller-value variable capacitors will make the tuning adjustments less sensitive at higher frequencies, as well.

All-Band Attic Antenna

This design by Kai Siwiak, KE4PT, describes an inverted L antenna installed in the attic of his home. The system uses an automatic antenna tuner, similarly to the antennas shown in Figures 20.3 and 20.4. The full article is included with this book's downloadable supplemental information.

The L is horizontal and laid out as shown in **Figure 20.7**. It comprises two parallel lengths of #9 AWG aluminum wire connected together at the far end, and spaced about 38 inches apart. The horizontal portion is about 48 feet long and a bit more than 14 feet above the ground, under the roof of the house. The horizontal length is approximately one wavelength at 21 MHz so the antenna pattern is very nearly omnidirectional from 20 meters down to 80 meters.

The parallel wires are brought together and emerge from the ceiling on a far wall of the house in a storage closet. Both of the parallel wires are joined together and connected to the antenna post of the AH-4 tuner. Connecting the wires together in this way creates a "thick" radiating element for which the feed point impedance varies more smoothly with frequency and eases the job of the antenna tuner.

A copper ground wire runs from the tuner ground connection to an outside 8-foot ground rod. The antenna shares this ground rod with a conductive mast supporting a 2 meter J-pole that tops out at 21.7 feet. This mast also functions as part of the HF radiating system.

A length of 50-Ω coaxial cable connects the tuner through an eight-turn, 5-inch diameter choke balun to the transceiver at the operating position in the ham shack on the other side of the wall of the storage closet.

Indoor antennas should be very carefully considered from the RF exposure point of view, especially for those within the dwelling. A spot check of near fields of the antenna both near the vertical and near the horizontal parts of the wires shows that for this antenna, the 6 meter band *4nec2* result of 3.3 feet gives sufficient compliance distance safety margin on all lower frequency bands. Evaluate unusual antennas very carefully, especially if a ground or ground post is part of the system!

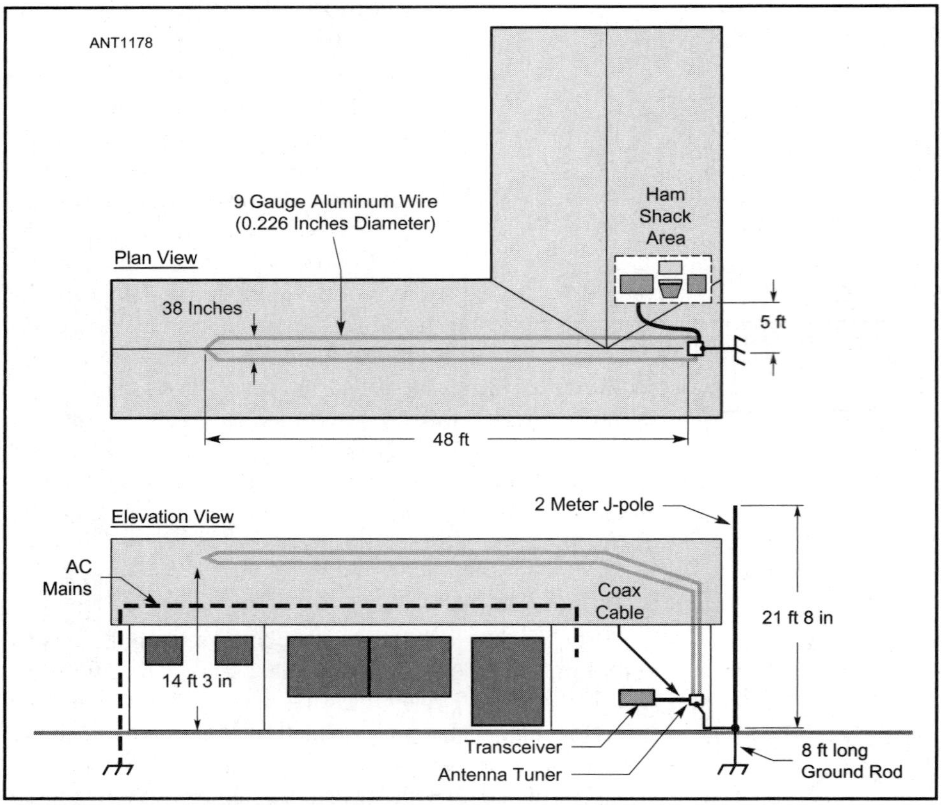

Figure 20.7 — Plan and elevation views of the attic inverted L antenna.

Cool That Hot-Spot with Quarter-Wave Wires

Using indoor, portable, and temporary antennas often results in an RF "hot spot" on the station equipment. The antennas are usually quite close to the station equipment and in the case of a random-wire antenna, may actually use the station equipment as part of the radiating system. If the hot spot is causing RF burns or otherwise upsetting the operator or equipment, the trick of attaching a λ/4 piece of wire to the equipment at the hot spot is often employed. If one end of the wire is left unconnected (open) the other end will present a low impedance at the λ/4 frequency. This can reduce the RF voltage substantially but the other end of the wire will be at a high RF voltage. Be sure to keep the other end of the wire clear of anything conductive, flammable, or where a person can touch it. The hot spot isn't gone, it just got moved to the unconnected end of the wire! Having a set of wires cut for different bands with an alligator clip on one end can be a very handy problem-solving addition to your tool kit.

20.4.2 MOBILE HF ANTENNAS INDOORS

Another popular option for indoor HF use is antennas intended for mobile operation. After all, mobiling is certainly another example of a limited-space application! (See the chapter **Mobile and Maritime HF Antennas** for more information about the mobile antennas described in this section.)

The same general concerns for mobile antennas mounted on vehicles apply to mobile antennas used indoors regarding the importance of how the antennas are mounted and having a large conductive surface to act as a ground plane. A mobile whip can be used quite effectively when mounted on a sufficiently large metal surface. For example, a windowsill (see **Figure 20.8**) or balcony railing will suffice. If those metal structures are also tied into a building's steel frame, the antenna will be very effective.

When using a mobile antenna in this way, if the metal item to which the antenna is clamped is not sufficiently large, a counterpoise wire should be added to the system. The counterpoise should be approximately λ/4 long at the frequency of operation and acts as the "missing half" of the antenna in lieu of a full ground plane. The counterpoise in this case is actually a radiating element and should be kept away from the operator and any electronics. If above the ground floor, the counterpoise can be allowed to hang down alongside the building. There may be significant RF voltage present at the end of the counterpoise so place it where it cannot be touched or arc to another surface.

The popular "screwdriver" mobile antenna (see the **Mobile and Maritime HF Antennas** chapter) can also make

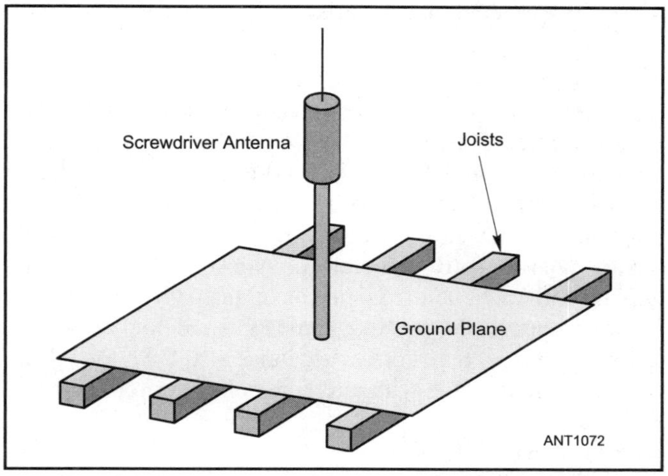

Figure 20.9 — A screwdriver antenna can be mounted on a ground plane for an effective, tunable attic antenna.

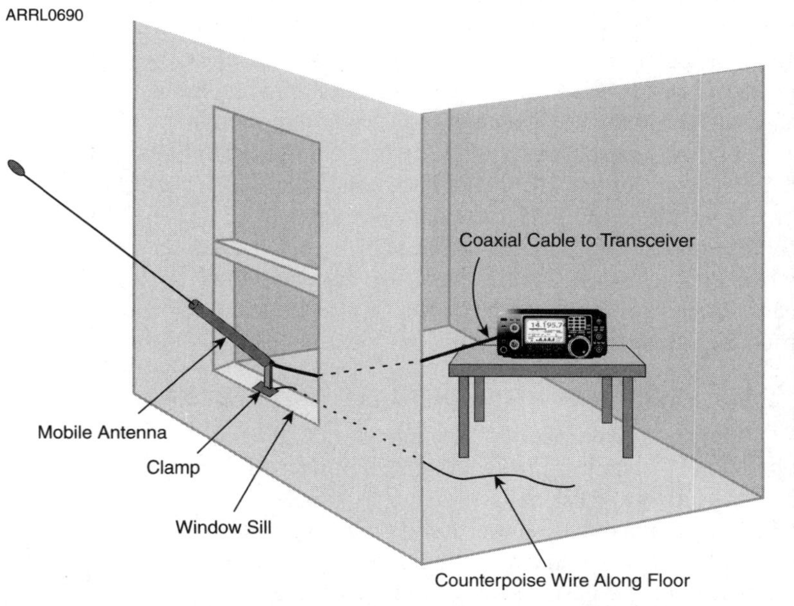

Figure 20.8 — A mobile antenna can be clamped to a windowsill or balcony railing. A counterpoise wire approximately λ/4 long at the operating frequency provides an additional radiating element to complete the antenna. For multiband operation, a counterpoise cut for each band should be used. If the frame or railing is tied into the building's metal structure, the counterpoise may not be necessary.

Figure 20.10 — This pair of CB mobile antennas were trimmed slightly to resonate on 10 meters then attached to a mounting bracket. This created an effective apartment-sized antenna.

an effective and tunable HF antenna in an attic or unused room. **Figure 20.9** shows the screwdriver mounted on a ground plane that in turn rests on the ceiling joists. Shorter models are small enough to fit comfortably under a peaked roof. Along with sheet metal any mesh will do for the ground plane, such as hardware cloth or chicken wire. Even aluminum foil could be used, such as on insulation panels. The more extensive the ground plane, the more effective the antenna will be. Screwdriver antennas also have the advantage of being tunable with a remote controller for use on all HF bands.

To lower the frequency range of a screwdriver antenna, the whip can be extended with horizontal wires, either as an Inverted L or as a T antenna. A capacitance hat can be added at the top of a sturdy whip or at the top of the adjustable coil. (See the **Multiband HF Antennas** chapter) The adjustable coil is then used to bring the entire antenna to resonance. Adding whip length (either physically or electrically) may lower the operating range such that a reasonable match on the upper HF bands and 6 meters is no longer attainable. In this case, an auto-tuner at the antenna feed point may be used.

It is also possible to use mobile whips configured to form a dipole as in **Figure 20.10**. Many antenna parts dealers sell brackets with an SO-239 coax connector and tapped fittings for the popular ⅜-24 threaded antenna base. A pair of mobile whips can be attached as in the figure and supported on a camera tripod or other suitable base. This makes an excellent portable antenna, too.

20.4.3 INDOOR VHF AND UHF ANTENNAS

Operating with indoor antennas for VHF and UHF operation is much less difficult than creating an effective HF antenna indoors. For example, placing a simple mag mount whip on top of a refrigerator or filing cabinet makes a reasonable base station antenna for local 2 meter or 70 cm FM contacts. Any of the designs for ground-plane antennas in the **VHF and UHF Antenna Systems** chapter is easily adapted to indoor use. The "roll up" J pole designs are particularly good for portable and travel antennas.

An excellent "make do" antenna for 2 meters can be as simple as two pieces of wire. **Figure 20.11** shows the idea. The antenna can be installed permanently, for example on an apartment window, or as a portable antenna that can be taken along when traveling or as part of a "go kit." The wires need not be stiff — small-gauge stranded wire also works quite well. In an emergency situation, this is an easy antenna to construct from almost any source of wire and dimensions are not critical. A short (less than 10 feet) feed line of RG-174 miniature coax is sufficient and keeps the entire package small.

Creating an effective installation for SSB and CW operation — the so-called *weak signal* modes — is more challenging. Horizontal polarization is required for sustained success but it is not always necessary to have multi-element beams. 6 meters provides a lot of opportunities for long-distance contacts to amateurs who can't put up outdoor antennas. Relatively omnidirectional antennas such as a horizontal "halo" (**Figure 20.12**) or dipole can make many contacts, including with distant stations when sporadic E propagation is occurring. (See the **Radio Wave Propagation** chapter.)

Nevertheless, if you can manage an antenna with some directivity, it will help. The 2-element Moxon design for 6 meters described by Allen Baker, KG4JJH, measures 84 × 31 inches and being flat, is a natural candidate for ceiling mounting. The 3-element wire "stealth" Yagi for 6 meters

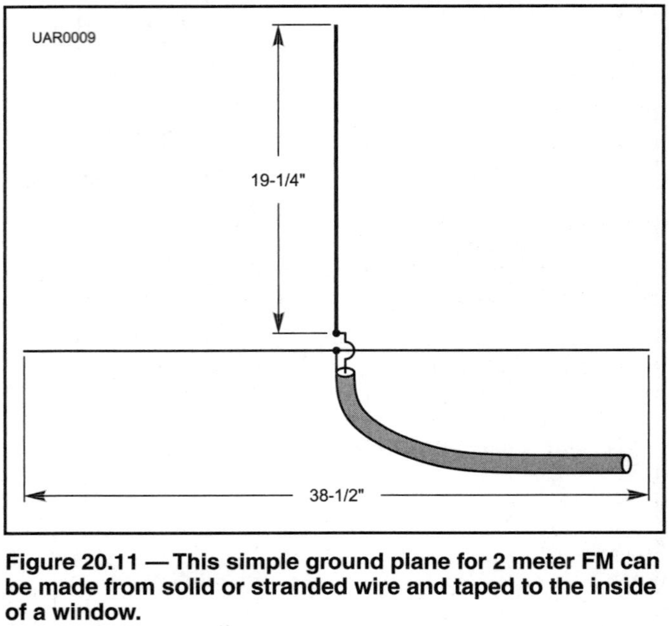

Figure 20.11 — This simple ground plane for 2 meter FM can be made from solid or stranded wire and taped to the inside of a window.

Figure 20.12 — A typical 6 meter horizontal full-wave loop antenna can be used either indoors or outdoors. The radiation pattern is omnidirectional with horizontal polarization.

Figure 20.13 — The 2 meter PortaQuad by National RF isn't intended for permanent outdoor use, but it would be a fine directional antenna inside a room or attic.

designed by Bruce Walker, N3JO, is about 10 feet by 5 feet is another good ceiling mount antenna. Both of these articles are included in this book's downloadable supplemental information and the book *Magic Band Antennas for Ham Radio* is full of useful antenna designs for limited-space stations.

Quad beams for VHF and UHF are also fairly small antennas, even on 6 meters where quad elements are only 5 feet on a side. A 2-element quad for 6 meters can fit many attic spaces or be suspended from a ceiling mount.

Quads and small beams for 2 meters and higher frequencies are even smaller. **Figure 20.13** shows an example for 2 meters. A light-duty TV rotator can turn any of these antennas. A note of caution — the higher the frequency of operation, the higher the attenuation from building materials as well as rain and snow on roofs, especially at UHF and microwaves.

20.5 OUTDOOR ANTENNAS

This book contains plenty of candidates for outdoor antenna designs in spaces of limited size. The antennas in the chapter **Portable Antennas** address similar limited-space needs as the amateur with a limited fixed space. The builder should start with a good idea of the available supports or ground area, decide on a horizontal or vertical antenna, and begin reviewing the antenna books and articles.

The main challenge addressed in this chapter, however, is how to put up such an antenna in the face of restrictions against them or when esthetics just don't permit the usual construction techniques. There are two basic approaches to putting up such a stealth antenna; invisibility and disguise.

20.5.1 INVISIBLE ANTENNAS

An invisible antenna is one that is constructed so as to be difficult to see. Many amateurs have been able to operate for long periods using invisible antennas without being detected. The secret to making an antenna invisible is to think small and thin. Thin wire, small coax, placing the antenna in trees or other foliage — all of these are time-tested techniques for making an antenna "disappear."

Thin wire can be used up to surprisingly high power before its resistance becomes an issue. Assuming you'll be using power levels of 100 W or less, you can use wire as small as #30 AWG. For sizes below #24 AWG, however, the challenge of keeping it up due to breakage becomes the bigger issue. Use stranded wire for better flexibility and be careful not to tension the wire too heavily — it will stretch, then break.

Think "small," too. Insulators, feed points, supporting lines, and coaxial feed line all need to be small so as not to attract the eye. Insulators and feed points can be homebrewed from scrap plastic or fishing supplies. Woven fishing line is usually tough, UV-resistant, and very hard to see against the sky or foliage (just ask the fish!). If possible, use colors that blend in to the surroundings.

Small diameter coax such as RG-174 can be dismayingly lossy (see the table of coaxial cable parameters in the

Transmission Lines chapter) and should only be used for very short runs. RG-58, RG-59, and RG-6 can be used for longer runs and have the added benefit of looking very much like the cable TV service drop. Parallel-wire lines have much lower loss and are lighter than coax but are much harder to conceal. If you get a good deal on a long length of subminiature Teflon-insulated cable such as RG-393 or similar, it makes a very good miniature feed line.

20.5.2 DISGUISED ANTENNAS

A disguised antenna is an antenna that is easy to see but the viewer doesn't recognize it as an antenna! The classic example of the disguised antenna is a flagpole antenna such as that described by Geoff Haines, N1GY in the December 2010 issue of *QST*. To the non-ham, it's a basic flagpole. To the ham, it's a 23-foot ground-plane vertical with an automatic tuner at the base. Albert Parker, N4AQ took a different tack by hiding a Hustler 4-BTV 4-band trap vertical inside a flagpole made of PVC pipe (see Bibliography).

Making Radials Disappear

How do you create an effective ground screen of radial wires without an unsightly mess covering your lawn? The answer is to let the lawn do the work for you!

Get a large pizza cutter — it will be ruined for kitchen use so don't use the family's prize pie divider. You'll also need a spool of thin stiff iron wire — rebar tie wire will do fine. Cut at least a half-dozen 6-inch lengths of wire for each radial you plan on installing and bend them in half to form a narrow U — these are radial pins. Your radial wire can be any convenient type although a dark insulation or enamel coating will help with the disappearing act. Bare wire is fine, too.

Start by mowing the grass as short as you reasonably can. Attach a radial to the base of the antenna and cut a narrow slot in the grass into which you lay your radial wire. As you move away from the antenna, hold the radial down with the radial pins every few feet. The cost of each pin is quite low so use as many as you need.

Once all of the radials are in, water the grass well. A little fertilizer won't hurt. In a matter of days, the grass will have grown high enough to completely hide the radial wires — you won't be able to see them even if you know they are there! Over time, the grass (and the worms) will conspire to pull the wires deeper toward and even below the surface of the ground. The radial pins will also quickly rust away and disappear if you used iron wire. The only thing sticking up out of the yard will be the ends of the radials at the antenna.

(A)

(B)

Figure 20.14 — Martin, G8JNJ, converted a scrap laundry drying rack into a stealthy HF vertical. At A is the complete antenna showing the top and bottom counterpoise and capacity hat, respectively. B shows the upper capacity hat. [Photos courtesy of the RSGB and Martin Ehrenfried, G8JNJ]

Another long-time favorite method is hiding the antenna near an approved structure such as a drain pipe or gutter. Hams have even used metal gutters and downspouts as antennas with a variety of results but it can be difficult to maintain good connections at joints. With plastic guttering so common, why not put a wire antenna directly into the gutter? With horizontal gutters, pooling water can be a problem but most vertical gutters are immune. Put your antenna in the gutter itself! The challenge will be to get the feed line to the antenna and keep water out of the feed line.

If your gutters or downspouts are metallic, try loading them up as described by Craig LaBarge, WB3GCK at **www.qsl.net/wb3gck/spout.htm**. Craig's example is just one way of using an automatic antenna tuner and counterpoise wires to create a surprisingly effective, yet completely invisible antenna.

Take a look around and see what metal objects are outside in your yard or around your home. Almost anything can be made into an antenna as the photo in **Figure 20.14** shows. Martin Ehrenfried, G8JNJ (**www.g8jnj.webs.com**) converted an outdoor drying rack into a vertical dipole with end loading. Lawn chairs, garden tools, sports equipment — any metal object can be made to radiate. The Ventenna (**www.ventenna.com**) is a roof-mounted antenna for VHF or UHF that looks just like an ordinary drain pipe.

20.5.3 MODIFIED TV ANTENNAS

That's not a typo, TV antennas can really be modified for use on the amateur bands! With over-the-air broadcast DTV having established a sizeable presence, TV antennas are once again popping up on rooftops and chimneys. The most familiar TV antennas are an LPDA with V-shaped elements for the lower frequency channels. (See the **Log-Periodic Dipole Array** chapter.) The lower TV bands, VHF Channels 2 – 6 (54 – 88 MHz) are received with the four largest elements, while Channels 7 – 13 (175 – 216 MHz) use the same elements operating in the third harmonic mode. A corner reflector with a dipole at its focal point is often used to receive the lower UHF channels while multiple parasitic directors at the front of the antenna are used for the higher UHF channels.

John Stanley, K4ERO, has contributed an article about converting one of these antennas to cover the 50, 144, and 222 MHz bands. It is included with the downloadable supplemental information for this book. The procedure involves lengthening some of the elements and removing the higher UHF elements. The 300 Ω feed system impedance was retained and the antenna used with 300 Ω twin-lead which is very light and has the additional benefit of maintaining the disguise of the antenna as a TV receive antenna. A 6:1 impedance transformer could be used to convert 300 Ω to 50 Ω or a 4:1 transformer could be used with low-loss RG-6 cable. A tuner at the transceiver could then take care of any resulting mismatch.

It is a very effective disguise to look like something familiar. In this case, people are used to TV receive antennas, various covenants and restrictions usually allow them, and they are often available for free. In fact, K4ERO used pieces from a second TV antenna to lengthen the lower-channel elements for use on 6 meters.

20.6 SMALL TRANSMITTING LOOPS

Small transmitting loops such as the one shown in **Figure 20.15** have become very popular for portable and temporary operation. They are small enough to fit on an apartment balcony or patio, in a garage, or in an attic, as well. The section on these antennas in the **Loop Antennas** chapter covers them in detail and includes references to articles describing how they are built.

As noted earlier in this chapter's section on RF Safety, amateurs using small transmitting loops should be cautious about RF exposure from high field strengths near the antenna. It is common to see photos of the operator and radio on a picnic table with the loop antenna just a few feet away. A table of safe distances is provided in the **Loop Antennas** chapter section on Small Transmitting Loops. Because these popular loop antennas are often used in portable operation, careful attention should be paid to insuring RF exposure limits are not exceeded and that people cannot inadvertently get too close to the antenna.

When building or assembling these loops, take extra care to avoid loose or corroded connections. Radiation resistance of small loops is very, very low and any resistance in a connection or component will reduce efficiency dramatically. Connectors should be tight and adjustable joints clean and snug. Avoid placing the loop near conductive surfaces or

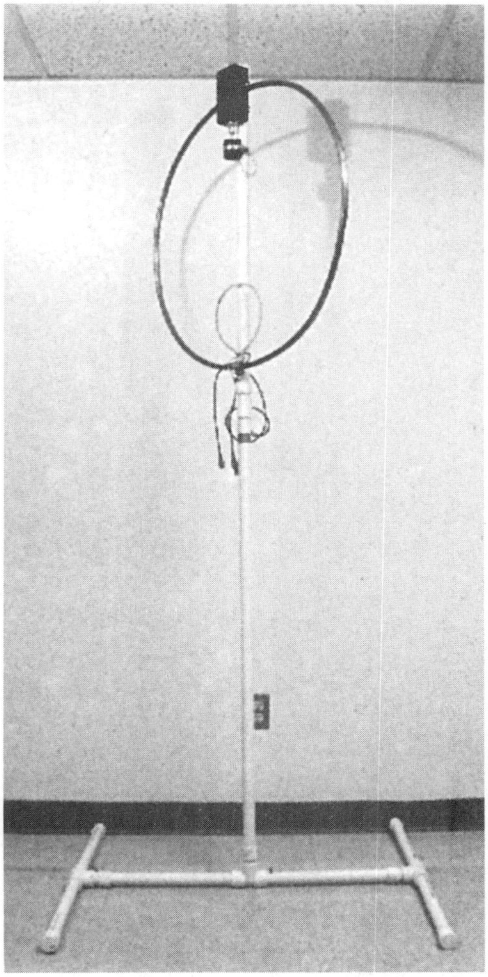

Figure 20.15 — Photo of compact transmitting loop designed by Robert Capon, WA3ULH. This uses a 1-inch PVC H-frame to support the loop made of flexible ⅝-inch copper tubing. The small coupling loop made of RG-8 couples the loop to the coax feed line. The tuning capacitor and drive motor are at the top of the loop, shown here in the ARRL Laboratory during testing.

structures where the antenna's field can couple to lossy elements. Ferrite chokes (see the **Transmission Line System Techniques**) should be used to decouple the feed line from the antenna, as well.

If you use the loop inside a building constructed with large amounts of iron or other conductive materials, you will simply have to live with the loss if the loop cannot otherwise be relocated. For that reason, avoid placing loops in attics with metal roofs or where metal siding is nearby.

20.7 BIBLIOGRAPHY

A. Baker, "A 6-Meter Moxon Antenna," *QST*, Apr 2004, pp 65-69.

A. Brogdon, *Low Profile Amateur Radio*, 2nd edition (Newington: ARRL, 2006). (out of print but available used)

F. Brown, "Better Results with Indoor Antennas," *QST*, Oct 1979, pp 18-21.

J. Brown, "RFI, Ferrites, and Common Mode Chokes For Hams," **www.audiosystemsgroup.com/publish.htm**.

S. Ford, *Small Antennas for Small Spaces* (Newington: ARRL, 2011).

M. Gruber, Ed., *The ARRL RFI Book*, 3rd Edition (Newington: ARRL, 2010).

G. Haines, "Constructing a Flagpole Antenna," *QST*, Dec 2010, pp 30-32.

E. Hare, *RF Exposure and You* (Newington: ARRL, 1998). (Out of print, but available for download from **www.arrl.org/rf-exposure**.)

I. Grigorov, *Urban Antennas*, *Vol. 1*, *Antennex* Online Magazine, 2001.

J. Malone, "Can a 7 foot 40m Antenna Work?." *73*, Mar 1975, pp 33-38.

R. Marris, "An In-Room 80-Meter Transmitting Multiturn Loop Antenna," *QST*, Feb 1996, pp 43-45. Also see Feedback, *QST*, May 1996, p 48.

S. Nichols, *Stealth Antennas,* 2nd edition (Potters Bar: RSGB, 2014).

A. Parker, "A Disguised Flagpole Antenna," *QST*, May 1993, p 65.

A. Peterson, "Apartment Dwellers' Slinky Jr Antenna," *QST*, Oct 1974, pp 22-23.

T. Phelps, "A Hidden Loop Antenna," *The ARRL Antenna Compendium*, *Vol 7* (Newington: ARRL, 2002), pp 160-162.

B. Walker, *Magic Band Antennas for Ham Radio* (Newington: ARRL, 2018).

TABLE OF CONTENTS

Chapter 21 — Downloadable Supplemental Content

Supplemental Articles
- "How To Build A Capacity Hat" by Ken Muggli, KØHL
- "Screwdriver Mobile Antenna" by Max Bloodworth, KO4TV
- "Table of Mobile Antenna Manufacturers" by Alan Applegate, KØBG

Chapter 21

Mobile and Maritime HF Antennas

Mobile antennas are designed for use while in motion. At the mention of mobile antennas, most amateurs think of a whip antenna mounted on an automobile or other vehicle. While it is true that most mobile antennas are vertical whips, mobile antennas can also be found in other places. For example, antennas intended for use aboard a boat or ship are usually called *marine* or *maritime antennas*. Whip antennas are common in maritime service, but wire antennas installed on masts are also common.

Few amateurs construct their own antennas for HF mobile and maritime use, since safety requirements dictate very sound mechanical construction. (A short directory table of mobile antenna manufacturers is included with this book's downloadable supplemental information.) Even if commercially made antennas are installed, most require some adjustment to optimize the particular installation and type of operation desired. The information in this chapter will provide a better understanding of the requirements for designing and choosing HF mobile antennas and using them effectively.

The chapter begins with a discussion of mobile antenna fundamentals at HF, updated from previous editions by Alan Applegate, KØBG. The following sections explain the more important attributes of the most popular designs and how to get the best from them. This will include mounting, impedance matching, and other important issues to all types of mobile antennas. Several examples of mobile antenna installation are provided. Information on constructing a capacitive hat-loaded whip and an adjustable "screwdriver" HF mobile antenna is included with this book's downloadable supplemental information.

The second half of the chapter covers maritime HF antennas for sail and power boats and was updated by John Thompson, K3MD, along with the material originally provided by Rudy Severns, N6LF. The text discusses important issues regarding placement and safety of the maritime HF system. Several examples of common installation practices are given, based on antenna designs presented elsewhere in this book.

21.1 HF MOBILE ANTENNA FUNDAMENTALS

High frequency mobile antennas come in every imaginable configuration of efficiency, overall length, quality, design, sturdiness, ease of mounting, and selling price. The design, mounting method employed, and most importantly where the antenna is mounted, all have an effect on maximum efficiency — the holy grail of HF mobile operation. The right combination of strengths and weaknesses depends on how you expect to use the antenna.

Propagation conditions and ignition noise are usually the limiting factors for mobile operation on 10 through 28 MHz. Antenna size restrictions affect operation somewhat on 7 MHz and much more on 3.5 and 1.8 MHz. From this perspective, perhaps the optimum band for HF-mobile operation is 7 MHz. The popularity of regional mobile nets on 7 MHz is perhaps the best indication of how effective mobile communication can be on that band.

If you intend to chase DX, 20 meters and above are perhaps the best choices as antennas for those bands offer the best efficiency for a given physical size. For local communication, 28 MHz is also useful as a full-size whip without

Figure 21.1 — A simple HF mobile whip can be mounted on almost any vehicle. (*NØAX photo*)

loading coils is not too large for convenient use and is easy to build. In fact, a slightly shortened CB whip works very well.

On the HF bands, the physical size of full-size whips becomes a problem and some form of electrical loading is usually employed to shorten the antenna. Commonly used loading techniques consist of placing a coil at the base of the whip (base loading), or at the center of the whip (center loading). **Figure 21.1** shows a typical mobile whip installation. These and other techniques for reducing the physical size of antennas are discussed in this chapter.

For typical antenna lengths used in mobile operation, the difficulty in constructing suitable loading coils increases as the frequency of operation is lowered. Radiation resistance of the antenna decreases as the antenna becomes electrically shorter, which is the same as lowering the frequency of operation for a fixed-length antenna. In addition, the required inductance to resonate the antenna gets larger. The result is that the fraction of the applied power lost as heating in ohmic losses increases and the antenna becomes less efficient.

Designing short HF mobile antennas requires a careful balance of loading coil Q, loading coil position in the antenna, ground loss resistance, and length-to-diameter ratio of the antenna. The optimum balance of these parameters can be realized only through a thorough understanding of how they interact. This section presents a mathematical approach to designing mobile antennas for maximum radiation efficiency. Bruce Brown, W6TWW, first presented this approach in *The ARRL Antenna Compendium Volume 1*. (See the Bibliography following the sections on mobile antennas.)

21.1.1 THE EQUIVALENT CIRCUIT OF A TYPICAL MOBILE ANTENNA

It is customary in solving problems involving electric and magnetic fields (such as antenna systems) to try to find an equivalent network with which to replace the antenna for analysis reasons. In many cases, the network may be an accurate representation over only a limited frequency range. However, this is often a valuable method in matching the antenna to the transmission line.

Antenna resonance is defined as the frequency at which the input impedance at the antenna terminals is purely resistive. The shortest length at which this occurs for a vertical antenna over a ground plane is when the antenna is an electrical quarter-wavelength at the operating frequency; the impedance value for this length (neglecting losses) is about 36 Ω. The idea of resonance can be extended to antennas shorter (or longer) than a quarter-wave and means only that the input impedance is purely resistive.

When the frequency of operation is lowered below the antenna's resonant frequency, the antenna looks like a series RC circuit, as shown in **Figure 21.2**. For the average 8-foot whip, the capacitive reactance may range from about –150 Ω at 21 MHz to as high as –8000 Ω at 1.8 MHz, while the radiation resistance R_R, varies from about 15 Ω at 21 MHz to as low as 0.1 Ω at 1.8 MHz.

For an antenna less than 0.1 λ long, the approximate radiation resistance may be determined from the following:

$$R_R = 273 \times (\ell f)^2 \times 10^{-8} \qquad (1)$$

where ℓ is the length of the whip in inches and f is the frequency in MHz.

Since the radiation resistance is low, considerable current must flow in the circuit if any appreciable power is to be

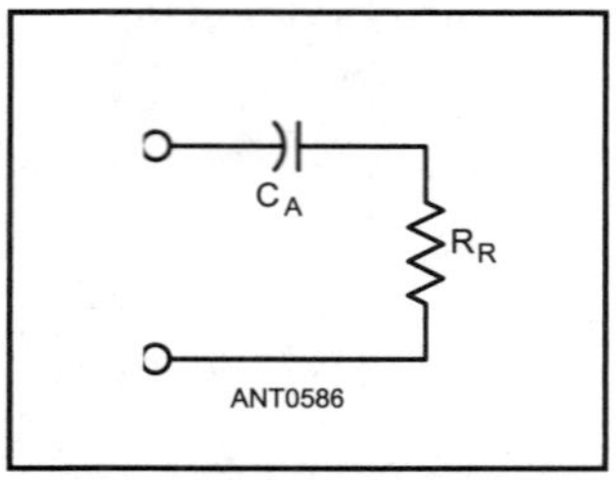

Figure 21.2 — At frequencies below resonance, the whip antenna will show capacitive reactance as well as resistance. R_R is the radiation resistance, and C_A represents the antenna capacitance.

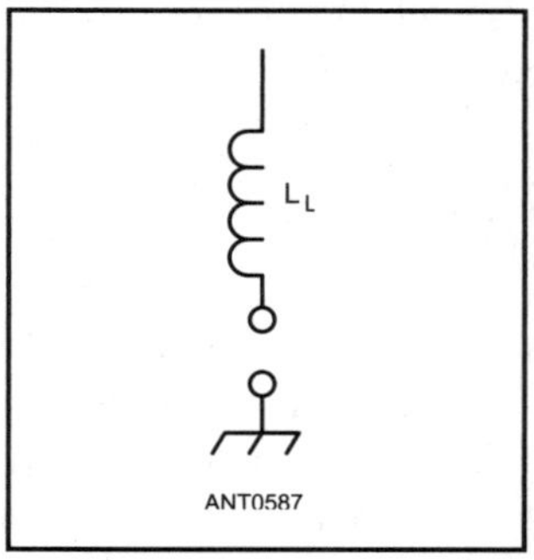

Figure 21.3 — The capacitive reactance at frequencies below the resonant frequency of the whip can be canceled by adding an equivalent inductive reactance in the form of a loading coil in series with the antenna.

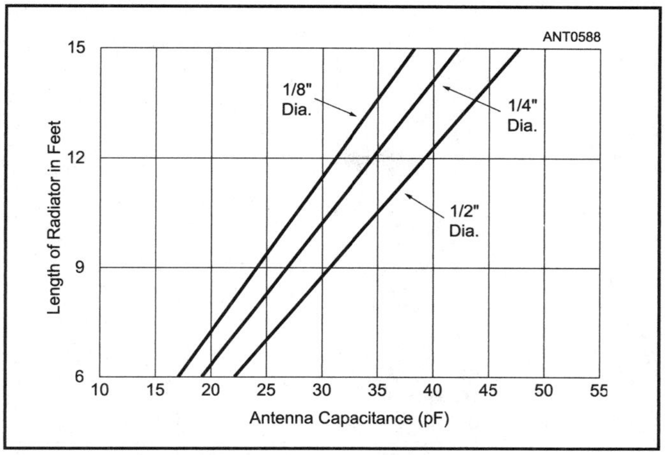

Figure 21.4 — Graph showing the approximate capacitance of short vertical antennas for various diameters and lengths. These values should be approximately halved for a center-loaded antenna.

dissipated in the form of radiation in R_R. Yet it is apparent that little current can be made to flow in the circuit as long as the comparatively high series reactance remains.

Antenna Capacitance

Capacitive reactance can be canceled by connecting an equivalent inductive reactance (coil) in series, as shown in **Figure 21.3**, thus tuning the system to resonance.

The capacitance of a vertical antenna shorter than one-quarter wavelength is given by:

$$C_A = \frac{17\ell}{\left[\left(\ln\frac{24\ell}{D}\right)-1\right]\left[1-\left(\frac{f\ell}{234}\right)^2\right]} \qquad (2)$$

where

C_A = capacitance of antenna in pF
ℓ = antenna height in feet
D = diameter of radiator in inches
f = operating frequency in MHz

Figure 21.4 shows the approximate capacitance of whip antennas of various average diameters and lengths. For 1.8, 4 and 7 MHz, the loading coil inductance required (when the loading coil is at the base) would be approximately the inductance required to resonate in the desired band (with the whip capacitance taken from the graph). For 10 through 21 MHz, this rough calculation will give more than the required inductance, but it will serve as a starting point for the final experimental adjustment that must always be made.

21.1.2 LOADING A SHORT MOBILE ANTENNA

To minimize loading coil loss, the coil should have a high ratio of reactance-to-resistance (that is, a high unloaded Q). A loading coil for use at 4 MHz, wound with small wire on a small-diameter solid form of poor quality and enclosed in a metal protector, may have a Q as low as 50, with a loss resistance of 50 Ω or more. High-Q coils require a large conductor, air-wound construction, large spacing between turns, and the best insulating material available. A diameter not less than half the length of the coil (not always mechanically feasible) and a minimum of metal in the field of the coil are also necessities for optimum efficiency. Such a coil may show a Q of 300 or more at 4 MHz, with a resistance of 12 Ω or less.

The coil could then be placed at the base of the antenna in series with the feed line and the antenna to tune out the unwanted capacitive reactance, as shown in Figure 21.3. Such a method is often referred to as *base-loading*, and many practical mobile antenna systems have been built using this scheme.

Over the years, the question has come up as to whether more efficient designs than simple base loading are possible. While many ideas have been tried with varying degrees of success, only a few have been generally accepted and incorporated into actual antenna systems. These are *center loading*, *continuous loading*, and combinations of the latter with more conventional antennas.

Base Loading and Center Loading

If a whip antenna is short compared to a wavelength and the current is uniform along the length ℓ, the electric field strength E, at a distance d, away from the antenna is approximately:

$$E = \frac{120\,\pi\,I\,\ell}{d\,\lambda} \qquad (3)$$

where

I = the antenna current in amperes
λ = the wavelength in the same units as d and ℓ.

A uniform current flowing along the length of the whip is an idealized situation, however, since the current is greatest at the base of the antenna and goes to a minimum at the top. In practice, the field strength will be less than that given by the above equation, because it is a function of the current distribution on the whip.

The reason that the current is not uniform on a whip antenna can be seen from the circuit approximation shown in **Figure 21.5**. A whip antenna over a ground plane is similar in many respects to a tapered coaxial cable where the center conductor remains the same diameter along its length, but with an increasing diameter outer conductor. The inductance per unit length of such a cable would increase along the line, while the capacitance per unit length would decrease. In Figure 21.5 the antenna is represented by a series of LC circuits in which C1 is greater than C2, which is greater than C3, and so on. L1 is less than L2, which is less than succeeding inductances. The net result is that most of the antenna current returns to ground near the base of the antenna, and very little near the top.

Two things can be done to improve this distribution and

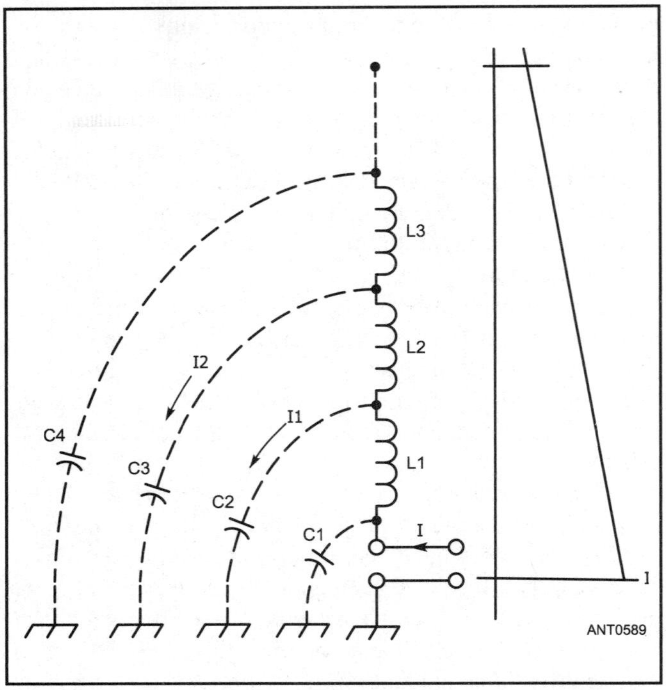

Figure 21.5 — A circuit approximation of a simple whip over a perfectly conducting ground plane. The shunt capacitance per unit length gets smaller as the height increases, and the series inductance per unit length gets larger. Consequently, most of the antenna current returns to the ground plane near the base of the antenna, giving the current distribution shown at the right.

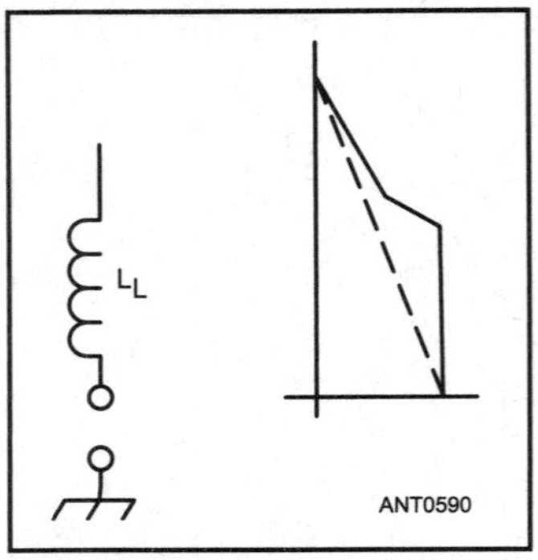

Figure 21.6 — Improved current distribution resulting from center loading.

make the current more uniform in order to increase field strength. One would be to increase the capacitance of the top of the antenna to ground throughthe use of *top loading* or a *capacitance hat*, as discussed in the chapter on **Single Band MF and HF Antennas**. Unfortunately, the wind resistance of the hat makes it somewhat unwieldy for mobile use. The other method is to place the loading coil farther up the whip, as shown in **Figure 21.6**, rather than at the base. If the coil is resonant (or nearly so) at the frequency of operation with the capacitance to ground of the section above the coil, the current distribution is improved as also shown in Figure 21.6. The result with either top loading and center loading is that the radiation resistance is increased, offsetting the effect of losses and making matching easier.

Table 21.1 shows the approximate loading coil inductance for the various amateur bands. Also shown in the table are approximate values of radiation resistance to be expected with an 8-foot whip, and the resistances of loading coils — one group having a Q of 50, the other a Q of 300. A comparison of radiation and coil resistances will show the importance

Table 21.1
Approximate Values for 8-foot Mobile Whip

f(MHz)	*Loading L (μH)*	*R_C(Q50) (Ω)*	*R_C(Q300) (Ω)*	*R_R (Ω)*	*Feed R* (Ω)*	*Matching L (μH)*
Base Loading						
1.8	345	77	13	0.1	23	3
3.8	77	37	6.1	0.35	16	1.2
7.2	20	18	3	1.35	15	0.6
10.1	9.5	12	2	2.8	12	0.4
14.2	4.5	7.7	1.3	5.7	12	0.28
18.1	3.0	5.0	1.0	10.0	14	0.28
21.25	1.25	3.4	0.5	14.8	16	0.28
24.9	0.9	2.6	—	20.0	22	0.25
29.0	—	—	—	—	36	0.23
Center Loading						
1.8	700	158	23	0.2	34	3.7
3.8	150	72	12	0.8	22	1.4
7.2	40	36	6	3.0	19	0.7
10.1	20	22	4.2	5.8	18	0.5
14.2	8.6	15	2.5	11.0	19	0.35
18.1	4.4	9.2	1.5	19.0	22	0.31
21.25	2.5	6.6	1.1	27.0	29	0.29

R_C = loading coil resistance; R_R = radiation resistance.
*Assuming loading coil Q = 300, and including estimated ground-loss resistance.

Table 21.2
Suggested Loading Coil Dimensions

Req'd L (μH)	*Turns*	*Wire Size*	*Dia. (Inches)*	*Length (Inches)*
700	190	22	3	10
345	135	18	3	10
150	100	16	2.5	10
77	75	14	2.5	10
77	29	12	5	4.25
40	28	16	2.5	2
40	34	12	2.5	4.25
20	17	16	2.5	1.25
20	22	12	2.5	2.75
8.6	16	14	2	2
8.6	15	12	2.5	3
4.5	10	14	2	1.25
4.5	12	12	2.5	4
2.5	8	12	2	2
2.5	8	6	2.375	4.5
1.25	6	12	1.75	2
1.25	6	6	2.375	4.5

of reducing the coil resistance to a minimum, especially on the three lower frequency bands. **Table 21.2** shows suggested loading-coil dimensions for the inductance values given in Table 21.1.

21.1.3 RADIATION RESISTANCE OF A SHORT MOBILE ANTENNA

The determination of radiation efficiency requires the knowledge of resistive power losses and radiation losses. Radiation loss — the power radiated by the antenna as electromagnetic energy — is expressed in terms of radiation resistance. Radiation resistance is defined as the resistance that would dissipate the same amount of power as is radiated by the antenna. The variables used in the equations that follow are defined once in the text and are summarized in **Table 21.3**. Radiation resistance of vertical antennas shorter than 45 electrical degrees (⅛ wavelength) is approximately:

$$R_R = h^2/312 \quad (4)$$

where

R_R = radiation resistance in Ω

h = antenna length in electrical degrees.

Antenna height in electrical degrees is expressed by:

$$H = \frac{\ell}{984} \times f(\text{MHz}) \times 360 \quad (5)$$

where

ℓ = antenna length in feet

f (MHz) = operating frequency in MHz.

Table 21.3
Variables used in Eqs 4 through 20

A = area in degree-amperes
a = antenna radius in English or metric units
dB = signal loss in decibels
E = efficiency in percent
f (MHz) = frequency in megahertz
H = height in English or metric units
h = height in electrical degrees
h_1 = height of base section in electrical degrees
h_2 = height of top section in electrical degrees
I = I_{base} = 1 ampere base current
k = 0.0128
k_m = mean characteristic impedance
k_{m1} = mean characteristic impedance of base section
k_{m2} =mean characteristic impedance of top section
L = length or height of the antenna in feet
P_I = power fed to the antenna
P_R = power radiated
Q = coil figure of merit
R_C = coil loss resistance in Ω
R_G = ground loss resistance in Ω
R_R = radiation resistance in Ω
X_L = loading-coil inductive reactance

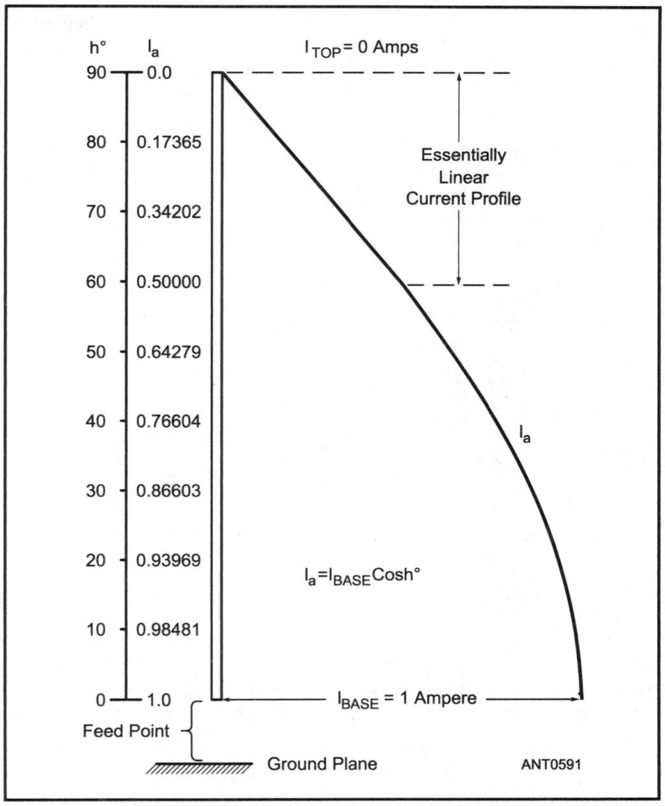

Figure 21.7 — Relative current distribution on a vertical antenna of height h = 90 electrical degrees.

End effect is purposely omitted to ensure that an antenna is electrically long. This is so that resonance at the design frequency can be obtained easily by removing a turn or two from the loading coil.

Eq 4 is valid only for antennas having a sinusoidal current distribution and no reactive loading. However, it can be used as a starting point for deriving an equation that is useful for shortened antennas with other than sinusoidal current distributions.

Refer to **Figure 21.7**. The current distribution on an antenna 90° long electrically (¼ wavelength) varies with the cosine of the length in electrical degrees. The current distribution over the top 30° of the antenna is essentially linear. It is this linearity that allows for derivation of a simpler, more useful equation for radiation resistance.

The radiation resistance of an electrically-short, base-loaded vertical antenna can be conveniently defined in terms of a geometric figure, a triangle, as shown in **Figure 21.8**. The radiation resistance is given by:

$$R_R = KA^2 \quad (6)$$

where

K = a constant (to be derived shortly)

A = area of the triangular current distribution in degree-amperes.

Degree-ampere area is a product of current and electrical

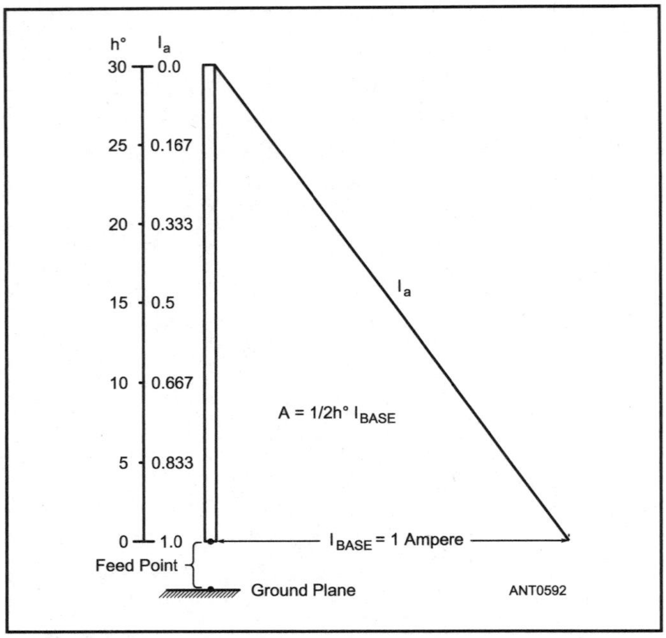

Figure 21.8 — Relative current distribution on a base-loaded vertical antenna of height H = 30 electrical degrees (linearized). The base loading coil is not shown here.

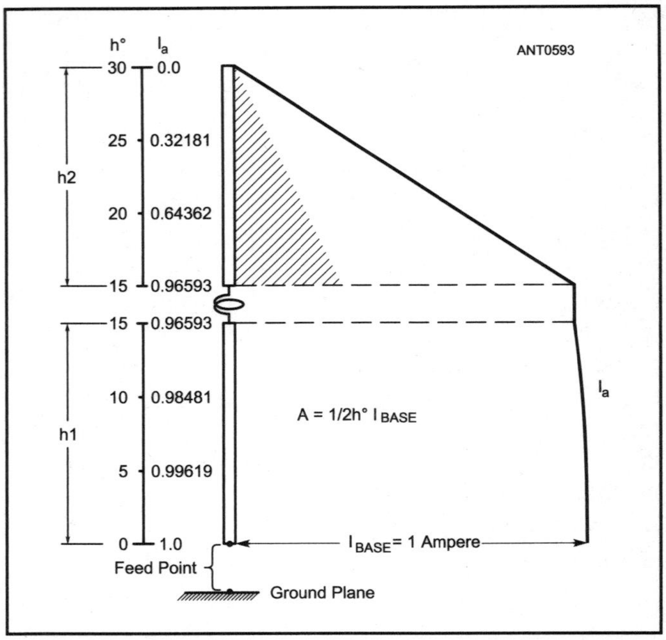

Figure 21.9 — Relative current distribution on a center-loaded antenna with base and top sections each equal to 15 electrical degrees in length. The cross-hatched area shows the current distribution that would exist in the top 15° of a 90°-high vertical fed with 1 ampere at the base.

length, calculated for a triangular current distribution as

$$A = \tfrac{1}{2} h \times I_{BASE} \tag{7}$$

It is referred to as "area" because it is the area between a plot of current and the electrical length axis, as shown in Figures 21.7 and 21.8. More current flowing over a longer electrical distance in degrees results in a higher degree-ampere area and more power being radiated.

By combining Eqs 4 and 6 and solving for K, we get

$$K = \frac{h^2}{312 \times A^2} \tag{8}$$

By substituting the values from Figure 21.8 into Eq 8 we get

$$K = \frac{30^2}{312 \times (0.5 \times 30 \times 1)^2} = 0.0128$$

and by substituting the derived value of K into Eq 6 we get

$$R_R = 0.0128 \times A^2 \tag{9}$$

Eq 9 is useful for determining the radiation resistance of coil-loaded vertical antennas less than 30° in length. The derived constant differs slightly from that presented by Laport (see Bibliography) as he used a different equation for radiation resistance than Eq 4.

21.1.4 OPTIMUM LOADING COIL INDUCTANCE AND PLACEMENT

The optimum location for a loading coil in an antenna can be found experimentally, but it requires many hours of designing and constructing models and making measurements to ensure the validity of the design. A faster and more reliable way of determining optimum coil location is through the use of a personal computer. This approach allows the variation of any single variable, while observing the cumulative effects on the system. When plotted graphically, the data reveals that the placement of the loading coil is critical if maximum radiation efficiency is to be realized. (See the program *MOBILE.EXE*, which may be downloaded from **www.arrl.org/antenna-book-reference**.)

When the loading coil is moved up the antenna (away from the feed point), the current distribution is modified as shown in **Figure 21.9**. The current varies with the cosine of the height in electrical degrees at any point in the base section. Therefore, the current flowing into the bottom of the loading coil is less than the current flowing at the base of the antenna.

But what about the current in the top section of the antenna? Because the loading coil is a lumped constant, disregarding losses and radiation from the coil, it maintains the same current flow throughout. As a result, the current at the top of a high-Q coil is essentially the same as that at the bottom. This is easily verified by measuring RF current immediately above and below the loading coil in a test antenna. Thus, the coil "forces" much more current into the top section than would flow in the equivalent section of an antenna that is a full 90° long. This occurs as a result of the extremely high voltage that appears at the top of the loading coil. This higher current flow results in more radiation than would

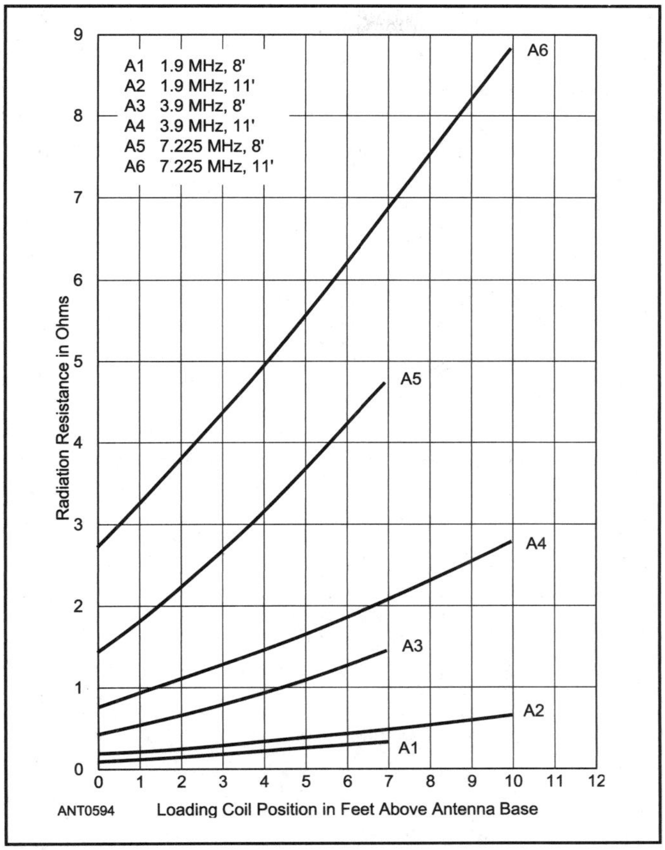

Figure 21.10 — Radiation resistance plotted as a function of loading coil position.

occur from the equivalent section of a quarter-wave antenna. (This is true for conventional coils. However, radiation from long thin coils allows coil current to decrease, as in helically wound antennas.)

The cross-hatched area in Figure 21.9 shows the current that would flow in the equivalent part of a 90° high antenna, and reveals that the degree-ampere area of the whip section of the short antenna is greatly increased as a result of the modified current distribution. The current flow in the top section decreases almost linearly to zero at the top. This can be seen in Figure 21.9.

The degree-ampere area of Figure 21.9 is the sum of the triangular area represented by the current distribution in the top section, and the nearly trapezoidal current distribution in the base section. Radiation from the coil is not included in the degree-ampere area because it is small and difficult to define. Any radiation from the coil can be considered a bonus.

The degree-ampere area is expressed by:

$$A = ½ [h_1(1 + \cos h_1) + h_2 (\cos h_1)] \quad (10)$$

where

h_1 = electrical length in degrees of the base section
h_2 = electrical height in degrees of the top section.

The degree-ampere area (calculated by substituting Eq 10 into Eq 9) can be used to determine radiation resistance when the loading coil is at any position other than the base of the antenna. Radiation resistance has been calculated with these equations and plotted against loading coil position at three different frequencies for 8- and 11-foot antennas in **Figure 21.10**. Eight feet is a typical length for commercial antennas, and 11-foot antennas are about the maximum practical length that can be installed on a vehicle.

In Figure 21.10 the curves reveal that the radiation resistance increases almost linearly as the loading coil is moved up the antenna. They also show that the radiation resistance rises rapidly as the frequency is increased. If the analysis were stopped at this point, one might conclude that the loading coil should be placed at the top of the antenna. This is not so, and the reason will become apparent shortly.

Required Loading Coil Inductance

Calculation of the loading coil inductance needed to resonate a short antenna can be done easily and accurately by using the antenna transmission-line analog described by Boyer in *Ham Radio*. For a base-loaded antenna as in Figure 21.8, the loading coil reactance required to resonate the antenna is given by

$$X_L = -j\, K_m \cot h \quad (11)$$

where

X_L = inductive reactance required
K_m = mean characteristic impedance (defined in Eq 12).

The $-j$ term indicates that the antenna presents capacitive reactance at the feed point. A loading coil must cancel this reactance.

The mean characteristic impedance of an antenna is expressed by

$$K_m = 60 [(\ln (2H/a) - 1] \quad (12)$$

where

H = physical antenna height (excluding the length of the loading coil)
a = radius of the antenna in the same units as H.

From Eq 12 you can see that decreasing the height-to-diameter ratio of an antenna by increasing the radius results in a decrease in K_m. With reference to Eq 11, a decrease in K_m decreases the inductive reactance required to resonate an antenna. As will be shown later, this will increase radiation efficiency. In mobile applications, we quickly run into wind-loading problems if we attempt to use an antenna that is physically large in diameter.

If the loading coil is moved away from the base of the antenna, the antenna is divided into a base and top section, as depicted in Figure 21.9. The loading coil reactance required to resonate the antenna when the coil is away from the base is given by

$$X_L = j\, K_{m2} (\cot h_2) - j\, K_{m1} (\tan h_1) \quad (13)$$

In mobile-antenna design and construction, the top section is usually a whip with a much smaller diameter than the base section. Because of this, it is necessary to compute separate values of K_m for the top and base sections. K_{m1} and K_{m2} are the mean characteristic impedances of the base and top sections, respectively.

Loading coil reactance curves for the 3.8-MHz antennas of Figure 21.10 have been calculated and plotted in **Figure 21.11**. These curves show the influence of the loading coil position on the reactance required for resonance. The curves in Figure 21.11 show that the required reactance decreases with longer antennas. The curves also reveal that the required loading coil reactance grows at an increasingly rapid rate after the coil passes the center of the antenna. Because the highest possible loading coil Q is needed, and because optimum Q is attained when the loading coil diameter is twice the loading coil length, the coil would grow very quickly to an impractical size above the center of the antenna. It is for this reason that the highest loading coil position is limited to one foot from the top of the antenna in all computations.

Loading Coil Resistance

Loading coil resistance constitutes one of the losses consuming power that could otherwise be radiated by the antenna. Heat loss in the loading coil is not of any benefit, so it should be minimized by using the highest possible loading coil Q. Loading coil loss resistance is a function of the coil Q and is given by

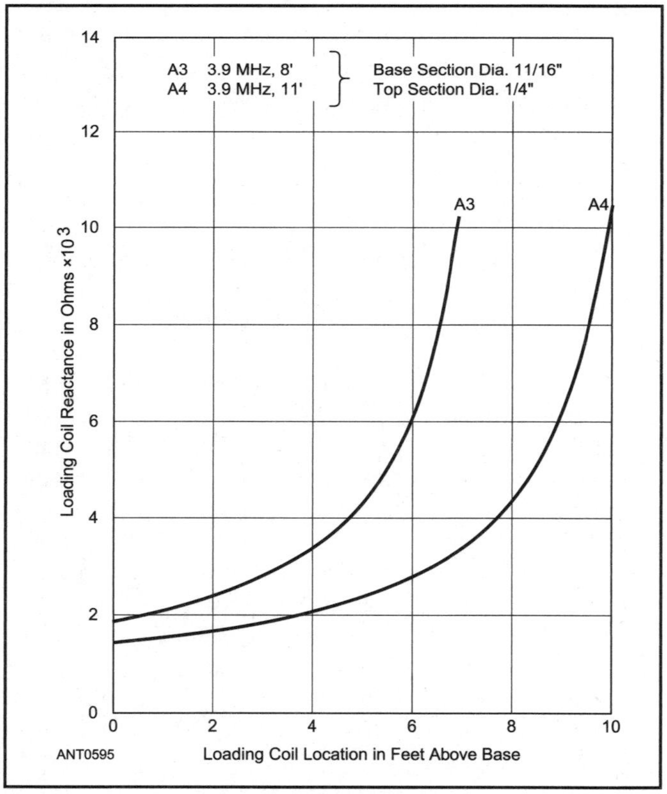

Figure 21.11 — Loading coil reactance required for resonance, plotted as a function of coil height above the antenna base. The resonant frequency is 3.9 MHz.

$$R_C = \frac{X_L}{Q} \qquad (14)$$

where

R_C = loading coil loss resistance in Ω
X_L = loading coil reactance
Q = coil figure of merit

Inspection of Eq 14 reveals that, for a given value of inductive reactance, loss resistance will be lower for higher Q coils. Measurements made with a Q meter show that typical, commercially manufactured coil stock produces a Q between 150 and 160 at 3.8 MHz.

Higher Q values can be obtained by using larger diameter coils having a diameter-to-length ratio of two, by using larger diameter wire, by using more spacing between turns, and by using low-loss polystyrene supporting and enclosure materials. In theory, loading coil turns should not be shorted for tuning purposes because shorted turns somewhat degrade Q. Pruning to resonance should be done by removing turns from the coil.

In fairness, it should be pointed out that many practical mobile antennas use large-diameter loading coils with shorted turns to achieve resonance. The popular "Texas Bug Catcher" coils come to mind here. (See the section "HF Mobile Antenna Types.") Despite general proscriptions against shorting turns, these systems are often more efficient than antennas with small, relatively low-Q, fixed loading coils.

21.1.5 RADIATION EFFICIENCY

The ratio of power radiated to power fed to an antenna determines the radiation efficiency. It is given by:

$$E = \frac{P_R}{P_I} \times 100\% \qquad (15)$$

where

E = radiation efficiency in percent
P_R = power radiated
P_I = power fed to the antenna at the feed point.

In a short, coil-loaded mobile antenna, a large portion of the power fed to the antenna is dissipated in ground and coil resistances. A relatively insignificant amount of power is also dissipated in the antenna conductor resistance and in the leakage resistance of the base insulator. Because these last two losses are both very small and difficult to estimate, they are here neglected in calculating radiation efficiency.

Another loss worth noting is matching network loss. Because we are concerned only with power fed to the antenna in the determination of radiation efficiency, matching network loss is not considered in any of the equations. Suffice it to say that matching networks should be designed for minimum loss in order to maximize the transmitter power available at the antenna.

The radiation efficiency equation may be rewritten and expanded as follows:

$$E = \frac{I^2 R_R \times 100}{I^2 R_R + I^2 R_G + (I \cos h_1)^2 R_C} \quad (16)$$

where

I = antenna base current in amperes

R_G = ground loss resistance in Ω

R_C = coil loss resistance in Ω

R_R = radiation resistance in Ω

Each term of Eq 16 represents the power dissipated in its associated resistance. All the current terms cancel, simplifying this equation to

$$E = \frac{R_R \times 100}{R_R + R_G + R_C \cos^2 h_1} \quad (17)$$

For base-loaded antennas the term $\cos^2$ drops to unity and may be omitted.

Ground Loss

Eq 14 shows that the total resistive losses in the antenna system are:

$$R_T = R_R + R_G + R_C (\cos^2 h_1) \quad (18)$$

where R_T is the total resistive loss. Ground loss resistance can be determined by rearranging Eq 18 as follows:

$$R_G = R_T - R_R - R_C \cos^2 h_1 \quad (19)$$

R_T may be measured in a test antenna installation on a vehicle using an R-X noise bridge or an SWR analyzer. You can then calculate R_R and R_C.

Ground loss is a function of vehicle size, placement of the antenna on the vehicle, and conductivity of the ground over which the vehicle is traveling. It is only feasible to control the first two variables. Larger vehicles provide better ground planes than smaller ones. The vehicle ground plane is only partial, so the result is considerable RF current flow (and ground loss) in the ground around and under the vehicle.

By raising the antenna base as high as possible on the vehicle, ground losses are decreased. This results from a decrease in antenna capacitance to ground that also increases the capacitive reactance to ground. This, in turn, reduces ground currents and ground losses.

This effect has been verified by installing the same antenna at three different locations on two different vehicles, and by determining the ground loss from Eq 19. In the first test, the antenna was mounted 6 inches below the top of a large station wagon, just behind the left rear window. This placed the antenna base 4 feet 2 inches above the ground, and resulted in a measured ground loss resistance of 2.5 Ω. The second test used the same antenna mounted on the left rear fender of a mid-sized sedan, just to the left of the trunk lid. In this test, the measured ground loss resistance was 4 Ω. The third test used the same mid-sized car, but the antenna was mounted on the rear bumper. In this last test, the measured ground loss resistance was 6 Ω.

The same antenna therefore sees three different ground

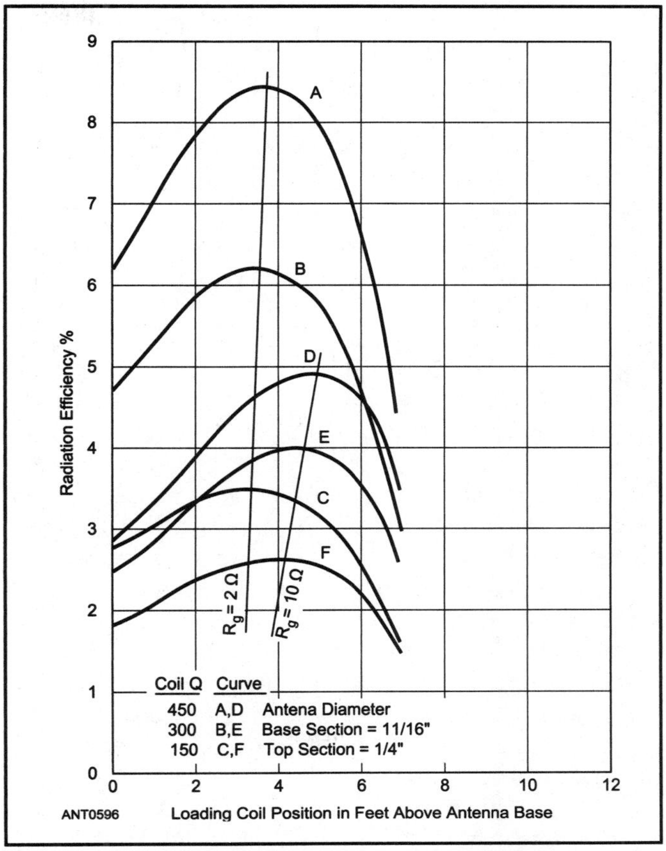

Figure 21.12 — Radiation efficiency of 8-foot antennas at 3.9 MHz.

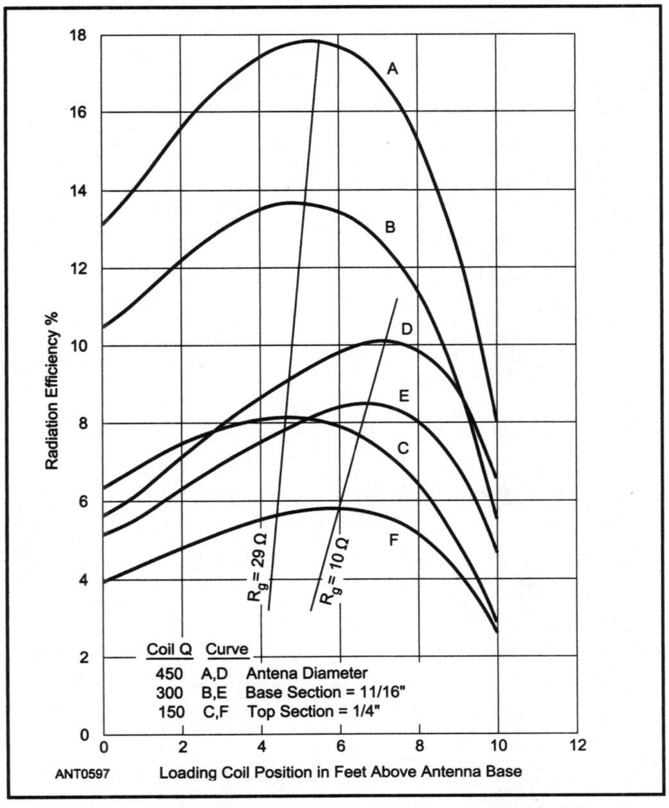

Figure 21.13 — Radiation efficiency of 11-foot antennas at 3.9 MHz.

loss resistances as a direct result of the antenna mounting location and size of the vehicle. It is important to note that the measured ground loss increases as the antenna base nears the ground. The importance of minimizing ground losses in mobile antenna installations cannot be overemphasized.

Efficiency Curves

With the equations defined previously, a computer was used to calculate the radiation efficiency curves depicted in **Figures 21.12** through **21.15**. These curves were calculated for 80 and 40 meter antennas of 8- and 11-foot lengths. Several values of loading coil Q were used, for both 2 and 10 Ω of ground loss resistance. For the calculations, the base section is ½-inch diameter electrical EMT which has an outside diameter of 11⁄16 inch. The top section is fiberglass bicycle-whip material covered with Belden braid. These are readily available materials, which can be used by the average amateur to construct an inexpensive but rugged antenna.

Upon inspection, these radiation-efficiency curves reveal some significant information:

1) higher coil Q produces higher radiation efficiencies,

2) longer antennas produce higher radiation efficiencies,

3) radiation efficiency increases at high frequencies,

4) lower ground loss resistances produce higher radiation efficiencies,

5) higher ground loss resistances force the loading coil above the antenna center to reach a peak in the radiation-efficiency curve, and

6) higher coil Q sharpens the radiation-efficiency curves, resulting in the coil position being more critical for optimum radiation efficiency.

Note that the radiation efficiency curves reach a peak and then begin to decline as the loading coil is raised farther up the antenna. This is because of the rapid increase in loading coil reactance required above the antenna center. Refer to Figure 21.11. The rapid increase in coil size required for resonance results in the coil loss resistance increasing much more rapidly than the radiation resistance. This results in decreased radiation efficiency, as shown in Figure 21.10.

A slight reverse curvature exists in the curves between the base-loaded position and the one-foot coil-height position. This is caused by a shift in the curve that resulted from insertion of a base section of larger diameter than the whip when the coil is above the base.

The curves in Figures 21.12 through 21.15 were calculated with constant (but not equal) diameter base and whip sections. Because of wind loading, it is not desirable to increase the diameter of the whip section. However, the base-section diameter can be increased within reason to further improve radiation efficiency. **Figure 21.16** was calculated for base-section diameters ranging from 11⁄16 inch to 3 inches. The curves reveal that a small increase in radiation efficiency results from larger diameter base sections.

The curves in Figures 21.12 through 21.15 show that radiation efficiencies can be quite low at 3.9 MHz compared to 7 MHz. They are lower yet at 1.8 MHz. To gain some perspective on what these low efficiencies mean in terms of

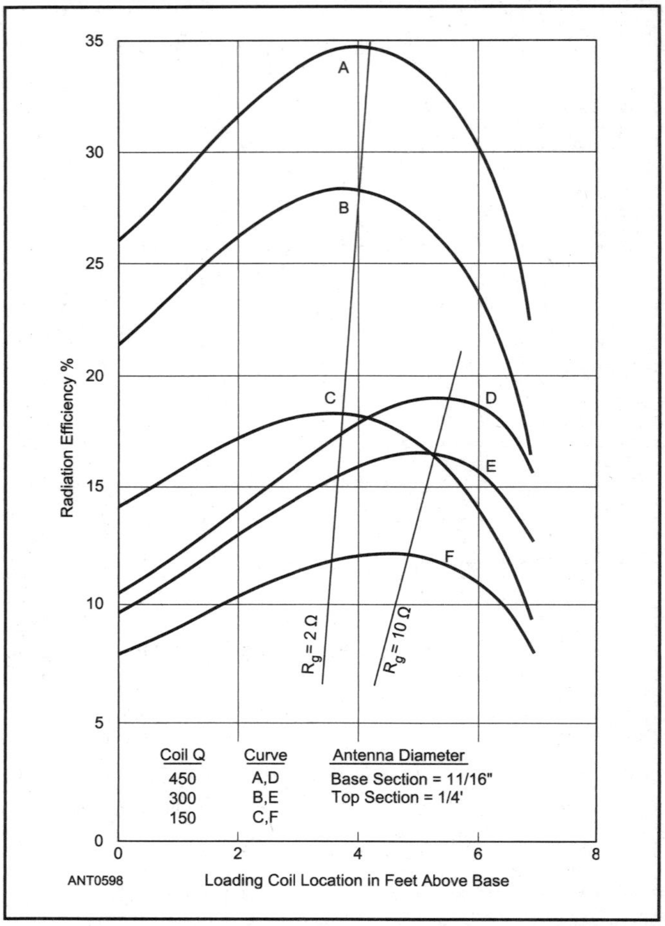

Figure 21.14 — Radiation efficiency of 8-foot antennas at 7.225 MHz.

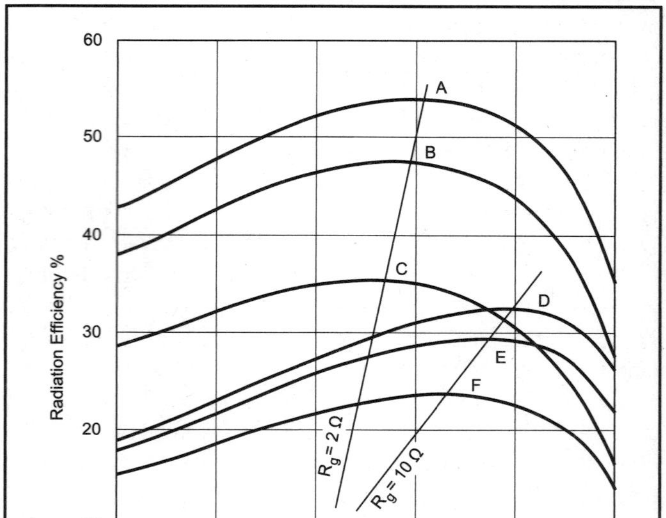

Figure 21.15 — Radiation efficiency of 11-foot antennas at 7.225 MHz.

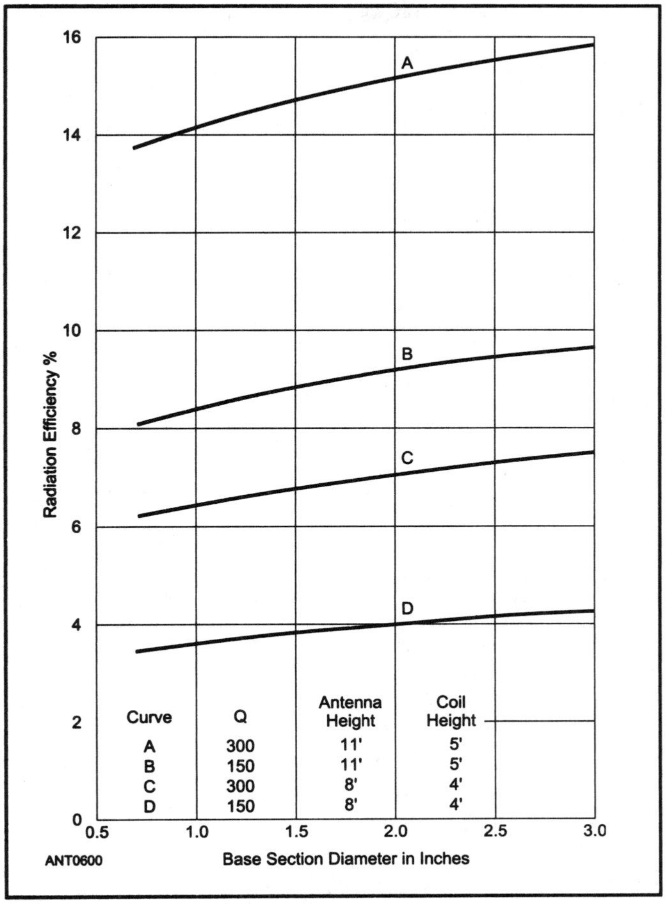

Figure 21.16 — Radiation efficiency plotted as a function of base section diameter. Frequency = 3.9 MHz, ground loss resistance = 2 Ω, and whip section = 1/4-inch diameter.

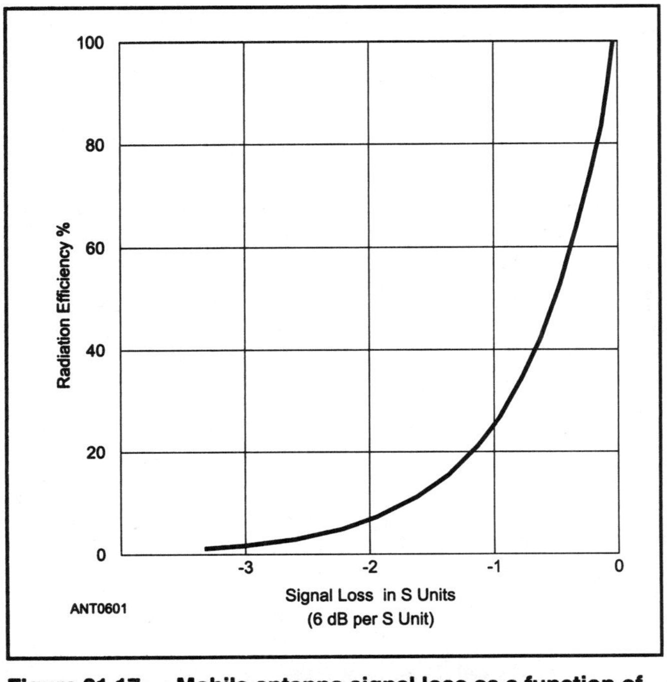

Figure 21.17 — Mobile antenna signal loss as a function of radiation efficiency, compared to a quarter-wave vertical antenna over perfect ground.

signal strength, **Figure 21.17** was calculated using the following equation:

$$dB = \log\frac{100}{E} \qquad (20)$$

where

dB = signal loss in decibels

E = efficiency in percent.

The curve in Figure 21.17 reveals that an antenna having 25% efficiency has a signal loss of 6 dB (approximately one S unit) below a quarter-wave vertical antenna over perfect ground. An antenna efficiency in the neighborhood of 6% will produce a signal strength on the order of two S units or about 12 dB below the same quarter-wave reference vertical. By careful optimization of mobile-antenna design, signal strengths from mobiles can be made fairly competitive with those from fixed stations using comparable power. Additional improvement can be obtained by operating in an open area and over or near good ground, such as wetlands and fresh or saltwater.

21.1.6 IMPEDANCE MATCHING

The input impedance of short, high-Q coil-loaded antennas is quite low. For example, an 8-foot antenna optimized for 3.9 MHz with an unloaded coil Q of 300 and a ground-loss resistance of 2 Ω has a base input impedance of about 13 Ω. This low impedance value causes a standing wave ratio of 4:1 in 50-Ω coax at resonance. This high SWR is not compatible with the requirements of solid-state transmitters. Also, the bandwidth of shortened vertical antennas is very narrow. This severely limits the capability to maintain transmitter loading over even a small frequency range.

Impedance matching can be accomplished by means of L networks or impedance-matching transformers, but the narrow bandwidth limitation remains. A more elegant solution to the impedance matching and narrow band- width problem is to install an automatic tuner at the antenna base. Such a device matches the antenna and feed line automatically, and permits operation over a wide frequency range.

The tools are now available to tailor a mobile antenna design to produce maximum radiation efficiency. Mathematical modeling with a personal computer reveals that loading coil Q factor and ground loss resistance greatly influence the optimum loading coil position in a short vertical antenna. It also shows that longer antennas, higher coil Q, and higher operating frequencies produce higher radiation efficiencies.

End effect has not been included in any of the equations to assure that the loading coil will be slightly larger than necessary. Pruning the antenna to resonance should be done by removing coil turns, rather than by shorting turns or shortening the whip section excessively. Shortening the whip reduces radiation efficiency, by both shortening the antenna and moving the optimum coil position. Shorting turns in the loading coil degrades the Q of the coil.

Matching to the Transmitter

Most modern transmitters require a 50-Ω load and because the feed point impedance of a mobile whip is quite low, a matching network is usually necessary. Although calculations are helpful in the initial design, considerable experimenting is often necessary in final tune-up. This is particularly true for the lower bands, where the antenna is electrically short compared with a quarter-wave whip. The reason is that the loading coil is required to tune out a very large capacitive reactance, and even small changes in component values result in large reactance variations. Since the feed point resistance is low to begin with, the problem is even more aggravated.

You can transform the low resistance of the whip to a value suitable for a 50-Ω system with an RF transformer or with a shunt-feed arrangement, such as an L network. The latter may only require a shunt coil or shunt capacitor at the base of the whip since the net series capacitive or inductive reactance of the antenna and its loading coil may be used as part of the network. The following example illustrates the calculations involved.

Assume that a center-loaded whip antenna, 8.5 feet in overall length, is to be used on 7.2 MHz. From Table 21.1 earlier in this chapter we see that the feed point resistance of the antenna will be approximately 19 Ω and from Figure 21.4 that the capacitance of the whip, as seen at its base, is approximately 24 pF. Since the antenna is to be center loaded, the capacitance value of the section above the coil will be cut approximately in half, to 12 pF. From this, it may be calculated that a center-loading inductor of 40.7 μH is required to resonate the antenna by canceling out the capacitive reactance. (This figure agrees with the approximate value of 40 μH shown in Table 21.1. The resulting feed point impedance would then be $19 + j\,0$ Ω.)

Solution: The antenna can be matched to a 52-Ω line such as RG-8 by tuning it either above or below resonance and then canceling out the undesired component with an appropriate shunt element, capacitive or inductive. The way in which the impedance is transformed up can be seen by plotting the admittance of the series RLC circuit made up of the loading coil, antenna capacitance, and feed point resistance. Such a plot is shown in **Figure 21.18** for a constant feed point resistance of 19 Ω. There are two points of interest, P1 and P2, where the input conductance is 19.2 millisiemens, corresponding to 52 Ω. The undesired susceptance is shown as $1/X_P$ and $-1/X_P$, which must be canceled with a shunt element of the opposite sign but with the same magnitude. The value of the canceling shunt reactance, X_P, may be found from the formula:

$$X_P = \frac{R_f Z_0}{\sqrt{R_f (Z_0 - R_f)}} \tag{21}$$

where X_P is the reactance in Ω, R_f is the feed point resistance, and Z_0 is the feed line impedance. For Z_0 = 52 Ω and R_f = 19 Ω, X_P = ±39.5 Ω. A coil or good quality mica capacitor may be used as the shunt element. With the tune-up procedure described later, the value is not critical and a fixed-value component may be used.

To arrive at point P1, the value of the center loading-coil inductance would be less than that required for resonance. The feed point impedance would then appear capacitive, and

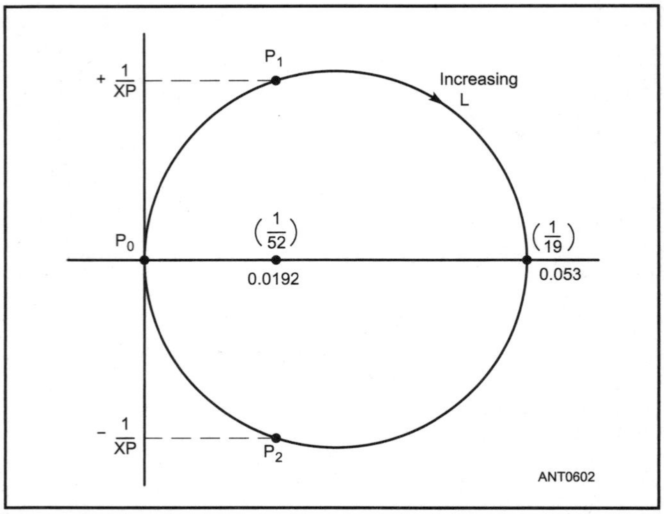

Figure 21.18 — Admittance diagram of the RLC circuit consisting of the whip capacitance, radiation resistance and loading coil discussed in text. The horizontal axis represents conductance, and the vertical axis susceptance. The point P_0 is the input admittance with no whip loading inductance. Points P_1 and P_2 are described in the text. The conductance equals the reciprocal of the resistance, if no reactive components are present. For a series RX circuit, the conductance is given by

$$G = \frac{R}{R^2 + X^2}$$

and the susceptance is given by

$$B = \frac{-X}{R^2 + X^2}$$

Consequently, a parallel equivalent G-B circuit to the series RX circuit can be found that makes computations easier. This is because conductances and susceptances add in parallel the same way resistances and reactances add in series.

an inductive shunt matching element would then be required. To arrive at point P2, the center loading coil should be more inductive than required for resonance, and the shunt element would need to be capacitive. The value of the center loading coil required for the shunt-matched and resonated condition may be determined from the equation:

$$L = \frac{10^6}{4\pi^2 f^2 C} \pm \frac{X_S}{2\pi f} \tag{22}$$

where addition is performed if a capacitive shunt is to be used and subtraction performed if the shunt is inductive, and where L is in μH, f is the frequency in MHz, C is the capacitance of the antenna section being matched in pF, and

$$X_S = \sqrt{R_f (Z_0 - R_f)} \tag{23}$$

For the example given, where Z_0 = 52 Ω, R_f = 19 Ω, f = 7.2 MHz, and C = 12 pF, X_S is found to be 25.0 Ω. The required antenna loading inductance is either 40.2 μH or

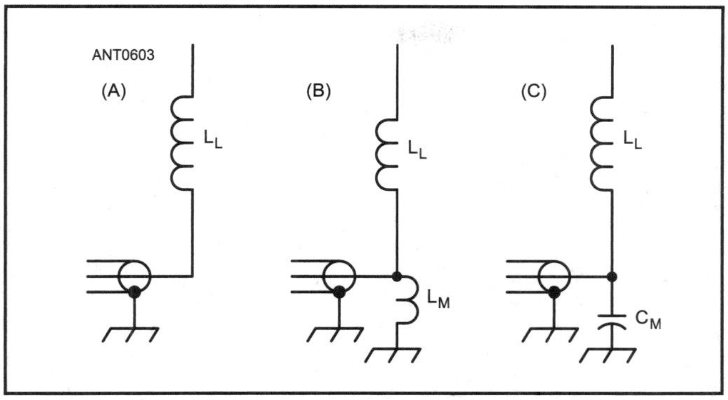

Figure 21.19 — At A, a whip antenna that is resonated with a center loading coil. At B and C, the value of the loading coil has been altered slightly to make the feed point impedance appear reactive, and a matching component is added in shunt to cancel the reactance. This provides an impedance transformation to match the Z_0 of the feed line. An equally acceptable procedure, rather than altering the loading coil inductance, is to adjust the length of the top section above the loading coil for the best match, as described in the tune-up section of the text.

Shunt Coil Matching

The use of a shunt coil is the preferred matching methodology for two reasons. First, it provides a dc ground for the antenna which helps control static buildup. Second, once adjusted, no further adjustment is needed to cover all of the HF bands between 80 and 10 meters. Thus it is an ideal matching scenario for remotely-controlled (tuned) antennas. Capacitive matching, on the other hand, requires changing capacitance for every band, and sometimes within a band. It should be noted that any HF mobile antenna for bands at frequencies below 20 MHz that do not require matching to obtain a low SWR are less than optimal performers.

41.3 µH, depending on the type of shunt. Various matching possibilities for this example are shown in **Figure 21.19**. At A, the antenna is shown as tuned to resonance with L_L, a 40.7 µH coil, but with no provisions included for matching the resulting 19-Ω impedance to the 52-Ω line. At B, L_L has been reduced to 40.2 µH to make the antenna appear net capacitive, and L_M, having a reactance of 39.5 Ω, is added in shunt to cancel the capacitive reactance and transform the feed point impedance to 50 Ω. The arrangement at C is similar to that at B except that L_L has been increased to 41.3 µH, and C_M (a shunt capacitor having a negative reactance of 39.5 Ω) is added, which also results in a 52-Ω nonreactive termination for the feed line.

The values determined for the loading coil in the above example point out an important consideration concerning the matching of short antennas — relatively small changes in values of the loading components will have a greatly magnified effect on the matching requirements. A change of less than 3% in the loading coil inductance value necessitates a completely different matching network! Likewise, calculations show that a 3% change in antenna capacitance will give similar results, and the value of the precautions mentioned earlier becomes clear. The sensitivity of the circuit with regard to frequency variations is also quite critical, and an excursion around practically the entire circle in Figure 21.18 may represent only 600 kHz, centered around 7.2 MHz, for the above example. This is why tuning up a mobile antenna can be very frustrating unless a systematic procedure is followed.

Tune-Up

Assume that inductive shunt matching is to be used with the antenna in the previous example, Figure 21.19B, where 39.5 Ω is needed for L_M. This means that at 7.2 MHz, a coil of 0.87 µH will be needed across the whip feed point terminal to ground. With a 40-µH loading coil in place, the adjustable whip section above the loading coil should be set for minimum height. Signals in the receiver will sound weak and the whip should be lengthened a bit at a time until signals start to peak. Turn the transmitter on and check the SWR at a few frequencies to find where a minimum occurs. If it is below the desired frequency, shorten the whip slightly and check again. It should be moved approximately ¼ inch at a time until the SWR reaches a minimum at the center of the desired range. If the frequency where the minimum SWR occurs is above the desired frequency, repeat the procedure above, but lengthen the whip only slightly.

If a shunt capacitance is to be used, as in Figure 21.19C, a value of 560 pF would correspond to the required –39.5 Ω of reactance at 7.2 MHz. With a capacitive shunt, start with the whip in its longest position and shorten it until signals peak up.

21.2 HF MOBILE ANTENNA TYPES

21.2.1 THE SCREWDRIVER ANTENNA

No doubt the biggest change in HF mobile operation has been brought about by the screwdriver antenna. Originally conceived by Don Johnson, W6AAQ, the basic design has become ubiquitous, available from many different manufacturers. They consist of a large, hollow lower mast, an extendable coil assembly, and a whip, typically 60 to 96 inches long.

The unused portion of the coil is stored in the mast of the antenna. Finger stock at the top of the mast makes contact with the coil. A dc motor, controlled remotely, drives a screw arrangement that extends or retracts the coil to tune lower or higher in frequency, respectively. That tuning can be done while in motion is an attractive feature, hence their popularity.

A decent quality, high-Q, screwdriver antenna is not inexpensive and can cost upward of $1000, although most are about half this amount. They're relatively heavy and require both a feed line (coax), and a motor control lead. Some varieties also use a reed switch to count the turns of the screw (see the "Mobile Antenna Controllers and Tuners" section).

Shortened versions of the screwdriver are available from several manufacturers and have become very popular. Their light weight, short length, and ease of mounting, account for their popularity. However, because of their short overall length and low-Q coils, they take a big hit in performance over their full-sized cousins, especially when mounted on lip mounts. They also require some special considerations when coupled to automatic antenna controllers, as covered later.

It should be noted that not all models use the same mounting scheme. Some use standard ⅜-24 bolts, and at least one uses a ¾-inch bolt. Some form of base insulator is also required in most cases.

If you wish to build your own screwdriver antenna, plans for doing so are included with this book's downloadable supplemental information.

21.2.2 MONOBAND ANTENNAS

There are several types of monoband antennas, including the "bug catcher", linear-loaded varieties, and the ever-popular Hustler series.

The bug catcher shown in **Figure 21.20** can be the most efficient of all of the mobile antenna types, if mounted correctly. (The name derives from the tendency of the coil to "catch bugs" while driving.) However, it has several drawbacks, not the least of which is wind-loading, especially when equipped with a capacitive top-hat, which is discussed later.

Bug catcher antennas, in which a large air-wound loading coil is used for center loading, are monoband by nature but can be made multiband. The usual practice is to make the coil large enough in reactance to resonant the antenna on 80 meters. Then a jumper wire is used to short coil turns to resonate the antenna on the higher bands. However, shorting turns reduces coil Q and lowers efficiency.

They tend to be heavier than other monoband antennas, requiring heavy-duty mounting and base springs — even guys to keep them stable at highway speeds.

Figure 21.20 — A "bug catcher" style antenna showing the large, air-wound center-loading coil in the center of the antenna with a capacitance-hat at the top. This antenna was designed and constructed by VE6AB.

Helical-Wound Antennas

These lightweight antennas are quite popular due to their low cost and reasonable performance. They look similar to the continuously loaded antennas covered below except they use a single, fixed-value loading coil.

The antenna itself is basically a fiberglass tube or rod with a small-gauge wire wound around it. Toward the top of the tube, the wire is close-wound in a loading coil and the antenna is topped off with a short, adjustable-length whip, commonly referred to as a *stinger*.

Due to their light weight, a mag-mount, angle, or trunk lip mount may be used with surprisingly good results considering their low Q, and relatively short length (≈7 feet). Changing bands requires changing the complete antenna, but most models have quick disconnects available making the task quicker and easier. As a general rule, they don't require impedance matching, as their overall losses bring the input impedance very close to 50 Ω.

Continuously-Loaded Antennas

There are several manufacturers of both monoband and multiband antennas that could be described as continuously-loaded. (Sometimes referred to as "linear-loaded," this is not the linear-loading technique used to shorten dipoles and beam antennas.) For these antennas, loading is done using multiple fixed-value inductors spaced over the length of the

Extending Bandwidth

Monoband antennas have a finite bandwidth. Depending on the band and installation parameters, the 2:1 bandwidth may be as little as 12 kHz on 80 meters to as much as 1 MHz or more on 10 meters. Since modern solid state transceivers start to reduce on their output at SWR above 2:1, it would be convenient to extend the bandwidth.

One way to do this is to use an internal (or external) auto-coupler (antenna tuner or ATU for short). The technique works well, as long as we don't try to match an antenna on a band it is not resonant on as this greatly increases the overall losses. However, few if any made-for-mobile transceivers have built in ATUs. Using an external unit will certainly suffice if you're willing to put up with the added complexity.

As we learned in the "HF Mobile Antenna Fundamentals" section, we can use a shunt element to match the antenna's input impedance to 50-Ω feed line. If we substitute a ¼-wave shorted coaxial stub for the fixed-value shunt element, we can effectively increase the bandwidth in the process. This is possible because the shorted stub's reactance swing is opposite that of the antenna's as we change frequencies — the ¼-wave stub's reactance will become more capacitive above resonance as the antenna's feed point reactance becomes more inductive.

Typically, the useable SWR bandwidth will increase from 30% to as much as 50%, again based on the frequency and installation parameters. The drawback is that we have to use a different stub for each band of operation.

antenna or winding a continuous coil with a large pitch (ratio of turn length to turn diameter) along the antenna.

The multiband versions use what is commonly called a "flying lead" connected at the base, which in turn connects to taps along the coil making up the body of the antenna to select the band.

Proponents incorrectly argue that the large length-to-diameter, up to 25 to 1, allows the coil to radiate, thus increasing efficiency. However, what little advantage this form of loading has, it is more than offset by the low coil Q, and short overall length (4 to 7 feet).

These antennas typically do not require matching but a few models exhibit input impedances of greater than 100 Ω and thus need to be matched.

Shortened Dipoles

A few amateurs opt to purchase two identical mobile antennas, and mount them in a V configuration. Knowing that ground loss is the dominate factor in determining antenna efficiency, they reason that replacing the ground loss with a second antenna is a viable solution. While they're correct that it increases radiation resistance as well as the feed point input impedance, efficiency remains largely the same because ground loss has been replaced with the second antenna's loss of about the same magnitude. Gain claims are often exaggerated, as well. A full-size, lossless dipole in free space has a maximum theoretical gain of 2.15 dBi — higher values assume the presence of ground reflections and antenna heights of ½ wavelength or more which are impractical at best for a mobile station.

Stainless Steel Whips

Almost without exception, most whips referred to as "CB whips" are made from 17-7 stainless steel wire. Their overall length is 102 inches but at one time 108- and 120-inch versions were available. They are made from wire about 0.220 to 0.250 inch in diameter that is straightened and ground down to an OD of 0.200 inch. Beginning at about 60 inches above the base, they're tapered down to 0.100 inch OD at the tip. The whip is finished off with a swaged-on ⅜-24 threaded brass base fitting and a small corona ball added at the tip.

Stainless steel isn't the best of RF conductors, especially on the lower HF bands. When compared to an aluminum conductor of the same size, the additional resistive losses may reduce the ERP (effective radiated power) by ≈3 dB on 160 meters, depending on the overall length of the whip in use.

The unfortunate truth is, there is no viable alternative with the strength and flexibility of 17-7 stainless steel! Whips can be copper plated (a costly step) but the improvement is minimal. Covering the whip with silver-plated copper braid is easy to do, but again, the ERP improvement versus the additional wind loading might not be worth the effort.

Corona Balls

The small corona balls supplied atop standard CB whips provide a slight amount of eye protection but their effect on reducing corona is questionable. What is corona and how does a corona ball prevent it?

As we learned in the **HF Mobile Antenna Fundamentals** section, the highest RF voltage occurs at the very top of the whip. Under the right weather conditions, it is possible to see the corona discharge from the end of a pointed whip even when running modest power levels. *Corona discharge* is caused by the small radius of the whip's tip creating large differences in voltage that exceed the breakdown voltage of air across small distances. This causes the air to ionize and conduct. The discharge then extends away from the antenna as "streamers" until voltage is reduced below the level of ionization. Static discharges from the pointed tip can also become a problem on receive.

The solution is to replace the pointed end with a smoother, larger surface. The corona ball's smooth, round surface creates reduces voltage changes with distance that cause corona discharge. The corona ball must be large enough to be effective — at least 0.5 inch in diameter and preferably 1 inch — and are available from several *QST* advertisers. Above 1 inch, wind loading becomes a problem.

Capacitance hats, or cap-hats or top-hats for short, are a method of increasing the efficiency of HF mobile antennas at the expense of complexity and higher wind loading. They increase efficiency by adding capacitance to that portion of the antenna above the loading coil, effectively increasing the overall electrical length.

They may consist of a single stiff wire, two or more wires, a disc made up of several more wires like the spokes of a wheel, a set of loops, or wire arranged as the spokes of a wheel as shown in **Figure 21.21**. The larger the hat (physically), the greater the capacitance and the greater the effective increase in electrical length. Since less inductance is then required to resonate the electrically longer antenna, coil Q losses will also decrease.

No matter where the hat is located, the added capacitance will be the same. However, if placed too close to the coil, the added capacitance will decrease efficiency rather than improve it. The most effective position is at the very top of the antenna. At a minimum, hats should be placed at least half their diameter above the coil (Figure 21.21 shows the hat in the center of the whip) and as far away from vehicle sheet metal as possible. These facts require robust antenna construction and mounting techniques but the increase in performance is worth the effort.

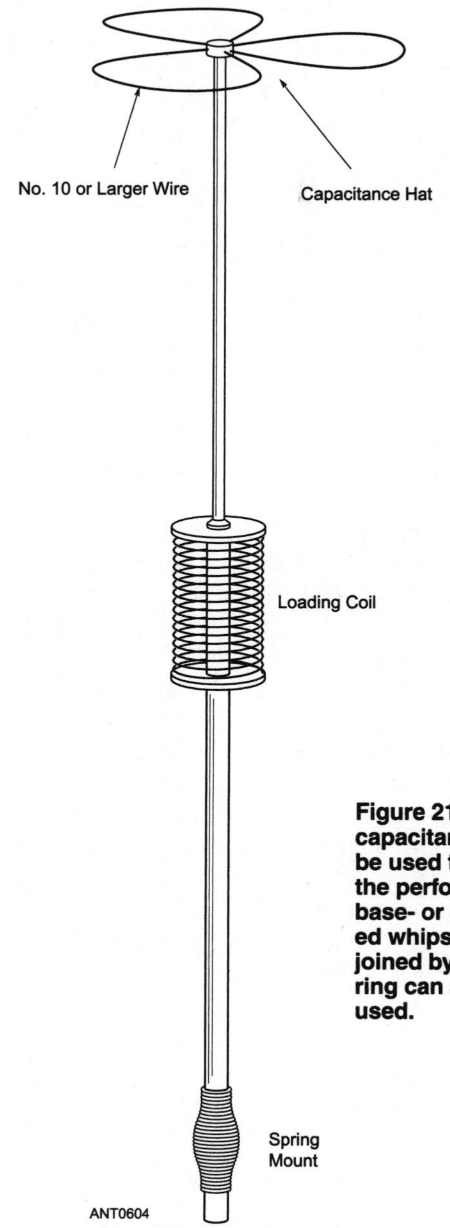

Figure 21.21 — A capacitance hat can be used to improve the performance of base- or center-loaded whips. Spokes joined by an outer ring can also be used.

Plans for a capacitive hat hub designed and made by Ken Muggli, KØHL are provided with this book's downloadable supplemental information, and include suggestions on where to buy materials. The supporting whip in this case is a 102-inch CB whip that has been cut down to 60 inches.

As described and when mounted atop a Scorpion 680 screwdriver antenna, 80 through 17 meter operation is possible. Measured field strength improvement over an unloaded 102-inch whip is between 3 dB, and 6 dB, depending on the band.

21.2.3 ANTENNA MOUNTING

Antenna mounts come in so many different styles that it is difficult to decide which is best for any specific installation. Ball mounts, clip mounts, bracket mounts, stake pocket mounts, trailer hitch mounts, and even "mag" (magnet) mounts are popular. Which mount you pick and where you install it depends on many factors. Among them are weight, overall length, frequency of operation, the vehicle in question, and personal preferences.

Weight may be a few ounces for a UHF antenna to as much as 20 pounds for a full-sized, high Q, "bug catcher" antenna. The length may be a few inches for a UHF antenna, to as much as 13 feet or more for an HF one.

Some vehicles lend themselves to antenna mounting and some don't. In general, pickup trucks make better antenna platforms than vans and SUVs. No doubt the biggest decision for many hams is whether or not to drill holes in body sheet metal.

Another often-overlooked requirement is deciding on which side of the vehicle the antenna should be mounted. For rear-mounted antennas, the driver's side of the vehicle is preferred. This can be very important if you live in an area with low bridges and overhanging trees as there is typically more clearance toward the center of the street. Further, it is easier to see the antenna in the side mirrors if they are on the driver's side. If you've chosen front mounting, common when pulling a trailer or RV, then it should be mounted to the right in order to avoid distraction or obstruction of your vision.

Whatever method you choose for mounting your antenna, it must be sturdy enough to hold the weight and withstand the wind loading imposed by the antenna without too much flexing. It should be attached in such a way to maximize what little ground plane a vehicle represents. The key phrase for mounting the antenna is: *It is the metal mass directly under the antenna, not what's alongside, that counts the most!* Keep in mind, no matter what the antenna, permanent and secure mounting maximizes performance and safety.

HF Mobile Antenna Mounts

Figure 21.22 shows a typical center-loaded, remote-controlled, 80 through 10 meter screwdriver antenna, a Scorpion Antennas SA-680. This homebrew mount was made by Joe McEneaney, KG6PCI. The 18-pound antenna is supported by a steel mast welded to a frame extension. There is a stainless steel plate at the top of the mast, bolted to the top of the bed rail, that secures the antenna and reduces ground losses. A quick disconnect at the base of the antenna facilitates removal when desired.

Because of the difficulty in designing and finding someone to weld a special mount, most mobile operators opt for a commercial trailer hitch mount from one of the many *QST* advertisers. While secure, trailer hitch mounting schemes increase ground losses, and should be avoided if possible.

If you drive a pickup truck, mounts in the top of the bed rail or in the bed offer more efficient operation. A stake pocket mount like the Breedlove model shown in **Figure 21.23** is a good, no-holes choice. Its offset design allows it to extend from beneath most bed covers.

Figureure 21.22 — A Scorpion 680 screwdriver antenna mounted on the truck of KG6PCI. *(Photo courtesy of Alan Applegate, KØBG and Ron Douglass, NI7J)*

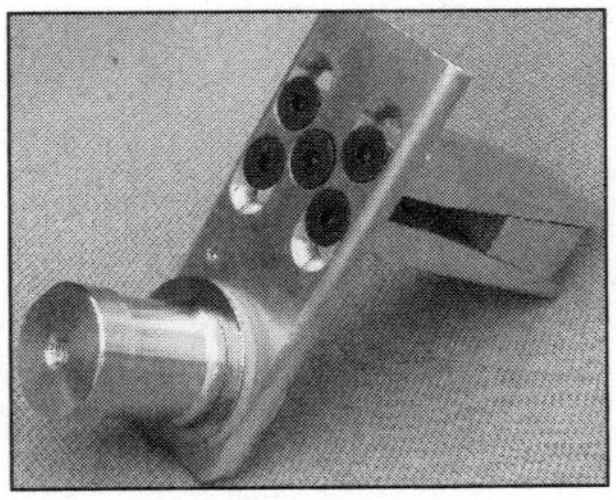

Figure 21.23 — Stake-pocket mounts are designed to fit into the square holes in the walls of a pickup truck's bed. An offset mount as shown in the photo will also clear most bed covers.

3/8-Inch Threaded Mounts

Most monoband, a few screwdriver types, and some VHF antennas mount via a male or female ⅜-24 threaded stud. Ball mounts, clip and lip mounts, and mag mounts are frequently supplied with this type of threaded base. Mounts so equipped often require base insulators to isolate the antenna from the mounting hardware. Feed line connections may be simple wire lugs, an SO-239 connector, or a coaxial cable pigtail with or without a female RF connector installed.

The studs themselves are often stainless steel, but some are mild steel or brass. If the antenna in question is a heavy bug-catcher, a strong stud is in order. A replacement stud can be easily made from a 2-inch, class-8 bolt by cutting off and redressing the threaded portion. The resulting stud has over twice the tensile strength of the stainless steel version.

Ball Mounts

Ball mounts like the one shown in **Figure 21.24** aren't used much anymore as late-model automotive sheet metal isn't as strong as it once was or has been replaced by plastic or composite materials. Further, most hams don't have the necessary tools to fabricate heavy-duty insulators and large backing plates to overcome the thin sheet metal problem for the larger, heavier antennas. However, for ham-sticks and shortened CB whips, ball mounts are more than adequate, even on lighter sheet metal.

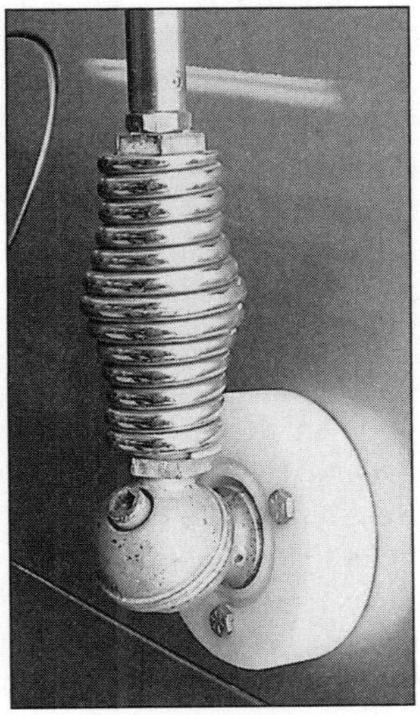

Figure 21.24 — A ball mount is attached to a vertical or nearly-vertical vehicle panel and can be adjusted so that the antenna is vertical. The spring shown in this photo may or may not be included with the mount. The length of the spring must be included in the antenna's total length.

Clip or Lip Mounts

Clip mounts are a mixed bag of tricks. Most are quite adaptable to any surface angle including those offered by trunk lids, rear hatches, and even side doors. For light-duty VHF and UHF antennas, they offer a convenient mounting method. If you're careful in closing the door or hatch they're attached to, they work quite well. Clearance between the mount and the vehicle body structure should be checked before purchase, however.

Typical clip mounts are secured by setscrews. The

folded-over sheet metal of the car body to which the set screws make contact is often jagged and thus offers a less than secure electrical connection. Even modest and lightweight antennas tend to stress the connection. When the connection loosens, intermittent SWR and RFI problems are often the result. Therefore, as a general rule, clip mounts should be restricted to antennas weighing less than 2 pounds. (Larger antennas can be used if guyed or otherwise stabilized above the mount.)

All modern vehicles are dipped in a zinc compound before final assembly and painting. When exposed to air, zinc rapidly oxidizes but in this case the oxidation is a good thing! When a piece of road debris nicks the paint down to the zinc layer, it quickly oxidizes, and protects the base metal underneath. Do not remove this zinc coating to bare metal! This removes the protective coating, allowing the underlying steel to rust and creates an intermittent connection.

All lip mounts bring the coax cable into the trunk or passenger cabin through the weather seal potentially allowing water to enter. The problem is often exacerbated by the larger control cable most screwdriver antennas require. Take care to dress the cables and seals to direct water toward a drain hole or other exit.

Angle Brackets

Angle brackets come in a variety of sizes, shapes, angles, hole size, attachment style, strength, and colors. They're great for lightweight antennas like ham-sticks and VHF antennas, but shouldn't be used for heavier ones. There are special hood seam versions for some models of trucks and other vehicles. They require holes for attachment screws. Some mounts can be clamped on mirror arms or other tubes and struts.

Magnet "Mag" Mounts

Lots of folks use mag mounts with good success for both HF and VHF antennas. Models are available that can secure just about any size antenna. In fact, some VHF antennas come preassembled with mag mounts. Although they're meant for temporary mounting, it is common for them to be used as permanent mounts as a way to avoid drilling holes. Mag mounts have several drawbacks that tend to limit them to temporary installation.

Coax routing is always a problem if for no other reason than weather sealing. The magnet tends to collect road debris, primarily metallic brake dust that eventually gets under the magnet and rusts or scratches the vehicle's finish.

Regardless of the number or size of the magnets, the ultimate holding power relies on the metal surface. For example, some newer vehicles use steel-reinforced composite materials and although the magnets stick to the surface, the force with which they do so is less than on an all-steel surface. In these cases, mag mounts *should not* be used.

For larger antennas mounts are available with from three to five large magnets. These mounts tend to be very heavy and are difficult to install and remove. When used with large antennas, even large mag mounts should be securely tethered and/or guyed to keep them in place for very obvious reasons.

High ground loss and common-mode currents on the coax shield can be a problem when using mag mounts, as they rely on capacitive coupling to the vehicle body for RF return current. Installing a ground strap to the nearest chassis hard point is often recommended but does little to solve these problems.

21.2.4 MOBILE ANTENNA CONTROLLERS AND TUNERS

Screwdriver antennas have become very popular in part because their operating frequency can be changed while in motion. Most manufacturers offer some form of manual control box as an option. However, manual controllers require the operator to watch either an internal or external SWR indicator during tuning, which isn't safe while in motion. Fortunately, there is a solution — the automatic antenna controller.

There are two basic types with several variations, SWR sensing and turn counters. Both types require special attention with respect to RF on the antenna's control leads and we'll cover that issue, as well. Most have a built-in *park* feature which retracts the coil all the way into the mast. If you have garage or carport clearance issues, this is a nice feature.

Automatic Screwdriver Antenna Controllers

The West Mountain Radio TARGETuner (**www.westmountainradio.com**) shown in **Figure 21.25** is a typical example of an automatic controller that can retune an antenna based on SWR or based on frequency data from a radio. Frequency data directly from a radio's computer control port and the SWR level from a separate sensing unit. Commanding the radio to activate a TUNE function varies with the manufacturer and/or radio.

One clear advantage of most automatic controllers is that they store the previous operating frequency. Therefore, when you change frequency, the controller always moves the

Figure 21.25 — An SWR-sensing controller adjusts the length of the screwdriver coil for minimum SWR automatically.

antenna in the correct direction, saving wear and tear on the motor assembly. The controllers also have manual modes that allow an operator to adjust the screwdriver length for initial setup or fine-tuning.

Turn Counter Controllers

Most screwdriver antennas come equipped with a turns counter, usually in the form of a magnet attached to the drive assembly that closes a magnetic reed switch. As the motor turns, the switch opens and closes once or twice every 360°. The controller counts the closures and moves the antenna to a *predetermined* resonance point. **Figure 21.26**, an Ameritron SDC-104, is an example of this type of turns-counting controller. "Jog" buttons are included to touch up the SWR once the predetermined point is reached.

Like some SWR type controllers, turn counters are prone to RF currents on their control leads, so proper RF choking is essential.

Common-Mode Current Problems

In an ideal world, RF flows down the outer surface of the center conductor of coaxial cable and returns on the inner surface of the coax shield. In the real world, RF current will flow on the *outside* of the coax shield, completely independently of the currents inside. The skin effect electrically separates the inside and outside of the shield. This creates a "third wire" — the outside of the shield — that is often connected directly to one side of an antenna. For mobile antennas, the outside of the shield is usually connected to the vehicle body. In addition, if the coax is not itself shielded from the antenna's radiated field, the outside of the shield will pick up RF energy radiated by the antenna. This unbalanced RF current is called "common-mode current" as opposed to the balanced differential-mode currents inside the coax. The common-mode RF current can radiate a signal of its own, just like from any antenna carrying RF, and it can also cause RFI to your radio and to the vehicle's electronic systems.

In the case of HF mobile antennas, the magnitude of common-mode current on feed lines and other cables increases as ground impedance increases which also increases ground losses. As a result the coax and control cables running to clamp or lip-mount and mag-mount antennas will typically carry more common-mode current than body-mounted antennas.

Because of the potential for RFI from common-mode currents, it is prudent to add RF chokes to reduce common-mode currents in a mobile installation, even though there may be no direct indication of a problem. The best place to install a common-mode RF choke is near the base of the antenna where the feed line is connected and not inside the vehicle.

The most convenient way to create an RF choke is to use the "split bead" or "split core" ferrite cores. A mix 31, ¾-inch ID split bead may be utilized with great effect. Depending on the coax size, between five and seven turns of either RG-58 or RG-8X can be wound through that size bead as shown in **Figure 21.27A**. The impedance will be somewhat greater than 1.8 kΩ at 10 MHz which is adequate in most cases. If not, a second split bead can be used effectively doubling the impedance. Take care not to bend the coaxial cable too sharply in making the choke, particularly for foam-insulation cables, as the center conductor can be forced through the insulation over time, creating a short circuit. For more information on ferrite common-mode chokes, see the **Transmission Line System Techniques** chapter.

Control Lead RF Chokes

All screwdriver antennas have one thing in common: Their control motor and any reed switches are housed inside the antenna. Therefore, the control leads will be "hot" with RF during transmissions. This RF must be prevented from reaching the controller or erratic operation may result. This is especially important when utilizing short antennas on clip mounts with their inherent ground losses.

Figure 21.27A shows a motor lead choke utilizing a ¾-inch ID, mix 31 split bead. These specific split beads are available from a variety of *QST* advertisers. The one shown is

Figure 21.26 — A turns-counting controller keeps track of coil position by counting switch closures from a reed switch mounted on the antenna.

(A)

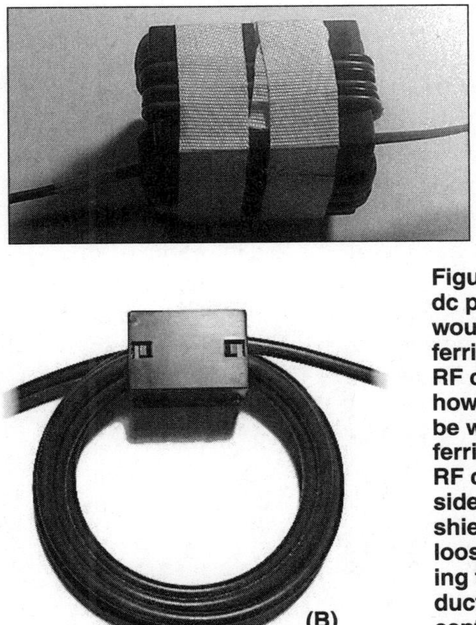

(B)

Figure 21.27 — At A, dc power leads are wound around a split ferrite bead to form an RF choke. B shows how coaxial cable can be wound on a split ferrite bead to form an RF choke on the outside of the cable shield. Wind coax loosely to avoid forcing the center conductor through the center insulation.

wound with 13 turns of #18, nylon insulated wire with an OD of 0.068 inches. Larger diameter wire will not allow enough turns to be wound on the core. It is important that the turns not be overlapped or twisted as this will reduce the choke's effective impedance. In this case, the choke presents approximately 10 kΩ of impedance at 10 MHz, an amount adequate in all but the most severe cases. It is important to wind as many non-overlapping turns on the core as possible.

21.3 BIBLIOGRAPHY FOR HF MOBILE ANTENNAS

Source material and more extended discussions of topics covered in this chapter can be found in the references given below and in the textbooks listed at the end of the **Antenna Fundamentals** chapter.

J. S. Belrose, "Short Antennas for Mobile Operation," *QST*, Sep 1953, pp 30-35.

J. M. Boyer, "Antenna-Transmission Line Analog," *Ham Radio*, April 1977, pp 52-58 and May 1977, pp 29-39.

B. F. Brown, "Tennamatic: An Auto-Tuning Mobile Antenna System," *73*, Jul 1979, p 132.

B. F. Brown, "Optimum Design of Short Coil-Loaded High-Frequency Mobile Antennas," *ARRL Antenna Compendium Volume 1* (Newington: ARRL, 1985), p 108.

C.W. Frazell and T.D. Allison, "Another Look at an Old Subject: The Bug Catcher," *QST*, Dec 1980, pp 30-32.

E. A. Laport, *Radio Antenna Engineering* (New York: McGraw-Hill Book Co., 1952), p 23.

C. E. Smith and E. M. Johnson, "Performance of Short Antennas," *Proceedings of the IRE*, Oct 1947.

F. E. Terman, *Radio Engineering Handbook*, 3rd edition (New York: McGraw-Hill Book Co., 1947), p 74.

21.4 HF ANTENNAS FOR SAIL AND POWER BOATS

21.4.1 PLANNING YOUR INSTALLATION

Many of the mobile antennas discussed earlier in this chapter can be applied to sailboats. (For readers who might not be fully conversant with nautical jargon, the Wikipedia's online glossary of nautical terms at **en.wikipedia.org/wiki/Glossary_of_nautical_terms** will help you keep port and starboard straight.) However, the presence of the mast and rigging, plus the prevalence of nonconducting fiberglass hulls complicates the issue:

- On most boats the spars, standing rigging and some running rigging will be conductors. Stainless steel wire is usually used for rigging and aluminum for spars.
- Topping lifts, running backstays, jackstays, etc may also be made from conducting materials on occasion and often change position while the boat is underway. This changes the configuration of the rigging and may affect radiation patterns and feed point impedances. For example, when tacking you may discover that the SWR on starboard tack is quite different from that on port tack. A conducting topping lift can do this as well as running backstays.
- The antennas on a boat will always be close (in terms of wavelength) to the mast and rigging. Some antennas may in fact be part of the rigging. This means very tight electrical coupling between the antenna and the rigging.
- The feed point impedance, SWR and radiation pattern can be strongly influenced by the presence of spars and rigging.
- The behavior of a given antenna will depend on the details of the rigging on a particular vessel. The performance of a given antenna can vary widely on different boats, due to differences in dimensions and arrangement of the rigging.
- Even though you may be floating on a sea of saltwater, grounding still requires careful attention!
- The radio will typically be an HF transceiver with an output power of 100 W. This low power operation means you must pay careful attention to the efficiency of the "antenna system" and take into account the radiation pattern which will normally be asymmetric with significant signal reduction in some directions.

The First Step

An effective antenna system for a sailboat can require a good deal of effort and some expense. It may be necessary for example, to modify the rigging and do considerable work inside the hull to install a grounding system. For this reason it is important at the beginning to define your goals: Do you simply want to have a little fun at anchor on a summer vacation or are you planning to go blue water cruising and perhaps need to communicate back home from the middle of the Indian Ocean? Is the installation primarily for emergencies to summon assistance or will you want to have daily communications with other boats and shore stations? Or do you want all these plus lots of time for just DXing or chatting with friends back home?

You need to think about what bands you want to operate on. As we'll see shortly, multiband operation poses some problems. Your intended use for Amateur Radio will determine the time, effort and money you have to invest in the antenna system and it will also directly impact your final choice of antenna.

Note the use of the words "antenna system" above. This includes not only the antenna itself but the grounding system, the feed arrangements and very possibly an antenna tuner. All of these components interact and affect the final result.

Antenna Modeling

Because of the strong interaction between the rigging and the antenna, accurate prediction of radiation patterns and a reasonable guess at feed point impedances requires that you model both the antenna and the rigging with CAD software. Fortunately, easy-to-use antenna modeling software such as *EZNEC* (**www.eznec.com**) and *4NEC2* (**www.qsl.net/4nec2/**) is available at low cost. Unless you accurately model the system, considerable cut-and-try may be needed and even then you won't have any real idea of how your system is performing. Cut-and-try can be expensive when it has to be done in 1 × 19 stainless steel wire with $300 swaged insulator fittings!

Modeling allows you to try a number of different ideas and see which approach works best for your installation. While the software is very helpful, it has to be used with some caution:

1) You will need a reasonably accurate model using the physical dimensions of the spars and rigging unique to your boat. Take the time to carefully measure the dimensions and create a model that includes all the spars and conductive rigging.

2) The connections between the spars and rigging will have many small intersection angles and radically different conductor diameters — this can cause problems for *NEC* and *MININEC* programs. In general, sufficient accuracy can be obtained by using the same diameter for all the parts of the *NEC* model including the spars. Make all the conductors 0.25 inch which is typical for standing rigging.

3) Be careful to make the segment lengths at a junction the same for each wire connected to that junction.

4) For more information on antenna modeling, see the **Antenna Modeling** chapter.

From *NEC* modeling, you can expect the predicted radiation patterns to be close to reality but the feed point impedance predictions will be approximate. Some final adjustment will usually be required. Because of the wide variation between boats, even those of the same class, each new installation is unique and should be analyzed separately.

NEC modeling with *EZNEC-Pro/4* will be used for much of the following discussion. The model uses the dimensions and rigging arrangements for a Crealock 37 sailboat. The author (N6LF) and his wife lived aboard this boat for many years and cruised off-shore extensively. Some of the ideas shown are taken directly from experience on this boat, other boats he has owned and boats belonging to fellow cruisers.

Pre-Installation Evaluation

When the antenna is going to be integrated into the standing rigging, it's a very good idea (after modeling) to try your designs out at the dock. For example, suppose you want to insulate part of your backstay and use it as your primary antenna. Temporarily you could replace the backstay with a stout Dacron line and use wire and inexpensive insulators for the initial tests to determine the antenna final dimensions. Then finalize the backstay in stainless wire and swaged insulators. This approach can save a lot of money and aggravation.

A Safety Note

Ungrounded rigging near deck level can have high RF potentials when you transmit. For example, the shrouds on a fiberglass boat connect to chainplates that are bolted to the hull, but may not be grounded. The lower ends of the shrouds can inflict painful RF burns on the unwary, even while operating at low power. This is not hypothetical! As a general rule all rigging, spars and lifelines near deck level should be grounded. This also makes good sense for lightning protection. For antennas with parts near deck level that can be touched, a sleeve of schedule 80 PVC pipe can be placed over the lower end as a protective shield. It's not uncommon to stand at the stern with a hand grasping the backstay. You don't want to be able to grasp the backstay above the insulator without an insulating shield over it! Many commercial verticals for marine use are insulated.

As shown in the chapter **Effects of Ground**, it is possible to determine in advance the potentials that may exist on a given system using the near-field calculations provided by most software combined with some simple calculations using a spreadsheet.

21.4.2 ANTENNA OPTIONS

There are a number of possibilities for antennas on a sailboat. One of the simplest is to install a separate vertical as shown in **Figure 21.28.** An alternative is to insulate a portion of the backstay and use that as a vertical as shown in **Fig-**

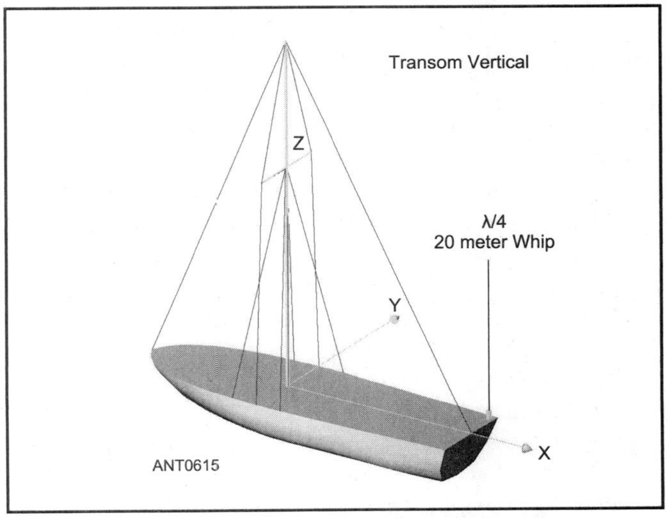

Figure 21.28 — An example of a 20 meter λ/4 whip mounted on the transom. A local ground system must also be provided, as described in the section on grounding.

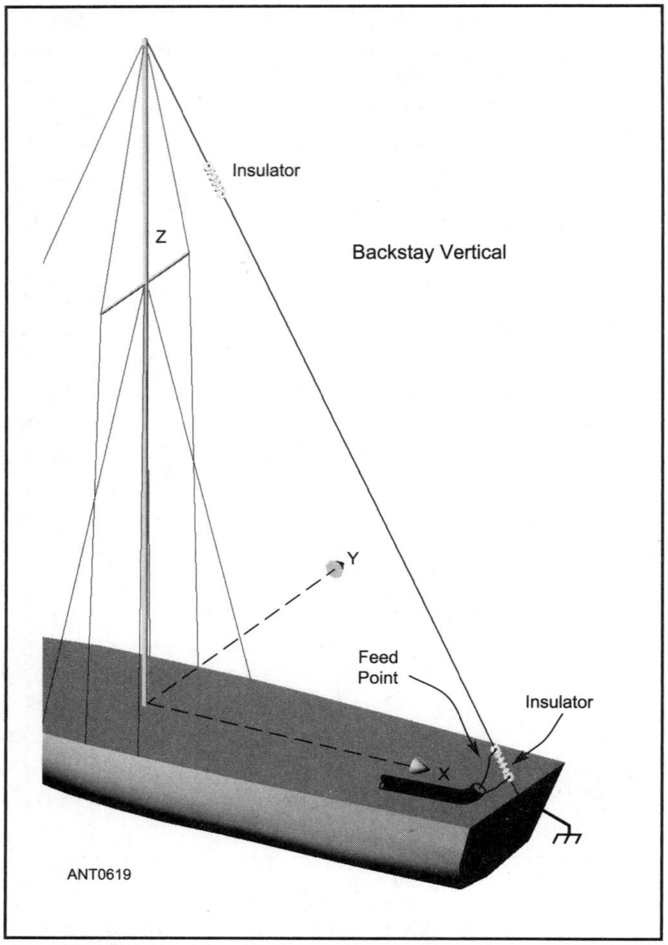

Figure 21.29 — An example of a backstay vertical fed at deck level. A local ground point must be established on the transom next to the base of the backstay.

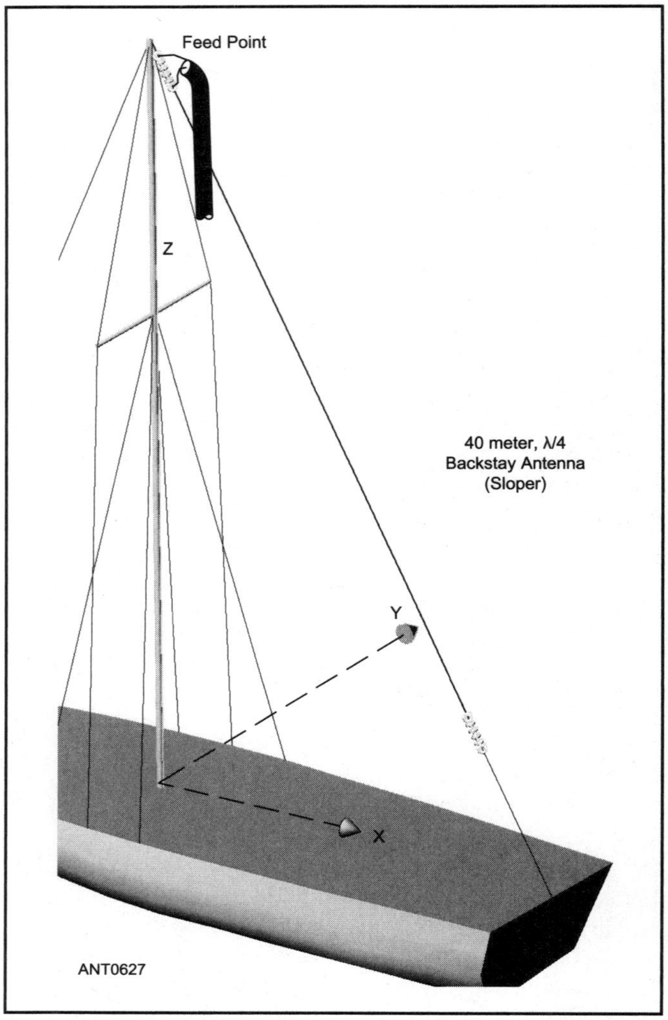

Figure 21.30 — An insulated stay 40 meter half-sloper fed at the masthead.

ures 21.29 and **21.30**. The backstay vertical can be fed at deck level or at the masthead.

This is the same idea as the λ/4-sloper discussed in the chapter on **Single-Band MF and HF Antennas**. One problem with this antenna is that the lower end of the antenna is a very high potential point. You don't want the lower end of the sloper to be anywhere it could be reached from the deck. Another possibility is to place a self-supporting dipole at the masthead as shown in **Figure 21.31**.

These basic antennas can be applied in a number of ways:

1) For single-band operation you can make the vertical shown in Figure 21.28 λ/4 resonant or insulate a portion of the backstay that is λ/4 resonant (Figure 21.29 or 21.30). If the length of the backstay or the vertical is not long enough to reach resonance on the desired band you can use the loading techniques described earlier in this chapter for mobile antennas and there is also some useful information regarding loading in the chapter **Single-Band MF and HF Antennas**.

2) Another single-band option is the use of a self-supporting dipole at the masthead as shown in Figure 21.31. The antenna shown was fabricated from a pair of 12 foot fiberglass fly-fishing rod blanks (with a copper wire inside!) that were attached to ¾ inch by 6 foot aluminum tubes. Although it looks a bit ungainly this antenna survived several years of cruising and two 24 day passages in the north Pacific including the long beat back from Hawaii. The antenna was very effective for the 20 meter maritime nets. A 15 meter version of this antenna was installed on another boat for a passage from Australia back to the US via South Africa. With this masthead dipole they were able to work back to the US regularly from the Indian Ocean. One half of this antenna would make a good homebrew vertical on the transom.

3) For multiband operation it is possible to build or purchase multiband antennas, some of which are intended for mobile operation (see the **Multiband HF Antennas** chapter and material on mobile antennas earlier in this chapter). These come in many forms: multiple traps, replaceable upper sections, interchangeable loading coils for each band or motorized tuning of a loading coil. Unfortunately most commercial products of this type are not intended for a marine environment. In addition, close proximity to the rigging can have a strong effect on multiband trap verticals, preventing

Figure 21.31 — A rigid dipole can be made from aluminum tubing, fiberglass poles or a combination of these and attached to the mast such as is visible in the photo at the top of the mast.

them from being tuned properly.

4) Another option for multiband operation is the SteppIR family of self-adjusting verticals (**www.steppir.com**). The antenna consists of a fiberglass tube, 18 feet or 34 feet long, inside of which is a variable length of conductive metal tape. The tape is motor driven so that its length can be adjusted to be resonant at any frequency from 40 or 20 meters (depending on the tube length) through 6 meters. It is even possible to purchase a tuning unit for operation on 80 meters. The antenna controller comes with pre-programmed length settings for the amateur bands but these can be custom adjusted to compensate for the interaction with the rigging. These antennas can be quite efficient and a tuner is not needed in most installations.

5) A common solution for multiband operation is to use a fixed length antenna, such as a vertical mounted on the transom or integrated into the backstay, combined with a tuner to provide a match to the transmitter.

6) It is also possible to use more than one antenna. For example, you could use an insulated backstay resonant on 40 meters combined with a shorter transom vertical for the higher bands.

Temporary Antennas

Not everyone needs permanent antennas. A variety of temporary antennas can be arranged. A few of these are shown in **Figures 21.32**, **21.33**, and **21.34**. All of these options will

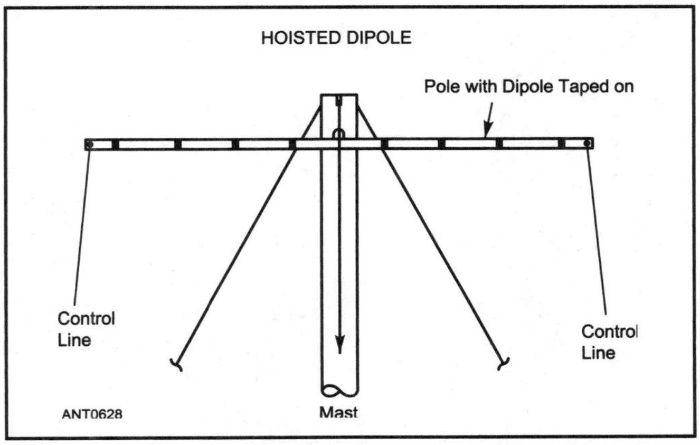

Figure 21.32 — A dipole can be taped to a wood or bamboo pole and hoisted to the masthead with the main halyard while at anchor. It is possible to make this a multiband dipole.

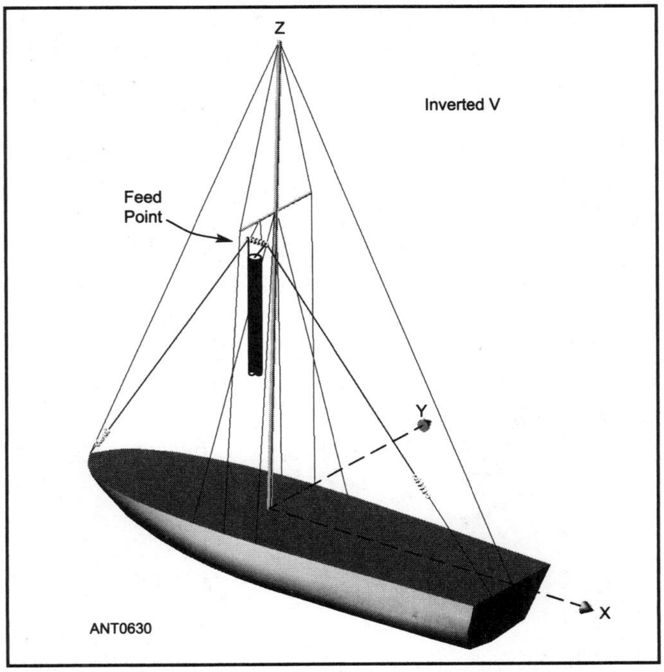

Figure 21.33 — The flag halyard can be used to hoist the center of an inverted V to the spreaders, or alternatively, the main halyard can be used to hoist the center of the antenna to the masthead. Interaction between the rigging and the antenna will be very pronounced and the length of the antenna will have to be adjusted on a cut-and-try basis.

be strongly affected by their close proximity to the rigging but by employing a tuner, they may work well for temporary operation. You can also try altering the wire lengths to get a better match.

21.4.3 THE EFFECT OF MAST AND RIGGING

A vertical can be placed on the transom as shown in Figure 21.28. (Note that the vertical is offset a short distance from the backstay to reduce coupling to the rigging slightly). This vertical could be a mobile whip, a fixed length commercial marine vertical or an insulated section of backstay. It turns out that the length of the antenna and whether it's part of the backstay or separate has only a modest effect on the radiation pattern so we will use 23 foot independent vertical that will give us a general idea what to expect from verticals of other lengths. **Figure 21.35** shows the radiation patterns for this antenna at 7.2, 14.2 and 21.25 MHz.

Unlike a vertical standing alone, this antenna doesn't have an omnidirectional pattern. It is asymmetrical, with pattern distortion of 8-10 dB depending on the band. Further, the pattern is offset in the direction the antenna is placed on the transom. With the backstay vertical that offset is absent. The pattern distortion shown in Figure 21.35 is very typical for a wide range of boats. The directive gain can be useful but only if you point the boat in the right direction! Otherwise you may have significant reduction in your signal.

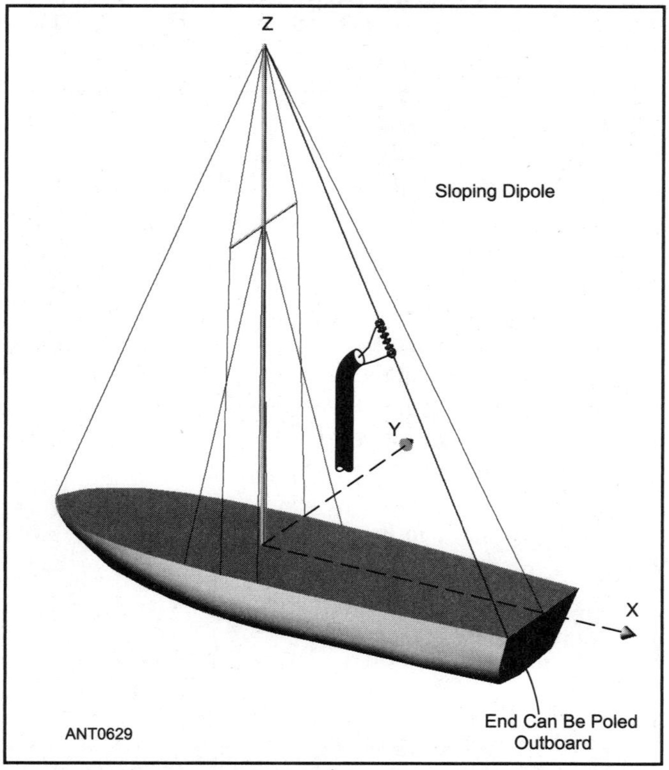

Figure 21.34 — One end of dipole can be attached to the main halyard and pulled up to the masthead. The bottom end of the dipole should be pulled out away from the rigging as much as possible to reduce the impact of the rigging on the impedance.

Figure 21.36 shows Smith chart graphs for the feed point impedance at the base of a 23 foot vertical with and without the rig. Figures 21.35 and 21.36 are very good examples of the profound effect the mast and rigging can have on an antenna installed on a sailboat.

What if we chose a length other than 23 feet for either the vertical or an insulated backstay? Is there a better choice? **Figure 21.37** shows Z_{in} for various vertical lengths from 15 to 40 feet on 40, 20 and 15 meters. For a backstay vertical it would be common to set L=33 feet which gives a good match on 40 and 15 meters. Usually no tuner would be needed or at least the internal tuner found in most transceivers would have little difficulty matching those bands. However, L=33 feet is a very poor length for 20 meters — the impedance is very high and even the best tuner might have difficulty matching to that load. Instead of 33 feet you could set L=17 feet which will have $Z_{in} = 11 - j384\ \Omega$ at 7.15 MHz, $36 + j8\ \Omega$ at 14.175 MHz and $220 + j451\ \Omega$ at 21.25 MHz. On 20 meters a tuner is not required and the impedances on 40 and 15 meters are reasonable for an automatic tuner.

Common lengths for commercial marine antennas intended for HF SSB service are 23 feet and 28 feet. From Figure 21.37 we can see these lengths have impedances that are a bit high (though not impossible) for many automatic tuners. A better choice would be 26 feet. However, this observation applies only to this particular example, on this boat! Other boats, with different rigging dimensions might be better (or worse) with a given vertical length. That is why it is a good idea to model each boat individually before choosing an antenna. Each installation will be unique!

The message here is that some lengths are better than others for verticals or insulated backstay antennas and these lengths may not be resonant on any of the bands. The choice of length will depend on the specifics of the boat, the desired operating bands and whether a tuner is used.

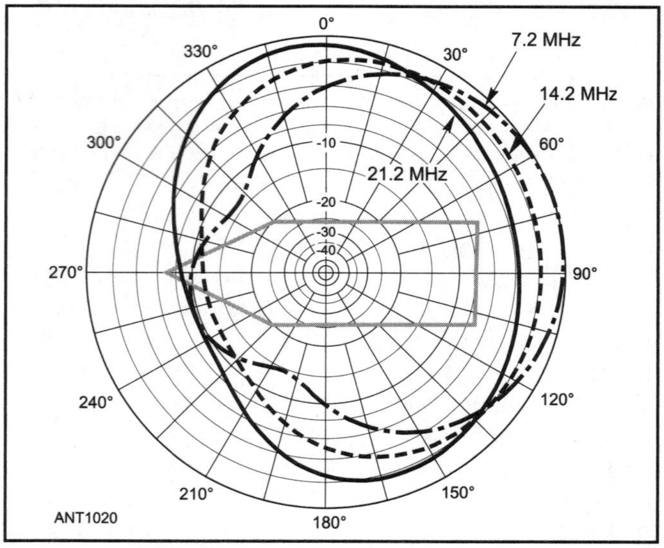

Figure 21.35 — Azimuth radiation pattern of a vertical at 15° elevation at 7.2, 14.2 and 21.2 MHz.

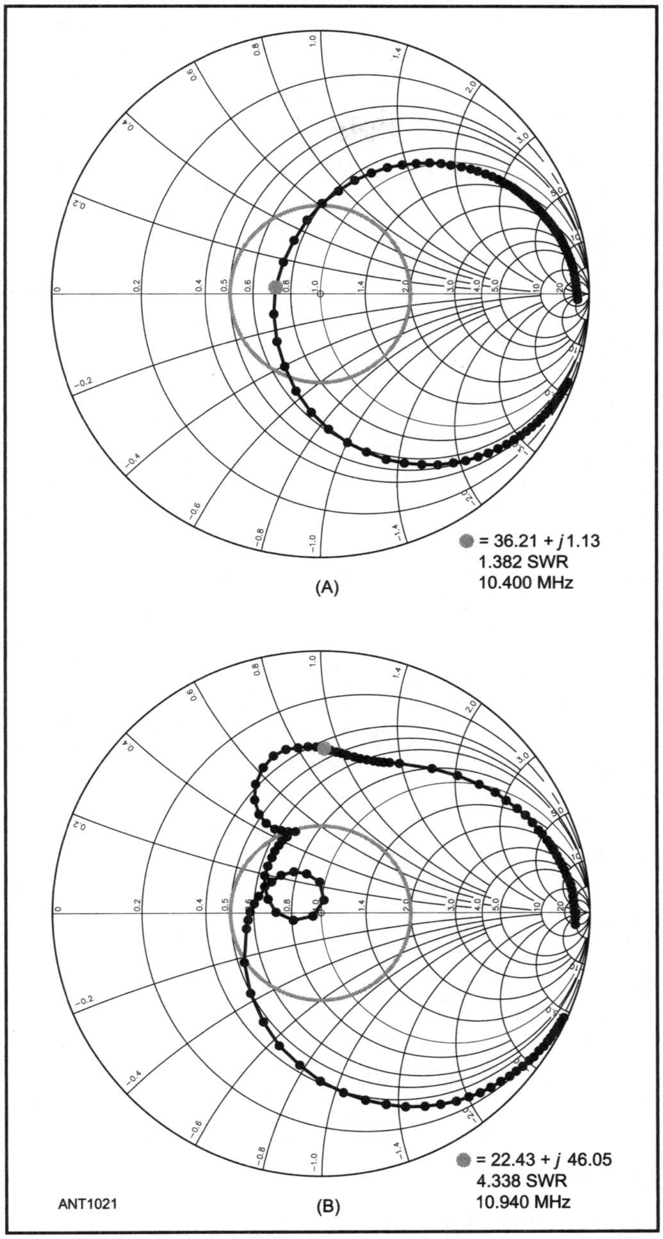

Figure 21.36 — Feed point impedance of a 23 foot free-standing vertical with the mast and rigging present. (Z_0 = 50 Ω)

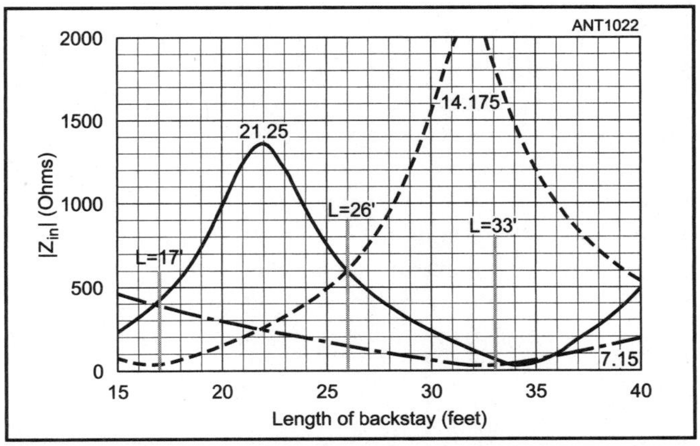

Figure 21.37 — Feed point impedance as a function of vertical length at 7.150, 14.175 and 21.250 MHz. (Z_0 = 50 Ω)

21.4.4 ANTENNAS FOR POWER BOATS

Power boaters are not usually faced with the problems and opportunities created by the mast and rigging on a sailboat. A powerboat may have a small mast, but usually not on the same scale as a sailboat. Antennas for power boats have much more in common with automotive mobile operation, but the motion of a powerboat, especially in rough seas, can be quite severe. This places additional mechanical strain on the antennas and exposure to wet and possibly salt-water environments.

The simplest situation for HF is to install a regular mobile vertical on the bow-rail of a cabin cruiser. The bowrail and any attached bonding conductor act as a counterpoise for the vertical. Band-changing then becomes a simple matter of replacing the antenna or attaching a different resonator. The ground system then becomes a critical part of the antenna system as discussed in the following section.

Sometimes a number of radial wires are used for a vertical, much like that for a ground-plane antenna. This is not a very good idea unless the "wires" are actually wide copper foil strips that can lower the Q substantially. The problem is the high voltage present at the ends of the radials. On a boat these radials are likely to be in close proximity to the cabin, which in turn contains both people and electronic equipment. The high voltage at the ends of the radials is both a safety hazard and can result in RF coupling back into the equipment, including ham gear, navigational instruments and entertainment devices. Decoupling the counterpoise from the transmission line, as discussed in the chapter **Effects of Ground**, can be very helpful to keep RF out of other equipment.

One way to avoid many of problems associated with grounding is to use a rigid dipole antenna as suggested in Figure 21.31. For short-range communication, a low dipole over saltwater can be effective. However, if long-range communication is needed, then a well-designed vertical, operating over seawater, will work much better. For these to work, of course, you must have the ground system associated with a vertical.

It is not uncommon for large powerboats to have a two or three-element multiband Yagi installed on a short mast. While these can be effective, if they are not mounted high above the waterline (> λ/2) they may be disappointing for longer-range communication. Over saltwater, vertical polarization is very effective for longer distances. A simple, well-designed, vertical system on a boat may outperform a low Yagi.

Remember that in the case of a thunderstorm, a VHF/marine SSB/ham antenna may be the highest thing on the water for a mile or so and therefore liable to be struck by lightning. Antennas should be lowered if possible. A direct strike on antennas will do a lot of damage to the entire RF system.

21.4.5 GROUND SYSTEMS

You may be sitting in the middle of a thousand miles of saltwater. This is great for propagation but you will still have to connect to that ground, particularly if you want to use a vertical antenna. If the boat has a steel or aluminum

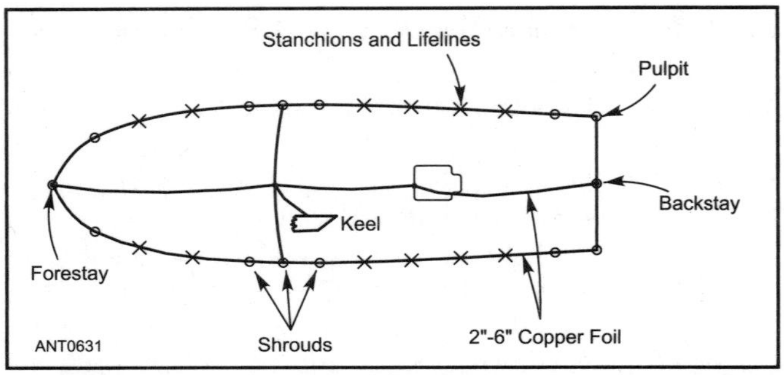

Figure 21.38 — A typical sailboat grounding scheme.

hull, no additional ground system is required. For wooden or fiberglass hulls, there are many possibilities, but the scheme shown in **Figure 21.38** is representative for sailboats.

First, a wire, strap, or most preferably 3-inch by 0.003-inch ground foil, is installed as a grounding conductor from bow-to-stern on each side. If strap or foil is not available, a pair of parallel wires (such as #12 AWG) spaced a few inches apart will have an impedance similar to a wide copper strap and may be easier to install. This system couples to the water through the hull and is not directly immersed. Do not use braided strap as it will corrode when exposed to water, fresh or salt. Some fiberglass hulls have embedded copper mesh that is used for RF bonding.

Bond the lifeline stanchions, chainplates, bow and stern pulpits, and any rails. On sailboats, include the forestay and backstay and create a common connection at the base of the mast. The bonding conductor can also be attached to the engine and to the keel bolts.

It is not recommended to bond everything below the waterline, as that may result in unexpected additional electrolysis. (Marine literature is inconsistent on this point.) This has to be dealt with on a case-by-case basis. If the protective zinc sacrificial anodes (**www.boatus.com/boattech/casey/sacrificial-zincs.asp**) deplete more rapidly after a ground system is installed or modified, change it by disconnecting some part of the system — the engine-shaft-propeller, for example. Ground systems vary with every installation and must be customized to each vessel. However, just as on shore, the better the ground system, the better the performance of a vertical antenna!

A common recommendation for powerboat grounds is two or three porous-zinc through-hull ground plates. Each through-hull porous plate provides an equivalent grounding area of 10 to 20 square feet. These must be professionally installed with leakproof techniques. Bonded through-hulls using #8 AWG wire are recommended by the America Boat and Yacht Council for controlling galvanic corrosion and the effects of nearby (not direct) lightning strikes. To connect the bonding foil or strap, wire-brush the post, wrap the foil or strap around it, and tighten with a stainless-steel hose clamp. There is no need for soldering or welding.

Consult with your ship builder before connecting the grounding system to though-hull ground plates installed at the factory. The completed grounding system should be inspected by a certified marine electrician in order to ensure that it does not interfere with the boat's anti-galvanic corrosion system.

Some power boats have a ground-plane equivalent built into the roof of a flying bridge. The bridge is the most common location of RF communications equipment, including VHF ship-to-shore, marine SSB, and ham radio equipment. This built-in ground plane should be connected to the ground system with foil or strap.

In modern cabin cruisers, the ability to install a bonding conductor in the bow or passenger compartment of the boat is limited, due to the extensive woodwork involved in the typical cabin cruiser. However, an equivalent ground might be created in a more accessible portion of the hull, particularly the engine compartment.

A ground conductor can be attached with adhesive to the inside of the engine compartment or just formed to the interior of the engine compartment. Using adhesive is preferable to avoid having unsecured items in the engine compartment. The ground system should not be connected directly to the negative battery terminal. If practical run a separate grounding conductor from an antenna mount directly to the through-hull. This minimizes inductance of the connection.

Icom recommends that HF transceivers be connected to the ground system via foil or strap. The foil can be folded so that it is easy to remove the radio for servicing but this also increases the inductance of the connection substantially. Keep the conductor as short as possible while still allowing the radio to be removed for service.

The negative lead of many HF radios is fused. This can allow false ground paths from winches, etc., to blow the fuse rather than damaging the expensive radio. Be careful to route the ground conductor in a way that it does not interfere with the power connections.

When transmitting, it is common to see meters reacting to voice or CW peaks. With the antenna mounted directly on the boat, the strong RF field is rectified by dissimilar-metal or corroded connections. This creates dc currents that affect metering circuits.

21.4.6 ANTENNA TUNERS

Tuners can only match a limited range of impedances. In general, very low and very high impedances lead to higher voltages and/or currents in the tuner components, which can lead to much lower tuner efficiency. The worst case is usually when the resistive component at the feed point is very low and the reactive component is high. This happens when whip antennas are used at frequencies below their $\lambda/4$ resonance (see Table 21.1 for examples of feed point resistance as an 8-foot whip is excited at lower frequencies). As the antenna is made longer and approaches $\lambda/2$ resonance, the resistive part of Z_{in} can become very large, $>1000\ \Omega$. From the point of view of tuner efficiency and the ability to provide a match, the antenna feed point impedance should be kept between $10\ \Omega$ and $500\ \Omega$, if possible.

The tuner should be placed physically as close to the antenna feed point as possible. The best design is to have a good ground connection immediately adjacent to the feed point and tuner. Using a remote tuner at the base of a ham/marine-SSB antenna will also help eliminate RF feedback and "hot spots" such as on a microphone or enclosure.

Running an insulated wire from the feed point back through the boat to a tuner at or in the transceiver is a very bad practice. There is the danger of exposure to high potentials on the wire and the probability of RF coupling to the boat's wiring and other electronics. *Do not do this*!

If you have a good ground connection next to the feed point and another at the transmitter, it is possible to use a length of coaxial cable to connect the feed point to the tuner, allowing you to use a conventional manual tuner collocated with the transceiver. However, the coax is a transmission line and it will transform the feed point impedance to some new value that may or may not be suitable for the tuner. (See the **Transmission Lines** chapter for more on impedance transformation by feed lines.) In addition, there can be very high voltages on the transmission line. The best general advice is to locate the tuner as close as possible to the antenna feed point!

Locating the tuner close to the feed point may have disadvantages however. The tuner may need to be installed in a locker or cabinet that may not be completely shielded from the weather so you have to use a weather-tight tuner. Such a location makes it difficult to use a manual tuner since you may have to reach into the locker to adjust the tuner for a new band. Typically weather resistant automatic tuners are chosen for this application.

The chapter **Transmission Line System Techniques** has information on tuners you can build yourself. Another good resource is *The ARRL Guide to Antenna Tuners* by Joel Hallas, W1ZR.

TABLE OF CONTENTS

Chapter 22 — Downloadable Supplemental Content

Supplemental Articles

Chapter 22

Receiving and Direction-Finding Antennas

22.1 RECEIVING ANTENNAS

The following introduction is excerpted from the section "Introduction to Receiving Antennas" written by Robye Lahlum, W1MK, in *ON4UN's Low-Band DXing*.

Separate antennas are necessary because optimum receiving and transmitting have different requirements. For a transmit antenna, we want maximum possible field strength in a given direction (or directions) at the most useful elevation (wave) angles. We cannot tolerate unnecessary power loss in a transmit antenna, because any amount of transmitting loss decreases signal-to-noise ratio at the distant receiver.

A receiving antenna on the other hand has a different design priority. The goal is obtaining a signal that can be read comfortably, which means having the greatest possible signal-to-noise (S/N) and signal-to-QRM ratio. Receiving antennas providing the best performance can and will be different under different circumstances, even at the same or similar locations. There is no such thing as a universal "best low-band receiving antenna."

Typical low band receiving antennas like the Beverage require more space that most hams have available. In recent years, computer modeling has enabled the development of small loops and arrays that provide meaningful improvements in receiving ability without requiring large areas or overly specialized construction techniques.

22.1.1 DIRECTIVITY AND COUPLING

Directivity is the main concern for a receiving antenna on the low bands. There are currently two methods to quantify this directivity described in the fifth edition of ON4UN's *Low-Band DXing* — Directivity Merit Figure and Receiving Directivity Factor. Both are described in this chapter. In addition, Jukka Klemola, OH6LI, develops the idea of Noise Margin and Leaking Index in his presentation made available by the World Wide Radio Operators Foundation (WWROF) at **wwrof.org/wp-content/uploads/2018/02/Receiving-Antenna-Metrics-With-Examples-v20p.pdf**. The presentation includes a detailed comparison of the performance for popular receiving antennas.

Directivity Merit Figure (DMF)

The average front-to-back (the peak forward lobe versus what happens in the back 180° over the entire elevation angle range) gives a good indication of directivity. The DMF is the forward gain of the antenna at a chosen elevation angle (usually the elevation angle producing maximum gain) minus the average back half-hemisphere's gain. The back quadrisphere is the area between 90° and 270° azimuth — provided the forward lobe is aiming at 0° azimuth — and 0° to 90° elevation. (DMF can be calculated from the table of pattern gain values and using a spreadsheet or other software to perform the averaging function. W8WWV's *DBDXView* will perform the calculations from *EZNEC* data files and is available with *Low-Band DXing*.)

This method of evaluating a receive antenna applies to a case where a dominant noise arrives from a relatively wide half-hemisphere. If the noise is evenly distributed in all directions (eg, in a very quiet location), the RDF ranking system discussed below should be used.

Many noise sources vary in direction, arrival angle and polarization tilt. The same is true for desired signals. Because of this, we really only are considering "average" results over time. Averages are not foolproof under every condition. For example, if you have a strong single-point noise and if that noise arrives in a deep notch in your receiving antenna pattern, the S/N improvement may be much greater than expected. If noise arrives predominantly from a higher antenna response area, the S/N improvement will be proportionally less. Another important thing to consider: Signals almost never arrive from a single angle or direction. A range of angles is involved, and a single-angle evaluation does not fully represent the real world.

Receiving Directivity Factor (RDF)

Developed by Tom Rauch, W8JI (**www.w8ji.com**), RDF goes a step further and compares the forward lobe gain to the average gain of the antenna in all directions (both azimuth and elevation).

While the Directivity Merit Factor (DMF) compares forward gain at the desired wave angle to the average gain in the rear half hemisphere, RDF compares forward gain at a desired direction and elevation angle to average gain over the entire hemisphere above ground. RDF includes all areas around and above the antenna, considering noise to be evenly distributed and aligned with the element polarization. RDF tells you not only how good the average front-to-back ratio is, but also how narrow your forward (wanted) lobe is.

Losses are factored out, and we find the directivity of the array. If noise, on average, is evenly distributed in all directions (including forward and side lobe areas) this method provides an accurate picture of receiving ability. (Keep in mind most antenna modeling programs used by amateurs calculate pattern at infinite distances and ignore ground wave response. RDF models, like DMF models, are not reliable when ground wave noise dominates skywave noise.)

For everything but an omnidirectional antenna, the RDF will be different from the DMF. You have to decide if your location has dominant skywave noise in the rearward area (DMF), or if skywave noise is evenly distributed on average (RDF). Do not compare RDF with DMF.

Calculating the RDF with *EZNEC* is very simple. After ensuring the model is correct, model the antenna with lossy elements and real ground and plot the 3D pattern. The main *EZNEC* window shows average gain at the very bottom. Now, go to a two-dimensional elevation or azimuth pattern and select the desired elevation angle and/or azimuth of the desired signal with the gain cursor and note the gain. The difference between the overall average gain and gain at the desired direction and elevation angle is the RDF. The front lobe does not have to align with the desired signal. You can also move the cursor around and look at the RDF for off-path signals. (W8WWV's *LBDXView* software will also calculate RDF from *EZNEC* tables.)

Using DMF and RDF

Both evaluation systems have their merits. If you're in a location that's always very quiet, with no specific noise or QRM sources from a particular direction, then RDF is most meaningful. The exception would be if you always had grossly dominant noise (or QRM) only from one direction. For a front-to-rear (F/R) selection to be valid, the dominant noise would have to be so strong as to consistently exceed distributed background noise by the null-depth ratio between an antenna selected by RDF compared to one selected by F/R.

John Kaufmann, W1FV, also made the following observation on the Topband email reflector (**lists.contesting.com/mailman/listinfo/Topband**): "As RDF gets higher, the beamwidth of the antenna system generally gets narrower. By making the RDF very high, you are necessarily restricting the angular sector over which the antenna delivers its best performance. This is fine as long as the angular sector coincides with a direction that is important to you. The flip side is you give up some of that performance outside that sector. For switched arrays with a finite number of selectable directions, that could be a disadvantage when a direction of interest falls halfway between contiguous switching directions. Looking at the pattern of the array will tell you what you give up in the "in between" directions."

Polarization of the signals and the noise are assumed to be the same on average for RDF calculations. If the signal and noise have different polarizations, the antenna will have different responses to each and the RDF metric is not valid. For example, if your local noise source has a different polarization than the sky-wave signals you are trying to receive, RDF can be greatly misleading.

Coupling

Most antenna models are developed and evaluated without other antennas or conductive surfaces nearby except for ground under the antenna. This is rarely the case in the real world, with transmitting antennas, metal surfaces and structures, power lines, and numerous other conductors in the vicinity. Especially on the low bands with their long wavelengths, it is common for other antennas to be as close as a few hundredths of a wavelength away. As a result, there will likely be a significant amount of interaction. As W8JI observed, "If [the antenna] receives, it will receive from the mess of things all around it from the dirt below it to the wires down the road."

Coupling can significantly distort an antenna's radiation pattern, whether receiving or transmitting. Separating the antenna from whatever it is coupling to is the best remedy but that is not an option in many cases. De-tuning an antenna when not in use by shifting its resonance out of band is a common technique of reducing coupling. The exact technique depends on the antenna.

Coupling can also result in significant amounts of power being picked up and overloading or damaging receivers. Out-of-band energy can be rejected with filters, but in-band coupling is harder to manage. Front-end protection circuits may be required, or a relay to interrupt the signal path during transmit periods is often used.

Noise pickup from coupling occurs on the outer surface of feed lines where it can then get into the feed line at a termination. It is particularly important to insure that common-mode current on the feed line shield is blocked from entering the feed line where it mixes with the desired signal and cannot be removed. Ferrite chokes (see the **Transmission Line System Techniques** chapter) at the end of the cable can be quite effective against noise *ingress* from coupling. As an added bonus, this also reduces coupling of the feed line's outer surface to other antennas.

22.1.2 THE BEVERAGE ANTENNA

Perhaps the best known type of wave antenna is the *Beverage*. Many 160 meter enthusiasts have used Beverage antennas to enhance the signal-to-noise ratio while attempting to extract weak signals from the often high levels of atmospheric noise and interference on the low bands. Alternative antenna systems have been developed and used over the years, such as loops and long spans of unterminated wire on or slightly above the ground, but the Beverage antenna seems to be the best for 160 meter weak-signal reception. The information in this section was prepared originally by Rus Healy, K2UA.

A Beverage is simply a directional wire antenna, at least one wavelength long, supported along its length at a fairly low height and terminated at the far end in its characteristic impedance. This antenna is shown in **Figure 22.1A**. It takes its name from its inventor, Harold Beverage, W2BML.

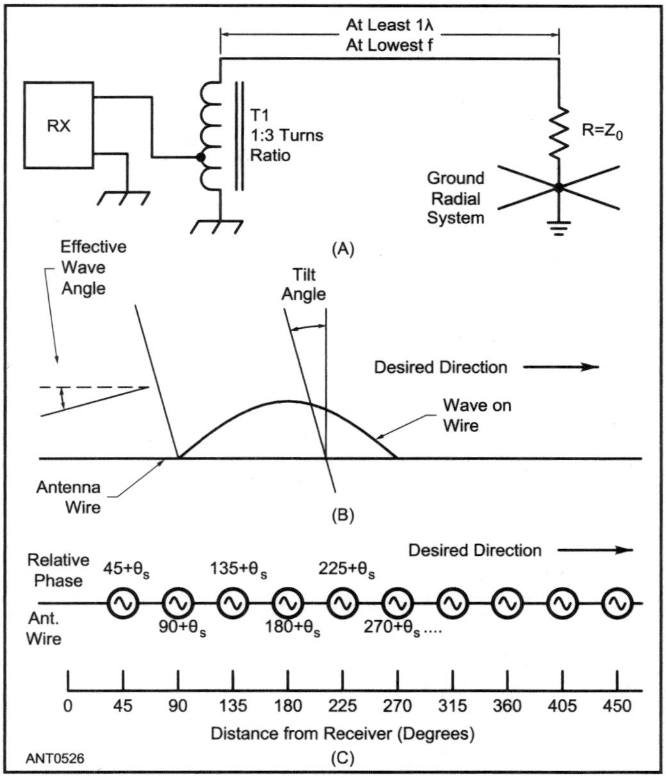

Figure 22.1 — At A, a simple one-wire Beverage antenna with a variable termination impedance and a matching 9:1 autotransformer for the receiver impedance. At B, a portion of a wave from the desired direction is shown traveling down the antenna wire. Its tilt angle and effective takeoff angle are also shown. At C, a situation analogous to the action of a Beverage on an incoming wave is shown. See text for discussion.

Many amateurs choose to use a single-wire Beverage because they are easy to install and they work well. The drawback is that Beverages are physically long and they do require that you have the necessary amount of real estate to install them. Sometimes, a neighbor will allow you to put up a temporary Beverage for a particular contest or DXpedition on his land, particularly during the winter months.

Beverage antennas can be useful into the HF range, but they are most effective at lower frequencies, mainly on 160 through 40 meters. The antenna is responsive mostly to low-angle incoming waves that maintain a constant (vertical) polarization. These conditions are nearly always satisfied on 160 meters, and most of the time on 80 meters. As the frequency is increased, however, the polarization and arrival angles are less and less constant and favorable, making Beverages less effective at these frequencies. Many amateurs have, however, reported excellent performance from Beverage antennas at frequencies as high as 14 MHz, especially when rain or snow (precipitation) static prevents good reception on the Yagi or dipole transmitting antennas used on the higher frequencies.

Beverage Operation

The Beverage antenna acts like a long transmission line with one lossy conductor (the ground), and one good conductor (the wire). Beverages have excellent directivity if erected properly, but they are quite inefficient because they are mounted close to the ground. This is in contrast with the terminated long-wire antennas described earlier, which are typically mounted high off the ground. Beverage antennas are not suitable for use as transmitting antennas.

Because the Beverage is a traveling wave, terminated antenna, it has no standing waves resulting from radio signals. As a wave strikes the end of the Beverage from the desired direction, the wave induces voltages along the antenna and continues traveling in space as well. Figure 22.1B shows part of a wave on the antenna resulting from a desired signal. This diagram also shows the tilt of the wave. The signal induces equal voltages in both directions. The resulting currents are equal and travel in both directions. The component traveling toward the termination end moves against the wave and thus builds down to a very low level at the termination end. Any residual signal resulting from this direction of current flow will be absorbed in the termination (if the termination is equal to the antenna impedance). The component of the signal flowing in the other direction, as we will see, becomes a key part of the received signal.

As the wave travels along the wire, the wave in space travels at approximately the same velocity. (There is some phase delay in the wire, as we shall see.) At any given point in time, the wave traveling along in space induces a voltage in the wire in addition to the wave already traveling on the wire (voltages already induced by the wave). Because these two waves are nearly in phase, the voltages add and build

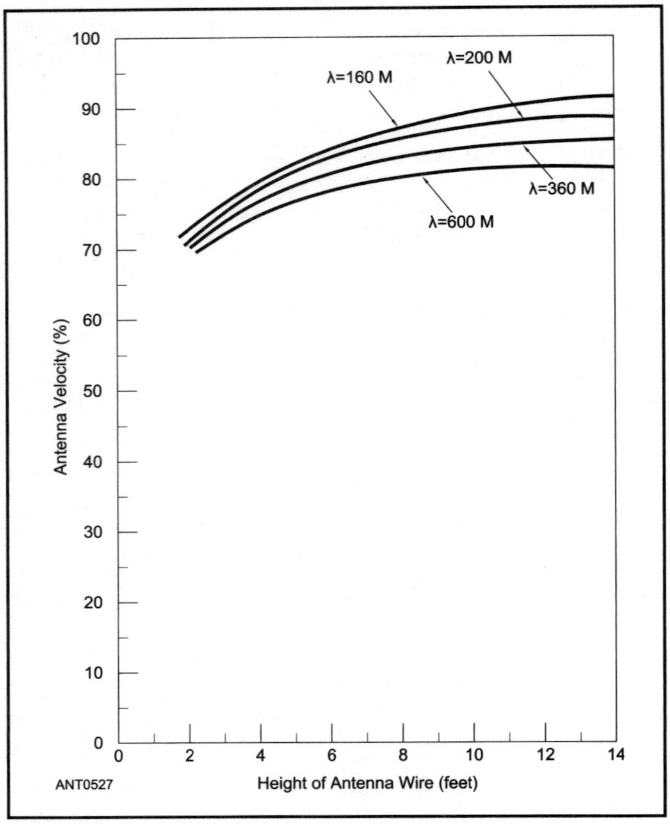

Figure 22.2 — Signal velocity on a Beverage increases with height above ground, and reaches a practical maximum at about 10 feet. Improvement is minimal above this height. (100% represents the velocity of light.)

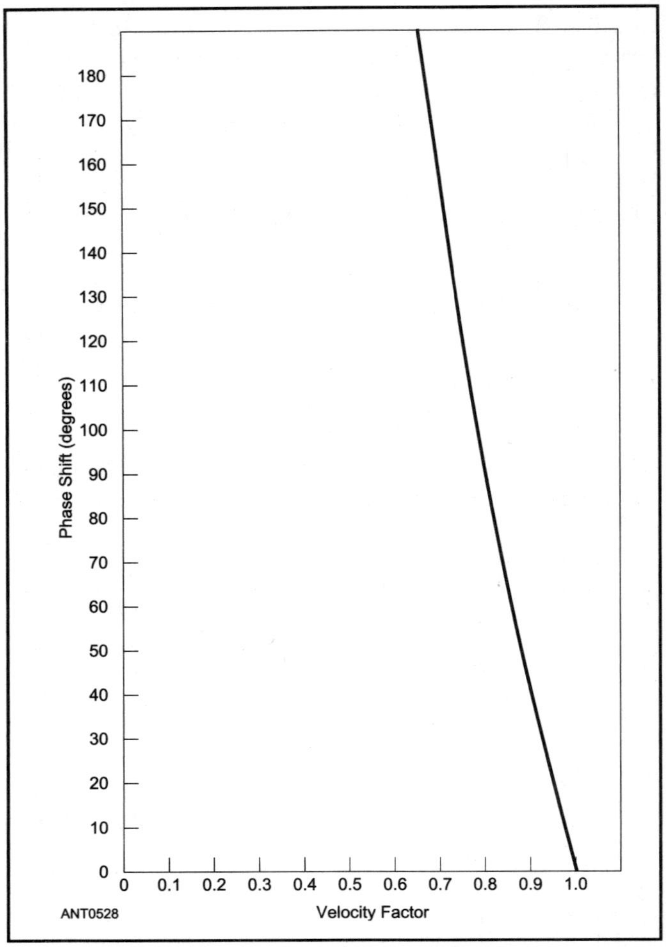

Figure 22.3 — This curve shows phase shift (per wavelength) as a function of velocity factor on a Beverage antenna. Once the phase shift for the antenna goes beyond 90°, the gain drops off from its peak value, and any increase in antenna length will decrease gain.

toward a maximum at the receiver end of the antenna.

This process can be likened to a series of signal generators lined up on the wire, with phase differences corresponding to their respective spacings on the wire (Figure 22.1C). At the receiver end, a maximum voltage is produced by these voltages adding in phase. For example, the wave component induced at the receiver end of the antenna will be in phase (at the receiver end) with a component of the same wave induced, say, 270° (or any other distance) down the antenna, after it travels to the receiver end.

In practice, there is some phase shift of the wave on the wire with respect to the wave in space. This phase shift results from the velocity factor of the antenna. (As with any transmission line, the signal velocity on the Beverage is somewhat less than in free space.) Velocity of propagation on a Beverage is typically between 85 and 98% of that in free space. As antenna height is increased to a certain optimum height (which is about 10 feet for 160 meters), the velocity factor increases. Beyond this height, only minimal improvement is afforded, as shown in **Figure 22.2**. These curves are the result of experimental work done in 1922 by RCA, and reported in a *QST* article (November 1922) entitled "The Wave Antenna for 200-Meter Reception," by H. H. Beverage. The curve for 160 meters was extrapolated from the other curves.

Phase shift (per wavelength) is shown as a function of velocity factor in **Figure 22.3**, and is given by:

$$\theta = 360\left(\frac{100}{k} - 1\right) \qquad (1)$$

where k = velocity factor of the antenna in percent.

The signals present on and around a Beverage antenna are shown graphically in A through D of **Figure 22.4**. These curves show relative voltage levels over a number of periods of the wave in space and their relative effects in terms of the total signal at the receiver end of the antenna.

Performance in Other Directions

The performance of a Beverage antenna in directions other than the favored one is quite different than previously discussed. Take, for instance, the case of a signal arriving perpendicular to the wire (90° either side of the favored direction). In this case, the wave induces voltages along the wire that are essentially *in phase*, so that they arrive at the receiver end more or less out of phase, and thus cancel. (This can be likened to a series of signal generators lined up along the antenna as before, but having no progressive phase differences.)

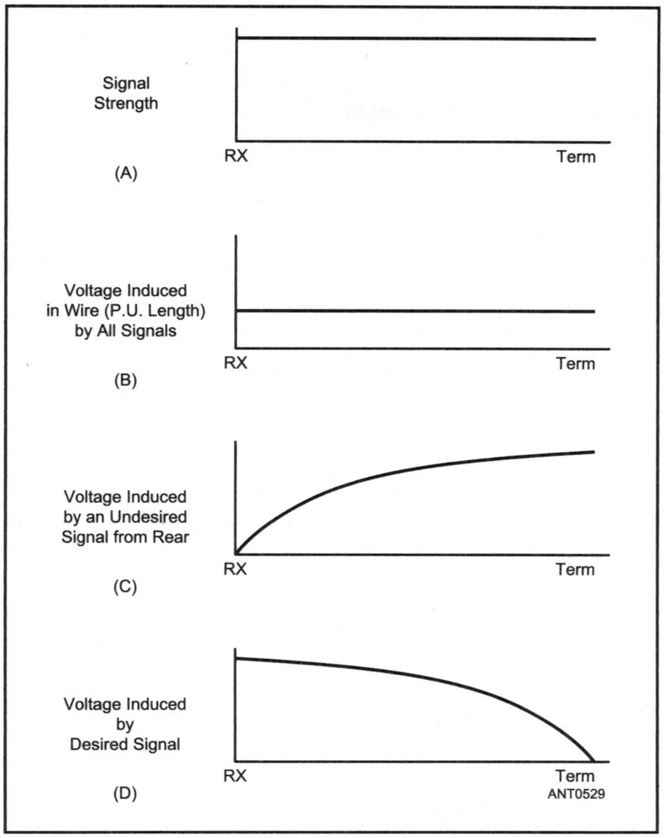

Figure 22.4 — These curves show the voltages that appear in a Beverage antenna over a period of several cycles of the wave. Signal strength (at A) is constant over the length of the antenna during this period, as is voltage induced per unit length in the wire (at B). (The voltage induced in any section of the antenna is the same as the voltage induced in any other section of the same size, over the same period of time.) At C, the voltages induced by an undesired signal from the rearward direction add in phase and build to a maximum at the termination end, where they are dissipated in the termination (if $Z_{term} = Z_0$). The voltages resulting from a desired signal are shown at D. The wave on the wire travels closely with the wave in space, and the voltages resulting add in phase to a maximum at the receiver end of the antenna.

As a result of this cancellation, Beverages exhibit deep nulls off the sides. Some minor sidelobes will exist, as with other long-wire antennas, and will increase in number with the length of the antenna.

In the case of a signal arriving from the rear of the antenna, the behavior of the antenna is very similar to its performance in the favored direction. The major difference is that the signal from the rear adds in phase at the termination end and is absorbed by the termination impedance. **Figure 22.5** compares the azimuth and elevation patterns for a 2-λ (1062 foot) and a 1-λ (531 foot) Beverage at 1.83 MHz. The wire is mounted 8 feet above flat ground (to keep it above deer antlers and away from humans too) and is terminated with a 500-Ω resistor in each case, although the exact value of the terminating resistance is not very critical. The ground constants assumed in this computer model are conductivity of 5 mS/m and a dielectric constant of 13. Beverage dielectric performance tends to decrease as the ground becomes better. Beverages operated over saltwater do not work as well as they do over poor ground.

For most effective operation, the Beverage should be terminated in an impedance equal to the characteristic impedance Z_{ANT} of the antenna. For maximum signal transfer to the receiver you should also match the receiver's input impe-

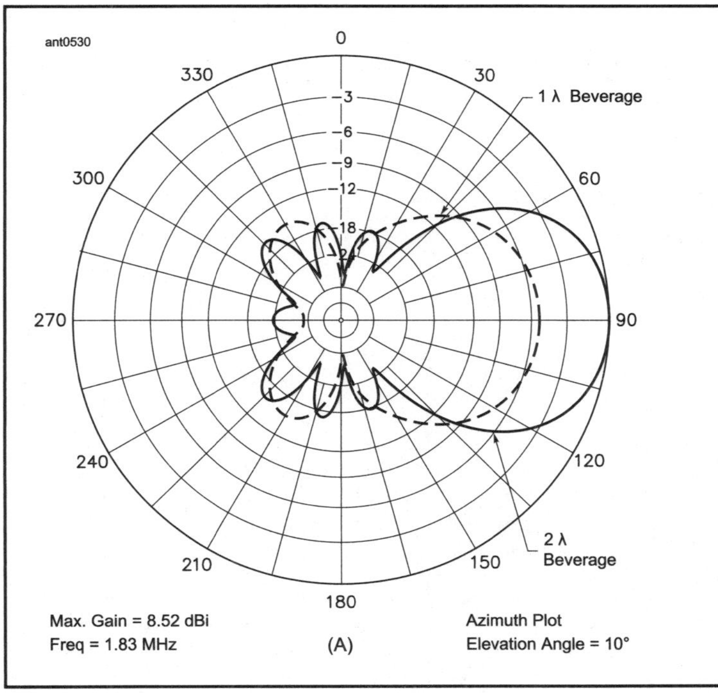

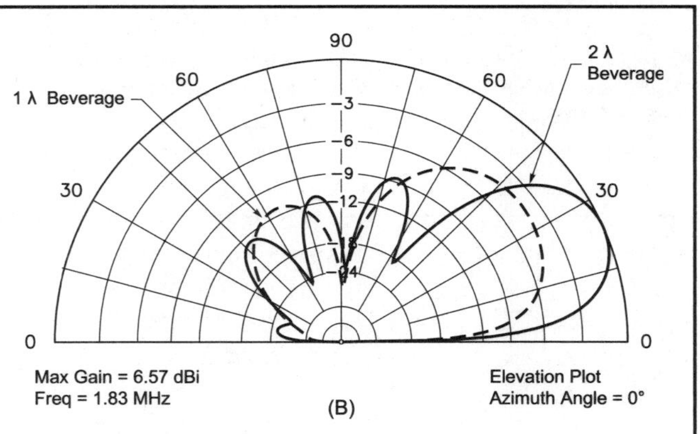

Figure 22.5 — At A, azimuthal patterns of a 2-λ (solid line) and a 1-λ (dashed line) Beverage antenna, terminated with 550-Ω resistor at 1.83 MHz, at an elevation angle of 10°. The rearward pattern around 180° is more than 20 dB down from the front lobe for each antenna. At B, the elevation-plane patterns. Note the rejection of very high-angle signals near 90°.

dance to the antenna. If the termination impedance is not equal to the characteristic impedance of the antenna, some part of the signal from the rear will be reflected back toward the receiver end of the antenna.

If the termination impedance is merely an open circuit (no terminating resistor), total reflection will result and the antenna will exhibit a bidirectional pattern (still with very deep nulls off the sides). An unterminated Beverage will not have the same response to signals in the rearward direction as it exhibits to signals in the forward direction because of attenuation and re-radiation of part of the reflected wave as it travels back toward the receiver end. **Figure 22.6** compares the response from two 2-λ Beverages, one terminated and the other unterminated. Just like a terminated long-wire transmitting antenna (which is mounted higher off the ground than a Beverage, which is meant only for receiving), the terminated Beverage has a reduced forward lobe compared to its unterminated sibling. The unterminated Beverage exhibits about a 5 dB front-to-back ratio for this length because of the radiation and wire and ground losses that occur before the forward wave gets to the end of the wire.

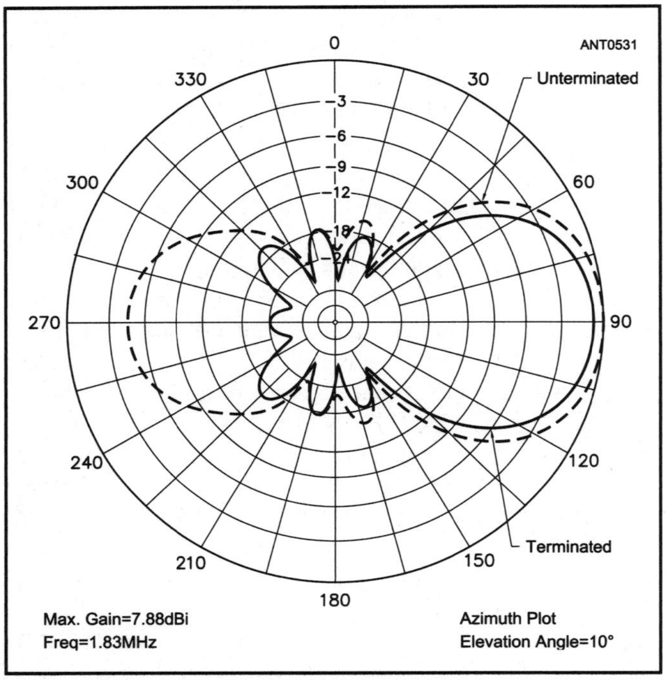

Figure 22.6 — Comparing the azimuthal patterns for a 2-λ Beverage, terminated (solid line) and unterminated (dashed line).

If the termination is between the extremes (open circuit and perfect termination in Z_{ANT}), the peak direction and intensity of signals off the rear of the Beverage will change. As a result, an adjustable reactive termination can be employed to *steer* the nulls to the rear of the antenna (see **Figure 22.7**). This can be of great help in eliminating a local interfering signal from a rearward direction (typically 30° to 40° either side of the back direction). Such a scheme doesn't help much for interfering skywave signals because of variations encountered in the ionosphere that constantly shift polarity, amplitude, phase and incoming elevation angles.

To determine the appropriate value for a terminating resistor, you need to know the characteristic impedance (surge impedance), Z_{ANT}, of the Beverage. It is interesting to note that Z_{ANT} is not a function of the length, just like a transmission line.

$$Z_{ANT} = 138 \times \log\left(\frac{4h}{d}\right) \tag{2}$$

where

Z_{ANT} = characteristic impedance of the Beverage = terminating resistance needed

h = wire height above ground

d = wire diameter (in the same units as h)

Another aspect of terminating the Beverage is the quality of the RF ground used for the termination. For most types of soil a ground rod is sufficient, since the optimum value for the termination resistance is in the range of 400 to 600 Ω for typical Beverages and the ground-loss resistance is in series with this. Even if the ground-loss resistance at the

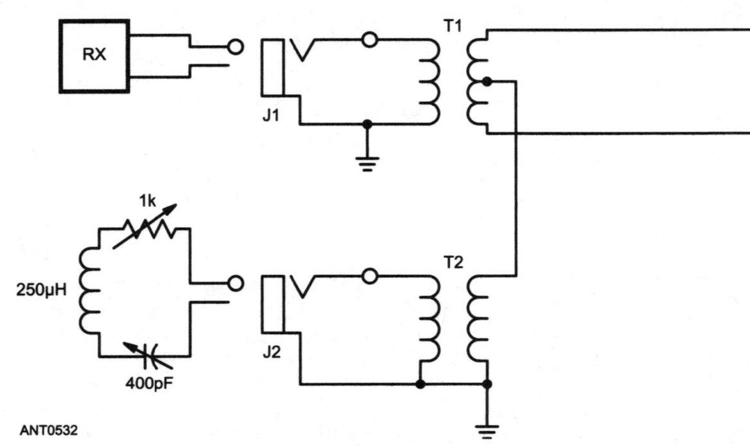

Figure 22.7 — A two-wire Beverage antenna that has provisions for direction switching and null steering in the rear quadrant. Performance improves with height to a point, and is optimum for 1.8-MHz operation at about 10 to 12 feet. Parts identifications are for text reference.

termination point is as high as 40 or 50 Ω, it still is not an appreciable fraction of the overall terminating resistance. For soil with very poor conductivity, however, (such as sand or rock) you can achieve a better ground termination by laying radial wires on the ground at both the receiver and termination ends. These wires need not be resonant quarter-wave in length, since the ground detunes them anyway. Like the ground counterpoise for a vertical antenna, a number of short radials is better than a few long ones. Some amateurs use chicken-wire ground screens for their ground terminations.

As with many other antennas, improved directivity and gain can be achieved by lengthening the antenna and by arranging several antennas into an array. One item that must be kept in mind is that by virtue of the velocity factor of the antenna, there is some phase shift of the wave on the antenna with respect to the wave in space. Because of this phase shift, although the directivity will continue to sharpen with increased length, there will be some optimum length at which the gain of the antenna will peak. Beyond this length, the current increments arriving at the receiver end of the antenna will no longer be in phase, and will not add to produce a maximum signal at the receiver end. This optimum length is a function of velocity factor and frequency, and is given by:

$$L = \frac{\lambda}{4\left(\frac{100}{k} - 1\right)} \quad (3)$$

where

L = maximum effective length

λ = signal wavelength in free space (same units as L)

k = velocity factor of the antenna in percent

Because velocity factor increases with height (to a point, as mentioned earlier), optimum length is somewhat longer if the antenna height is increased. The maximum effective length also increases with the number of wires in the antenna system. For example, for a two-wire Beverage like the bidirectional version shown in Figure 22.7, the maximum effective length is about 20% longer than the single-wire version. A typical length for a single-wire 1.8-MHz Beverage (made of #16 AWG wire and erected 10 feet above ground) is about 1200 feet.

Feed Point Transformers for Single-Wire Beverages

Most users are not concerned with obtaining a low SWR on the transmission line feeding their Beverages. For example, let us assume that the Z_{ANT} of a particular Beverage is 525 Ω and the terminating resistance is made equal to that value. If a 3:1 turns-ratio autotransformer is used at the input end of the antenna, the nominal impedance transformation 50 Ω × 3^2 = 450 Ω. This transformer is a *9:1 transformer*, referring to its impedance transformation. The resulting SWR on the feed line to the receiver would be 525/450 = 1.27:1, not enough to be concerned about. For a Z_{ANT} of 600 Ω, the SWR is 600/450 = 1.33:1, again not a matter of concern.

Matching transformer T1 in Figure 22.1 is easily constructed as a flux-coupled transformer or as an auto-transformer. Small toroidal ferrite cores are best for this application, with those of high permeability (μ_i = 125 to 5000, type 77 ferrite is recommended for 160 meters) being the easiest to wind (requiring fewest turns) and having the best high-frequency response (because few turns are used).

A 9:1 transformer can be made from a pair of ferrite beads as described on the K9AY website at **www.aytechnologies.com/TechData/9-to-1_XFMR.htm**. **Figure 22.8A** shows the basic design. If a binocular core is available, that simplifies construction. If high-frequency noise or signals are present, additional isolation between primary and secondary can be obtained by using a toroidal core and placing the windings on opposite sides. K9YC has written a detailed paper on the subject, "Chokes and Isolation Transformers For Receiving Antennas" which is downloadable from **k9yc.com/RXChokesTransformers.pdf** and is available as an *NCJ* article, as well. (See the Bibliography.)

Trifilar-wound autotransformers are convenient but do not provide galvanic isolation and have significant distributed capacitance between the primary and secondary windings. You can make a matching autotransformer suitable for use from 160 to 40 meters using eight trifilar turns of #24 AWG enameled wire wound over a stack of two Amidon FT-50-75 or two MN8-CX cores. See Figure 22.8B.

Make your own trifilar cable bundle by placing three 3-foot lengths of #24 AWG wire side-by-side and twisting them in a hand drill so that there is a uniform twist about one twist-per-inch. This holds the three wires together in a bundle that can be passed through the two stacked cores, rather like

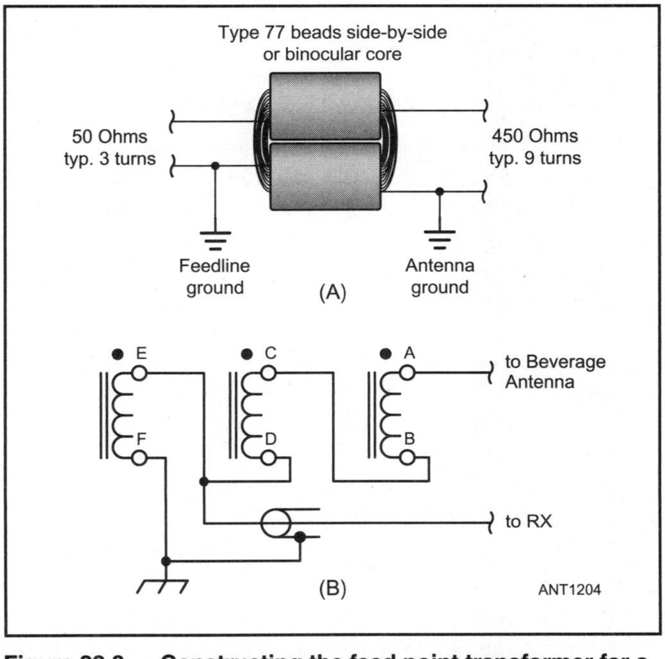

Figure 22.8 — Constructing the feed point transformer for a single-wire Beverage. See text for details.

threading a needle. Remember that each time you put the bundle through the center of the cores counts as one turn.

After you finish winding, cut the individual wires to leave about 3/4-inch leads, sand off the enamel insulation and tin the wires with a soldering iron. Identify the individual wires with an ohmmeter and then connect them together following Figure 22.8B. Coat the transformer with Q-dope (liquid polystyrene) to finalize the transformer. White glue will work also. See the chapter **Transmission Line System Techniques** for more information. *The ARRL Handbook* and the chapter **Receiving Antennas** of *ON4UN's Low-Band DXing* book are also good sources of more information on winding toroidal transformers

Practical Considerations

Even though Beverage antennas have excellent directive patterns if terminated properly, gain never exceeds about –3 dBi in most practical installations. However, the directivity that the Beverage provides results in a much higher signal-to-noise ratio for signals in the desired direction than almost any other real-world antenna used at low frequencies.

A typical situation might be a station located in the US Northeast (W1), trying to receive Top Band signals from Europe to the northeast, while thunderstorms behind him in the US Southeast (W4) are creating huge static crashes. Instead of listening to an S7 signal with 10-dB over S9 noise and interference on a vertical, the directivity of a Beverage will typically allow you to copy the same signal at perhaps S5 with only S3 (or lower) noise and interference. This is certainly a worthwhile improvement. However, if you are in the middle of a thunderstorm, or if there is a thunderstorm in the direction from which you are trying to receive a signal, no Beverage is going to help you!

There are a few basic principles that must be kept in mind when erecting Beverage antennas if optimum performance is to be realized.

1) Plan the installation thoroughly, including choosing an antenna length consistent with the optimum length values discussed earlier.

2) Keep the antenna as straight and as nearly level as possible over its entire run. Avoid following the terrain under the antenna too closely — keep the antenna level with the average terrain.

3) Minimize the lengths of vertical downleads at the ends of the antenna. Their effect is detrimental to the directive pattern of the antenna. It is best to slope the antenna wire from ground level to its final height (over a distance of 50 feet or so) at the feed point end. Similar action should be taken at the termination end. Be sure to seal the transformers against weather.

4) Use a noninductive resistor for terminating a single-wire Beverage. If you live in an area where lightning storms are common, use 2-W terminating resistors, which can survive surges due to nearby lightning strikes.

5) Use high-quality insulators for the Beverage wire where it comes into contact with the supports. Plastic insulators designed for electric fences are inexpensive and effective.

6) Keep the Beverage away from parallel conductors such as electric power and telephone lines for a distance of at least 200 feet. Perpendicular conductors, even other Beverages, may be crossed with relatively little interaction, but do not cross any conductors that may pose a safety hazard.

7) Run the coaxial feed line to the Beverage so that it is not directly under the span of the wire. This prevents common-mode currents from appearing on the shield of the coax. It may be necessary to use a ferrite-bead choke on the feed line if you find that the feed line itself picks up signals when it is temporarily disconnected from the Beverage.

8) If you use elevated radials in your transmitting antenna system, keep your Beverage feed lines well away from them to avoid stray pickup that will ruin the Beverage's directivity.

The Two-Wire Beverage

The two-wire antenna shown in Figure 22.7 has the major advantage of having signals from both directions available at the receiver at the flip of a switch between J1 and J2. Also, because there are two wires in the system (equal amounts of signal voltage are induced in both wires), greater signal voltages will be produced. (The April 2006 *QST* article "A Cool Beverage Four Pack" by Ward Silver, NØAX, describes a four-directional array created from a pair of two-wire Beverages at right angles.)

A signal from the left direction in Figure 22.7 induces equal voltages in both wires, and equal in-phase currents flow as a result. The *reflection transformer* (T3 at the right-hand end of the antenna) then inverts the phase of these signals and reflects them back down the antenna toward the receiver, using the antenna wires as a balanced open-wire transmission line. This signal is then transformed by T1 down to the input impedance of the receiver (50 Ω) at J1.

Signals traveling from right to left also induce equal voltages in each wire, and they travel in phase toward the receiver end, through T1, and into T2. Signals from this direction are available at J2.

T1 and T2 are standard 9:1 wideband transformers capable of operating from 1.8 to at least 10 MHz. Like any two parallel wires making up a transmission line, the two-wire Beverage has a certain characteristic impedance — we'll call it Z_1 here — depending on the spacing between the two wires and the insulation between them. T3 transforms the terminating resistance needed at the end of the line to Z_1. Keep in mind that this terminating resistance is equal to the characteristic impedance Z_{ANT} of the Beverage — that is, the impedance of the parallel wires over their images in the ground below. For example, if Z_1 of the Beverage wire is 300 Ω (that is, you used TV twin-lead for the two Beverage wires), T3 must transform the balanced 300 Ω to the unbalanced 500 Ω Z_{ANT} impedance used to terminate the Beverage.

The design and construction of the reflection transformer used in a two-wire Beverage is more demanding than that for the straightforward matching transformer T1 because the exact value of terminating impedance is more critical for good F/B. See the **Receiving Antennas** chapter in *ON4UN's Low-Band DXing* for details on winding the reflection transformers for a two-wire Beverage.

Another convenient feature of the two-wire Beverage is the ability to steer the nulls off either end of the antenna while receiving in the opposite direction. For instance, if the series RLC network shown at J2 is adjusted while the receiver is connected to J1, signals can be received from the left direction while interference coming from the right can be partially or completely nulled. The nulls can be steered over a 60° (or more) area off the right-hand end of the antenna. The same null-steering capability exists in the opposite direction with the receiver connected at J2 and the termination connected at J1.

The two-wire Beverage is typically erected at the same height as a single-wire version. The two wires are at the same height and are spaced uniformly — typically 12 to 18 inches apart for discrete wires. Some amateurs construct two-wire Beverages using "window" ladder-line, twisting the line about three twists per foot for mechanical and electrical stability in the wind.

The characteristic impedance Z_{ANT} of a Beverage made using two discrete wires with air insulation between them depends on the wire size, spacing and height and is given by:

$$Z_{ANT} = \frac{69}{\sqrt{\varepsilon}} \times \log\left[\frac{4h}{d}\sqrt{1+\left(\frac{2h}{S}\right)^2}\right] \quad (4)$$

where

Z_{ANT} = Beverage impedance = desired terminating resistance

S = wire spacing

h = height above ground

d = wire diameter (in same units as S and h)

ε = 2.71828

22.1.3 BEVERAGE ON GROUND (BOG)

A number of low-band DXers have reported improved received signal-to-noise ratios using a Beverage On Ground (BOG). This consists of a wire placed directly on the ground, as if a regular Beverage antenna were simply installed on the ground. Results are mixed as discussed by Guy Olinger, K2AV, in the following excerpt from a discussion on the Topband reflector: "What is often called a BOG is really a ground-mounted low-velocity-factor receive antenna, which has its own set of rules. The technique of terminating the far end of a wire in what amounts to a characteristic impedance, to dissipate the standing wave on the wire, does not produce an optimum BOG.

"160 meter BOGs longer than 220 feet start to not model or perform well. One can easily model a BOG that has a pattern *reversal*. The various serious quirks of BOGs make them [difficult to use].

"Notching the BOG into the ground during installation prevents a large change in velocity factor as over seasons the wire gradually works itself through the grass and into the dirt. To get the BOG adjusted and with a somewhat constant behavior really requires that the BOG be in the actual ground, not laying on the grass where it can move vertically.

"The BOG's pattern will also vary with the ground's water content, which is in turn varying the velocity factor and the best termination strategy. This effect, along with the wire gradually growing down into the grass, can be responsible for the difficulty in obtaining repeatable and satisfactory results."

22.1.4 EWE ANTENNA

The EWE antenna invented by Floyd Koontz, WA2WVL, combines two short vertical wires and one horizontal wire as shown in **Figure 22.9**. (See the Bibliography.) Although the EWE looks similar to a Beverage antenna as described previously, the EWE is essentially a two-element driven array. The antenna receives best in the plane of the array in the direction opposite the termination. The pattern is a broad cardioid with a null in the direction of the terminated "rear" element. The horizontal gain of the antenna is about 20 dB lower than the vertical gain and is directed at a high angle off the side.

The version in Figure 22.9 is designed to operate from 1.8 to 4.0 MHz with a front-to-back ratio of greater than 25 dB without adjustment. The EWE can be bottom fed as shown in the figure or at the top of the front vertical element. If separate feed lines and transformers are used for each of the vertical elements, the termination can be switched between elements, creating a reversible pattern. Arrays can also be created as described in the referenced articles, creating a steerable pattern. The technique of creating an array of vertical elements by using loops is discussed in the article "Introducing the Shared-Apex Loop Array" by Mark Bauman, KB7GF that is included with this book's downloadable supplemental information.

22.1.5 LF AND MF REVERSIBLE EWE

This version of the EWE designed by Mike Sapp, WA3TTS, was optimized for weak signal reception on the 2200 and 630 meter bands. It is also useful on the 160 and 80 meter bands with a typical SWR of 1.3:1 throughout its design range. It can be used down into the 30 kHz range, as

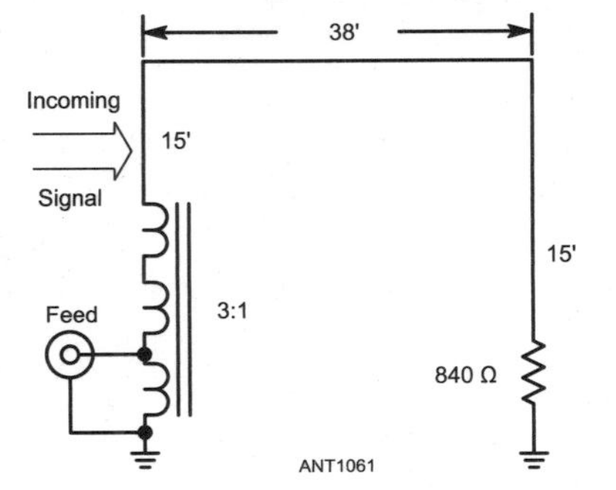

Figure 22.9 — The EWE antenna designed for use on 160 and 80 meters.

well. As with other EWE antennas, the dimensions are not critical and can be reduced to fit a small lot with some corresponding reduction in signal capture. The full article, "A Reversible LF and MF EWE Receive Antenna for Small Lots" is included in the downloadable supplemental information and includes detailed construction directions and complete descriptions of the specialized components associated with this antenna.

This version of the EWE improves the grounding of the antenna to reduce dependence on ground properties observed with the original design. A perimeter ground wire ties the four antenna ground rods together along with the center ground wires and rods. The coaxial feed line pair is grounded as well. Feed line chokes and isolation transformers are used to prevent noise pickup from common-mode current.

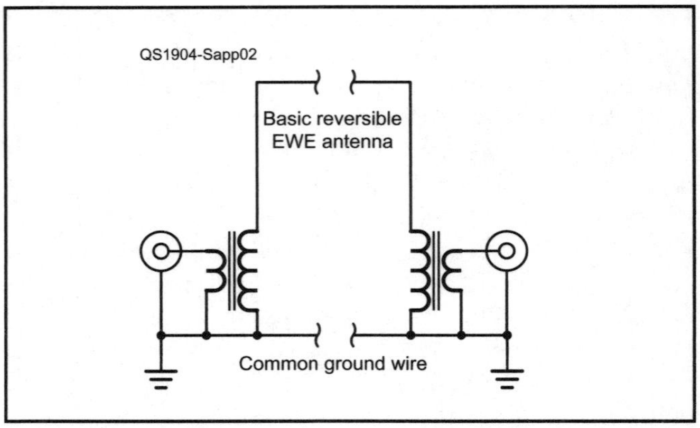

Figure 22.10 — The LF/MF reversible EWE antenna at WA3TTS.

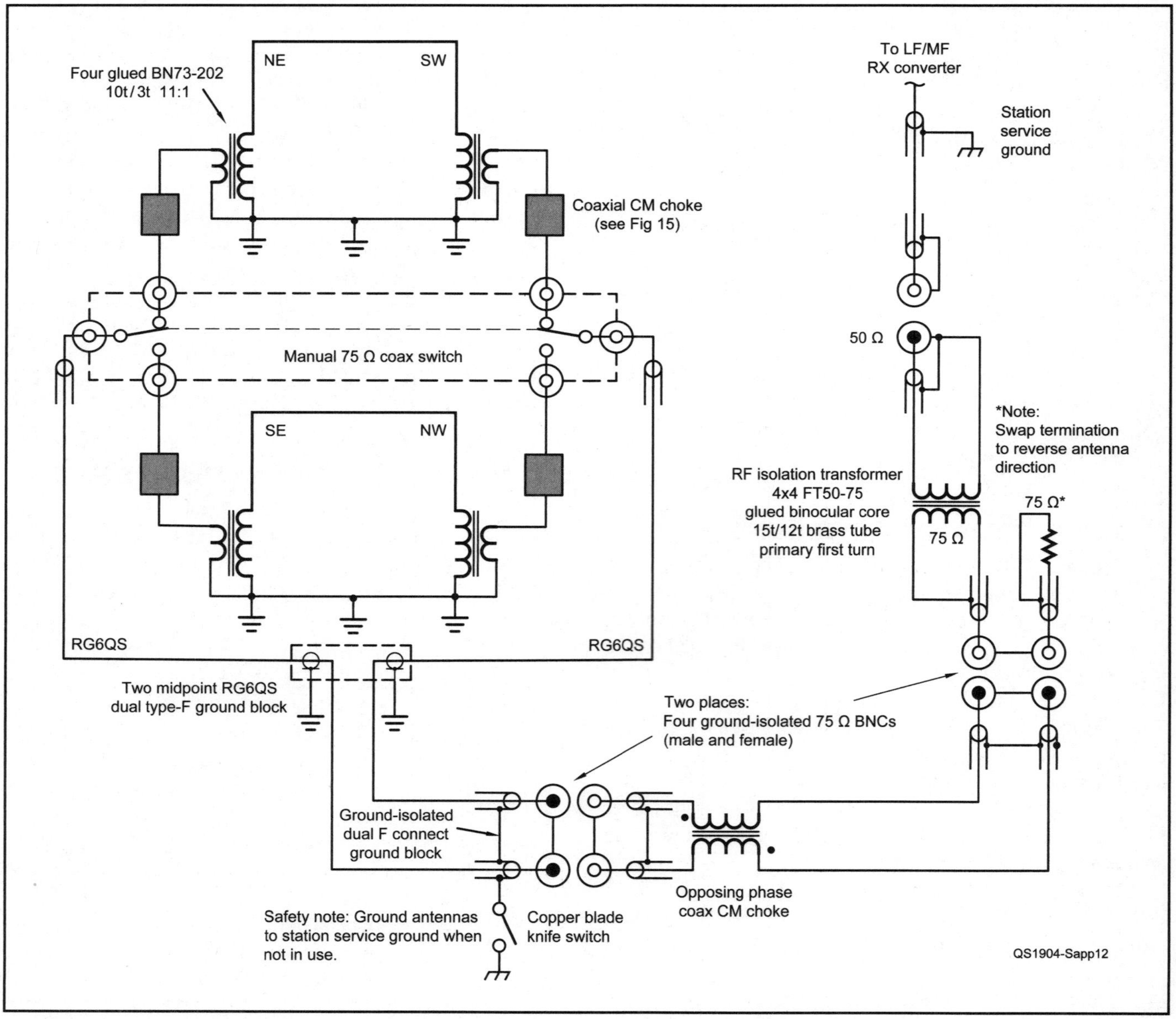

Figure 22.11 — The essential design details of the four-way LF/MF EWE antenna system.

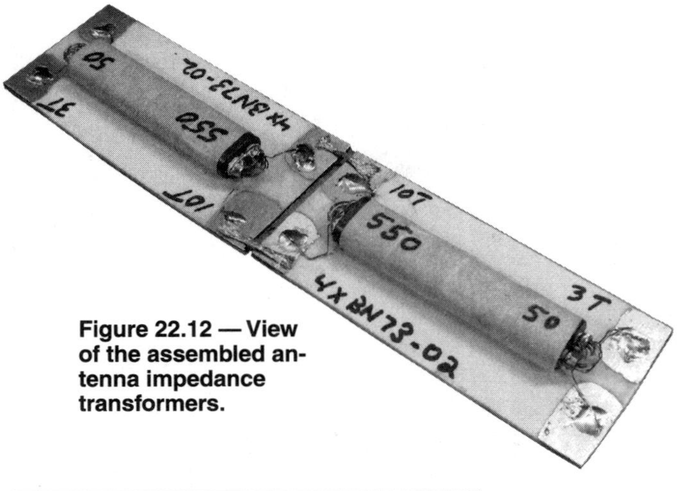

Figure 22.12 — View of the assembled antenna impedance transformers.

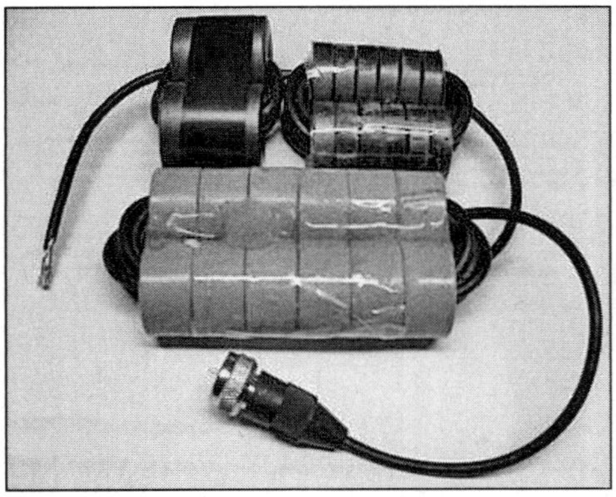

Figure 22.13 — The coaxial common-mode choke, used on each antenna termination.

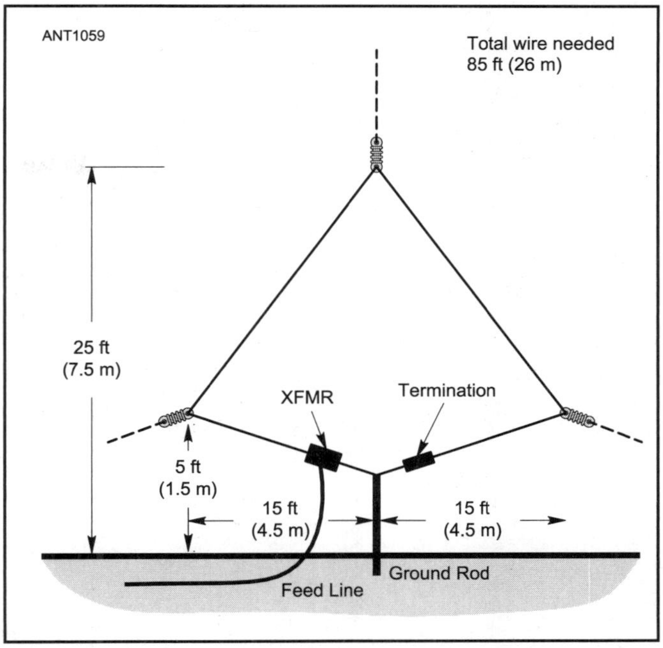

Figure 22.14 — Configuration of the K9AY Loop at the maximum size that allows coverage of both 160 and 80 meter ham bands with a resistive termination.

The wire shared at the antenna ground points enables the original EWE design to be made reversible as in **Figure 22.10**. An antenna transformer is used at each end with a separate feed line for each direction. If two of these reversible antennas are positioned at right angles, a four-way receiving antenna system is obtained as shown in **Figure 22.11**.

Because the frequency of operation is much lower than most amateur receiving antennas, the impedance transformer and common-mode choke construction use multiple ferrite cores taped together. In addition, special common-mode chokes are used and careful attention is paid to block common-mode noise and transmit signal pickup on the receive feed lines. An impedance transformer is shown in **Figure 22.12** and the coaxial common-mode choke is shown in **Figure 22.13**.

Switching the antenna requires 75 Ω TV-type A/B switches which automatically terminate the unused port in 75 Ω. This allows separate receivers to be used on the individual EWE antennas. A two-port 180° combiner makes it possible to obtain a bi-directional pattern aimed between the main lobes of the individual antennas.

22.1.6 K9AY LOOP

Described here by its inventor, Gary Breed, K9AY, the loop achieves modest, but useful directivity in a small area, making it a popular choice for hams wanting to improve their receiving ability. (See the Bibliography for additional information about the antenna.)

The K9AY loop is a hybrid that combines two antenna types. Referring to **Figure 22.14**, if the termination resistor is zero — a short circuit — the antenna becomes a classic "small loop" (usually defined as less than 0.1 λ diameter). The near-field response of small loops is predominantly to the magnetic field (H-field) component of an electromagnetic wave. Next, with an infinite resistor — an open circuit — the antenna becomes a short, bent monopole. Short monopole antennas respond most strongly to the electric field (E-field) component of an electromagnetic wave.

In the K9AY Loop, the terminating resistor serves to balance the ratio of the small loop and monopole responses, with energy from the two modes summed at the feed point. When the value of the resistor is adjusted to the optimum value (typically near 400 Ω), there is cancellation of arriving signals in one of the directions in line with the plane of the loop. This cancellation occurs because of the rotational "sense" of the H-field. While the E-field is one-dimensional (amplitude only), the H-field obeys the "right hand rule" that can be visualized as spiral rotation as a wave travels through space. Waves arriving from opposite directions will thus have opposite rotation. From one direction, the E- and H-field contributions are summed at the feed point. But for signals from the opposite direction, the antenna output is the difference of these contributions.

This same type of behavior is present in two other devices familiar to hams; a directional coupler such as those used in the familiar Bird wattmeter, and the direction-finding (DF) loop with sense antenna described in many (mostly older) antenna reference books.

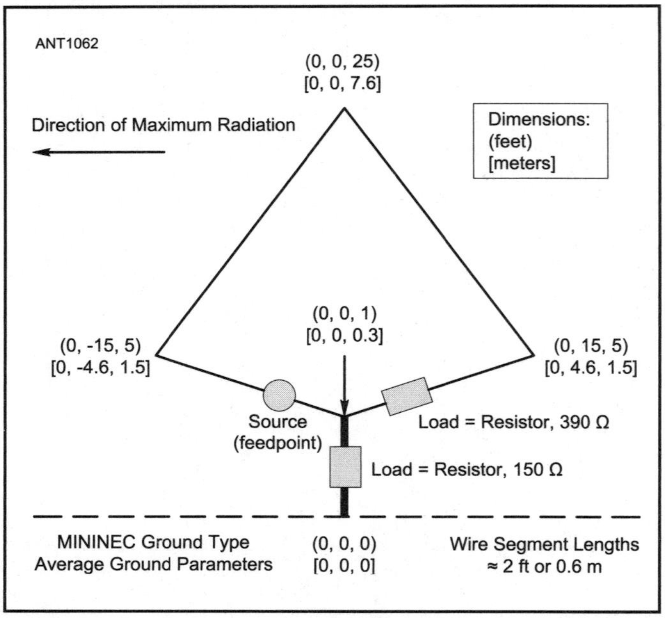

Figure 22.15 — Diagram of the K9AY Loop with dimensions and parameters for computer modeling.

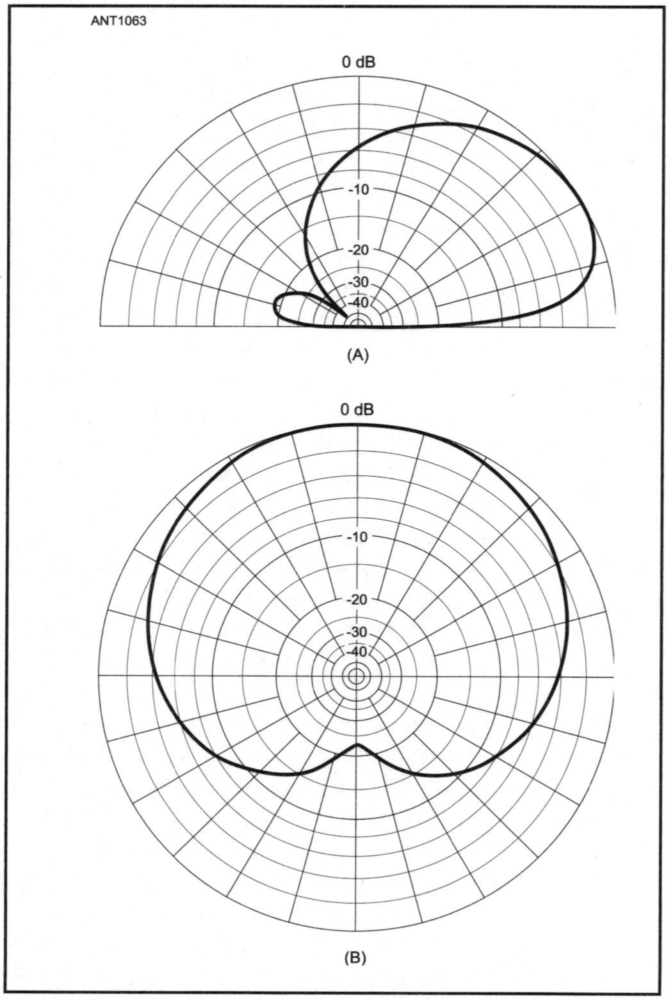

Figure 22.16 — Vertical (A) and horizontal (B) radiation patterns for the K9AY Loop at 1.825 MHz.

The tradeoff for obtaining a directional pattern with small size is low efficiency. With the dimensions given above, the K9AY Loop has a gain of approximately –26 dBi. For comparison, a ¼-wave vertical has a gain near 0 dBi, and a typical one-wavelength Beverage antenna has a gain about –11 dBi. The loop should be used with a good high dynamic range preamplifier for best results. It is not suitable for transmitting, since most of the RF energy will be absorbed by the resistor.

Computer Modeling

One of the challenges of designing the K9AY Loop was developing an accurate computer model, since *NEC*-based modeling programs will give inconsistent results for an antenna connected directly to lossy ground. K9AY's approach was to first create a free-space model of the loop, doubled in size with its mirror-image — just like making a ¼-wave vertical into a ½-wave dipole. This model is repeatable and shows the actual gain and pattern shape, including the location of the rearward null.

K9AY then returned to the as-built dimensions, installed over ground. The final model uses the *MININEC* ground option, which assumes perfect ground when calculating impedance. Ground losses are simulated by placing a resistor in the ground connection. A little trial-and-error determined that a resistor in the range of 100 to 150 Ω results in a pattern that matched the free-space model (and on-air behavior, as best as it can be determined). **Figure 22.15** is a diagram showing the modeling dimensions and parameters. This model has proven accurate for modeling loops of different sizes and shapes, and for arrays of loops. (K9AY updated his model for the loop in the article "Modeling the K9AY Loop" in the March/April 2015 issue of the *National Contest Journal* which is included with this book's downloadable supplemental information.)

For the chosen shape of the loop, and with the influence of lossy ground, the resulting null appears at an angle about 45° above horizontal, in line with the plane of the loop and toward the side with the resistor. This is shown in the pattern plots of **Figure 22.16**.

Construction

Construction of the K9AY Loop is shown in Figure 22.14. Approximately 85 feet of wire is arranged into a four-sided shape that is almost triangular. This shape was chosen primarily for its mechanical arrangement — it has a single center support approximately 25 feet high, and it can share that support with a second loop installed at right angles (see **Figure 22.17**).

Connections are made at the bottom. One end of the loop wire goes to the high impedance side of a 9:1 matching transformer; the other end to a resistor with an optimum value that is typically about 400 Ω. (See the previous section "Feed Point Transformers for Single-Wire Beverages" for more information on the transformer design.) Because the connections to each end are at a central point, it is a simple matter to include a relay at this point to reverse the connections, which

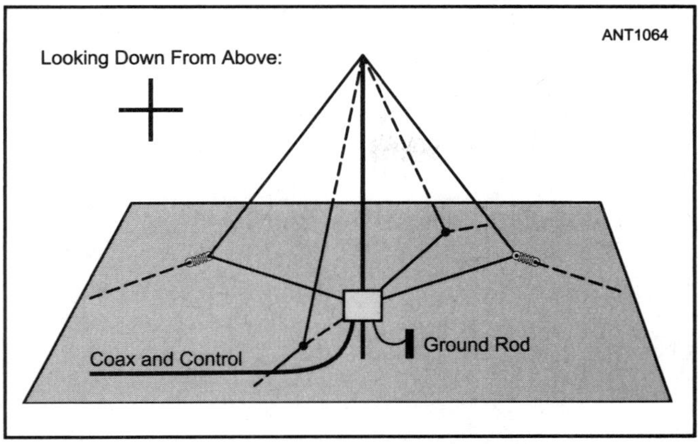

Figure 22.17 — Two loops can be installed with the same central support, creating a two-loop system that can be switched to cover four different directions. In a typical installation for 160 and 80 meter operation, the loops are 25 feet high and ±15 feet from the center (30 feet across).

reverses the directional pattern of the loop. As noted above, a second loop can be installed. Since its connections are also located in the same place, a switching system with four directions is easily implemented. The ability to switch the pattern to several directions is the primary advantage of the K9AY Loop over other small receiving antenna designs. A schematic diagram of four-direction relay switching is shown in **Figure 22.18**.

Installation and Operating Notes

Location — Because the K9AY Loop will often be installed where there is limited space, there may be interaction with nearby objects. Other antennas, house wiring, metal siding and gutters, overhead utilities, metal fences and other conductors can distort the pattern and reduce the depth of the null. The key test for proper operation is good front-to-back ratio. If F/B is poor, you will need to identify the problem. It is usually easiest to change the loop location compared to changing the surroundings!

Transmitting Antennas — Proximity to transmitting antennas may result in high RF levels on the loop, sent into the shack on the feed line. Your receiver should be protected! Protective devices are available from ham radio dealers, or you can make a simple relay box that disconnects the feed line when transmitting. It's best to open both the center conductor and shield connections.

Ground Connection — Experience has shown that locations with almost any type of "real dirt" soil only require a single ground rod for proper operation. However, some installations may experience seasonal changes in soil moisture. Desert and salt water installations will change the behavior, too. It sometimes helps to install additional ground radials to maintain consistent performance. Four or eight short radials are sufficient. Make them the same length, and place the first four directly under the loop wires. Note that the optimum value of the resistor will likely be different when using radials.

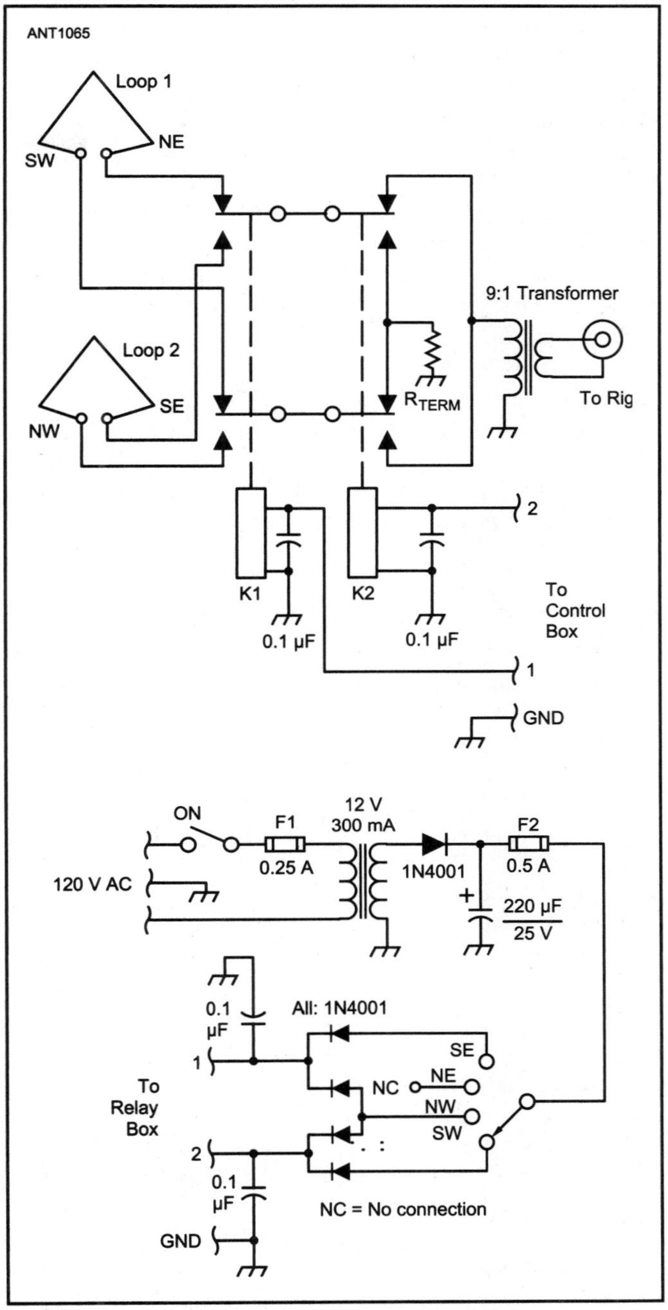

Figure 22.18 — Outdoor antenna switching (top) and indoor control (bottom) circuits for a four-direction, two-loop system.

Common-Mode Isolation — While many installations will work just fine with feed line and antenna both connected to the ground rod, some will require better isolation to avoid having the feed line shield become part of the antenna. One method is to wind the feed line and control wires through a high-permittivity (µ) toroid that is large enough to accommodate several turns. Ferrite cores of type 73 or 31 material are appropriate choices. Alternatively, the 9:1 matching transformer can have separate primary and secondary windings, with the antenna side connected to the ground rod. The feed line side may work well "floating," although another ground rod for the feed line may be wise, especially with long feed lines. Feed lines that are buried, or placed directly on the ground will be the least susceptible to common mode problems. If at all possible, avoid elevating feed lines above ground (along fences or on posts, for example).

Lack of directivity — If you don't see a deep rearward null and you're sure there is no installation problem, coupling to nearby things, or common-mode issues with feed line and control lines, or you see obvious changes with the seasons (typically in dry summer or with winter frost), then install some radials to stabilize the ground connection. A minimum of four radials located under the loop wires may be okay, but reports suggest that a total of eight radials is a better choice. Radials should extend 10 feet or so beyond the footprint of the loop.

Loop Size — As designed, the size is the maximum for 80 meter use. If made larger, the rearward null could not be obtained with just a resistor as the termination. If made smaller, the directional pattern will remain the same, but the signal level will be lower. The voltage (or current) at the feed point is proportional to the area enclosed by the loop. For example, a loop with half-size dimensions will have ¼ the area, and thus, 12 dB lower signal level. A smaller version of the K9AY Loop scaled to the 30 and 40 meter bands was developed by Bob Lombardi, W4ATM. (See the Bibliography entry for Lombardi.) K9AY has also done some experimentation with multi-turn versions of the loop as noted in the Bibliography.

Arrays of K9AY Loops

Although the K9AY Loop has useful directivity, its pattern is modest compared to a one-wavelength or longer Beverage. One way to improve performance, while keeping most of the antenna's limited-space appeal, is to combine two or more of them in an array. One of the simplest arrays is to install two crossed-loop sets with a spacing of ½-wavelength (140 feet on 80 meters, 270 feet on 160 meters). For simplicity, a phase shift of 0° for broadside operation and 180° for end-fire operation can be used to avoid the need for additional phase shift circuitry — phasing can be accomplished by simply reversing the windings of one matching transformer when the array is in the end-fire mode.

Figure 22.19 compares the radiation patterns of a single loop and the two-elements in line with the loops (end-fire mode, phasing = 180°). The array adds two very deep side nulls to the horizontal pattern, and increases the gain by 3 dB. Also, the vertical directivity is enhanced with a deep overhead null. The main forward lobe is narrower than a single loop, but remains quite wide.

Figure 22.20 shows the horizontal pattern for the broadside mode (phase shift = 0°). The main forward lobe is much narrower than a single loop, and good side nulls are present. The vertical pattern is not shown because it is the same shape as a single loop, plus the 3 dB array gain.

Of course, other arrays with different spacings and phase shifts can be designed. The K9AY Loop is a good candidate for an array element. Its inherent directivity results in performance that is better than the same array using omnidirectional elements such as verticals. The loops also have a low VSWR on the feed line, which simplifies the design of a phasing network.

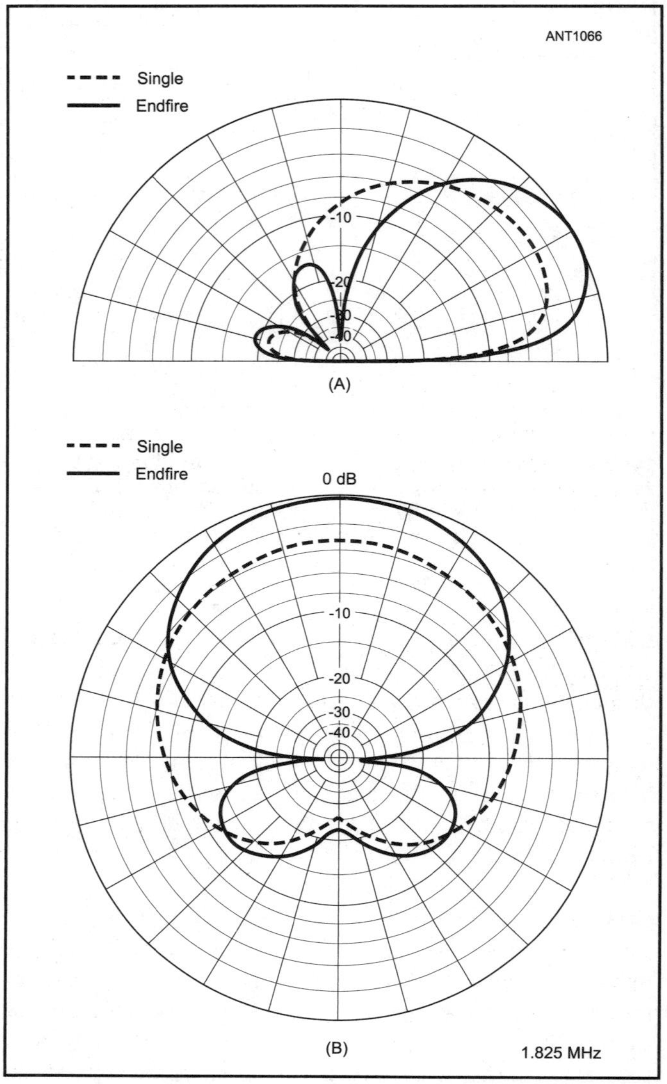

Figure 22.19 — Vertical (A) and horizontal (B) radiation patterns for two K9AY Loops, spaced ½ λ, fed in end-fire mode with 180° phasing. Frequency is 1.825 MHz

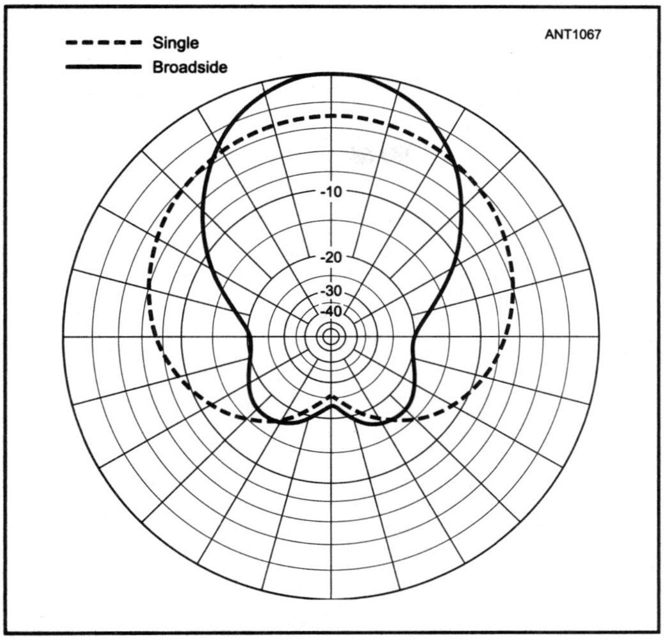

Figure 22.20 — Horizontal pattern for two K9AY Loops, spaced ½ λ, fed as a broadside array with 0° phasing. Frequency is 1.825 MHz.

22.1.7 FLAG AND PENNANT ANTENNAS

Jose Mata, EA3VY, and Earl Cunningham, K6SE, developed the pennant and flag receiving antennas in **Figure 22.21** which have become popular for the low band DXer. The antennas were developed to eliminate the need for a good ground for predictable low noise directional reception. Their small size makes them practical for those DXers without the room to construct a Beverage or Four Square. The basic premise for these antennas is to create a hybrid of the small loop pattern and a bent monopole pattern that has useful directivity. (See the previous section on K9AY Loops for more information.)

Configured as either a rectangle, triangle or diamond loop in the vertical plane, the 160 and 80 meter version is about 29 feet long and 14 feet high and mounted about 6 feet above the ground. Charles Kluttz, W4TMR, developed a version of the flag antenna with the bottom wire buried and Jerome Kahn, ACØRL, extended the design to a four-direction array. The FoG design article also includes a band-pass filter design for the 160 meter band. (See the Bibliography entries for Kluttz and for Kahn, respectively.) The reader is referred to the Bibliography for more information along with the original article included with this book's downloadable supplemental information.

Pennant and flag antennas have a feed point impedance in the range of 945 Ω (the termination opposite the feed point is also 945 Ω). The flag version shows about 5.5 dB higher "gain" than the pennant version. Their directivity is toward the feed point direction and appears cardioidal. The front-to-back ratio is in excess of 35 dB. A simple 16 to 1 toroidal or balun transformer can be used to couple to low impedance coax lines.

Mark Connelly, WA1ION, (**www.qsl.net/wa1ion**) has come up with a modification to allow a flag antenna to be electrically reversed in direction and also to allow remote optimization of the termination. In his version 16:1 transformers are put at both the termination and feed point locations and a coax cable is brought from the low impedance winding of both of these into the shack. The user can then attach one of these to the receiver and the other to a noninductive potentiometer and adjust the potentiometer so that it is in the range of 55 to 70 Ω to see an impedance at the antenna in the 880 to 1120 Ω range (when the transformer ratio is taken into effect). This allows an in-shack switching box to be constructed to allow these receiver and termination connections to be reversed to allow the null to be moved in the opposite direction.

Steve Lawrence, WB6RSE, took the steering solution to the next level and designed a flag antenna that is mechanically rotatable. The article "Rebuilding a Receiving Flag Antenna for 160 Meters" describes a 29-by-14 foot flag with a frame made from telescoping fiberglass poles. The assembly is sturdy enough to be turned with a small rotator. The full article is included in the downloadable supplemental information.

Don Kirk, WD8DSB, has published a design for a three-element point-fed pennant array with a common feed point (**sites.google.com/site/pennantflagantennas**). A single BN-73-202 binocular core transformer is used to

Figure 22.21 — Configurations of the flag and pennant antennas. The dimensions of the Flag, both Pennants, and the Diamond (a modification of the Flag) are 29 feet by 14 feet. The Delta (a type of half-Diamond) is 17 feet high and 28 feet long. The ground-independent antennas are 6 feet above ground.

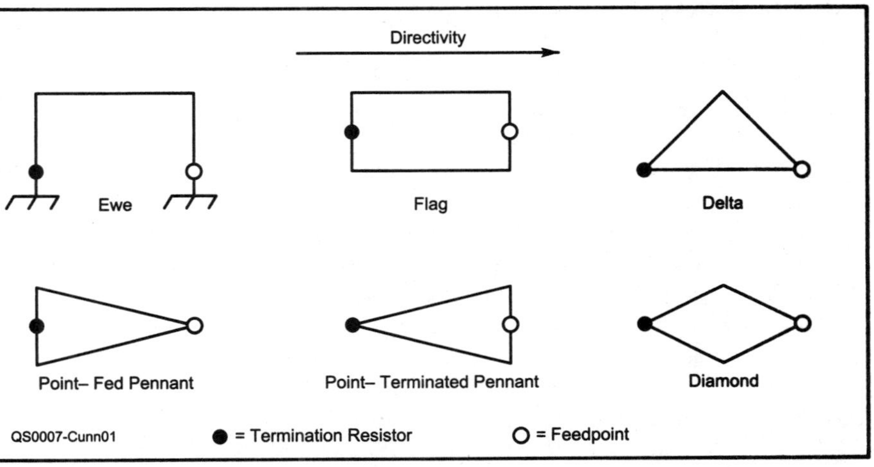

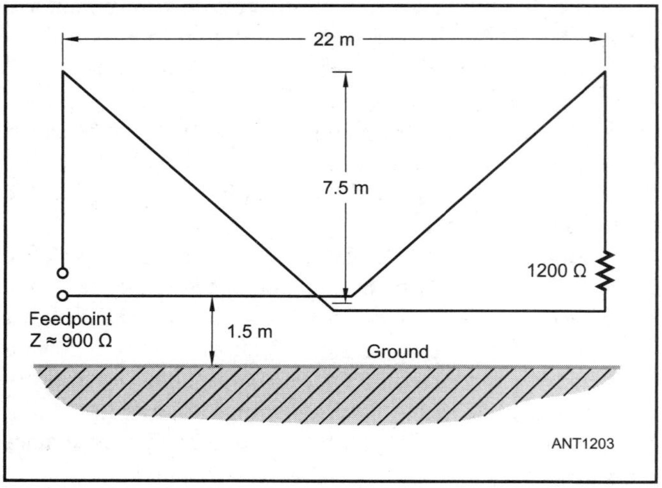

Figure 22.22 — The Double Half-Delta Loop (DHDL) antenna designed by AA7JV is an improved version of the flag and pennant receiving antennas. Note that the loops cross in the center of the antenna without a connection between them.

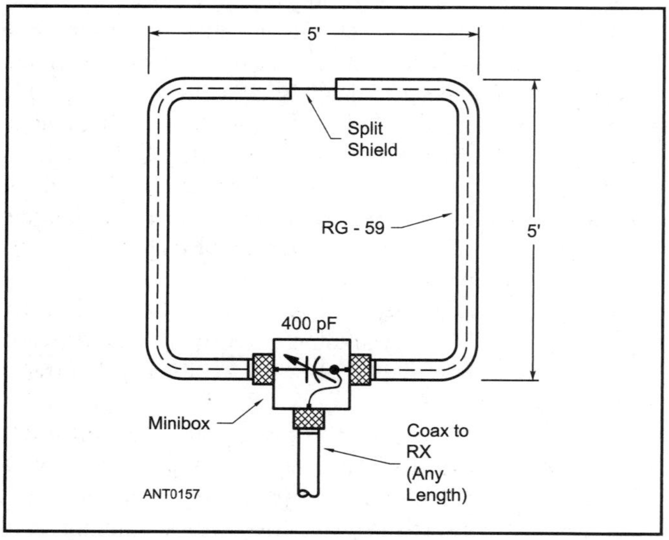

Figure 22.23 — Schematic diagram of the loop antenna. The dimensions are not critical provided overall length of the loop element does not exceed approximately 0.1 λ. Small loops which are one half or less the size of this one will prove useful where limited space is a consideration.

match whichever antenna is selected. Two relays are used for antenna switching with a single control line supplying +12/0/–12 V. This same basic switching controller design can be used with any balanced antenna design.

As part of the TX3A DXpedition to Chesterfield Island that emphasized low-band operation, George Wallner, AA7JV, developed a variation on the pennant antenna known as the Double Half Delta Loop (DHDL), shown in **Figure 22.22**. A complete description of the antenna by AA7JV is available at **www.ok1rr.com/index.php/antennas/42-double-half-delta-loop-rx-antenna**. An illustration of how the antenna is installed at contest station ED1R was published by Tobias Wellnitz, DH1TW, at **dh1tw.de/double-half-delta-loop-dhdl-receiving-antenna**. The improvement in RDF over a flag antenna of similar size is about 2.5 dB.

Jukka Klemola, OH6LI, extended the DHDL, separating the individual loops by several meters to create the LIXA (Linear Inline target Antenna). The additional separation improved the RDF leading to an array of two LIXAs separated by approximately 25 meters — the 2x LIRA (Linear Inline Receiving Antenna) with an excellent RDF of 12.1 dB. Finally, the 4x LIRA which is approximately 216 meters long, achieves an RDF of approximately 14.8 dB, similar to two staggered 320-meter long Beverages (see the article "Beverages in Echelon" in the downloadable supplemental information). The development and configuration for the LIXA and LIRA antennas is provided along with pattern comparisons to Beverage antennas at **wwrof.org/wp-content/uploads/2018/02/Receiving-Antenna-Metrics-With-Examples-v20p.pdf**.

22.1.8 A RECEIVING LOOP FOR 1.8 MHz

To obtain the sharp bidirectional pattern of a small loop, the overall length of the conductor must not exceed 0.1 λ. (See the discussion of small loops in the **Loop Antennas** chapter and the section on Direction-Finding Antennas later in this chapter.) The loop of **Figure 22.23** has a conductor length of 20 feet. At 1.81 MHz, 20 feet is 0.037 λ. With this style of loop, 0.037 λ is about the maximum practical dimension if you want to tune the element to resonance. This limitation results from the distributed capacitance between the shield and inner conductor of the loop. RG-59 was used for the loop element in this example. The capacitance per foot for this cable is 21 pF, resulting in a total distributed capacitance of 420 pF. An additional 100 pF was needed to resonate the loop at 1.810 MHz.

Therefore, the approximate inductance of the loop is 15 μH. The effect of the capacitance becomes less pronounced at the higher end of the HF spectrum, provided the same percentage of a wavelength is used in computing the conductor length. The ratio between the distributed capacitance and the lumped capacitance used at the feed point becomes greater at resonance. These facts should be contemplated when scaling the loop to those bands above 1.8 MHz.

There will not be a major difference in the construction requirements of the loop if coaxial cables other than RG-59 are used. The line impedance is not significant with respect to the loop element. Various types of coaxial line exhibit different amounts of capacitance per foot, however, thereby requiring more or less capacitance across the feed point to establish resonance.

Balanced loops are not affected noticeably by nearby objects, and therefore they can be installed indoors or out after being tuned to resonance. Moving them from one place to another does not significantly affect the tuning.

A supporting structure was fashioned from bamboo poles. The X frame is held together at the center with two U bolts. The loop element is taped to the cross-arms to form a square. You could likely use metal cross arms without seriously degrading the antenna performance. Alternatively, wood can be used for the supporting frame.

Maintaining symmetry is important to preserving the depth of the pattern's null. Using flexible cable to build the loop will achieve satisfactory results but even better performance and stability result from using semi-rigid 50 or 75 Ω hardline cable. A wooden or plastic center mast is sufficient to hold a loop made from hardline, even up to several feet in diameter.

A Minibox was used at the feed point of the loop to hold the resonating variable capacitor. In this model a 50 to 400-pF compression trimmer was used to establish resonance. You must weatherproof the box for outdoor installations.

Remove the shield braid of the loop coax for one inch directly opposite the feed point. You should treat the exposed areas with a sealing compound once this is done.

For receiving applications it is not necessary to match the feed line to the loop, though doing so may enhance the performance somewhat. If no attempt is made to obtain an SWR of 1, the builder can use 50- or 75-Ω coax for a feeder, and no difference in performance will be observed. The Q of this loop is sufficiently low to allow the operator to peak it for resonance at 1.9 MHz and use it across the entire 160 meter band. The degradation in performance at 1.8 and 2 MHz will be so slight that it will be difficult to discern.

Propagation Effects on Null Depth

After building a balanced loop you may find it does not approach the theoretical performance in the null depth. This problem may result from propagation effects. Tilting the loop away from a vertical plane may improve performance under some propagation conditions, to account for the vertical angle of arrival. Basically, the loop performs as described above only when the signal is arriving perpendicular to the axis of rotation of the loop. At incidence angles other than perpendicular, the position and depth of the nulls deteriorate. Bond explained this issue in his book on direction finding in 1944 along with the math to calculate the performance.

The problem can be even further influenced by the fact that if the loop is situated over less than perfectly conductive ground, the wave front will appear to tilt or bend. (This bending is not always detrimental; in the case of Beverage antennas, sites are chosen to take advantage of this effect.)

Another cause of apparent poor performance in the null depth can be from polarization error. If the polarization of the signal is not completely linear, the nulls will not be sharp. In fact, for circularly polarized signals, the loop might appear to have almost no nulls. Propagation effects are discussed further in the sections on direction finding.

Siting Effects on the Loop

The location of the loop has an influence on its performance that at times may become quite noticeable. For ideal performance the loop should be located outdoors and clear of any large conductors, such as metallic downspouts and towers. A VLF loop, when mounted this way, will show good sharp nulls spaced 180° apart if the loop is well balanced. This is because the major propagation mode at VLF is by ground wave. At frequencies in the HF region, a significant portion of the signal is propagated by sky wave, and nulls are often only partial.

Most hams locate their loop antennas near their operating position. If you choose to locate a small loop indoors, its performance may show nulls of less than the expected depth, and some skewing of the pattern. For precision direction finding there may be some errors associated with wiring, plumbing, and other metallic construction members in the building. Also, a strong local signal may be reradiated from the surrounding conductors so that it cannot be nulled with any positioning of the loop. There appears to be no known method of curing this type of problem. All this should not discourage you from locating a loop indoors; this information is presented here only to give you an idea of some pitfalls. Many hams have reported excellent results with indoor mounted loops, in spite of some of the problems.

Locating a receiving loop in the field of a transmitting antenna may cause a large voltage to appear at the receiver antenna terminals. This may be sufficient to destroy sensitive RF amplifier transistors or front-end protection diodes. This can be solved by disconnecting your loop from the receiver during transmit periods. This can obviously be done automatically with a relay that opens when the transmitter is activated.

22.1.9 ACTIVE ANTENNAS

The following material is based on the September 2001 *QST* article, "The AMRAD Active LF Antenna," by Frank Gentges, KØBRA. (This article is also included with this book's downloadable supplemental information.) A detailed treatment of active whip antennas and several active impedance-conversion circuits was also published by Dr Ulrich Rhode, N1UL, in *RF Design* (see the Bibliography) and he has published an excellent overview presentation, "Electrically Short Antennas" with co-authors Salazar-Palma and Sarkar at **synergymwave.com/articles/2016/Antenna_presentation.pdf**.

An active antenna is an electrically and physically small antenna combined with an active electronic circuit, such as an amplifier. An active antenna uses a small whip — one that is a fraction of a wavelength long at the desired frequency — connected to an active impedance-conversion circuit. Active antennas are used at HF and lower frequencies through VLF. A commercially available model, the DX Engineering DXE-ARAV3-1P (**www.dxengineering.com**), can be used from 100 kHz through 30 MHz and can be combined with other units into highly directional arrays.

An electrically short whip has a high output impedance. For example, a 1 meter whip at 100 kHz has an input impedance higher than 100 kΩ, mostly capacitive reactance. If such a whip were connected directly to a 50-Ω load, signals would be attenuated more than 80 dB than those from a 50-Ω antenna! Thus, some kind of active impedance-conversion is required, usually a high-input-impedance FET-based amplifier.

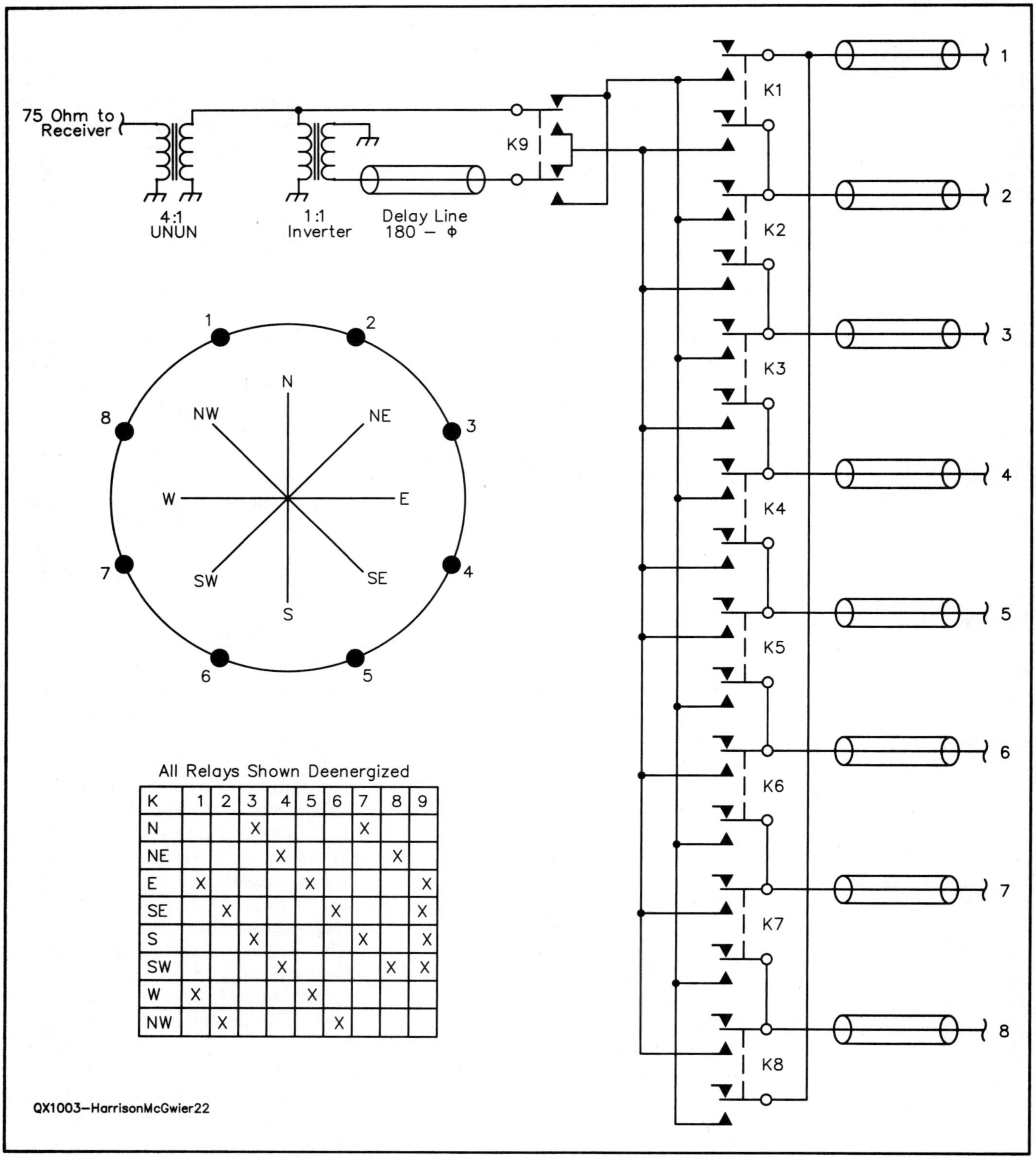

K	1	2	3	4	5	6	7	8	9
N			X				X		
NE				X				X	
E	X				X				X
SE		X				X			X
S			X				X		X
SW				X				X	X
W	X				X				
NW		X				X			

Figure 22.24 — The schematic of the eight-circle receiving array at W5ZN.

Signal-to-noise ratio (SNR) is a primary concern for active antennas due to the antenna's small size. Nevertheless, if the noise contributed by the transistor is less than the noise picked up by the antenna, SNR can be comparable to an optimized passive antenna for the same frequency. Below about 4 MHz, atmospheric and man-made noise dominates the antenna output signal. Above 4 MHz, a circuit using an FET with a noise figure of 1-2 dB or less will provide satisfactory results.

Chris Trask, N7ZWY, has published the design of a broadband preamp for active antennas covering 30 kHz to 70 MHz. (See Bibliography entry for Demmer) The input amplifier is a pair of U310 JFETs in cascode followed by a 2N2222/2N2905 cascode. The article is in German but the schematic is easy to read, including a power-over-feed line circuit.

The recently opened amateur bands of 630 and 2200 meters can also benefit from active antennas, since full-size antennas are quite large. The active whips described above are useful on these low frequencies. Preamps and impedance converters can make use of op amps and other analog ICs designed for use below 1 MHz. For example, the active antenna project by Robert Dildine, W6SFH (see the Bibliography entry for R. Dildine) uses a 1-meter dipole and an op amp signal conditioning circuit. The lower frequency also allows the use of common CAT5 network cable between the antenna package and receiver.

The major challenges to the impedance conversion circuit are nonlinearity and the resulting intermodulation distortion products. Intermodulation products generated in the signal conditioning circuit can create a significant amount of noise and other interference. This is a particularly difficult issue close to transmitting antennas and filters may be required.

22.1.10 RECEIVE ARRAYS

"Circle arrays" of four to nine vertical antennas have become popular, using active whip antennas as described in the previous section. (A number of examples can be seen in the Dayton Hamvention Antenna Forum presentations by Lee Strahan, K7TJR, and Mark Bauman, KB7GF, at **www.kkn.net/dayton2014/dayton-2014-antenna-forum.html** and in the PowerPoint presentation "Receiving Antennas" by Frank Donovan, W3LPL, from the 2014 Contest University at **www.contestuniversity.com/attachments/W3LPL_Receiving_Antennas_2014.pptx.**) These designs provide an unprecedented ability to reject noise and improve receive SNR without requiring large pieces of property. The small footprint (electrically small) of these arrays requires careful attention to design and construction detail, however.

The design and construction of an 8-element array was detailed in an exhaustive article by Joel Harrison, W5ZN, and Bob McGwier, N4HY, in the 2010 *QEX* article "Design, Construction and Evaluation of the Eight Circle Vertical Array for Low Band Receiving" that is included with this book's downloadable supplemental information and shown schematically in **Figure 22.24**.

Dan Maguire, AC6LA, has done some modeling of various circle arrays and published comparative radiation patterns at **ac6la.com/adhoc** — look for filenames beginning with "8circle." Dan also provided additional discussion and links to models in his Topband reflector post from 23 Dec 2014 (**lists.contesting.com/_topband/2014-12/msg00379.html**).

22.1.11 RECEIVING ANTENNAS BIBLIOGRAPHY

Source material and more extended discussion of topics covered in this chapter can be found in the references given below and in the textbooks listed at the end of the **Antenna Fundamentals** chapter.

Beverage Antennas

A. Bailey, S. W. Dean and W. T. Wintringham, "The Receiving System for Long-Wave Transatlantic Radio Telephony," *The Bell System Technical Journal*, Apr 1929.

J. S. Belrose, "Beverage Antennas for Amateur Communications," Technical Correspondence, *QST*, Sep 1981, p 51.

H. Beverage, C. Rice, and E. Kellogg, "The Wave Antenna — A New Type of Highly Directive Antenna," *Transactions of the AIEE*, Feb 1923, pp 215-266.

H. H. Beverage, "Antennas," *RCA Review*, Jul 1939.

H. H. Beverage and D. DeMaw, "The Classic Beverage Antenna Revisited," *QST*, Jan 1982, pp 11-17.

B. Boothe, "Weak-Signal Reception on 160 — Some Antenna Notes," *QST*, Jun 1977, pp 35-39.

J. Brown, "Chokes and Isolation Transformers for Receiving Antennas," *National Contest Journal*, Mar/Apr 2019, pp 7-10.

M. F. DeMaw, *Ferromagnetic-Core Design and Application Handbook* (Englewood Cliffs, NJ: Prentice-Hall Inc, 1981).

J. Devoldere, *ON4UN's Low-Band DXing, Fifth Edition* (Newington: ARRL, 2010). See the chapter "Receiving Antennas," for many practical details on Beverage antennas.

V. A. Misek, *The Beverage Antenna Handbook* (Wason Rd., Hudson, NH: W1WCR, 1977).

W. Silver, "A Cool Beverage Four Pack," *QST*, Apr 2006, pp 33-36.

Active Antennas

P. Bertini, "Active Antenna Covers 0.5-30 MHz," *Ham Radio*, May 1985, pp 37-43.

R. Burhans, "Active Antenna Preamplifiers," *Ham Radio*, May 1986, pp 47-54.

W. Demmer, "Breitbandige Aktivantenne nach N7ZWY," *CQ DL*, Jul 2013, pp 492-493.

R. Dildine, "An Active Dipole for Long- and Medium-Wave Frequencies," *QST*, Oct 2018, pp 30-34.

R. Fisk, "Voltage-Probe Receiving Antenna," *Ham Radio*, Oct 1970, pp 20-21.

F. Gentges, "The AMRAD Active LF Antenna," *QST*, Sep 2001, pp 31-37.

U. Rohde, "Active Antennas," *RF Design*, May/Jun 1981, pp 38-42.

Loops, Flags, and Pennants

B. Beezley, "A Receiving Antenna that Rejects Local Noise," *QST*, Sep 1995, pp 33-36.

D. Bond, *Radio Direction Finders*, 1st ed. (New York: McGraw-Hill Book Co, 1944).

G. Bramslev, "Loop Aerial Reception," *Wireless World*, Nov 1952, pp 469-472.

G. Breed, "The K9AY Terminated Loop — A Compact, Directional Receiving Antenna," *QST*, Sep 1997, pp 43-46.

G. Breed, "Hum Problems When Switching the K9AY Loops," Technical Correspondence, *QST*, May 1998, p 73.

G. Breed, "Introduction to Multi-Wire Loops," *QRP Quarterly*, Jan 2019, pp 36-38.

G. Breed, Additional notes on the K9AY Loop are available at **k9ay.com** under the "Tech Notes" tab.

R. Burhans, "Experimental Loop Antennas for 60 kHz to 200 kHz," *Technical Memorandum (NASA) 71*, (Athens, OH: Ohio Univ, Dept of Electrical Engr), Dec 1979.

R. Burhans, "Loop Antennas for VLF-LF," *Radio-Electronics*, Jun 1983, pp 83-87.

M. Connelly, "New Termination Control Method for Flag, Pennant and Similar Antennas," International Radio Club of America reprint A162, Nov 2002.

M. Connelly, "Pennant Antenna with Remote Termination Control," **www.qsl.net/wa1ion/pennant.htm**.

E. Cunningham, "Flag, Pennants and Other Ground-Independent Low-Band Receiving Antennas," *QST*, Jul 2000, pp 34-37.

R. Devore and P. Bohley, "The Electrically Small Magnetically Loaded Multiturn Loop Antenna," *IEEE Trans on Ant and Prop*, Jul 1977, pp 496-505.

R. J. Edmunds, Ed. "An FET Loop Amplifier with Coaxial Output," *N.R.C. Antenna Reference Manual, Vol 2*, 1st ed. (Cambridge, WI: National Radio Club, Oct 1982), pp 17-20.

S. Goldman, "A Shielded Loop for Low Noise Broadcast Reception," *Electronics*, Oct 1938, pp 20-22.

J. V. Hagan, "A Large Aperture Ferrite Core Loop Antenna for Long and Medium Wave Reception," *Loop Antennas Design and Theory*, M.G. Knitter, Ed. (Cambridge, WI: National Radio Club, 1983), pp 37-49.

F. M. Howes and F. M. Wood, "Note on the Bearing Error and Sensitivity of a Loop Antenna in an Abnormally Polarized Field," *Proc IRE*, Apr 1944, pp 231-233.

J. Kahn, "Remotely Switched Directional FoG Array," *QST*, Feb 2019, pp 36-38.

C. Kluttz, "The Flag on Ground (FoG) Antenna," *QST*, Sep 2017, pp 30-31.

F. Koontz, "Is this EWE for You?," *QST*, Feb 1995, pp 31-33. See also Feedback, Apr 1995 *QST*, p 75.

F. Koontz, "More EWEs for You," *QST*, Jan 1996, spp 32-34.

F. Koontz, "The Horizontal EWE Antenna," *QST*, Dec 2006, pp 37-38.

S. Lawrence, "Rebuilding a Receiving Flag Antenna for 160 Meters," *QST*, July 2015, pp 35-38.

G. Levy, "Loop Antennas for Aircraft," *Proc IRE*, Feb 1943, pp 56-66. Also see correction, *Proc IRE*, Jul 1943, p 384.

R. Lombardi, "Field Deployable Mini-K9AY Loop," *QST*, Feb 2019, pp 39-41.

R. C. Pettengill, H. T. Garland and J. D. Meindl, "Receiving Antenna Design for Miniature Receivers," *IEEE Trans on Ant and Prop*, Jul 1977, pp 528-530.

W. J. Polydoroff, *High Frequency Magnetic Materials — Their Characteristics and Principal Applications* (New York: John Wiley and Sons, Inc, 1960).

E. Robberson, "QRM? Get Looped," *Radio and Television News*, Aug 1955, pp 52-54, 126.

M. Sapp, "A Reversible LF and MF EWE Receive Antenna for Small Lots," *QST*, April 2019, pp 37-43.

D. Sinclair, "Flag and Pennant Antenna Compendium," **www.angelfire.com/md/k3ky**.

G. S. Smith, "Radiation Efficiency of Electrically Small Multiturn Loop Antennas," *IEEE Trans on Ant and Prop*, Sep 1972, pp 656-657.

E. C. Snelling, *Soft Ferrites — Properties and Applications* (Cleveland, OH: CRC Press, 1969).

C. R. Sullivan, "Optimal Choice for the Number of Strands in a Litz-Wire Transformer Winding," *IEEE Trans on Power Electronics*, Vol. 14 No. 2, Mar 1999, pp 283-291 (also available on line at **engineering.dartmouth.edu/inductor/papers.shtml**).

G. Thomas, "The Hot Rod — An Inexpensive Ferrite Booster Antenna," *Loop Antennas Theory and Design*, M. G. Knitter, Ed. (Cambridge, WI: National Radio Club, 1983), pp 57-62.

22.2 DIRECTION-FINDING ANTENNAS

The use of radio for direction finding purposes (RDF) is almost as old as its application for communications. Radio amateurs have learned RDF techniques and found much satisfaction by participating in hidden-transmitter hunts. Other hams have discovered RDF through an interest in boating or aviation, where radio direction finding is used for navigation and emergency location systems. (Amateur RDF which finds a transmitter from its transmitted signal, should be distinguished from aviation's radio direction-finding, which finds a direction based on a signal transmitted from a known location.)

In many countries of the world, the hunting of hidden amateur transmitters takes on the atmosphere of a sport, as participants wearing jogging togs or track suits dash toward the area where they believe the transmitter is located. The sport is variously known as *fox hunting*, *bunny hunting*, ARDF (Amateur Radio direction finding) or simply transmitter hunting. In North America, most hunting of hidden transmitters is conducted from automobiles, although hunts on foot are gaining popularity. Most ARDF activity uses 80 meter or 2 meter transmitters.

There are less pleasant RDF applications as well, such as tracking down noise sources or illegal operators from unidentified stations. Jammers of repeaters, traffic nets and other amateur operations can be located with RDF equipment. Or sometimes a stolen amateur rig will be operated by a person who is not familiar with Amateur Radio and by being lured into making repeated transmissions, the operator unsuspectingly permits their location to be determined with RDF equipment. The ability of certain RDF antennas to reject signals from selected directions has also been used to advantage in reducing noise and interference. Through APRS (Amateur Packet Reporting System), radio navigation is becoming a popular application of RDF. The locating of downed aircraft is another, and one in which amateurs often lend their skills. Indeed, there are many useful applications for RDF.

Although sophisticated and complex equipment pushing the state of the art has been developed for use by governments and commercial enterprises, relatively simple equipment can be built at home to offer the radio amateur an opportunity to RDF. This section deals with antennas suitable for that purpose.

The major types of RDF antennas used by amateurs are covered here, with a project or referenced article included for each. In ARDF events, it's very common to use integrated receiver/antenna combinations to reduce the amount of gear the competitor has to carry. Examples of this type of gear can be found through the Homing In website maintained by Joe Moell, KØOV (**www.homingin.com**). In ARDF, both magnetic loop and ferrite rod antennas are popular with magnetic loops being the more popular. On VHF, three-element Yagis are by far the most popular

How accurate should an RDF antenna be? In mobile and portable use, accuracy to a few degrees is fine. While the uncertainty of a few degrees sounds large, as the distance to the transmitter is reduced and more bearings are taken for triangulation, the amount of error also shrinks. If the antenna is fixed, such as for taking sky-wave bearings, precision is more important since distance to the transmitter does not change. In competitive events where the most common technique is to move toward peak signal on a relatively continuous basis, it is more important to be able to take a reading quickly and consistently.

22.2.1 RDF BY TRIANGULATION

It is impossible, using amateur techniques, to pinpoint the whereabouts of a transmitter from a single receiving location. With a directional antenna you can determine the direction of a signal source, but not how far away it is. To find the distance, you can then travel in the determined direction until you discover the transmitter location. However, that technique can be time consuming and often does not work very well.

A preferred technique is to take at least one additional direction measurement from a second receiving location. Then use a map of the area and plot the bearing or direction measurements as straight lines from points on the map representing the two locations. The approximate location of the transmitter will be indicated by the point where the two bearing lines cross. Even better results can be obtained by taking direction measurements from three locations and using the mapping technique just described. Because absolutely precise bearing measurements are difficult to obtain in practice, the three lines will almost always cross to form a triangle on the map, rather than at a single point. The transmitter will usually be located inside the area represented by the triangle. Additional information on the technique of triangulation and much more on RDF techniques may be found at the Homing In website mentioned above.

It is important to note that the directions determined by a DF receiver can be affected by skew paths (HF) and reflections (VHF). In addition, signals arriving by sky wave can appear to be coming from different azimuths than by ground wave. Knowing about and avoiding these errors are part of successful RDF.

22.2.2 DIRECTION-FINDING ANTENNAS

Required for any RDF system are a directive antenna and a device for detecting the radio signal. In amateur applications the signal detector is usually a transceiver and for convenience it will usually have a meter to indicate signal strength. Unmodified, commercially available portable or mobile receivers are generally quite satisfactory for signal detectors. At very close ranges a simple diode detector and dc microammeter may suffice for the detector.

On the other hand, antennas used for RDF techniques are not generally the types used for normal two-way communications. Directivity is a prime requirement, and here the word *directivity* takes on a somewhat different meaning than is commonly applied to other amateur antennas. Normally we associate directivity with gain, and we think of the ideal antenna pattern as one having a long, thin main lobe. Such a pattern may be of value for coarse measurements in RDF work, but precise bearing measurements are not possible. There is always a spread of a few (or perhaps many) degrees on the *nose* of the lobe, where a shift of antenna bearing produces no detectable change in signal strength. In RDF measurements, it is desirable to correlate an exact bearing or compass direction with the position of the antenna. In order to do this as accurately as possible, an antenna exhibiting a *null* in its pattern is used. A null can be very sharp in directivity, to within a half degree or less.

Loop Antennas

A simple antenna for HF RDF work is a small loop tuned to resonance with a capacitor. (Resonant loops are too small for VHF DFing and other antennas must be used.) Several factors must be considered in the design of an RDF loop. The loop must be small in circumference compared with the wavelength. In a single-turn loop, the conductor should be less than 0.08 λ long. For 28 MHz, this represents a length of less than 34 inches (a diameter of approximately 10 inches). Maximum response from the loop antenna is in the plane of the loop, with nulls exhibited at right angles to that plane. (A more detailed treatment is presented in the **Loop Antennas** chapter.)

To obtain the most accurate bearings, the loop must be balanced electrostatically with respect to ground. Otherwise, the loop will exhibit two modes of operation. One is the mode of a true loop, while the other is that of an essentially non-directional vertical antenna of small dimensions. This second mode is called the *antenna effect*. The voltages introduced by the two modes are seldom in phase and may add or subtract, depending upon the direction from which the wave is coming.

The theoretical true loop pattern is illustrated in **Figure 22.25A**. When properly balanced, the loop exhibits two nulls that are 180° apart. Thus, a single null reading with a small loop antenna will not indicate the exact direction toward the transmitter — only the line along which the transmitter lies. Ways to overcome this ambiguity are discussed later.

When the antenna effect is appreciable and the loop is tuned to resonance, the loop may exhibit little directivity, as shown in Figure 22.25B. However, by detuning the loop to shift the phasing, a pattern similar to Figure 22.25C may be obtained. Although this pattern is not symmetrical, it does exhibit a null. Even so, the null may not be as sharp as that obtained with a loop that is well balanced, and it may not be at exact right angles to the plane of the loop, making determining a bearing more difficult.

By suitable detuning, the unidirectional cardioid pattern of Figure 22.25D may be approached. This adjustment is sometimes used in RDF work to obtain a unidirectional bearing, although there is no complete null in the pattern. A cardioid pattern can also be obtained with a small loop antenna by adding a *sensing element*. Sensing elements are discussed in a later section of this chapter.

An electrostatic balance can be obtained by shielding the loop, as described in the earlier section "Receiving Loop Antenna for 1.8 MHz." The shield is represented by the broken lines in the drawing, and eliminates the antenna effect. The response of a well-constructed shielded loop is quite close to the ideal pattern of Figure 22.25A.

For the low-frequency amateur bands, single-turn loops of convenient physical size for portability are generally found to be too large for RDF work. Therefore, multi-turn loops are generally used instead. Such a loop is shown in **Figure 22.26**. This loop may also be shielded, and if the total conductor length remains below 0.08 λ, the directional pattern is that of Figure 22.25A. A sensing element may also be used with a multi-turn loop.

Loop Circuits and Criteria

No single word describes a direction-finding loop of high performance better than *symmetry*. To obtain an

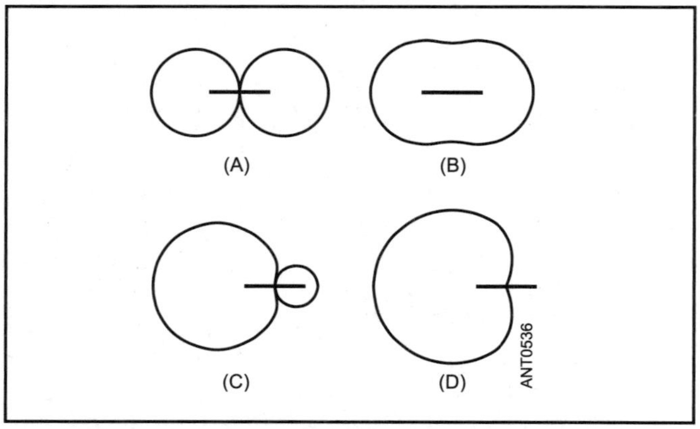

Figure 22.25 — Small-loop field patterns with varying amounts of antenna effect — the undesired response of the loop acting merely as a mass of metal connected to the receiver antenna terminals. The straight lines show the plane of the loop.

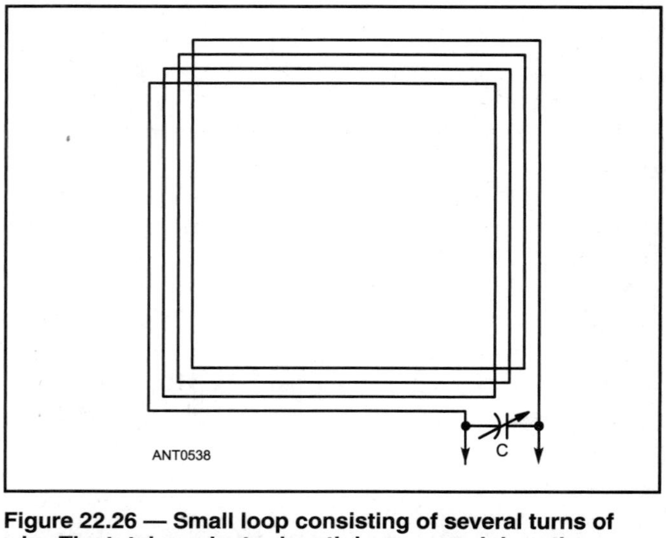

Figure 22.26 — Small loop consisting of several turns of wire. The total conductor length is very much less than a wavelength. Maximum response is in the plane of the loop.

undistorted response pattern from this type of antenna, you must build it in the most symmetrical manner possible. The next key word is *balance*. The better the electrical balance, the deeper the loop null and the sharper the maxima.

The physical size of the loop for 7 MHz and below is not of major consequence. A 4-foot diameter loop will exhibit the same electrical characteristics as one which is only an inch or two in diameter. The smaller the loop, however, the lower its efficiency. This is because its aperture samples a smaller section of the wave front. Thus, if you use loops that are very small in terms of a wavelength, you will need preamplifiers to compensate for the reduced efficiency.

An important point to keep in mind about a small loop antenna oriented in a vertical plane is that it is vertically polarized. It should be fed at the bottom for the best null response. Feeding it at one side, rather than at the bottom, will not alter the polarization and will only degrade performance. To obtain horizontal polarization from a small loop, it must be oriented in a horizontal plane, parallel to the earth. In this position the loop response is essentially omnidirectional.

The earliest loop antennas were of the *frame antenna* variety. These were unshielded antennas built on a wooden frame in a rectangular format. The loop conductor could be a single turn of wire (on the larger units) or several turns if the frame was small. Later, shielded versions of the frame antenna became popular, providing electrostatic shielding — an aid to noise reduction from such sources as precipitation static.

Ferrite Rod Antennas

With advances in technology, magnetic-core loop antennas came into use. Their advantage was reduced size, and this appealed especially to the designers of aircraft and portable radios. Most of these antennas contain ferrite bars or cylinders, which provide high inductance and Q with a relatively small number of coil turns. Because of their reduced-size advantage, ferrite-rod *loopstick* antennas are used almost exclusively for portable work at frequencies below 150 MHz. Design of ferrite-core loop antennas is described in the article "Ferrite-Core Loops" included in this book's downloadable supplemental information. Loopstick antennas for construction are described later in this chapter.

Maximum response of the loopstick antenna is broadside to the axis of the rod as shown in **Figure 22.27**, whereas maximum response of the ordinary loop is in a direction at right angles to the plane of the loop. Otherwise, the performances of the ferrite-rod antenna and of the ordinary loop are similar. The loopstick may also be shielded to eliminate the antenna effect, such as with a U-shaped or C-shaped channel of aluminum or other type of metal. The length of the shield should equal or slightly exceed the length of the rod.

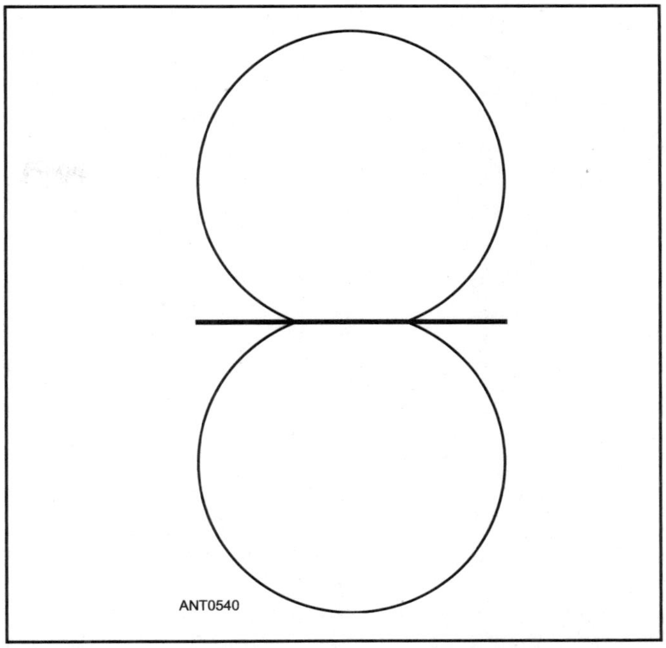

Figure 22.27 — Field pattern for a ferrite rod antenna. The dark bar represents the rod on which the loop turns are wound.

Sensing Antennas

Because there are two nulls that are 180° apart in the directional pattern of a loop or a loopstick, an ambiguity exists as to which one indicates the true direction of the station being tracked. For example, assume you take a bearing measurement and the result indicates the transmitter is somewhere on a line running approximately east and west from your position. With this single reading, you have no way of knowing for sure if the transmitter is east of you or west of you.

If more than one receiving station takes bearings on a single transmitter, or if a single receiving station takes bearings on the transmitter from more than one position, the ambiguity may be worked out by triangulation, as described earlier. However, it is sometimes desirable to have a pattern with only one null, so there is no question about whether the transmitter in the above example would be east or west from your position.

A loop or loopstick antenna may be made to have a single null if a second antenna element is added. The element is called a *sensing antenna*, because it gives an added sense of direction to the loop pattern. The second element must be omnidirectional, such as a short vertical. When the signals from the loop and the vertical element are combined with a 90° phase shift between the two, a cardioid pattern results. The development of the pattern is shown in **Figure 22.28A**.

Figure 22.28B shows a circuit for adding a sensing antenna to a loop or loopstick. R1 is an internal adjustment and is used to set the level of the signal from the sensing antenna. For the best null in the composite pattern, the signals from the loop and the sensing antenna must be of equal amplitude, so R1 is adjusted experimentally during setup. In practice, the null of the cardioid is not as sharp as that of the loop, so the usual measurement procedure is to first use the loop alone to obtain a precise bearing reading, and then to add the sensing antenna and take another reading to resolve the ambiguity. (The null of the cardioid is 90° away from the nulls of the loop.) For this reason, provisions are usually made for switching the sensing element in an out of operation.

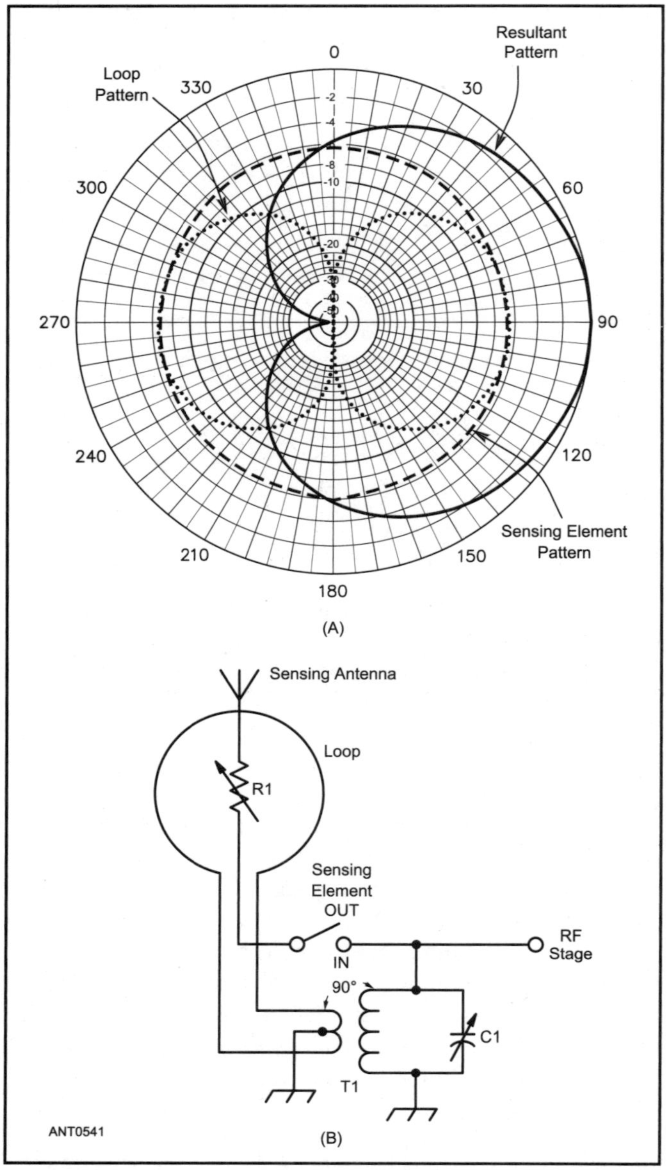

Figure 22.28 — At A, the directivity pattern of a loop antenna with sensing element. At B is a circuit for combining the signals from the two elements. C1 is adjusted for resonance with T1 at the operating frequency.

22.2.3 DIRECTION-FINDING ARRAYS

Phased arrays are also used in amateur RDF work. Two general classifications of phased arrays are end-fire and broadside configurations. Depending on the spacing and phasing of the elements, end-fire patterns may exhibit a null in one direction along the axis of the elements. At the same time, the response is maximum off the other end of the axis, in the opposite direction from the null. A familiar arrangement is two elements spaced ¼ λ apart and fed 90° out of phase. The resultant pattern is a *cardioid*, with the null in the direction of the leading element. Other arrangements of spacing and phasing for an end-fire array are also suitable for RDF work. One of the best known is the *Adcock array*, discussed in the next section.

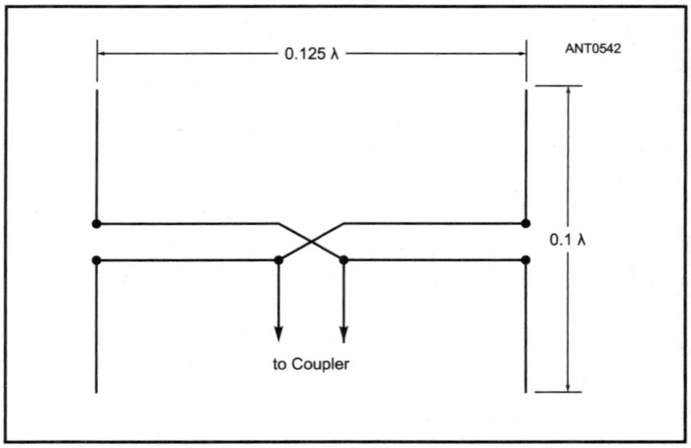

Figure 22.29 — A simple Adcock antenna.

Broadside arrays are inherently bidirectional, which means there are always at least two nulls in the pattern. Ambiguity therefore exists in the true direction of the transmitter, but depending on the application, this may be no handicap. Broadside arrays are seldom used for amateur RDF applications however.

The Adcock Antenna

Loops are adequate in RDF applications where only the ground wave is present. The performance of an RDF system for sky-wave reception can be improved by the use of an Adcock antenna, one of the most popular types of end-fire phased arrays. A basic version is shown in **Figure 22.29**.

This system was invented by F. Adcock and patented in 1919. The array consists of two vertical elements fed 180° apart, and mounted so the system may be rotated. Element spacing is not critical, and may be in the range from 0.1 to 0.75 λ. The two elements must be of identical lengths, but need not be self-resonant. Elements that are shorter than resonant are commonly used. Because neither the element spacing nor the length is critical in terms of wavelengths, an Adcock array may be operated over more than one amateur band.

The response of the Adcock array to vertically polarized waves is similar to a conventional loop and the directive pattern is essentially the same. Response of the array to a horizontally polarized wave is considerably different from that of a loop, however. The currents induced in the horizontal members tend to balance out regardless of the orientation of the antenna, preserving the null. This effect has been verified in practice, where good nulls were obtained with an experimental Adcock under sky-wave conditions with rapidly varying polarization that produced poor nulls in small loops (both conventional and ferrite-loop models).

Generally speaking, the Adcock antenna has attractive properties for amateur RDF applications. Unfortunately, its portability leaves something to be desired, making it more suitable to fixed or semi-portable applications. While a metal support for the mast and boom could be used, wood, PVC or fiberglass are preferable because they are nonconductors and would therefore cause less pattern distortion.

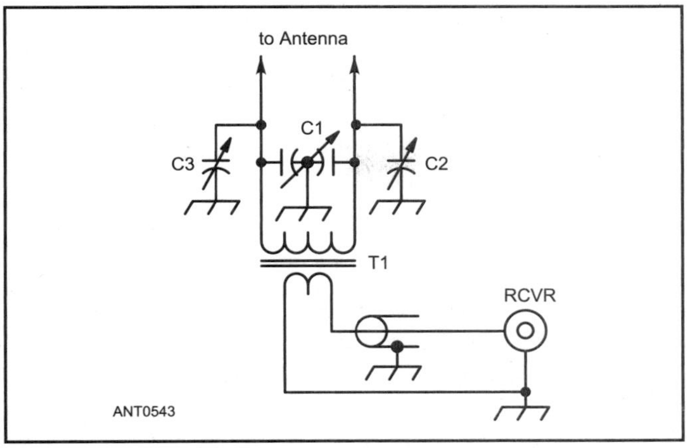

Figure 22.30 — A suitable coupler for use with the Adcock antenna.

Since the array is balanced, an antenna tuner is required to match the unbalanced input of a typical receiver. **Figure 22.30** shows a suitable link-coupled network. C2 and C3 are null-balancing capacitors. A low-power signal source is placed some distance from the Adcock antenna and broadside to it. C2 and C3 are then adjusted until the deepest null is obtained. The tuner can be placed below the wiring-harness junction on the boom. Connection can be made by means of a short length of 300-Ω twinlead.

The radiation pattern of the Adcock is shown in **Figure 22.31A**. The nulls are in directions broadside to the array, and become sharper with greater element spacings. However, with an element spacing greater than 0.75 λ, the pattern begins to take on additional nulls in the directions off the ends of the array axis. At a spacing of 1 λ the pattern is that of Figure 22.31B, and the array is unsuitable for RDF applications.

Short vertical monopoles over a ground plane are often used in what is sometimes called the *U-Adcock*, so named because the elements with their feeders take on the shape of the letter U. In this arrangement the elements are worked against the earth as a ground or counterpoise. (Replace the bottom half of the elements and feeders in Figure 22.29 with a ground plane.) If the array is used only for reception, earth losses are of no great consequence. Short, elevated vertical dipoles are also used in what is sometimes called the *H-Adcock*.

The Adcock array, with two nulls in its pattern, has the same ambiguity as the loop and the loopstick. Adding a sensing element to the Adcock array has not met with great success. Difficulties arise from mutual coupling between the array elements and the sensing element, among other things. Because Adcock arrays are used primarily for fixed-station applications, the ambiguity presents no serious problem. The fixed station is usually one of a group of stations in an RDF network.

Loops Versus Phased Arrays

Although loops can be made smaller than suitable phased arrays for the same frequency of operation, the phased arrays are preferred by some for a variety of reasons. In general, sharper nulls can be obtained with phased arrays, but this is also a function of the care used in constructing and feeding the individual antennas, as well as of the size of the phased array in terms of wavelengths. The primary constructional consideration is the shielding and balancing of the feed line against unwanted signal pickup, and the balancing of the antenna for a symmetrical pattern.

Loops are not as useful for skywave RDF work because of random polarization of the received signal. Phased arrays are somewhat less sensitive to propagation effects, probably because they are larger for the same frequency of operation and therefore offer some space diversity. In general, loops and loopsticks are used for mobile and portable operation, while phased arrays are used for fixed-station operation. However, phased arrays are used successfully above 144 MHz for portable and mobile RDF work. Practical examples of both types of antennas are presented later in this chapter.

The Goniometer

An early-day device that permits finding directions without moving the elements is called a *radiogoniometer*, or simply a *goniometer*. Various types of goniometers are still

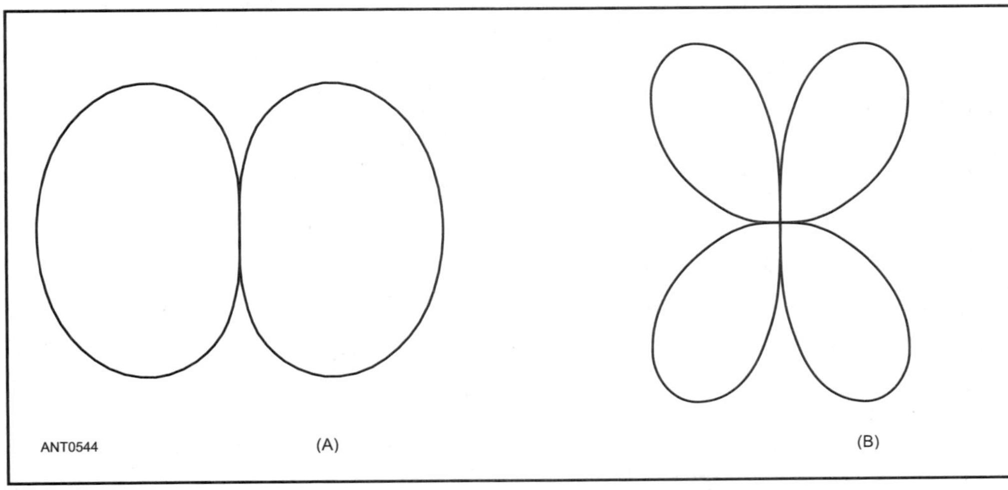

Figure 22.31 — At A, the pattern of the Adcock array with an element spacing of ½ wavelength. In these plots the elements are aligned with the horizontal axis. As the element spacing is increased beyond ¾ wavelength, additional nulls develop off the ends of the array, and at a spacing of 1 wavelength the pattern at B exists. This pattern is unsuitable for RDF work.

used today in many installations, and offer the amateur some possibilities.

The early style of goniometer is a special form of RF transformer, as shown in **Figure 22.32**. It consists of two fixed coils mounted at right angles to one another. Inside the fixed coils is a movable coil, not shown in Figure 22.32 to avoid cluttering the diagram. The pairs of connections marked A and B are connected respectively to two elements in an array, and the output to the detector or receiver is taken from the movable coil. As the inner coil is rotated, the coupling to one fixed coil increases while that to the other decreases. Both the amplitude and the phase of the signal coupled into the pickup winding are altered with rotation in a way that corresponds to actually rotating the array itself. Therefore, the rotation of the inner coil can be calibrated in degrees to correspond to bearing angles from the station location.

Electronic Antenna Rotation

With an array of many fixed elements, beam formation and rotation can be performed electronically by sampling and combining signals from various individual elements in the array. Contingent upon the total number of elements in the system and their physical arrangement, almost any desired antenna pattern can be formed by summing the sampled signals in appropriate amplitude and phase relationships. Delay networks are used for some of the elements before the summation is performed. In addition, attenuators may be used for some elements to develop patterns such as from an array with binomial current distribution.

One system using these techniques is the *Wullenweber* antenna, employed primarily in government and military installations. The Wullenweber consists of a very large number of elements arranged in a circle, usually outside of (or in front of) a circular reflecting screen. Delay lines and electronic switches create a beam-forming network that can be steered in any direction and with a wide variety of patterns.

For the moment, consider just two elements of a Wullenweber antenna, shown as A and B in **Figure 22.33**. Also shown is the wavefront of a radio signal arriving from a distant transmitter. As drawn, the wavefront strikes element A first, and must travel somewhat farther before it strikes element B. There is a finite time delay before the wavefront reaches element B.

The propagation delay may be measured by delaying the signal received at element A before summing it with that from element B. If the two signals are combined directly, the amplitude of the resultant signal will be maximum when the delay for element A exactly equals the propagation delay. This results in an in-phase condition at the summation point. Or if one of the signals is inverted and the two are summed, a null will exist when the element-A delay equals the propagation delay; the signals will combine in a 180° out-of-phase relationship. Either way, once the time delay is known, it may be converted to distance. Then the direction from which the wave is arriving may be determined by trigonometry.

By altering the delay in small increments, the peak of the antenna lobe (or the null) can be steered in azimuth. This is true without regard to the frequency of the incoming wave. Thus, as long as the delay is less than the period of one RF cycle, the system is not frequency sensitive, other than for the frequency range that may be covered satisfactorily by the array elements themselves. Surface acoustic wave (SAW) devices or lumped-constant networks can be used for delay lines in such systems if the system is used only for receiving. Rolls of coaxial cable of various lengths are used in installations for transmitting. In this case, the lines are considered for the time delay they provide, rather than as simple phasing lines. The difference is that a phasing line is ordinarily designed for a single frequency (or for an amateur band), while a delay line offers essentially the same time delay at all frequencies.

A four-element, electronically-rotating RDF antenna system for amateur RDF was described in an article by Malcolm C. Mallette, WA9BVS, in November 1995 *QST* and included with this book's downloadable supplemental information. The system is designed to be used while mobile and is based on *time-difference-of-arrival* techniques.

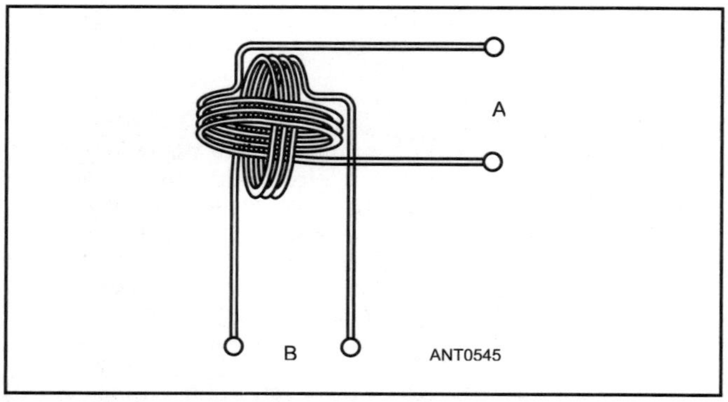

Figure 22.32 — An early type of goniometer that is still used today in some RDF applications. This device is a special type of RF transformer that permits a movable coil in the center (not shown here) to be rotated and determine directions even though the elements are stationary.

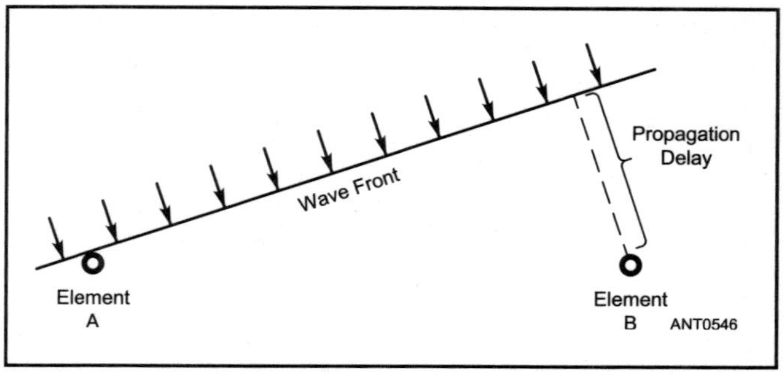

Figure 22.33 — This diagram illustrates one technique used in electronic beam forming. By delaying the signal from element A by an amount equal to the propagation delay, the two signals may be summed precisely in phase, even though the signal is not in the broadside direction. Because this time delay is identical for all frequencies, the system is not frequency sensitive.

22.2.4 RDF SYSTEM CALIBRATION AND USE

Once an RDF system is initially assembled, it should be calibrated or checked out before actually being put into use. Of primary concern is the balance or symmetry of the antenna pattern. A lop-sided figure-8 pattern with a loop, for example, is undesirable; the nulls are not 180° apart, nor are they at exact right angles to the plane of the loop. If you didn't know this fact in actual RDF work, measurement accuracy would suffer.

It is also common to add a regular magnetic compass to an RDF antenna. This provides numeric bearings for events that combine orienteering or if reporting numeric bearings is important.

Initial checkout can be performed with a low-powered transmitter at a distance of a few hundred feet. It should be within visual range and if transmitting on HF must be operating into a vertical antenna. (A quarter-wave vertical or a loaded whip is quite suitable. Omni-directional horizontally polarized antennas work fine on VHF.) The site must be reasonably clear of obstructions, especially steel and concrete or brick buildings, large metal objects, nearby power lines, and so on. If the system operates above 30 MHz, you should also avoid trees and large bushes. An open field makes an excellent site.

The procedure is to find the transmitter with the RDF equipment as if its position were not known, and compare the RDF null indication with the visual path to the transmitter. For antennas having more than one null, each null should be checked.

If imbalance is found in the antenna system, there are two options available. One is to correct the imbalance. Toward this end, pay particular attention to the feed line. Using a coaxial feeder for a balanced antenna invites an asymmetrical pattern, unless an effective balun is used. A balun is not necessary if the loop is shielded, but an asymmetrical pattern can result with misplacement of the break in the shield itself. The builder may also find that the presence of a sensing antenna upsets the balance slightly, due to mutual coupling. Experiment with its position with respect to the main antenna to correct the error. You will also note that the position of the null shifts by 90° as the sensing element is switched in and out, and the null is not as deep. This is of little concern, however, as the intent of the sensing antenna is only to resolve ambiguities. The sensing element should be switched out when accuracy is desired.

The second option is to accept the imbalance of the antenna and use some kind of indicator to show the true directions of the nulls. Small pointers, painted marks on the mast, or an optical sighting system might be used. Sometimes the end result of the calibration procedure will be a compromise between these two options, as a perfect electrical balance may be difficult or impossible to attain.

Because of nearby obstructions or reflecting objects, the null in the pattern may not appear to indicate the precise direction of the transmitter. Do not confuse this with imbalance in the RDF array. Check for imbalance by rotating the array 180° and comparing readings.

The discussion above is oriented toward calibrating portable RDF systems such as would be used for competitive ARDF events and general-purpose fox hunting. The same general suggestions apply if the RDF array is fixed, such as an Adcock. However, it won't be possible to move it to an open field. Instead, the array must be calibrated in its intended operating position through the use of a portable or mobile transmitter and a table of bearing errors compiled that can be used during actual operation. Fixed DF antennas are rare in amateur service however.

22.2.5 A FRAME LOOP

It was mentioned earlier that the earliest style of receiving loops was the frame antenna. If carefully constructed, such an antenna performs well and can be built at low cost. **Figure 22.34** illustrates the details of a practical frame type of loop antenna. This antenna was designed by Doug DeMaw, W1FB, and described in *QST* for July 1977. (See the Bibliography at the end of this chapter.) The circuit in Figure 22.34A is a 5-turn system tuned to resonance by C1. If the layout is symmetrical, good balance should be obtained. L2 helps to achieve this objective by eliminating the need for direct coupling to the feed terminals of L1. If the loop feed were attached in parallel with C1, a common practice, the

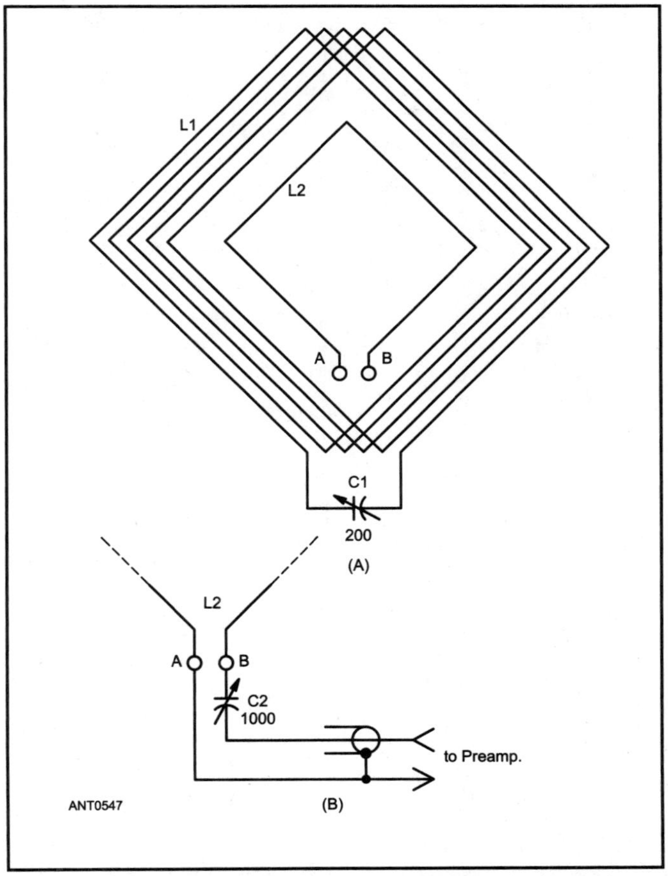

Figure 22.34 — A multiturn frame antenna is shown at A. L2 is the coupling loop. The drawing at B shows how L2 is connected to a preamplifier.

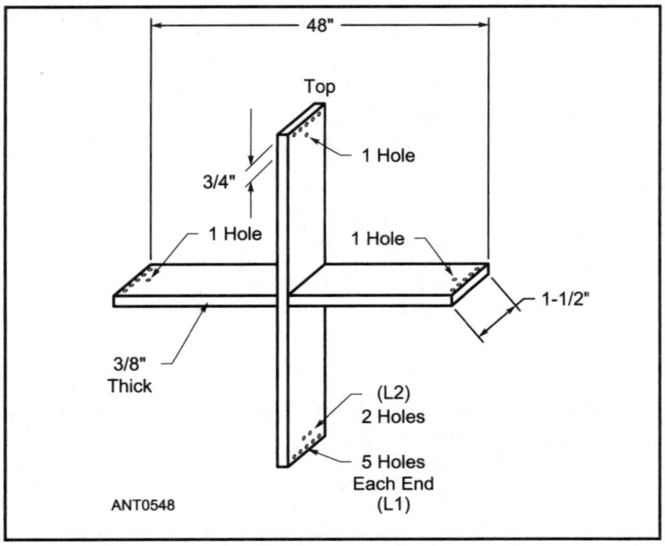

Figure 22.35 — A wooden frame can be used to contain the wire of the loop shown in Figure 12.

Figure 22.36 — An assembled table-top version of the electrostatically shielded loop. RG-58 cable is used in its construction.

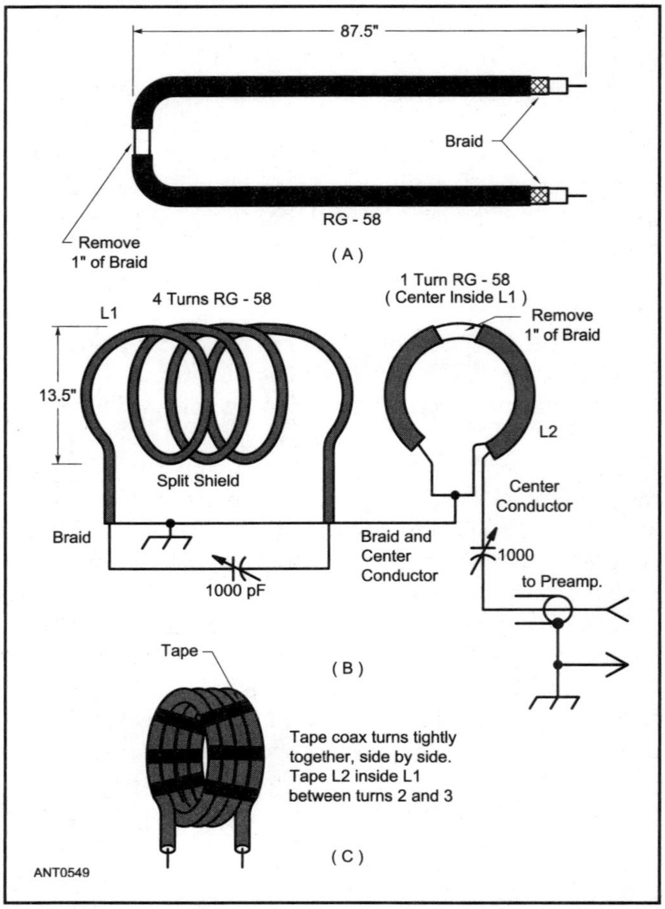

Figure 22.37 — Components and assembly details of the shielded loop shown in Figure 22.36. The dimensions and values given are for 1.8 MHz operation.

chance for imbalance would be considerable.

L2 can be situated just inside or slightly outside of L1; a 1-inch separation works nicely. The receiver or preamplifier can be connected to terminals A and B of L2, as shown in Figure 22.34B. C2 controls the amount of coupling between the loop and the preamplifier. The lighter the coupling, the higher is the loop Q, the narrower is the frequency response, and the greater is the gain requirement from the preamplifier. It should be noted that no attempt is being made to match the extremely low loop impedance to the preamplifier.

A supporting frame for the loop of Figure 22.34 can be constructed of wood, as shown in **Figure 22.35**. The dimensions given are for a 1.8-MHz frame antenna. For use on 75 or 40 meters, L1 of Figure 22.34A will require fewer turns, or the size of the wooden frame should be made somewhat smaller than that of Figure 22.35.

If electrostatic shielding is desired, the format shown in **Figure 22.36** and **Figure 22.37** can be adopted. In this example, the loop conductor and the single-turn coupling loop are made from RG-58 coaxial cable. The number of loop turns should be sufficient to resonate with the tuning capacitor at the operating frequency. Antenna resonance can be checked by first connecting C1 (Figure 22.34A) and setting it at mid-range. Then connect a small 3-turn coil to the loop feed terminals, and couple to it with a dip meter. Just remember that the pickup coil will act to lower the frequency slightly from actual resonance.

22.2.6 A FERRITE-CORE LOOP FOR 160 METERS

Figure 22.38 contains a diagram for a rod loop (loopstick antenna). This antenna was also designed by Doug DeMaw, W1FB, and described in July 1977 *QST*. The article "Ferrite-Core Loop Antennas" analyzes this antenna in more detail, including the effects of rod permeability and winding configuration. (The article is available in the downloadable supplemental information.)

The winding (L1) has the appropriate number of turns to permit resonance with C1 at the operating frequency. L1 should be spread over approximately ⅓ of the core center. Litz wire will yield the best Q but enameled magnet wire can be used if desired. A layer of electrical tape is recommended as a covering for the core before adding the wire since ferrite is somewhat abrasive.

L2 functions as a coupling link over the exact center of L1. C1 is a dual-section variable capacitor, although a differential capacitor might be better toward obtaining optimum balance. The loop Q is controlled by means of C2, which is a mica-compression trimmer.

Electrostatic shielding of rod loops can be effected by centering the rod in a U-shaped aluminum, brass or copper channel, extending slightly beyond the ends of the rod loop (1 inch is suitable). The open side (top) of the channel can't be closed, as that would constitute a shorted turn and render the antenna useless. This can be proved by shorting across the center of the channel with a screwdriver blade when the loop is tuned to an incoming signal. The shield-braid gap in the coaxial loop of Figure 22.37 is maintained for the same reason.

Figure 22.39 shows the shielded rod loop assembly. This antenna was developed experimentally for 160 meters and uses two 7-inch ferrite rods, glued together end-to-end with epoxy cement. The longer core resulted in improved sensitivity for weak-signal reception. The other items in the photograph were used during the evaluation tests and are not pertinent to this discussion. This loop and the frame loop discussed in the previous section have bidirectional nulls, as shown in Figure 22.24A.

Obtaining a Cardioid Pattern

Although the bidirectional pattern of loop antennas can be used effectively in tracking down signal sources by means of triangulation, an essentially unidirectional loop response will help to reduce the time spent finding the fox. Adding a sensing antenna to the loop is simple to do, and it will provide the desired cardioid response. The theoretical pattern for this combination is shown in Figure 22.24D.

Figure 22.40 shows how a sensing element can be added to a loop or loopstick antenna. The link from the loop is connected by coaxial cable to the primary of T1, which is a tuned toroidal transformer with a split secondary winding.

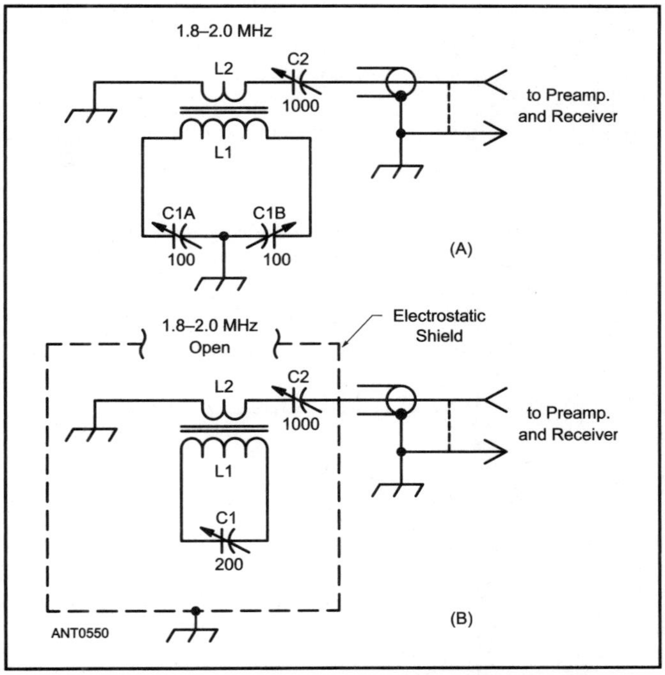

Figure 22.38 — At A, the diagram of a ferrite loop. C1 is a dual-section air-variable capacitor. The circuit at B shows a rod loop contained in an electrostatic shield channel (see text). A suitable low-noise preamplifier is shown in Figure 22.41.

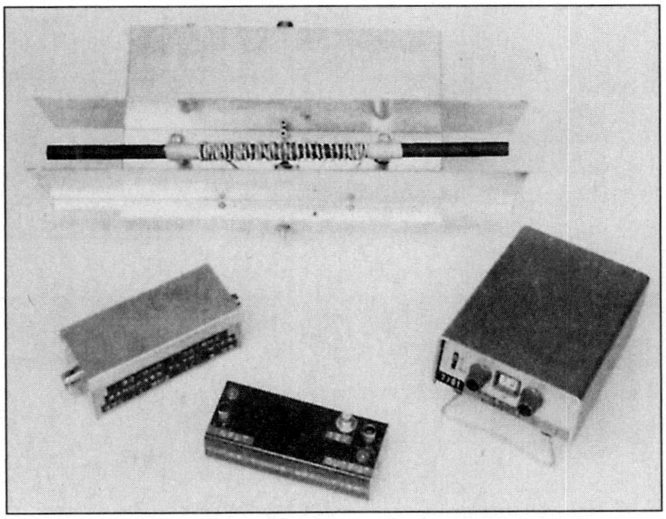

Figure 22.39 — The assembly at the top of the picture is a shielded ferrite-rod loop for 160 meters. Two rods have been glued end to end (see text). The other units in the picture are a low-pass filter (lower left), broadband preamplifier (lower center) and a Tektronix step attenuator (lower right). These were part of the test setup used when the antenna was evaluated.

C3 is adjusted for peak signal response at the frequency of interest (as is C4), then R1 is adjusted for minimum back response of the loop. It will be necessary to readjust C3 and R1 several times to compensate for the interaction of these controls. The adjustments are repeated until no further null depth can be obtained. Tests at ARRL Headquarters showed that null depths as great as 40 dB could be obtained with the circuit of Figure 22.40 on 80 meters. A near-field weak-signal source was used during the tests.

The greater the null depth, the lower the signal output from the system, so plan to include a preamplifier with 25 to 40 dB of gain. Q1 shown in Figure 22.40 will deliver approximately 15 dB of gain. In the interest of maintaining a good noise figure, even at 1.8 MHz, Q1 should be a low-noise device. A 2N4416, an MPF102, or a 3N201 MOSFET would be satisfactory. The circuit of **Figure 22.41** can be used following T2 to obtain an additional 24 dB of gain. The sensing antenna can be mounted from a few mm to 6 inches from the loop. The vertical whip need not be more than 12 inches long. Some experimenting may be necessary in order to obtain the best results. Optimization will also change with the operating frequency of the antenna.

22.2.7 A SIMPLE DIRECTION-FINDING SYSTEM FOR 80 METERS

This section gives an overview of the article by the same name in September 2005 *QST* by Dale Hunt, WB6BYU. (The full article is included with this book's downloadable supplemental information.) The antenna (a multi-turn loop) and receiver are combined into a single package as shown in

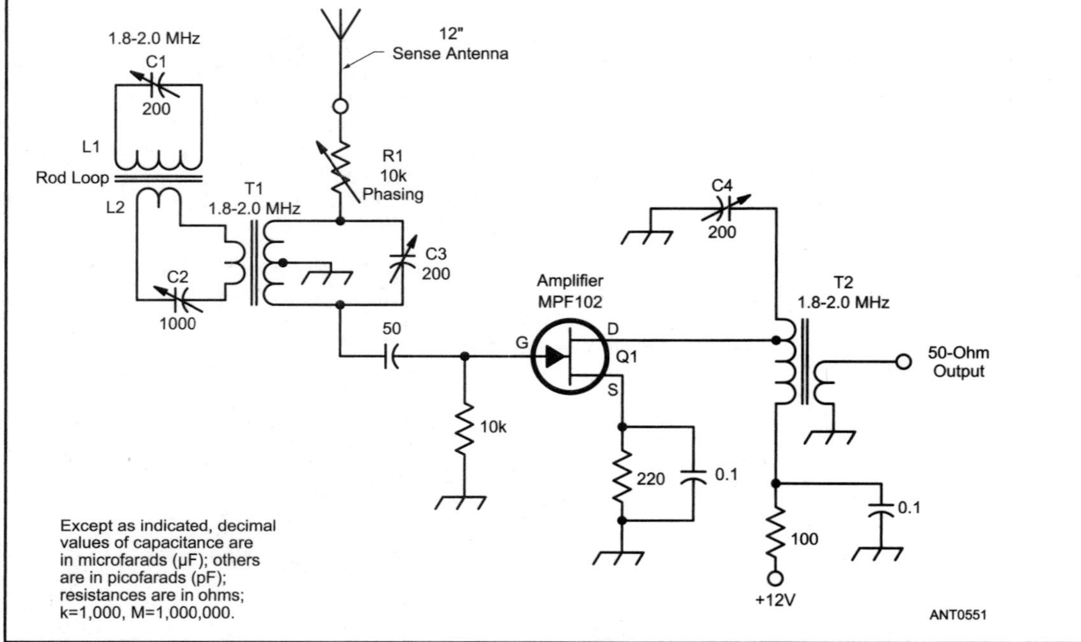

Figure 22.40 — Schematic diagram of a rod-loop antenna with a cardioid response. The sensing antenna, phasing network and a preamplifier are shown also. The secondary of T1 and the primary of T2 are tuned to resonance at the operating frequency of the loop. T-68-2 to T-68-6 Amidon toroid cores are suitable for both transformers. Amidon also sells ferrite rods for this type of antenna.

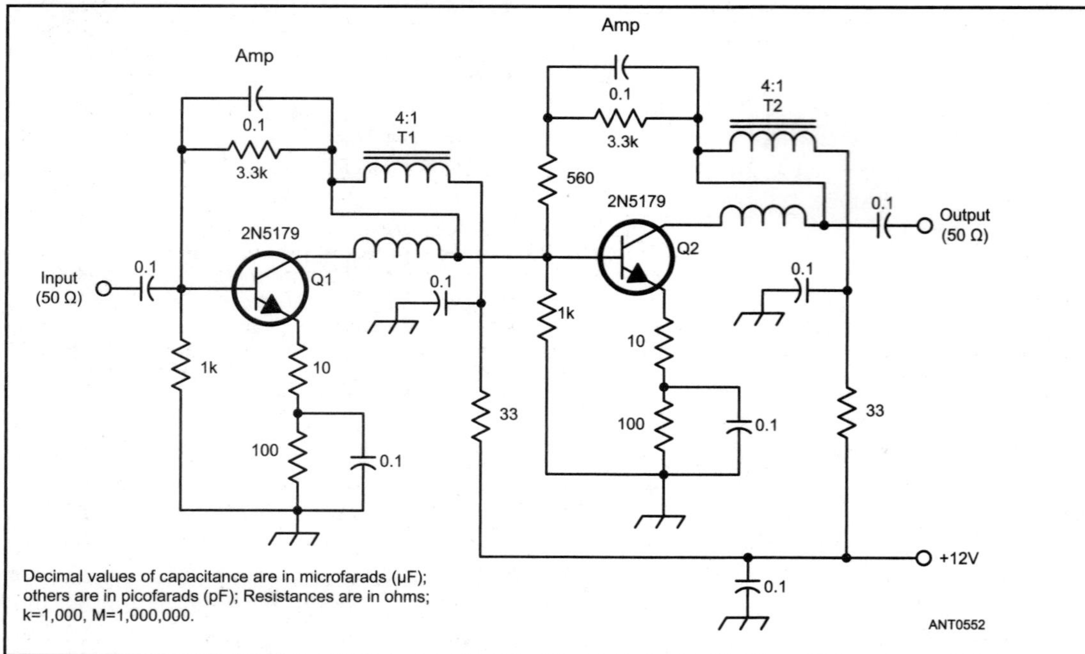

Figure 22.41 — Schematic diagram of a two-stage broadband amplifier patterned after a design by Wes Hayward, W7ZOI. T1 and T2 have a 4:1 impedance ratio and are wound on FT-50-61 toroid cores (Amidon) which have a μ_i of 125. They contain 12 turns of #24 AWG enamel wire, bifilar wound. The capacitors are disc ceramic. This amplifier should be built on double-sided circuit board for best stability.

Figure 22.42. The receiver was designed to hear a 1-W signal from up to 3 miles away, to have low battery drain and to be lightweight and rugged for competitive RDF use.

The four-turn loop is tuned to resonance to provide RF selectivity. Without the sense antenna, the loop alone is bidirectional. With the sense antenna switched in, a cardioid pattern is obtained. A shielded coupling loop of RG-174 coaxial cable is used to transfer the signal to the receiver which is described in detail in the article.

Operation is straightforward — plug in the headphones and turn on the radio. Adjust the RF gain to max and tune in the desired signal. Rotate the receiver to find the null in the pattern that is perpendicular to the loop. If the signal is too loud, reduce RF gain and try again. To resolve the direction of the transmitter (the loop's natural pattern is bidirectional) rotate the receiver 90° in either direction, switch in the sense antenna, and check signal strength. Then rotate the loop 180° and compare — one direction should be stronger than the other.

22.2.8 THE DOUBLE-DUCKY VHF DIRECTION FINDER

For direction finding, most amateurs use antennas having pronounced directional effects, either a null or a peak in signal strength. FM receivers are designed to eliminate the effects of amplitude variations, and so they are difficult to use for direction finding without looking at an S meter. Most modern HT transceivers do not have S meters.

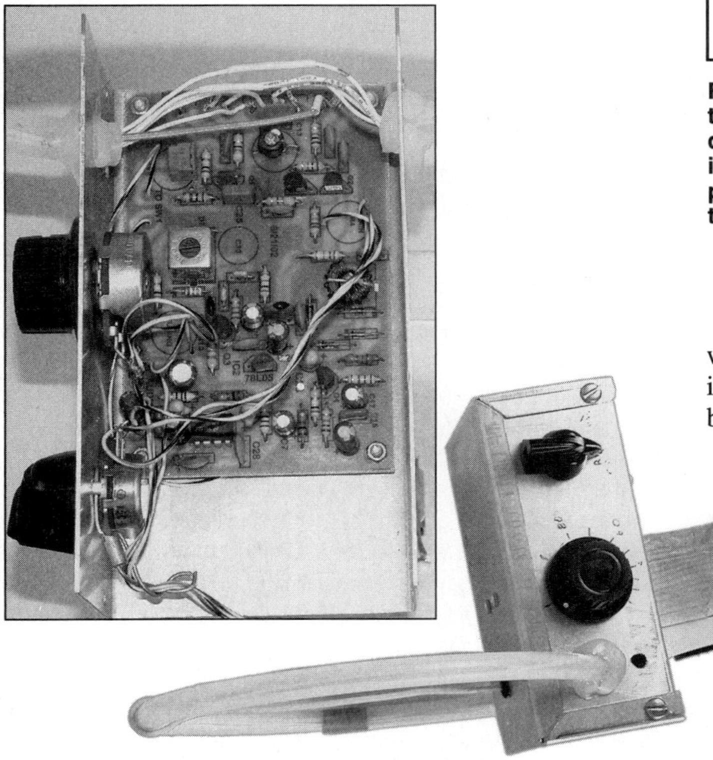

Figure 22.42 — The integrated antenna, handle, and receiver are built into a RadioShack aluminum box. The controls are made to be operated with one hand while using the antenna.

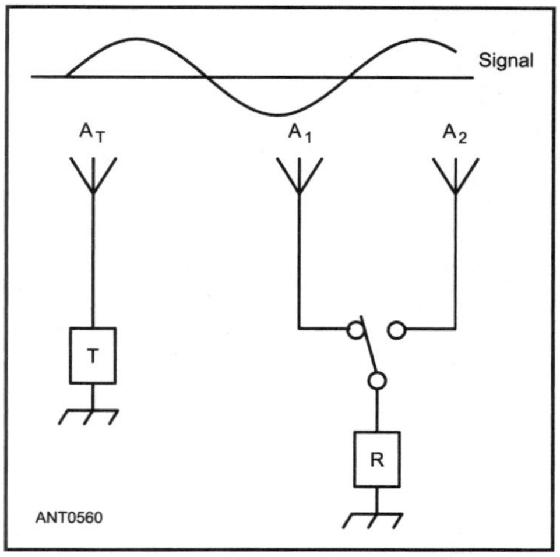

Figure 22.43 — At the left, A_T represents the antenna of the hidden transmitter, T. At the right, rapid switching between antennas A_1 and A_2 at the receiver samples the phase at each antenna, creating a pseudo-Doppler effect. An FM detector detects this as phase modulation.

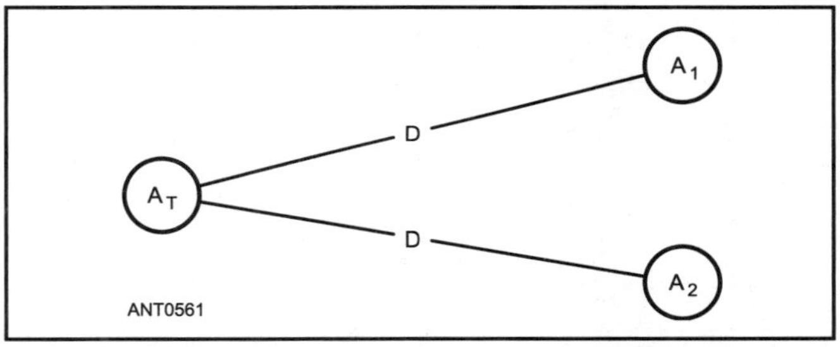

Figure 22.44 — If both receiving antennas are an equal distance (D) from the transmitting antenna, there will be no difference in the phase angles of the signals in the receiving antennas. Therefore, the detector will not detect any phase modulation, and the audio tone will disappear from the output of the detector.

This classic "Double-Ducky" direction finder (DDDF) was designed by David Geiser, WA2ANU, and was described in *QST* for July 1981. It works on the principle of switching between two nondirectional antennas, as shown in **Figure 22.43**. This creates phase modulation on the incoming signal that is heard easily on the FM receiver. When the two antennas are exactly the same distance (phase) from the transmitter, as in **Figure 22.44**, the tone disappears. (This technique is also known in the RDF literature as *Time-Difference-of-Arrival,* or TDOA, since signals arrive at each antenna at slightly different times, and hence at slightly different phases, from any direction except on a line perpendicular to and halfway in-between the two antennas. Another general term for this kind of two-antenna RDF technique is *interferometer. — Ed.*)

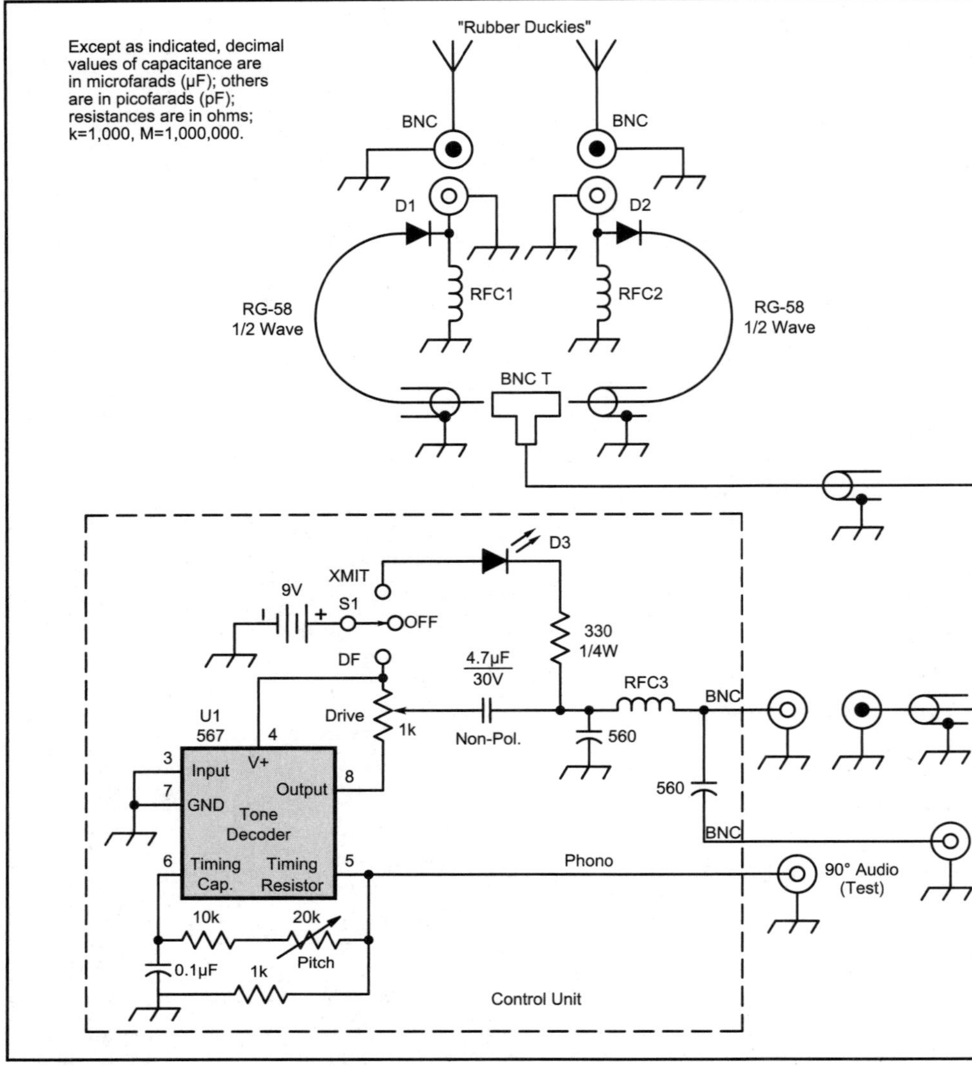

Figure 22.45 — Schematic diagram of the DDDF circuit. Construction and layout are not critical. Components inside the broken lines should be housed inside a shielded enclosure. Most of the components are available from RadioShack, except D1, D2, the antennas and RFC1-RFC3. These components are discussed in the text. S1 — See text.

In theory the antennas may be very close to each other, but in practice the amount of phase modulation increases directly with the spacing, up to spacings of a half wavelength. While ½ λ separation on 2 meters (40 inches) is pretty large for a mobile array, ¼ λ gives entirely satisfactory results, and even ⅛ λ (10 inches) is acceptable.

Think in terms of two antenna elements with fixed spacing. Mount them on a ground plane and rotate that ground plane. The ground plane held above the hiker's head or car roof reduces the needed height of the array and the directional-distorting effects of the searcher's body or other conducting objects.

The DDDF is bidirectional and, as described, its tone null points both toward and away from the signal origin. An L-shaped search path would be needed to resolve the ambiguity. Use the techniques of triangulation described earlier in this chapter.

Specific Design

It is not possible to find a long-life mechanical switch operable at a fairly high audio rate, such as 1000 Hz. Yet we want an audible tone, and the 400- to 1000-Hz range is perhaps most suitable considering audio amplifiers and average hearing. Also, if we wish to use the transmit function of a transceiver, we need a switch that will carry perhaps 10 W without much problem.

A solid-state switch, the PIN diode is used. The intrinsic region of this type of diode is ordinarily free of current carriers and, with a bit of reverse bias, looks like a low-capacitance open space. A bit of forward bias (20 to 50 mA) will load the intrinsic region with current carriers that are happy to dance back and forth at a 148-MHz rate, looking like a resistance of an ohm or so. In a 10-W circuit, the diodes do not dissipate enough power to damage them.

Because only two antennas are used, the obvious approach is to connect one diode *forward* to one antenna, to connect the other *reverse* to the second antenna and to drive the pair with square-wave audio-frequency ac. **Figure 22.45** shows the necessary circuitry. RF chokes (Ohmite Z144, J. W. Miller RFC-144 or similar VHF units) are used to let the audio through to bias the diodes while blocking RF. Of course, the reverse bias on one diode is only equal to the forward bias on the other, but in practice this seems sufficient.

A number of PIN diodes were tried in the particular setup built. These were the Hewlett-Packard HP5082-3077, the Alpha LE-5407-4, the KSW KS-3542 and the Microwave Associates M/A-COM 47120. All worked well, but the HP diodes were used because they provided a slightly lower SWR (about 3:1).

A type 567 IC is used as the square-wave generator. The output does have a dc bias that is removed with a nonpolarized coupling capacitor. This minor inconvenience is more than rewarded by the ability of the IC to work well with between 7 and 15 V (a nominal 9-V minimum is recommended).

The nonpolarized capacitor is also used for dc blocking when the function switch is set to XMIT. D3, a light-emitting diode (LED), is wired in series with the transmit bias to indicate selection of the XMIT mode. In that mode there is a high battery current drain (20 mA or so). S1 should be a center-off locking type toggle switch. An ordinary center-off switch may be used, but beware. If the switch is left on XMIT you will soon have dead batteries.

Cables going from the antenna to the coaxial T connector were cut to an electrical ½ λ to help the open circuit, represented by the reverse-biased diode, look open at the coaxial T. (The length of the line within the T was included in the calculation.)

The length of the line from the T to the control unit is not particularly critical. If possible, keep the total of the cable length from the T to the control unit to the transceiver under 8 feet, because the capacitance of the cable does shunt the square-wave generator output.

Ground-plane dimensions are not critical. See **Figure 22.46**. Slightly better results may be obtained with a larger ground plane than shown. Increasing the spacing between the pickup antennas will give the greatest improvement. Every doubling (up to a half wavelength maximum) will cut the width of the null in half. A 1° wide null can be obtained with 20-inch spacing.

DDDF Operation

Switch the control unit to DF and advance the drive potentiometer until a tone is heard on the desired signal. Do not advance the drive high enough to distort or "hash up" the voice. Rotate the antenna for a null in the fundamental tone. Note that a tone an octave higher may appear.

If the incoming signal is quite out of the receiver linear region (10 kHz or so off frequency), the off-null antenna aim may present a fairly symmetrical AF output to one side. It may also show instability at a sharp null position. Aimed to the other side of a null, it will give a greatly increased AF output. This is caused by the different parts of the receiver FM detector curve used. The sudden tone change is the tip-off that the antenna null position is being passed.

The user should practice with the DDDF to become acquainted with how it behaves under known situations of signal direction, power and frequency. Even in difficult nulling situations where a lot of second-harmonic AF exists, rotating the antenna through the null position causes a very distinctive tone change. With the same frequencies and amplitudes present, the quality of the tone (timbre) changes. It is as if a note were first played by a violin, and then the same note played by a trumpet. (A good part of this is the change of phase of the fundamental and odd harmonics with respect to the even harmonics.) The listener can recognize differences (passing through the null) that would give an electronic analyzer indigestion.

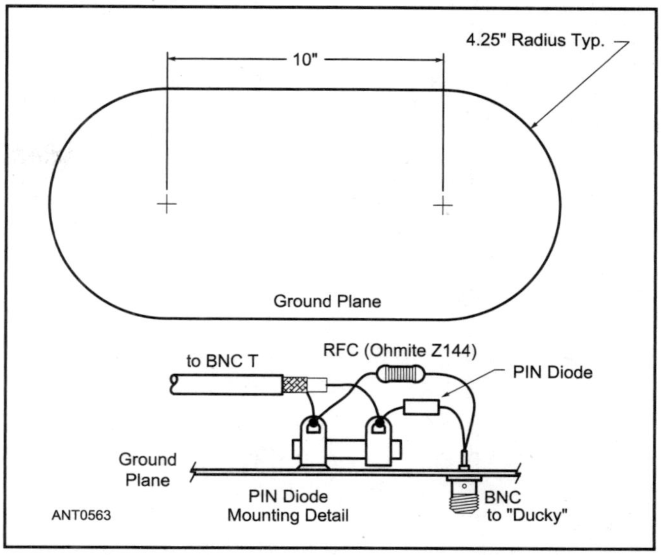

Figure 22.46 — Ground-plane layout and detail of parts at the antenna connectors.

22.2.9 A COMBINED YAGI — INTERFEROMETER VHF ANTENNA

Interferometers give sharp bearings, but they lack sensitivity for distant work. Yagis are sensitive, but they provide relatively broad bearings. The Oct 1998 *QST* article by R. F. Gillette, W9PE, "A Fox-Hunting DF Twin 'Tenna" describes a three-element Yagi antenna that blends both on a single boom to cover both ends of the hunt. (The article is included with this book's downloadable supplemental information.) Being rigid, the elements of the antenna described in the article make it somewhat impractical for competitive DFing in brushy or wooded areas, but the design provides a starting point for experimentation and modification.

This antenna uses slide switches to configure it as either a Yagi or a single-channel interferometer. When used as an interferometer, a GaAs RF microcircuit switches the FM receiver between two matched dipoles at an audio frequency. To make the antenna compact W9PE used hinged, telescopic whips as the elements; they collapse and fold parallel to the boom for storage.

To form the interferometer, the two end elements are converted to dipoles and the center element is disabled. The feed line to the receiver is switched from the center element to the RF switch output, and the end elements are connected via feed lines to the RF switch inputs.

Now if both interferometer coax cables are of equal

length (between the antennas and switch) and the two antennas are the same distance from the transmitter (broadside to it), the signals from both antennas will be in phase. Switching from one antenna to the other will have no effect on the received signal. If one antenna is a little closer to the transmitter than the other, however, there will be a phase shift when we switch antennas. When the antenna switch is at an audio rate, say 700 Hz, the repeated phase shifts result in a set of 700 Hz sidebands that can be heard by the operator as in the preceding DDDF design.

22.2.10 A TAPE-MEASURE ELEMENT YAGI FOR 2 METERS

Joe Leggio, WB2HOL, designed this antenna while searching for a beam with a really great front-to-back ratio to use in hidden transmitter hunts. It exhibits a very clean pattern and is perfect for RDF use. You can construct this beam using only simple hand tools, and it has been duplicated many times.

WB2HOL's first design requirement was to be able to get in and out of his car easily when hunting for a hidden transmitter. He accomplished this by using steel "tape-measure" elements, which fold easily when putting the antenna into a car and yet are self supporting. They also hold up well while crashing through the underbrush on a fox hunt. (This antenna isn't designed for mobile use — *Ed.*)

WB2HOL decided to use three elements to keep the boom from getting too long. He used inexpensive schedule-40 PVC pipe, crosses and tees that can be found at any hardware store for the boom and element supports. He used a simple hairpin match, consisting of a 5-inch length of #14 AWG solid wire bent into the shape of a U, with the two legs about ¾ inch apart. This gave in a very good match across the 2 meter band after he tweaked the distance (1-inch on his prototype) between the halves of the driven element for minimum SWR.

You can cut the 1-inch wide tape-measure elements with a pair of shears, chamfering the ends of the elements. Be very careful — the edges are very sharp and will inflict a nasty cut if you are careless. Use some sandpaper to remove the sharp edges and burrs and put some vinyl electrical tape or conformal coating such as Plasti-Dip on the ends of the elements to protect yourself from getting cut. Wear safety glasses while cutting the elements. See **Figure 22.47** for dimensions.

Ken Harker, WM5R recommends using wider tape measures to provide stiffer elements or stacking thinner elements. He also notes that when taking apart a tape measure, the internal spring tension can cause the pieces to fly apart. Covering the entire element with heat shrink provides additional stiffness and comes in a variety of colors. Ken also notes that a handheld-size receiver can be mounted to the boom of a beam to further integrate the package. Plastic brackets or hook-and-loop fasteners both work well.

Make sure you scrape or sand the paint off the tape-measure elements where the feed line is attached. Most tape measures have a very durable paint finish designed to stand up to heavy use. You do not want the paint to insulate your feed line connection!

If you are careful, you can solder the feed line to the element halves, but take care since the steel tape measure does not solder easily and the PVC supports can be easily melted. Tin the tape-measure elements before mounting them to the PVC cross if you decide to connect the feed line in this fashion.

If you decide not to solder to the tape-measure elements, you can use two other methods to attach the feed line. One method employs ring terminals on the end of the coax. The ring terminals are then secured under self-tapping screws or with 6-32 bolts and nuts into holes drilled in the driven-element halves. However, with this method you cannot fine-tune the antenna by moving the halves of the driven element in and out.

The simplest method is simply to slide the ends of the feed line under the driven element hose clamps and tighten the clamps to hold the ends of the coax. This is low-tech but it works just fine.

WB2HOL used 1½-inch stainless-steel hose clamps to attach each driven-element half to the PVC cross that acts as its support. This allowed him to fine-tune his antenna for lowest SWR simply by loosening the hose clamps and sliding the halves of the driven element in or out to lengthen or shorten the element. He achieved a 1:1 SWR at 146.565 MHz (the local fox-hunt frequency) when the two elements were spaced about 1 inch apart. **Figure 22.48** shows the hose-clamp method for attaching the driven element to the PVC cross, along with the hairpin wire and feed line coax. **Figure 22.49** shows the completed antenna.

Some builders have used rubber faucet washers between the tape-measure elements and the PVC-cross fittings on the director and reflector. These allow for the tape to fit the contour of the PVC fitting better and will make the antenna look nicer. It is normal for the reflector and director elements to buckle a bit as they are tightened to the PVC tee and cross if you don't use faucet washers. You can also eliminate the buckling if you use self-tapping screws to attach these elements instead of hose clamps. The beam will not be as rugged, however, as when you use hose clamps.

The RG-58 coax feed line is wound into an 8-turn coil along the boom to form the choke balun required to prevent feed line interaction from distorting the antenna pattern. (RG-174 is much lighter and does not introduce significant loss in the short length used here — *Ed.*) The coil is covered with electrical tape or tennis racket grip tape to secure it to the boom.

This beam has been used on fox hunts, on mountain tops, at local public-service events, outdoors, indoors in attics — just about everywhere. The SWR is typically very close to 1:1 once adjusted. Front-to-back performance is exactly as predicted. The null in the rear of the pattern is perfect for transmitter hunts.

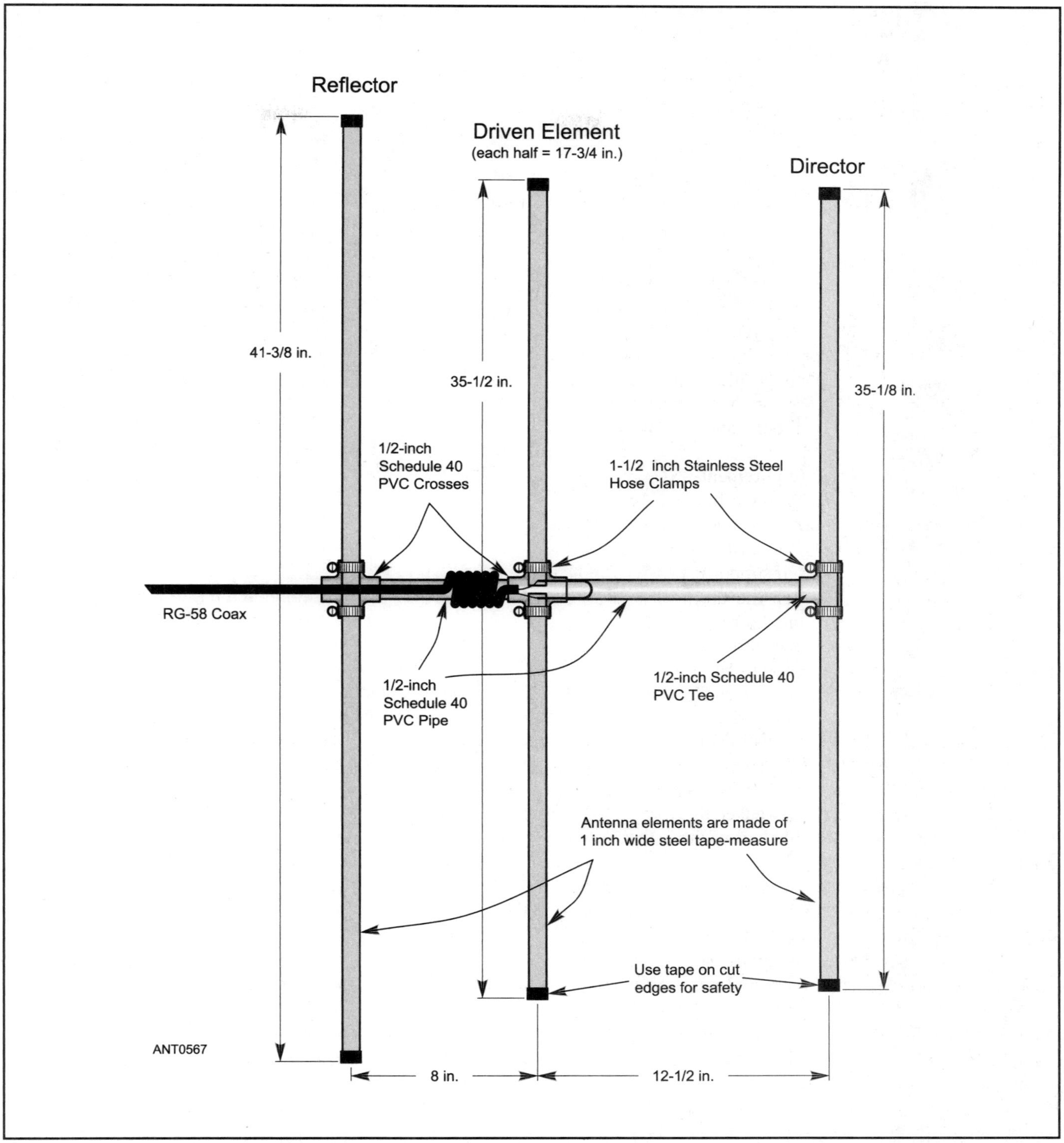

Figure 22.47 — Tape-measure beam dimensions.

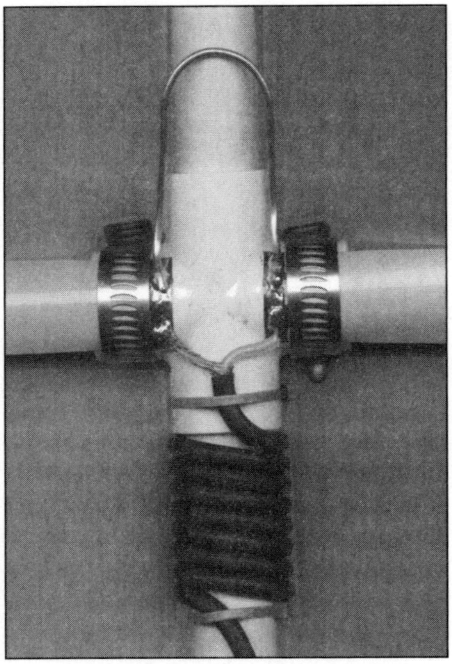

Figure 22.48 — Photo of driven-element mounted to PVC tee using hose clamps. The hairpin match wires are shown here soldered to the tape-measure elements, along with the RG-58 feed line.

Figure 22.49 — Photo of complete tape-measure beam, ready to hunt foxes!

22.2.11 DIRECTION FINDING BIBLIOGRAPHY

Source material and more extended discussion of topics covered in this chapter can be found in the references given below and in the textbooks listed at the end of the **Antenna Fundamentals** chapter.

W. U. Amfahr, "Unidirectional Loops for Transmitter Hunting," *QST*, Mar 1955, pp 28-29.

G. Bonaguide, "HF DF — A Technique for Volunteer Monitoring," *QST*, Mar 1984, pp 34-36.

D. S. Bond, *Radio Direction Finders*, 1st edition (New York: McGraw-Hill Book Co).

R. E. Cowan and T. A. Beery, "Direction Finding with the Interferometer," *QST*, Nov 1985, pp 33-37.

D. DeMaw, "Beat the Noise with a Scoop Loop," *QST*, Jul 1977, pp 30-34.

D. DeMaw, "Maverick Trackdown," *QST*, Jul 1980, pp 22-25.

T. Dorbuck, "Radio Direction-Finding Techniques," *QST*, Aug 1975, pp 30-36.

D. T. Geiser, "Double-Ducky Direction Finder," *QST*, Jul 1981, pp 11-14.

D. T. Geiser, "The Simple Seeker," *The ARRL Antenna Compendium, Vol 3*, p 126.

G. Gercke, "Radio Direction/Range Finder," *73*, Dec 1971, pp 29-30.

N. K. Holter, "Radio Foxhunting in Europe," Parts 1 and 2, *QST*, Aug 1976, pp 53-57 and Nov 1976, pp 43-46.

J. Isaacs, "Transmitter Hunting on 75 Meters," *QST*, Jun 1958, pp 38-41.

H. Jasik, *Antenna Engineering Handbook*, 1st edition (New York: McGraw-Hill, 1961).

R. Keen, *Wireless Direction Finding*, 3rd edition (London: Wireless World).

J. Kraus, *Antennas*, 2nd edition (New York: McGraw-Hill Book Co, 1988).

J. Kraus, *Electromagnetics*, 4th edition (New York: McGraw-Hill Book Co, 1992).

C. M. Maer, Jr., "The Snoop-Loop," *QST*, Feb 1957, pp 11-14.

M. C. Mallette, "The Four-Way DFer," *QST*, Nov 1995, pp 29-35.

L. R. Norberg, "Transmitter Hunting with the DF Loop," *QST*, Apr 1954, pp 32-33.

P. O'Dell, "Simple Antenna and S-Meter Modification for 2-Meter FM Direction Finding," Basic Amateur Radio, *QST*, Mar 1981, pp 43-47.

Ramo and Whinnery, *Fields and Waves in Modern Radio* (New York: John Wiley & Sons, 1944).

F. Terman, *Electronic and Radio Engineering* (New York: McGraw-Hill Book Co, 1955).

For more information on direction finding, see *Radio Orienteering-The ARDF Handbook* by Bob Titterington, G3ORY, David Williams, M3WDD and David Deane, G3ZOI and *Transmitter Hunting: Radio Direction Finding Simplified*, by Joe Moell, KØOV, and Thomas Curlee, WB6UZZ. These books are available from your local dealer or can be ordered directly from ARRL(**www.arrl.org/shop**).

Notes

Notes

Notes

Notes

The ARRL

ANTENNA BOOK

FOR RADIO COMMUNICATIONS

24th EDITION

Volume 1: Antenna Fundamentals — Ch. 1-8

Volume 2: Antennas for LF/MF/HF — Ch. 9-14

Volume 3: Antennas for VHF through Microwave and Specialty Antennas — Ch. 15-22

► **Volume 4: Transmission Lines and Building Antenna Systems, and Index — Ch. 23-28**

Editor

H. Ward Silver, NØAX

Contributing Editors

Steven R. Ford, WB8IMY

Mark J. Wilson, K1RO

Editorial Assistant

Maty Weinberg, KB1EIB

Production

Michelle Bloom, WB1ENT

Sue Fagan, KB1OKW

— Cover Art

Jodi Morin, KA1JPA

David F. Pingree, N1NAS

Contributors to the 24th Edition

Alan Applegate, KØBG
Gary Breed, K9AY
Jim Brown, K9YC
Glen Brown, W6GJB
David Conn, VE3KL
Remco den Besten, PA3FYM
Wyatt Dirks, ACØRA
James Duffey, KK6MC
Darryl Holman, WW7D
Justin Johnson, GØKSC
Matt Kastigar, N9ES
Steve Kostro, N2CEI
Sean Kutzko, KX9X
Carl Luetzelschwab, K9LA
Brian Machesney, K1LI
Paul Marsh, MØEYT
Tino Pavic, VK3EGN
Stu Phillips, K6TU
Tom Planer, KJ9P
Gilles Renucci, VA2EW
Ulrich Rohde, N1UL
Rick Rosen, K1DS
Rudy Severns, N6LF
Corey Shields, KB9JHU
Kai Siwiak, KE4PT
Andrea Slack, K2EZ
Steve Stearns, K6OIK
Steve Sutterer, AKØM
John Thompson, K3MD
Paul Wade, W1GHZ
Mike Willis, GØMJW
Ken Wolff, K1EA
Grant Zehr, AA9LC

Published by:

ARRL The national association for AMATEUR RADIO®

225 Main Street, Newington, CT 06111-1400 USA

www.arrl.org

Printed in the USA

ISBN: 978-1-62595-111-3 Softcover
978-1-62595-114-4 Four-Volume Boxed Set

Kindle eBook Editions
ISBN: 978-1-62595-115-1 — Volume 1
ISBN: 978-1-62595-116-8 — Volume 2
ISBN: 978-1-62595-118-2 — Volume 3
ISBN: 978-1-62595-119-9 — Volume 4

Twenty-Fourth Edition
First Printing

Contents

A more detailed Table of Contents is included at the beginning of each chapter.

VOLUME 1
ANTENNA FUNDAMENTALS

VOLUME 2
ANTENNAS FOR LF/MF/HF

VOLUME 3
ANTENNAS FOR VHF THROUGH MICROWAVE AND SPECIALTY ANTENNAS

VOLUME 4
TRANSMISSION LINES AND BUILDING ANTENNA SYSTEMS, AND INDEX

TABLE OF CONTENTS

Chapter 23 — Downloadable Supplemental Content

Supplemental Articles

- "Coaxial RF Connectors for Microwaves" by Tom Williams, WA1MBA
- "Hands-On Radio: Open Wire Transmission Lines" by Ward Silver, NØAX
- "Hands-On Radio: SWR and Transmission Line Loss" by Ward Silver, NØAX
- "Hands-On Radio: Choosing a Feed Line" by Ward Silver, NØAX
- "Hands-On Radio: Feed Line Comparison" by Ward Silver, NØAX
- "Installing Coax Crimp Connectors" by Dino Papas, KLØS
- "Microwave Plumbing" by Paul Wade, W1GHZ
- "Multiband Operation with Open-wire Line" by George Cutsogeorge, W2VJN
- "My Feedline Tunes My Antenna" by Byron Goodman W1DX
- RF Connectors and Transmission Line Information — ARRL Handbook
- Smith Chart supplement
- "The Doctor Is In: Yes, Window Line Can be Spliced — If You Must" by Joel Hallas, W1ZR
- "Using RG58 coaxial crimp connectors with RG6 cable" by Garth Jenkinson, VK3BBK

Chapter 23

Transmission Lines

23.1 BASIC THEORY OF TRANSMISSION LINES

The connecting link between a source of ac power, such as a transmitter, and a load, such as an antenna, is a *transmission line*, *feeder* or *feed line*. Its purpose is to carry the power from one place to another and to do it as efficiently as possible. That is, the ratio of the power *transferred* by the line to the power *lost* in or from it should be as large as the circumstances permit. This is the goal, whether the ac power is RF or low-frequency ac utility power.

23.1.1 CURRENT FLOW IN LONG LINES

The simplest transmission line is a pair of parallel conductors, so we will develop our theory based on that model. In **Figure 23.1**, imagine that the connection between the battery and the two wires is made instantaneously and then broken. During the time the wires are in contact with the battery terminals, electrons in wire 1 will be attracted to the positive battery terminal and an equal number of electrons in wire 2 will be repelled from the negative terminal. This happens only near the battery terminals at first, because electromagnetic waves do not travel at infinite speed. Some time does elapse before the currents flow at the more extreme parts of the wires. By ordinary standards, the elapsed time is very short. Because the speed of wave travel along the wires may approach the speed of light at 300,000,000 meters per second, it becomes necessary to measure time in millionths of a second (microseconds, μs).

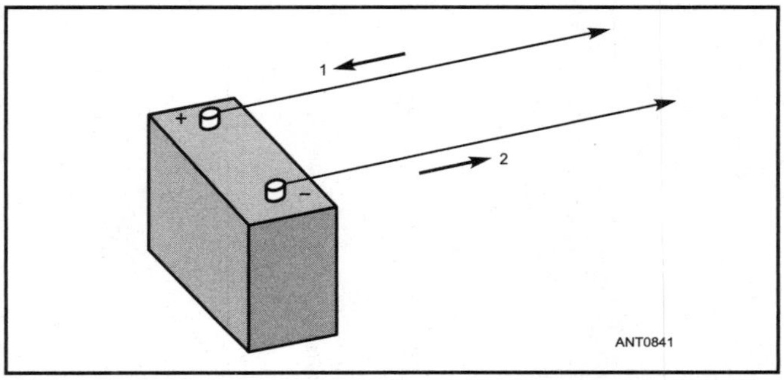

Figure 23.1 — A representation of current flow on a long transmission line.

For example, suppose that the contact with the battery is so short that it can be measured in a very small fraction of a microsecond. Then the "pulse" of current that flows at the battery terminals during this time can be represented by the vertical line in **Figure 23.2**. At the speed of light this pulse travels 30 meters along the line in 0.1 μs, 60 meters in 0.2 μs, 90 meters in 0.3 μs, and so on, as far as the line reaches.

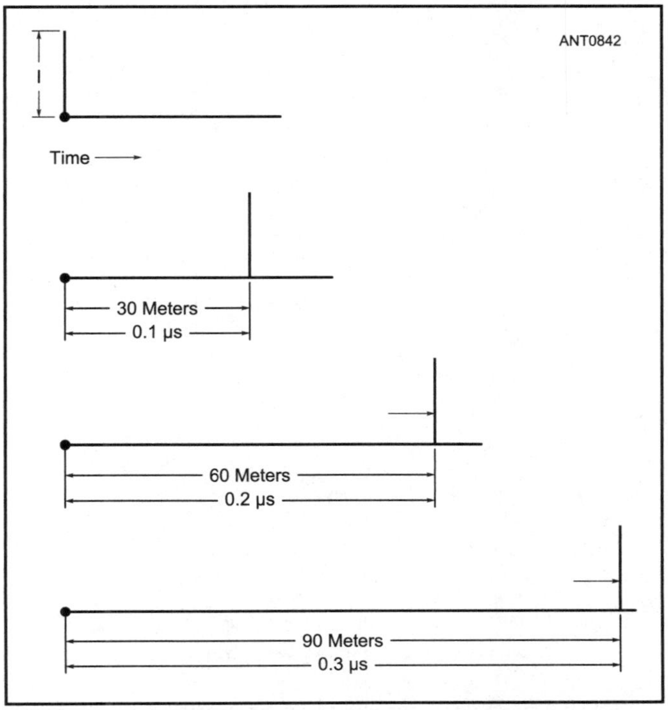

Figure 23.2 — A current pulse traveling along a transmission line at the speed of light would reach the successive positions shown at intervals of 0.1 μs.

The current does not exist all along the wires; it is only present at the point that the pulse has reached in its travel. At this point it is present in both wires, with the electrons moving in one direction in one wire and in the other direction in the other wire. If the line is infinitely long and has no resistance (or other cause of energy loss), the pulse will travel undiminished forever.

By extending the example of Figure 23.2, it is not hard to see that if, instead of one pulse, a whole series of them were started on the line at equal time intervals, the pulses would travel along the line with the same time and distance spacing between them, each pulse independent of the others. In fact, each pulse could even have a different amplitude if the battery voltage were varied between pulses. Furthermore, the pulses could be so closely spaced that they touched each other, in which case current would be present everywhere along the line simultaneously.

It follows from this that an alternating voltage applied to the line would give rise to the sort of current flow shown in **Figure 23.3**. If the frequency of the ac voltage is 10,000,000 hertz or 10 MHz, each cycle occupies 0.1 ms, so a complete cycle of current will be present along each 30 meters of line. This is a distance of one wavelength. Any currents at points B and D on the two conductors occur one cycle later in time than the currents at A and C. Put another way, the currents initiated at A and C do not appear at B and D, one wavelength away, until the applied voltage has gone through a complete cycle.

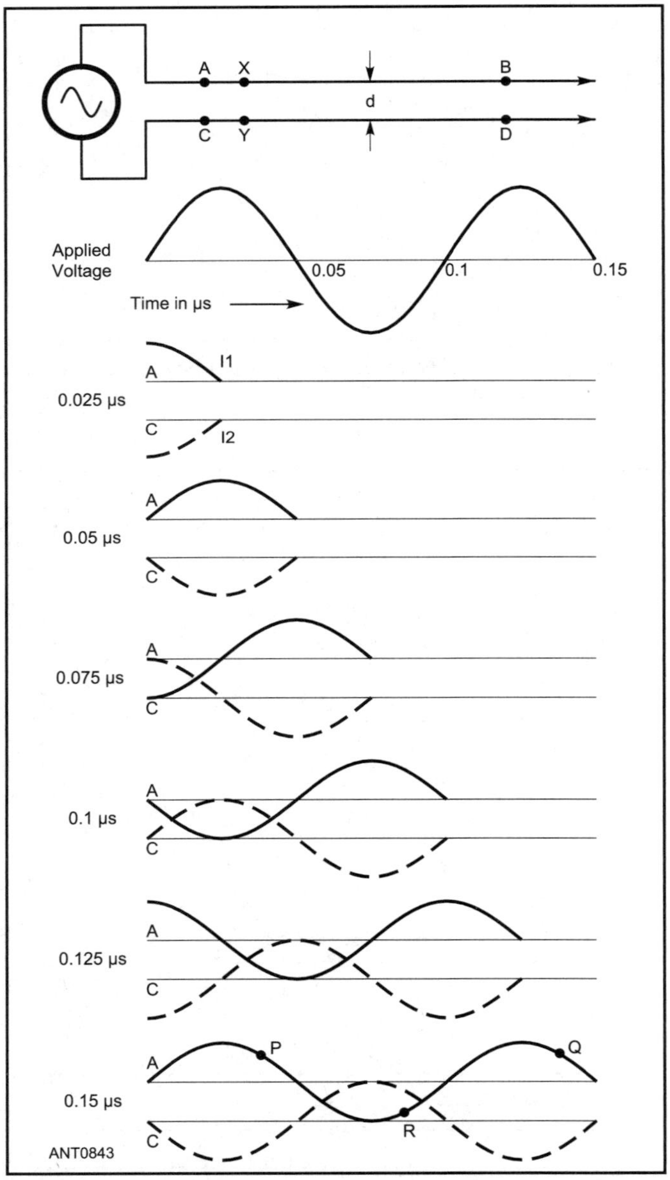

Figure 23.3 — Instantaneous current along a transmission line at successive time intervals. The frequency is 10 MHz; the time for each complete cycle is 0.1 µs.

Because the applied voltage is always changing, the currents at A and C change in proportion. The current a short distance away from A and C — for instance, at X and Y — is not the same as the current at A and C. This is because the current at X and Y was caused by a value of voltage that occurred slightly earlier in the cycle. This situation holds true all along the line; at any instant the current anywhere along the line from A to B and C to D is different from the current at any other point on that section of the line.

The remaining series of drawings in Figure 23.3 shows how the instantaneous currents might be distributed if we could take snapshots of them at intervals of ¼ cycle. The current travels out from the input end of the line in waves. At any given point on the line, the current goes through its complete range of ac values in one cycle, just as it does at the input end. Therefore (if there are no losses) an ammeter inserted in either conductor reads exactly the same current at any point along the line, because the ammeter averages the current over a whole cycle. (The phases of the currents at any two separate points are different, but the ammeter cannot show phase.)

23.1.2 VELOCITY OF PROPAGATION

In the example above it was assumed that energy travels along the line at the velocity of light. The actual velocity is very close to that of light only in lines in which the insulation between conductors is air. The presence of dielectrics other than air reduces the velocity.

Current flows at the speed of light only in a vacuum, although the speed in air is close to that in a vacuum. Therefore, the time required for a signal of a given frequency to travel down a length of practical transmission line is *longer* than the time required for the same signal to travel the same distance in free space. Because of this propagation delay, 360° of a given wave exists in a physically shorter distance on a given transmission line than in free space. The exact delay for a given transmission line is a function of the properties of the line, mainly the dielectric constant of the insulating material between the conductors. This delay is expressed in terms of the speed of light (either as a percentage or a decimal fraction), and is referred to as velocity factor (VF). The velocity factor is related to the dielectric constant (ε) by

$$VF = \frac{1}{\sqrt{\varepsilon}} \qquad (1)$$

The wavelength in a practical line is always shorter than the wavelength in free space, which has a dielectric constant ε = 1.0. Whenever reference is made to a line as being a half wavelength or quarter wavelength long (λ/2 or λ/4), it is understood that what is meant by this is the *electrical* length of the line. The physical length corresponding to an electrical wavelength on a given line is given by

$$\lambda\text{ (feet)} = \frac{983.6}{f} \times VF \qquad (2)$$

where

f = frequency in MHz

VF = velocity factor

Values of VF for several common types of lines are given later in this chapter. The actual VF of a given cable varies slightly from one production run or manufacturer to another, even though the cables may have exactly the same specifications.

As we shall see later, a quarter-wavelength line is frequently used as an impedance transformer, and so it is convenient to calculate the length of a quarter-wave line directly by

$$\lambda / 4 = \frac{245.9}{f} \times VF \qquad (2A)$$

It is important to note that Equation 1 is based on some simplifying assumptions about the cable and the frequency of use. At frequencies below 100 kHz, these assumptions become progressively less valid and VF drops dramatically. This is generally not an issue at amateur frequencies (except slightly on the 2200 meter band) but could become significant when coaxial or twisted-pair transmission lines are used for software-defined radio applications. This is discussed more in the paper "Transmission Lines at Audio Frequencies, and a Bit of History" by Jim Brown, K9YC listed in the Bibliography.

23.1.3 CHARACTERISTIC IMPEDANCE

If the line could be *perfect* — having no resistive losses — a question might arise: What is the amplitude of the current in a pulse applied to this line? Will a larger voltage result in a larger current, or is the current theoretically infinite for an applied voltage, as we would expect from applying Ohm's Law to a circuit without resistance? The answer is that the current does depend directly on the voltage, just as though resistance were present.

The reason for this is that the current flowing in the line is something like the charging current that flows when a battery is connected to a capacitor. That is, the line has capacitance. However, it also has inductance. Both of these are "distributed" properties. We may think of the line as being composed of a whole series of small inductors and capacitors, connected as in **Figure 23.4**, where each coil is the inductance of an extremely small section of wire, and the capacitance is that existing between the same two sections. Each series inductor acts to limit the rate at which current can charge the following shunt capacitor, and in so doing establishes a very important property of a transmission line: its *surge impedance*, more commonly known as its *characteristic impedance*. This is abbreviated by convention as Z_0. While relatively constant at RF, Z_0 increases below 100 kHz, becoming much higher at and below audio frequencies as described in the previously noted Bibliography entry for Brown.

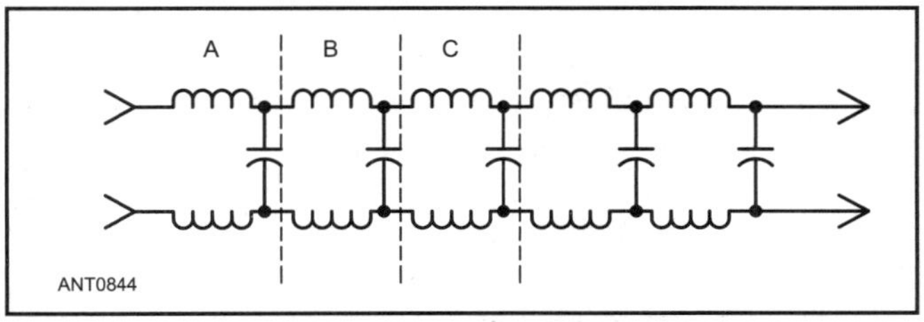

Figure 23.4 — Equivalent of an ideal (lossless) transmission line in terms of ordinary circuit elements (lumped constants). The values of inductance and capacitance depend on the line construction.

But Why 50 Ohms?

Coaxial cable burst on the scene as ham radio re-booted after World War II and the 50 Ω characteristic impedance of RG-8 became the de facto standard from then on. But why 50 Ω? The answer comes from Volume 9 of the MIT Radiation Lab Series, *Microwave Transmission Circuits*, by George L. Ragan, published in 1948. (**web.mit.edu/klund/www/books/radlab.html**) On page 147, after several pages deriving the optimum geometries, Ragan writes, "Obvious economy both in test equipment and in design work can be achieved if a single impedance can be chosen as a compromise standard. It has been found convenient to adopt 50 ohms as an impedance level offering a satisfactory compromise." His Table 4.2 shows the relative loss and power-handling capability loss of 50 Ω air- and polyethylene-insulated lines. The latter achieves better than 50% of the optimum value based either on wavelength or outer conductor size, including 100% of the optimum attenuation. Thus, 50 Ω was selected based on available types and sizes of materials to give good (but mostly not best) performance for both power and loss. (Thanks to Gene Pentecost, W4IMT, for researching this question.)

23.1.4 TERMINATED LINES

The value of the characteristic impedance is equal to $\sqrt{L/C}$ in a perfect line — that is, one in which the conductors have no resistance and there is no leakage between them — where L and C are the inductance and capacitance, respectively, per unit length of line. The inductance decreases with increasing conductor diameter, and the capacitance decreases with increasing spacing between the conductors. Hence a line with closely spaced large conductors has relatively low characteristic impedance, while one with widely spaced thin conductors has high impedance. Practical values of Z_0 for parallel-conductor lines range from about 200 to 800 Ω. Typical coaxial lines have characteristic impedances from 30 to 100 Ω. Physical constraints on practical wire diameters and spacings limit Z_0 values to these ranges.

In the earlier discussion of current traveling along a transmission line, we assumed that the line was infinitely long. Practical lines have a definite length, and they are terminated in a load at the output or load end (the end to which the power is delivered). In **Figure 23.5**, if the load is a pure resistance

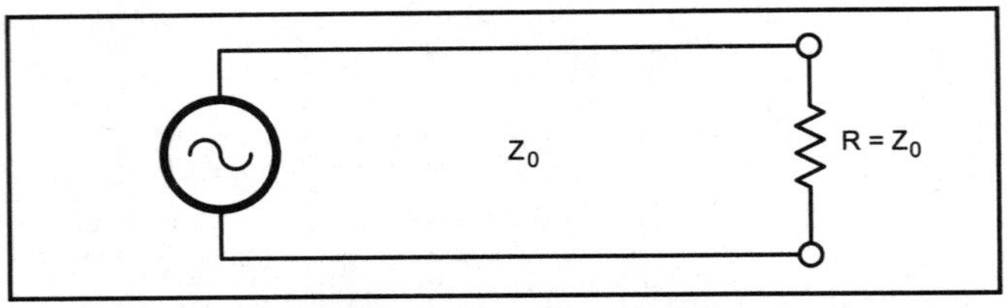

Figure 23.5 — A transmission line terminated in a resistive load equal to the characteristic impedance of the line.

of a value equal to the characteristic impedance of a perfect, lossless line, the current traveling along the line to the load finds that the load simply "looks like" more transmission line of the same characteristic impedance.

The reason for this can be more easily understood by considering it from another viewpoint. Along a transmission line, power is transferred successively from one elementary section in Figure 23.4 to the next. When the line is infinitely long, this power transfer goes on in one direction — away from the source of power.

From the standpoint of Section B, Figure 23.4, for instance, the power transferred to section C has simply disappeared in C. As far as section B is concerned, it makes no difference whether C has absorbed the power itself or has transferred it along to more transmission line. Consequently, if we substitute a load for section C that has the same electrical characteristics as the transmission line, section B will transfer power into it just as if it were more transmission line. A pure resistance equal to the characteristic impedance of C, which is also the characteristic impedance of the line, meets this condition. It absorbs all the power just as the infinitely long line absorbs all the power transferred by section B.

Matched Lines

A line terminated in a load equal to the complex characteristic line impedance is said to be *matched*. In a matched transmission line, power is transferred outward along the line from the source until it reaches the load, where it is completely absorbed. Thus with either the infinitely long line or its matched counterpart, the impedance presented to the source of power (the line-input impedance) is the same *regardless of the line length.* It is simply equal to the characteristic impedance of the line. The current in such a line is equal to the applied voltage divided by the characteristic impedance, and the power put into it is E^2/Z_0 or I^2Z_0, by Ohm's law.

Mismatched Lines

Now take the case where the terminating load is *not* equal to Z_0, as in **Figure 23.6**. The load no longer looks like more line to the section of line immediately adjacent. Such a line is said to be *mismatched*. The more the load impedance differs from Z_0, the greater the mismatch. The power reaching the load is not totally absorbed, as it was when the load was equal to Z_0, because the load requires a voltage to current ratio that is different from the one traveling along the line. The result is that the load absorbs only part of the power reaching it (the *incident* power); the remainder acts as though it had bounced off a wall and starts back along the line toward the source. This is known as *reflected power*, and the greater the mismatch, the larger the percentage of the incident power that is reflected. In the extreme case where the load is zero (a short circuit) or infinity (an open circuit), *all* of the power reaching the end of the line is reflected back toward the source.

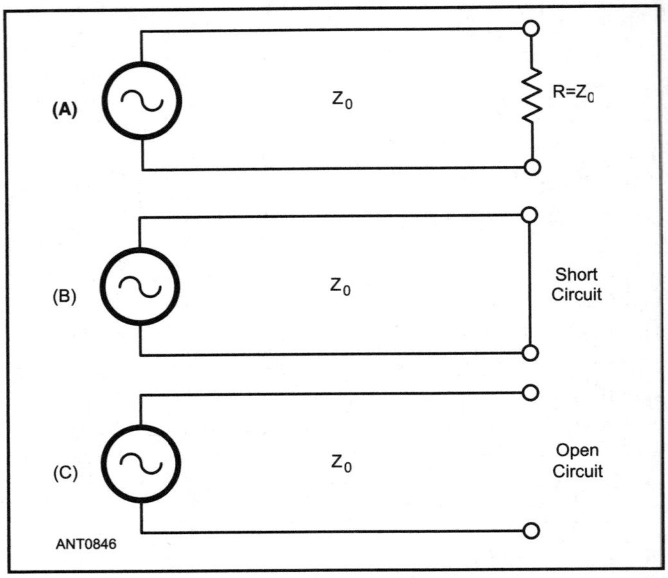

Figure 23.6 — Mismatched lines; extreme cases. At A, termination not equal to Z_0; at B, short-circuited line; At C, open-circuited line.

Whenever there is a mismatch, power is transferred in both directions along the line. The voltage to current ratio is the same for the reflected power as for the incident power, because this ratio is determined by the Z_0 of the line. The voltage and current travel along the line in both directions in the same wave motion shown in Figure 23.3. If the source of power is an ac generator, the incident (outgoing) voltage and the reflected (returning) voltage are simultaneously present all along the line. The actual voltage at any point along the line is the vector sum of the two components, taking into account the *phases* of each component. The same is true of the current.

The effect of the incident and reflected components on the behavior of the line can be understood more readily by considering first the two limiting cases — the short-circuited line and the open-circuited line. If the line is short-circuited as in Figure 23.6B, the voltage at the end must be zero. Thus the incident voltage must disappear suddenly at the short. It can do this only if the reflected voltage is opposite in phase and of the same amplitude. This is shown by the vectors in **Figure 23.7**. The current, however, does not disappear in the short circuit. In fact, the incident current flows through the short and in addition, there is the reflected component in phase of the same amplitude as the incident current.

The reflected voltage and current must have the same amplitudes as the incident voltage and current, because no power is dissipated in the short circuit; all the power starts back toward the source. Reversing the phase of *either* the

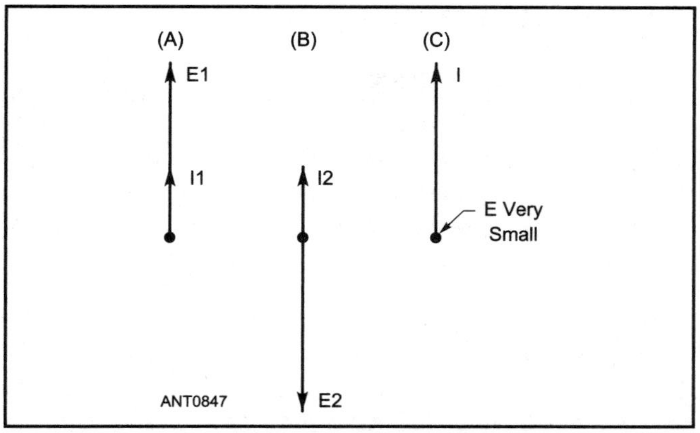

Figure 23.7 — Voltage and current at the short circuit on a short-circuited line. These vectors show how the incident voltage and current (A) combine with the reflected voltage and current (B) to result in high current and very low voltage in the short circuit (C).

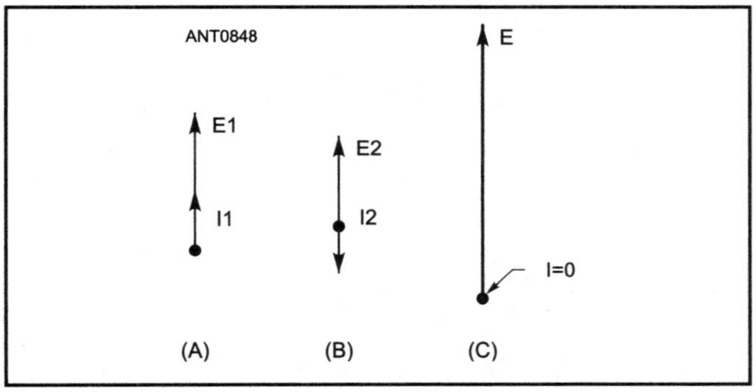

Figure 23.8 — Voltage and current at the end of an open-circuited line. At A, incident voltage and current; At B, reflected voltage and current; At C, resulting voltage and current.

current or voltage (but not both) reverses the direction of power flow. In the short-circuited case the phase of the voltage is reversed on reflection, but the phase of the current is not.

If the line is open-circuited (Figure 23.6C) the current must be zero at the end of the line. In this case the reflected current is 180° out of phase with the incident current and has the same amplitude. By reasoning similar to that used in the short-circuited case, the reflected voltage must be in phase with the incident voltage, and must have the same amplitude. Vectors for the open-circuited case are shown in **Figure 23.8**.

Where there is a finite value of resistance (or a combination of resistance and reactance) at the end of the line, as in Figure 23.6A, only part of the power reaching the end of the line is reflected. That is, the reflected voltage and current are smaller than the incident voltage and current. If R is less than Z_0, the reflected and incident voltage are 180° out of phase, just as in the case of the short-circuited line, but the amplitudes are not equal because all of the voltage does not disappear at R. Similarly, if R is greater than Z_0, the reflected and incident currents are 180° out of phase (as they were in the open-circuited line), but all of the current does not appear

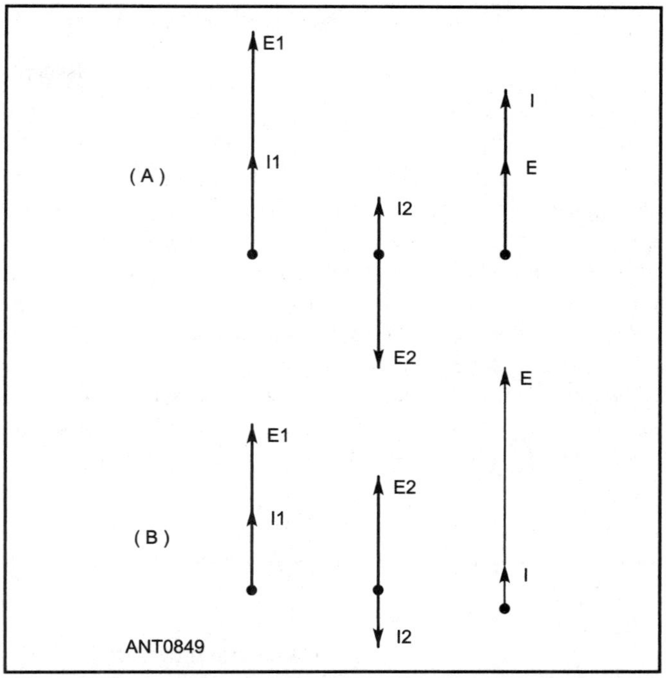

Figure 23.9 — Incident and reflected components of voltage and current when the line is terminated in a pure resistance R not equal to Z_0. In the case shown, the reflected components have half the amplitude of the incident components. At A, R less than Z_0; at B, R greater than Z_0.

in R. The amplitudes of the two components are therefore not equal. These two cases are shown in **Figure 23.9**. Note that the resultant current and voltage are in phase in R, because R is a pure resistance.

Non-Resistive Terminations

In most of the preceding discussions, we considered loads containing only resistance. Furthermore, our transmission line was considered to be lossless. Such a resistive load will consume some, if not all, of the power that has been transferred along the line. However, a non-resistive load such as a pure reactance can also terminate a length of line. Such terminations, of course, will consume no power, but will reflect all of the energy arriving at the end of the line. In this case the theoretical SWR (covered later) in the line will be infinite, but in practice, losses in the line will limit the SWR to some finite value at line positions back toward the source.

At first you might think there is little or no point in terminating a line with a non-resistive load. In a later section we shall examine this in more detail, but the value of input impedance depends on the value of the load impedance, on the length of the line, the losses in a practical line, and on the characteristic impedance of the line. There are times when a line terminated in a non-resistive load can be used to advantage, such as in phasing or matching applications. Remote switching of reactive terminations on sections of line can be used to reverse the beam heading of an antenna array, for example. The point of this brief discussion is that a line need not always be terminated in a load that will consume power.

23.2 PRACTICAL TRANSMISSION LINES

Transmission lines consisting of two parallel conductors as in **Figure 23.10**, parts E, F, and G are called *open- or parallel-wire lines*, *parallel-conductor lines* or *two-wire lines*. The specific styles shown here are called *twin-lead* (E), *ladder line* (F), and *window line* (G). Current flowing on one conductor is balanced by an equal-and-opposite current flowing on the other conductor. In almost all cases, both conductors have an equal impedance to the system's ground reference and so these are referred to as *balanced lines*.

A second general type of line construction called *coaxial cable* or coax (pronounced "KOH-ax") or *concentric line* is shown in Figures 23.10A, B, C, and D. In coax, one of the conductors is tube-shaped and encloses the other conductor. Current flowing on the inner conductor is balanced by an equal current flowing in the opposite direction on the inside surface of the outer conductor. Because of skin effect, the current on the inner surface of the outer conductor does not penetrate far enough to appear on the outside surface. In fact, the total electromagnetic field outside the coaxial line (as a result of currents flowing on the conductors inside) is always zero, because the outer conductor acts as a shield at radio frequencies, reducing radiation from coax to nearly zero. The separation between the inner conductor and the outer conductor is therefore unimportant from the standpoint of reducing radiation. (This is not true at very low frequencies where the skin depth is greater than the shield thickness and

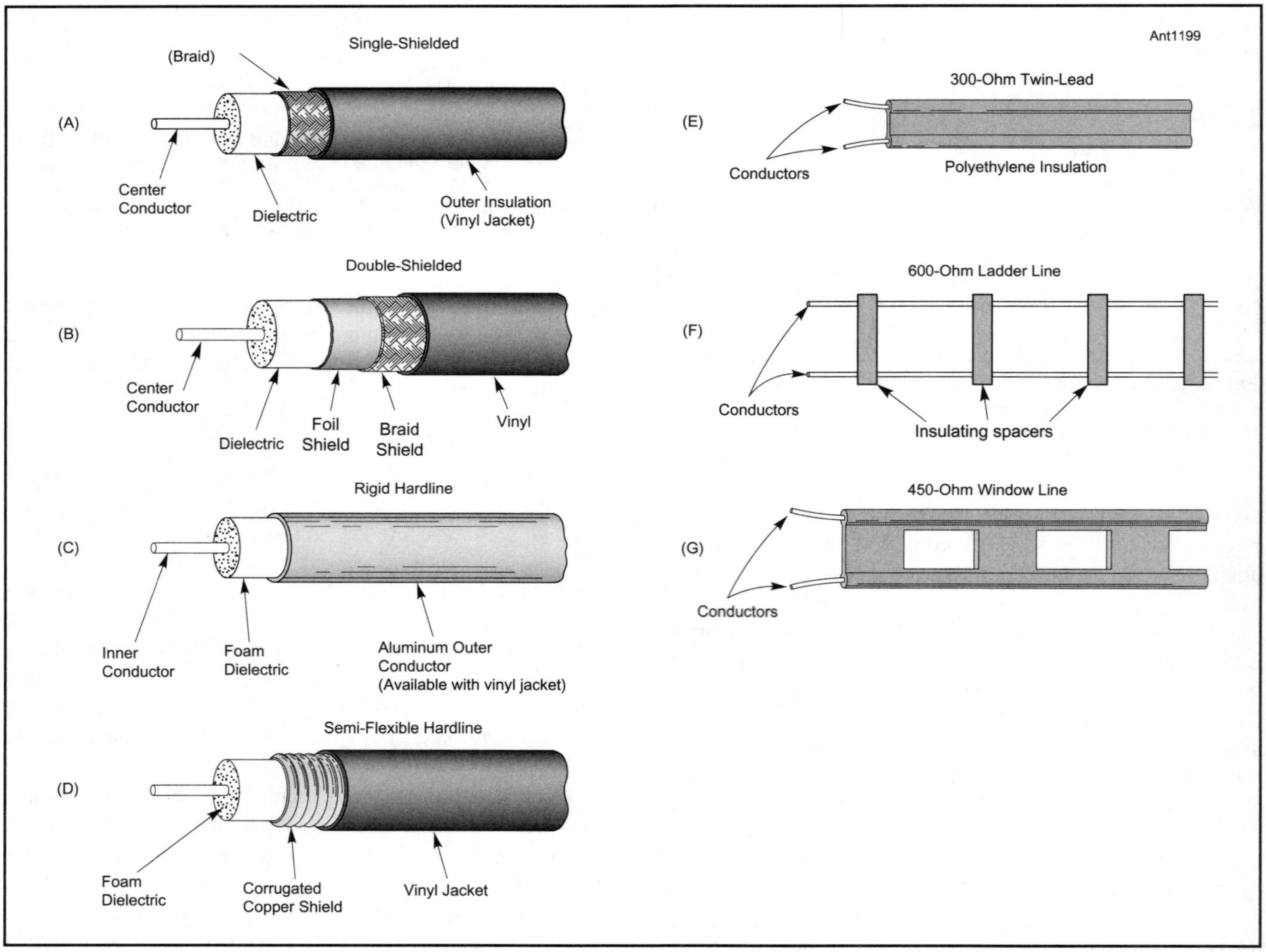

Figure 23.10 — Common types of transmission lines used by amateurs below microwave frequencies. Coaxial cables are shown at A, B, C, and D. Parallel-conductor lines are shown at E, F, and G.

at microwave frequencies where openings in the braided shield of flexible coax becomes significant with respect to a wavelength.)

A third general type of transmission line is the *waveguide* which is not shown here. Waveguides are discussed in the chapter **VHF and UHF Antenna Systems**.

Common-Mode and Differential-Mode Current

It is important to recognize the two types of currents that may flow in and on transmission lines: differential-mode (DM) and common-mode (CM). **Figure 23.11** shows DM and CM current for typical unshielded paired conductors at A and a coaxial line at B.

DM signals are what we often think of as "balanced" in that the signal consists of identical currents flowing in opposite directions along two closely-matched paths, neither of which is connected directly to ground or a grounded enclosure. CM signals flow equally on all conductors of a multiconductor cable or on the common (shield) conductor of a coaxial or shielded cable.

Taking a close look at Figure 23.11B, you can see that a single cable can support both DM and CM signals at the same time. In fact, at RF the outside of a braided or foil shield is electrically independent from the inside because the skin effect restricts ac current flow to the exterior surfaces of a conductor. At frequencies above 1 MHz, current penetrates copper or aluminum less than 0.1 mm.

CM current is often caused by the conductors acting as an antenna and picking up a transmitted signal. It can also result from signals being present on a ground conductor or enclosure or the signal can leak from an enclosure. As discussed in the next section, CM current can be converted to a DM signal by the cable's transfer impedance. CM current also radiates a signal just as current on an antenna does.

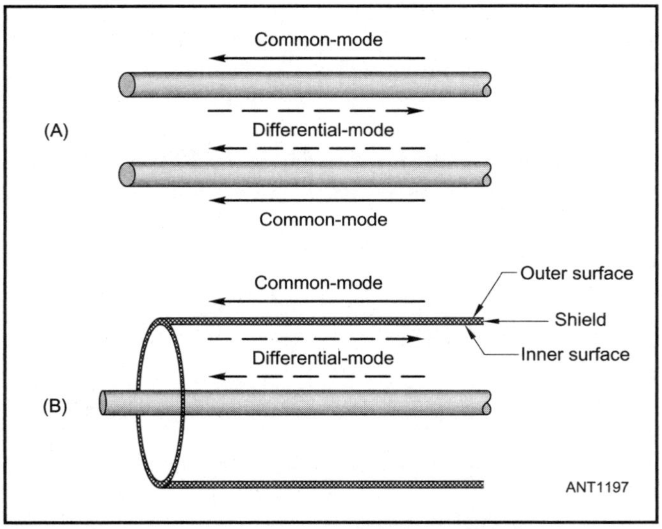

Figure 23.11 — Common-mode (CM) and differential-mode (DM) current can flow on parallel-conductor and coaxial cables at the same time. CM current can be converted to a DM signal by the cable's transfer impedance.

23.2.1 ATTENUATION

Every practical line will have some inherent loss, partly because of the resistance of the conductors, partly because power is consumed in the dielectric used for insulating the conductors, and partly because in many cases a small amount of power escapes from the line by radiation.

Line Radiation and Transfer Impedance

At RF, every conductor that has appreciable length compared with the wavelength in use *radiates* power — every conductor is an antenna. Special care must be used, therefore, to minimize radiation from the conductors used in RF transmission lines. Without such care, the power radiated by the line may be much larger than that which is lost in the resistance of conductors and dielectrics (insulating materials). Power loss in resistance is inescapable, at least to a degree, but loss by radiation is largely avoidable.

Radiation loss from differential-mode signals carried by transmission lines can be prevented by using two conductors arranged and operated so the electromagnetic field from one is balanced everywhere by an equal and opposite field from the other. In such a case, the resultant field is zero everywhere in space — there is no radiation from the line. This requires that the spacing between the conductors making up the line be very small compared with the wavelength of the energy flowing in the line. Through the UHF range, the transmission lines used by amateurs satisfy this requirement with plenty of margin and line radiation is not significant.

Figure 23.3 shows two parallel conductors having currents I1 and I2 flowing in opposite directions. If the current I1 at point Y on the upper conductor has the same amplitude as the current I2 at the corresponding point X on the lower conductor, the fields set up by the two currents are equal in magnitude. Because the two currents are flowing in opposite directions, the field from I1 at Y is 180° out of phase with the field from I2 at X. However, it takes a measurable interval of time for the field from X to travel to Y.

If I1 and I2 are alternating currents, the phase of the field from I1 at Y changes in such a time interval, so at the instant the field from X reaches Y, the two fields at Y are not exactly 180° out of phase. The two fields are exactly 180° out of phase at every point in space only when the two conductors occupy the same space — an obviously impossible condition if they are to remain separate conductors.

The best that can be done is to make the two fields cancel each other as completely as possible. This can be achieved by keeping the distance d between the two conductors small enough so the time interval during which the field from X is moving to Y is a very small part of a cycle. When this is the case, the phase difference between the two fields at any given point is so close to 180° that cancellation is nearly complete.

Practical values of d (the separation between the two conductors) are determined by the physical limitations of line construction. A separation that meets the condition of being "very small" at one frequency may be quite large at another. For example, if d is 6 inches, the phase difference between the two fields at Y is only a fraction of a degree if the frequency is 3.5 MHz. This is because a distance of 6 inches is such a small fraction of a wavelength (1 λ = 281 feet) at 3.5 MHz. But at 144 MHz, the phase difference is 26°, and at 420 MHz, it is 77°. In neither of these cases could the two fields be considered to "cancel" each other. Conductor separation must be very small in comparison with the wavelength used; it should never exceed 1% of the wavelength, and smaller separations are desirable.

Common-mode current flowing on the outside of a coaxial line's shield can also create differential-mode signals inside the line due to *transfer impedance*. (See the Bibliography entry for Jim Brown, K9YC on "A Ham's Guide to RFI, Ferrites, Baluns, and Audio Interfacing" and by Brown and Bill Whitlock on "Common-Mode to Differential-Mode Conversion in Shielded Twisted-Pair Cables (Shield-Current-Induced Noise)".) From Brown's paper, transfer impedance is defined as ratio of the differential voltage induced inside the cable to common-mode current on the shield. Its units are ohms, a low value is better, and the lower limit is the resistance of the shield at the frequency of interest. The overall quality, percent coverage, and uniformity of the shield also contribute to the transfer impedance — a less dense braid or a shield with poor uniformity raise the transfer impedance, causing more noise to couple by this method. Transfer impedance varies with frequency and its effect is significant below a few MHz, particularly for inexpensive audio cables used in consumer equipment.

Matched-Line Losses

The most important causes of transmission line loss for amateurs are conductor and dielectric losses. Power lost in a transmission line is not directly proportional to the line length, but varies logarithmically with the length. That is, if 10% of the input power is lost in a section of line of certain length, 10% of the remaining power will be lost in the next section of the same length, and so on. For this reason it is customary to express line losses in terms of decibels per unit length, since the decibel is a unit of logarithmic ratios. Calculations are very simple because the total loss in a line is found by multiplying the decibel loss per unit length by the total length of the line.

The power lost in a matched line (that is, where the load is equal to the characteristic impedance of the line) is called *matched-line loss*. Matched-line loss is usually expressed in decibels per 100 feet. It is necessary to specify the frequency for which the loss applies, because the loss does vary with frequency.

Conductor and dielectric loss both increase as the operating frequency is increased, but not in the same way. This, together with the fact that the relative amount of each type of loss depends on the actual construction of the line, makes it impossible to give a specific relationship between loss and frequency that will apply to all types of lines.

One relationship that does apply is that for lines made of the same materials (for example, copper and solid polyethylene) higher impedance lines will have lower losses. This is because the current is lower in a higher impedance line, reducing resistive (I^2R) losses.

In practice, when selecting a feed line, each type of line must be considered individually. Actual loss values for practical lines are given in a later section of this chapter along with a discussion of how to select a feed line.

One effect of matched-line loss in a real transmission line is that the characteristic impedance, Z_0, becomes complex, with a non-zero reactive component X_0. Thus,

$$Z_0 = R_0 - jX_0 \tag{3}$$

$$X_0 = -R_0 \frac{\alpha}{\beta} \tag{4}$$

where

$$\alpha = \frac{\text{Attenuation (dB / 100 feet)} \times 0.1151 \text{ (nepers / dB)}}{\text{100 feet}}$$

the matched-line attenuation, in nepers per unit length. (Nepers are a unitless non-logarithmic radio and 1 neper = 8.686 dB.)

$\beta = \frac{2\pi}{\lambda}$, the phase constant in radians/unit length.

The reactive portion of the complex characteristic impedance is always capacitive (that is, its sign is negative) and the value of X_0 is usually small compared to the resistive portion R_0.

23.2.2 REFLECTION COEFFICIENT

The ratio of the reflected voltage at a given point on a transmission line to the incident voltage is called the *voltage reflection coefficient*. The voltage reflection coefficient

Coaxial Feed Line Loss Coefficients

High-precision calculations of loss in coaxial feed lines require three constants, K0, K1, and K2, which are specified by manufacturers for each type of cable. You may encounter these coefficients in online calculators and other tools for determining feed line characteristics, loss, and so on.

- K0 is associated with the dc resistance of the conductors and does not vary with frequency.
- K1 is associated with the skin effect of the conductors which varies in proportion to the square root of frequency.
- K2 is associated with the dielectric loss which varies directly with frequency.

is also equal to the ratio of the incident and reflected currents. Thus

$$\rho = \frac{E_r}{E_f} = \frac{I_r}{I_f} \tag{5}$$

where

ρ = reflection coefficient
E_r = reflected voltage
E_f = forward (incident) voltage
I_r = reflected current
I_f = forward (incident) current

The reflection coefficient is determined by the relationship between the line Z0 and the actual load at the terminated end of the line. In most cases, the actual load is not entirely resistive — that is, the load is a complex impedance, consisting of a resistance in series with a reactance, as is the complex characteristic impedance of the transmission line.

The reflection coefficient is thus a complex quantity, having both amplitude and phase, and is generally designated by the Greek letter ρ (rho), or sometimes as Γ (Gamma). The relationship between R_a (the load resistance), X_a (the load reactance), Z_0 (the complex line characteristic impedance, whose real part is R_0 and whose reactive part is X_0) and the complex reflection coefficient ρ is

$$\rho = \frac{Z_a - Z_0}{Z_a + Z_0} = \frac{(R_a \pm jX_a) - (R_0 \pm jX_0)}{(R_a \pm jX_a) + (R_0 \pm jX_0)} \tag{6}$$

For high-quality, low-loss transmission lines at low frequencies, the characteristic impedance Z_0 is almost completely resistive, meaning that $Z_0 \cong R_0$ and $X_0 \cong 0$. The magnitude of the complex reflection coefficient in Eq 6 then simplifies to:

$$|\rho| = \sqrt{\frac{(R_a - R_0)^2 + X_a^2}{(R_a + R_0)^2 + X_a^2}} \tag{7}$$

For example, if the characteristic impedance of a coaxial line at a low operating frequency is 50 Ω and the load impedance is 120 Ω in series with a capacitive reactance of –90 Ω, the magnitude of the reflection coefficient is

$$|\rho| = \sqrt{\frac{(120-50)^2 + (-90)^2}{(120+50)^2 + (-90)^2}} = 0.593$$

Note that the vertical bars on each side of ρ mean the *magnitude* of rho. If R_a in Eq 7 is equal to R_0 and if X_a is 0, the reflection coefficient, ρ, also is 0. This represents a *matched condition*, where all the energy in the incident wave is transferred to the load. On the other hand, if R_a is 0, meaning that the load has no real resistive part, the reflection coefficient is 1.0, regardless of the value of R_0. This means that all the forward power is reflected, since the load is completely reactive. As we shall see later on, the concept of reflection coefficient is a very useful one to evaluate the impedance seen looking into the input of a mismatched transmission line.

Another representation of the reflection coefficient concept is the *return loss*, which is the reflection coefficient expressed in dB.

$$RL = -20 \log |\rho| \text{ dB} \tag{8}$$

For example, a reflection coefficient of 0.593 is a return loss of –20 log (0.593) = 4.5 dB. (Note that some texts express return loss as negative numbers, but most define it as positive.)

23.2.3 STANDING WAVES

As might be expected, reflection cannot occur at the load without some effect on the voltages and currents all along the line. To keep things simple for a while longer, let us continue to consider only resistive loads, without any reactance. The conclusions we shall reach are valid for transmission lines terminated in complex impedances as well.

The effects are most simply shown by vector diagrams. **Figure 23.12** is an example where the terminating resistance R is less than Z_0. The voltage and current vectors at R are shown in the reference position; they correspond with the vectors in Figure 23.9A, turned 90°. Back along the line from R toward the power source, the incident vectors, E1 and I1, lead the vectors at the load according to their position along the line measured in electrical degrees. (The corresponding distances in fractions of a wavelength are also shown.) The vectors representing reflected voltage and current, E2 and I2, successively lag the same vectors at the load.

This lag is the natural consequence of the direction in which the incident and reflected components are traveling,

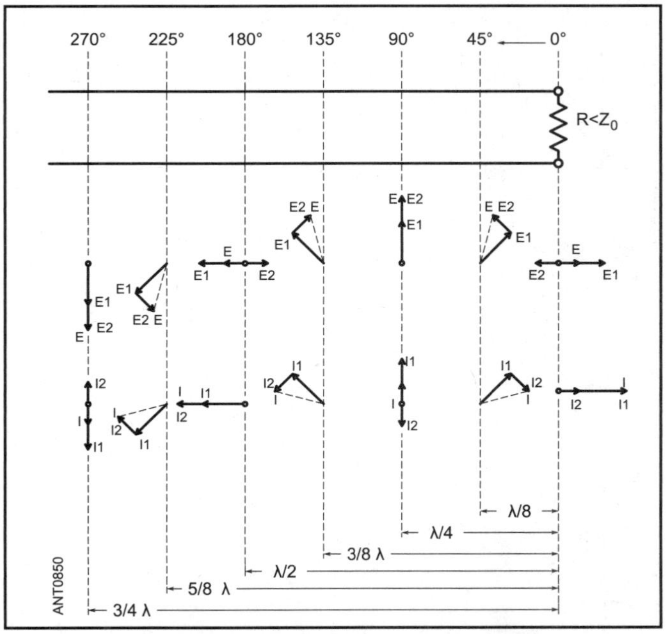

Figure 23.12 — Incident and reflected components at various positions along the transmission line, together with resultant voltages and currents at the same positions. The case shown is for R less than Z_0.

together with the fact that it takes time for power to be transferred along the line. The resultant voltage E and current I at each of these positions is shown as a dotted arrow. Although the incident and reflected components maintain their respective amplitudes (the reflected component is shown at half the incident-component amplitude in this drawing), their phase relationships vary with position along the line. The phase shift causes both the amplitude and phase of the *resultants* to vary with position on the line.

If the amplitude variations (disregarding phase) of the resultant voltage and current are plotted against position along the line, graphs like those of **Figure 23.13A** will result. If

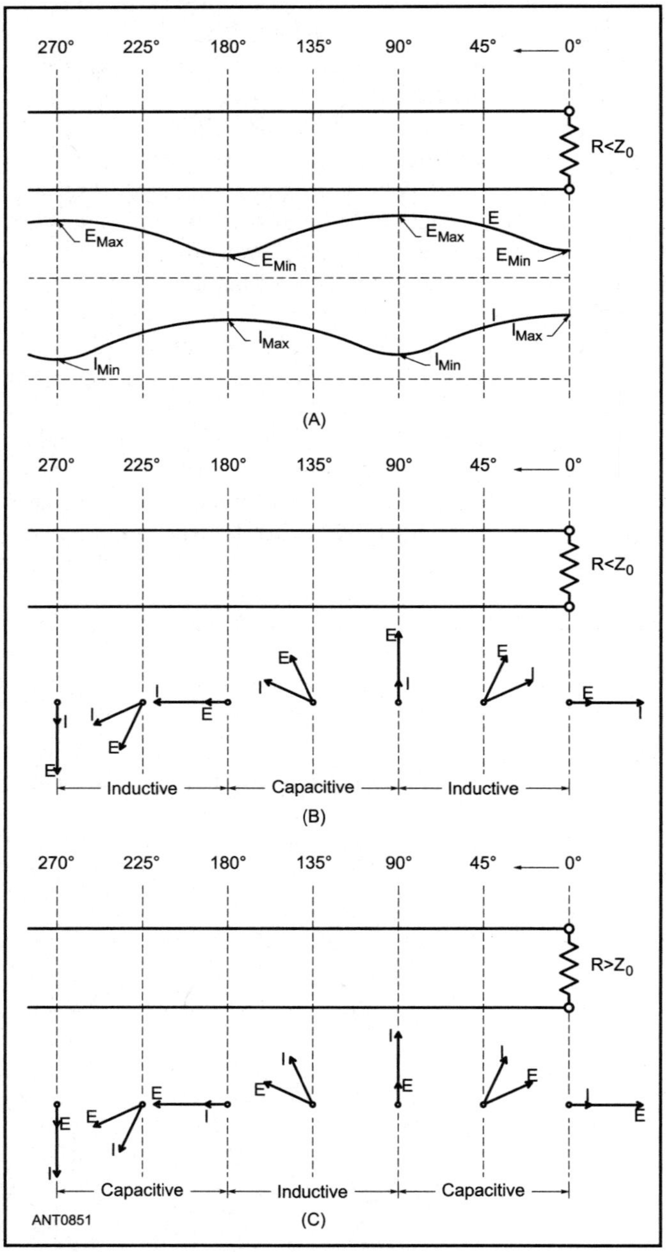

Figure 23.13 — Standing waves of current and voltage along the line for R less than Z_0. At A, resultant voltages and currents along a mismatched line are shown at B and C. At B, R less than Z_0; At C, R greater than Z_0.

we could go along the line with a voltmeter and ammeter measuring the current and voltage at each point, plotting the collected data would give curves like these. In contrast, if the load matched the Z_0 of the line, similar measurements along the line would show that the voltage is the same everywhere (and similarly for the current). The mismatch between load and line is responsible for the variations in amplitude which, because of their stationary, wave-like appearance, are called *standing waves.*

Some general conclusions can be drawn from inspection of the standing-wave curves: At a position 180° (λ/2) from the load, the voltage and current have the same values they do at the load. At a position 90° from the load, the voltage and current are "inverted." That is, if the voltage is lowest and current highest at the load (when R is less than Z_0), then 90° from the load the voltage reaches its highest value. The current reaches its lowest value at the same point. In the case where R is greater than Z_0, so the voltage is highest and the current lowest at the load, the voltage is lowest and the current is highest 90° from the load.

Note that the conditions at the 90° point also exist at the 270° point (3λ/4). If the graph were continued on toward the source of power it would be found that this duplication occurs at every point that is an odd multiple of 90° (odd multiple of λ/4) from the load. Similarly, the voltage and current are the same at every point that is a multiple of 180° (any multiple of λ/2) away from the load.

Standing-Wave Ratio

The ratio of the maximum voltage (resulting from the interaction of incident and reflected voltages along the line) to the minimum voltage — that is, the ratio of E_{max} to E_{min} in Figure 23.13A, is defined as the *voltage standing-wave ratio* (VSWR) or simply *standing-wave ratio* (SWR).

$$\mathrm{SWR} = \frac{E_{max}}{E_{min}} = \frac{I_{max}}{I_{min}} \tag{9}$$

The ratio of the maximum current to the minimum current is the same as the VSWR, so either current or voltage can be measured to determine the standing-wave ratio. The standing-wave ratio is an index of many of the properties of a mismatched line. It can be measured with fairly simple equipment, so it is a convenient quantity to use in making calculations on line performance.

The SWR is related to the magnitude of the complex reflection coefficient by

$$\mathrm{SWR} = \frac{1+|\rho|}{1-|\rho|} \tag{10}$$

and conversely the reflection coefficient magnitude may be defined from a measurement of SWR as

$$|\rho| = \frac{\mathrm{SWR}-1}{\mathrm{SWR}+1} \tag{11}$$

We may also express the reflection coefficient in terms of

forward and reflected power, quantities which can be easily measured using a directional RF wattmeter. The reflection coefficient may be computed as

$$\rho = \sqrt{\frac{P_r}{P_f}} \tag{12}$$

where

P_r = power in the reflected wave

P_f = power in the forward wave.

From Eq 11, SWR is related to the forward and reflected power by

$$SWR = \frac{1+|\rho|}{1-|\rho|} = \frac{1+\sqrt{P_r / P_f}}{1-\sqrt{P_r / P_f}} \tag{13}$$

Figure 23.14 converts Eq 13 into a convenient nomograph. In the simple case where the load contains no reactance, the SWR is numerically equal to the ratio between the load resistance R and the characteristic impedance of the line. When R is greater than Z_0,

$$SWR = \frac{R}{Z_0} \tag{14}$$

When R is less than Z_0,

$$SWR = \frac{Z_0}{R} \tag{15}$$

(The smaller quantity is always used in the denominator of the fraction so the ratio will be a number greater than 1).

It is important to note that in a lossless transmission line, SWR does not change with length of the line or along the line. While the values of voltage and current do change along the line, the ratio of their maximum and minimum values does not. The value of SWR shown by typical amateur SWR measuring instruments may change with line length but that can result from a number of causes; inaccuracy of the voltage or current sensing circuits, common-mode current on the outside of a coaxial feed line shield, and signals from a nearby transmitter upsetting the voltage or current measurement being the most common reasons.

Flat Lines

As discussed earlier, all the power that is transferred along a transmission line is absorbed in the load if that load is a resistance value equal to the Z_0 of the line. In this case, the line is said to be *perfectly matched.* None of the power is reflected back toward the source. As a result, no standing waves of current or voltage will be developed along the line. For a line operating in this condition, the waveforms drawn in Figure 23.13A become straight lines, representing the voltage and current delivered by the source. The voltage along the line is constant, so the minimum value is the same as the maximum value. The voltage standing-wave ratio is therefore 1:1. Because a plot of the voltage standing wave is a straight line, the matched line is also said to be *flat.*

23.2.4 ADDITIONAL POWER LOSS DUE TO SWR

The power lost in a given line is least when the line is terminated in a resistance equal to its characteristic impedance, and as stated previously, that is called the *matched-line loss.* There is however an *additional loss* that increases with an increase in the SWR. (Modern transmitters will also reduce output power to protect the solid-state output devices from elevated SWR but this is not power lost in the feed line.)

Additional loss in the line occurs because the effective values of both current and voltage become greater on lines with standing waves. The increase in effective current raises the ohmic losses (I^2R) in the conductors, and the increase in effective voltage increases the losses in the dielectric (E^2/R). (The nature of feed line loss is discussed at length in *Reflections* by W2DU — see the Bibliography entries for M. W. Maxwell.)

The increased loss caused by an SWR greater than 1:1 may or may not be serious. If the SWR at the load is not greater than 2:1, the additional loss caused by the standing waves, as compared with the loss when the line is perfectly matched, does not amount to more than about ½ dB, even on very long lines. One-half dB is an undetectable change in signal strength. Therefore, it can be said that, from a

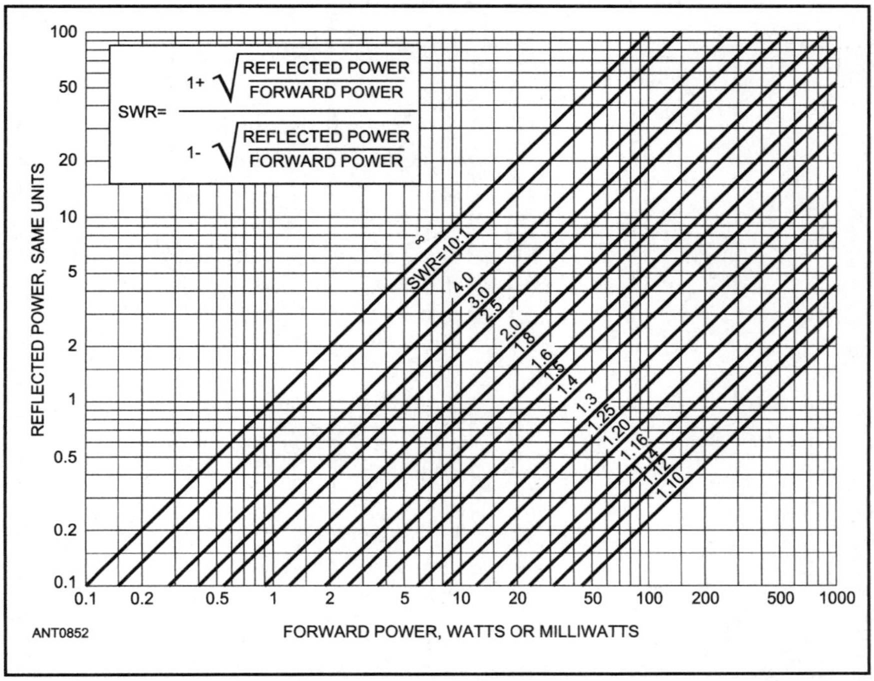

Figure 23.14 — SWR as a function of forward and reflected power.

SWR and Resonance

It is a common misunderstanding that for a transmission line connected to an antenna, minimum SWR occurs when the antenna is resonant. In a general sense, this is not true — minimum SWR occurs when the magnitude of the load's reflection coefficient, |r|, is at a minimum (see Eq 7). Viewing the load impedance on a Smith Chart as in **Figure 23.A**, the value of |r| is represented by the distance from the origin (center) to the point representing the load impedance. (The Smith Chart is explored in the PDF supplement, "The Smith Chart" with this book's downloadable supplemental information.)

As the frequency changes, the impedance of an antenna changes. The example in Figure 23.A shows points A, B and C — three plausible load impedances for an antenna at different frequencies. Point O is the origin. The antenna is resonant at both A and C since the points are on the X=0 line through the middle of the chart. At point A the impedance is 0.2 + *j*0 or 10 Ω in a 50-Ω system and C represents 4.0 + *j*0 Ω or 200 Ω. The magnitude of ρ at A is 0.67 and the SWR = 5:1. The magnitude of ρ at C is 0.6 and the SWR = 4:1. Point B represents the normalized load impedance 0.8 + *j*0.8, which is 40 + *j*40 Ω in a 50-Ω system. The magnitude of ρ at B is 0.42 and the SWR = 2.44. Even though the load impedance at B is reactive (nonresonant) the SWR is lower than at either of the two resonant points at A and C.

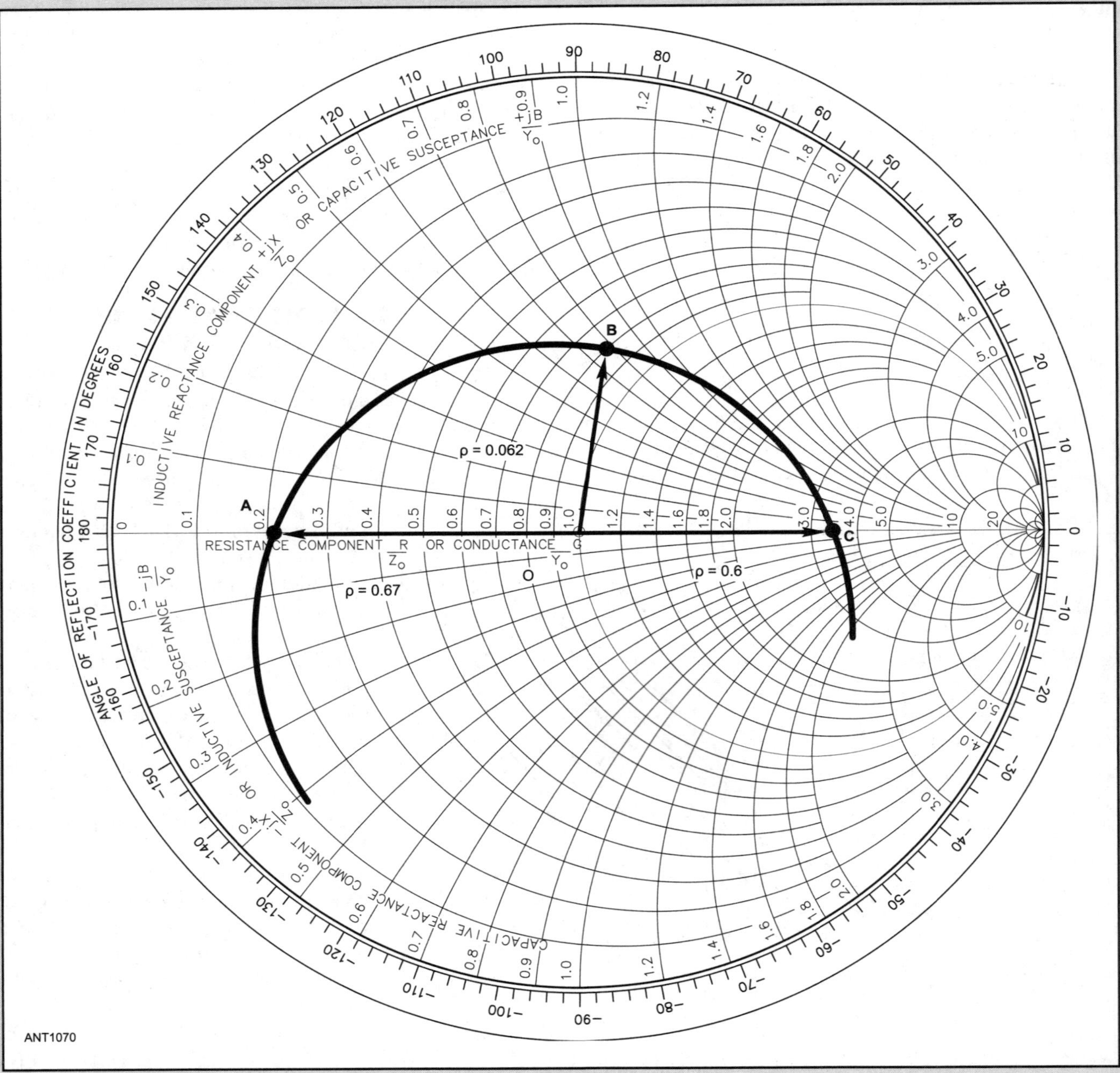

Figure 23.A — Load impedance viewed on a Smith Chart.

practical standpoint in the HF bands, an SWR of 2:1 or less is every bit as good as a perfect match, so far as additional losses due to SWR are concerned.

As is illustrated by the examples of a 100-foot-long doublet and a 66-foot-long Inverted V at the beginning of the chapter on **Transmission Line System Techniques**, both non-resonant antennas that are in widespread use on HF, the impedance mismatch and SWR can be quite high. In such cases, losses in even modest lengths of feed line can be unacceptably high. (See the supplemental article "Multiband Operation with Open-wire Line" by George Cutsogeorge, W2VJN, with this book's downloadable supplemental information.)

Above 30 MHz, in the VHF and especially the UHF range, where low receiver noise figures are essential for effective weak-signal work, matched-line losses for commonly available types of coax can be relatively high. This means that even a slight mismatch may become a concern regarding overall transmission line losses. At UHF one-half dB of additional loss may be considered intolerable!

The total loss in a line, including matched-line and the additional loss due to standing waves may be calculated from Eq 16 below for moderate levels of SWR (less than 20:1).

$$\text{Total Loss (dB)} = 10 \log \left(\frac{a^2 - |\rho|^2}{a\,(1 - |\rho|^2)} \right) \tag{16}$$

where

$a = 10^{0.1\,ML}$ = matched-line loss ratio

ML = the matched-line loss in dB for the particular length of line

$|\rho|$ = the reflection coefficient at the load, calculated as in Eq 7

and reflected power is assumed to be re-reflected at the source. Thus, the additional loss caused by the standing waves is calculated from:

$$\text{Additional Loss (dB)} = \text{Total Loss} - \text{ML} \tag{17}$$

For example, RG-213 coax at 14.2 MHz is rated at 0.795 dB of matched-line loss per 100 feet. A 150-foot length of RG-213 would have an overall matched-line loss of

$$(0.795/100) \times 150 = 1.193 \text{ dB}$$

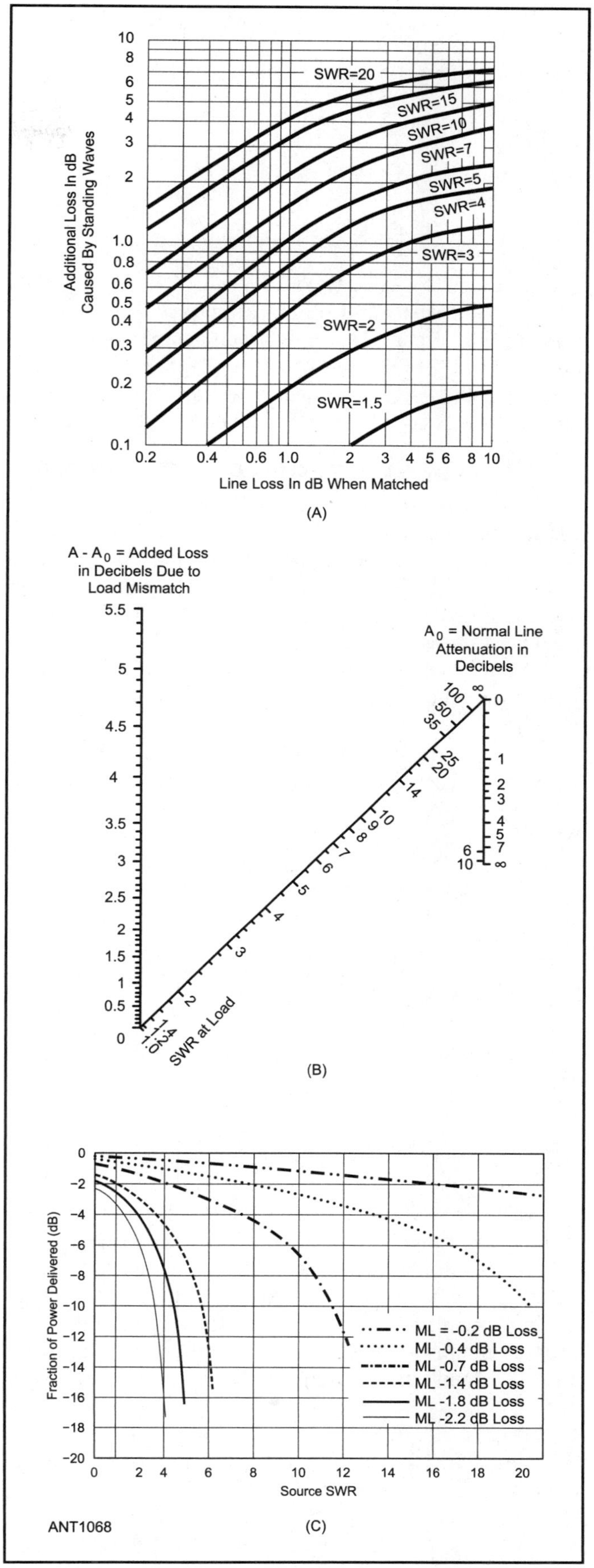

Figure 23.15 — (A) Additional line loss due to standing waves (SWR, measured at the load). See Figure 23.24 for matched-line loss. To determine the total loss in dB, add the matched-line loss to the value from this graph. (B) Nomograph showing Added Loss in dB due to mismatch (SWR at Load) with a known line attenuation. Place a straightedge along the points representing load SWR and line attenuation. Read additional loss on the left-hand scale. (C) Fractional amount of the input power delivered to the load given source or input SWR and line attenuation. (Graph provided courtesy of Refined Audiometrics Laboratory, LLC by David McLain, N7AIG.)

Thus, if the SWR at the load end of the RG-213 is 4:1,

$$\alpha = 10^{1.193/10} = 1.316$$

$$|\rho| = \frac{4\ \ 1}{4\ \ 1} = 0.600$$

and the total line loss

$$= 10 \log \left(\frac{1.316^2 - 0.600^2}{1.316\,(1 - 0.600^2)} \right) = 2.12 \text{ dB}$$

The additional loss due to the SWR of 4:1 is 2.12 – 1.19 = 0.93 dB. **Figure 23.15A** is a graph of additional loss versus SWR. Figure 23.15B is a nomograph equivalent to Figure 23.15A. Figure 23.15C is an alternative graph that shows the fraction of input power actually delivered to the load for a given source SWR and line Matched Loss (ML).

23.2.5 LINE VOLTAGES AND CURRENTS

It is often desirable to know the maximum voltages and currents that are developed in a line operating with standing waves. (We'll cover the determination of the exact voltages and currents along a transmission line later.) The voltage maximum may be calculated from the equations below, and the other values determined from the result.

The following equation is the standard for calculating peak RMS voltage as a function of SWR at the load:

$$E_{max} = \left(1 + \frac{SWR - 1}{SWR + 1}\right)\sqrt{P \times Z_0} \qquad (18A)$$

where

E_{max} = voltage maximum along the line in the presence of standing waves

P = power delivered by the source to the line input in watts

Z_0 = characteristic impedance of the line in ohms

SWR = SWR at the load

For example, if P = 100 W in a 50 Ω line with an SWR of 4:1,

$$E_{max} = \left(1 + \frac{4-1}{4+1}\right)\sqrt{100 \times 50} = 113 \text{ V}$$

The value of E_{max} for an infinite SWR is twice the incident voltage according to this equation. Strictly speaking, this value of E_{max} only applies near the load in the case of lines with appreciable losses. However, the resultant values are the maximum possible that can exist along the line under normal circumstances. For this reason the value is useful as a rule-of-thumb in determining whether or not a particular line can operate safely with a given SWR. Voltage ratings for various cable types are given in a later section.

Figure 23.16 shows the peak ratio of current or voltage, in the presence of standing waves, to the current or voltage that would exist with the same power in a perfectly matched line. As with Eq 18 and related calculations, the curve literally applies only near the load.

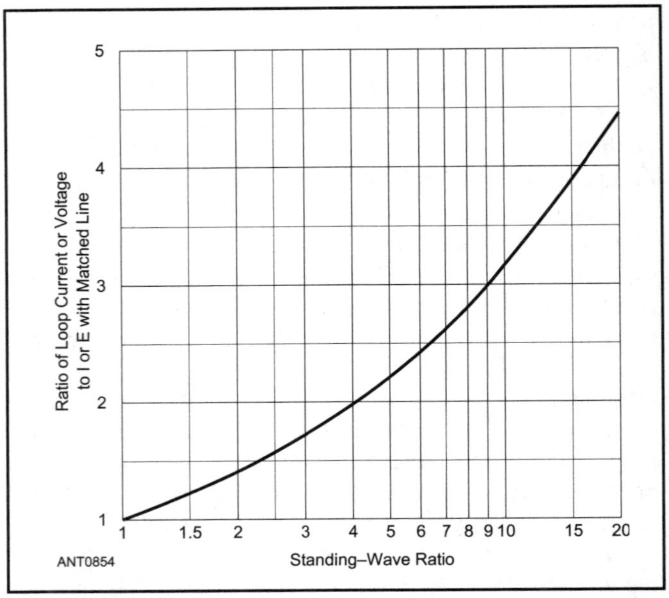

Figure 23.16 — Increase in maximum value of current or voltage on a line with standing waves, as referred to the current or voltage on a perfectly matched line, for the same power delivered to the load. Voltage and current at minimum points are given by the reciprocals of the values along the vertical axis. The curve is plotted from the relationship, current (or voltage) ratio = the square root of SWR.

An alternate calculation applies if P is the net input power, which on a directional wattmeter equals $P_{fwd} - P_{refl}$, and none of the reflected power is absorbed by the source (such as a transmitter's output stage) or by line loss. In such a case, power is continually "pumped" into the line. If the termination is infinite, such as for a short or open, power is only dissipated by line loss and voltage can become very high.

$$E_{max} = \sqrt{P \times Z_0 \times SWR} \qquad (18B)$$

An alternate equation provided by Bob Zavrel, W7SX, is:

$$E_{max} = \left(\frac{1}{1 - |\rho|}\right)\sqrt{P \times Z_0} \qquad (18C)$$

If $P_{fwd} - P_{refl}$ = 100 W of power is applied to the same 50-Ω line with an SWR at the load of 4:1, using equation 18b the maximum voltage is:

$$E_{max} = \sqrt{100 \times 50 \times 4} = 141.4 \text{ V}$$

In practice, when SWR is very high, line losses and transmitter output amplifier protection circuitry limit the peak line voltage caused by standing waves to a lower value.

Regardless of which equation is used, from Eq 9, E_{min}, the minimum voltage along the line equals E_{max}/SWR. The maximum current may be found by using Ohm's law. $I_{max} = E_{max}/Z_0$. The minimum current equals I_{max}/SWR.

The voltages determined in the various forms of Eq 18 are RMS values — that is, the voltages that would be measured with an ordinary RF voltmeter. If voltage breakdown is a consideration, the value from Eq 18 should be converted to an *instantaneous peak voltage* by multiplying by 1.414 and by 2.828 to find the instantaneous peak-to-peak voltage.

23.2.6 INPUT IMPEDANCE

The effects of incident and reflected voltage and current along a mismatched transmission line can be difficult to envision, particularly when the load at the end of the transmission line is not purely resistive, and when the line is not perfectly lossless.

If we can put aside for a moment all the complexities of reflections, SWR and line losses, a transmission line can simply be considered to be an *impedance transformer*. A certain value of load impedance, consisting of a resistance and reactance, at the end of a particular transmission line is transformed into another value of impedance at the input of the line. The amount of transformation is determined by the electrical length of the line, its characteristic impedance, and by the losses inherent in the line. The input impedance of a real, lossy transmission line is computed using the following equation, called the *Transmission Line Equation*, which uses the hyperbolic cosine and sine functions.

$$Z_{in} = Z_0 \frac{Z_L \cosh(\gamma \ell) + Z_0 \sinh(\gamma \ell)}{Z_L \sinh(\gamma \ell) + Z_0 \cosh(\gamma \ell)} \quad (19)$$

where

Z_{in} = complex impedance at input of line

Z_L = complex load impedance at end of line = $R_a \pm j X_a$

Z_0 = characteristic impedance of line = $R_0 - j X_0$

ℓ = physical length of line

γ = complex loss coefficient = $\alpha + j \beta$

α = matched-line loss attenuation constant, in nepers/unit length (1 neper = 8.686 dB; cables are rated in dB/100 ft)

β = phase constant of line in radians/unit length (related to physical length of line ℓ by the fact that 2π radians = one wavelength, and by Eq 2)

$$\beta = \frac{2\pi}{VF \times 983.6 / f(MHz)} \text{ for } \ell \text{ in feet}$$

VF = velocity factor

For example, assume that a half-wave dipole terminates a 50-foot long piece of RG-213 coax. This dipole is assumed to have an impedance of 43 + j 30 Ω at 7.15 MHz, and its velocity factor is 0.66. The matched-line loss at 7.15 MHz is 0.54 dB/100 feet, and the characteristic impedance Z_0 for this type of cable at this frequency is 50 – j 0.45 Ω. Using Eq 19, we compute the impedance at the input of the line as 65.8 + j 32.0 Ω.

Solving this equation manually is quite tedious, but it may be solved using a traditional paper Smith Chart or a computer program. (The PDF file "The Smith Chart" explains how to use the chart and is available with this book's downloadable supplemental information.) *SimSmith* by AE6TY (**www.ae6ty.com/Smith_Charts.html**) is available for free download and there are several on-line calculators available if you search for "smith chart calculator" on the Internet. *TLW* (Transmission Line for Windows) is an ARRL program that performs this transformation, but without Smith Chart graphics. *TLW* is available with this book's downloadable supplemental information.

One caution should be noted when using any of these computational tools to calculate the impedance at the input of a mismatched transmission line — the velocity factor of practical transmission lines can vary significantly between manufacturing runs of the same type of cable. For highest accuracy, you should measure the velocity factor of a particular length of cable before using it to compute the impedance at the end of the cable. See the chapter **Antenna and Transmission Line Measurements** for details on measurements of line characteristics.

Input SWR and Line Loss

If the line is not perfectly matched to the load the loss in the line reduces the amount of reflected power that returns to the source end of the line. This makes SWR appear lower at the source (transmitter) end of the line than it is at the load (antenna) end of the line. The longer the line or the higher the loss, the more power is dissipated as heat and the lower the input SWR. In fact, a long (many wavelengths) lossy transmission line can be used as a dummy load at VHF and higher frequencies.

A nomograph is given in **Figure 23.17** that relates load SWR, line attenuation, and load SWR. If you know any two of those three parameters, place a ruler between those two points and read the third from the intersection of the ruler with the scale for the unknown parameter.

Series and Parallel Equivalent Circuits

Once the series-form impedance $R_S \pm j X_S$ at the input of a particular line has been determined, either by measurement or by computation, you may wish to determine the equivalent parallel circuit $R_P \parallel \pm j X_P$, which is equivalent to the series form only at a single frequency. The equivalent parallel circuit is often useful when designing a matching circuit (such as an antenna tuner, for example) to transform the impedance at the input of the cable to another impedance. The following equations are used to make the transformation from series to parallel and from parallel to series. See **Figure 23.18**.

$$R_p = \frac{R_s^2 + X_s^2}{R_s} \quad (20A)$$

$$X_p = \frac{R_s^2 + X_s^2}{X_s} \quad (20B)$$

and

$$R_s = \frac{R_p X_p^2}{R_p^2 + X_p^2} \quad (21A)$$

$$X_s = \frac{R_p^2 X_p}{R_p^2 + X_p^2} \quad (21B)$$

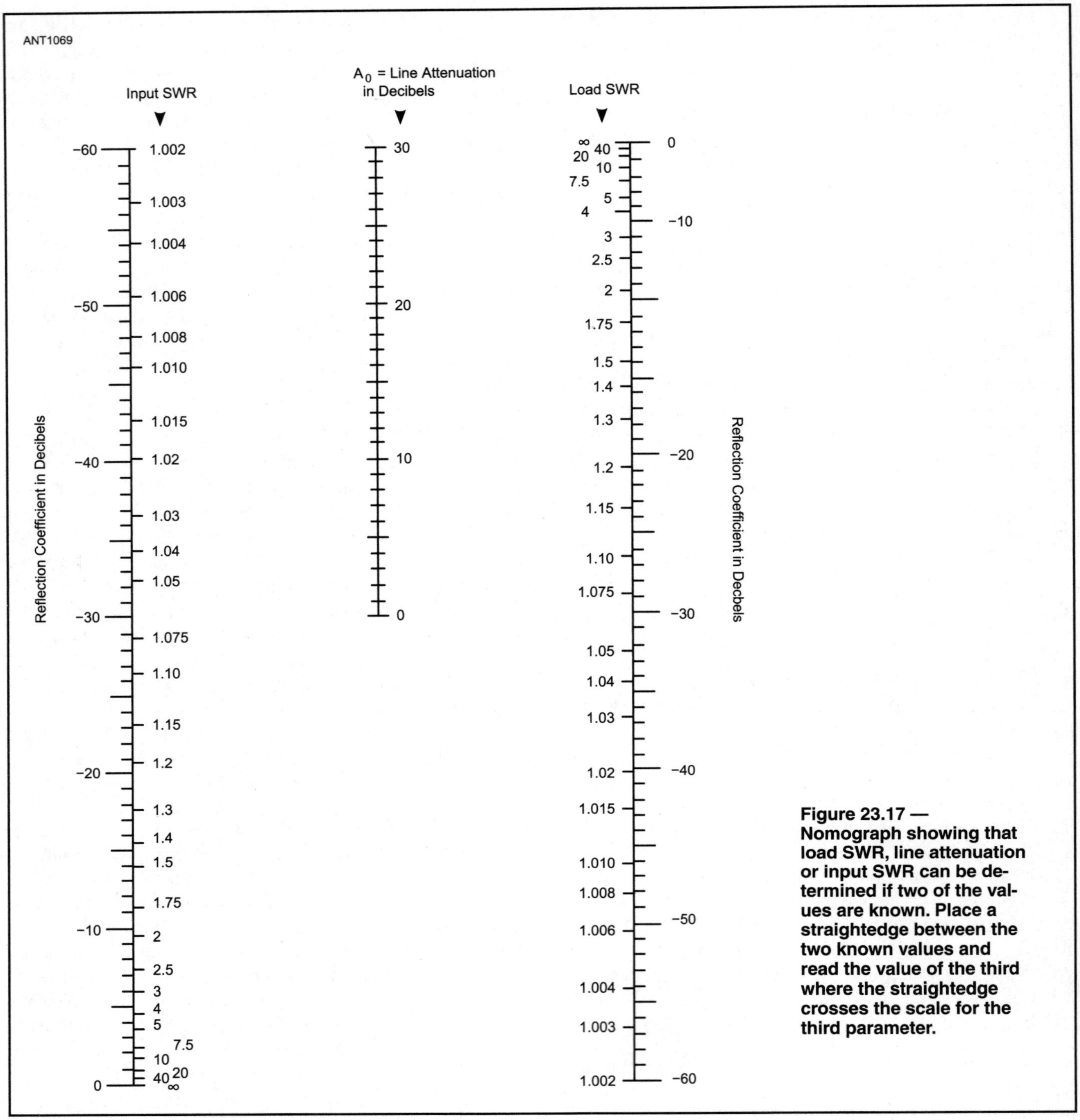

Figure 23.17 — Nomograph showing that load SWR, line attenuation or input SWR can be determined if two of the values are known. Place a straightedge between the two known values and read the value of the third where the straightedge crosses the scale for the third parameter.

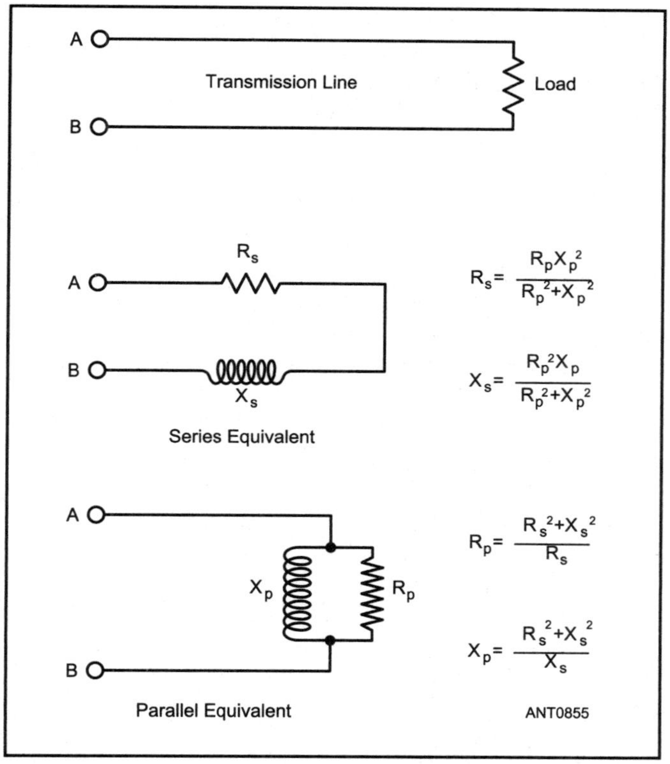

Figure 23.18 — Input impedance of a line terminated in a resistance. This impedance can be represented by either a resistance and reactance in series, or a resistance and reactance in parallel, at a single frequency. The relationships between the R and X values in the series and parallel equivalents are given by the equations shown. X may be either inductive or capacitive, depending on the line length, Z_0 and the load impedance, which need not be purely resistive.

The individual values in the parallel circuit are not the same as those in the series circuit (although the overall result is the same, but only at one frequency), but are related to the series-circuit values by these equations. For example, let us continue the example in the section above, where the impedance at the input of the 50 feet of RG-213 at 7.15 MHz is 65.8 + *j* 32.0 Ω. The equivalent parallel circuit at 7.15 MHz is

$$R_p = \frac{65.8^2 + 32.1^2}{65.8} = 81.46\ \Omega$$

$$X_p = \frac{65.8^2 + 31.2^2}{31.2} = 169.97\ \Omega$$

If we were to put 100 W of power into this parallel equivalent circuit, the voltage across the parallel components would be

$$\text{Since } P = \frac{E^2}{R},\quad E = \sqrt{P \times R} = \sqrt{100 \times 81.46} = 90.26\ \text{V}$$

Thus, the current through the inductive part of the parallel circuit would be

$$I = \frac{E}{X_p} = \frac{90.26}{169.97} = 0.53\ \text{A}$$

Highly Reactive Loads

When highly reactive loads are used with practical transmission lines, especially coax lines, the overall loss can reach staggering levels. For example, a popular multiband antenna is a 100-foot long center-fed dipole located some 50 feet over average ground. At 1.83 MHz, such an antenna will exhibit a feed-point impedance of 4.5 – *j* 1673 Ω, according to the analysis program *EZNEC*. The high value of capacitive reactance indicates that the antenna is extremely short electrically — after all, a half-wave dipole at 1.83 MHz is almost 270 feet long, compared to this 100 foot long antenna. If an amateur attempts to feed such a multiband antenna directly with 100 feet of RG-213 50-Ω coaxial cable, the SWR at the antenna terminals would be (using the *TLW* program from this book's downloadable supplemental information) 1740:1. An SWR of more than 1700 to one is a very high level of SWR indeed! At 1.83 MHz the *matched-line loss* of 100 feet of the RG-213 coax by itself is only 0.26 dB. However, the *total line loss* due to this extreme level of SWR is 26 dB.

This means that if 100 W is fed into the input of this line, the amount of power at the antenna is reduced to only 0.25 W. Admittedly this is an extreme case. It is more likely that an amateur would feed such a multiband antenna with open-wire *ladder* or *window* line than coaxial cable. The matched-line loss characteristics for 450-Ω window open-wire line are far better than coax, but the SWR at the end of this line is still 793:1, resulting in an overall loss of 8.9 dB. Even for low-loss open-wire line, the total loss is significant because of the extreme SWR.

This means that only about 13% of the power from the transmitter is getting to the antenna, and although this is not very desirable, it is a lot better than the losses in coax cable feeding the same antenna. However, at a transmitter power level of 1500 W, the maximum voltage in a typical antenna tuner used to match this line impedance is almost 9200V with the open-wire line, a level which will certainly cause arcing or burning inside. (As a small compensation for all the loss in coax under this extreme condition, so much power is lost that the voltages present in the antenna tuner are not excessive.) Keep in mind also that an antenna tuner can lose significant power in internal losses for very high impedance levels, even if it has sufficient range to match such impedances in the first place.

Clearly, it would be far better to use a longer antenna at this 160 meter frequency. Another alternative would be to resonate a short antenna with loading coils (at the antenna). Either strategy would help avoid excessive feed line loss, even with low-loss line.

23.2.7 SPECIAL CASES

Beside the primary purpose of transporting power from one point to another, transmission lines have properties that are useful in a variety of ways. One such special case is a line an exact multiple of λ/4 (90°) long. As shown earlier, such a line will have a purely resistive input impedance when the termination is a pure resistance. Also, short-circuited or open-circuited lines can be used in place of conventional inductors and capacitors since such lines have an input impedance that is substantially a pure reactance when the line losses are low. (An alternate way of explaining the interesting behavior of transmission lines — "My Feedline Tunes My Antenna!" by Byron Goodman, W1DX — is included with this book's downloadable supplemental information. Originally published in 1956, this classic *QST* article is still useful today.)

The Half-Wavelength Line

When the line length is a multiple of 180° (that is, a multiple of λ/2), the input resistance is equal to the load resistance, regardless of the line Z_0. As a matter of fact, a line an exact multiple of λ/2 in length (disregarding line losses) simply repeats, at its input or sending end, whatever impedance exists at its output or receiving end. It does not matter whether the impedance at the receiving end is resistive, reactive, or a combination of both. Sections of line having such length can be added or removed without changing any of the operating conditions, at least when the losses in the line itself are negligible.

Impedance Transformation with Quarter-Wave Lines

The input impedance of a line an odd multiple of λ/4 long is

$$Z_i = \frac{Z_0^{\ 2}}{Z_L} \qquad (22)$$

where Z_i is the input impedance and Z_L is the load impedance. If Z_L is a pure resistance, Z_i will also be a pure resistance. Rearranging this equation gives

$$Z_0 = \sqrt{Z_i Z_L} \qquad (23)$$

This means that if we have two values of impedance that we wish to "match," we can do so if we connect them together by a λ/4 transmission line having a characteristic impedance equal to the square root of their product.

A λ/4 line is, in effect, a transformer, and in fact is often referred to as a *quarter-wave transformer*. It is frequently used as such in antenna work when it is desired, for example, to transform the impedance of an antenna to a new value that will match a given transmission line. This subject is considered in greater detail in a later chapter.

Lines as Circuit Elements

Two types of non-resistive line terminations are quite useful — short and open circuits. The impedance of the short-circuit termination is 0 + *j*0, and the impedance of the open-circuit termination is infinite. Such terminations are used in *stub matching* as described in the **Transmission Line System Techniques** chapter. Applications of line sections as circuit elements in connection with antenna and transmission-line systems are discussed in later chapters.

An open- or short-circuited line does not deliver any power to a load, and for that reason is not, strictly speaking a "transmission" line. However, the fact that a line of the proper length has inductive reactance makes it possible to substitute the line for a coil in an ordinary circuit. Likewise, another line of appropriate length having capacitive reactance can be substituted for a capacitor.

Sections of lines used as circuit elements are usually λ/4 or shorter. The desired type of reactance (inductive or capacitive) or the desired type of resonance (series or parallel) is obtained by shorting or opening the far end of the line. The circuit equivalents of various types of line sections are shown in **Figure 23.19**. Longer lengths of line are not necessary since any value of impedance available from a particular type of feed line is attainable in λ/4 or less.

When a line section is used as a reactance, the amount of reactance is determined by the characteristic impedance and the electrical length of the line. The type of reactance exhibited at the input terminals of a line of given length depends on whether it is open- or short-circuited at the far end.

The equivalent *lumped* value for any inductor or capacitor may be determined with the aid of the Smith Chart or Eq 19. Line losses may be taken into account if desired, as explained for Eq 19. In the case of a line having no losses, and to a close approximation when the losses are small, the inductive reactance of a short- circuited line less than λ/4 in length is

$$X_L \text{ in } \Omega = Z_0 \tan \ell \qquad (24)$$

where ℓ is the length of the line in electrical degrees and Z_0 is the characteristic impedance of the line.

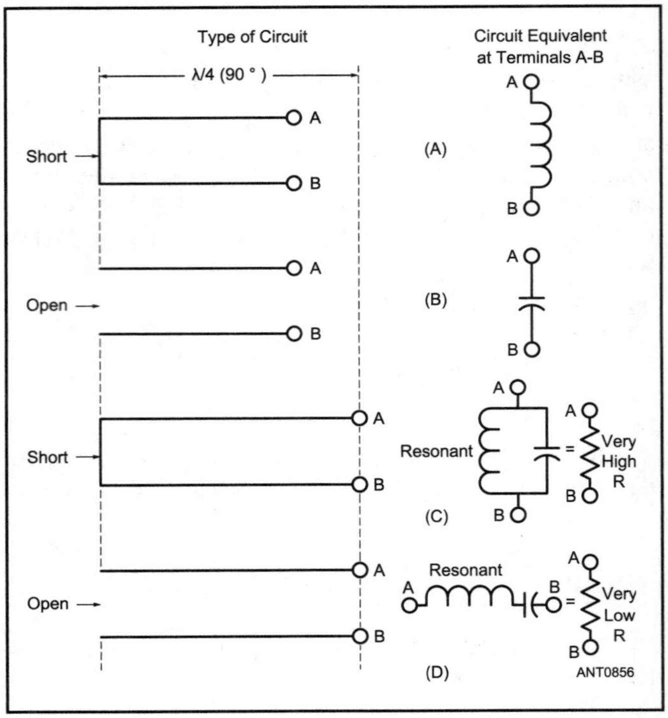

Figure 23.19 — Lumped-constant circuit equivalents of open- and short-circuited transmission lines.

The capacitive reactance of an open-circuited line less than λ/4 in length is

$$X_C \text{ in } \Omega = Z_0 \cot \ell \qquad (25)$$

Lengths of line that are exact multiples of λ/4 have the properties of resonant circuits. With an open-circuit termination, the input impedance of the line acts like a series-resonant circuit. With a short-circuit termination, the line input simulates a parallel-resonant circuit. The effective Q of such linear resonant circuits is very high if the line losses, both in resistance and by radiation, are kept down. This can be done without much difficulty, particularly in coaxial lines, if air insulation is used between the conductors. Air-insulated open-wire lines are likewise very good at frequencies for which the conductor spacing is very small in terms of wavelength.

23.2.8 VOLTAGE AND CURRENT ALONG A LINE

The voltage and current along a transmission line will vary in a predictable manner, whether that line is matched or mismatched at its load end. (The voltage and current along a matched line vary because of loss in the line.) Eq 26 below describes the voltage at point ℓ, while Eq 27 describes the current at point ℓ, each as a function of the voltage at the input of the line.

$$E_x = E_{in}\left(\cosh \gamma\ell - \frac{Z_0}{Z_{in}} \sinh \gamma\ell\right) \text{ volts} \qquad (26)$$

$$I_x = \frac{E_{in}}{Z_{in}}\left(\cosh \gamma\ell - \frac{Z_{in}}{Z_0} \sinh \gamma\ell\right) \text{ amperes} \qquad (27)$$

where γ = complex loss coefficient used in Eq 19, and cosh and sinh are the hyperbolic cosine and sine functions. The load end of the transmission line is, by definition, at a length of ℓ.

A useful identity for working with the $\cosh^{-1}$ or acosh function encountered in transmission line calculations is:

$$\cosh^{-1}(x) = \ln\left(x + \sqrt{x^2 - 1}\right)$$

The inverse hyperbolic cosine (cosh) is sometimes accessed on calculators by using the INV (inverse) key before COSH.

The power at the input and the output of a transmission line may be calculated using Eq 28 and Eq 29 below.

$$P_{in} = \left|E_{in}\right|^2 G_{in} \text{ watts} \qquad (28)$$

$$P_{load} = \left|E_{load}\right|^2 G_{load} \text{ watts} \qquad (29)$$

where G_{in} and G_{load} are the admittance at the input (the real part of $1/Z_{in}$) and the admittance at the load (the real part of $1/Z_{load}$) ends respectively of the line. Z_{in} is calculated using Eq 19 for a length of ℓ.

The power loss in the transmission line in dB is:

$$P_{loss} = 10 \log\left(\frac{P_{in}}{P_{load}}\right) \text{ dB} \qquad (30)$$

23.3 FEED LINE CONSTRUCTION AND OPERATING CHARACTERISTICS

The two basic types of transmission lines, parallel conductor and coaxial, can be constructed in a variety of forms. Both types can be divided into two classes, (1) those in which the majority of the insulation between the conductors is air, where only the minimum of solid dielectric necessary for mechanical support is used, and (2) those in which the conductors are embedded in and separated by a solid dielectric. The first variety (air-insulated) has the lowest loss per unit length, because there is no power loss in dry air if the voltage between conductors is below the level at which corona forms. At the maximum power permitted for amateur transmitters, it is seldom necessary to consider corona unless the SWR on the line is very high.

Transmission lines in which the conductors are separated by a flexible dielectric have a number of advantages over the air-insulated type. They are less bulky, weigh less in comparable types and maintain more uniform spacing between conductors. They are also generally easier to install, and are neater in appearance. Both parallel conductor and coaxial lines are available with flexible insulation.

The chief disadvantage of such lines is that the power loss per unit length is greater than in air-insulated lines. Power is lost in heating of the dielectric, and if the heating is great enough (as it may be with high power and a high SWR) the line may break down mechanically and electrically.

23.3.1 AIR-INSULATED LINES

Figure 23.20 shows four different types of air-insulated transmission lines. The two-wire and coaxial lines are common in amateur use. The four-wire line is most common at high-power commercial and military installations. The single-wire line is useful in some types of point-to-point construction.

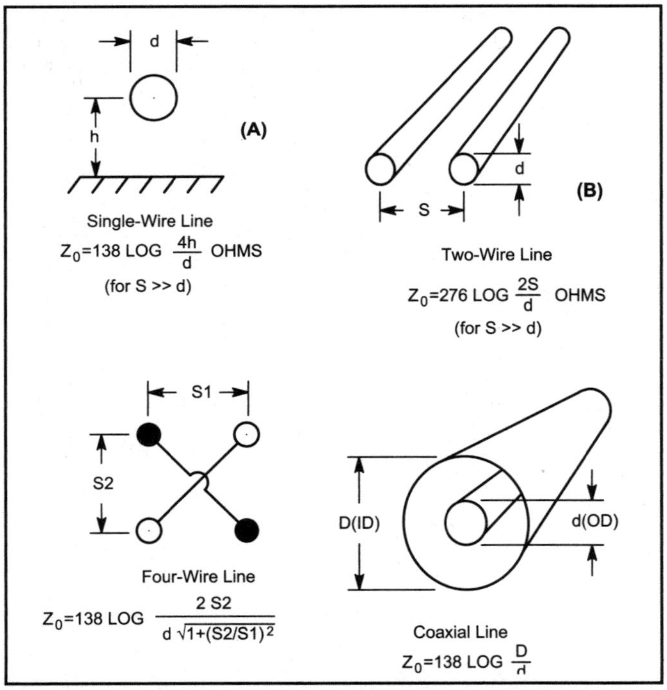

Figure 23.20 — Construction of air-insulated transmission lines.

The characteristic impedance of an air-insulated parallel conductor line, neglecting the effect of the spacers, is given by

$$Z_0 = \frac{120}{\sqrt{\varepsilon}} \cosh^{-1}\left(\frac{S}{d}\right) = \frac{276}{\sqrt{\varepsilon}} \log\left[\frac{S}{d} + \sqrt{\left(\frac{D}{d}\right)^2 - 1}\right] \quad (31A)$$

where

Z_0 = characteristic impedance in ohms

ε = relative permittivity of insulating medium (1 for dry air)

S = center-to-center distance between conductors

d = outer diameter of conductor (in the same units as S)

An approximation that can be used when S >> d and ε=1 is:

$$Z_0 = 276 \log\left(\frac{2S}{d}\right) \quad (31B)$$

The error of the approximation becomes significant for S/d < 3.

For single-wire lines, similar formulas are used with the same caveat about errors for 2h/d < 3:

$$Z_0 = 60\ \cosh^{-1}\left(\frac{2h}{d}\right) = 138 \log\left(\frac{4h}{d}\right) \quad (31C)$$

Impedances for two-wire lines using common sizes of conductors over a range of spacings are given in **Figure 23.21**.

At very close spacings, such as for the parallel-wire lines used for winding chokes and baluns, the exact formula should be used. **Figure 23.22** shows the difference in calculated values for very close spacings.

Four-Wire Lines

Another parallel conductor line that is useful in some applications is the four-wire line (Figure 23.20C). In cross section, the conductors of the four-wire line are at the corners of a square. Spacings are on the same order as those used in two-wire lines. The conductors at opposite corners of the square are connected to operate in parallel. This type of line has a lower characteristic impedance than the simple two-wire type. Also, because of the more symmetrical construction, it has better electrical balance to ground and other objects that are close to the line. The spacers for a four-wire line may be discs of insulating material, X-shaped members, etc.

Air-Insulated Coaxial Lines

In air-insulated coaxial lines (Figure 23.20D), a considerable proportion of the insulation between conductors may actually be a solid dielectric, because the separation between the inner and outer conductors must be constant. This is particularly likely to be true in small diameter lines. The inner conductor, usually a solid copper wire, is supported at the center of the copper tubing outer conductor by insulating beads or a helically wound strip of insulating material. The beads are usually a ceramic such as isolantite or Steatite, and the wire is generally crimped on each side of each bead to prevent the beads from sliding. The material of which the beads are made, and the number of beads per unit length of line, will affect the characteristic impedance of the line. The greater the number of beads in a given length, the lower the

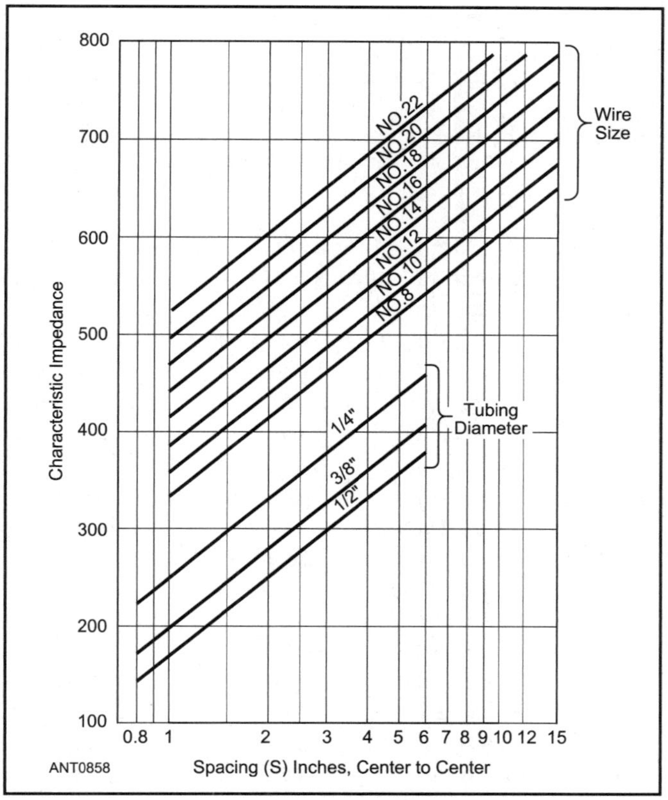

Figure 23.21 — Characteristic impedance as a function of conductor spacing and size for parallel conductor lines.

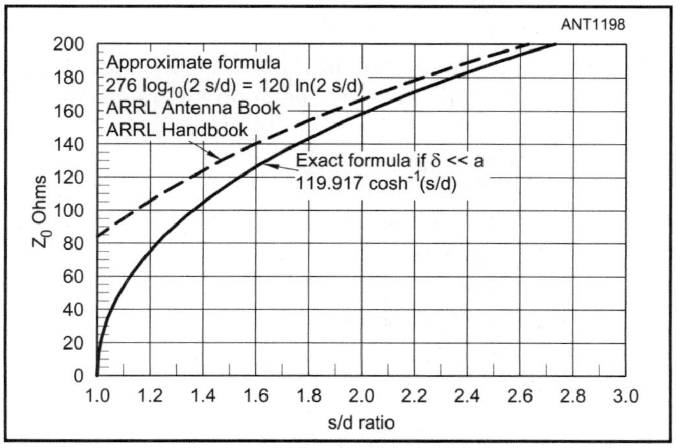

Figure 23.22 — A graph showing the approximate and the exact calculations of characteristic impedance for close-spaced parallel-wire lines. [Contributed by Steve Stearns, K6OIK, Pacificon, Oct 2010]

characteristic impedance compared with the value obtained with air insulation only. Teflon is ordinarily used as a helically wound support for the center conductor. A tighter helical winding lowers the characteristic impedance.

The presence of the solid dielectric also increases the losses in the line. On the whole, however, a coaxial line of this type tends to have lower actual loss, at frequencies up to about 100 MHz, than any other line construction, provided the air inside the line can be kept dry. This usually means that air-tight seals must be used at the ends of the line and at every joint. The characteristic impedance of an air-insulated coaxial line is given by

$$Z_0 = 138 \log \frac{D}{d} \qquad (32)$$

where

Z_0 = characteristic impedance in ohms
D = inside diameter of outer conductor
d = outside diameter of inner conductor (in same units as D)

Values for typical conductor sizes are graphed in **Figure 23.23**. The equation and the graph for coaxial lines are approximately correct for lines in which bead spacers are used, provided the beads are not too closely spaced.

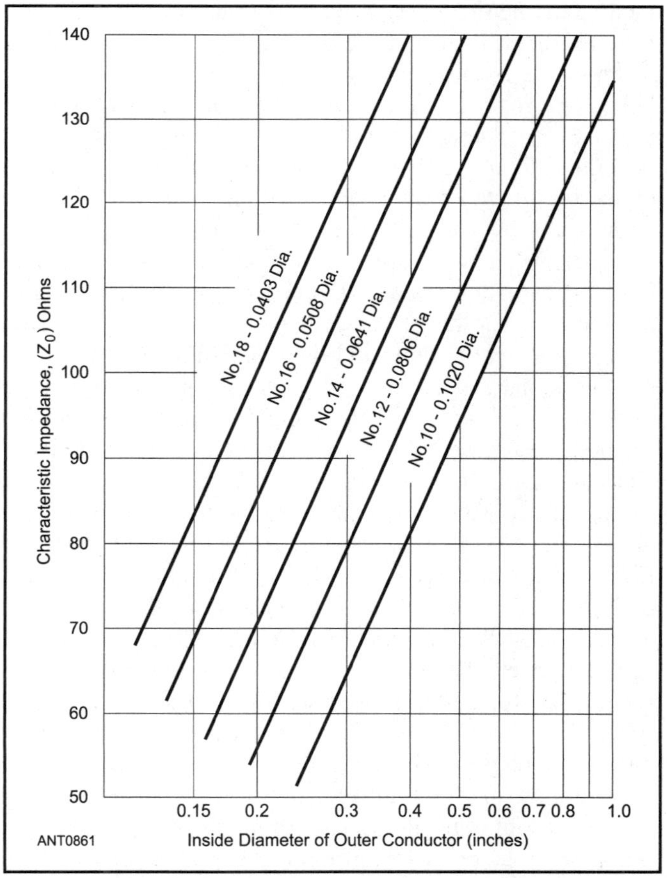

Figure 23.23 — Characteristic impedance of typical air insulated coaxial lines.

23.3.2 PARALLEL-CONDUCTOR LINES

For common *twin-lead* (see Figure 23.10E) the conductors are stranded wire equivalent to #20 AWG in cross-sectional area, and are molded in the edges of a polyethylene ribbon about ½-inch wide that keeps the wires spaced a constant amount away from each other. The effective dielectric is partly solid and partly air, and the presence of the solid dielectric lowers the characteristic impedance of the line as compared with the same conductors in air. The resulting impedance is approximately 300 Ω. This type of feed line is most commonly used for TV and broadcast FM receiving antennas.

Because part of the field between the conductors exists outside the solid dielectric, dirt and moisture on the surface of the ribbon tend to change the characteristic impedance of the line. The operation of the line is therefore affected by weather conditions. The effect will not be very serious in a line terminated in its characteristic impedance, but if there is a considerable mismatch, a small change in Z_0 may cause wide fluctuations of the input impedance. Weather effects can be minimized by cleaning the line occasionally and giving it a thin coating of a water repellent material such as silicone grease or car wax.

To overcome the effects of weather on the characteristic impedance and attenuation of ribbon type line, another type of twin-lead is made using an oval polyethylene tube with an air core or a foamed dielectric core. The conductors are molded diametrically opposite each other in the walls. This increases the leakage path across the dielectric surface. Also, much of the electric field between the conductors is in the hollow (or foam-filled) center of the tube. This type of line is fairly impervious to weather effects. Care should be used when installing it, however, so any moisture that condenses on the inside with changes in temperature and humidity can drain out at the bottom end of the tube and not be trapped in one section. This type of line is made in two conductor sizes (with different tube diameters), one for receiving applications and the other for transmitting.

Ladder line as shown in Figure 23.10F is one of the oldest forms of transmission lines used by amateur. Although once used nearly exclusively, such homemade lines are enjoying a renaissance of sorts because of their high efficiency and low cost. A typical construction technique is shown in **Figure 23.24**. The two wires are supported a fixed distance apart by means of insulating spacers. Spacers may be made from material such as polycarbonate, phenolic, polystyrene, or ABS plastics. Ceramic spacers such as isolantite or Steatite are also used and may be found on the surplus market or at flea markets. Several vendors also sell spacers designed specifically for building open-wire line. The spacer length varies from 2 to 6 inches. Smaller spacings are desirable at higher frequencies (28 MHz and above) so radiation from the transmission line is minimized.

Spacers must be used at small enough intervals along the line to keep the two wires from moving appreciably with respect to each other. For amateur purposes, lines using this construction ordinarily have #12 AWG or #14 AWG conductors

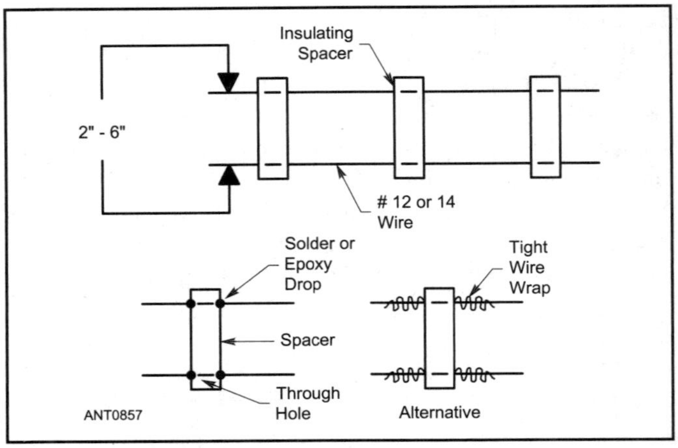

Figure 23.24 — Typical open-wire line construction. The spacers may be held in place by beads of solder or epoxy cement. Wire wraps can also be used, as shown.

(such as THHN wire used for house wiring and discussed in the chapter **Antenna Materials and Construction**), and the characteristic impedance is between 500 to 600 Ω.

Where an air-insulated line with still lower characteristic impedance is needed, metal tubing from ¼ to ½-inch diameter is frequently used. With the larger conductor diameter and relatively close spacing, it is possible to build a line having a characteristic impedance as low as about 200 Ω. This construction technique is principally used for $\lambda/4$ matching transformers at the higher frequencies and for use with log-periodic dipole arrays having feed point impedances near 200 Ω.

A third type of commercial parallel-line is so-called *window line*, illustrated in Figure 23.10G. This is a variation of twin-lead construction, except that *windows* are cut in the polyethylene insulation at regular intervals. This reduces weight of the line, and also breaks up the amount of surface area where dirt, dust and moisture can accumulate. Such window line is commonly available with a nominal characteristic impedance of 450 Ω, although actual impedance varies from about 390 to 450 Ω. A conductor spacing of about 1 inch is used in the 450-Ω line with a conductor size of about #18 AWG. The impedances of such lines are somewhat lower than given by Figure 23.21 for the same conductor size and spacing, because of the effect of the dielectric constant of the spacer material used. The attenuation is quite low and lines of this type are entirely satisfactory for transmitting applications at amateur power levels.

23.3.3 COAXIAL CABLES

Coaxial cable is available in flexible and semi-flexible varieties. The fundamental design is the same in all types, as shown in Figure 23.10. The outer diameter varies from 0.06 inch to over 5 inches. Power handling capability and cable size are directly proportional, as larger dielectric thickness and larger conductor sizes can handle higher voltages and currents. Generally, losses decrease as cable diameter increases. The extent to which this is true is dependent on the properties of the insulating material.

Some coaxial cables have stranded wire center conductors

RG-8, RG-213 and Type Cables

The most common coax used for amateur applications is RG-8/U — a 50-Ω cable approximately 0.4 inch in diameter, with solid or foamed polyethylene center insulation, and capable of handling full legal power. A close second to RG-8/U is RG-213/U, also a 50-Ω cable and nearly identical. The two cable types are almost identical as seen in Table 23.1, but RG-213/U is slightly lossier than RG-8.

Many amateurs are unaware that RG-8/U is an obsolete military specification designation, meaning that the part number RG-8/U does not confer any particular level of quality or performance on the cable. RG-213/U, on the other hand, is a current military designation that can only be used for cables manufactured to the military specification for that cable, both for materials as well as manufacturing processes. This results in a more consistent product.

It is also common for manufacturers to add "type" after a military specification label, such as "RG-8 Type" or "RG-213 Type". This means that the cable has much the same performance characteristics as the "non-type" cable but is not guaranteed to meet that higher level of performance.

Should you decide to use RG-8/U or a "type" cable, read the specifications carefully. The shield coverage (the percentage of the center insulator covered by the copper braid shield) should be from 95 to 97% for a high-quality cable. You should not be able to easily see the center insulation through holes in the shield.

Another advantage of RG-213/U is that the jacket is made from non-contaminating PVC and many types of RG-213/U are rated for direct burial.

while others use a solid copper conductor. Similarly, the outer conductor (shield) may be a single layer of copper braid, a double layer of braid (more effective shielding), solid aluminum (hardline and Heliax), aluminum foil or aluminized mylar, or a combination of these.

Voltage, Power and Loss Specifications

Selection of the correct coaxial cable for a particular application is not a casual matter. Not only is the attenuation loss of significance, but breakdown and heating (voltage and power) also need to be considered. If a cable were lossless, the power handling capability would be limited only by the breakdown voltage. There are two types of power ratings: *peak power* and *average power*. The peak power rating is limited by a voltage breakdown between the inner and outer conductors and is independent of frequency. The average power rating is governed by the safe long-term operating temperature of the dielectric material and decreases as the frequency increases. Excessive RF operating voltage in a coaxial cable can cause noise generation, dielectric damage and eventual breakdown between the conductors.

The power handling capability and loss characteristics of coaxial cable depend largely on the dielectric material between the conductors and the size of the conductors. The commonly used cables and many of their properties are listed in **Table 23.1**. The pertinent characteristics of unmarked coaxial cables can be determined from the equations in **Table 23.2**. The most common impedance values are 50, 75 and 95 Ω. However, impedances from 25 to 125 Ω are available in special types of manufactured line. The 25-Ω cable (miniature) is used extensively in magnetic-core broadband transformers.

In practical coaxial cables the copper and dielectric losses, rather than breakdown voltage, limit the maximum power than can be accommodated. If 1000 W is applied to a cable having a loss of 3 dB, only 500 W is delivered to the load. The remaining 500 W must be dissipated in the cable. The dielectric and outer jacket are good thermal insulators, which prevent the conductors from efficiently transferring the heat to free air. As a result the cable can heat up, softening the plastic insulation and allowing the geometry of the conductors and the characteristic impedance to change or even short-circuit. Many amateur transmitter duty cycles are so low that substantial overload is permissible on current peaks so long as the SWR is relatively low, such as less than 2:1. **Figure 23.25** is a graph of the matched-line attenuation characteristics versus frequency for the most popular lines

A cable with a solid dielectric will handle higher power than a cable with a foam dielectric. RG-8/U with a solid dielectric will handle 5000 V maximum while the same cable with foam dielectric only has a 600 V rating. In addition, heating of the center conductor from cable loss can soften the center insulation. (See the following section on Center Conductor Migration.)

As the operating frequency increases, the power-handling capability of a cable decreases because of increasing conductor loss (skin effect) and dielectric loss. RG-58 with foam dielectric has a breakdown rating of only 300 V, yet it can handle substantially more power than its ordinary solid dielectric counterpart because of the lower losses. Normally, the loss is inconsequential (except as it affects power handling capability) below 10 MHz in amateur applications. This is true unless extremely long runs of cable are used.

In general, full legal amateur power can be safely applied to inexpensive RG-58 coax in the bands below 10 MHz. RG-8 and similar cables can withstand full amateur power through the VHF spectrum, but connectors must be carefully chosen in these applications. Connector choice is discussed in a later section.

As inexpensive RG-6-type cables gain wider use for receiving antennas, cable loss on the MF and LF bands becomes more important, particularly with copper-clad steel (CCS) center conductors. These cables are designed for use at VHF and higher frequencies, so the copper plating on the center conductor may be extremely thin. This increases resistive loss on the lower frequency bands and may also cause problems if dc power is supplied through the cable. Be particularly wary of surplus or off-brand cable that is intended for TV and data use. It is recommended that a long run of the cable be tested

Table 23.1

Nominal Characteristics of Commonly Used Transmission Lines

RG or Type	*Part Number*	*Nom.* Z_0 Ω	*VF* %	*Cap. pF/ft*	*Cent. Cond. AWG*	*Diel. Type*	*Shield Type*	*Jacket Matl*	*OD inches*	*Max V (RMS)*	*Matched Loss (dB/100')* 1 MHz	10	100	1000
RG-6	Belden 1694A	75	82	16.2	#18 Solid BC	FPE	FC	P1	0.275	300	0.3	.7	1.8	5.9
RG-6	Belden 8215	75	66	20.5	#21 Solid CCS	PE	D	PE	0.332	2700	0.4	0.8	2.7	9.8
RG-8	Belden 7810A	50	86	23.0	#10 Solid BC	FPE	FC	PE	0.405	300	0.1	0.4	1.2	4.0
RG-8	TMS LMR400	50	85	23.9	#10 Solid CCA	FPE	FC	PE	0.405	600	0.1	0.4	1.3	4.1
RG-8	Belden 9913	50	84	24.6	#10 Solid BC	ASPE	FC	P1	0.405	300	0.1	0.4	1.3	4.5
RG-8	CXP1318FX	50	84	24.0	#10 Flex BC	FPE	FC	P2N	0.405	600	0.1	0.4	1.3	4.5
RG-8	Belden 9913F	50	83	24.6	#11 Flex BC	FPE	FC	P1	0.405	300	0.2	0.6	1.5	4.8
RG-8	Belden 9914	50	82	24.8	#10 Solid BC	FPE	FC	P1	0.405	300	0.2	0.5	1.5	4.8
RG-8	TMS LMR400UF	50	85	23.9	#10 Flex BC	FPE	FC	PE	0.405	600	0.1	0.4	1.4	4.9
RG-8	DRF-BF	50	84	24.5	#9.5 Flex BC	FPE	FC	PE	0.405	600	0.1	0.5	1.6	5.2
RG-8	WM CQ106	50	84	24.5	#9.5 Flex BC	FPE	FC	P2N	0.405	600	0.2	0.6	1.8	5.3
RG-8	CXP008	50	78	26.0	#13 Flex BC	FPE	S	P1	0.405	600	0.1	0.5	1.8	7.1
RG-8	Belden 8237	52	66	29.5	#13 Flex BC	PE	S	P1	0.405	3700	0.2	0.6	1.9	7.4
RG-8X	Belden 7808A	50	86	23.5	#15 Solid BC	FPE	FC	PE	0.240	300	0.2	0.7	2.3	7.4
RG-8X	TMS LMR240	50	84	24.2	#15 Solid BC	FPE	FC	PE	0.242	300	0.2	0.8	2.5	8.0
RG-8X	WM CQ118	50	82	25.0	#16 Flex BC	FPE	FC	P2N	0.242	300	0.3	0.9	2.8	8.4
RG-8X	TMS LMR240UF	50	84	24.2	#15 Flex BC	FPE	FC	PE	0.242	300	0.2	0.8	2.8	9.6
RG-8X	Belden 9258	50	82	24.8	#16 Flex BC	FPE	S	P1	0.242	300	0.3	0.9	3.2	11.2
RG-8X	CXP08XB	50	80	25.3	#16 Flex BC	FPE	S	P1	0.242	300	0.3	1.0	3.1	14.0
RG-9	Belden 8242	51	66	30.0	#13 Flex SPC	PE	SCBC	P2N	0.420	5000	0.2	0.6	2.1	8.2
RG-11	Belden 8213	75	84	16.1	#14 Solid BC	FPE	S	PE	0.405	300	0.1	0.4	1.3	5.2
RG-11	Belden 8238	75	66	20.5	#18 Flex TC	PE	S	P1	0.405	300	0.2	0.7	2.0	7.1
RG-58	Belden 7807A	50	85	23.7	#18 Solid BC	FPE	FC	PE	0.195	300	0.3	1.0	3.0	9.7
RG-58	TMS LMR200	50	83	24.5	#17 Solid BC	FPE	FC	PE	0.195	300	0.3	1.0	3.2	10.5
RG-58	WM CQ124	52	66	28.5	#20 Solid BC	PE	S	PE	0.195	1400	0.4	1.3	4.3	14.3
RG-58	Belden 8240	52	66	29.9	#20 Solid BC	PE	S	P1	0.193	1400	0.3	1.1	3.8	14.5
RG-58A	Belden 8219	53	73	26.5	#20 Flex TC	FPE	S	P1	0.195	300	0.4	1.3	4.5	18.1
RG-58C	Belden 8262	50	66	30.8	#20 Flex TC	PE	S	P2N	0.195	1400	0.4	1.4	4.9	21.5
RG-58A	Belden 8259	50	66	30.8	#20 Flex TC	PE	S	P1	0.192	1400	0.5	1.5	5.4	22.8
RG-59	Belden 1426A	75	83	16.3	#20 Solid BC	FPE	S	P1	0.242	300	0.3	0.9	2.6	8.5
RG-59	CXP 0815	75	82	16.2	#20 Solid BC	FPE	S	P1	0.232	300	0.5	0.9	2.2	9.1
RG-59	Belden 8212	75	78	17.3	#20 Solid CCS	FPE	S	P1	0.242	300	0.2	1.0	3.0	10.9
RG-59	Belden 8241	75	66	20.4	#23 Solid CCS	PE	S	P1	0.242	1700	0.6	1.1	3.4	12.0
RG-62A	Belden 9269	93	84	13.5	#22 Solid CCS	ASPE	S	P1	0.240	750	0.3	0.9	2.7	8.7
RG-62B	Belden 8255	93	84	13.5	#24 Flex CCS	ASPE	S	P2N	0.242	750	0.3	0.9	2.9	11.0
RG-63B	Belden 9857	125	84	9.7	#22 Solid CCS	ASPE	S	P2N	0.405	750	0.2	0.5	1.5	5.8
RG-83	WM165	35	66	44.0	#10 Solid BC	PE	S	P2	0.405	2000	0.23	0.8	2.8	9.6
RG-142	CXP 183242	50	69.5	29.4	#19 Solid SCCS	TFE	D	FEP	0.195	1900	0.3	1.1	3.8	12.8
RG-142B	Belden 83242	50	69.5	29.0	#19 Solid SCCS	TFE	D	TFE	0.195	1400	0.3	1.1	3.9	13.5
RG-174	Belden 7805R	50	73.5	26.2	#25 Solid BC	FPE	FC	P1	0.110	300	0.6	2.0	6.5	21.3
RG-174	Belden 8216	50	66	30.8	#26 Flex CCS	PE	S	P1	0.110	1100	0.8	2.5	8.6	33.7
RG-213	Belden 8267	50	66	30.8	#13 Flex BC	PE	S	P2N	0.405	3700	0.2	0.6	2.1	8.0
RG-213	CXP213	50	66	30.8	#13 Flex BC	PE	S	P2N	0.405	600	0.2	0.6	2.0	8.2
RG-214	Belden 8268	50	66	30.8	#13 Flex SPC	PE	D	P2N	0.425	3700	0.2	0.7	2.2	8.0
RG-216	Belden 9850	75	66	20.5	#18 Flex TC	PE	D	P2N	0.425	3700	0.2	0.7	2.0	7.1
RG-217	WM CQ217F	50	66	30.8	#10 Flex BC	PE	D	PE	0.545	7000	0.1	0.4	1.4	5.2
RG-217	M17/78-RG217	50	66	30.8	#10 Solid BC	PE	D	P2N	0.545	7000	0.1	0.4	1.4	5.2
RG-218	M17/79-RG218	50	66	29.5	#4.5 Solid BC	PE	S	P2N	0.870	11000	0.1	0.2	0.8	3.4
RG-223	Belden 9273	50	66	30.8	#19 Solid SPC	PE	D	P2N	0.212	1400	0.4	1.2	4.1	14.5
RG-303	Belden 84303	50	69.5	29.0	#18 Solid SCCS	TFE	S	TFE	0.170	1400	0.3	1.1	3.9	13.5

RG or Type	*Part Number*	*Nom. Z_0 Ω*	*VF %*	*Cap. pF/ft*	*Cent. Cond. AWG*	*Diel. Type*	*Shield Type*	*Jacket Matl*	*OD inches*	*Max V (RMS)*	*Matched Loss (dB/100') 1 MHz*	*10*	*100*	*1000*
RG-316	CXP TJ1316	50	69.5	29.4	#26 Flex BC	TFE	S	FEP	0.098	1200	1.2	2.7	8.0	26.1
RG-316	Belden 84316	50	69.5	29.0	#26 Flex SCCS	TFE	S	FEP	0.096	900	0.8	2.5	8.3	26.0
RG-393	M17/127-RG393	50	69.5	29.4	#12 Flex SPC	TFE	D	FEP	0.390	5000	0.2	0.5	1.7	6.1
RG-400	M17/128-RG400	50	69.5	29.4	#20 Flex SPC	TFE	D	FEP	0.195	1400	0.4	1.3	4.3	15.0
LMR500	TMS LMR500UF	50	85	23.9	#7 Flex BC	FPE	FC	PE	0.500	2500	0.1	0.4	1.2	4.0
LMR500	TMS LMR500	50	85	23.9	#7 Solid CCA	FPE	FC	PE	0.500	2500	0.1	0.3	0.9	3.3
LMR600	TMS LMR600	50	86	23.4	#5.5 Solid CCA	FPE	FC	PE	0.590	4000	0.1	0.2	0.8	2.7
LMR600	TMS LMR600UF	50	86	23.4	#5.5 Flex BC	FPE	FC	PE	0.590	4000	0.1	0.2	0.8	2.7
LMR1200	TMS LMR1200	50	88	23.1	#0 Copper Tube	FPE	FC	PE	1.200	4500	0.04	0.1	0.4	1.3
Hardline														
1/2"	CATV Hardline	50	81	25.0	#5.5 BC	FPE	SM	none	0.500	2500	0.05	0.2	0.8	3.2
1/2"	CATV Hardline	75	81	16.7	#11.5 BC	FPE	SM	none	0.500	2500	0.1	0.2	0.8	3.2
7/8"	CATV Hardline	50	81	25.0	#1 BC	FPE	SM	none	0.875	4000	0.03	0.1	0.6	2.9
7/8"	CATV Hardline	75	81	16.7	#5.5 BC	FPE	SM	none	0.875	4000	0.03	0.1	0.6	2.9
LDF4-50A	Heliax – ½"	50	88	25.9	#5 Solid BC	FPE	CC	PE	0.630	1400	0.02	0.2	0.6	2.4
LDF5-50A	Heliax – ⅞"	50	88	25.9	0.355" BC	FPE	CC	PE	1.090	2100	0.03	0.10	0.4	1.3
LDF6-50A	Heliax – 1¼"	50	88	25.9	0.516" BC	FPE	CC	PE	1.550	3200	0.02	0.08	0.3	1.1
Parallel Lines														
TV Twinlead (Belden 9085)		300	80	4.5	#22 Flex CCS	PE	none	P1	0.400	**	0.1	0.3	1.4	5.9
Twinlead (Belden 8225)		300	80	4.4	#20 Flex BC	PE	none	P1	0.400	8000	0.1	0.2	1.1	4.8
WM CQ 554		400	90.2	2.7	#14 Flex CCS	PE	none	P1	1.000	10000	0.04	0.01	0.6	3.0
WM CQ 552		380	91.8	2.5	#16 Flex CCS	PE	none	P1	1.000	10000	0.05	0.2	0.6	2.6
WM CQ 553		395	90.2	2.5	#18 Flex CCS	PE	none	P1	1.000	10000	0.06	0.2	0.7	2.9
WM CQ 551		400	91	2.5	#18 Solid CCS	PE	none	P1	1.000	10000	0.05	0.02	0.6	2.8
Open-Wire Line		600	0.95-99***	1.7	#12 BC	none	none	none	**	12000	0.02	0.06	0.2	—

Note – WM CQ parallel line products are no longer available but are representative of parallel lines available from several manufacturers

Approximate Power Handling Capability (1:1 SWR, 40°C Ambient):

	1.8 MHz	*7*	*14*	*30*	*50*	*150*	*220*	*450*	*1 GHz*
RG-58 Style	1350	700	500	350	250	150	120	100	50
RG-59 Style	2300	1100	800	550	400	250	200	130	90
RG-8X Style	1830	840	560	360	270	145	115	80	50
RG-8/213 Style	5900	3000	2000	1500	1000	600	500	350	250
RG-217 Style	20000	9200	6100	3900	2900	1500	1200	800	500
LDF4-50A	38000	18000	13000	8200	6200	3400	2800	1900	1200
LDF5-50A	67000	32000	22000	14000	11000	5900	4800	3200	2100
LMR500	18000	9200	6500	4400	3400	1900	1600	1100	700
LMR1200	52000	26000	19000	13000	10000	5500	4500	3000	2000

Legend:

**	Not Available or varies
***	Varies with spacer material and spacing
ASPE	Air Spaced Polyethylene
BC	Bare Copper
CC	Corrugated Copper
CCA	Copper Cover Aluminum
CCS	Copper Covered Steel
CXP	Cable X-Perts, Inc.
D	Double Copper Braids
DRF	Davis RF
FC	Foil + Tinned Copper Braid
FEP	Teflon ® Type IX
Flex	Flexible Stranded Wire
FPE	Foamed Polyethylene
Heliax	Andrew Corp Heliax
N	Non-Contaminating
P1	PVC, Class 1
P2	PVC, Class 2
PE	Polyethylene
S	Single Braided Shield
SC	Silver Coated Braid
SCCS	Silver Plated Copper Coated Steel
SM	Smooth Aluminum
SPC	Silver Plated Copper
TC	Tinned Copper
TFE	Teflon®
TMS	Times Microwave Systems
UF	Ultra Flex

Table 23.2
Coaxial Cable Equations

$$C\ (\text{pF/foot}) = \frac{7.26\varepsilon}{\log (D / d)} \quad \text{(Eq A)}$$

$$L\ (\mu\text{H/foot}) = 0.14 \log \frac{D}{d} \quad \text{(Eq B)}$$

$$Z_0\ (\text{ohms}) = \sqrt{\frac{L}{C}} = \left(\frac{138}{\sqrt{\varepsilon}}\right)\left(\log \frac{D}{d}\right) \quad \text{(Eq C)}$$

$$\text{VF \% (velocity factor, ref. speed of light)} = \frac{100}{\sqrt{\varepsilon}} \quad \text{(Eq D)}$$

$$\text{Time delay (ns/foot)} = 1.016 \sqrt{\varepsilon} \quad \text{(Eq E)}$$

$$f\ (\text{cutoff/GHz}) = \frac{7.50}{\sqrt{\varepsilon}\,(D + d)} \quad \text{(Eq F)}$$

$$\text{Reflection Coefficient} = |\rho| = \frac{Z_L - Z_0}{Z_L + Z_0} = \frac{SWR - 1}{SWR + 1} \quad \text{(Eq G)}$$

$$\text{Return Loss (dB)} = -20 \log |\rho| \quad \text{(Eq H)}$$

$$SWR = \frac{1 + |\rho|}{1 - |\rho|} \quad \text{(Eq I)}$$

$$V\ \text{peak} = \frac{(1.15\ S\ d)(\log D / d)}{K} \quad \text{(Eq J)}$$

$$A = \frac{0.435}{Z_0 D}\left(\frac{D}{d}(K1 + K2)\right)\sqrt{f} + 2.78\sqrt{\varepsilon}\,(PF)(f) \quad \text{(Eq K)}$$

where

- A = attenuation in dB/100 foot
- d = OD of inner conductor
- D = ID of outer conductor
- S = max voltage gradient of insulation in volts/mil
- ε = dielectric constant
- K = safety factor
- K1 = strand factor
- K2 = braid factor
- f = freq in MHz
- PF = power factor

Note: Obtain K1 and K2 data from manufacturer.

Splicing Window Line

In keeping with the amateur ethic of re-use, feed lines are often spliced. While connectors can be installed on coaxial line to join sections, that luxury is not available for the common window line. The ARRL's take on splicing window line is included in the downloadable supplemental information from The Doctor Is In column in *QST*.

for loss and resistance before being placed into service. Cable with a solid-copper center conductor is more expensive but avoids low-frequency and resistance problems.

Deterioration

Deterioration of coaxial cable is most commonly caused by water or moisture infiltration which causes corrosion of the shield, dramatically increasing its losses. This usually occurs at the ends of cables where connectors are installed or the cable is separated into two conductors for attachment to an antenna.

Exposure of the inner insulating material to moisture and chemicals over time contaminates the center insulation and increases cable losses. Newer types of foam-dielectric cables are less prone to contamination than are older types of solid-polyethylene insulated cables.

Impregnated cables, such as Times Wire LMR-400-DB, are immune to water and chemical damage, and may be buried if desired. They also have a self-healing property that is valuable when rodents chew into the line. Cable loss should be checked at least every two years if the cable has been outdoors or buried. See the section on testing transmission lines.

The outer insulating jacket of the cable (usually PVC) is used solely as protection from dirt, moisture and chemicals. (The jacket's only electrical function is compressing the shield braid to keep the strands in good contact with each other.) If the jacket is breached, it generally leads to corrosion of the shield and contamination of the center insulation, again causing high losses.

The ultra-violet (UV) radiation in sunlight causes a chemical reaction in standard PVC jacket material that causes the plastic to break down into products that migrate from the jacket into the braid and center insulation, degrading the electrical properties of both. If your cable will be exposed to strong sunlight, use a cable with a non-contaminating jacket.

Cable Capacitance

The capacitance between the conductors of coaxial cable varies with the impedance and dielectric constant of the line. Therefore, the lower the impedance, the higher the capacitance per foot, because the conductor spacing is decreased. Capacitance also increases with dielectric constant.

Bending Radius

A normal amateur installation will create bends and turns in the feed line run. It is common to wind coax into a coil to form a common-mode RF choke or to store excess cable. Bending coax is acceptable as long as the *minimum bending radius* is not violated. A typical minimum bending radius is a multiple of the coax diameter. For example, a common minimum bending radius specification for RG-8 is 4 inches, which is a multiple of 8 (½ inch OD × 8). Coax with more rigid shield materials such as hardline or Heliax will have a larger minimum bending radius.

If the cable will be subjected to regular flexing, such as if it is attached to a rotating antenna, use a cable with a stranded center conductor. When repeatedly bent or flexed,

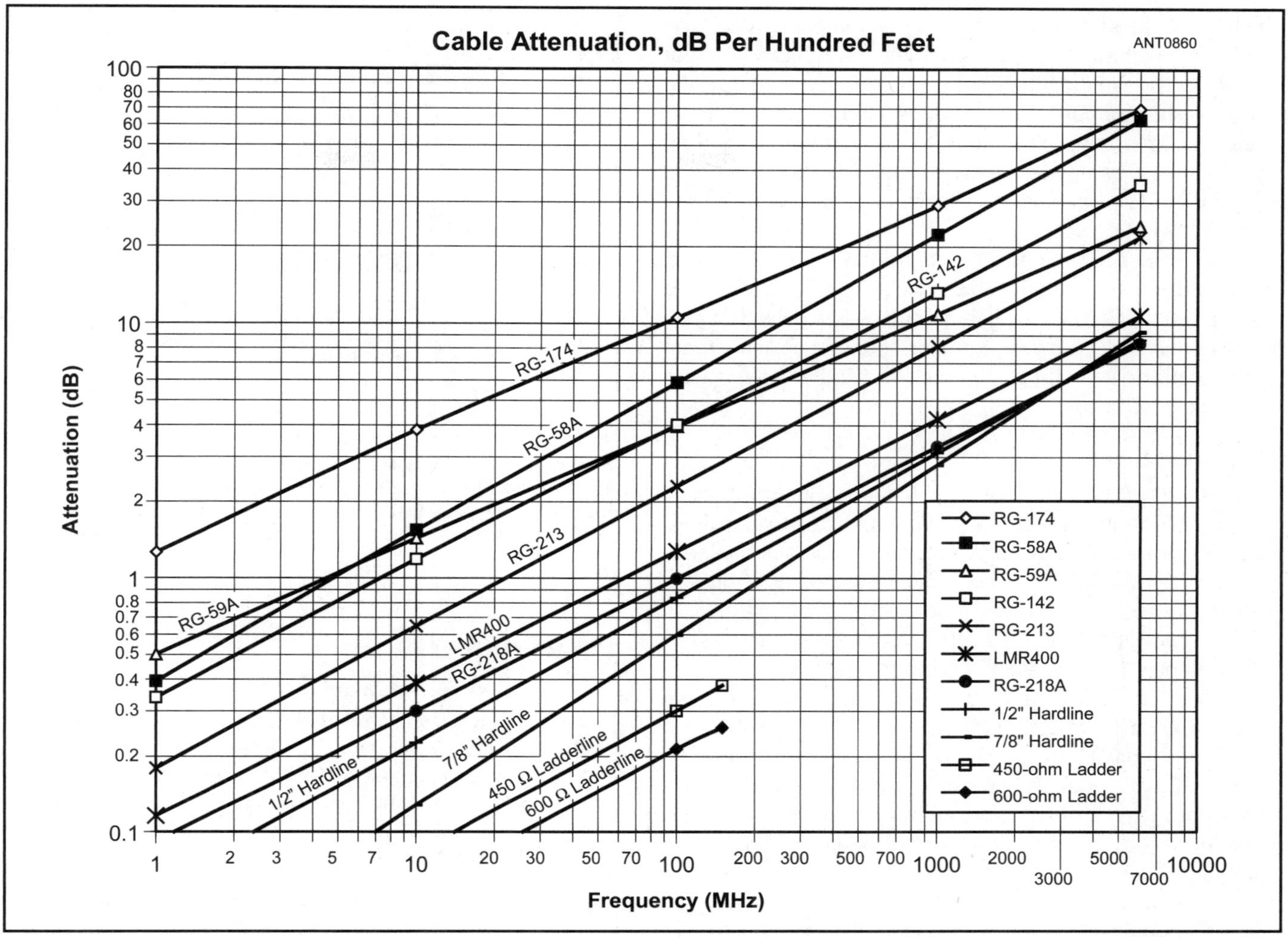

Figure 23.25 — Nominal matched-line attenuation in decibels per 100 feet of various common transmission lines. Total attenuation is directly proportional to length. Attenuation will vary somewhat in actual cable samples, and generally increases with age in coaxial cables having a type 1 jacket. Cables grouped together in the above chart have approximately the same attenuation. Types having foam polyethylene dielectric have slightly lower loss than equivalent solid types, when not specifically shown above.

solid center conductors will develop *metal fatigue* and break.

Miniature and sub-miniature TFE-insulated cables such as RG-400 are often used for winding choke baluns. The cable is wound around a toroid core or rod, usually with a turn radius several times smaller than the minimum specified. There are few reports of failure from this practice in both commercial and home-made chokes. While no specification is available, the consensus of experienced antenna system builders is that if the power carried by the cable is well below its maximum rating, not at an elevated temperature, and not repeatedly flexed, smaller radius bends do not lead to failure of this type of cable.

Center Conductor Migration

The most common center insulation materials are solid polyethylene (PE), extended or "foamed" polyethylene (FPE), and solid Teflon (TFE). Teflon dielectric coax is usually trouble-free and often used at VHF and UHF frequencies due to its low loss characteristics.

Foam polyethylene dielectric coax is used extensively on the HF bands. RG-8X and RG-11/U (Belden 8213) are examples found in many stations. An unfortunate property of the foam dielectric coax is a lack of mechanical stability under some conditions. The center conductor in foam coax can migrate toward the shield causing an "impedance bump," or worse, a center conductor-to-shield short.

Several user-created conditions can lead to foam coax developing a short circuit. A major culprit is bending or coiling foam coax with a tight radius. For example, RF choke baluns are often made by wrapping several turns of coax into a tight bundle with a tight radius. Coaxial cable stubs are also wrapped into a coil of small radius to keep them small overall and out of the way. Coax is sometimes coiled up just to use up extra length. These practices are all potential trouble.

An additive factor is the self-heating caused by the cable's loss — a direct function of the amount of power applied and SWR. RG-8X is not rated for 1500 W, but lots of amateurs use it successfully at that power level. RG-8X gets warm to the touch at 1500 W. Increasing internal temperature softens the foam which facilitates center conductor migration. Tight radius bends taken together with heating are a recipe for an eventual short circuit. Tightly coiled baluns used outdoors receive solar heating in addition to self-heating and a tight bend radius. A balun made and used this way has a very high probability of shorting out over time - particularly when used at high power.

To avoid center conductor migration: don't use sharp bends, particularly at high power. Use solid dielectric coax to make tightly coiled coaxial baluns and if stubs must be coiled up, use solid dielectric coax for those too. Use up spare foam coax length by laying it flat on the floor and avoiding sharp radius turns or bends.

Paralleled Lines

In order to obtain feed lines with intermediate or unusual characteristic impedances, identical lengths of line with Z_0 can be connected in parallel. The resulting characteristic impedance, $Z_{COMB} = Z_0 / N$, where N is the number of lines in parallel. For example, to create a section of line with $Z_0 = 37.5\ \Omega$, two sections of 75 Ω RG-11 or RG-59 can be connected in parallel to create a λ/4 matching section for a 25 Ω load. Paralleled cables have the same loss as a single cable would with an equal degree of mismatch.

Either coaxial or parallel-conductor lines may be combined in parallel. When using paralleled coaxial lines, if standard connectors and adaptors are not used and lines are spliced together, precautions must be taken to maintain shielding at the junctions or RF chokes must be placed on the line to block noise currents on the shield from entering the line and to prevent signals from inside the line escaping to flow on the outside of the shield. If parallel-conductor lines are combined they must be kept well apart (at least one line width) to avoid coupling between the lines.

Shielded Balanced Lines

Shielded balanced lines made from parallel coaxial cables have several advantages over open-wire lines. They can be buried and they can be routed through metal buildings or inside metal piping the same as for single coaxial lines. The outer surface of the shields can pick up noise and common-mode signals just as for single coaxial lines, as well.

The shields are connected together (see **Figure 23.26A**), and the two inner conductors constitute the balanced line. At the input, the coaxial shields should be connected to chassis ground; at the output (the antenna side), they are joined but left floating. (See the previous section's caution about blocking shield current at the open end of the cable.)

The characteristic impedance of a balanced shielded line is twice that of each single line — as if they were in series. Shielded balanced lines having impedances of 140 or 100 Ω can be constructed from two equal lengths of 70-Ω or 50-Ω cable (RG-59 or RG-58 would be satisfactory for amateur power levels). Paralleled RG-63 (125-Ω) cable would make a balanced transmission line more in accord with traditional 300-Ω twin-lead feed line ($Z_0 = 250\ \Omega$). Note that the losses for these shielded types of balanced lines will generally be higher than those for classic open-wire lines.

A high power, low-loss, low-impedance 70-Ω (or 50-Ω) balanced line can be constructed from four coaxial cables as in Figure 23.26B. The characteristic impedance of each pair of cables is one-half that of the single lines as described in the previous section. The net result is that the overall characteristic impedance is that of a single cable. Again, the shields are all connected together. The center conductors of the two sets of coaxial cables that are connected in parallel provide the balanced feed.

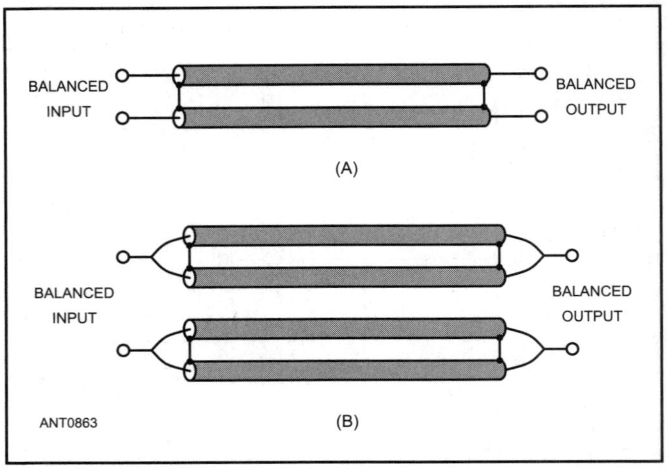

Figure 23.26 — Shielded balanced transmission lines utilizing standard small-size coaxial cable, such as RG-58 or RG-59. These balanced lines may be routed inside metal conduit or near large metal objects without adverse effects.

Waveguide and Microwave Cable

Rigid waveguide is used above 1 GHz and is uncommon below 10 GHz in amateur installations. Amateurs use special low-loss coaxial cables for short runs, along with special connectors such as the SMA family and others developed for consumer use in mobile networks and other microwave systems. The special techniques for working with these transmission lines at microwave frequencies are introduced in the chapter on **VHF and UHF Antenna Systems**. See the article "Microwave Plumbing" in this book's downloadable supplemental information.

Other useful references include the RSGB's *International Microwave Handbook* and the ARRL's *UHF/Microwave Experimenter's Manual*, which is out of print but available used. (See the Bibliography.) In addition, *QST*'s "Microwavelengths" column by Paul Wade, W1GHZ, often often contains information about working with transmission lines above 1 GHz.

23.4 RF CONNECTORS

There are many different types of RF connectors for coaxial cable, but the three most common for amateur use are the UHF, Type N and BNC families. Type F connectors are becoming popular for use with receiving antennas and low-loss RG-6 coaxial cable. Type SMA connectors are commonly found on hand-held transceivers and microwave equipment. The type of connector used for a specific job depends on the size of the cable, the frequency of operation and the power levels involved.

If the connector is to be exposed to the weather, select a waterproof design such as Type N or take care to thoroughly waterproof the connector as discussed in the chapter **Building Antenna Systems and Towers.**

23.4.1 UHF CONNECTORS

The so-called UHF connector (the series name is not related to frequency) is found on most HF and some VHF equipment. PL-259 is another name for the UHF male, and the female is also known as the SO-239. These connectors are rated for full legal amateur power at HF and can be used through VHF without concerns. Above the 70 cm band, the connectors are poor for UHF work because of variable impedance and inconsistent insulator characteristics of different brands. PL-259 connectors are designed to fit RG-8 and RG-11 size cable (0.405-inch OD). Adapters are available for use with smaller RG-58, RG-59 and RG-8X size cable. UHF connectors are not weatherproof.

Figure 23.27 shows how to install the solder type of PL-259 on RG-8 cable. Note that this is only one of many different methods hams have developed to attach these popular connectors. The key to any successful solder-based method is to have a sturdy soldering gun or iron that can heat the connector body quickly and thoroughly without melting the center insulation from having to apply heat for a long time. For soldered connectors, do not pay attention to suggestions that it is sufficient to capture braid in the connector threads or between the connector body and adaptors. Such an installation will inevitably fail and presents a poor connection on VHF and UHF bands from the outset. If you don't want to solder a PL-259, use good-quality crimp connectors with the proper installation tools.

Proper preparation of the cable end is the key to success. Follow these simple steps. Measure back about ¾-inch from the cable end and slightly score the outer jacket around its circumference. With a sharp knife, cut through the outer jacket, through the braid, and through the dielectric — almost to the center conductor. Be careful not to score the center conductor. Cutting through all outer layers at once keeps the braid from separating. (Using a coax stripping tool with preset blade depth makes this and subsequent trimming steps much easier.)

Pull the severed outer jacket, braid and dielectric off the end of the cable as one piece. Inspect the area around the cut, looking for any strands of braid hanging loose and snip them off. There won't be any if your knife was sharp enough. Next, score the outer jacket about 5⁄16-inch back from the first cut. Cut through the jacket lightly; do not score the braid. This step takes practice. If you score the braid, start again. Remove the outer jacket.

Tin the exposed braid and center conductor, but apply the solder sparingly and avoid melting the dielectric. Slide the coupling ring onto the cable. Screw the connector body onto the cable. If you prepared the cable to the right dimensions, the center conductor will protrude through the center

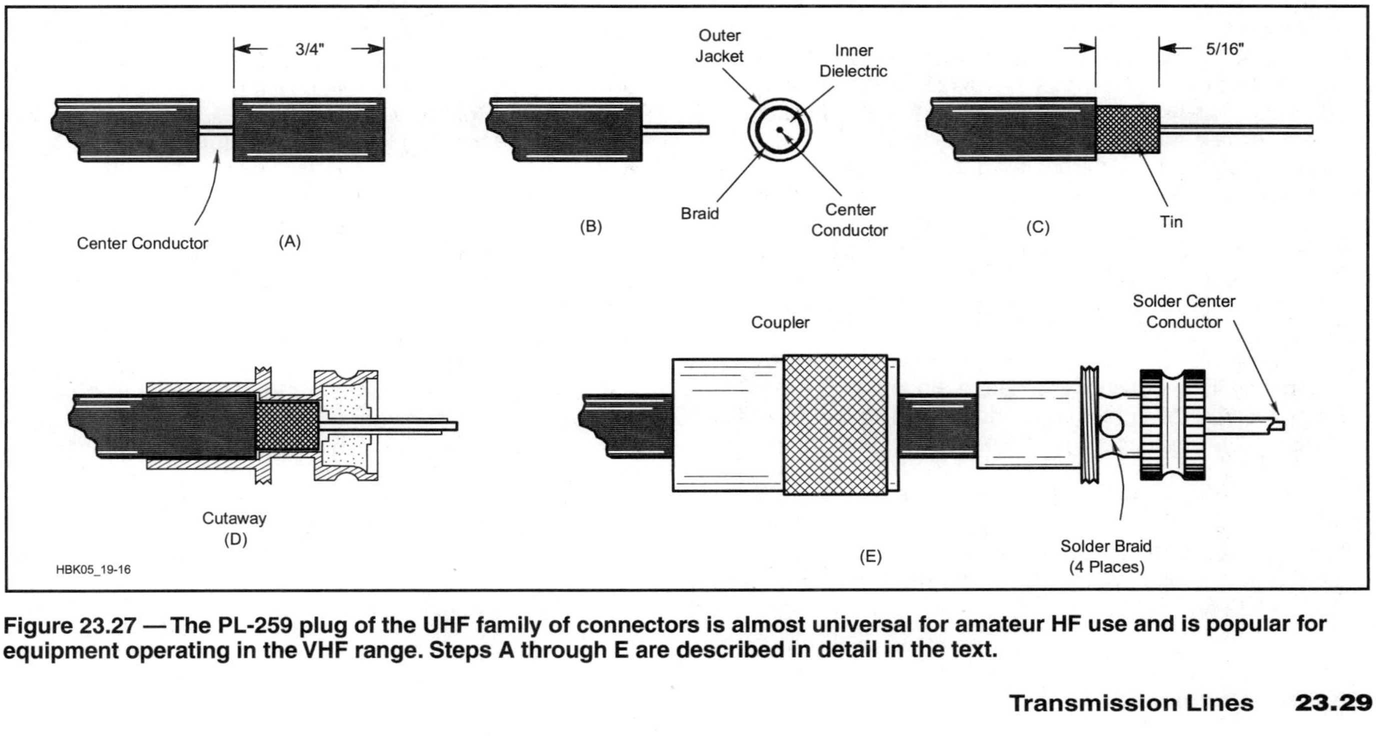

Figure 23.27 — The PL-259 plug of the UHF family of connectors is almost universal for amateur HF use and is popular for equipment operating in the VHF range. Steps A through E are described in detail in the text.

pin, the braid will show through the solder holes, and the body will actually thread onto the outer cable jacket. A very small amount of lubricant on the cable jacket will help the threading process.

Solder the braid through the solder holes. Solder through all four holes; poor connection to the braid is the most common form of PL-259 failure. A good connection between connector and braid is just as important as that between the center conductor and connector. Use a large soldering iron for this job. With practice, you'll learn how much heat to use. If you use too little heat, the solder will bead up, not really flowing onto the connector body. If you use too much heat, the dielectric will melt, letting the braid and center conductor touch. Most PL-259s are nickel plated, but silver-plated connectors are much easier to solder and only slightly more expensive.

Solder the center conductor to the center pin. The solder should flow on the inside, not the outside, of the center pin. If you wait until the connector body cools off from soldering the braid, you'll have less trouble with the dielectric melting. Trim the center conductor to be even with the end of the center pin. Use a small file to round the end, removing any solder that built up on the outer surface of the center pin. Use a sharp knife, very fine sandpaper or steel wool to remove any solder flux from the outer surface of the center pin. Screw the coupling ring onto the body, and you're finished.

Figure 23.28 shows how to install a PL-259 connector on RG-58 or RG-59 cable. An adapter is used for the smaller cable with standard RG-8 size PL-259s. (UG-175 for RG-58 and UG-176 for RG-59) Prepare the cable as shown. Once the braid is prepared, screw the adapter into the PL-259 shell and finish the job as you would a PL-259 on RG-8 cable.

Figure 23.29 shows the instructions and dimensions for crimp-on UHF connectors that fit all common sizes of coaxial cable.

While amateurs have been reluctant to adopt crimp-on connectors, the availability of good quality connectors and inexpensive crimping tools make crimp technology a good choice, even for connectors used outside. Soldering the center conductor after crimping in the connector tip is optional. The crimping process is illustrated in the article "Installing Coax Crimp Connectors" by Dino Papas, KLØS, that is included with the downloadable supplemental information.

Coax Connectors — Not as Simple as They Appear

"You get what you pay for" was never more true than when it comes to common UHF connectors, including PL-259s, SO-239s, adapters, and so on. Every hamfest seems to have at least one vendor selling "mystery" UHF connectors, sometimes for as little as $1.00 each. What are you buying when you buy a $1.00 PL-259? It's pretty much a guess. For the difference of a dollar or two, "mystery" UHF connectors are a very poor investment.

PL-259s have four parts: the outer sleeve called the "knurled nut," the connector body, the insulator/dielectric and the center pin. All four components can be compromised to the point of making a bargain connector useless.

Problems frequently encountered:

• Finish: Bargain connectors sometimes have a finish you can't solder to! They may have a chrome-like appearance, but the plating may not take solder well and has to be filed down for a good connection.

• Threading: The internal threads at the rear of the body are there to accept a UG-style insert that narrows the connector barrel to accept smaller diameter coax such as RG-8X or RG-58. The threads may be metric! UG inserts also sometimes appear in the US market with metric threads. Either way, the insert will not screw into the body.

• Dielectric: Good connectors use quality phenolic or Teflon insulation between the center pin and the body. Bargain connectors might use anything, including materials like polystyrene, which will melt when the center pin is soldered.

• Center pin diameter: This is one of the most common and insidious problems in mystery PL-259s. The center pin ODs are almost always slightly smaller than they should be and it's hard to notice. The center pin connection between a PL-259 and an SO-239 or barrel connector depends on the male side pin OD being correct and the matching fingers on the female side being the correct diameter and made of the proper spring material.

• Center socket spring tension: If the SO-239 socket metal relaxes over time and/or temperature, an intermittent connection will be created that can be very hard to track down.

• Mating indentions: The indentations on the end of the SO-239 that mates to a PL-259 (the annulus flange) may only have four indentations to match up with the short prongs on the body of the male connector. A quality SO-239 or barrel connector has indentations all the way around. If the PL-259 and SO-239 don't seat completely, an intermittent connection is likely to develop.

• Tee and right-angle (elbow) UHF adapters: The center conductor makes a right-angle turn inside the shell. In poor-quality adapters the right-angle connection is done with a spring contact — these do not hold up. Quality tee and right-angle adapters are reliable because the internal conductors are tapped and threaded — the conductors are screwed together within the body at the right-angle junction.

How can we tell the good connectors? If the price is too good to be true — well, it is. PL-259s with good silver plating have a dull appearance. Good connectors have a part number and manufacturer's name stamped into them. You can look up the connector's specifications if it's marked. An example is the connectors made by Amphenol — all of which have parts numbers such as 83-1SP (PL-259) or 83-1R (SO-239) stamped into or onto the connector body. [Contributed by Hal Kennedy, N4GG]

83-1SP (PL-259) Plug with adapters
(UG-176/U OR UG-175/U)

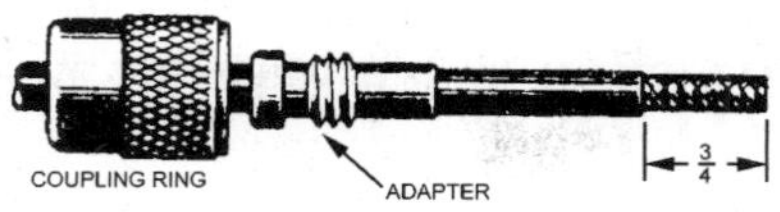

1. Cut end of cable even. Remove vinyl jacket 3/4" - don't nick braid. Slide coupling ring and adapter on cable.

2. Fan braid slightly and fold back over cable.

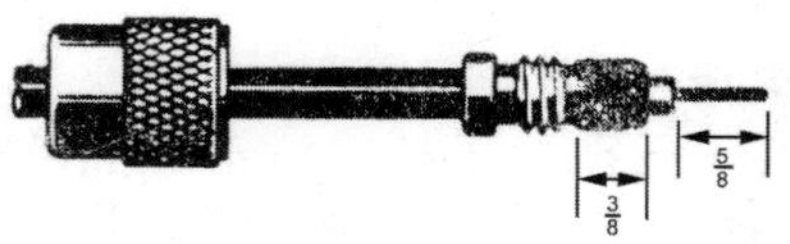

3. Position adapter to dimension shown. Press braid down over body of adapter and trim to 3/8". Bare 5/8" of conductor. Tin exposed center conductor.

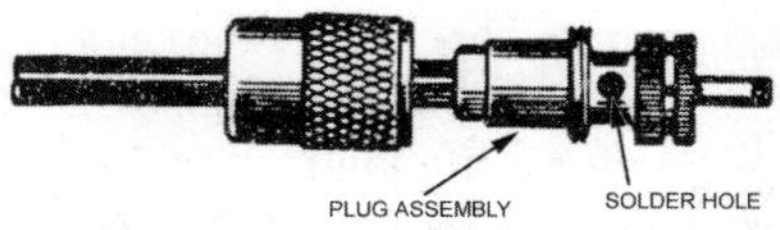

4. Screw the plug assembly on adapter. Solder braid to shell through solder holes. Solder conductor to contact sleeve.

5. Screw coupling ring on plug assembly.

HBK0460

Figure 23.28 — Installing PL-259 plugs on RG-58 or RG-59 cable requires the use of UG-175 or UG-176 reducing adapters, respectively. The adapter screws into the plug body using the threads of the connector to grip the jacket on larger cables. ***(Courtesy Amphenol Electronic Components)***

UHF Connectors

Braid Crimp - Solder Center Contact

Ferrule · Coupling Nut · Body assembly

Amphenol	Cable RG-/U	Cable Attachment		Hex Crimp Data			Stripping Dims, inches (mm)		
		Outer	Inner	Cavity for Outer Ferrule	Die Set Tool 227-994	CTL Series Tool No.	a	b	c
83-58SP	58, 141	Crimp	Solder	0.213(5.4)	227-1221-11	CTL-1	1.14 (29.0)	0.780 (19.9)	0.250 (6.4)
83-58SP-1002	400	Crimp	Solder	0.213(5.4)	227-1221-11	CTL-1	1.14 (29.0)	0.780 (19.9)	0.250 (6.4)
83-59DCP-RFX	59	Crimp	Solder	0255(6.5)	227-1221-13	CTL-1	1.22 (30.9)	0.890* (22.6)	0.543 (13.8)
83-58SCP-RFX	58	Crimp	Solder	0.213(5.4)	227-1221-11	CTL-1	1.22 (30.9)	0.890* (22.6)	0.543 (13.8)
83-59SP	59	Crimp	Solder	0.255(6.5)	227-1221-13	CTL-1	1.22 (30.9)	0.890* (22.6)	0.543 (13.8)
83-8SP-RFX	8	Crimp	Solder	0.429(10.9)	227-1221-25	CTL-3	1.22 (30.9)	0.890* (22.6)	0.543 (13.8)

See www.AmphenolRF.com for assembly instructions for all other connectore types. These dimensions only apply to Amphenol connectors and may not be correct for other manufacturers.
* Manufacturer's assembly dimensions incorrectly show 0.574 inches.

Step 1

Step 1 Cut end of cable even. Strip cable to dimensions shown in table. All cuts are to be sharp and square. Do not nick braid, dielectric or center conductor. Tin center conductor avoiding excessive heat.

Step 2

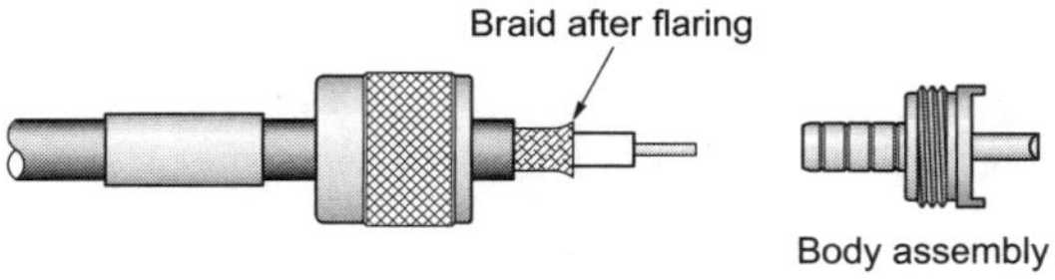

Step 2 Slide coupling nut and ferrule over cable jacket. Flair braid slightly as shown. Install cable into body assembly, so inner ferrule portion slides under braid, until braid butts shoulder. Slide outer ferrule over braid until it butts shoulder. Crimp ferrule with tool and die set indicated in table.

Step 3

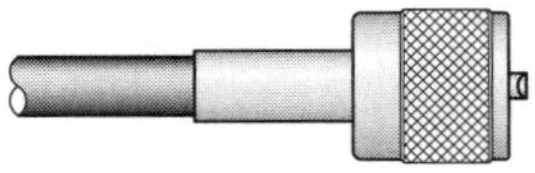

Step 3 Soft solder center conductor to contact. Avoid heating contact excessively to prevent damaging insulator. Slide/screw coupling nut over body.

HBK0475

Figure 23.29 — Crimp-on UHF connectors are available for all sizes of popular coaxial cable and save considerable time over soldered connectors. The performance and reliability of these connectors is equivalent to soldered connectors, if crimped properly. ***(Courtesy Amphenol Electronic Components)***

23.4.2 OTHER RF CONNECTORS

BNC Connectors

The BNC connectors illustrated in **Figure 23.30** are popular for low power levels at VHF and UHF. They accept RG-58 and RG-59 cable and are available for cable mounting in both male and female versions. Several different styles are available, so be sure to use the dimensions for the type you have. Follow the installation instructions carefully. If you prepare the cable to the wrong dimensions, the center pin will not seat properly with connectors of the opposite gender. Sharp scissors are a big help for trimming the braid evenly. Crimp-on BNC connectors are also available, with a large number of variations, including a twist-on version. A guide to installing these connectors is available with this book's downloadable supplemental information.

Type N Connectors

The Type N connector, illustrated in **Figure 23.31**, is a must for high-power VHF and UHF operation. N connectors are available in male and female versions for cable mounting and are designed for RG-8 size cable. Unlike UHF connectors, they are designed to maintain a constant impedance at cable joints. Like BNC connectors, it is important to prepare the cable to the right dimensions. The center pin must be positioned correctly to mate with the center pin of connectors of the opposite gender. Use the right dimensions for the connector style you have. Crimp-on N connectors are also available, again with a large number of variations. A guide to installing these connectors is available with this book's downloadable supplemental information.

Type F Connectors

Type F connectors, used primarily on cable TV connections, are also popular for receive-only antennas and can be used with RG-59 or the increasingly popular RG-6 cable available at low cost. Crimp-on is the only option for these connectors and **Figure 23.32** shows a general guide for installing them. The exact dimensions vary between connector styles and manufacturers — information on crimping is generally provided with the connectors. There are two styles of crimp — ferrule and compression. The ferrule crimp method is similar to that for UHF, BNC and N connectors in which a metal ring is compressed around the exposed coax shield. The compression crimp forces a bushing into the back of the connector, clamping the shield against the connector body. In all cases, the exposed center conductor of the cable — a solid wire — must end flush with the end of the connector. A center conductor that is too short may not make a good connection.

SMA Connectors

The SMA connector in **Figure 23.33** is the most common microwave connector. The cable center insulation is taken directly to the connector interface without air gaps. A standard SMA is rated for use to 12.4 GHz but high-quality connectors, properly installed, can be used to 24 GHz. For more information about SMA and other microwave connectors, see the Bibliography entry for Williams (the article is also available with this book's downloadable supplemental information).

SMA connectors have become popular on handheld VHF/UHF transceivers. Some models use a "reverse SMA" that requires a double-receptacle adapter for a feed line terminated in an SMA plug to be attached.

Hardline Connectors

Surplus hardline cable comes in various sizes (½, ⅝, ¾, 1 inch and so on) that are not compatible with standard RF connectors such as UHF or N. There have been dozens of inventive schemes published over the years that use plumbing hardware or other materials to fabricate an adaptor compatible with a standard connector. If you decide to make your own adapter, be cautious about using dissimilar metals and waterproof the connector carefully. Otherwise, use the recommended connectors from the manufacturer — these are often available as surplus on Internet websites.

Using RG-6 with RG-58 Crimp Connectors

RG-6 coaxial cable is readily and cheaply available as it is commonly used for domestic cable and satellite TV. Crimp-type BNC, N, PL-259 and others are readily obtainable for RG-58 cables. Crimp connectors for RG-6 other than Type F are becoming difficult to find. However RG-58 crimp connectors can be satisfactorily used on RG-6 and some other cables as described on the article by Garth Jenkinson, VK3BBK, with this book's downloadable supplemental information.

BNC CONNECTORS

Standard Clamp

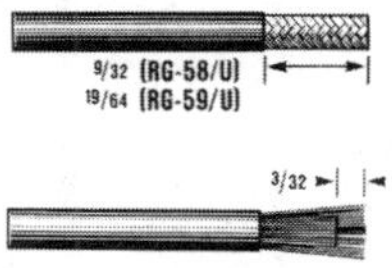

1. Cut cable even. Strip jacket. Fray braid and strip dielectric. ***Don't nick braid or center conductor.*** Tin center conductor.

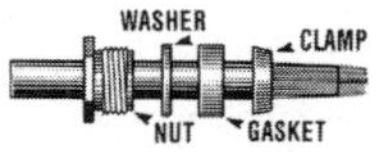

2. Taper braid. Slide nut, washer, gasket and clamp over braid. Clamp inner shoulder should fit squarely against end of jacket.

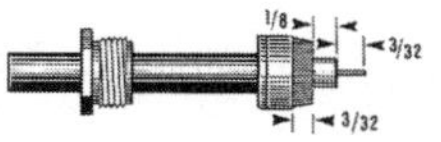

3. With clamp in place, comb out braid, fold back smooth as shown. Trim center conductor.

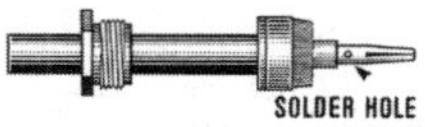

4. Solder contact on conductor through solder hole. Contact should butt against dielectric. Remove excess solder from outside of contact. Avoid excess heat to prevent swollen dielectric which would interfere with connector body.

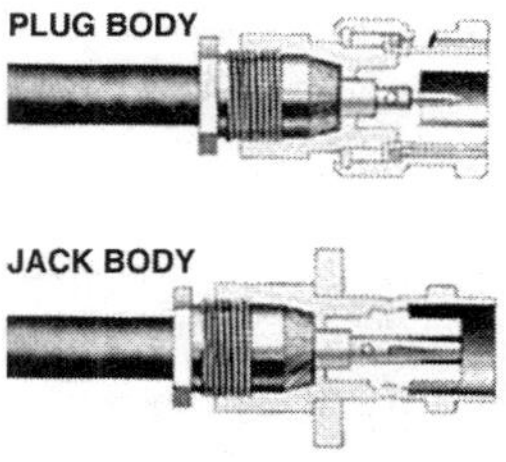

5. Push assembly into body. Screw nut into body with wrench until tight. ***Don't rotate body on cable to tighten.***

Improved Clamp

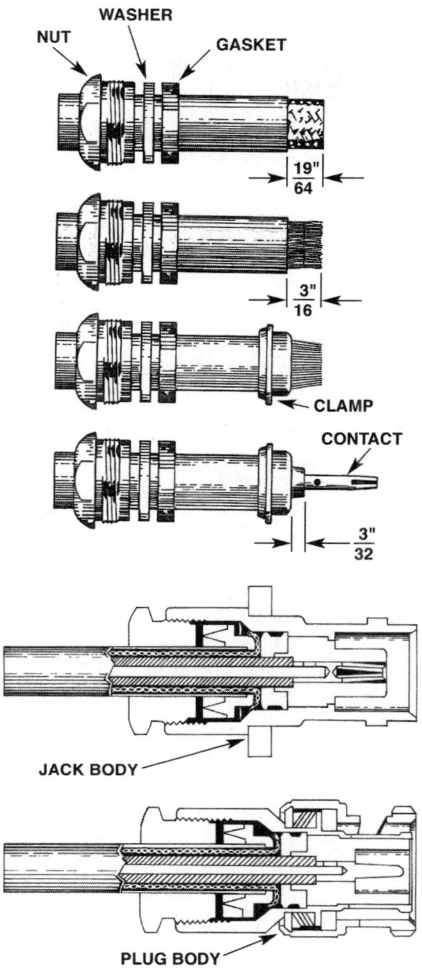

Follow 1, 2, 3 and 4 in BNC connectors (standard clamp) exceptas noted. Strip cable as shown. Slide gasket on cable *with groove facing clamp.* Slide clamp *with sharp edge facing gasket.* Clamp *should* cut gasket to seal properly.

HBK05_19-18

C. C. Clamp

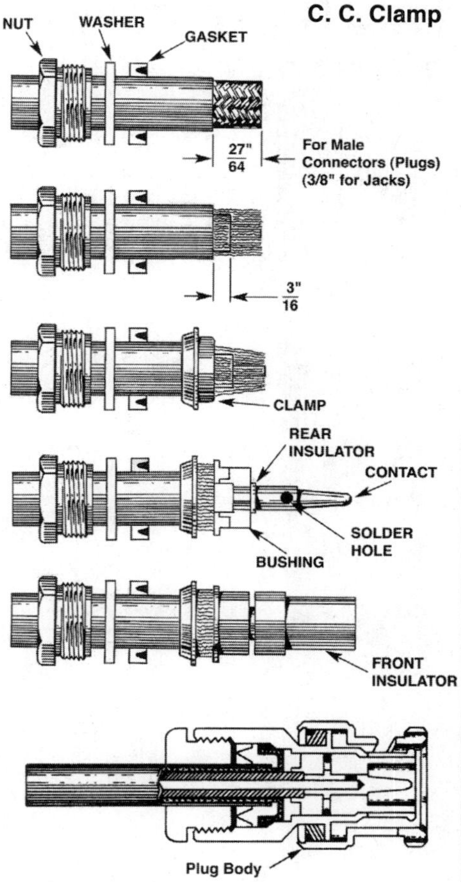

1. Follow steps 1, 2, and 3 as outlined for the standard-clamp BNC connector.

2. Slide on bushing, rear insulator and contact. The parts must butt securely against each other, as shown.

3. Solder the center conductor to the contact. Remove flux and excess solder.

4. Slide the front insulator over the contact, making sure it butts against the contact shoulder.

5. Insert the prepared cable end into the connector body and tighten the nut. Make sure the sharp edge of the clamp seats properly in the gasket.

Figure 23.30 — BNC connectors are common on VHF and UHF equipment at low power levels. ***(Courtesy Amphenol Electronic Components)***

Type N assembly instructions

HBK05_19-19

CLAMP TYPES

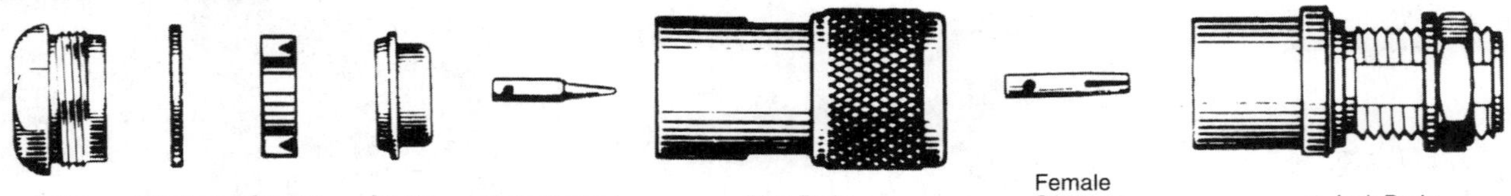

Step 1

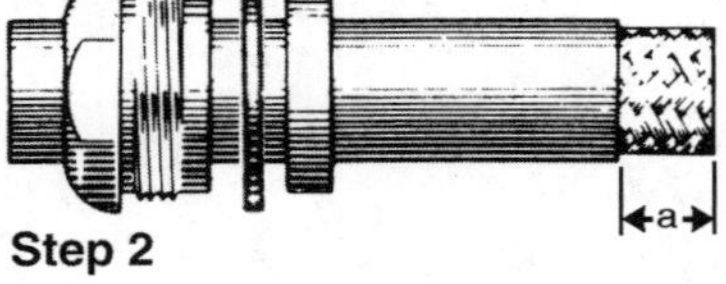

Step 2

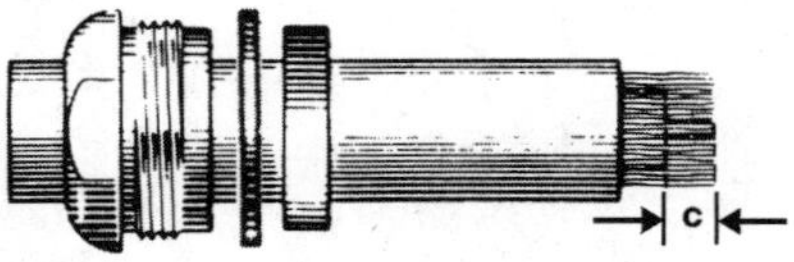

Step 3

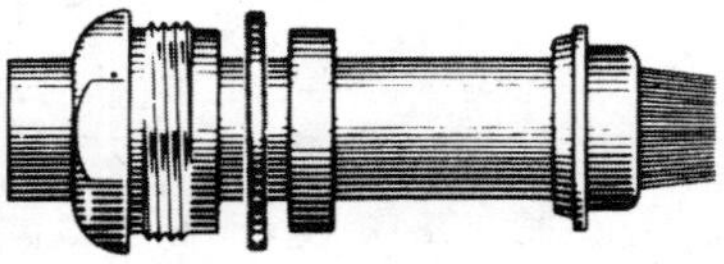

Step 4

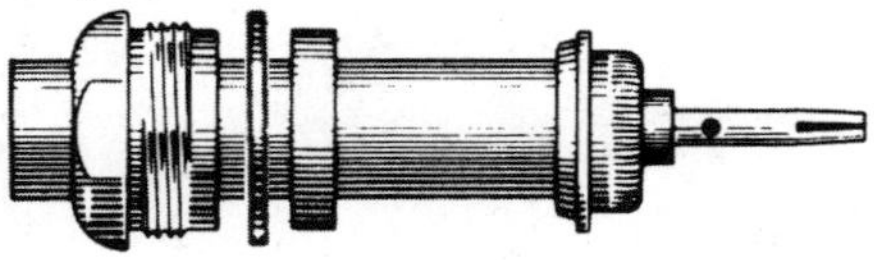

Step 5

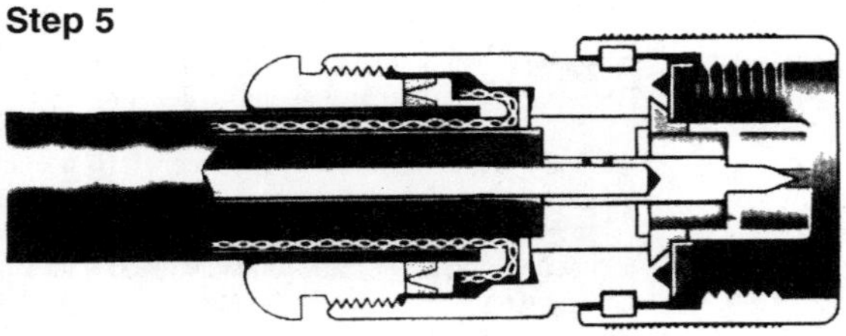

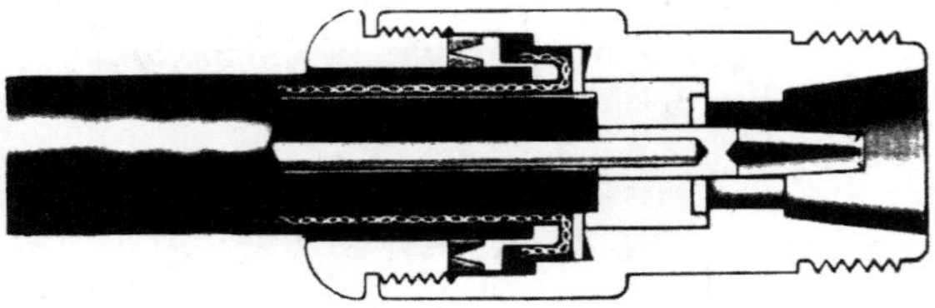

Amphenol Number	Connector Type	Cable RG-/U	Strip Dims., inches (mm)	
			a	c
82-61	N Plug	8, 9, 144, 165, 213, 214, 216, 225	0.359(9.1)	0.234(6.0)
82-62	N Panel Jack	8, 9, 87A, 144, 165, 213, 214, 216, 225	0.312(7.9)	0.187(4.7)
82-63	N Jack		0.281(7.1)	0.156(4.0)
82-67	N Bulkhead Jack			
82-202	N Plug	8, 9, 144, 165, 213, 214, 216, 225	0.359(9.1)	0.234(6.0)
82-202-RFX	N Plug	8, 213, 214	0.315(8.0)	0.177(4.5)
82-202-1006	N Plug	Belden 9913	0.359(9.1)	0.234(6.0)
82-835	N Angle Plug	8, 9, 87A, 144, 165, 213, 214, 216, 225	0.281(7.1)	0.156(4.0)
18750	N Angle Plug	58, 141, 142	0.484(12.3)	0.234(5.9)
34025	N Plug		0.390(9.9)	0.203(5.2)
34525	N Plug	59, 62, 71, 140, 210	0.410(10.4)	0.230(5.8)
35025	N Jack	58, 141, 142	0.375(9.5)	0.187(4.7)
36500	N Jack	59, 62, 71, 140, 210	0.484(12.3)	0.200(5.1)

See www.AmphenolRF.com for assembly instructions for all other connector types. These dimensions only apply to Amphenol connectors and may not be correct for other manufacturers.

Step 1 Place nut, washer, and gasket, with "V" groove toward clamp, over cable and cut off jacket to dimension a.

Step 2 Comb out braid and fold out. Cut off cable dielectric to dim. c as shown.

Step 3 Pull braid wires forward and taper toward center conductor. Place clamp over braid and push back against cable jacket.

Step 4 Fold back braid wires as shown, trim braid to proper length and form over clamp as shown. Solder contact to center conductor.

Step 5 Insert cable and parts into connector body. Make sure sharp edge of clamp seats properly in gasket. Tighten nut.

Figure 23.31 — Type N connectors are required for high-power VHF and UHF operation. ***(Courtesy Amphenol Electronic Components)***

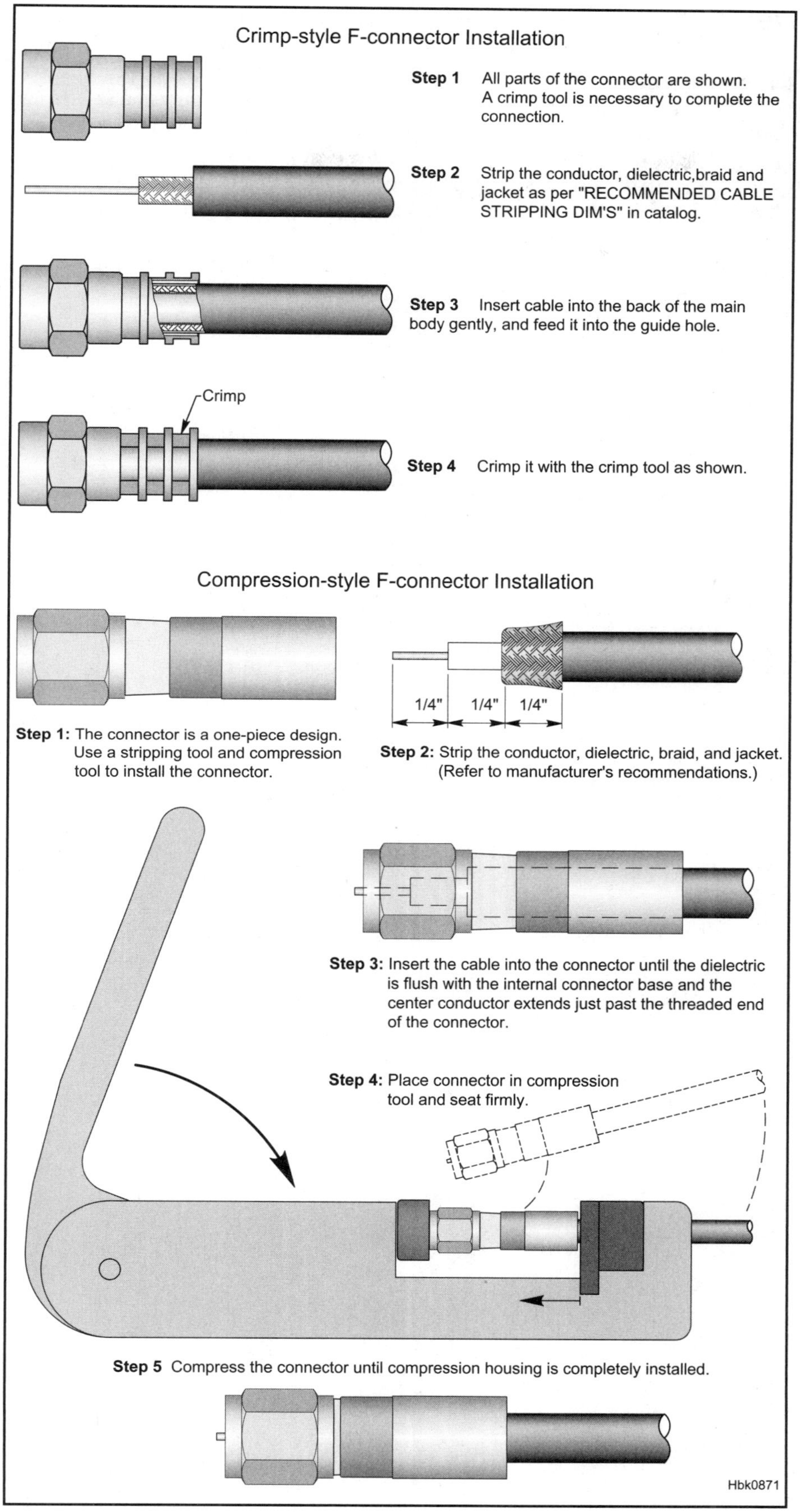

Figure 23.32 — Type F connectors, commonly used for cable TV connections, can be used for receive-only antennas with inexpensive RG-59 and RG-6 cable.

Figure 23.33 — A pair of SMA connectors, with male on the left and female on the right. SMA connectors are available in nickel, stainless steel, or gold finish.

23.4.3 CONNECTOR IDENTIFIER AND RANGE CHART

Table 23.3 provides a list of the military and industry part numbers for the most common RF connectors and adaptors used by amateurs on the MF/HF, VHF, and UHF bands.

Figure 23.34 provides dimensions and side views to help identify the different types of connectors used for RF through microwave frequencies. Dimensions are provided in both imperial and metric units as appropriate. For mm-wave and microwave connectors, calipers or a micrometer may be required to provide an accurate measurement capable of distinguishing between similar connectors. These specifications are intended for connector identification only and should not be the sole dimensions used when laying out a circuit board or drilling a mounting hole. **Figure 23.35** shows the frequency ranges appropriate for popular connector types.

These figures and chart were provided by Pasternack (**www.pasternack.com**), a major distributor of coaxial connectors, cable, tools, and other RF materials and supplies.

Table 23.3
Coaxial Cable Connectors

UHF Connectors

Military No.	*Style*	*Cable RG- or Description*
PL-259	Str (m)	8, 9, 11, 13, 63, 87, 149, 213, 214, 216, 225
UG-111	Str (m)	59, 62, 71, 140, 210
SO-239	Pnl (f)	Std, mica/phenolic insulation
UG-266	Blkhd (f)	Rear mount, pressurized, copolymer of styrene ins.

Adapters

PL-258	Str (f/f)	Polystyrene ins.
UG-224,363	Blkhd (f/f)	Polystyrene ins.
UG-646	Ang (f/m)	Polystyrene ins.
M-359A	Ang (m/f)	Polystyrene ins.
M-358	T (f/m/f)	Polystyrene ins.

Reducers

UG-175		55, 58, 141, 142 (except 55A)
UG-176		59, 62, 71, 140, 210

Family Characteristics:

All are nonweatherproof and have a nonconstant impedance. Frequency range: 0-500 MHz. Maximum voltage rating: 500 V (peak).

N Connectors

Military No.	*Style*	*Cable RG-*	*Notes*
UG-21	Str (m)	8, 9, 213, 214	50 Ω
UG-94A	Str (m)	11, 13, 149, 216	70 Ω
UG-536	Str (m)	58, 141, 142	50 Ω
UG-603	Str (m)	59, 62, 71, 140, 210	50 Ω
UG-23, B-E	Str (f)	8, 9, 87, 213, 214, 225	50 Ω
UG-602	Str (f)	59, 62, 71, 140, 210	—
UG-228B, D, E	Pnl (f)	8, 9, 87, 213, 214, 225	—
UG-1052	Pnl (f)	58, 141, 142	50 Ω
UG-593	Pnl (f)	59, 62, 71, 140, 210	50 Ω
UG-160A, B, D	Blkhd (f)	8, 9, 87, 213, 214, 225	50 Ω
UG-556	Blkhd (f)	58, 141, 142	50 Ω
UG-58, A	Pnl (f)		50 Ω
UG-997A	Ang (f)		50 Ω

Panel mount (f) with clearance above panel

M39012/04-	Blkhd (f)	Front mount hermetically sealed
UG-680	Blkhd (f)	Front mount pressurized

N Adapters

Military No.	*Style*	*Notes*
UG-29,A,B	Str (f/f)	50 Ω, TFE ins.
UG-57A.B	Str (m/m)	50 Ω, TFE ins.
UG-27A,B	Ang (f/m)	Mitre body
UG-212A	Ang (f/m)	Mitre body
UG-107A	T (f/m/f)	—
UG-28A	T (f/f/f)	—
UG-107B	T (f/m/f)	—

Family Characteristics:

N connectors with gaskets are weatherproof. RF leakage: –90 dB min @ 3 GHz. Temperature limits: TFE: –67° to 390°F (–55° to 199°C). Insertion loss 0.15 dB max @ 10 GHz. Copolymer of styrene: –67° to 185°F (–55° to 85°C). Frequency range: 0-11 GHz. Maximum voltage rating: 1500 V P-P. Dielectric withstanding voltage 2500 V RMS. SWR (MIL-C-39012 cable connectors) 1.3 max 0-11 GHz.

BNC Connectors

Military No.	*Style*	*Cable RG-*	*Notes*
UG-88C	Str (m)	55, 58, 141, 142, 223, 400	

Military No.	*Style*	*Cable RG-*	*Notes*
UG-959	Str (m)	8, 9	
UG-260,A	Str (m)	59, 62, 71, 140, 210	Rexolite ins.
UG-262	Pnl (f)	59, 62, 71, 140, 210	Rexolite ins.
UG-262A	Pnl (f)	59, 62, 71, 140, 210	nwx, Rexolite ins.
UG-291	Pnl (f)	55, 58, 141, 142, 223, 400	
UG-291A	Pnl (f)	55, 58, 141, 142, 223, 400	nwx
UG-624	Blkhd (f)	59, 62, 71, 140, 210	Front mount Rexolite ins.
UG-1094A	Blkhd		Standard
UG-625B	Receptacle		
UG-625			

BNC Adapters

Military No.	*Style*	*Notes*
UG-491,A	Str (m/m)	
UG-491B	Str (m/m)	Berylium, outer contact
UG-914	Str (f/f)	
UG-306	Ang (f/m)	
UG-306A,B	Ang (f/m)	Berylium outer contact
UG-414,A	Pnl (f/f)	# 3-56 tapped flange holes
UG-306	Ang (f/m)	
UG-306A,B	Ang (f/m)	Berylium outer contact
UG-274	T (f/m/f)	
UG-274A,B	T (f/m/f)	Berylium outer contact

Family Characteristics:

Z = 50 Ω. Frequency range: 0-4 GHz w/low reflection; usable to 11 GHz. Voltage rating: 500 V P-P. Dielectric withstanding voltage 500 V RMS. SWR: 1.3 max 0-4 GHz. RF leakage –55 dB min @ 3 GHz. Insertion loss: 0.2 dB max @ 3 GHz. Temperature limits: TFE: –67° to 390°F (–55° to 199°C); Rexolite insulators: –67° to 185°F (–55° to 85°C). "Nwx" = not weatherproof.

HN Connectors

Military No.	*Style*	*Cable RG-*	*Notes*
UG-59A	Str (m)	8, 9, 213, 214	
UG-1214	Str (f)	8, 9, 87, 213, 214, 225	Captivated contact
UG-60A	Str (f)	8, 9, 213, 214	Copolymer of styrene ins.
UG-1215	Pnl (f)	8, 9, 87, 213, 214, 225	Captivated contact
UG-560	Pnl (f)		
UG-496	Pnl (f)		
UG-212C	Ang (f/m)		Berylium outer contact

Family Characteristics:

Connector Styles: Str = straight; Pnl = panel; Ang = Angle; Blkhd = bulkhead. Z = 50 Ω. Frequency range = 0-4 GHz. Maximum voltage rating = 1500 V P-P. Dielectric withstanding voltage = 5000 V RMS SWR = 1.3. All HN series are weatherproof. Temperature limits: TFE: –67° to 390°F (–55° to 199°C); copolymer of styrene: –67° to 185°F (–55° to 85°C).

Cross-Family Adapters

Families	*Description*	*Military No.*
HN to BNC	HN-m/BNC-f	UG-309
N to BNC	N-m/BNC-f	UG-201,A
	N-f/BNC-m	UG-349,A
	N-m/BNC-m	UG-1034
N to UHF	N-m/UHF-f	UG-146
	N-f/UHF-m	UG-83,B
	N-m/UHF-m	UG-318
UHF to BNC	UHF-m/BNC-f	UG-273
	UHF-f/BNC-m	UG-255

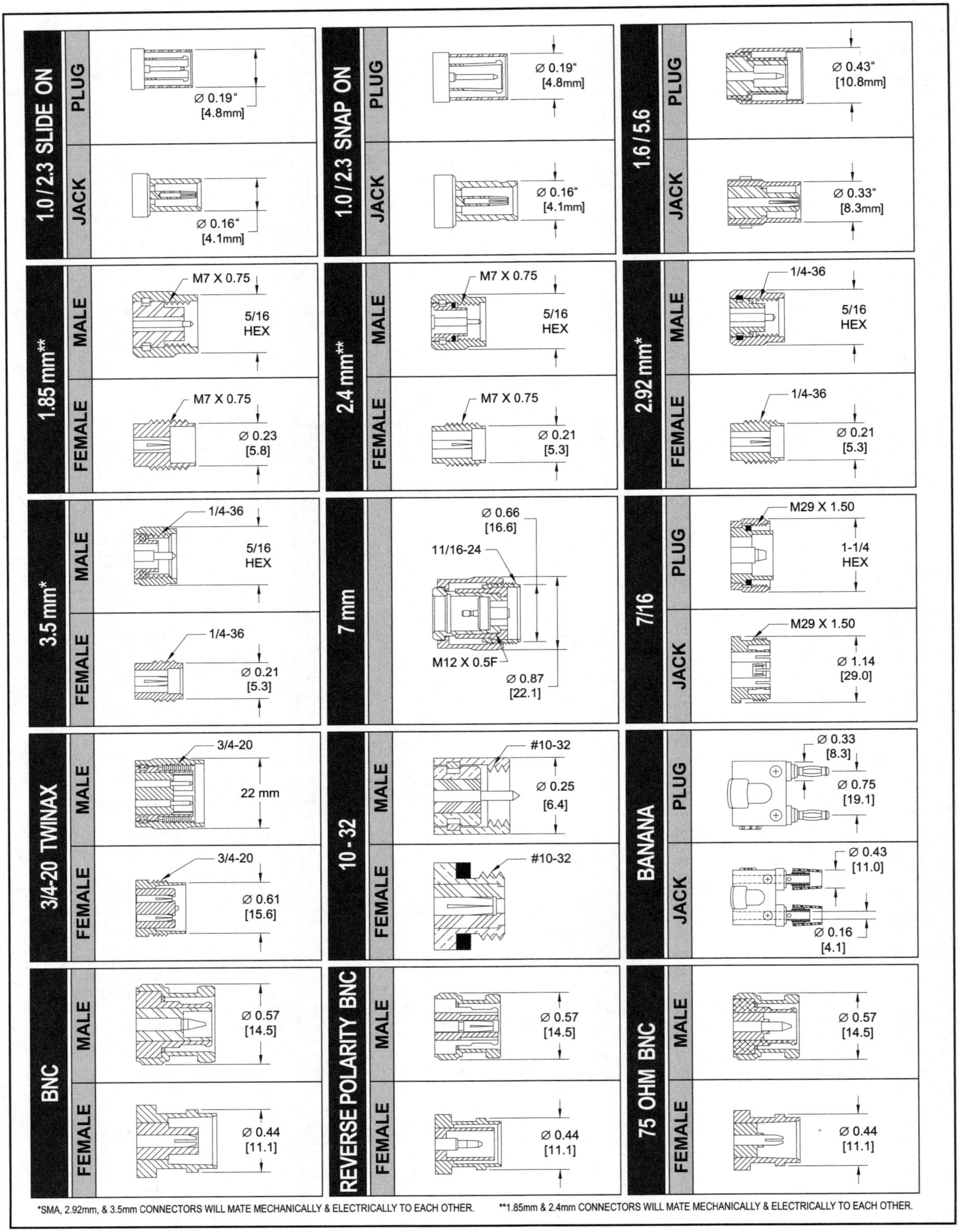

Figure 23.34A – Connector side views, set 1 of 4. (Courtesy of Pasternak)

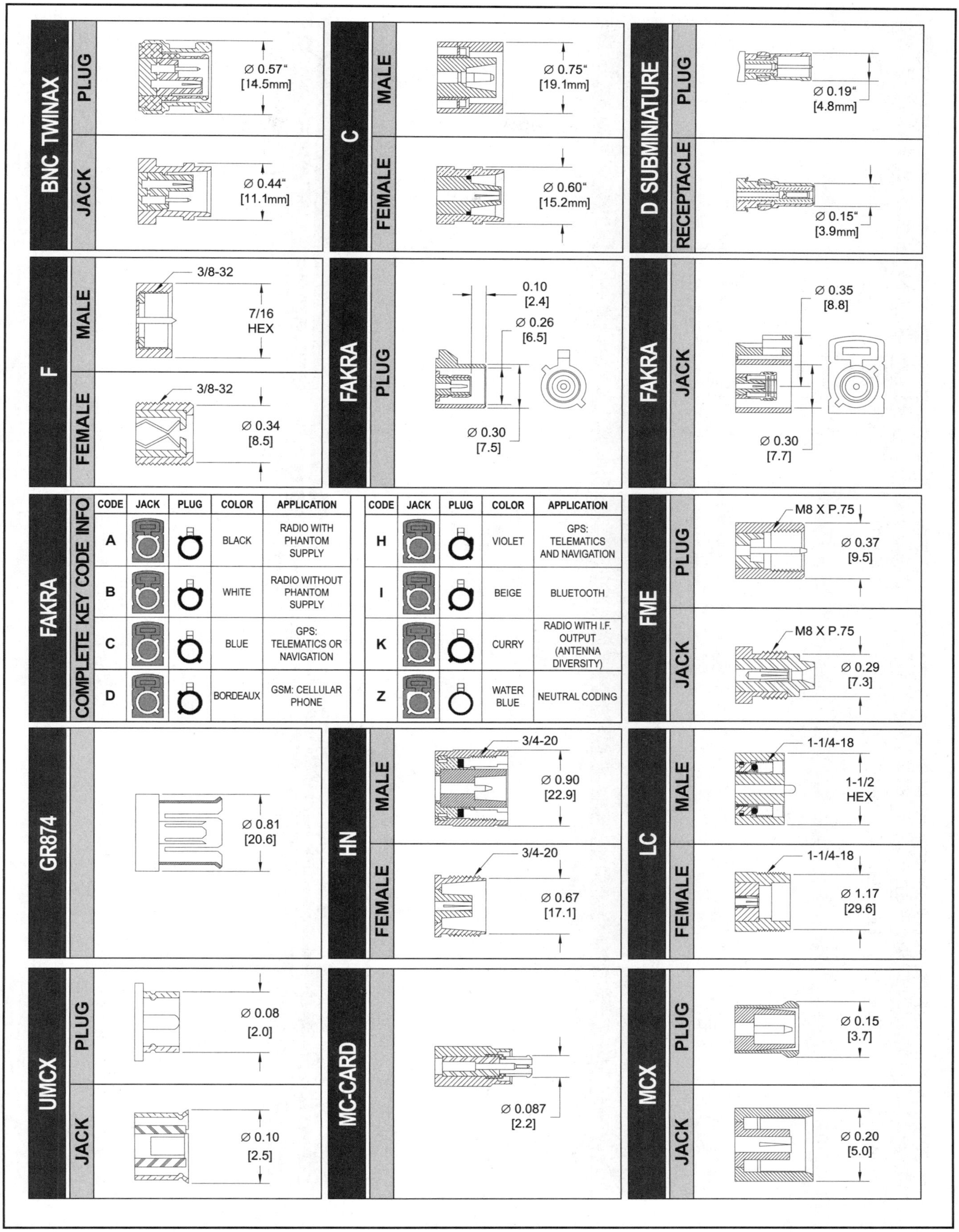

Figure 23.34B – Connector side views, set 2 of 4. (Courtesy of Pasternak)

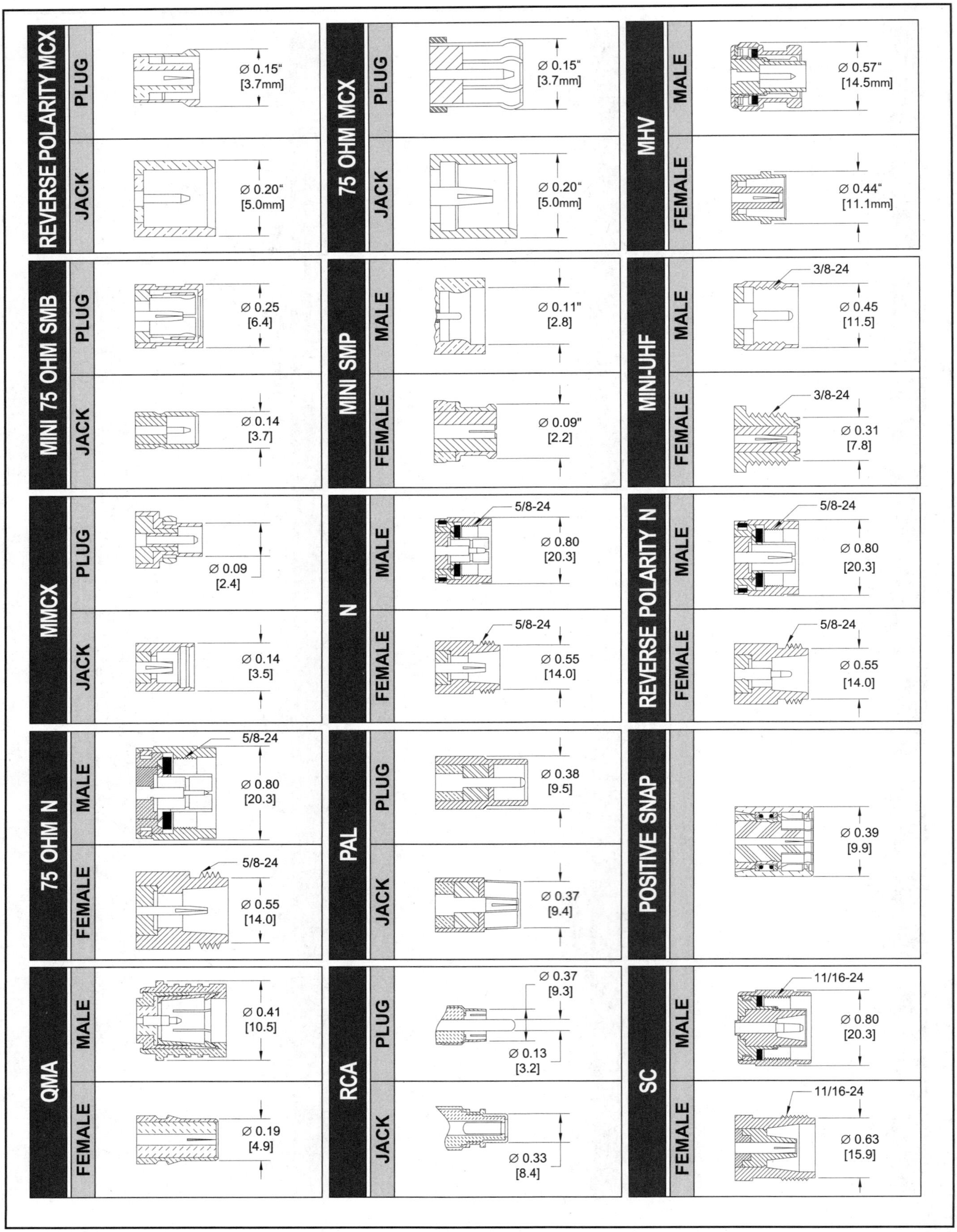

Figure 23.34C – Connector side views, set 3 of 4. (Courtesy of Pasternak)

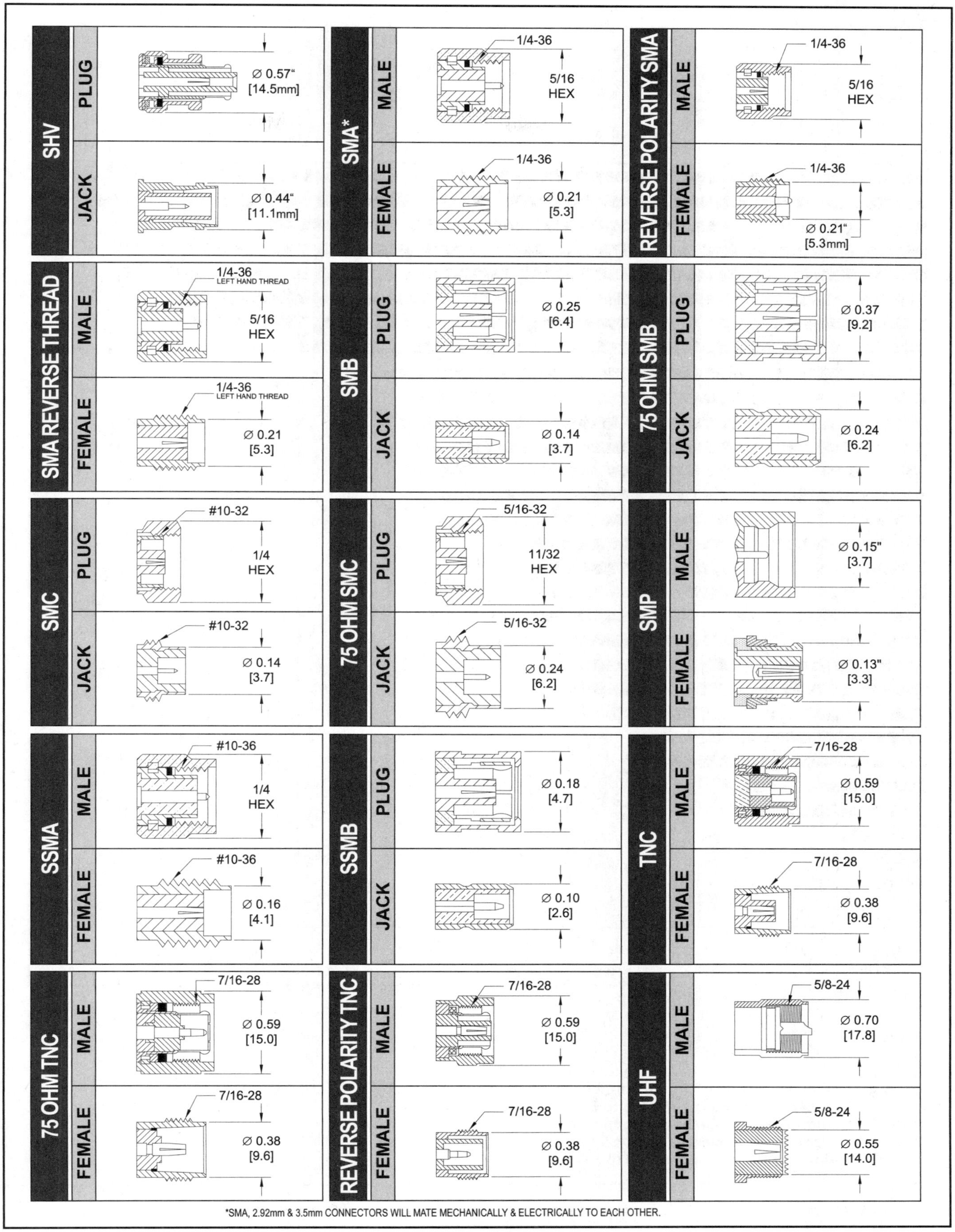

Figure 23.34D – Connector side views, set 4 of 4. (Courtesy of Pasternak)

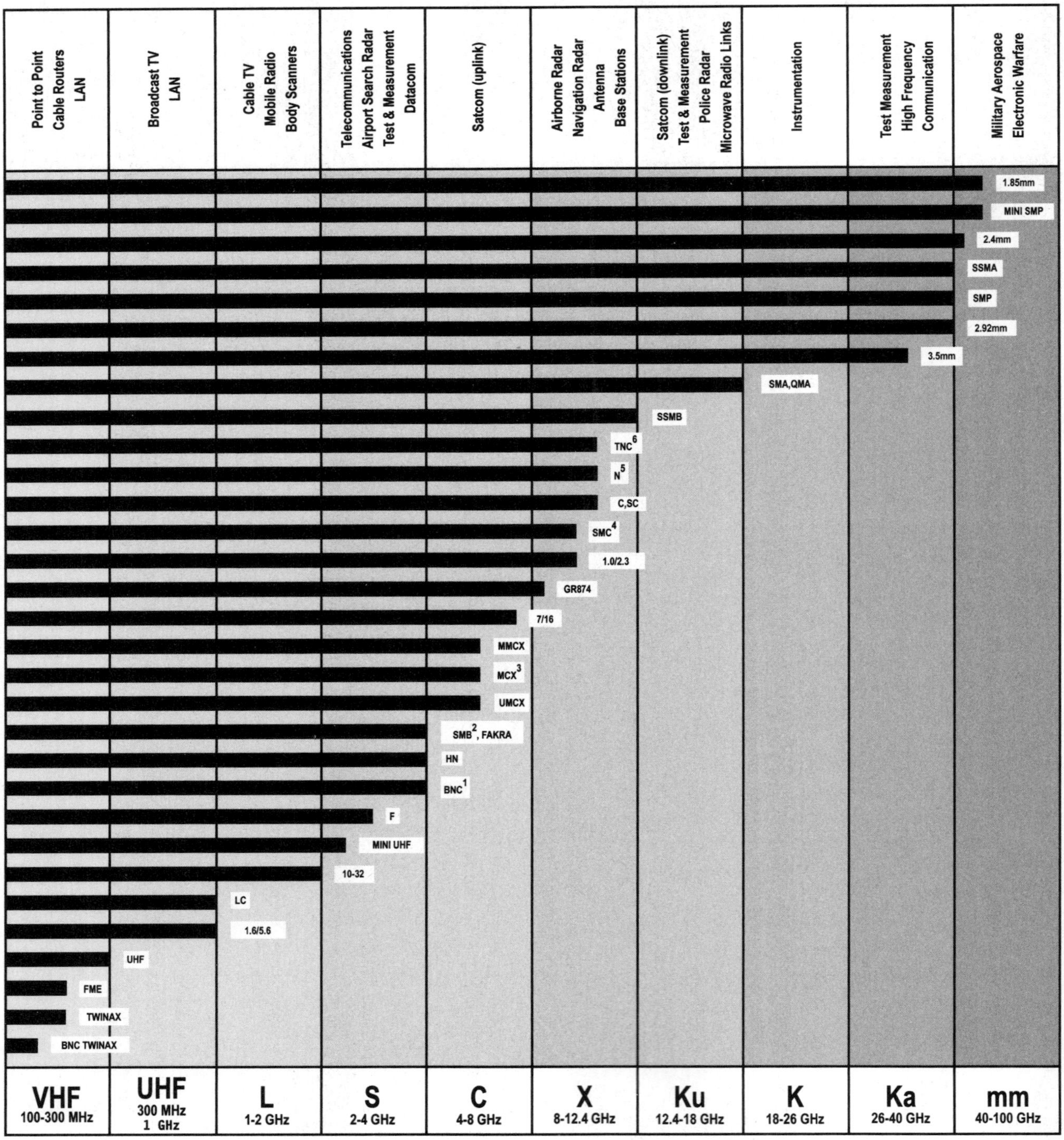

Notes:

1: BNC-75 Ohm connectors operate up to 1 GHz
2: SMB-75 Ohm & Mini SMB-75 Ohm connectors operate up to 4 GHz
3: MCX-75 Ohm connectors operate up to 6 GHz
4: SMC-75 Ohm connectors operate up to 10 GHz
5: N-75 Ohm connectors operate up to 1.5 GHz
6: TNC-75 Ohm connectors operate up to 1 GHz

Figure 23.35 – Recommended frequency ranges by connector type. (Courtesy of Pasternak)

23.5 CHOOSING AND INSTALLING FEED LINES

23.5.1 COMPARING FEED LINES

Begin by studying the section on Transmission Line System Design in the chapter **Transmission Line System Techniques**. It is important to understand the requirements for your feed line before making a purchase. By approaching your antenna and feed line as a whole, you may be able to improve performance and save money at the same time. At the least, you will have a better appreciation for the different parts of your antenna system.

The usual two primary considerations for choosing a feed line are loss at the frequency of use and cost. Starting with the impedance of the load attached to the feed line (usually an antenna feed point) determine the matched loss for types of feed line you are considering. **Table 23.4** and **Table 23.5**, published by Frank Donovan, W3LPL in 2008 give typical losses for various types of coaxial cable at frequencies in the amateur bands by using a calculator by VK1OD. (Most manufacturers specify losses at 1, 10, 100 and 1000 MHz.) Table 23.5 specifies the length of line that will exhibit a loss of 1 dB.

To use Table 23.4, multiply the loss figure by the length of your feed line divided by 100 feet. For example, to find the loss of a 250-foot run of RG-213 at 28.4 MHz, multiply the table loss (1.2 dB) by 250/100 = 1.2 × 2.5 = 3.0 dB. Now use Equation 16 or one of the charts in Figure 23.15 to determine the total loss of the line at that frequency and SWR. If one of the cables is acceptable to you in performance and affordability, your job is done.

If you are operating with full power, you must also consider the peak voltage and power handling capability of the line. There may be other considerations in special circumstances. For example, operators who carry QRP equipment may elect to use RG-174 coax, even though it has high losses, because of its low weight.

Table 23.4
Cable Attenuation (dB per 100 feet)

MHz	*1.8*	*3.6*	*7.1*	*14.2*	*21.2*	*28.4*	*50.1*	*144*	*440*	*1296*
LDF7-50A	0.03	0.04	0.06	0.08	0.10	0.12	0.16	0.27	0.5	0.9
FHJ-7	0.03	0.05	0.07	0.10	0.12	0.15	0.20	0.37	0.8	1.7
LDF5-50A	0.04	0.06	0.09	0.14	0.17	0.19	0.26	0.45	0.8	1.5
FXA78-50J	0.06	0.08	0.13	0.17	0.23	0.27	0.39	0.77	1.4	2.8
3/4" CATV	0.06	0.08	0.13	0.17	0.23	0.26	0.38	0.62	1.7	3.0
LDF4-50A	0.09	0.13	0.17	0.25	0.31	0.36	0.48	0.84	1.4	2.5
RG-17	0.10	0.13	0.18	0.27	0.34	0.40	0.50	1.3	2.5	5.0
LMR-600	0.10	0.15	0.20	0.29	0.35	0.41	0.55	0.94	1.7	3.1
SLA12-50J	0.11	0.15	0.20	0.28	0.35	0.42	0.56	1.0	1.9	3.0
FXA12-50J	0.12	0.16	0.22	0.33	0.40	0.47	0.65	1.2	2.1	4.0
FXA38-50J	0.16	0.23	0.31	0.45	0.53	0.64	0.85	1.5	2.7	4.9
9913	0.16	0.23	0.31	0.45	0.53	0.64	0.92	1.6	2.7	5.0
LMR-400	0.16	0.23	0.32	0.46	0.56	0.65	0.87	1.5	2.7	4.7
RG-213	0.25	0.37	0.55	0.75	1.0	1.2	1.6	2.8	5.1	10.0
RG-8X	0.49	0.68	1.0	1.4	1.7	1.9	2.5	4.5	8.4	13.2
RG-58	0.56	0.82	1.2	1.7	2.0	2.4	3.2	5.6	10.5	20.0
RG-174	1.1	1.5	2.1	3.1	3.8	4.4	5.9	10.2	18.7	34.8

Table 23.5
Cable Attenuation (feet per dB)

MHz	*1.8*	*3.6*	*7.1*	*14.2*	*21.2*	*28.4*	*50.1*	*144*	*440*	*1296*
LDF7-50A	3333	2500	1666	1250	1000	833	625	370	200	110
FHJ-7	2775	2080	1390	1040	833	667	520	310	165	92
LDF5-50A	2108	1490	1064	750	611	526	393	227	125	69
FXA78-50J	1666	1250	769	588	435	370	256	130	71	36
3/4" CATV	1666	1250	769	588	435	385	275	161	59	33
LDF4-50A	1145	809	579	409	333	287	215	125	70	39
RG-17	1000	769	556	370	294	250	200	77	40	20
LMR-600	973	688	492	347	283	244	182	106	59	33
SLA12-50J	909	667	500	355	285	235	175	100	53	34
FXA12-50J	834	625	455	300	250	210	150	83	48	25
FXA38-50J	625	435	320	220	190	155	115	67	37	20
9913	625	435	320	220	190	155	110	62	37	20
LMR-400	613	436	310	219	179	154	115	67	38	21
RG-213	397	279	197	137	111	95	69	38	19	9
RG-8X	257	181	128	90	74	63	47	27	14	8
RG-58	179	122	83	59	50	42	30	18	9	5
RG-174	91	67	48	32	26	23	17	10	5	3

Table 23.6
Advantage from Upgrading Feed Line

Feet Required For 1 dB Advantage If Replaced By LDF5-50A (7/8-inch Heliax)

MHz	*1.8*	*3.6*	*7.1*	*14.2*	*21.2*	*28.4*	*50.1*	*144*	*440*	*1296*
LDF4-50A	2500	1430	1250	910	715	625	475	279	158	90
RG-17	1666	1430	1110	770	560	475	420	120	60	30
FXA12-50J	1250	1000	770	525	435	355	255	120	75	40
9913	935	590	455	320	280	220	150	85	53	29

Feet Required For 1 dB Advantage If Replaced By LDF4-50A (1/2-inch Heliax)

MHz	*1.8*	*3.6*	*7.1*	*14.2*	*21.2*	*28.4*	*50.1*	*144*	*440*	*1296*
RG-17	-	-	-	-	-	-	-	220	90	40
FXA12-50J	-	-	2000	1250	1100	835	625	250	145	65
9913	1430	1000	715	500	455	345	235	135	75	40
RG-213	618	434	306	212	171	146	106	58	29	14

For situations in which SWR is very high (such as for a nonresonant doublet used on multiple bands) or a very long run of feed line is required, open-wire line may be the best solution. Be sure to include the cost of impedance transformers in your system budget to connect the higher-impedance open-wire line to 50-Ω equipment and antennas.

If you are considering replacing a long run of cable with hardline or Heliax, **Table 23.6** should be helpful. This is a common situation for stations with antennas far from the transceiver and for VHF/UHF stations of any size. The cable lengths in the table are the lengths for which replacing them with Heliax would yield a 1-dB benefit. For example, replacing a 146-foot run of RG-213 with ½-inch Heliax would yield a 1 dB benefit on 10 meters. Similarly, an 85-foot run of Belden 9913 used on 2 meters could be replaced by ⅞-inch Heliax for a 1 dB benefit. The longer the cable run, the greater the benefit of replacing them with the lower loss of Heliax. (LDF4-50A and LDF5-50A are available at reasonable prices on auction websites, ham websites such as **www.eham.net** or **www.qrz.com**, and at hamfests.)

23.5.2 INSTALLING COAXIAL CABLE

One great advantage of flexible coaxial line is that it can be installed with almost no regard for its surroundings. It requires no insulation, can be run on or in the ground or in piping, can be bent around corners with a reasonable radius, and can be snaked through places such as the space between walls where it would be impractical to use other types of lines. In addition, coaxial lines are unaffected by proximity to other conductors and can be run inside metal conduit or attached to metal structures.

Coax must still be treated with care as described in the following paragraphs, especially when being pulled through a conduit. Cable grips should be used to spread the gripping force over a large area of the cable's surface and the amount of force should be limited to prevent distorting the cable's cross section.

Jacket Protection

When installing coaxial cable, it is important to protect the cable jacket to prevent water from entering the cable at any point. First, handle the cable with care during storage and installation so that the jacket is not damaged. If damage to the

Coaxial Feed Line Loss Calculators

Should you need exact loss calculations for a specific feed line, the loss may be found by using ARRL's TLW software available from this book's downloadable supplemental information. A good online feed line loss calculator is provided by Times-Microwave at **www.timesmicrowave.com/calculator**. Another free calculator has been created by Dan McGuire, AC6LA, at **www.ac6la.com/tldetails1.html**.

Using Coax Braid

It is common to loosen and strip the shield braid from old coax and reuse it as a ground strap. Unfortunately, cable braid is not a very good RF conductor without its jacket! What makes braid work well in coaxial cable is the continuous pressure of the jacket that compresses the braid, keeps all of the strands in good contact, and protects it from water. This allows the braid to act as a continuous conducting surface.

When braid is removed from the cable, the jacket is no longer present to protect and compress the strands. This allows them to move away from each other and for the strand surfaces to corrode, greatly reducing the effectiveness of the braid at RF. This is why the commercial and military standard for this type of connection is solid copper strap or heavy solid copper wire.

Used coax braid may be used for dc and low-frequency connections as long as it is protected from the weather but for a reliable RF connection use copper strap or heavy wire. Flat-weave tinned braid designed for unprotected use may be used as an RF conductor but never where it is exposed to water.

Coaxial cable inner conductor and center insulation can be used as a high-voltage wire to the rating of the coaxial cable as long as the insulation is not cracked or compromised in some other way.

jacket is noticed immediately and no water is allowed to enter the cable, limited amounts of damage can be repaired using the same technique for waterproofing splices made with RF connectors as described in the **Building Antenna Systems and Towers** chapter.

Secure the cable after it has been connected to the antenna so that the jacket is not abraded or chafed by motion due to wind or antenna rotation. Cables hanging vertically should be supported in such a way that any bending is gradual and with a radius comfortably above the minimum bending radius. Cable grips are available that clamp over a short length, spreading the pressure and avoiding damage to the jacket. If wire or plastic cable ties are used, do not over-tighten them so that the jacket is crimped.

An important part of jacket protection is the waterproofing of RF connectors. Exposed coaxial cable braid will act as a wick, drawing in moisture. To a lesser extent, cables with stranded center conductors or partially hollow center insulation will draw in moisture as well. Coaxial cable infiltrated by water or moisture, either in the braid or center conductor, rapidly becomes unusable due to loss. Coax with a discolored or tarnished shield is not repairable and should be discarded.

Burying Coax

There are several reasons why you might choose to bury coaxial cable feed lines. One is that buried cable is virtually free from storm and UV damage, and usually has lower maintenance costs than cable that is exposed to the weather. Another reason might be that underground cable interacts less with the radiation pattern of antennas, picks up less noise, and carries less common-mode RF on the outside of the shield. A buried cable will be aesthetically acceptable in almost all communities, as well.

Although any cable can be buried, a cable that is specifically designed for burial will have a longer life. *Direct-burial* cable has a high-density polyethylene jacket because it is both nonporous and will withstand a relatively high amount of compressive loads. In impregnated direct burial cables, an additional moisture barrier of polyethylene grease may be applied under the jacket; this allows the material to leak out, thus "healing" small jacket penetrations. These are referred to as "flooded" cables and the grease can make installing connectors more difficult. Neither RG-8/U or RG-213/U are automatically rated for direct burial — the cable vendor must specify the direct burial rating. The cable jacket is usually stamped with "Direct Burial" or the equivalent.

Here are some direct burial tips:

1) Because the outer jacket is the cable's first line of defense, any steps which can be taken to prevent damage to it will go a long way toward maintaining cable quality.

2) Bury the cable in sand or finely pulverized soil, free of sharp stones, cinders or rubble. If the soil in the trench does not meet these requirements, tamp four to six inches of sand into the trench and lay the cable. Tamp in another six to eleven inches of sand above the cable. Place a creosoted or pressure-treated board in the trench above the sand prior to the final filling of the trench. This will provide some protection against damage that could be caused by digging or driving stakes.

3) When laying buried cable, leave some slack in the cable. A tightly stretched cable is more likely to be damaged as it is being covered with fill material.

4) Examine the cable as it is being installed to be sure the jacket has not been damaged during storage or by being dragged over sharp edges.

5) It is important that burial is below the frost line to avoid damage by the expansion and contraction of the soil and water during freezing and thawing cycles.

Using Conduit

You may want to consider burying the coax in plastic pipe or electrical conduit. While plastic pipe provides a mechanical barrier, water incursion is practically guaranteed — water will either leak in directly or will condense from moisture in the air. Be careful to drill holes in the bottom of solid conduit at all low spots so that any moisture can drain out or use the perforated pipe that allows the water to drain out into the surrounding ground.

Whether the conduit is above or below ground, use large-radius sweeps to create bends instead of elbows. It is much easier to pull cable through the gradual bend of a sweep and pulling cables through too sharp a bend can damage it. Metal conduit and fittings frequently have sharp edges and burrs that will cut or even strip the jacket from coax being pulled over them. Before assembling each section, file off sharp or rough edges.

When choosing the size of the conduit, leave plenty of extra space — at least double the expected total diameter of your cable bundle. A 3 to 4 inch-diameter pipe is recommended. This greatly eases the pulling process and gives the cables plenty of room to move around connectors and joints in the conduit. Be sure to include a "fish rope" or "fish wire" with the final cable you pull so you can add or replace cables later.

If you also have rotator or other control cables, there may be local building codes that limit the number and type of cables that can share the same conduit.

23.5.3 INSTALLING PARALLEL-CONDUCTOR LINE

Open-Wire Line

In installing an open-wire line, care must be used to prevent it from being affected by moisture, snow and ice. If the line is home-made, only spacers that are impervious to moisture and are unaffected by sunlight and weather should be used on air-insulated lines. Ceramic spacers meet this requirement although they are somewhat heavy. The wider the line spacing, the longer the leakage path across the spacers, but this cannot be carried too far without running into line radiation, particularly at the higher frequencies. Six inches should be considered a maximum practical spacing for HF use.

The line should be kept away from other conductors, including downspouts, metal window frames, flashing, etc, by a distance of two or three times the line spacing. Conductors that are very close to the line will be coupled to it to some degree, and the effect is that of placing an additional load across the line at the point where the coupling occurs. Reflections take place from this coupled load, raising the SWR. The effect is at its worst when one wire is closer than the other to the external conductor. In such a case one wire carries a heavier load than the other, with the result that the line currents are no longer equal. The line then becomes unbalanced.

Twin-lead and Window Lines

Solid dielectric, two-wire lines have a relatively small external field because of the small spacing, and can be mounted within a few inches of other conductors without much danger of coupling between the line and such conductors. Standoff insulators are available for supporting lines of this type when run along walls or similar structures.

As with open-wire lines, avoid installing the line in such a way that snow, ice, or liquid water can build up on the line. This presents an additional dielectric to the conductors and can change the line impedance or create loss.

Mechanical Issues

Where a parallel-wire line must be anchored to a building or other structure, standoff insulators of a height comparable with the line spacing should be used if mounted in a spot that is open to the weather. Electric fence insulators are an excellent source of standoffs for this type of feed line. They are available from farm supply dealers and are fairly inexpensive.

Lead-in bushings for bringing the line into a building also should have a long leakage path. You may want to install a feed line feedthrough panel designed to fit in a window frame. Ceramic feed-through insulators can be used and are available as replacement parts from the panel vendors.

When running any kind of parallel-wire line down the side of a tower or other conducting surface, balance can be preserved by twisting the line every few feet. This results in approximately equal coupling by each conductor. Twisting the line also reduces the tendency of the line to move in the wind.

Parallel-line also has more wind resistance than coaxial cable and tends to move quite a bit more. The continual flexing can cause the conductors to break at soldered or otherwise fixed joints. This is a particular problem for lines with solid conductors as is common with window line. Support the line where it is attached to an antenna with insulators designed to provide stress relief to parallel-wire lines. (See the **Antenna Materials and Construction** chapter.)

Sharp bends should be avoided in any type of parallel-wire line, because it causes a change in the characteristic impedance at that point. The result is that reflections take place from each bend. This is of less importance when the SWR is high than when an attempt is being made to match the load to the line Z_0. It may be impossible to get the SWR to the desired figure until bends in the line are made very gradual.

23.5.4 TESTING TRANSMISSION LINES

Coaxial cable loss should be checked at least every two years if the cable is installed outdoors or buried. (See earlier sections on losses and deterioration.) Testing of any type of line can be done using the technique illustrated in **Figure 23.36**. If the measured loss in watts equates to more than 1 dB over the rated matched-line loss per 100 feet, the line should be replaced. The matched-line loss in dB can be determined from

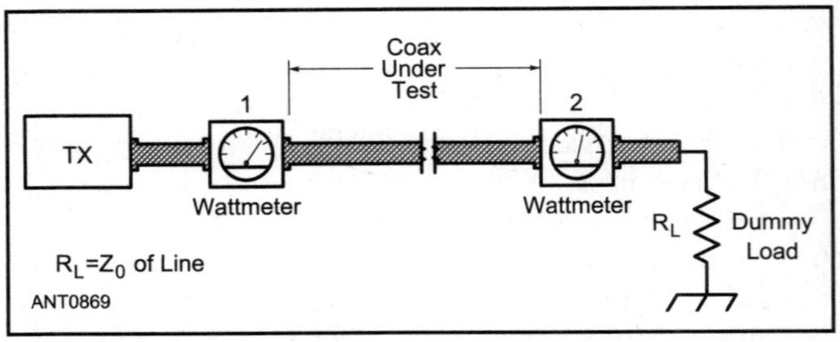

Figure 23.36 — Method for determining losses in transmission lines. The impedance of the dummy load must equal the Z_0 of the line for accurate results.

$$dB = 10 \log \frac{P_1}{P_2} \tag{33}$$

where

P_1 is the power at the transmitter output

P_2 is the power measured at R_L of Figure 23.36.

Yet other methods of determining line losses may be used. If the line input impedances can be measured accurately with a short- and then an open-circuit termination, the electrical line length (determined by velocity factor) and the matched-line loss may be calculated for the frequency of measurement.

Determining line characteristics as just mentioned requires the use of a laboratory style of impedance bridge, or at least an impedance or noise bridge calibrated to a high degree of accuracy. But useful information about a transmission line can also be learned with just an SWR indicator, if it offers reliable readings at high SWR values.

A lossless line theoretically exhibits an infinite SWR when terminated in an open or a short circuit. A practical line will have losses, and therefore will limit the SWR at the line input to some finite value. Provided the signal source can operate safely into a severe mismatch, an SWR indicator can be used to determine the line loss. The instruments available to most amateurs lose accuracy at SWR values greater than about 5:1, so this method is useful principally as a go/no-go check on lines that are fairly long. For short, low-loss cables, only significant deterioration can be detected by the open-circuit SWR test.

First, either open or short circuit one end of the line. It makes no difference which termination is used, as the terminating SWR is theoretically infinite in either case. Then measure the SWR at the other end of the line. The matched-line loss for the frequency of measurement may then be determined from

$$ML = 10 \log \left(\frac{SWR + 1}{SWR - 1} \right) \tag{34}$$

where SWR = the SWR value measured at the line input.

23.6 BIBLIOGRAPHY

Source material and more extended discussion of topics covered in this chapter can be found in the references given below and in the textbooks listed at the end of Chapter 2.

A. Barter, *International Microwave Handbook*, 2nd edition, RSGB, 2008.

C. Brainard and K. Smith, "Coaxial Cable — The Neglected Link," *QST*, Apr 1981, pp 28-31.

J. Brown, "A Ham's Guide to RFI, Ferrites, Baluns, and Audio Interfacing," Jan 2019, Audio Systems Group (**www.audiosystemsgroup.com**).

J. Brown, "Transmission Lines at Audio Frequencies, and a Bit of History," Audio Systems Group (**www.audiosystemsgroup.com**).

J. Brown and B. Whitlock, "Common-Mode to Differential-Mode Conversion in Shielded Twisted-Pair Cables (Shield-Current-Induced Noise), AES Preprint 5747," Audio Systems Group (**www.audiosystemsgroup.com**).

D. DeMaw, "In-Line RF Power Metering," *QST*, Dec 1969, pp 11-16.

A. Ferreira, Jr., W. Pereira, J. Ribeiro, "Determine Twisted-Line Characteristic Impedance," *Microwaves & RF*, Jan 2008, **mwrf.com/test-and-measurement/determine-twisted-line-characteristic-impedance**.

D. Geiser, "Resistive Impedance Matching with Quarter-Wave Lines," *QST*, Feb 1963, pp 56-57.

R. C. Johnson and H. Jasik, *Antenna Engineering Handbook*, 2nd ed. (New York: McGraw-Hill, 1984), pp 43-27 to 43-31.

E. Jordan, Ed., *Reference Data for Engineers: Radio, Electronics, Computer, and Communications*, 7th Edition (Howard W. Sams, 1985).

R. W. P. King, H. R. Mimno and A. H. Wing, *Transmission Lines, Antennas and Waveguides* (New York: Dover Publications, Inc., 1965).

J. D. Kraus, *Antennas* (New York: McGraw-Hill Book Co., 1950).

Kurokawa, "Power Waves and the Scattering Matrix," *IEEE Transactions on Microwave Theory and Techniques*, Vol MTT-13, Mar 1965, pp 194-202.

Z. Lau, "RF: Mounting RF Connectors," *QEX*, Nov 1996, pp 21-22.

M. W. Maxwell, "Another Look at Reflections (Parts 1-7)," *QST*, Apr 1973, pp 35-41; Jun 1973, pp 20-23, 27; Aug 1973, pp 36-43; Oct 1973, pp 22-29; Apr 1974, pp 26-29, 160-165; Dec 1974, pp 11-14, 158-166; Aug 1976, pp 15-20.

M. W. Maxwell, *Reflections III* (New York: CQ Communications, 2010; available on CD from **store.cq-amateur-radio.com/shop/**).

T. McMullen, "The Line Sampler, an RF Power Monitor for VHF and UHF," *QST*, Apr 1972, pp 21-25.

D. Papas, "Installing Coax Crimp Connectors," *QST*, Feb 2019, pp 44-46.

J. Reisert, "RF Connectors, Part I and Part II," *Ham Radio*, Sep 1986, pp 77-80, and Oct 1986, pp 59-64.

H. H. Skilling, *Electric Transmission Lines* (New York: McGraw-Hill Book Co, Inc, 1951).

W. Silver, "Hands-On Radio: Experiment 94 — SWR and Transmission Line Loss," *QST*, Nov 2010, pp 63-64.

W. Silver, "Hands-On Radio: Experiment 96 — Open Wire Transmission Lines," *QST*, Jan 2011, pp 59-60.

W. Silver, "Hands-On Radio: Experiment 137 — Choosing a Feed Line," *QST*, Jun 2014, pp 55-56.

W. Silver, "Hands-On Radio: Experiment 177 — Feed Line Comparison," *QST*, Oct 2017, pp 71-72.

G. Southworth, *Principles and Applications of Waveguide Transmission* (New York: D. Van Nostrand Co, 1950).

UHF/Microwave Experimenter's Manual, ARRL, 2000 (out of print).

H. Weinstein, "RF Transmission Cable for Microwave Applications," *Ham Radio*, May 1985, pp 106-112.

T. Williams, "Microwavelengths: Coaxial RF Connectors for Microwaves," *QST*, Nov 2004, pp 92-94.

TABLE OF CONTENTS

Chapter 24 — Downloadable Supplemental Content

Supplemental Articles

- "Baluns in Matching Units" by Robert Neece, KØKR
- "Broadband Antenna Matching"
- "Coiled-Coax Balun Measurements" by Ed Gilbert, K2SQ
- "Compact 100-W Z-Match Antenna Tuner" by Phil Salas, AD5X
- "Don't Blow Up Your Balun" by Dean Straw, N6BV
- "Factors to be Considered in Matching Unit Design" by Robert Neece, KØKR
- "Hairpin Tuners for Matching Balanced Antenna Systems" by John Stanley, K4ERO
- "High-Power ARRL Antenna Tuner" by Dean Straw, N6BV
- "Matching with Inductive Coupling"
- "Matching-Unit Circuit Comparison Table" by Robert Neece, KØKR
- "Optimizing the Performance of Harmonic Attenuation Stubs" by George Cutsogeorge, W2VJN
- "Tapered Lines" from previous editions
- "The AAT — Analyze Antenna Tuner — Program" by Dean Straw, N6BV
- "The EZ Tuner — Parts 1, 2, and 3," by Jim Garland, W8ZR
- "The Quest for the Ideal Antenna Tuner" by Jack Belrose, VE2CV
- "Why Do Baluns Burn Up?" by Zack Lau, W1VT

Chapter 24

Transmission Line System Techniques

The **Transmission Lines** chapter presented the fundamentals of transmission line operation and characteristics. This chapter covers methods of getting energy into and out of the transmission line at the transmitter and at the antenna. This requires *coupling* — the transfer of energy between two systems — from a transmitter to the feed line or from the feed line to the antenna. For coupling to be the most efficient, both systems should have the same ratio of voltage to current (impedance) wherever the two systems meet so that no energy is reflected at that interface. This often requires *impedance matching* to convert energy at one ratio of voltage to current to another ratio — all as efficiently as possible. This can be done with LC circuits, special structures, and even transmission lines themselves.

The initial portions of this chapter discuss methods used at the transmitter to effectively transfer power into the antenna system feed line using LC impedance-matching circuits and antenna tuners. The subject then turns to choosing a transmission line and deciding the best configuration of feed line and impedance-matching devices. Finally, at the "other end" of the feed line, several sections address methods of impedance matching at the antenna and minimizing unwanted interaction between the feed line and antenna.

24.1 COUPLING THE TRANSMITTER AND LINE

A lot of effort is expended to ensure that the impedance presented to the transmitter by the antenna system feed line is close to 50 Ω. Is all that effort worthwhile? Like most broadly phrased questions, the answer begins, "It depends…" Vacuum-tube transmitters, with the wide adjustment range of the output amplifier's pi-network, could comfortably deliver rated output power into a wide variety of loads. The drawback was that the output network needed to be readjusted whenever the operating frequency changed significantly.

The modern amateur transceiver does not require output tuning adjustment at all for its broadband, untuned solid-state final amplifiers that are designed to operate into 50 Ω. Such a transmitter is able to deliver its rated output power — at the rated level of distortion — only when it is operated into the load for which it was designed. Generating full power from such a transmitter into loads far from 50 Ω can result in distortion products causing interference to other stations.

Further, modern radios often employ protection circuitry to reduce output power automatically if the SWR rises above 2:1. Protective circuits are needed because the higher voltages or currents encountered at such loads can quickly destroy solid-state amplifier transistors. Modern solid-state transceivers often include built-in antenna tuners to match impedances when the SWR isn't 1:1.

The impedance at the input of a transmission line is determined by the frequency, the characteristic impedance (Z_0) of the line, the physical length, velocity factor and the matched-line loss of the line, as well as the impedance of the load (the antenna) at the output end of the line. The section on Transmission Line System Design later in this chapter presents an example of this effect for a typical multiband dipole. (See the **Transmission Lines** chapter for an explanation.)

If the impedance at the input of the transmission line connected to the transmitter differs appreciably from the load resistance into which the transmitter output circuit is designed to operate, an impedance-matching circuit must be inserted between the transmitter and the line input terminals.

These circuits, called *networks* in professional literature, have one of several configurations with the L, pi, and T being the most common. The name of the network reflects the letter (L, π or T) that the usual shape of the circuit schematic most closely resembles.

The use of impedance-matching networks in a standalone piece of equipment is usually referred to as an *antenna tuner* or just *tuner*. This is somewhat of a misnomer since the network does not "tune" the antenna at all, even if located directly at the terminals of the antenna. The network only transforms the impedance presented to its output terminals into a different impedance at its input terminals. Many modern transceivers feature an internal antenna tuner that can compensate for SWR up to 3:1 (sometimes more).

In many publications, such an impedance-matching network is often called a *transmatch*, meaning a "transmitter matching" network. Another common name is *matchbox* (after the E.F. Johnson product line). A network operated automatically by a microprocessor is often called an *auto tuner*. Regardless of the name, the function of an antenna tuner is to transform the impedance at the input end of the transmission line — whatever it may be — to the 50 Ω needed for the transmitter to operate properly. An antenna tuner does *not* alter the SWR between its output terminals and the load, such as on the transmission line going to the antenna. It only ensures that the transmitter sees the 50-Ω load for which it was designed.

Antenna tuners come in three basic styles: *manual* (adjusted by the operator), *automatic* (adjusted under the control of a microprocessor) and *remote* (an automatic version designed to be mounted away from the operating position). Manual tuners are the most common and often include an SWR or power meter to aid the operator in adjusting the tuner. Automatic tuners may be internal to the transmitter or external, standalone equipment. Since the controlling microprocessor measures SWR on its own, there is rarely a need for power or SWR metering on automatic antenna tuners. Automatic models are available that are activated manually, or that sense the RF frequency and tune immediately, or that tune based on a computer control input or control link to the host transceiver. Remote antenna tuners are essentially automatic antenna tuners in enclosures designed to be mounted outside or out of sight of the operator and have no operating controls or displays.

As an example of the impedance-matching task, column one of **Tables 24.1** and **24.2** list the computed impedance at the center of two common dipoles mounted over average ground (with a conductivity of 5 mS/m and a dielectric constant of 13). The dipole in Table 24.1 is 100 feet long, and is mounted as a flattop, 50 feet high. The dipole in Table 24.2 is 66 feet long overall, mounted as an inverted-V whose apex is 50 feet high and whose legs have an included angle of 120°. The second column in Tables 24.1 and 24.2 shows the computed impedance at the transmitter end of a 100-foot long transmission line using 450-Ω window open-wire line. Please recognize that there is nothing special or "magic" about these antennas — they are merely representative of typical antennas used by real-world amateurs.

The intent of the tables is to show that the impedance at the input of the transmission line varies over an extremely wide range when antennas like these are used over the entire range of amateur bands from 160 to 10 meters. The impedance at the input of the line (that is, at the antenna tuner's output terminals) *will be different* if the length of the line or the frequency of operation is changed. It should be obvious that an antenna tuner used with such a system must be very flexible to match the wide range of impedances encountered under ordinary circumstances — and it must do so without arcing from high voltage or overheating from high current.

Table 24.1
Impedance of Center-Fed 100 Foot Flattop Dipole, 50 Feet High Over Average Ground

Frequency (MHz)	*Antenna Feed point Impedance (Ω)*	*Impedance at Input of 100 ft 450-Ω Line (Ω)*
1.83	4.5 – *j* 1673	2.0 – *j* 20
3.8	39 – *j* 362	888 – *j* 2265
7.1	481 + *j* 964	64 – *j* 24
10.1	2584 – *j* 3292	62 – *j* 447
14.1	85 – *j* 123	84 – *j* 65
18.1	2097 + *j* 1552	2666 – *j* 884
21.1	345 – *j* 1073	156 + *j* 614
24.9	202 + *j* 367	149 – *j* 231
28.4	2493 – *j* 1375	68 – *j* 174

Table 24.2
Impedance of Center-Fed 66 Foot Inverted-V Dipole, 50 Feet at Apex 120° Included Angle Over Average Ground

Frequency (MHz)	*Antenna Feed point Impedance (Ω)*	*Impedance at Input of 100 ft 450-Ω Line (Ω)*
1.83	1.6 – *j* 2257	1.6 – *j* 44
3.8	10 – *j* 879	2275 + *j* 8980
7.1	65 – *j* 41	1223 – *j* 1183
10.1	22 + *j* 648	157 – *j* 1579
14.1	5287 – *j* 1310	148 – *j* 734
18.1	198 – *j* 820	138 – *j* 595
21.1	103 – *j* 181	896 – *j* 857
24.9	269 + *j* 570	99 – *j* 140
28.4	3089 + *j* 774	74 – *j* 223

24.1.1 THE IMPEDANCE MATCHING SYSTEM

Over the years, radio amateurs have derived a number of circuits for use as antenna tuners. At one time, when parallel-conductor transmission line was more widely used, link-coupled tuned circuits were in vogue. With the increasing popularity of coaxial cable used as feed lines, other circuits have become more prevalent. The most common form of antenna tuner in recent years is some variation of a *T-network* configuration.

The basic system of a transmitter, impedance-matching network, transmission line and antenna is shown in **Figure 24.1**. As usual, we assume that the transmitter is designed to deliver its rated power into a load of 50 Ω. The problem is one of designing a matching circuit that will transform the actual line impedance at the input of the transmission line into a resistive impedance of 50 + *j*0 Ω. This impedance will be unbalanced; that is, one side will be grounded, since modern transmitters universally ground one side of the output

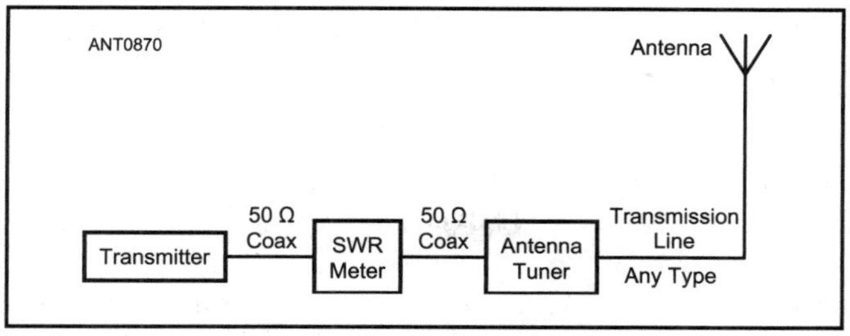

Figure 24.1 — Essentials of an impedance-matching system between transmitter and transmission line. The SWR meter indicates the quality of the match provided by the antenna tuner and may be part of the antenna tuner or the transmitter.

connector to the chassis. The line to the antenna, however, may be unbalanced (coaxial cable) or balanced (parallel-conductor line), depending on whether the antenna itself is unbalanced or balanced.

The antenna tuner in such a system may only consist of the LC network necessary to transform impedance. This is typical of custom LC networks constructed to match an antenna used on a single band that may be located away from the transmitter. An antenna tuner used on multiple bands and located in the station usually includes some type of SWR bridge or meter. (See the **Antenna and Transmission Line Measurements** chapter.)

Other features common in commercial antenna tuners include directional wattmeters, switches for the use of multiple feed lines and for bypassing the tuner, and balanced and single-wire outputs. An overview of antenna tuner functions and features is provided in *The ARRL Guide to Antenna Tuners* by Joel Hallas, W1ZR. (See Bibliography.)

24.1.2 HARMONIC ATTENUATION

This is a good place to bring up the topic of harmonic attenuation, as it is related to antenna tuners. One potentially desirable characteristic of an antenna tuner is the degree of extra harmonic attenuation it can provide by acting as a tuned circuit. While this is desirable in theory, it is not always achieved in practice. For example, if an antenna tuner is used with a single, fixed-length antenna on multiple bands, the impedances presented to the tuner at the fundamental frequency and at the harmonics will often be radically different as shown in Table 24.2. For example, at 7.1 MHz, the impedance seen by the antenna tuner for the 66-foot inverted-V dipole is $1223 - j\,1183\ \Omega$. At 14.1 MHz, roughly the second harmonic, the impedance is $148 - j\,734\ \Omega$. The amount of harmonic attenuation for a particular network will vary dramatically with the impedances presented at the different frequencies.

Harmonics and Multiband Antennas

There are some antennas for which the impedance at the second harmonic is essentially the same as that for the fundamental. This often involves trap antenna systems or wideband log-periodic designs. For example, a system used by many amateurs is a triband Yagi that works on 20, 15 and 10 meters. The second harmonic of a 20 meter transmitter feeding such a tribander can be objectionably strong for nearby amateurs operating on 10 meters such as at a Field Day or other multi-position special event or contest station, even with the approximately 60 dB of attenuation of the second harmonic provided by the low-pass filters at the output of modern solid-state transceivers. The third harmonic of a 144.2 MHz fundamental can cause interference on the 432 MHz band, as well. A linear amplifier can exacerbate the problem, since its second harmonic may be suppressed only about 46 dB by the typical pi-network output circuit used in many older amplifiers.

Most amateur antenna tuners will not attenuate the 10 meter harmonic much at all, especially if the tuner uses a high-pass T-network. This is the most common network used commercially because of the wide range of impedances it will match. Some T-network designs have attempted to improve the harmonic attenuation using parallel inductors and capacitors instead of a single inductor for the center part of the tee. Unfortunately, this often leads to more loss and more critical tuning at the fundamental, while providing little, if any, additional harmonic suppression in actual installations. The lesson here is to not depend on the antenna tuner for harmonic suppression — use filters at the transmitter.

Harmonics and Pi-Network Tuners

If a low-pass pi-network is used for an antenna tuner, there will be additional attenuation of harmonics, perhaps as much as 30 dB for a loaded Q of 3. The exact degree of harmonic attenuation, however, is often limited due to the stray inductance and capacitance present in most tuners at harmonic frequencies. Further, the matching range for a pi-network tuner is fairly limited because of the range of input and output capacitance needed for widely varying loads.

Harmonics and Stubs

Far more reliable suppression of harmonics can be achieved using quarter-wave and half-wave transmission line stubs at the transmitter output. For example, a typical 20 meter $\lambda/4$ shorted stub (which is an open circuit at 20 meters, but a short circuit at 10 meters) will provide about 25 dB of attenuation to the second harmonic. It will handle full legal amateur power too. The characteristics of such stubs are covered in the sections of this chapter on the use of stubs as filters and on impedance matching at the antenna. The use of stubs as filters is also covered in excellent book *Managing Interstation Interference* by George Cutsogeorge, W2VJN. (See Bibliography.)

24.1.3 MYTHS ABOUT SWR

There are some enduring and quite misleading myths in Amateur Radio concerning SWR.

• Despite some claims to the contrary, a high SWR *does not by itself* cause RF interference, or TVI or telephone interference. While it is true that an antenna located close to such devices can cause overload and interference, the SWR in the feed line to that antenna has nothing to do with it, providing of course that the tuner, feed line or connectors are not arcing.

The antenna is merely doing its job, which is to radiate. The transmission line is doing its job, which is to convey power from the transmitter to the radiator.

• A second myth, often stated in the same breath as the first one above, is that a high SWR will cause radiation from a transmission line. SWR has nothing to do with excessive radiation from a line. Common-mode currents on feed lines do radiate just like on antennas, but they are not directly related to SWR. An asymmetric arrangement of a transmission line and antenna can result in common-mode currents being induced on the outside of the shield of coax or as an imbalance of currents in an open-wire line. Common-mode current will radiate just as if it were on an antenna. If that current is flowing close to electronic equipment such as a telephone or entertainment system, RFI can result. A *choke* (also called a *choke balun*) is used on coaxial feed lines to reduce these currents as described in the section "Current and Choke Baluns" later in this chapter.

• A third and perhaps even more prevalent myth is that you can't "get out" if the SWR on your transmission line is higher than 1.5:1 or 2:1 or some other such arbitrary figure. On the HF bands, if you use reasonable lengths of good coaxial cable (or even better yet, open-wire line), the truth is that you need not be overly concerned if the SWR at the load is kept below about 6:1. This sounds pretty radical to some amateurs who have heard horror story after horror story about SWR. The fact is that if you can load up your transmitter without any arcing inside, or if you use a tuner to make sure your transmitter is operating into its rated load resistance, you can enjoy a very effective station, using antennas with feed lines having high values of SWR. For example, a 450-Ω open-wire line connected to the multiband dipole shown in Table 24.1 would have a 19:1 SWR on it at 3.8 MHz. Yet time and again this antenna has proven to be a great performer at many installations.

• A fourth myth is that changing the length of a feed line changes the SWR. Changing a feed line's length does *not* change the SWR (except for losses) inside the line. When someone tells you that adding or subtracting length changes the SWR, they are really telling you that their SWR meter reading was affected by the changing impedance in the line or that common-mode currents were affecting the measurement. Changing the feed line length can affect the impedance of the line to common-mode current and thus how much common-mode current is flowing at a particular point, including at the antenna's feed point.

24.2 IMPEDANCE MATCHING NETWORKS

This section reviews the operation of several common impedance matching networks that are used as antenna tuners. As a supplement to this chapter, a review of impedance-matching circuit designs and characteristics contributed by Robert Neece, KØKR is included with this book's downloadable supplemental information. The material includes:

• Factors to be Considered in Creating or Assessing Matching-Unit Designs for the MF/HF Spectrum

• Comparison Table of Matching-Unit Designs

• Baluns in Matching Units

Along with the discussion is an extensive collection of references. The student of impedance matching will find the material to supplement and complement the material here, giving examples of commercial equipment and addressing the general advantages and disadvantages of each type. The student will also enjoy the excellent three-part series of articles by George Grammer, W1DF, listed in the Bibliography.

When designing and constructing impedance matching networks, particularly for power levels of 100 W and higher, it is important to take into account the high voltages and currents that may be present. The larger the difference between the input and output impedances, the higher those voltages and currents will be. Inductors should be constructed from low-loss wire or tubing. Variable inductors should be rated for transmitting applications. Capacitors should have sufficient voltage rating and variable capacitors should have heavy contacts to the moving plates. Switches must be heavy enough to handle both the current and voltage. Connections between components should be made with short lengths of heavy wire or strap. For more information on these heavy-duty components and wiring techniques, see the *ARRL Handbook* chapter on **RF Power Amplifiers** and projects for building high-power equipment.

24.2.1 THE L-NETWORK

A comparatively simple but very useful matching circuit for unbalanced loads is the L-network, as shown in **Figure 24.2A**. L-network antenna tuners are normally used for only a single band of operation, although multiband versions can be made with switched or variable coil taps. To determine the range of circuit values for a matched condition, the input and load impedance values must be known or assumed. Otherwise a match may be found by trial and error.

There are several versions of the L-network. In Figure 24.2A, L is shown as the series reactance, X_S, and C1 as the shunt or parallel reactance, X_P. However, a capacitor may be used for the series reactance and an inductor for the shunt reactance, to satisfy mechanical or other considerations. The version shown in Figure 24.2A is the most popular with amateurs because of its low-pass characteristics that reduce harmonics, reasonable component values, and convenient construction from available component styles. A complete discussion of L-networks is available in the *ARRL Handbook*.

The ratio of the series reactance to the series resistance, X_S/R_S, is defined as the network Q. The four variables, R_S, R_P, X_S and X_P, for lossless components are related as given

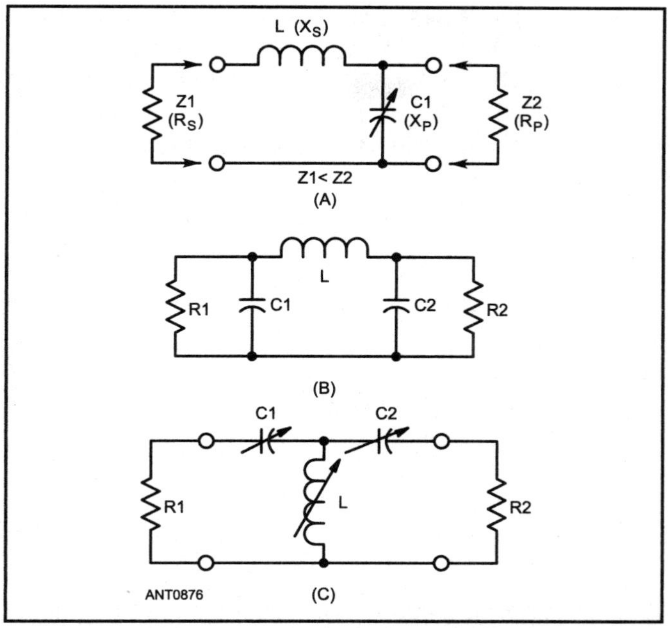

Figure 24.2 — At A, the L-matching network, consisting of L and C1, to match Z1 and Z2. The lower of the two impedances to be matched, Z1, must always be connected to the series-arm side of the network and the higher impedance, Z2, to the shunt-arm side. The positions of the inductor and capacitor may be interchanged in the network. At B, the pi-network tuner, matching R1 to R2. The pi-network provides more flexibility than the L as an antenna-tuner circuit. See equations in the text for calculating component values. At C, the T-network tuner. This has more flexibility in that components with practical values can match a wide variety of loads. The drawback is that this network can be inefficient, particularly when the output capacitor is small.

in the equations below. When any two values are known, the other two may be calculated.

$$Q = \sqrt{\frac{R_P}{R_S} - 1} = \frac{X_S}{R_S} = \frac{R_P}{X_P} \tag{1}$$

$$X_S = QR_S = \frac{QR_P}{1+Q^2} \tag{2}$$

$$X_P = \frac{R_P}{Q} = \frac{R_P R_S}{X_S} = \frac{R_S^{\,2} + X_S^{\,2}}{X_S} \tag{3}$$

$$R_S = \frac{R_P}{Q^2+1} = \frac{X_S X_P}{R_P} \tag{4}$$

$$R_P = R_S(1+Q^2) = QX_P = \frac{R_S^{\,2} + X_S^{\,2}}{R_S} \tag{5}$$

The reactance of loads that are not purely resistive may be taken into account and absorbed or compensated for in the reactances of the matching network. Inductive and capacitive reactance values may be converted to inductor and capacitor values for the operating frequency with standard reactance equations.

It is important to recognize that Eq 1 through 5 are for *lossless* components. When real components with real unloaded Qs are used, the transformation changes and you must compensate for the losses. Real coils are represented by a perfect inductor in series with a loss resistance, and real capacitors by a perfect capacitor in parallel with a loss resistance. At HF, a physical coil will have an unloaded Q_U between 100 and 400, with an average value of about 200 for a high-quality airwound coil mounted in a spacious metal enclosure. A variable capacitor used in an antenna tuner will have an unloaded Q_U of about 1000 for a typical air-variable capacitor with wiper contacts. An expensive vacuum-variable capacitor can have an unloaded Q_U as high as 5000.

The power loss in coils is generally larger than in variable capacitors used in practical antenna tuners. The circulating RF current in both coils and capacitors can also cause severe heating. The ARRL Laboratory has seen coils forms made of plastic melt when pushing antenna tuners to their extreme limits during product testing. The RF voltages developed across the capacitors can be pretty spectacular at times, leading to severe arcing.

Note that L-networks cannot match all impedances to 50 Ω. The load and source impedances must have the proper relationship for the equations to solve to obtainable component values. The reactance at the load must also be cancellable by the reactance of the L-network. If the load impedance is such that it cannot be matched by an L-network try (a) reversing the network or (b) adding λ/8 to λ/4 of transmission line between the load and network. This does not change the SWR but it does transform the load impedance to a new combination of resistance and reactance that the L-network may be able to match.

L-Network Construction

Building an L-network is straightforward and there have been many construction articles about constructing antenna tuners based on an L-network. If you are trying to match an antenna for a single band, the network can be constructed with fixed-value components as in **Figure 24.3A** if you know the impedance to be matched and are willing to do the calculations. (See the Bibliography entry for Hands-On Radio Experiment 157 by Silver.)

Dick Sanders, K5QY, uses the variable, re-configurable L-network in Figure 24.3B as a test set. (See his Bibliography entry.) He connects the L-network to the antenna and an antenna analyzer to the input of the network. Then he adjusts the network for the best match, measures the value of the L-network components, and builds an L-network with those values.

The L-network can form the basis of an adjustable antenna tuner for high or low power. The article "On the Quest for an Ideal Antenna Tuner" by Jack Belrose, VE2CV, begins with a simple, reversible L-network and extends it to a more versatile configuration that can place the L and C in both series and shunt. (The article is included in the downloadable supplemental information for this chapter.)

Finally, the L-network can be tuned automatically by a microcontroller. Most automatic antenna tuners are built this

(A)

(B)

Figure 24.3 — Two examples of L-networks. At A is a full-power L-network for matching a base-fed tower on 160 meters using a vacuum variable capacitor and inductor wound from ¼-inch refrigerator tubing. At B is a low-power L-network that is used as an adjustable test set for determining what component values are required for matching a load impedance. [Dick Sander, K5QY, photo]

way. Relays are used to select from a wide variety of fixed-value components. If a match is not reached, other relays "turn the network around" and move the shunt component to the other end of the network.

24.2.2 THE PI-NETWORK

The impedances at the feed point of an antenna used on multiple HF bands varies over a very wide range, particularly if thin wire is used. This was described in detail in the **Dipoles and Monopoles** chapter. The transmission line feeding the antenna transforms the wide range of impedances at the antenna's feed point to another wide range of impedances at the transmission line's input. This often mandates the use of a more flexible antenna tuner than an L-network.

The pi-network, shown in Figure 24.2B, offers more flexibility than the L-network, since there are three variables instead of two. The only limitation on the circuit values that may be used is that the reactance of the series arm, the inductor L in the figure, must not be greater than the square root of the product of the two values of resistive impedance to be matched. The following equations are for lossless components in a pi-network. For R1 > R2

$$X_{C1} = \frac{R1}{Q} \tag{6}$$

$$X_{C2} = R2\sqrt{\frac{R1/R2}{Q^2+1-R1/R2}} \tag{7}$$

$$X_L = \frac{(Q \times R1) + \dfrac{R1 \times R2}{X_{C2}}}{Q^2+1} \tag{8}$$

The pi-network may be used to match a low impedance to a rather high one, such as 50 to several thousand ohms. Conversely, it may be used to match 50 Ω to a quite low value, such as 1 Ω or less. For antenna-tuner applications, C1 and C2 may be independently variable. L may be a roller inductor or a coil with switchable taps.

Alternatively, a lead fitted with a suitable clip may be used to short out turns of a fixed inductor. In this way, a match may be obtained through trial. It will be possible to match two values of impedances with several different settings of L, C1 and C2. This results because the Q of the network is being changed. If a match is maintained with other adjustments, the Q of the circuit rises with increased capacitance at C1.

Of course, the load usually has a reactive component along with resistance. You can compensate for the effect of these reactive components by changing one of the reactive elements in the matching network. For example, if some reactance were shunted across R2, the setting of C2 could be changed to compensate for inductive or capacitive shunt reactance.

As with the L-network, the effects of real-world unloaded Q for each component must be taken into account in the pi-network to evaluate real-world losses.

Pi-networks are used in vacuum-tube amplifiers to match the high tube output impedance to the 50-Ω impedance of most feed lines and antenna systems. See the *ARRL Handbook* chapter **RF Power Amplifiers** for more information on and design software for the pi-network.

24.2.3 THE T-NETWORK

Both the pi-network and the L-network often require unwieldy values of capacitance — that is, *large* capacitances are often required at the lower frequencies — to make the desired transformation to 50 Ω. Often, the range of capacitance from minimum to maximum must be quite wide when the impedance at the output of the network varies radically with frequency, as is common for multiband, single-wire antennas.

The high-pass T-network shown in Figure 24.2C is

capable of matching a wide range of load impedances and uses practical values for the components. However, as in almost everything in radio, there is a price to be paid for this flexibility. The T-network can be very lossy compared to other network types. This is particularly true at the lower frequencies, whenever the load resistance is low. Loss can be severe if the maximum capacitance of the output capacitor C2 in Figure 24.2C is low.

For example, **Figure 24.4** shows the computed values for the components at 1.8 MHz for four types of networks into a load of $5 + j\,0\ \Omega$. In each case, the unloaded Q of the inductor used is assumed to be 200, and the unloaded Q of the capacitor(s) used is 1000. The component values were computed using the program *TLW* (described later in this chapter).

Figure 24.4A is a low-pass L-network; Figure 24.4B is a high-pass L-network and Figure 24.3C is a pi-network. At more than 5200 pF, the capacitance values are pretty unwieldy for the first three networks. The loaded Q_L for all three is only 3.0, indicating that the network loss is small. In fact, the loss is only 1.8% for all three because the loaded Q_L is much smaller than the unloaded Q_U of the components used.

The T-network in Figure 24.4D uses more practical, realizable component values. Note that the output capacitor C2 has been set to 500 pF and that dictates the values for the other two components. The drawback is that the loaded Q in this configuration has risen to 34.2, with an attendant loss of 22.4% of the power delivered to the input of the network. For the legal limit of 1500 W, the loss in the network is 335 W. Of this, 280 W ends up in the inductor, which will probably melt! Even if the inductor doesn't burn up, the output capacitor C2 might well arc over, since it has more than 3800 V peak across it at 1500 W into the network.

Due to the losses in the components in a T-network, it is quite possible to "load it up into itself," causing real damage inside. For example, *TLW* analyzed a T-network loaded up into a short circuit at 1.8 MHz. The component values look quite reasonable; C_{IN} = 78 pF, L = 13 µH, C_{OUT} = 500 pF, but unfortunately *all* the power is dissipated in the network itself. The current through the output capacitor C2 at 1500 W input to the antenna tuner would be 35 A, creating a peak voltage of more than 8700 V across C2. Either C1 (also at more than 8700 V peak) or C2 will probably arc over before the power loss is sufficient to destroy the coil. However, the loud arcing might frighten the operator pretty badly.

The point you should remember is that the T-network is indeed very flexible in terms of matching to a wide variety of loads. However, it must be used judiciously, lest it burn itself up. Even if it doesn't fry itself, it can waste that precious RF power you'd rather put into your antenna. Additional discussion of the T-network as an antenna tuner is provided in the article by Sabin listed in the Bibliography. A fully-automated, full-power T-network, was described by Jim Garland, W8ZR, in his series of *QST* articles "The EZ Tuner" which are included in the downloadable supplemental information.

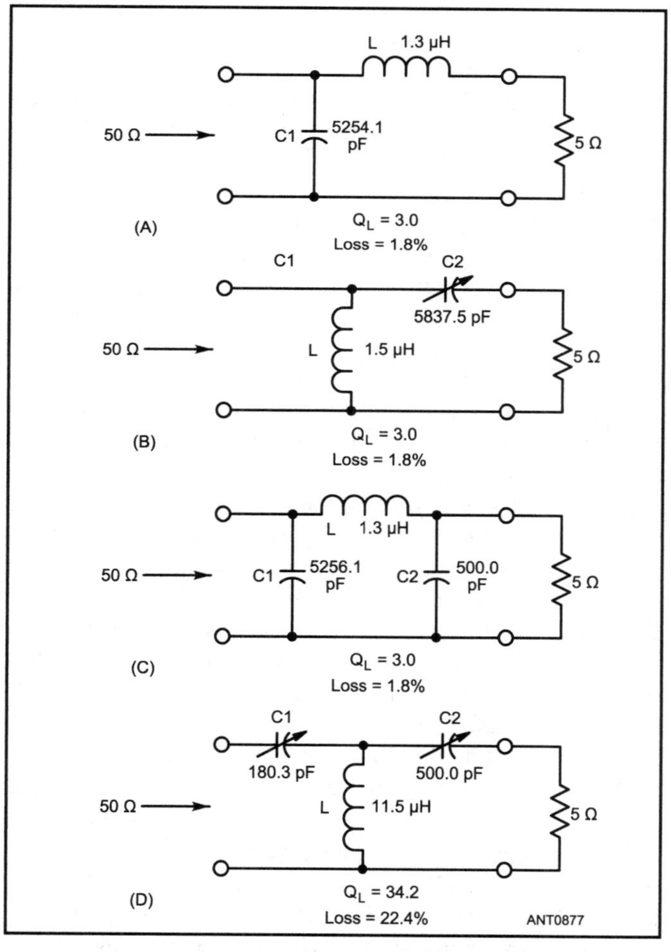

Figure 24.4 — Computed values for real components (Q_U = 200 for coil, Q_U = 1000 for capacitor) to match 5-Ω load resistance to 50-Ω line. At A, low-pass L-network, with shunt input capacitor, series inductor. At B, high-pass L-network, with shunt input inductor, series capacitor. Note how large the capacitance is for these L-networks. At C, low-pass pi-network and at D, high-pass T-network. The component values for the T-network are practical, although the loss is highest for this particular network, at 22.4% of the input power.

Adjusting T-Network Antenna Tuners

The process of adjusting an antenna tuner can be simplified greatly by using a process that not only results in minimum SWR to the transmitter, but also minimizes power losses in the tuner circuitry. If you have a commercial tuner and read the user's manual, the manufacturer will likely provide a method of adjustment that you should follow, including initial settings. If you do not have a user's manual, first open the tuner and determine the circuit for the tuner. To adjust a T-network type of tuner:

1) Set the series capacitors to maximum value. This may not correspond to the highest number on the control scale — verify that the capacitor's plates are fully meshed.

2) Set the inductor to maximum value. This corresponds to placing a switch tap or roller inductor contact so that it is electrically closest to circuit ground.

3) If you have an SWR analyzer, connect it to the TRANSMITTER connector of the tuner. Otherwise, connect the

transceiver and tune it to the desired frequency, but do not transmit.

4) Adjust the inductor throughout its range watching the SWR analyzer for a dip in the SWR or listen for a peak in the received noise. Return the inductor to the setting for lowest SWR or highest received noise.

a) If no SWR minimum or noise peak is detected, reduce the value of the capacitor closest to the transmitter in steps of about 20% and repeat.

b) If still no SWR minimum or noise peak is detected, return the input capacitor to maximum value and reduce the output capacitor value in steps of about 20%.

c) If still no SWR minimum or noise peak is detected, return the output capacitor to maximum value and reduce both input and output capacitors in 20% steps.

5) Once a combination of settings is found with a definite SWR minimum or noise peak:

a) If you are using an SWR analyzer, make small adjustments to find the combination of settings that produce minimum SWR with the maximum value of input and output capacitance.

b) If you do not have an SWR analyzer, set the transmitter output power to about 10 W, ensure that you won't cause interference, identify with your call sign, and transmit a steady carrier by making the same adjustments as in step 5a.

c) For certain impedances, the tuner may not be able to reduce the SWR to an acceptable value. In this case, try adding feed line at the output of the tuner from ⅛- to ½ λ electrical wavelength long. This will not change the feed line SWR, but it may transform the impedance to a value more suitable for the tuner components.

In general, for any type of tuner, begin with the maximum reactance to ground (maximum inductance or minimum capacitance) and the minimum series reactance between the source and load (minimum inductance or maximum capacitance). The configuration that produces the minimum SWR with maximum reactance to ground and minimum series reactance will generally have the highest efficiency and broadest tuning bandwidth.

24.2.4 THE *TLW* (TRANSMISSION LINE FOR WINDOWS) PROGRAM AND ANTENNA TUNERS

The ARRL program *TLW* (Transmission Line for Windows) included with this book's downloadable supplemental information does calculations for transmission lines and antenna tuners. *TLW* evaluates four different networks: a low-pass L-network, a high-pass L-network, a low-pass pi-network, and a high-pass T-network. **Figure 24.5** shows the *TLW* output screen for an L-network design example.

Not only does *TLW* compute the exact values for network components, but also the full effects of voltage, current and power dissipation for each component. Depending on the load impedance presented to the antenna tuner, the internal losses in an antenna tuner can be disastrous. See the documentation file TLW.PDF for further details on the use of *TLW*, which some call the "Swiss Army Knife" of transmission line

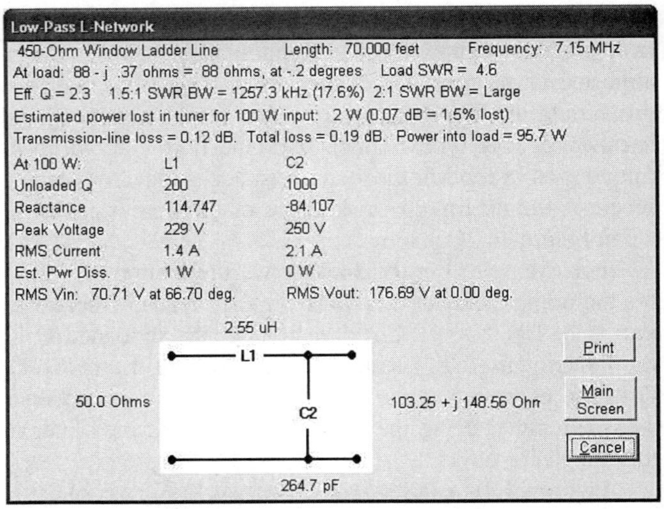

Figure 24.5 — Antenna tuner output screen of *TLW* software. Note the tuner schematic with parts values shown. The data above the schematic provide additional important information.

software. Also see the Bibliography entry for Birnbaum for another analysis of losses in the popular internal and external automatic L-network tuners.

TLW's author, Dean Straw, N6BV, also wrote the article "A Beginner's Guide to Transmission-Line and Antenna-Tuner Modeling," which is included in this chapter's downloadable supplemental material. The article provides some examples of how to use *TLW* for common design tasks.

24.2.5 BALANCED ANTENNA TUNERS

Modern antenna tuners often include a toroid-wound balun at their output for use with balanced or parallel-conductor feed lines. This allows a transmitter's unbalanced coaxial output to be connected to the balanced feed line. Be aware that at very high or very low impedances, the balun's power rating may be exceeded at high transmitted power levels.

The inductive- or link-coupling circuits seen in **Figure 24.6** are sometimes used but have largely been replaced by the toroid-wound balun. A more detailed discussion on inductive coupling is included with this book's downloadable supplemental information, as is a low-power link-coupled tuner project that uses the configuration shown in Figure 24.6D and instructions for building the 100-W "Z-Match" antenna tuner designed by Phil Salas, AD5X. The article "*FilTuners*-a New (Old) Approach to Antenna Matching" by John Stanley, K4ERO (see Bibliography) also discusses tuned link-coupling from the standpoint of the matching network providing both filtering and impedance matching.

A fully-balanced tuner has a symmetrical internal circuit with a tuner circuit for each side of the feed line and the balun at the input to the tuner where the impedance is close to 50 Ω. Several examples are shown in **Figure 24.7** that can be recognized as being formed from the unbalanced networks described earlier with a mirror-image of the network being inserted in the "ground" side of the circuit.

A balun is inserted on the 50-Ω side of the circuit to allow connection to unbalanced coaxial feed lines. Some tuners are designed to use a 1:1 balun for this purpose while others transform the load impedance to 200 Ω and use a 4:1 balun. This allows the balun to operate at its design impedances regardless of load impedance. A balun at the output of an unbalanced tuner must operate at whatever load impedance is presented, which can lead to significant losses or arcing in the balun.

A disadvantage of balanced tuners is the higher cost from the additional components and the more complex mechanical arrangements to adjust more than one component at the same time with a single control. The hairpin tuner configuration in **Figure 24.8** is a balanced tuner for use at VHF and UHF where solenoid-wound coils may have too much inductance. The tuner is described in the April 2009 *QST* article "Hairpin Tuners for Matching Balanced Antenna Systems" by John Stanley, K4ERO (the article is included with this book's downloadable supplemental information).

Figure 24.6 — Simple antenna tuners for coupling a transmitter to a parallel-conductor feed line presenting a load different from the transmitter's design load impedance, usually 50 Ω. A and B, respectively, are series and parallel tuned circuits using variable inductive coupling between coils. C and D are similar but use fixed inductive coupling and a variable series capacitor, C1. A series tuned circuit works well with a low-impedance load; the parallel circuit is better with high impedance loads (several hundred ohms or more).

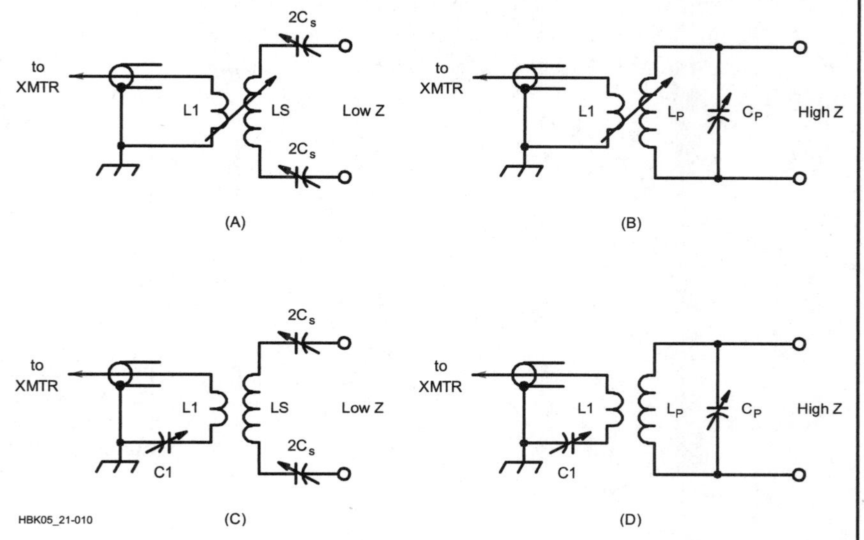

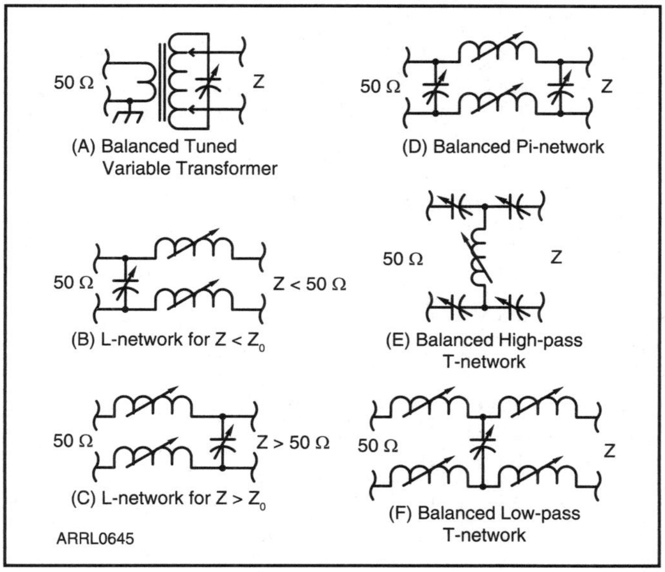

Figure 24.7 — Configurations of balanced antenna tuners.

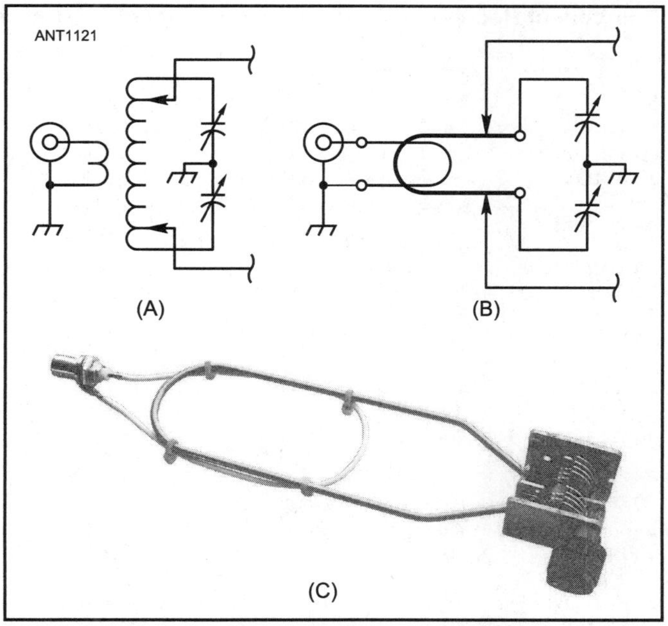

Figure 24.8 — Balanced tuner configurations. At (A) conventional tapped coil based tuner, at (B) the hairpin equivalent. (C) shows a hairpin tuner for 144 MHz. The technique can be used from 10 meters through 70 cm.

24.2.6 GENERAL PURPOSE TUNER DESIGNS

Several antenna tuner designs were created by Joel Hallas, W1ZR, for the book *The ARRL Guide to Antenna Tuners*. The *TLW* program was used to determine component values for a set of common load impedances and three popular antenna tuner circuits shown in **Figure 24.9**. **Tables 24.3** to **24.5** show the required component values to match those load impedances at 1.8, 3.5 and 30 MHz, the extremes of HF operation for antenna tuners.

Former *ARRL Antenna Book* editor, Dean Straw, N6BV, designed a high-power tuner with a 1:1 balun at the input to allow the tuner to work into balanced or unbalanced loads. The tuner has a very wide range and is designed for low losses. See the article "High-Power ARRL Antenna Tuner" that is included in this chapter's downloadable supplemental material.

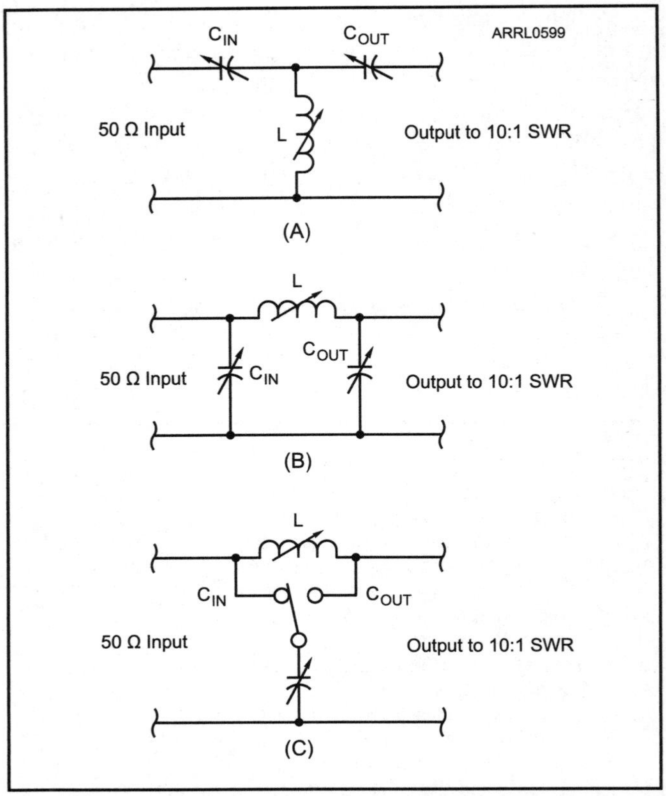

Figure 24.9 — Schematic diagrams of a high-pass T-network (A), pi-network (B), and a low-pass L-network (C). Tables 24.3 to 24.5 give component values at 1.8, 3.5, and 30 MHz to match different values of load impedances to 50 Ω.

Table 24.3
Component Requirements for High-Pass (Shunt L) T-Network Antenna Tuners at 10:1 SWR

Frequency/Z (Ω)	*Capacitor*		*Inductor (μH)*	*Capacitor Voltage (V_P)*		*Efficiency (%)*
1.8 MHz	*Input (pF)*	*Output (pF)*		*100 W*	*1500 W*	
5	1136	3000	2.1	180	710	96
500	548	500	13.9	323	1250	98
25 + *j*100	343	300	10.3	790	3070	92
25 – *j*100	170	300	20	1040	4030	86
250 + *j*250	308	200	10.5	380	1470	98
250 – *j*250	337	300	16.9	525	2030	96
Frequency/Z (Ω)	*Capacitor*		*Inductor (μH)*	*Capacitor Voltage (V_P)*		*Efficiency (%)*
3.5 MHz	*Input (pF)*	*Output (pF)*		*100 W*	*1500 W*	
5	563	1500	1.1	190	720	96
500	265	200	7.3	343	1330	98
25 + *j*100	275	200	3.5	613	2373	95
25 – *j*100	104	200	8.6	880	3403	88
250 + *j*250	333	100	5.6	381	1475	98
250 – *j*250	136	100	10.8	670	2600	94
Frequency/Z (Ω)	*Capacitor*		*Inductor (μH)*	*Capacitor Voltage (V_P)*		*Efficiency (%)*
30 MHz	*Input (pF)*	*Output (pF)*		*100 W*	*1500 W*	
5	79	200	0.12	160	640	96
500	29	50	0.77	370	1470	97
25 + *j*100	91	30	0.24	400	1560	98
25 – *j*100	24	100	0.46	440	1710	93
250 + *j*250	36	100	0.9	300	1150	98
250 – *j*250	29	100	0.6	360	1410	97

Table 24.4
Component Requirements for Low-Pass (Series L) L-Network Antenna Tuners at 10:1 SWR

Frequency/Z (Ω)	*Capacitor*		*Inductor (µH)*	*Capacitor Voltage (V_P)*		*Efficiency (%)*
1.8 MHz	*Input (pF)*	*Output (pF)*		*100 W*	*1500 W*	
5	5254	n/a	1.34	100	390	98
500	n/a	536	13.5	310	1210	98
25 + *j*100	n/a	1408	12	290	1120	98
25 – *j*100	1760	n/a	11	100	390	97
250 + *j*250	n/a	713	13	310	1210	98
250 – *j*250	n/a	359	13	310	1210	98
Frequency/Z (Ω)	*Capacitor*		*Inductor (µH)*	*Capacitor Voltage (V_P)*		*Efficiency (%)*
3.5 MHz	*Input (pF)*	*Output (pF)*		*100 W*	*1500 W*	
5	2700	n/a	0.69	100	400	98
500	n/a	275	6.8	310	1200	98
25 + *j*100	n/a	720	6.2	290	1120	98
25 – *j*100	926	n/a	5.6	100	390	97
250 + *j*250	n/a	367	6.8	310	1210	98
250 – *j*250	n/a	184	6.8	310	1210	98
Frequency/Z (Ω)	*Capacitor*		*Inductor (µH)*	*Capacitor Voltage (V_P)*		*Efficiency (%)*
30 MHz	*Input (pF)*	*Output (pF)*		*100 W*	*1500 W*	
5	315	n/a	0.08	100	390	98
500	n/a	32	0.79	310	1210	98
25 + *j*100	n/a	85	0.72	290	1120	98
25 – *j*100	140	n/a	0.58	100	390	97
250 + *j*250	n/a	43	0.79	310	1210	98
250 – *j*250	n/a	22	0.79	310	1210	98

Table 24.5
Component Requirements for Low-Pass Pi-Network Antenna Tuners at 10:1 SWR

Frequency/Z (Ω)	*Capacitor*		*Inductor (µH)*	*Capacitor Voltage (V_P)*		*Efficiency (%)*
1.8 MHz	*Input (pF)*	*Output (pF)*		*100 W*	*1500 W*	
5	5256	500	1.4	100	390	98
500	2602	1000	9.6	310	1200	96
25 + *j*100	966	1500	12.5	280	1110	97
25 – *j*100	3410	500	7.5	280	1100	96
250 + *j*250	1931	1000	11.3	310	1210	97
250 – *j*250	1284	500	12.9	310	1210	97
Frequency/Z (Ω)	*Capacitor*		*Inductor (µH)*	*Capacitor Voltage (V_P)*		*Efficiency (%)*
3.5 MHz	*Input (pF)*	*Output (pF)*		*100 W*	*1500 W*	
5	2706	500	0.7	100	390	98
500	1287	500	5.1	310	1200	96
25 + *j*100	643	800	6.2	280	1110	97
25 – *j*100	1886	300	3.7	280	1430	95
250 + *j*250	934	500	6.0	310	1200	97
250 – *j*250	859	300	6.2	310	1200	97
Frequency/Z (Ω)	*Capacitor*		*Inductor (µH)*	*Capacitor Voltage (V_P)*		*Efficiency (%)*
30 MHz	*Input (pF)*	*Output (pF)*		*100 W*	*1500 W*	
5	321	200	0.08	100	390	98
500	118	50	0.7	310	1200	97
25 + *j*100	103	100	0.7	290	1100	97
25 – *j*100	205	30	0.5	285	1100	96
250 + *j*250	71	50	0.8	310	1200	97
250 – *j*250	77	30	0.8	310	1200	97

24.3 TRANSMISSION LINE SYSTEM DESIGN

The previous sections of this chapter looked at system design from the point of view of the transmitter, examining what could be done to ensure that the transmitter load is its design load of 50 Ω. In this section, we will look at antenna system design from the point of view of the transmission line.

24.3.1 TRANSMISSION LINE IMPEDANCE TRANSFORMATION

For the purposes of designing a transmission line system, the line can be also be used for its impedance transforming properties. A certain value of load impedance, consisting of a resistance and reactance, at the end of the line is transformed into another value of impedance at the input of the line. The amount of transformation is determined by the electrical length of the line, its characteristic impedance, and by the losses inherent in the line. The input impedance of a real, lossy transmission line is computed using the following equation

$$Z_{in} = Z_0 \times \frac{Z_L \cosh(\eta\ell) + Z_0 \sinh(\eta\ell)}{Z_L \sinh(\eta\ell) + Z_0 \cosh(\eta\ell)} \tag{9}$$

where

Z_{in} = complex impedance at input of line = $R_{in} \pm j\,X_{in}$

Z_L = complex load impedance at end of line = $R_l \pm j\,X_l$

Z_0 = characteristic impedance of line = $R_0 \pm j\,X_0$

η = complex loss coefficient = $\alpha + j\,b$

α = matched line loss attenuation constant, in nepers/unit length (1 neper = 8.688 dB, so multiply line loss in dB per unit length by 8.688)

β = phase constant of line in radians/unit length (multiply electrical length in degrees by 2π radians/360 degrees)

ℓ = electrical length of line in same units of length as used for α.

Solving this equation manually is tedious, since it incorporates hyperbolic cosines and sines of the complex loss coefficient, but it may be solved using a traditional paper Smith Chart or software that performs the Smith Chart operations. *TLW* can perform this transformation, but without Smith Chart graphics.

There are many antenna analyzers available to amateurs that will measure the complex impedance at the input to a transmission line. Given the impedance in the series format, R + *j*X, *TLW* can make the transformations.

Let us go through an example. Use some of the values shown in the table for the 100-foot center-fed dipole in **Table 24.4**. Suppose we would like to use the antenna on 3.8 MHz and are feeding it with a 100-foot length of 450-Ω window line. The antenna's feed point impedance of 39 – *j*362 Ω creates an SWR of 17.7:1. At the transmitter end of the feed line, using *TLW* shows the impedance is transformed to 233 – *j*1066 Ω for an SWR of 13.9:1. Line loss would be 1.2 dB due to the high SWR. Remember that the high SWR will be present in the feed line even if an antenna tuner converts the line's input impedance to 50 Ω.

Table 24.6
Impedance of Center-Fed 100-Foot Flattop Dipole, 50 Feet High Over Average Ground

Frequency (MHz)	*Antenna Feed point Impedance (Ω)*	*Total Loss for 100 ft 450-Ω Line (dB)*	*Feed Point SWR*
1.83	4.5 – *j* 1673	13.1	390
3.8	39 – *j* 362	1.18	18.3
7.1	481 + *j* 964	0.55	6.7
10.1	2584 – *j* 3292	1.46	16.8
14.1	85 – *j* 123	0.67	5.2
18.1	2097 + *j* 1552	1.05	8.1
21.1	345 – *j* 1073	1.43	10.1
24.9	202 + *j* 367	0.63	3.9
28.4	2493 – *j* 1375	1.26	8.1

If we were using RG-213 coax to feed this antenna, the situation would be quite different: feed point SWR would be 62.34, impedance at the transmitter would be 6.9 – *j*62.4 Ω for an SWR of 16.7:1, and the feed line loss would be 5.7 dB. Entering the feed point impedance values for the different frequencies and switching feed line types between parallel conductor and coax is very instructive.

Table 24.6 shows a similar set of impedances for a 66-foot inverted-V dipole with the center 50 feet above the ground. This might be a very good 40 meter antenna but when it is fed with 100 feet of 450 Ω window line, the impedance is no longer anywhere close to 50 Ω on the dipole's fundamental frequency. Again, using *TLW* to check the SWR and total line loss is a useful exercise.

Smith Chart Software

The standard way of visualizing transmission line and impedance matching mechanics is by using a Smith chart. (If you are unfamiliar with the Smith chart, the supplemental information for the **Transmission Lines** chapter includes a detailed tutorial on the Smith chart.) Paper charts, however, have been replaced by interactive computer software such as the easy-to-use *jjSmith* (Windows only) by Jim Tonne, W4ENE, available on the *ARRL Handbook's* reference website (**www.arrl.org/arrl-handbook-reference**) and *SimSmith* (**www.ae6ty.com/Smith_Charts.html**) by Ward Harriman, AE6TY. *SimSmith* is written in Java and runs on a number of operating systems. Learning about the Smith chart will be a great aid in understanding the mechanics of transmission lines and impedance matching.

24.3.2 TRANSMISSION LINE SELECTION

Until you get into the microwave region where waveguides become practical, there are only two practical choices for transmission lines: coaxial cable and parallel-conductor lines such as open wire or ladder line and window line. (Refer to the **Transmission Lines** chapter for information about the different types of feed lines.)

The shielding of coaxial cable offers advantages in incidental radiation and routing flexibility. Coax can be tied or taped to the legs of a metal tower without problem, for example. Some varieties of coax can even be buried underground. Coaxial cable can perform acceptably even with significant SWR. A drawback of coaxial line is its loss, particularly at moderate to high SWR. For example, a 100-foot length of RG-213 coax has 1.1 dB matched-line loss at 30 MHz. If this line were used with a load of $250 + j0\ \Omega$ (an SWR of 5:1), the total line loss would be 2.2 dB. This represents about a half S unit on most receivers.

On the other hand, open-wire line has the advantage of both lower loss and lower cost compared to coax. At 30 MHz, 600-Ω open-wire line has a matched loss of only 0.1 dB. If you use such open-wire line with the same 5:1 SWR, the total loss would about 0.3 dB. In fact, even if the SWR rose to 20:1, the total loss would be less than 1 dB.

Despite their inherently low-loss characteristics, open-wire lines are not often employed above about 100 MHz. This is because the physical spacing between the two wires begins to become an appreciable fraction of a wavelength, leading to undesirable radiation by the line itself. Some form of coaxial cable is almost universally used in the VHF and UHF amateur bands.

Open-wire line is enjoying a renaissance of sorts with amateurs wishing to cover multiple HF bands with a single-wire antenna. Doublets of various lengths (44, 88, and 105 feet are popular lengths) fed with open-wire line into an antenna tuner have become popular as a simple all-band antenna. The simple 135-foot long 80 meter dipole, fed with 450-Ω window line, is also very popular as an all-band antenna.

So, apart from concerns about convenience and the matter of cost, how do you go about choosing a transmission line for a particular antenna? Let's start with some simple cases.

Feeding a Single-Band Antenna

If the antenna system is only required to operate on a single band and if the feed point impedance of the antenna doesn't vary too radically across the band, then the choice of transmission line is easy. Most amateurs would opt for convenience — they would use coaxial cable to feed the antenna, usually without an antenna tuner.

An example of such an installation is a half-wave 80 meter dipole fed with 50-Ω coax. The matched-line loss for 100 feet of 50-Ω RG-213 coax at 3.5 MHz is only 0.33 dB. At each end of the 80 meter band, this dipole will exhibit an SWR of about 6:1. The additional loss caused by this level of SWR at this frequency is less than 0.6 dB, for a total line loss of 0.9 dB. Since 1 dB represents an almost undetectable change in signal strength at the receiving end, it does not matter whether the line is "flat" (low SWR) or not for this 80 meter system.

This is true provided that the transmitter can operate properly into the load presented to it by the impedance at the input of the transmission line. Even if the feed line loss is low, an antenna tuner is sometimes required to ensure that the transmitter operates into its design load impedance. On the other amateur bands, where the percentage bandwidth is smaller than that on 75/80 meters, a simple dipole fed with coax will provide an acceptable SWR for most transmitters without an antenna tuner.

If you want a better match at the antenna feed point of a single-band antenna to coax, you can provide some sort of matching network at the antenna. We'll look further into schemes for achieving matched antenna systems later in this chapter, when we'll examine single-band methods of matching feed point and feed line impedances.

Feeding a Multiband Antenna

A multiband antenna is one where special techniques are used to make a single antenna present a consistent feed point impedance on each of several amateur bands. Often, trap circuits are employed. (Information on traps is given in the **Multiband HF Antennas** chapter.) For example, a trap dipole presents a feed point impedance similar to that of a $\lambda/2$ dipole on each of the bands for which it is designed.

Note that "resonance" only means that the self-impedance of the antenna is completely resistive (no reactance) and does not imply that the value of the impedance is low. For example, the 135-foot dipole may be resonant on 3.5 MHz and all harmonics but its feed point impedance will vary from low values at the fundamental and odd harmonics (10.5, 17.5, 24.5 MHz) to very high impedances at even harmonics (7.0, 14.0, 21.0, 28.0 MHz). Yet it may be resonant at all of those frequencies.

Another common multiband antenna is constructed from several dipoles cut for different frequencies and connected in parallel at a common feed point and fed with a single coaxial

Using *TLW* to Determine SWR

The program *TLW* can be used in two important ways: to determine SWR and impedance on the "other end" of transmission lines. The first case occurs when you are given a certain load impedance, such as that of an antenna feed point, and wish to know what the SWR and impedance will be at the input of the feed line. This type of information is used to design impedance-matching networks and antenna tuners for use in the station. From the program's main screen, select the feed line type and length. Enter frequency and the load resistance and reactance, specifying LOAD for the location of the impedance. The SWR and impedance at the input of the feed line will be displayed at the bottom of the window. The additional loss due to SWR is also calculated.

The second case works in reverse. It occurs when you know the SWR (or impedance) at the input to the feed line and want to know the SWR (or impedance) at the load (antenna) end of the feed line. Enter the cable type and length, frequency, and a value for RESISTANCE equal to SWR × Z_0. (If you know the input impedance, enter it instead.) Specify INPUT for the location where SWR is specified. The SWR (and impedance) will be displayed at the bottom of the window along with the additional line loss due to SWR.

cable. This arrangement acts as an independent λ/2 dipole on each band. (Interaction between the individual dipoles is discussed in the **Multiband HF Antennas** chapter.)

Another type of multiband antenna is a log-periodic dipole array (LPDA), which features moderate gain and pattern with a low SWR across a fairly wide band of frequencies. See the **Log-Periodic Dipole Arrays** chapter for more details.

Yet another popular multiband antenna is the trap triband Yagi, or a multiband interlaced quad. On the amateur HF bands, the triband Yagi is almost as popular as the simple λ/2 dipole. See the **HF Yagi and Quad Antennas** chapter for more information on this antenna.

A multiband antenna doesn't present much of an antenna system design challenge — you simply feed it with coax that has characteristic impedance close to the antenna's feed point impedance. Usually, 50-Ω cable, such as RG-213, is used.

Table 24.7
Impedance of Center-Fed 66-Foot Inverted-V Dipole, 50-Foot High Apex Over Average Ground

Frequency (MHz)	*Antenna Feed point Impedance (Ω)*	*Total Loss for 100 ft 450-Ω Line (dB)*	*Feed Point SWR*
1.83	1.6 – *j* 2257	19.7	622
3.8	10 – *j* 879	7.2	153
7.1	65 – *j* 41	0.6	6.3
10.1	22 + *j* 648	4.0	73
14.1	5287 – *j* 1310	1.5	13.9
18.1	198 – *j* 820	1.4	10.8
21.1	103 – *j* 181	0.73	4.8
24.9	269 + *j* 570	0.84	4.9
28.4	3089 + *j* 774	1.3	8.1

Feeding a Multiband Nonresonant Antenna

Let's say that you wish to use a single antenna, such as a 100-foot long doublet, on multiple amateur bands. You know from the **Antenna Fundamentals** chapter that since the physical length of the antenna is fixed, the feed point impedance of the antenna will vary on each band. In other words, except by chance, the antenna will *not* be resonant — or even close to resonant — on multiple bands. This presents special challenges with regard to feed line selection.

For multiband nonresonant antenna systems, the most appropriate transmission line is often a parallel-conductor line, because of the inherently low matched-line loss characteristic of these types of lines. Such a system is called an *unmatched* system, because no attempt is made to match the impedance at the antenna's feed point to the Z_0 of the transmission line. Commercial 450-Ω window ladder line has become popular for this kind of application. It is almost as good as traditional open-wire or ladder-line for most amateur systems.

The transmission line will be mismatched most of the time and on some frequencies it will be severely mismatched. Because of the mismatch, the SWR on the line will vary widely with frequency. As shown in the **Transmission Lines** chapter, such a variation in load impedance has an impact on the loss created in the feed line. Let's look at the losses in a typical multiband nonresonant system.

Table 24.6 summarizes the feed point information over the HF amateur bands for a 100-foot long dipole, mounted as a flattop, 50 feet high over typical ground. In addition, the table shows the total line loss created in 100 feet of 450-Ω ladder line by the SWR at the antenna feed point. As usual, there is nothing particularly significant about the choice of a 100-foot long antenna or a 100-foot long transmission line. Both are practical lengths that could very well be encountered in a real-world situation. At 1.8 MHz, the loss in the transmission line is large — 13.1 dB. This is due to the fact that the SWR at the feed point is a very high 390:1, a direct result of the fact that the antenna is extremely short in terms of wavelength.

Table 24.7 summarizes the same information as in Table 24.6, but this time for a 66-foot long inverted-V dipole, with the apex 50 feet over typical ground and an included angle between its two legs of 120°. The situation at 1.83 MHz is even worse, as might be expected because this antenna is even shorter electrically than its 100-foot flattop cousin. The line loss has risen to 19.7 dB!

Under such severe mismatches, another problem can arise. Transmission lines with solid dielectric have voltage and current limitations. At lower frequencies with electrically short antennas, this can be a more compelling limitation than the amount of power loss. The ability of a line to handle RF power is inversely proportional to the SWR. For example, a line rated for 1.5 kW when matched, should be operated at only 150 W when the SWR is 10:1. At the mismatch on 1.83 MHz illustrated for the 100-foot doublet or the 66-foot inverted-V dipole in Tables 24.6 and 24.7, the line may well arc over, burning the insulation, due to the extremely high SWR. (To calculate the maximum voltage, see the "Line Voltages and Current" section of the **Transmission Lines** chapter.)

To use *TLW* to see the voltage and current along the feed line for 1500 W of input power, select VOLT/CURRENT and click GRAPH. On 160 meters, where the feed point SWR is highest, the maximum voltage is 6600 V. This would exceed the voltage rating for RG-213 (3700 V) by nearly a factor of two and probably result in a voltage breakdown near the load.

A feed line of 450-Ω window-type ladder line using two #16 AWG conductors should be safe up to the 1500 W level for frequencies where the antenna is at least a half-wavelength long. For the 100-foot dipole, this would be above 3.8 MHz, and for the 66-foot long inverted-V, this would be above 7 MHz. For the very short antennas illustrated above, however, even 450-Ω window line may not be able to take full amateur legal power. Check the line's maximum rated voltage in the table in the **Transmission Lines** chapter and compare with that expected at your maximum power and expected maximum SWR. The article "Don't Blow Up Your Balun" by Dean Straw, N6BV, includes several excellent examples of antenna systems that place a lot of stress on chokes, baluns and antenna tuners. The article is included in the downloadable supplemental material.

24.3.3 MEASURING TRANSMISSION LINE LOSS

The most obvious method is to use a calibrated wattmeter and dummy load. With the wattmeter at the input to the line and the dummy load at the output, apply power to the line and measure forward power, P_{IN}. (With the dummy load attached, there should be no reflected power.) Remove power and connect the input of the line directly to the power source. Connect the wattmeter between the output of the line and the dummy load. Apply the same amount of power and read forward power at the dummy load, P_{OUT}. The loss in the line is equal to 10 log (P_{OUT} / P_{IN}).

Without a wattmeter, loss can be measured by using a calibrated mismatch. Assuming a 50-Ω system, select a non-inductive resistor between 150 Ω (3:1 SWR) and 270 Ω (5.4:1 SWR). Convert the resistor's expected SWR to return loss (RL), using **Table 24.8**. For example, a 220-Ω resistive load results in a 4.4:1 SWR which is a return loss of 4.0 dB. Connect the resistor to the output of the line. Make sure the resistor leads are very short so that they do not add a significant amount of inductance. Measure SWR at the input to the line and convert to return loss. The line loss is the difference between return loss at the line input and return loss of the load. For example, with the 220-Ω load (4.0 dB RL) and 100 feet of RG-58 coax at 10 MHz, the input SWR might be 3.0:1 (RL = 6.0 dB). The line loss at this frequency is 6.0 dB – 4.0 dB = 2.0 dB.

Some methods use an open or short circuit at the load end of the line (an infinite SWR and RL = 0) to measure line loss. Most amateur instrumentation is not well-calibrated at

Table 24.8
Reflection Coefficient, Attenuation, SWR and Return Loss

Reflection Coefficient (%)	*Attenuation (dB)*	*Max SWR*	*Return Loss (dB)*
1.000	0.000434	1.020	40.00
1.517	0.001000	1.031	36.38
2.000	0.001738	1.041	33.98
3.000	0.003910	1.062	30.46
4.000	0.006954	1.083	27.96
4.796	0.01000	1.101	26.38
5.000	0.01087	1.105	26.02
6.000	0.01566	1.128	24.44
7.000	0.02133	1.151	23.10
7.576	0.02500	1.164	22.41
8.000	0.02788	1.174	21.94
9.000	0.03532	1.198	20.92
10.000	0.04365	1.222	20.00
10.699	0.05000	1.240	19.41
11.000	0.05287	1.247	19.17
12.000	0.06299	1.273	18.42
13.085	0.07500	1.301	17.66
14.000	0.08597	1.326	17.08
15.000	0.09883	1.353	16.48
15.087	0.10000	1.355	16.43
16.000	0.1126	1.381	15.92
17.783	0.1396	1.433	15.00
18.000	0.1430	1.439	14.89
19.000	0.1597	1.469	14.42
20.000	0.1773	1.500	13.98
22.000	0.2155	1.564	13.15
23.652	0.2500	1.620	12.52
24.000	0.2577	1.632	12.40
25.000	0.2803	1.667	12.04
26.000	0.3040	1.703	11.70
27.000	0.3287	1.740	11.37
28.000	0.3546	1.778	11.06
30.000	0.4096	1.857	10.46
31.623	0.4576	1.925	10.00
32.977	0.5000	1.984	9.64
33.333	0.5115	2.000	9.54
34.000	0.5335	2.030	9.37
35.000	0.5675	2.077	9.12
36.000	0.6028	2.125	8.87
37.000	0.6394	2.175	8.64
38.000	0.6773	2.226	8.40
39.825	0.75000	2.324	8.00
40.000	0.7572	2.333	7.96
42.000	0.8428	2.448	7.54
42.857	0.8814	2.500	7.36
44.000	0.9345	2.571	7.13
45.351	1.0000	2.660	6.87
48.000	1.1374	2.846	6.38
50.000	1.2494	3.000	6.02
52.000	1.3692	3.167	5.68
54.042	1.5000	3.352	5.35
56.234	1.6509	3.570	5.00
58.000	1.7809	3.762	4.73
60.000	1.9382	4.000	4.44
60.749	2.0000	4.095	4.33
63.000	2.1961	4.405	4.01
66.156	2.5000	4.909	3.59
66.667	2.5528	5.000	3.52
70.627	3.0000	5.809	3.02
70.711	3.0103	5.829	3.01

$$\rho = \frac{SWR - 1}{SWR + 1}$$

where $\rho = 0.01 \times$ (reflection coefficient in %)

$$\rho = 10^{-RL/20}$$

where RL = return loss (dB)

$$\rho = \sqrt{1 - (0.1^{X})}$$

where X = A/10 and A = attenuation (dB)

$$SWR = \frac{1 + \rho}{1 - \rho}$$

high SWR and will give an unreliable reading for SWR and RL. Using a moderate mismatch improves the accuracy of the final result. You can replace the feed line with inline attenuators to check this more accurate method with the known amounts of loss.

24.3.4 ANTENNA TUNER LOCATION

To meet the goal of presenting a 50-Ω load to the transmitter, in many antenna systems it is necessary to place an antenna tuner between the transmitter and the transmission line going to the antenna. This is particularly true for a single-wire antenna used on multiple amateur bands.

The tuner is usually located near the transmitter in order to adjust it for different bands or antennas. If a tuner is in use for one particular band and does not need to be adjusted once set up for minimum VSWR, it can be placed in a weatherproof container near the antenna. Some automatic tuners are designed to be installed at the antenna, for example. For some situations, placing the tuner at the base of a tower can be particularly effective and eliminates having to climb the tower to perform maintenance on the tuner.

It is useful to consider the performance of the entire antenna system when deciding where to install the antenna tuner and what types of feed line to use in order to minimize system losses. Here is an example, using the program *TLW*. Let's use the familiar 100-foot doublet described previously. As extreme examples, we will use 3.8 and 28.4 MHz with 200 feet of transmission line. There are many ways to configure this system, but three examples are shown in **Figure 24.10**. A low-pass L-network is assumed for all three systems.

Example 1 in Figure 24.10A shows a 200-foot run of RG-213 going to a 1:1 balun that feeds the antenna. The tuner in the station reduces the VSWR for proper matching in the transmitter. Example 2 (Figure 24.10B) shows a similar arrangement using 450-Ω window line. Example 3 (Figure 24.10C) shows a 50-foot run of 450-Ω line dropping straight down to a remote tuner near the ground and 150 feet of RG-213 going to the shack. **Table 24.9** summarizes the losses and the L-network component values required. Balun losses are not included.

Some interesting conclusions can be drawn. First, direct feeding this antenna with coax through a balun is very lossy — a poor solution. If the flattop were λ/2 long — a resonant half-wave dipole — direct coax feed would be a good method. In the second example, direct feed with 450-Ω low-loss line does not give the lowest loss. The combination method in Example 3 provides the best solution. (Note the very high C value at 3.8 MHz and the very low L value at 28.4 MHz in Example 1

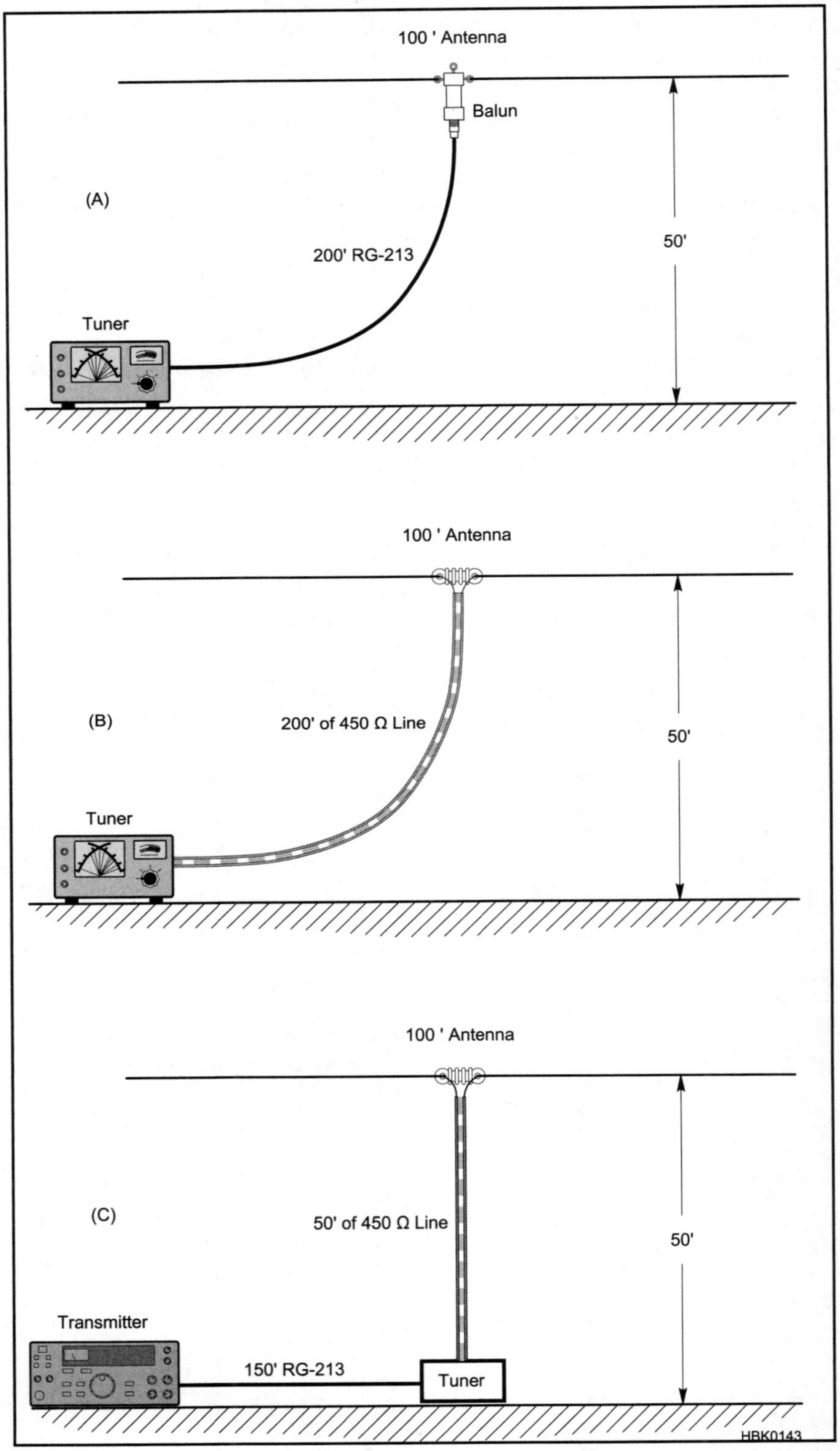

Figure 24.10 — Variations of an antenna system with different losses. The examples are discussed in the text.

Table 24.9
Low-Pass L-Network Tuner Settings and Performance

Example (Fig 24.10)	*Frequency (MHz)*	*L (µH)*	*C (pF)*	*Line Loss (dB)*	*Tuner Loss (dB)*	*Total Loss (dB)*
1	3.8	1.5	2308	8.4	0.1	8.5
	28.4	0.13	182	12.8	0.1	12.9
2	3.8	20.5	47.5	1.2	0.6	1.8
	28.4	0.8	59	2.3	0.1	2.4
3	3.8	12.5	290	1.0	0.2	1.2
	28.4	1.7	9	0.7	0.2	0.9

and the very low C value at 28.4 MHz in Example 3. A pi- or T-network might be a better choice for these frequencies and impedances.)

Example 3 has some additional advantages. It feeds the antenna in a symmetrical arrangement which is best to reduce common-mode current pickup on the shield of the feed line. The shorter feed line will not weigh down the antenna as much, and the balun's additional weight and expense are also avoided. The coax back to the transmitter can be buried or laid on the ground and it is perfectly matched. Burial of the cable will also prevent any additional common-mode currents from being induced on the coax shield. The tuner is then adjusted for minimum SWR on the cable as measured in the station at the transmitter.

24.3.5 TRANSMISSION LINE STUBS

The impedance-transformation properties of a transmission line are useful in a number of applications. If the terminating resistance is zero (that is, a short) at the end of a low-loss line with length $\ell < \lambda/4$, the input impedance is a reactance given by:

$$X_{in} \cong Z_0 \tan \ell \quad (10)$$

If the line termination is an open circuit, the input reactance is given by

$$X_{in} \cong Z_0 \cot \ell \quad (11)$$

The input of a short (less than $\lambda/4$) length of line with a short circuit as a terminating load appears as an inductance, while an open-circuited line appears as a capacitance. This is a useful property of a transmission line, since it can be used as a low-loss inductor or capacitor in matching networks. Such lines are often referred to as stubs.

A line that is electrically $\lambda/4$ long is a special kind of a stub. When a $\lambda/4$ line is short circuited at its load end, it presents an open circuit at its input. Conversely, a $\lambda/4$ line with an open circuit at its load end presents a short circuit at its input. Such a line inverts the impedance of a short or an open circuit at the frequency for which the line is $\lambda/4$ long. This is also true for frequencies that are odd multiples of the $\lambda/4$ frequency. However, for frequencies where the length of the line is $\lambda/2$, or integer multiples thereof, the line will duplicate the termination at its end.

Building a Coax Stub

This procedure results in a shorted stub tuned to be $\lambda/2$ long because this is the easiest frequency at which to measure an impedance null. The stub will be $\lambda/4$ long at one-half the $\lambda/2$ frequency. For example, if you want to build a stub that is $\lambda/4$ long at 7.1 MHz, tune it to be $\lambda/2$ long a 14.2 MHz. The short can either be left in place for a shorted stub or removed for an open stub. If you are unfamiliar with stub building, look up the approximate stub length in a published table such as in the next section. As you begin your measurements, check to be sure the stub will be about the same length as in the table and not off by a factor of two, which indicates a calculation problem.

Begin by installing the desired connector on one end of a piece of coax, cutting the coax about 10% longer than the computed value. Strip ½ inch or so at the far end and short the shield to the center conductor with a direct, minimum-length connection.

Connect the stub to an impedance measuring device, and find the lowest frequency at which impedance Z and reactance (X) are minimum, near zero ohms, repeating the termination impedance which is a short. (If you are using an antenna analyzer, ignore the SWR measurement — use only the Z and X values.) At this frequency the stub is $\lambda/2$ long. It will be $\lambda/4$ long at ½ the measured frequency.

The frequency should be below your desired frequency by about 10%, meaning the stub is too long. Use the actual percentage below your target frequency to tell you how much to cut, then cut about half that much. Repeat until the stub is at the desired frequency. Carefully solder the shorted end and weatherproof it.

Tuning a Transmission Line Stub

Because different manufacturing runs of coax will have slightly different velocity factors, a quarter-wave stub is usually cut a little longer than calculated, and then carefully pruned by snipping off short pieces, while using an antenna analyzer or VNA to monitor the response at the harmonic frequency. Velocity factor (VF) also changes a small amount with frequency, enough to be significant when measuring and cutting a stub. VF error can be a fraction of a percent at HF which is enough to move the resonant frequency substantially. For example, the 20 meter band is about 2.5% wide so a 0.5% error represents about 70 kHz. Either measure VF at the frequency being used or leave enough margin in the initial length to accommodate variations.

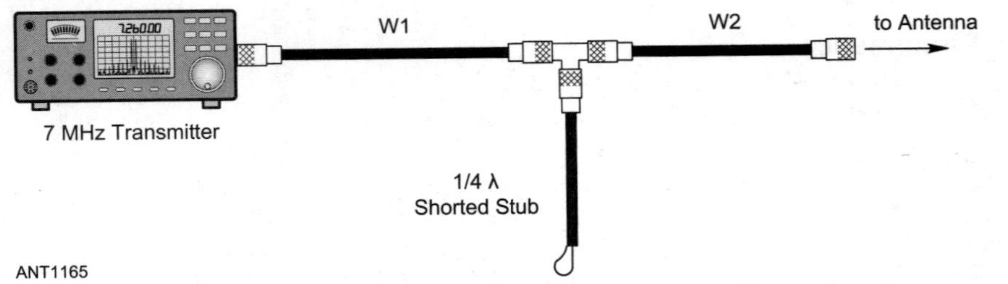

Figure 24.11 — Method of attaching a stub to a feed line.

Because the end of the coax is an open circuit while pieces are being snipped away, the input of a λ/4 line will show a short circuit exactly at the fundamental frequency. Once the coax has been pruned to frequency, a short jumper is soldered across the end, and the response at the second harmonic frequency is measured. **Figure 24.11** shows how to connect a shorted stub to a transmission line and **Figure 24.12** shows a typical frequency response.

The shorted quarter-wave stub shows low loss at 7 MHz and at 21 MHz where it is 3λ/4 long. It nulls 14 and 28 MHz. This is useful for reducing the even harmonics of a 7 MHz transmitter. It can be used for a 21 MHz transmitter as well, and will reduce any spurious emissions such as phase noise and wideband noise which might cause interference to receivers operating on 14 or 28 MHz. (Note that spurious emissions *must* be filtered out *at the transmitter* or they become in-band signals to a receiver and cannot be removed.)

The open-circuited quarter-wave stub has a low impedance at the fundamental frequency, so a transmitter must operate at two times the frequency for which the stub is cut. For example, a quarter-wave open stub cut for 3.5 MHz will present a high impedance at 7 MHz where it is λ/2 long. It will present a high impedance at those frequencies where it is a multiple of λ/2, or 7, 14 and 28 MHz. It would be connected in the same manner as Figure 24.11 and the frequency plot is shown in **Figure 24.13**.

This open stub can protect a receiver operating on 7, 14, 21 or 28 MHz from interference by a 3.5 MHz transmitter. It also has nulls at 10.5, 17.5 and 24.5 MHz — the 3rd, 5th and 7th harmonics. The length of a quarter-wave stub may be calculated as follows:

$$L_e = \frac{VF \times 983.6}{4f} \qquad (12)$$

where

L_e = length in feet

VF = propagation constant for the coax in use

f = frequency in MHz.

For the special case of RG-213 (and any similar cable with VF = 0.66), equation 11 can be simplified to:

$$L_e = \frac{163.5}{f} \qquad (13)$$

where

L_e = length in feet

f = frequency in MHz.

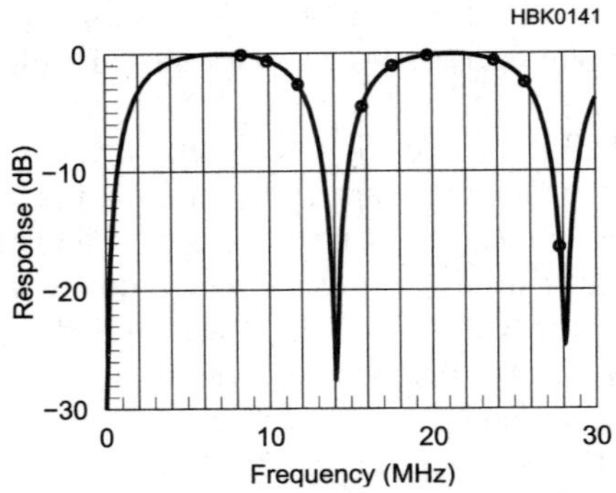

Figure 24.12 — Frequency response of a shorted λ/4 stub cut for 14 MHz.

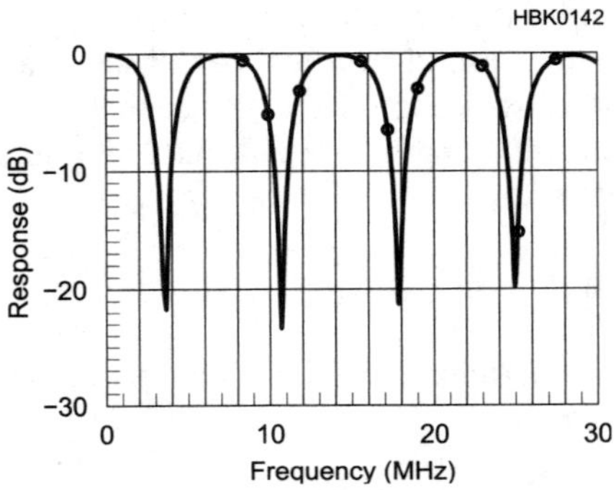

Figure 24.13 — Frequency response of an open λ/4 stub cut for 7 MHz.

Table 24.10
Quarter-Wave Stub Lengths for the HF Contesting Bands

Freq (MHz)	*Length (L_e)**	*Remove per 100 kHz*
1.8	90 ft, 10 in	57⅜ in
3.5	46 ft, 9 in	15½ in
7.0	23 ft, 4 in	4 in
14.0	11 ft, 8 in	1 in
21.0	7 ft, 9 in	7/16 in
28.0	5 ft, 10 in	¼ in

*Lengths shown are for RG-213 and any similar cable, assuming a 0.66 velocity factor (L_e = 163.5/f).

Table 24.10 solves this equation for the major contesting bands where stubs are often used. The third column shows how much of the stub to cut off if the desired frequency is 100 kHz higher in frequency. For example: To cut a stub for 14.250 MHz, reduce the overall length shown by 2.5 × 1 inches, or 2.5 inches. There is some variation in dielectric constant of coaxial cable from batch to batch or manufacturer to manufacturer, so it is always best to measure the stub's fundamental resonance before proceeding.

Measuring Stubs with One-Port Instruments

Many of the common measuring instruments used by amateurs are one-port devices, meaning they have one connector at which the measurement — typically VSWR — is made. Probably the most popular instrument for this type of work is the antenna analyzer, available from a number of manufacturers.

To test a stub using an antenna analyzer, connect the stub to the meter by itself and tune the meter for a minimum reactance value (or impedance, if reactance is not displayed), ignoring the VSWR display. If practical, tune the stub with one end shorted so as to determine the stub's λ/2 frequency, then dividing the frequency by two to get the λ/4 frequency. This will be easier to read accurately on the analyzer and give more accurate results. It is almost impossible to get an accurate reading on the higher HF bands, particularly with open stubs. For example, when a quarter-wave open stub cut for 20 meters was swept to determine the frequency of the null on an MFJ-259 SWR analyzer, the frequency measured 14.650 MHz, with a very broad null. A recheck with a professional-quality network analyzer measured 14.018 MHz. (Resolution on the network analyzer is about ±5 kHz.) Running the same test on a λ/4 shorted stub gave a measurement of 28.320 MHz on the MFJ-259 and 28.398 MHz on the network analyzer. (These inaccuracies are typical of amateur instrumentation and are meant to illustrate the difficulties of using inexpensive instruments for sensitive measurements.)

Other one-port instruments that measure phase can be used to get a more accurate reading. The additional length added by the required T must be accounted for. If a measurement is made without the T and then with the T, the average value will be close to correct. An alternative is to use a double-female adaptor of the same length as the T connection when making measurements.

Measuring Stubs with Two-Port Instruments

A two-port measurement is made with a signal generator and a separate detector, such as provided by a vector network analyzer (VNA) as described in the chapter on **Antenna and Transmission Line Measurements**. If a VNA is not available, attach a T connector to the generator with the stub connected to one side. The other side is connected to a cable of any length that goes to the detector. The detector should present a 50-Ω load to the cable. This is how the network analyzer is configured, and it is similar to how the stub is connected in actual use. If the generator is accurately calibrated, the measurement can be very good. There are a number of ways to do this without buying an expensive piece of lab equipment.

An antenna analyzer can be used as the signal generator. Measurements will be quite accurate if the detector has 30 to 40 dB dynamic range. Two setups were tested by W2VJN for accuracy. The first used a digital voltmeter (DVM) with a diode detector. (A germanium diode must be used for the best dynamic range.) Tests on open and shorted stubs at 14 MHz returned readings within 20 kHz of the network analyzer. Another test was run using an oscilloscope as the detector with a 50-Ω load on the input. This test produced results that were essentially the same as the network analyzer.

A noise generator can be used in combination with a receiver as the detector. (An inexpensive noise generator kit is available from Elecraft, **www.elecraft.com**.) Set the receiver for 2-3 kHz bandwidth and turn off the AGC. An ac voltmeter connected to the audio output of the receiver will serve as a null detector. The noise level into the receiver without the stub connected should be just at or below the limiting level. With the stub connected, the noise level in the null should drop by 25 or 30 dB. Connect the UHF T to the noise generator using any necessary adapters. Connect the stub to one side of the T and connect the receiver to the other side with a short cable. Tune the receiver around the expected null frequency. After locating the null, snip off pieces of cable until the null moves to the desired frequency. Accuracy with this method is within 20 or 30 kHz of the network analyzer readings on 14 MHz stubs.

Connecting Stubs

To connect a stub to a coaxial transmission line it is necessary to insert a T adaptor in the line. If the stub is to be connected directly at the transmitter, a female-male-female T is used with the male port connected directly to the transmitter and the antenna feed line and stub connected to the two female ports. If the stub is to be inserted in the feed line, an all-female port T can be used.

It should be noted that the T inserts a small additional length in series with the stub that lowers the resonant frequency. The additional length for an Amphenol UHF T is about ⅜ inch. This length is negligible at 1.8 and 3.5 MHz, but on the higher bands the additional length should be accounted for when measuring the stub.

24.3.6 TRANSMISSION LINE STUBS AS FILTERS

[Material in this section was adapted from papers and articles by George Cutsogeorge, W2VJN; Jim Brown, K9YC (**audiosystemsgroup.com/publish.htm**); and Ward Harriman, AE6TY (**ae6ty.com/Smith_Charts.html**), which are included with this book's downloadable supplemental information and/or online. (See this book's downloadable supplemental information directory and this chapter's Bibliography.) The ARRL appreciates the contributions of these authors. — Ed.]

The impedance transformation properties of stubs can

be put to use as filters. For example, if a shorted line is cut to be λ/4 long at 7.1 MHz, the impedance looking into the input of the line will be an open circuit. The line will have no effect if placed in parallel with a transmitter's output terminals. However, at *twice* the frequency, 14.2 MHz, that same line is now λ/2 and the line looks like a short circuit. This *quarter-wave stub* will act as a filter for not only the second harmonic, but also for higher even-order harmonics, such as the fourth or sixth harmonics. Quarter-wave stubs made of good-quality coax, such as RG-213, can provide 20 to 30 dB of harmonic attenuation or more if located properly in the feed line.

This filtering action is extremely useful in multi-transmitter situations, such as during Field Day, emergency operations centers, portable communications facilities and multioperator contest stations. Transmission line stubs can operate at high power where lumped-constant filters would be expensive. Using stub filters reduces noise, harmonics and strong fundamental signals from the closely-spaced antennas which cause overload and interference to receivers.

One caveat is that there may be other inter-station paths for harmonic energy to get from one radio to another. This coupling is not addressed by adding stubs and may be a reason why applying stubs or bandpass filters may not give the results you expect. Another reason for poor harmonic suppression is that harmonics may be generated by non-linear junctions or devices in the antenna system or in the vicinity of the antenna system. If you suspect these or other sources for harmonic generation or coupling, use test equipment to build and then test the stub. Troubleshoot harmonic generation or coupling separately.

Stub filters can also be used as receive filters to remove a strong fundamental signal received by an antenna system operating at a harmonic of the fundamental. In the following discussion, of stub placement, when placing a stub for receive filtering, reverse the references to transmitter and antenna. Also, do not alter the position of any transmit filter stubs when adding stubs for receive filtering.

Positioning a Stub Connection

This discussion will focus on the common application of using a shorted stub to act as a harmonic filter at even integer multiples of a transmitted signal's fundamental frequency. A stub works to suppress a harmonic by placing a short circuit across the line at the harmonic frequency. When a stub is placed in the line somewhere between the transmitter and antenna, the impedance at that point determines how well the stub will work. i.e. – attenuating the harmonic. If the stub is located at a low impedance point in the line, the short circuit is in parallel with the low impedance and so provides little additional attenuation. Additionally, if the length of coax between stub and transmitter output degrades the suppression provided by the transmitter output network, the total suppression (output network plus stub) may be no better than without the stub. ("Transmitter" in this section will refer to either a transceiver or power amplifier, including any filters that will be used.)

It is important to remember that for this application, impedance is measured or calculated at the frequency of the second harmonic, *not* the fundamental. The assumption is made that the antenna is reasonably well-matched to the line at the fundamental (SWR < 2:1) and poorly matched at the harmonic. This procedure is intended to be applied to monoband antenna systems and may be unreliable when the antenna in use is a multiband antenna matched to the line at the fundamental and harmonic(s) in question.

Note also that this procedure does not include the effects of an adjustable antenna tuner, such as an auto-tuner in a transmitter. If a tuner is used, the stub should be located with the tuner adjusted for operation at the fundamental. (This includes any tuning or impedance matching networks or stubs that match the antenna to the line at the fundamental frequency.)

Before beginning, you may not have to undertake a detailed process to achieve acceptable results. Build a stub λ/4 long at the fundamental frequency and prepare to attach it at a convenient point in your transmission line. Measure the strength of the harmonic to be suppressed by either using a receiver S-meter or a spectrum analyzer. Install the stub and determine the amount of attenuation of the harmonic. If you have sufficient attenuation, you need go no further!

Another option is to build the double-stub combination described in the next section as that is nearly guaranteed to provide at least 30 dB of harmonic attenuation at the expense of the extra stub, adaptors, and coupling line.

To optimize the location of the stub in the feed line, each of the three authors mentioned above approach the problem somewhat differently but the basic procedure is as follows:

Step 1: With the antenna connected, measure the complex impedance (at the second harmonic) at the input to the feed line.

Step 2: Use *TLW* or a Smith chart program such as *SimSmith* by AE6TY to find the location of impedance peaks on the line.

Step 3: Break the line at one of those points, insert a coax T (tee) adaptor and add the stub. The length of line from the stub to the antenna corresponds to cable W2 in Figure 24.11. (If you have acceptable results, you can stop here.)

Step 4: Make the line between the stub and the output of the transmitter (cable W1 in Figure 24.11) a length that preserves the harmonic suppression of the transmitter output network. This length of line is relatively non-critical with an error of up to 45° resulting in only 3 dB less attenuation than at the optimum point.

If the element of the transmitter's output matching network (including any filter circuits) nearest the point of connection to the antenna feed line is a series inductor (such as for a Pi-L output network), make the coax as short as possible or some even multiple of λ/2 at the harmonic. If that component is a capacitor, make cable W1 some odd multiple (1, 3, 5, etc.) of λ/4 at the harmonic. If you are using a double stub as below, W1 is the length of coax to the stub closest to the transmitter.

An alternate method is suggested by W2VJN in which the impedance is measured looking back into the transmitter output network through W1. Step 2 from above can then be repeated to find the optimum length of cable that results in

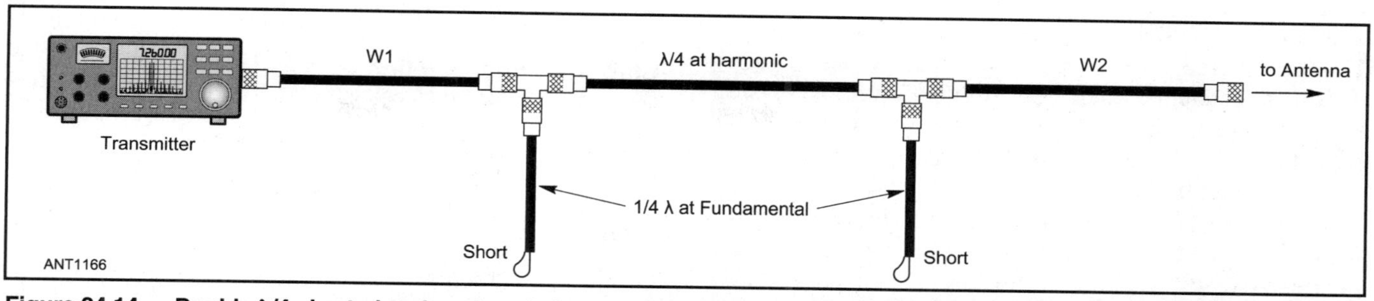

Figure 24.14 — Double λ/4 shorted stubs, placed λ/4 apart at the harmonic, guarantee the full effectiveness of at least one of the stubs, regardless of where the combination is placed in the feed line. If optimally placed, total attenuation is the sum of attenuation from each stub.

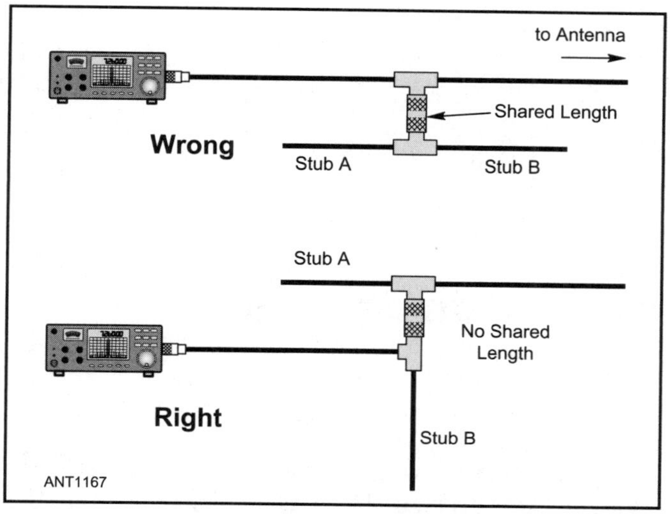

Figure 24.15 — When connecting stubs at a common point, do not connect them so that they share any length. Separate them with double female or "barrel" adaptor. This avoids interaction between the stubs which would shift the assembly's resonant frequencies.

a high impedance point at the stub connection point. By optimizing both W1 and W2, W2VJN has observed more than 50 dB of attenuation from a single stub.

Stub Combinations

A single stub will give 20 to 30 dB attenuation in the null if connected at a high-impedance point in the feed line as described above. A second stub can be added for additional attenuation if separated from the first stub by λ/4 at the frequency of the harmonic to be attenuated. This is shown in **Figure 24.14**. This technique will also provide good attenuation if you are unable to determine an optimum location for the stubs or are required to install the stubs in a non-optimum location. The stubs both force low-impedance points on the line at the harmonic, guaranteeing that at least one stub will have its full effect.

Open and shorted stubs can be combined together to attenuate higher harmonics as well as lower frequency bands. The stubs may be cut to the same frequency for maximum attenuation, or to two slightly different frequencies such as the CW and SSB frequencies in one band. Stubs should not be connected together at exactly the same point in the feed line, but separated by a very short length of line or a double female adaptor. Stubs should also not share any length. The correct way to connect multiple stubs is shown in **Figure 24.15**.

An interesting combination is the parallel connection of two ⅛ λ stubs, one open and the other shorted. The shorted stub will act as an inductor and the open stub as a capacitor. Their reactance will be equal and opposite, forming a resonant circuit. The null depth with this arrangement will be a bit better than a single quarter-wave shorted stub. This presents some possibilities when combinations of stubs are used in a band switching system. W2VJN's book *Managing Interstation Interference* presents a number of useful combinations. (See the Bibliography.)

24.3.7 PROJECT: A FIELD DAY STUB ASSEMBLY

Figure 24.16 shows a simple stub arrangement that can be useful in a two-transmitter Field Day station. The stubs reduce out-of-band noise produced by the transmitters that

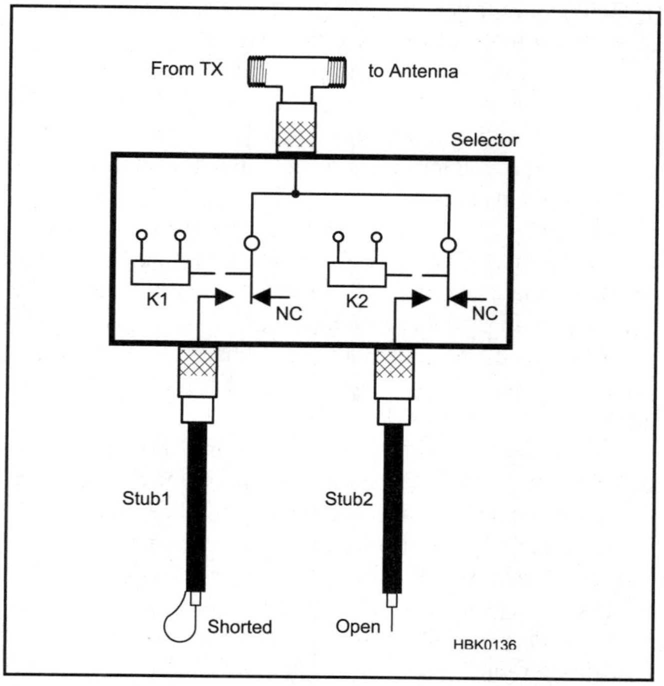

Figure 24.16 — Schematic of the Field Day stub switching relay control box. Table 24.11 shows which relays should be closed or for the desired operating band.

would cause interference to the other stations — a common Field Day problem where the stations are quite close together. This noise cannot be filtered out at the receiver and must be removed at the transmitter. One stub assembly would be connected to each transmitter output and manually switched for the appropriate band.

Two stubs are connected as shown. The two-relay selector box can be switched in four ways. Stub 1 is a shorted quarter-wave 40 meter stub. Stub 2 is an open quarter-wave 40 meter stub. Operation is as shown in **Table 24.11**.

The stubs must be cut and tuned while connected to the selector relays. RG-213 may be used for any amateur power level and will provide 25 to 30 dB reduction in the nulls. For power levels under 500 W or so, RG-8X may be used. It will provide a few dB less reduction in the nulls because of its slightly higher loss than RG-213.

Table 24.11
Stub Selector Operation
See Fig 24.16 for circuit details

Relay K1 Position	*Relay K2 Position*	*Bands Passed (meters)*	*Bands Nulled (meters)*
Open	Open	All	None
Energized	Energized	80	40, 20, 15, 10
Energized	Open	40, 15	20, 10
Open	Energized	20, 10	40, 15

24.4 TRANSMISSION LINE MATCHING DEVICES

Baluns, Chokes, and Transformers

It is useful to begin with the terminology of this important topic. The term "balun" applies to any device that transfers differential-mode signals between a balanced (*bal-*) system and an unbalanced (*un-*) system while maintaining symmetrical energy distribution at the terminals of the balanced system. The term only applies to the function of energy transfer, not to how the device is constructed. It doesn't matter whether the balanced-unbalanced transition is made through transmission line structures, flux-coupled transformers, or simply by blocking unbalanced current flow. A *common-mode choke*, for example, can perform the balun function by putting impedance in the path of common-mode currents at the load terminals, such as antenna feed point, and is therefore a balun.

A *current balun* forces symmetrical current at the balanced terminals. This is of particular importance in feeding antennas, since antenna currents determine the antenna's radiation pattern. A *voltage balun* forces symmetrical voltages at the balanced terminals. Voltage baluns are less effective in causing equal currents at their balanced terminals, such as at an antenna's feed point.

An *impedance transformer* may or may not perform the balun function. Impedance transformation (changing the ratio of voltage and current) is not required of a balun nor is it prohibited. There are balanced-to-balanced impedance transformers (transformers with isolated primary and secondary windings, for example) just as there are unbalanced-to-unbalanced or *unun* impedance transformers (autotransformer and transmission-line designs). A *transmission-line transformer* is a device that performs the function of power transfer (with or without impedance transformation) by utilizing the characteristics of transmission lines.

Multiple devices are often combined in a single package called a "balun." For example, a "4:1 current balun" is a 1:1 current balun in series with a 4:1 impedance transformer or voltage balun. Other names for baluns are common, such as "line isolator" for a choke balun. Baluns are often referred to by their construction — "bead balun," "coiled-coax balun," "sleeve balun," and so forth. What is important is to separate the function (power transfer between balanced and unbalanced systems) from the construction.

Types of Matching Devices

There are two types of devices discussed in this section. The first are reflective, in that they perform impedance transformation by setting up a series of reflections in the transmission line. These are called *synchronous transformers* because the reflections have precise phase relationships. The forward and reflected waves combine to create a different ratio of voltage and current, the definition of impedance.

The second type, *transmission line transformers*, isolate the output of short transmission lines from the input by blocking the common-mode signal path with a high impedance created by winding the line on ferrite material. That allows the differential-mode signals from each line to be combined as if they were independent signal sources. The signals can be combined in and out of phase, just as conventional transformer windings can be connected together to create different combinations of voltages and current.

24.4.1 QUARTER-WAVE TRANSFORMERS

The impedance-transforming properties of a $\lambda/4$ transmission line *synchronous transformer* or *Q-section* shown in **Figure 24.17A** can be used to good advantage for matching the feed point impedance of an antenna to the characteristic

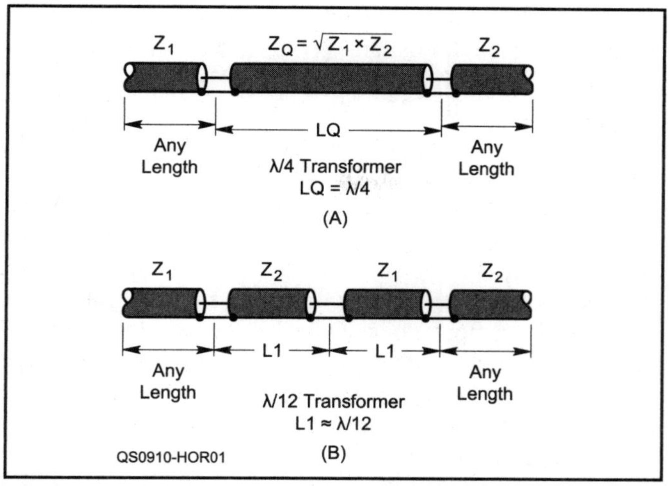

Figure 24.17 — The ¼-wave (A) Q-section and 1⁄12 wave (B) synchronous transformers.

impedance of the line. As described in the **Transmission Lines** chapter, the input impedance of a λ/4 line terminated in a resistive impedance Z_R is

$$Z_i = \frac{Z_0^{\ 2}}{Z_L} \tag{14}$$

where

Z_i = the impedance at the input end of the line
Z_0 = the characteristic impedance of the line
Z_L = the impedance at the load end of the line

Rearranging this equation gives

$$Z_0 = \sqrt{Z_i Z_L} \tag{15}$$

This means that any value of load impedance Z_L can be transformed into any desired value of impedance Z_i at the input terminals of a λ/4 line that has a characteristic impedance Z_0 equal to the square root of the product of the other two impedances. The factor that limits the range of impedances that can be matched by this method is the range of values for Z_0 that is physically realizable — approximately 50 to 600 Ω. Practically any type of line can be used for the matching section, including both air-insulated and solid-dielectric lines.

The λ/4 transformer may be adjusted to resonance before being connected to the antenna by following the procedures for determining line length in the chapter **Antenna and Transmission Line Measurements**.

Yagi Driven Elements

Another application for the λ/4 transformer is in matching the low antenna impedance encountered in close-spaced, monoband Yagi arrays to a 50-Ω transmission line. The impedances at the antenna feed point for typical Yagis range from about 8 to 30 Ω. Let's assume that the feed point impedance is 25 Ω. A matching section is needed. Since there is no commercially available cable with a Z_0 of 35.4 Ω, a pair of λ/4-long 75-Ω RG-11 coax cables connected in parallel will have a net Z_0 of 75/2 = 37.5 Ω, close enough for practical purposes.

24.4.2 TWELFTH-WAVE TRANSFORMERS

The Q-section is really a special case of series-section matching described below. There's no restriction (other than complexity) that there be just one matching section. In fact, the two-section variation shown in Figure 24.17B is quite handy for matching two different impedances of transmission line, such as 50-Ω coax and 75-Ω hardline. Best of all, special transmission line impedances are not required, only sections of line with the same impedances that are to be matched.

This configuration is referred to as a *twelfth-wave transformer* because when the ratio of the impedances to be matched is 1.5:1 (as is the case with 50- and 75-Ω cables), the electrical length of the two matching sections between the lines to be matched is 0.0815 λ (29.3°), quite close to λ/12 (0.0833 λ or 30°). **Figure 24.18** shows that the SWR bandwidth of the twelfth-wave transformer is quite broad. You can use this technique to make good use of surplus low-loss 75-Ω CATV hardline between 50-Ω antennas and radios.

24.4.3 SERIES-SECTION TRANSFORMERS

The *series-section transformer* has advantages over either stub tuning or the λ/4 transformer. Illustrated in **Figure 24.19**, the series-section transformer bears considerable resemblance to the λ/4 and λ/12 transformers described earlier. (Actually, these are special cases of the series-section transformer.) The important differences are (1) that the matching section need not be located exactly at the load, (2) the

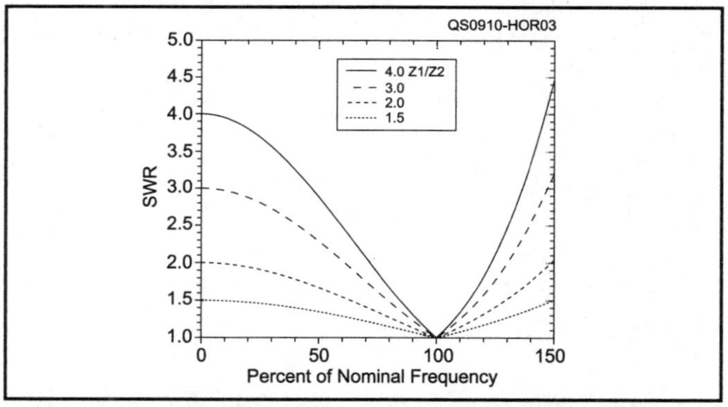

Figure 24.18 — The bandwidth of the λ/12 transformer is fairly broad as shown in this family of curves for different impedance transformation ratios. For 75- and 50-Ω impedances (a ratio of 1.5:1), the points at which an SWR of 1.2:1 are reached are approximately 75% and 125% of the design frequency.

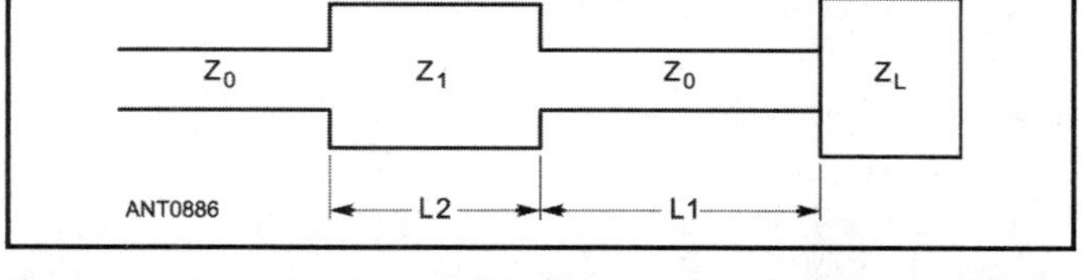

Figure 24.19 — Series section transformer Z_1 for matching transmission line Z_0 to load Z_L.

matching section may be less than a quarter wavelength long, and (3) there is great freedom in the choice of the characteristic impedance of the matching section.

In fact, the matching section can have *any* characteristic impedance that is not too close to that of the main line. Because of this freedom, it is almost always possible to find a length of commercially available line that will be suitable as a matching section. As an example, consider a 75-Ω line, a 300-Ω matching section, and a pure-resistance load. It can be shown that a series-section transformer of 300-Ω line may be used to match *any* resistance between 5 Ω and 1200 Ω to the main line.

Frank Regier, OD5CG, described series-section transformers in July 1978 *QST*. (See Bibliography.) This information is based on that article. The design of a series-section transformer consists of determining the length L2 of the series or matching section and the distance L1 from the load to the point where the section should be inserted into the main line. Three quantities must be known. These are the characteristic impedances of the main line and of the matching section, both assumed purely resistive, and the complex-load impedance. Either of two design methods may be used. One is a graphic method using the Smith Chart, and the other is algebraic. You can take your choice. (Of course the algebraic method may be adapted to obtaining a computer solution.) The Smith Chart graphic method is described in an article included with this book's downloadable supplemental information.

Algebraic Design Method

The two lengths L1 and L2 are to be determined from the characteristic impedances of the main line and the matching section, Z_0 and Z_1, respectively, and the load impedance $Z_L = R_L + j X_L$. The first step is to determine the normalized impedances.

$$n = \frac{Z_1}{Z_0} \tag{16}$$

$$r = \frac{R_L}{Z_0} \tag{17}$$

$$x = \frac{X_L}{Z_0} \tag{18}$$

Next, L2 and L1 are determined from

L2 = arctan B, where

$$B = \pm\sqrt{\frac{(r-1)^2 + x^2}{r\left(n - \frac{1}{n}\right)^2 - (r-1)^2 - x^2}} \tag{19}$$

L1 = arctan A, where

$$A = \frac{\left(n - \frac{r}{n}\right)B + x}{r + xnB - 1} \tag{20}$$

Lengths L2 and L1 as thus determined are electrical lengths in degrees (or radians). The electrical lengths in wavelengths are obtained by dividing by 360° (or by 2π radians). The physical lengths (main line or matching section, as the case may be), are then determined from multiplying by the free-space wavelength and by the velocity factor of the line.

The sign of B may be chosen either positive or negative, but the positive sign is preferred because it results in a shorter matching section. The sign of A may not be chosen but can turn out to be either positive or negative. If a negative sign occurs and a computer or calculator is then used to determine L1, a negative electric length will result for L1. If this happens, add 180°. The resultant electrical length will be correct both physically and mathematically.

In calculating B, if the quantity under the radical is negative, an imaginary value for B results. This would mean that Z_1, the impedance of the matching section, is too close to Z_0 and should be changed.

Limits on the characteristic impedance of Z_1 may be calculated in terms of the SWR produced by the load on the main line without matching. For matching to occur, Z_1 should either be greater than $Z_0\sqrt{SWR}$ or less than $Z_0 / \sqrt{SWR}$.

An Example

As an example, suppose we want to feed a 29-MHz ground-plane vertical antenna with RG-58 type foam-dielectric coax. We'll assume the antenna impedance to be 36 Ω, pure resistance, and use a length of RG-59 foam-dielectric coax as the series section. See **Figure 24.20**.

Z_0 is 50 Ω, Z_1 is 75 Ω, and both cables have a velocity factor of 0.79. Because the load is a pure resistance we may determine the SWR to be 50/36 = 1.389. From the above, Z_1 must have an impedance greater than $50\sqrt{1.389}$. From the earlier equations, n = 75/50 = 1.50, r = 36/50 = 0.720, and x = 0.

Further, B = 0.431 (positive sign chosen), and L2 = 23.3° or 0.065 λ. The value of A is -1.570. Calculating L1 yields –57.5°. Adding 180° to obtain a positive result gives L1= 122.5°, or 0.340 λ.

To find the physical lengths L1 and L2 we first find the free-space wavelength.

$$\lambda = \frac{984}{f(\text{MHz})} = 33.93 \text{ feet}$$

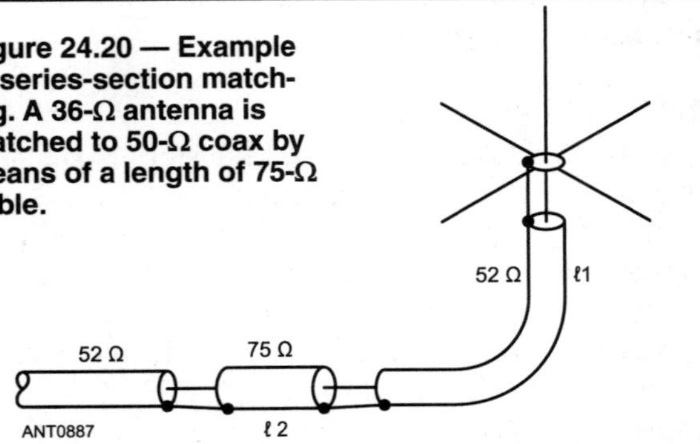

Figure 24.20 — Example of series-section matching. A 36-Ω antenna is matched to 50-Ω coax by means of a length of 75-Ω cable.

Multiply this value by 0.79 (the velocity factor for both types of line), and we obtain the electrical wavelength in coax as 26.81 feet. From this, L1 = 0.340 × 26.81 = 9.12 feet, and L2 = 0.065 × 26.81 = 1.74 feet.

This completes the calculations. Construction consists of cutting the main coax at a point 9.12 feet from the antenna and inserting a 1.74-foot length of the 75-Ω cable.

The antenna in the preceding example could also have been matched by a λ/4 transformer at the load. Such a transformer would use a line with a characteristic impedance of 42.43 Ω. It is interesting to see what happens in the design of a series-section transformer if this value is chosen as the characteristic impedance of the series section.

Following the same steps as before, we find n = 0.849, r = 0.720, and x = 0. From these values we find B = 8 and L2 = 90°. Further, A = 0 and l1 = 0°. These results represent a λ/4 section at the load, and indicate that, as stated earlier, the λ/4 transformer is indeed a special case of the series-section transformer.

24.4.4 MULTIPLE QUARTER-WAVE SECTIONS

An alternate to the smooth-impedance transformation of the tapered line is provided by using two or more λ/4 transformer sections in series, as shown in **Figure 24.21**. (See article "Tapered Lines" in the downloadable supplemental information). Each section has a different characteristic impedance, selected to transform the impedance at its input to that at its output. Thus, the overall impedance transformation from source to load takes place as a series of gradual transformations. The frequency bandwidth with multiple sections is greater than for a single section. This technique is useful at the upper end of the HF range and at VHF and UHF. Here, too, the total line length that is required may become unwieldy at the lower frequencies.

A multiple-section line may contain two or more λ/4 transformer sections; the more sections in the line, the broader is the matching bandwidth. Coaxial transmission lines may be used to make a multiple-section line, but standard coax lines are available in only a few characteristic impedances. Open-wire lines can be constructed rather easily for a specific impedance, designed from:

$$S = \frac{d \times 10^{Z_0/276}}{2} \qquad (21)$$

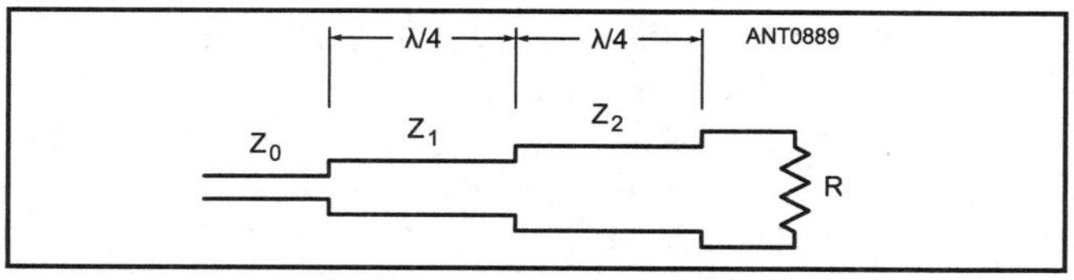

Figure 24.21 — Multiple quarter-wave matching sections approximate the broadband matching transformation provided by a tapered line. Two sections are shown here, but more may be used. The more sections in the line, the broader is the matching bandwidth. Z_0 is the characteristic impedance of the main feed line, while Z_1 and Z_2 are the intermediate impedances of the matching sections. See text for design equations.

where S is the center-to-center spacing between the conductors, d is the diameter of the conductors (same units as S), and Z_0 is the characteristic impedance in ohms.

The following equations may be used to calculate the intermediate characteristic impedances for a two-section line.

$$Z_1 = \sqrt[4]{RZ_0^{\,3}} \qquad (22A)$$

$$Z_2 = \sqrt[3]{R^2 Z_1} \qquad (22B)$$

where terms are as illustrated in Figure 24.21. For example, assume we wish to match a 75-Ω source (Z_0) to an 800-Ω load. From Eq 21, calculate Z_1 to be 135.5 Ω. Then from Eq 22A, calculate Z_2 to be 442.7 Ω. As a matter of interest, for this example the virtual impedance at the junction of Z_1 and Z_2 is 244.9 Ω. (This is the same impedance that would be required for a single-section λ/4 matching section.)

Multisection λ/4 transformers are discussed by Randy Rhea in *High-Frequency Electronics* magazine. (See Bibliography.) This technique is related to the "equal delay" transmission line transformers.

Double Quarter-Wave Transformer

The double λ/4 transformer is a special case of the multisection λ/4 transformer. If two λ/4 sections of feed line, one with impedance Z_0 followed by another with an impedance of $2Z_0$ as the input impedance as in **Figure 24.22**, the input to the transformer will be the load impedance divided by 4. The transformer can be "turned around" to step up the load impedance. In general, the transformation ratio is the square of the impedance ratio of the two λ/4 sections and it is independent of the impedances of the input and output. The larger the difference in Z_0 between the sections, the smaller the bandwidth of the impedance transformation.

You are not restricted to the Z_0 of single cables. Paralleled cables with characteristic impedances of Z_0 act as a combined cable with a characteristic impedance of $Z_0/2$. So for example, a λ/4 section of two 50-Ω cables in parallel (Z_0 = 25 Ω) connected to a λ/4 section of 50-Ω line has an impedance ratio of 2:1 and an impedance transformation ratio of 4:1. This design could match 75-Ω line to a 300-Ω load — using 50-Ω cable! If the input section were composed of three cables in parallel, the impedance ratio would be 3:1 and the transformation ratio 9:1 — this could match 50 Ω at the input to 450 Ω at the output.

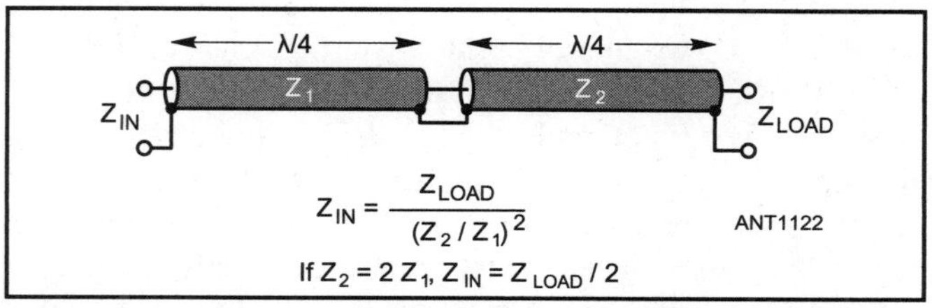

Figure 24.22 — The impedance transformation ratio of the double quarter-wave transformer is the square of the difference between the characteristic impedances of the two λ/4 sections.

24.4.5 TRANSMISSION LINE TRANSFORMERS (TLT)

From Sevick's paper analyzing TLTs, "A Transmission line transformer transmits the energy from input to output by a transmission line mode and not by flux-linkages as in the conventional transformer." (See Bibliography.) The TLT may or may not perform an impedance transformation and may have a balanced-balanced, balanced-unbalanced, or unbalanced-unbalanced configuration.

The basic transmission line transformer, from which other transformers are derived, is the 1:1 choke balun or current balun, shown in **Figure 24.23A**. To construct this type of balun, a length of coaxial cable or a pair of close-spaced, parallel wires forming a transmission line are wrapped around a ferrite rod or toroid or inserted through a number of beads. (See the Current and Choke Balun section of this chapter.) The Z_0 of the line should equal the load resistance, R.

Because of the ferrite, a high impedance exists between points A and C and a virtually identical impedance between B and D. This is true for parallel conductor lines and for coax. The ferrite affects the A to C impedance of the coax inner conductor and the B to D impedance of the outer braid equally.

The conductors (two close-spaced parallel wires or coaxial cable's braid and center conductor) are tightly coupled by electromagnetic fields and therefore constitute a good conventional transformer with a turns ratio of 1:1. The voltage from A to C is equal to and in-phase with that from B to D. These are common-mode (CM) voltages.

A CM current is one that has the same value and direction in both wires (or on the shield and center conductor). Because of the ferrite, the CM current encounters a high impedance that acts to reduce (choke) the current. The normal *differential-mode* (*DM*) signal does not encounter this CM impedance because the electromagnetic fields due to equal and opposite currents in the two conductors cancel each other in the ferrite, so the magnetic flux in the ferrite is virtually zero. (See the section on Ferrite Core Choke Baluns.)

The main idea of the transmission line transformer is that although the CM impedance may be very large, the DM signal is virtually unopposed, especially if the line length is a small fraction of a wavelength. But it is very important to keep in mind that the common-mode voltage across the ferrite winding that is due to this current is efficiently coupled to the center conductor by conventional transformer action, as mentioned before and easily verified. This equality of CM voltages, and also CM impedances, reduces the *conversion* of a CM signal to an *undesired* DM signal that can interfere with the *desired* DM signal in both transmitters and receivers. In other words, the undesired CM signal is blocked or "choked."

The CM current, multiplied by the CM impedance due to the ferrite, produces a CM voltage. The CM impedance has L and C reactance and also R. So L, C and R cause a broad parallel self-resonance at some frequency. The R component also produces some dissipation (heat) in the ferrite. This dissipation is an excellent way to dispose of a small amount of unwanted CM power. (The section on Power Dissipation in Ferrite Transmitting Chokes discusses the effect of large CM voltages across the ferrite material in transmitting applications.)

Because of the high CM impedance, the two output wires of the balun in Figure 24.23A have a high impedance with respect to, and are therefore "isolated" from, the generator. This feature is very useful because now any point of R at the output can be grounded. In a well-designed balun circuit almost all of the current in one conductor returns to the generator through the other conductor, despite this ground connection. In a coax balun the return current flows on the inside surface of the braid.

Note also that the ground connection introduces some CM voltage across the balun cores and this has to be taken into account. This CM voltage is a maximum if point C is grounded. If point D is grounded and if all "ground" connections are at the same potential, which they often are not, the CM voltage is zero and the balun may no longer be needed.

The Guanella Transformer

We now look briefly at a transmission line transformer that is based on the choke balun. Figure 23.23B shows two identical choke baluns whose inputs are in parallel and whose outputs are in series. The output voltage amplitude of each balun is identical to the common input, so the two outputs add in-phase (equal time delay) to produce twice the input voltage. It is the high CM impedance that makes this voltage addition possible. For the power to remain constant the load current must be one-half the generator current, and the load resistance must be 2 V/0.5 I = 4 V/I = 4 R.

The CM voltage in each balun is V/2, so there is some flux in the cores. The right side floats. This is named the *Guanella* transformer after its inventor. Guanella transformers are also referred to as current baluns since they create equal currents in the load terminals. If Z_0 of the lines equals 2R and if the load is a pure resistance of 4R then the input resistance R is independent of line length. If the lines are exactly one-quarter wavelength, then $Z_{IN} = (2R)^2 / Z_L$, an impedance inverter, where Z_{IN} and Z_L are complex. The quality of balance can often be improved by inserting a 1:1 balun (Figure 24.23A) at the left end so that both ends of the 1:4 transformer are floating and a ground is at the far left side as shown. The Guanella transformer can also be operated from a grounded right end to a floating left end. The 1:1 balun at the left then allows a grounded far left end.

The Ruthroff Transformer

Figure 24.23C is the *Ruthroff transformer* (named after its inventor) in which the input voltage V is divided into two equal in-phase voltages AC and BD (they are tightly coupled), so the output is V/2. And because power is constant, $I_{OUT} = 2I_{IN}$ and the load is R/4. There is a CM voltage V/2 between A and C and between B and D, so in normal operation the core is not free of magnetic flux. The input and output both return to ground so it can also be operated from right to left for a 1:4 impedance step-up. Since the Ruthroff transformer creates equal voltages at the load terminals, it is referred to as a *voltage balun*. It is important to note that if the impedances connected

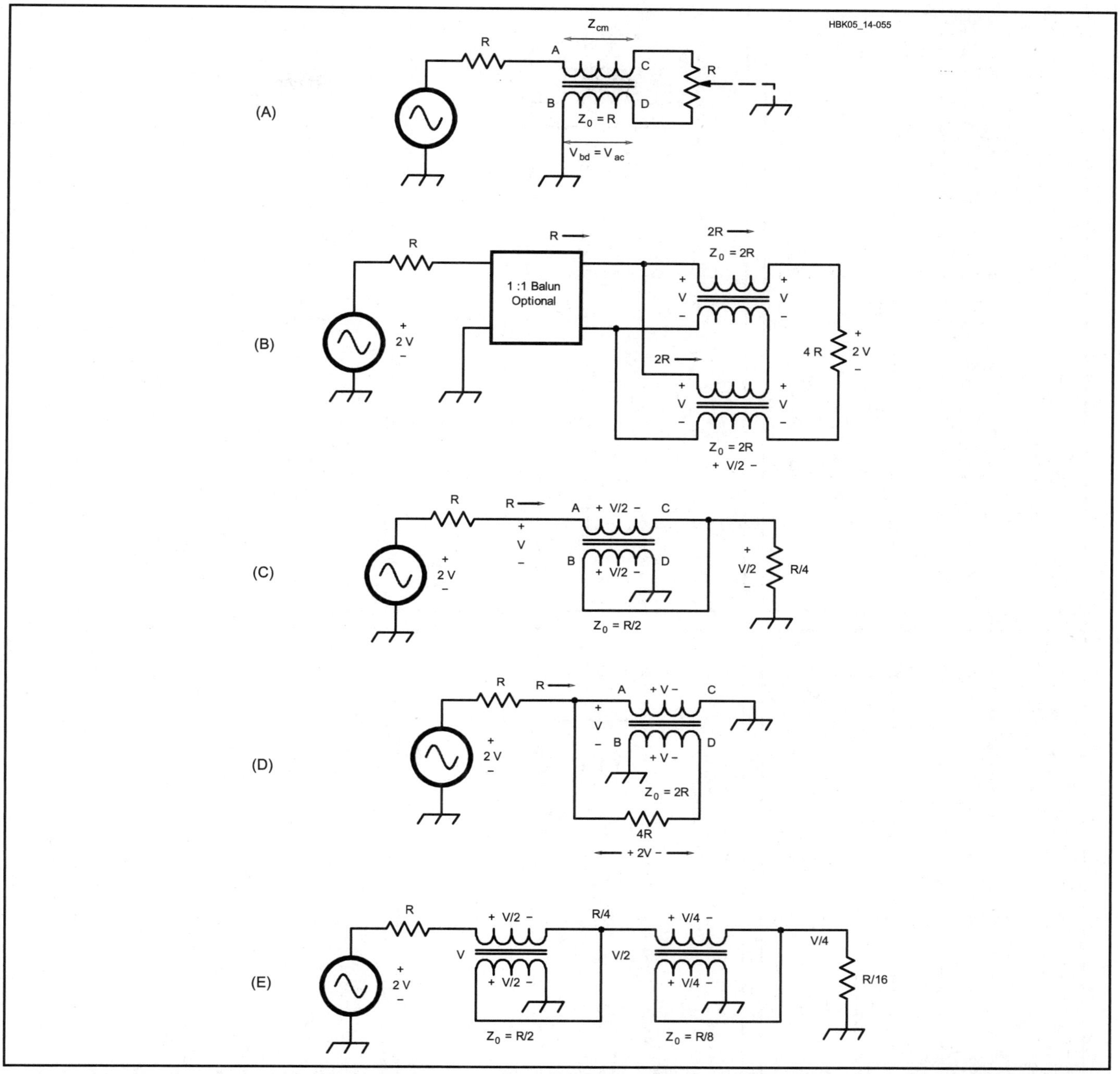

Figure 24.23 — (A) Basic current or choke balun. (B) Guanella 1:4 transformer. (C) Ruthroff 4:1 unbalanced transformer. (C) Ruthroff 1:4 balanced transformer. (E) Ruthroff 16:1 unbalanced transformer.

to the load terminals are not the same, the currents will not be the same. This makes the Ruthroff transformer less effective than the Guanella transformer in creating equal load currents in antennas where impedance imbalances are common.

To maintain low attenuation the line length should be much less than one-fourth wavelength at the highest frequency of operation, and its Z_0 should be R/2. A balanced version is shown in Figure 24.23D, where the CM voltage is V, not V/2, and transmission is from left-to-right only. Because of the greater flux in the cores, no different than a conventional transformer, this is not a preferred approach, although it could be used with air wound coils (for example in antenna tuner circuits) to couple 75-Ω unbalanced to 300-Ω balanced. The tuner circuit could then transform 75 Ω to 50 Ω.

Applications of Transmission-Line Transformers

There are many transformer schemes that build on the basic ideas of Figure 24.23. Several of them, with their toroid winding instructions, are shown in **Figure 24.24**. Two of the most commonly used devices are the 1:1 choke balun (discussed later in this chapter) and 4:1 impedance transformer wound on toroid cores as shown in **Figure 24.25**. For more information, see the Bibliography entry for Sevick on baluns and ununs.

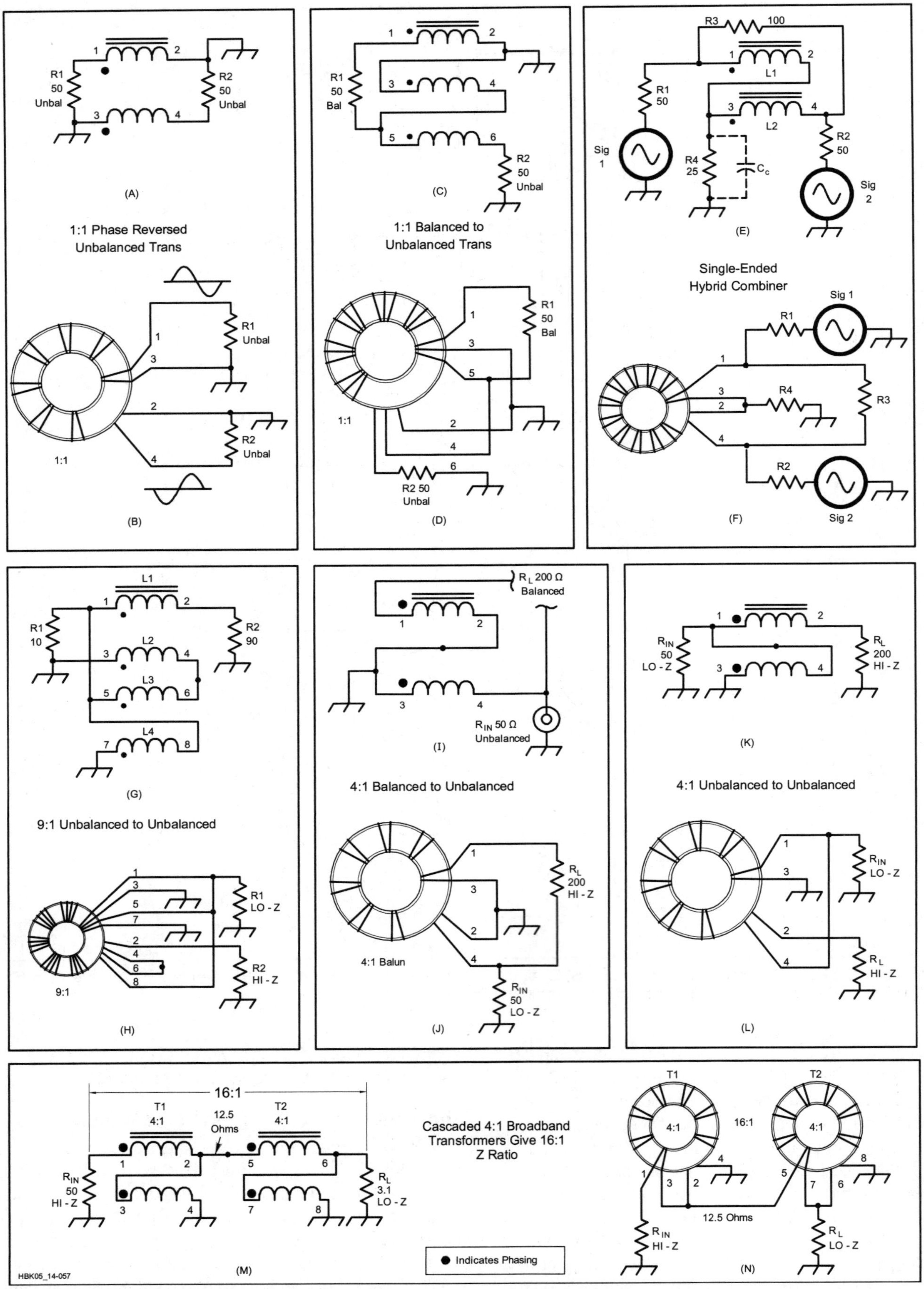

Figure 24.24 — Schematics and construction instructions for a variety of transmission-line transformers.

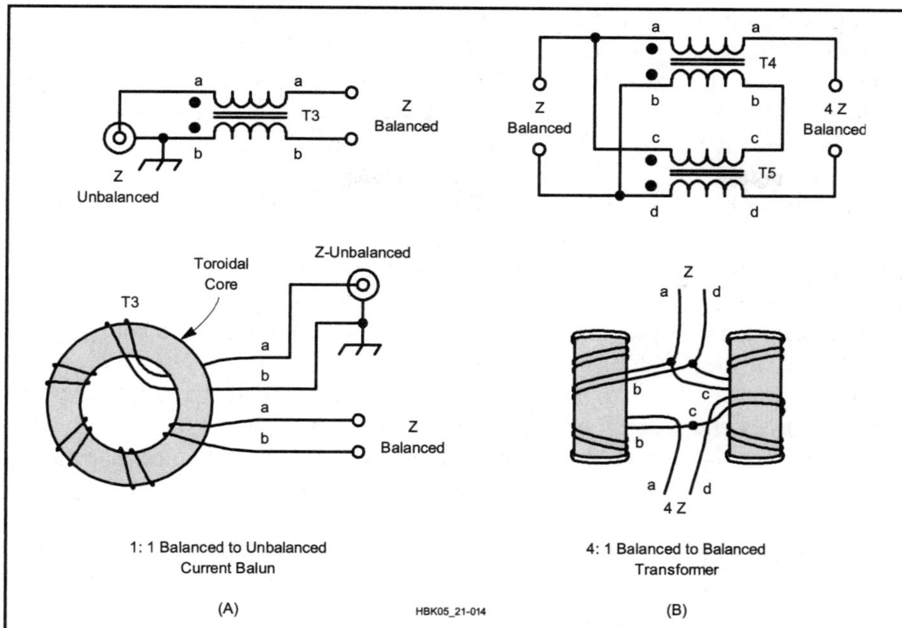

Figure 24.25 — (A) 1:1 current balun and (B) Guanella 4:1 impedance transformer. Use 12 bifilar turns of #14 AWG enameled or THHN wire, on a 2.4-inch type 31 ferrite core for HF use. Turns should be distributed evenly around the core.

24.4.6 BROADBAND MATCHING TRANSFORMERS

Broadband transformers have been used widely because of their inherent bandwidth ratios (as high as 20,000:1) from a few tens of kilohertz to over a thousand megahertz. This is possible because of the transmission line nature of the windings. The interwinding capacitance is a component of the characteristic impedance and therefore, unlike a conventional transformer, forms no resonances that seriously limit the bandwidth.

At low frequencies, where interwinding capacitances can be neglected, these transformers are similar in operation to a conventional transformer. The main difference (and a very important one from a power standpoint) is that the windings tend to cancel out the induced flux in the core. Thus, high permeability ferrite cores, which are not only highly nonlinear but also suffer serious damage even at flux levels as low as 200 to 500 gauss, can be used. This greatly extends the low frequency range of performance. Since higher permeability also permits fewer turns at the lower frequencies, HF performance is also improved since the upper cutoff is determined mainly from transmission line considerations. At the high frequency cutoff, the effect of the core is negligible.

The most popular cores used in these applications are 2.5-inch OD ferrites of low-loss type #61 material with a permeability (μ) of 125. Transformers wound on these cores can be made to operate over the 1.8 to 28-MHz bands with full power capability and very low loss. Type #61 material requires 10 turns to cover the 1.8-MHz band. (A 2-inch OD Type E powdered iron core with μ of 10 requires 14 turns, leading to possible problems at higher ratios because more turns are required on a somewhat smaller core.) When you are working with low impedance levels, unwanted parasitic inductances come into play, particularly on 14 MHz and above. In this case lead lengths should be kept to a minimum.

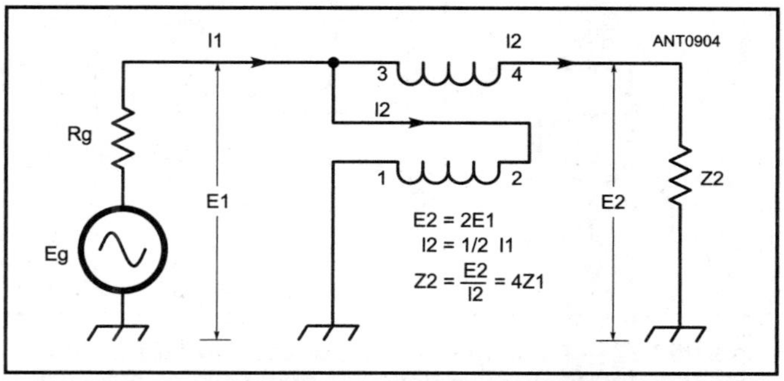

Figure 24.26 — Broadband bifilar transformer with a 4:1 impedance ratio. The upper winding can be tapped at appropriate points to obtain other ratios such as 1.5:1, 2:1, and 3:1. Terminal numbering corresponds to the ends of the wires of the windings. Odd numbered wire ends (1 and 3) are at the same end of the winding.

Unun Transformers

Bifilar matching transformers lend themselves to unbalanced operation. That is, both input and output terminals can have a common ground connection. This eliminates the third magnetizing winding required in balanced to unbalanced (*voltage balun*) operation as shown below. These are *unun* transformers, which stands for unbalanced-to-unbalanced.

By adding third and fourth windings, as well as by tapping windings at appropriate points, various combinations of broadband matching can be obtained. **Figure 24.26** shows a 4:1 unbalanced to unbalanced configuration. Using #14 AWG wire it will easily handle 1000 W of power. By tapping at points ¼, ½, and ¾ of the way along the top winding, ratios of approximately 1.5:1, 2:1, and 3:1 can also be obtained. One of the wires should be covered with electrical tape in order to prevent voltage breakdown between the windings. This is necessary when a step-up ratio is used at high power to match antennas with impedances greater than 50 Ω.

Figure 24.27 shows a transformer with four windings, permitting wideband matching ratios as high as 16:1. **Figure 24.28** shows a four-winding transformer with taps at 4:1, 6:1 (point b in Figure 24.27), 9:1, and 16:1. In tracing the current flow in the windings when using the 16:1 tap, one sees that the top three windings carry the same current. The bottom winding, in order to maintain the proper potentials, sustains a current three times greater. The bottom current cancels out the core flux caused by the other three windings. If this transformer is used to match into low impedances, such as 3 to 4 Ω, the current in the bottom winding can be as high as 15 amperes. This value is based on the high side of the transformer being fed with 50-Ω cable handling a kilowatt of power. If one needs a 16:1 match like this at high power, then cascading two 4:1 transformers is recommended. In this case, the transformer at the lowest impedance side requires each winding to handle only 7.5 A. Thus, even #14 AWG wire would suffice in this application. See the Bibliography entry for Johnson that presents a similar 9:1 design if you are only interested in the single impedance ratio.

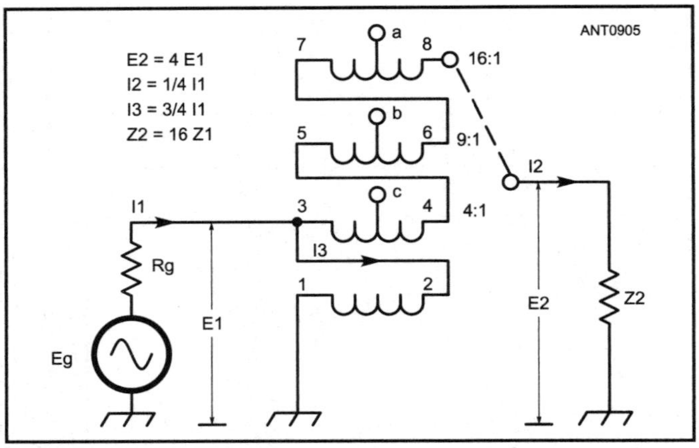

Figure 24.27 — Four-winding, broadband, variable impedance transformer. Connections a, b and c can be placed at appropriate points to yield various ratios from 1.5:1 to 16:1. See Figure 24.26 for an explanation of the wire numbering scheme.

Figure 24.28 — A 4-winding, wideband transformer with connections made for matching ratios of 4:1, 6:1, 9:1 and 16:1. The 16:1 ratio is the top coaxial connector and, from left to right, 6:1, 9:1 and 4:1 are the others. There are 10 quadrifilar turns of #14 AWG enameled wire on a type #61, 2.5-inch OD ferrite core. (see text for winding taps and numbers of turns on different core materials)

1:1 Three-Winding Voltage Balun

The voltage balun shown in **Figure 24.29** is a flux-linked impedance auto-transformer, similar to conventional power transformers. It causes equal and opposite voltages to appear at the two output terminals, relative to the voltage at the ground side of the input.

If the impedances of the two antenna halves are perfectly balanced with respect to ground, the currents flowing from the output terminals will be equal and opposite and no common-mode current will flow on the line. If the line is coaxial, there will be no current flowing on the outside of the shield; if the line is balanced, the currents in the two conductors will be equal and opposite. These are the conditions for a nonradiating line.

Under this condition, the 1:1 voltage balun of Figure 24.29 performs exactly the same function as a current balun since there is no current in winding b. If the antenna isn't perfectly balanced, however, unequal currents will appear at the balun output, causing antenna current to flow on the line, an undesirable condition. Voltage baluns can be used as impedance transformers in this application if a 1:1 current or choke balun is added at the unbalanced input to prevent the common-mode current flow.

Another potential shortcoming of the 1:1 voltage balun is that winding b appears across the line. If this winding has insufficient impedance (a common problem, particularly near the lower frequency end of its range), the impedance transformation ratio will be degraded. In general, voltage baluns are not recommended in favor of a choke or 1:1 current balun. An impedance transformer can then be used on the balanced side of the current balun.

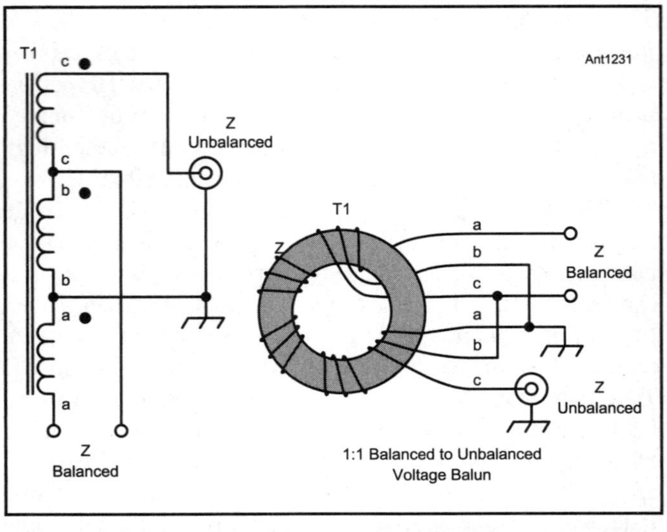

Figure 24.29 — Three-winding 1:1 voltage balun. These have largely been supplanted by the current or choke balun.

24.5 MATCHING IMPEDANCE AT THE ANTENNA

Since operating a transmission line at a low SWR requires that the line be terminated in a load matching the line's characteristic impedance, the problem can be approached from two standpoints:

(1) selecting a transmission line having a characteristic impedance that matches the antenna impedance at the point of connection, or

(2) transforming the antenna resistance to a value that matches the Z_0 of the line selected.

The first approach is simple and direct, but its application is obviously limited — the antenna impedance and the line impedance are alike only in a few special cases. Commercial transmission lines come in a limited variety of characteristic impedances while antenna feed point impedances vary over a wide range.

The second approach provides a good deal of freedom in that the antenna and line can be selected independently. The disadvantage of the second approach is that it is more complicated in terms of actually constructing the matching system at the antenna. Further, this approach sometimes calls for a tedious routine of measurement and adjustment before the desired match is achieved.

24.5.1 ANTENNA IMPEDANCE

Impedance Change with Frequency

Most antenna systems show a marked change in impedance when the frequency is changed greatly. For this reason it is usually possible to match the line impedance only on one frequency. A matched antenna system is consequently a one-band affair, in most cases. It can, however, usually be operated over a fair frequency range within a given band.

The frequency range over which the SWR is low is determined by how rapidly the impedance changes as the frequency is changed. If the change in impedance is small for a given change in frequency, the SWR will be low over a fairly wide band of frequencies. However, if the impedance change is rapid (implying a sharply resonant or high-Q antenna), the SWR will also rise rapidly as the operating frequency is shifted away from antenna resonance, where the line is matched. See the discussion of Q in the **Dipoles and Monopoles** chapter in the section dealing with changes of impedance with frequency.

Material from previous editions in the chapter "Broadband Antenna Matching" by Frank Witt, AI1H, is included for reference with this book's downloadable supplemental information. It presents and analyzes various techniques used to increase the bandwidth of antenna feed point impedance.

Antenna Resonance

In general, achieving a good match to a transmission line means that the antenna is resonant. (Some types of long-wire antennas, such as rhombics, are exceptions. Their input impedances are resistive over a wide band of frequencies, making such systems essentially nonresonant.) Antennas that are not resonant may also be matched to transmission lines, of course, but the additional cancellation of reactance complicates the task.

The higher the Q of an antenna system, the more essential it is that resonance be established before an attempt is made to match the line. This is particularly true of close-spaced parasitic arrays. With simple dipole antennas, the tuning is not so critical, and it is usually sufficient to cut the antenna to the length given by the appropriate equation. The frequency should be selected to be at the center of the range of frequencies (which may be the entire width of an amateur band) over which the antenna is to be used.

24.5.2 CONNECTING DIRECTLY TO THE ANTENNA

As discussed previously, the impedance at the center of a resonant $\lambda/2$ antenna at heights of the order of $\lambda/4$ and more is resistive and is in the neighborhood of 50 to 70 Ω. The dipole may be fed through 75-Ω coaxial cable such as RG-11, as shown in **Figure 24.30**. Cable having a characteristic impedance of 50 Ω, such as RG-213, may also be used. RG-213 may actually be preferable, because at the heights many amateurs install their antennas, the feed point impedance is closer to 50 Ω than it is to 75 Ω.

With a parallel-conductor feed line the system would be symmetrical but with coaxial line it is inherently unbalanced. Stated broadly, the unbalance with coaxial line is caused by the fact that the outside surface of the outer braid is not coupled to the antenna in the same way as the inner conductor and the inner surface of the outer braid. The overall result is that common-mode current will flow on the outside of the outer conductor in the simple arrangement shown in Figure 24.30. The unbalance is small if the line diameter is very small compared with the length of the antenna, a condition that is met fairly well at the lower amateur frequencies. It is not negligible in the VHF and UHF range, however, nor should it be ignored at 28 MHz. If the feed line is oriented asymmetrically with respect to the antenna so that it is closer

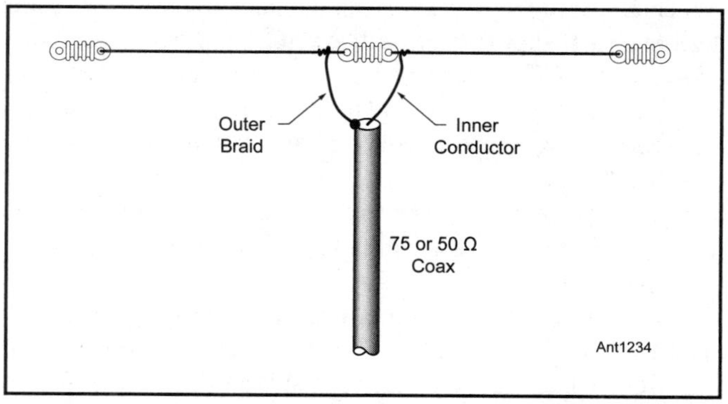

Figure 24.30 — A ½ λ antenna fed with 75-Ω coaxial cable. The outside of the shield of the line acts as a "third wire" connected to the dipole's left leg. A choke balun can be used to reduce current flowing on this conductor.

to one side of the antenna than the other, higher common-mode currents will flow on the outside of the feed line. The system can be detuned for currents on the outside of the line by using a choke.

This system is designed for single-band operation, although it can be operated at *odd* multiples of the fundamental. For example, an antenna that is resonant near the low-frequency end of the 7-MHz band will operate with a relatively low SWR across the 21-MHz band.

At the fundamental frequency, the SWR should not exceed about 2:1 within a frequency range ±2% from the frequency of exact resonance. Such a variation corresponds approximately to the entire width of the 7-MHz band, if the antenna is resonant at the center of the band. A wire antenna is assumed. Antennas having a greater ratio of diameter to length will have a lower change in SWR with frequency.

Direct-Feed Yagis

Direct-feed Yagis are designed to have a feed point impedance of 50- or 75-Ω so that a coaxial feed line can be connected directly to the antenna without additional impedance matching. These have become more common in recent years as antenna modeling has produced designs without the gain and pattern tradeoffs previously required for the higher feed point impedances required for direct-feed.

There is some question as to whether a choke balun is required for direct-feed antennas. The same questions of symmetry and radiation from common-mode current apply to direct-feed Yagis as to dipoles and other types of antennas. If re-radiation is an issue, a choke balun should be used. For commercial antennas, if the manufacturer specifies that a balun be used or makes no recommendation, use a choke balun at the feed point. If the manufacturer specifies that *no* balun be used, that is an indication that the feed line affects antenna performance in some way and the manufacturer's instructions for feed line placement and attachment should be followed exactly.

24.5.3 THE DELTA MATCH

Among the properties of a coil and capacitor resonant circuit is that of transforming impedances. If a resistive impedance, Z_1 in **Figure 24.31**, is connected across the outer terminals AB of a resonant LC circuit, the impedance Z_2 as viewed looking into another pair of terminals such as BC will also be resistive, but will have a different value depending on the mutual coupling between the parts of the coil associated with each pair of terminals. Z_2 will be less than Z_1 in the circuit shown. Of course this relationship will be reversed if Z_1 is connected across terminals BC and Z_2 is viewed from terminals AB.

As stated in the **Antenna Fundamentals** chapter, a resonant antenna has properties similar to those of a tuned circuit. The impedance presented between any two points symmetrically placed with respect to the center of a λ/2 antenna will depend on the distance between the points. The greater the separation, the higher the value of impedance, up to the limiting value that exists between the open ends of the antenna.

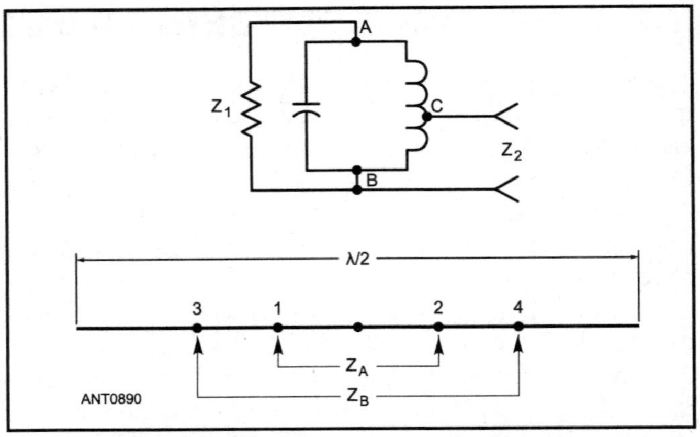

Figure 24.31 — Impedance transformation with a resonant circuit, together with antenna analogy.

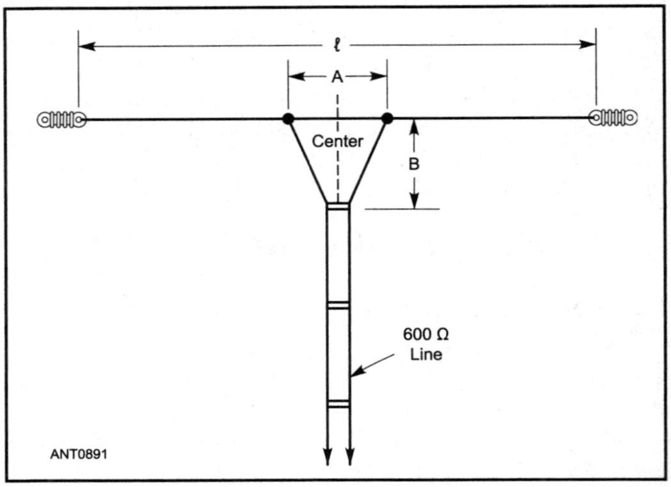

Figure 24.32 — The delta matching system.

This is also suggested in Figure 24.31, in the lower drawing. The impedance Z_A between terminals 1 and 2 is lower than the impedance Z_B between terminals 3 and 4. Both impedances, however, are purely resistive if the antenna is resonant.

This principle is used in the *delta matching system* shown in **Figure 24.32**. The center impedance of a λ/2 dipole is too low to be matched directly by any practical type of air-insulated parallel-conductor line. However, it is possible to find, between two points, a value of impedance that can be matched to such a line when a "fanned" section or delta is used to couple the line and antenna. The antenna length ℓ is that required for resonance. The ends of the delta or "Y" should be attached at points equidistant from the center of the antenna. When so connected, the terminating impedance for the line will be resistive. Obviously, this technique is useful only when the Z_0 of the chosen transmission line is higher than the feed point impedance of the antenna.

Based on experimental data for the case of a typical λ/2 antenna coupled to a 600-Ω line, the total distance, A, between the ends of the delta should be 0.120 λ for frequencies below 30 MHz, and 0.115 λ for frequencies above 30 MHz. The length of the delta, distance B, should be 0.150 λ. These values are based on a wavelength in air, and on the assumption that the center impedance of the antenna is approximately 70 Ω. The dimensions will require modifications if the actual impedance is very much different.

The delta match can be used for matching the driven element of a directive array to a transmission line, but if the impedance of the element is low — as is frequently the case — the proper dimensions for A and B must be found by experimentation.

The delta match is somewhat awkward to adjust when the proper dimensions are unknown, because both the length and width of the delta must be varied. An additional disadvantage is that there is always some radiation from the delta. This is because the conductor spacing does not meet the requirement for negligible radiation: The spacing should be very small in comparison with the wavelength.

24.5.4 FOLDED DIPOLES

Basic information on the folded dipole antenna appears in chapter **Dipoles and Monopoles**. The input impedance of a two-wire folded dipole is so close to 300 Ω that it can be fed directly with 300-Ω twinlead or with open-wire line without any other matching arrangement, and the line will operate with a low SWR. The antenna itself can be built like an open-wire line; that is, the two conductors can be held apart by regular feeder spreaders. TV ladder line is quite suitable at low power. It is also possible to use 300-Ω line for the antenna, in addition to using it for the transmission line.

Since the antenna section does not operate as a transmission line, but simply as two wires in parallel, the velocity factor of twinlead can be ignored in computing the antenna length. The reactance of the folded-dipole antenna varies less rapidly with frequency changes away from resonance than a single-wire antenna. Therefore it is possible to operate over a wider range of frequencies, while maintaining a low SWR on the line, than with a simple dipole. This is partly explained by the fact that the two conductors in parallel form a single conductor of greater effective diameter.

A folded dipole will not accept power at twice the fundamental frequency. However, the current distribution is correct for harmonic operation on odd multiples of the fundamental. Because the feed point resistance is not greatly different for a 3λ/2 antenna and one that is λ/2, a folded dipole can be operated on its third harmonic with a low SWR in a 300-Ω line. A 7-MHz folded dipole, consequently, can be used for the 21-MHz band as well.

Folded dipoles are sometimes used as the driven element of Yagi antennas at VHF and UHF. The low feed point impedance of a Yagi, often less than 20 Ω, when multiplied by four presents a good match to 75-Ω coaxial cable.

24.5.5 THE T AND GAMMA MATCHES

The T Match

The current flowing at the input terminals of the T match consists of the normal antenna current divided between the radiator and the T conductors in a way that depends on their relative diameters and the spacing between them, with a superimposed transmission line current flowing in each half of the T and its associated section of the antenna. See **Figure 24.33**. Each such T conductor and the associated antenna conductor can be looked upon as a section of transmission line shorted at the end. Because it is shorter than λ/4 it has inductive reactance. As a consequence, if the antenna itself

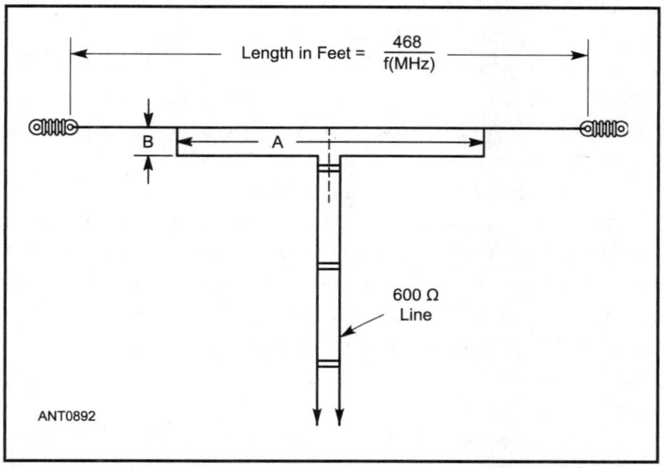

Figure 24.33 — The T matching system, applied to a ½ λ antenna and 600-Ω line.

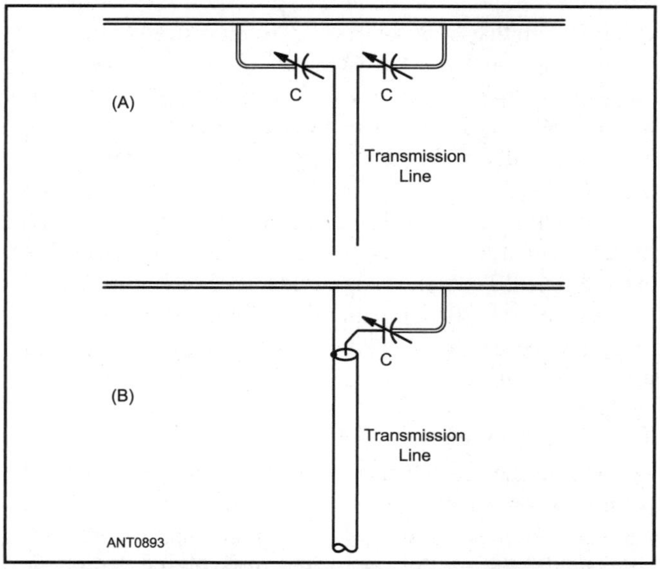

Figure 24.34 — Series capacitors for tuning out residual reactance with the T and gamma matching systems. A maximum capacitance of 150 pF in each capacitor should provide sufficient adjustment range, in the average case, for 14-MHz operation. Proportionately smaller capacitance values can be used on higher frequency bands. Receiving-type plate spacing will be satisfactory for power levels up to a few hundred watts.

is exactly resonant at the operating frequency, the input impedance of the T will show inductive reactance as well as resistance. The reactance must be tuned out if a good match to the transmission line is to be obtained. This can be done either by shortening the antenna to obtain a value of capacitive reactance that will reflect through the matching system to cancel the inductive reactance at the input terminals, or by inserting a capacitance of the proper value in series at the input terminals as shown in **Figure 24.34A**.

Analysis shows that the part of the impedance step-up arising from the spacing and ratio of conductor diameters is approximately the same as given for a folded dipole. The actual impedance ratio is, however, considerably modified by the length A of the matching section (Figure 24.33). The trends can be stated as follows:

1) The input impedance increases as the distance A is made larger, but not indefinitely. In general there is a distance A that will give a maximum value of input impedance, after which further increase in A will cause the impedance to decrease.

2) The distance A at which the input impedance reaches a maximum is smaller as d2/d1 is made larger, and becomes smaller as the spacing between the conductors is increased. (d1 is the diameter of the lower T conductor in Figure 24.33 and d2 is the diameter of the antenna.)

3) The maximum impedance values occur in the region where A is 40% to 60% of the antenna length in the average case.

4) Higher values of input impedance can be realized when the antenna is shortened to cancel the inductive reactance of the matching section.

The T match has become popular for transforming the balanced feed point impedance of a VHF or UHF Yagi up to 200 Ω. From that impedance a 4:1 balun is used to transform down to the unbalanced 50 Ω level for the coax cable feeding the Yagi. See the various K1FO-designed Yagis referred to in the **VHF, UHF and Microwave Antennas** chapter and the section later in this chapter concerning transmission-line baluns.

The structure of the T-match also affects the length of the driven element by increasing the element's electrical diameter. A typical T-match is approximately 5 to 10 times greater in diameter than the element alone. This results in the need to extend the length of the driven element by 2-3% to return it to resonance.

The Gamma Match

The gamma-match arrangement shown in Figure 24.34B is an unbalanced version of the T, suitable for use directly with coaxial lines. Except for the matching section being connected between the center and one side of the antenna, the remarks above about the behavior of the T apply equally well. The inherent reactance of the matching section can be canceled either by shortening the antenna appropriately or by using the resonant length and installing a capacitor C, as shown in Figure 24.34B.

For a number of years the gamma match has been widely used for matching coaxial cable to all-metal parasitic beams. Because it is well suited to *plumber's delight* construction, in which all the metal parts are electrically and mechanically connected, it has become quite popular for amateur arrays.

Because of the many variable factors — driven-element length, gamma rod length, rod diameter, spacing between rod and driven element, and value of series capacitors — a number of combinations will provide the desired match. The task of finding a proper combination can be a tedious one, as the settings are interrelated. A few rules of thumb have evolved that provide a starting point for the various factors. For matching a multielement array made of aluminum tubing to 50-Ω line, the length of the rod should be 0.04 to 0.05 λ, its diameter $\frac{1}{3}$ to $\frac{1}{2}$ that of the driven element, and its spacing (center-to-center from the driven element), approximately 0.007 λ. The capacitance value should be approximately 7 pF per meter of wavelength. This translates to about 140 pF for 20 meter operation. The exact gamma dimensions and value for the capacitor will depend on the radiation resistance of the driven element, and whether or not it is resonant. These starting-point dimensions are for an array having a feed point impedance of about 25 Ω, with the driven element shortened approximately 3% from resonance.

Calculating Gamma Dimensions

A starting point for the gamma dimensions and capacitance value may be determined by calculation. H. F. Tolles, W7ITB, has developed a method for determining a set of parameters that will be quite close to providing the desired impedance transformation. (See Bibliography.) The impedance of the antenna must be measured or computed for Tolles's procedure. If the antenna impedance is not accurately known, modeling calculations provide a very good starting point for initial settings of the gamma match.

The math involved in Tolles's procedure is tedious, especially if several iterations are needed to find a practical set of dimensions. The procedure has been adapted for computer calculations by R. A. Nelson, WBØIKN, who wrote his program in Applesoft BASIC (see Bibliography).The process of calculating the necessary gamma match dimensions and values has been implemented in software by Bill Wortman,

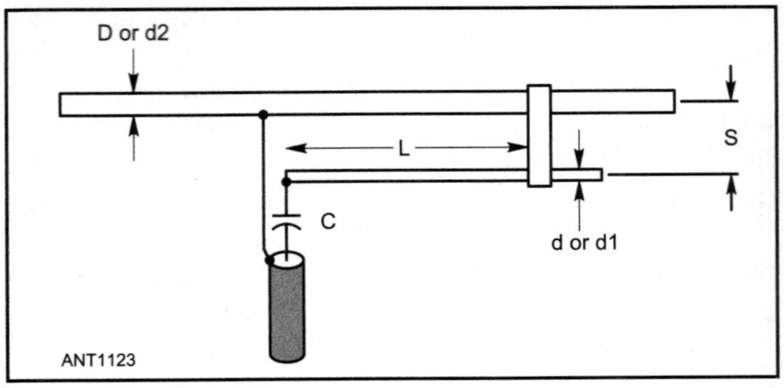

Figure 24.35 — The gamma match, as used with tubing elements. Parameters are those used for the *GAMMAMW4* dimension calculation software. Note that S is a center-to-center value, not surface-to-surface. The transmission line may be either 50-Ω or 75-Ω coax.

N6MW. His program *GAMMAMW4* is available for download from **www.arrl.org/arrl-antenna-book-reference** in the Software Utilities section. The inputs to *GAMMAMW4* are illustrated in **Figure 24.35**:

Z_a — the complex impedance of the unmatched antenna ($Z_a = R_a + j\,X_a$, normally measured with dipole halves split)

S — center-to-center spacing of the circular antenna element to the circular gamma rod

D — diameter of the circular antenna element

d — diameter of the circular gamma rod

Note that S is a center-to-center dimension, not a surface-to-surface value. The following is the *GAMMAMW4* dialog for a 14 MHz antenna with a feed point impedance of 20 + *j*0 Ω, element diameter of 1.5 inches, with a gamma tube diameter of 0.375 inches spaced 2 inches (center to center) from the element. Additional intermediate calculation values are also output but not shown in these examples.

```
Gamma Match Design
 N6MW, October 2012

Freq (MHz)? 14

Now input the unmatched antenna impedance
R +jX

Antenna feed point resistance R (ohms)? 20
Antenna feed point reactance X (ohms)? 0
Feed line impedance (ohms)? 50

 Gamma Match Quantities to be input:
 D = Driven element diameter
 d = Gamma rod diameter
 S = Gamma rod spacing (center-to-center)
 The units, such inches or cm, do not mat-
ter but all 3 must be the same
 Gamma rod spacing, S, must be greater than
(D/2 + d/2)

Driven element diameter, D? 1.5
Gamma element diameter, d? 0.375
Gamma rod spacing ( > 0.9) S? 2

Gamma length (deg) 31.81
Gamma length (feet) 6.21
Gamma length (inches) 74.49
Gamma length (cm) 189.19
Gamma capacitor (pF) 125.04
```

As another example, say we wish to shunt feed a tower at 3.5 MHz with 50-Ω line. The driven element (tower) is 12 inches in diameter, and #12 AWG wire (diameter = 0.0808 inch) with a spacing of 12 inches from the tower is to be used for the "gamma rod." The tower is 50 feet tall with a 5-foot mast and beam antenna at the top. The total height, 55 feet, is approximately 0.19 λ. We assume its electrical length is 0.2 λ or 72°. Modeling shows that the approximate base feed point impedance is 20 – *j* 100 Ω. *GAMMAMW4* says that the gamma rod should be 57.1 feet long, with a gamma capacitor of 32.1 pF.

```
Gamma Match Design
 N6MW, October 2012

Freq (MHz)? 3.5

Now input the unmatched antenna impedance
R +jX

Antenna feed point resistance R (ohms)? 20
Antenna feed point reactance X (ohms)? -100
Feed line impedance (ohms)? 50

 Gamma Match Quantities to be input:
 D = Driven element diameter
 d = Gamma rod diameter
 S = Gamma rod spacing (center-to-center)
 The units, such inches or cm, do not mat-
ter but all 3 must be the same
 Gamma rod spacing, S, must be greater than
(D/2 + d/2)

Driven element diameter, D? 12
Gamma element diameter, d? .0808
Gamma rod spacing ( > 6.0) S? 12

Gamma length (deg) 73.14
Gamma length (feet) 57.10
Gamma length (inches) 685.16
Gamma length (cm) 1740.30
Gamma capacitor (pF) 32.07
```

Immediately we see this set of gamma dimensions is impractical — the rod length (685 inches or 57.1 feet) is greater than the tower height. So we make another set of calculations, using a spacing of 24 inches between the rod and tower. The results this time are that the gamma rod is 44.2 feet long, with a capacitor of 51 pF. This gives us a practical set of starting dimensions for the shunt-feed arrangement.

The preferred method of building a gamma match is illustrated in **Figure 24.36**. The feed line is connected directly to the center element. This is usually done using a clamp or strap from an RF connector but depends on the physical size of the antenna. The gamma capacitor is created from an insulated wire inside the tube that forms the gamma rod. For ½ inch OD aluminum tube and the center conductor and insulation from RG-213, the capacitance is approximately 25 pF/ft of wire inserted into the tube. Do not use the center conductor and insulation from foam-dielectric coax as it will absorb water. Seal the end of the wire inserted into the tube to reduce the tendency to arc when wet or if insects or debris are present. After a satisfactory match has been obtained by adjusting the gamma capacitor as described below, the variable capacitor may be replaced with an equivalent length of wire in the gamma rod.

Adjustment

After installation of the antenna, the proper constants for the T and gamma generally must be determined experimentally. The use of the variable series capacitors, as shown in

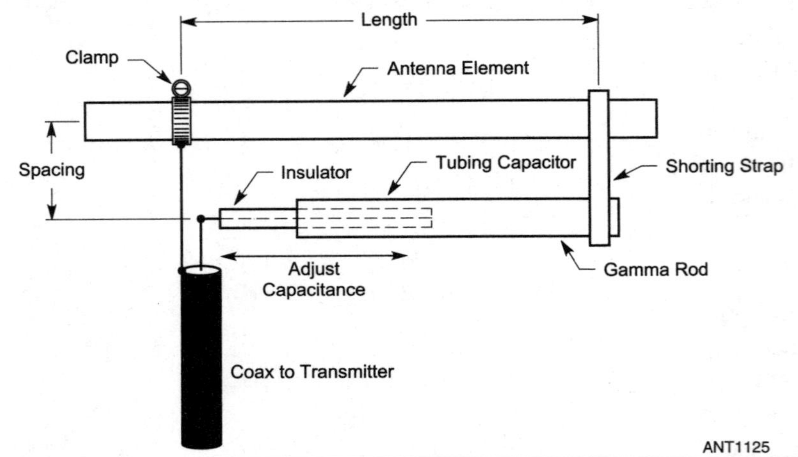

Figure 24.36 — Typical gamma match construction for HF and VHF Yagis.

Figure 24.34, is recommended for ease of adjustment. With a trial position of the tap or taps on the antenna, measure the SWR on the transmission line and adjust C (both capacitors simultaneously in the case of the T) for minimum SWR. If it is not close to 1:1, try another tap position and repeat. It may be necessary to try another size of conductor for the matching section if satisfactory results cannot be brought about. Changing the spacing will show which direction to go in this respect.

24.5.6 THE OMEGA MATCH

The omega match is a slightly modified form of the gamma match. In addition to the series capacitor, a shunt capacitor is used to aid in canceling a portion of the inductive reactance introduced by the gamma section. This is shown in **Figure 24.37**. C1 is the usual series capacitor. The addition of C2 makes it possible to use a shorter gamma rod, or makes it easier to obtain the desired match when the driven element is resonant. During adjustment, C2 will serve primarily to determine the resistive component of the load as seen by the coax line, and C1 serves to cancel any reactance.

24.5.7 THE HAIRPIN AND BETA MATCHES

The usual form of the *hairpin match* is shown in **Figure 24.38**. Basically, the hairpin is a form of an L-matching network in which the feed point's capacitive reactance forms the shunt capacitor. Because it is somewhat easier to adjust for the desired terminating impedance than the gamma match, it is preferred by many amateurs. Its disadvantages, compared with the gamma, are that it must be fed with a parallel-conductor line (a balun may be used with a coax feed line, as shown in Figure 24.38), and the driven element must be split at the center and insulated from the boom. This latter requirement complicates the mechanical mounting arrangement for the element, since the driven element cannot be mounted directly on the boom.

As indicated in Figure 24.38, the center point of the hairpin is electrically neutral. As such, it may be grounded or connected to the remainder of the antenna structure, restoring dc ground to the feed line and driven element. The hairpin itself is usually secured by attaching this neutral point to the boom of the antenna array. The Hy-Gain *beta match* is electrically identical to the hairpin match, the difference being in the mechanical construction of the matching section. With the beta match, the conductors of the matching section straddle the Yagi's boom, one conductor being located on either side, and the electrically neutral point consists of a sliding or adjustable shorting clamp placed around the boom and the two matching-section conductors.

The capacitive portion of the L-network circuit is produced by slightly shortening the antenna driven element,

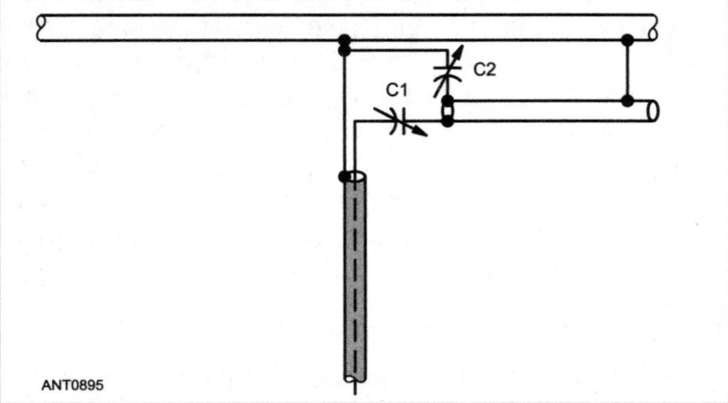

Figure 24.37 — The omega match.

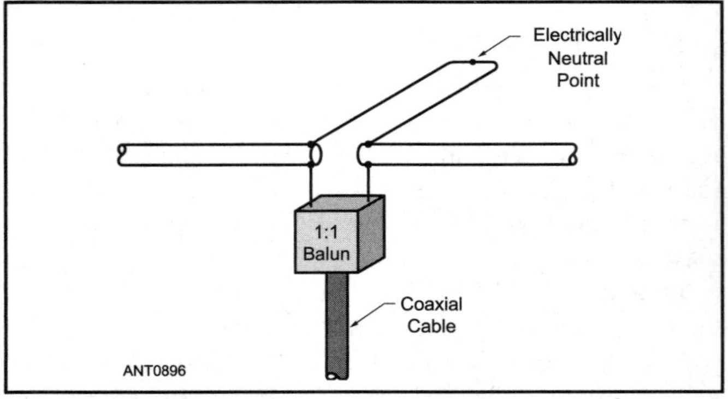

Figure 24.38 — The hairpin match.

shown in **Figure 24.39A**. For a given frequency the impedance of a shortened λ/2 element appears as the antenna resistance and a capacitance in series, as indicated schematically in Figure 24.39B. The inductive portion of the resonant circuit at C is a hairpin of heavy wire or small tubing that is connected across the driven-element center terminals. The diagram of C is redrawn in D to show the circuit in conventional L-network form. R_A, the resistive component of the feed point impedance, must be a smaller value than R_{IN}, the impedance of the feed line, usually 50 Ω.

If the approximate value of R_A for the antenna system is known, **Figures 24.40** and **24.41** may be used to gain an idea of the hairpin dimensions necessary for the desired match. The required value of X_A, the feed point impedance's capacitive reactance component is

$$X_A = -\sqrt{R_A(R_{IN} - R_A)} \quad (23)$$

The curves of Figure 24.40 were obtained from design equations for L-network matching presented earlier in this chapter. Figure 24.41 is based on the equation, $X_L/Z_0 = j \tan \theta$, which gives the inductive reactance as normalized to the characteristic impedance, Z_0, of the hairpin, looking at it as a length of transmission line terminated in a short circuit. For example, if an antenna-system impedance with a resistive component of 20 Ω is to be matched to 50-Ω line,

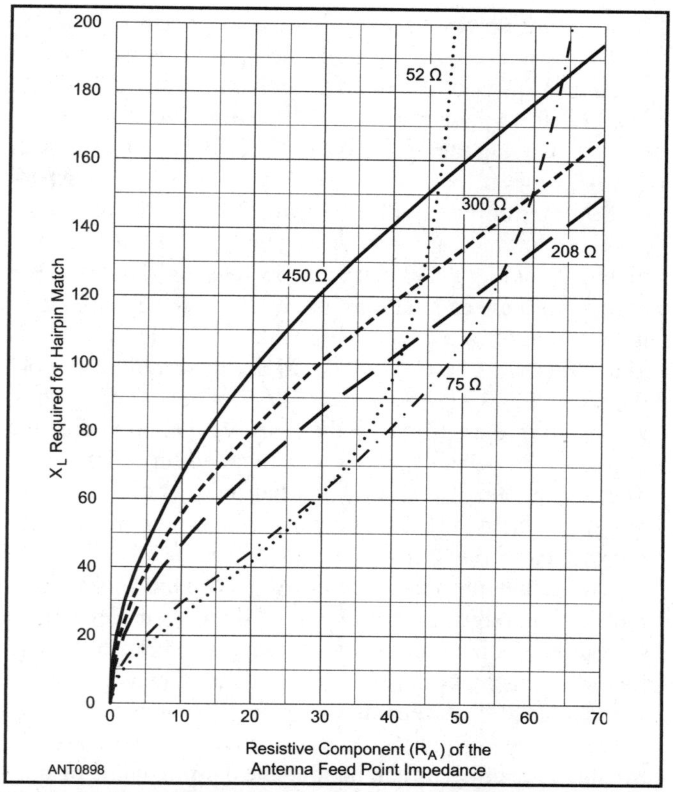

Figure 24.40 — Reactance required for a hairpin to match various antenna resistances to common line or balun impedance. The driven element's feed point impedance must exhibit a specific amount of capacitive reactance as shown in the text.

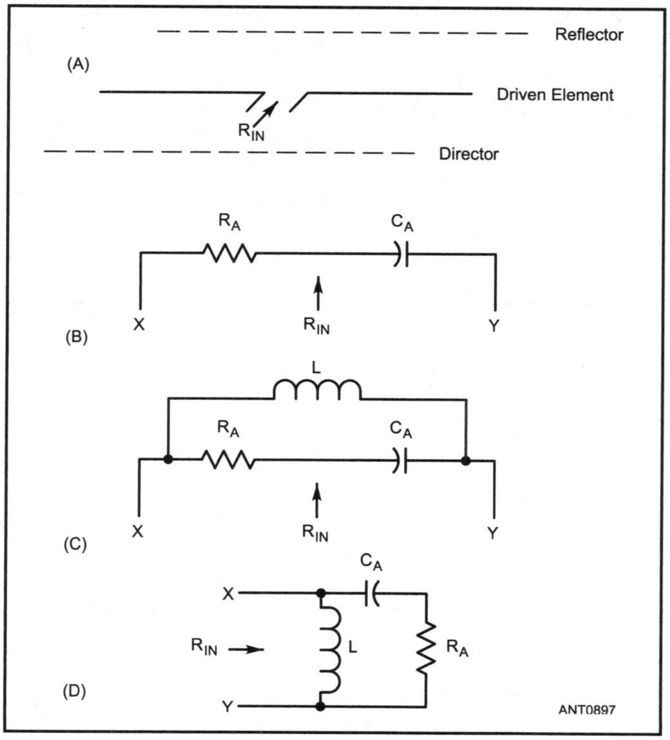

Figure 24.39 — For the Yagi antenna shown at A, the driven element is shorter than its resonant length with a capacitive feed point impedance as represented at B. By adding an inductor, as shown at C, the low value of R_A is made to appear as a higher impedance at terminals XY. At D, the diagram of C is redrawn in the usual L-network configuration.

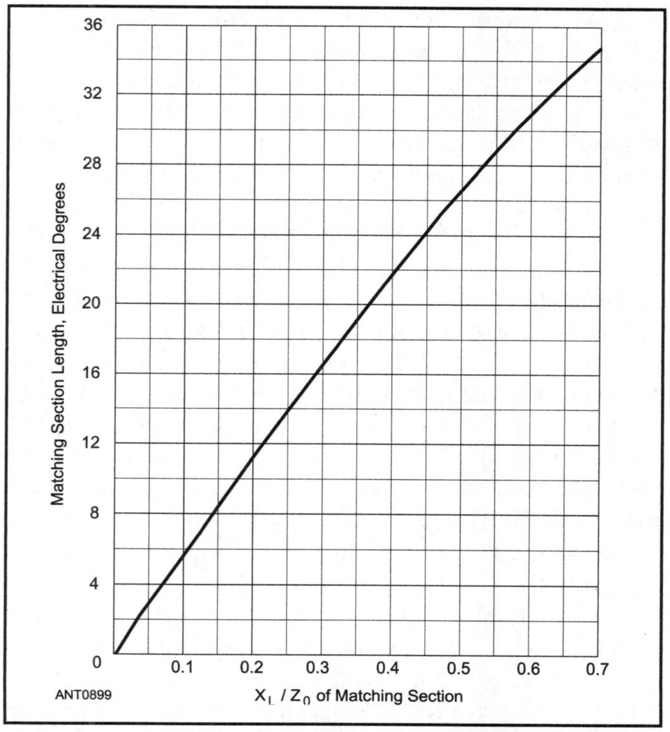

Figure 24.41 — Inductive reactance (normalized to Z_0 of matching section), scale at bottom, versus required hairpin matching section length, scale at left. To determine the length in wavelengths divide the number of electrical degrees by 360. For open-wire line, a velocity factor of 97.5% should be taken into account when determining the electrical length.

Figure 24.40 shows that the inductive reactance required for the hairpin is +41 Ω. If the hairpin is constructed of ¼ inch tubing spaced 1½ inches, its characteristic impedance is 300 Ω (from equations in the **Transmission Lines** chapter). Normalizing the required 41-Ω reactance to this impedance, 41/300 = 0.137.

By entering the graph of Figure 24.41 with this value, 0.137, on the scale at the bottom, you can see that the hairpin length should be 7.8 electrical degrees, or 7.8/360 λ. For purposes of these calculations, taking a 97.5% velocity factor into account, the wavelength in inches is 11,508/f (MHz). If the antenna is to be used on 14 MHz, the required hairpin length is 7.8/360 × 11,508/14.0 = 17.8 inches. The length of the hairpin affects primarily the resistive component of the terminating impedance, as seen by the feed line. Greater resistances are obtained with longer hairpin sections — meaning a larger value of shunt inductor — and smaller resistances with shorter sections.

The remaining reactance at the feed point terminals is tuned out by adjusting the length of the driven element, as necessary. If a fixed-length hairpin section is in use, a small range of adjustment may be made in the effective value of the inductance by spreading or squeezing together the conductors of the hairpin. Spreading the conductors apart will have the same effect as lengthening the hairpin, while placing them closer together will effectively shorten it.

Instead of using a hairpin of stiff wire or tubing, this same matching technique may be used with a lumped-constant inductor connected across the antenna terminals. Such a method of matching has been dubbed, tongue firmly in cheek, as the "helical hairpin." The inductor, of course, must exhibit the same reactance at the operating frequency as the hairpin it replaces. A cursory examination with computer calculations indicates that a helical hairpin may offer a very slightly improved SWR bandwidth over a true hairpin.

24.5.8 MATCHING STUBS

As explained in the **Transmission Lines** chapter, a mismatch-terminated transmission line less than λ/4 long has an input impedance that is both resistive and reactive. The equivalent circuit of the line input impedance at any one frequency can be formed either of resistance and reactance in series, or resistance and reactance in parallel. Depending on the line length, the series resistance component, R_S, can have any value between the terminating resistance Z_R (when the line has zero length) and Z_0^2/Z_R (when the line is exactly λ/4 long).The same thing is true of R_P, the parallel-resistance component.

R_S and R_P do not have the same values at the same line length, however, other than at zero and λ/4. With either equivalent there is some line length that will give a value of R_S or R_P equal to the characteristic impedance of the line. However, there will be reactance along with the resistance. But if provision is made for canceling or tuning out this reactive part of the input impedance, only the resistance will remain. Since this resistance is equal to the Z_0 of the transmission line, the section from the reactance-cancellation point back to the generator will be properly matched.

Tuning out the reactance in the equivalent series circuit requires that a reactance of the same value as X_S (but of opposite kind) be inserted in series with the line. Tuning out the reactance in the equivalent parallel circuit requires that a reactance of the same value as X_P (but of opposite kind) be connected across the line. In practice it is more convenient to use the parallel-equivalent circuit. The transmission line is simply connected to the load (which of course is usually a resonant antenna) and then a reactance of the proper value is connected across the line at the proper distance from the load. From this point back to the transmitter there are no standing waves on the line.

A convenient type of reactance to use is a section of transmission line less than λ/4 long, terminated with either an open circuit or a short circuit, depending on whether capacitive reactance or inductive reactance is called for. Reactances formed from sections of transmission line are called *matching stubs*, and are designated as *open* or *closed* depending on whether the free end is open or short circuited. The two types of matching stubs are shown in the sketches in **Figure 24.42**.

The distance from the load to the stub (dimension A in Figure 24.42) and the length of the stub, B, depend on the characteristic impedances of the line and stub and on the ratio of Z_R to Z_0. Since the ratio of Z_R to Z_0 is also the standing-wave ratio in the absence of matching (and with a resonant antenna), the dimensions are a function of the SWR. If the line and stub have the same Z_0, dimensions A and B are dependent on the SWR only. Consequently, if the SWR can be measured before the stub is installed, the stub can be properly located and its length determined even though the actual value of load impedance is not known.

Typical applications of matching stubs are shown in **Figure 24.43**, where open-wire line is being used. From inspection of these drawings it will be recognized that when an

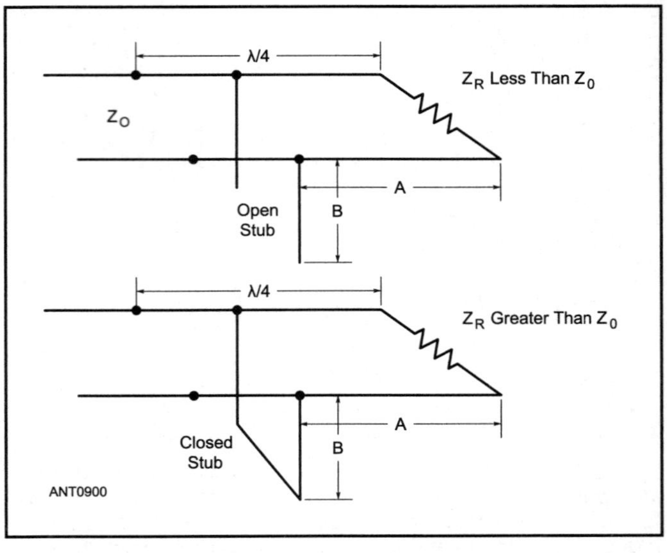

Figure 24.42 — Use of open or closed stubs for canceling the parallel reactive component of input impedance.

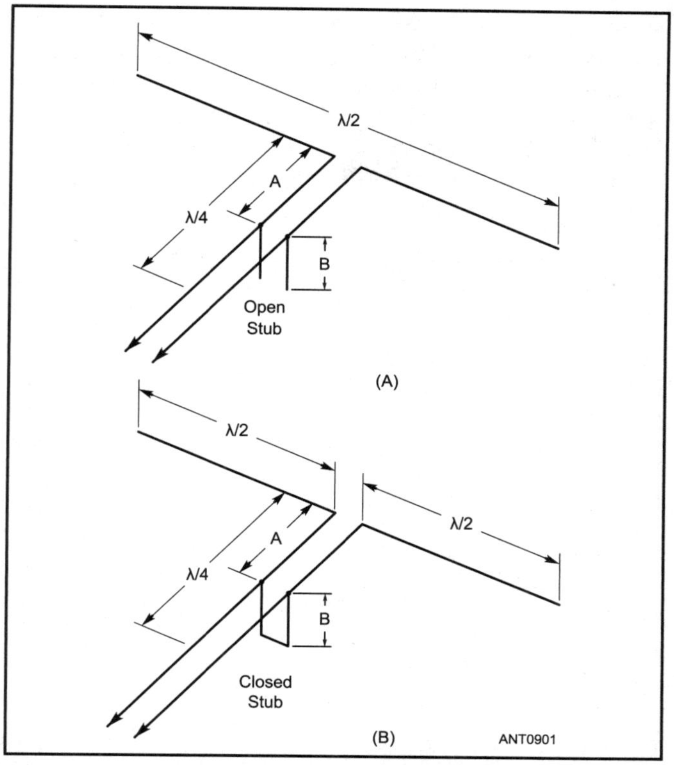

Figure 24.43 — Application of matching stubs to common types of antennas.

antenna is fed at a current loop, as in Figure 24.43A, Z_R is less than Z_0 (in the average case) and therefore an open stub is called for, installed within the first λ/4 of line measured from the antenna. Voltage feed, as at B, corresponds to Z_R greater than Z_0 and therefore requires a closed stub.

A Smith Chart may be used to determine the length of the stub and its distance from the load as described on the supplement included with this book's downloadable supplemental information or the ARRL program *TLW* (also included) may be used. If the load is a pure resistance and the characteristic impedances of the line and stub are identical, the lengths may be determined by equations. For the closed stub when Z_R is greater than Z_0, they are

$$A = \arctan \sqrt{SWR} \tag{24}$$

$$B = \arctan \frac{\sqrt{SWR}}{SWR - 1} \tag{25}$$

For the open stub when Z_R is less than Z_0

$$A = \arctan \frac{1}{\sqrt{SWR}} \tag{26}$$

$$B = \arctan \frac{SWR - 1}{\sqrt{SWR}} \tag{27}$$

In these equations the lengths A and B are the distance from the stub to the load and the length of the stub, respectively, as shown in Figure 24.43. These lengths are expressed in electrical degrees, equal to 360 times the lengths in wavelengths.

In using the above equations it must be remembered that the wavelength along the line is not the same as in free space. If an open-wire line is used the velocity factor of 0.975 will apply. When solid-dielectric line is used, the free-space wavelength as determined above must be multiplied by the appropriate velocity factor to obtain the actual lengths of A and B (see the **Transmission Lines** chapter.)

Although the equations above do not apply when the characteristic impedances of the line and stub are not the same, this does not mean that the line cannot be matched under such conditions. The stub can have any desired characteristic impedance if its length is chosen so that it has the proper value of reactance. Correct lengths can be determined using *TLW* or the Smith Chart for dissimilar types of line.

In using matching stubs it should be noted that the length and location of the stub should be based on the SWR at the load. If the line is long and has fairly high losses, measuring the SWR at the input end will not give the true value at the load. This point is discussed in the section on attenuation in the **Transmission Lines** chapter.

In the experimental adjustment of any type of matched line it is necessary to measure the SWR with fair accuracy in order to tell when the adjustments are being made in the proper direction. In the case of matching stubs, experience has shown that experimental adjustment is unnecessary, from a practical standpoint, if the SWR is first measured with the stub not connected to the transmission line, and the stub is then installed according to the design data.

Reactive Loads

In this discussion of matching stubs it has been assumed that the load is a pure resistance. This is the most desirable

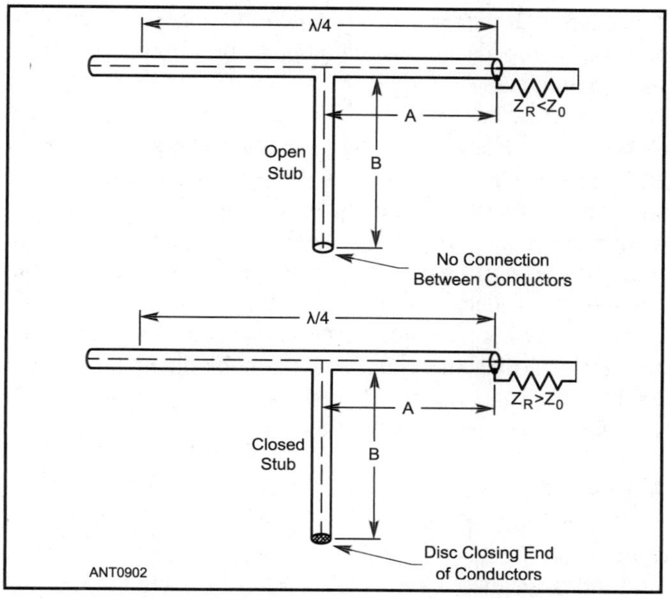

Figure 24.44 — Open and closed stubs on coaxial lines.

condition, since the antenna that represents the load preferably should be tuned to resonance before any attempt is made to match the line. Nevertheless, matching stubs can be used even when the load is considerably reactive. A reactive load simply means that the loops and nodes of the standing waves of voltage and current along the line do not occur at integral multiples of λ/4 from the load. If the reactance at the load is known, the Smith Chart or *TLW* may be used to determine the correct dimensions for a stub match.

Stubs on Coaxial Lines

The principles outlined in the preceding section apply also to coaxial lines. The coaxial cases corresponding to the open-wire cases shown in Figure 24.43 are given in **Figure 24.44**. The equations given earlier may be used to determine dimensions A and B. In a practical installation the junction of the transmission line and stub would be a T connector.

A special case is the use of a coaxial matching stub, in which the stub is associated with the transmission line in such a way as to form a balun. This is described in detail later on in this chapter. The antenna is shortened to introduce just enough reactance at its feed point to permit the matching stub to be connected there, rather than at some other point along the transmission line as in the general cases discussed here. To use this method the antenna resistance must be lower than the Z_0 of the main transmission line, since the resistance is transformed to a higher value. In beam antennas such as Yagis, this will nearly always be the case.

Matching Sections

If the two antenna systems in Figure 24.44 are redrawn in somewhat different fashion, as shown in **Figure 24.45**, a system results that differs in no consequential way from the matching stubs described previously, but in which the stub formed by A and B together is called a *quarter-wave matching section*. The justification for this is that a λ/4 section of line is similar to a resonant circuit, as described earlier in this chapter. It is therefore possible to use the λ/4 section to transform impedances by tapping at the appropriate point along the line.

Earlier equations give design data for matching sections, A being the distance from the antenna to the point at which the line is connected, and A + B being the total length of the matching section. The equations apply only in the case where the characteristic impedance of the matching section and transmission line are the same. Equations are available for the case where the matching section has a different Z_0 than the line, but are somewhat complicated. A graphic solution for different line impedances may be obtained with the Smith Chart (see the supplement included with this book's downloadable supplemental information).

Universal Stub

If the stub attached to the antenna is λ/2 long as in **Figure 24.46**, the combination of feed line attachment point and stub are called a *universal stub*. As its name implies, the double-adjustments are useful for many matching purposes. It is most commonly used at VHF and UHF as described in the **VHF, UHF and Microwave Antenna Systems** chapter.

The stub length is varied to resonate the system by moving the short circuit. The transmission line attachment point is varied until the transmission line and stub impedances are equal. In practice this involves moving both the sliding short

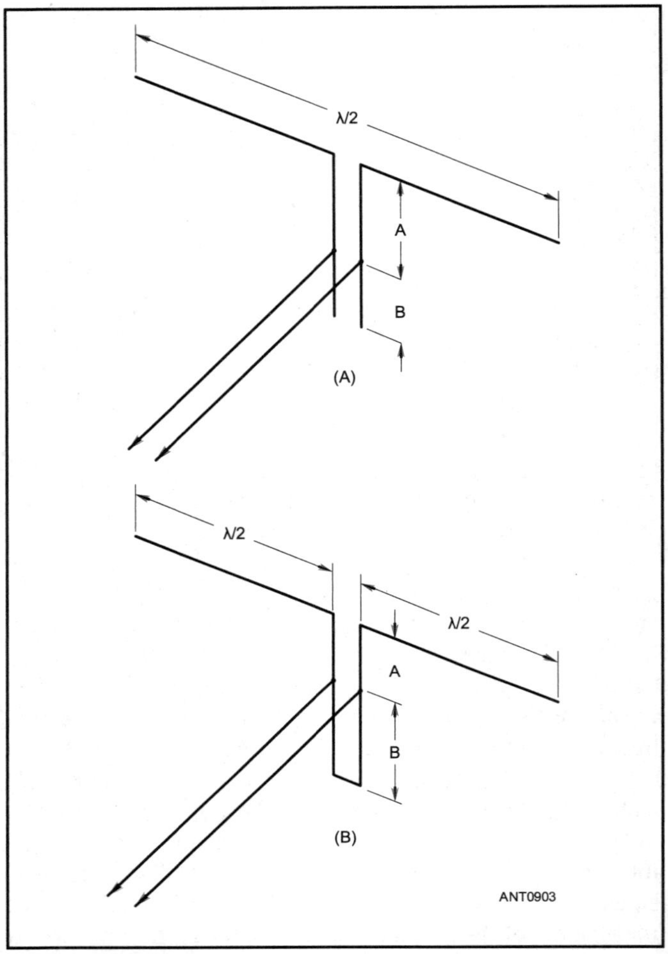

Figure 24.45 — Application of matching sections to common antenna types.

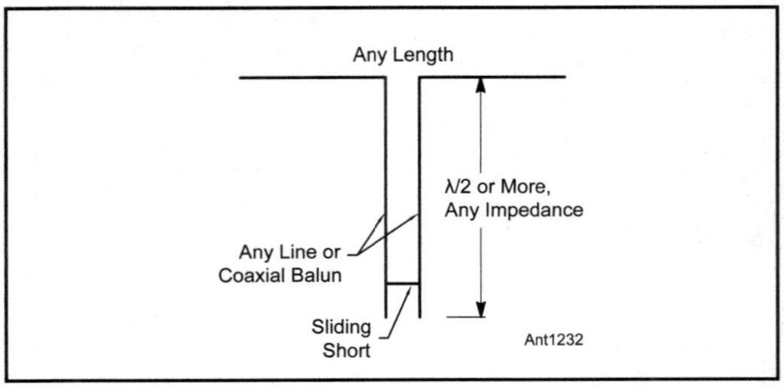

Figure 24.46 —The Universal Stub. An adjustable short on the stub and the points of connection of the transmission line are adjusted for minimum reflected power on the line.

and the point of line connection for zero reflected power, as indicated on an SWR bridge connected in the line.

The universal stub allows for tuning out any small reactance present in the driven part of the system. It permits matching the antenna to the line without knowledge of the actual impedances involved. The position of the short yielding the best match gives some indication of the amount of reactance present. With little or no reactive component to be tuned out, the stub must be approximately λ/2 from the load toward the short.

The stub should be made of stiff bare wire or rod, spaced no more than 1/20 λ apart. Preferably it should be mounted rigidly, on insulators. Once the position of the short is determined, the center of the short can be grounded, if desired, and the portion of the stub no longer needed can be removed.

It is not necessary that the stub be connected directly to the driven element. It can be made part of a parallel-wire line as a device to match coaxial cable to the line. The stub can be connected to the lower end of a delta match or placed at the feed point of a phased array. Examples of these uses are given later.

24.5.9 RESONANT CIRCUIT MATCHING

Antennas with a high feed point impedance, such as end-fed wires close to λ/2 in length and "voltage-fed" antennas such as the Bobtail Curtain often use a parallel-tuned circuit at the feed point to effect an impedance match. The circuit is adjusted to resonance and then the feed line attached to a tap on the inductor that is moved until an SWR minimum is obtained. The circuit may need a slight retuning following by a final position adjustment of the feed line. (See the chapters **Multiband HF Antennas** and **Broadside and End-Fire Arrays** for more information on these antennas and typical feed systems.)

The matching bandwidth of this technique is quite narrow, requiring frequent retuning or operation over a narrow bandwidth. In addition, the voltages at the "hot" or ungrounded end of the tank circuit can be very high. Caution must be used in construction to prevent contact with the high voltages and adequately rated components must be used.

24.6 COMMON-MODE TRANSMISSION LINE CURRENT

In discussions so far about transmission line operation, it was always assumed that the two conductors carry equal and opposite currents throughout their length. This is an ideal condition that may or may not be realized in practice. In the average case, the chances are rather good that the currents will not be balanced unless special precautions are taken. The degree of imbalance — and whether that imbalance is actually important — is what we will examine in the rest of this chapter, along with measures that can be taken to restore balance in the system.

It is important to note that common-mode current on the shield of a coaxial feed line is not entirely isolated from signals inside the cable. Because of *transfer impedance*, the common-mode current can create differential-mode signals as discussed in the **Transmission Lines** chapter.

There are two common conditions that will cause an imbalance of transmission line currents. Both are related to the symmetry of the system. The first condition involves the lack of symmetry when an inherently *unbalanced* coaxial line feeds a *balanced* antenna (such as a dipole or a Yagi driven element) directly. The second condition involves asymmetrical routing of a transmission line near the antenna or asymmetry in the environment around the antenna and transmission line such as unequal heights or lengths of conductors, ground slope, nearby conducting objects such as other antennas, towers, or buildings. Even trees can affect the fields near an antenna and transmission line.

24.6.1 UNBALANCED COAX FEEDING A BALANCED ANTENNA

Figure 24.47 shows a coaxial cable feeding a hypothetical balanced dipole fed in the center. The coax has been

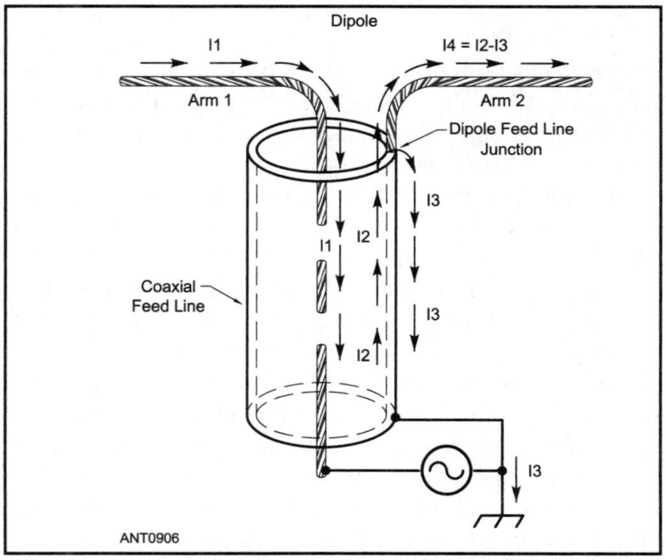

Figure 24.47 — Drawing showing various current paths at feed point of a balanced dipole fed with unbalanced coaxial cable. The diameter of the coax is exaggerated to show currents clearly.

drawn highly enlarged to show all currents involved. In this drawing the feed line drops at right angles down from the feed point and the antenna is assumed to be perfectly symmetrical. Because of this symmetry, one side of the antenna induces current on the feed line that is completely canceled by the current induced from the other side of the antenna. (See the Bibliography entry for Lewellan for a detailed paper about this situation and the use of baluns.)

Currents I1 and I2 from the transmitter flow on the inside of the coax. I1 flows on the *outer surface* of the coax's inner conductor and I2 flows on the *inner surface* of the shield. Skin effect keeps I1 and I2 inside the transmission line confined to where they are within the line. The field outside the coax is zero, since I1 and I2 have equal amplitudes but are 180° out of phase with respect to each other.

The currents flowing on the antenna itself are labeled I1 and I4, and both flow in the same direction at any instant in time for a resonant half-wave dipole. On Arm 1 of the dipole, I1 is shown going directly into the center conductor of the feed coax. However, the situation is different for the other side of this dipole. Once current I2 reaches the end of the coax, it splits into two components. One is I4, going directly into Arm 2 of the dipole. The other is I3 and this flows down the *outer surface* of the coax shield. Again, because of skin effect, I3 is separate and distinct from the current I2 on the inner surface. The antenna current in Arm 2 is thus equal to the difference between I2 and I3.

The magnitude of I3 is proportional to the relative impedances in each current path beyond the split. The feed point impedance of the dipole by itself is somewhere between 50 to 75 Ω, depending on the height above ground. The impedance seen looking into one half of the dipole is half, or 25 to 37.5 Ω. The impedance seen looking down the outside surface of the coax's outer shield to ground is called the *common-mode impedance*, and I3 is aptly called the *common-mode current*. (The term common-mode is more readily appreciated if parallel-conductor line is substituted for the coaxial cable used in this illustration. Current induced by radiation onto both conductors of a two-wire line is a common-mode current, since it flows in the *same direction* on both conductors, rather than in opposite directions as it does for differential-mode transmission line current. The outer braid for a coaxial cable shields the inner conductor from such an induced current, but the unwanted current on the outside braid is still called *common-mode* current.)

The common-mode impedance will vary with the length and diameter of the coaxial feed line, system of conductors and enclosures in the station, and the connection to any ground system. Note that the path from the station equipment to the ground system may go through a ground bus, the transmitter power supply's ac cord, the house wiring and even the power-line service ground. In other words, the overall length of the coaxial outer surface and the other components making up ground can actually be quite a bit different from what you might expect by casual inspection.

The best way to think about the common-mode path is to understand it is really an antenna, and possesses all the properties of an antenna. Voltage and current vary along it according to the conditions along it and its length. As part of the antenna system, it radiates and receives. What it radiates and receives is coupled to and from the "intentional" parts of the antenna.

The worst-case common-mode impedance occurs when the overall effective path length to ground is a multiple of λ/2, making this path half-wave resonant. In effect, the line and ground-wire system acts like a sort of transmission line, transforming the short circuit to ground at its end to a low impedance at the dipole's feed point. This causes I3 to be a significant part of I2.

I3 not only causes an imbalance in the amount of current flowing in each arm of the otherwise symmetrical dipole, but it also radiates by itself. The radiation in Figure 24.47 due to I3 would be mainly vertically polarized, since the coax is drawn as being mainly vertical. However the polarization is a mixture of horizontal and vertical, depending on the orientation of the ground wiring from the transmitter chassis to the rest of the station's grounding system.

Pattern Distortion for a Dipole with Symmetrical Coax Feed

Figure 24.48 compares the azimuthal radiation pattern for two λ/2-long 14-MHz dipoles mounted horizontally λ/2 above average ground. Both patterns were computed for a 28° elevation angle, the peak response for a λ/2-high dipole. The model for the first antenna, the reference dipole shown

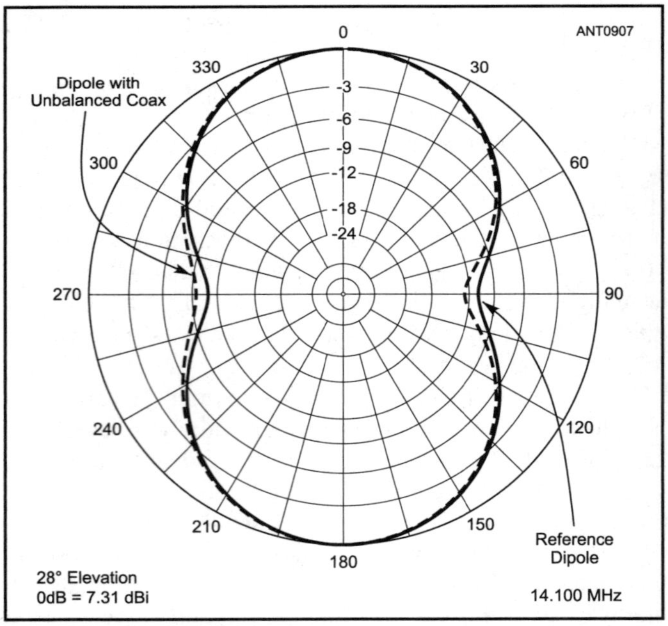

Figure 24.48 — Comparison of azimuthal patterns of two λ/2-long 14-MHz dipoles mounted λ/2 over average ground. The reference dipole without effect of feed line distortion (modeled as though the transmitter were located right at the feed point) is the solid line. The dashed line shows the pattern for the dipole affected by common-mode current on its feed line due to the use of unbalanced coax to feed a balanced antenna. The feed line is dropped directly from the feed point to ground in a symmetrical manner. The feed point impedance in this symmetrical configuration changes only a small amount compared to the reference antenna.

as a solid line, has no feed line associated with it — it is as though the transmitter were somehow remotely located right at the center of the dipole. This antenna displays a classical figure-8 pattern. Both side nulls dip symmetrically about 10 dB below the peak response, typical for a 20 meter dipole 33 feet above ground (or an 80 meter dipole placed 137 feet above ground).

The second dipole, shown as a dashed line, is modeled using a $\lambda/2$-long coaxial feed line dropped vertically to the ground below the feed point. Now, the azimuthal response of the second dipole is no longer perfectly symmetrical. It is shifted to the left a few dB in the area of the side nulls and the peak response is down about 0.1 dB compared to the reference dipole. Many would argue that this sort of response isn't all that bad! However, do keep in mind that this is for a feed line placed in a symmetrical manner, at a right angle below the dipole. Asymmetry in dressing the coax feed line will result in more pattern distortion.

SWR Change with Common-Mode Current

If an SWR meter is placed at the bottom end of the coax feeding the second dipole, it would show an SWR of 1.38:1 for a 50-Ω coax such as RG-213, since the antenna's feed point impedance is $69.20 + j\,0.69\ \Omega$. The SWR for the reference dipole would be 1.39:1, since its feed point impedance is $69.47 - j\,0.35\ \Omega$. As could be expected, the common-mode impedance in parallel with the dipole's natural feed point impedance has lowered the net impedance seen at the feed point, although the degree of impedance change is miniscule in this particular case with a symmetrical feed line dressed away from the antenna.

In theory at least, we have a situation where a change in the length of the unbalanced coaxial cable feeding a balanced dipole will cause the SWR on the line to change also. This is due to the changing common-mode impedance to ground at the feed point. The SWR may even change if the operator touches the SWR meter, since the path to RF ground is subtly altered when this happens. Even changing the length of an antenna to prune it for resonance may also yield unexpected, and confusing, results on the SWR meter because of the common-mode impedance.

When the overall effective length of the coaxial feed line to ground is not a multiple of a $\lambda/2$ resonant length but is an odd multiple of $\lambda/4$, the common-mode impedance transformed to the feed point is high in comparison to the dipole's natural feed point impedance. This will cause I3 to be small in comparison to I2, meaning that radiation by I3 itself and the imbalance between I1 and I4 will be minimal. Modeling this case produces no difference in response between the dipole with unbalanced feed line and the reference dipole with no feed line. Thus, a multiple of a half-wave length for coax and ground wiring represents the *worst case* for this kind of imbalance, when the system is otherwise symmetrical.

If the coax in Figure 24.47 were replaced with parallel-conductor transmission line, the SWR would remain almost constant along the line, no matter what the length. SWR would actually decrease slightly toward the transmitter end because of line loss due to increased SWR. However, the decrease would be slight, because the loss in parallel-conductor transmission line is small, even with relatively high SWR on the line. It is worth noting that window-line can be lossy when wet or covered with ice or snow. (See the **Transmission Lines** chapter for a thorough discussion on additional line loss due to SWR.)

Size of Coax

At HF, the diameter of the coax feeding a $\lambda/2$ dipole is only a tiny fraction of the length of the dipole itself. In the case of Figure 24.47 above, the model of the coax used assumed an exaggerated 9-inch diameter, just to simulate a worst-case effect of coax spacing at HF.

However, on the higher UHF and microwave frequencies, the assumption that the coax spacing is not a significant portion of a wavelength is no longer true. The plane bisecting the feed point of the dipole in Figure 24.47 down through the space below the feed point and in-between the center conductor and shield of the coax is the "center" of the system. If the coax diameter is a significant percentage of the wavelength, the center is no longer symmetrical with reference to the dipole itself and significant imbalance will result. Measurements done at microwave frequencies showing extreme pattern distortion for balun-less dipoles may well have suffered from this problem.

24.6.2 ASYMMETRICAL ROUTING OF THE FEED LINE

Figure 24.47 shows a symmetrically located coax feed line, one that drops vertically at a 90° angle directly below the feed point of the symmetrical dipole. What happens if the feed line is not dressed away from the antenna in a completely symmetrical fashion — that is, not at a right angle to the dipole?

Figure 24.49 illustrates a situation where the feed line

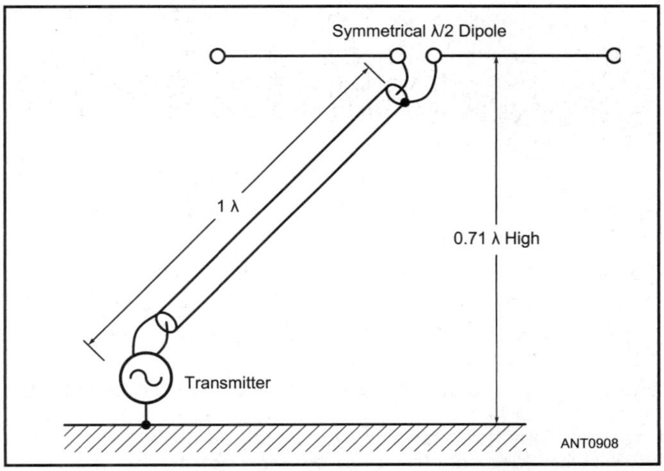

Figure 24.49 — Drawing of $\lambda/2$ dipole, placed 0.71 λ above average ground, with a 1-λ long coax feed line connected at far end to ground through a transmitter. Worst-case feed line radiation due to common-mode current induced on the outer shield braid occurs for lengths that are multiples of $\lambda/2$.

goes to the transmitter and ground at a 45° angle from the dipole. Now, one side of the dipole can radiate more strongly onto the feed line than the other half can. Thus, the currents radiated onto the feed line from each half of the symmetrical dipole won't cancel each other. In other words, the antenna itself radiates a common-mode current onto the transmission line. This is a different form of common-mode current from what was discussed above in connection with an unbalanced coax feeding a balanced dipole, but it has similar effects.

Figure 24.50 shows the azimuthal response of a 0.71-λ-high reference dipole with no feed line (as though the transmitter were located right at the feed point) compared to a 0.71-λ-high dipole that uses a 1-λ-long coax feed line, slanted 45° from the feed point down to ground through the transmitter. The 0.71-λ height was used so that the slanted coax could be exactly 1 λ long, directly grounded at its end through the transmitter and so that the low-elevation angle response could be emphasized to show pattern distortion. The feed line was made 1 λ long in this case, because when the feed line length is only 0.5 λ and is slanted 45° to ground, the height of the dipole is only 0.35 λ. This low height masks changes in the nulls in the azimuthal response due to feed line common-mode currents. Worst-case pattern distortion occurs for lengths that are multiplies of λ/2, as before.

The degree of pattern distortion is now slightly worse than that for the symmetrically placed coax, but once again, the overall effect is not really severe. Interestingly enough, the slanted-feed line dipole actually has about 0.2 dB more gain than the reference dipole. This is because the left-hand side null is deeper for the slanted-feed line antenna, adding power to the frontal lobes at 0° and 180°.

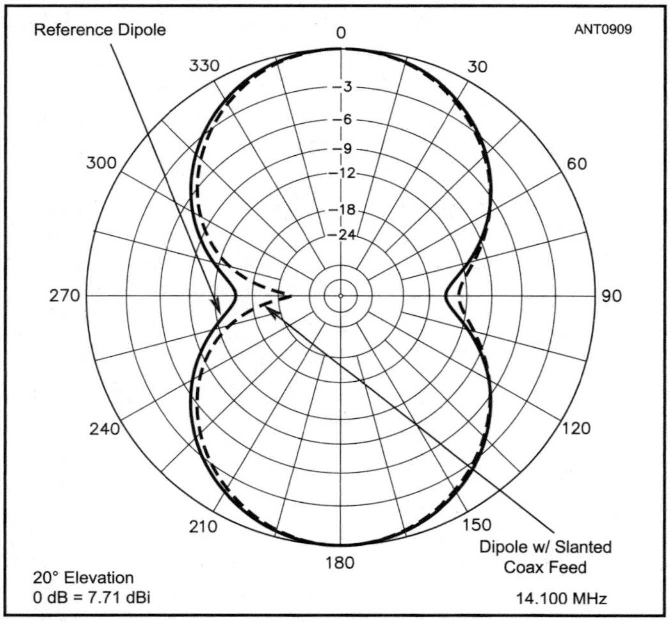

Figure 24.50 — Azimuthal response for two dipoles placed as shown in Figure 24.49. The solid line represents a reference dipole with no feed line (modeled as though the transmitter were located directly at the feed point). The dashed line shows the response of the antenna with feed line slanted 45° down to ground. Current induced on the outer braid of the 1-λ -long coax by its asymmetry with respect to the antenna causes the pattern distortion. The feed point impedance also changes, causing a different SWR from that for the unaffected reference dipole.

The feed point impedance for this dipole with slanted feed line is 62.48 – *j* 1.28 Ω for an SWR of 1.25:1, compared to the reference dipole's feed point impedance of 72.00 + *j* 16.76 Ω for an SWR of 1.59:1. Here, the reactive part of the net feed point impedance is smaller than that for the reference dipole, indicating that detuning has occurred due to mutual coupling to its own feed line. This change of SWR is slightly larger than for the previous case and could be seen on a typical SWR meter.

You should recognize that common-mode current arising from radiation from a balanced antenna back onto its transmission line due to a lack of symmetry occurs for *both* coaxial or balanced transmission lines. For a coax, the inner surface of the shield and the inner conductor are shielded from such radiation by the outer braid. However, the outer surface of the braid carries common-mode current radiated from the antenna and then subsequently reradiated by the line. For a parallel-conductor line, common-mode currents are induced onto both conductors, again resulting in reradiation from the feed line.

If the *antenna or its environment* are not perfectly symmetrical in all respects, there will also be some degree of common-mode current generated on the transmission line, either coax or balanced. Perfect symmetry means that the ground would have to be perfectly flat everywhere under the antenna, and that the physical length of each leg of the antenna would have to be exactly the same. It also means that the height of the dipole must be exactly symmetrical all along its length, and it even means that nearby conductors, such as power lines, must be completely symmetrical with respect to the antenna.

In the real world, where the ground isn't always perfectly flat under the whole length of a dipole and where wire legs aren't cut to the same length, a parallel-conductor line feeding a supposedly balanced antenna is no guarantee that common-mode transmission line currents will not occur! However, dressing the feed line so that it is symmetrical to the antenna will lead to fewer problems in all cases.

Note that the popular End-Fed Half-Wave (EFHW) is an extreme example of asymmetry with the feed line attached at one end of the antenna. (Also see the discussion of vertical half-wave dipoles in the **Single Band MF and HF Antennas** chapter.) Common-mode current is guaranteed to flow on the feed line because one conductor of the feed line is not attached directly to the antenna. The feed line's common-mode path, whether on both conductors of a parallel-conductor feed line or on the outer shield of coax, is part of the antenna. EFHW designs that depend on this common-mode path as part of the radiating element will not work properly if a choke is placed on the feed line at the antenna.

Some EFHW designs replace the common-mode path with an extra counterpoise wire which is simply the "missing" part of the antenna, allowing an isolation transformer to decouple the feed line from the antenna current.

24.6.3 COMMON-MODE CURRENT EFFECTS ON DIRECTIONAL ANTENNAS

For a simple dipole, many amateurs would look at Figure 24.48 or Figure 24.50 and say that the worst-case pattern asymmetry doesn't look very important, and they would be right. Any minor, unexpected change in SWR due to common-mode current would be shrugged off as inconsequential — if indeed it is even noticed. All around the world, there are many thousands of coax-fed dipoles in use, where no special effort has been made to smooth the transition from unbalanced coax to balanced dipole.

For antennas that are specifically designed to be highly directional, however, pattern deterioration resulting from common-mode currents is a very different matter. Much care is usually taken during design of a directional antenna like a Yagi or a quad to tune each element in the system for the best compromise between directional pattern, gain and SWR bandwidth. What happens if we feed such a carefully tailored antenna in a fashion that creates common-mode feed line currents?

Figure 24.51 compares the azimuthal response of two five-element 20 meter Yagis, each located horizontally $\lambda/2$ above average ground. The solid line represents the reference antenna, where it is assumed that the transmitter is located right at the balanced driven element's feed point without the need for an intervening feed line. The dashed line represents the second Yagi, which is modeled with a $\lambda/2$-long unbalanced coaxial feed line going to ground directly under the balanced driven element's feed point.

Minor pattern skewing evident in the case of the dipole now becomes definite deterioration in the rearward pattern of the otherwise superb pattern of the reference Yagi. The side nulls deteriorate from more than 40 dB to about 25 dB. The rearward lobe at 180° goes from 26 dB to about 22 dB. In short, the pattern gets a bit ugly and the gain decreases as well.

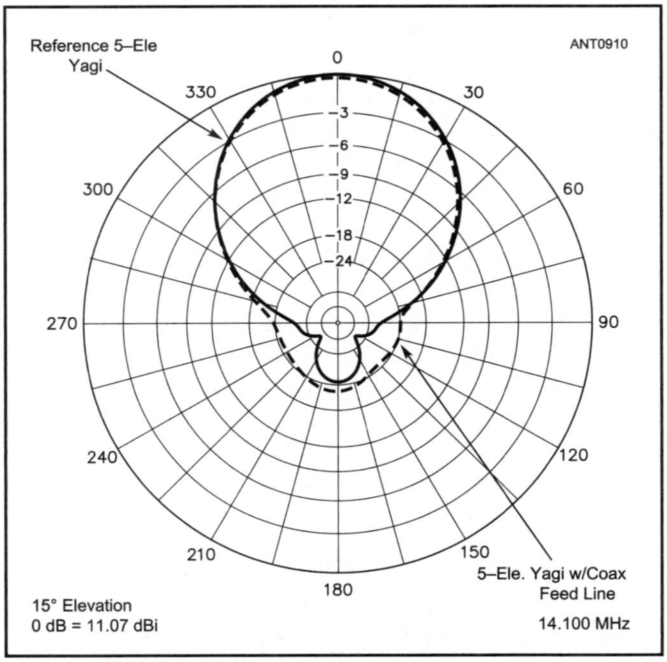

Figure 24.51 — Azimuthal response for two five-element 20 meter Yagis placed λ 2 over average ground. The solid line represents an antenna fed with no feed line, as though the transmitter were located right at the feed point. The dashed line represents an antenna fed with a $\lambda/2$ length of unbalanced coax line directly going to ground (through a transmitter at ground level). The distortion in the rearward pattern is evident, and the Yagi loses a small amount of forward gain (0.3 dB) compared to the reference antenna. In this case, placing a common-mode choke of $+j$ 1000 Ω at the feed point eliminated the pattern distortion.

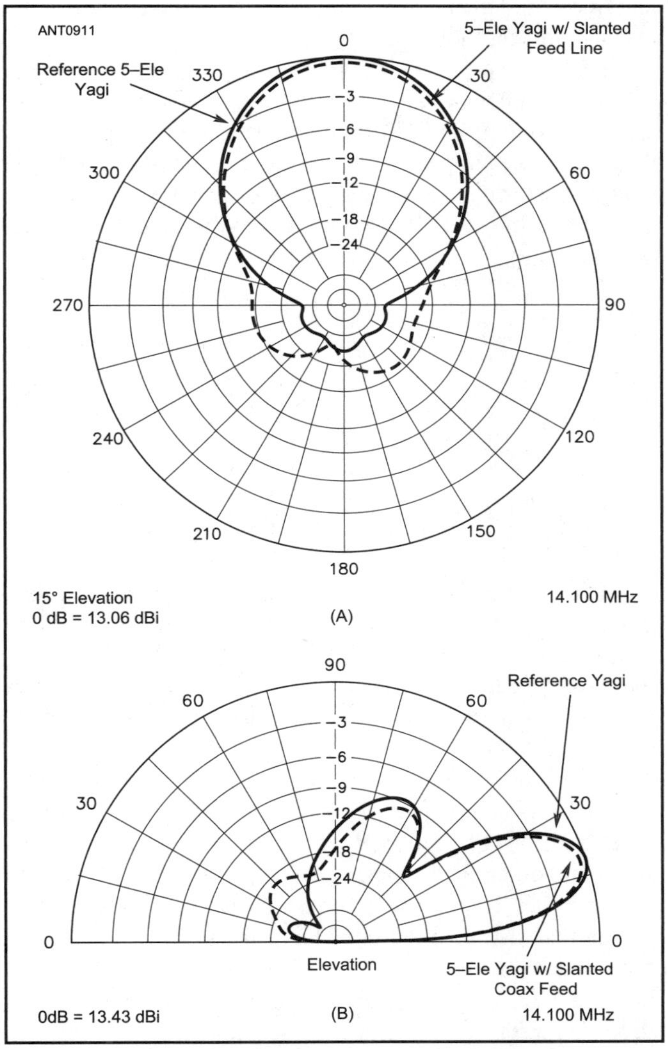

Figure 24.52 — At A, azimuthal response for two five-element 20 meter Yagis placed 0.71 λ over average ground. The solid line represents an antenna fed with no feed line. The dashed line represents an antenna fed with a 1-λ length of unbalanced coax line slanted at 45° to ground (through a transmitter at ground level). The distortion in the rearward pattern is even more evident than in Figure 24.49. This Yagi loses a bit more forward gain (0.4 dB) compared to the reference antenna. At B, elevation response comparison. The slant of the feed line causes more common-mode current due to asymmetry. In this case, placing a common-mode choke of $+j$ 1000 Ω at the feed point was not sufficient to eliminate the pattern distortion substantially. Another choke was required $\lambda/4$ farther down the transmission line to eliminate common-mode currents of all varieties.

Figure 24.52 shows a comparison at 0.71 λ height between a reference Yagi with no feed line and a Yagi with a 1-λ-long feed line slanted 45° to ground. Side nulls that were deep (at more than 30 dB down) for the reference Yagi have been reduced to less than 18 dB in the common-mode afflicted antenna. The rear lobe at 180° has deteriorated mildly, from 28 dB to about 26 dB. The forward gain of the antenna has fallen 0.4 dB from that of the reference antenna. As expected, the feed point impedance also changes, from $22.3 - j\,25.2\ \Omega$ for the reference Yagi to $18.5 - j\,29.8\ \Omega$ for the antenna with the unbalanced feed. The SWR will also change with line length on the balanced Yagi due to the common-mode path, just as it did for the simple dipole.

Clearly, the pattern of what is supposed to be a highly directional antenna can be seriously degraded by the presence of common-mode currents on the coax feed line. As in the case of the simple dipole, multiples of λ/2-long resonant feed line to ground represents the worst-case feed system, even when the feed line is dressed symmetrically at right angles below the antenna. And as found with the dipole, the pattern deterioration becomes even worse if the feed line is dressed at a slant under the antenna to ground, although this sort of installation with a Yagi is not very common. For least interaction, the feed line still should be dressed so that it is symmetrical with respect to the antenna.

In the computer models used to create Figures 24.48, 24.50 and 24.51, placing a common-mode choke (described in the next sections) with a reactance of $+\,j\,1000\ \Omega$ at the antenna's feed point removed virtually all traces of the problem. This was always true for the simple case where the feed line was dressed symmetrically, directly down under the feed point. Certain slanted-feed line lengths required additional common-mode chokes which should be placed at λ/4 intervals beginning λ/2 down the transmission line from the feed point. (Placing the first choke λ/2 from the antenna feed point avoids creating a low impedance point on the outside of the coax shield at the feed point.) Remember that the free-space wavelength is used on the *outside* of coax while the VF must be applied *inside* the coax.

24.7 CURRENT BALUNS, CHOKES, AND CHOKE BALUNS

In the preceding sections, problems associated with common-mode currents on transmission lines were described. Common-mode feed line currents have several causes — primarily physical asymmetry of the antenna, direct connection of unbalanced feed lines and balanced antennas, and coupling between the feed line and the antenna due to placement or orientation of the feed line. In addition, noise is picked up by the feed line as common-mode current and signals radiated by current on the feed line can cause interference to appliances and other electronics if they are near the feed line.

In order to reduce common-mode feed line current, *chokes* that create a high impedance in the current's path are used. If the choke is placed at the junction of a coaxial feed line and load, such as an antenna, the choke becomes a *choke balun* between the unbalanced feed line and the balanced load, such as the antenna. Choke and choke baluns come in a variety of forms, which we will explore in this section. See the earlier section Transmission Line Matching Devices for a discussion of the difference between chokes, baluns, and impedance transformers.

It is important to note that a number of the papers and articles referenced in this section were written before the advent of a wide variety of ferrite materials available today, in particular the type #31 mix which is used for EMI suppression in the MF, HF, and VHF ranges. (See **www.fair-rite.com/materials** for a table of ferrite types and their applications.) In addition, more applications for feed line chokes, such as for reducing received noise and breaking up resonant feed line length, have been developed for amateurs. This does not invalidate the information from those early sources but requires the reader to remember that current usage may be have evolved in light of a better understanding of antenna and feed line system behavior and new types of ferrite becoming available.

Material in this section has been updated from earlier editions based on the latest versions of Jim Brown, K9YC's paper "RFI, Ferrites, and Common Mode Chokes For Hams," (updated in April 2019) and a new paper on transmitting chokes, "A New Choke Cookbook for the 160–10M Bands," (Dec 2018) that are both available for download from **k9yc.com/publish.htm**.

24.7.1 CURRENT BALUNS

The *current balun* is a type of transmission line transformer with a high common-mode impedance providing isolation between the input and output terminals. It has the hybrid properties of a tightly coupled transmission line transformer (with a 1:1 transformation ratio) and the common-mode impedance of an inductance or resistance to provide common-mode impedance. (See the previous discussion of Transmission Line Transformers.) The transmission line transformer action forces the current at the output terminals to be equal, and the common-mode impedance blocks common-mode currents. The blocking action is why current baluns are often referred to as choke baluns. The current balun was originally developed for interstage coupling with inductive ferrite materials and not as an antenna system choke component. This causes confusion in amateur circles where the predominant use of baluns is in antenna systems where resistive (lossy) materials are the most useful.

See **Figure 24.53A** for a schematic representation of such a balun. This characterization is attributed to Frank Witt, AI1H. Z_W is the winding impedance that blocks common-mode currents. (This is the Guanella transformer discussed previously.) The winding impedance is determined by the material used for the core on which the transmission line is wound, usually a ferrite rod or toroid.

The *ideal transformer* in this characterization models what happens either inside a coax or for a pair of perfectly coupled parallel wires in a two-wire transmission line. Although Z_W is shown here as a single impedance, it could be split into two equal parts, with one placed on each side of the ideal transformer. The transmission line consists of coaxial cable (such as a small diameter Teflon-insulated cable like RG-303) or tightly coupled (side-by-side) bifilar wires. (Construction is discussed later in this section.)

Figure 24.53B and C show two common methods of winding 1:1 and 4:1 current baluns using a ferrite core. Type #31 material is recommended for the core as discussed in the section on Transmitting Ferrite-Core Coaxial Choke Baluns. Each bifilar winding forms a transmission line that is wound around the core which creates the choking impedance, Z_W.

In Figure 24.53C, note that two cores are required. A 4:1 current balun cannot be wound on a single core because of the coupling between the lines that would be created. The transmission lines must be independent and separate cores must be used.

24.7.2 COILED-COAX CHOKE BALUNS

The simplest method of constructing a feed line choke is simply to wind a length of coaxial cable into a coil (see **Figure 24.54**), creating an inductor from the shield's outer surface. (This construction technique cannot be used with parallel-conductor line because of coupling between the conductors in adjacent turns.) Common-mode current on the outside of the shield encounters the coil's reactance, while

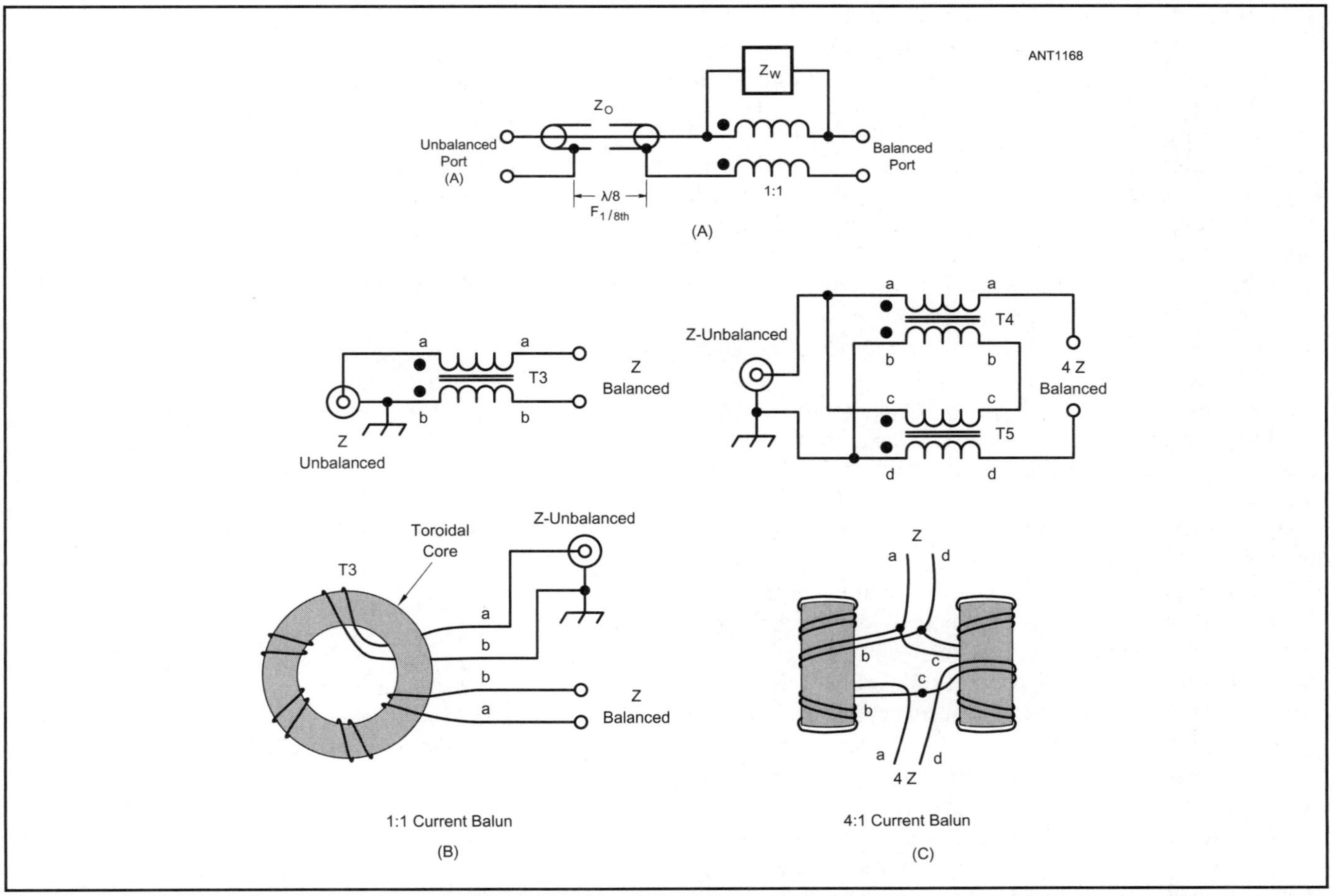

Figure 24.53 — Current or choke baluns. Section A shows the model for a 1:1 current or choke balun by Frank Witt, AI1H. The transformer is an ideal transformer. Z_W is the common-mode winding impedance. Section B shows how to wind a 1:1 version. The 4:1 balun in C is wound on two cores, which are physically separated from each other. Each winding is made from 9 turns of #12 AWG on a 2.4-inch OD type #31 ferrite core.

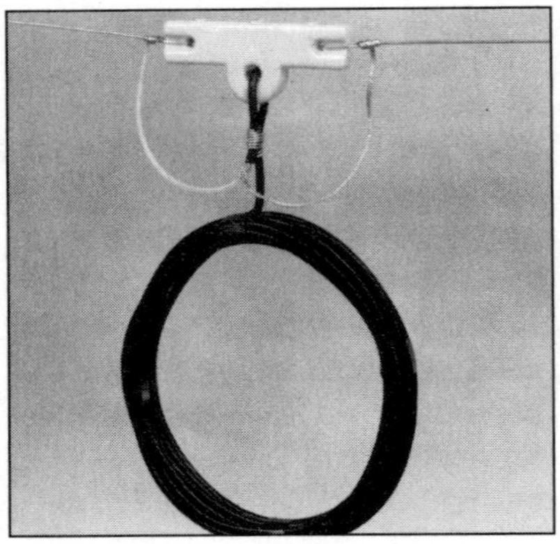

Figure 24.54 — Scramble-wound RF choke formed by coiling the feed line. The reactance of the choke isolates the antenna from the outer surface of the feed line. It is used as a choke balun at the point of connection to the antenna.

differential-mode currents on the inside are unaffected. The reactance creates an RF choke in the common-mode path. If used at the antenna feed point, the choke becomes a type of choke balun by blocking the common-mode current path.

While this type of choke has been used for many years, its performance is hard to control and often over-estimated. Winding style, diameter and organization, and coupling to nearby conductors all affect all affect choke reactance. The impedance of ferrite chokes can be controlled more easily and optimized for specific frequency ranges by selecting the appropriate mix. Ferrite chokes are much less sensitive to winding organization. If a ferrite core designed for EMI suppression is used, the impedance is mostly resistive and thus not affected by line length.

The coiled-coax choke's effectiveness depends on the impedance of the feed line's outer surface at that point: If the impedance is inductive, the choke will likely be effective. Otherwise, the line's capacitive reactance may actually cancel some of the coil's inductive reactance, *increasing* common-mode current on the line. Feed line common-mode impedance is hard to predict or measure accurately, so the antenna system builder must be aware of the possibility of this type of interaction. The G3TXQ web page (**www.karinya.net/g3txq/chokes**) shows a number of examples in which a choke's reactance combines with that of the feed line. G3TXQ suggests that a choke reactance of at least 1000 Ω is required to avoid this level of interaction. In addition, the feed line and choke impedances will change with frequency, making coiled-coax chokes a poor choice for multiband antennas.

Just as for any inductor, the coiled-coax choke's self-resonance is created by the distributed capacitance between the turns of the coil. At the parallel self-resonant frequency, series impedance is very high. The resonant frequency can be determined with an impedance analyzer or with a dip meter. If using a dip meter, leave the ends of the choke disconnected, couple the coil to the dip meter, and tune for a dip.

For all coiled-coaxial chokes, use cable with solid dielectric insulation, not foamed, to minimize migration of the center conductor through the insulation toward the shield. The diameter of the coil should be at least 10 times the cable diameter to avoid mechanically stressing the cable.

Scramble-Wound versus Single-Layer

Scramble-wound chokes (wound like a coil of rope as in Figure 24.54) described in **Table 24.12** were measured by Ed Gilbert, K2SQ, to have a high impedance at the indicated frequencies as measured with an impedance meter. Because the winding order and grouping are uncontrolled, it is unlikely for a choke wound in a slightly different way to have the same resonant frequency and impedance as described in the table. Given the better performance of ferrite chokes, scramble-wound chokes are not recommended for high-performance installations. However, these simple chokes can be created anywhere along the feed line simply by winding it up, adding reactance in order to reduce common-mode current.

The performance of a single-layer coiled-coax choke is more reproducible. This type of choke is created by winding the cable as a single-layer solenoidal coil on a section of plastic pipe or other suitable cylinder (**Figure 24.55**). The cable is secured with electrical tape as shown in Figure 24.55B. This type of construction reduces the stray capacitance of the coil and makes the coil's construction more consistent. If the choke will be used with a metal-boom Yagi, it is recommended that it not be held directly against the boom which

Table 24.12
Coiled-Coax Choke Baluns

Wind the indicated length of coaxial feed line into a coil (like a coil of rope) and secure with electrical tape.
Lengths of line specified are approximate.

Single Band, Scramble Wound

Freq (MHz)	*RG-213*	*RG-58*
3.5	22 ft, 8 turns	20 ft, 6-8 turns
7	22 ft, 10 turns	15 ft, 6 turns
10	12 ft, 10 turns	10 ft, 7 turns
14	10 ft, 4 turns	8 ft, 8 turns
21	8 ft, 6-8 turns	6 ft, 8 turns
28	6 ft, 6-8 turns	4 ft, 6-8 turns
50*	4-5 turns, 2½" dia	
144, 222*	2 turns, 2½" dia	
432*	1 turn, 2½" dia	

Multiple Band, Scramble Wound

Freq (MHz)	*RG-58, 59, 8X, 213*
3.5 – 30	10 ft, 7 turns
3.5 – 10	18 ft, 9-10 turns
1.8 – 3.5	40 ft, 20 turns
14 – 30	8 ft, 6-7 turns

Multiple Band, Single-layer Solenoid

Freq (MHz)	*RG-213*
7 – 24	12 turns, 4¼" dia
14 – 30	6 turns, 4¼" dia
14 – 30	4 turns, 6⅝" dia
7 – 24	8 turns, 6⅝" dia

*Recommended by Justin Johnson, GØKSC, **www.g0ksc.co.uk/creatingabalun.html**

will interact with the choke. As in Figure 24.55B, eye bolts in the form allow the coil to be suspended under the boom, improving electrical performance and giving a measure of mechanical strain relief.

A series of measurements by K2SQ on single-layer coiled-coax chokes determined several useful combinations of turns and diameter listed in Table 24.12. The 12-turn choke in Figure 24.55B, for example, is often used with common 2-element 40 meter Yagis. Although that choke only presents slightly more than 500 Ω of reactance, the low feed-point impedance of the beam over most of the 40 meter band (typical 50-Ω SWR>3:1), makes 500 Ω sufficient to reduce common-mode current to low levels, assuming the feed line impedance at the feed point is not capacitive. If the antenna feed point impedance was higher, a higher choke impedance would be necessary to maintain isolation of the feed line.

The single-layer chokes listed in the table were measured to have greater than 500 Ω of reactance on the bands shown. The measured self-resonant frequency and impedance are also given. While the single-layer chokes are more controlled than scramble-wound, expect a fair amount of variation in choke behavior. (The full table of measurements is included in the downloadable supplemental information for this chapter.)

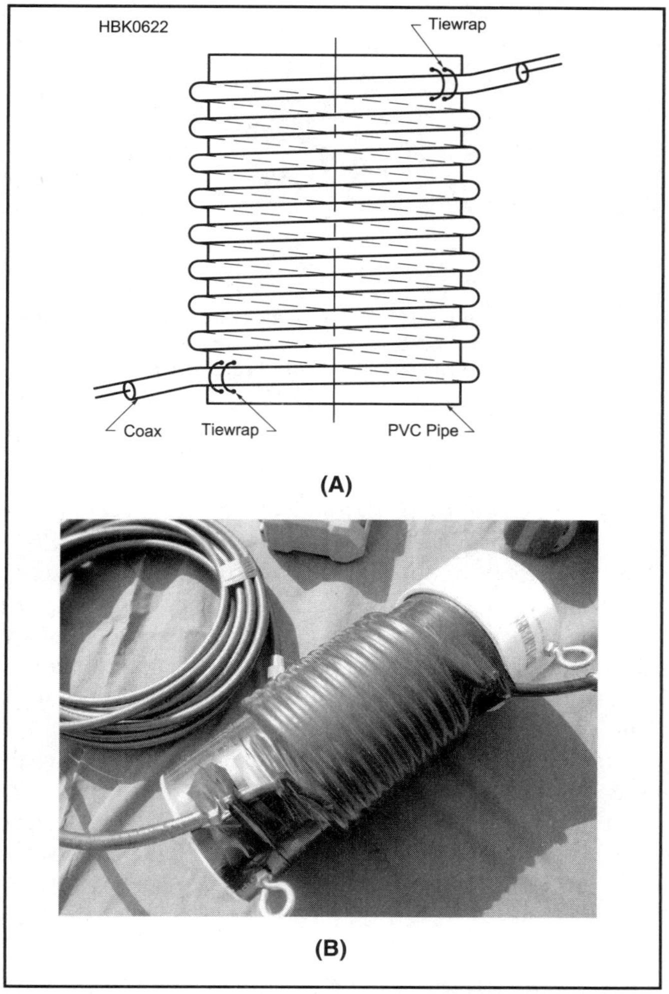

Figure 24.55 — Winding a coaxial choke as a single-layer solenoid (A) controls impedance and self-resonant frequency compared to a scramble-coil choke. The 12-turn 40 meter choke balun wound on a 4¼ inch diameter PVC pipe with eye bolts for attaching the choke to a Yagi boom.

24.7.3 COAX-WOUND FERRITE CHOKES

Transmitting chokes differ from other common-mode chokes because they must be designed to work well when the feed line they are choking carries high power. Excellent common-mode chokes having very high power-handling capability can be formed simply by winding multiple turns of coax through a sufficiently large ferrite core or multiple cores. (These chokes will be referred to as "coax-wound ferrite chokes" to distinguish them from the air-core coiled-coax chokes of the preceding section.)

Joe Reisert, W1JR, first introduced chokes made with coaxial cable wound on ferrite toroids to amateurs. He used low-loss cores, typically type #61 or #67 material in frequency ranges which produce primarily an inductive reactance. **Figure 24.56** shows that these high-Q chokes are quite effective near their resonance. However, the resonance is narrow and typically covers only one or two bands. Away from resonance, the choke becomes far less effective, as choking impedance falls rapidly and its reactive component interacts with the impedance of the feed line.

Today there are more types of ferrite, including mixes designed for EMI suppression that produce impedances in the MF, HF, and VHF range that are primarily resistive. Chokes made with these materials exhibit broad peaks in impedance that can be used across several amateur bands. Chokes designed for different frequency ranges can be placed in series for even wider frequency coverage.

Design Criteria

Traditionally, the rule-of-thumb for a transmission line choke was that the choking impedance needed to be at least 10 Z_0 of the line. I.e., 500 Ω for 50-Ω coax. If the load was well-balanced and the feed point impedance reasonably close to Z_0, that would block most of the common-mode current without too much power dissipation. Difficulties resulted if the antenna system was not well-balanced for some reason or if the feed point impedance was much higher than Z_0. Either the choke would overheat or there would be significant common-mode current on the line or both. Since these situations are fairly common, choke design must meet those requirements.

A choking impedance (R_S) of 5000 Ω is a good starting point for most applications, such as at the feed point of a reasonably well-balanced and well-matched antenna at power levels below about 600 W. Full-power, high duty-cycle, 1500 W operation such as for contesting and some types of digital mode operation, or use with a very unbalanced antenna, can result in high power dissipation in the choke. In such cases, more choking impedance is needed. (See the section Power Dissipation in Ferrite Transmitting Chokes.)

The best way to reduce power dissipation from common-mode current is to increase choking impedance. Doubling choke impedance divides the common-mode current by 2. This divides the power dissipated in the choke's series resistance (R_S) by 4 according to $P = I^2R_S$. Higher impedance

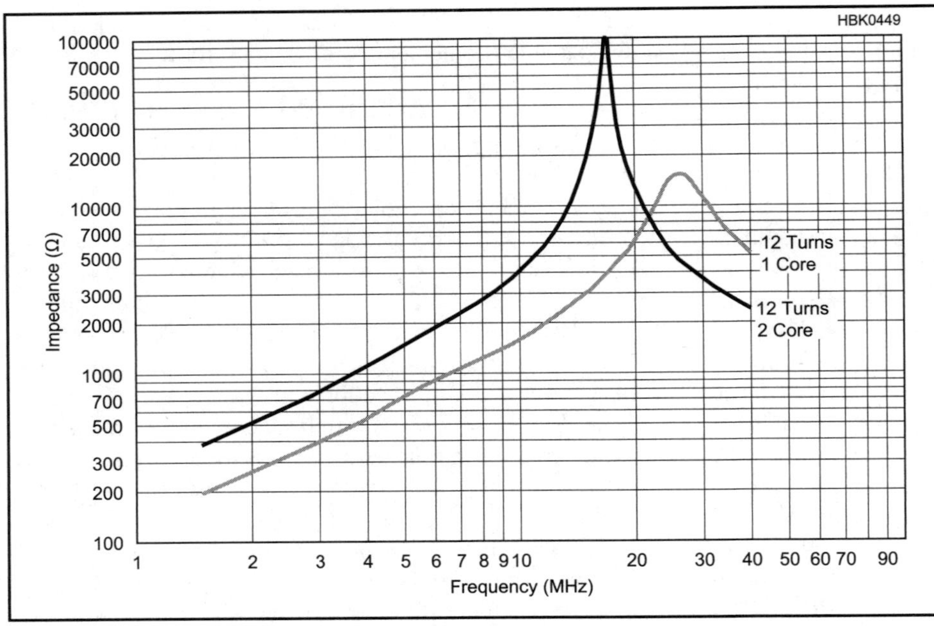

Figure 24.56 — Impedance versus frequency for HF coax-wound ferrite transmitting chokes wound with RG-142 coax on toroid cores of type #61 material.

For the 1-core choke: R = 15.6 kΩ, L = 25 µH, C = 1.4 pF, Q = 3.7.

For the 2-core choke: R = 101 kΩ, L = 47 µH, C = 1.9 pF, Q = 20.

can be obtained by winding more turns on a single core or by winding the choke on a stack of two or more cores.

In general, any combination of chokes can be used in series to provide the desired choking impedance over the desired bandwidth. Their combined choking impedance, R_S, will be the sum of their R_S values on each band. Chokes for different frequency ranges can be placed in series to create a choke with a higher impedance across a wider frequency range, as well.

Since the chokes are subjected to only common-mode voltage, the only effect of high SWR on power handling of coax-wound ferrite chokes is to increase the peaks of differential current and voltage along the line established by the mismatch in the antenna system. If SWR is very high, the extra mismatch loss may become an issue.

For receiving applications, a choke impedance of 500-1000 Ω is sufficient to prevent pattern distortion, ordinary cases of RFI, and noise coupling from other sources. Chuck Counselman, W1HIS, correctly observes that radiation and noise coupling from the feed line should be viewed as a form of pattern distortion that fills in the nulls of a directional antenna, reducing its ability to reject noise and interference. (See Jim Brown, K9YC's article on receiving chokes at **k9yc.com/RXChokesTransformers.pdf** or in the Bibliography.)

Chokes used to break up a feed line into segments too short to interact with another antenna should have a choking impedance on the order of 1000 Ω to prevent interaction with simple antennas. A value closer to 5000 Ω may be needed if the effects of common-mode current on the feed line are filling the null of directional antenna.

Practical Transmitting Chokes

Legacy Choke Designs

Legacy designs for coax-wound ferrite chokes from previous editions used RG-8 or RG-11 for full-power operation, and RG-58 for lower power levels. Those chokes were wound on 2.4-inch OD, 1.4-inch ID toroid of type #31 or #43 material, and the 1-inch ID × 1.125-inch long clamp-on of type #31 material. (Note the following section's caveat about material variation for these cores which affects choking performance.)

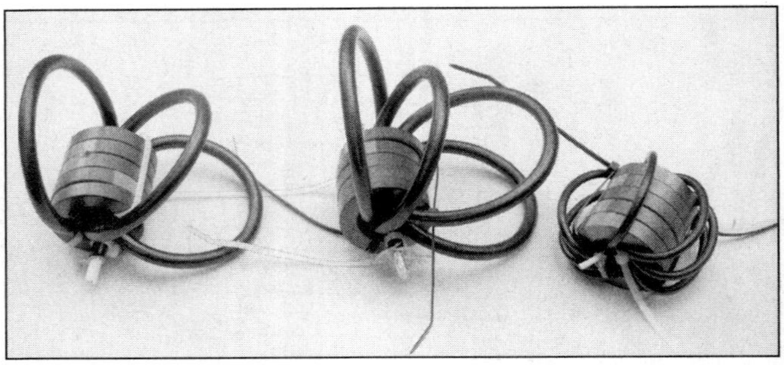

Figure 24.57 — Legacy design coax-wound ferrite transmitting chokes for use on the HF bands. Figure 24.59 shows examples of currently recommended choke construction.

The resonance curves for these chokes are affected by turn spacing, diameter, and organization, leading to a lot of variation with construction techniques. In addition, the larger minimum bend radius for the PE-insulated coax caused the full-power designs to be rather large and somewhat of a challenge to support at an antenna feed point. **Figure 24.57A** shows examples of the legacy design chokes and **Figures 24.58A-C** are graphs of the magnitude of the impedance for various numbers of turns, type of line, and types of core. These are presented here as reference information although they are not recommended for new installations. **Table 24.13** summarizes legacy designs that meet the 5000-Ω criteria for the 160 through 6 meter ham bands and several practical transmitting choke designs that are "tuned" or optimized for ranges of frequencies. (For VHF and UHF, note that parasitic capacitance makes an effective choke more difficult to create.)

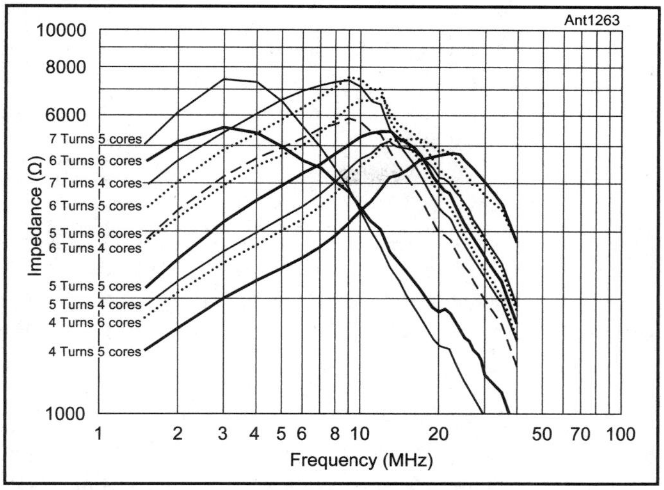

Figure 24.58A — Impedance versus frequency for legacy HF coax-wound ferrite transmitting chokes of RG-8X coax wound on 2.4-inch toroid cores of type #31 material. Turns are 5-inch diameter and wide-spaced unless noted.

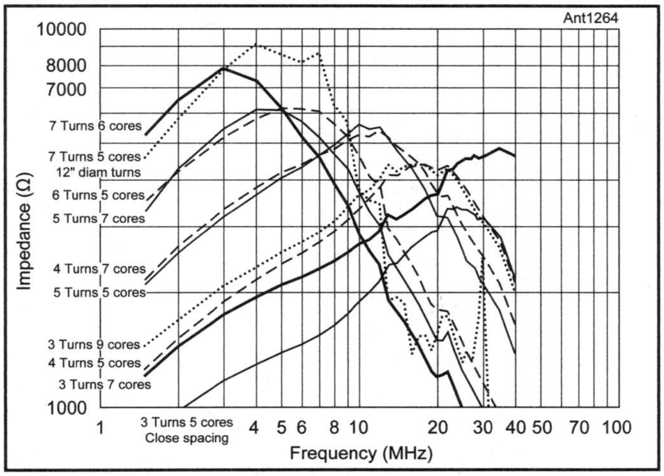

Figure 24.58B — Impedance versus frequency for legacy HF coax-wound ferrite transmitting chokes of RG-8 coax wound on 2.4-inch toroid cores of type #31 material. Turns are 5-inch diameter and wide-spaced unless noted.

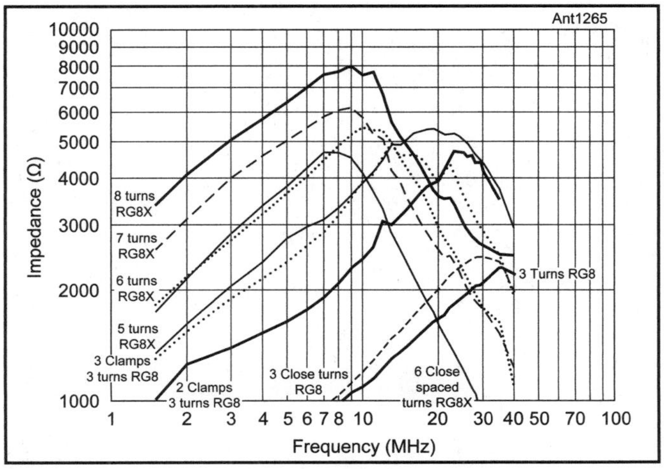

Figure 24.58C — Impedance versus frequency for legacy HF coax-wound ferrite transmitting chokes of RG-8X or RG-8 coax wound on big clamp-on cores of type #31 material. Turns are 6-inch diameter, wide-spaced except as noted.

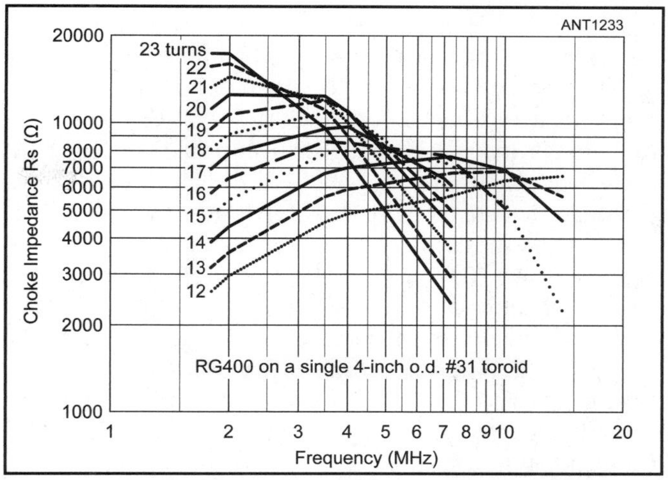

Figure 24.58D — Impedance versus frequency for currently recommended HF coax-wound ferrite transmitting chokes of RG-400 wound on a single 2.4-inch toroid core of type #31 material.

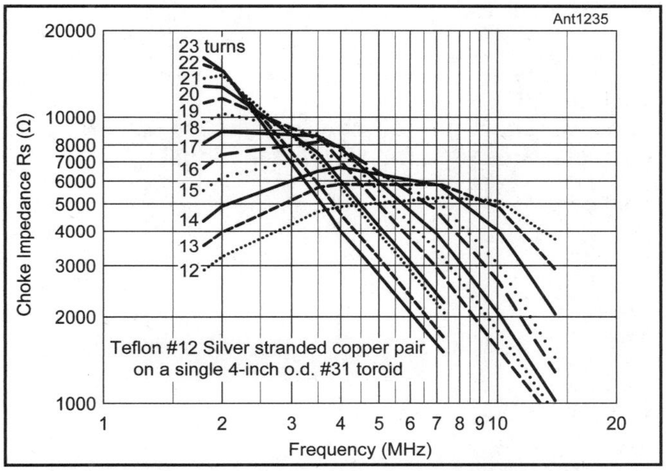

Figure 24.58E — Impedance versus frequency for currently recommended HF coax-wound ferrite transmitting chokes Teflon-insulated #12 AWG wire wound on a single 2.4-inch toroid core of type #31 material.

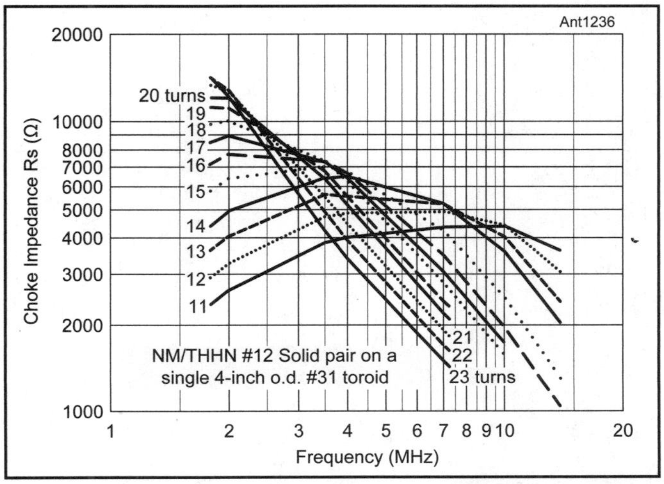

Figure 24.58F— Impedance versus frequency for currently recommended HF coax-wound ferrite transmitting chokes THHN wire wound on a single 2.4-inch toroid core of type #31 material.

Recommended Choke Designs

Since the previous edition of this book, Jim Brown, K9YC, and Glen Brown, W6GJB, built, tested, and measured numerous chokes constructed with RG-8-size coax, RG-400 (Teflon jacket, stranded silver-plated copper center, two silver-plated copper shields, TFE dielectric), #12 and #10 enameled copper wire pairs, THHN #12 and #10 pairs, a #12 Teflon-insulated wire pair (silver-plated stranded copper, 0.109-inch OD), and a pair formed by the black and white conductors removed from #10 and #12 Romex (NM) cable. The transmission characteristics were also measured at MF and HF. The data presented here is a summary of that information and the reader is encouraged to download the entire paper referenced at the beginning of this section (see Bibliography).

Their study also discovered wide variations in the fundamental properties of the 2.4-inch cores purchased over a period of 12 years. Variations of ±10% were measured for newly purchased cores. The choke designs in the tables are selected to have sufficient impedance values for average cores but variations at the upper and lower ends of the useful range for the choke will depend on the core characteristics.

Figures 24.58D-F are graphs of impedance magnitude for various numbers of turns, type of line, and types of core. **Tables 24.14** and **24.15** summarize designs for the 160 through 6 meter ham bands and several practical transmitting choke designs that are "tuned" or optimized for ranges of frequencies. The tables include designs meeting the 5000-Ω minimum impedance requirement and a higher-impedance design if available. Number of turns are limited on the smaller 2.4-inch OD cores.

An additional compilation of recommended air-core and ferrite-core designs is available from Steve Hunt, G3TXQ, at **www.karinya.net/g3txq/chokes**. The guidelines correspond roughly with measurements taken by others but should not be taken as guaranteed or representative of all methods of construction or materials. Note that a 500-Ω impedance may be quite inadequate for applications in which the load

Table 24.13
Legacy Transmitting Choke Designs for Solid PE-insulated Coax (not recommended for new installations)

Freq Band(s) (MHz)	*Mix*	*RG-8, RG-11 Turns*	*RG-8, RG-11 Cores*	*RG-6, RG-8X, RG-58, RG-59 Turns*	*RG-6, RG-8X, RG-58, RG-59 Cores*
1.8, 3.8	#31	7	5 toroids	7 8	5 toroids Big clamp-on
3.5-7		6	5 toroids	7 8	4 toroids Big clamp-on
10.1	#31 or #43	5	5 toroids	8 6	Big clamp-on 4 toroids
7-14		5	5 toroids	8	Big clamp-on
14		5 4	4 toroids 6 toroids	8 5-6	2 toroids Big clamp-on
21		4 4	5 toroids 6 toroids	4 5	5 toroids Big clamp-on
28		4	5 toroids	4 5	5 toroids Big clamp-on
7-28, 10.1 – 28 or 14 – 28	#31 or #43	Use two chokes in series: #1 — 4 turns on 5 toroids #2 — 3 turns on 5 toroids		Use two chokes in series: #1 — 6 turns on a big clamp-on #2 — 5 turns on a big clamp-on	
14-28		Two 4-turn chokes, each w/one big clamp-on		4 turns on 6 toroids, or 5 turns on a big clamp-on	
50		Two 3-turn chokes, each w/one big clamp-on			
144-432	#43	1-3 turns on a big clamp-on			

Notes:
"Core" refers to a 2.4-inch OD, 1.4-inch ID toroid
"Big clamp-on" refers to a 1-inch ID, 1.125-inch clamp-on core of type #31 material
Turn diameter is nor critical, but 6 inches is good.

Table 24.14
Transmitting Choke Designs for TFE Coax and Wire-Pair Lines on 2.4-inch OD Type #31 Toroid (5 kΩ min impedance design)

Freq Band(s) (MHz)	*RG-400 Turns*	*TFE #12 Pair Turns*	*NM/THHN #12 Pair Turns*
1.8	17	17	16
3.5	13	14	13
7	13	13	13
10	12	13	13-14
14	12	12	11
21	11-12 (4.8 kΩ)	11-12 (4.7 kΩ)	11
28	10 (4.4 kΩ)	10 (4.3 kΩ)	10-11 (4.2 kΩ)
1.8-3.5	17	17	16
3.5-10		15	14
3.5-14	13	13	13
7-21	13	12	

High impedance design, if available, given as "Turns (kΩ)"

1.8	18 (10)	18 (9.5)	18 (9.5)
3.5	16 (8)	15-16 (6.5)	14 (6)
7	14 (6.2)	15 (6.5)	14 (6)
10	14 (6.5)	14 (6)	13-14 (5.5)
14	13 (5.4)	13 (5.5)	12-13 (5)
3.5-14	14 (6, 6, 6, 6)	14 (5.8, 5.8, 6, 5)	

Table 24.15
Transmitting Choke Designs for TFE Coax and Wire-Pair Lines on 4-inch OD Type #31 Toroid (5 kΩ min impedance)

Freq Band(s) (MHz)	*RG-400 Turns*	*TFE #12 Pair Turns*	*NM/THHN #12 Pair Turns*
1.8	16	15	15
3.5	13	13	20
7.0	12	15	12-14
10	12	13-14	
14	12		
1.8-3.5	16	21	20
1.8-7	16	15	
1.8-10	16		
3.5-7	19	15	13
3.5-10	14	13	

High impedance design, if available, given as "Turns (kΩ)"

1.8	23 (17)	22-23 (15)	21-23 (12.5)
3.5	18-20 (11)	16-18 (7.5)	15-16 (6.7)
7	14 (7.5)	13-14 (5.7)	12-14 (5)
1.8-3.5	21 (13,10)	18 (9.5,8)	17 (8.5,6.5)
1.8-7	17 (7, 9.5, 6)	15 (5.5, 7.2, 5)	
1.8-10	16 (5.5, 8.5, 7.5, 5)		
3.5-7	15 (8.5, 7.5)	14 (6.5, 4.8)	14 (6.5, 5)
3.5-10	16 (8.5,7.5,5)	13 (5.8,5.8,5)	

Notes:
Chokes for 1.8, 3.5 and 7 MHz should have closely spaced turns.
Chokes for 14 – 28 MHz should have widely spaced turns.

impedance is high or if high isolation of the load is required. In such cases, a higher-impedance choke is necessary.

Selecting the Choke Transmission Line

Which line is recommended? The best compromise of size and power-handling capability was determined to be a miniature coax with TFE (Teflon) insulation such as RG-400 or a parallel-wire wound choke using TFE-insulated wire. **Table 24.16** was obtained from measured values of S11 (return loss) for short lengths with the far end open and the far end shorted, post-processed using AC6LA's *ZPlots* Excel spreadsheet (**ac6la.com/zplots.html**).

Chokes wound with higher Z_0 line (pairs of #12 THHN, NM, Teflon) work quite well at the feed point of various dipoles, but may not at the feed point of a complex array. (See the online paper's discussion of 75-Ω chokes for transmitting arrays.) Chokes wound with the #12 Teflon wire pair were found to have the lowest loss and the least dissipation for each band. The wire is expensive and best purchased from surplus vendors or in a quantity group purchase. Remember that for paired-wire lines, Z_0 will vary with insulation thickness and the dielectric properties of the insulation.

The other recommended choices, especially for antennas with feed point Z_0 near 50 Ω, is RG-400, followed by a pair made from the white and black conductors removed from Romex (NM) cable.

Previous editions have referred to leakage flux from a parallel-wire (bifilar) winding causing heating in the core. This concern does not appear to be warranted based on measurements. Heating in the core external to the transmission line, coaxial or bifilar, is attributed to flux created by common-mode current only. See the section Power Dissipation in Ferrite Transmitting Chokes for a discussion of heating from common-mode current.

Enameled copper pairs were found to have much greater loss than other paired lines. This is because the magnetic fields produced by currents in very closely spaced pairs used as transmission lines cause the current to be concentrated in the side of the conductors closest to each other. This mechanism, strongly related to skin effect, is called *proximity effect*, and causes differential current to flow on the inside of the coax shield. Just as skin effect forces current to the skin of the conductor, proximity effect forces it to only one half of the skin! Proximity effect rises rapidly as the center-to-center

Table 24.16
Measured Characteristic Impedance of Paired-Wire Lines

Line Type	*Z_0 @ 5 MHz*	*VF @ 5 MHz*	*10 MHz Loss*
#12 THHN Solid	91.2 Ω	0.725	1.2 dB/100 ft
#10 THHN Stranded	92.4 Ω	0.73	1.5 dB/100 ft
#12 Teflon (Ag/Cu)	96.6 Ω	0.833	76 dB/100 ft
#10 NM	86 Ω	0.725	1.5 dB/100 ft
#12 NM	91 Ω	0.73	1.2 dB/100 ft
#12 Enameled	43.4 Ω	0.77	2.45 dB/100 ft
#10 Enameled	41.3 Ω	0.66	2.36 dB/100 ft
RG-400	50.8 Ω	0.69	1.22 dB/100 ft

spacing approaches the conductor diameter, which is the case with enameled wire. As can be seen from the table of measured transmission line data in the online paper, the enameled pairs have significantly higher loss (and greater dissipation) than other paired cables. It's also possible for the enamel to be scraped by the ferrite core during winding, shorting to the core at multiple points and significantly degrading choke performance. For both reasons, using enameled wire pairs for ferrite-core chokes are not recommended.

Construction Guidelines

Starting The Winding: Wind a cable tie around the cross section of the toroid where you want to start the winding and pull it not quite tight. Feed the cable through the toroid from below, and use another cable tie to secure it to the first one, leaving enough free cable to connect the choke when it is complete. Leave enough cable tie for final tightening later. The choke in **Figure 24.59A** starts at 3 o'clock and is wound counterclockwise around the core.

Wind In Sequence: Take care that turns are wound in order around the core — out of sequence turns can cancel. Turns can be continued on a second layer when the first layer is filled by overlaying the starting turns of the winding. In Fig 24.59B, the winding starts at the upper left, completely fills the first layer around the core, and continues with five more turns overlaying the start of the winding.

Turn Spacing: Measured data are for windings tight to the core, with adjacent windings touching on the inside of the core.

Paired Lines: Take care that pairs are not twisted as they are wound. Twisting can reduce choking impedance. Using different colors for the two conductors makes it easier to see twisting, and also to count turns. Keep the wires parallel and flat against the core. Solid conductors are preferred over stranded because turns tend to stay in place. Stranded wire is much less disciplined. (The choke in the figure has short leads for measurement purposes.)

Maintain polarity between the two ends of the choke — that is, make sure that the same conductor of a parallel pair is connected to the coax shield at both ends of the choke. This is especially important with arrays, and can be an issue with lightning protection for a choke added to the line not at the feed point. If the polarity is reversed, the choke will still work but the array won't work as designed and static buildup on a coax shield may not be as well discharged.

Pairing the wire: Loss, VF, and Z_0 data are for the paired conductors touching, held in place every 3-6 inches with Scotch 33 or 35 (thinner than Scotch 88, it can help squeeze an extra turn on 2.4-in chokes for 160 meters). Wider spacing will increase Z_0 and decrease attenuation, especially with enameled pairs (because proximity effect is reduced).

Solid PE-insulated Coax: These legacy designs have been superseded by the RG-400 and paired-wire designs. These chokes are heavier, more expensive, and have greater loss (because they use more cores and more coax). These designs are repeatable only if turns pass through the core(s) sequentially, and if they have the same radius and spacing.

(A)

(B)

Figure 24.59 — At A is a coax-wound ferrite transmitting choke showing RG-400 winding technique. B shows how a wire-pair winding is constructed.

Space turns evenly around the toroid to minimize inter-turn capacitance. See the online paper for some suggestions for constructing these chokes.

Supporting the Choke: Ferrite-core chokes can be heavy, even if wound with the lightest line on a single core. This can lead to mechanical failure from wind or other flexing of the antenna and feed line. The referenced paper contains several photos of suggested construction techniques. **Figure 24.60** shows a center insulator assembly of GPO3 fiberglass supporting two chokes in series (see the paper or series performance tables), an SO-239 receptacle for convenient feed line attachment, and sturdy attachment points for the dipole legs and a support rope or cable. The photo was taken before

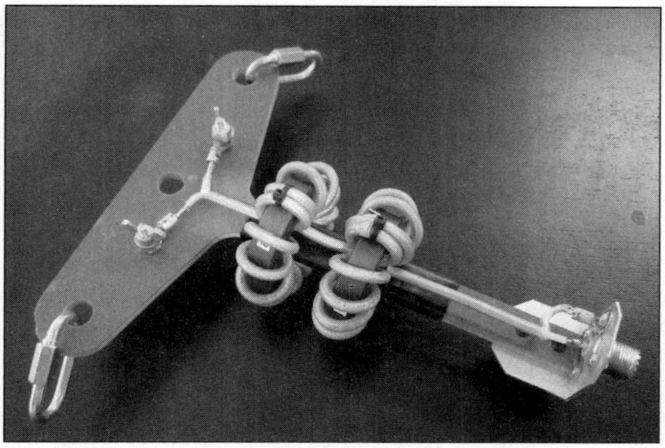

Figure 24.60 — A center insulator assembly designed by W6GJB to support one or two choke baluns in series for a wire antenna. An SO-239 is attached using a small bracket. Waterproofing can be provided by using silicone sealant.

a waterproofing coating was applied to seal the electrical connections and provide UV resistance. Silicone adhesive was used to waterproof the SO-239. Lexan or some other plastic will also work for the body of the assembly.

Coaxial Cable Minimum Bend Radius

Coaxial chokes should be wound with a bend radius sufficiently large that the coax is not deformed. When a line is deformed, the spacing between the center conductor and the shield varies, so voltage breakdown and heating are more likely to occur. Deformation also causes a discontinuity in the impedance; the resulting reflections may cause some waveform distortion and increased loss at VHF and UHF.

Chokes wound with any large diameter cable have more stray capacitance than those wound with small diameter wire. There are two sources of stray capacitance in a ferrite choke: the capacitance from end-to-end and from turn-to-turn via the core; and the capacitance from turn-to-turn via the air dielectric. Both sources of capacitance are increased by increased conductor size, so stray capacitance will be greater with larger coax. Turn-to-turn capacitance is also increased by larger diameter turns.

While the turn diameter on the ferrite toroid cores is smaller than the minimum specified bend radius for RG-400 coax, failures caused by center conductor migration have not been commonly reported. The consensus among experienced builders and manufacturers is that that cable will work as intended as long as it is not operated at its full power rating and repeatedly flexed. This is also discussed in the **Transmission Lines** chapter.

24.7.4 USING FERRITE BEADS IN CHOKE BALUNS

The ferrite bead current baluns developed by Walt Maxwell, W2DU, formed simply by stringing multiple beads in series on a length of coax to obtain the desired choking impedance, are really common-mode chokes. Maxwell's

Figure 24.61 — W2DU bead balun consisting of 50 FB-73-2041 ferrite beads over a length of RG-303 coax. See text for details.

designs utilized 50, 100, and 200 very small beads of type #73 material as shown in **Figure 24.61**. Product data sheets show that a single type #73 bead has a very low-Q resonance around 20 MHz, and has a predominantly resistive impedance of 10-20 Ω on all HF ham bands. Stringing 50 beads in series simply multiples the impedance of one bead by 50, so the W2DU balun has a choking impedance of 500-1000 Ω and because it is strongly resistive, any resonance with the feed line is minimal.

This is a fairly good design for moderate power levels, but suitable beads are too small to fit most coax. A specialty coaxial cable such as RG-303 must be used for high-power applications. Even with high-power coax, the choking impedance is often insufficient to limit current to a low enough value to prevent overheating. Equally important — the lower choking impedance is much less effective at rejecting noise and preventing the filling of nulls in a radiation pattern.

Newer bead balun designs use type #31 and #43 beads that are resonant around 150 MHz, are inductive below resonance, and have only a few tens of ohms of strongly inductive impedance on the HF bands. Even with 20 of the type #31 or #43 beads in the string, the choke is still resonant around 150 MHz, is much less effective than a wound coaxial ferrite choke, and is still inductive on the HF bands (so it will be ineffective at frequencies where it resonates with the line).

Be aware that the heat-dissipating capability of small-diameter ferrite beads can be exceeded where there is a serious imbalance that results in large common-mode currents. Beads nearest the feed point can become very warm and can even shatter under extreme conditions of imbalance. Use enough beads to provide the necessary choking impedance to keep power dissipation at safe levels. The original W2DU designs should be limited to use at 100 W power levels if there is significant imbalance in the antenna system.

24.7.5 MEASURING CHOKE BALUN IMPEDANCE

A ferrite RF choke creates a parallel resonant circuit from inductance and resistance coupled from the core and stray capacitance resulting from interaction of the conductor that forms the choke with the permittivity of the core. If the choke is made by winding turns on a core (as opposed to single-turn bead chokes) the inter-turn capacitance also becomes part of the choke's circuit.

These chokes are very difficult to measure for two fundamental reasons. First, the stray capacitance forming the parallel resonance is quite small, typically 0.4-5 pF, which is often less than the stray capacitance of the test equipment used to measure it. The key to accurate measurement of high impedance ferrite chokes is to set up the choke as the series element, Z_X, of a voltage divider with a calibrated load.

The coax-wound ferrite chokes in this section were measured with a two-port vector network analyzer (VNA) using a test fixture built by K9YC and W6GJB that places the choke in series between the input and output of the VNA, forming a voltage divider between the choke and the 50-Ω input impedance of the VNA. (See the *ARRL Handbook* for information about using a VNA.) The VNA was calibrated to a measurement plane at the point where the choke is inserted, and S21 (the gain from output to input) is measured.

In a vector network analyzer, S21 is complex — that is, the result contains both magnitude and phase data. Math functions built into the VNA operating and display software solves the voltage divider equation to convert S21 (the voltage divider ratio) to Z_{MAG}, R_S, and X_S. See the online paper "A New Choke Cookbook for the 160-10M Bands" for more information about the VNA test fixture.

Obtaining R, L, and C Values

The VNA will provide a data file including Z_{MAG}, R_S, and X_S. In a spreadsheet worksheet, create columns that compute parallel L and C values from the VNA data. (The required equations can be found in the section Parallel Circuits of Moderate to High Q of the **Electrical Fundamentals** chapter in the *ARRL Handbook*.)

The spreadsheet should also plot impedance of the same range of frequencies as the measurements and with the same plotted scale as the measurements.

1) R is equal to the resonant peak of the measured impedance.

2) At a point on the resonance curve below the resonant frequency with approximately one-third of the impedance at resonance compute L for that value of inductive reactance ($L = X_L / 2\pi f$).

3) Calculate a value for C that produces the same resonant frequency of the measurement.

The resulting values for R, L, and C form the equivalent circuit for the choke. The values can then be used in circuit modeling software (*NEC*, *SPICE*) to predict the behavior of circuits using ferrite chokes.

Accuracy

The test fixture can be constructed so that its stray capacitance is small but it won't be zero. A first approximation of the stray capacitance can be obtained by substituting for the unknown a noninductive resistor whose resistance is in the same general range as the chokes being measured, then sweeping through the VNA range to find the -3 dB point where $X_C = R$. This test for the author's setup yielded a stray capacitance value of 0.4 pF. A thin-film surface-mount or chip resistor will have the lowest stray reactances and devices with <0.1 pF capacitance are available.

Since the measured curve includes stray capacitance, the actual capacitance of the choke will be slightly less than the computed value. If you have determined the value of stray capacitance for your test setup, subtract it from the computed value to get the actual capacitance. You can also use this corrected value in the theoretical circuit to see how the choke will actually behave in a circuit — that is, without the stray capacitance of your test setup. You won't see the change in your measured data, only in the theoretical RLC equivalent.

Dual Resonances

In NiZn ferrite materials (type #61, #43), there is only circuit resonance, but MnZn materials (#77, #78, #31) have both circuit resonance and dimensional resonance. (See the **RF Techniques** chapter of the *ARRL Handbook* for a discussion of ferrite resonances.) The dimensional resonance of type #77 and #78 material is rather high-Q and clearly defined, so R, L, and C values can often be computed for both resonances. (Type #77 and #78 material are not recommended for common-mode chokes. Those materials are intended for low-frequency magnetic circuits.)

This is not practical with chokes wound on type #31 cores because the dimensional resonance occurs below 5 MHz, is very low-Q, is poorly defined, and blends with the circuit resonance to broaden the impedance curve. The result is a dual-sloped resonance curve — that is, curve fitting will produce somewhat different values of R, L, and C when matching the low-frequency slope and high frequency slope. When using these values in a circuit model, use the values that most closely match the behavior of the choke in the frequency range of interest.

24.7.6 POWER DISSIPATION IN FERRITE TRANSMITTING CHOKES

Current through a choke is caused by the voltage across the choke from the load to the common-mode path on the feed line. The resistive component of a choke's impedance will dissipate power like any resistor but tends to be fairly broadband. The reactive component will not dissipate power but tends to be highest in a narrower bandwidth than resistive chokes. (The following discussion refers only to power dissipation caused by common-mode current. Differential-mode losses in the short transmission line windings can become significant above 20 MHz and at high values of SWR.)

Ferrites used in chokes exhibit both resistive and inductive components that change with frequency so the type or mix and the frequency both affect choke impedance. (See the *ARRL Handbook's* **RF Techniques** chapter and K9YC's ferrite tutorials at **k9yc.com/publish.htm** for more information on ferrites.)

If the choke's impedance is primarily inductive reactance, such as for an air-core choke, there is little power dissipation. This is the case for wound-coax chokes and chokes made with ferrites designed for inductive applications. Feed line impedance at the choke can also affect the net choking impedance by adding to or subtracting from the choke's impedance.

Inductive chokes, such as air-core coiled coax chokes and chokes wound on high-Q ferrite materials (#43, #52, #61,

#67), tend to have limited bandwidths over which choking impedance is high. These chokes work best on the one or two bands containing the self-resonant frequency but impedance drops quickly above and below that range. As impedance decreases, the choke is not as effective.

For ferrite chokes with an impedance that is primarily resistive, choking impedance is less dependent on frequency and feed line reactance but power is dissipated by the choke's resistance. If the choke's impedance is high enough, current through the choke can be reduced to a safe level of power dissipation.

The antenna's feed point impedance also changes with frequency as does the impedance of the feed line's common-mode path. Determining the voltage a choke will have to withstand thus requires analyzing the whole antenna system, a job best done with careful modeling. The variability of antenna system impedance is why a choke might work properly on some bands and overheat on others. This problem is addressed in Zack Lau, W1VT's article, "Why Do Baluns Burn Up?" which is included with this chapter's downloadable supplemental information, and in Jim Brown K9YC's online paper "A New Choke Cookbook for the 160–10M Bands" at **k9yc.com/2018Cookbook.pdf**. The article "Don't Blow Up Your Balun" by Dean Straw, N6BV, includes several excellent examples of antenna systems that place a lot stress on ferrite chokes and antenna tuners. The article is included in the downloadable supplemental material.

Determining the voltage across the choke is done by modeling the system with various impedances inserted in the common-mode current path. A wire representing the common-mode current path is connected to one side of the antenna and follows the geometry of the feed line. (The feed line is not always connected to ground, such as in a link-coupled tuner.) The added wire should be the diameter of the coax shield or twice the diameter of the paired conductors, and with insulation corresponding to the outer jacket of the coax. Modeling software then determines the current at the choke. (See Lau's article for a description of how this is done in *EZNEC*.)

For example, Lau modeled an 80 meter dipole operating on both 20 meters and 80 meters with 1500 W. **Table 24.17** provides examples of different choke impedances, the resulting common-mode current, and loss in the choke in both watts and decibels. (Note that the paper does not evaluate power dissipation for a variety of ferrite materials. Using different materials would result in different common-mode impedance and power dissipation values.)

On 20 meters, where the feed point impedance is 2834 + j1214 Ω, almost all of the chokes dissipate significant power. The 12-turn wound-coax choke dissipates the least amount of power but that frequency is near the choke's self-resonance where it presents a very high resistive impedance. That choke will not present the same impedance on other bands. Conversely, on 80 meters, where feed point impedance in this example is less than 100 Ω, almost any of the chokes will work without significant temperature rise — because of the low feed point impedance, feed line shield current is minimal

Table 24.17
Balun Impedance and Loss

80 meter dipole operated on 20 meters

Balun Impedance (Ω)	*Common-Mode Current (A)*	*Balun Loss (W)*	*Balun Loss (dB)*
1000	0.5	253	1.3
4000	0.2	144	0.7
10000	0.08	72	0.3
1300 – j4001	0.44	258	1.3
449 + j58332	0.14	9	0.04

80 meter dipole operated on 80 meters

Balun Impedance (Ω)	*Common-Mode Current (A)*	*Balun Loss (W)*	*Balun Loss (dB)*
50	0.02	0.022	0.0
2000	0.015	0.45	0.002
5 + j5611	0.022	0.0024	0.0
No balun	0.021	0.000	0.0

Notes
1. W2DU bead balun
2. 12 turns of RG-213 on 4¼-inch form

even with no choke at all!

A high value of resistance increases the ability of a resistive choke to handle higher transmit power. Dissipation due to common-mode current is $I_{CM}^2R_S$ where R_S is the series equivalent resistance of the choke and I_{CM} is the common-mode current. Because power is proportional to the square of current, power dissipation is greatly reduced with very high R_S.

The power dissipated by a ferrite bead or core can result in a significant amount of heat buildup. Heat builds up throughout the material, so the problem is getting the heat out through its surface area. Lau also developed the following formula for temperature rise of ferrite components in free air (see the Bibliography entry):

$$\Delta T = \left(\frac{P_{dis}}{A}\right)^{0.833} \qquad (28)$$

where
ΔT = Temperature rise in °C
P_{dis} = Power dissipation in milliwatts
A = Surface area in cm²

As Lau determined, even a small amount of power can, over time, lead to a large amount of temperature rise. For example, 4 W of continuous power dissipation in a large 2-inch toroid creates a 25°C temperature rise. Putting the toroid in an enclosure can make the temperature rise even greater. See K9YC's updated choke cookbook for a discussion of power dissipation and enclosure ventilation. Chokes can be wound on multiple cores to reduce power dissipation in a single core and create more surface area.

You can compute an estimate the amount of power lost in a choke by transforming the polar representation of the winding impedance (impedance magnitude and phase angle) to its equivalent parallel form (R_p resistance and X_p shunt reactance). This procedure assumes the full feed point voltage appears across the choke impedance.

Power dissipated in the choke is estimated as the square of half the voltage across the feed point divided by the choke's equivalent parallel resistance: $(E/2)^2/R_p$. For example, a choke made with 8 turns of RG-213 on a 6⅝ inch diameter coil form has a series impedance at 14 MHz of 262 ∠–86.9°. (See the K2SQ table of coiled-coax choke impedances in this chapter's downloadable supplemental information.) Converting polar to rectangular form, this is equal to 14.17 – *j* 261.62 Ω, then converting series to parallel, we have 4844 – *j* 262.38 Ω. For an RF power of 1500 W in the antenna, one-half the feed point voltage is 273.9 V RMS. Thus, an estimate of the power lost in the choke is $(273.9/2)^2/(4844.8) = 3.9$ W, while for a 50-Ω load the power is $273.9^2/50 = 1500$ W.

The articles and papers by Lau and Brown go into considerably more detail than this short summary but it is clear that choke selection should be done carefully, with a good understanding of feed point impedance If the antenna will be used on several bands, the analysis should be done for each band.

24.7.7 DETERMINING BALUN POLARITY

Many baluns, impedance transformers, chokes (a.k.a. "line isolators"), and other similar items are manufactured as sealed units and markings for output polarity with respect to the input connector are not often clear. For designs in which one or more continuous coaxial cables or parallel-wire lines are connected between the input and output terminals, a resistance measurement will suffice to determine polarity. In flux-coupled designs there is no continuity between the input and output terminals at dc so a resistance measurement cannot be used. Similarly, for autotransformer designs there may be a low resistance across the input or output terminals. In these cases, it is necessary to test the units at RF.

The first method is to test the unit using a dual-trace oscilloscope. Analog scopes should be in "Chop" mode so that both traces show display waveforms synchronized in time. Digital scopes must also sample both waveforms at the same time. Do not use "Alt" or an alternating waveform display. Drive the input to the unit with a signal generator's output in the unit's specified operating frequency range. Connect one scope channel to the unit's input and the other channel to the output. If the waveforms are displayed in-phase, the connections to the scope have the same polarity.

The following procedure requires only a signal generator and RF voltmeter (see the **Test Equipment and Measurements** chapter in *The ARRL Handbook*) and is used to check two identical units. If the units are substantially different, the test may not be conclusive or reliable. The procedure assumes a 50-Ω system impedance. If the units operate at an impedance very different from 50 Ω, such as for 300-, 450-, or 600-Ω open-wire line, use a 6-10 dB attenuator in the generator output to isolate the generator from the mismatch.

Connect the signal generator output to the input of both units using a T connector and identical lengths of feed line. Connect one output terminal of unit "A" to an output terminal of unit "B" and measure the RF voltage across the combined balun outputs. Swap the output terminal connections on one of the units and measure the RF voltage again. One arrangement of connections should show a substantially higher output voltage – this is the arrangement with the same polarity for both units.

24.8 TRANSMISSION-LINE BALUNS AND MATCHING DEVICES

The properties of transmission lines, explored in the **Transmission Lines** chapter can be put to work isolating loads and transforming impedances. Here are a few useful designs for use with your antenna projects.

24.8.1 DETUNING SLEEVES

The detuning sleeve shown in **Figure 24.62B** is essentially an air-insulated λ/4 line, but of the coaxial type, with the sleeve constituting the outer conductor and the outside of the coax line being the inner conductor. Because the impedance at the open end is very high, the unbalanced voltage on the coax line cannot cause much current to flow on the outside of the sleeve. Thus the sleeve acts just like a choke to isolate the remainder of the line from the antenna. (The same viewpoint can be used in explaining the action of the λ/4 arrangement shown at Figure 24.62A, but is less easy to understand in the case of baluns less than λ/4 long.)

A sleeve of this type may be resonated by cutting a small longitudinal slot near the bottom, just large enough to take a single-turn loop which is, in turn, link-coupled to a dip meter. If the sleeve is a little long to start with, a bit at a time can be cut off the top until the stub is resonant.

The diameter of the coaxial detuning sleeve in Figure 24.62B should be fairly large compared with the diameter of the cable it surrounds. A diameter of two inches or so is satisfactory with half-inch cable. The sleeve should be symmetrically placed with respect to the center of the antenna so that it will be equally coupled to both sides. Otherwise a current will be induced from the antenna to the outside of the sleeve. This is particularly important at VHF and UHF.

In both the balancing methods shown in Figure 24.62 the λ/4 section should be cut to be resonant at exactly the same frequency as the antenna itself. These sections tend to have a beneficial effect on the impedance-frequency characteristic of the system, because their reactance varies in the opposite direction to that of the antenna. For instance, if the operating frequency is slightly below resonance the antenna has capacitive reactance, but the shorted λ/4 sections or stubs have inductive reactance. Thus the reactances tend to cancel, which prevents the impedance from changing rapidly and helps maintain a low SWR on the line over a band of frequencies.

The Pawsey stub in **Figure 24.63A** is similar to a sleeve balun but consists only of the single λ/4 wire which is attached to one terminal of the load and the shield of the feed line. This creates a λ/4-wave shorted stub that creates a high impedance in the common-mode current path at the connection of the feed line and the load. The stub creates a dc short-circuit at the load which is a disadvantage in some applications. The Pawsey stub is useful from UHF through microwave frequencies where the length of the connections at the load terminals becomes significant.

The Roberts or Collins balun in Figure 24.63B is similar to the Pawsey stub but does not place a dc short-circuit across the load terminals. The λ/4 open stub presents a low impedance to RF at the other end of the stub, allowing the same RF current to flow in both load terminals. It is most useful from 2 meters where the length of the stub starts to become unwieldy to above 23 cm where connection lengths start to become significant.

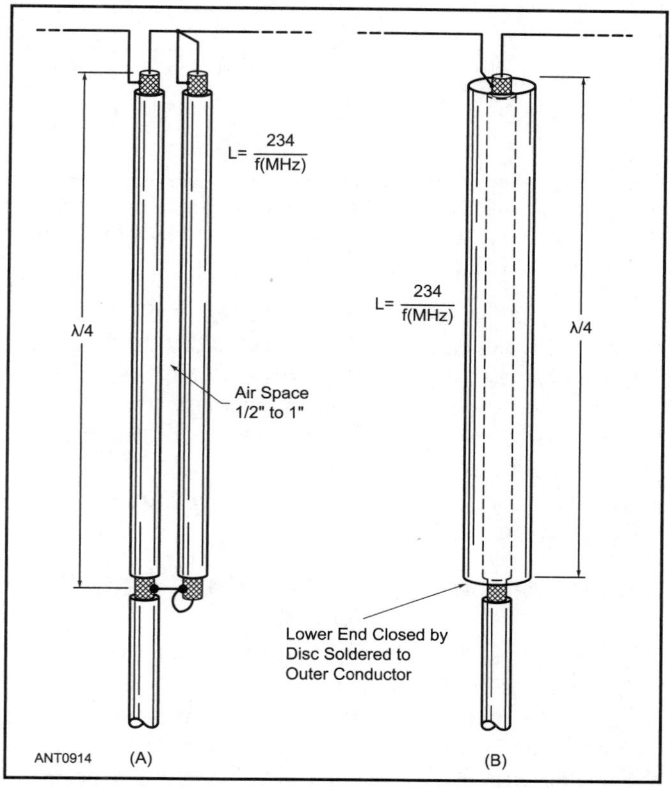

Figure 24.62 — Fixed-balun methods for balancing the termination when a coaxial cable is connected to a balanced antenna. These baluns work at a single frequency. The balun at B is known as a "sleeve balun" and is often used at VHF.

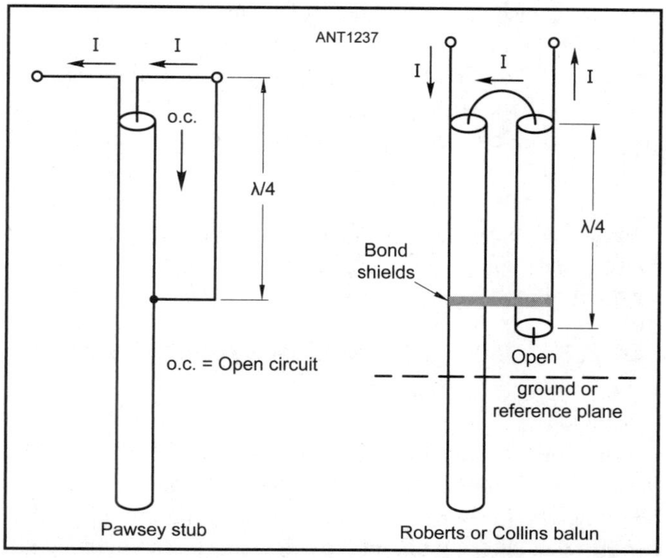

Figure 24.63 — The Pawsey stub (A) and Roberts or Collins baluns (B). See text for a description of how they function.

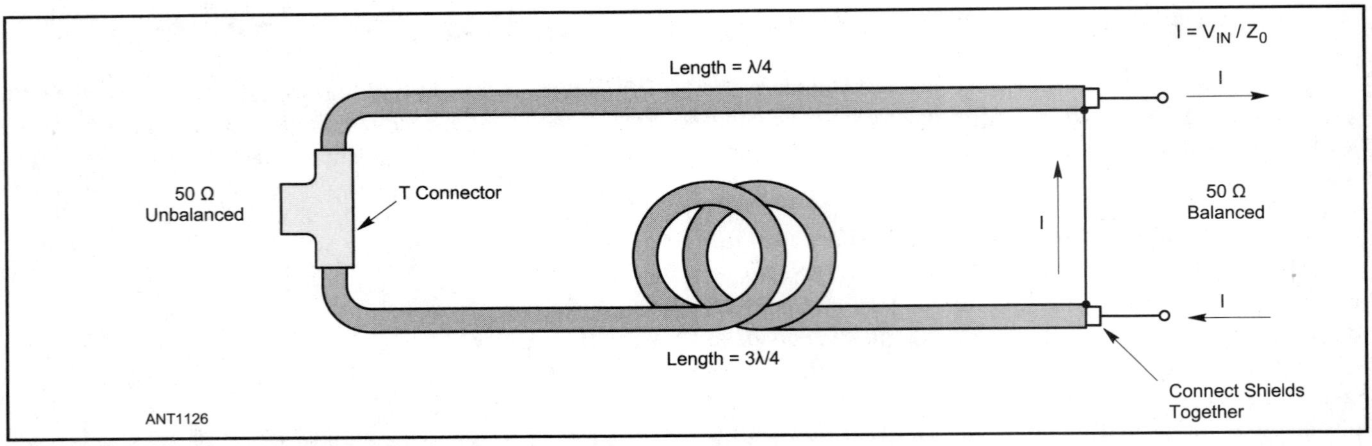

Figure 24.64 — The λ/4 – 3λ/4 balun uses the current-forcing function of odd-λ/4 feed lines and the λ/2 delay of the longer line to cause equal and opposite currents to flow in the antenna terminals.

The length of the open stub can be varied to act as a matching element or extend the bandwidth of the antenna. The stub can also act as a quarter-wave transformer for the load impedance. The usual construction is for a ground plane to create the bond between the stub and the feed line. A complete analysis is available from the MIT Haystack Observatory at **www.haystack.mit.edu/ast/arrays/Edges/EDGES_memos/087.pdf**.

24.8.2 QUARTER/THREE-QUARTER-WAVE BALUN

The coaxial balun in **Figure 24.64** is a 1:1 decoupling balun made from two pieces of coaxial cable. One leg is λ/4 long and the other 3λ/4 long. The two coaxes and the feed line are joined together with a T connector. At the antenna, the shields of the cables are connected together and the center conductors connected to the terminals of the antenna feed point. The balun has very little loss and is reported to have a bandwidth of more than 10%.

The balun works because of the current-forcing function of a transmission line an odd number of λ/4 long. The current at the output of such a transmission line is V_{IN} / Z_0 regardless of the load impedance, similarly to the behavior of a current source. Because both lines are fed with the same voltage, being connected in parallel, the output currents will also be equal.

The current out of the 3λ/4 line is delayed by λ/2 from the current out of the λ/4 line (and so is out of phase). The result is that equal and opposite currents are forced into the terminal of the load.

24.8.3 COMBINED BALUN AND MATCHING STUB

In certain antenna systems the balun length can be considerably shorter than λ/4; the balun is, in fact, used as part of the matching system. This requires that the radiation resistance be fairly low as compared with the line Z_0 so that a match can be brought about by first shortening the antenna to make it have a capacitive reactance, and then using a shunt inductor across the antenna terminals to resonate the antenna

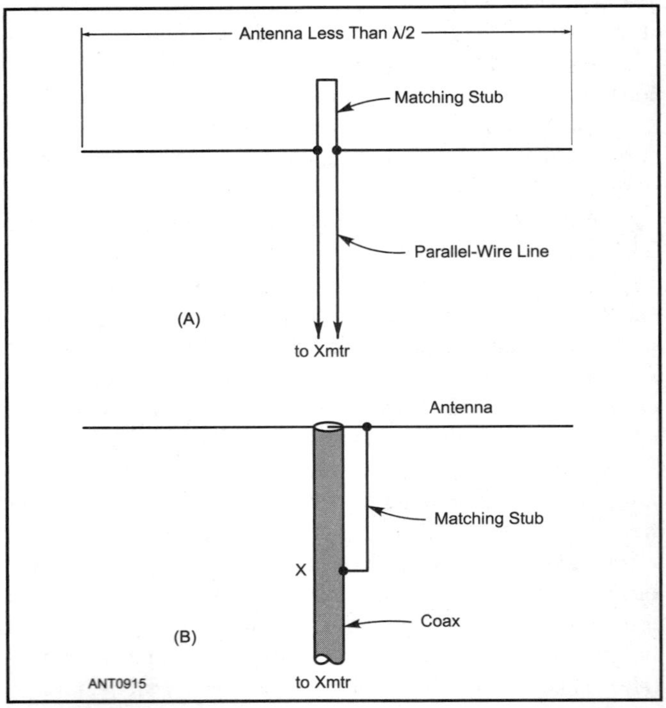

Figure 24.65 — Combined matching stub and balun. The basic arrangement is shown at A. At B, the balun arrangement is achieved by using a section of the outside of the coax feed line as one conductor of a matching stub.

and simultaneously raise the impedance to a value equal to the line Z_0. This is the same principle used for hairpin matches. The balun is then made the proper length to exhibit the desired value of inductive reactance.

The basic matching method is shown in **Figure 24.65A** for parallel-conductor line, and the balun adaptation to coaxial feed is shown in Figure 24.65B. The matching stub in Figure 24.66B is a parallel-line section, one conductor of which is the outside of the coax between point X and the antenna; the other stub conductor is an equal length of wire. (A piece of coax may be used instead, as in the balun in Figure 24.62A.)

The spacing between the stub conductors can be 2 to 3 inches. The stub of Figure 24.65 is ordinarily much shorter than λ/4, and the impedance match can be adjusted by altering the stub length along with the antenna length. With simple coax feed, even with a λ/4 balun as in Figure 24.62, the match depends entirely on the actual antenna impedance and the Z_0 of the cable; no adjustment is possible.

Adjustment

When a λ/4 balun is used it is advisable to resonate it before connecting the antenna. This can be done without much difficulty if a dip meter or impedance analyzer is available. In the system shown in Figure 24.62A, the section formed by the two parallel pieces of line should first be made slightly longer than the length given by the equation. The shorting connection at the bottom may be installed permanently. With the dip meter coupled to the shorted end, check the frequency and cut off small lengths of the shield braid (cutting both lines equally) at the open ends until the stub is resonant at the desired frequency. In each case leave just enough inner conductor remaining to make a short connection to the antenna. After resonance has been established, solder the inner and outer conductors of the second piece of coax together and complete the connections indicated in Figure 24.62A.

Another method is to first adjust the antenna length to the desired frequency, with the line and stub disconnected, then connect the balun and recheck the frequency. Its length may then be adjusted so that the overall system is again resonant at the desired frequency.

Construction

In constructing a balun of the type shown in Figure 24.62A, the additional conductor and the line should be maintained parallel by suitable spacers. It is convenient to use a piece of coax for the second conductor; the inner conductor can simply be soldered to the outer conductor at both ends since it does not enter into the operation of the device. The two cables should be separated sufficiently so that the vinyl covering represents only a small proportion of the dielectric between them. Since the principal dielectric is air, the length of the λ/4 section is based on a velocity factor of 0.95, approximately.

24.8.4 IMPEDANCE STEP-UP/STEP-DOWN BALUN

A coax-line balun may also be constructed to give an impedance step-up ratio of 4:1. This form of balun is shown in **Figure 24.66**. If 75-Ω line is used, as indicated, the balun will provide a match for a 300-Ω terminating impedance. If 50-Ω line is used, the balun will provide a match for a 200-Ω terminating impedance. The U-shaped section of line must be an electrical length of λ/2 long, taking the velocity factor of the line into account. In most installations using this type of balun, it is customary to roll up the length of line represented by the U-shaped section into a coil of several inches in diameter. The coil turns may be bound together with electrical tape.

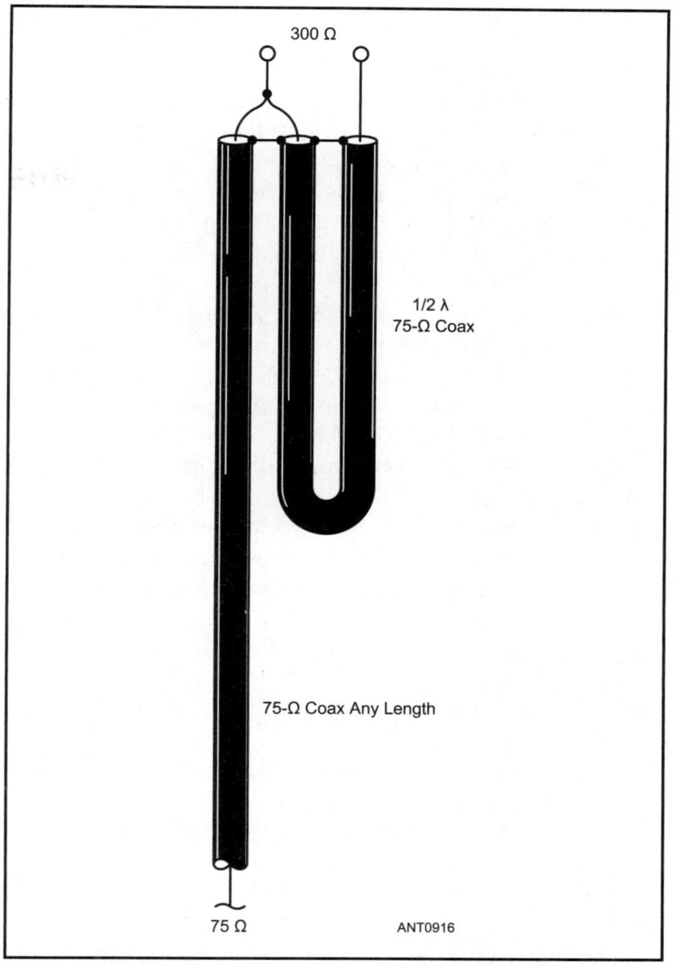

Figure 24.66 — A balun that provides an impedance step-up ratio of 4:1. The electrical length of the U-shaped section of line is λ/2.

Because of the bulk and weight of the balun, this type is seldom used with wire-line antennas suspended by insulators at the antenna ends. More commonly it is used with multielement Yagi antennas, where its weight may be supported by the boom of the antenna system. See the K1FO designs in the **VHF, UHF and Microwave Antennas** chapter, where 200-Ω T-matches are used with such a balun.

24.9 BIBLIOGRAPHY

Source material and more extended discussion of topics covered in this chapter can be found in the references given below and in the textbooks listed at the end of the **Antenna Fundamentals** chapter.

G. Barrere, "Magnetic Coupling in Transmission Lines and Transformers," *QEX*, Sep/Oct 2006, pp 28-36.

D. K. Belcher, "RF Matching Techniques, Design and Example," *QST*, Oct 1972, pp 24-30.

D. Birnbaum, "Direct Calculation of Antenna Tuner Losses," *QEX*, Nov/Dec 2018, pp 23-25.

J. Brown, "RFI, Ferrites, and Common Mode Chokes For Hams," April 2019, **k9yc.com/publish.htm**.

J. Brown, "A New Choke Cookbook for the 160–10M Bands," Dec 2018, **k9yc.com/publish.htm**.

J. Brown, "Optimizing the Location of Stubs For Harmonic Suppression," **audiosystemsgroup.com/publish.htm**.

J. Brown, "Chokes and Isolation Transformers for Receiving Antennas," *National Contest Journal*, Mar/Apr 2019, pp 7-10.

W. Bruene, "Introducing the Series-Parallel Network," *QST*, Jun 1986, pp 21-23.

W. Caron, *Antenna Impedance Matching* (Newington: ARRL, 1989). [out of print]

G. Cutsogeorge, *Managing Interstation Interference, 2nd edition*, International Radio, 2009.

T. Dorbuck, "Matching-Network Design," *QST*, Mar 1979, pp 26-30.

B. A. Eggers, "An Analysis of the Balun," *QST*, Apr 1980, pp 19-21.

D. Emerson, "Try a Twelfth-Wave Transformer," *QST*, Jun 1997, pp 43-44.

J. Garland, "The EZ Tuner — Parts 1, 2, and 3," *QST*, Apr 2002, pp 40-43, May 2002, pp 28-34 and Jun 2002, pp 89-96.

D. Geiser, "Resistive Impedance-matching with Quarter-Wave Lines," *QST*, Feb 1963, pp 63-67.

J. D. Gooch, O. E. Gardner, and G. L. Roberts, "The Hairpin Match," *QST* , Apr 1962, pp 11-14, 146, 156.

G. Grammer, "Simplified Design of Impedance-Matching Networks," *QST*, Part 1, Mar 1957, pp 38-42; Part 2, Apr 1957, pp 32-35; Part 3, May 1957, pp 29-34.

J. Hallas, *The ARRL Guide to Antenna Tuners* (Newington: ARRL, 2010).

W. Harriman, "Second Harmonic Suppression Using a Coax Stub," **ae6ty.com/Smith_Charts.html**.

D. J. Healey, "An Examination of the Gamma Match," *QST*, Apr 1969, pp 11-15, 57.

S. Johnson, "Build a 9 to 1 Unun Transformer," *QST*, Mar 2019, pp 34-35.

J. D. Kraus and S. S. Sturgeon, "The T-Matched Antenna," *QST*, Sep 1940, pp 24-25.

Z. Lau, "Why Do Baluns Burn Up?" *QEX*, Jan/Feb 2004, pp 55-58.

Z. Lau, "RF: Calculating the Power Limit of Circuits with Toroids," *QEX*, Mar/Apr 1995, pp 24-30.

R. W. Lewallen, "Baluns: What They Do and How They Do It," *The ARRL Antenna Compendium, Vol 1* (Newington: ARRL, 1985), pp 157-164.

R. Lindquist, "*QST* Compares: Four High-Power Antenna Tuners," Product Review, *QST*, Mar 1997, pp 73-77.

M. W. Maxwell, "Some Aspects of the Balun Problem," *QST*, Mar 1983, pp 38-40.

M. W. Maxwell, *Reflections III* (New York: CQ Communications, 2010).

R. A. Nelson, "Basic Gamma Matching," *Ham Radio*, Jan 1985, pp 29-31, 33.

B. Pattison, "A Graphical Look at the L Network," *QST*, Mar 1979, pp 24-25.

F. A. Regier, "Series-Section Transmission line Impedance-matching," *QST*, Jul 1978, pp 14-16.

R. Rhea, "Yin-Yang of Matching, Parts 1 and 2," *High Frequency Electronics,* Mar and Apr 2006. Also available from Keysight Technologies (**www.keysight.com**) as application notes 5989-9012EN and 5989-9015EN. Go to the Services & Support section, then Technical Support, and use the Search function.

W. Sabin, "Understanding the T-tuner (C-L-C) Transmatch," *QEX*, Dec 1997, pp 13-21.

J. Sevick, *Understanding, Building, and Using Baluns and Ununs*, (New York: CQ Communications, 2003).

J. Sevick, *Transmission Line Transformers, 4th edition,* Noble Publishing, 2001.

J. Sevick, "Simple Broadband Matching Networks," *QST*, Jan 1976, pp 20-23.

J. Sevick, "A Simplified Analysis of the Broadband Transmission Line Transformer," *High Frequency Electronics*, Feb 2004, pp 48-53.

J. Sevick, "Magnetic Materials for Broadband Transmission Line Transformers," *High Frequency Electronics*, Jan 2005, pp 46-52.

W. Silver, ed., *ARRL Handbook*, (Newington: ARRL, 2019).

W. Silver, "Hands-On Radio: Experiment #157 — Matching Network Design and Build," *QST*, Feb 2016, pp 65-66.

J. Stanley, "Hairpin Tuners for Matching Balanced Antenna Systems," *QST,* Apr 2009, pp 34-35.

J. Stanley, "*FilTuners* — a New (Old) Approach to Antenna Matching," *The ARRL Antenna Compendium, Vol. 6* (Newington: ARRL, 1999), pp 168-173.

R. E. Stephens, "Admittance Matching the Ground-Plane Antenna to Coaxial Transmission Line," Technical Correspondence, *QST*, Apr 1973, pp 55-57.

D. Straw, "A Beginner's Guide to Transmission-Line and Antenna-Tuner Modeling," *QST*, May 2001, pp 34-37.

H. F. Tolles, "How to Design Gamma-Matching Networks," *Ham Radio*, May 1973, pp 46-55.

E. Wingfield, "New and Improved Formulas for the Design of Pi and Pi-L Networks," *QST*, Aug 1983, pp 23-29.

F. Witt, "Baluns in the Real (and Complex) World," *The ARRL Antenna Compendium, Vol 5* (Newington: ARRL, 1997), pp 171-181.

F. Witt, "How to Evaluate Your Antenna Tuner," *QST*, Part 1, Apr 1995, pp 30-34 and May 1995, pp 33-37.

B. S. Yarman, *Design of Ultra Wideband Antenna Matching Networks*, (New York: Springer, 2008).

TABLE OF CONTENTS

Chapter 25 — Downloadable Supplemental Content

Supplemental Articles

- "K5GO Half-Element Designs" by Stan Stockton, K5GO
- "Conductors for HF Antennas" by Rudy Severns, N6LF
- "Insulated Wire and Antennas" by Rudy Severns, N6LF
- "3D-Printed Coax-to-Wire Connection Blocks" by John Portune, W6NBC

Chapter 25

Antenna Materials and Construction

This chapter contains information on materials and techniques amateurs use to construct antennas. Included is a discussion of useful material types that are readily available at reasonable cost, and tips on working with and using these materials.

The National Electric Code (NEC) of the National Fire Protection Association contains a section on amateur stations in which a number of recommendations are made concerning minimum size of antenna wire and the manner of bringing the transmission line into the station. The code in itself does not have the force of law but it is frequently made a part of local building regulations, which are enforceable. The provisions of the code may also be written into, or referred to, in fire and liability insurance documents. See the chapter **Building Antenna Systems and Towers** for more information on applying the NEC to your station's antenna system.

Although antennas are relatively simple structures, they can constitute a potential hazard unless properly constructed. Antennas and supporting ropes or wires should *never* be run under or over public utility (telephone or power) lines. Stay well clear of utility lines when erecting antennas and give yourself plenty of safety margins. Amateurs have lost their lives by failing to observe these precautions.

Basically any conductive material can be used as the radiating element of an antenna. Almost any insulating material can be used as an antenna insulator. An antenna system must also include some means to support those conductors and maintain their relative positions — the boom for a Yagi antenna, for example. The materials used for antenna construction are limited mainly by physical considerations (required strength and resistance to outdoor exposure) and by the availability of materials. Don't be afraid to experiment with radiating materials and insulators.

The two types of material most often used for antenna conductors are wire and tubing. Wire antennas are generally simple and therefore easier to construct, although arrays of multiple wire elements can become rather complex. When tubing is required, aluminum tubing is used most often because of its light weight, reasonable cost and strength. Aluminum tubing is discussed in a subsequent section of this chapter.

25.1 WIRE FOR ANTENNA SYSTEMS

25.1.1 WIRE TYPES

Solid copper wire is used for most wire antennas although the use of stranded wire is common. Solid wire is less flexible than stranded wire, but it is available "hard-drawn," which offers good tensile strength and negligible stretch. Special stranded wire with a larger-than-usual number of fine strands (such as Flex-Weave) is available for building antennas. It withstands vibration and bending in the wind better than common stranded wire and better than solid wire. Galvanized steel and aluminum wire are generally not used for antennas because of higher electrical resistance than copper. Galvanized wire also has a strong tendency to rust, and making good electrical connections to aluminum wire is difficult — it cannot be soldered directly without special solder fluxes.

Solid wire is also available with and without enamel coating. Enamel coating resists oxidation and corrosion, but bare wire is far more common. Solid wire is also available with a variety of different insulating coatings, including plastics, rubbers and PVC. Unless specifically rated for outdoor use however, wire insulation, including enamel, tends to break down when exposed to the UV in sunlight. Insulation also lowers the velocity factor of wire by a few percent (see the **Transmission Lines** chapter) making it electrically longer than its physical length — this will lower the resonant frequency of an antenna compared to one made of bare wire of equivalent diameter. In addition, insulation increases wind loading without increasing strength. If enameled or insulated wire is used, care should be taken to not nick the wire when removing the coating for an electrical connection. Wire will break at a nick when flexed repeatedly, such as by wind.

"Soft-drawn" or annealed copper wire is easy to handle and obtain. Common THHN-insulated "house wire" is soft-drawn. Unfortunately, soft-drawn wire stretches considerably under load. Soft-drawn wire should only be used in applications where there will be little or no tension, or where some change in length can be tolerated. For example, the length of a horizontal antenna fed at the center with open-wire line is not critical, although a change in length may require some readjustment of an impedance matching unit. Similarly, if the wire stretches significantly, it can be re-trimmed to the desired length. Repeated cycles of stretching followed by trimming and re-tensioning will result in loss of strength and possibly in mechanical failure.

Concerns about the effect of insulation on copper wire, such as the THHN-insulated wire referred to previously, appear to be unwarranted. In his *QEX* article "Insulated Wire and Antennas" (available in the downloadable supplemental information), N6LF reported on a study of using insulated wire. There are esthetic concerns — the outermost transparent sheath degrades with exposure to UV and is shed by the wire. N6LF also considers mechanical issues — adding insulation increases the weight but also causes ground surface or buried radials to last longer than bare wire. Overall, the effects of the insulation are insignificant with the exception being when used in sparse radial systems. Those effects disappear for more than 12 elevated radials and 16 to 20 radials on or below ground level.

"Hard-drawn" copper wire and CCS (copper-clad steel, usually sold as the trademarked product Copperweld) wire are more difficult to handle because of their mechanical stiffness and, in the case of CCS, the tendency to have "memory" when unrolled. These types of wire are ideal for applications where high strength for a given weight is required and/or significant stretch cannot be tolerated. Care should be exercised to make sure kinks do not develop in hard-drawn and CCS wire — the wire will have a far greater tendency to break at a kink. The "memory" or tendency of CCS wire to coil up can be reduced by suspending it a few feet above ground for a few days before final use. The wire should not be recoiled before it is installed. The electrical quality of CCS wire varies considerably. A conductivity class of 30% or higher is desirable, meaning the wire has 30% of the conductivity of copper wire of the same diameter but for RF applications at HF it will have close to 100% conductivity due to skin effect.

At MF and LF, such as 160 meters, 630 meters, and 2200 meters, CCS wire may have unacceptably high losses due to insufficient thickness of the copper layer. (See the **Transmission Lines** chapter's section on "Choosing and Installing Feed Lines" for the effect on feed line loss.) **Figure 25.1** compares the resistance of copper-clad and solid copper wires at 100 kHz and higher frequencies. As a general guideline, for resistance losses to be equivalent to solid

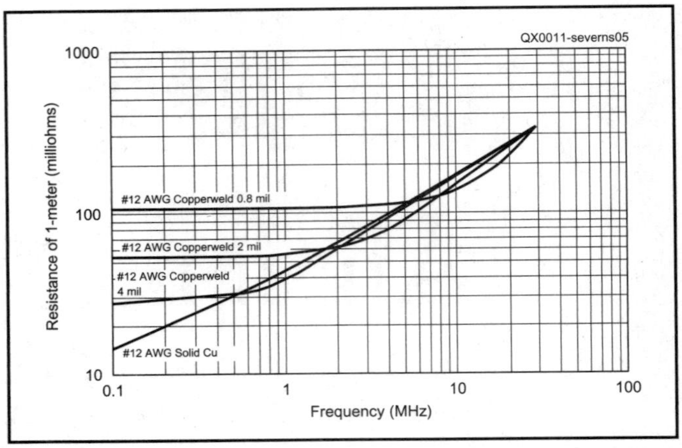

Figure 25.1 — Resistance comparison of 1-meter lengths of #12 AWG solid copper, #12 AWG Copperweld with 4-mil cladding, and an equivalent wire for 19- strand #26 AWG Copperweld with 0.8-mil cladding from 1 to 30 MHz. Derived by N6LF from FEM modeling.

copper, the cladding should be approximately 3 times the skin depth which is:

1.80 MHz (160 meters) —49 µm
475 kHz (630 meters) — 95 µm
136.5 kHz (2200 meters) — 177 µm

Assume the cladding thickness is the typical 10 percent of the overall conductor diameter at 30% conductivity. To have equivalent resistance to solid copper at 1.80 MHz the overall wire diameter must be 490 × 3 = 1470 µm or 0.058 inches and #14 AWG is the smallest wire gauge that is thick enough. Similarly, the smallest wire gauge is #8 AWG at 475 kHz. Less cladding such as for the 20% conductivity CCS will result in increased losses so at 630 and 2200 meters solid copper conductors are recommended. N6LF also notes that stranded CCS is inferior to solid CCS below 40 meters.

Copper cladding can be damaged by abrasion (typically at insulators) or sharp bends. Plastic insulators of sufficient strength are preferable to ceramic insulators when using CCS; they are soft in comparison and less likely to degrade the copper cladding over time. Induced defects in copper cladding eventually result in mechanical failure due to rusting of the steel core. Breaks in the copper cladding also form high resistance points to RF and will heat considerably when running high power. Heat accelerates oxidation (rusting).

Using Strap or Braided Conductors

Communications systems expert Frank Donovan, W3LPL, contributed these guidelines for the use of strap (solid metal) or braided conductors. Wide, flat, copper strap is the standard for grounding and bonding when flexibility isn't required — at least 10 mm wide, wider is better. Thin, round conductors are always inferior. Properly designed grounding and bonding systems use wide, flat, copper strap everywhere except for the short lengths where flexibility is required for the last foot or two of connections to moveable equipment.

Braided conductors should not be used for grounding (connections to a facility's grounding electrodes as discussed in the chapter on **Building Antenna Systems and Towers**) and should be as short as reasonably practical. Unnecessarily long pigtails should always be avoided. Terminals should be installed on both ends of the braid conductors, firmly and securely fastened to the equipment and conductors at each end of the braid. (Use a crimp terminal specified for use with braid.)

Tinned, tightly woven, wide (at least 10 mm, preferably much wider), flat copper braid is an excellent bonding conductor provided it is not corroded. Skin effect may force RF to jump across each wire crossover, but there are very many tight connections in parallel.

Braid removed from coaxial cable is an exceptionally poor choice for a bonding conductor because it is round, relatively small diameter, loosely meshed and usually not tinned. It works very well inside coaxial cable because the jacket maintains tight connections in the braid mesh and protects the copper from water and other corrosion agents.

Braid of any kind should never be used outdoors, especially on antennas and towers where lightning currents might be present. The standard is wide, flat, copper strap or #2 AWG solid copper wire where lightning currents might be present. Seven or nineteen strand copper wire can be used where flexibility is required.

25.1.2 WIRE SIZE AND TENSION

Many factors influence the choice of wire type and size (gage or gauge). Important considerations include the length of the unsupported span, the amount of sag that can be tolerated, the stability of the supports under wind pressure, the amount of wind and ice loading anticipated and whether or not a transmission line will be suspended from the span. Some sag is desirable. Removing most or all sag requires additional unnecessary tension and increases the likelihood of failure. **Table 25.1** shows the wire diameter, current-carrying capacity and resistance of various sizes of copper wire. **Table 25.2** shows the recommended maximum working tension of hard-drawn and CCS wire of various sizes. The recommended working tension is approximately 10% of the minimum guaranteed breaking strength of the wire. Together with a calculation of span sag, these two tables can be used to select the appropriate wire size for an antenna.

The National Electrical Code (see the chapter **Building Antenna Systems and Towers**) specifies minimum conductor sizes for different span-length wire antennas. For hard-drawn copper wire, the Code specifies #14 AWG wire for open (unsupported) spans less than 150 feet, and #10 AWG for longer spans. CCS, bronze or other high-strength conductors may be #14 AWG for spans less than 150 feet and #12 AWG for longer runs. Lead-in conductors (for open-wire transmission line) should be at least as large as those specified for antennas.

The RF resistance of copper wire increases as the size of the wire decreases. In most common wire antenna designs however, the antenna's radiation resistance will be much higher than the wire's RF resistance and the efficiency of the antenna will be adequate. Wire sizes as small as #30 AWG, or

Table 25.1
Copper-Wire Table

Wire Size AWG (B&S)	*Dia in Mils*[1]	*Dia in mm*	*Turns per Linear Inch Enamel*	*Feet per Pound Bare*	*Ohms per 1000 ft 25°C*[3]	*Cont.-duty current*[2,3] *Single Wire in Open Air*
1	289.3	7.348	—	3.947	0.1264	—
2	257.6	6.544	—	4.977	0.1593	—
3	229.4	5.827	—	6.276	0.2009	—
4	204.3	5.189	—	7.914	0.2533	—
5	181.9	4.621	—	9.980	0.3195	—
6	162.0	4.115	—	12.58	0.4028	—
7	144.3	3.665	—	15.87	0.5080	—
8	128.5	3.264	7.6	20.01	0.6405	73
9	114.4	2.906	8.6	25.23	0.8077	—
10	101.9	2.588	9.6	31.82	1.018	55
11	90.7	2.305	10.7	40.12	1.284	—
12	80.8	2.053	12.0	50.59	1.619	41
13	72.0	1.828	13.5	63.80	2.042	—
14	64.1	1.628	15.0	80.44	2.575	32
15	57.1	1.450	16.8	101.4	3.247	—
16	50.8	1.291	18.9	127.9	4.094	22
17	45.3	1.150	21.2	161.3	5.163	—
18	40.3	1.024	23.6	203.4	6.510	16
19	35.9	0.912	26.4	256.5	8.210	—
20	32.0	0.812	29.4	323.4	10.35	11
21	28.5	0.723	33.1	407.8	13.05	—
22	25.3	0.644	37.0	514.2	16.46	—
23	22.6	0.573	41.3	648.4	20.76	—
24	20.1	0.511	46.3	817.7	26.17	—
25	17.9	0.455	51.7	1031	33.00	—
26	15.9	0.405	58.0	1300	41.62	—
27	14.2	0.361	64.9	1639	52.48	—
28	12.6	0.321	72.7	2067	66.17	—
29	11.3	0.286	81.6	2607	83.44	—
30	10.0	0.255	90.5	3287	105.2	—
31	8.9	0.227	101	4145	132.7	—
32	8.0	0.202	113	5227	167.3	—
33	7.1	0.180	127	6591	211.0	—
34	6.3	0.160	143	8310	266.0	—
35	5.6	0.143	158	10480	335	—
36	5.0	0.127	175	13210	423	—
37	4.5	0.113	198	16660	533	—
38	4.0	0.101	224	21010	673	—
39	3.5	0.090	248	26500	848	—
40	3.1	0.080	282	33410	1070	—

[1]A mil is 0.001 inch.
[2]Max wire temp of 212° F and max ambient temp of 135° F.
[3]Ratings are for dc measurements and currents without skin effect.

Wiring Techniques

Working with antenna wire, cables, and terminals requires heavier tools and different techniques from ordinary electronic wiring. Manufacturers of tools and materials often supply "how to" tutorials on their websites and others can be found on YouTube and other Internet video sites. A comprehensive course by CED Engineering on wiring techniques can be found online at **www.cedengineering.com/upload/Wiring%20 Techniques.pdf.**

Table 25.2
Stressed Antenna Wire

American Wire Gauge	***Recommended Tension[1] (pounds)*** *Copper-clad steel[2]*	*Hard-drawn copper*	***Weight (pounds per 1000 feet)*** *Copper-clad steel[2]*	*Hard-drawn copper*
4	495	214	115.8	126.0
6	310	130	72.9	79.5
8	195	84	45.5	50.0
10	120	52	28.8	31.4
12	75	32	18.1	19.8
14	50	20	11.4	12.4
16	31	13	7.1	7.8
18	19	8	4.5	4.9
20	12	5	2.8	3.1

[1]Approximately one-tenth the guaranteed breaking strength. Might be increased 50% if end supports are firm and there is no danger of ice loading.
[2] Copperweld, 40% copper

even smaller, have been used successfully in the construction of "invisible" antennas in areas where more conventional antennas cannot be erected. In most cases, the selection of wire for an antenna will be based primarily on the mechanical properties of the wire, since the suspension of wire from elevated supports places the wire in tension.

Calculating Wire Sag

The following section is based on a *QST* "Technical Correspondence" item by Darrell Emerson, AA7FV, in the March 2014 issue of *QST.* Given the horizontal distance between two antenna masts supporting the wire, the weight per foot of the wire and the tension in the wire, it is possible to predict the wire sag at the lowest point of the wire, halfway between the supports (**Figure 25.2**). Previous editions of the *Antenna Book* used a nomograph based on the original article "Predicting Sag in Long Wire Antennas" in the January 1966 issue of *QST*, by John J. Elengo, Jr, K1AFR. Nowadays, most radio amateurs possess computers and perhaps quite sophisticated scientific calculators. The equations to calculate wire sag are fairly trivial by today's standards, and now it is much easier to use a simple calculator to determine the wire sag than to use a nomograph.

The equation describing the catenary, the curve of a rope or chain held horizontally between two supports, was first solved in 1691 by Johann Bernoulli and others. The equation is now found in many engineering and mathematical text books. One form of the solution is:

$$\text{Wire sag} = \frac{T}{w}\left[\cosh\left(w\frac{S}{2T}\right) - 1\right] \qquad (1)$$

where

cosh = the hyperbolic cosine
T = the tension in the wire in pounds
w = the weight of the wire in pounds per foot
S = the span of the wire, here defined as the *total* horizontal distance in feet between the two supports of the wire.

(There has been some confusion in previous publications about whether S represents half the distance or the total distance between supports. In Equation 1 it represents the total distance.) Some scientific calculators include hyperbolic functions and so can compute this directly, but there is a much simpler approximation that is valid in all cases likely to be of interest to the radio amateur.

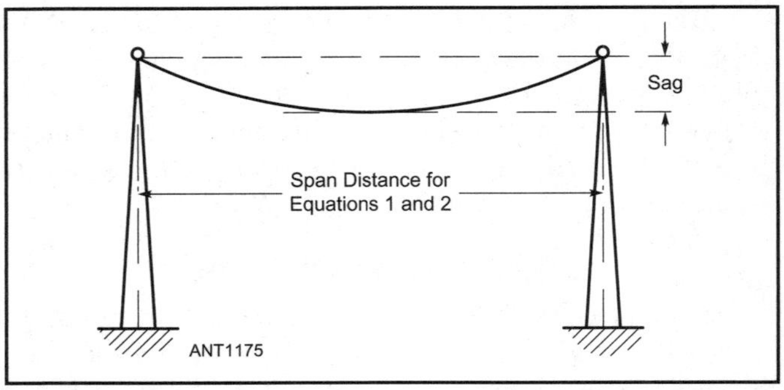

Figure 25.2 — This drawing applies to Equations 1 and 2 for calculating sag of wire antennas.

$$\text{Wire sag} = \frac{wS^2}{8T} \qquad (2)$$

Equation 2 is exactly that given in Edmund Laport's *Radio Antenna Engineering*, in his chapter on "Wire Stringing." (For sag between two supports of unequal height, see the "Miscellaneous Data" chapter of *Reference Data for Engineers* or **www.electricalengineeringinfo.com/2015/01/what-is-sag-tension-in-electrical-transmission-lines.html**)

An example calculation:

w = 0.011 (pounds per foot, 11 pounds per 1000 ft)

S = 420 feet (span, being the total distance between supports.

T = 50 pounds (wire tension).

Substituting w, S and T into the rigorous Equation 1, the computed result for sag is 4.860 feet. Using the much more convenient Equation 2, the result is 4.861 feet. The simpler formula is certainly adequate.

If the calculated sag is greater than allowable, it may be

reduced by any one or a combination of the following:

1) Providing additional supports, thereby decreasing the span

2) Increasing the tension in the wire

3) Decreasing the size (gage or gauge) of the wire

These calculations do not take into account the weight of a feed line supported by the antenna wire.

25.1.3 WIRE SPLICING AND CONNECTIONS

Wire antennas should preferably be made with unbroken lengths of wire. In instances where this is not feasible, wire sections should be spliced as shown in **Figure 25.3**. Any insulation should be removed for a distance of about 6 inches from the end of each section (take care not to nick the wire). Enamel may be removed by scraping with a knife or rubbing with sandpaper until the copper underneath is bright. The turns of wire should be brought up tight around the standing part of the wire by twisting with broad-nose pliers.

The crevices formed by the wire should be completely filled by using solder that does not contain an acid-core flux. A soldering iron or gun may not be sufficient for heavy wire or in cold temperatures; use a propane or butane torch instead. The joint should be heated sufficiently so the solder flows freely into the joint when the source of heat is removed momentarily. After the joint has cooled completely, it should be wiped clean with a cloth and then sprayed generously with acrylic to prevent corrosion.

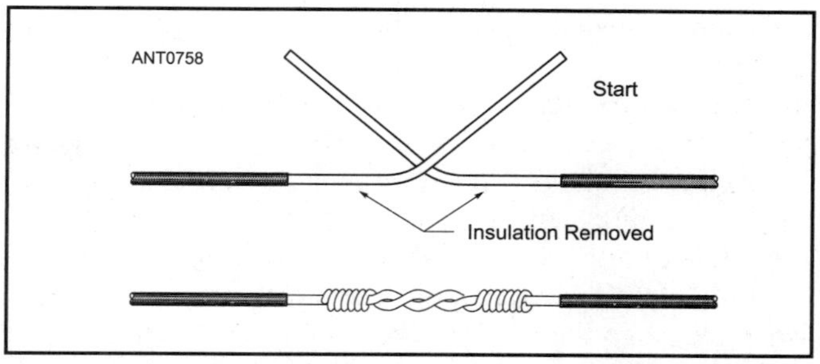

Figure 25.3 — Correct method of splicing antenna wire. Solder should be flowed into the wraps after the connection is completed. After cooling, the joint should be sprayed with acrylic to prevent oxidation and corrosion.

25.1.4 RADIAL SYSTEMS

See the chapter **Effects of Ground** for complete information on the requirements for ground radial systems, including references showing how to get the best results from a specific amount of wire.

Bare copper wire is the least expensive for radials with #18 or #20 AWG the smallest size likely to last due to mechanical abuse. Smaller wire will function electrically and is a good choice for temporary or portable installations. Good prices can be obtained by buying wire in bulk directly from a distributor. Copper will also withstand corrosive soils much better than aluminum.

When attaching radials to the antenna ground system, try to avoid direct contact with the ground due to corrosion from minerals in the ground. Tin-lead solder should not be used in connections in contact with the ground. If soldering is required, such as to a ground ring or plate, use silver-bearing plumbing solder or brazing rods. High-temperature MAPP gas torches are available at plumbing supply stores.

Radials need not be in direct contact with soil except for appearances. Shallow burial slits in a lawn can be made with an edging tool or a wire burial plow. See the previous cautions about avoiding direct contact between soil and solder joints.

Radials can also be placed on closely-cropped grass and the grass will grow over and around them in a few weeks, allowing them to lie directly on top of the soil. To hold radials firmly to the ground, landscaping staples can be used or iron rebar tie wire can be cut into 6 to 10 inch pieces and bent double.

25.2 ANTENNA INSULATORS

To prevent loss of RF power, the antenna should be well insulated from ground, unless of course it is a shunt-fed system. This is particularly important at the outer end or ends of wire antennas, since these points are always at a comparatively high RF potential. If an antenna is to be installed indoors, it should not touch any building materials. Electric fence insulators are inexpensive and work well for this purpose. Much greater care should be given to the selection of proper insulators when the antenna is located outside where it is exposed to wet weather. Antenna insulators should be made of material that will not absorb moisture. The best insulators for antenna use are made of glass or glazed porcelain although plastic insulators are widely available and suitable for most antennas.

The length of an insulator relative to its surface area is indicative of its comparative voltage stand-off and RF leakage abilities. A long thin insulator will have less leakage than a short thick insulator. Some antenna insulators are deeply ribbed to increase the surface leakage path without increasing the physical length of the insulator. Shorter insulators can be used at low-potential points, such as at the center of a dipole. If such an antenna is to be fed with open-wire line and used on several bands however, the center insulator should be the same as those used at the ends, because high RF potential may exist across the center insulator on some bands.

Insulator Stress

As with the antenna wire, the insulator must have sufficient physical strength to carry the mechanical load of the antenna without danger of breaking. Elastic line ("bungee cord" or "shock cord") or woven fishing line can provide long leakage paths and be used to provide both the end-insulator and support functions at antenna ends, subject to their ability to carry mechanical load. They are often used in antennas of the "invisible" type mentioned in the **Stealth Antennas** and **Portable Antennas** chapters. Abrasion between a woven line and a wire loop will cut through the line fairly quickly unless a fishing swivel or similar metal attachment point is used. Use of high power approaching and up to the US legal limit of 1500 W may cause sufficient leakage current to melt woven or monofilament line directly connected to a wire loop at the end of a dipole or similar antenna. A suitable antenna insulator as explained below must be used in this case.

For low-power operation with short antennas not subject to appreciable stress, almost any small plastic, glass, or glazed-porcelain insulator will do. Homemade insulators of plastic rod or sheet are usually satisfactory. Many plastics rated for outdoor use make good insulators — this includes Lucite (polycarbonate), Delrin, plexiglass, and even the high-density polyethylene (HDPE) used in cutting boards. More care is required in the selection of insulators for longer spans and higher transmitter power.

For a given material, the breaking tension of an insulator will be proportional to its cross-sectional area. It should be remembered that the wire hole at the end of the insulator decreases the effective cross-sectional area. For this reason, insulators designed to carry heavy strains are fitted with heavy metal end caps, the eyes being formed in the metal cap, rather than in the insulating material itself.

The following stress ratings of ceramic antenna insulators are typical:

- ⅝ inch square by 4 inches long — 400 pounds
- 1 inch diameter by 7 or 12 inches long — 800 pounds
- 1-½ inches diameter by 8, 12 or 20 inches long, with special metal end caps — 5000 pounds

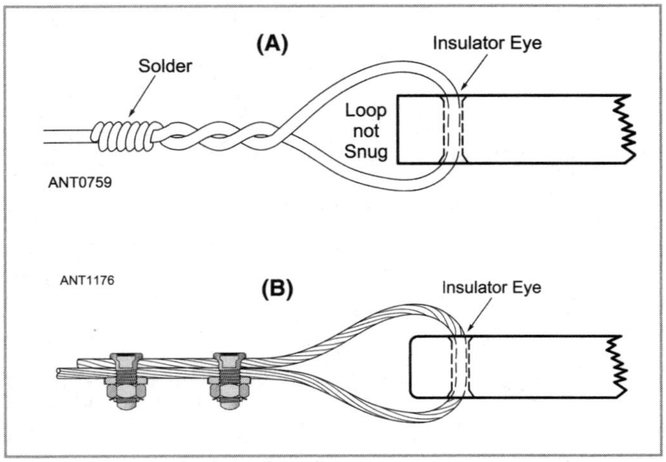

Figure 25.4 — The insulator at A uses a conventional twisted attachment which is soldered with a non-acid flux solder and can be sprayed with outdoor acrylic for protection. At B, split bolts may be used to provide a secure connection between heavy wires, such as at an insulator or splice. Using a pair of split bolts provides a more mechanically secure connection. For both types of connection, do not make the wire loop too snug to allow the wire loop to move in the insulator and flex.

These are rated breaking tensions. The actual working tensions should be limited to not more than 25% of the breaking rating. Plastic insulators have significantly lower tension ratings.

The antenna wire should be attached to the insulators as shown in **Figure 25.4A**. Care should be taken to avoid sharp angular bends in the wire when it is looped through the insulator eye. The loop should be generous enough in size that it will not bind the end of the insulator tightly. If the length of the antenna is critical, the length should be measured to the outward end of the loop, where it passes through the eye of the insulator. (See the note below about the loop area affecting the antenna's electrical length.)

Soldering should be done as described earlier for the wire splice. If CCS wire is used, care should be taken to ensure insulator holes and edges are smooth. Any roughness at contact points between the wire and the insulator will cause the copper to be abraded away over time, exposing the wire's steel core and eventually leading to mechanical failure from rust. Assuming they are of sufficient size to handle the mechanical load, plastic insulators are a good choice for use with CCS wire.

An alternative to soldering antenna wires is the use of "split bolts" to clamp wires together as in Figure 25.4B. This allows wire connections to be adjusted, such as when trimming a dipole length. If the proper-size split bolt is used, the connection is secure even for large conductors. Using a pair of split bolts provides a more secure attachment and less stress on the wire than a single bolt.

Note that the large area of the loop through the insulator adds capacitance to the antenna. The larger the insulator loop, the more capacitance is created, and the greater its effect in lowering the resonant frequency of the antenna. This effect increases with operating frequency. When building a wire antenna, attach the insulators temporarily (without soldering) and adjust the resonant frequency of the antenna before soldering the insulator loop.

Strain Insulators

Strain or "egg" insulators have their holes at right angles, since they are designed to be connected as shown in **Figure 25.5**. It can be seen that this arrangement places the insulating material in compression rather than tension. An insulator connected this way can withstand very high mechanical load.

The principal attribute of strain insulators is that the wire will not fall or fail to carry load if the insulator breaks,

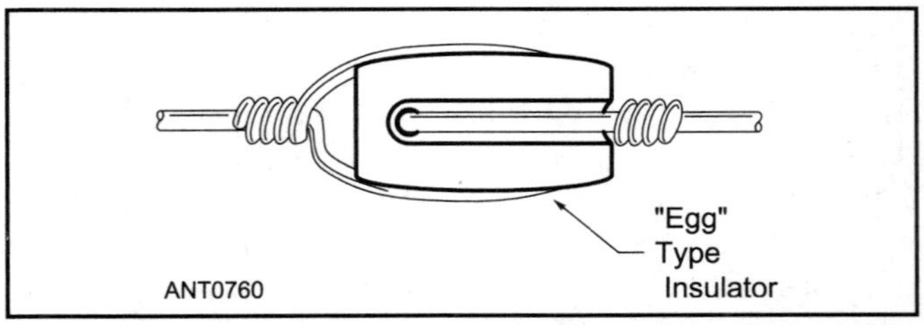

Figure 25.5 — Conventional manner of fastening wire to a strain insulator. This method decreases the leakage path and increases capacitance, as discussed in the text.

since the two loops are interlocked. Insulator failure may go unnoticed however — strain insulators should be visually checked periodically. Because the wires are wrapped around each other, the leakage path is shorter than it would be otherwise and both leakage and capacitive end effects are higher compared to insulators where the wires are not interlinked. For this reason, strain insulators are typically confined to applications such as breaking up resonances in guy wires, where there is high mechanical load and where RF insulation is of minor importance.

Strain insulators are suitable for use at low-potential points on an antenna, such as at the center of a dipole. They may also be used at the ends of antennas used for low power operation.

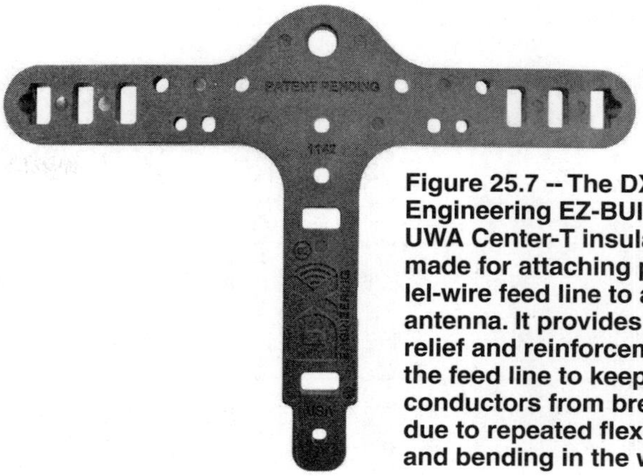

Figure 25.7 -- The DX Engineering EZ-BUILD UWA Center-T insulator is made for attaching parallel-wire feed line to a wire antenna. It provides strain relief and reinforcement to the feed line to keep the conductors from breaking due to repeated flexing and bending in the wind.

Feed Point Insulators

Often referred to as "center insulators," the insulators used at the feed point of a wire antenna often have special features that help attach and support feed lines. A "dog bone" style insulator as in **Figure 25.6A** is the most common. To attach a coaxial feed line using this style of insulator, the cable's shield and center conductor are separated into "pigtails" that are soldered to the wire at each eye. The cable can be supported by looping it over the insulator and securing it with tape. Note that the length of the separated shield and center conductor count as part of the antenna length — that may be significant at higher frequencies. The cable must be carefully waterproofed with a coating such as silicone sealant or Liquid Electrical Tape to prevent water from being wicked into the cable by the exposed shield.

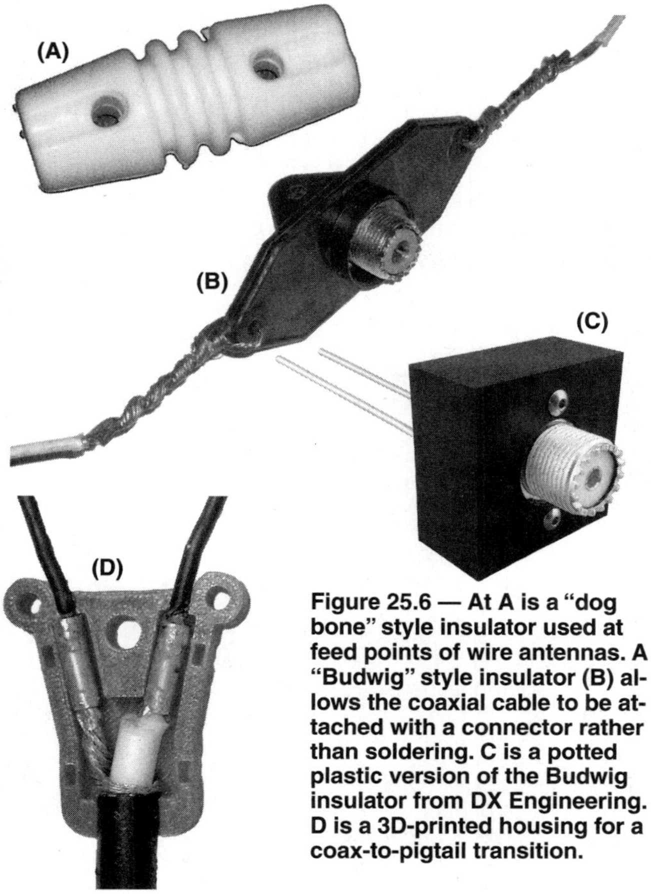

Figure 25.6 — At A is a "dog bone" style insulator used at feed points of wire antennas. A "Budwig" style insulator (B) allows the coaxial cable to be attached with a connector rather than soldering. C is a potted plastic version of the Budwig insulator from DX Engineering. D is a 3D-printed housing for a coax-to-pigtail transition.

The "Budwig" style of insulator in Figure 25.6B includes an SO-239 so that the coaxial cable can be attached with a connector instead of soldered to the antenna. The PL-259 and exposed portion of the SO-239 connectors in this case should be waterproofed. This type of center insulator can be made from a PVC pipe cap or other plumbing fittings as shown later in this chapter. An updated style of insulator is available from DX Engineering (part number DXE-FPC-SO239) as a potted plastic assembly seen in Figure 25.6C. W6NBC has designed a 3D-printed connection block shown in Figure 25.6D for coax terminated in pigtail leads without a connector. (See the downloadable supplemental information for details.)

Figure 25.7 shows a feed point insulator intended for use with parallel-wire feed line. The dog bone style of insulator may be used but cannot support the feed line in the same way as for coaxial cable. Parallel-wire line cannot be looped back on itself with the conductors close together. If left unsupported, the conductors of the feed line continually flex and bend in the wind which causes them to break. The tee-style of insulator in the figure captures the parallel-wire feed line and provides mechanical support, greatly reducing breakage.

Insulators for Ribbon-Line Antennas

Figure 25.8A shows the sketch of an insulator designed to be used at the ends of a folded dipole or a multiple dipole made of parallel conductor line. It should be made approximately as shown, out of insulating material about ¼ inch thick. The advantage of this arrangement is that the strain of the antenna is shared by the conductors and the plastic webbing of the line, which adds considerable strength. After soldering, the screw should be sprayed with acrylic.

Figure 25.8B shows a similar arrangement for suspending one dipole from another in a stagger-tuned dipole system. If better insulation is desired, these insulators can be wired to a conventional insulator.

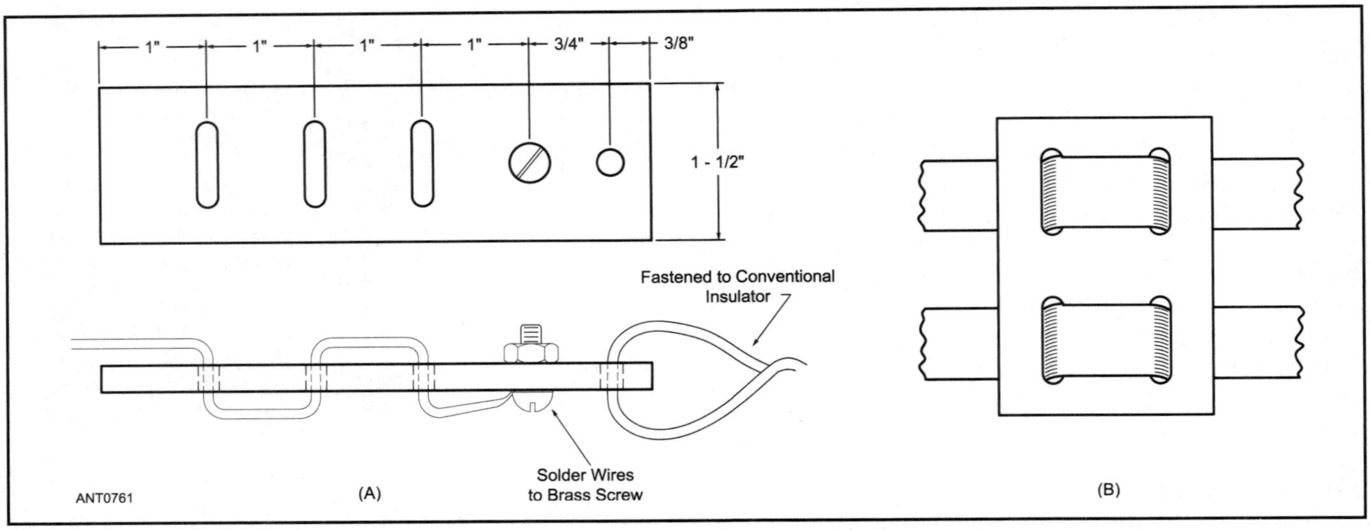

Figure 25.8 — At A, an insulator for the ends of folded dipoles, or multiple dipoles made of parallel-wire line. At B, a method of suspending one ribbon dipole from another in a multiband dipole system.

25.3 ANTENNAS OF ALUMINUM TUBING

Aluminum is a non-toxic, malleable, ductile metal with a density approximately 35% that of iron and 30% that of copper. Aluminum can be polished to a high brightness, and it will retain this polish in dry air. In the presence of oxygen, aluminum forms an oxide coating (Al_2O_3) that protects the metal from further corrosion. Direct contact between aluminum and certain metals (particularly ferrous metals such as iron or steel) in an outdoor environment can bring about galvanic corrosion of aluminum and its alloys. Some protective coating such as Noalox or Penetrox should be applied to any point of contact between dissimilar metals. (See the section on Corrosion in the chapter **Building Antenna Systems and Towers**.)

The ease with which aluminum can be drilled or sawed makes it a pleasure to work with. Aluminum alloys can be used to build amateur antennas, towers and supports. Light weight and high conductivity make aluminum ideal for these applications. Alloying typically lowers conductivity, but significantly increases tensile strength. Aluminum is typically alloyed with metals such as manganese, silicon, copper, magnesium and zinc. Cold rolling can be employed to further increase the strength.

A four-digit system is used to identify aluminum alloys, such as 6061. Aluminum alloys starting with a 6 contain di-magnesium silicide (Mg_2Si). The second digit indicates modifications of the original alloy or impurity limits. The last two digits designate different aluminum alloys within the category indicated by the first digit.

In the 6000-series, the 6061 and 6063 alloys are commonly used for antenna applications. Both types have good resistance to corrosion, medium strength and are widely available. A further designation like T6 denotes thermal treatment (heat tempering). In recent years 6063-T832 drawn aluminum tubing has become an attractive alternative to 6061-T6, given its good mechanical properties (typical yield strength of 35,000 psi) and comparatively low cost. Often found in commercial antennas, this alloy's low cost is derived from ubiquitous use in household items including aluminum folding chairs. More information on the available aluminum alloys can be found in **Table 25.3**.

Table 25.3
Aluminum Numbers and Alloy Types for Amateur Use

Common Alloy Numbers

Type	*Characteristics*
2024	Good formability, high strength
5052	Excellent surface finish, excellent corrosion resistance, normally not heat treatable for high strength
6061	Good machinability, good weldability
6063	Good machinability, good weldability
7075	Good formability, high strength

Common Tempers

Type	*Characteristics*
T0	Special soft condition
T3	Hard
T6	Hardest, possibly brittle
TXXX	Three digit tempers — usually specialized high strength heat treatments, similar to T6

General Uses

Type	*Uses*
2024-T3	Chassis boxes, antennas, anything that will be bent or
7075-T3	Flexed repeatedly
6061-T6	Tubing and pipe; angle channel and bar stock
6063-T832	Tubing and pipe; angle channel and bar stock

25.3.1 SELECTING ALUMINUM TUBING

Table 25.4 shows the standard sizes of aluminum tubing that are stocked by most aluminum suppliers or distributors in the United States and Canada. Note that all tubing comes in 12-foot lengths (local hardware stores sometimes stock 6- and 8-foot lengths) and larger-diameter sizes may be available in lengths up to 24 feet. Note also that any diameter tubing will fit snugly into the next larger size, if the larger size has a 0.058-inch wall thickness. For example, ⅝-inch tubing has an outside diameter of 0.625 inch. This will fit into ¾-inch tubing with a 0.058-inch wall, which has an inside diameter of 0.634 inch. A clearance of 0.009 inch is just right for a slip fit or for slotting the tubing and then using hose clamps. Always get the next larger size and specify a 0.058-inch wall to obtain the 0.009-inch clearance.

A little figuring with **Table 25.5** will give you all the information you need to build a beam, including what the antenna will weigh. 6061-T6 aluminum has relatively high strength and good workability. It is highly resistant to corrosion and will bend without taking a "set."

25.3.2 SOURCES OF ALUMINUM TUBING AND MOUNTING MATERIALS

Aluminum tubing can be purchased new and is available from local metal suppliers and some Amateur Radio dealers. Materials for attaching pieces of tubing, such as boom-to-mast or boom-to-element brackets can be purchased from ham radio antenna manufacturers either as separate products or as replacement parts for a commercial antenna. Stauff clamps (**us.stauff.com**) are a relatively new product for amateurs; they are used in industrial applications to support pipe and tubing. The polyamide version is preferred.

Don't overlook sources for used tubing, such as a local metal scrap yard. Surplus metal dealers often have odd lengths and sizes of aluminum tubing. Understand the difference between "tubing" which is extruded and rated for structural use and "pipe" and tubing for household products which are not as strong. Tubing often has an alloy number printed on it.

Some items to look for include irrigation tubing (fairly common in rural areas), tent poles for small antennas, tubing and fittings from scrapped antennas, and aluminum angle, rod, and round or square extrusions stock. Occasionally, aluminum tower sections can be found in scrap yards. Garage sales are also good sources of used tubing, and every hamfest flea market has a broken or bent antenna or two that can be "parted out." By being a good scavenger, you can build up a "bone yard" of materials for antenna construction.

Irrigation pipe may be usable as a boom or for longer element sections, although it may require extra support from a truss. Tent poles range in length from 2½ to 4 feet, are usually tapered and can be split on the larger end and mated with the smaller end of another pole of the same diameter. A small stainless-steel hose clamp can be used to fasten the poles at this junction. These make fine elements for small beams, particularly at VHF, and even booms for VHF and UHF Yagis.

For vertical antennas, consumer items such as window-washing and painter's poles can sometimes be used. These are not made of structural strength tubing but are often suitable and are low cost. For larger low-band verticals, irrigation pipe is often used.

25.3.3 CONSTRUCTION WITH ALUMINUM TUBING

Although there is endless variation in the type of antennas designed and built with aluminum tubing, Yagis are by far the most common. Yagi antennas can be successfully built using rules-of-thumb for element and boom material and sizing. Some of these approaches and a set of element point designs are provided in the following paragraphs. *YagiStress*, a commercially available software program developed and supported by Kurt Andress, K7NV (**k7nv.com/yagistress**), can be used to accurately calculate the loads and survivability of Yagi designs. Designers and builders of large Yagi antennas are well advised to use modeling software such as *YagiStress* to ensure survivability of the antenna while at the same not using more material than required to achieve desired mechanical performance. *YagiStress* was used to calculate the wind-speed ratings of the half-element designs in this chapter and is based on the EIA-222-C "Structural Standard for Antenna Supporting Structures and Antennas." Antenna mechanical design spreadsheets from *Physical Design of Yagi Antennas* by David Leeson, W6NL (see Bibliography), are available from **www.realhamradio.com/Download.htm** (the URL is case-sensitive) and have been updated to EIA-222-F.

Antennas for frequencies of 14 MHz and above are usually made to be rotated. Rotatable antennas require materials that are strong, lightweight and easy to obtain. Material selection is dependent on many factors, with weather conditions typically being the most demanding requirement. High winds alone may not cause as much damage to an antenna as does ice loading. Ice in combination with high wind is typically the worst-case condition.

As explained in Section 25.2.1, elements and booms can be made from telescoping tubing to provide the necessary total length. This is referred to as tapering. The boom diameter for a rotatable Yagi or quad should be selected to provide required structural strength and to stably support the elements. The appropriate tubing diameter for a boom depends on many factors. Among them are element weight, element length, number of elements and environmental loads, including static loads such as ice and dynamic loads, principally from wind gusts. Tubing of 1¼-inch diameter can easily support a three-element 28-MHz antenna and marginally a two-element 21-MHz antenna. A 2-inch diameter boom will be adequate for larger 28-MHz antennas or for harsh weather conditions and for antennas up to three elements on 14 MHz or four elements on 21 MHz. It is not recommended that 2-inch diameter booms be made any longer than 24 feet unless additional support is added to carry both vertical and horizontal loads. Suitable reinforcement for a long 2-inch boom can consist of a truss or a truss and lateral support, as shown in **Figure 25.9**.

For boom lengths in excess of 24 feet, 3-inch diameter material is usually required. Three-inch diameter booms provide considerable mechanical stability as well as large clamping surface area for boom-to-element hardware. Clamping surface area is particularly important if heavy icing is anticipated, and helps prevent rotation of elements around the axis of the boom. Pinning an element to the boom with a bolt or, preferably, a swaged, hardened pin, can eliminate this possibility, but the hole introduces a stress riser that can materially reduce the strength of the boom. Element rotation about the boom axis can be minimized by mounting elements under the boom rather than on top. Pinned elements sometimes work loose and elongate the pinning holes in both the element and the boom. This is a progressive condition resulting in elements that can be so loose-fitting to the boom that their rotational positions change frequently. Although this condition typically does not adversely affect the electrical performance of a Yagi, the mechanical strength of the members involved degrades as the holes elongate. A Yagi with elements at various angles is unsightly as well.

A 3-inch diameter boom with a wall thickness of 0.065 inch is satisfactory for antennas up to about a five-element, 14-MHz array that is spaced on a 40-foot long boom. A truss is recommended for any boom longer than 24 feet.

Per theory, there is no RF voltage at the center of a parasitic element and insulation is not required at the boom-to-element interface for elements centered on the boom. Driven elements may or may not be electrically connected to the boom depending on the feed system employed. In practice, parasitic

Table 25.4
Aluminum Tubing Sizes
6061-T6 (61S-T6) Round Aluminum Tube In 12-Foot Lengths

	Wall Thickness			***Approximate Weight***	
Tubing Diameter	*Inches*	*Stubs Ga.*	*ID, Inches*	*Pounds Per Foot*	*Pounds Per Length*
3/16 in.	0.035	(#20)	0.117	0.019	0.228
(0.1875 in.)	0.049	(#18)	0.089	0.025	0.330
1/4 in.	0.035	(#20)	0.180	0.027	0.324
(0.25 in.)	0.049	(#18)	0.152	0.036	0.432
	0.058	(#17)	0.134	0.041	0.492
5/16 in.	0.035	(#20)	0.242	0.036	0.432
(0.3125 in.)	0.049	(#18)	0.214	0.047	0.564
	0.058	(#17)	0.196	0.055	0.660
3/8 in.	0.035	(#20)	0.305	0.043	0.516
(0.375 in.)	0.049	(#18)	0.277	0.060	0.720
	0.058	(#17)	0.259	0.068	0.816
	0.065	(#16)	0.245	0.074	0.888
7/16 in.	0.035	(#20)	0.367	0.051	0.612
(0.4375 in.)	0.049	(#18)	0.339	0.070	0.840
	0.065	(#16)	0.307	0.089	1.068
1/2 in.	0.028	(#22)	0.444	0.049	0.588
(0.5 in.)	0.035	(#20)	0.430	0.059	0.708
	0.049	(#18)	0.402	0.082	0.984
	0.058	(#17)	0.384	0.095	1.040
	0.065	(#16)	0.370	0.107	1.284
5/8 in.	0.028	(#22)	0.569	0.061	0.732
(0.625 in.)	0.035	(#20)	0.555	0.075	0.900
	0.049	(#18)	0.527	0.106	1.272
	0.058	(#17)	0.509	0.121	1.452
	0.065	(#16)	0.495	0.137	1.644
3/4 in.	0.035	(#20)	0.680	0.091	1.092
(0.75 in.)	0.049	(#18)	0.652	0.125	1.500
	0.058	(#17)	0.634	0.148	1.776
	0.065	(#16)	0.620	0.160	1.920
	0.083	(#14)	0.584	0.204	2.448
7/8 in.	0.035	(#20)	0.805	0.108	1.308
(0.875 in.)	0.049	(#18)	0.777	0.151	1.810
	0.058	(#17)	0.759	0.175	2.100
	0.065	(#16)	0.745	0.199	2.399
1 in.	0.035	(#20)	0.930	0.123	1.476
	0.049	(#18)	0.902	0.170	2.040
	0.058	(#17)	0.884	0.202	2.424
	0.065	(#16)	0.870	0.220	2.640
	0.083	(#14)	0.834	0.281	3.372

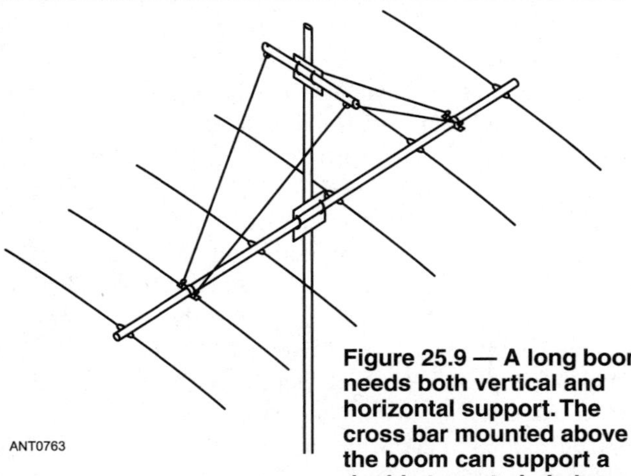

Figure 25.9 — A long boom needs both vertical and horizontal support. The cross bar mounted above the boom can support a double truss to help keep the antenna in position.

Table 25.5
Aluminum Alloy Strength

Tubing	*Tensile Strength PSI min*	*Yield Strength PSI min*
6005A-T61 extruded	38,000	35,000
6061-T6	45,000	40,000
6061-T8 drawn	45,000	40,000
6063-T832 drawn	42,000	39,000
6063-T6 extruded	35,000	31,000
6063-T52 extruded	27,000	21,000
6082-T6*	42,100	36,300
AW-6060-T66**	31,180	23,200
AW-6005-T6**	36,260	29,000

*<5 mm wall
**<3 mm wall
Strengths shown are approximate. Consult manufacturer data sheets for specifications of materials chosen.

Tubing Diameter	Wall Thickness Inches	Stubs Ga.	ID, Inches	Approximate Weight Pounds Per Foot	Pounds Per Length
1⅛ in.	0.035	(#20)	1.055	0.139	1.668
(1.125 in.)	0.058	(#17)	1.009	0.228	2.736
1¼ in.	0.035	(#20)	1.180	0.155	1.860
(1.25 in.)	0.049	(#18)	1.152	0.210	2.520
	0.058	(#17)	1.134	0.256	3.072
	0.065	(#16)	1.120	0.284	3.408
	0.083	(#14)	1.084	0.357	4.284
1⅜ in.	0.035	(#20)	1.305	0.173	2.076
(1.375 in.)	0.058	(#17)	1.259	0.282	3.384
1½ in.	0.035	(#20)	1.430	0.180	2.160
(1.5 in.)	0.049	(#18)	1.402	0.260	3.120
	0.058	(#17)	1.384	0.309	3.708
	0.065	(#16)	1.370	0.344	4.128
	0.083	(#14)	1.334	0.434	5.208
	*0.125	1/8 in.	1.250	0.630	7.416
	*0.250	1/4 in.	1.000	1.150	14.832
1⅝ in.	0.035	(#20)	1.555	0.206	2.472
(1.625 in.)	0.058	(#17)	1.509	0.336	4.032
1¾ in.	0.058	(#17)	1.634	0.363	4.356
(1.75 in.)	0.083	(#14)	1.584	0.510	6.120
1⅞ in.	0.058	(#17)	1.759	0.389	4.668
(1.875 in.)					
2 in.	0.049	(#18)	1.902	0.350	4.200
	0.065	(#16)	1.870	0.450	5.400
	0.083	(#14)	1.834	0.590	7.080
	*0.125	1/8 in.	1.750	0.870	9.960
	*0.250	1/4 in.	1.500	1.620	19.920
2¼ in.	0.049	(#18)	2.152	0.398	4.776
(2.25 in.)	0.065	(#16)	2.120	0.520	6.240
	0.083	(#14)	2.084	0.660	7.920
2½ in.	0.065	(#16)	2.370	0.587	7.044
(2.5 in.)	0.083	(#14)	2.334	0.740	8.880
	*0.125	1/8 in.	2.250	1.100	12.720
	*0.250	1/4 in.	2.000	2.080	25.440
3 in.	0.065	(#16)	2.870	0.710	8.520
	*0.125	1/8 in.	2.700	1.330	15.600
	*0.250	1/4 in.	2.500	2.540	31.200

*These sizes are extruded. All other sizes are drawn tubes.

Table 25.6
Hose-Clamp Diameters

Size No.	Clamp Diameter (In.) Min	Max
06	7/16	7/8
08	7/16	1
10	½	1⅛
12	⅝	1¼
16	¾	1½
20	⅞	1¾
24	1⅛	2
28	1⅜	2¼
32	1⅝	2½
36	1⅞	2¾
40	2⅛	3
44	2 5/16	3¼
48	2⅝	3½
52	2⅞	3¾
56	3⅛	4
64	3½	4½
72	4	5
80	4½	5½
88	5⅛	6
96	5⅝	6½
104	6-⅛	7

elements are usually directly connected to the boom both mechanically and electrically for designs from HF through lower UHF. At upper UHF grounded elements are subject to detuning because the element-to-boom contact no longer acts as a point but rather as a complex shape of significant area. At HF, unanticipated and unwanted resonances, though very unlikely, can occur in center-grounded elements. Highly conservative HF designs and many UHF designs insulate all elements from the boom, typically using Garolite at HF and suitable materials such as Teflon at UHF and above.

Metal booms have a small "shortening effect" on elements that run through them. With materials sizes commonly employed, this is not more than one percent of the element length, and may not be noticeable. It is just perceptible with ½-inch tubing booms used on 432 MHz, for example. At VHF and UHF, standard design-formula lengths can be used as given and driven element matching can be adjusted at the desired operating frequency. The center frequency of an all-metal array will tend to be 0.5 to 1 percent higher than a similar system built with insulated elements.

Element Assembly

Figure 25.10 shows tapered Yagi element designs contributed by Stan Stockton, K5GO, that will survive winds in excess of 80 mi/h. With a ½-inch thickness of radial ice, these designs will withstand winds from 45 to 77 mi/h. Ice increases the surface area subject to wind loading but does not increase the strength of the element. More rugged designs are shown in **Figure 25.11**. With no ice loading, these elements will survive in 118 to 172-mi/h winds, and in winds from 78 to 92 mi/h with ½ inch of radial ice. Deviations from the designs provided require analysis with a program such as *YagiStress* to ensure survivability in the environmental conditions of interest. Except for the very largest 40 meter elements, all required tubing lengths are 6 feet or shorter that can be shipped by parcel services. The file "K5GO Half-Element Designs" showing all element segment lengths, overlaps, tubing specifications and more information on ice loading is included with this book's downloadable supplemental information.

Figures 25.10 and 25.11 show only half elements. When the element is assembled, the largest size tubing for each element should be double the length shown in the

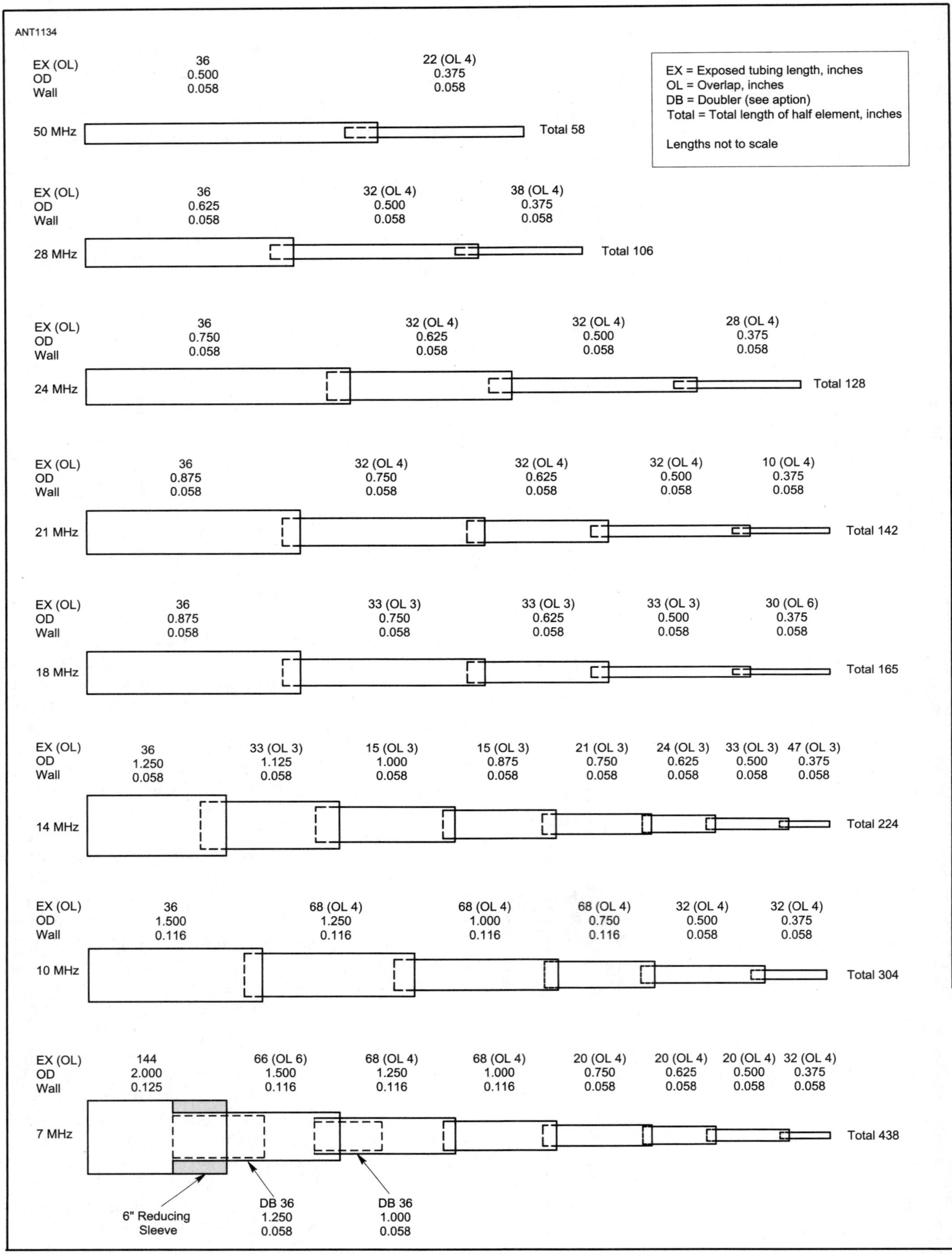

ANT1134
EX = Exposed tubing length, inches
OL = Overlap, inches
DB = Doubler (see aption)
Total = Total length of half element, inches
Lengths not to scale
EX (OL)
OD
Wall
50 MHz
36
0.500
0.058
22 (OL 4)
0.375
0.058
Total 58
28 MHz
36
0.625
0.058
32 (OL 4)
0.500
0.058
38 (OL 4)
0.375
0.058
Total 106
24 MHz
36
0.750
0.058
32 (OL 4)
0.625
0.058
32 (OL 4)
0.500
0.058
28 (OL 4)
0.375
0.058
Total 128
21 MHz
36
0.875
0.058
32 (OL 4)
0.750
0.058
32 (OL 4)
0.625
0.058
32 (OL 4)
0.500
0.058
10 (OL 4)
0.375
0.058
Total 142
18 MHz
36
0.875
0.058
33 (OL 3)
0.750
0.058
33 (OL 3)
0.625
0.058
33 (OL 3)
0.500
0.058
30 (OL 6)
0.375
0.058
Total 165
14 MHz
36
1.250
0.058
33 (OL 3)
1.125
0.058
15 (OL 3)
1.000
0.058
15 (OL 3)
0.875
0.058
21 (OL 3)
0.750
0.058
24 (OL 3)
0.625
0.058
33 (OL 3)
0.500
0.058
47 (OL 3)
0.375
0.058
Total 224
10 MHz
36
1.500
0.116
68 (OL 4)
1.250
0.116
68 (OL 4)
1.000
0.116
68 (OL 4)
0.750
0.116
32 (OL 4)
0.500
0.058
32 (OL 4)
0.375
0.058
Total 304
7 MHz
144
2.000
0.125
66 (OL 6)
1.500
0.116
68 (OL 4)
1.250
0.116
68 (OL 4)
1.000
0.116
20 (OL 4)
0.750
0.058
20 (OL 4)
0.625
0.058
20 (OL 4)
0.500
0.058
32 (OL 4)
0.375
0.058
Total 438
6" Reducing Sleeve
DB 36
1.250
0.058
DB 36
1.000
0.058

drawing, with its center being the point of attachment to the boom. These designs are somewhat conservative, in that they are self-resonant slightly below the frequency indicated for each design. Telescoping the outside end sections to shorter lengths for resonance will increase the survival wind speeds. Conversely, lengthening the outside end sections will reduce the survival wind speeds. [See Bibliography listing for David Leeson,W6NL (ex-W6QHS), at the end of this chapter.]

Figure 25.12 shows several methods of fastening antenna element sections together. The slot and hose-clamp method shown in Figure 25.12A works well for joints that require adjustment. Generally, one adjustable joint per element half is sufficient to tune an antenna. Stainless-steel hose clamps work well and are inexpensive. Some do not have stainless steel screws however. This can be checked with a magnet. Table 25.5 shows available hose-clamp sizes. Wherever tubing sections overlap, a small amount of anti-oxidation compound such as Noalox or Penetrox should be used. This prevents aluminum oxide from forming between the tubing surfaces that can create a high impedance electrical connection and/or mechanically "freeze" the joint.

Figures 25.12B, 12C and 12D show possible fastening methods for joints that do not require adjustment. At B, machine screws and nuts hold the elements in place. At C, sheet metal screws are used. At D, rivets secure the tubing. If the antenna is to be assembled permanently, rivets are the best choice. Once in place they are permanent, although they can be drilled out if necessary. They will not work free, regardless of vibration or wind, if properly installed and seated. If aluminum rivets with aluminum mandrels are used, they will never rust. In addition, there is no danger of dissimilar-metal corrosion with aluminum rivets and aluminum antenna elements. If the antenna is to be disassembled and moved periodically, either B or C will work. If machine screws are used, however, take all possible precautions to keep the nuts from vibrating free. Use Nylock nuts or lock washers and a thread-locking compound.

Very strong elements can be made by using a double thickness of tubing, made by telescoping one size inside another for a portion of, or for the total length. This is usually done at the center of an element where more strength is desired at the boom support point, as in the 14-MHz element in Figure 25.11. Other materials can be used as well, such as wood dowels, fiberglass rods, etc.

Metal antenna elements have high mechanical Q, resulting in a tendency to vibrate in the wind. One way to dampen vibrations is by placing a piece of polypropylene or similar material line inside the element throughout its entire length. Choice of damping line material is not critical — the line will not be exposed to the sun's UV. The line will mildew or rot however if something like inexpensive clothesline is used. Cap or tape the end of the element to secure the damping line. If mechanical requirements dictate (a U-bolt going through the center of the element, for instance), the line may be cut into separate pieces for each element half.

Antennas for 50 MHz need not have elements larger than ½-inch diameter, although up to 1 inch is used occasionally. At 144 and 222 MHz the elements are usually ⅛ to ¼ inch in diameter. For 432 MHz, elements as small as 1⁄16 inch diameter work well if made of stiff rod. Aluminum welding rod of 3⁄32 to ⅛ inch diameter is fine for 432-MHz arrays, and ⅛ inch or larger is good for the 222-MHz band. Aluminum rod or hard-drawn wire works well at 144 MHz.

Tubing and rod sizes recommended in the paragraph above are usable with most formula dimensions for VHF/UHF antennas. Larger diameter material reduces Q and increases bandwidth; smaller diameter material raises element and overall antenna Q and reduces bandwidth. Much smaller diameters than those recommended will require longer elements, particularly for antennas for 50-MHz and above.

Element Taper and Electrical Length

The builder should be aware of one important aspect of telescoping or tapered elements. When the element diameter tapers, as shown in Figures 25.10 and 25.11, the electrical length is not the same as it would be for a constant diameter element of the same total length. Length corrections for tapered elements are discussed in the chapter on **HF Yagi and Quad Antennas**.

Figure 25.10 — Light-duty half-element designs for Yagi antennas. The other side of the element is identical and the center section should be a single piece twice as long as the length shown here for the largest diameter section. Tubing with 0.116-inch wall thickness consists of doubled 0.058-inch wall sections of the same length. Tubing with 0.125-inch or 0.250-inch wall thickness is 6061-T6 alloy, all other tubing is 6063-T832. Doubler (DB) sections consist of a length of tubing inserted completely into the next larger segment, flush with the inner end of that larger segment. Included with this book's downloadable supplemental information is a text file file "K5GO Half-Element Designs" gives complete specifications for each half-element along with survivability ratings for ½ inch and 1 inch of radial ice loading.

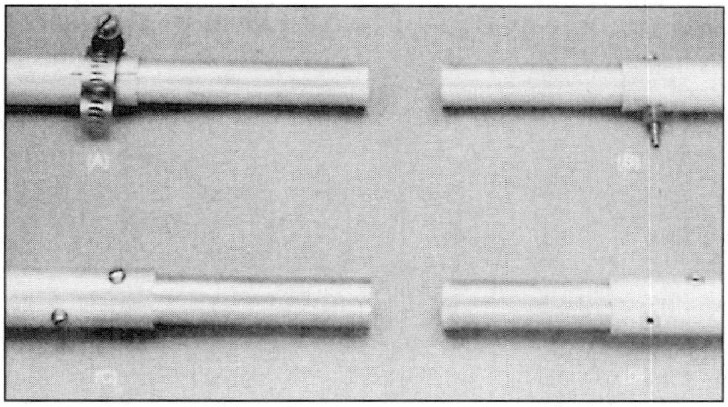

Figure 25.12 — Methods of connecting telescoping tubing sections to build beam elements. See text for a discussion of each method.

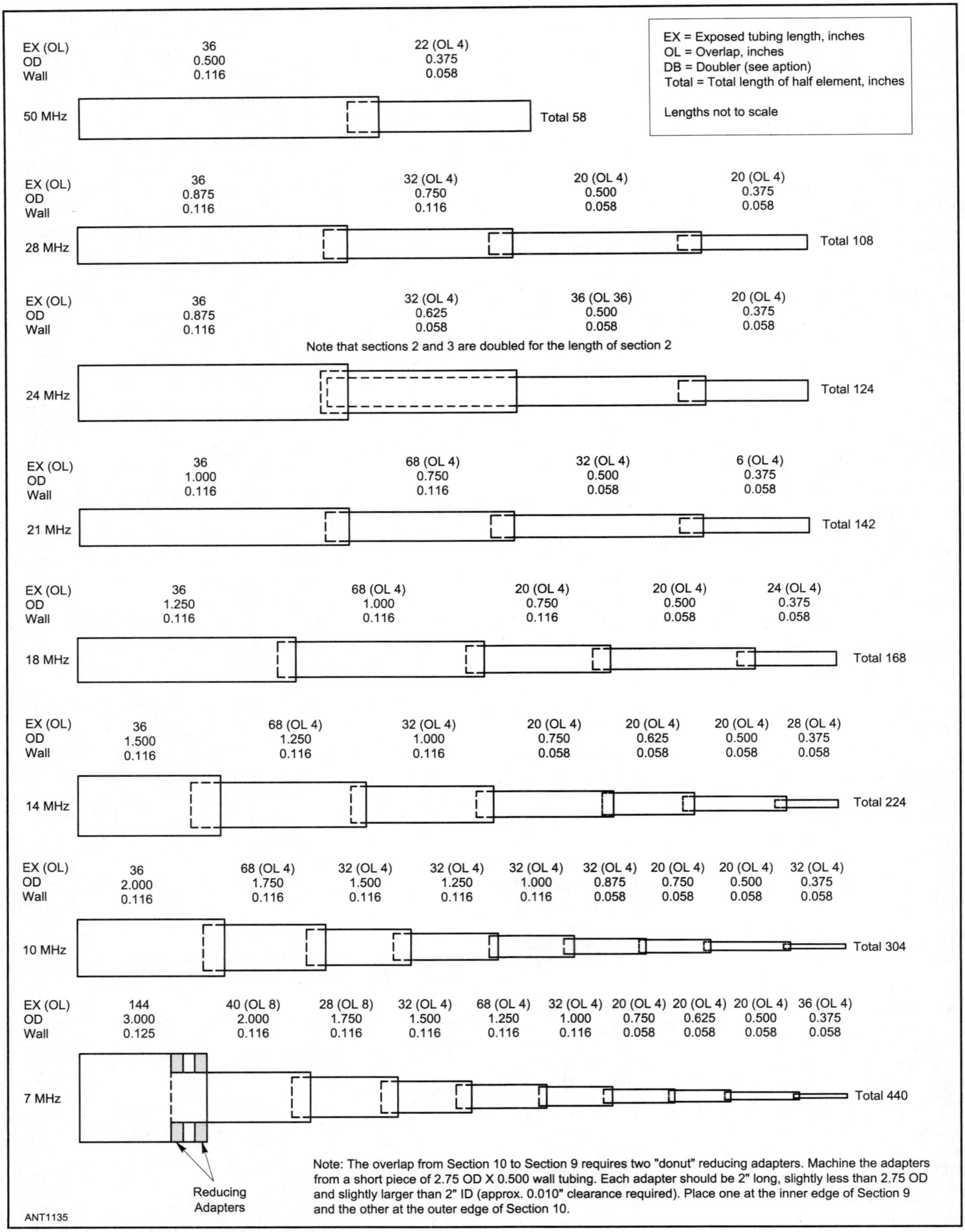

Figure 25.11 — A heavy-duty schedule of Yagi half-element segments. See the Figure 25.10 caption for details. Table 25.4 gives details of aluminum tubing sizes.

25.4 OTHER MATERIALS FOR ANTENNA CONSTRUCTION

25.4.1 WOOD AND BAMBOO

Wood is very useful in antenna work. It is available in a great variety of types and sizes. Rug poles of wood or bamboo make fine booms. Bamboo is quite satisfactory for spreaders in quad antennas.

Round wood stock (doweling) is found in many hardware stores in sizes suitable for small arrays. Wood is good for the framework of multi-bay arrays for the higher bands, as it keeps down the amount of metal in the active area of the array. Square or rectangular boom and frame materials can be cut to order in most lumber yards if they are not available from the racks in suitable sizes.

Wood used for antenna construction should be well seasoned and free of knots or damage. Available materials vary, depending on local sources. Your lumber dealer can help you better than anyone else in choosing suitable materials. Joining wood members at right angles can be done with gusset plates, as shown in **Figure 25.13**. These can be made of thin outdoor-grade plywood. Construction with round material can be handled in ways similar to those used with metal components, such as with U-bolts.

In the early days of radio, hardwood was used as insulating material for antennas, such as at the center and ends of dipoles, or for the center insulator of a driven element made of tubing. Wood dowels cut to length were the most common approach. To drive out moisture and prevent the subsequent absorption of moisture into the wood, it was treated before use by boiling in paraffin. Of course today's technology has produced superior materials for insulators in terms of both strength and insulating qualities. However, the technique is worth consideration in an emergency situation or if low cost is a prime requirement. "Baking" the wood in an oven for a short period at 200° F should drive out any moisture. Then treatment as described in the next paragraph should prevent moisture absorption. The use of wood insulators should be avoided at high-voltage points if high power is being used.

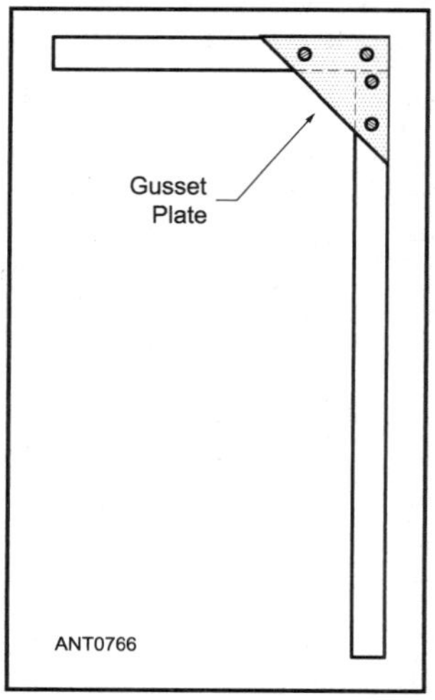

Figure 25.13 — Wood members can be joined at right angles using gusset plates.

All wood or bamboo used in outdoor installations should be protected from the weather with varnish or paint. A good grade of marine spar varnish or UV-stable polyurethane varnish will offer protection for years in mild climates, and one or more seasons in harsh climates. Epoxy-based paints also offer good protection. Bamboo can also be protected by wrapping it with electrical tape. Spray varnish is sometimes applied after wrapping with tape and will provide excellent longevity.

25.4.2 PLASTICS

Plastic tubing and rods of various sizes are available from many building-supply stores. The uses for the available plastic materials are limited only by your imagination. PVC pipe and electrical conduit is quite useful for antenna construction at VHF and UHF. For permanent antennas, be sure the plastic will withstand UV exposure or paint it.

Plastic plumbing and irrigation fittings can also be used to enclose baluns and as the center insulator or end insulators of a dipole, as shown in **Figure 25.14**. The same fittings and adapters can be used to create a portable antenna that is assembled using friction fits between pipe and fittings.

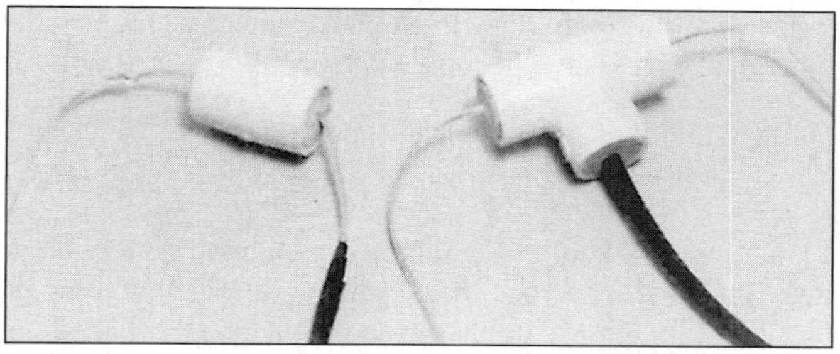

Figure 25.14 — Plastic plumbing parts can be used as antenna center and end insulators.

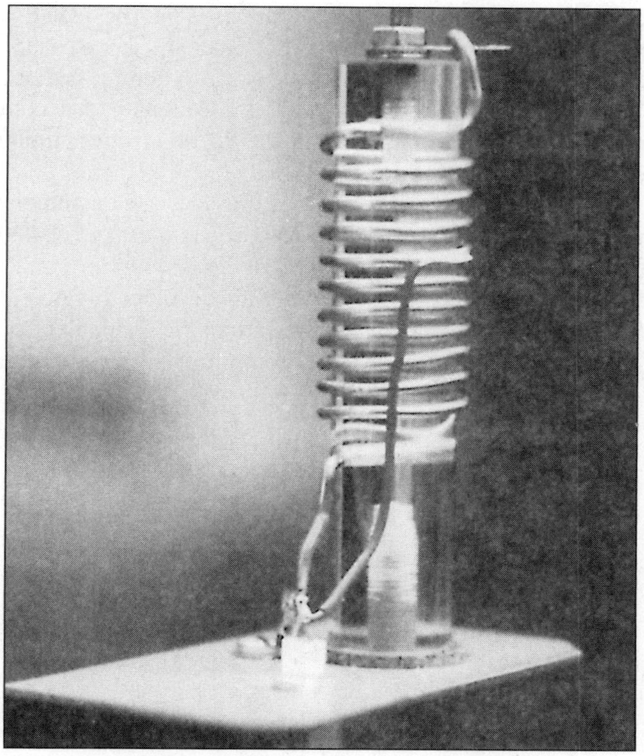

Figure 25.15 — A mobile-antenna loading coil wound on a polystyrene rod.

Plastic or Teflon rod can be used as the core of antenna loading coils, including for mobile antennas (**Figure 25.15**), but the material for this use should be selected carefully. Some plastics, particularly PVC, become warm in the presence of a strong RF field. This can result in the core deforming or even catching fire. Where high RF fields are anticipated, fiberglass or Teflon solid rod, or open polycarbonate cylinders are recommended. Home goods stores frequently carry inexpensive drinking glasses made of polycarbonate, in a variety of sizes. These make excellent coil forms for high-power RF applications.

25.4.3 FIBERGLASS

Fiberglass is lightweight, withstands harsh weather well, and has excellent insulating qualities. Fiberglass rod and tubing are excellent for the nonconductive structure of an antenna. Fiberglass poles are the preferred material for spreaders for quad antennas, for example. Fiberglass rod or tubing can be used as the boom for VHF and UHF antennas. Extendable fiberglass poles have become very popular as supports for portable wire antennas. The SteppIR family of tunable Yagi antennas use fiberglass tubes with flexible metal tape inside as the elements.

Fiberglass should be painted or coated to protect it from exposure to UV when used outdoors. UV breaks down the resin holding the glass fibers together and the surface begins to shed fibers, leading to cracks and water ingress.

Whenever working with fiberglass materials — sawing, cutting, sanding, drilling — gloves and eye protection against loose fiber fragments should be used. If heavy dust is being generated, a dust mask should be worn.

A disadvantage of hollow fiberglass poles is that they may be crushed rather easily. Fracturing occurs at the point where the pole is crushed, causing it to lose its strength. A crushed pole is next to worthless. Some amateurs have repaired crushed poles with fiberglass cloth and epoxy, but the original strength is nearly impossible to regain. Inserting a wooden dowel into the tubing provides additional crush resistance.

25.5 HARDWARE

Antennas should be assembled with good quality hardware intended for outdoor use. Stainless steel is a good choice for long life. Rust will quickly attack plated steel hardware, making nuts difficult, if not impossible, to remove. Stainless-steel nylon-insert or "nyloc" nuts are a good choice for antennas since they are subjected to vibration from the wind.

If stainless-steel muffler or saddle clamps and hose-clamps are not available, steel hardware can be plated or painted with a good zinc-chromate primer and a one or more finish coats. Rust inhibiting paints are also good protection. When using stainless-steel hardware, use an anti-seize compound on the threads to prevent the threads from jamming due to galling of the thread surfaces.

Larger antennas and tower fixtures are often assembled with bolts that are rated to have specific strengths and characteristics. The ratings are identified by *grade markings* on the bolt head. A complete list of the markings developed by ASTM, SAE, and ISO standards organizations is available from American Fastener at **www.americanfastener.com/astm-sae-and-iso-grade-markings-for-steel-fasteners**. It is important to use hardware with the required ratings to prevent failure from overloaded hardware.

Galvanized steel generally has a longer life than plated steel, but this depends on the thickness of the galvanizing coat. In harsh climates rust will usually develop on galvanized fittings in a few years. For the ultimate in long-term protection, galvanized steel should be further protected with zinc-chromate primer and then paint or enamel before exposing it to the weather. Cold-galvanizing spray is useful in repairing damage to galvanized surfaces and preventing rust. It is available in home goods stores.

Good quality hardware is expensive, but over time is less expensive and much less frustrating than poor quality "equivalents." Antennas built of high quality hardware need to be taken down and refurbished much less often. When the time does come to repair or modify an antenna, rusty hardware, particularly at the top of a tower, will seem in retrospect to have been a very poor investment.

25.6 BIBLIOGRAPHY

Source material and more extended discussion of topics covered in this chapter can be found in the following references:

ARRL's Wire Antenna Classics, (Newington, CT: ARRL)

More Wire Antenna Classics, (Newington, CT: ARRL)

ARRL's Yagi Antenna Classics, (Newington, CT: ARRL)

Reference Data for Radio Engineers: Radio, Electronics, Computer, and Communications (Boston, MA: Newnes, an Imprint of Elsevier, 2001)

D. Daso, K4ZA, *Antenna Towers for Radio Amateurs* (Newington, CT: ARRL, 2010)

J. Elengo, K1AFR, "Predicting Sag in Long Wire Antennas," *QST*, Jan 1966, pp 57-58.

E. Laport, *Radio Antenna Engineering*, (New York: McGraw-Hill, 1952), Chapter 4, "Wire Stringing," p 466.

D. Leeson, W6NL, *Physical Design of Yagi Antennas* (Newington, CT: ARRL). [out of print]

D. Leeson, W6NL, "Joint Design for Yagi Booms," *QEX*, Jun 1993, pp 6-8.

D. Leeson, W6NL, "Strengthening the Cushcraft 40-2CD," *QST*, Nov 1991, pp 36-42.

S. Morris, K7LXC, *Up the Tower* (Seattle: Champion Radio Products, 2009)

R. Weber, K5IU, "More on Strengthening Yagi Elements," *QST*, Oct 1992, pp 65-66

R. Weber, K5IU, "Structural Evaluation of Yagi Elements," *Ham Radio*, Dec 1988, pp 29-46.

TABLE OF CONTENTS

Chapter 26 — Downloadable Supplemental Content

Supplemental Articles

- "A One Person, Safe, Portable and Easy to Erect Antenna Mast" by Bob Dixon, W8ERD
- "Antenna Feed Line Control Box" by Phil Salas, AD5X
- "Homeowners Insurance and Your Antenna System" by Ray Fallen, ND8L
- "Installing Yagis in Trees" by Steve Morris, K7LXC
- "Is Your Tower Still Safe?" by Tony Brock Fisher, K1KP
- Ladder Mast and PVRC Mount
- "Lightning Protection for the Amateur Station, Parts 1, 2 and 3" by Ron Block, KB2UYT
- "Removing and Refurbishing Towers" by Steve Morris, K7LXC
- Rotator Specifications
- "The Care and Feeding of an Amateur's Favorite Antenna Support — The Tree" by Doug Brede, W3AS
- "The Tower Shield" by Baker Springfield, W4HYY and Richard Ely, WA4VHM

Chapter 26

Building Antenna Systems and Towers

Getting an antenna in the air and keeping it there requires decisions and challenges. For example, what kind of antenna support? How do you build it? What tools and techniques should be used? There are many other questions. In this chapter, you'll find material from experienced tower workers Don Daso, K4ZA, and Steve Morris, K7LXC, along with contributions from earlier editions.

The information here is by no means exhaustive. For a more complete treatment, the reader is directed to two books written specifically for the ham installing or working on towers and antennas:

- *Antenna Towers for Radio Amateurs: A Guide for Design, Installation and Construction* by Don Daso, K4ZA, and published by ARRL.
- *Up the Tower: The Complete Guide to Tower Construction* by Steve Morris, K7LXC, and published by Champion Radio Products (**www.championradio.com**).

These books are great tutorials on working successfully and safely with towers and antennas. They also provide information for working with masts and trees. The two books provide complementary perspectives on many subjects, and reinforcing views on many others. If you are contemplating either a simple or significant tower or antenna project, you should read either or both of these books before beginning. You are also encouraged to read the articles listed in the Bibliography and to attend presentations by experienced individuals. Consider hiring professional assistance if you are not comfortable with doing such work yourself.

Many of the safety and tower work products mentioned in this chapter are available from numerous *QST* advertisers. Hardware and materials are widely available for all project sizes. There's no need to use an under-rated item for such important jobs. You should be able to supply everything you need in order to do the job safely and correctly, resulting in years of trouble-free service at the least possible risk.

Learning and practicing the right way to do things will save you time, money and worries. Let's start with safety!

26.1 SAFETY AND SAFETY EQUIPMENT

Working aloft is dangerous, pure and simple. Whether it's 20 or 200 feet tall, climbing towers is dangerous. You're always at risk. Fear of heights is one of the most common phobias, affecting an estimated 3 to 5 percent of the population.

Due to the dangers inherent in such work, working safely is paramount. That translates into having and using the proper equipment to ensure one does not get hurt. Today, that means a proper harness, proper clothing and tools, along with some training or instruction. This focus on safety and equipment is critical.

OSHA and Tower Work

OSHA is the federal Occupation Safety and Health Agency (**www.osha.gov**) that sets minimum safety standards for workers. Each state has an agency that is responsible for enforcing the OSHA regulations in that state. In addition, your state agency may have stricter regulations than OSHA; OSHA regulations are just the minimum requirements.

If you are getting paid or paying someone to do tower work, you or they must comply with the federal and state regulations. If you are simply working on your own system, or someone else's without pay, then you don't fall under the OSHA/state laws. But you should still observe them! You should use only OSHA/state approved safety equipment and follow the regulations applicable to your activity. By doing this, you'll be giving yourself a large and acceptable safety margin while working.

26.1.1 FALL-ARREST EQUIPMENT

The most important pieces of safety equipment are the *fall-arrest harness* (FAH) and the accompanying lanyards (see **Figure 26.1**). Leather safety equipment was outlawed years ago by OSHA so please don't use any of it. This includes the old-fashioned safety belt that was used for years but offers no fall-arrest capability.

If you drop down while wearing a safety belt, your body weight can cause the safety belt to rise up your waist to your ribcage, where it will immobilize your diaphragm, potentially suffocating you! On the other hand, you can use your safety belt for positioning when it's used in conjunction with your FAH. Just don't depend on it to catch you in case of a fall.

The FAH is the part that you wear and to which the lanyards attach. The FAH has leg loops and suspenders to help spread the fall forces over more of your body. It has the ability to catch you in a natural position — with your arms and legs hanging below your body, so you're able to breathe normally. Plan on spending $300 or more for a new FAH and lanyards.

There are two primary types of lanyards. One is the *positioning lanyard* shown in **Figure 26.2**. That is, it holds you in working position and attaches to the D-rings at your waist. Positioning lanyards can be adjustable or fixed and are made from materials such as nylon rope, steel chain or special synthetic materials. An adjustable positioning lanyard will adjust to fit various tower diameters, while a fixed-length lanyard is often either too long or too short for the job. The rope type is the least expensive version.

The other lanyard is the *fall-arrest lanyard* that attaches to a D-ring between your shoulder blades. The other end attaches to the tower above your work position and catches you in case of a fall. The simplest is a 6-foot rope lanyard that is inexpensive, but doesn't offer any shock absorption. There are also shock absorbing varieties that typically have bar-tacked stitches that pull apart under force and decelerate you (see **Figure 26.3**).

(A) (B) (C)

Figure 26.1 — KI4TZ wearing a Personal Fall Arrest Harness system (A). With shock-absorbing lanyard, positioning lanyard, and a safety hook, he's ready to work aloft. Long pants, hard hat, steel shank boots, and eye protection are included. Shock-absorbing lanyard is attached to the harness's rear D-ring (B). The waist-level pouch (C) allows easy access to required tools.

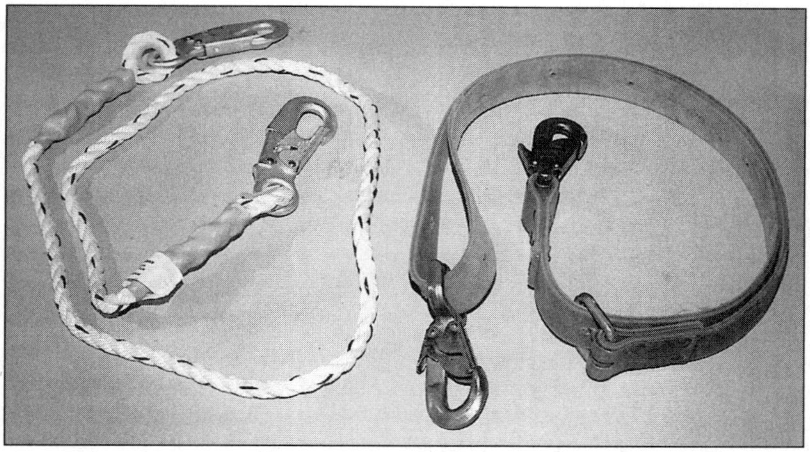

Figure 26.2 — A fixed-length rope positioning lanyard on the left and a versatile Klein adjustable lanyard on the right. They both use double-locking snap-hooks.

Figure 26.4 — A climber on a tower. Note the fall arrest lanyard attached to the tower above him.

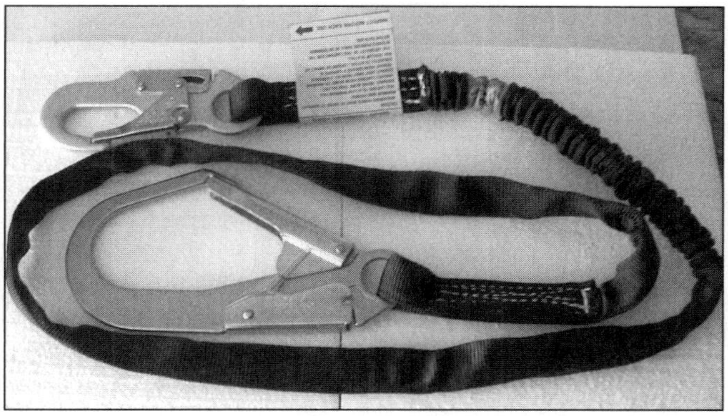

Figure 26.3 — A shock absorbing fall arrest lanyard. Portions of the nylon webbing are sewn together and pull apart under the weight of a climber falling on it, thus decelerating the fall.

26.1.2 SAFELY CLIMBING A TOWER

Common sense, as well as current OSHA rules, say you should be attached to the tower 100% of the time. You can do this several ways. One is to attach the fall-arrest lanyard above you and climb up to it as shown in **Figure 26.4**. Use your positioning lanyard to hold you while you detach the fall-arrest lanyard and move it up again. Repeat while you climb. An alternative is to use two fall-arrest lanyards, alternating them as you climb.

It's not a race! Take your time and climb safely. If you become tired or uncomfortable, stop and rest with your lanyards securely fastened to the tower. If you feel unsafe at any time for any reason — stop and return to a safe position or configuration!

Safety Climb Systems

Most commercial towers have a safety climb system, typically a ⅜-inch steel cable that runs from the top to the bottom of the tower. The climber attaches to a special trolley with a cable from the climber's FAH. The trolley will slide up freely, but clamps the safety cable if weight is put on it, thus preventing you from sliding down the cable and tower. Such installations are rare on amateur towers, but are worth considering.

Mountain Climbing Harnesses — Problems

Some amateurs feel that mountain climbing harnesses offer a less-expensive option for a safety belt. The first problem with using a mountain climbing harness is that most require you to tie the harness directly to a rope or to a carabiner and most hams are not skilled at tying climbing knots properly. You could use a locking carabiner as an attachment point but it is another piece of hardware that could fail or open up at the wrong time.

Second, there are no D-rings for attaching any sort of positioning lanyard; you can only connect one carabiner to the loops in the front. The nylon loop on the front of the climbing harness is only designed to position the leg loops and is intended to be used only with a climbing rope or carabiner, not the metal snaps of your lanyard that are frequently snapped on and off.

Mountain climbing belts are designed to be used only with climbing ropes and hardware, not with tower tools or equipment. They also don't have any provisions for convenient attachment of tool or bolt bags.

The final problems are that a mountain climbing harness may be designed for a force of only 1000 pounds while OSHA-approved fall-arrest gear must be designed for 5000 pounds of strength. Also, the mountain climbing harness has no fall-arrest capability. Although the main advantage of a mountain climbing harness is low cost, its limitations prevent it from being recommended for tower work.

Working on a Crank-up Tower

One of the advantages of a crank-up is the ability to bring the antennas down to rooftop level or close to ground level where it's easier for the station owner to work on it. For this convenience, the price that you pay is the added mechanical complexity and cost of the crank-up apparatus. They can cost two to three times the cost of a guyed tower of the same height.

Another limitation is the fact that a crank-up cannot be climbed safely once it is extended. Do not climb a crank-up tower unless it is totally nested and locked in the lowered position! Again, all of the weight of the system is on the cable and pulley systems and if something breaks or comes loose, your toes and fingers are in the path of the tower sections as they fall! If the tower is jammed and won't come down, don't climb it to fix it. Get a boom truck or crane in to lift you up to work on it. Better yet, get professional help.

It is possible to climb a crank-up if you can lock it into place. One method is to use 3 to 4 foot long pieces of 2×4s or pipes. Another is to place a U-bolt on at least one leg under each section. Insert them at the bottom of each section through the bracing and they'll catch each section before it can move down very far. You can also gently lower the tower until it rests on the safety pieces, thus jamming them into place and eliminating any tower movement at all.

It will still be quite difficult to climb the nested latticework sections. Havng small feet is an advantage here, as silly as that may sound. It may even be difficult to find a suitably rated attachment point for your lanyard. Again, the safest and simplest method of working on a crank-up tower is to utilize a manlift.

Principles of Working Safely

The following safety tenets are founded on three fundamental principles: Do it safely or not at all; There's always time to do it right; and If it's worth doing, do it better.

1. Never load or operate structures or equipment outside the design limits. Be careful with tools, ropes, pulleys, and other equipment that can cause injury or damage if they fail due to overload. Use the right stuff!

2. Always move to a safe, controlled condition and seek assistance when a situation is not understood. This is particularly important when working on towers and antennas. If something doesn't look right or isn't going according to plan, return to a safe state and figure out what to do.

3. Always operate with the safety mechanisms engaged. If a safety mechanism prevents you from doing something, either the task is unsafe or you may not be using the right equipment.

4. Always follow safe work practices and procedures. Make a plan before you start and don't do something you know is unsafe.

5. Act to stop unsafe practices. The team's safety depends on every team member. Do not hesitate to stop work if you see it is unsafe. Don't be afraid to speak up or ask for help! Regroup and do it right.

6. Clarify and understand procedures before proceeding. This is particularly important when working with a crew. Be sure everyone understands the procedure and how to communicate.

7. Involve people with expertise and firsthand knowledge in decisions and planning. Ask for advice and guidance from experienced hams when planning a task with which you are unfamiliar.

Do not even consider using harnesses not designed for climbing work, such as lightweight tethers or belts for hunting or other recreational uses. Please: use only the tools designed specifically for the job!

26.1.3 WORKING SAFELY

The Mental Game

One of the most important aspects of safety is having the knowledge and awareness that will enable you to perform work safely and efficiently. You must have the mental ability to climb and work at altitude while constantly rethinking all connections, techniques and safety factors. Climbing and working on towers safely is 90% mental. Mental preparedness is something that must be learned. This is an instance when there's simply no substitute for experience.

When it comes to tower climbing, only a small percentage of people are willing to climb and work aloft. The biggest obstacle is making the mental adjustment. Properly installed towers are inherently safe and accidents are relatively rare. The only thing stopping most people is their own mind and attitude.

Would you have any trouble standing on a 24 × 24 inch piece of plywood on the ground? Probably not! But, could you stand on that same four-square-foot platform 100 feet in the air? The only difference is in your mind. It's easier said than done, but you must make the mental adjustment if you are going to do any tower work.

An important lesson learned from mountain climbing that is directly applicable to tower climbing is that when you climb, you have four points of attachment and security — two hands and two feet. When tower climbing, move only one point at a time. That leaves you with three points of contact on the tower and a wide margin of safety if you ever need it. This is in addition to having your fall-arrest lanyard connected at all times.

Another recommended technique to excel at the mental game is to always do everything the same way every time. That is, always wear your positioning lanyard on the same D-ring and always connect it in the same way. Always look at your belt D-ring while clipping in with your safety strap. This way you'll always confirm that you're belted in. Don't rely on the "clicking sound," or assume you're belted in and clipped on. Always look — always!

Check Your Safety Equipment

You should also check your safety equipment every time before you use it. Inspect it for any nicks or cuts to your belt and safety strap. Professional tower workers are required to check their safety equipment every day; follow their example.

Inclement Weather

Tower work is the easiest when the weather is nice and the sun is shining. Unfortunately, that doesn't always coincide with your construction schedule or repair priority. Don't hesitate to call off your project. If you're not sure if the weather is good enough, it probably isn't.

For raising tower sections or antennas, a relatively windless day is preferred. Professional climbers usually do their trickiest lifts first thing in the morning when the chance of wind is the least. Don't push on in marginal conditions; you may wind up doing more harm than good. Obviously you don't ever want to climb during a lightning storm.

As far as rain goes, unless it's coming in horizontally it's more of a nuisance. For ham towers, you'll always be belted in and you won't be walking across any rain-slicked surfaces, so working in the rain is possible. Just dress with good rain gear and you'll be able to still get some work done. Some ham towers have been painted, and their surfaces become slick when wet, so exercise extreme caution if that's what you're working on. And while the workers aloft may find they can continue working, the ground crew (or the client) suffers more, getting wet while waiting for something to happen. Again, don't be afraid to wait for better conditions.

Electrical Safety

Electrocution due to metal antenna or tower parts touching power lines is the biggest cause of tower related electrical injuries. *Be very careful if you're anywhere near power lines.*

Even without touching a power line, you can still be electrocuted while working on a tower, which is a large, grounded conductor. A major cause of tower injuries and deaths is electrocution. While there usually isn't much 120 V ac circuitry on amateur towers, care should still be taken around ac power. Use battery-powered equipment if possible, both for the convenience and safety. If you do use ac extension cords, make sure they're plugged into a GFCI (ground fault circuit interrupter) for your protection. Power tools operated from ac should be double-insulated. Part of your pre-work safety meeting should be pointing out where the circuit breaker box is in case someone has to turn off the power.

Safety Tips for Tower Work

- Don't climb with anything in your hands; attach it to your harness if you must climb with it or have your ground crew send it up in a bucket after you're in position.
- Don't put any hardware in your mouth; you could swallow it or choke on it.
- Remove any rings and/or neck chains; they can get hooked on things.
- Be on the lookout for bees, wasps and their nests; there aren't too many bigger surprises when you're climbing a tower. If you do get stung, apply a meat tenderizing powder containing the enzyme papain, such as Adolph's Meat Tenderizer, directly on the sting moistened with a little water or saliva. The enzyme neutralizes the venom and reduces the pain within a minute or two. Keep a bottle in your tower tool kit.
- Don't climb when tired; that's when most accidents occur.
- Don't try to lift anything by yourself; one person on a tower has very little leverage or strength. Let the ground crew use their strength; save your strength for when you really need it or you'll quickly run out of arm strength.
- If something doesn't work one way, re-rig, and then try again.

26.1.4 SAFETY EQUIPMENT

Boots

Boots should be leather with a steel or fiberglass shank. Diagonal bracing on Rohn 25G tower is only 5⁄16-inch rod — spending all day standing on that small step will take a toll on your feet. The stiff shank will support your weight and protect your feet; tennis shoes will not. Leather boots are mandatory on towers such as Rohn BX that have sharp X-cross braces, plus your feet are always on a slant and that combination can be quite painful and hard on your feet.

Hard Hats

The hard hat is highly recommended. Just make sure hard hats are OSHA-approved and that you and your crew wear them. As you'll be looking up and down a lot while wearing your hard hat, a chin strap is essential to keep it from falling off. Look for the ANSI or OSHA label on the hard hat; that should be the minimum safety compliance for your helmet.

Safety Goggles

Approved safety goggles should be worn to prevent eye injury. Look for ANSI or OSHA approval.

Gloves

If you do a lot of tower work, your hands will take a beating — gloves are essential. Keep several spare pairs for ground crew members who show up without them. Cotton gloves are fine for gardening, but not for tower work; they don't provide enough friction for climbing or working with a haul rope. Leather gloves are the only kind to use; either full leather or leather-palmed are fine.

The softer the gloves the more useful they'll be. Stiff leather construction gloves are fine for the ground crew but the pigskin and other soft leathers allow you to thread a nut or do just about any other delicate job without removing (and possibly dropping) your gloves.

Framers or mechanics gloves (with the fingertips removed) are K4ZA's glove of choice over the past several years. A pair typically lasts for about two to three months of near-daily use.

Safety Equipment Suppliers

Chances are that you've got a safety equipment store in your area, but your best bet is to search the Internet for what you need since tower climbing equipment is not very common. Manufacturers such as Klein, Petzl, DBI-Sala and others all provide OSHA-approved safety equipment. These are more expensive products, but they're preferred by professionals who wear and work in them all day. These companies will have many other useful accessories and rigging supplies, such as rope, canvas buckets, tool pouches and other hardware.

26.1.5 INSURANCE

It is important that you have insurance that covers any potential liabilities (someone getting hurt on the tower, damage caused by tower failure, and so on) as well as the physical equipment itself.

The ARRL also offers the Ham Radio Equipment Insurance Plan (**www.arrlinsurance.com**). Your mobile and home station equipment is covered on an all-risk form which includes fire, lightning, theft, collision, and other accidents and natural hazards. Loss or damage to antennas, towers or rotators is covered. Review the policy's coverage at the insurance plan's website for complete information.

Ray Fallen, ND8L, an agent for State Farm Insurance for over 20 years, wrote an informative article on insurance in the February 2009 issue of *QST*, titled "Homeowners Insurance and Your Antenna System," which is included with this book's downloadable supplemental information. Ray also wrote Chapter 12 of *Antenna Towers for Radio Amateurs*, which is focused on insurance.

The National Electrical Code (NEC)

The National Electrical Code (a.k.a. — "the Code") is a comprehensive document that details safety requirements for all types of electrical installations. In addition to setting safety standards for house wiring and grounding, the Code also contains a section on Radio and Television Equipment — Article 810. Sections C and D specifically cover "Amateur Transmitting and Receiving Stations". Highlights of the section concerning Amateur Radio stations follow. If you are interested in learning more about electrical safety, you may purchase a copy of *The National Electrical Code* or *The National Electrical Code Handbook*, edited by Peter Schram, from the National Fire Protection Association, Batterymarch Park, Quincy, MA 02269. Both are available at libraries, as well.

Antenna installations are covered in some detail in the Code. It specifies minimum conductor sizes for different length wire antennas. For hard-drawn copper wire, the Code specifies #14 AWG wire for open (unsupported) spans less than 150 feet, and #10 AWG for longer spans. Copper-clad steel, bronze or other high-strength conductors may be #14 AWG for spans less than 150 feet and #12 AWG wire for longer runs. Lead-in conductors (for open-wire transmission line) should be at least as large as those specified for antennas.

The Code also says that antenna and lead-in conductors attached to buildings must be firmly mounted at least 3 inches clear of the surface of the building on nonabsorbent insulators. The only exception to this minimum distance is when the lead-in conductors are enclosed in a "permanently and effectively grounded" metallic shield. The exception covers coaxial cable.

According to the Code, lead-in conductors (except those covered by the exception) must enter a building through a rigid, noncombustible, nonabsorbent insulating tube or bushing, through an opening provided for the purpose allowing a clearance of at least 2 inches or through a drilled window pane. All lead-in conductors to transmitting equipment must be arranged so that accidental contact is difficult.

Transmitting stations are required to have a means of draining static charges from the antenna system. An antenna discharge unit (lightning arrester) must be installed on each lead-in conductor (except where the lead-in is protected by a continuous metallic shield that is permanently and effectively grounded, or the antenna is permanently and effectively grounded). An acceptable alternative to lightning arrester installation is a switch that connects the lead-in to ground when the transmitter is not in use.

Grounding conductors are described in detail in the Code. Grounding conductors may be made from copper, aluminum, copper-clad steel, bronze or similar erosion-resistant material. Insulation is not required. The "protective grounding conductor" (main conductor running to the ground rod) must be as large as the antenna lead-in, but not smaller than #10 AWG. The "operating grounding conductor" (to bond equipment chassis together) must be at least #14 AWG. Grounding conductors must be adequately supported and arranged so they are not easily damaged. They must run in as straight a line as practical between the mast or discharge unit and the ground rod.

26.2 TREES AND MASTS

26.2.1 TREES

Trees were among the first antenna supports and have been used successfully by many amateurs over the years. If you're in an area with suitable trees — congratulations! They're free (compared to towers) and generally unregulated for use as antenna supports. Trees make good temporary antenna supports and with care can support an antenna for many years — even a large one. When attaching an antenna to a tree, it's important to traumatize the tree as little as possible. This will ensure a strong, enduring attachment.

Although it's relatively easy to get a wire up into a tree, it's certainly more difficult to keep it there for the long term. Tree-mounted antennas require more maintenance, but their height and low cost more than make up for the added work. (Although uncommon, even Yagi antennas have been installed in trees using the techniques in the short article "Installing Yagis in Trees" included with this book's downloadable supplemental information.)

Using a Line Launcher or Drone

In this method, you use some sort of line launcher from the ground by which a lightweight line (usually fishing line of a few pounds capacity) with a weight on the end of it is propelled over a branch high up in the tree. Hopefully, the weight drops to the ground and you use the small line to pull up a bigger line with your antenna attached. Such launchers include slingshots, compressed air cannons, fishing rod and reel, bow and arrow, and even tennis ball throwing aids.

Keep people out of the fall zone around the tree since there will be falling weights, plus lines and antennas at some point. Safety glasses and gloves are always a good idea for these kinds of activities.

Somewhat slower but a lot more controllable, a multi-rotor drone can lift light lines over the highest trees, although not through them. A light line is carried over the tree by the drone, and then the light line is used to pull a heavier line over the tree, just as when using a launcher. The process is described in a pair of recent *QST* articles: See the Bibliography entries for an article by Kam Sirageldin, N3KS (better known as TI5W and TI7W), and another by Michael Shandblatt, W3MAS, and Joe Warwick, KB3ZED.

Attaching an Anchor

A stouter method of securing a rope in a tree is to climb the tree to install an anchor. For light antenna loads, such as the end of a dipole, a threaded eye-screw is the method of choice. (Use welded or forged (closed end) eye-screws and bolts to prevent them from opening up under load.) Just drill a hole into the tree about 1⁄16 inch smaller than the screw diameter, then twist in the screw as shown in **Figure 26.5**. Be certain you use a cadmium-plated eye-screw threaded for use in wood. A screw thread length of two or three inches should secure most antennas. Allow ½ inch of space or more between the trunk and the eye; this allows for outward growth of the tree with time.

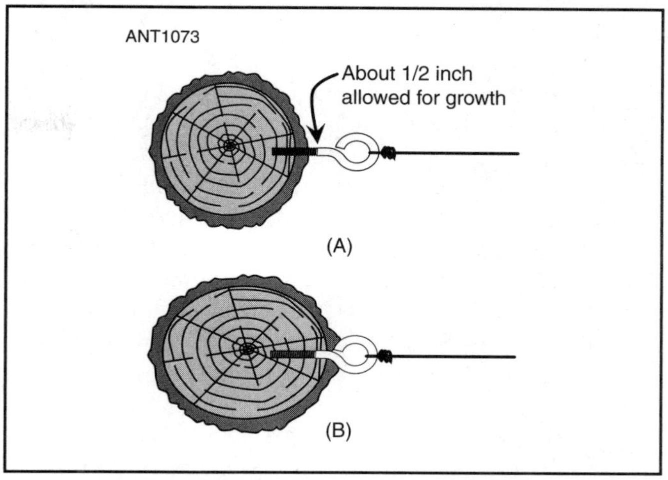

Figure 26.5 — The best way to secure a wire to a tree is with an eye-screw threaded into the wood (A). As the tree grows and expands, however, the eye-screw will become embedded (B) and must be removed and replaced.

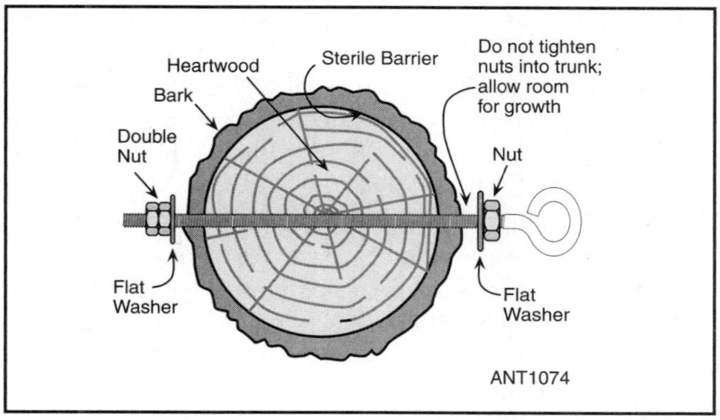

Figure 26.6 — For heavy antenna loads, an eyebolt passed through the trunk or limb will support more weight than an eye-screw. Allow about ½ inch of play between the bolt and trunk or limb. Don't tighten the bolt completely; this allows for tree growth.

For stouter antennas, such as multielement wire beams, a different method for securing wires to trees is recommended (see **Figure 26.6**). This procedure involves using an eyebolt longer than the tree diameter, drilling completely through the tree, and securing the eyebolt on each side of the tree with flat washers and nuts. Drilling a hole through a tree causes much less trauma to the tree than wrapping something around it. Much of the core of a tree is dead tissue, used mainly for physical support.

Although there will be some wounding of the tree at the site of a bolt or screw, such trauma will be far less than that which occurs from wrapping a wire around the trunk. Wrapping a line around a tree's branch or trunk strangles the veins in the sapwood the same way a noose around your neck would strangle you. It's important not to wrap anything around the trunk.

You can find a professional tree climber/arborist in the *Yellow Pages* or perhaps use the services of a talented friend to install a pulley and rope system in your trees of choice. A ⅜ or ½ inch eyebolt screwed into the tree as described above with a pulley attached is the best method. Use a threaded chain link or "cold shut" (a type of chain attachment link) to attach the pulley to the eye.

A non-swiveling pulley is preferred because the lay of the rope can cause the pulley to turn, twisting the rope and possibly jamming the pulley. Use only all-metal pulleys for permanent installations, preferably ones made from stainless or galvanized materials. Plastic parts will either break or be damaged by UV (ultraviolet) radiation from sunlight. Check your local hardware stores for inexpensive stainless steel pulleys.

Pulleys intended for marine use are excellent candidates for tree-mounted antennas but they are expensive. Years of trouble-free service offset this expense, however. Harken and Schaeffer are two brands offering quality products.

Keep in mind that with pulleys and haul ropes there should be minimal clearance between the sheave (the wheel in the pulley) and the pulley body; the rope or halyard should be larger in diameter than that clearance so it can't get jammed between the sheave and the pulley — a major annoyance. The best type of rope for this purpose is black Dacron UV-resistant line because it doesn't deteriorate when used outdoors. (See the section "Ropes and Rope Care" later in this chapter for more information.)

Have the climber go up the tree to the desired location, screw in the eye-screw, then attach the pulley. It's all but certain that the tree will have to be pruned to clear a decent window through which the line can travel. It's better to over-prune since new growth will invariably grow back in just a few years. Small branches are incredibly strong and resilient and can cause major problems in any tree project or installation.

Having brought the line along, the climber will put the line through the *back* side of the newly installed pulley (closest side to the tree), attach a weight to the end of the line, and throw it out in the direction that your wire antenna will take. The wire antenna must clear all branches to successfully install your antenna. It's very difficult to install an inverted V in a tree from the ground because it's just about impossible to get both sides of the antenna through the branches. A climber can help by throwing each leg of the antenna through the branches separately.

When the end of the line reaches the ground, remove the weight, then tie the ends of the line together, making the rope into a loop (see **Figure 26.7**). This is because in almost all cases it is the antenna that breaks, not the rope. Without the loop, when the antenna breaks the end of the support rope will be at the top of the pulley and you'll have to send someone up to retrieve it. If you have a loop system, all you have to do is pull the line down and reattach the antenna. Tie an overhand knot loop to form the antenna attachment point (this is usually an insulator) where the rope ends are tied together and you're ready to start hoisting.

In a strong wind that will get the trees swaying, you'll want to have a method that allows the trees to move without breaking the antenna. You can attach a weight of some sort (cement block, plastic milk container filled with water, a bucket with rocks, etc.) to the rope or place tension on it with an elastic cord or strap.

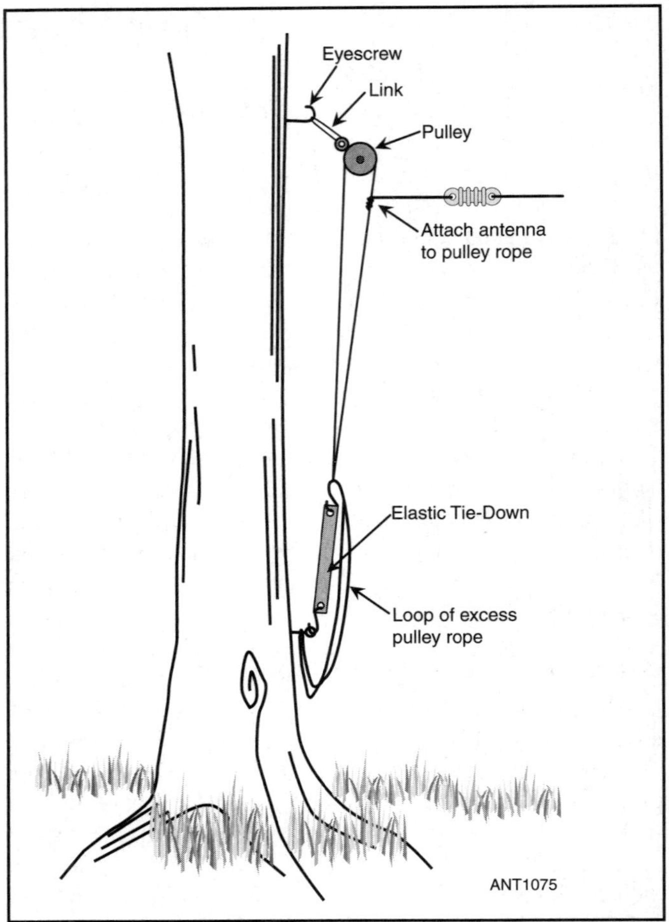

Figure 26.7 — By using a pulley, raising and lowering the antenna for repairs can be done without the need to climb the tree. Elastic cords or straps can be used to apply tension to the antenna. Loop the excess pulley rope to a second eye-screw in case the cord or strap fails.

Tree Climbing

If you're going to climb the tree yourself, you'll need sturdy boots, hard hat, a safety belt with two lanyards and possibly tree climbing spurs. You'll need the two lanyards to leapfrog your belts around branches so that you'll be belted to the tree 100% of the time.

Newer tree climbing techniques don't use steel climbing spikes as it's deemed harmful to the tree. The latest methods use a line thrown or shot over a branch and then the rope is used to climb the tree using rope ascenders like the ones used by mountain climbers and cavers. You don't even touch the trunk of the tree using this technique. The same techniques used to get a line over a branch for an antenna can be used to position a tree-climbing line.

Tree climbing has even become a recreational activity

similar to the way that rock climbing has. There are clubs and resources available and you can find them online. Be sure to check out the equipment and techniques and you can learn to utilize such tools yourself.

26.2.2 GROUND-MOUNTED MASTS AND POLES

TV and Push-up Masts

Stacking TV mast is available in 5- and 10-foot lengths, 1¼ inches diameter, in both steel and aluminum. These sections are swaged or crimped at one end to permit sections to be joined together. This type of mast is usually mounted on a chimney or some sort of house-mounted bracket and is not intended to be permanently guyed. This mast is suitable for VHF/UHF verticals and small beams and holding up light wire antennas for HF.

Galvanized steel push-up masts such as Rohn H30 or H40 are intended primarily for TV antennas and wireless Internet antennas. The masts may be obtained with three, four or five 10-foot sections and come complete with guying rings and a means of locking the sections in place after they have been extended. These masts are inherently more suitable for guyed mast installations than the non-telescoping type because the diameters of the sections increase toward the bottom of the mast. For instance, the top section of a 50-foot mast is 1¼ inches diameter, and the bottom section is 2½ inches diameter. The mast can be mounted on the ground or on a roof.

While tricky to install (each 10-foot segment must be guyed separately while pushing the mast up section by section), they can provide years of reliable service if not overloaded with anything larger than small VHF/UHF beams and verticals or HF wire antennas. If you are unfamiliar with push-up masts, a local TV antenna installer can perform the actual installation quickly and properly. They cannot be climbed and must be lowered to work on the antennas. Do not attempt to "walk up" these masts when extended.

Push-up masts are available from numerous sources but the shipping cost often exceeds the cost of the mast. These masts can be ordered online (search for antenna, pushup and mast), through hardware stores and from TV antenna installers.

AB-155 Multi-Section Masts

The AB-155 is the prototype for multi-section mast kits with aluminum or fiberglass sections. Kits are available with and without a base tripod. Most kits have 4-foot sections which can be stacked safely up to about 40 feet. If a tripod is available, the mast can be assembled like a push-up mast with each new section being added at the bottom with guys attached as the mast grows. Without a tripod base, the mast will have to be assembled lying down and walked up.

The masts are not heavy enough to hold more than very small HF and mid-sized 6 meter beams. They are well-suited to hold wire antennas and VHF beams and verticals. If there is a significant side load, such as holding one end of a dipole, an additional back-guy may be needed or the guys should be arranged so that one set of guys is aligned to take the extra load.

A critical part sometimes missing from the kits or that may be sold separately are the guy attachment rings. In the original design, the rings slip over the top of each section and rest on collars where the section attaches to the next lowest section. Rings from different types of kits may not fit properly and some kits use a clamp-on ring. If you purchase a used kit, be sure all of the rings are included.

The US Army manual for AB-155, including instructions for putting it up and taking it down safely, is widely available online. The kit also includes a parts list, so be sure all of the necessary items are present before purchasing the kit or starting to put it together. If you are purchasing a used kit, do a careful inspection of all sections, especially where the sections fit together, to be sure the section is not cracked or split.

AB-577 Masts

The AB-577 mast is an all-aluminum crank-up mast kit that was sold as military surplus. It is designed to be field deployed by one or more people and does not require a prepared surface or foundation of any kind. The complete kit in **Figure 26.8** consists of a "launcher" (the base section), eight tube sections, guy wires and all hardware and tools to assemble the 50-foot mast. The standard AB-577 system, with three sets of guys, will support a modest triband Yagi at 45 feet (see **Figure 26.9**).

Figure 26.8 — An AB-577 temporary tower system in its transport case. (Photo by Alan Biocca, WB6ZQZ)

Figure 26.9 — Installation of surplus AB-577 tower with tribander at 45 feet at K7NV. (Photo by Kurt Andress, K7NV)

The supply from military surplus dealers has largely been exhausted but kits are available from other hams. Before purchasing a used kit, be sure that all the required pieces are present (a parts list is included with the kits) and no pieces are damaged beyond normal wear-and-tear.

A total height of 75 feet is possible with the addition of the MK-806 extension kit. It's useful for any application requiring a temporary or permanent tower such as lighting, surveillance, emergency communications, or RF survey work. The quick erection time also makes the mast very useful in neighborhoods where a permanently installed tower is not allowed.

The system consists of several short sections of aluminum tubing, with special end clamp connectors used to join sections. These can be erected from the base fixture, which has a crank-up type winch-driven elevator platform. The tubing sections are installed in the base fixture and connected to the section above it with an over-center locking *Marmon*-style clamp. Then, the elevator platform is raised with the winch and the new tube is locked in place, high on the base fixture. Then the elevator is lowered to accept the next section. While the tower is extended, the supporting guys are adjusted via the unique *snubber* assemblies at the anchor connection. One person can erect this system, even in windy conditions, when special care is given to keeping the guys properly adjusted during each extension. There are several videos online showing how the system goes up and the original US Army manual is also widely available.

Fiberglass Poles

Telescoping fiberglass poles have become widely available in recent years. While they are too light to support rotatable antennas, they are popular as supports for wire antennas. Primarily intended for portable use, if you decide to use one in a permanent installation make sure the surface is coated to resist UV from sunlight or paint it. There is more information on these poles in the **Portable Antennas** chapter.

Wooden Poles

A seldom-used but sturdy alternative is to use a wooden utility pole. They vary from new ones to used poles that have been pulled from service by utility companies. Make some inquiries to find out the availability and installed cost in your area. You'll need to add pole steps to climb it and may have to fabricate your own antenna mounting hardware. Pole steps are available from suppliers such as MacLean Power Systems. Utility poles are very sturdy, require no guys, and might satisfy your use and budget.

26.2.3 MAST GUYING

Three guy wires in each set are usually adequate for a mast. These should be spaced equally (every 120 degrees) around the mast. The required number of sets of guys depends on the height of the mast, its stiffness, and the required antenna tension if supporting a wire antenna in one end. A 30-foot-high mast usually requires two sets of guys, and a 50-foot mast needs at least three sets. If supporting the end of a wire antenna, one guy of the top set should be anchored to a point directly opposite the antenna. The other two guys of the same set should be spaced 120° with respect to the first, as shown in **Figure 26.10**.

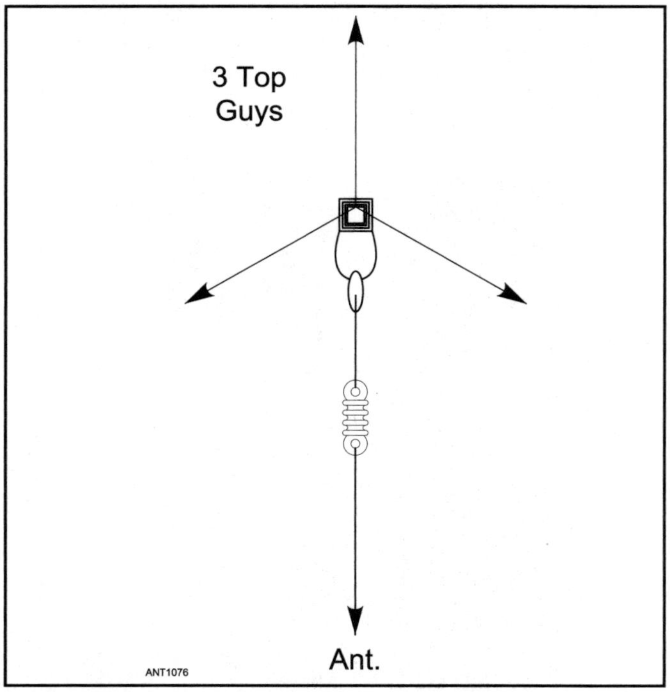

Figure 26.10 — For a mast supporting a wire antenna, the guys should be equally spaced at 120 degrees around the mast with one guy directly in line with the antenna.

Generally, the top guys should be anchored at distances from the base of the mast at least 60% of the mast height. The separation of the guy anchors from the mast determines the guy loads and the vertical load compressing the mast. At an anchor distance of 60% of the mast height, the load on the guy wire opposite the wire antenna is approximately twice the antenna tension. The compression in the mast will be 1.66 times the antenna tension. For 80% of the mast height, the guy tension will be 1.6 times larger than the antenna load and the mast compression will be 1.25 times larger.

The largest available and practical anchor spacing should be used. Additional compression on the mast caused by closer anchor spacing increases the tendency of the mast to buckle. Buckling occurs when the compression on the unsupported spans between guys become too great for the unsupported length. The section then bows out laterally and will usually fold over, collapsing the mast. Additional sets of guys reduce the tendency for the mast to buckle under the compression by decreasing the unsupported span lengths and stabilizing the mast, keeping it straight where it best withstands compression.

A natural phenomenon, called *vortex shedding*, can occur when the wind passes over the sections of a guyed mast. For every section size, shape, and length, there is a wind speed that can cause the sections to oscillate mechanically. When all the sections of an antenna support mast are close to the same size and length, it is possible for all of the mast sections to vibrate simultaneously between the guys. To reduce the potential for this, you can place the guys at locations along the mast that will result in different span lengths. This creates different mechanical resonant frequencies for each span, eliminating the possibility of all sections oscillating at the same time.

When determining the guy locations along the mast to treat this problem, you also need to consider the mast buckling requirements. Since compression of the mast is greatest in the bottom span and the least in the top span, the guys should be placed to make the bottom span the shortest and the top span the longest. A general guide for determining the different span lengths is to make the unguyed lengths increase by 10 to 20% with increasing height.

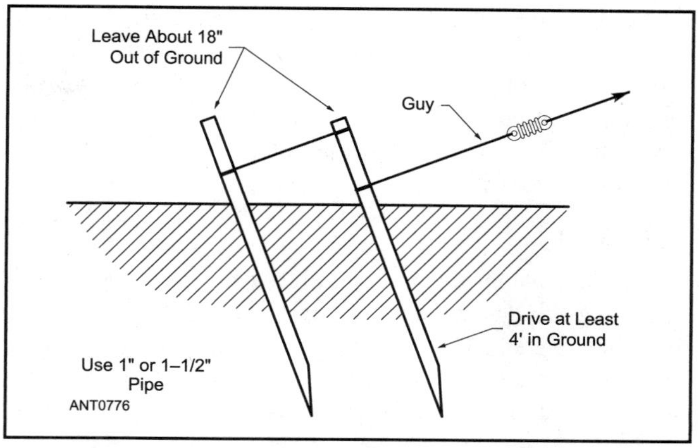

Figure 26.12 — Driven guy anchors. One pipe is usually sufficient for a small mast. For added strength, a second pipe may be added as shown.

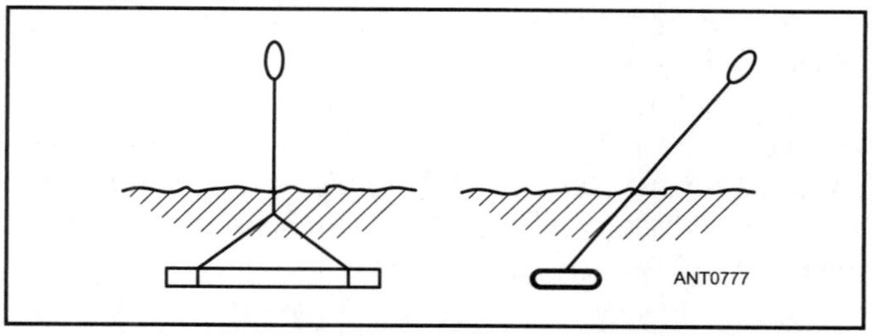

Figure 26.13 — Buried "dead-man" guy anchors (see text).

Guy Material

When used within their safe load ratings, you may use any of the ropes listed later in the chapter for mast guys. Nonmetallic materials have the advantage that there is no need to break them up into sections to avoid unwanted resonant interactions, also discussed later in the chapter. All of these materials are subject to *stretching*, however, which causes mechanical problems in permanent installations. At rated working loads, dry manila rope stretches about 5%, while nylon rope stretches about 20%. Usually, after a period of wind load and wet/dry cycles, the lines will become fairly stable and require less frequent adjustment.

Solid galvanized steel wire is also widely used for guying. This wire has approximately twice the load ratings of similar sizes of copper-clad wire, but it is more susceptible to corrosion. Stranded galvanized wire sold for guying TV masts is also suitable for light-duty applications, but is also susceptible to corrosion. It is prudent to inspect the guys every six months for signs of deterioration or damage. **Figure 26.11** shows how to attach guy wire to strain insulators.

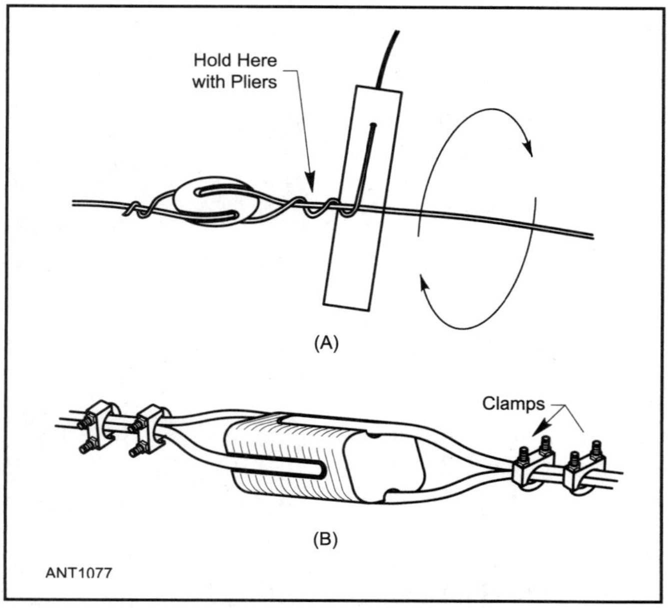

Figure 26.11 — Attaching guy wires to strain insulators. At (A) a simple lever is used to twist solid wire and at (B) standard cable clamps are used for stranded wire.

Guy Anchors

Figures 26.12 and **26.13** show two different kinds of guy anchors. In Figure 26.12 one or more pipes are driven into the ground at right angles to the guy wire. If a single pipe proves to be inadequate, another pipe can be added in tandem, as shown, and connected with a galvanized steel cable. Heavy-gauge galvanized pipe is preferred for corrosion resistance. Steel fence posts may be used in the same manner. Figure 26.13 shows a *dead-man* type of anchor. The buried anchor may consist of one or more pipes 5 or 6 feet long, or scrap automobile parts, such as bumpers or wheels. The anchors should be buried 3 or 4 feet in the ground. The cable connecting the dead-man to the guys should be galvanized wire rope, such as EHS guy cable. You should coat the buried part of the cable with roofing tar to well above the ground and thoroughly dry it prior to burial to enhance resistance to corrosion.

Heavy auger-type anchors that screw into the ground are also used and are commonly used by utilities to anchor power poles. These anchors are usually heavier than required for guying a mast, although they may be more convenient to install. You should conduct annual inspections of the anchors by digging several inches below grade around the anchor to inspect for corrosion.

Trees and buildings may also be used as guy anchors if they are located appropriately. Care should be exercised, however, to make sure that the tree is of adequate size and that any fastening to a building can be made sufficiently secure. See the section above on using trees as antenna supports regarding anchoring to trees.

Guy Tension

Many troubles encountered in mast guying are a result of pulling the guy wires too tight. Guy-wire tension should never be more than necessary to correct for obvious bowing or movement under wind pressure. Approximately 10% to 15% of the working load is sufficient. In most cases, achieving the necessary tension does not require the use of turnbuckles, with the possible exception of the guy opposite a wire antenna. If any great difficulty is experienced in eliminating bowing from the mast, the guy tension should be reduced or additional sets of guys are required. The mast should be checked periodically, especially after strong winds, to ensure the guys and anchors have not stretched or moved, allowing the mast to bend away from the required straight alignment.

In the case of rope guys, use of a "trucker's hitch" (see the section on knots) will provide much more tension than can be obtained by just pulling on the rope since it has a 2:1 mechanical advantage.

26.3 TYPES OF TOWERS

A tower is the best answer to a reliable, permanent antenna support structure and they basically come in two types — self-supporting and guyed. Beginning with the small, roof-mounted "four-footed tripod" models, amateurs use towers up to and beyond 200-foot tall broadcast-size structures. This section is an overview of various common types of towers with some of their key characteristics.

Lattice towers consist of two kinds of *members*: *legs* (often called siderails) and diagonal and horizontal *braces*. Members can either be round, such as used with Rohn G-series (**www.rohnnet.com**), or 90- or 60-degree angled metal. Round-member towers are the most common for amateur towers. The *tower face* is that outward facing area between the legs with the braces between them. Free-standing and guyed lattice towers are built of pre-assembled *sections*, usually 8 to 10 feet long, stacked on top of each other to reach some desired height. Lattice towers are constructed from steel or aluminum, with steel the most common for guyed towers. *Tubular* towers are constructed from telescoping sections of steel tubing. These are referred to as monopoles; some models rotate and can carry significant loads.

Figure 26.14 — A roof mounted tower will give your antennas a chance to get up in the air with a minimal impact and cost. (Photo by Redd Swindells, AI2N)

26.3.1 ROOF-MOUNTED TOWERS

The self-supporting roof-mounted tower is a modest way to support small to mid-sized antennas. This might be your first foray into a tower and directional antenna and a roof-mounted tower offers an inexpensive way to get started. Glen Martin Engineering (**www.glenmartin.com**) offers several models of four-leg aluminum towers and is a representative source of roof-mounted towers ranging in height from 4.5 to 26 feet. **Figure 26.14** shows a typical installation. Follow the manufacturer's recommendations for installation and grounding.

A roof-mounted tower is attached to the roof with anchor bolts that extend completely through the roof. Do not use lag bolts into the roof trusses. Use a 2×4 or 2×6 across the trusses inside the attic for a backing plate and attach the anchor bolts to them as in **Figure 26.15**. Another similar board can be placed on top of the roof to further distribute the load. Any wood

Figure 26.15 — The strengthened anchoring for the roof-mounted tower. Bolts run through the roof and through the anchor plate (2 × 6) between joists. (Photo by Jane Wolfert)

exposed to the weather should be pressure-treated or coated with roofing tar. Roofing tar is also used to seal around the mounting bolt holes to prevent leaks (see **Figure 26.16**).

Roof-mounted antennas and structures provide practical, easy solutions to getting a directional antenna in the air, but roof mounting can be dangerous work. State and federal safety laws require fall-arrest equipment and it's highly recommended that you use it as well. A fall-arrest harness (FAH) should be attached to an anchor point on the peak of the roof. Most of these small roof-mounted supports cannot be climbed, but require a ladder support against them to provide access to the antenna.

26.3.2 SELF-SUPPORTING TOWERS

Self-supporting towers have a smaller footprint, but are generally more expensive to install. Significantly more concrete is required for the base of a free-standing tower and the amount of steel or aluminum (which ultimately determines the cost of a tower) is higher. The advantage of a self-supporting tower is that no guy wires are required. This appeals to hams without enough room for the necessary guying system and the cleaner "look" sometimes helps with aesthetic concerns.

Because there are no guys to keep them standing, self-supporting towers depend on bending strength and a large concrete base. The base is generally required to have a volume of at least five to six cubic yards, requiring significant digging and preparation. The weight of the base keeps the tower system's center of gravity low or below ground level, minimizing the overturning force from wind. The soil around the base must be solid enough to withstand the pressure from overturning forces on the tower system. If you have any questions about your ability to properly construct the base, consult a professional engineer or hire a concrete contractor.

Figure 26.16 — Lengths of 2 × 6 on the roof act as footing for the tower legs and are coated by roofing tar to protect against weathering and prevent leaks. (Photo by Jane Wolfert)

Freestanding Towers

Towers specifically designed and installed for TV antennas are at the low end of suitability for typical HF beams. TV antenna towers have a maximum height of 40 to 60 feet. The most common are the Rohn AX, BX and HDBX series and a tubular-legged type similar to but lighter than Rohn 25G. Universal Manufacturing (**www.universaltowers.com**) offers similar towers made of aluminum.

The common BX-series towers sketched in **Figure 26.17** are made from stamped steel with X-bracing of the legs. The X braces are not connected to each other and the most common failure point is between the braces. Also, the rotator and top plates are made from sheet metal and can crack from wind-induced metal fatigue. For small triband HF beams and VHF arrays they are fine, but be careful of overloading towers

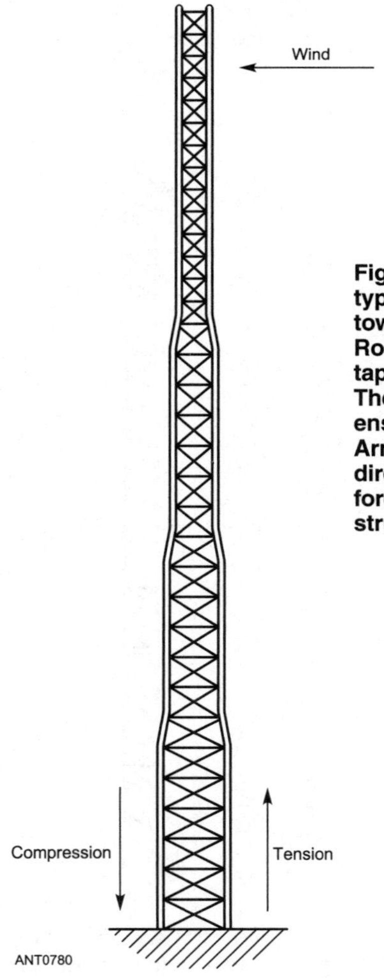

Figure 26.17 — A typical freestanding tower similar to Rohn BX. The tower tapers as it rises. The wide stance ensures stability. Arrows indicate the directions of the forces acting on the structure.

using the smaller stacking sections. These towers should be limited to antennas with boom lengths less than 10 feet since they have minimal resistance to torsion (twisting).

For larger antenna arrays, heavier towers are available that are designed for broadcast and commercial applications. These look much the same as the "TV antenna" towers but are made of heavier material and have heavier and stiffer bracing. The most common models of these towers are the Rohn SSV, Trylon (**www.trylon.com**), Universal and AN Wireless (**www.anwireless.com**). While significantly more expensive, they can handle very large loads, including high winds and icing conditions.

Crank-up Towers

Crank-ups are a popular type of self-supporting tower. These towers use either a motorized or manual system of cables and pulleys to extend or retract the tower. They are the most expensive tower for the height due to more materials and hardware, but satisfy many hams with limited space, or those who dislike guy wires. When cranked down, a telescoping tower can maintain a low-profile system, out of sight of the neighbors and family.

Tubular crank-ups are generally limited to a single antenna since the rotator is mounted on a plate at the top of the tower without any additional bracing. This limits the size of the antenna and how far above the rotator it can be mounted. Lattice crank-ups generally have the same top structure as a guyed tower and can support much larger antenna and mast combinations.

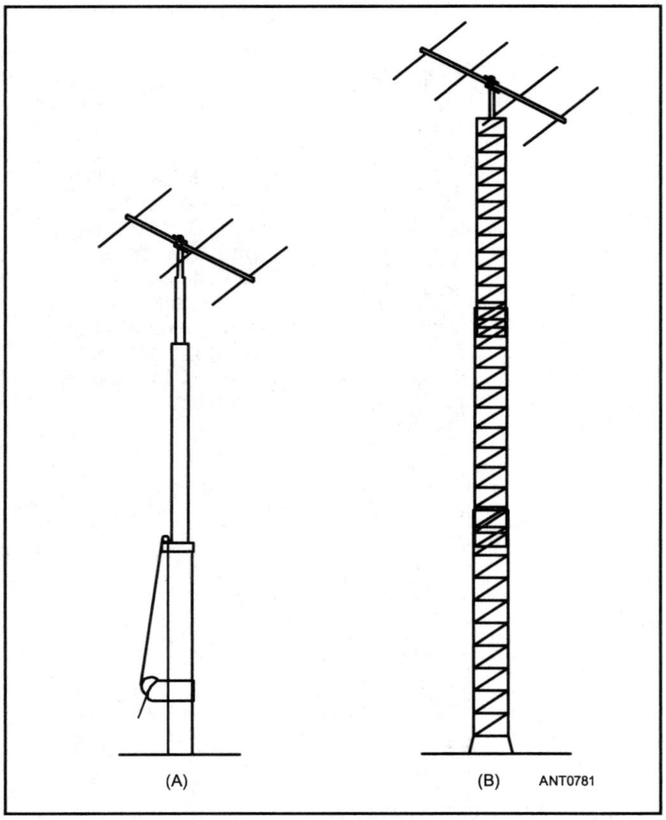

Figure 26.18 — Two examples of crank-up towers. At (A) a tubular style and at (B) a lattice style.

US Tower (**www.ustower.com**) dominates the market for crank-ups, manufacturing good products and offering good customer support. Both lattice- and tubular-type crank-up towers are available as shown in **Figure 26.18**.

Do not use guys with normal crank-up towers (those that have no locking devices between sections)! The increased tower compression will be carried by the hoisting cable, which will eventually cause it to fail.

Tilt-over Towers

Some free-standing towers have another convenience feature — a hinged section that permits the owner to fold over all or a portion of the tower. The primary benefit is in allowing antenna work to be done close to ground level, without the necessity of removing the antenna and lowering it for service. **Figure 26.19** shows a hinged base used with stacked, guyed tower sections. Many crank-up towers come with optional tilt-over base fixtures that are equipped with a winch and cable system for tilting the fully nested tower between horizontal and vertical positions.

The hinged section can also be designed for portions of the tower above the base. These are usually referred to as *guyed tilt-over towers*, where a conventional guyed tower can be tilted over for installing and servicing antennas.

Misuse of hinged sections during tower erection is a dangerously common practice among radio amateurs. Unfortunately, these episodes can end in accidents. If you do not have a good grasp of the fundamentals of physics, it might be wise to avoid hinged towers or to consult an expert if there are any questions about safely installing and using such a tower. It is often far easier (and safer) to erect a regular guyed tower or self-supporting tower with gin pole and climbing belt than it is to try to walk up an unwieldy hinged tower.

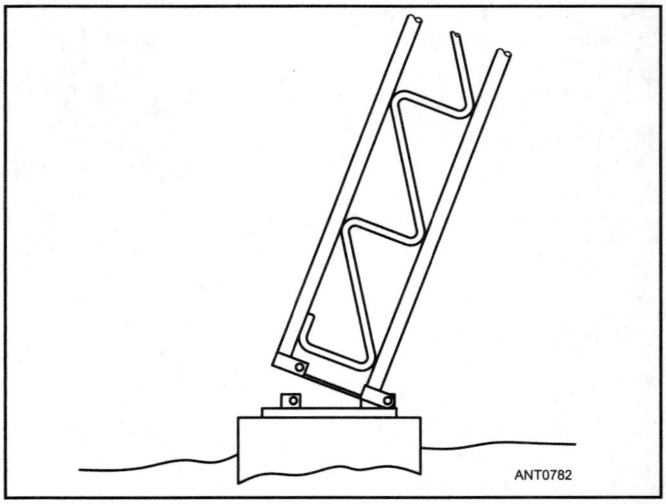

Figure 26.19 — Fold-over or tilting base. There are several different kinds of hinged sections permitting different types of installation. Great care should be exercised when raising or lowering a tilting tower.

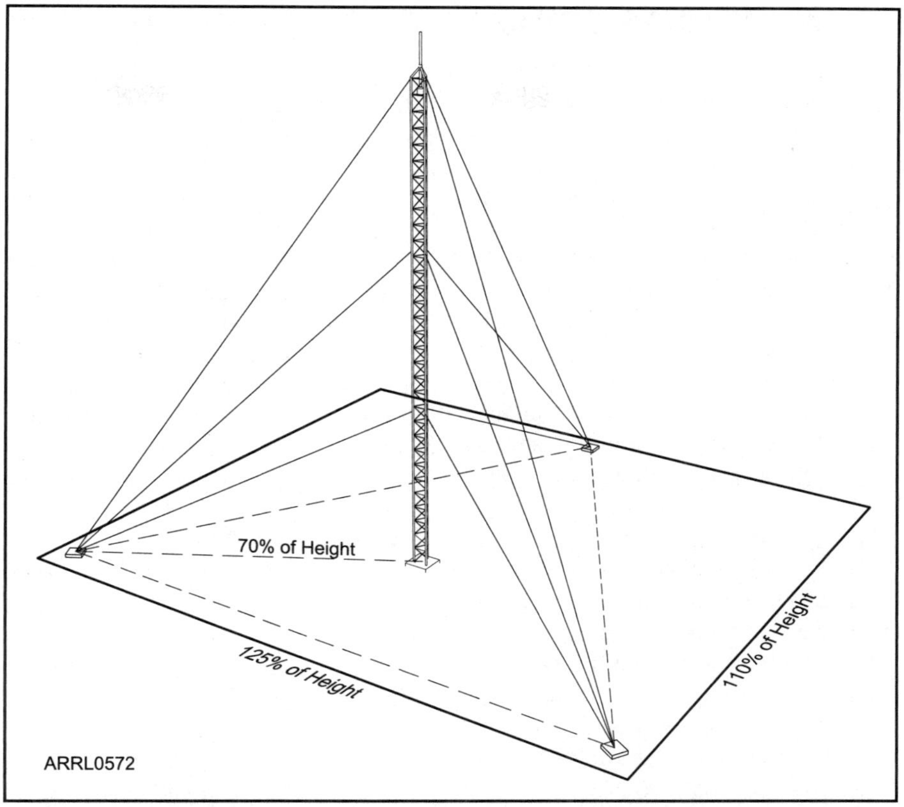

Figure 26.20 — Guyed towers are built from stackable sections that are usually identical except for the base that attaches to the concrete and the top section that supports the rotator and mast. Guy requirements are specified by the manufacturer, but spacing the anchors 70 to 80% of the tower height is typical. As seen in the drawing, the tower and guy wires do take up quite a bit of space.

26.3.3 GUYED TOWERS

Guyed tubular-leg lattice towers are strong, reliable, relatively easy to erect, and have a wide array of accessories designed and intended for ham use. They are usually less expensive to install, but need a big footprint for the guying system. Since the typical recommended guy anchor distance from the tower is 80% of the height, the guys for a 100-foot tower need to be anchored 80 feet away from the tower. A set of three guys spaced 120° around the tower is repeated every 30 to 40 feet up the tower (see **Figure 26.20**).

The most widely used guyed towers for amateur applications are the Rohn 25G and 45G. They are well constructed, are hot-dipped galvanized, and have enough accessory items for any use. These towers have tubular legs and Z-bracing rods welded to the legs. The Rohn product catalog (available for downloading from the company website) provides calculations for rated wind load at various heights and all base and guying requirements.

Rohn 25G has a face width of 12 inches and a 10-foot section weighs 40 pounds. A gin pole and a ground crew is the recommended way to install these towers. A practical height limit of 190 feet at 90 MPH wind speed provides 7.8 square feet of antenna load capacity. A 100-foot tower yields 9.1 square feet of antenna capacity, enough for a small stack of monoband Yagis or a high-performance triband beam. An experienced crew can erect up to a hundred feet a day of this popular tower.

Rohn 45G is 18 inches across the face and a 10-foot section weighs 70 pounds. This robust tower is rated up to 240 feet in 90 MPH winds, with a wind load rating of 16.3 square feet. At a height of 100 feet the wind loading is 21.5 square feet.

Rohn 55G is also 18 inches across the face, weighs 100 pounds per section, and can be installed up to 300 feet with 90 MPH wind ratings. It has a gross capacity of 17.4 square feet in that maximum configuration. The standard Rohn gin pole is not rated for 55G because of its weight.

Tubular-leg towers can also be supported by attaching them to a building with a *house bracket*. The manufacturer will specify how far above a bracket the tower can be extended without guys.

26.4 ENGINEERING THE TOWER PROJECT

Engineering in this sense means to plan, construct, or manage the practical applications of your tower project. The engineering should be done *before* you begin digging, pouring, or constructing!

The process you go through to design your system may begin with site selection ("What is a suitable location for a tower?") or it may start with selecting a tower ("What tower can I put up on this site?"). Everyone's circumstances are different.

It's not unusual to repeat the process of planning and tower selection for several iterations as you work through the various types of towers and associated costs and constraints. The important thing is to work through the various interacting issues until you are satisfied you have addressed all of them.

It is often very helpful to the novice tower installer to visit other local amateurs who have installed towers. Look over their installations and ask questions. Ask about local permitting processes and requirements. If possible, have a few local experienced amateurs look over your design plans — before you commit yourself. They may be able to offer a great deal of help. If someone in your area is planning to install a tower and antenna system, be sure to offer your assistance. There is no substitute for experience when it comes to tower work and your experience there may prove invaluable to you later.

26.4.1 SITE PLANNING AND PERMITTING

Local Ordinances and CC&Rs

Local ordinances, deed restrictions, and any CC&Rs (Covenants, Conditions and Restrictions) should be checked to determine if any legal restrictions affect the proposed installation. While compliance with local building regulations may be pretty straightforward, your CC&Rs may specifically rule out any type of outdoor structure that would make tower or antenna installation impossible.

The FCC's PRB-1 memorandum specifies that local regulations must make "reasonable accommodation" for Amateur Radio antennas and support structures, but does not pre-empt local regulations. For more information on PRB-1, consult the information at **www.arrl.org/prb-1**.

The best book for Amateur Radio tower zoning issues is *Antenna Zoning for the Radio Amateur* by Fred Hopengarten, K1VR, now in its second edition and available from the ARRL or Radioware (**www.radio-ware.com**). Fred is a telecommunications attorney and this book is filled with valuable information on legal issues. Besides covering the legal issues, it also contains many practical insights and examples of real world aspects of working with the local building departments and navigating the permitting process.

Building permits will dictate setbacks from property lines and are likely to place other constraints on where your tower can be located. For example, you may have to stay a certain distance from septic systems or buried utilities.

Safety

You must consider the safety aspects of your installation. For example, a tower should not be installed in a location where it could fall onto a neighbor's property. Imagine what would happen if your tower or antenna fell — where would it be likely to land? What could it hit on the way down? You may not be able to mitigate every possible outcome but thinking about it before construction may lead to a better plan.

The antenna must be located in such a position that it cannot possibly come in contact with power lines, either during normal operation or if the structure should fall. Consider the proximity of power lines to the tower. Safety rules dictate that all parts of a tower and antenna must remain at least 10 feet from power lines when being erected or after being installed. This is the smallest separation you should consider and a greater safety margin is strongly recommended.

Area and Access

For a guyed tower, there must be sufficient space for proper guying. The guy anchors should be between 70% and 80% of the tower height in distance from the base of the tower on level ground — sloping terrain may require larger areas (see Figure 26.20).

Erecting the tower and installing the antennas will require some space. Is there enough room to lay out a tower on a tilt-over base and how should the hinged base be oriented? Think about where antennas will be assembled and how they'll be hoisted to the top of the tower. Where will any necessary equipment need to be positioned and how will it get there?

Another part of choosing a tower site has to do with arranging for access. That is, access for base excavation and access for concrete. If you aren't sure, ask a local contractor to evaluate your site and make suggestions. They may spot something important that you've overlooked.

26.4.2 SELECTING A TOWER

The selection of a tower, its height, and the type of antennas and rotator is probably one of the more complex issues faced by station builders. All aspects of the tower, antenna, and rotator system are interrelated, and you should consider the overall system before making any decisions regarding specific system components.

Selecting a tower must be based on your requirements for what the tower must support, along with considerations such as total budget, permit restrictions, aesthetics, and the specifics of where you intend to install the tower. You should also consider the climate and your ability to maintain a tower. You may already know what general type of tower you want — self-supporting or guyed, lattice or tubular, and so on. Or you may have to select a tower based on the constraints of the available site or other factors.

One of the first things you need to determine in the tower selection process is the type of specification required by the local authorities, if any. Then, you must determine the *Basic Wind Speed* appropriate for the site. The Basic Wind Speed used in most specifications is the average wind speed for one mile of wind passing across the structure. It will be a lower

The 10 Most Common Tower Building Mistakes

1. Not following the manufacturer's specifications

Commercially manufactured towers have to comply with current standards for wind loading and structural integrity. Engineers design the towers and make the calculations to make them safe. If you don't follow their specifications at a minimum, the tower will not take the stresses and loads to which it is subjected. In other words, it'll probably fail.

2. Overloading

This is the most common reason for amateur tower failure. You must not exceed the wind load rating. This is even more important for self-supporting and crank-up towers. While you might get away with exceeding the ratings due to built-in design margins, it's never a good idea to overload any part of the tower system. When in doubt, err on the conservative side — you won't regret it.

3. Underestimating wind forces

Wind pressure on a tower and antenna system can be tremendous. Unless you've been on a tower during a windstorm to feel the pressure and the forces, it's difficult to appreciate how significant they are. Increases in wind pressure are not linear; wind loading goes up with the *cube* of wind speed. An increase of 10 MPH in wind speed can increase the wind force by almost 50% in some cases as shown in **Table 26.A**.

4. Not building for the wind speed rating in your county

While many counties and even whole states in the US are only rated for 70 MPH winds (the minimum rating), many other counties have ratings much higher. For example, Dade and Broward counties in Florida have ratings of 140 MPH. Find out what the wind speed rating is for your county or your specific location and use that as the *minimum* wind speed design parameter for your tower and antenna system. Champion Radio Tech Notes provides the wind speed ratings for all 3076 counties (**www.championradio.com/tech.notes.html**).

5. Using the wrong mast for the job

This is an all too common failure. Stacks of medium to large HF beams can put huge stresses on your mast. Pipe may be fine for small installations where you don't have much wind speed or loading or when there is only one antenna at the top of the tower. Structural tubing is carbon alloy steel rated for strength and is the preferred material.

6. Not having the guy wires tensioned properly

Proper guy wire tension is a critical part of a tower's ability to handle wind stresses. Having the wrong tension can be like driving your car with over or under-inflated tires; it is potentially dangerous and is not the proper specification from the manufacturer. Having too little tension can result in wind slamming of the tower and guys as the tower is blown back and forth. Too much tension puts excess preload on the guys and lowers the safety margin significantly.

Around 90% of ham towers use 3/16 inch EHS steel guy wires. Guy wire tension is typically 10% of the breaking strength — in the case of 3/16 inch EHS that would be 400 pounds. The only inexpensive and accurate way to measure this is to use a Loos Tension Gauge, such as the Loos PT-2 for 3/16 and 1/4 inch wire rope sizes.

7. Not having a proper ground system

A good ground system is necessary not only for lightning protection but will also protect your equipment, your home and your life. Proper grounding is discussed elsewhere in this chapter and in *The ARRL Handbook's* chapter on safety.

8. Not doing an annual inspection

Your tower and antennas are undergoing a slow, but constant process of deterioration. The best way to find and fix small problems before they become big problems and potential calamities is by doing an annual inspection.

Look at everything and push and pull on the hardware. You also want to put a wrench on 10% or more of the tower nuts to check for tightness as well as all of the nuts on accessories like antennas, mounts, U-bolts, etc.

9. Not fitting the tower sections on the ground

Tower sections, new or used, may not fit together easily. It's much easier to correct alignment problems on the ground than up on the tower during construction. A handy tool for getting tower sections together (or apart) is the Tower*Jack Combo that combines a leg aligner along with a lever for pulling sections together or pushing them apart.

10. Using the wrong hardware

To slow the process of deterioration, use only hardware that minimizes corrosion. Galvanized or stainless steel materials are the only ones that will survive outdoor use reliably. (See the section on "Corrosion" in this chapter.)

Substituting the wrong hardware can also lead to failure, for example using general hardware store bolts for tower legs when the manufacturer calls for a specific SAE grade. Using hardware totally unsuited for the task is common, i.e. installing the wrong type of 'screw-in' anchor or anchor rods; use of non-closed-eye eyebolts (use only welded or forged ones); use of the wrong guy material (EHS only!); and more.

Table 26.A
Wind Speed and Pressure

Mean Velocity Pressure	*Wind*
50.0 MPH	10.0 PSF
60.0 MPH	14.4 PSF
70.7 MPH	20.0 PSF
86.6 MPH	30.0 PSF
100.0 MPH	40.0 PSF
111.8 MPH	50.0 PSF
122.5 MPH	60.0 PSF

value than the peak readings from an anemometer (wind gauge) installed at the site. For example, a Basic Wind Speed of 70 mph could have a maximum value of 80 mph and a minimum of 60 mph, equally distributed during the passage of the mile of wind. Basic wind speeds can be found in tables or maps contained in the appropriate specifications. Often, the basic wind speed used for the location may be obtained from the local permit authority.

Many building regulations base their specifications for maximum wind speed on TIA-222, "Structural Standard for Antenna Supporting Structures and Antennas." (TIA-222G is the latest revision as of mid-2011.) County wind speeds for all 3076 counties in the US from TIA-222 are also online at **www.championradio.com** under Tech Notes. Remember — these are the minimums and some building departments use a slightly higher figure for issuing building permits.

Add up the total square feet of antenna area (commercial antennas include area in the antenna specifications) you plan on installing. Compare that combination of wind area and your maximum wind speed rating to manufacturer specifications for the specific models of acceptable towers.

Most tower manufacturers provide catalogues or data packages that represent engineered tower configurations. These are provided as a convenience for users to help determine the most suitable tower configurations. The most commonly used design specifications for towers are the previously mentioned TIA-222 and the UBC (Uniform Building Code). These specifications define how the tower, antenna and guy loads are determined and applied to the system, and establish general design criteria for the analysis of the tower. Local authorities often require the review and approval of the installation by a state licensed Professional Engineer (P.E.) to obtain building permits. All local authorities in the United States do not subscribe to the same design standards, so often the manufacturers' general-purpose engineering is not applicable.

Determining Tower Load

Most manufacturers rate their towers in terms of the maximum allowable antenna load that can safely be carried at a specific wind speed. Ensuring that the specific antennas you plan to install meet the tower's design criteria, however, may not always be a straightforward task.

For most towers, the manufacturer assumes that the allowable antenna load is a horizontal force applied at the top of the tower. The allowable load represents a defined amount of exposed antenna area, at a specified wind velocity. Most tower manufacturers rate the load in terms of *Flat Projected Area* (FPA). This is simply the equivalent area of a flat rectangular surface at right angles to the wind. The FPA is not related to the actual shape of the antenna itself, only its rectangular projected area. Some manufacturers provide separate FPAs for antennas made from cylindrical sections and those made from rectangular sections.

In the realm of antenna manufacturers, however, you may encounter another wind load rating called the *Effective Projected Area* (EPA). This attempts to take into account the actual shape of antenna elements. The problem is that there is no agreed-upon standard for the conversion from EPA to load numbers. Different manufacturers may use different conversion factors.

Since most tower manufacturers have provided FPA figures for their towers — allowing us in effect to ignore design-specification details — it would be easiest for us to work only with FPA values for our antennas. This would be fine, if indeed we had good FPA figures for the specific antennas

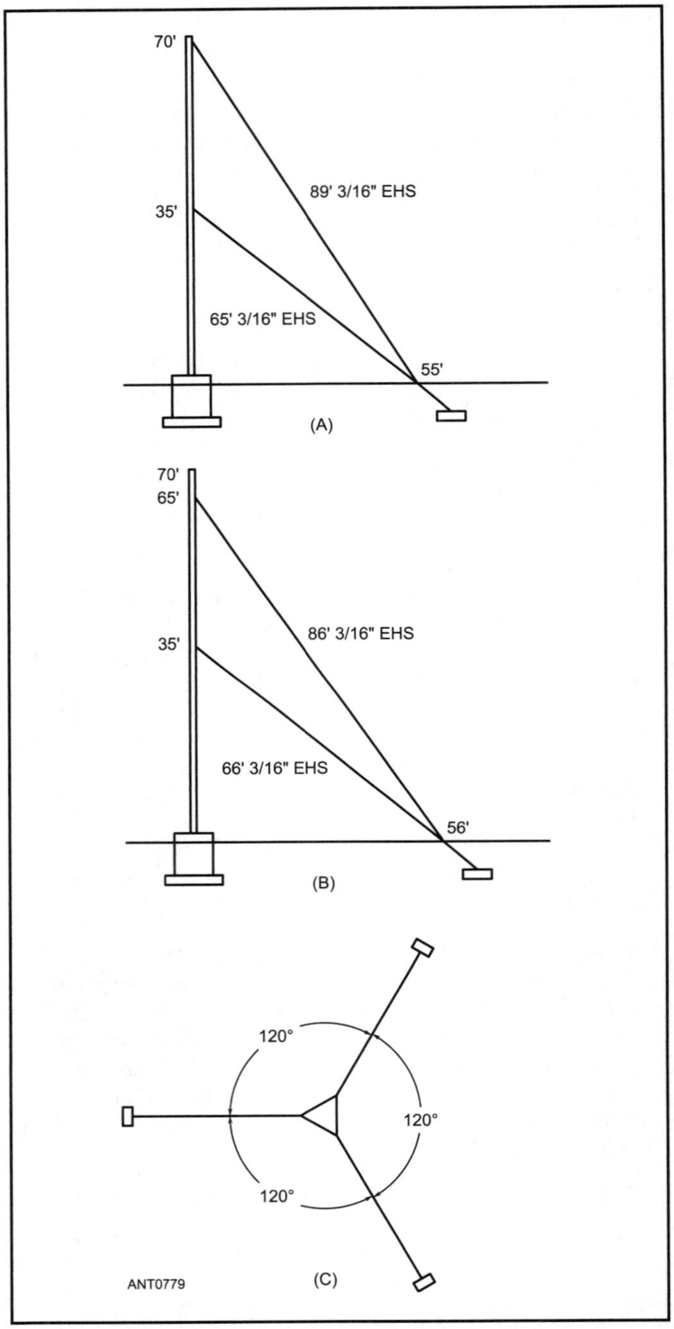

Figure 26.21 — The proper method of installation of a guyed tower. At (A) is the method recommended for most amateur installations. At (B), the method shown in current Rohn catalogs that places considerable stresses on the top section of the tower when large antennas are mounted above the tower (see text). (C) shows the recommended orientation of guy wires, symmetrically spaced around the tower.

we plan to use! Unfortunately, FPAs are rarely specified for commercially built amateur antennas. Instead, most antenna manufacturers provide effective areas in their specification sheets. You may need to contact the antenna manufacturer directly for the FPA antenna area or for the antenna dimensions so that you can do your own FPA calculations as discussed in **Appendix A** of this chapter.

26.4.3 DESIGNING THE GUYS

The configuration shown in **Figure 26.21A** is taken from an older (1983) Unarco-Rohn catalog. This configuration has the top set of guys placed at the top of the tower with the lower set halfway up the tower. This configuration is best for most amateur installations, which usually have the antennas mounted on a rotatable mast extending out the top of the tower — thereby placing the maximum lateral loads when the wind blows at the top of the tower (and the bottom of the rotating mast). This configuration can limit the ability to easily tram and install antennas on the mast, or at the tower top, but will work fine for one's first tower installation.

The configuration shown in Figure 26.21B is from the current Rohn catalog (Catalog 2). It shows 5 feet of unsupported tower extending above the top guy set. The lower guy set is approximately halfway between the top guys and the base. The newer configurations are tailored for commercial users who populate the top region of the tower with fixed arrays and/or dishes. The installation in Figure 26.21B cannot safely withstand the same amount of horizontal top load as can the configuration shown in Figure 26.21A, simply because the guys start farther down from the top of the tower.

An overhead view of a guyed tower is given in Figure 26.21C. Common practice is to use equal angular spacings of 120° between guy wires. If you must deviate from this spacing, the engineering staff of the tower manufacturer or a civil engineer should be contacted for advice.

Amateurs should understand that most catalogs show generic examples of tower configurations that work within the cited design specifications. They are by no means the only solution for any specific tower/antenna configuration. You can usually substantially change the load capability of any given tower by varying the size and number of guys. Station builders are encouraged to utilize the services of professional engineers to get the most out of their guyed towers.

Guy Anchors

The most common type of guy anchor is the buried "dead man" concrete anchor shown in **Figure 26.22A**. The Rohn catalog contains drawings and specifications for anchors suitable for typical 25G, 45G, and 55G towers. Rohn makes all of the necessary hardware to attach guys to buried anchors.

Screw in earth anchors shown in Figure 26.22B are widely used in commercial tower work for anchoring utility poles and other similar jobs. Smaller anchors are not suited for typical tower installations. Larger anchors that require hydraulic drivers are available from Rohn, AB Chance, and other commercial vendors. Expanding earth anchors are installed in a

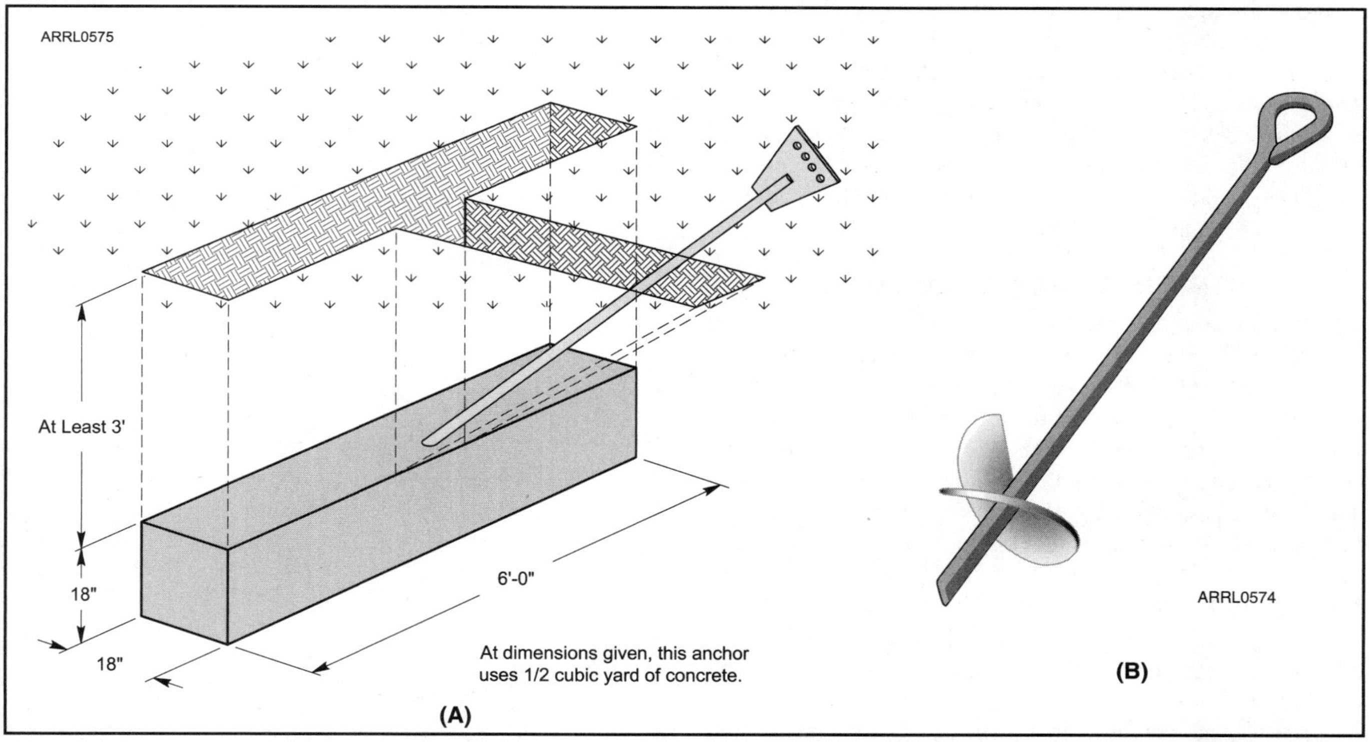

Figure 26.22 — At (A) a "dead man" anchor for guyed towers is basically a block of concrete buried in the ground. Block dimensions are specified by the manufacturer or calculated by an engineer and will vary depending on the height of the tower and wind and ice loading requirements. Various anchor rods are available, depending on the length and strength needed. The typical screw-in anchor is shown at B. Pullout strength is determined by soil characteristics, anchor rod length and helical screw diameter.

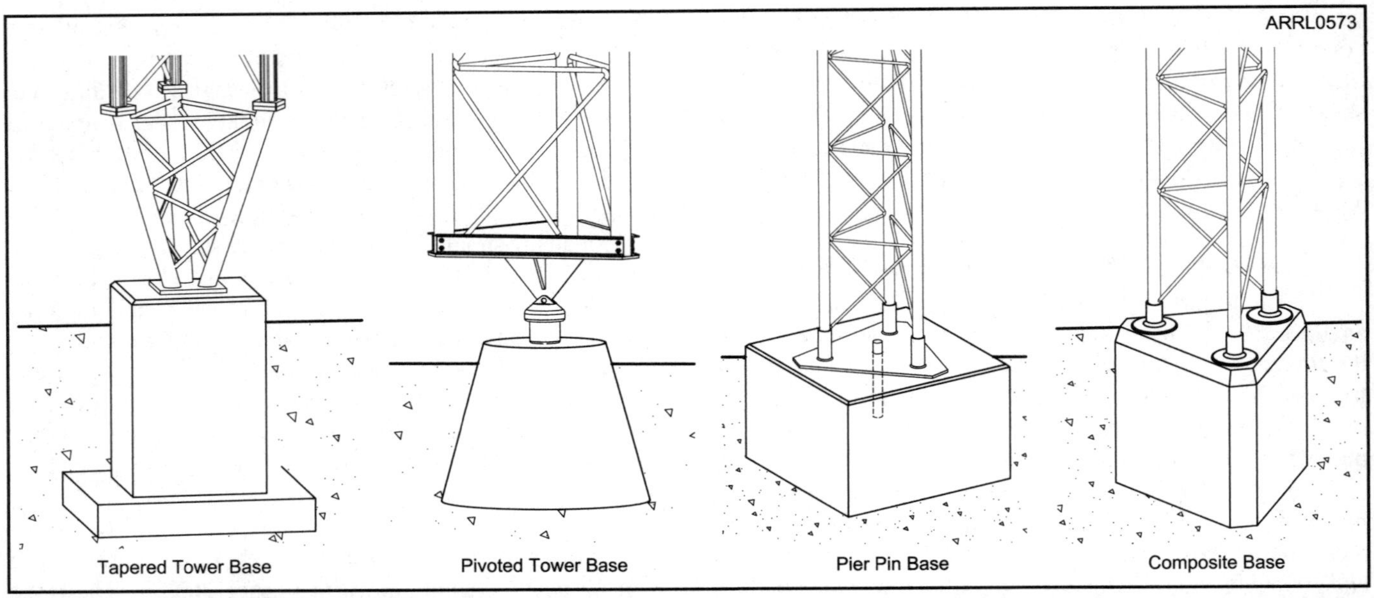

Figure 26.23 — Tower bases can take different forms. Most ham towers use the composite base (or a variation on that with a buried base section) or the pier pin base.

hole, hammered to secure the anchor fingers in place, and the hole backfilled.

The AB Chance guide *Encyclopedia of Anchoring* is available online as a PDF document. Selecting the proper anchor is highly dependent on the soil properties at the tower. If you are unsure of how to install this type of anchor or how to assess soil properties, consult a structural or soils engineer.

Other types of anchors, such as elevated anchors made of steel pipe or I-beams may be more suitable for your circumstances. Guys can also be attached to the structural elements of a building — do not rely on expansion bolts or lugs in masonry. When using an alternative to buried anchors, consult a engineer to be sure your guys will stand up to the load your tower will present in local conditions.

26.4.4 DESIGNING THE BASE

Several common types of tower bases are shown in **Figure 26.23**. Amateurs use all types of bases. A tower base is its foundation — what supports and carries the weight of the tower itself, along with force directed down the legs from wind and guying tension. Hams often use a variation of the composite base in which part of a tower section or a "base burial" section is buried in the concrete. Hams also use the pier pin base. A pin in the center of the concrete pier protrudes through a hole in the center of the base plate and holds it in place. The base plate is not bolted down or anchored to the concrete so that some side-to-side and twisting movement is allowed. The pivoted and tapered bases are only used on the largest towers.

Tower manufacturers can provide customers with detailed plans for properly constructing tower bases. **Figure 26.24** is an example of one such plan. This plan calls for a hole that is 3.5 × 3.5 × 6 feet deep. Steel reinforcement bars are tied together to form a cage and placed in the hole.

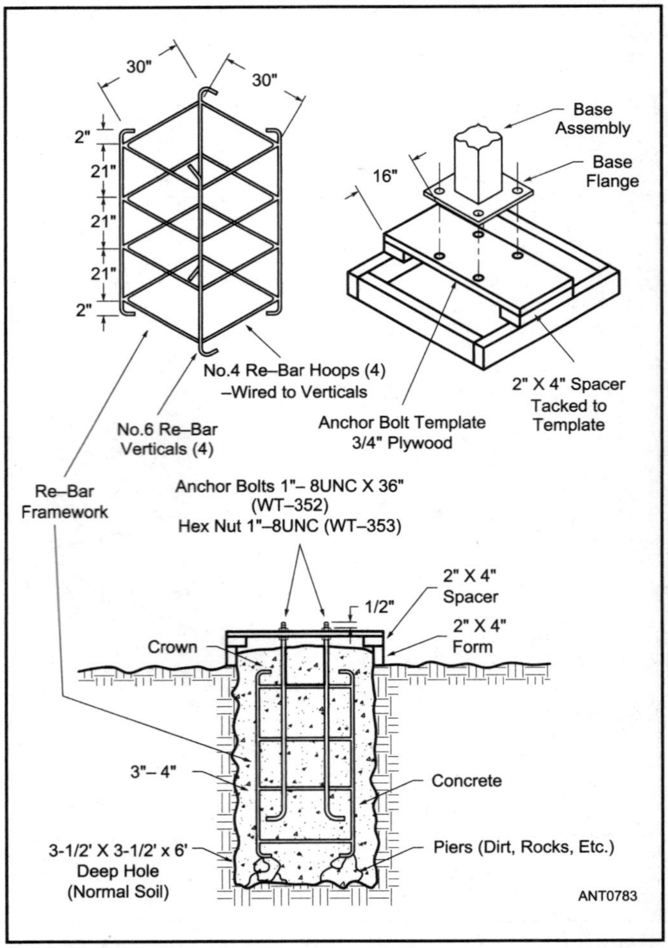

Figure 26.24 — Plans for installing concrete base for a 70-foot tubular crank-up tower. Although the instructions vary from tower to tower, this is representative of the type of concrete base specified by most manufacturers.

A strong wooden form is constructed around the top of the hole. The hole and the wooden form are filled with concrete so that the resultant block will be 4 inches above grade. Before it hardens, the anchor bolts are embedded in the concrete, and aligned with the plywood template. The template serves to align the anchor bolts to properly mate with the tower itself. Once the concrete has cured, the tower base is installed on the anchor bolts and the base connection is adjusted to bring the tower into vertical alignment.

For a tower that bolts to a flat base plate mounted to the footing bolts (as shown in Figure 26.24), you can bolt the first tower section on the base plate to ensure that the base is level and properly aligned. Use temporary guys or wooden braces to hold things exactly vertical while the concrete cures. (The use of such temporary guys also works well when you place the first tower section in the base hole and plumb it vertically before pouring in the concrete.) Manufacturers can provide specific, detailed instructions for the proper mounting procedure. **Figure 26.25** shows a slightly different design for a tower base.

The one assumption so far is that *normal* soil is predominant in the area in which the tower is to be installed. Normal soil is a mixture of clay, loam, sand and small rocks. More conservative design parameters for the tower base should be adopted (usually, using more concrete) if the soil is sandy, swampy or extremely rocky. If there are any doubts about the soil, the local agricultural extension office can usually provide specific technical information about the soil in a given area. When this information is in hand, contact the engineering department of the tower manufacturer or a civil engineer for specific recommendations with regard to compensating for any special soil characteristics.

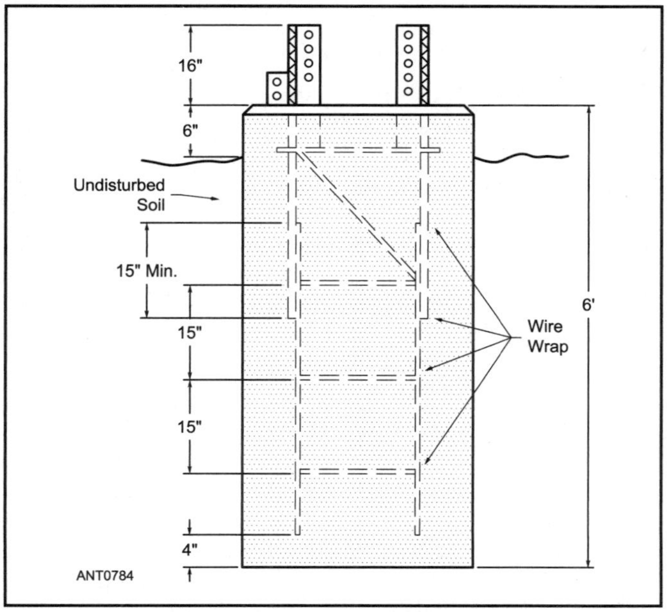

Figure 26.25 — Another example of a concrete base for a 70-foot lattice crank-up tower.

Pier-Pin Bases

An important phenomenon in a guyed tower is stretching of the guy cables. All guys stretch under load and when the wind blows the elongated guys allow the tower to lean over somewhat. If the tower base is buried in the concrete footing — as is commonly done in amateur installations — the bending stress at the tower base can become a significant factor. Towers that have been installed with tapered pier-pin bases much more freely absorb tower leaning, and they are far less sensitive to guy-elongation problems.

The tapered pier-pin tower installation is not without some drawbacks. These installations often require torque-arm guy brackets or six-guy torque-arm assemblies to control tower rotation due to antenna torque. They also require temporary guys when they are being installed to hold the base steady until the permanent guys are mounted. Some climbers also don't like the flexing when they start to climb these types of towers.

On the positive side, pier-pin base towers have all structural members above the concrete footing, eliminating concerns about hidden corrosion that can occur with buried towers. Most decisions regarding the type of base installation are made according to the preference of the tower builder/maintainer. While either type of base configuration can be successfully used, you would be wise to do the stress calculations (or have a professional engineer do them) to ensure safety, particularly when large antenna loads are contemplated and particularly if guys that can easily stretch are used, such as Phillystran guys.

26.4.5 DESIGNING THE ANTENNA MAST

The antenna mast is the pipe or tubing that extends from the top of the rotator through the top of the tower. Wind loading on the mast can be significant for large antenna systems or for antennas mounted well above the top of the tower. This requires careful selection of the mast material and is an important part of completing your tower system design. **Table 26.1** gives yield strengths for various mast materials. For all but the smallest systems, do not depend on unknown materials for this critical component!

There are two types of round material used for masts — pipe and structural tubing. Pipe is commonly water pipe or conduit and has extremely limited value. Pipe is designed to carry liquids and is not rated for bending strength. While pipe may have a *yield strength* of 30,000 psi (pounds-per-square-inch), that will only accommodate small loads and wind speeds. Another problem is that the OD (outside diameter) of pipe is 1.9 inches which is smaller than the 2.0 inch ham hardware standard. Conduit should not be used as antenna mast at all except for very small antennas.

Tubing on the other hand does come in 2.0 inch sizes and is rated for strength. There are many different materials and manufacturing processes for tubing that may be used for a mast. Yield strengths range from 25,000 psi to nearly 100,000 psi. Knowing the minimum yield strength of the material used

Table 26.1
Yield Strengths of Mast Materials

Material Specification	*Yield Strength (lb/in.²)*
Drawn aluminum tube	
6063-T5	15,000
6063-T832	35,000
6061-T6	35,000
6063-T835	40,000
2024-T3	42,000
Aluminum pipe	
6063-T6	25,000
6061-T6	35,000
Extruded alum. tube	
7075-T6	70,000
Aluminum sheet and plate	
3003-H14	17,000
5052-H32	22,000
6061-T6	35,000
Structural steel	
A36	33,000
Carbon steel, cold drawn	
1016	50,000
1022	58,000
1027	70,000
1041	87,000
1144	90,000
Alloy steel	
2330 cold drawn	119,000
4130 cold worked	75,000
4340 1550 °F quench	162,000
1000 °F temper Stainless steel	
AISI 405 cold worked	70,000
AISI 440C heat-treated	275,000

(From *Physical Design of Yagi Antennas* by David B. Leeson, W6NL)

for a mast is an important part of determining if it will be safe.

When evaluating a mast with multiple antennas attached to it, special care should be given to finding the worst-case condition (wind direction) for the system. What may appear to be the worst load case, by virtue of the combined flat projected antenna areas, may not always be the exposure that creates the largest mast bending moment. Masts with multiple stacked antennas should always be examined to find the exposure that produces the largest mast bending moment. The antenna flat projected areas at 0° and 90° azimuths are particularly useful for this evaluation.

A manual procedure for determining the mast bending stress is available in **Appendix B** of this chapter. There are also several online calculators and the *MARC* (Mast, Antenna and Rotator Calculator) program is available from Champion Radio Products for a modest price. If you have any doubts about the strength requirements for your antenna mast, consult a professional installer or engineer.

The often-asked question, "How much mast should be inside the tower?" is certainly important. A good rule-of-thumb is to have ⅓ of the total mast length inside the tower. When selecting the length of the mast, allow for four feet or more of mast extending above the top of the highest antenna on the tower. This extra mast can then be used as a gin pole/pulley attachment point for other antenna or tower work.

26.5 TOOLS AND EQUIPMENT

Any job anywhere is easier and safer if you've got the right tools and tower work is no exception. If you are a weekend mechanic or handyman, you've probably already got most of what you need; all you need to do is add a few specialized items and you're good to go. If, on the other hand, all you have is a hammer, pair of pliers and a screwdriver, you'll need to make a trip or two to the tool store before you can really do anything. Once you have them, you'll be all set whenever any of your friends need help on their tower, too. Have the right tools and be prepared; you'll never go wrong.

26.5.1 THE TOWER TOOLBOX

Most amateur tower and antenna work can be done with a minimum of hand tools. Nut sizes of 7⁄16, ½ and 9⁄16 inch are the most common wrench sizes needed. **Table 26.2** lists the tools necessary for building and working on a typical ham tower. Your club may have a gin pole or guy wire tension gauge for members to borrow or you may be able to rent one.

26.5.2 SPECIALIZED TOWER TOOLS

Come-alongs

A come-along or hand cable winch, is very useful for pulling tower sections together, tightening tramlines and tensioning guy wires. You'll probably find more uses for it. Cheap ones cost $15-20 and are fine for occasional use. The best ones for tower work have spring-loaded safety latches over the end of the hooks, and very rugged (not stamped) ratchets and pawls.

Table 26.2
Essential tools

1	set of combination wrenches: 7⁄16, ½ and 9⁄16 inch
1	set of sockets ⅜ inch drive
1 each	deep sockets: 7⁄16, ½, 9⁄16 inch
1 each	screwdrivers (blade and Phillips)
2	adjustable pliers
1	diagonal cutter
1	razor blade utility knife
2	pulleys
1	drift pin or centering punch (for lining up tower sections)
1	hammer (attach some line for hanging on the tower)
3 each	adjustable wrenches — small, medium, and large
1	bubble level
6	carabiners
6	one-inch nylon webbing slings — 2 feet long
250 ft	rope (or more — this is enough for working on a 100 ft tower)
1	canvas bucket (for parts hauling and storage)
1	Loos PT-2 Tension Gauge
1 set	nutdrivers
1 (or more)	come-along or hand cable winch
1 (or more)	cable grips
1	circular saw with aggregate blade or hand grinder (for cutting metal, including guywires)
1	tag line (¼ inch is fine — you chose the size and length)
1	cordless ½ inch drill, with assorted bits and socket driver, 18 V recommended
1	set drill bits including step-drill, e.g. Uni-Bit
1	antenna analyzer
1	gin pole
1	soldering gun and solder

Cable Grips

The cable grip in **Figure 26.26** complements the come-along to tighten guy wires. It is a spring-loaded device that slides up the guy wire but clamps down when you put tension on it. Klein is the primary supplier of cable grips and they come in lots of sizes and designs for use with various materials. For amateur use, the Klein 1613-40 is for 3⁄16 and ¼ inch EHS guy material — used on the majority of amateur towers. If you have three come-alongs and cable grips you can put initial tension on a full set of three guy wires at the same time.

Steel Cutter

A portable (6.5-inch) circular saw with a steel-cutting aggregate blade will work to cut EHS guy wire, well, as will a 4½ inch hand grinder with 1/8-inch steel-cutting blades. Always use safety goggles when cutting metal!

Gin Pole

The purpose of a gin pole (see **Figure 26.27**) is to provide a support point high above the top of the tower for lifting and positioning an object. This allows the necessary work to be done on the object without whoever is doing the work having to support its weight at the same time. The Rohn gin pole (Rohn Erection Fixture EF2545) is rated for sections of Rohn 25G and 45G and comes with clamps to secure it to a leg of the assembled sections. Towers made of angled legs require a special gin pole — contact the manufacturer.

Typical gin pole loads are tower sections (10 feet long) and masts (6 to 22 feet long). Pick up these loads just above their balance point so they will hang naturally in the correct upright position for installation. The Rohn gin pole is 12 feet long, just right for lifting a 10-foot tower section. For 20-foot masts, a 12-foot gin pole is marginal because there is barely 10 feet of working length available from the gin pole. A large mast will probably exceed the rating for the Rohn gin pole

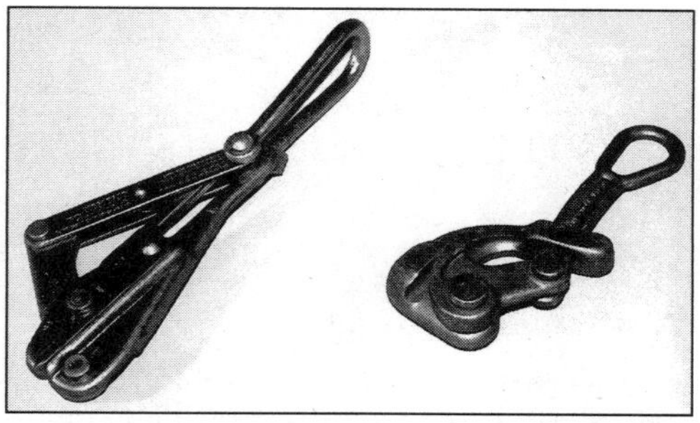

Figure 26.26 — Klein Chicago cable grip on the left and Klein Haven's grip on the right.

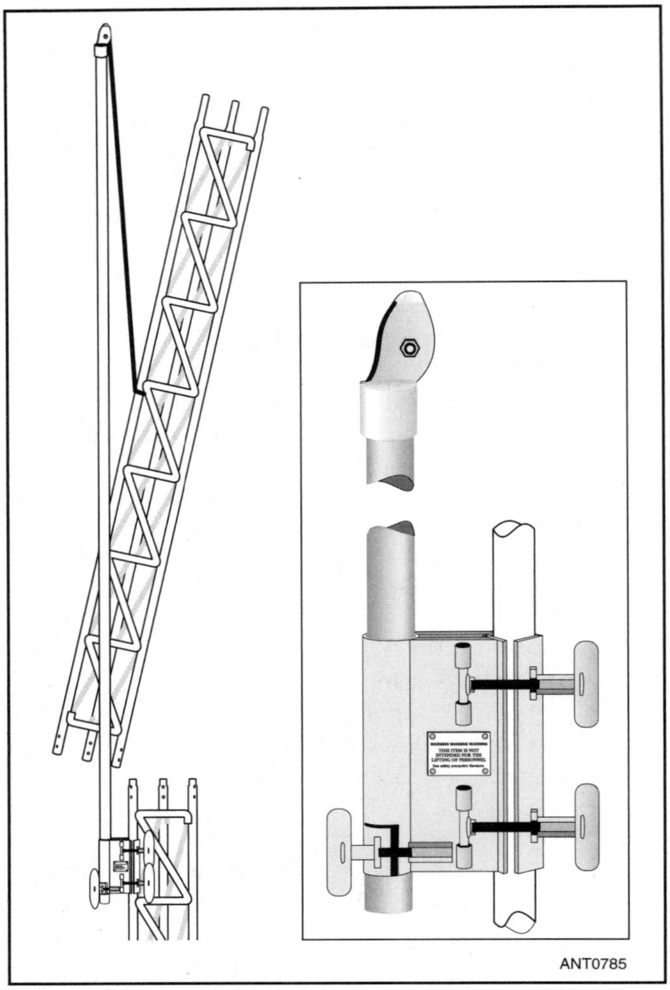

Figure 26.27 — Rohn "Erection Fixture" EF2545 also known commonly as a "gin pole."

(rated for 70 pounds). Large, heavy-duty masts require special handling; consult an experienced tower worker for instructions on installing large masts.

Carabiners

Carabiners are steel or aluminum snap-links with spring loaded gates as seen in **Figure 26.28A** and **26.28B**; they are invaluable for dozens of tower work tasks. A carabiner at the end of your haul rope can be attached to virtually anything that needs to be raised or lowered. A carabiner can be a third hand on the tower; you can clip a carabiner to almost anything with a rung or diagonal brace. You can instantly hang a pulley from a tower rung. Lightweight, they can be clipped on to your climbing harness for easy access. Experienced tower workers may carry twelve to fifteen carabiners on typical jobs. They typically cost $6 to $10 and will last for years with little or no maintenance. If the gate no longer opens and closes smoothly, the carabiner should be discarded.

A word of caution: mountain climbing carabiners are considered to be for private use and not OSHA-approved. Current ratings for mountain climbing carabiners are typically in the 6 to 10 kN (1350-2250 pounds of force) range with the gate open and 18-25 kN (4050-5625 pounds) with the gate closed. A typical rating for an OSHA-approved commercial carabiner — called a *safety hook* — is 40kN (9000 pounds). If you don't feel that mountain-climbing carabiners are adequately rated, safety hooks are available from safety equipment vendors.

Larger carabiners are available with locking gates; these will give you an added degree of safety, particularly if you are using them for your own protection or if you just want to be doubly safe. They're only a couple of dollars more than the standard, non-locking types.

Big carabiners are used for rescue work and other applications where a wider gate opening is needed. These are sometimes called *gorilla hooks* or *rebar hooks* and are used for larger tower rungs (Rohn BX, for example) and larger

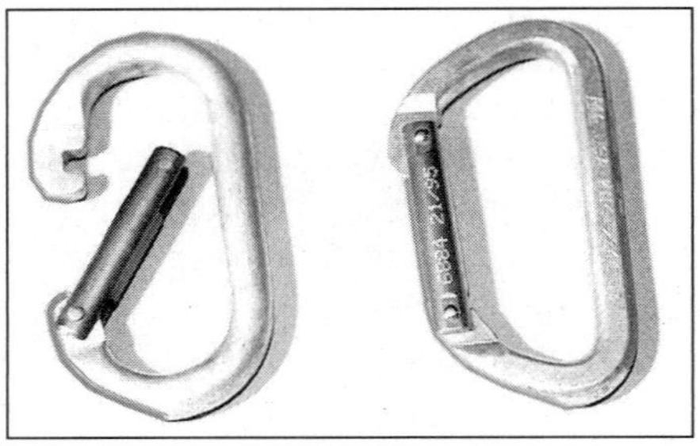

(A)

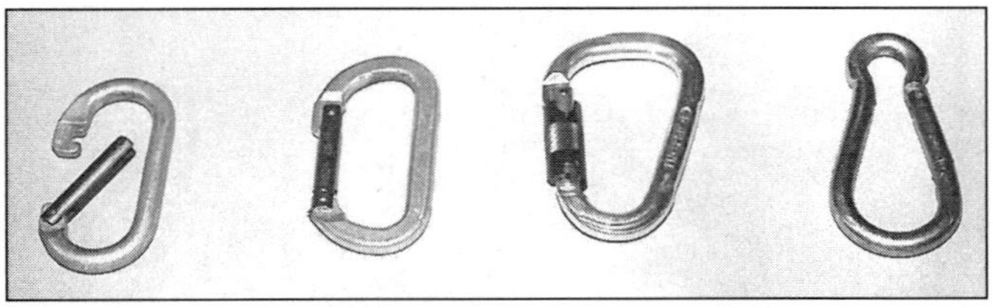

(B)

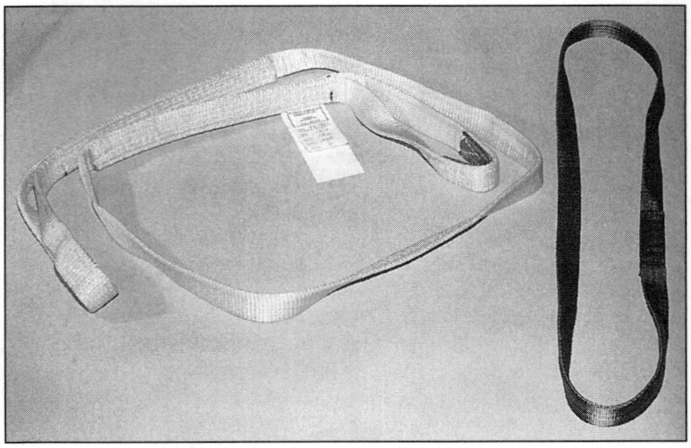

(C)

Figure 26.28 — (A) Oval mountain climbing type carabiners are ideal for tower workloads and attachments. The gates are spring loaded — the open gate is shown for illustration. (B) An open aluminum oval carabiner; a closed oval carabiner; an aluminum locking carabiner; a steel snap link. (C) A heavy duty nylon sling of the left for big jobs and a lighter-duty loop sling on the right for everything else.

loads. OSHA-compliant devices are offered by safety equipment vendors.

Using Carabiners

Here are some common ways that carabiners are used on tower projects:

1) Attach a sling to a guy anchor rod as an attachment point for the come-along when pulling guy wires.

2) Clip a carabiner onto a rung at the bottom of the tower then attach the haul rope snatch block pulley to it. This will change the direction of the haul rope from vertical to horizontal, making it much easier to pull. It also allows the ground crew workers to watch the load as it goes up or down the tower (without having to strain to look upward) and it removes them from the fall danger zone at the bottom of the tower.

3) Dedicate a sling and carabiner to the gin pole for easy lifting as the tower is assembled.

4) Put a loop through a frequently used tool, then clip it to your belt with a carabiner.

5) Always have a carabiner clipped into the bowline at the end of your haul rope and tag line for quick load attachment.

6) Clip a carabiner into the U-bolt on your rotator to haul it up.

Slings

A loop sling is made from one-inch nylon tubular webbing as seen in Figure 26.28C. Mountain-climbing slings are a continuous loop of webbing. A configuration with a sewn loop at each end is also useful. Slings can be wrapped around large or irregularly shaped objects and attached to a rope or tower member with a carabiner. Slings have around the same breaking strength as carabiners (approximately 4000 pounds, or 18.1 kN force) and are very handy for amateur applications and loads. Wrapping one around a tower rung or leg provides a convenient place to hang tools, parts or a pulley. Like carabiners, slings are not OSHA-approved but they're used for mountain climbing protection. OSHA-approved slings are available from a safety equipment vendor.

Lifting Loads with Slings

Slings are typically used in one of three rigging configurations shown in **Figure 26.29**:

1) *Straight pull* — A simple direct vertical attachment such as for a tower section. Run the sling around a tower member and clip both ends in a carabiner for lifting.

2) *Choker* — Wrap the sling around the load one or more times, insuring that you pull the loop through itself on each wrap, cinch it tight, clip it into a carabiner and pull it up. The more tension you put on the sling, the tighter it gets. Chokers are the best way to lift a mast.

A choker will work in many other cases where you have an irregular load to haul, not just masts. Using a sling as a choker reduces the lifting capacity of the sling by as much as 30% though. A U-clamp can be installed above the sling when raising a mast for redundant protection if desired.

3) *Basket* — Basket hitches distribute a load equally between the two legs of a sling. The greater the angle between the two legs, the smaller the capacity of the sling.

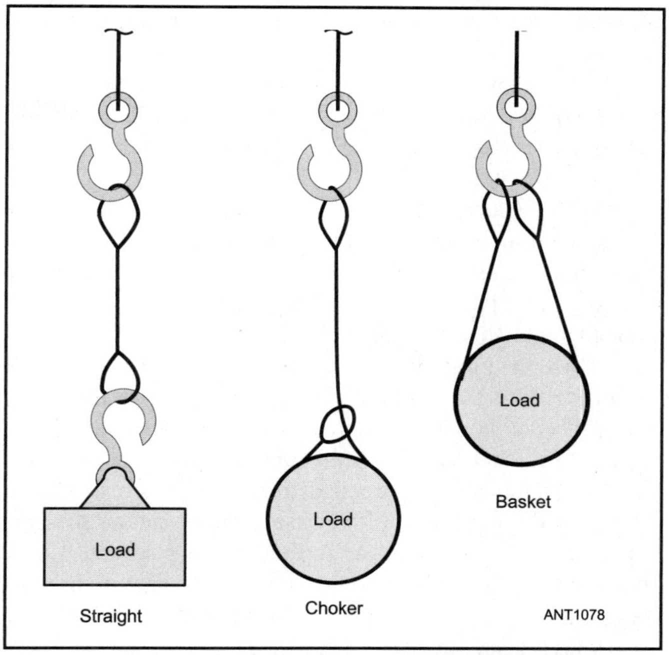

Figure 26.29 — Three basic lifting hitches used with slings and ropes.

26.5.3 USING A GIN POLE

This section was condensed from the ARRL book *Simple and Fun Antennas for Hams*. We're going to assume in the following discussion that you are using a Rohn EF2545 to install sections of Rohn 45G, which weigh about 70 pounds.

The main working part of the gin pole is the pulley mounted at the top of the 12-foot long heavy-wall aluminum tubing. This pulley has a haul rope going down to the ground crew through the center of the aluminum tube.

An adjustable, sliding clamp toward the bottom of the aluminum tubing is clamped to the tower using a swinging L-bracket-type clamp with two clamping bolts. These have T-bar handles that can be tightened by hand. In fact, this gin pole can be moved and deployed without any tools. The clamp is positioned just below the top braces of the tower section onto which the next tower section is to be installed. Once clamped to the top of the tower, you would loosen the T-bar handle that tightens the clamp against the sliding aluminum tube and slide the tubing up to its maximum extent.

In practice, the following steps are taken as each 10-foot section of tower is installed, one-by-one. We're assuming here that the gin pole starts out on the ground, with at least one person harnessed safely at the top of the tower. We're also assuming that the haul rope has been threaded through the aluminum tube and the top pulley, with a carabiner to prevent it from falling back down the tube.

Here's a rope tip — If the wind is blowing it may be difficult to lower the end of the rope to the ground. Attach a weight to the end of the rope; a wrench works well. If added weight isn't enough, use a carabiner to clip the free end of the haul rope around the other side of the rope. The carabiner will guide the free end back down the haul rope without blowing around.

1) The clamp holding the aluminum tubing is loosened so that the pulley on the tube can be lowered to where it is just above the bottom clamp. Then the T-bar handle for the tube clamp is tightened.

2) The climber lowers a work rope for the ground crew to tie to the gin-pole pull rope. (This work rope has been looped through a temporary pulley clipped to the top of the tower. It is also used to pull up tools and other materials.) The ground crew then pulls the gin pole up to the climber, using the work rope. Once the gin-pole head reaches the top of the tower, the climber clamps the gin pole clamp securely to the top of the tower. The tag line is then removed from the gin pole.

3) The T-bar handle for the tube clamp is loosened, and the aluminum tube is extended to its maximum height, as shown in Figure 26.27. Make sure the free end of the haul rope cannot slip through the top pulley, or else you'll have to lower the gin pole and go through this step again. In other words, the climber keeps the "business end" of the gin pole rope while raising the pole.

4) The free end of the haul rope is then dropped to the ground, often using a weight to keep the rope from waving about. (See the rope tip above.)

5) The ground crew then attaches the free end of the rope *above* the balance point of the tower section. For Rohn 25G or 45G there are eight horizontal cross braces per section. The crew should attach the rope to the fifth horizontal brace from the bottom. Please remember that the tower section should hang with its bottom down so that it is properly oriented when it reaches the top of the tower.

6) Once the bottom of the tower section has been lifted to just above the top of the legs of the bottom tower section, the tower crew can guide the section down onto the top of the three legs, while calling out to the ground crew instructions about *slowly lowering* the new section down onto the legs. See **Figure 26.30**, which illustrates guiding the new section of tower onto the previous section's legs.

Figure 26.30 — Tower worker lowering a new section onto the top of the assembled stack of sections. The gin pole attached to the left leg is bearing the weight as the tower worker gives verbal instructions to the ground crew pulling on the haul rope. (Mike Hammer, N2VR, photo)

7) Once the new tower section has been guided down onto the male ends, the pinning bolts are inserted and tightened with nuts. Note that Rohn uses two different sized bolts on 25G and 45G sections, with the larger diameter bolt on the bottom.

8) Finally, reposition the gin pole for the next section of tower. The T-bar at the clamp is loosened, the tube is dropped down to the level of the clamp, and the climber walks the gin pole up to the top of the section just installed and clamps it there, ready to pull up the next tower section.

26.5.4 ROPES AND ROPE CARE

If you are going to do tower and antenna work, you'll be using ropes. The most common uses are for haul rope, tag lines or work rope and temporary guys. A *halyard* is a rope used for hoisting.

Manila

Manila is the best known natural fiber rope. Manila must be handled and stored with care as any dampness will cause it to rot and damage its effectiveness and safety.

Polypropylene

Polypropylene makes lightweight, strong ropes that float on water, are rot-proof and are unaffected by water, oil, gasoline and most chemicals. Polypropylene rope is relatively stiff and doesn't take a knot well.

Nylon

Nylon is the strongest fiber rope commercially available. Due to its elasticity, nylon ropes can absorb sudden shock loads that would break ropes of other fibers. Nylon is particularly recommended for antennas using trees as supports. A disadvantage of new nylon rope is that it stretches by a significant percentage.

Nylon has very good resistance to abrasion and will last four to five times longer than natural fiber ropes. Nylon ropes are rot-proof and are not damaged by oils, gasoline, grease, marine growth or most chemicals.

Dacron

Dacron rope comes in three sizes (3⁄32, 3⁄16 and 5⁄16 inch) and is UV resistant. This is an excellent candidate for any rope used permanently outside such as for wire antenna halyards.

Rope Lay

All rope is twisted, or laid; and nearly all laid rope is *three-strand* construction, typically what you'll find at your local hardware store. Another type of rope is known as *braid-on-braid*, or *kernmantle*. This rope has a laid core covered with a braided jacket to produce a strong, easy-handling rope. In most instances, braid-on-braid rope is stronger than twisted rope of the same material and diameter. It is available in various synthetic fibers. Marine supply stores and mountain climbing stores carry a large variety of braid-on-braid types as well as a variety of types and sizes.

Which Rope to Use

The best rope for holding up wire antennas with spans up to 150 or 200 feet is ¼-inch nylon rope. Nylon is somewhat more expensive than ordinary rope of the same size, but it weathers much better. UV-resistant Dacron rope is also popular. After an installation with any new rope, it will be necessary to repeatedly take up the slack created by stretching. This process will continue over a period of several weeks, at which time most of the stretching will have taken place. Even a year after installation, however, some slack may still arise from stretching.

For ropes to be used on tower work, first decide which size will suit your needs based on working load. Most amateur loads are less than 100 pounds and very rarely do they exceed 250 pounds. A haul rope having a working load between 100 and 250 pounds will handle just about anything. **Table 26.3** summarizes the sizes and working loads for different types of rope.

Second, choose the type and material of your rope. Polypropylene rope is stiffer and more difficult to knot than nylon. Nylon and braid-on-braid ropes are softer and will take a knot very easily. The softer ropes also coil more easily and are more resistant to kinking.

Finally, choose the length that will be most useful for you. If you double the height of your tower and add 25%, you'll have plenty. A 100-foot tower requires $(100 \times 2) + (100 \times 2 \times 0.25) = 200 + 50 = 250$ feet.

Price varies from less than $20 for 600 feet of ¼ inch polypropylene rope to more than $100 for 165 feet of high quality kernmantle climbing rope. K4ZA recommends having a variety of ropes. All are doubled-braided construction. Lengths vary from 100 feet to 600 feet. Each rope is carried and stored in simple plastic tubs, which are labeled appropriately, including dates of purchase. If you simply feed the rope loosely into its container, it will pull back out without kinking or knotting.

Make certain that the rope ends will not unravel. Most supply stores will cut the length with a hot knife; that will do the best job of sealing the ends. You can do it at home by simply melting the ends with a lighter. An alternative is to tightly wrap a few layers of electrical tape or heatshrink tubing around the ends. Be sure to tape the ends of all your ropes to protect them.

Table 26.3
Rope Sizes and Safe Working Load Ratings in Pounds

3-strand twisted line

Diameter	*Manila*	*Nylon*	*Dacron*	*Polypropylene*
¼	120	180	180	210
⅜	215	405	405	455
½	420	700	700	710
⅝	700	1140	1100	1050

Double braided line

Diameter	*Nylon*	*Dacron*
¼	420	350
⅜	960	750
½	1630	1400
⅝	2800	2400

Rope Care

Inspect your rope periodically and replace it if there is any visible serious abrasion or damage. Here are some additional tips for using ropes:

1) Be certain your rope size is adequate for the job; don't use a rope that is too small.

2) Dry your rope before storing it. Natural fiber (Manila) ropes will mildew and rot if stored wet. You can put nylon ropes in the clothes dryer on low heat if they are really soaked.

3) Don't store ropes in direct sunlight; UV deterioration will significantly weaken them.

4) Cut out and discard any badly worn or abraded portions of a rope; better to have two shorter ropes you can trust than one long one that is suspect.

5) Keep your rope clean. Don't drag it through the mud, or over a rough or gritty surface. Try not to even step on your ropes, especially on wet or muddy soils.

6) Watch for kinks; they can cause permanent damage and weakening.

7) Protect ropes from all chemicals such as acids, oils, gasoline, paints, solvents, etc.

8) Avoid sudden strains; shock loading or jerking may cause failure.

9) Avoid overloading. A safe working load for a rope is 10-20% of its breaking strength.

10) Avoid abrasion. If the rope must run over a tower leg or any surface with a sharp edge, protect it with a layer or two of canvas or other such material.

11) Avoid bending a rope around corners or at sharp angles.

26.5.5 KNOTS

You can do about 98% of your tower and antenna work with only three knots — and you already know one of them. Remember that any knot will decrease the breaking strength of the rope — usually 40% or more. Choose and use the correct rope and knots for the job, and you should have no problems. Knots not listed here and additional knot-tying know-how can be found online at Animated Knots (**www.animatedknots.com**) and Real Knots (**www.realknots.com/knots**). **Figure 26.31** shows several common knots.

Overhand Knot

Start with an overhand loop, then passing the end under and up through the loop and then tightening. To form an overhand loop in the middle of a rope, double the rope for about two feet and tie an overhand knot with the doubled rope.

Bowline

The bowline forms a loop that will not slip or jam, yet unties easily. It is used for hoisting, joining two ropes and fastening a rope to a ring or carabiner. To tie it, form a small

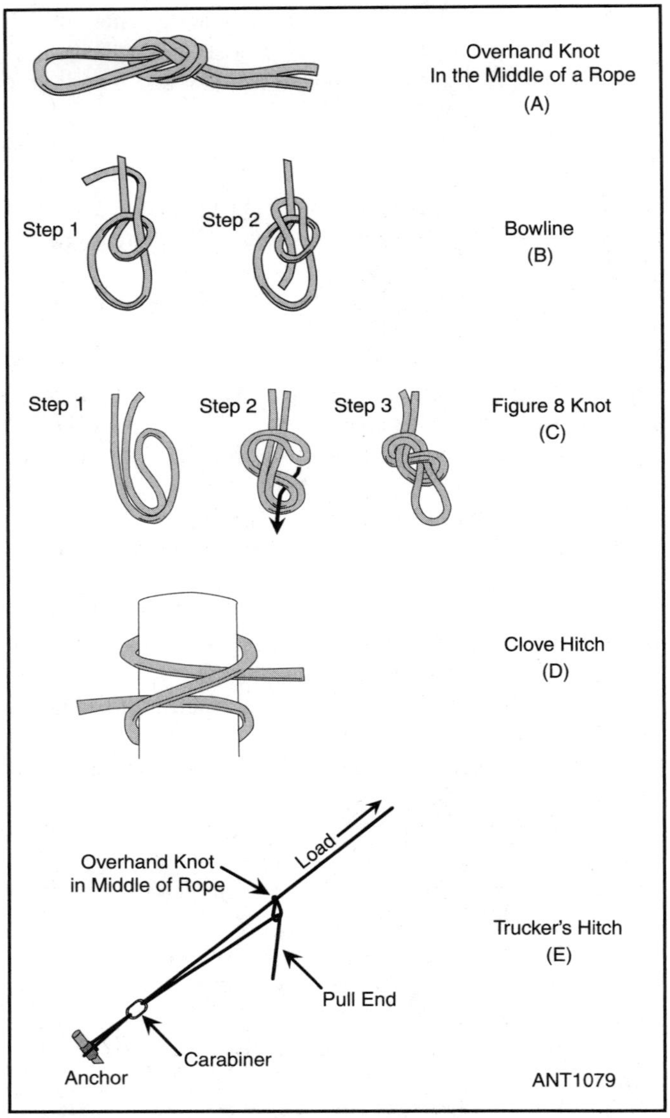

Figure 26.31 — Common knots used in tower and antenna work.

loop in the rope. Run the end up through the loop, behind the standing part, then back down through the loop. Pull tight. Practice this one until you can make it almost automatically.

Figure-eight

Simpler than the bowline, a figure-eight knot may be used in most situations in place of a bowline. It is tied like a doubled overhand except that the rope is twisted an additional half-turn before the knot is pulled through the loop. It is one of the few knots that can be easily untied after holding a severe impact load, such as a falling tower section. Its only disadvantage for tower work is that it is a physically larger knot, and it takes a bit more rope than a bowline.

Clove Hitch

The clove hitch can be invaluable when you're working with round objects, and it can be put on or around almost any object very quickly.

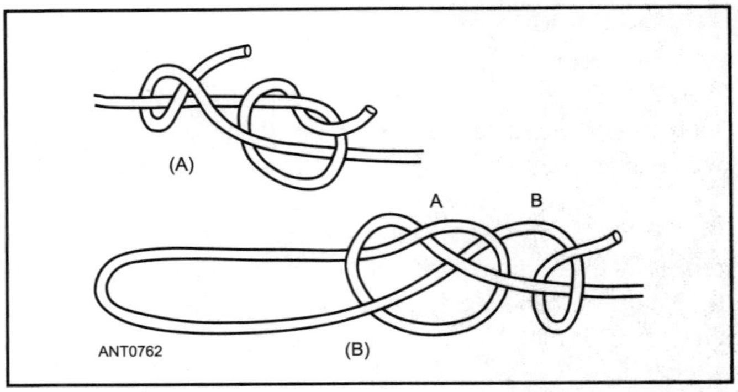

Figure 26.32 — This is one type of knot that will hold with slick types of line. Avoid these types of lines for lifting or safety uses. Shown at A, the knot for splicing two ends. B shows the use of a similar knot in forming a loop, as might be needed for attaching an insulator to a halyard. Knot A is first formed loosely 10 or 12 in. from the end of the rope; then the end is passed through the eye of the insulator and knot A. Knot B is then formed and both knots pulled tight. (courtesy Richard Carruthers, K7HDB)

Truckers' Hitch

The trucker's hitch allows you to tighten the rope as much as you can without a come-along. Tie an overhand loop (see above) toward the load end, run the end of the rope through a carabiner or shackle at a convenient anchor point, pass the end through the loop and then pull to tighten the rope. This technique gives twice the mechanical advantage of pulling on the single rope.

Plastic Line

For types of plastic line that are too slick to hold common knots well, **Figure 26.32** shows a more suitable knot. Needless to say, these lines should probably not be used for lifting loads or holding climbers.

26.5.6 PULLEYS

Pulleys are used constantly in tower and antenna projects. One should always be placed at the top of the tower for a haul rope to bring up materials. Steel pulleys costing $25-35 are found in many hardware stores or rigging shops but are heavy. Both K4ZA and K7LXC recommend lightweight nylon pulleys used by utility company line crews for tower work. Wood-sheathed pulleys used in "block and tackle" devices and for sail hoisting should work well for very heavy loads. K4ZA prefers lightweight (aluminum) pulleys designed for "rescue" work. These can be placed on the line at any point, and have load ratings comparable to carabiners as well.

Two important things to consider when shopping for pulleys are sheave size and sheave clearance. A sheave is the pulley wheel with a groove in it. A two-inch diameter sheave is the minimum size to use and larger sizes are better. Use a jam-proof pulley with minimal clearance between the sheave and the pulley body. If there is any way for your haul rope or cable to jump the pulley and get jammed, it almost certainly will.

A *snatch-block* is a pulley with a body that opens up

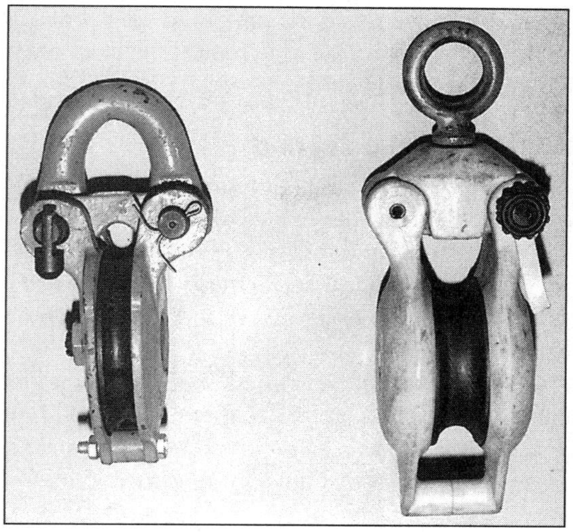

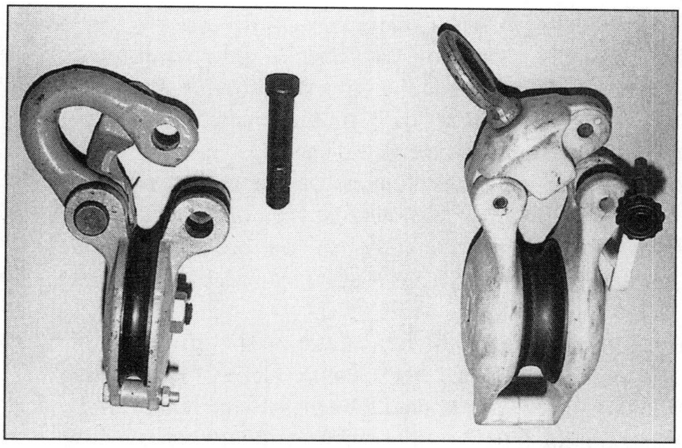

Figure 26.33 — (A) closed snatch-block pulleys. (B) open snatch-block pulleys.

so that it can be placed directly anywhere on a rope without needing one end of the rope to be free. This is useful when the rope is under tension (see **Figure 26.33**).

For supporting wire antennas, avoid small galvanized pulleys designed for awnings and clothesline pulleys. Use heavier and stronger pulleys intended for outdoor and marine installations with good-quality bearings.

An important consideration for pulleys to be constantly exposed to the weather is corrosion resistance. Use a good-quality pulley made entirely of alloys and materials that do not corrode readily. Galvanized pulleys will quickly rust. Marine pulleys have good weather-resisting qualities since they are usually made of bronze but they are comparatively expensive and the smaller pulleys are not designed to carry heavy loads.

26.6 TOWER CONSTRUCTION

Now that you have done all the planning and purchased the materials, it's time to start "growing" your tower. We'll start at the bottom!

26.6.1 THE LXC PRIME DIRECTIVE

After working on more than 225 Amateur Radio tower and antenna systems, Steve Morris, K7LXC, has seen many problems and failures that could have, and should have, been avoided. By avoiding these mistakes, your tower and antenna system will be safer and more reliable. You'll sleep better when that big storm blows through, too.

When it comes to tower construction, you are strongly advised to always observe the 'LXC Prime Directive; that is, to "DO what the manufacturer says." Similarly, "DON'T do what the manufacturer doesn't say to do." Follow the specifications for materials, concrete and wind load and you'll minimize the chances for failure, small or large. Follow the directions for assembling equipment and using tools and supplies. Professional engineers have designed every aspect of these systems for safe, long-term and reliable use and it's in your best interests to follow their specifications and directions. Pretty straightforward and simple to follow advice. K4ZA observes that there are many situations where nothing matches or is covered by the directions. In cases like these, either carefully devise a plan or seek professional advice.

26.6.2 BASE EXCAVATION AND REBAR

To avoid underground utility lines, please don't dig without calling one of the utility locator services. There are several websites such as **www.call811.com** that can help or you can call your local utility for assistance. Avoid expensive and embarrassing surprises. It may even be illegal in your area to begin digging without determining the location of buried utilities!

Hand-digging the hole for a large self-supporting tower base entails a lot of work! Excavating the necessary hole can be done quickly and effectively by a professional contractor. You can also rent excavating equipment and do the job yourself. No matter how you dig the hole, extreme caution should be used when someone is in the hole due to the risk of wall collapse. Many building regulations make it illegal to be in a hole or trench more than 4 feet deep without shoring up the sides of the hole. If you're doing the work yourself, never work alone in a hole that is deeper than your waist.

Building a Rebar Cage

Once the hole is dug you'll be installing the reinforcing bar, or rebar. The tower manufacturer will provide a recommended design for the rebar "cage" in the concrete base. **Figure 26.34** shows a typical completed cage.

Rebar is sized in eighths of an inch. For example, #4 rebar is 4⁄8 of an inch, or ½ inch, and #6 rebar is 6⁄8, or ¾ inch. Rebar vendors will cut and bend the rebar to your order which is a lot easier than buying long lengths of it at your local hardware store and trying to cut it yourself.

You can either build the rebar cage on the ground or in the hole. You'll need a backhoe or other piece of equipment to lift the completed cage up and lower it into the hole. Building the cage in the hole is harder since room to work is really restricted. Remember to shore up the hole and don't work by yourself.

To tie the rebar together to form the cage use bailing/tie wire at each joint. Take about 2 feet of bailing wire and bend it in half. Wrap the tie wire through one of the Xs of the joint twice. Next wrap it twice through the other axis of the joint, bring the ends together and wrap them together several times. Use a large pair of pliers, or a wire tie tool, to twist it until snug. To stiffen the cage, add an X cross brace, using two pieces of rebar across each face.

Guy anchors are easy to deal with since they're smaller, take less concrete and you don't have to move as much soil. The easiest way to locate the anchors is to temporarily put up a tower section at the desired location and then sight through each face across the opposite leg — that'll give you the angle. Then run your measuring tape out the appropriate distance to the anchor location. A more accurate way of measuring is to use a transit, which will ensure each guy anchor is spaced exactly 120 degrees apart. Suitable transits can be rented quite reasonably.

Once the rebar cage has been placed in the hole, a wooden form surrounding the top of the base hole provides for a neater appearance and also raises the top of the base above ground a few inches. This allows water to run off the base and not pool around the legs or bolts of the tower.

Figure 26.34 — The rebar cage for KX8D's tower base. (Duane Durflinger, KX8D, photo)

Installing the Base Section

If you're installing a guyed tower such as Rohn 25G or 45G with tubular legs, be sure to put 4 inches or so of crushed stone at the bottom for drainage and set the legs of the base in the gravel. Water will condense in the legs, and if there's no place for the water to drain out, it will build up and split the leg when it freezes.

Place the base section, if used, in the hole without touching the rebar cage and use wooden braces to hold it precisely vertical. Alternately, you can join one of the tower sections to the base section and use temporary guys to hold it up. For bigger tower bases, it's sometimes convenient to attach the leg(s) to the rebar cage with tie wire. A properly constructed rebar cage will be strong enough to support it and you can stand on it if needed.

If anchor bolts are being used, a piece of plywood with the proper hole pattern can be used to hold the bolts in position while the concrete is being poured.

26.6.3 CONCRETE FOR BASES

The tower manufacturer will specify the type of concrete required for the base and your building permit may also impose some requirements. The strength specification is generally 2500 to 4000 PSI for tower bases and a slump (a measure of the concrete's workability) of 4. Consult an engineer if you are unfamiliar with ordering or working with concrete. The Wikipedia entry for concrete (**en.wikipedia.org/wiki/Concrete**) provides a great deal of good information.

You can mix the concrete yourself by using bags of premixed concrete and a powered mixer. It takes about 45 80-pound bags of concrete mix to make one cubic yard of concrete so for large bases ordering ready-mix concrete is more practical. The delivery truck will need to be relatively close to the hole (within 10 to 15 feet) to be able to position the delivery chute properly. If the truck cannot get close enough to the hole, you'll have to move the concrete yourself.

To avoid moving tons of concrete (a yard of concrete weighs about 4000 pounds!) in long runs to the hole with a wheelbarrow, use a concrete line pumper — a truck-mounted pump that uses 3-4-inch hoses laid on the ground for concrete distribution. They're not that expensive and can pump up to 400 feet. There are big hydraulic boom pumpers that can work over obstacles such as buildings and fences, and much greater distances, but they are more expensive to hire. In either case, using professional equipment makes the job of moving tons of concrete much easier.

Concrete takes a long time to cure to its rated strength — at least three weeks until it reaches 90% of its rated strength. The concrete supplier can give you complete instructions on how long to wait and whether the concrete needs to be kept damp during the curing period or any other special treatment. It's hard to sit and wait a month before beginning work on the tower but be safe and don't put any load on the base until it is ready to support it. Your building permit may require inspection of the base before tower work can begin.

26.6.4 WORKING WITH GUY WIRES

Guy wires are the heart of a reliable guyed tower system. Almost any tall amateur tower is going to be guyed. Rohn 25G, 45G and 55G are the most common towers used by amateurs and they all need to be guyed. Before you begin building the tower, familiarize yourself with guy wires and the associated equipment, hardware and techniques. Practice until you are confident of being able to handle guy wires correctly.

Guy Wire Grades

Steel guy wire comes in several different grades. Rohn specifications call for EHS (Extra High Strength) cable exclusively. As you can see from **Table 26.4**, this is the strongest steel cable available.

Guy Wire Terminations

The three most common methods of terminating guy wires are to use cable clamps, swaged or crimped pressed fittings, or preformed guy grips. With the advent of the preformed guy grips, cable clamp and swage fitting use has declined dramatically.

Cable Clamps

The least expensive and most common cable fittings are cable clamps consisting of two parts; the U-bolt and the saddle. The guy wire is put through a thimble or insulator and doubled back for clamping (this is called a *turnback*) as shown in **Figure 26.35**. A thimble is used to prevent the wire from breaking because of a sharp bend at the point of intersection. Conventional wisdom strongly recommends the use of thimbles that are at least two wire sizes larger than the cable to provide a more gentle wire bend radius.

Wrapping the wire around the thimble results in two parallel guy wires. The wire that bears the tension of the guy wire forces is called the "live" end and the short piece that is turned back is called the "dead" end. It's "dead" because it is not load bearing.

Table 26.4
Guy Wire Specifications

Typical 3⁄16 inch steel guy wire breaking strengths

Common Grade	1540 pounds
Utility Grade	2400 pounds
Siemens-Martin Grade	2550 pounds
High Strength Grade	2850 pounds
Stainless Steel Aircraft	3700 pounds
Extra High Strength Grade	3990 pounds
Phillystran HPTG4000	4000 pounds

EHS guy wire sizes and breaking strengths

3⁄16 inch	3990 pounds
1⁄4 inch	6650 pounds
5⁄16 inch	11,200 pounds
3⁄8 inch	15,400 pounds

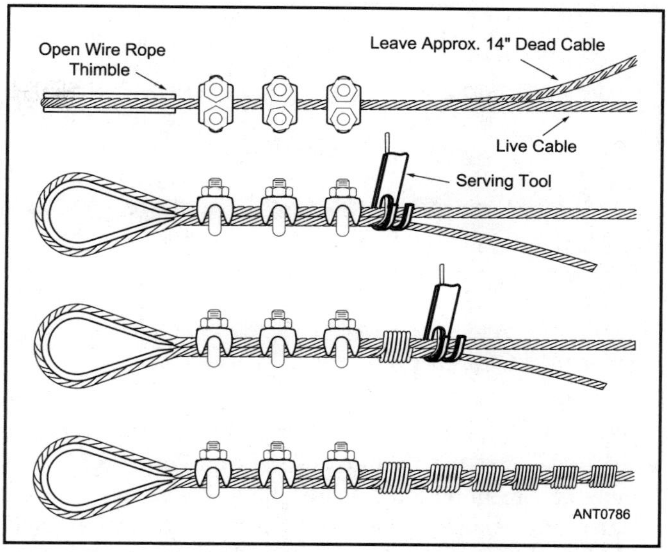

Figure 26.35 — Traditional method for securing the end of a guy wire. This technique is becoming increasingly uncommon as Preforms replace cable clamps.

Always use three cable clamps per joint and make certain that the saddle is on the live (load-bearing) side of the guy wire. The saddle portion provides the majority of the holding capacity of the clamp and goes on the "live" side of the cable. To remember the correct method, use the saying "Don't saddle a dead horse." In other words, don't put the saddle on the dead side of the turnback. A clamp mounted backwards loses 40% of the holding capacity of a properly installed clamp.

At one time, the guy wire end strands were unwoven and wrapped around the guy wire itself. This process was known as "serving," and was best done using a special tool. Not only is this procedure quite difficult with EHS, the wrapped bundle will trap water running down the cable, which will accelerate the rusting process. With the near-universal adoption of Big Grips, this practice is no longer used very much.

Swaged Fittings

Swaged fittings produce a strong, clean connection. If you don't like the look of lots of cable clamps, swaging may be for you. The most common swages are *Nicopress* fittings shown in **Figure 26.36**. While the fittings themselves are relatively inexpensive, you have to buy or rent a Nicopress tool to crimp them onto the guy wire. Once they're crimped on they can't be removed.

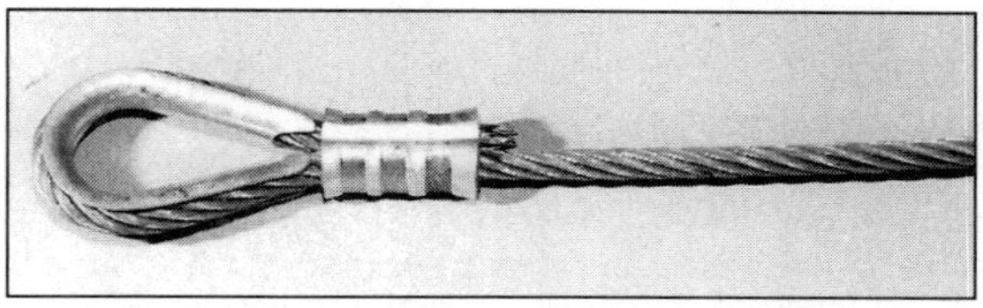

Figure 26.36 — Swaged guy wire end using Nicopress fitting.

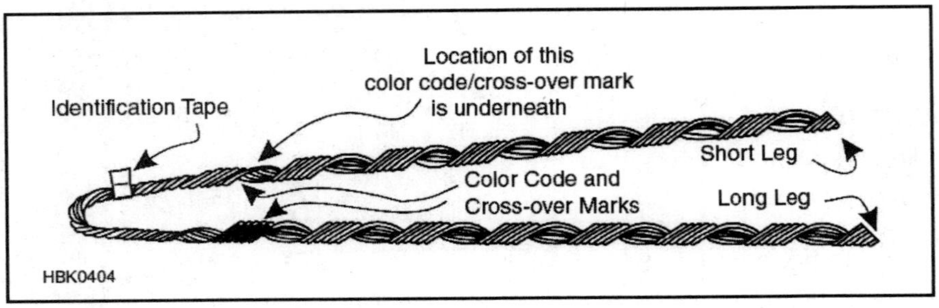

Figure 26.37 — Preformed guy wire "dead end" grip. The grip is wound around the guy wire and holds the load through friction.

Preformed Guy Grips

Preformed guy grips (or *Big-Grip Dead-Ends* from Preformed Line Products — **www.preformed.com**) are the easiest to use and the most expensive (see **Figure 26.37**). You simply curl them onto the end of the guy wire to produce a permanent termination. Preformed cable grips have virtually replaced cable clamps for power, telephone, and communications companies. Factory specs say that you can remove and reapply the grips twice. If removal is necessary after a guy grip has been installed for a period greater than three months, it must be replaced. If you can't find them locally, they are available from several *QST* advertisers.

Preforms are color-coded for guy wire sizes, as follows:

⅛ inch — blue
3/16 inch — red
¼ inch — yellow
9/32 inch — blue
5/16 inch — black
⅜ inch — orange

Use only the correct size Preforms for the guy wire you are using. Guy wire and related hardware, including cable clamps and Preforms, are designed for a certain number of strands in the wire rope, and for a specific lay for each cable size. Do not mix different hardware. Note that Preformed grips have two sets of crossover marks. The set closest to the loop is for normal guy wire attachment. The set farthest from the loop is for when the guy wire goes through an insulator.

Installing Preforms

Preformed guy grips are precision devices, designed to be installed by hand; do not use any tools to install them. They should be installed only in conjunction with heavy-duty wire rope thimbles.

1) Insert a heavy-duty thimble into the eye of the Preform, then through the attaching hardware (shackle, etc.).

2) Wrap the first leg (either one) around the guy wire with two complete wraps. Simply wrap them around the guy wire. Line up the crossover marks, then wrap the second leg with two complete wraps, ending opposite the first leg.

3) Complete the installation by either simultaneously wrapping both legs (keeping the legs opposite each other) or alternating between the legs a couple of wraps at a time. Bending the EHS guy wire as you wrap the Preform leg around it will make it easier to attach.

4) Finish the short leg first, then the long leg.

5) Seat the ends of the legs by hand or use a flat blade screwdriver under the end of the strands. For Phillystran guy wire you may need to separate the strands to finish the ends of the Preform.

6) Attach a black tie-wrap or end sleeve around the grip at the end to secure it.

Cutting Guy Cable

Many different methods have been used over the years to cut guy cable. These days, EHS (extra high strength) guy wire is the standard and special cutters are needed to cut this hard wire. Always wear safety goggles when working with guy wires. There can be lots of metal chips floating around when you cut them or the guy wire can easily whip around and hit you in the face or other body parts.

Table 26.5
Guy Cable Comparisons

Cable	*Nominal Dia. (inches)*	*Breaking Strength (lbs)*	*Weight (lbs/100 ft)*	*Elongation (inches/100 ft)*	*Elongation (%)*
3/16 inch 1×7 EHS	0.188	3990	7.3	6.77	0.56%
¼ inch 1×7 EHS	0.250	6700	12.1	3.81	0.32%
HPTG6700	0.220	6700	3.1	13.20	1.10%
HPTG8000	0.290	8000	3.5	8.90	0.74%
5/16 inch 1×7 EHS	0.313	11200	20.5	2.44	0.20%
HPTG11200	0.320	11200	5.5	5.45	0.45%
⅜ inch fiberglassrod	0.375	13000	9.7	5.43	0.45%

EHS steel cable information is taken from ASTM A 475-89, the industry standard specification for steel wire rope.
The HPTG listings are for Phillystran aramid cables, and are based on the manufacturers' data sheets. The elongation (stretch) values are for 100 feet of cable with a 3000-pound load.

Resonance in Guy Wires

If steel guy wires are resonant at or near the operating frequency, they can receive and reradiate RF energy. By behaving as parasitic elements, the guy wires may alter and thereby distort the radiation pattern of a nearby antenna. For low frequencies, where a dipole or other simple antenna is used, this is generally of little or no consequence. But at higher frequencies, where a unidirectional antenna is installed, it is desirable to avoid pattern distortion if at all possible. The symptoms of re-radiating guy wires are usually a lower front-to-back ratio and a lower front-to-side ratio than the antenna is capable of producing. The gain of the antenna and the feed point impedance will usually not be significantly affected, although sometimes changes in SWR can be noted as the antenna is rotated. (Of course other conductors in the vicinity of the antenna can also produce these same symptoms.)

The amount of re-radiation from a guy wire depends on two factors — its resonant frequency, and the degree of coupling to the antenna. Resonant guy wires near the antenna will have a greater effect on performance than those that are farther away. Therefore, the upper portion of the top level of guy wires should warrant the most attention with horizontally polarized arrays. The lower guy wires are usually closer to horizontal than the top level, but by virtue of their increased distance from the antenna, are not coupled as tightly to the antenna.

To avoid resonance, the guys should be broken up by means of egg or strain insulators.

Figure 26.A shows wire lengths that fall within 10% of ½-λ resonance (or a multiple of ½ λ) over all the HF amateur bands.

Unfortunately, no single length greater than about 14 feet avoids resonance in all bands. If you operate just a few bands, you can locate greater lengths from the chart that will avoid resonance. For example, if you operate only the 14, 21 and 24 MHz bands, guy wire lengths of 27 feet or 51 feet would be suitable, along with any length less than 16 feet.

Of course, you could neutralize the whole problem by using Phillystran at some expense. One way to minimize the cost is to use Phillystran on only the top or top two sets of guys. Further, it's not necessary to use Phillystran all the way down to the anchor. Even using Phillystran for the top 50% will reap benefits.

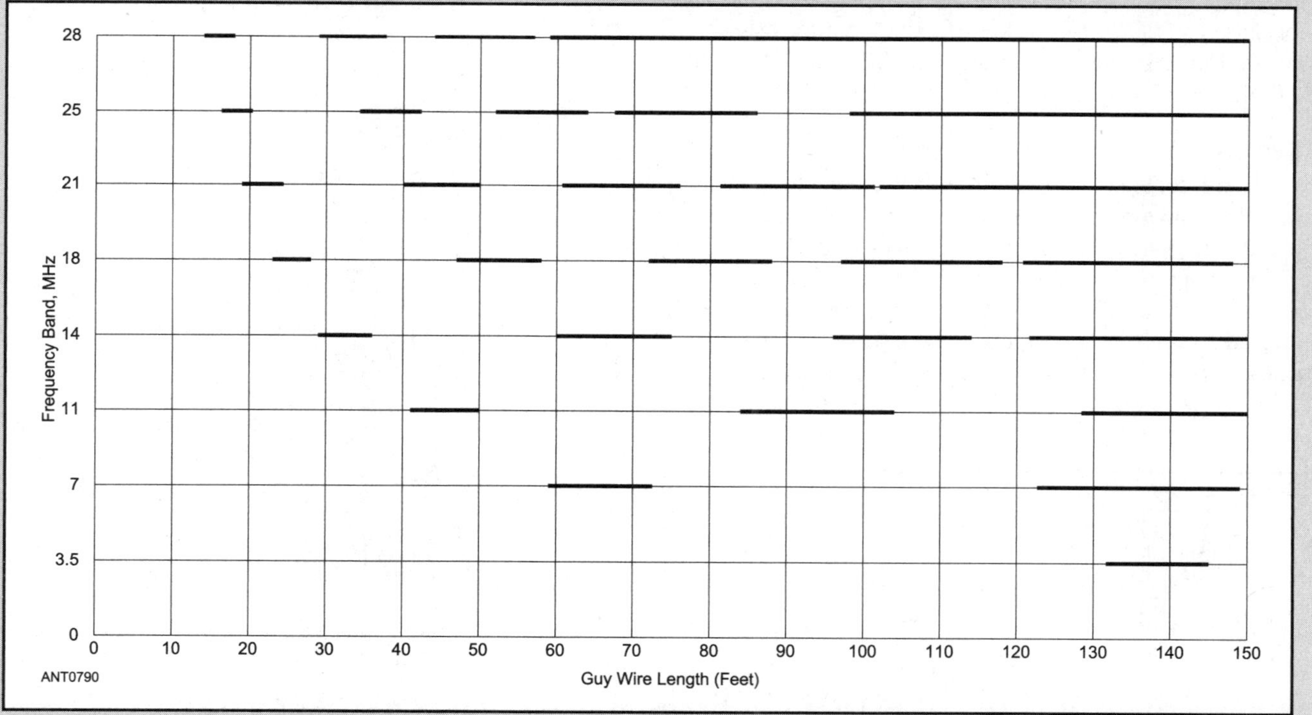

Figure 26.A — The black bars indicate ungrounded guy wire lengths to avoid for the eight HF amateur bands. This chart is based on resonance within 10% of any frequency in the band. Grounded wires will exhibit resonance at odd multiples of a quarter wavelength. (chart by Jerry Hall, K1TD)

To cut the guy wire, rent or borrow a bolt cutter. Be certain it will cut EHS, not just soft metal. Another method is to use a circular saw or hand grinder with a metal cutting aggregate blade. These blades are less than $4 at your neighborhood hardware store and will cut pipe mast material as well. Use electrical tape not only to mark where you want to cut, but also to prevent the guy wire from unraveling after it's cut.

Phillystran

Introduced in 1973, Phillystran offers the strength of EHS guy wire with the added advantage that it is nonconducting and electrically transparent to RF. It consists of a polyurethane resin-impregnated aramid fiber rope with a thick extruded jacket of specially formulated polyurethane. Its non-conductivity makes it ideal for tower systems where some antennas will be under or close to guy wires. Guy wire interaction with stacks and wire antennas will be eliminated by using Phillystran. **Table 26.5** compares EHS, Phillystran and fiberglass rod guying material.

Recommended Phillystran installation calls for at least 10 to 25 feet of steel cable from the end of the Phillystran to the anchor. This prevents damage from vandalism, accidents and ground fires that can weaken Phillystran and cause a tower failure.

Phillystran Cable Grips

Preformed Line Products now manufactures Phillystran-compatible Preformed guy grips. These are different from those used with ¼ or ⅜ inch EHS with a different lay (twist) to match the characteristics of Phillystran. The grips for Phillystran cannot be interchanged with the grips for EHS.

The guy grips are installed generally the same way, except that you must keep some tension on the *Phillystran* while installing them, and you may have to split the strands on the end of the Preform in order to finish wrapping them on. This is because the *Phillystran* is very flexible, particularly when compared to EHS. Other than that, they're installed just like the Preforms for steel guys.

Attaching Guy Wires to the Tower

Figure 26.38 shows two different methods for attaching guy wires to towers. At Figure 26.38A, the guy wire is simply looped around the tower leg and terminated in the usual manner. At Figure 26.38B, a *guy bracket*, with *torque arms* has been added. Even if the torque arms are not required, it is preferred to use the guy bracket to distribute the load from the tower/guy connection to all three tower legs, instead of just one. The torque bracket is more effective at resisting torsion on the tower than simply wrapping the Big Grip or EHS around the tower leg. Rohn offers another guy attachment bracket, called a *Torque Arm Assembly* (sometimes called a "star guy" bracket), which allows six guys to be connected between the bracket and anchors. This is by far the best method of stabilizing a tower against high torque loads, and is recommended for installations with large antennas.

Attaching Guys to Anchors

Turnbuckles and associated hardware are used to attach guy wires to anchors and to provide a convenient method for adjusting tension. **Figure 26.39A** shows a turnbuckle with a single guy wire attached to the eye of the anchor. Turnbuckles are usually fitted with either two eyes, or one eye and one jaw. The eyes are the oval ends, while the jaws are U-shaped with a bolt through each tip. Figure 26.39B shows two turnbuckles attached to the eye of an anchor. The procedure for installation is to remove the bolt from the jaw, pass the jaw over the eye of the anchor and reinstall the bolt through the jaw, through the eye of the anchor and through the other side of the jaw.

If two or more guy wires are attached to one anchor,

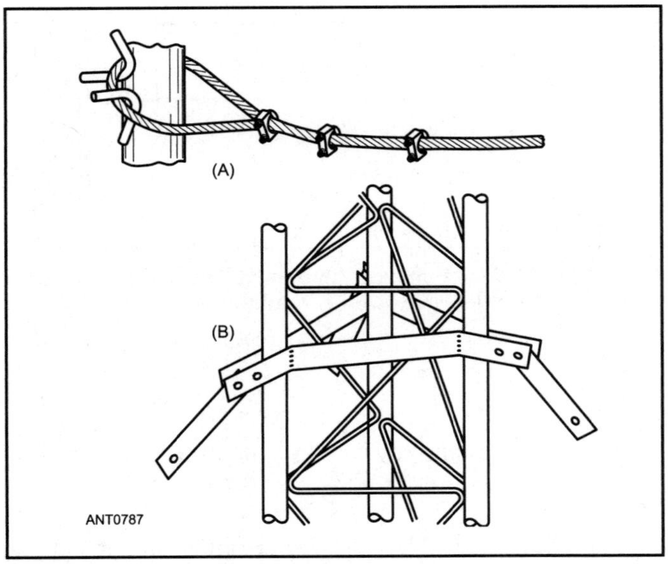

8Figure 26.38 — Two methods of attaching guy wires to tower. See text for discussion.

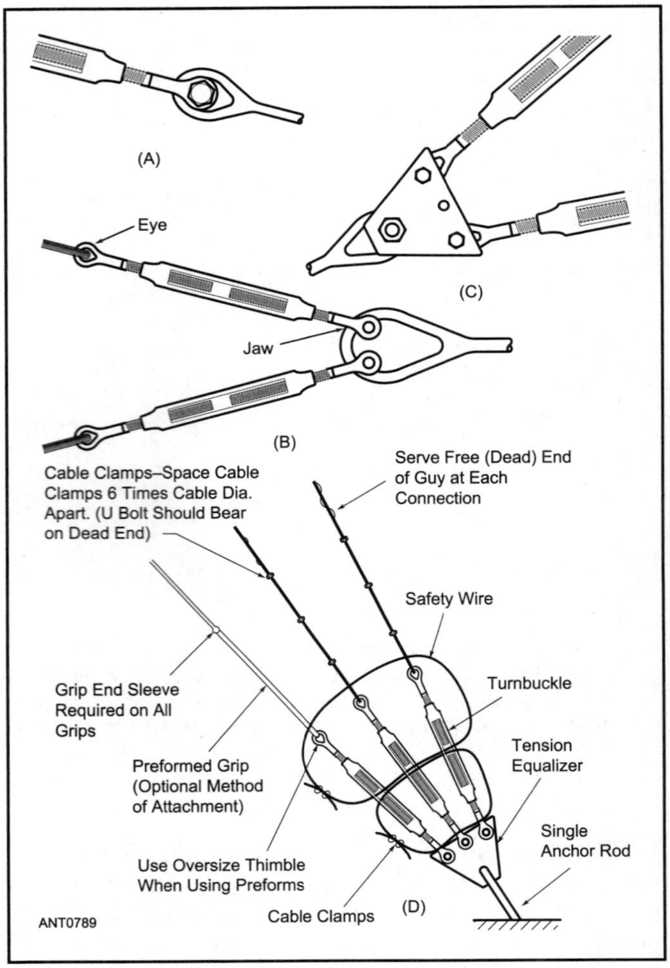

Figure 26.39 — Variety of means available for attaching guy wires and turnbuckles to anchors.

equalizer plates should be installed (Figure 26.39C). In addition to providing a convenient point to attach the turnbuckles, the plates pivot slightly to equalize the various guy loads and produce a single load applied to the anchor. Once the installation is complete, a safety wire should be passed through the turnbuckles in a figure-eight fashion to prevent the turnbuckles from turning and getting out of adjustment (Figure 26.39D).

Pulling and Tensioning Guy Wires

Once the guys are cut to their appropriate lengths and are attached to the tower, you need to pull them so you can attach them to the turnbuckle at the guy anchor. One method is to pull them by hand with a moderate amount of force (100-200 pounds of pre-tension will stabilize the tower under construction) and then secure them to the anchor. This will deflect the tower slightly but will put some initial tension on them. Another method shown in **Figure 26.40** is to use a come-along and cable grip. Place a nylon sling around the guy anchor for attachment of the other end of the come-along.

Most manufacturers require the final tension of the guy wire to be 10% of its breaking strength. That amount of tension is necessary to eliminate looseness in the cable caused by the spiral wire construction and to eliminate excessive dynamic guy and tower motion under wind loading. For 3/16-inch EHS that amount of tension would be approximately 400 pounds.

How do you know when you've got the right amount of tension? A calibrated dynamometer can be used, but such tools are quite expensive. The Loos Tension Gauge in **Figure 26.41** is an accurate, inexpensive device for measuring guy tension. While originally designed for accurate, repeatable tuning of a sailboat's standing rigging (which typically uses 7X19 SS cable), the accuracy of measurement is quite good

Figure 26.40 — To tighten guy wires a nylon sling (see at the lower right of the photo) is attached to the guy anchor and a come-along. The come-along is then hooked to a Klein cable grip on the guy wire. The come-along is then tightened until the required guy tension is achieved as measured with a Loos tension gauge or dynamometer. The guy wire can then be attached to the guy anchor and the Klein grip released. (courtesy of Dale Boggs, K7MJ)

Figure 26.41 — Loos PT-2 guy wire tension gauge.

Figure 26.42 — A length of guy cable is used to assure that the turnbuckles do not loosen after they are tightened. This procedure is an absolute requirement in guyed tower systems, as shown by Jodi Morin, KA1JPA (left) and Helen Dalton, KB1HLF.

enough for ham radio towers, using EHS. It works by measuring the deflection of the guy wire and does not need to be inserted into the guy wire. (If you are using Phillystran, measure tension in the recommended section of steel EHS between the Phillystran and the ground anchor.)

The guy is gripped with a cable grip, which is connected to the anchor below the eye (or equalizer plate) with a block and tackle arrangement (see Figure 26.40) or a come-along. Then the turnbuckle is adjusted to take up the load, the cable grip is released and the final guy tension is adjusted and checked.

Regardless of how you measure guy tension, the important thing is to tighten all the guys so tension is approximately the same within each set of guys. Having all tensions equal avoids pulling the tower out of alignment. When you adjust the guys at each level, you should check the tower for vertical alignment and straightness. This is often done with a transit from two ground points located 90° from each other. After plumbing the tower up to the first set of guys, another method is to look up the face of the tower from the bottom. It will be obvious if the sections above the guys are out of plumb.

Safety Wiring Turnbuckles

The final step in installing guy wires is to safety wire them as shown in **Figure 26.42**. This keeps turnbuckles from loosening from normal vibration and discourages vandalism. Use some pieces of leftover guy cable and loop it through the anchor shackle and the turnbuckles, securing the ends with a cable clamp.

26.6.5 BEFORE WORKING ON A TOWER

The Work Crew

For small antenna jobs, two people (one on the tower and one on the ground) are usually enough. Even erecting 25G tower (40 pounds per section) can be accomplished with two people but a third person to handle the tag line is very handy. For 45G, it takes two people on the haul rope as these sections weigh 70 pounds each and a section with guy brackets is close to 100 pounds.

Commercial riggers commonly use some type of winch or windlass to haul up heavy loads. For working with large antennas, such as 40 meter beams, two people on the tower along with one or two tag line handlers, plus two to four on the haul rope, makes for a large crew.

Regardless of size, take care of your crew! Roll out the red carpet for them. They're giving up their time to help you and they deserve it. Make an effort to provide lots of water or iced tea and by all means feed everybody a nice lunch. *No alcohol* until after the work is done!

Pre-Work Meeting

On project day, the first thing you should do is have a session with the entire crew and go over what is going to be accomplished and the order and manner in which it is going to be done. Cover all safety issues, commands and equipment related to the job. Identify any hazards in the work area, such as power lines. Explain any specialized equipment or tools, including carabiners and slings, come-alongs, hoisting grips and so on. If a come-along or other special tool is going to be used, be sure that someone on the tower and ground crews knows how to use it properly.

One of the most important jobs for the ground crew is to act as a spotter and take care of the safety of the tower crew and the whole team. Point out where a phone is and any phone numbers that may be needed in an emergency. Also discuss and understand what to do in an emergency situation. For minor emergencies, knowing where the closest medical facility is will be valuable. Since just about everyone will have a mobile phone, calling 911 won't present any problems for bigger emergencies. Not many emergency services professionals have been trained for high-angle rescue such as lowering someone off of a tower, so you're probably going to be on your own at least initially. Search and rescue crews are used to working with ropes and other hardware for extrications, so hopefully your 911 operator will be able to put you in touch with them. Physical trauma can set in quickly even with a fall-arrest harness so fast action is vital.

Let your ground crew know not to be standing around the bottom of the tower unless they must specifically be there. This is the danger zone for dropped tools and hardware which reaches high speeds and can bounce a long way from the tower.

Rule #1. The tower crew is in charge. The ground crew should do what the tower crew tells them and not do what the tower crew doesn't tell them. Being on the ground crew is usually pretty boring, but they should not do anything that would have any impact up on the tower. With very few exceptions, the ground crew shouldn't do anything unless directed to. If they are not sure about something, ask the tower crew.

Rule #2. When the ground crew is talking to the tower crew, look up and talk in a loud, concise voice. Although it may be still and quiet on the ground, the ambient noise level on the tower is always significantly higher 50 feet or more in the air and you have major communication obstacles. VHF/UHF handhelds, FRS handhelds, or VOX-operated 47 MHz headsets all work. Make sure that all have fully charged batteries before work begins.

Rule #3. Really communicate. Insist that the ground crew keeps the tower crew really informed. If something is lowered to the ground, the ground crew should tell the tower crew that it's "on the ground." If the tower crew is waiting for the ground crew to do something, they should keep the tower crew informed about status. This prevents the "everybody waiting on everybody" problem.

Commands

Make certain that everyone understands each of the commands — whether they are the ones given here as examples or your own preferred set — and that they all use the same ones. All of the following commands refer to the "load" (antenna, tower section, etc.) and are applied to the "haul rope" (the line to which the load is attached). There are also several common hand signals to use. Simple ones for up, down and stop can be useful, particularly in high-noise situations. Make certain everyone knows what they are. For example:

■ "Tension" tells the ground crew to put tension on the line, to take up any slack. Once you have some tension, move the load with "Up" or "Down" commands. Add "Slow" for slower lifting and lowering.

■ "Slack" means giving the load some slack.

■ "All slack" means the ground crew may gradually and gently release their grip on the load.

■ "Stop" is obvious and "Stand by" indicates that they should maintain their assignment while awaiting the next command. Again, the tower crew is in charge; don't do anything without their instruction.

If something drops or falls, alert the ground crew immediately. Yell "Look out below!" or "Headache!" so that they can get out of the way of the wayward bolt, nut or tool. Their hardhats only provide minimal protection against this occurrence. Dropped items are not only dangerous, but it also means sloppy work. Take your time and concentrate on not dropping anything.

The Tower Crew

If you're on the tower crew, you should know what you're doing or be working with someone who does. If you are working on a standing tower, before climbing walk around it and make a thorough visual inspection. Look at the base for cracked or rusted legs or missing hardware. Go out to the anchors to check the turnbuckles, clamps and other hardware. Look for bee or wasp nests. Never assume that any tower is safe to climb — always inspect it thoroughly before you take that first step.

Before beginning any maneuver, discuss how you're going to do it and the sequence that will be used. This way, everyone will understand the process and will hopefully do the right thing at the right time. This is particularly important if you're up there with someone you've never worked with before. Sometimes you both assume that the other person is going to do something obvious that needs doing and then neither of you does it — this can be dangerous. Go over everything. This trains an inexperienced person and makes it easier the next time you work together.

Keep your tools either in your bucket or tool bags on your belt or tied to the tower. Try to avoid putting anything on a flat surface such as the rotator plate or thrust bearing plate; they can roll off.

Avoid using ac-powered tools on the tower. Battery powered tools are safer; you can buy, borrow or rent them. If you must use ac-powered tools, make certain they are insulated and that the extension cords are suitable. Zip cord extensions are dangerous. Make certain the ground crew knows where to disconnect the extension cords and where the breaker box is located.

Managing the Work to be Done

Break everything down into bite-sized pieces and only do one step at a time. Trying to combine two or more steps in the same task is asking for trouble. For example, don't try to bring up the guy wires already attached to the tower section; bring them up after the section and guy brackets are installed. Trying to combine too many steps often results in doing things twice, along with undoing what you've already done. You'll be more efficient and safe by doing things one step at a time.

Prepping the Materials

Many tasks are a lot easier to do on the ground than up on the tower. Take the time to prepare all of the materials before hoisting them so that the tower crew's job is as simple as possible.

For a tubular-legged lattice tower, there are several things you can do to make the job easier while the tower sections are still on the ground. First, there will be excess galvanizing from the hot-dip process in many of the leg bolt holes on new tower sections. This will prevent a bolt from going through the hole. Except as a last resort, do not drill out the holes as it exposes the steel. Use a drift pin or taper punch and a hammer to enlarge the hole only enough for a bolt to clear the hole. Next, check the inside of each lower leg for that same excess galvanizing and remove it carefully with a round file. These steps are much easier to do on the ground than in the air.

Check that the sections fit together. It's not uncommon that one leg won't line up, particularly with new sections. Using a piece of pipe or another tower section as a lever, gently bend the out-of-line leg until it slips on properly. This also is easier to do on the ground. Lay out the sections in order of fit and mark one pair of the mating legs with tape or a felt marker to ensure they can be assembled the same way they were on the ground. Be sure to send the sections up the tower in the same order they were checked for fit.

Put some grease around the *inside* of each *lower* leg of a tubular-legged tower section. Not only will they slide on more easily during installation, but the grease will help minimize corrosion and oxidation between the sections and make later removal easier. Skipping this step at assembly makes disassembly harder to the point where a jack may be required to get the sections apart! If the tower is to be conductive, for example if it's to be used as a vertical antenna, then use a conductive antioxidant compound instead.

Inspect all of the remaining metal pieces and parts for blocked holes, damaged threads, bent braces or arms — anything that will make it hard to assemble on the tower. These are much easier to repair on the ground. Use a file to round the sharp edges of all plates, steps, brackets or arms to keep them from damaging you.

If more than one antenna is to be installed on the mast, measure and mark where each antenna will be mounted and where the thrust bearing, if any, will be.

Hook the rotator up to its control box and test its operation. Turn the rotator until it indicates North or another known direction, then get it ready for hoisting. It doesn't really matter which way the rotator is physically installed in the tower as the antennas can be oriented when mounting them on the mast. By knowing the rotator's indicated direction the antennas can be aligned properly without stopping work.

If you are assembling an antenna for the project, let it sit overnight then retighten all of the nuts and bolts the next day. The hardware will have temperature cycled from warm to cold and warm again and some of the hardware will have loosened up during that temperature-induced expansion and contraction. This is the time to be sure it's all tight!

Antenna element hose clamps invariably catch on anything — wire antennas, guy wires, cables, and so on. To minimize this annoying characteristic, wrap the hose clamp with a layer or two of electrical tape while it's still on the ground. This is another good reason to use rivets instead of hose clamps for beam assembly.

If your rotator doesn't have a connector for the control cable, you can add one using vehicle trailer connectors — they come in a flat 4-wire polarized configuration. Get two sets and install a pigtail to the rotator terminated in one male and one female connector. Do the opposite at the end of your control cable to the station. This will ensure that the cable is always connected correctly. Another system is to use a European Molex connector to connect a short jumper from the rotator to the longer control cable run to the station. Weatherproof the connector by inserting it into a short piece of 2-inch capped PVC tubing taped to a tower leg. Being able to access the rotator wiring at the rotator, without having to look underneath or open up a connector, can be extremely time-saving during troubleshooting.)

When putting something together "temporarily," always install it as though you won't be coming back; "temporary" sometimes means it will be up and used for years!

Hardware Prep

Make sure all hardware is stainless or galvanized hardware. Avoid plated hardware.

Never place a load on eyebolts with eyes that can open. Only eyebolts that are forged or welded closed should be use on tower or antenna projects if they will be carrying a load.

Always take extra hardware, nuts and bolts up the tower in case you run short or drop something. If you don't have them, you'll invariably need them.

26.6.6 ASSEMBLING THE TOWER

Route the haul rope through a snatch block at the bottom of the tower to transfer the hoisting effort from pulling down to pulling horizontally. Pulling vertically is all arm strength plus the ground crew is exposed to falling objects. Pull horizontally by putting the rope around your hips and walking backward to hoist the load. This uses larger muscle groups and hoisting will be much easier. In addition, those hoisting can watch the load while staying out of the danger zone. Of course, working with ropes under load near the tower means wearing leather gloves, and a hard hat.

To hold onto a haul rope, put it around your hips then bring the tail or dead end in front of you. *Do not* tie the rope around your waist — this is potentially dangerous. Aiming the tail end in the same direction as the load rope, grasp both ropes with one or both hands. This is the best way to hold or brake a rope load. Don't depend on just using your hands; it's not as reliable and your hands and arms will quickly tire. With the rope secured around you, it can be held comfortably for quite some time.

Section Stacking

After rigging the gin pole as in Figure 26.27 (the haul rope goes up the middle of the pipe, across the pulley, then down to the load), attach the leg bracket to the top of the top section, *below* the top brace. Make certain that it's secure before you push the gin pole mast up to the extended position where it'll be ready for the lift. (This is a good procedure to rehearse on the first section above the base with the ground crew watching.) K4ZA recommends placing a suitably sized piece of plywood or OSB right at the tower base, on which to "stage" or set the sections. This prevents the legs from getting dirt stuck in them. (If you're installing used sections, make sure each siderail is clear of any debris before hauling them aloft.)

The tower section should be rigged so that it hangs more or less vertically; the heavier the section, the more important this becomes. Here are a couple of rigging options: Put a sling around a leg at about ¾ of the way up the section (double-check for proper top and bottom orientation) to establish the pick-point. Attach the haul rope just above the section mid-point and, on the command of the tower crew, start to pull on the haul rope. Or, a carabiner can be clipped to the third horizontal brace down from the section top, and a second carabiner (simply clipped on to the haul rope) can be attached to the topmost horizontal brace.

As soon as it clears the top of the tower, the tower crew should yell "stop," then "down slow" when ready to have the section lowered onto the top of the tower.

If leg alignment problems are discovered (see item 9 in the sidebar on tower building mistakes), use a come-along around the bottom of the whole section and tighten it up to pull the legs together. (This is common practice when putting up angle-legged self-supporting towers.) If you don't have a come-along, a ratchet-operated truck strap may suffice. One person on a tower doesn't have a whole lot of leverage and if the sections line up but won't slide down, use a come-along or TowerJack and pull the section down into place.

Stack an appropriate number of sections (typically up to the next guy point), then bring up the first set of guys and attach them. Your ground crew can use their cable grips and come-alongs to put the initial tension on them, then attach them to the anchors. You'll be able to tell them which ones to tighten and which ones to loosen by using a level on the leg to plumb the tower. Once that's done, repeat the same steps until all the sections are in place and guyed.

It's important to plumb the first set of sections including the first set of guys. Once that segment is plumb, you can look up the face of the tower to see if everything above it lines up — it'll be pretty obvious. If it doesn't, just adjust the come-alongs or turnbuckles to get it straight.

Installing the Mast

For small and medium masts, use the gin pole to bring it up using a sling as a choker. The choker should be above the balance point so that the mast goes up vertically. Lower the mast into the tower from the top.

Large and heavy masts more than 20 feet long are bigger

Tower Climbing Shield

A tower can be legally classified as an "attractive nuisance" that could cause injuries and/or lawsuits. You should take some precautions to ensure that "unauthorized climbers" can't get hurt on your tower.

Generally, the attractive-nuisance doctrine applies to your responsibility to trespassers on your property. (The law is much stricter with regard to your responsibility to an invited guest.) You should expect your tower to attract children, whether they are already technically trespassing or whether the tower itself lures them onto your property. A tower is dangerous to children, especially because of their inability to appreciate danger. (What child could resist trying to climb a tower once they see one?) Because of this danger, you have a legal duty to exercise reasonable care to eliminate the danger or otherwise protect children against the perils of the attraction.

An article describing such a tower shield by Baker Springfield, W4HYY and Richard Ely, WA4VHM was published in September 1976 *QST*. It has been added to this book's downloadable supplemental information, including construction diagrams. Installing it should eliminate the worry.

than the usual gin pole can control properly. When building the tower, put the mast inside the bottom sections. Remove any rotator shelves or other obstructions so the gin pole can lift the mast up through the tower. Once the mast is captured at the top of the tower, it can be raised gradually. The books referenced at the beginning of this chapter provide more details.

Once the mast extends slightly above the top of the tower and is captured by the thrust bearing or a clamp acting as a collar, install the top antenna on the mast if more than one is to be installed. Once the first antenna is installed, pull the mast up with a come-along to where the next antenna is to be installed. Repeat the sequence until all the antennas are installed.

One "trick" to making this vertical lift easier is to replace one of the thrust bearing mounting bolts with a forged eye or eyebolt. This provides an attachment point for your come-along, making it as close to vertical as possible. This helps ensure the mast comes up as plumb as possible. The eye can, of course, be left in place.

Installing the Rotator

Clip a carabiner and haul rope onto a U-bolt on the rotator clamp or lift it with a bucket. Bring up the rotator, install it under the mast, and lower the mast into the rotator clamp. To haul up the control cable, tie an overhand knot in the cable and snap that into the haul rope carabiner.

To minimize the possibility of binding in the rotator/mast/thrust bearing system, work down when doing the final tightening. Do the thrust bearing first, the rotator mast clamps next, the rotator shelf bolts, and the rotator base bolts last.

When connecting the multiconductor control cable, one way to keep wire colors straight and consistent is to use the resistor color code: black, brown, red, orange, yellow, green, blue, violet, grey and white.

Rotation Loops

The rotation loop should be made with the rotator oriented north (typically its midpoint here in North America), ensuring the loop itself is centered. There are two ways to make a rotation loop for your cables. One way is to tape all the cables coming down the mast into a bundle, leaving an extra 4-5 feet of slack before securing the bundle to a tower leg. The bundle will have some rigidity that will help keep it out of harm's way. Make sure that it doesn't snag on anything as the system rotates and you'll be good to go. If you have a flat-topped tower, wind the cable around the mast 2-3 times in a diameter smaller than the top plate so that the coil lays on the flat surface.

26.7 RAISING AND LOWERING ANTENNAS

While small antennas can simply be pulled up directly on a haul rope, working with HF beams requires some technique. If done properly, the actual work of getting the antenna into position can be executed quite easily with only one person at the top of the tower. The ground crew does all the lifting by using a large pulley attached to the antenna mast or a gin pole with its pulley a foot or two above the point at which the antenna is to be mounted. Because raising an antenna often requires the load to be pulled away from the tower — either to avoid guy wires or as part of a tram or V-track system — this places significant bending forces on a mast or gin pole and may bend them if the pulley is too far above where they are attached to the tower.

The advice and suggestions in this section also apply to removing antennas by following the procedures in reverse. An antenna should probably be removed the same way it was installed. If installing it required a crane, it will most likely have to be removed by a crane.

26.7.1 AVOIDING GUY WIRES

Guy wires often obstruct the antenna's path to the top of the tower. One method of avoiding them is to tie a tag line to the middle of the boom and to a middle element for leverage (but within reach of the tower crew). The ground crews then pull the antenna out away from the guys as the antenna is raised. With this method, some crew members are pulling up the antenna to raise it while others are pulling down and out to keep the beam clear of the guys. Obviously, the opposing crews must act in coordination to avoid damaging the antenna.

A second method is to tie the haul rope to the center of the antenna. A crew member, wearing a climbing harness, walks the antenna up the tower as the ground crew raises it. Because the haul rope is tied at the balance point, the tower climber can rotate the elements around the guys. A tag line can be tied to the bottom end of the boom so that a ground crew member can help move the antenna around the guys. The tag line must be removed while the antenna is still vertical.

The third method is characterized as the "wig-wag" system by Tom Schiller, N6BT in his book *Array of Light*. It is particularly useful when other antennas are already installed on the antenna mast. The new antenna is lifted until it is immediately below the lowest antenna on the mast and rotated so that its elements are parallel to the boom of the installed antenna. The new antenna's elements are then tipped up to clear the elements of the installed antenna so that the new antenna is rotated around the installed antenna until its boom is above that of the installed antenna. Once above the installed antenna, the new antenna can be lifted so that its elements can be rotated to clear those of the installed antenna and then returned to horizontal and lowered for installation. This can be difficult if more than one antenna is already installed on the antenna mast.

26.7.2 USING A TROLLEY OR TRAM SYSTEM

Sometimes one of the top guys can provide a track to support the antenna as it is pulled upward. Insulators in the guys, however, may obstruct the movement of the antenna. A better track made with rope is an alternative. One end of the rope is secured outside the guy anchors. The other end is passed over the top of the tower and back down to an anchor near the first anchor. So arranged, the rope forms a narrow V-track strung outside the guy wires. Once the V-track is secured, the antenna may simply be pulled up, resting on the track. This is known as the trolley or V-track system. It is not an easy method to use. It requires two trolley cables spread apart some distance with the same tension on each line or the beam will tip. Plus there is a lot of added friction to the system from the weight of the antenna on the lines.

A much easier system is the tram line in which one line runs from the top of the tower to an anchor on the ground and the antenna is slung below the tramline. The system is illustrated in **Figure 26.43**.

Install one long (6-foot) sling on each side of the center mounting point of the antenna with two or three wraps around the boom; then bring them together to form a truss with the pick point directly above where the boom plate will attach to the mast.

This assures that the antenna is balanced and will arrive in the correct mounting position. Using two slings on the boom enables you to hoist the beam while it remains horizontal. Even if the antenna is mechanically off balance, you can adjust the slings so that it will remain basically horizontal.

You'll need three pulleys, a haul rope, a length of wire rope for the tram line, an anchor on the ground and miscellaneous slings and carabiners. K7LXC's preference is to use a wire rope tram line with the antenna suspended below the tram wire. Small diameter aircraft cable or wire rope such as ⅛ inch or $^{3}/_{16}$ inch ($^{3}/_{16}$-inch EHS works well) is sufficient to take the static load of just about any amateur antenna.

To set up the tram line, first secure a sling choker on the antenna mast about three feet above the place where the antenna will be mounted. Use two or three wraps and bring the choker through itself as described earlier.

Clip a carabiner or shackle to the tail of the sling. Then clip a large pulley into the carabiner. Bring up one end of the tram line and clip it into the same carabiner. Obviously, it's easiest if the tram line can "bisect" the guys, which provides the most clearance for the antenna coming up. This may require using some sort of temporary anchor point. A good rule of thumb for tramming is to try and have 1.5 times the tower height of working room; having a shallow angle makes tram work easier.

Secure the other end of the tram line to an anchor. You can use a tree, a fence post, a car, a stake driven into the ground or any other convenient strong point. Use a come-along and cable grip to tighten the cable until most of the slack is taken up. Do not over-tighten; you could damage your mast. If the sling on the mast is now high enough to create a significant bending force on your mast (more than four or five feet), back guy it in the opposite direction with another wire line or rope that is anchored to a convenient spot.

Run the haul rope through the back of the antenna mast pulley and out the front in the direction of the ground anchor. Lower the end of the haul rope directly to the ground or tie it to a carabiner clipped onto the tram line and let it slide down the wire. Figure 26.43A shows how the system should look at the top of the tower.

You may have to drop one or two of the top guy wires or any wire antennas closest to the antenna tram path if the antenna is going to be installed close to the top of the tower. Guys should be detached at ground level.

On the ground, attach the tram pulley (**Figure 26.44**) to the tramline. Turn the pulley upside-down (the antenna will be suspended under the tramline) then clip in the load end of the haul rope. Lift the two slings forming the antenna truss to the tram pulley and clip it in. The boom should be at a right angle to the tram line (elements parallel to the line) with the boom-to-mast bracket pointed toward the mast ready to accept U-bolts.

At this point, the haul rope should be attached to the tramline pulley. It goes up through the pulley on the mast, then down the tower to the ground. The third pulley is used at the bottom of the tower to change the direction of the haul rope from vertical to horizontal. At this point the system should look like Figure 26.43.

With antennas that have the elements mounted above the boom the antenna will attempt to flip over or "turn turtle." Minimize that tendency by tying the slings with opposite wraps (one around the boom in one direction, the other wrapped in the other direction).

Another method that helps counteract this unwanted tendency is to use a "tiller" as shown in **Figure 26.45**. It's a 4-foot long or so piece of angle iron or aluminum that is U-bolted to the boom on one end and has a small U-bolt on the front that captures the tramline and acts as a guide. Alternately, the

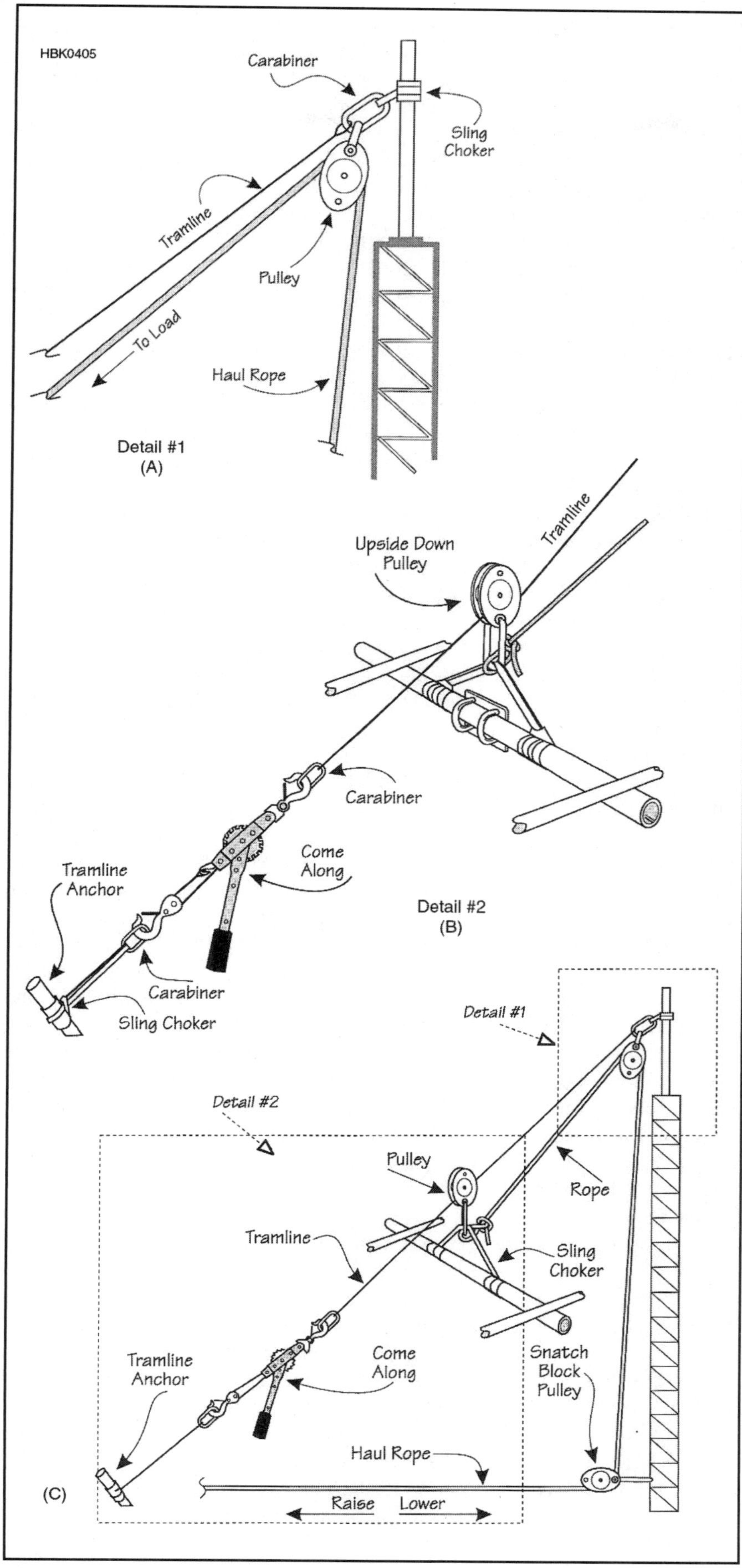

Figure 26.43 — A schematic drawing of the tram line system. At A, rigging the top of the tower for tramming antennas. Note the use of a sling and carabiner. (B) Rigging the anchor of the tramline. A come-along is used to tension the tramline. (C) The tram system for getting antennas up and down. Run the antenna part way up the tramline for testing before installation. It just takes a couple of minutes to run an antenna up or down once the tramline is rigged.

Figure 26.44 — A sturdy all-metal pulley suitable for tramming. (Don Daso, K4ZA, photo)

Figure 26.45 — Photo of the tram suspension system used by K7NV. Note that the tiller is attached to the haul rope in this system. The boom of the antenna can be rotated in the U-bolt holding it to the tiller to adjust the tilt of the elements to clear guy wires. (Kurt Andress, K7NV, photo)

front of the tiller can be attached to the haul rope. The tiller holds the antenna boom in a relatively fixed position, thus preventing it from turning over. Once the antenna has been lifted off the ground, the boom can be rotated in the tiller's U-bolt so that the element halves facing the tower are raised to clear the guy wires.

Next, attach any tag lines. Use a small line such as ¼ inch polypropylene because it's light and stiff enough to resist hanging up on any clamps or hardware sticking out on the elements. Tie one end to the boom at a convenient spot that the tower crew can reach to untie it. Wrap the tag line around an adjacent element two or three times. You can add one or two wraps of electrical tape to hold it in place on the element to keep the fulcrum out on the element and away from the boom. The tag line will pull easily through the tape when you're done. If the tag line does hang up on a guy wire, lower the antenna to free it then tram it back up again.

When it's time to launch the antenna, have the ground crew pull the haul rope while another person helps the antenna off the ground. Once the antenna is launched, crew members holding the tag lines can guide it as it goes up. (For big beams, such as 40 meter antennas, more than one person may be required to maneuver it up and on to the tram line and get the lift started.)

Use the tag lines to pull the element halves pointing away from the tower down so that they'll clear the guys. You'll be pulling against the haul rope so don't pull too hard on the tag line. The tag lines can also be used to move the boom so that the antenna will be in the proper mast-mounting orientation.

The tower crew can guide the antenna when it gets close to the tower. Once the antenna has cleared all obstacles and if everything was rigged correctly, the antenna should come right up to the mast. (If using the tiller, once the beam arrives at the mast, you'll find it's now in the way. Having a come-along or a second haul rope you can transfer the load to will allow you to move it out of the way. A second pair of hands can help greatly at this point, too.)

Another advantage is that while on the tram line you can run any on-the-air tests you'd like. Just attach a run of coax before you lift the antenna. To make any adjustments, lower the antenna, make the changes and pull it up again. Make measurements with the boom 90° to the tram line if possible (elements parallel to the tramline).

To take antennas down, rig everything the same way, then lower the antenna down the tram line. Be certain as it comes up from the ground, the haul rope goes behind the boom before it goes through the mast pulley.

26.7.3 BUILDING ANTENNAS ON THE TOWER

A fourth method is to build the antenna on the tower and then swing it into position. Building the Yagi on the tower works particularly well for Yagis mounted partway up the tower, as you might do in a stacked array. The technique works best when the vertical spacing between the guys is greater than the length of the Yagi boom.

Figure 26.46 illustrates the steps involved. A haul rope through a gin-pole or tower-mounted pulley is secured to the boom at the final balance point and the ground crew raises the boom in a vertical position up the tower. A tie rope is used to temporarily secure the upper end of the boom to keep it stable while the boom is being raised. The tower person removes the tie-rope once the boom is raised to the right level and has been temporarily secured to the tower.

The elements are then brought up one at a time and mounted to the boom. It helps if you have a 2- or 3-foot long spotting mast temporarily attached to the boom to form a 90° frame of reference. This allows the ground crew to spot from below so that the elements are all lined up in the same plane. After all the elements are mounted and aligned properly, the temporary rope securing the boom to the tower is released, suspending the antenna on the haul rope. The tower person then rotates the boom 90° so that the elements are vertical. Next, the elements are rotated 90° into the tower so that they are parallel to the ground. The ground crew then moves the completed antenna up or down using the haul rope to the final point where it is mounted to the tower.

A modification of this technique also works for building a medium-sized Yagi on the top of the tower. This technique will work if the length of the gin pole at maximum safe extension is long enough (see **Figure 26.47**). (This method is much easier if the top guy set is not exactly at the tower top, as previously mentioned. The extra working space helps immeasurably!)

As usual, the gin pole haul rope is attached to the balance point of the boom and the boom is pulled up the tower in the vertical position, using a rope to temporarily tie the haul rope to the top end of the boom for stability. The boom is temporarily secured to the tower with slings or a short length of rope in the vertical position so that the top end is just higher than the top of the tower. In order to clear the gin pole when the elements are mounted and the boom is raised higher to mount the next element, you must tilt the boom slightly so that the element mounted to the top end of the boom will be behind the mast. This is very important!

The elements are first mounted to the bottom side of the boom to provide weight down below for stability. Then the top-most element is mounted to the boom. The tower person removes the temporary rope securing the boom to the tower and the ground crew uses the haul rope to move the mast vertically upwards to the point where the next element from the top can be mounted. Once all the elements are mounted and aligned in the same plane (the center element closest to the mast-to-boom bracket can be left off until the boom is in place), the temporary securing rope is removed. The boom is now swung so that the elements can be maneuvered to clear the top guy wires. Once the elements are horizontal the boom is secured to the mast and the center element is mounted if necessary.

A special boom-to-mast mounting plate that supports both building and working on antennas at the top of the tower was designed by members of the Potomac Valley Radio Club. It is described in a short article ("The PVRC Mount") included with this book's downloadable supplemental information.

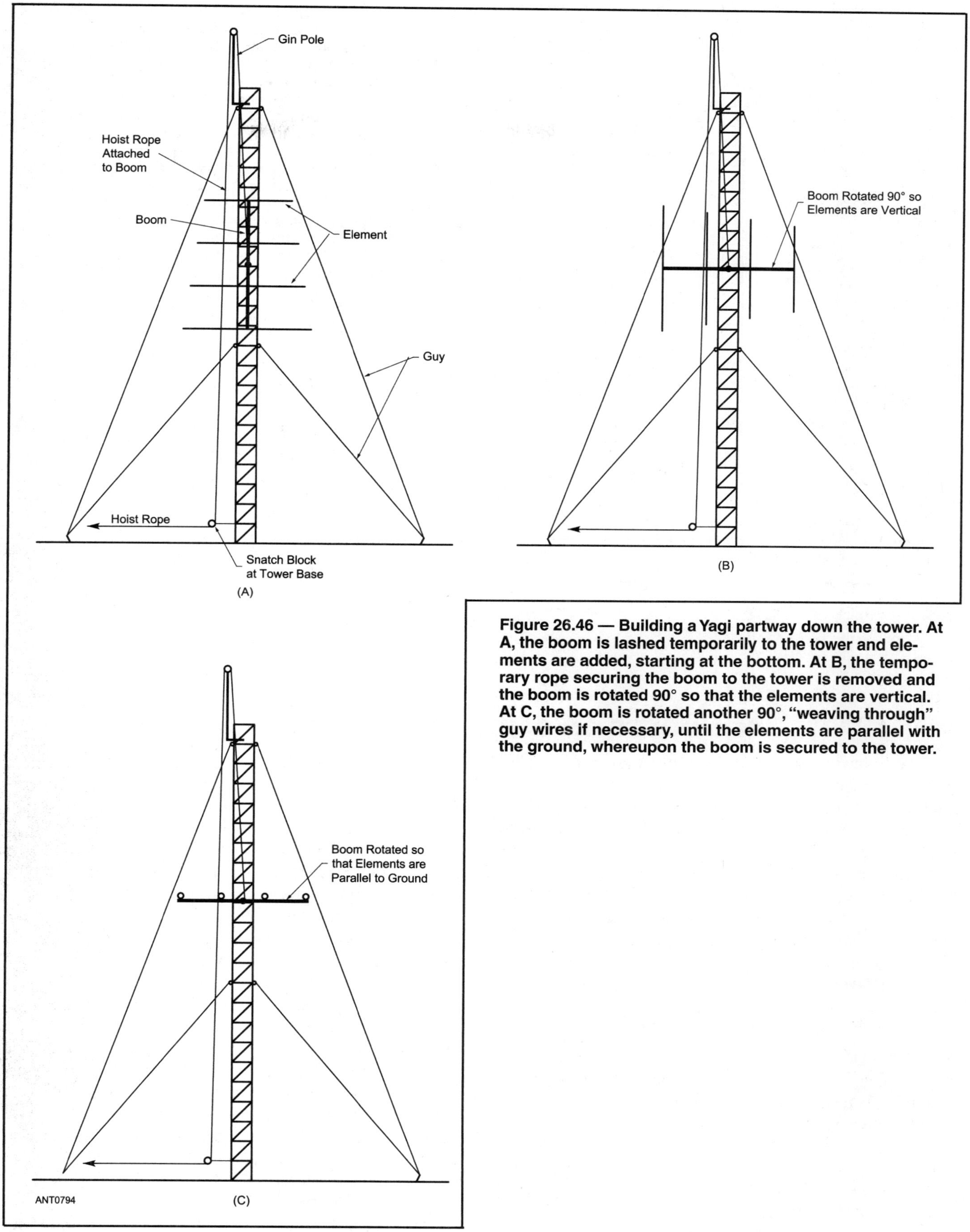

Figure 26.46 — Building a Yagi partway down the tower. At A, the boom is lashed temporarily to the tower and elements are added, starting at the bottom. At B, the temporary rope securing the boom to the tower is removed and the boom is rotated 90° so that the elements are vertical. At C, the boom is rotated another 90°, "weaving through" guy wires if necessary, until the elements are parallel with the ground, whereupon the boom is secured to the tower.

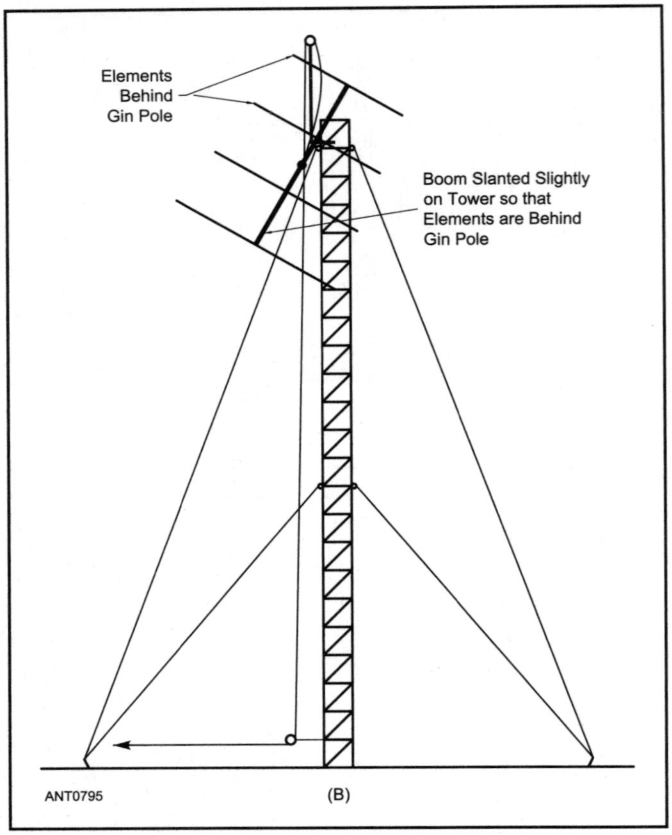

Figure 26.47 — Building a Yagi at the top of the tower. The length of the gin pole must be longer than ½ the boom so that the boom can be hoisted upwards to the place where it is mounted to the mast. Usually the boom is initially lashed to the tower slanted slightly from vertical so that the top element ends up behind the gin pole. The elements are mounted at the bottom end of the boom first to provide stability. Then the element at the top of the boom is mounted and the boom is moved upwards using the gin-pole hoist rope so that the next-to-top element may be mounted, again behind the gin pole. This process is repeated until all elements are mounted (save possibly the middle element if it can be reached easily from the tower once the beam has been mounted to the mast). Then the boom is tilted to the final position, weaving the elements to clear guy wires if necessary.

26.8 NOTES ON CABLES AND CONNECTORS

The following sections contain information that applies to the construction of antenna and tower systems. For more information on the characteristics of coaxial cable and RF connectors, including cable selection, see the **Transmission Lines** chapter.

A general tip for handling cable and wire — when removing it from a reel or spool, unroll it so that it lies straight and flat along the ground. Pulling it straight up and off the end of the coil twists the cable, leading to strength-reducing kinks in the braid and endless aggravation as you attempt to get it untwisted and untangled.

26.8.1 COAXIAL CABLE

Bending Radius

Bending coax is acceptable as long as the radius of the bend is larger than the specified minimum bending radius. For example, a common minimum bending radius specification for RG-8 is 4 inches (8 times the cable diameter). Coax with more rigid shield materials will have a larger bending radius. Bending the coax tighter than the minimum bending radius can cause impedance "bumps" in the line by distorting the geometry of the conductors. It can also cause the center conductor to migrate through the plastic insulation and eventually short to the outer shield.

Burying Coax

There are several reasons why you might choose to go to all the work of burying your coax. One is that direct burial cable is virtually free from storm and UV damage, and usually has lower maintenance cost than cable that is out in the open. Another reason might be aesthetics; a buried cable will be acceptable in almost all communities. Also, being underground reduces common-mode feed line current on the outside of the shield, helping to reduce interstation interference and RFI.

Although any cable can be buried, a cable that is specifically designed for direct burial will have a longer life. The best cable to use is one that has a high-density polyethylene jacket because it is both nonporous and will take a relatively high amount of compressive loads. "Flooded" direct burial cables contain an additional moisture barrier of non-conductive grease under the jacket; this allows the material to leak out, thus "healing" small jacket penetrations. (These can be messy to work with when installing connectors.)

Here are some direct burial tips:

1) Because the outer jacket is the cable's first line of defense, any steps that can be taken to protect it will go a long

way toward maintaining the internal quality of the cable.

2) Bury the cable in sand or finely pulverized dirt, without sharp stones, cinders or rubble. If the soil in the trench does not meet these requirements, tamp four to six inches of sand into the trench, lay the cable and tamp another six to eleven inches of sand above it. A pressure-treated board placed in the trench above the sand prior to backfilling will provide some protection against subsequent damage that could be caused by digging or driving stakes.

3) Lay the cable in the trench with some slack. A tightly stretched cable is more likely to be damaged as the fill material is tamped.

4) Examine the cable as it is being installed to be sure the jacket has not been damaged during storage or by being dragged across sharp edges.

5) You may want to consider burying it in plastic pipe or conduit. Be careful to drill holes in the bottom of the pipe at all low spots so that any moisture can drain out. While PVC pipe provides a mechanical barrier, water incursion is practically guaranteed — you can't keep it out. It will leak in directly or condense from moisture in the air. Use the perforated type so that any water will just drain out harmlessly.

6) It is important that direct burial is below the frost line to avoid damage by the expansion and contraction of the earth during freezing and thawing of the soil and any water surrounding the buried cables.

Coax Jumpers

With many beam antennas, the feed point is out of reach from the tower and should be connected to a jumper just long enough to reach from the feed point to the antenna mast. That way, the feed line connection and waterproofing can be done at the most convenient location. If you ever have to remove the antenna in the future you can just disconnect the jumper and lower the antenna.

Coax "Pigtails"

Most manufacturers use some type of feed point system that accepts a PL-259 or N connector. Some antennas require you to split the coax and attach the shield and center conductor to machine screws on the driven element. The exposed end of the coax is very difficult to seal; indeed, it's nearly impossible. Water will wick down the outer shield and into your station unless you take great pains to weatherproof it. Coating the entire pigtail and attachment terminals with Liquid Electrical Tape or some other conformal sealant is a good approach, although UV will degrade such coatings over time. Another approach for HF beams is to use a "Budwig HQ-1" style insulator with the integral SO-239 and wires for connecting to the terminals (See the **Antenna Materials and Construction** chapter for alternatives.) As always, follow the manufacturer's directions.

26.8.2 CONTROL CABLES

In addition to coaxial cables, most towers will have some sort of control cable for rotators, antenna switches or other accessories. The manufacturer should provide the size that is necessary and again, you should follow their specifications.

In the case of rotator cables, some rotators are sensitive to voltage drop so bigger sizes should be used. For really long runs, some amateurs use THHN house wire or UF-Romex, (with the motor start capacitor installed at the rotator) from the local hardware store to get reasonably-priced bigger wire. Only the motor and solenoid (if used) conductors typically require the larger wire.

26.8.3 WEATHERPROOFING RF CONNECTORS

The primary purpose of weatherproofing is to keep moisture and contaminants out of your coaxial cable connections. Whether it is rain or condensation, water in a connector can put you off the air.

Properly sealed connector joints will be very effective and reliable in maintaining electrical and mechanical integrity. Here's how to do it as illustrated in **Figure 26.48**:

1) Install the connector correctly on the end of the coax.

2) Use pliers when attaching a PL-259 to a SO-239 or PL-258 barrel connector. Hand-tightened connections are not tight enough! Do not crimp or deform the connector.

3) Apply two wraps of premium electrical tape such as Scotch 33+ or 88.

4) Apply a layer of vapor-wrap material. Vapor-wrap is a butyl rubber material that comes in rolls or sheets and does an excellent job of isolating the joint from the elements. A commercial vapor-wrap, such as from Andrew Solutions or Decibel Products won't stick to connectors and comes off easily. By putting one or two wraps of tape over the joint first, your connector will be protected from the vapor-wrap and it will look as good as new if you ever have to take it apart. To remove, simply take your razor knife, slice down the joint and peel off the weatherproofing.

Putty-type "coax seals" are *not* recommended as the surface can crack and dry out with age. If applied directly to a connector, the connector will become unusable as the inner putty forms a sticky mess. If you want to use putty-type sealants, wrap the connector with a layer of tape first.

5) Apply two or three layers of tape over the vapor wrap.

6) When your coax joint will be vertical, always apply the final layer of tape in an upward direction. This way the tape will overlap in such a way that water will not be conducted into the tape layers (like the shingles on your house). Tape wrapped downward will form little pockets that will trap the rain and conduct it right into your joint.

7) Do not stretch the tape when applying the final few inches. If you put it on under tension, it will eventually "flag," meaning it will come loose and blow around in the wind.

8) Paint the whole joint with a UV-resistant protective layer such as clear acrylic spray paint. That joint should never fail.

9) K4ZA recommends installing a UV-rated tie wrap above the weather-proofed connector, leaving the free end loose to guide any water running down the coax away from the connector.

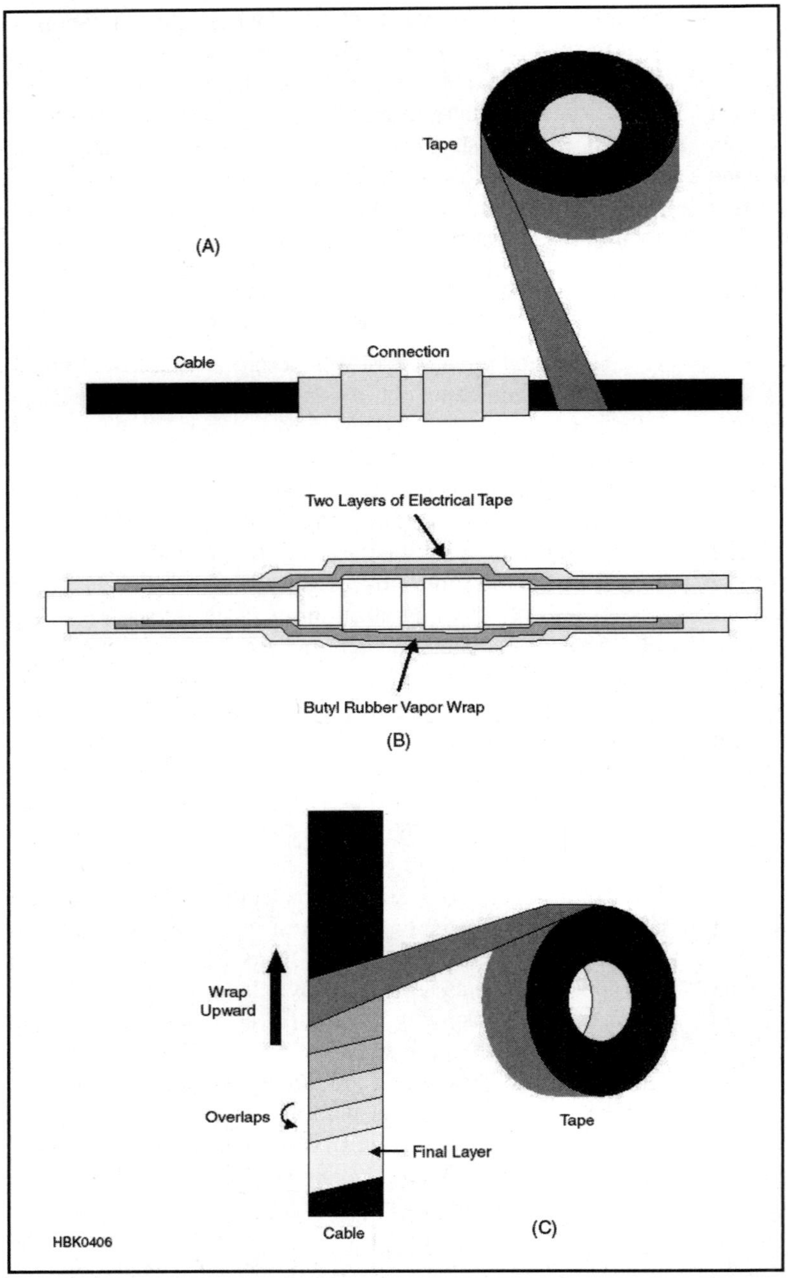

Figure 26.48 — Waterproofing a connector in three steps. At A, cover the connectors with a layer of good-quality electrical tape. B shows a layer of butyl rubber vapor wrap between the two layers of electrical tape. C shows how to wrap tape of a vertical cable so that the tape sheds water away from the connection. (Drawing (C) reprinted courtesy of *Circuitbuilding for Dummies*, Wiley Press)

Shrink-Fit Tubing

A recent product for coax joints is shrink-fit tubing impregnated with hot-melt glue along the inside. As you apply heat to the shrink-fit tubing, it shrinks while the glue melts and oozes inside between the fitting and the tubing. It not only keeps the tubing from slipping, but it also fills in the voids in the joint and provides an additional seal. It's an expensive alternative (approximately $1 per inch) but is very simple to use and remove if necessary.

Silicone Sealants

Do not use silicone sealant that gives off acetic acid (a vinegary smell) and absorbs water when curing. Acid and water will migrate into the connection causing problems later. Use only aquarium-type sealants or Dow-Corning 3145 for reliable connections. Be aware that once cured, silicone sealants are very hard to remove from connectors — practically impossible.

Giving off that vinegar-like odor means the silicone is "out-gassing," and K4ZA has found that once the curing period has passed, the silicone does not corrode or otherwise damage materials. Extensive tests have shown this to be the case.

26.8.4 TAPE AND TIES

Every amateur installation has many feet of electrical tape used outdoors in a variety of applications. The "3 rolls for $1.00" bargain specials are not recommended for demanding outdoor use, particularly for weatherproofing. Scotch Super 88 is the recommended standard for waterproofing connectors. Besides being conformable to 0 °F (–18 °C), it will perform continuously in ambient temperatures of up to 220 °F (105 °C) and it is UV-resistant. The data sheet says it provides "moisture-tight electrical protection" and it retails in the $4 to $5 range per roll. Another Scotch tape, Super 33+, is another "premium grade, all-weather vinyl insulating tape" with many of the same properties and specs as the Super 88. The only difference is that Super 88 is slightly thicker than Super 33+ (10 mils for 88 vs 7 mils for 33+). Both tapes are easily applied at low temperatures, and will even stick to a wet aluminum antenna boom.

Another specialized tape is the Scotch 130C Linerless Rubber Splicing Tape. This is a fairly thick (30 mils vs 7 mils for Super 33+) tape intended for high-voltage splices and is moisture-sealing. 3M makes many products for demanding electrical use — these are just several of them. You may have your own favorite.

Cable ties or tie-wraps are locking plastic fasteners intended to bundle cables and secure them to brackets and other supports, such as tower legs. They come in a variety of lengths, strengths, and materials at the local hardware store. For outside work, do not use white or translucent tie-wraps; they'll deteriorate quickly from UV exposure, often in less than a year. Black, UV-resistant tie-wraps are better, but they still eventually break down. A wrap of electrical tape will protect the tie.

A tie-wrap also makes a simple drip loop for coax and control cables. Attach a medium-size tie to the cable just before it enters the building with the tie's free end pointing down.

26.8.5 CABLE SUPPORT

When a long run of feed line or control cable is suspended vertically, it is important to provide some strain relief so that the load is not all carried by a connector or terminal strip. Commercial cable support arms such as from KF7P Metalwerks (**www.kf7p.com**) are available to hold cables away from a crank-up tower or take the load of a long vertical cable run. Another popular solution is the family of Kellems grips that are widely available from electrical distributors such as Graybar (**www.graybar.com**). The smaller grips can be used with larger coaxial cables.

Using electrical tape or wire ties to secure cables to tower legs or other vertical supports will work but makes replacement more difficult since the tape or tie will have to be cut away. An alternative is to use pieces of solid #12 or #14 AWG wire from house wiring cable, twisted around the tower leg and the cables. Such twist-ties can be reused many times.

When running cables down a tower, place them where they will not be stepped on, snag a boot or belt, or compromise your grip on the tower. If possible, run them inside the tower. This also reduces their exposure to picking up RF from the antennas.

Suspending a horizontal run of cables above ground is best done with a *catenary wire* or *messenger wire* anchored to supports on each end. This technique is also referred to as *aerial cable*. The suspended wire supports the weight of the electrical cables, such as feed lines and control cables. The cables can be lashed to the supporting wire (typical of CATV systems) or allowed to move in the supporting hardware.

The tools and materials are very similar to guy wires, using turnbuckles, thimbles, and Crosby clips to secure the catenary ends. The techniques and hardware used are also similar to installing overhead residential power drops and suspended lighting systems.

For amateur installations, 1/8-inch galvanized or stainless-steel wire rope will be sufficient for typical run lengths. Commercial installers support the cables with J-hooks and bridle rings so they can move and cables can be removed or added to the bundle. As on tower legs, #12 or #14 AWG solid wire can also be used as reusable ties.

26.9 ROTATORS

The rotator is an important component of directional antenna systems, turning the antenna to any direction with a repeatable accuracy of a few degrees. Once in position, the rotator must hold the antenna in place against the wind. The rotator must do this while supporting the weight of the mast and all of the antennas. **Figure 26.49** is a photo of a popular type of rotator with its control box (a Hy-Gain Ham-V rotator with a DCU-1 controller).

Rotators consist of a base assembly mounted to a fixed mast or tower and a rotating assembly atop it with a clamp in which the antenna support mast is held. **Figure 26.50** shows several common ways of attaching rotators to towers, masts, and antennas.

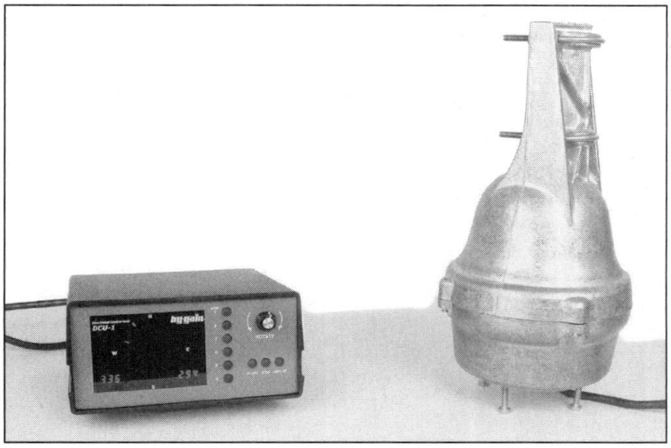

Figure 26.49 — A Ham-V rotator (right) with a DCU-1 digital control unit.

The turning motor and gear train, brake, position indicator, and limit switches are installed in or on the base. The rotating assembly sits on a bearing race resting on the base assembly. A ring gear is the most common method of transferring the motor's rotation to the rotating housing although worm gears are also used.

26.9.1 ROTATOR RATINGS

Rotators are expected to work for many years over a very wide range of temperatures while exposed to the elements, with little or no maintenance. To achieve those performance goals, the rotator's specifications and installation requirements must be respected.

There are three primary rotator ratings: *wind load*, *braking ability*, and *turning torque*. *Effective moment* is the product of antenna weight and turning radius. It is a specification for maximum antenna system size used by the Hy-Gain family of

"Rotator" or "Rotor"?

The piece of equipment installed on the tower that makes the antennas turn is a "rotator." A "rotor" is the rotary part of a motor or vehicle. For example, the blades of a helicopter form its rotor and the spinning shaft and armature of an electric motor form its rotor. The rotator includes the entire machine, both the stationary and moving parts, making the antenna system turn. Amateurs use both words, rotator and rotor, somewhat interchangeably, regardless.

rotators. Many rotators also specify a maximum *vertical load* in pounds or kilograms. **Table 26.6** lists manufacturers for rotators intended for fixed-station installations and **Table 26.7** contains the primary specifications for common rotators.

Wind load is specified both with the rotator mounted inside a tower and with the rotator outside a tower mounted on a mast. When mounted inside a tower section, the tower holds the mast in place straight above the rotator, often using a thrust bearing to hold the mast in place. This eliminates any sideways load on the rotating assembly relative to the base. Wind load is usually specified as a maximum antenna area in square feet, and antenna manufacturers specify the area of their beams for this reason. In the

Table 26.6
Rotator Manufacturers (Fixed Station)

Manufacturers	
AlfaSpid	**www.alfaradio.ca**
Channel Master	**www.channelmaster.com**
Hy-Gain	**www.hy-gain.com**
M²	**www.m2inc.com**
TIC	**www.ticgen.com**
Yaesu	**www.yaesu.com**

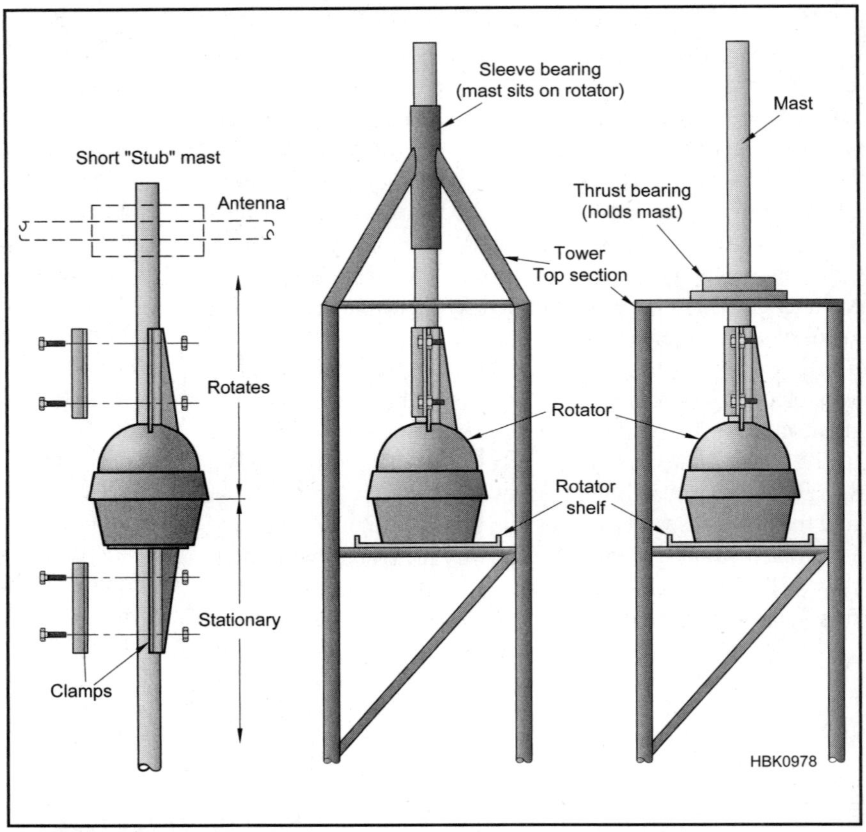

Figure 26.50 — Rotators can be mounted directly on masts or inside lattice-style towers. Rotators can also be mounted directly on the top of towers (not shown).

Table 26.7
Common Rotator Specifications

Manufacturer	*Model*	*Wind Load (in tower, sq ft)*	*Wind Load (outside tower, sq ft)*	*Turning Torque (in-lb)*	*Braking Ability (in-lb)*	*Effective Moment (ft-lb)*	*Brake Type*	*Notes*
AlfaSpid	RAK1			1400	>14,000		Worm gear	Heavy-duty
Channel Master	9521HD			100				Light-duty
DX Engineering	RT4500HD*	>37	n/a	>3300	>20,000		Gear reduction	Heavy-duty
Hy-Gain	T2X	20	10	1000	9000	3400	Wedge	Heavy-duty
	AR-40	3	1.5	350	450	300	Disc	Light-duty
	CD-45II	8.5	5	600	800	1200	Disc	Medium-duty
	HAM-IV	15	7.5	800	5000	2800	Wedge	Medium-duty
	HDR-300A	25	n/a	5000	7500		Solenoid lock	Heavy-duty
M²	OR2800	35	n/a	3200	17,000		Worm drive	Heavy-duty
TIC	1022D			6500	6500		Gear reduction	1 motor, heavy-duty
	1032D			7881	7530		Gear reduction	1 motor, heavy-duty
Yaesu	G-450A	10.8	5.4	516	2604		Gear reduction	Light-duty
	G-800DXA	21.5	8	955	3472		Mech and elec	Medium-duty
	G-1000DXA	23.7	8	955	5207		Mech and elec	Medium-duty
	G-2800DXA	32.3	10.8	2170	21700		Mech and elec	Heavy-duty
Az-El Rotators								
Yaesu	G-5500	10.8	10.8	528	3468		Gear reduction	
AlfaSpid	RAS-1	30		1400	14,000		Worm gear	At 12 V
	RAS-2			5000	24,000		Worm gear	At 12 V
	REAL-1			1400	14,000		Worm gear	At 12 V

*Preliminary specifications, final data not available at publication.

US, wind load calculations are based on the standard EIA/TIA-222-G:2005-08-02. In Europe, EN 1991-1-4 is the current standard, corresponding to the German standard DIN 1055-4.

Braking ability is the maximum twisting force the rotator can withstand. This force is primarily by the wind. The rotator's braking action is provided by either a solenoid-controlled wedge or bar inside the housing, or by a worm-gear drive that does not allow backward rotation of the mast under load. Turning torque is the maximum amount of torque the rotator can produce to turn the antennas. Both braking ability and turning torque are given in inch-pounds.

Effective moment is the product of antenna weight in pounds (or kilograms) and turning radius in feet (or meters). Heavy antennas and bigger antennas are harder to turn and to hold in place against the wind, requiring a higher effective moment rating for the rotator.

It is important not to overload a rotator. If you live in a location that is prone to high winds, persistent winds, or large gusts, include a safety factor when selecting a rotator. Persistent twisting from winds can wear out a rotator's brake wedge or housing indentations that hold the brake in place. This can cause the brake to slip or jam. Rotators are not inexpensive and a failed rotator brake can allow an antenna to "freewheel," damaging the feed line as well. A thrust bearing above the rotator can be used to hold the weight of a large antenna array, leaving only the turning load on the rotator.

26.9.2 TYPES OF ROTATORS

Amateur rotators range from very light-duty models intended for TV antennas all the way to reconditioned "prop-pitch" rotators designed originally to control the pitch or angle of aircraft propeller blades. There are also models for portable and temporary use.

Light-duty antenna rotators are suitable for small VHF and UHF Yagis or log-periodics. They should not be used with HF antennas, large microwave dishes, or antennas with a significant wind load.

Medium-duty rotators can handle a single, mid-sized HF tribander or log-periodic. A small VHF/UHF Yagi can be stacked with the HF beam. These rotators are also good choices for a stack of VHF/UHF antennas. Dish antennas should be evaluated to be sure they won't overload these rotators.

Heavy-duty rotators are able to handle the biggest amateur HF Yagis, including stacks of two or three antennas. Instead of a solenoid brake, some of these rotators use a gear train or worm-drive to provide the braking action. Be sure the tower and supporting hardware is rated to handle the antenna and mast load. These rotators are somewhat larger than the more common medium-duty models and may be difficult to install in smaller lattice-style towers.

Ring rotators, or *orbital ring rotators*, are a special type of rotator installed outside the tower, attached to its legs. The antenna is carried by a motorized cradle that moves around the tower on a circular, toothed track that acts as a drive gear. Ring rotators are generally used at larger stations that use large, stacked HF Yagis.

It is also possible to simply rotate the entire tower with a variety of antennas mounted directly on the tower. The guy wires are attached to bearing rings, allowing the tower to turn inside them.

What is an Armstrong Rotator?

The term "armstrong" refers to anything turned or lifted manually, requiring a "strong arm." There are many examples of hams using gears or cranks to turn antennas but the most common is a rope tied to the antenna's boom and pulled from ground level. The antenna's mast turns freely in the tower or the antenna mount turns on the mast. This is a common temporary solution during antenna system repair or when operating during Field Day and portable.

26.9.3 ROTATOR INSTALLATION

Rotators are usually installed inside a lattice tower section. The top section is usually where the rotator is located although it can be placed anywhere in the tower that can be reached by a mast.

A sleeve or thrust bearing at the top of the section holds the mast so that it is vertical and stabilized against sideways torque. The sleeve is part of the tower's top section. A thrust bearing is mounted on a bearing plate at the top of the tower. The rotator is mounted on a rotator shelf that sits inside the tower and is sold as an accessory by the tower manufacturer. (See **Figure 26.51**.) Smaller rotators usually come with a mast

Figure 26.51 — The accessory shelf in a Rohn 25G top section is pre-drilled with a standard bolt layout to fit the popular Ham-M/1/2/3/4/V series of rotator base plates. This rotator uses a terminal strip for connections although rotators are available with waterproof connectors. After-market kits for converting rotators with terminal strips to waterproof connectors are also available.

clamp so they can be mounted on a pipe or similar mast with the antenna directly above them.

The common Hy-Gain/CDE rotators (Ham-IV, T2X, and similar models) are designed to accept masts with a maximum of 2¹⁄₁₆-inch OD. Smaller masts, such as 2-inch OD tubing or smaller water pipes will be off-center from the tower section holding the rotator. This can lead to binding in the top sleeve or bearing. The mast can be centered by placing strips of aluminum or brass shim between the mast and the portion of the clamp that is part of the bell housing.

Some crank-up tubular towers have the ability to place the rotator at the base of the tower. The tower is supported on a bearing and the rotator turn the entire tower. This is more convenient for working with the rotator but incurs extra expense.

Thrust Bearings

A thrust bearing is mounted at the top of the tower and the antenna mast passes through it to the rotator. The thrust bearing clamps the mast and supports the weight of the antenna system, leaving the rotator to handle the torque load without carrying any weight.

Except in unusual circumstances, this is unnecessary since rotator bearings are designed to operate properly at full vertical load. A substitute for an actual thrust bearing is a bushing of heavy plastic or wood that supports a collar clamped to the antenna mast.

Do not use machine shop type pillow-blocks for thrust bearings. They are not intended to be exposed to the weather and will quickly rust solid. Use only outdoor grade (Rohn, galvanized, and so on) thrust bearings.

Clamp Hardware and Mounting Bolts

Use galvanized or stainless-steel U-bolts and mounting bolts to install the rotator and mast clamp. Do not use plated hardware as it will rust and become very difficult to remove. If stainless-steel hardware is used, apply a small amount of anti-seize compound to the threads before tightening to prevent galling. Split-O lock washers should be used on all bolts.

Because the rotator experiences considerable and repeated twisting, it is possible for the mast clamp or mounting bolts to work loose over time. Heavy-duty aftermarket mast clamps are available for some rotators. If a rotator has worked loose on its rotator shelf or mounting plate, it can be seen from the ground through binoculars in most cases — when the rotator begins to turn, it will turn in the tower before lodging against a strut or leg or a bolt hits the side of a mounting hole. The antenna will begin to turn after that. This must be repaired quickly to avoid damage to the rotator, rotator shelf, or rotator control lines. Make inspection of rotator mounting part of your regular station maintenance.

Rotator or Rotation Loop

Leave enough slack in all antenna feed lines for the rotator to turn completely in either direction plus another half-turn in case the mast slips during a high-wind situation. The feed lines can be left hanging below the antenna boom or wrapped around the top sleeve or mast once or twice like a spring. Have someone turn the antenna system completely through its travel with someone on the tower to watch the feed lines as the mast turns. Be sure the feed lines are not chafing against a metal surface that can wear a hole in the jacket or outer insulation, allowing water to get in. In extreme cases, a feed line or control cable can snag on something and break completely. (See "Assembling the Tower" earlier in this chapter.)

26.9.4 ROTATOR CONTROL

Turning Control

There are two steps in controlling turning: releasing the brake, if any, and energizing a motor to turn in the desired direction.

An electrically controlled brake consists of a heavy-duty solenoid and a spring-loaded brake wedge or bar that fits into indentations inside the rotating assembly. The rotator's braking torque is determined by how securely the brake is held by the indentations or, if worm gears are used, by the resistance to the gears turning backward under load. To turn the rotator, the solenoid is energized, pulling the brake out of the indentations. Energizing the solenoid is usually the largest current draw of the rotator.

The most common rotator motor is a 2-phase ac motor with a starting capacitor. The capacitor is switched between phases to control direction of rotation. Because of gear reduction, the motor can be fairly small and does not draw much current. Unless blocked by an obstruction, rotators turn a full 360 degrees. Limit switches open at the ends of rotation, removing power from the motor at the extreme ends of travel to prevent feed line damage.

Rotator Brake Control

When rotation is complete, the solenoid is de-energized and the brake re-engages the indentations, holding the mast in place. Over time, the indentations or brake can wear out, allowing the rotating housing to slip under heavy loads. Wear is accelerated by de-energizing the solenoid while the mast

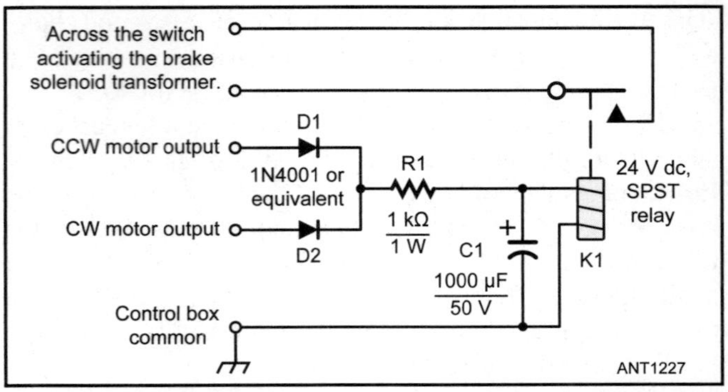

Figure 26.52 — Brake delay circuit for Hy-Gain HAM-series and Tailtwister T2X rotators. D1 and D2 charge C1 through R1, closing the contacts of K1 whenever the motor is energized. The contacts are wired in parallel with the control unit brake and motor power transformer, holding the solenoid on until the relay is no longer energized. When the motor is turned off, C1 discharges through the coil of K1 and power is removed from the brake solenoid when the relay opens.

is still turning, causing the brake to impact the sides of the indentations.

To reduce the impact of sudden stops, some controllers allow the mast to stop turning before de-energizing the solenoid. Typical delays are about 5 seconds. Retrofit delay modules are available for the Hy-Gain family of rotators. (See the RBD-5 from Hy-Gain, and rotator repair shops also have modules.) You can make your own brake delay module from the circuit in **Figure 26.52**. It is installed inside the control unit and can be fabricated on perf-board. Whenever power is applied to the rotator motors, C1 is charged and the relay contacts then close, keeping power applied to the brake and motor transformer. When power is removed from the motors, C1 discharges through the relay coil for a few seconds before the relay de-energizes, removing power from the transformer and releasing the brake solenoid. Depending on what relay you select, you may have to experiment with the value of C1 to get the delay you want.

If your rotator does not have a brake delay, practice keeping the brake energized for a few seconds after you release the turning controls to allow the antennas to stop moving first.

Position Indication

There are two basic types of position indication — resistance and pulse counting. The most common circuit is a potentiometer ("pot") contained in the rotator's housing and turned in sync with the rotator motor. Current through the pot (typically only a few milliamps) drives an analog meter in the control unit calibrated in degrees. Rotators using pulse counters use a switch to generate pulses that the control unit counts to calculate the number of degrees from one end of travel.

Most rotators in North America are configured as "North center," meaning they can turn an antenna from pointing directly south at one limit, through north at mid-travel, and all the way to south again at the opposite limit. North is the center position on the meter displaying the antenna's direction. (South center meter scales are an option for most rotators.)

To calibrate a pot-indicator rotator's direction, assuming north center, first adjust any meter calibration controls to mid-scale. Then move the rotator to its mid-travel orientation. Loosen the antenna mast clamp and rotate the mast until the antennas point directly north and re-tighten the clamp. (Using a compass or landmark is sufficient resolution for most amateur antennas.) When storing or testing a rotator, make a practice of leaving it set to mid-travel for ease of position calibration and mark or tag it for later reference. For a pulse-count rotator, the manufacturer's manual will provide the necessary directions.

26.9.5 ROTATOR WIRING

The ARRL appreciates being granted permission by the Hy-Gain Company to reproduce the wiring diagram of the control unit for its widely used Ham-IV/Ham-IVX and Tailtwister T2X rotators as a convenience for readers. (See **Figure 26.53**.)

The connection from the control unit to the rotator requires a multi-conductor control cable (no shield necessary). Most rotators require either 6- or 8-conductor cable. Solenoid brake circuits need heavier wire due to the higher current. If wire is used that is too small, the extra resistance may cause enough voltage drop to result in erratic brake operation or slow turning. Check the manufacturer's recommendation for minimum wire size, which depends on the length of the cable. For the popular Ham-IV series and the Tailtwister T2X rotators, minimum recommended wire sizes are:

•Up to 125 feet: #18 AWG (brake solenoid), #20 AWG (all others)

•125 to 200 feet: #16 AWG (brake solenoid), #18 AWG (all others)

•200 to 300 feet: #14 AWG (brake solenoid), #16 AWG (all others)

Other rotators have similar requirements — consult the manufacturer's instructions.

At the rotator, connections can be made directly to a terminal strip under the unit or to a weatherproofed connector at the end of a short "pigtail." A nearby junction box where the pigtail and cable are attached can also be used. Retrofit kits to replace terminal strips are available from several vendors. The Ham-IV family suggests an 8-pin Cinch-Jones connector with wiring and color code as shown in **Table 26.8**.

For terminal strip connections, use a weatherproofing

One Control for All

Each rotator family (Ham-IV, Yaesu, M², and so on) comes with a custom control unit for turning and position display. There are also aftermarket control units that operate with any of the common rotators. The most widely used are the Green Heron controllers (**www.greenheronengineering.com**) and the EA4TX interfaces (**ea4tx.com**). Both can control most available models of rotators, allowing you to standardize in the shack and customize on the tower.

Rotator Software Control

Recently-designed rotator control units have RS-232 or USB interfaces which are used as COM ports by PC software. There are several different protocols, the Yaesu protocol being the most common. The Rotor-EZ and ERC interfaces can be added to most rotators that don't have a software interface.

Green Heron makes a control unit that can work with almost any common rotator and can be controlled by software, as well. The Green Heron product line includes a number of rotator control accessories and consoles.

Logging software often supports several different protocols and standalone software packages and utilities are also available - Internet searches for "antenna rotator software control" will find many programs.

Going beyond PC interfaces to legacy controllers, popular microcontrollers are being employed to create "smart" rotator systems. For an example, see the SatNOGS system described in the **Space Antennas** chapter. VK1DSH describes his Arduino-based rotator controller in the July 2016 issue of *Amateur Radio*, the Wireless Institute of Australia's magazine.

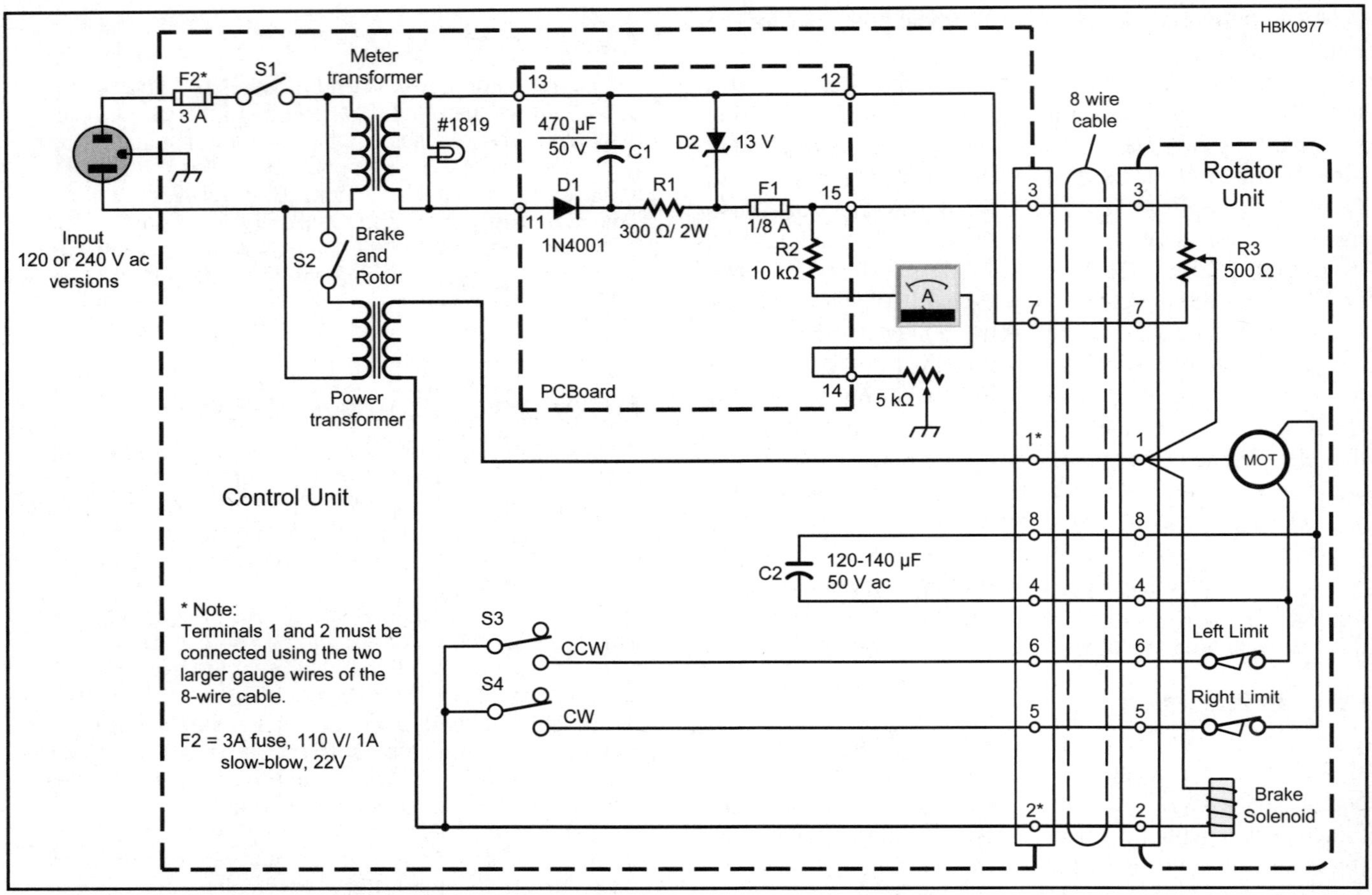

Figure 26.53 — The Hy-Gain Ham-IV/IVX control unit schematic. This control unit will also work with T2X rotators. (Circuit provided courtesy of Hy-Gain, Inc.)

Table 26.8
Ham-IV/IVX Connector and Cable Wiring
Pin numbers, colors, and resistance values from Ham-IV/IVX Instruction Manual

Pin	*Color*	*Circuit*
1	Black	Solenoid and common
2	White	Solenoid
3	Green	Position pot element, + end
4	Blue	Motor winding 1
5	Orange	Right limit switch
6	Yellow	Left limit switch
7	Brown	Position pot element, – end
8	Red	Motor winding 2

Resistance Checks — Read Between Terminals

1-2	Brake solenoid	0.75 Ω + cable or leads
1-8	1/2 Motor winding	2.5 Ω + cable or leads
1-4	1/2 Motor winding	2.5 Ω+ cable or leads
1-6	1/2 Motor + switch	2.5 Ω + cable or leads
1-5	1/2 Motor + switch	2.5 Ω + cable or leads
8-4	Entire motor	5 Ω + cable or leads
8-5	Right limit switch	0 Ω + cable or leads
4-6	Left limit switch	0 Ω + cable or leads
3-7	Entire pot element	500 Ω
3-1	Pot wiper to element end 1	0 to 500 Ω
7-1	Pot wiper to element end 2	0 to 500 Ω

Note: readings 3-1 and 7-1 should add to 3-7 reading

Keeping Rotators Rotating

Rotators are designed for years of trouble-free service as long as they are not overloaded and subjected to high winds, tightly secured to the mast and tower, and water kept away from the control cable connections and out of the motors and gears. It's your job as the station owner to check on them now and then with regular inspections and make sure the controller and wiring are working properly. Regular resistance and voltage checks at the controller are a good way to look for developing electrical problems.

If your rotator does need repair, there are several service shops that will fix up an old rotator or provide a rebuilt unit. You can also do the job yourself if you are careful and have access to replacement parts — check before opening up the housing! You can find instructions and videos online for most of the common rotators. The *CQ VHF* article "CDE/Hy-Gain Rotors, How to Keep 'em Turning, Parts 1 and 2," by W9FX in the Winter and Spring 2009 issues goes into some detail with photographs of key steps and assemblies.

grease found at electrical and automotive stores. Run the connecting cable down and away from the rotator to guide water away from it. It is highly recommended to use a consistent color code at the rotator and the control unit.

Lightning protection is also recommended for rotator control cables. Several vendors make 8-line lightning protectors for rotators. The protector must be well-grounded and should be installed at a common entry point for all antenna system cables. See the **Safety** chapter for more about grounding and lightning protection practices.

Troubleshooting a rotator electrically can be done from the ground through resistance checks. Table 26.8 shows the nominal resistance values for the Ham-IV family of rotators. When making resistance checks, the control unit must be disconnected. Include the resistance of the cable or test leads when making resistance checks.

For the Hy-Gain family of rotators, if the rotator has been turned to the limit of rotation and can't be turned in the other direction, it is possible to bypass the limit switches at the control box. Jumpering pins 4-6 and 2-5 bypass the limit switches so you can turn the rotator off the limits. This should only be done temporarily.

26.10 GROUNDING AND LIGHTNING PROTECTION

The subject of grounding and lightning protection is very broad, covering everything from low-frequency ac safety through RF electromagnetics. As such, a thorough treatment is well beyond the scope of this section although certain important points and concepts can be introduced and discussed. This section covers the requirements for safety grounding of the antenna system components and discusses ground or earth connections used for lightning protection.

Providing "cookbook" solutions for grounding and lightning protection is unrealistic because every station and antenna system is different. Local codes, soils, and lightning environment all vary from location to location. Thus, the goal is to provide general guidance, define common terms, and identify authoritative sources of information so that the underlying principles can be applied to a specific station's needs.

It is recommended that station builders study the references and articles cited in this section, including those provided with this book's downloadable supplemental information, when designing and constructing their own station. The Bibliography lists several well-known and respected industry standards for lightning protection of military and commercial communications and broadcast facilities. While a professional-quality installation may be out of reach for amateurs, the references provide guidance for how best to make use the limited resources available.

This section also includes material from the **Safety** chapter of *The ARRL Handbook* and other ARRL publications such as *Grounding and Bonding for the Radio Amateur*. (See Bibliography). The ARRL's Technical Information Service web page on Safety (**www.arrl.org/safety**) also contains lists of useful references and guidelines for installing protective systems in your station.

26.10.1 STATION GROUNDING

Permitting

Most locations impose some kind of permit process on significant outdoor building projects, such as towers. Along with mechanical and civil engineering concerns for whether the structure is sound and appropriately sited, electrical requirements for grounding and lightning protection are also included.

Find out what building codes apply in your area and have someone explain the regulations about antenna installation and safety. For more help, look in your telephone directory or online for professional engineers, electricians, and contractors. Accommodating local code requirements at the beginning of your project is usually a lot less expensive than trying to bring a non-compliant system up to code later on.

Your local electrical supply houses and distributors are good sources for both references to contractors, and materials.

AC Safety Grounding

The National Electrical Code (NEC) specifies standard methods for dealing with electrical shock and fire hazards. Article 250 deals with grounding and bonding. Article 810 deals with radio and television equipment. Your local code may refer to these sections or may impose different or more stringent requirements. In either case, the local code has authority over your installation. The NEC is published by the National Fire Protection Agency (NFPA) — **www.nfpa.org**.

Reducing the detailed language of the NEC to simple terms, you must connect all exposed metal from ac-powered equipment to a central, common ground. All equipment electrically connected to an ac-powered device should have a permanent safety connection, even if the equipment is unpowered, such as an antenna tuner or audio switch. This includes masts and towers, along with any other outdoor equipment.

This connection is usually referred to as the *ac safety ground* and the connection is made through the "third wire" of your ac power wiring; the bare or "green" wire. If a short circuit develops between the ac wiring and the enclosure of a piece of equipment, the resulting fault current in the ground connection trips a circuit breaker in the hot conductor. Leakage current is mostly due to capacitance between the phase (hot) ac conductor and the equipment chassis or enclosure. This includes capacitors used for ac line filtering and stray capacitances such as between a power transformer's windings and its metallic frame, which is usually bonded to the equipment enclosure and thus to the equipment's ground connection.

Ground-Fault Circuit Interrupter (GFCI) breakers go one step further and monitor the balance of current on the hot and neutral lines of an ac circuit. If an imbalance is detected, it is assumed that the missing current is flowing on the equipment chassis or enclosure, where it can present a shock hazard and the GFCI trips to remove power.

Since the ac safety ground is concerned with currents at the power line frequency and its first few harmonics, the length of the connection is relatively unimportant. Similarly, resistance in the ac safety ground path or imbalances of a few ohms between circuits doesn't matter much from the perspective of safety. (Imbalances might be significant for signal-level connections.) The important thing is that hazardous current takes a path that doesn't go through a human being.

Bonding

Bonding refers to connecting equipment enclosures and earth connections (ground rods) together so they are at the same electrical potential, even if there is a short-circuit in the ac power connection or a lightning strike. The goal of bonding is to minimize the voltage between exposed metal surfaces to reduce shock hazards. In the amateur station, bonding also minimizes RF current flow between pieces of equipment that can cause improper or degraded operation.

Equipment can be bonded together regardless of whether there is an earth connection. Bonding connections should be made with conductors that are heavy enough to be mechanically secure and that have minimal resistance.

The minimum recommended grounding conductor for bonding earth connections together is #6 AWG stranded wire. Copper strap (or flashing) should be a minimum of 1.5 inches wide and 0.051 inch thick. In the station, bonding equipment enclosures together can be done with #12 or #14 AWG wire or flat-woven braided strap. Use grounding fittings and blocks for connecting the bonding wires and strap together.

Do not use braided strap outdoors or where exposed to moisture because the individual strands oxidize over time, greatly reducing the effectiveness of braid at RF. Use bare copper for buried ground wires. (There are some exceptions; seek an expert's advice if your soil is corrosive.) Braid removed from coaxial cable should not be used as an RF bonding conductor. Without the protection and compression of the jacket, the weave of round braid loosens and the individual wires will oxidize.

Exposed runs above ground that are subject to physical damage may require additional protection (such as a conduit) to meet code requirements. Wire size depends on the application but never use anything smaller than #6 AWG for bonding conductors. Local lightning-protection experts, electricians, or building inspectors can recommend sizes for each application.

Static Dissipation

Wind and precipitation can develop a large static charge on any ungrounded antenna or tower, up to thousands of volts. If not discharged to ground, the charge will eventually build up and arc to a convenient grounded point. This can obviously lead to equipment damage. There are several methods of dissipating static charge without affecting the antenna system. The first two suggestions are primarily useful at HF.

- High-value, non-inductive resistors of 10 kΩ or more connected from ungrounded feed line conductors to ground allow small currents from static electricity to be discharged safely. The resistors should be rated for at least 1 kV to avoid arcing from high RF power levels and induced voltage surges from nearby lightning strikes. Metal-oxide resistors of ½-W or higher power rating can withstand short pulse overloads and are inexpensive.
- RF chokes below their self-resonant frequency provide a dc path to ground for static while having sufficiently high reactance to have a minimal effect on impedance. Note that wire-wound chokes use fine wire that can act as a fuse and become an open circuit from a lightning-induced transient.
- DC-grounded antenna designs use shunt inductors to ground at the feed point or have driven elements connected to a supporting structure, such as a gamma-matched Yagi. These antennas dissipate static charges continually.
- Quarter-wave shorted stubs (see the **Transmission Line System Techniques** chapter) act as an open-circuit at the design frequency while providing a direct path to ground for static electricity. This technique only works on a single band and can't be used on multiband antennas.

26.10.2 LIGHTNING PROTECTION

Effective lightning protection system design is a complex topic. There are a variety of system tradeoffs that must be made and that determine the type and amount of protection needed. Hams can easily follow some general guidelines that will protect their stations against high-voltage events that are induced by nearby lightning strikes or that arrive via utility lines. The basic techniques are thoroughly explored in the three-part 2002 series of *QST* articles "Lightning Protection for the Amateur Station" by Ron Block, KB2UYT, that are included with this book's downloadable supplemental information and online at **www.arrl.org/lightning-protection**. Another useful document on lightning protection is available from the IEEE, "How to Protect Your House and Its Contents from Lightning" (see the Bibliography).

You may also wish to use the services of a local lightning protection expert to advise you on specific techniques appropriate for your area. Companies that sell lightning-protection products may offer considerable help to apply their products to specific installations. One such source is PolyPhaser (**www.polyphaser.com**). The Bibliography of this chapter contains a partial list of PolyPhaser's publications.

Tower and Feed Line Grounding

Because a tower is usually the highest metal object on the property, it is the most likely strike target. Proper tower grounding is essential to lightning protection. The goal is to establish short multiple paths to the earth so that the strike energy is divided and dissipated.

Connect each tower leg and each fan of metal guy wires

to a separate ground rod. Space the rods at least 6 feet apart. Bond the leg ground rods together with #6 AWG or larger copper bonding conductor (form a ring around the tower base, see **Figure 26.54**). Connect a continuous bonding conductor between the tower ring ground and the station's cable entrance panel.

Make all connections with fittings approved for grounding applications. Do not use lead-tin solder for these connections — it will be destroyed in the heat of a lightning strike. If the fitting is to be buried, use welded connections (see the sidebar) or clamps that are specifically rated for direct burial.

Because galvanized steel (which has a zinc coating) reacts with copper when combined with moisture, use stainless steel hardware between the galvanized metal and the copper grounding materials.

To provide an alternate path for strike energy to entering your home or station via the feed line, ground the feed line outside the home. Ground the coax shield to the tower at the antenna and the base to keep the tower and line at the same potential. Several companies offer grounding blocks that make this job easy to do properly.

Bonding Earth Connections

Significant voltages can be created between separated earth connections, especially during lightning surges. The solution is to bond all external earth connections together, creating a *perimeter ground* as shown in **Figure 26.55**. The perimeter ground may extend completely around the building but if that is not practical, extend the ground system as far as you can with ground rods every 10 feet or so.

The ground rods and buried bonding conductor provide a low impedance path for the lightning's charge outside the building and help keep equipment at close to the same voltage at low frequencies. Both are important — keep as much of the lightning energy as possible outside while minimizing large voltage differences and current surges that damage equipment inside.

The *service entrance ground* connection from the ac power distribution panel to a ground rod establishes a local earth connection for lightning protection of ac-powered equipment and appliances. All other earth connections should be bonded to the service entrance ground.

All earth connection bonding requires at least #6 AWG copper wire. This includes lightning protection conductors, electrical service, telephone, antenna system grounds and underground metal pipes. Any ground rods used for lightning protection or entrance panel grounding should be spaced at least 6 feet from each other and the electrical service or other utility grounds and then bonded to the ac service entrance ground as required by the NEC and local codes.

Ufer Ground

If you live in a dry or rocky area where ground rods are difficult to install or ineffective, a Ufer ground or "concrete-encased electrode" is often used. The Ufer ground relies on the conductivity of concrete to make contact with the soil over the large area of a foundation slab or tower footing. Reinforcing bar (rebar) inside the concrete is bonded to building steel or a tower with a heavy bonding conductor.

More information on Ufer grounds is available in NEC section 250.52, the PolyPhaser book *Lightning Protection and Grounding,* and in *Lightning Protection & Grounding Solutions for Communication Sites* (see Bibliography).

Cable Entrance Panel

The basic concept for lightning protection is to make sure that all the radio and other equipment is bonded so that it "moves together" in the presence of a transient voltage. It's not so important that the station be at "ground" potential, but, rather, that everything is at the *same* potential. For fast rise-time transients, such as the individual strokes that make up a lightning strike, even a short wire has enough inductance that the voltage drop along the wire is significant, so whether you are on the ground floor, or the 10th floor of a building, your station is "far" from Earth potential.

The easiest way to ensure that everything is at the same potential is to tie all the signals to a common reference. In

Welding Earth Connections

The best way to ensure that a buried ground rod connection remains effective is to weld it. Conventional welding may be used but a far easier method is to use exothermic welding in which a fast-burning fuel melts the rod and connecting wire together, resulting in a mechanically and electrically secure connection. Often referred to as "one-shots," the best known products in this line are the CADWELD products by Erico (**www.erico.com**) and the Harger Uni-Shot (**www.harger.com**)

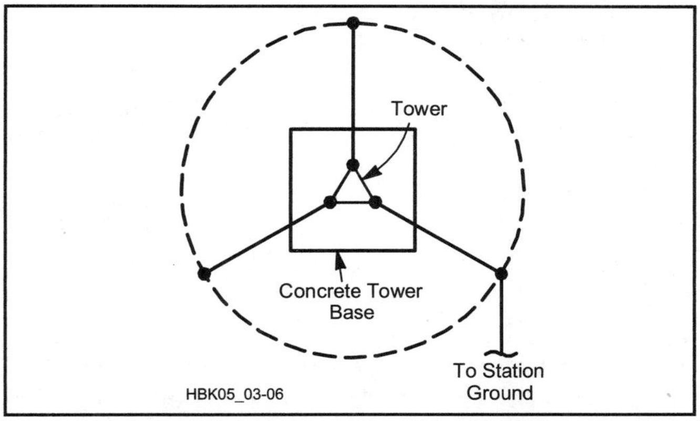

Figure 26.54 — Schematic of a properly grounded tower. A bonding conductor connects each tower leg to a ground rod and a buried (1 foot deep) bare, tinned copper ring (dashed line), which is also connected to the station ground and then to the ac safety ground. Locate ground rods on the ring, as close as possible to their respective tower legs. All connectors should be compatible with the tower and conductor materials to prevent corrosion. See text for conductor sizes and details of lightning and voltage transient protection.

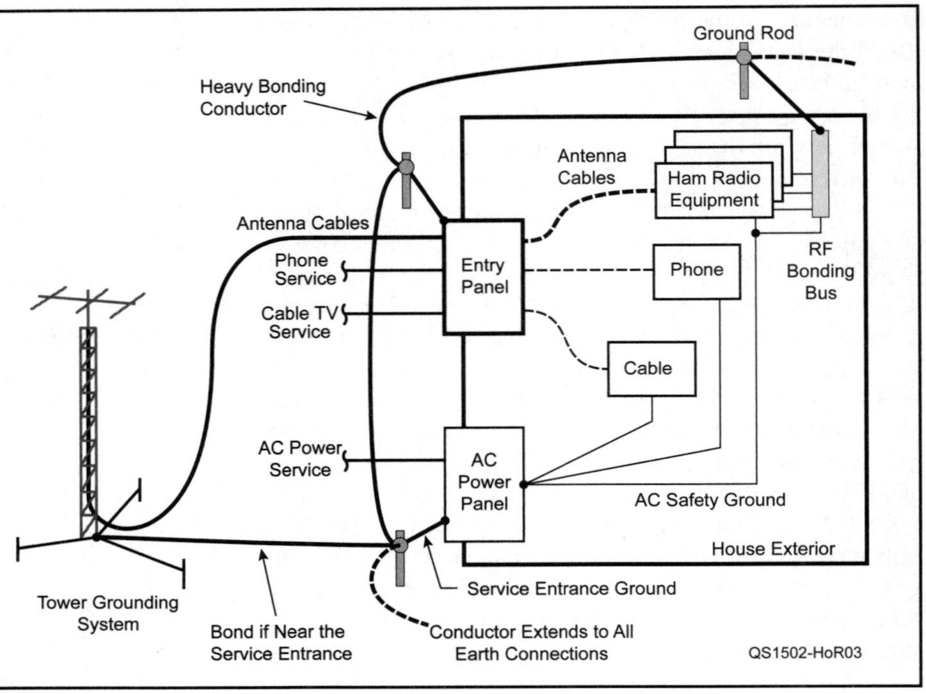

Figure 26.55 — A lightning protection system attempts to dissipate charge outside the home or station. All earth connections are bonded together to provide a low-impedance path for lightning, and to minimize voltage differences and current flow between equipment and circuits.

large facilities, this reference would be provided by a grid of large diameter cables under the floor, or by wide copper bars, or even a solid metal floor. A more practical approach for smaller facilities like a ham station is to have a common connection point for all the cables. Often referred to as an *entrance panel* or *single-point ground panel* (SPGP), the object is to provide a common potential reference for shields and signal connections.

The easiest way to create an entrance panel is to install a large metal enclosure or a metal panel as a bulkhead and grounding block in the exterior wall. The panel should be bonded to the lightning dissipation ground with a short wide conductor, and, like all grounds, bonded to the electrical system's ac service entry ground. This is illustrated in Figure 26.55 which shows the various grounding systems at a typical home station. (W8JI's website at **www.w8ji.com/station_ground.htm** shows examples of an entrance panel system and wiring practices.)

If multiple entry panels or lightning arrestors are used for different services, such as telephone or cable TV, connect those panels or lightning arrestors to the outside bonding conductor that connects all of the ground rods together.

Every conductor that enters the structure, including antenna system control lines, should have its own surge suppressor on an entrance panel. Suppressors are available from a number of amateur equipment vendors, as well as the usual electrical equipment suppliers such as Square-D, Graybar, and so forth. (See Parts 1 and 2 of the *QST* articles by Block for illustrations.)

Mount all lightning arrestors, protective devices, switches and relay disconnects on the outside facing wall of the bulkhead. The enclosure or panel should be installed in a way that if lightning currents cause a component to fail, the molten metal and flaming debris do not start a fire. To avoid creating another path to ground around the panel, route the feed lines, rotator control cables, and so on at least six feet away from other nearby grounded metal objects.

Lightning Arrestors and Surge Suppressors

Feed line lightning arrestors (known as *antenna discharge units* in the NEC) are available for both coaxial cable and parallel-conductor or balanced line. Most of the balanced line arrestors use a simple spark gap arrangement, but a balanced line impulse suppressor is available from several vendors.

DC blocking arrestors for coaxial cable have a fixed frequency range. They present a high-impedance to lightning energy below 1 MHz while offering a low impedance to higher-frequency RF.

DC-continuous arrestors (gas tubes and spark gaps) can

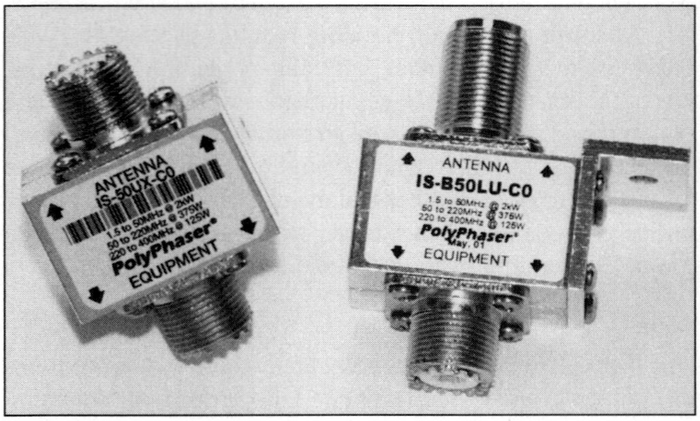

Figure 26.56 — Typical coaxial lightning arrestors from PolyPhaser. These are mounted on an cable entrance panel that is connected to a ground rod.

be used over a wider frequency range than those that block dc. Where the coax carries supply voltages to remote devices (such as a mast-mounted preamp or remote coax switch), dc-continuous arrestors must be used. **Figure 26.56** shows examples of typical arrestors for coaxial cable.

Upper Floor Stations

A common situation is for an amateur station to be on the floor of a building well above ground level. For these stations, a grounded entrance panel as described above can still be constructed outside the building at ground level as in **Figure 26.57A**. Antenna feed lines and other cables are run to the entrance panel where they are connected to arrestors and suppressors. Cables to the station are then run outside the building from the entrance panel to an entry point on the higher floor.

Running antenna feed lines and other cables directly into an upper-floor station as in Figure 26.57B creates a very difficult lightning protection challenge. An entrance panel on the upper floor will help equalize voltage differences between the cables but unless the building's steel framework is available as a low-impedance earth connection, the long bonding wire to the ground rod will result in significant voltage differences with respect to other ground-referenced wiring such as ac power. In such cases, it is best to disconnect all cables at the entrance panel when not in use or when storms are in the area.

26.10.3 ANTENNA FEED LINE PROTECTION BOX

This project was originally published as "Antenna Feed Line Control Box" by Phil Salas, AD5X, in the August 2014 issue of *QST*. The complete article, including a parts list, all construction details, design formulas, and performance measurements, is included with this book's downloadable supplemental information. Commercial versions of this project are sold as "antenna disconnectors" by Inrad (**www.vibroplex.com**) and Paradan Radio (**paradanradio.com**) — see the Product Review of these items in the April 2019 issue of *QST*.

Regardless of whether you build the device yourself or purchase it, the connection to your station's ground system is very important. The connection should be direct, low-impedance, and short, using heavy wire or strap. This will help reduce the voltage difference between the protector and any other piece of station equipment also connected to the ground system. The commercial versions completely disconnect both conductors of the feed line from the radio. See this chapter's section on "Grounding and Lightning Protection" for more information about lightning protection.

Design

While the design in **Figure 26.58** is not a substitute for a fully grounded entrance panel with lightning arrestors, it can make a good backup protection system, particularly for stations on upper floors of buildings or with marginal lightning protection grounding. The intent is to deal with voltage pulses caused by nearby lightning strikes and static buildup on antennas, both of which can damage equipment in the station.

Static buildup (often termed precipitation static) on antennas can reach thousands of volts.8 This can be prevented with bleeder resistors connected from the coax center conductor to ground.

As most of the energy in a lightning strike is concentrated well below 500 kHz, the high reactance of the blocking capacitors will attenuate much of this low frequency energy.

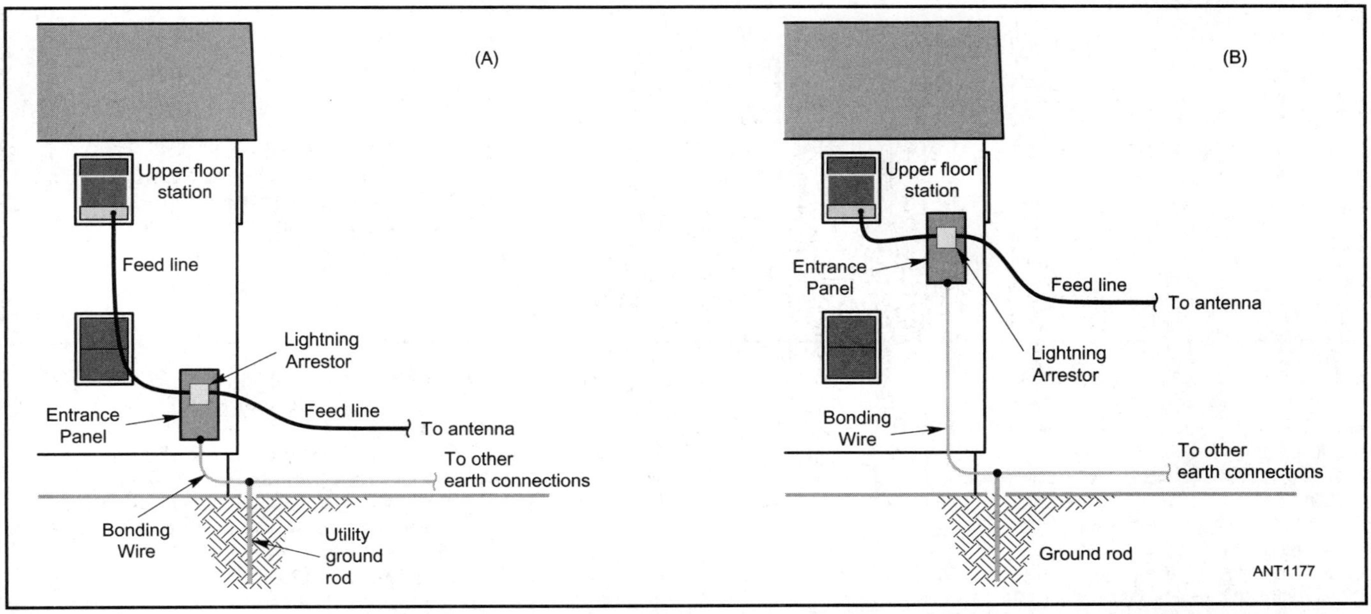

Figure 26.57 — Protecting an upper-floor station against lightning is a challenge. If possible, construct an entrance panel at ground level as in A and run feed lines (and a ground wire – not shown) to the station. If the entrance panel must be at the station level as in B, it should still be grounded but the long bonding wire will create significant voltages at the station. Disconnecting all cables when not in use on when storms are nearby is highly recommended in this case.

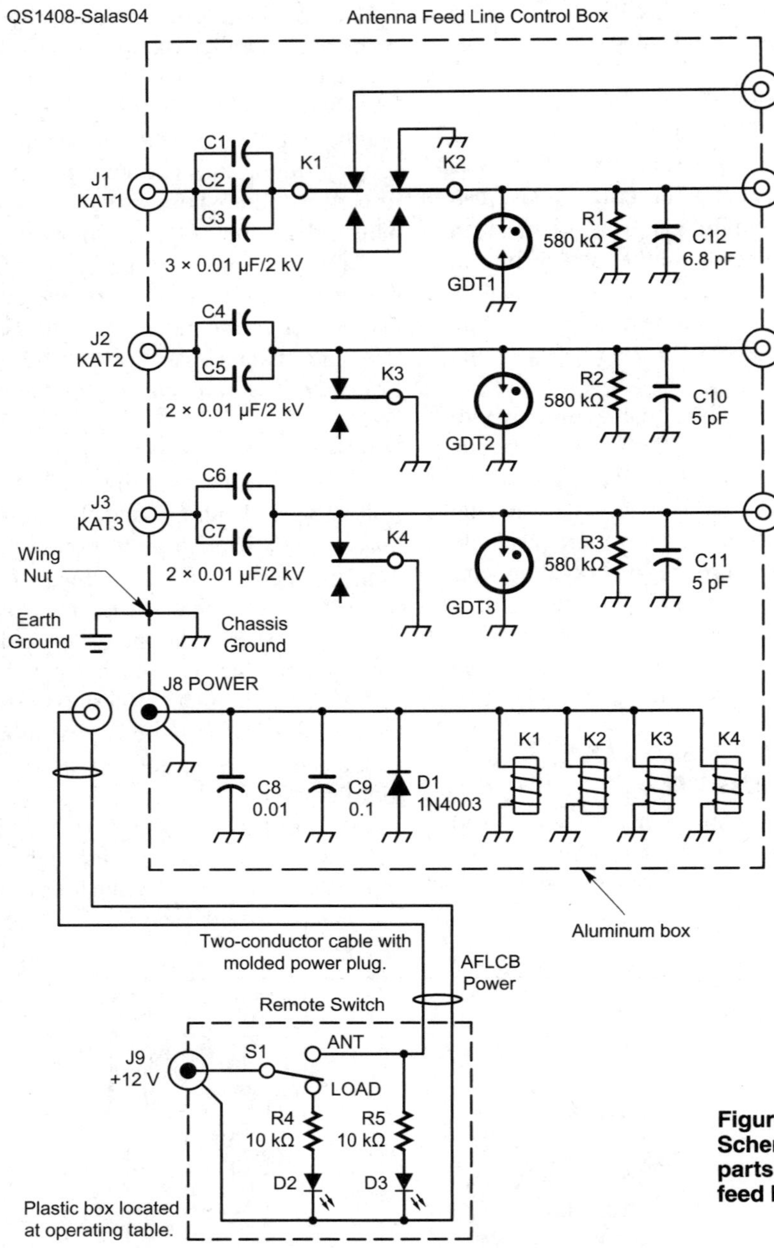

Figure 26.58 — Schematic diagram and parts list for the antenna feed line protection box.

C1 – C7 — 0.01 µF, 2 kV capacitor (Mouser 594-S103M69Z5UP63K7R).
C8 — 0.01 µF, 100 V ceramic disc capacitor (Mouser 140-100Z5-103Z-RC).
C9 — 0.1 µF, 50 V ceramic disc capacitor (Mouser 140-50U5-104M-RC).
C10, C11 — 5 pF, 1 kV capacitor (Mouser 75-561R10TCCV50).
C12 — 6.8 pF, 1 kV capacitor (Mouser 75-561R10TCCV68).
D1 — 1N4003 diode (Mouser 512-1N4003).
D2, D3 — Green LED (Mouser 941-C5SMFGJSCV14Q7S1).
GDT1 – GSD3 — Gas discharge tube 800 V (Mouser 652-2095-80-BLF).
R1 – R3 — 580 kΩ ½ W 3.5 kV resistor (Mouser 594-HVR3700005903FR5)
R4 – R5 — 10 kΩ, ¼ W resistor (Mouser 66-CMF1/41002FLFTR).
J1 – J7 — SO-239 connector (Mouser 601-25-7350).
J8, J9 — DC jack 2.1 × 5.5 mm (Mouser 163-1060-EX).
K1 – K4 — SPDT power relay (Mouser 655-RTB14012F).
S1 — SPDT toggle switch (Mouser 108-0009-EVX).
DC power cable (with compatible plug for J8) — 2.1 × 5.5 mm × 3 feet (Mouser 172-4204).
Plastic box — 1.38 × 1.38 × 0.79 inches (Mouser 546-1551MBK).
Aluminum box — 4.3 × 3.3 × 1.6 inches (Mouser 563-CU-5471).

This high reactance also allows the voltage to spike. Therefore gas discharge tubes will fire for impulse voltages greater than about 800 V, shunting that energy to ground.

Normally the blocking capacitors will simply serve to pass RF current from the unit's inputs to the ANT outputs. Capacitors passing heavy current are subject to heating and will dissipate power P_d proportional to the product of the equivalent series resistance ESR and the square of the RF current I: $P_d = I^2 \times ESR$. This power dissipation can be minimized by choosing capacitors with a low dissipation factor DF. Because $ESR = DF \times X_c$ where X_c is the capacitor's reactance, the power dissipated by the capacitor can now be expressed as $P_d = I^2 \times DF \times X_c$. Stating X_c in terms of the frequency f and capacitance C yields $P_d = (I^2 \times DF) / (2\pi \times f \times C)$.

Capacitor heating can be further reduced by paralleling capacitors, which reduces the current through each capacitor. Assuming that the aggregate current remains the same, paralleling two equal-value capacitors will reduce the current through each by a factor of 2. Because the power dissipated is proportional to the square of the current, the net effect will be to reduce the individual capacitor power dissipation by a factor of 4.

Schematic

When remote switch S1 is set to LOAD, power is removed from SPDT relays K1 – K4. The disposition of the relay contacts shown in the schematic is for the power off condition, which is also the state of the unit when the station is off the air. In the power off state, relays K2 – K4 connect signals ANT1 – ANT3 (J5 – J7) to chassis ground, which in turn is connected to the station single point ground via a wing nut connection on the outside of the aluminum box. This prevents static charge buildup on the antennas and also provides a path to ground for pulses due to nearby lightning strikes. Additionally, when S1 is set to LOAD, relay K1 connects KAT1 to DUMMY LOAD through SO-239 connectors J1 and J4 respectively.

When remote switch S1 is set to ANTS, +12 V is supplied to the unit through POWER input J8, which in turn is connected to the coils of relays K1 – K4. Diode D1 suppresses the kickback voltage from the relay coils when power is removed and capacitors C8 and C9 bypass any RF voltage to ground.

In the power on state, the ground shunt connections made by relays K2 – K4 of signals ANT1 – ANT3 are removed along with the KAT1 connection to DUMMY LOAD through K1. Then, KAT1 is connected to ANT1 via K1 and K2 and blocking capacitors C1 – C3. The author paralleled three capacitors on this port because this is his only 160 meter connection.

The paths through the unit are similar, so we'll take the path from KAT2 (J2) to ANT2 (J6) as a representative case. Capacitors C4 and C5 are wired in parallel to share RF current in order to minimize heating due to their equivalent series resistance. In the power on state, since ANT1 – ANT3 are no longer grounded, the unit is vulnerable to pulses from nearby lightning strikes and to static charge buildup on the antennas. In the event of a nearby lightning strike, the high reactance of C4 and C5 will block much of the energy from the pulse.

Figure 26.59 — View of parts placement inside the aluminum box housing the unit. The wing nut at the upper left connects the chassis ground of the unit to the station single-point ground at the cable entrance panel.

And if the voltage spike should reach 800 V, gas discharge tube GDT2 will fire and the energy will be shunted to ground. While operating, static charge buildup is prevented by bleeder resistor R2 connected from the signal line to chassis ground.

The small-value capacitor C10 compensates for the impedance bump due to the unit's internal wiring. Without the capacitor the SWR of the unit degrades to about 1.3:1 on 6 meters when the unit is perfectly terminated. With the capacitor, the SWR is less than 1.03:1 (36 dB return loss) on 6 meters. Of course these capacitors are not really necessary as the protection box follows any antenna tuner. However any impedance bump can degrade a less-than perfect feed line SWR enough to make the difference between bypassing a tuner and the need for a tuner to be in-line, especially at the higher frequencies.

Note that the voltage ratings of the components in this path are higher than typical: R2 is rated at 3.5 kV, where an ordinary resistor is only rated for a few hundred volts; blocking capacitors C4 and C5 are rated at 2 kV and C10 is rated at 1 kV. The relays, while inexpensive, work well through 6 meters, providing 1 kV RMS of isolation between contacts, 5 kV RMS of isolation between the coil and the contacts, and contacts rated at 12 A continuous current.

Construction

Figure 26.59 shows a photo of the completed unit built into a cast aluminum box that has a mounting bracket that permits it to be rigidly mounted in place. The relays (with pins up) are hot-glued to the aluminum box. A step-drill or ⅝-inch Greenlee punch works well for cutting the SO-239 connector holes. Note that there is also a ground stud consisting of a #8 stainless steel screw, nut, lock washer, and wing nut for connecting to your station's single-point ground.

26.11 CORROSION

Corrosion is one of the biggest problems in tower and antenna installations. Knowing more about it will help you to use appropriate materials and stay away from problematic combinations. For detailed information on corrosion, visit the website of Corrosion Source (**www.corrosionsource.com**), where there are a number of free reports and other downloadable documents on corrosion.

Any metal by itself will eventually oxidize due to exposure to the oxygen in the atmosphere. The aluminum in our antennas combines with oxygen to create the powdery aluminum oxide you find when you take an antenna apart, while oxidation of steel (which is iron) produces the rust that you want to avoid.

When two metals with the right properties are in contact in the presence of an electrolyte, *bimetallic corrosion* takes place. It's the same chemical process that takes place in batteries. Specifically, ions from one metal (called the *anodic* metal) flow across the joint or junction to the other metal (called the *cathodic* metal). In bimetallic joints, the more anodic metal is the one that loses material.

The electrolyte is typically some kind of salt or other compound (such as zinc) dissolved in water making the solution conductive. Rain (particularly acid rain), mist or condensation are sufficient for bimetallic corrosion to begin.

Galvanically incompatible metals are combinations of metals that readily corrode when in contact because of their ranking on the galvanic chart. The farther apart the metals are in the table, the faster they will corrode when in contact. When you must use different materials, it is best to use metals that are close together in **Table 26.9**. You can see that on a zinc galvanized tower, aluminum and mild steel are the most compatible. If you use materials such as copper and brass when installing your tower ground system on a galvanized tower, you can see that you will have problems with corrosion almost immediately.

Table 26.9
Relative Galvanic Series In Sea Water

MORE ANODIC
Magnesium
Zinc
Galvanized steel
Aluminum
Mild Steel
Iron
50-50 lead/tin solder
Stainless Steel
Tin
Nickel (active)
Brass
Aluminum-bronze
Copper
Nickel (passive)
Silver
Gold
MORE CATHODIC

One technique for avoiding corrosion on towers is to use an intermediate corrosion-resistant material between two otherwise incompatible metals. For example, to connect a copper ground conductor to a galvanized tower, use a stainless steel washer or shim between the copper and zinc galvanizing and stainless steel hardware to hold them together.

Another technique is to use *sacrificial anodes* that give up material to prevent corrosion of the main structure. A complete discussion of this technique is beyond the scope of this chapter but the recent *QST* article by Tony Brock-Fisher, K1KP, "Is Your Tower Still Safe?" covers the topic well (see the Bibliography or this book's downloadable supplemental information).

26.11.1 ANTIOXIDANTS

Various compounds are available for combating corrosion. These are *antioxidants* and most commonly-used metals such as copper, aluminum, and steel have several products designed specifically for each of them.

For aluminum antennas, most manufacturers provide a packet of antioxidant with their products. Retarding oxidation is not only a good electrical idea but the compound also functions as an anti-seize coating, aiding you in taking the antenna apart at a later date.

Antioxidants are sometimes incorrectly called "conductive pastes or greases." In general, these antioxidant compounds are comprised of a carrier material with metallic chips in suspension. It is these conductive chips, not the carrier, that give the compound its conductive properties. What happens is that the particles will pierce the layer of oxidation while preventing corrosion by isolating the joint from the air. The compound that comes with Butternut antennas, *Butter-It's-Not*, uses copper dust in a molybdenum suspension while the paste supplied by M^2 Antennas uses copper and graphite flakes in a petroleum base. There are other commercial products available for copper joints which should be used on ground systems. Just be certain to use the right one for the job. **Table 26.10** lists several compounds and their manufacturers. In addition to using antioxidants on towers and antennas, they should be used in ground system joints as well as in marine environments.

26.11.2 RUST

Steel towers and hardware will rust unless steps are taken to prevent it. In the case of towers, use galvanized steel or aluminum. Hardware, including U-bolts, nuts, bolts and other fasteners should either be made out of stainless steel (SS) or

Table 26.10
Antioxidant Compounds

Product	*Manufacturer*	*Use with*
OX-GARD	GB Electrical — **www.gardnerbender.com**	Aluminum-aluminum, aluminum-copper
NOALOX	Ideal Industries, Inc — **www.idealind.com**	Aluminum-aluminum
NO-OX-ID "A-SPECIAL"	Sanchem, Inc. — **www.sanchem.com**	Steel rust preventative
Penetrox	Burndy — **www.hubbell.com/burndy**	Aluminum-aluminum, aluminum-copper
DE-OX	ILSCO Corporation — **www.ilsco.com**	Aluminum-aluminum, aluminum-copper

be galvanized. Because the galvanizing process deposits a thin coating of zinc on the hardware, you can't interchange SS and galvanized nuts and bolts.

Surface rust is rust that is either deposited when you have water from a rusted piece of hardware run down a surface such as a tower leg or active rust that hasn't yet penetrated the layer of galvanizing. Neither condition is serious but you should repair those spots during your annual inspection. Use a wire brush to scrub off the rust and then spray the spot with a cold-galvanizing paint. "Cold-galvanizing" paint is available at almost any spray paint rack. Check the contents to make sure that it contains zinc. The LPS Company (**www.lpslabs.com**) makes a very good cold-galvanizing spray that is relatively expensive but adheres very well.

26.12 GENERAL MAINTENANCE

Having invested time and money installing your dream antenna and tower system, you'll need periodic preventive maintenance (PM) and inspections. The key is to catch anything before it becomes a problem.

If you've followed the directives and steps described in this chapter you've already taken the most important steps in ensuring the safety and reliability of your tower and antenna system. Following the manufacturer's specifications, using the right hardware, using antioxidants and following conservative designs are the true keys to success.

26.12.1 ANNUAL INSPECTION

An annual inspection is a critical part of your PM program. Most commercial companies do it religiously; many insurance companies require it as a condition of their coverage. An annual inspection entails examining everything in the tower and antenna system, including the ground system, concrete anchors and footings, and the tower structure. In addition to annual inspections, all installations should be inspected after ice storms or wind storms that exceed 60 mph.

You should correct any problems you discover in your inspection. If you're not sure about the seriousness of something you've found, talk to a knowledgeable friend or contact the manufacturer for advice. When you do a tower inspection, you should have enough supplies to redo several coax connector joints if necessary, as well as a note pad and pencil to write down any discrepancies that may require further action. You'll be able to take care of most problems on the spot, along with knowing what else you may need to finish the repairs. Push and pull on antennas and appurtenances (anything that's attached to the tower) to see if anything is loose. Something might look okay but pushing on it might reveal loose hardware or some other problem.

You should get in the habit of doing a quick visual check every time you climb the tower. Carry a wire brush, a can of cold-galvanizing spray, a roll of electrical tape, and a utility knife to perform small repairs along the way. A station notebook of relevant information found during inspection, along with exceptions and repairs is a handy reference item. The information that follows is based on commercial and *TIA-222* tower inspection standards.

Tower Structure

1) Check for damaged or faulty tower legs and braces. With welded towers such as Rohn *25G* and *45G,* the members cannot be replaced without replacing the whole section; minor bends or damage that do not alter the structural integrity can usually be tolerated.

2) Check all welds for integrity.

3) Examine the condition of the finish and any corrosion. Look for rust patches; use a wire brush and cold galvanizing paint to repair it.

4) In addition to visually checking any bolted connections, you should put a wrench to at least 10% of them to check for tightness. Any loose nuts or bolts should be retightened. Also look for missing hardware and replace it immediately.

Tower Alignment

1) The tower should be checked for plumb. A guyed tower is allowed a maximum deviation of one part in 400, or three inches per 100 feet. While a transit is the best way to check tower alignment, an electronic level will give you 0.1° accuracy, or a bubble level will indicate relative plumb. Even simpler is a long piece of string with a weight on the end, held an arm's length away from the tower; sight the string along the tower leg for a very quick and fairly accurate indication of tower plumb. For self-supporting towers, the allowed deviation allowed is 1 part in 250 or 4.8 inches in 100 feet.

Even if the tower is perfectly plumb, perform all of the guy wire and hardware checks that follow to be sure nothing is loose or about to fail.

2) Check the guy wires and guy insulators, using binoculars for the ones that aren't close to the ground or the tower.

3) Examine all guy wire and guy wire hardware including preformed grips, turnbuckles, clamps, and shackles for damage. Make sure that all turnbuckle safety ties are intact. Make sure all bolts and nuts are tight.

4) Check guy wire tension with an instrument or another technique.

5) Examine the tower base and guy anchors. Look for any cracking of the concrete. Also look for evidence of movement in the soil of the anchor rods or base. Look for rust and/or corrosion. Excavate a buried anchor rod for twelve inches

to inspect for hidden corrosion — some sources recommend inspecting anchor rods all the way to the concrete anchor.

Antennas, Cables and Appurtenances

1) Inspect antenna, boom-to-mast bracket and boom truss hardware for loose or missing hardware. Test nuts for tightness.

2) Look at each feed point joint and coax cable joint for compromised weatherproofing.

3) Check all cables for abrasion, binding and attachment.

4) Examine all appurtenances for missing hardware or corrosion.

Rotator

1) Check that all mounting bolts are tight and that they are not slipping in the rotator shelf or plate.

2) Check that the rotator mast clamp is securely holding the mast.

Grounding System

Do a visual inspection of the grounding system. Redo any connections that are corroded.

26.12.2 CRANK-UP MAINTENANCE

Crank-up towers are complex mechanical contrivances. While some are hand cranked, many have a motor, gearbox, cables, pulleys and limit switches — all of which should be carefully inspected twice a year.

The electric motors and gearbox are generally bulletproof and the only inspections are to check the oil level in the gearbox, the condition of the drive belt or chain (some sort of conditioner is helpful for each), and the operation of the cable drum (there are probably some Zerk grease fittings that need attention).

Pulleys are sometimes custom made by the manufacturer so you may not be able to run down to the local store and buy one. Some sheaves are made by the manufacturer and then an off-the-shelf bearing is inserted in the middle. This one you probably can replace.

Pulleys need to turn and not bind so a good thing to do is to watch the pulleys if they're exposed enough while the tower is being raised or lowered and see if there are any problems. (A simple dot or line drawn on the sheave itself will quickly show, even at a distance, whether it's turning or not.)

Crank-Up Cables

Crank-up towers depend almost entirely on their cables to operate reliably and safely. Exercise the cables by running the tower up and down a couple of times a month and don't always leave the tower in the same spot all the time, for example at the limit switches. Over time the cable can take a set if it's always at the same place so leaving it at different places spreads the wear over much more of the cable length.

The cables should be lubricated at least annually; twice a year would be even better. Do not use heavy grease or motor oil which will just attract grime and particles. Use a cable lubricant such as PreLube 6 and be sure to check for damage while you're doing the lube job. If you see any of the following, the cables should be replaced:

1) Damage in which a cable is significantly kinked or flattened.

2) Rust. This means serious rust, not surface rust that can be easily wiped or scraped off.

3) Excessive broken strands. Most crank-ups use 7×19 galvanized cable which means it has 133 strands in it. You're allowed to have six total broken strands and three in the same bundle before replacing the cable.

26.12.3 ROTATOR MAINTENANCE

Most rotator problems are first noticed as misalignment of the antennas with regard to where the control box indicator says they are pointing. With a light duty rotator, this happens frequently when the wind blows the antenna to a different heading. With no brake, the force of the wind can move the gear train and motor of the rotator, while the indicator remains fixed. Such rotator systems have a mechanical stop to prevent continuous rotation during operation, and provision is usually included to realign the indicator against the mechanical stop from inside the station. During installation, the antenna must be oriented correctly for the mechanical stop position, which is usually North.

In larger rotator systems with an adequate brake, indicator misalignment is caused by mechanical slippage in the antenna boom-to-mast hardware. Many texts suggest that the boom be pinned to the mast with a heavy-duty bolt and the rotator be similarly pinned to the mast. There is a trade-off here. If there is sufficient wind to cause slippage in the couplings without pins, with pins the wind could break a rotator casting or transmission parts. The slippage will act as a clutch release, which may prevent serious damage to the rotator. On the other hand, you might not like to climb the tower and realign the system after each heavy windstorm.

26.12.4 WHEN SOMETHING FAILS

Failures to your installation can come in many forms, but wind is generally the common denominator. Rust, metal fatigue and overloading aren't usually a problem until the wind starts to blow. Other causes of failure could be lightning strikes, ice, vandalism or accidents.

Assess the Damage

The first thing to do is a visual inspection. Using binoculars if possible, take a look at everything from the ground to see if anything is bent or broken. If something is swinging in the wind, that's a major problem. If there is obvious damage, try to determine if it is in danger of falling. If so, evacuate the endangered area immediately and alert local emergency services. This is especially true if it looks as though it could fall on power lines, sidewalks or roadways. If you have damage that isn't an imminent danger to life or property, keep an eye on it until the storm is over to ensure that it doesn't get worse. If you have the opportunity, take some snapshots or video of the damage for documentation.

Prevent Further Damage

Your next task is to take prudent steps to prevent further damage, both to your property and to the property of others. This is not only common sense but also a requirement of the insurance company. You want to avoid or minimize the possibility of liability lawsuits for personal injury or the property damage of others. Tie anything off you can but *do not* attempt to climb the tower!

File an Insurance Claim

After the storm is over, call your homeowner's or renter's insurance agent and notify them of the loss. Do it orally first, then follow up with a letter. The insurance company may require a *"Proof of Loss."* They'll give you a claim number that you'll need to use in all written and verbal communications. Start a file with all your documentation, plus the other paperwork that you'll start accumulating. (See the article on insurance by Ray Fallen, ND8L, included with this book's downloadable supplemental information.)

Keep notes of every conversation with your insurance agent or claims adjuster with dates and times; you may have to refer to them in the future. At this point, you may want to write down all pertinent facts surrounding the loss for reference also. Send copies of your photos with your loss letter.

Estimate of Repairs

You'll make things very easy for your claims adjuster if you include an estimate of repair along with your letter and photos. The adjuster has probably never handled a radio tower loss before and will appreciate your help in getting a quote. Contact your local commercial rigger or antenna installation company and they'll give you the quote.

Insurance companies will want professional workers to perform professional repairs to your loss; they expect to pay the going rate and they expect licensed contractors to do the work. Be sure that your estimate for tower repair covers *all* of the work including: dismantling damaged parts, hauling away damaged parts and disposal, clean-up, labor for reinstallation including assembly of antennas, labor for reinstallation of tower, replacing all damaged materials including hardware, cables, rotators, and other items.

Don't be surprised if the estimate comes in quite a bit higher than you expect. Not only are you paying professionals to do all of the work, but a damaged tower or antenna system can be hazardous and a crane or other piece of equipment may be needed to remove it safely.

Stay in Your Comfort Zone

Needless to say, don't consider getting involved in the removal and repair of the damage unless you feel comfortable with it. If there is *any* doubt at all in your mind, either get the professionals in or bring in a piece of equipment such as a crane or boom truck. If anything is at a precarious or dangerous angle, don't touch it — send for the professionals!

26.13 BIBLIOGRAPHY

Source material and more extended discussions of the topics covered in this chapter can be found in the references listed below.

L. H. Abraham, "Guys for Guys Who Have To Guy," *QST*, Jun 1955, pp 33-34, 142.

K. Andress, "The K7NV Notebook", **k7nv.com/notebook**

R.W. Block, "Lightning Protection for the Amateur Radio Station," Parts 1-3, *QST*, Jun 2002, pp 56-59; Jul 2002, pp 48-52; Aug 2002, pp 53-55.

G. Brede, "The Care and Feeding of the Amateur's Favorite Antenna Support — The Tree," *QST*, Sep 1989, pp 26-28, 40.

T. Brock-Fisher, "Is Your Tower Still Safe?," *QST*, Oct 2010, p 43-47.

The Complete Guide to Wiring, 6th edition, Cool Springs Press, 2014.

D. Daso, *Antenna Towers for Radio Amateurs* (Newington: ARRL, 2010).

D. Daso, "Workshop Chronicles," columns in *National Contest Journal.*

M. Frydeniund, *Lightning Protection for People and Property*, Van Nostrand Reinhold, 1993.

W. R. Gary, "Toward Safer Antenna Installations," *QST*, Jan 1980, p 56.

W. Hart, and E. Malone, *Lightning and Lightning Protection*, Interference Control Technologies, Inc, 1988

S. F. Hoerner, "Fluid Dynamic Drag," (Bricktown, NJ: Hoerner Fluid Dynamics, 1993), pp 1-10.

C. L. Hutchinson, R. D. Straw, *Simple and Fun Antennas for Hams* (Newington: ARRL, 2002).

M. P. Keown and L. L. Lamb, "A Simple Technique for Tower-Section Separation," *QST*, Sep 1979, pp 37-38.

S. Morris, *Up the Tower*, (Seattle: Champion Radio Products, 2009).

S. Morris, "Up the Tower," columns in *National Contest Journal.*

P. O'Dell, "The Ups and Downs of Towers," *QST*, Jul 1981, pp 35-39.

S. Phillabaum, "Installation Techniques for Medium and Large Yagis," *QST*, Jun 1979, pp 23-25.

B. Pioveson, "CDE/Hy-Gain Rotors, How to Keep 'em Turning, Parts 1 and 2," CQ VHF, Winter 2009, pp 38-46, and Spring 2009, pp 18-26.

PolyPhaser, see **www.polyphaser.com** and look under the Resources link for White Papers on lightning protection.

K. Rand, *Lightning Protection & Grounding Solutions for Communication Sites*, Polyphaser Corporation, 2000.

C. J. Richards, "Mechanical Engineering in Radar and Communications" (London: Van Nostrand Reinhold Co., 1969), pp 162-165.

T. Schiller, *Array of Light*, Third edition, **www.n6bt.com.**

M. Shanblatt and J. Warwick, "Hanging a Treetop Antenna with a Drone," *QST*, Mar. 2018, pp 67-68.

W. Silver, *Grounding and Bonding for the Radio Amateur*, (Newington: ARRL, 2017.)

K. Sirageldin, "Using a Drone for Antenna Installation at TI5W," *QST*, Nov 2017, pp 85-86.

H.G. Ufer, "Investigation and Testing of Footing Type Grounding Electrodes for Electrical Installations" IEEE Transactions Paper #63-1505, Power Apparatus Systems Vol. 83 pp 1042-1048: Oct 1964.

D. Weber "Determination of Yagi Wind Loads Using the Cross-Flow Principle," *Communications Quarterly*, Spring 1993.

B. White, E. White and J. White, "Assembling Big Antennas on Fixed Towers," *QST*, Mar 1982, pp 28-29.

L. Wolfert, "The Tower Alternative," *QST*, Nov 1980, pp 36-37.

W. C. Young., "Roark's Formulas for Stress & Strain" (New York: McGraw-Hill Co., 1989), pp 67, 96.

"How to Protect Your House and Its Contents Against Lightning," IEEE, 2005.

Lightning Protection for Engineers, National Lightning Safety Institute (NLSI), 2004.

Lightning Protection for Radio Transmitter Stations, Nautel Corporation, 1998.

Military Handbook MIL-HDBK-419A, Vol. 1(Basic Theory) and 2 (Applications), Grounding,

Bonding and Shielding for Electronic Equipments and Facilities, 1987 (**www.tscm.com/MIL-HDBK-419A.PDF**)

National Electrical Code, NFPA 70, National Fire Protection Association, Quincy, MA (**www.nfpa.org**).

Standard for the Installation of Lightning Protection Systems, NFPA 780, National Fire Protection Association, Quincy, MA (**www.nfpa.org**).

Standards and Guidelines for Communications Sites, document 68P81089E50-B, Motorola, Inc., 2005. Also referred to as "R56" in the communications industry as it is administered by the R56 committee at Motorola.

Structural Standards for Steel Antenna Towers and Antenna Supporting Structures, TIA Standard TIA-222-G, Telecommunications Industry Association, Aug 2005 (**www.tiaonline.org**). May be purchased from IHS/Global Engineering Documents, 15 Inverness Way East, Englewood, CO, 80112-5704, 1-800-854-7179 (**www.global.ihs.com**).

APPENDIX A

DETERMINING ANTENNA AREAS AND WIND LOAD

The method for determining the flat projected area (FPA) of an antenna is quite simple. We'll use a Yagi antenna as an example. There are two worst-case areas that should be considered here. The first is the FPA of all the elements when the wind blows in the direction along the boom; that is, at right angles to the elements. The second FPA for a Yagi is when the wind is at right angles to the boom. One of these two orientations produces the worst-case exposed antenna area — all other wind angles present lower exposed areas. The idea is to take the highest of the FPAs for these two wind directions and call that the FPA of the antenna structure. See **Figure 26.60A.**

The element FPA is calculated by multiplying each element's dimension of length by its diameter and then summing the FPAs for all elements. The boom's FPA is computed by multiplying the boom's length by its diameter.

The reason for considering two potential peak-load orientations becomes clear when different frequency antennas are stacked on a mast or tower. Some antennas produce peak loads when the elements are broadside to the wind. This is typical of low-frequency Yagis, where the elements are very long lengths of aluminum tubing. On the other hand, the boom can dominate the surface area computations in higher-frequency Yagis.

The fundamentals responsible for the need to examine both potential FPAs for Yagis relates to how wind flows over a structure and develops loads. Called *The Cross-Flow Principle*, this was introduced to the communications industry by Dick Weber, K5IU, in 1993. The principle is based on the fact that the loads created by wind flowing across an antenna member only produce forces that are normal to (or perpendicular to) the major axis of the member. The resultant and component load calculations for this method are shown in Figure 26.60A.

For a Yagi, this means that wind forces on the elements act in-line with the boom, while forces on the boom act in-line with the elements. Figure 26.60B shows a force diagram for a typical Yagi. Figure 26.60C shows the FPA for a Yagi rotated through 90° of azimuth.

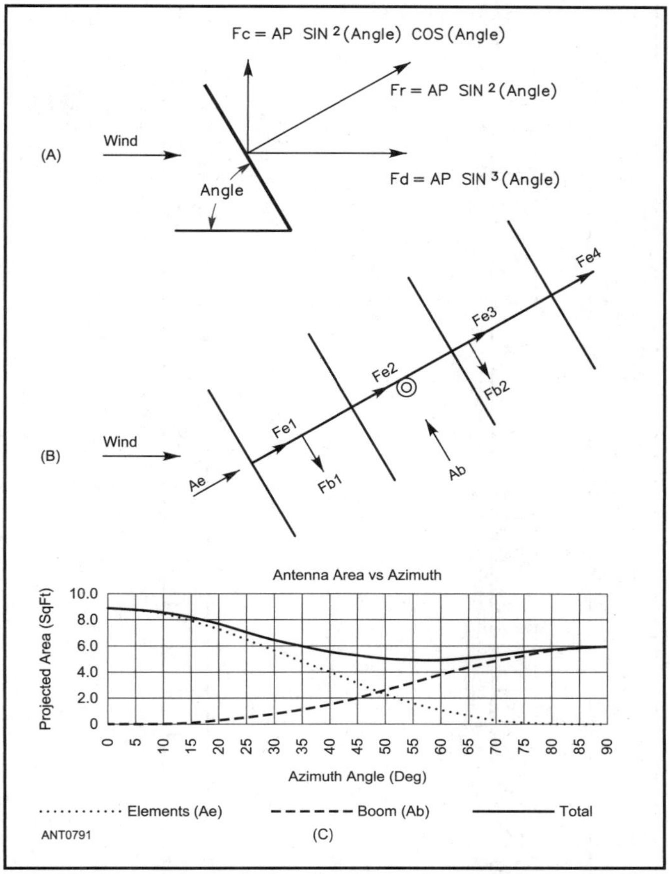

Figure 26.60 — Description of how loads are developed on a Yagi. At A, F_r is the resultant force from the wind load on a generalized member. F_d is the load acting downwind (drag) that creates the load on the tower. F_c is the lateral component of the wind load. The term A is the flat projected area (FPA), which is the broadside area normal to the wind. The term P is the wind pressure. At B, A_e is the total element area, while Ab is the total boom area. All the loads due to the wind act normal to the antenna sections—the force on element #1 (F_{e1}) acts along the axis of the boom, for example. At C, a plot of the effective FPA as a function of the azimuthal wind direction for a Yagi, ignoring drag coefficients. The Yagi in this example has 9.0 square feet of element FPA and 6.0 square feet of boom FPA. The worst-case FPAs occur with the beam pointed in the wind and with the boom broadside to the wind. To determine the actual tower loading, the actual drag coefficients and wind pressures must be used.

Antenna Placement on the Mast/Tower

Another important consideration is where the antenna(s) will be placed on the tower. As mentioned before, most generic tower specifications assume that the entire antenna load is applied at the top of the tower. Most amateur installations have a tubular mast extending above the tower top, turned by a rotator mounted down inside the tower. Multiple Yagi antennas are often placed on the mast above the tower top, and you must make sure that both the tower and the mast can withstand the wind forces on the antennas.

For freestanding towers, you can determine how a proposed antenna configuration compares to the tower manufacturer's rating by using an *Equivalent Moment* method. The method computes the bending moment generated at the base of the tower by wind loads on the tower's rated antenna area located right at the top of the tower and compares that to the case when the antenna is mounted on a mast sticking out of the top of the tower.

The exact value of wind pressure is not important, so long as it is the same for both comparisons. The wind load on the tower itself can be ignored because it is the same in both comparisons and the drag coefficients for the antennas can also be ignored if all calculations are performed using flat projected antenna areas, as we've recommended previously.

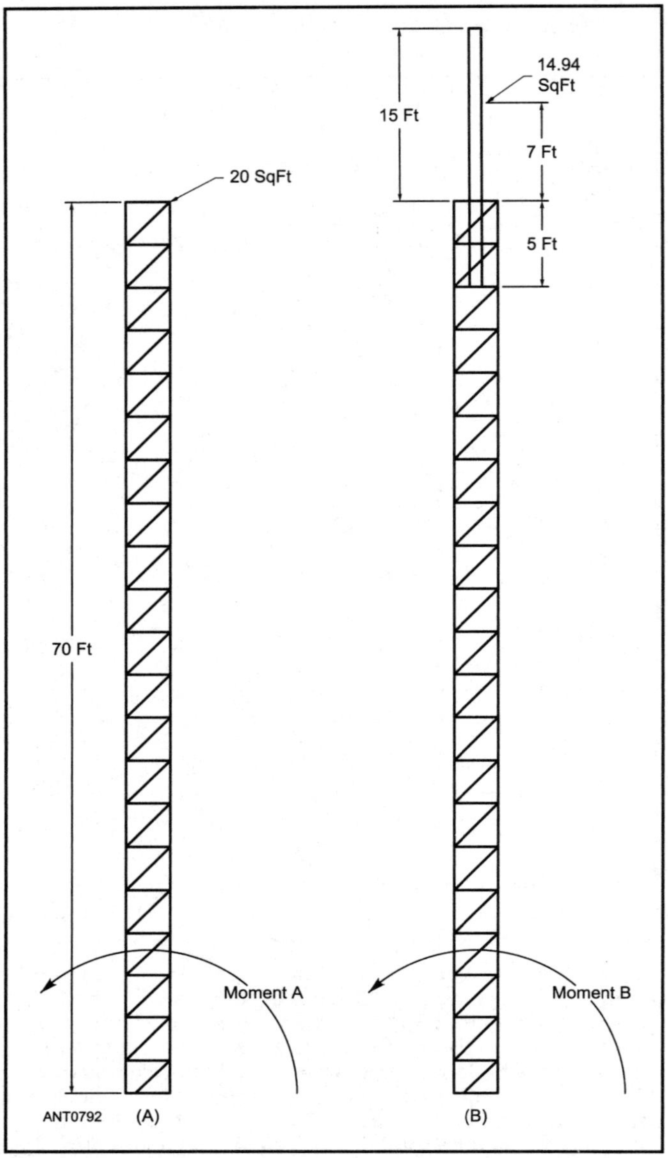

Figure 26.61 — At A, a 70-foot tower rated for 20 square feet of antenna load at the top. At B, the same tower with a 2-inch OD, 20-foot long mast, with an antenna mounted 7 feet above the top of the tower. Both configurations produce the same tower load.

Keep in mind that this approach does not calculate *actual* loads and moments relevant to any specific tower design standard, but it does allow equivalent comparisons when the wind pressure is constant and all the antenna areas are of the same type. An example is in order.

Figure 26.61A shows a generic tower configuration, with a concentrated antenna load at the top of the tower. We'll assume that the tower manufacturer rates this tower at 20 square feet of flat projected antenna area. Figure 26.61B shows a typical amateur installation with a rotating mast and an antenna mounted 7 feet above the top of the tower. To make the calculations easy, we select a wind pressure of 1 pound per square foot (1 psf). This makes the tower base moment calculation for Figure 26.61A:

Antenna load = 20 feet^2 × 1 psf = 20 pounds
Base moment = 70 feet × 20 pounds = 1400 foot-pounds.

This is the target value for the comparison. An equivalent configuration would produce the same base moment. For the configuration in Figure 26.61B, we assume a tubular 2-inch diameter mast that is 20 feet long, mounted 5 feet down inside the tower. Note that the lattice structure of the tower allows the wind to "see" the whole length of the mast and that we can consider the force distributed along the mast as being a single force concentrated at the mast's center. The flat projected area of the mast by itself, without the antenna, is:

Mast area = 20 feet × 2 inches / 12 inches/foot = 3.33 square feet

The center of the mast is located at a height of 75 feet. Using the same 1-psf-wind load, the base bending moment due to the mast alone is:

Base moment (due to mast) = 3.33 feet^2 × 1 psf × 75 feet = 249.75 foot-pounds

Including the mast in the configuration reduces the allowable antenna load. The remaining target base moment left for the antenna is found by subtracting the moment due to the mast from the original target value:

New base target moment = 1400 – 249.75 foot-pounds = 1150.25 foot-pounds.

The antenna in Figure 26.61B is located at a height of 77 feet. To obtain the allowable antenna area at this elevation we divide the new base target moment by the antenna height, yielding an allowable antenna load of:

1150.25 foot-pounds / 77 feet = 14.94 pounds.

Since we chose a wind load of 1 psf, the allowable antenna FPA has been reduced to 14.94 square feet from 20 square feet. If the projected area of the antenna we are planning to mount in the new configuration is less than or equal to this value, we have satisfied the requirements of the original design. You can use this equivalent-moment method to evaluate different configurations, even ones involving multiple antennas on the mast or situations with additional antennas placed along the tower below the tower top.

For guyed towers, the analyses become much more rigorous to solve. Because the guys and their behaviors are such a significant portion of the tower support mechanism, these designs can become very sensitive to antenna load placements. A general rule of thumb for guyed towers is never to exceed the original tower-top load rating, regardless of distributed loads along its length. Once you redistribute the antenna load placements along a guyed tower, you should do a fresh analysis, just to be sure.

You can run evaluations using the above method for antennas placed on the mast above a guyed tower top. The use of the Equivalent-Moment method for antennas mounted below the top of a guyed tower, however, can become quite suspect, since many generic tower designs have their intermediate guys sized for zero antenna loads lower down the tower. The proper approach in this case is to have a qualified mechanical engineer check the configuration, to see if guy placement and strength is adequate for the additional antennas down the tower.

Mounting the mast and antenna as shown in Figure 26.61B increases tower loads in the region of the mast. You should investigate these loads to ensure that the tower bracing in that area is sufficient.

APPENDIX B

CALCULATING THE REQUIRED MAST STRENGTH

When you mount antennas on a mast above the tower top, you should examine the bending loads on the mast to ensure that it will be strong enough. This section explains how to perform mast stress calculations for a single sustained wind speed. This procedure does not include height, exposure and gust-response factors found in most tower design standards.

Here are some fundamental formulas and values used to calculate the bending stress in a mast mounted in the top of a tower. The basic formula for wind pressure is:

$$P = 0.00256\ V^2 \qquad (1)$$

where

P is the wind pressure is in pounds per square foot (psf)
V = wind speed in miles per hour (mph)

This assumes an air density for standard temperature and atmospheric pressure at sea level. The wind speed is not the Basic Wind Speed discussed in other sections of this chapter. It is simply a steady state (static) wind velocity.

The formula for calculating the force created by the wind on a structure is:

$$F = P \times A \times C_d \qquad (2)$$

where

P = the wind pressure from Eq 1
A = the flat projected area of the structure (square feet)
C_d = drag coefficient for the shape of the structure's members.

The commonly accepted *drag coefficient* for long cylindrical members like the tubing used for the mast and antenna is 1.20. The coefficient for a flat plate is 2.0.

The formula used to find the *bending stress* in a simple beam like our mast is:

$$\sigma = (M \times c) / I \qquad (3)$$

where

σ = the stress in pounds per square inch (psi)
M = *bending moment* at the base of the mast (inch-pounds)
c = ½ of the mast outside diameter (inches)
I = *moment of inertia* of the mast section ($inches^4$)

In this equation you must make sure that all values are in the same units. To arrive at the mast stress in pounds per square inch (psi), the other values need to be in inches and pounds also. The equation used to find the moment of inertia for the round tubing mast section is:

$$I = \pi/4\ (R^4 - r^4) \qquad (4)$$

where

I = Moment of Inertia of the section ($inches^4$)
R = Radius of tube outside diameter (inches)
r = Radius of tube inside diameter (inches)

This value describes the distribution of material about the mast *centroid*, which determines how it behaves under load. The equation used to compute the *bending moment* at the base of the mast (where it is supported by the tower) is:

$$M = (F_M \times L_M) + (F_A \times L_M) \qquad (5)$$

where

F_M = wind force from the mast (pounds)
L_M = Distance from tower top to center of mast (inches)
F_A = Wind force from the antenna (pounds)
L_A = Distance from tower top to antenna attachment (inches)
L_M is the distance to the center of the portion of the mast extending above the tower top. Additional antennas can be added to this formula by including their F × L. In the installation shown in Figure 26.61B, a wind speed of 90 mph, and a mast that is 2 inches OD, with a 0.250-inch wall thickness, the steps for calculating the mast stress are:

1) Calculate the wind pressure for 90 mph, from Eq 1:

$$P = .00256\ V^2 = .00256 \times (90)^2 = 20.736 \text{ psf}$$

2) Determine the flat projected area of the mast. The portion of the mast above the tower is 15 feet long and has an outside diameter of 2 inches, which is 2/12 feet.

Mast FPA, A_M = 15 feet × (2 inches / 12 inches/feet) = 2.50 square feet.

3) Calculate the wind load on the mast, from Eq 2:

Mast Force, $F_M = P \times A \times C_d = 20.736 \text{ psf} \times 2.50 \text{ feet}^2 \times 1.20 = 62.21$ pounds

4) Calculate the wind load on the antenna: From Eq 2:

Antenna Force, $F_A = P \times A \times C_d$ = 20.736 psf × 14.94 feet^2 × 1.20 = 371.76 pounds

5) Calculate the mast *Bending Moment*, from Eq 5:

$M = (F_M \times L_M) + (F_A \times L_A)$ = (62.21 pounds × 90 inches) + (371.76 pounds × 84 inches) = 36827 inch-pounds

where

L_M = 7.5 feet × 12 inches/foot = 90 inches

L_A = 7.0 feet × 12 inches/foot = 84 inches.

6) Calculate the mast *Moment of Inertia*, from Eq 4:

$$I = \frac{\pi}{4}(R^4 - r^4) = \frac{\pi}{4}(1.0^4 - 0.75^4) = 0.5369 \text{ inches}^4$$

where, for a 2.0-inch OD and 0.250-inch wall thickness tube, R= 1.0 and r = 0.75.

7) Calculate the mast *Bending Stress*, from Eq 3:

$$\sigma = \frac{M \times c}{I} = \frac{36827 \text{ inch-pounds} \times 1.0 \text{ inches}}{0.5369} = 68592 \text{ psi}$$

If the yield strength of the mast material is greater than the calculated bending stress, the mast is considered safe for this configuration and wind speed. If the calculated stress is higher than the mast yield strength, a stronger alloy, or a larger mast, or one with a thicker wall is required.

When evaluating a mast with multiple antennas attached to it, special care should be given to finding the worst-case condition (wind direction) for the system. What may appear to be the worst load case, by virtue of the combined flat projected antenna areas, may not always be the exposure that creates the largest mast bending moment. Masts with multiple stacked antennas should always be examined to find the exposure that produces the largest mast bending moment. The antenna flat projected areas at 0° and 90° azimuths are particularly useful for this evaluation.

One way of reducing the net wind torque on a mast holding multiple antennas is to mount antennas on opposite sides of the mast. This alternate mounting scheme causes the wind torque from each antenna to cancel at least partially, reducing the total torque experienced by the mast.

TABLE OF CONTENTS

Chapter 27 — Downloadable Supplemental Content

Supplemental Articles
- "A Reflectometer for Twin-Lead" by Fred Brown, W6HPH
- "An Inexpensive VHF Directional Coupler" and "A Calorimeter for VHF and UHF Power Measurements"
- "Antenna Analyzer Pet Tricks" by Paul Wade, W1GHZ
- "Build a Super-Simple SWR Indicator" by Tony Brock-Fisher, K1KP
- "Improving and Using R-X Noise Bridges" by John Grebenkemper, KI6WX
- "Microwavelengths — Directional Couplers" by Paul Wade, W1GHZ
- "On Tuning, Matching and Measuring Antenna Systems Using a Hand Held SWR Analyzer" by John Belrose, VE2CV
- RF Power Meter (Kaune) support files
- "QRP Person's VSWR Indicator" by Doug DeMaw, W1FB
- "Smith Chart Calculations"
- "SWR Analyzer Tips, Tricks, and Techniques" by George Badger, W6TC, et al
- "Technical Correspondence — A High-Power RF Sampler" by Tom Thompson WØIVJ (plus "More on a High-Power RF Sampler" by Thompson, two files)
- "The Noise Bridge" by Jack Althouse, K6NY
- "Time Domain Reflectometry"
- "The Gadget — An SWR Analyzer Add-On" byFred Hauff, W3NZ
- "The No Fibbin RF Field Strength Meter" by John Noakes, VE7NI
- "The SWR Analyzer and Transmission Lines" by Peter Schuch, WB2UAQ
- "The Tandem Match — An Accurate Directional Wattmeter" by John Grebenkemper, KA3BLO (plus corrections and updates, four files)
- "Using Single-Frequency Antenna Analyzers"

Chapter 27

Antenna and Transmission Line Measurements

The principal quantities measured on transmission lines are current or voltage, including phase. From these measurements, forward and reflected power and standing wave ratio (SWR) may be obtained. For antennas, the primary measurement of interest to amateurs is field strength in order to determine an antenna's radiation pattern or to compare relative antenna performance. It is important to note that for most practical purposes, a relative measurement is sufficient. An uncalibrated indicator that shows when the largest possible amount of power is being put into the line is just as useful, in most cases, as an instrument that measures the power accurately. It is seldom necessary to know the actual number of watts going into the line unless the overall efficiency of the system is being investigated. An instrument that shows when the SWR is close to 1:1 is all you need for most impedance-matching adjustments.

Absolute quantitative measurements of amplitude or time (phase) become increasingly difficult at frequencies above a few MHz with numerous sources of error becoming more and more significant. Quantitative measurements of reasonable accuracy demand good design and careful construction in the measuring instruments. They also require intelligent use of the equipment, including knowledge not only of its limitations but also of stray effects in the instrument and also of the test configuration that often lead to false results. Until you know the complete conditions of the measurements, a certain amount of skepticism regarding numerical data resulting from amateur measurements with simple equipment is justified.

Accurate measurement of SWR, for example, is necessary only in studies of antenna characteristics such as bandwidth, or for the design of some types of matching systems, such as a stub match. If such measurements are required, surplus lab equipment of very high quality is commonly available although usually not "in calibration."

On the other hand, purely qualitative or relative measurements, such as comparing one antenna to another, before-and-after, or max/min adjustments are easy to make and quite useful. This chapter presents methods and devices for making these measurements.

27.1 LINE CURRENT AND VOLTAGE

A current or voltage indicator that can be used with coaxial line is a useful piece of equipment. It need not be elaborate or expensive. Its principal function is to show when the maximum power is being taken from the transmitter for any given set of line conditions (length, SWR, etc). This will occur when you adjust the transmitter output circuits for maximum current or voltage into the transmission line. Although a final-amplifier plate or collector current meter is frequently used for this purpose, it is not always a reliable indicator. In many cases, particularly with a screen-grid tube in the final stage, minimum loaded plate current does not occur simultaneously with maximum power output.

27.1.1 RF VOLTMETERS

You can combine a germanium or Schottky diode in conjunction with a low-range milliammeter and a few resistors to form an RF voltmeter suitable for connecting across the two conductors of a coaxial line, as shown in **Figure 27.1**. It

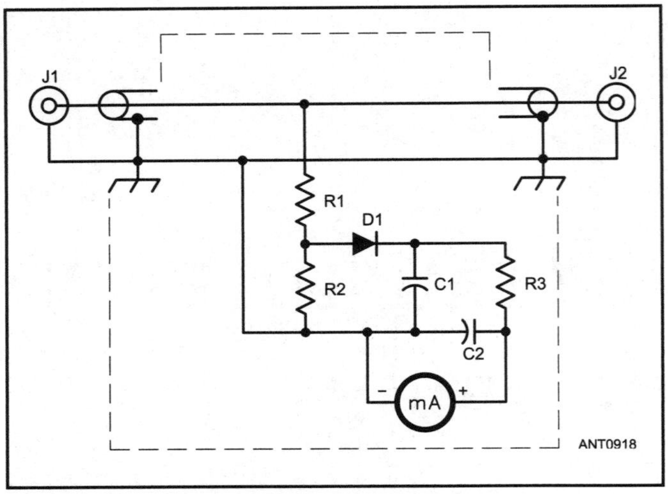

Figure 27.1 — RF voltmeter for coaxial line.
C1, C2 — 0.005- or 0.01-µF disc ceramic.
D1 — 1N34A germanium or 1N5817 Schottky diode.
J1, J2 — Coaxial fittings, chassis-mounting type.
M1 — 0-1 milliammeter (more sensitive meter may be used if desired; see text).
R1 — 6.8 kΩ, metal-oxide, 1 W for each 100 W of RF power.
R2 — 680 Ω, ½ or 1 W carbon-film or metal-oxide.
R3 — 10 kΩ, ½ W (see text).

consists of a voltage divider, R1-R2, having a total resistance about 100 times the Z_0 of the line (so the power consumed will be negligible) with a diode rectifier and milliammeter connected across part of the divider to read relative RF voltage. The purpose of R3 is to make the meter readings directly proportional to the applied voltage, as nearly as possible, by swamping the resistance of D1, since the diode resistance will vary with the amplitude of the current through the diode.

You may construct the voltmeter in a small metal box, indicated by the dashed line in the drawing, and fitted with coax receptacles. R1 and R2 should be noninductive resistors such as carbon-film or metal-oxide types. The power rating for R1 should be 1 W for each 100 W of carrier power in the matched line; separate 1- or 2-W resistors should be used to make up the total power rating required, to the total resistance as given. Any type of resistor can be used for R3; the total resistance should be such that about 10 V dc will be developed across it at full scale. For example, a 0-1 milliammeter would require 10 kΩ, a 0-500 microammeter would take 20 kΩ, and so on. R1 may be a variable resistor so the sensitivity can be adjusted for various power levels.

If more than one resistor is used for R1, the units should be arranged end-to-end with very short leads. R1 and R2 should be kept ½ inch or more from metal surfaces parallel to the body of the resistor. These precautions must be observed if consistent measurements are to be obtained above a few MHz. Stray capacitance and stray coupling limit the accuracy at higher frequencies but do not affect the utility of the instrument for comparative measurements.

Calibration

You may calibrate the meter for RF voltage at low frequencies by comparison with a standard such as an RF ammeter, wattmeter or oscilloscope. If a wattmeter is used, the line must be well matched so the impedance at the point of measurement is equal to the actual Z_0 of the line. The power can be calculated as $E = \sqrt{PZ_0}$. By making voltage measurements at a number of different power levels, you can obtain enough points to draw a calibration curve for your particular setup. Be advised that stray effects and nonlinearities inherent in this simple circuit make a true calibration questionable above a few MHz.

27.1.2 RF CURRENT METERS

The following project was designed by Tom Rauch, W8JI (**w8ji.com/building_a_current_meter.htm**). The circuit of **Figure 27.2** is based on a current transformer (T1) consisting of a T157-2 powdered-iron toroid core with a 20-turn winding. The meter is used with the current-carrying wire or antenna inserted through the middle of the core as a one-turn primary

When 1 A is flowing in the single-turn primary, the secondary current will be 50 mA (equal to primary current

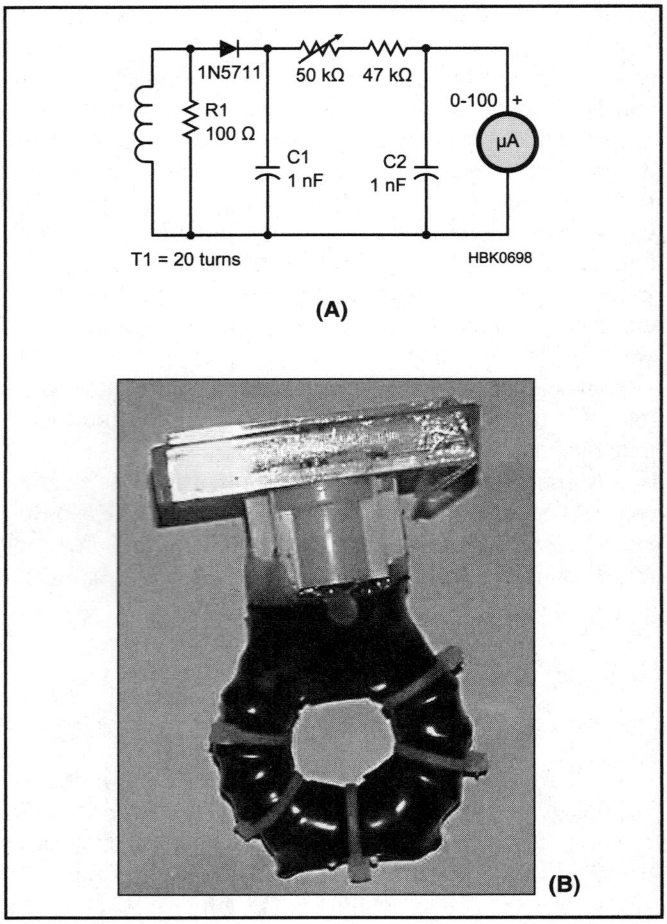

Figure 27.2 — The schematic of the RF current probe (A) and assembly of the RF current probe (B). Use an all-plastic meter and mount the circuits and toroid directly on the back of the meter case.

divided by the turns ratio of 20:1). R1 across the transformer flattens the frequency response and limits the output voltage. The RF voltage is then detected and filtered by D1 (a low-threshold Schottky diode for minimum voltage drop) and C1. The adjustable sum of R2 and R3 allow for full-scale (FS) calibration of the 100 μA meter. C2 provides additional filtering. The toroid core and all circuitry are glued to the back of the meter case with only R2 exposed — a screwdriver-adjustable calibration pot.

It is important to minimize stray capacitance by using a meter with all-plastic construction except for the electrical parts. The meter in Figure 27.2B has an all-plastic case including the meter scale. The meter movement and all metallic areas are small. The lack of large metallic components minimizes stray capacitance from the proximity of the meter. Low stray capacitance ensures the instrument has the least possible effect on the circuit being tested.

A value of 100 Ω for R1 gave the flattest response from 1.8 to 30 MHz. With 50 mA of secondary current, the voltage across R1 is $0.05 \times 100 = 5\ V_{RMS}$. The peak voltage is then $1.414 \times 5 = 7.1$ V. At full current, power dissipation in R1 = $50\ mA \times 5\ V_{RMS} = 0.25$ W so a ½-W or larger resistor should be used.

The meter used here was a 10,000 Ω/V model so for full-scale deflection from a primary current of 1 A producing a secondary voltage of ~7 V, the sum of R2 and R3 must be set to $7 \times 10{,}000 = 70$ kΩ. The low-current meter combined with high detected voltage improves detector linearity.

Calibration of the meter can be performed by using a calibrated power meter and a test fixture consisting of two RF connectors with a short piece of wire between them and through the transformer core. With 50 W applied to a 50-Ω load, the wire will be carrying 1 A of current. Full-scale accuracy is not required in comparison measurements, since the meter references against itself, but linearity within a few percent is important.

This transformer-based meter is much more reliable and linear than thermocouple RF ammeters and perturbs systems much less. Stray capacitance added to the system being tested is very small because of the proximity of the meter and the compact wiring area. Compared to actually connecting a meter with its associated lead lengths and capacitance in line with the load, the advantages of a transformer-coupled meter become apparent.

Clamp-on RF Current Probe

Sometimes it is not practical to disconnect a wire in order to sense RF current on it, such as a power cord or speaker wire. In such cases a *clamp-on* probe can be used as described in the February 1999 *QST* article by Steve Sparks, N5SV, and shown in **Figure 27.3**. The core is a split-core type — any common material will suffice (type 31, 75, 61, 43, etc) for HF use. If the enclosure is hand-held size, the instrument can be used as a handy detector and "sniffer" for RFI trouble-shooting. Because the split core does not close completely and consistently every time, this is not a precision instrument but is effective for relative comparison.

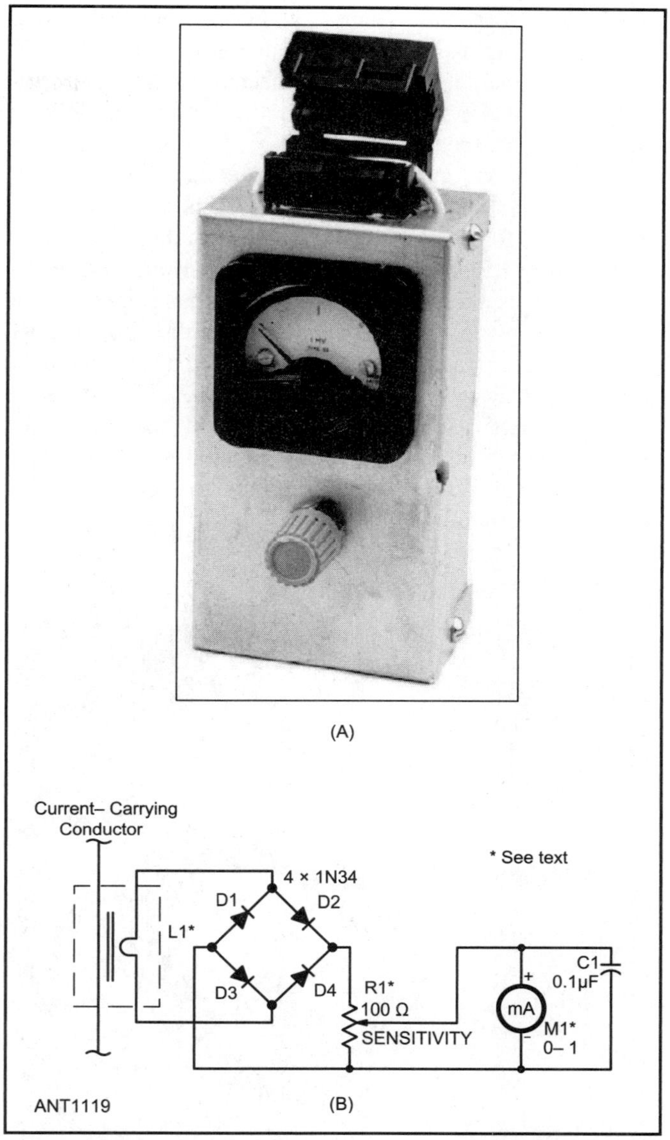

Figure 27.3 — The RF current probe at A is small enough to be hand-carried as an effective RF "sniffer." At B is the schematic of the RF current probe. Use a metal enclosure for the probe.
C1 — 0.1 μF disc ceramic.
D1-D4 — 1N34A germanium or 1N5817 Schottky diodes.
L1 — Single turn of #14 AWG wire through a snap-on ferrite split-core, type 31, 43, 61, 73, or 75 material will work. Glue core to top of metal enclosure.
M1 — 1 mA analog meter. Substitute lower full-scale current for higher sensitivity.
R1 — 100 to 500 Ω panel-mount potentiometer.

27.1.3 RF AMMETERS

An RF ammeter is a good way to gauge output power. You can mount an RF ammeter in any convenient location at the input end of the transmission line, the principal precaution being that the capacitance to ground, chassis and nearby conductors should be low. A Bakelite-case instrument can be mounted on a metal panel without introducing enough shunt capacitance to ground to cause serious error up to 30 MHz. When installing a metal-case instrument on a metal panel, you should mount it on a separate sheet of insulating material so that there is ⅛ inch or more separation between the edge of the case and the metal.

A 2-inch instrument can be mounted in a 2 × 4 × 4-inch metal box, as shown in **Figure 27.4**. This is a convenient arrangement for use with coaxial line. Installed this way, a good quality RF ammeter will measure current with an accuracy that is entirely adequate for calculating power in the line. As discussed above in connection with calibrating RF voltmeters, the line must be closely matched by its load so the actual impedance is resistive and equal to Z_0. The scales of such instruments are cramped at the low end, however, which limits the range of power that can be measured by a single meter. The useful current range is about 3 to 1, corresponding to a power range of about 9 to 1.

Figure 27.4 — A convenient method of mounting an RF ammeter for use in a coaxial line. This is a metal-case instrument mounted on a thin bakelite panel. The cutout in the metal clears the edge of the meter by about ⅛ inch.

New RF ammeters are expensive and even surplus pricing can vary widely between $10 and $100 in today's market. AM radio stations are the main users of new units. The FCC defines the output power of AM stations based on the RF current in the antenna, so new RF ammeters are made mainly for that market. They are quite accurate, and their prices reflect that!

The good news is that used RF ammeters are often available. For example, Fair Radio Sales in Lima, Ohio, has been a consistent source of RF ammeters. Ham flea markets are also worth trying. Some grubbing around in your nearest surplus store or an older ham's junk box may provide just the RF ammeter you need.

Before buying a used RF ammeter, check to be sure it is actually an RF ammeter — it is common to find meters labeled "RF Amps" that are simple current meters intended to be used with an external RF current sensing unit.

RF Ammeter Substitutes

Don't despair if you can't find a used RF ammeter. It's possible to construct your own. Both hot-wire and thermocouple units can be homemade. Pilot lamps in series with antenna wires, or coupled to them in various ways, can indicate antenna current or even forward and reflected power. (See the Bibliography entries for Sutter and Wright.)

Another approach is to use a small low-voltage lamp as the heat/light element and use a photodetector driving a meter as an indicator. (Your eyes and judgment can serve as the indicating part of the instrument.) A feed line balance checker could be as simple as a couple of lamps with the right current rating and the lowest voltage rating available. You should be able to tell fairly well by eye which bulb is brighter or if they are about equal. You can calibrate a lamp-based RF ammeter with 60-Hz or dc power.

The optical approach is often taken in QRP portable equipment where an LED is used to replace a meter in an SWR bridge as described by Phil Salas, AD5X, in his Z-Match antenna tuner described in the **Transmission Line System Techniques** chapter.

As another alternative, you can build an RF ammeter that uses a dc meter to indicate rectified RF from a current transformer that you clamp over a transmission line wire as described by Zack Lau, W1VT. (See Bibliography.)

27.2 SWR MEASUREMENTS

On parallel-conductor lines it is possible to measure the standing wave ratio by moving a current (or voltage) indicator along the line, noting the maximum and minimum values of current (or voltage) and then computing the SWR from these measured values. This cannot be done with coaxial line since it is not possible to make measurements of this type inside the cable. The technique is, in fact, seldom used with open lines because it is not only inconvenient but sometimes impossible to reach all parts of the line conductors. Also, the method is subject to considerable error from antenna currents flowing on the line.

Present-day SWR measurements made by amateurs practically always use some form of *directional coupler* or RF-bridge circuit. The indicator circuits themselves are fundamentally simple, but they require considerable care in construction to ensure accurate measurements. The requirements for indicators used only for the adjustment of impedance-matching circuits, rather than actual SWR measurement, are not so stringent, and you can easily make an instrument for this purpose.

27.2.1 BRIDGE CIRCUITS

Two commonly used bridge circuits are shown in **Figure 27.5**. The bridges consist essentially of two voltage dividers in parallel, with an RF voltmeter connected between the junctions of each pair of *arms*, as the individual elements are called. When the equations shown to the right of each circuit are satisfied there is no potential difference between the two junctions, and the RF voltmeter indicates zero voltage. The bridge is then said to be in *balance*.

Taking Figure 27.5A as an illustration, if R1 = R2, half the applied voltage, E, will appear across each resistor. Then if $R_S = R_X$, ½ E will appear across each of these resistors and the RF voltmeter reading will be zero. Remember that a matched transmission line has essentially a purely resistive input impedance. Suppose that the input terminals of such a line are substituted for R_X. Then if R_S is a resistor equal to the Z_0 of the line, the bridge will be balanced.

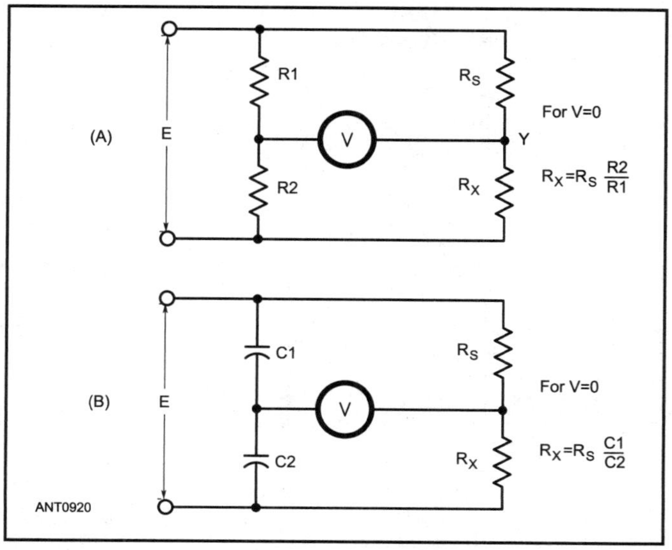

Figure 27.5 — Bridge circuits suitable for SWR measurement. At A, Wheatstone type using resistance arms. At B, capacitance-resistance bridge ("Micromatch"). Conditions for balance are independent of frequency in both types. The voltmeter must be an RF voltmeter.

If the line is not perfectly matched, its input impedance will not equal Z_0 and hence will not equal R_S, since you chose the latter to be equal to Z_0. There will then be a difference in potential between points X and Y, and the RF voltmeter will show a reading. Such a bridge therefore can be used to show the presence of standing waves on the line, because the line input impedance will be equal to Z_0 only when there are no standing waves.

Considering the nature of the incident and reflected components of voltage that make up the actual voltage at the input terminals of the line, as discussed in the **Transmission Lines** chapter, it should be clear that when $R_S = Z_0$, the bridge is always in balance for the incident component. Thus the RF voltmeter does not respond to the incident component at any time but reads only the reflected component. The incident component can be measured across either R1 or R2, if they are equal resistances. The standing wave ratio is then

$$SWR = \frac{E1 + E2}{E1 - E2} \qquad (1)$$

where E1 is the incident voltage and E2 is the reflected voltage. It is often simpler to normalize the voltages by expressing E2 as a fraction of E1, in which case the formula becomes

$$SWR = \frac{1 + k}{1 - k} \qquad (2)$$

where k = E2/E1.

The operation of the circuit in Figure 27.5B is essentially the same, although this circuit has arms containing reactance as well as resistance.

It is not necessary that R1 = R2 in Figure 27.5A; the bridge can be balanced, in theory, with any ratio of these two resistances provided R_S is changed accordingly. In practice, however, the accuracy is highest when the two are equal; this circuit is most commonly used.

A number of types of bridge circuits appear in **Figure 27.6**, many of which have been used in amateur products or amateur construction projects. The bridge at E is most often used in common low-cost SWR meters. (See the Bibliography entry for Silver for a description of how these meters work.) All circuits except that at G can have the ground returns of the generator and load at a common potential. At G, the generator and detector ground returns are at a common potential. You may interchange the positions of the detector and transmitter (or generator) in the bridge, and this may be advantageous in some applications.

The bridges shown at D, E, F and H may have one terminal of the generator, detector and load common. Bridges

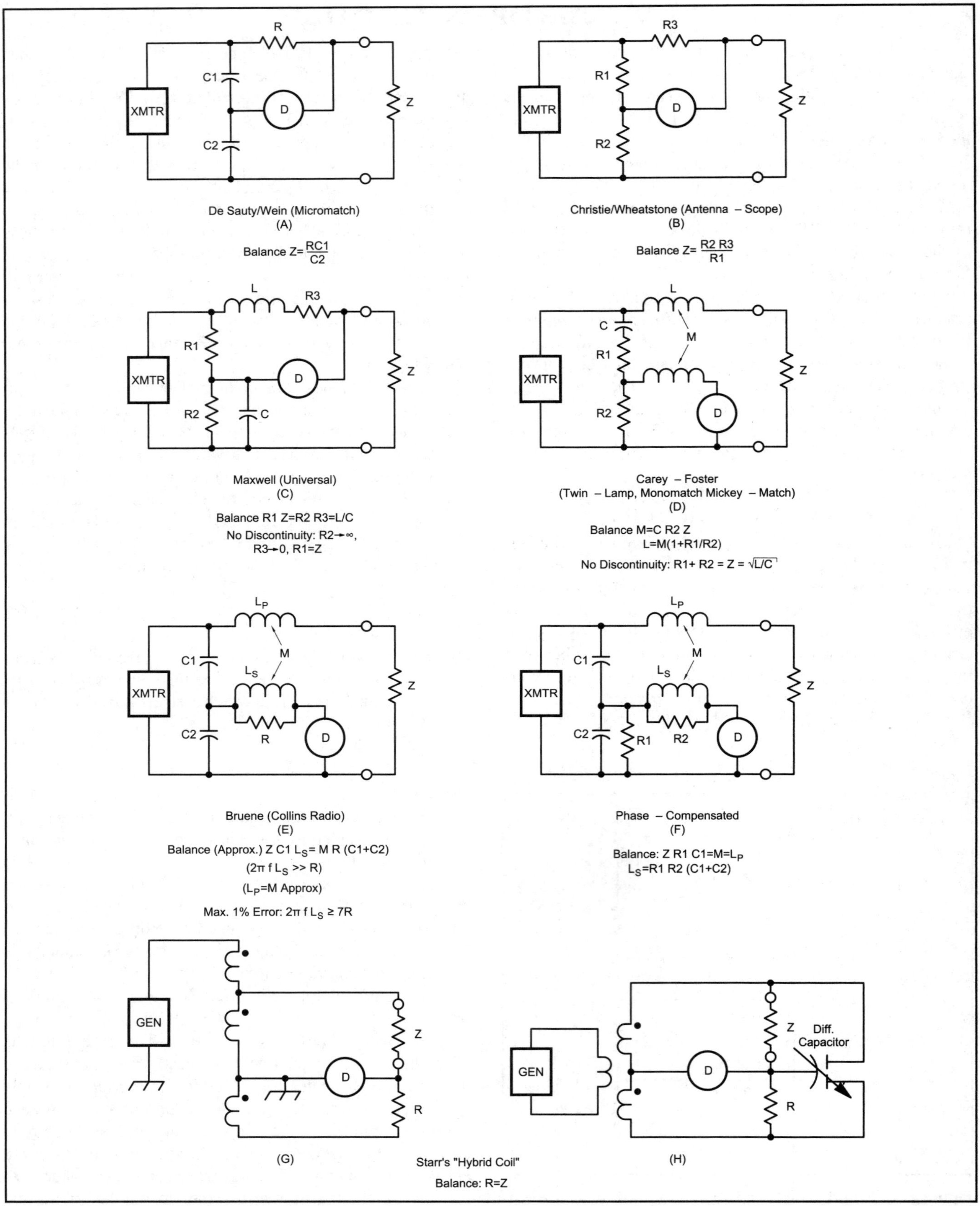

Figure 27.6 — Various types of SWR bridge indicator circuits and commonly known names of bridge circuits or devices in which they have been used. Detectors (D) are usually semiconductor diodes with meters, isolated with RF chokes and capacitors. However, the detector may be a radio receiver. In each circuit, Z represents the load being measured. (*This information provided by David Geiser, WA2ANU*)

at A, B, E, F, G and H have constant sensitivity over a wide frequency range. Bridges at B, C, D and H may be designed to show no discontinuity (impedance bump) with a matched line, as shown in the drawing. Discontinuities with A, E and F may be small.

Bridges are usually most sensitive when the detector bridges the midpoint of the generator voltage, as in G or H, or in B when each resistor equals the load impedance. Sensitivity also increases when the currents in each leg are equal.

27.2.2 SWR RESISTANCE BRIDGE

The basic bridge configuration shown in Figure 27.5B may be home constructed and is reasonably accurate for SWR measurement at HF. A practical circuit for such a bridge is given in **Figure 27.7A** and a representative layout is shown in Figure 27.7B. Properly built, a bridge of this design can be used for measurement of SWRs up to about 15:1 with good accuracy. Resistance bridges cannot be left in the transmission during regular operation due to the power dissipation limits of the resistors. This bridge should be used for test purposes only.

You must also observe these important construction points:

1) Keep leads in the RF circuit short, to reduce stray inductance.

2) Mount resistors two or three times their body diameter away from metal parts, to reduce stray capacitance.

3) Place the RF components so there is as little inductive and capacitive coupling as possible between the bridge arms.

In the instrument shown in Figure 27.7B, the input and line connectors, J1 and J2, are mounted fairly close together so the standard resistor, R_S, can be supported with short leads directly between the center terminals of the connectors. R2 is mounted at right angles to R_S, and a shield partition is used between these two components and the others.

The two 47-kΩ resistors, R5 and R6 in Figure 27.7A, are voltmeter multipliers for the 0-100 microammeter used as an indicator. This is sufficient resistance to make the voltmeter approximately linear (that is, the meter reading is directly proportional to the RF voltage) and no voltage calibration curve is needed. D1 is the rectifier for the reflected voltage and D2 is for the incident voltage. Because of manufacturing variations in resistors and diodes, the readings may differ slightly with two multipliers of the same nominal resistance value, so a correction resistor, R3, is included in the circuit. You should select its value so that the meter reading is the same with S1 in either position, when RF is applied to the bridge with the line connection open. In the instrument shown, a value of 1000 Ω was required in series with the multiplier for reflected voltage; in other cases different values probably would be needed and R3 might have to be put in series with the multiplier for the incident voltage. You can determine this by experiment.

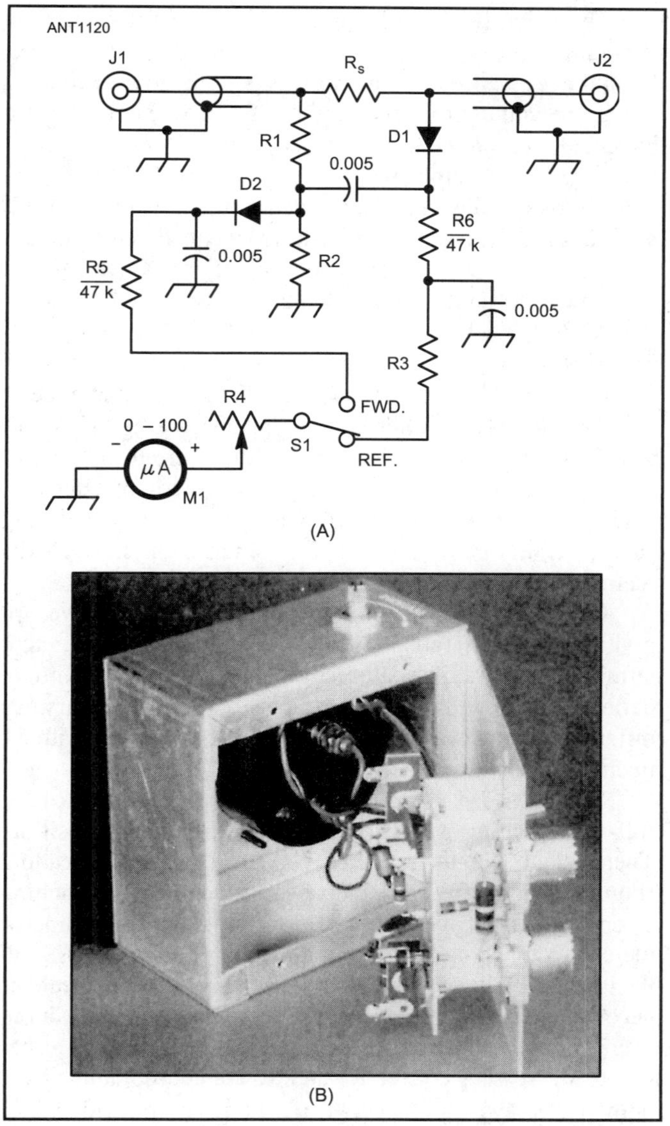

Figure 27.7 — At A, schematic of the resistance bridge for SWR measurement. Capacitors are disc ceramic. Resistors are ½-W composition except as noted below.

D1, D2 — 1N34A germanium or 1N5817 Schottky diodes.
J1, J2 — Coaxial connectors, chassis-mounting type.
M1 — 0-100 dc microammeter.
R1, R2 — 47 Ω, ½-W carbon-film or metal-oxide (see text).
R3 — See text.
R4 — 50-kΩ volume control.
R_s — Resistance equal to line Z_0 (½ or 1 W composition).
S1 — SPDT toggle.

At B, a 2 × 4 × 4-inch aluminum box is used to house this SWR bridge. The variable resistor, R4, is mounted on the side. The bridge components are mounted on one side plate of the box and a subchassis formed from a piece of aluminum. The input connector is at the top in this view. R_s is connected directly between the two center posts of the connectors. R2 is visible behind it and perpendicular to it. One terminal of D1 projects through a hole in the chassis so the lead can be connected to J2. R1 is mounted vertically to the left of the chassis in this view, with D2 connected between the junction of R1-R2 and a tie point.

The value used for R1 and R2 is not critical, but you should match the two resistors within 1% or 2% if possible. Keep the resistance of R_S as close as possible to the actual Z_0 of the line you use (generally 50 or 75 Ω). Select the resistor by actual measurement with an accurate resistance bridge, if you have one available.

R4 is for adjusting the incident-voltage reading to full scale in the measurement procedure described below. Its use is not essential, but it offers a convenient alternative to exact adjustment of the RF input voltage.

Testing

Measure R1, R2 and R_S with a reliable digital ohmmeter or resistance bridge after completing the wiring. This will ensure that their values have not changed from the heat of soldering. Disconnect one side of the microammeter and leave the input and output terminals of the unit open during such measurements to avoid stray shunt paths through the rectifiers.

Check the two voltmeter circuits as described above, applying enough RF (about 10 V peak, 1 V RMS) to the input terminals to give a full scale reading with R4 set for maximum deflection and with the line terminals open. If necessary, try different values for R3 until the reading is the same with S1 in either position.

With J2 open, adjust the RF input voltage and R4 for full-scale reading with S1 in the incident-voltage position. Then switch S1 to the reflected-voltage position. The reading should remain at full scale. Next, short-circuit J2 by touching a screwdriver between the center terminal and the frame of the connector to make a low-inductance short. Switch S1 to the incident-voltage position and readjust R4 for full scale, if necessary. Then throw S1 to the reflected-voltage position, keeping J2 shorted, and the reading should be full scale as before. If the readings differ, R1 and R2 are not the same value, or there is stray coupling between the arms of the bridge. You must read the reflected voltage at full scale with J2 either open or shorted, when the incident voltage is set to full scale in each case, to make accurate SWR measurements.

The circuit should pass these tests at all frequencies at which it is to be used. It is sufficient to test at the lowest and highest frequencies, usually 1.8 or 3.5 and 28 or 50 MHz. If R1 and R2 are poorly matched but the bridge construction is otherwise good, discrepancies in the readings will be substantially the same at all frequencies. A difference in behavior at the low and high ends of the frequency range can be attributed to stray coupling between bridge arms, or stray inductance or capacitance in the arms.

To check the bridge for balance, apply RF and adjust R4 for full scale with J2 open. Then connect a resistor identical with R_S (the resistance should match within 1% or 2%) to the line terminals, using the shortest possible leads. It is convenient to mount the test resistor inside a cable connector (PL-259), a method of mounting that also minimizes lead inductance. When you connect the test resistor the reflected-voltage reading should drop to zero. The incident voltage should be reset to full scale by means of R4, if necessary. The reflected reading should be zero at any frequency in the range to be used. If a good null is obtained at low frequencies but some residual current shows at the high end, the trouble may be the inductance of the test resistor leads, although it may also be caused by stray coupling between the arms of the bridge itself.

If there is a constant low (but not zero) reading at all frequencies the problem is poor matching of the resistance values. Both effects can be present simultaneously. You should make sure you obtain a good null at all frequencies before using your bridge.

Bridge Operation

You must limit the RF power input to a bridge of this type to 2 W at most, because of the power-dissipation ratings of the resistors. If the transmitter has no provision for reducing power output to this value a simple power-absorber circuit can be made up, as shown in **Figure 27.8**. Lamp DS1 changes resistance as it heats up — from a few ohms when cold to more than 100 Ω at full power. This increasing resistance tends to maintain constant current through the resistor over a fairly wide power range, so the voltage drop across the resistor also tends to be constant. This voltage is applied to the bridge, and with the constants given is in the right range for resistance-type bridges.

To make a measurement, connect the unknown load to J2 and apply sufficient RF voltage to J1 to give a full-scale incident-voltage reading. Use R4 to set the indicator to exactly full scale. Then throw S1 to the reflected voltage position and note the meter reading. The SWR is then found by using these readings in Eq 1.

For example, if the full-scale calibration of the dc instrument is 100 μA and the reading with S2 in the reflected-voltage position is 40 μA, the SWR is

$$\text{SWR} = \frac{100+40}{100-40} = \frac{140}{60} = 2.33:1$$

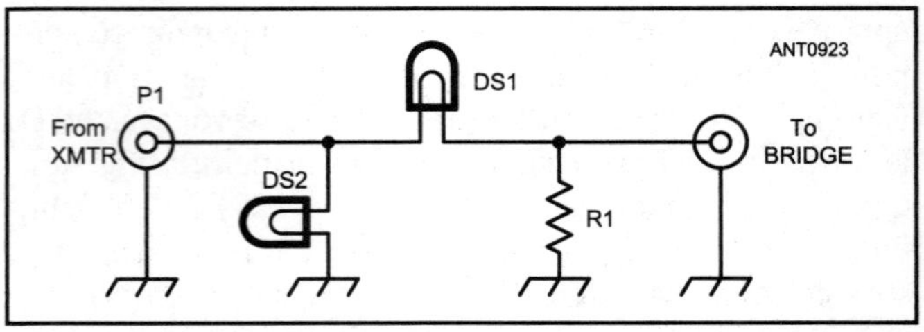

Figure 27.8 — Power-absorber circuit for use with resistance-type SWR bridges when the transmitter has no special provisions for power reduction. For RF powers up to 50 W, DS1 is a 120-V 40-W incandescent lamp and DS2 is not used. For higher powers, use sufficient additional lamp capacity at DS2 to load the transmitter to about normal output; for example, for 250-W output DS2 may consist of two 100-W lamps in parallel. R1 is made from three 1-W 68-Ω resistors connected in parallel. P1 and P2 are cable-mounting coaxial connectors. Leads in the circuit formed by the lamps and R1 should be kept short, but convenient lengths of cable may be used between this assembly and the connectors.

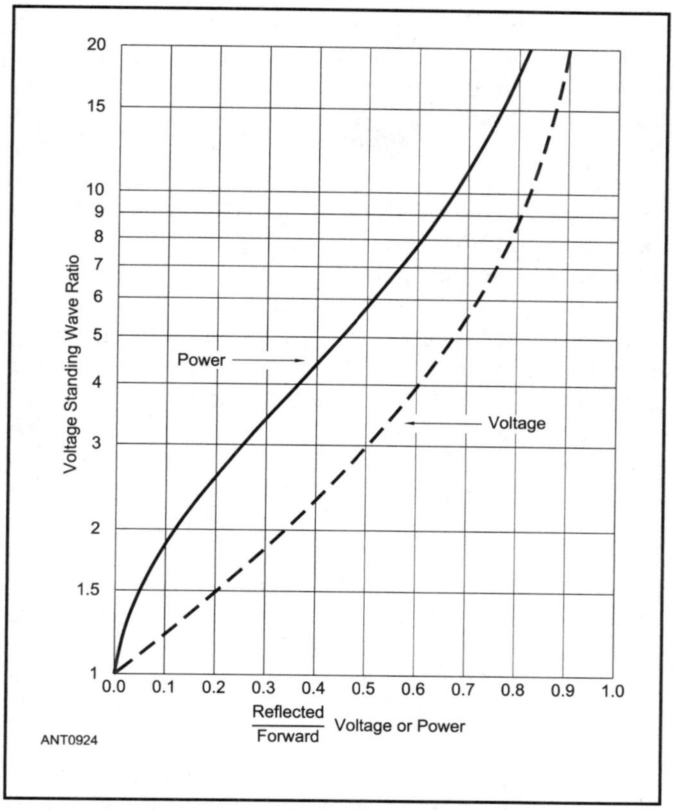

Figure 27.9 — Chart for finding voltage standing wave ratio when the ratio of reflected-to-forward voltage or reflected-to-forward power is known.

Instead of calculating the SWR value, you could use the voltage curve in **Figure 27.9**. In this example the ratio of reflected to forward voltage is 40/100 = 0.4, and the SWR value is about 2.3:1.

You may calibrate the meter scale in any arbitrary units, so long as the scale has equal divisions. It is the ratios of the voltages, and not the actual values, that determine the SWR.

27.2.3 AVOIDING ERRORS IN SWR MEASUREMENTS

The principal causes of inaccuracies within the bridge are differences in the resistances of R1 and R2, stray inductance and capacitance in the bridge arms, and stray coupling between arms. If the checkout procedure described above is followed carefully, the bridge in Figure 27.6 should be sufficiently accurate for practical use. The accuracy is highest for low standing wave ratios because of the nature of the SWR calculation; at high SWR the divisor in the equation above represents the difference between two nearly equal quantities, so a small error in voltage measurement may mean a considerable difference in the calculated SWR.

Detector nonlinearity is another source of error. A diode peak detector is approximately linear if the load impedance is high enough, and the signal is much greater than the diode forward-conduction voltage, but it will still have significant nonlinearity at the low end of the scale.

The standard resistor R_S must equal the actual Z_0 of the line. The actual Z_0 of a sample of line may differ by a few percent from the nominal figure because of manufacturing variations, but this has to be tolerated. In the 50- to 75-Ω range, the RF resistance of a noninductive resistor of ½- or 1-W rating is essentially identical with its dc resistance at VHF and below.

Common-Mode Currents

As explained in the **Transmission Line System Techniques** chapter, there are two ways in which unwanted *common-mode* (sometimes called *antenna*) currents can flow on the outside of a coaxial line — currents induced onto the line because of its spatial relationship to the antenna and currents that result from the direct connection between the coax outer conductor and (usually) one side of the antenna. Such currents can cause significant SWR measurements error and SWR that changes with line length but for different reasons.

Induced current usually will not be troublesome if the bridge and the transmitter (or other source of RF power for operating the bridge) are shielded so that any RF currents flowing on the outside of the line cannot find their way into the bridge. This point can be checked by inserting an additional section of line (⅛ to ¼ electrical wavelength preferably) of the same Z_0. The SWR indicated by the bridge should not change except for a slight decrease because of the additional line loss. If there is a marked change, you may need better shielding.

Common-mode currents can also flow on the outside of coaxial transmission lines if the outside surface of the shield is connected directly to one side of the antenna. Even if the antenna itself is balanced, this "extra" conductor will unbalance the system and common-mode current will flow on the outside of the line. In such cases, the SWR will vary with line length, even though the bridge and transmitter are well-shielded and the shielding is maintained throughout the system by the use of coaxial fittings. Often, merely moving the transmission line around will cause the indicated SWR to change. This is because the outside of the coax has become part of the antenna system by being connected to the antenna at the feed point. The outside shield of the line thus constitutes a load, along with the desired load represented by the antenna itself. The SWR on the line then is determined by the composite load of the antenna and the outside of the coax. Since changing the line length (or position) changes one component of this composite load, the SWR changes too. This is an undesirable condition since the line is usually operating at a higher SWR than it should — and would if the common-mode current on the outside of the coax were eliminated.

The remedy for both situations is generally to use a common-mode choke balun as described in the **Transmission Line System Techniques** chapter or to detune the outside of the line by proper choice of length so that it presents a high impedance at the frequency of operation. Note that this is not a *measurement error*, since what the instrument reads is the actual SWR on the line.

Spurious Frequencies

Off-frequency components in the RF voltage applied to the bridge may cause considerable error. The principal components of this type are harmonics and low-frequency subharmonics that may be fed through the final stage of the transmitter driving the bridge. The antenna is almost always a fairly selective circuit, and even though the system may be operating with a very low SWR at the desired frequency, it is almost always mismatched at harmonic and subharmonic frequencies. If such spurious frequencies are applied to the bridge in appreciable amplitude, the SWR indication will be very much in error. In particular, it may not be possible to obtain a null on the bridge with any set of adjustments of the matching circuit. The only remedy is to filter out the unwanted components by increasing the selectivity of the circuits between the transmitter final amplifier and the bridge.

27.2.4 REFLECTOMETERS

A reflectometer consists of a coupled pair of transmission-line impedance bridges (see Figure 27.6) operated back-to-back so that the generator and load are reversed in one bridge. The resulting imbalance between bridges is displayed on a meter with a scale calibrated so as to convert the imbalance to SWR. Various simple reflectometers have been described from time to time in *QST* and in *The ARRL Handbook*. (See Bibliography.)

Bridges of this type are usually frequency-sensitive — that is, the meter response increases with increasing frequency for the same applied voltage so that a CAL (calibration) potentiometer is required to set the meter sensitivity for each use.

Because most of these designs are frequency sensitive, it is difficult to calibrate them accurately for power measurement. Similarly, without a guaranteed power calibration, they cannot make accurate quantitative measurements of SWR but their low cost and suitability for use at moderate power levels, combined with the ability to show accurately when a matching circuit has been properly adjusted, make them a worthwhile addition to the amateur station.

A pair of typical reflectometer designs are given in **Figures 27.10** and **27.11**. (Both original *QST* articles are included with this book's downloadable supplemental information.) The classic circuit by DeMaw in Figure 27.10 is a very useful circuit at low power levels. It can be scaled up to be used at higher power levels by reducing the number of turns on the toroid primary and increasing the voltage ratings of the voltage sensing capacitors, C1 and C2. (The article by Bruene in the Bibliography should be consulted, as well.) The design by Brown in Figure 27.11 is for use with 300-Ω twin-lead and may be used with parallel-wire feed lines of other characteristic impedances such as 450-Ω window line by changing R1 and R2 to match the impedance of the line.

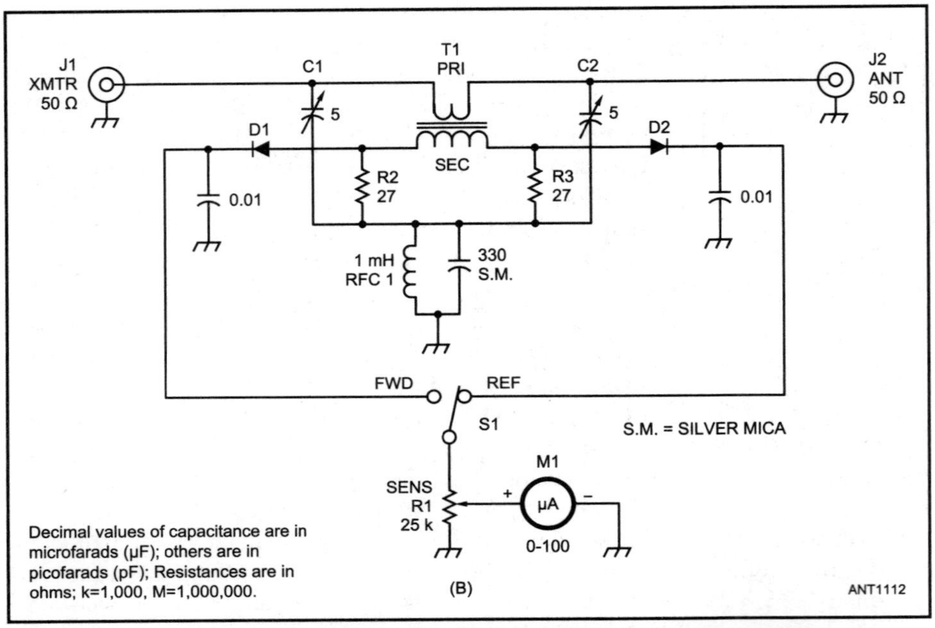

Figure 27.10 — Schematic diagram of the QRP VSWR indicator. Fixed-value capacitors are disc ceramic except those marked with S.M., which are silvered-mica. R2 and R3 and ¼-W carbon-film or metal-film units.

C1, C2 — Miniature PC board mount air trimmer.
D1, D2 — Silicon switching diode, 1N4148 type, matched for equivalent forward resistance by using an ohmmeter.
J1, J2 — RF connector receptacle (phono jack, BNC, UHF).
M1 — Miniature 50- or 100-μA dc meter.
R1 — Linear-taper miniature control, 25 kΩ.
RFC1 — Miniature 1-mH RF choke.
S1 — Miniature SPDT slide or toggle switch.
T1 — Toroidal transformer. Secondary: 60 turns #30 AWG enameled wire on a T68-2 powdered-iron core. Primary is two turns over secondary winding (see text).

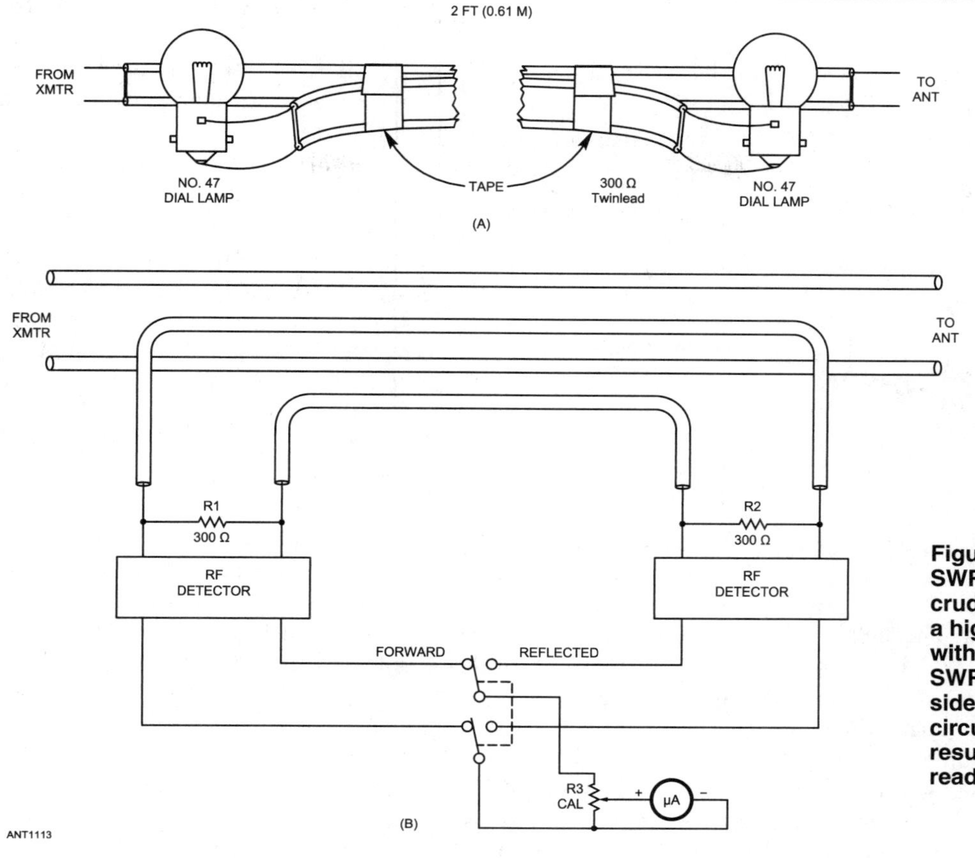

Figure 27.11 — The twin-lamp SWR indicator, shown at A, is a crude form of reflectometer. With a high SWR, both lamps will light with equal brightness. With low SWR, only the lamp on the left side will light. The reflectometer circuit at B yields more accurate results that can be calibrated to read SWR directly.

27.3 RF POWER MEASUREMENT

The standard commercial instruments amateurs use to measure RF power are the various models of the Thruline *directional wattmeters* from Bird Technologies (**www.birdrf.com**) such as the popular Model 43. The meter consists of a section of transmission into which is inserted a selectable power-sensing element, popularly referred to as a "slug." The transmission line in the wattmeter is designed to have an element inserted without disrupting normal power flow through the meter.

The element consists of a pickup loop and terminating resistor that form a *directional coupler* — a circuit that couples to a transmission line and extracts a small amount of power flowing in one direction. (See the Bibliography entry by Wade for a tutorial on directional couplers, also included with this book's downloadable supplemental information.) The construction of the Bird transmission line and sensing element are shown as Figure 3 in the Model 43 operating manual, available for download at **www.birdrf.com** (look for the Model 43 product information). The element can be rotated so that the directional coupler picks up either forward or reflected power.

The energy from the directional coupler in the element then passes through a rectifying diode and filter capacitor that form an RF detector as described earlier in this chapter. The output of the RF detector then drives a meter that is calibrated in watts. The standard series of elements covers from 2 to 1000 MHz and from 5 W to 5000 W full-scale. A variety of specialty elements are also available.

For a close look at the construction of the Bird Thruline wattmeter and a typical power sensing element, see the Repeater Builders website article, "Photo Tour of a Bird Wattmeter Element," by Robert Meister, WA1MIK at **www.repeater-builder.com/projects/bird-element-tour/bird-element-tour.html**. A number of excellent white papers and application notes on the use of these ubiquitous instruments are available on the Bird Technologies website under "Resources and Tools."

27.3.1 DIRECTIONAL POWER/SWR METER

The following section is an overview of the January 2011 *QST* article by Bill Kaune, W7IEQ, "A Modern Directional Power/SWR Meter." The complete article including firmware and printed circuit board artwork is included with this book's downloadable supplemental information.

The primary use for this unit is to monitor the output

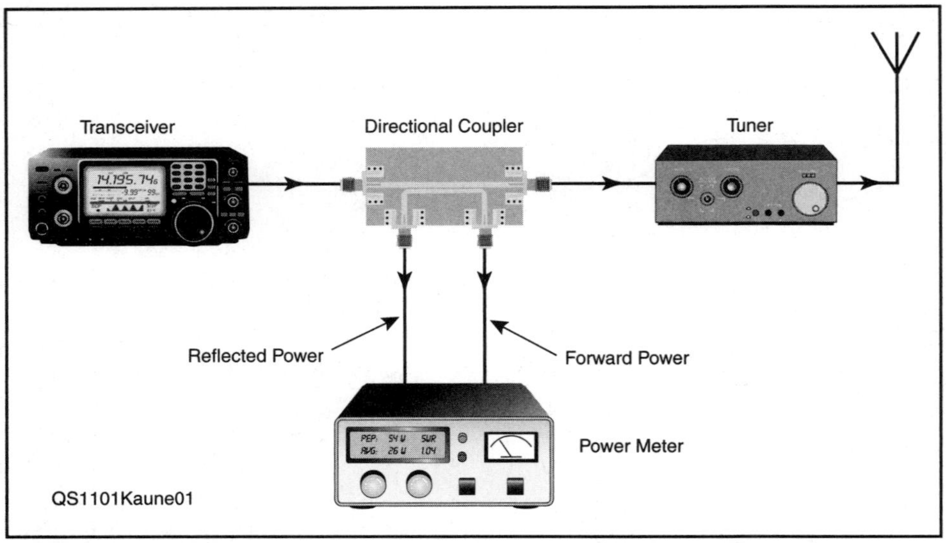

Figure 27.12 — W7IEQ station setup, including the power meter being described here.

power and tuning of a transceiver. The author's station configuration is shown in **Figure 27.12**. RF power generated by the transmitter is routed via RG-8 coaxial cable through a directional coupler to an antenna tuner, which is connected to the antenna with RG-8. The directional coupler contains circuits that sample the RF power flowing from the transmitter to the tuner (the forward power) and the RF power reflected back from the tuner to the transmitter (the reflected power). These samples are sent via RG-58 cable to the two input channels of the power meter. This project includes the directional coupler and the power meter. Enough detail is provided in the full article so that an amateur can duplicate the device or modify the design.

Directional Coupler

The directional coupler is based on the unit described in "The Tandem Match" by John Grebenkemper, KI6WX in the January 1987 issue of *QST* and also included with this book's downloadable supplemental information. A pair of FT-82-67 toroids with 31 turns of #26 AWG magnet wire over lengths of RG-8 form the basis of the directional coupler shown in **Figure 27.13**.

The forward and reflected power samples coupled are reduced by a factor of $1/N^2$, where N = 31 is the number of turns of wire on each toroid. Thus the forward and reflected power samples are reduced by about 30 dB. For example, if a transceiver were delivering a power of 100 W to a pure 50 Ω load, the forward power sample from the directional coupler would be about 0.1 W (20 dBm).

The directivity of a directional coupler is defined as the ratio of the forward power sample divided by the reflected power sample when the coupler is terminated in 50 Ω. In this coupler, the directivity measured using an inexpensive network analyzer is at least 35 dB at 3.5 MHz and 28 dB at 30 MHz.

Power/SWR Meter — Circuit Description

Figure 27.14 shows a front panel view of the power meter. An LCD displays the measured peak (PEP) and average (AEP) envelope powers as well as the standing wave ratio (SWR). The power meter calculates either the peak and average envelope power traveling from the transceiver to load (the forward power) or the peak and average envelope powers actually delivered to the load (the forward power minus reflected power). The average envelope power (AEP) represents an average of the forward or load powers over an averaging period of either 1.6 or 4.8 seconds.

A 1 mA-movement analog meter on the front panel facilitates antenna tuning. This meter continuously displays the quantity 1 – 1/SWR, where SWR is the standing wave ratio on the line. Thus, an SWR of 1.0 corresponds to a meter

Figure 27.13 — Completed directional coupler.

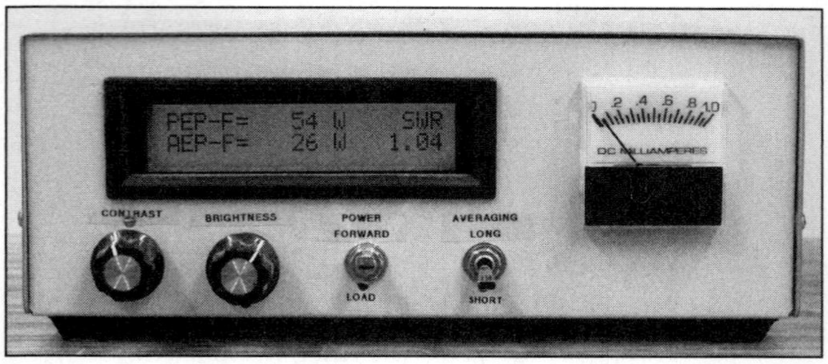

Figure 27.14 — Front panel of power meter. The LCD shows the peak envelope power (PEP), the average envelope power (AEP) and the SWR. The two knobs control the contrast and back lighting of the LCD. One toggle switch determines whether forward or load powers are displayed. A second switch sets the averaging time for the AEP calculation. The meter displays SWR and is used for tuning purposes.

reading of 0 — no deflection of the meter. An SWR of 2 results in a 50% deflection of the meter, while an SWR of 5 produces an 80% deflection of the meter.

The forward and reflected power samples from the directional coupler are applied to a pair of Analog Devices AD8307 logarithmic detectors. External 20 dB attenuators (Mini-Circuits HAT-20) reduce the signals from the directional coupler to levels compatible with the AD8307. As noted earlier, the directional coupler has an internal attenuation of about 30 dB, so the total attenuation in each channel is about 50 dB. Thus, a rig operating at a power level of 1 kW (60 dBm) will result in an input to the forward power channel of about 10 dBm. (The schematic diagram and parts list of the power meter are included with this book's downloadable supplemental information.) The detectors are configured such that the time constant of their output follows the modulation envelope of the RF signal.

LF398 sample-and-hold ICs stabilize the voltages from the forward and reflected power logarithmic detectors. In this way both voltages can be sampled at the exact same time and held for subsequent analog-to-digital conversion and calculation of power and SWR by the PIC16F876A microprocessor (**www.microchip.com**). The processor also includes a pulse-width-modulated (PWM) output used to drive the analog SWR meter on the front panel.

27.3.2 HIGH-POWER RF SAMPLERS

If one wants to measure characteristics of a transmitter or high-power amplifier, some means of reducing the power of the device to 10 or 20 dBm must be used. The most straightforward way to do this is to use a 30 or 40 dB attenuator capable of handling the high power. A 30 dB attenuator will reduce a 100 W transmitter to 20 dBm. A 40 dB attenuator will reduce a 1 kW amplifier to 20 dBm. If further attenuation is needed, a simple precision attenuator may be used after the signal has been reduced to the 20 dBm level.

The problem with high-power attenuators is that they are expensive to buy or build because the front end of the attenuator must handle the output power of the transmitter or amplifier. If one already has a dummy load, an RF sampler may be used to produce a replica of the signal at a reduced power level. The sampler described here was originally presented in *QST* Technical Correspondence for May 2011 by Tom Thompson, WØIVJ. (The original article with construction information plus some supplemental information is included with this book's downloadable supplemental information.)

A transformer sampler passes a single conductor (usually the insulated center conductor from a piece of coaxial cable) from the transmitter or amplifier to the dummy load through a toroidal inductor forming a transformer with a single turn primary. The secondary of the transformer is connected to a resistor network and then to the test equipment as shown in **Figure 27.15** The source, whether a transmitter or amplifier, is assumed to be a pure voltage source in series with a 50-Ω resistor. This most likely is not exactly the case but is sufficient for analysis.

If a current, I, flows into the dummy load, then a current, I / N flows in the secondary of the transformer, where N is the number of turns on the secondary. Figure 27.15 also shows the equivalent circuit, substituting a current source for the transformer. 40 dB is selected for the attenuation and 15 turns for the secondary of the transformer. If R_{SHUNT} = 15 Ω, and R_{SERIES} = 35 Ω, then the voltage across a 50-Ω load resistor, R_{SAMPLE}, is 1/100 of the voltage across the dummy load, which is 40 dB of attenuation.

Reflecting this resistor combination back through the transformer yields 0.06 Ω in series with the 50-Ω dummy load impedance. This is an insignificant change. Furthermore, reflecting 100 Ω from the primary to the secondary places 22.5 kΩ in parallel with R_{SHUNT}, which does not significantly affect its value. The test equipment sees a 50-Ω load looking back into the sampler. Even at low frequencies, where the reactance of the secondary winding is lower than 15 Ω, the impedance looking back into the sample port remains close to 50 Ω.

The samplers described here use an FT37-61 ferrite core followed by two resistors as described above. The through-line SWR is good up to 200 MHz, the SWR is fair looking into the sampled port, and the useful bandwidth extends from 0.5 MHz to about 100 MHz. If you are interested in an accurate representation of the third harmonic of your HF transmitter or amplifier, it is important for the sampler to give

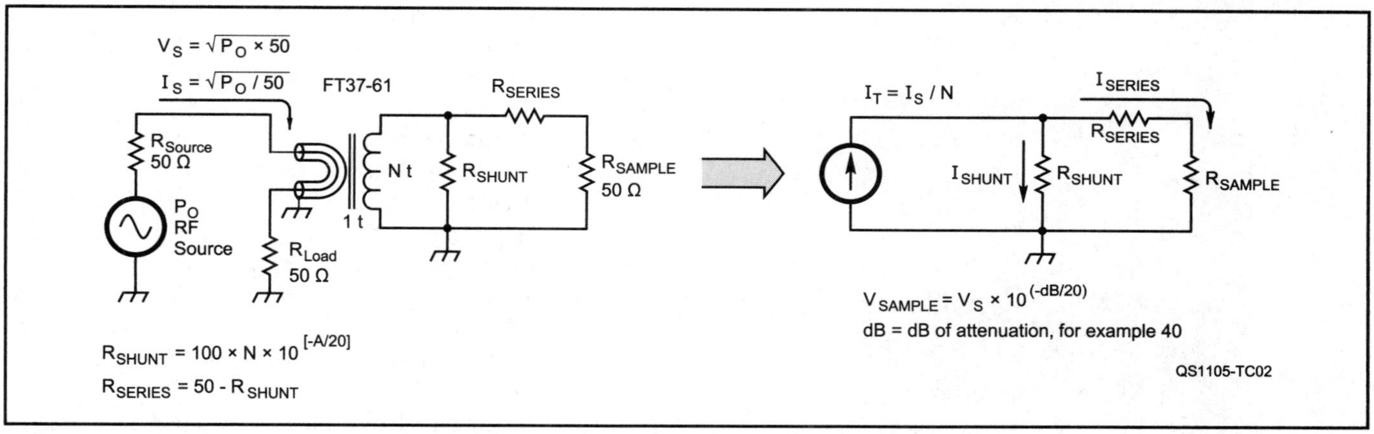

Figure 27.15 — RF sampler circuit diagram and equivalent circuit showing calculations.

Figure 27.16 — RF sampler using box construction.

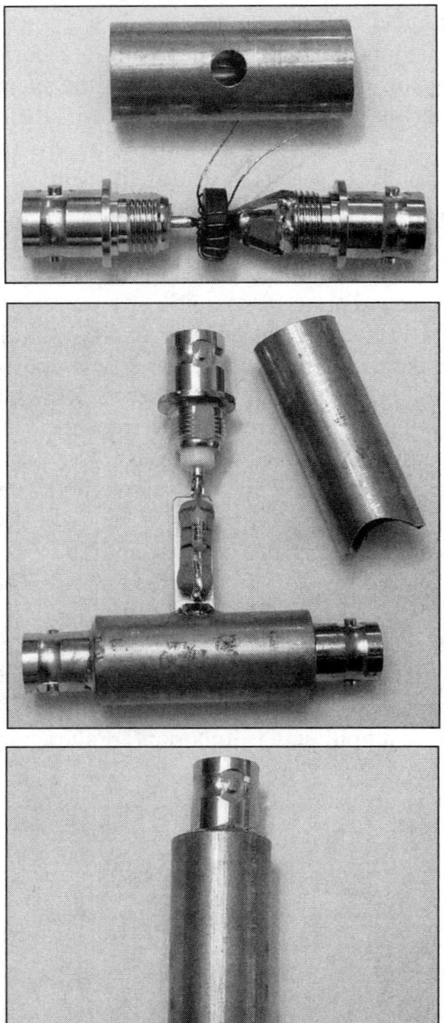

Figure 27.17 — RF sampler using tube construction.

accurate attenuation into the VHF range.

Figure 27.16 shows a photo of a sampler built into a 1.3 × 1.3 × 1 inch (inside dimensions) box constructed from single-sided circuit board material. The through-line connection is made with a short piece of UT-141 semi-rigid coax with the shield grounded only on one side to provide electrostatic shielding between the toroid and the center conductor of the coax. (Do not ground both ends of the shield or a shorted turn is created.) R_{SHUNT} is hidden under the toroid, and R_{SERIES} is shown connected to the sample port. This construction technique looks like a short piece of 200-Ω transmission line in the through-line which affects the SWR at higher frequencies. This can be corrected by compensating with two 3 pF capacitors connected to the through-line input and output connectors as shown in the photo. The through-line SWR was reduced from 1.43:1 to 1.09:1 at 180 MHz by adding the capacitors. This compensation, however, causes the attenuation to differ at high frequencies depending on the direction of the through-line connection. A sampler constructed using the box technique is useable from below 1 MHz through 30 MHz.

Figure 27.17 shows a different approach using 9⁄16 inch diameter, 0.014 inch wall thickness, hobby brass tubing. This lowers the impedance of the through-line so that no compensation is needed. The through-line SWR for the tube sampler is 1.08:1 at 180 MHz which is as good as the box sampler and the sensitivity to through-line direction is reduced. Although the high frequency attenuation is not as good as the box sampler, the construction technique provides a more consistent result. A sampler constructed using the tube technique should be usable through 200 MHz.

27.3.3 AN INEXPENSIVE VHF DIRECTIONAL COUPLER

Precision inline metering devices capable of reading forward and reflected power over a wide range of frequencies are very useful in amateur VHF and UHF work, but their rather high cost puts them out of the reach of many VHF enthusiasts. The device shown in **Figures 27.18** through **27.20** is an inexpensive adaptation of their basic principles. It can be made for the cost of a meter, a few small parts, and bits of copper pipe and fittings that can be found in the plumbing section at many hardware stores.

The sampler consists of a short section of handmade coaxial line, in this instance, of 50-Ω impedance, with a reversible probe coupled to it. A small pickup loop built into the probe is terminated with a resistor at one end and a diode at the other. The resistor matches the impedance of the loop, not the impedance of the line section. Energy picked up by the loop is rectified by the diode, and the resultant current is fed to a meter equipped with a calibration control.

The principal metal parts of the device are a brass plumbing T, a pipe cap, short pieces of 3⁄4-inch ID and 5⁄16-inch OD copper pipe, and two coaxial fittings. Other available tubing combinations for 50-Ω line may be usable. The ratio of outer conductor ID to inner conductor OD should be 2.4/1. (The complete article with more detail is included with

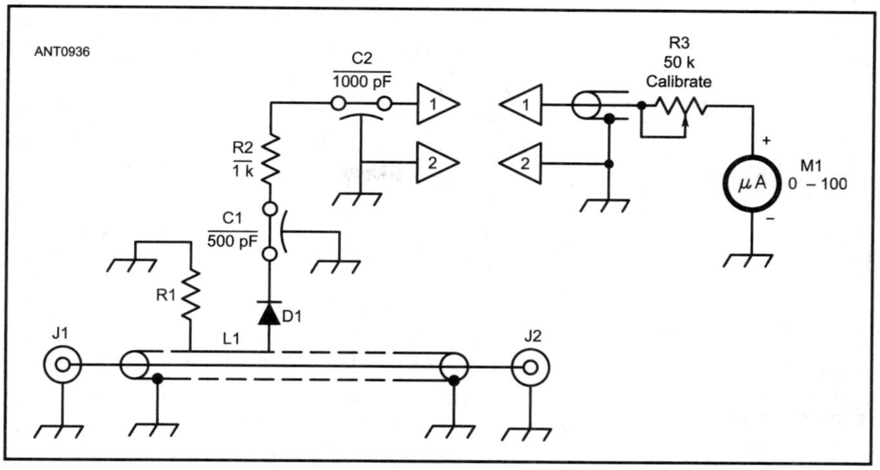

Figure 27.18 — Circuit diagram for the line sampler.
C1 — 500-pF feedthrough capacitor, solder-in type.
C2 — 1000-pF feedthrough capacitor, threaded type.
D1 — 1N34A germanium or 1N5817 Schottky diode.
J1, J2 — Coaxial connector, type N (UG-58A).
L1 — Pickup loop, copper strap 1-inch long × 3⁄16-inch wide. Bend into "C" shape with flat portion 5⁄8-inch long.
M1 — 0-100 μA meter.
R1 — 82 to 100 Ω, carbon-film or metal film.
R3 — 50-kΩ composition control, linear taper.

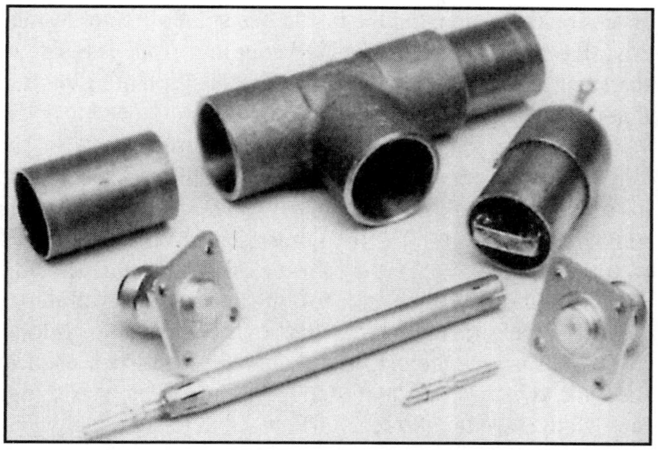

Figure 27.19 — Major components of the line sampler. The brass T and two end sections are at the upper left in this picture. A completed probe assembly is at the right. The N connectors have their center pins removed. The pins are shown with one inserted in the left end of the inner conductor and the other lying in the right foreground.

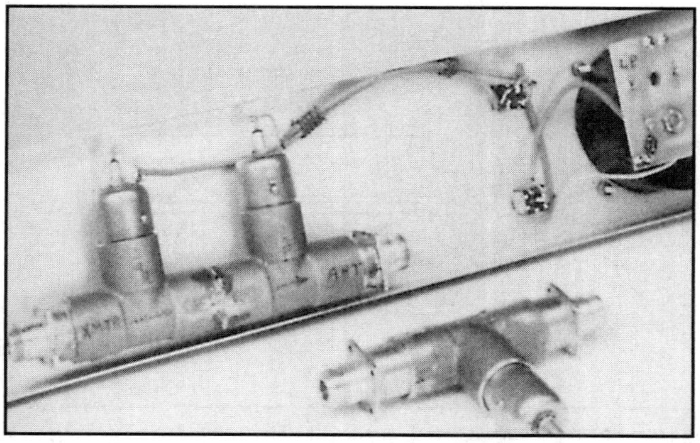

Figure 27.20 — Two versions of the line sampler. The single unit described in detail here is in the foreground. Two sections in a single assembly provide for monitoring forward and reflected power without probe reversal.

this book's downloadable supplemental information.)

The sampler is very useful for many jobs even if it is not accurately calibrated, although it is desirable to calibrate it against a wattmeter of known accuracy as described in the complete article.

27.3.4 RF STEP ATTENUATOR

A good RF step attenuator is one of the key pieces of equipment that belongs on your workbench. The attenuator in this project offers good performance yet can be built with a few basic tools. The attenuator is designed for use in 50-Ω systems, provides a total attenuation of 71 dB in 1-dB steps, offers respectable accuracy and insertion loss through 225 MHz and can be used at 450 MHz as shown in **Table 27.1**. This material was originally published as "An RF Step Attenuator" by Denton Bramwell, K7OWJ, in the June 1995 *QST*.

The attenuator consists of 10 resistive pi (π) attenuator sections such as the one in **Figure 27.21**. Each section consists of a DPDT slide switch and three ¼-W, 1%-tolerance metal-film resistors. The complete unit contains single 1, 2, 3 and 5-dB sections, and six 10-dB sections. **Table 27.2** lists the resistor values required for each section.

Table 27.1
Step Attenuator Performance at 148, 225, and 250 MHz
Measurements made in the ARRL Laboratory

Attenuator set for Maximum attenuation (71 dB)		***Attenuator set for minimum attenuation (0 dB)***	
Frequency (MHz)	*Attenuation (dB)*	*Frequency (MHz)*	*Attenuation (dB)*
148	72.33	148	0.4
225	73.17	225	0.4
450	75.83	450	0.84

Note: Laboratory-specified measurement tolerance of ±1 dB

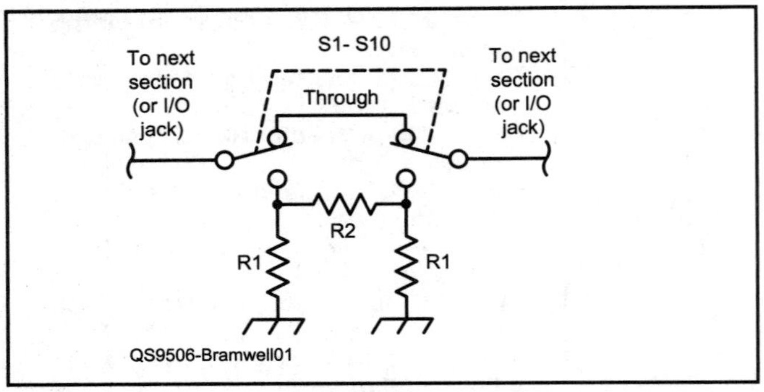

Figure 27.21 — Schematic of one section of the attenuator. All resistors are ¼-W, 1%-tolerance metal-film units. See Table 27.2 for the resistor values required for each attenuator section. There are six 10 dB sections and one each of 1, 2, 3, and 5 dB.

Table 27.2
Closest 1%-Tolerance Resistor Values

Attenuation (dB)	*R1 (Ω)*	*R2 (Ω)*
1.00	866.00	5.60
2.00	436.00	11.50
3.00	294.00	17.40
5.00	178.00	30.10
10.00	94.30	71.50

The enclosure is made of brass sheet stock, readily available at hardware and hobby stores. By selecting the right stock, you can avoid having to bend the metal and need only perform a minimum of cutting.

Construction

The enclosure can be built using only a nibbling tool, drill press, metal shears, and a soldering gun or heavy soldering iron. (Use a regular soldering iron on the switches and resistors.) One method of cutting the small pieces of rectangular tubing to length is to use a drill press equipped with a small abrasive cutoff wheel.

Brass is easy to work and solder. For the enclosure, you'll need two precut 2 × 12 × 0.025-inch sheets and two 1 × 12 × 0.025-inch sheets. The 2-inch-wide stock is used for the front and back panels; the 1-inch-wide stock is used for the ends and sides. For the internal wiring, you need a piece of ⁵⁄₃₂ × ⁵⁄₁₆-inch rectangular tubing, a ¼ × 0.032-inch strip, and a few small pieces of 0.005-inch-thick stock to provide interstage shields and form the 50-Ω transmission lines that run from the BNC connectors to the switches at the ends of the step attenuator.

For the front panel, nibble or shear a piece of 2-inch-wide brass to a length of about 9½ inches. Space the switches from each other so that a piece of the rectangular brass tubing lies flat and snugly between them. See **Figure 27.22**. Drill holes for the #4-40 mounting screws and nibble or punch rectangular holes for the bodies of the slide switches.

Before mounting any parts, solder in place one of the 1-inch-wide chassis side pieces to make the assembly more rigid. Solder the side piece to the edge of the top plate that faces the "through" side of the switches; this makes later assembly easier (see **Figure 27.23**). Although the BNC input and output connectors are shown mounted on the top (front) panel, better lead dress and high-frequency performance may result from mounting the connectors at the ends of the enclosure.

DPDT slide switches designed for sub-panel mounting often have mounting holes tapped for #4-40 screws. Enlarge the holes to allow a #4-40 screw to slide through. Before mounting the switches, make the "through" switch connection (see Figure 27.21) by bending the two lugs at one end of each switch toward each other and soldering the lugs together or solder a small strip of brass between the lugs and clip off the lug ends. Mount the switches above the front panel, using ⁵⁄₃₂-inch-high by ⁷⁄₃₂-inch-OD spacers. Use the same size spacer on the inside. On the inside, the spacer creates a small post that helps reduce capacitive coupling from one side of the attenuator to the other. The spacers position the switch so that the 50-Ω stripline can be formed later.

The trick to getting acceptable insertion loss in the "through" position is to make the attenuator look as much as possible like 50-Ω coax. That's where the rectangular tubing and the ¼ × 0.032-inch brass strip come into the picture (see Figure 27.22); they form a 50-Ω stripline. (See the **Transmission Lines** chapter for information on stripline.)

Cut pieces of the rectangular tubing about ¾-inch long, and sweat solder them to the front panel between each of the slide switches. Next, cut lengths of the ¼-inch strip long enough to conveniently reach from switch to switch, then cut one more piece. Drill ¹⁄₁₆-inch holes near both ends of all but one of the ¼-inch strips. The undrilled piece is used as a temporary spacer, so make sure it is flat and deburred.

Lay the temporary spacer on top of the rectangular tubing between the first two switches, then drop one of the drilled

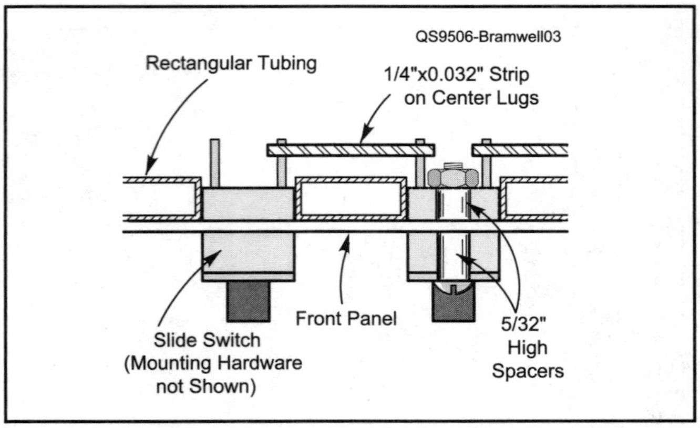

Figure 27.22 — Key to obtaining acceptable insertion loss in the "through" position is to make the whole device look as much as possible like 50-Ω coax. The rectangular tubing and the ¼ × 0.032-inch brass strip between the switch sections form a 50-Ω stripline.

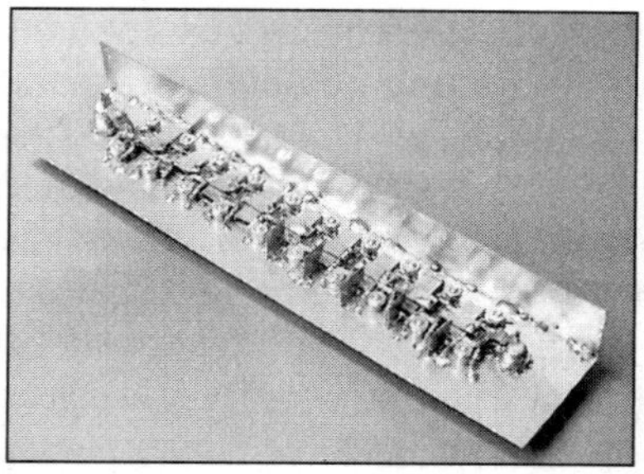

Figure 27.23 — Solder one of the 1-inch-wide chassis side pieces in place to make the assembly more rigid during construction. Solder the side piece to the edge of the top plate that faces the "through" side of the switches; this makes the rest of the assembly easier.

Figure 27.24 — The attenuator before final mechanical assembly. The ¼-inch strips are spaced 0.033 inch apart to form a 50-Ω connection from the BNC connector to the stripline. There are ½-inch square shields between 10-dB sections. The square shields have a notch in one corner to accommodate the end of the rectangular tubing.

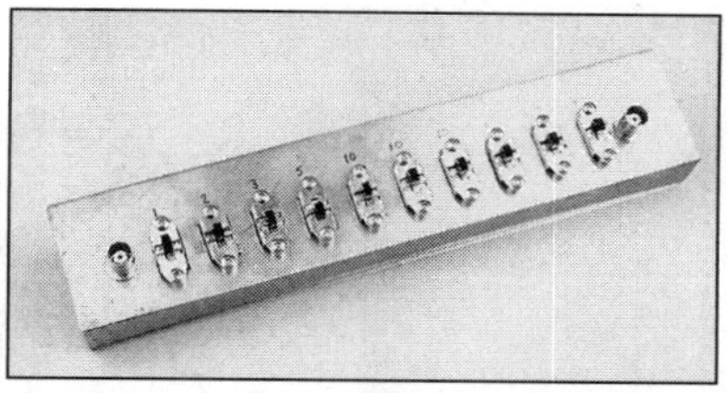

Figure 27.25 — The completed step attenuator in the enclosure of brass sheet. The BNC connectors may be mounted on the front panel at the end of the switches or on the end panels.

¼-inch pieces over it, with the center switch lugs through the ¹⁄₁₆-inch holes. Before soldering, check the strip to make sure there's sufficient clearance between the ¼-inch strip and the switch lugs; trim the corners if necessary. Use a screwdriver blade to hold the strip flat and solder the lugs to the strip. Remove the temporary spacer. Repeat this procedure for all switch sections. This creates a 50-Ω stripline running the length of the attenuator.

Next, solder in place the three 1%-tolerance resistors of each section, keeping the leads as short as possible. Use a generous blob of solder on ground leads to make the lead less inductive. Install a ½-inch-square brass shield between each 10-dB section to ensure that signals don't couple around the sections at higher frequencies.

Use parallel ¼-inch strips of 0.005-inch-thick brass spaced 0.033 inch apart to form 50-Ω feed lines from the BNC connectors to the switch contacts at each end of the stripline as shown in Figure 27.23. (Use the undrilled piece of 0.032-inch-thick brass to insure the proper line spacing.) The attenuator with all switches and shields in place is shown ready for final mechanical assembly in **Figure 27.24**

Finally, solder in place the remaining enclosure side, cut and solder the end pieces, and solder brass #4-40 nuts to the inside walls of the case to hold the rear (or bottom) panel. Drill and attach the rear panel and round off the sharp corners to prevent scratching or cutting anyone or anything. Add stick-on feet and labels and your step attenuator of **Figure 27.25** is ready for use.

Remember that the unit is built with ¼-W resistors, so it can't dissipate a lot of power. Remember, too, that for the attenuation to be accurate, the input to the attenuator must be a 50-Ω source and the output must be terminated in a 50-Ω load.

27.4 FIELD STRENGTH METERS

Few amateur stations, fixed or mobile, are without need of a *field-strength meter* (*FSM*). An instrument of this type serves many useful purposes during antenna experiments and adjustments. In its simplest form, the field strength meter is simply a diode detector and a sensitive meter with a potentiometer wired as a resistive divider to act as a sensitivity control as in **Figure 27.26**. This type of meter is commonly and inexpensively available both new and used. (See the Bibliography and this book's downloadable supplemental information for the *QST* article describing how to build this simple FSM.)

When work is to be done from many wavelengths away from the antenna, however, such a simple instrument lacks the necessary sensitivity. Further, such a device has a serious fault because its linearity leaves much to be desired and it is very wideband so that the measurement may be upset from any other strong nearby transmitter, such as an AM broadcast station. Thus, a more capable instrument is needed.

27.4.1 PORTABLE FIELD STRENGTH METER

The field-strength meter described here takes care of the problems associated with a simple FSM. Additionally, it is small, measuring only 4 × 5 × 8 inches. The power supply consists of two 9-V batteries. Sensitivity can be set

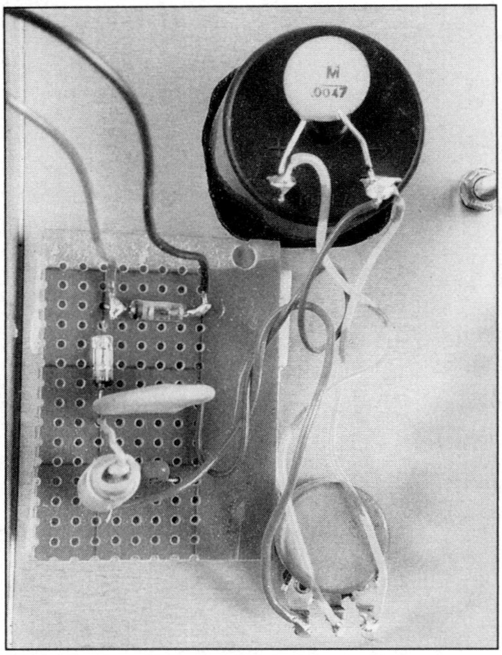

(A)

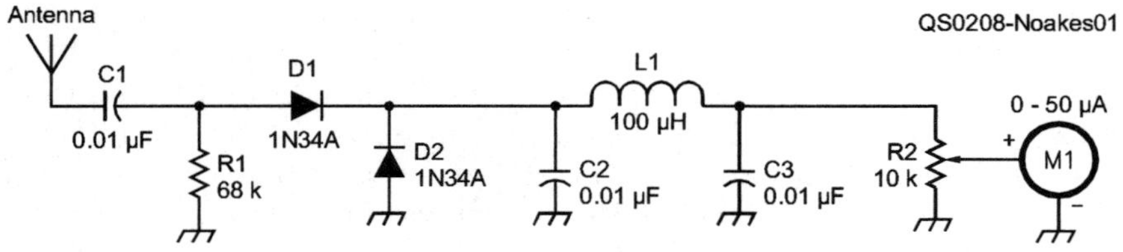

(B)

Figure 27.26 — With the sensitivity control at mid-range, the simple FSM shown at A can easily detect a 1-W, 2 meter signal. B gives the schematic and parts list for the FSM. A metal enclosure is mandatory.
C1-C3 — 0.01 µF disc ceramic capacitor.
D1, D2 — 1N34A (germanium) or 1N5817 (Schottky) diode.
L1 — 100 µH inductor.
M1 — 50 µA analog meter.
R1 — 68 kΩ, ¼-W carbon-film or metal-film resistor.
R2 — 10 kΩ linear or audio taper potentiometer.
Antenna — BNC chassis-mount receptacle.

for practically any amount desired. However, from a usefulness standpoint, the circuit should not be too sensitive or it will respond to unwanted signals. This unit also has excellent linearity with regard to field strength. (The field strength of a received signal varies inversely with the distance from the source, all other things being equal.) The frequency range includes all amateur bands from 3.5 through 148 MHz, with band-switched circuits, thus avoiding the use of plug-in inductors. All in all, it is a quite useful instrument. The information in this section is based on a January 1973 *QST* article by Lew McCoy, W1ICP. (See the Bibliography.)

The unit is pictured in **Figures 27.27** and **27.28**, and the schematic diagram is shown in **Figure 27.29**. A type 741 op-amp IC is the heart of the unit. (Any general-purpose op-amp can be substituted for the 741.) The antenna is connected to J1, and a tuned circuit is used ahead of a diode detector. The rectified signal is coupled as dc and amplified in the op amp. Sensitivity of the op amp is controlled by inserting resistors R3 through R6 in the circuit by means of S2.

With the circuit shown, and in its most sensitive setting, M1

Figure 27.27 —The linear field strength meter. The control at the upper left is for C1 and the one to the right for C2. At the lower left is the band switch, and to its right the sensitivity switch. The zero-set control for M1 is located directly below the meter.

Figure 27.28 — Inside view of the field-strength meter. At the upper right is C1 and to the left, C2. The dark leads from the circuit board to the front panel are the shielded leads described in the text.

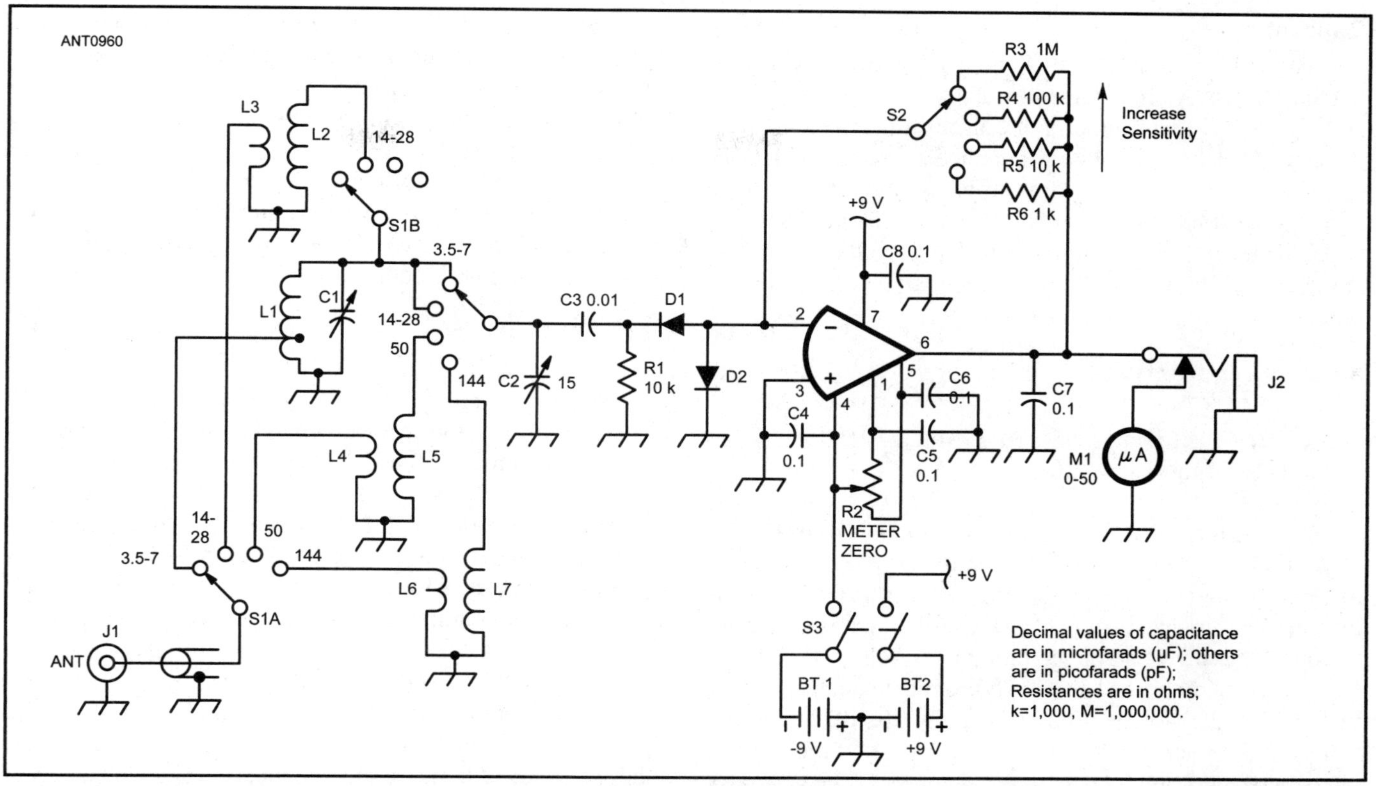

Figure 27.29 — Circuit diagram of the linear field strength meter. All resistors are ¼- or ½-W carbon-film or metal-film types.

C1 — 140 pF variable.
C2 — 15-pF variable
D1, D2 — 1N4148 or equiv.
L1 — 34 turns #24 AWG enameled wire wound on an T-68-2 core, tapped 4 turns from ground end.
L2 — 12 turns #24 AWG enameled wire wound on T-68-2 core.
L3 — 2 turns #24 AWG enameled wire wound at ground end of L2.
L4 — 1 turn #26 AWG enameled wire wound at ground end of L5.
L5 — 12 turns #26 AWG enameled wire wound on T-25-12 core.
L6 — 1 turn #26 AWG enameled wire wound at ground end of L7.
L7 — 1 turn #18 AWG enameled wire wound on T-25-12 core.
M1 — 50 or 100 µA dc.
R2 — 10-kΩ control, linear taper.
S1 — Rotary switch, 3 poles, 5 positions, 3 sections.
S2 — Rotary switch, 1 pole, 4 positions.
S3 — DPST toggle.
U1 — Type 741 op amp or equivalent. Pin numbers shown are for a 14-pin package.

will detect a signal from the antenna on the order of 100 µV. Linearity is poor for approximately the first ⅕ of the meter range, but then is almost straight-line from there to full-scale deflection. The reason for the poor linearity at the start of the readings is because of nonlinearity of the diodes at the point of first conduction. However, if gain measurements are being made this is of no real importance, as accurate gain measurements can be made in the linear portion of the readings.

The 741 op amp requires both a positive and a negative voltage source. This is obtained by connecting two 9-V batteries in series and grounding the center. One other feature of the instrument is that it can be used remotely by connecting an external meter at J2. This is handy if you want to adjust an antenna and observe the results without having to leave the antenna site.

L1 is the 3.5/7 MHz coil and is tuned by C1. The coil is wound on a toroid form. For 14, 21 or 28 MHz, L2 is switched in parallel with L1 to cover the three bands. L5 and C2 cover approximately 40 to 60 MHz, and L7 and C2 from 130 MHz to approximately 180 MHz. The two VHF coils are also wound on toroid forms.

Construction Notes

The majority of the components may be mounted on an etched circuit board. A shielded lead should be used between pin 4 of the IC and S2. The same is true for the leads from R3 through R6 to the switch. Otherwise, parasitic oscillations may occur in the IC because of its very high gain.

In order for the unit to cover the 144-MHz band, L6 and L7 should be mounted directly across the appropriate terminals of S1, rather than on a circuit board. The extra lead length adds too much stray capacitance to the circuit. It isn't necessary to use toroid forms for the 50- and 144 MHz coils. They were used in the version described here simply because they were available. You may substitute air-wound coils of the appropriate inductance.

Calibration

The field strength meter can be used as is for a relative-reading device. A linear indicator scale will serve admirably. However, it will be a much more useful instrument for antenna work if it is calibrated in decibels, enabling the user to check relative gain and front-to-back ratios. If you have access to a calibrated signal generator, connect it to the field-strength meter and use different signal levels fed to the device to make a calibration chart. Convert signal-generator voltage ratios to decibels by using the equation

$$dB = 20 \log (V1/V2) \quad (3)$$

where V1/V2 is the ratio of the two voltages and log is the common logarithm (base 10).

Let's assume that M1 is calibrated evenly from 0 to 10. Next, assume we set the signal generator to provide a reading of 1 on M1, and that the generator is feeding a 100 µV signal into the instrument. Now we increase the generator output to 200 µV, giving us a voltage ratio of 2:1. Also let's assume M1 reads 5 with the 200 µV input. From the equation above, we find that the voltage ratio of 2 equals 6.02 dB between 1 and 5 on the meter scale. M1 can be calibrated more accurately between 1 and 5 on its scale by adjusting the generator and figuring the ratio. For example, a ratio of 126 µV to 100 µV is 1.26, corresponding to 2.0 dB. By using this method, all of the settings of S2 can be calibrated. In the instrument shown here, the most sensitive setting of S2 with R3, 1 MΩ, provides a range of approximately 6 dB for M1. Keep in mind that the meter scale for each setting of S1 must be calibrated similarly for each band. The degree of coupling of the tuned circuits for the different bands will vary, so each band must be calibrated separately.

Another method for calibrating the instrument is using a transmitter and measuring its output power with an RF wattmeter. In this case we are dealing with power rather than voltage ratios, so this equation applies:

$$dB = 10 \log (P1/P2) \quad (4)$$

where P1/P2 is the power ratio.

With most transmitters the power output can be varied, so calibration of the test instrument is rather easy. Attach a pickup antenna to the field-strength meter (a short wire a foot or so long will do) and position the device in the transmitter antenna field. Let's assume we set the transmitter output for 10 W and get a reading on M1. We note the reading and then increase the output to 20 W, a power ratio of 2. Note the reading on M1 and then use Eq 4. A power ratio of 2 is 3.01 dB. By using this method the instrument can be calibrated on all bands and ranges.

With the tuned circuits and coupling links specified in Figure 27.29, this instrument has an average range on the various bands of 6 dB for the two most sensitive positions of S2, and 15 dB and 30 dB for the next two successive ranges. The 30-dB scale is handy for making front-to-back antenna measurements without having to switch S2.

27.5 ANTENNA ANALYZER MEASUREMENTS

Traditionally, amateurs have measured coax-fed antennas using a standing wave ratio (SWR) meter as described above. It is a good method for determining an antenna's resonant frequency and how well-matched its feed point impedance is to the characteristic impedance of the feed line. More information is often required, however. An RF impedance analyzer capable of measuring both the magnitude and the phase of impedance is often called an *antenna analyzer*, since the most common use by amateurs is for measuring antennas. Such an instrument can obtain more detailed information about the complex impedance versus frequency anywhere in the antenna system.

To keep size and cost to a minimum, portable antenna analyzers usually use a narrow-band source (an internal oscillator) and wide-band detector (a diode). Some units include a microprocessor and can display SWR, return loss, resistance, reactance, and the magnitude and phase of the impedance. The latest versions can also take *swept measurements* and display data graphically over a range of frequencies. Antenna analyzers suitable for amateur use are available from a number of manufacturers — search for "antenna analyzers" on the internet to find them.

When shopping for an antenna analyzer, pay careful attention to the capabilities and limitations. Several basic designs are available with tradeoffs between performance and cost. Be aware that some units measure only the SWR or impedance magnitude, while others measure both the resistive and reactive parts of the impedance. Some units give the magnitude of the reactance but not the sign, requiring the operator to change frequency a small amount and watch the change in impedance magnitude to determine the sign and thus the type of the impedance, inductive or capacitive.

Analyzers are available today with a wide range of capabilities, accessories, and supporting software. A thorough treatment of how to use these analyzers is provided in the manual or help functions for each unit. The ARRL's book

Understanding Your Antenna Analyzer by Joel Hallas, W1ZR is also available. Two additional articles are provided in this book's downloadable supplemental information: "Using Single-Frequency Antenna Analyzers" from previous editions of this book and "Antenna Analyzer Pet Tricks" by Paul Wade, W1GHZ.

27.5.1 BASIC OPERATION

Figure 27.31 shows the block diagram of a typical antenna analyzer. The functions in solid lines are required and those in dashed lines are included depending on feature set and price.

Figure 27.32 shows a relatively simple circuit that uses diodes for detecting voltages corresponding to voltage and current at the external load. This inexpensive circuit is useful, but at low signal levels the diodes introduce some non-linearity and temperature drift which may be an issue. This type of diode detector responds to signals over a wide frequency range, and there may be stray pickup from nearby broadcasting stations that makes the measurement results inaccurate.

The rectified voltages can be digitized by a microprocessor and the results displayed numerically. The signal source is typically a varactor-tuned LC oscillator in the "analog" units or a direct digital synthesizer (DDS) in more sophisticated models. The DDS signal source is very stable since it is controlled by a crystal oscillator and it can be set to the desired frequency quickly with a keyboard entry. The DDS version costs somewhat more, but it has significant performance and operating conveniences compared to the varactor-tuned oscillator.

For a more detailed analysis of the antenna system, an instrument with a narrowband detector such as for a radio receiver gives much better performance than the broadband diode detector. **Figure 27.33** shows how two DDSs can be used with one applied to the antenna system and the other used as a reference. Typically, the clock oscillator is crystal-controlled

Noise Bridges

Noise bridges (see **Figure 27.30**) were a very common test instrument until the modern antenna analyzer became widespread. The noise bridge includes an adjustable bridge circuit to which a wide-band noise generator is connected as the source and a conventional receiver is attached to the detector port. The receiver is tuned to the desired frequency and the resistance and reactance controls are adjusted for minimum noise in the receiver. If the receiver has a panadapter display, the null frequency can be seen on the screen, speeding the adjustment. The *QST* article "The Noise Bridge" by Jack Althouse, K6NY, gives a more complete description of how a noise bridge works and how it is used. The article is included in the downloadable supplemental information.

Figure 27.30 — A noise bridge is an alternative to the antenna analyzer, pairing a noise source with an external receiver as the detector. The bridge is adjusted for minimum noise in the receiver and values for R and X are read from calibrated dials. An article on using the noise bridge is downloadable with this book's supplemental information.

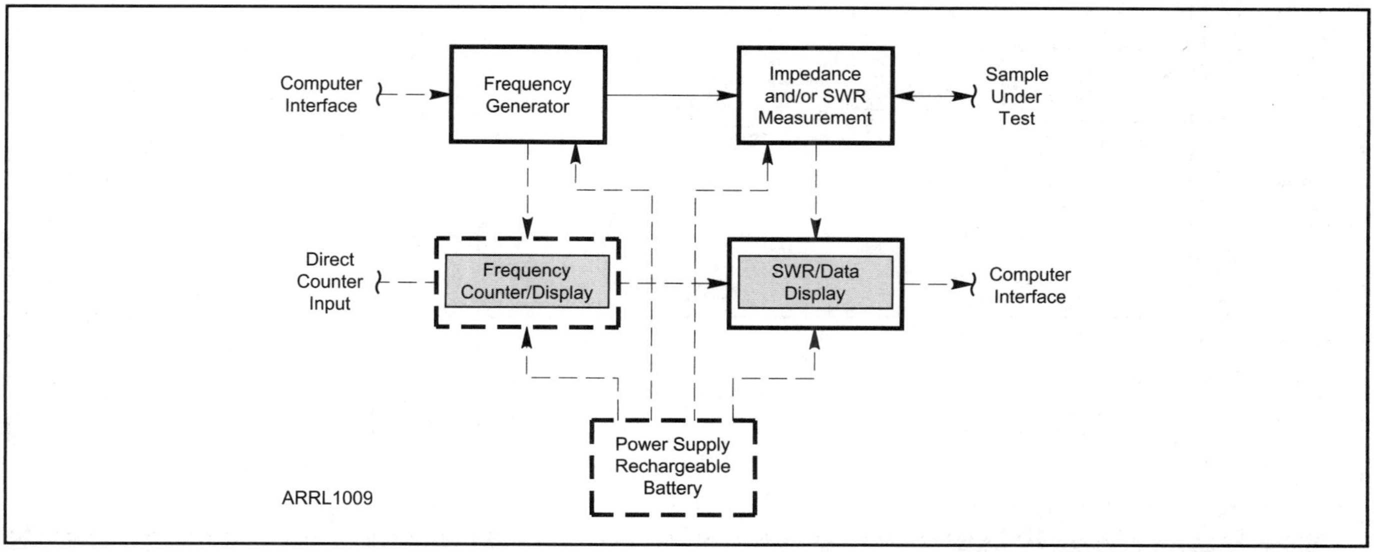

Figure 27.31 — Block diagram showing the elements of typical antenna analyzers. The items shown with dashed lines may not be part of every model.

for high accuracy. One DDS is programmed to output a signal at the actual test frequency and the other DDS is programmed to a slightly higher frequency in the 1 to 10 kHz range, shown in the figure as 2 kHz. See the reference entry for an article by Michael Knitter, DG5MK, that gives a detailed design description of this type of analyzer.

The signals are then mixed to produce a low frequency output) that can easily digitized by an inexpensive analog-to-digital converter (ADC). The measurements are then processed mathematically in a microprocessor or PC to yield full information about the complex impedance being measured. This type of analyzer is actually a one-port, swept-frequency impedance meter that measures both the magnitude and phase of a test impedance over a wide range of frequencies. A two-port vector network analyzer (VNA) can also be configured to do one-port swept frequency measurements.

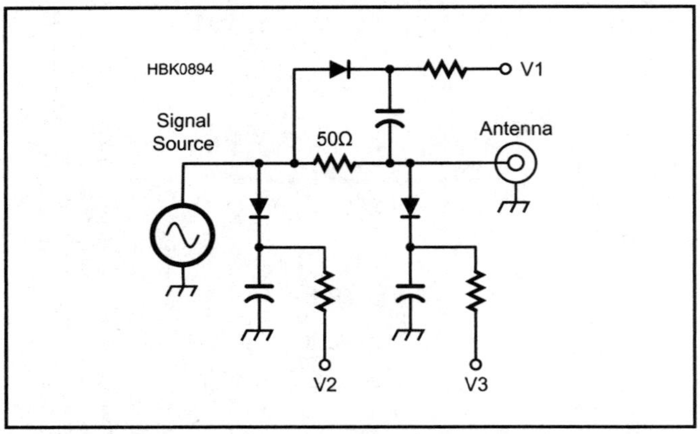

Figure 27.32 — A relatively simple diode detector circuit for measuring impedance that gives adequate results for many applications.

One signal corresponds to the voltage applied to the antenna system and the other signal corresponds to the current flowing in the antenna system. The ratio of these signals is the impedance of the circuit and the difference of their phases is the phase angle of the circuit:

Magnitude(Z) = Magnitude(V1)/Magnitude(V2)

Phase(Z) = Phase(V1) - Phase(V2)

The PC shown in the figure can be a desktop computer or a small tablet computer. The tablet provides good portability but if the size of the screen is too small it may be hard to read. The analyzer is able to generate a lot of data and it's helpful to be able to see as much as possible at one time on one screen, especially when making tuning adjustments. Another tradeoff is the size of the menu buttons on a tablet. If they are too small it may be hard to make menu selections.

Some analyzers can store sets of measurements in a file for review later and transfer to a PC for further processing and display. The standard format for swept impedance data (frequency and impedance) is called *Touchstone* (**en.wikipedia.org/wiki/Touchstone_file**). Files in the Touchstone format can be read and processed by a wide variety of software, including as the input to design software.

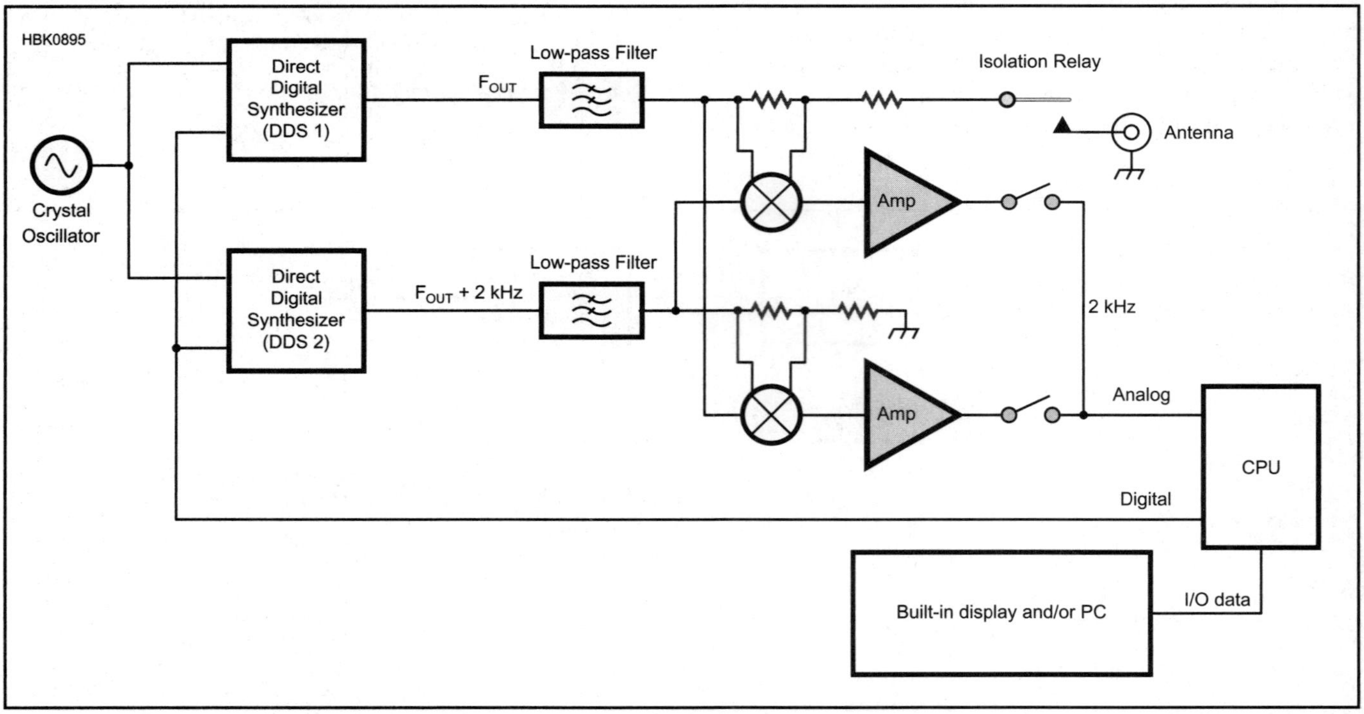

Figure 27.33 — Block diagram of a dual-DDS-based antenna analyzer. By mixing two signal sources that are very close in frequency, with one of the sources applied to the load (antenna), low-frequency signals are generated. The signals contain the necessary information to measure impedance magnitude and phase.

Many analyzers can create a calibration table to automatically correct for imperfections in the analyzer. The calibration process takes data at selected frequencies over the measurement range. This is usually done by sequentially attaching three known loads to the input of the analyzer and running a special calibration routine that saves the data for each load in memory. (See this chapter's section on Vector Network Analyzers.) This process is very quick and easy, and the final results of any measurement are much more accurate than from a simple analyzer that does not have a calibration procedure. The calibration is performed with three known loads: a short circuit, an open circuit, and a resistor of known value. The mathematics to apply this correction data is very complex but the microprocessor does it easily and the user does not have to worry about the details.

The impedance data can be used to calculate several parameters for the antenna system. Using the specified value for the system reference impedance, which can be any value (it doesn't have to be 50 Ω), For example, the reflection coefficient (ρ or rho) can be calculated as:

$$\rho = (Z_L - Z_0) / (Z_L + Z_0)$$

Where Z_L is the measured impedance of the load and Z_0 is the specified impedance of the transmission line which can be any value. Z_L is a complex number; therefore, ρ is, in general, a complex number with a magnitude between zero and one. Rho is approximately equal to zero when the line is matched to the antenna because there is no reflection, so all the transmitter power is absorbed by the antenna. When the antenna is poorly matched to the line, ρ is larger and it approaches 1 when the mismatch is large.

$$SWR = (1 + |\rho|) / (1 - |\rho|)$$

Note that SWR only depends on the *magnitude* of ρ denoted by the vertical bars as $|\rho|$ so it is not a complex number.

27.5.2 CALIBRATION

Different test situations may require adapters, interconnecting cables, baluns, or filters. The calibration process is able to compensate for the externally connected accessories so their exact properties are not critical. By placing the calibration loads *after* the external hardware, characteristics of the whole measurement system can be accounted for in the calibration table. The point at which the calibration loads are attached is called the analyzer's *reference plane*. (See the Agilent application note on vector network analyzers in the references.) For example, a filter with a response that is less than perfect can be used as long as it is included in the measurement system during calibration. The effects of the filter on measurements can then be cancelled mathematically.

Most antenna analyzers have a single-ended (unbalanced) output with a coax connector. For making measurements on a balanced transmission line, like window line or ladder line, a balun can be added between the analyzer's RF connector and the input to the transmission line as in **Figure 27.34.** The calibration loads are attached to the output side of this balun so that its imperfections are automatically canceled during the measurement. The measurement results displayed by the analyzer program then correspond to the input to the transmission line itself.

Broadcast Interference to Analyzers

Some users have reported difficulties in obtaining accurate impedance measurements on low-band antennas when an AM broadcast station is nearby. This is due to the wideband detector responding to the incoming signal from the AM station. Some analyzer manufacturers offer external high-pass broadcast-reject filters to allow the analyzers to be used in the presence of these strong signals. The filter can affect measurements near the broadcast band, particularly in the 3.5 MHz and lower-frequency bands. Check with the filter or analyzer manufacturer about the limitations of using filters with the analyzer.

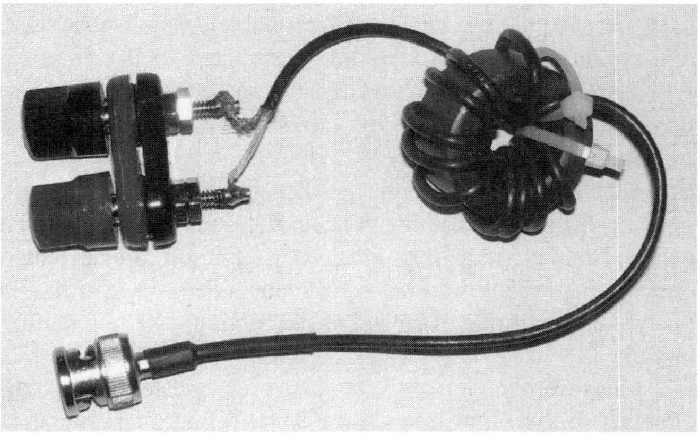

Figure 27.34 — A simple choke balun made by winding multiple turns of coax through a ferrite toroid, creating a high-impedance on the shield's outer surface. The choke is made of 12 turns of RG-193 miniature coax through a 2.4-inch OD, Type 31 core (Fair-Rite 2631803802 or Amidon FT-240-31) and is effective from 1.8 through 30 MHz.

27.5.3 MEASURING ANTENNA IMPEDANCE

The impedance at the end of a transmission line can be easily measured using an antenna analyzer. In many cases, however, you really want to measure the impedance of an antenna — that is, the impedance of the load at the far end of the line. There are several ways to handle this.

1) Measurements can be made with the analyzer at the antenna. This is usually not practical because the antenna must be in its final position for the measurement to be accurate. Even if it can be done, making such a measurement is certainly not very convenient.

2) Measurements can be made at the source end of a feed

line — if its length is an exact integer multiple of 1/2 λ. This effectively restricts measurements to a single frequency.

3) Measurements can be made at the source end of a coaxial cable and corrected using a Smith Chart. (See this book's downloadable supplemental information on the Smith Chart.) This graphic method can result in reasonable estimates of antenna impedance — as long as the SWR is not too high and the cable is not too lossy. However, it doesn't compensate for the complex impedance characteristics of real-world coaxial cables. Also, compensation for cable loss can be tricky to apply. These problems, too, can lead to significant errors.

4) Measurements at the source end of a feed line can be corrected using this book's downloadable *TLW* software. This is the best method for calculating antenna impedances from measured parameters, but it requires that you measure the feed line characteristics beforehand — measurements for which you need access to both ends of the feed line.

The procedure for determining antenna impedance is to first measure the electrical length, characteristic impedance, and attenuation of the feed line connected to the antenna. After making these measurements, connect the antenna to the feed line and measure the input impedance at a number of frequencies. Then use *TLW* to determine the actual antenna impedance at each frequency. When doing the conversions, be careful not to introduce measurement errors as discussed earlier. Such errors will be carried through into the corrected data. This problem is most significant when the feed line is near an odd multiple of 1/4 λ and the SWR and/or attenuation is high.

Measurement errors are probably present if small changes in the input impedance or feed line characteristics appear as large changes in antenna impedance or if changing the physical orientation of the line or instruments cause significant changes in the measured data. These effects can be minimized by decoupling the line from the antenna and by making the measurements with a feed line that is approximately an integer multiple of 1/2 λ. Another clue that there is something amiss with the system is final data that changes erratically with frequency or in ways that aren't typical of antennas or transmission lines. If the data "looks funny," apply extra scrutiny before accepting it as fact.

5) The calibration procedure in the previous section can be extended to allow measuring the actual driving point impedance of the antenna. The feed line is disconnected at the antenna and the calibration loads are attached at the far end instead of the antenna. This shifts the measurement point (the reference plane) to the antenna itself which is handy when designing matching networks. The final result is much more accurate than using a feed line that is 1/2 λ long because the calibration of the analyzer compensates for the transmission line parameters: length, velocity factor, and loss.

A word of caution when using an antenna analyzer is in order. These are sensitive instruments with low-power components at their input. They can be damaged by static electricity if care is not exercised. Antennas can collect a significant static charge from rain or wind. Be sure to momentarily ground the transmission line before connecting it to an analyzer to reduce the risk of damage to the sensitive components on the input.

Having a dc path to ground from the antenna protects station equipment as well as analyzers. The dc path can be the wire used for an inductor in a tuning circuit or it can be a large value resistor with a power rating suitable for the transmitter power. (Antennas with elements mounted directly on a grounded boom or support are also dc-grounded.)

Using the analyzer when another transmitter is active can also cause damage if enough signal is picked up by the antenna under test. The analyzer illustrated in Figure 27.33 includes an isolation relay that protects the input when a measurement is not in progress.

27.5.4 MEASURING COMPONENT VALUES

The antenna analyzer can be used to measure components other than antennas. For example, an inductor can be measured over a wide frequency range to see if it is resonant within the frequency range where it will be used.

Figure 27.35 shows a graph generated from swept-frequency impedance data collected by an antenna analyzer of the type in Figure 27.33. The figure shows the impedance of an air-core inductor with a nominal inductance of 7.4 μH at low frequencies. (The traces are labeled with the measurement they represent.) The self-resonant frequency is 45.4 MHz. This resonance occurs because of the coil's inter-turn capacitance.

Below the resonant frequency the inductance has a positive reactance and the coil presents its expected value, 7.4 μH. As the test frequency approaches the self-resonant frequency, the inductive reactance actually increases and the inductance appears to be larger. Above the self-resonant frequency, the component acts like a capacitor, as indicated by the negative phase angle.

The analyzer is also very handy for determining the material of a toroid core. Cores of different ferrite or powdered iron mixes cannot be told apart by their physical appearance but you can separate them by comparison with a core of known material. Small inductances of one or two turns can be tested side by side to differentiate the cores of different mixes. A single turn through the center of a core or bead will create enough inductance for an accurate measurement on a good analyzer. Be wary of confusing mixes that are designed for EMI suppression with mixes intended for inductive applications. The permeability of the different mixes has resistive and reactive components that dominate over different frequency ranges. See the discussion of ferrites in the **Transmission Line System Techniques** chapter for an explanation. Comparison to cores of known material is much more reliable than a simple calculation of μ (mu — permeability) or A_L, the inductance index.

Capacitors are usually closer to the ideal component than inductors, but they do have some inductance in their leads and eventually at some high frequency they too become self-resonant. This self-resonance should be checked for capacitors that will be used in the VHF/UHF range. Above the self-resonant frequency, a capacitor looks like an inductor.

Resistors have an effective capacitance in parallel with them as well as inductance in their leads so they are not ideal over a wide frequency range. Physically large power resistors used for dummy loads have larger parasitic components. (Thin-film power resistors in TO-220 packages are available with significantly lower reactance.) Tubular metal and carbon film resistors are often trimmed with a laser to create a spiral track in the deposited film, creating inductance. If the resistor is to be used in an RF circuit, it is prudent to verify its effective frequency range.

Transmission Line Measurements

Sections of transmission line material can be used to make tuning stubs for antennas as discussed in the **Transmission Lines** chapter. Tuning stubs can be measured with the antenna analyzer as shown in **Figure 27.36** and cut to the proper length for the required phase shift. The analyzer program can measure the actual phase shift of a piece of coax and quickly show how much needs to be trimmed to achieve the desired phase shift.

As discussed in the next section on time domain reflectometry (TDR), some analyzers have a software feature called *Distance to Fault*. This measures the length of a transmission line to an open or short circuit. If the line is disconnected from the antenna, the distance to fault is the total length of the line. If the line has been damaged somewhere this measurement gives you an idea where the damage is, which is very handy when the line is buried or otherwise requires special access. TDR can also locate impedance discontinuities or other changes in the line's characteristic impedance.

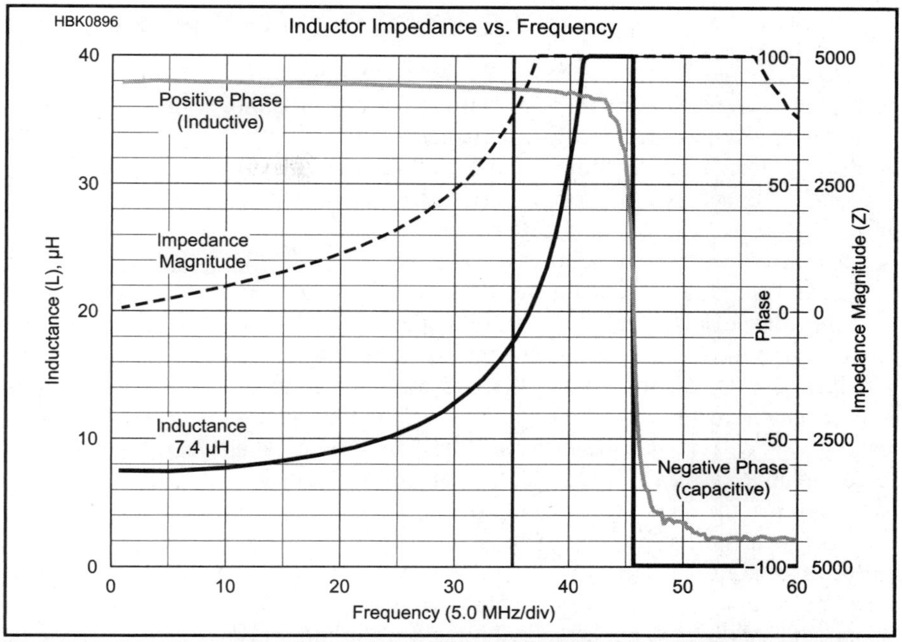

Figure 27.35 — Example of an antenna analyzer (AIM-4170 and companion software) being used to measure an air-core inductor's behavior. The inductor has a nominal value of 7.4 μH and a self-resonant frequency of 45.4 MHz.

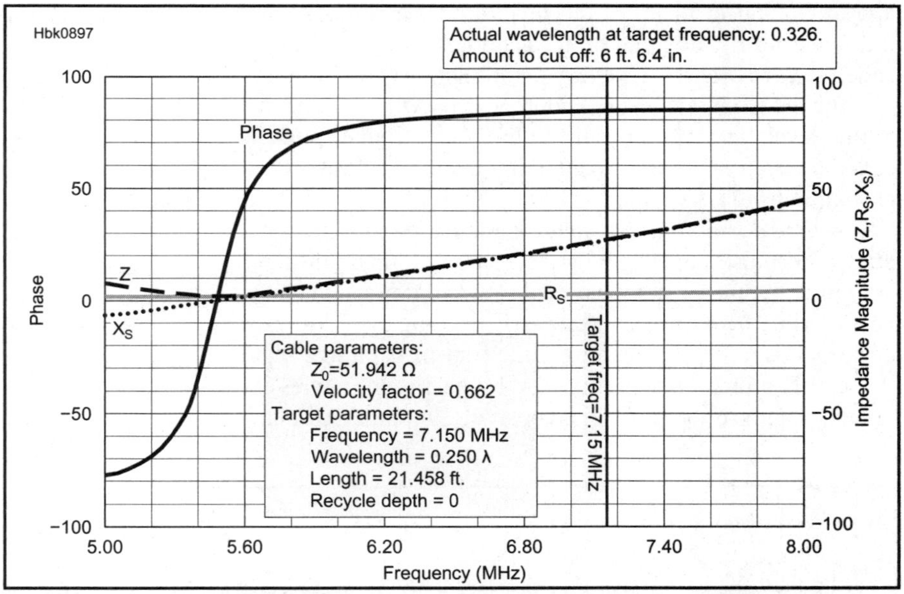

Figure 27.36 — Example of an antenna analyzer (AIM-4170 and companion software) being used to trim a transmission line stub. The cable is being trimmed to get a phase shift of 90° (0.25 wavelengths) at 7.15 MHz. From the current length (where the three curves intersect at the left), cut off 6 feet 6.4 inches (199.1 cm). As the cable is trimmed, the phase plot will move toward the target line at the right.

Determining Reactance Type

Some antenna analyzers can show the positive or negative sign of the reactance. Less expensive units may only show a reactance magnitude. To determine whether reactance is inductive or capacitive on a unit that doesn't indicate the sign, make a slight increase in frequency. If the reactance increases, it is inductive, and if reactance decreases, it is capacitive. This is a helpful trick when adjusting antennas with a portable analyzer that doesn't indicate reactance sign.

27.6 TIME-DOMAIN REFLECTOMETRY

Time domain reflectometry (TDR) shows what happens to a short, abrupt pulse as it travels through a transmission line. The pulse is reflected by any changes in impedance, such as an open or short (complete reflection) or a change in the line's characteristic impedance (partial reflection). The resulting series of pulses and reflections is displayed as a sequence in time, thus the name of the technique.

In an ideal transmission line terminated by its characteristic impedance, Z_0, the pulse will travel to the far end and be dissipated in the termination, so the trace will be a perfectly flat line. But at any point along the line where the impedance changes (called a *discontinuity*) some of the pulse's energy will be reflected back toward the line's input. The reflected component of the pulse creates an artifact (visually, a "bump") on the otherwise straight line.

The sequence of pulses and their reflections is the *impulse response* of the line. An *impulse* is basically a very short pulse that begins and ends before the system can respond and stabilize. A mathematical impulse is an infinitely narrow pulse made up of all frequencies from zero to infinity.

While it is not possible to create an ideal (perfect) impulse, a very fast rising edge of a longer pulse is a good enough approximation to measure the line's impulse response and the same information can be measured. The longer pulse is called a *step function*. The ideal step function is an infinitely fast change from one level to another, after which it remains at that level. The response of the line to the longer pulse is called the *step response*. Like the impulse, the infinitely fast change in level also contains all frequencies.

A *time domain reflectometer* is the instrument that generates the pulse and displays the results. A TDR displays amplitude (voltage) on the vertical axis and time on the horizontal axis. The position of each artifact along the TDR trace corresponds to the distance from the transmission line input to the discontinuity that produced it. Large discontinuities occur when a line is open-circuited or short-circuited, or when it is connected to an antenna. (Most antennas are matched to the line at their operating frequency, but at other frequencies they are not. Since the pulse contains all frequencies, an antenna is a large discontinuity.) Small discontinuities occur at splices or when a line is damaged.

The delay between the input pulse's rising edge and the artifact is the round-trip time in the line from the TDR to the discontinuity. If the line's velocity of propagation (VF) is known, the physical distance from the input to the discontinuity can be calculated. The shape of each reflection can sometimes provide a clue as to the nature of the discontinuity.

In this sense, the TDR is very much like a radar display in which a pulse is transmitted (shown at the center on a radar display) and any echoes from discontinuities in the air (i.e. targets) reflect some of the pulse back toward the transmitter. The farther away the target, the longer it takes for the pulse to travel to the target and back to the receiver. A radar screen shows echoes from all directions. The TDR only shows echoes from one direction, along the line. The larger the echo, the larger the target or discontinuity.

The usefulness of TDR is not limited to RF systems. Some of the first uses of TDR were for finding faults in cabling systems carrying all sorts of signals, including ordinary telephone lines, and it is still widely used for that purpose.

27.6.1 DIRECT METHOD TDR

There are two common TDR implementations, with variations of both. In the "direct method," which is the oldest and simplest, the line is driven by a pulse. This can be a single pulse or it a train of pulses like a square wave.

The pulse and all of the reflections are displayed on an oscilloscope trace triggered by the pulse's rising edge. The rise time of the pulse must be much shorter than the round-trip time for the impulse to travel to and from the discontinuity. **Figure 27.37** shows an example of a direct method TDR with the pulse generator and cable attached to the oscilloscope

Figure 27.37 — Example of a direct method TDR (see text) connected to a length of RG-58 coaxial cable (50 Ω impedance) followed by a short length of 75 Ω RG-59 and a 100 Ω load. The discontinuities are clearly shown as the reflections add to the input pulse.

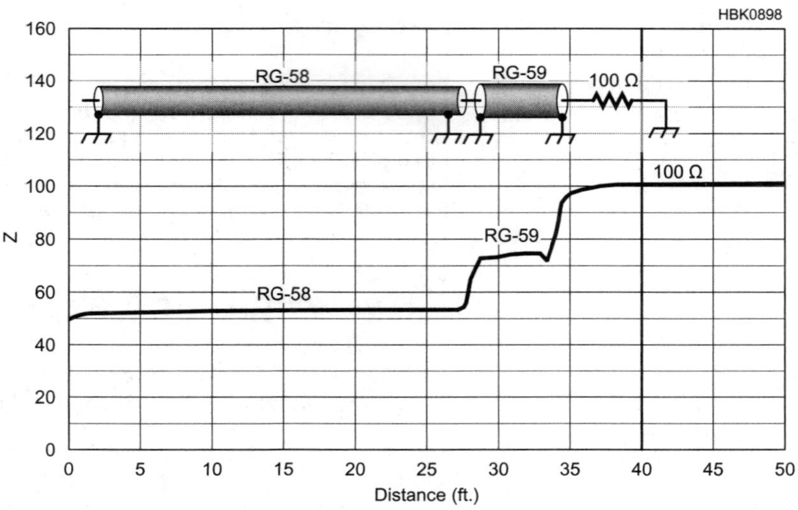

which is displaying the pulse.

Although a digital scope can capture a single pulse and its reflections, making the pulse repetitive means that multiple responses can be averaged to improve the signal to noise ratio. The signal to noise ratio of a system excited by a single pulse can be rather limited. Repeated pulses also sustain the trace so the operator to see it if the scope is an analog model. The repetition rate of the pulse must be much slower than it takes for the impulse to make a complete round trip time through the line, however. This insures the line's response dies out completely before the next pulse excites the line again. See the reference article by King about this type of TDR. The section on TDR in previous editions of the *ARRL Antenna Book* is also included in the downloadable supplemental information.

Modern antenna analyzers can use the direct method, as well. For example, the AIM family of analyzers, designed by W5BIG and sold by Array Solutions (**www.arraysolutions.com**), excite the line with a step function waveform having a very fast rise time. This implementation provides a display of the impedance at every point on the line — it can, for example, show the relative impedance of cables having different Z_0, as well as the position of discontinuities. Figure 27.37 shows a TDR display from an AIM analyzer connected to a length of RG-58 (50 Ω cable), a short length of RG-59 (75 Ω), and a 100 Ω load. The discontinuities at the cable and load transitions are clearly shown. Software converts the raw data from the pulse amplitudes into impedance and the time is converted into distance along the line.

The TDR function can be used to determine if the line has been degraded, for example, by water leaking into the coax or if the line has been shorted or cut somewhere between the transmitter and the antenna. Damage or defects can be located within a few inches and this reduces the effort required to repair the line. Defective connectors can also be indicated by short glitches in the trace corresponding to the location of the connectors.

Transform Method TDR

The other common implementation could be described as the "transform method." Instead of determining the impulse response of the cable with a pulse, the excitation is a sine wave swept over a range of frequencies and the analyzer captures the *frequency response*. An *inverse Fourier transform* (IFT) is performed on that frequency response, producing the time-domain response. (See the *ARRL Handbook* for more information on Fourier transforms.)

Frequency and time are the inverse of each other; the complete frequency response of a system contains its time response and the response to an ideal impulse contains the frequency response. A Fourier transform of the time response provides the frequency response, an inverse Fourier transform of the frequency response provides the time response.

Some antenna analyzers and vector network analyzers use this method. (Several well-suited for amateur use can be found by an internet search for "vector antenna analyzer" or "vector network analyzer.") One example is the hand-held SARK-110 Vector Impedance Antenna Analyzer (**www.sark110.com**). The sine wave exciting the cable need not be a continuous sweep — rather, it can be stepped over a wide range of frequencies and the frequency response is computed from that data. Sweep range, spacing between data points, and the settling time at each data point are set by the user.

An IFT produces spurious artifacts which must be removed by applying a mathematical windowing function to the transformed data. Several mathematically different windowing functions are commonly used, and which of the windows provides the most useful display depends on the shape of the impulse response.

The frequency content of the excitation strongly influences the degree of detail that the measurement can reveal. When the excitation is an impulse, a very fast rise time reveals greater detail. When the excitation is a swept sine wave, a wider frequency range reveals the greatest detail. Currently available analyzers can sweep from 1 kHz to more than 1 GHz.

For TDR studies using the sweep method, a sweep from 5 to 500 MHz (or from 500 MHz to 1 GHz) will clearly show detail that would be missed with a sweep to only 100 MHz, while a 5 MHz to 1GHz sweep may provide too much detail

Transforming Analyzer Data

Like the trace on a simple oscilloscope, the TDR plot of the impulse response contains all frequencies (or the range of frequencies if it is transformed from a sweep). The scope and the TDR plot are "frequency blind" — that is, they display information only about the time response, and no information about the frequency response. However, the data does contain information that can be useful.

An impulse or sweep measurement can, theoretically, be manipulated mathematically to compute the impedance at every point in the line over the same range of frequencies. The precision of that computation and whether it is practical, depends on how the data is gathered (sweep rate, sweep range, spacing of data points) and the software tools available. Frequency sweep ranges chosen for TDR may be inappropriate for examination of other line properties.

Free software like *SimSmith* (**www.ae6ty.com/smith_charts.html**) and *ZPlots* (**ac6la.com/zplots.html**) can accept swept measurements made at discrete frequencies to compute and plot the impedance at any point on a line if the characteristics of the line are known. Data is interchanged between a measurement device and software programs (and between one software program and another) by means of a plain text file. These files, defined by the Touchstone format (see text) can take several forms that are defined by the first line(s), called a "header." The filename extension indicates the type of measurements: s1p files describe single port measurements, like impedance or a time response and s2p files describe two-port measurements such as the S21 (gain) transfer function produced by a vector network analyzer.

(or show discontinuities that don't matter below 50 MHz). Beginning the sweep in the HF range avoids smearing of the data due to the variation of VF with frequency (see section below on Effect of Velocity Factor).

Examples of Using the Transform Method

Figure 27.38 is the impulse response of the feed line for a 30 meter half-wave dipole at a height of 100 feet, computed from a sweep over the range of 50 – 500 MHz. Marker 1 shows the effect of lightning protectors at the station entry bulkhead. Marker 2 is a coax splice (two PL-259s and a PL-258 double-receptacle). Markers 3, 4, and 5 are coax defects. Marker 6 is the antenna feed point. Marker 7 is the end of the antenna (displayed distances are for the feed line, so for the antenna are divided by 0.795). Marker 8 is unexplained, but most TDR sweeps show multiple reflections after the antenna.

Figure 27.39 is the step response (similar to that from the direct method shown in Figure 27.37) computed from the same sweep as that used for Figure 27.38. The data revealed (and a visual inspection confirmed) that the cable inside the

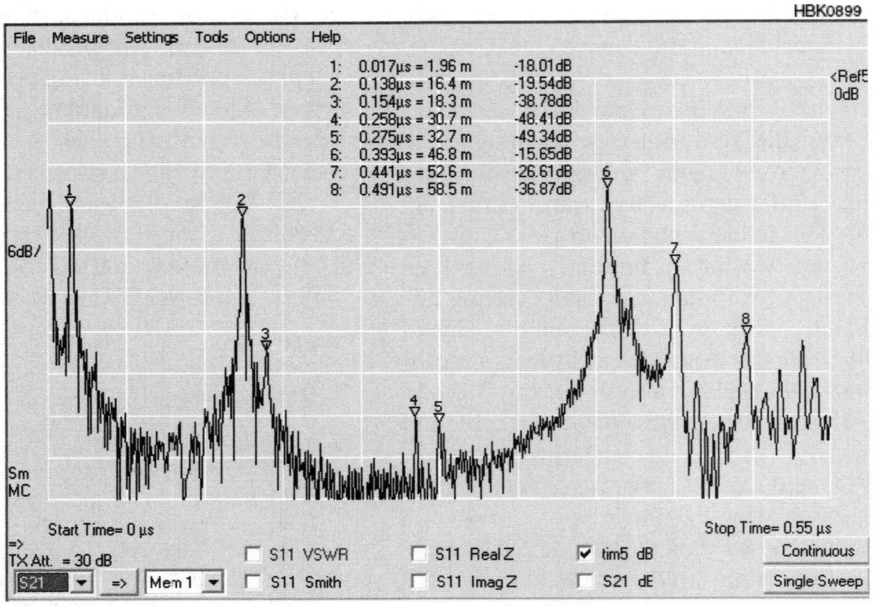

Figure 27.38 — The impulse response of a feed line attached to a 30 meter dipole. The system is swept from 50 to 500 MHz. See text for an explanation of the markers.

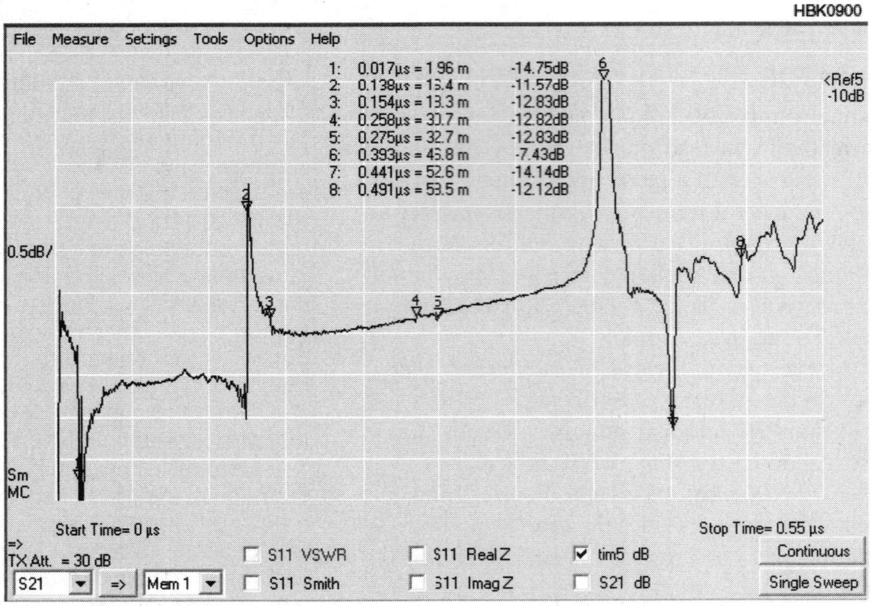

Figure 27.39 — The step response similar to the direct method for the same antenna system in Figure 27.38. See text for an explanation of the graph.

shack and from the bulkhead to the coax splice is 50 Ω, but that the cable from there to the antenna is 75 Ω.

TDR measures time. To convert that measurement to physical distance, we must provide the velocity factor. The 75 Ω cable is Belden 8213, this sample of which has a measured VF of 0.795 at VHF. The 50 Ω cable has a measured VF of 0.8425 at VHF. In the setup screen for this TDR measurement, VF was set at 0.795, so distance measurements will be correct for the 75 Ω cable, but wrong for the 50 Ω cable. Computed results could be made correct for the 50 Ω cable by changing VF in that setup screen, or by leaving VF at 0.795 and applying a correction factor of (0.8425/0.795) to the dimensions of the 50 Ω cable.

The Effect of Velocity Factor

The velocity of propagation in any transmission line is not constant — it varies with frequency. At the lowest audio frequencies, the velocity factor (VF) is quite a bit lower than the published specification, rising rapidly throughout the audio spectrum, continuing to increase through the radio spectrum until it reaches a nearly constant value in the VHF range. It is this constant value that is computed by simple equations for VF that don't take frequency into account.

For most cables, VF at 2 MHz is typically 1-2% slower than this constant value. In other words, an actual transmission line is 1-2% percent longer electrically than using the "nominal" (VHF) value that the simplified equation for VF predicts. Because of this change, the physical length of a stub for the lower frequency bands is 1-2 percent shorter than predicted from the specified value.

When using software to transform antenna measurements made in the station to the actual impedance at the feed point, the variability of VF must be applied to data for antennas for the lower bands (14 MHz and below). AC6LA's free *Zplots* shareware (based on *Excel* spreadsheets, see **ac6la.com/zplots.html**) computes and plots VF, Z_0, and attenuation versus frequency from measurements of a known length of a transmission made with the far end open and with the far end shorted. *ZPlots* can accept data in the Touchstone format discussed earlier.

Figure 27.40 is a plot of VF and attenuation computed by *ZPlots* from such measurements on a 176-foot length of RG-11 cable with a #14 AWG solid copper center conductor, a foam dielectric, and a copper braid shield. This behavior and general curve shape are typical of all transmission lines as predicted by fundamental transmission line equations. Exact values for each line will differ based on their physical dimensions and their dielectric.

It should also be noted that Z_0 also varies with frequency and below VHF is complex – that is, not a pure resistance, and is slightly capacitive. The *TLW* program (*Transmission Lines for Windows* by N6BV), included with this book's downloadable supplemental information, provides Z_0 data for most commonly used cables and can plot voltage and current along the line. These plots clearly show standing waves on a line at 2 MHz when the termination is only resistive. The mismatch is small and the effect on attenuation is insignificant, but it clearly shows up in carefully made measurements of long cable lengths over a range of frequencies as a small ripple in attenuation values.

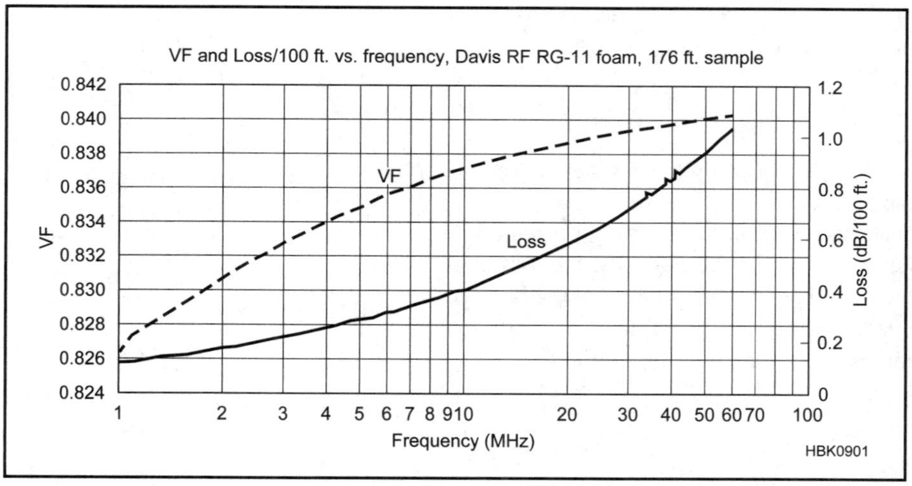

Figure 27.40 — VF and characteristic impedance for an RG-11 cable computed by *ZPlots* software from a swept-frequency measurement. See text.

27.7 VECTOR NETWORK ANALYZER

Professionals make transmission line measurements by employing a *vector network analyzer* (VNA) or the somewhat simpler *reflection-transmission test set* (more on this later). These instruments can make all the necessary measurements quickly and with great accuracy. However, in the past VNAs have been very expensive, out of reach for general amateur use. But thanks to modern digital technology VNAs that work with a laptop computer are now becoming available at prices an amateur might consider. As Paul Kiciak, N2PK (**n2pk.com**) and others have demonstrated, it's even possible to homebrew a VNA with performance that approaches a professional instrument. In addition, the data taken in the frequency domain by the VNA can be transformed to the time domain as a type of time-domain reflectometry as described in the Agilent application note "Comparison of Measurement Performance between Vector Network Analyzer and TDR Oscilloscope." (See Bibliography.)

VNAs are based on reflection and transmission measurements. To use a VNA it is very helpful to have a basic understanding of *scattering parameters* (S-parameters). Microwave engineers have long used these because they have to work with circuits that are large in terms of wavelength, where measurements of forward and reflected power are not easy.

27.7.1 S-PARAMETERS

In the chapter **Transmission Lines**, the reflection coefficient rho (ρ) is defined as the ratio of the reflected voltage (V_r) to the incident voltage (V_i):

$$\rho = \frac{V_r}{V_i} \qquad (5)$$

If we know the load impedance (Z_L) and the transmission line impedance (Z_0) we can calculate ρ from:

$$\rho = \frac{Z_L - Z_0}{Z_L + Z_0} \qquad (6)$$

Keep in mind that ρ is a complex number (a vector), which we represent by either amplitude and phase (|Z|, θ) or by real and imaginary parts ($R \pm jX$). The two representations are equivalent. Neglecting phase, from |ρ| (the magnitude of ρ) we can then calculate SWR. That's very handy, but here we want to do something different. If we have an instrument that measures ρ and we know Z_0 then we can determine Z_L from:

$$Z_L = Z_0\left(\frac{1+\rho}{1-\rho}\right) \qquad (7)$$

Measuring ρ is one of the things that VNAs do very well. With a VNA, the measurement can be made at one end of a long transmission line with the load at the other end. The effect of the line can be calibrated out, as mentioned above, so that we are in effect measuring right at the load. Note that the symbol Γ (gamma) is also used to represent the reflection coefficient. The two symbols may be used interchangeably.

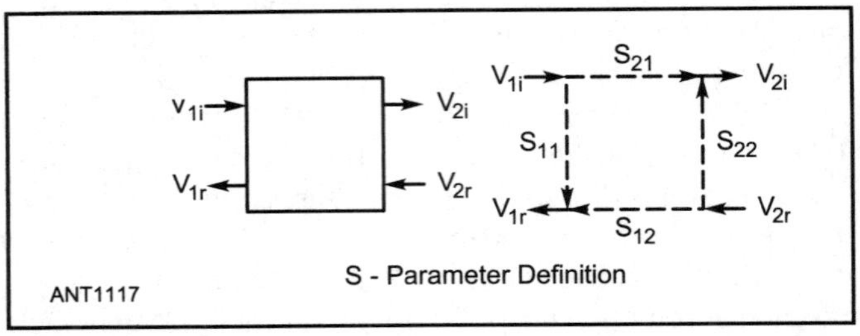

Figure 27.41 — Two-port network with incident and reflected waves.

This approach can be used directly to measure the impedance and resonant frequency of a single antenna element. By open and short circuiting elements in an array of antenna elements we can determine the mutual as well as self impedances for, and between, all the elements. We can also use this approach to measure component values, inductor Q, etc.

This is an example of a *one-port* measurement; that is, a load at the end of a transmission line. However, to get the most out of a VNA, you need to generalize the above procedure. This is where S-parameters come into play.

VNAs usually have at least two RF connections: the transmit port (T) and the receive port (R). Professional units may have more RF connections. The T output provides a signal from a 50-Ω source and the R port is a detector with a 50-Ω input impedance. Basically we have a transmitter and a receiver. The transmit port uses a directional coupler to provide measurements of the forward and reflected signals at that output. The receive port measures the signal transmitted through the network.

Using incident and reflected voltages, the two-port network representation is now changed, as shown in **Figure 27.41**, where:

V_{1i} = incident voltage at port 1
V_{1r} = reflected voltage at port 1
V_{2i} = incident voltage at port 2
V_{2r} = reflected voltage at port 2

We can write an expression in terms of the incident and reflected voltages:

$$b_1 = S_{11}a_1 + S_{12}a_2$$
$$b_2 = S_{21}a_1 + S_{22}a_2 \qquad (8)$$

where:

$$a_1 - \frac{V_{1i}}{\sqrt{Z_0}} \qquad b_1 - \frac{V_{1r}}{\sqrt{Z_0}}$$
$$a_2 - = \frac{V_{2i}}{\sqrt{Z_0}} \qquad b_2 - \frac{V_{2r}}{\sqrt{Z_0}} \qquad (9)$$

We see that a_n and b_n are simply the incident and reflected voltages at the two ports divided by $\sqrt{Z_0}$. Because this is a linear network, $S_{21} = S_{12}$.

What are the S_{ij} quantities? These are called the *S-parameters*, which are defined by:

$$
\begin{aligned}
S_{11} &\equiv \left.\frac{b_1}{a_1}\right|_{a_2=0} = \left.\frac{V_{1r}}{V_{1i}}\right|_{V_{2i}=0} \\
S_{21} &\equiv \left.\frac{b_2}{a_1}\right|_{a_2=0} = \left.\frac{V_{2r}}{V_{1i}}\right|_{V_{2i}=0} \\
S_{12} &\equiv \left.\frac{b_1}{a_2}\right|_{a_1=0} = \left.\frac{V_{1r}}{V_{2i}}\right|_{V_{1i}=0} \\
S_{22} &\equiv \left.\frac{b_2}{a_2}\right|_{a_1=0} = \left.\frac{V_{2r}}{V_{2i}}\right|_{V_{1i}=0}
\end{aligned}
\tag{10}
$$

Note that the S_{ij} parameters are all ratios of reflected and incident voltages, and they are usually complex numbers. The condition that $a_2 = 0 = V_{2i}$ is the same as saying that port 2 is terminated in a load equal to Z_0 and the network is excited at port 1. This means there is no reflection from the load on port 2, which makes $V_{2i} = 0$. Similarly, if we terminate port 1 with Z_0 and excite port 2, then $V_{1i} = 0 = a_1$.

If we compare Eq 17 to the first line of Eq 22 we see that $S_{11} = \rho_1$, the reflection coefficient at port 1. We can now restate Eq 19 in terms of S_{11}:

$$
Z = Z_0\left(\frac{1+S_{11}}{1-S_{11}}\right) \tag{11}
$$

where Z is the impedance looking into port 1 with port 2 terminated in Z_0. In the case where port 2 does not exist — that is, you are measuring a single impedance (for example, measuring an impedance at port 1 with port 2 open-circuited) or a component, then Z is simply the impedance at that port. Since S_{11} is a standard measurement for VNAs you can calculate Z using Eq 23. In many cases the VNA software will do this calculation for you automatically. You can also measure an impedance at port 2 with port 1 open and determine Z_{22}.

S_{21} represents the ratio of the signal coming out of port 2 (V_{2r}) to the input signal on port 1 (V_{1i}) and is another standard VNA measurement. S_{21} is a measurement of the signal transmission between the ports through the network with port 2 terminated in Z_0; forward gain in most applications.

A full-feature VNA will measure all the S_{ij} parameters at once, but most of the lower-cost units of interest to amateurs are what we call reflection-transmission test sets. What this means is that they only measure S_{11} and S_{21}. To obtain S_{22} and S_{12} we have to interchange the test cables at the ports and run the measurements again. Normally the software will accommodate this as a second entry and we end up with the full set of S_{ij} parameters.

If we do run a full set of S_{ij} parameters then we can transform these to Z_{ij} using the following expressions, assuming that $S_{21} = S_{12}$:

$$
\begin{aligned}
Z_{11} &= \frac{(1+S_{11})(1-S_{22})+S_{12}^2}{(1-S_{11})(1-S_{22})-S_{12}^2} \\
Z_{22} &= \frac{(1-S_{11})(1+S_{22})+S_{12}^2}{(1-S_{11})(1-S_{22})-S_{12}^2} \\
Z_{12} &= \frac{2S_{12}}{(1-S_{11})(1-S_{22})-S_{12}^2}
\end{aligned}
\tag{12}
$$

27.7.2 RETURN LOSS

Return loss (RL) is another term for S_{11}, the ratio of the reflected voltage to the incident voltage, usually expressed in dB.

$$
RL = -20\log\left(\frac{V_{1i}}{V_{1r}}\right) = -10\log\left(\frac{P_{1i}}{P_{1r}}\right)
$$

RL is measured as S_{11} by a VNA.

The name stems from measuring how much voltage is returned from a transmission line wave encountering a termination or impedance discontinuity. If the line is terminated in its characteristic impedance, the entire wave is absorbed and none is returned so the "loss" at the reflection is total and RL is infinite. If the line is open- or short-circuited, the entire wave is returned to the source and RL is 0. Note that RL is a positive quantity range from 0 (no transfer of wave energy at the termination) to infinite (all wave energy transferred to the termination). Negative RL would describe a voltage gain.

To convert from return loss to SWR, the following formulas are used:

$$
|\rho| = 10^{-\frac{RL}{20}}
$$

and

$$
SWR = \frac{1+|\rho|}{1-|\rho|}
$$

So, for example, a return loss of 20 dB is a reflection coefficient of 0.1, and an SWR of 1.22. A return loss of 10 dB is a reflection coefficient of 0.316, and an SWR of 1.92.

One of the most common measurements made is the standing wave ratio of an antenna. A low SWR means that the antenna input impedance is close to that of the measuring reference impedance. These measurements are from the July/August 2004 *QEX* article by McDermott and Ireland (see Bibliography) and show the magnitude of the return loss versus frequency for a KT34XA triband Yagi antenna at the end of 300 feet of hardline cable.

The resonance points are clearly visible. **Figure 27.42** shows the return loss of the antenna swept from 1 MHz to 50 MHz. The 20 meter, 15 meter and 10 meter band resonances are easily seen. (RL increases toward the bottom of the chart.) **Figure 27.43** shows a close-up of the return loss from 13.5 to 14.5 MHz. **Figure 27.44** shows this same close-up on a Smith Chart.

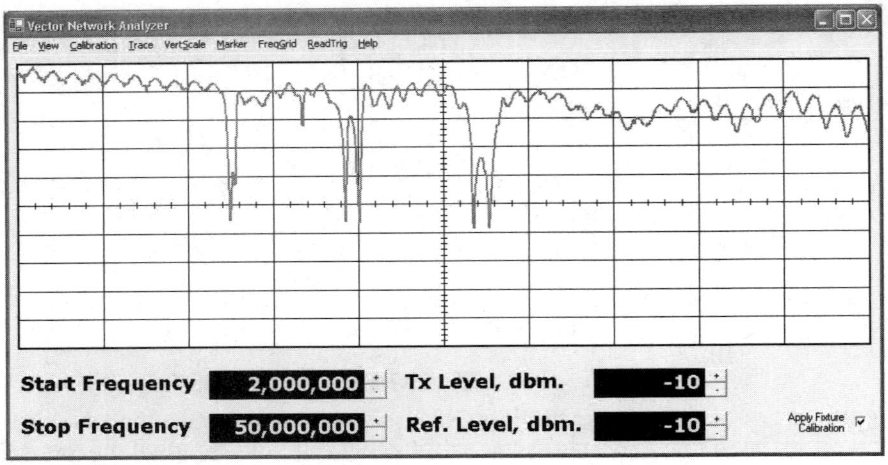

Figure 27.42 — Return loss of KT34XA antenna through 300 feet of hardline. Vertical scale is 5 dB/div. The three resonances at 20, 15, and 10 meters are clearly visible.

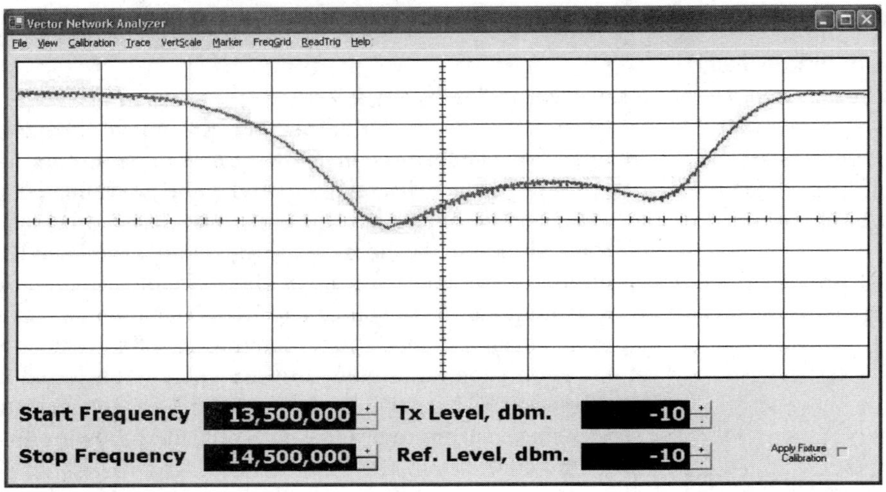

Figure 27.43 — Return loss of Figure 27.42 from 13.5 MHz to 14.5 MHz. A 26 dB return loss (best case at 13.94 MHz) is an SWR of 1.105 (at the ham-shack end of the feed line). Vertical scale is 5 dB/div.

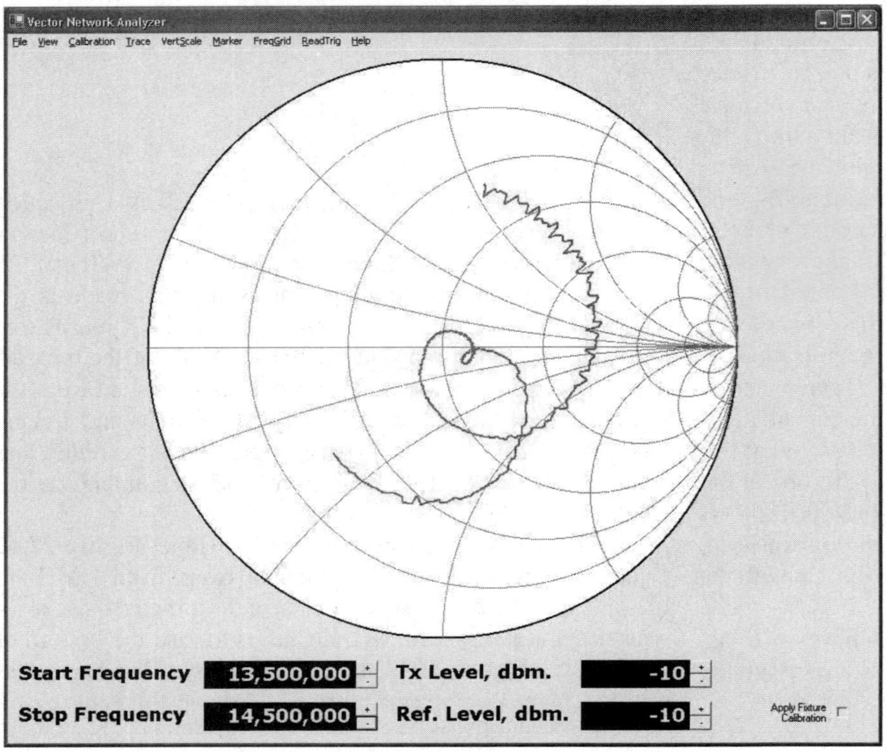

Figure 27.44 — Return loss of Figure 27.43 on a Smith Chart.

27.7.3 USING A VECTOR NETWORK ANALYZER

Discussing how to use a VNA is beyond the scope of this chapter but the user's manual for a VNA will explain the technique of calibrating that particular VNA and using it to make measurements. The second step will be the use of the measurements by computer software to display and transform the measurements into the desired parameters.

In addition, there are many online tutorials and application notes (see the Bibliography entries for Agilent) and the text *Microwave Electronics* by Pozar also goes into some detail about what the various measurements are and how they are made.

Array Measurement Example

The process of building and properly tuning a phased array often involves making a number of different measurements to achieve a desired level of performance, as was pointed out in the **Multielement Arrays** chapter. This section is adapted from material written by Rudy Severns, N6LF.

After erecting an array we would like to measure the resonant frequency of each element, the self-impedances of each element and the mutual impedances between the elements. We will also want to know these impedances over the whole operating band to help design a feed network. When building the feed network, we may need to check the values and Qs of the network elements and we will want to determine the electrical lengths of transmission lines.

Final tuning of the array requires that the relative current amplitudes and phases in each element be measured and adjusted, if necessary. We also will want to determine the SWR at the feed point. Doing all of this even moderately well can require quite a bit of equipment, some of which is heavy and requires ac line power. This can be a nuisance in the field, especially if the weather is not cooperating.

In a completed array with its feed network, the network can be excited by the VNA at the feed point and the relative current amplitudes and phases at each element can be measured over a frequency band. Then, adjustments can be made as needed. When the final values for the current amplitudes and phases are known, these values can be put back into an array model in a program like *EZNEC* to determine the pattern of the array across the whole frequency band. A multielement array actually behaves as a multiport network, so using a VNA is a natural solution to the measurement problem.

HF arrays are also large in terms of wavelength. The techniques for measuring forward and reverse powers work well even at 160 meters. For example, even though the array elements may be 100 feet apart, you can place your instruments in a central location and run cables out to each element. The effect of the cables from the VNA to the elements can be absorbed in the initial calibration procedure so the measurements read out at the VNA are effectively those at each element. In other words, the measurement reference points can be placed electrically at the base of the element, regardless of the physical location of the instrumentation and the interconnecting cables.

The discussion of S-parameters in the previous section can be viewed as measuring the characteristics of a 2-element array (see **Figure 27.45**) if one element is attached to the end of the transmission lines at each port as in **Figure 27.46.**

In the case of such an array, S_{21} represents the signal transmission due to the coupling between the elements. i.e. the signal coupled to element 2 as a result of a signal applied to element 1. Transmission lines are assumed to have Z_0 = 50 Ω (or the characteristic impedance of the overall system) and may be of any length required by the size of the array.

S-parameters can be determined for an array with any number of elements. In an n-port S-parameter measurement, all ports are terminated in Z_0 at the same time. Measurements are made between one set of ports at a time and repeated until all pairs of ports are measured.

To illustrate the principles of using a VNA we will use a simple 2-element array like that shown in Figure 27.45. To design a feed network to drive this array we need to know the input impedance of each element (Z_1 and Z_2) as a function of the drive currents (I_1 and I_2). The input impedances will depend on the self impedance of each element, the coupling between them (the mutual impedance) and the drive currents in each element. To manage this problem we can represent a 2-element array as a two-port network, as shown in **Figure 27.47**. And we can relate the port voltages, currents and impedances with Eq 25:

$$V_1 = Z_{11}I_1 + Z_{12}I_2$$
$$V_2 = Z_{21}I_1 + Z_{22}I_2 \quad (13)$$

Normally we know I_1 and I_2 from the design of the array, but we need to determine the resulting element impedances. That's the challenge. Fortunately, an array is a linear network,

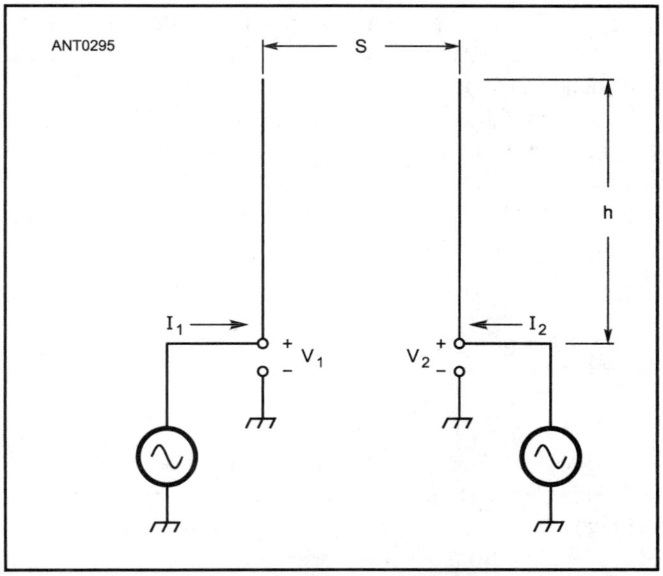

Figure 27.45 — A 2-element array, where h is the element height and S is the spacing between the elements.

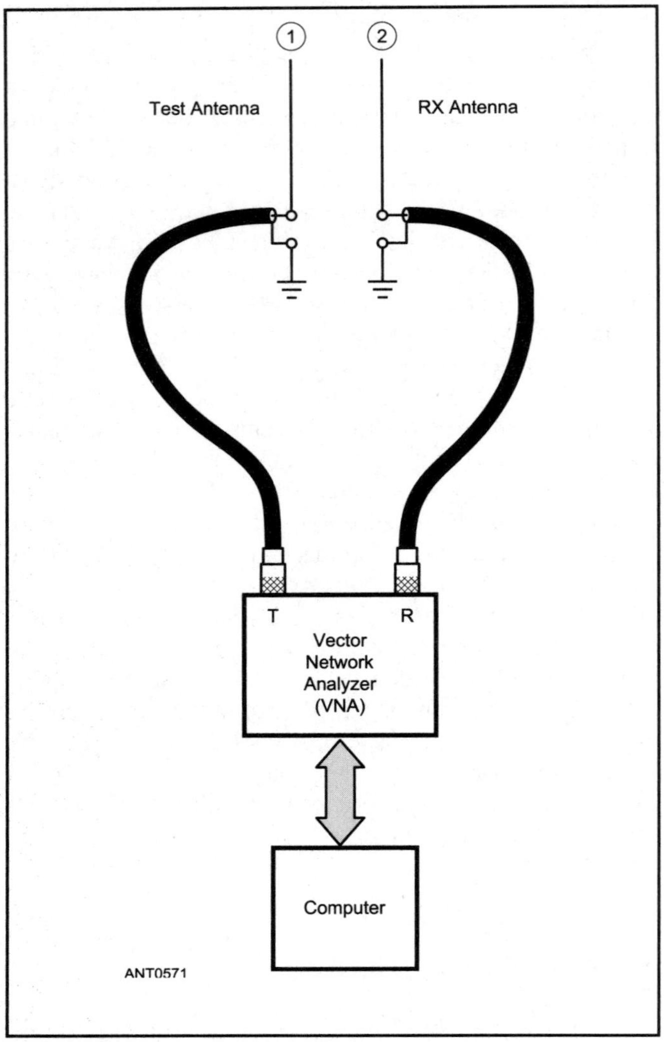

Figure 27.46 — Test setup to measure a 2-element array using a VNA.

so $Z_{12} = Z_{21}$, which means we need only determine three variables: the self impedances Z_{11} and Z_{22} and the mutual impedance, Z_{12}.

Once we know Z_{11}, Z_{12}, Z_{22} and are given I_1 and I_2, we can determine the feed point impedances at each element from:

$$Z_1 = Z_{11} + \left(\frac{I_2}{I_1}\right) Z_{12}$$

$$Z_2 = Z_{22} + \left(\frac{I_1}{I_2}\right) Z_{12} \tag{14}$$

This is the conventional approach. However, there are some problems here. We have to be able to accurately measure either voltages and currents or impedances in multiple elements that may be separated by large fractions of a wavelength. In addition, accurate measurements of current, voltage and impedance become increasingly more difficult as we go up in frequency.

It turns out that we can get the information more easily by measuring incident and reflected voltages at the ports and from those measurements determine the feed point impedances. A VNA is an instrument for measuring these voltages. It turns out to be easier to measure the ratios of two voltages rather than their absolute values.

The measurement setup using a VNA for a 2-element array is shown in Figure 27.46. A good way to illustrate the use of a VNA for array measurements is to work through an example with a real array. **Figure 27.48** is a picture of a 2-element 20 meter phased array built by Mark Perrin, N7MQ.

Each element is λ/4 (self resonant at 14.150 MHz) and spaced λ/4 (17 feet 5 inches). In the ideal case, both elements would have the same current amplitude with a 90° phase difference. This gives the cardioid pattern shown in the **Multielement Arrays** chapter. There are many schemes for correctly feeding such an array. The one used in this example uses two different 75-Ω transmission lines (one λ/4 and the other λ/2, electrically), as described by Roy Lewallen, W7EL and in Orr and Cowan. (See Bibliography.)

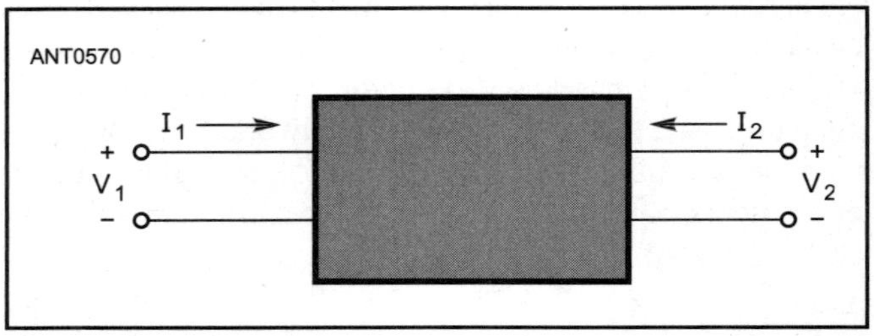

Figure 27.47 — Two-port representation of currents and voltages in the 2-element array in Figure 27.45.

Figure 27.48 — 2-element 20 meter phased array (*Photo courtesy N7MQ*).

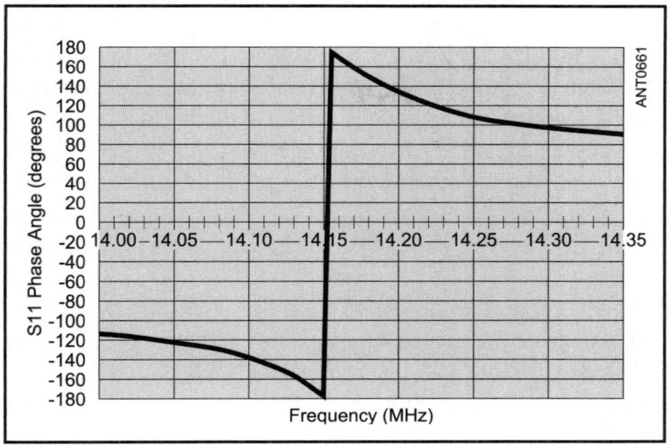

Figure 27.49 — S_{11} phase plot for an individual element.

The first task is to resonate the elements individually. With the VNA set to measure S_{11} phase, we will get a graph like that shown in **Figure 27.49**.

At the λ/4 resonant frequency (f_r) we will see a sharp phase transition as we go from −180° to +180°. This is typical of any series resonant circuit. The length of each element is adjusted until the desired f_r is achieved. This is a very sensitive measurement. You can see the shift in f_r due to the wind blowing, the length of the element changing as it heats up in the sun or any interactions between the feed line and the antenna as you move the feed line around. In fact this is a very good point in the process to make sure everything is mechanically stable and free of unexpected couplings. Usually you will find it necessary place choke baluns on each element to reduce stray coupling.

The next step is to determine the self (Z_{11} and Z_{22}) and mutual (Z_{12}) impedances from which the actual driving point impedances present when the array is excited can be determined. There are two ways to go.

First, we can simply use the VNA as an impedance bridge — ie, make two S_{11} measurements at one element, first with the other element open (Z_{11} or Z_{22}) and then with it shorted (Z_1 or Z_2). We can convert the S_{11} measurements to impedances using Eq 23. The value for Z_{12} can be obtained from:

$$Z_{12} = \pm\sqrt{Z_{11}(Z_{11} - Z_1)}$$

$$Z_{12} = \pm\sqrt{Z_{22}(Z_{22} - Z_2)} \qquad (15)$$

The second approach is to do a full two-port S-parameter measurement (S_{11}, S_{21}, S_{12} and S_{22}) and derive the impedances using Eq 23. Both approaches will work but the second approach has the advantage that the ± ambiguity in Eq 27 is eliminated.

For this example, the impedance values from the measurements at 14.150 MHz, turn out to be:

$$Z_{11} = 51.4 + j0.35$$

$$Z_{22} = 50.3 + j0.299 \qquad (16)$$

$$Z_{12} = 15.06 + j19.26$$

With these values we can now determine the feed point impedances from:

$$Z_1' = Z_{11} + \frac{I_2}{I_1} Z_{12}$$

$$Z_2' = Z_{22} + \frac{I_1}{I_2} Z_{12} \qquad (17)$$

$$\frac{I_1}{I_2} = -j$$

Note that $-j$ represents the 90° phase shift between the currents. Substituting the values from Eq 28 into Eq 29:

$$Z_1 = 32.09 - j14.7 \qquad (18)$$

$$Z2 = 69.61 + j15.32$$

With these impedances in hand we can now design the feed network. In this particular example however, we have decided to use the λ/4 and λ/2 cables as described by Lewallen and accept the results. So we now proceed to cut and trim the two cables to length.

Again, there are two ways to go. First we can determine the frequency at which each cable is λ/4 long. At this point the input impedance of the cable will be equivalent to a series-resonant circuit and we can simply measure the phase of S_{11} as we did earlier for f_r and get a plot like that shown in Figure 27.49. In this example the λ/4 resonant frequencies of the two cables are 7.075 MHz and 14.150 MHz.

The second approach would be to measure S_{21} for each cable at 14.150 MHz. The phase shift in S_{21} tells you how long the cable is, in degrees, at a given frequency. Because there is a small variation in cable characteristics with frequency (dispersion) this approach is slightly more accurate since it is done at the desired operating frequency. But this is not very large effect at HF.

This brings us down to the final measurements, which are to check that the relative current amplitudes and phases between the two elements are correct. We can then determine the feed point SWR. The phase and amplitude ratios are made using the S_{12} capability of the VNA and the test setup shown in **Figure 27.50**.

The VNA transmit port is connected to the normal feed point. A current sensor (see the **Multielement Arrays** chapter for a discussion of current sensors) is inserted at the base of element 1 and the output of the sensor is returned to the detector or receive port of the VNA. A calibration run is then made to normalize this path. That makes it the reference.

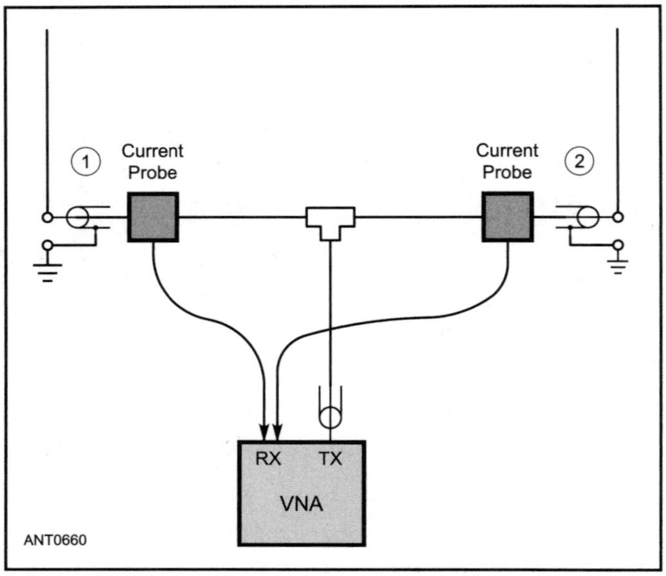

Figure 27.50 — Current phase and amplitude ratio test setup.

Next, the current sensor is shifted to element 2. The amplitude and phase plots for S_{12} obtained at this point will be the desired relative phase shift and amplitude ratio between the currents in the array when driven at the normal feed point. **Figures 27.51** and **27.52** show the behavior of the example array over the 20 meter band. Note that the amplitude ratio has been converted from dB. We can now use these values in a *EZNEC* model of the array to determine the actual radiation pattern.

Obviously the W7EL feed scheme is not perfect, but it has a definite advantage of simplicity. If better performance is desired we can use the values of Z_1' and Z_2' determined earlier to design and fabricate a new feed network and then proceed to evaluate its performance in the same way.

The final measurement is to connect the transmit port of the VNA to the feed point and measure S_{11}. From this we can calculate the SWR:

$$SWR = \frac{1+|S_{11}|}{1-|S_{11}|}$$

In this example, the return loss, $|S_{11}|$, is about 19 dB over the entire 20 meter band. This corresponds to SWR= 1.25:1.

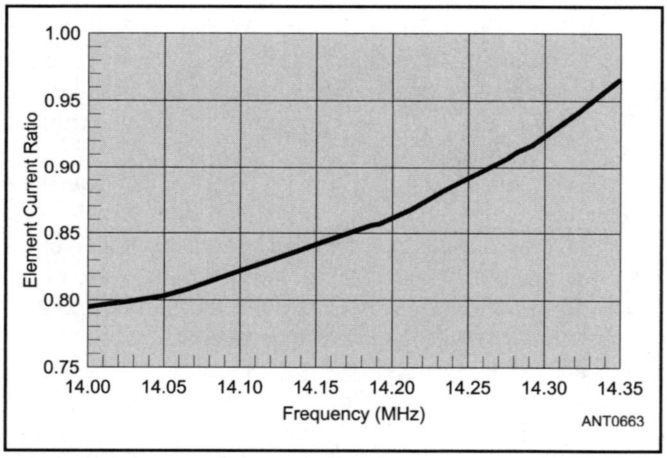

Figure 27.51 — Measured element current ratio over the 20 meter band.

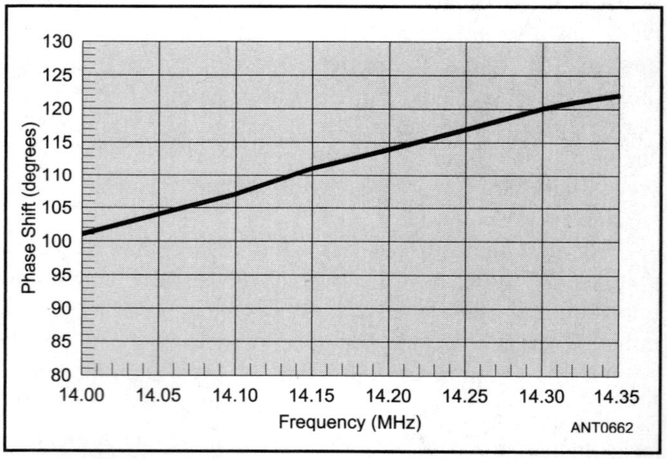

Figure 27.52 — Measured relative current phase shift over the 20 meter band.

27.8 ANTENNA FIELD MEASUREMENTS

Of all the measurements made in Amateur Radio systems, perhaps the most difficult and least understood are various measurements of the radiated field from antennas. For example, it is relatively easy to measure the frequency and CW power output of a transmitter, the response of a filter, or the gain of an amplifier. These are all what might be called *bench measurements* because, when performed properly, all the factors that influence the accuracy and success of the measurement are under control. In making antenna measurements, however, the "bench" is probably your backyard. In other words, the environment surrounding the antenna can affect the results of the measurement.

Control of the environment is not at all as simple as it was for the bench measurement, because now the work area may be rather spacious. This section describes antenna measurement techniques that are closely allied to those used in an antenna measuring event or contest. With these procedures you can make measurements successfully and with meaningful results. These techniques should provide a better understanding of the measurement problems, resulting in a more accurate and less difficult task. The information in this section was provided by Dick Turrin, W2IMU, and was originally published in November 1974 *QST*. The conventions used by amateurs to plot radiation patterns and antenna measurements are covered in the **Antenna Fundamentals** chapter.

27.8.1 FIELD MEASUREMENT BASICS

An antenna is simply a transducer or coupler between a suitable feed line and the environment surrounding it. In addition to the efficient transfer of power from feed line to environment, an antenna at VHF or UHF is most frequently required to concentrate the radiated power into a particular region of the environment.

To be consistent while comparing different antennas, you must standardize the environment surrounding the antenna. Ideally, you want to make measurements with the measured antenna so far removed from any objects causing environmental effects that it is literally in outer space — a very impractical situation. The purpose of the measurement techniques is therefore to simulate, under practical conditions, a *controlled environment.* At VHF and UHF, and with practical-size antennas, the environment can be controlled so that successful and accurate measurements can be made in a reasonable amount of space.

The electrical characteristics of an antenna that are most desirable to obtain by direct measurement are: (1) gain (relative to an isotropic source, which by definition has a gain of unity); (2) space-radiation pattern; (3) feed point impedance (mismatch) and (4) polarization.

Polarization

In general the polarization can be assumed from the geometry of the radiating elements. That is to say, if the antenna consists of a number of linear elements (straight lengths of rod or wire that are resonant and connected to the feed point) the polarization of the electric field will be linear and polarized parallel to the elements. If the elements are not consistently parallel with each other, then the polarization cannot easily be assumed. The following techniques are directed to antennas having polarization that is essentially linear (in one plane), although the method can be extended to include all forms of elliptic (or mixed) polarization.

Feed Point Mismatch

The feed point mismatch, although affected to some degree by the immediate environment of the antenna, does not affect the gain or radiation characteristics of an antenna. If the immediate environment of the antenna does not affect the feed point impedance, then any mismatch intrinsic to the antenna tuning reflects a portion of the incident power back to the source. In a receiving antenna this reflected power is reradiated back into the environment, and can be lost entirely.

In a transmitting antenna, the reflected power travels back down the feed line to the transmitter, where it changes the load impedance presented to that transmitter. The amplifier output controls are customarily altered during the normal tuning procedure to obtain maximum power transfer to the antenna. You can still use a mismatched antenna to its full gain potential, provided the mismatch is not so severe as to cause heating losses in the system, especially the feed line and matching devices. (See also the discussion of additional loss caused by SWR in the **Transmission Lines** chapter.)

Similarly, a mismatched receiving antenna may be matched into the receiver front end for maximum power transfer. In any case you should clearly keep in mind that the feed point mismatch does not affect the radiation characteristics of an antenna. It can only affect the system efficiency when heating losses are considered.

Why then do we include feed point mismatch as part of the antenna characteristics? The reason is that for efficient system performance, most antennas are resonant transducers and present a reasonable match over a relatively narrow frequency range. It is therefore desirable to design an antenna, whether it be a simple dipole or an array of Yagis, such that the final single feed point impedance is essentially resistive and matched to the feed line. Furthermore, in order to make accurate, absolute gain measurements, it is vital that the antenna under test accept all the power from a matched-source generator, or that the reflected power caused by the mismatch be measured and a suitable error correction for heating losses be included in the gain calculations. Heating losses may be determined from information contained in the **Transmission Lines** chapter.

While on the subject of feed point impedance, mention should be made of the use of baluns in antennas. A balun is simply a device that permits a lossless transition between a balanced system feed line or antenna and an unbalanced feed line or system. If the feed point of an antenna is symmetric, such as with a dipole, and it is desired to feed this antenna with an unbalanced feed line such as coax, you should provide a balun between the line and the feed point. Without the balun, current will be allowed to flow on the outside of the coax. The current on the outside of the feed line will cause radiation, and thus the feed line will become part of the antenna radiation system. In the case of beam antennas, where it is desired to concentrate the radiated energy is a specific direction, this extra radiation from the feed line will be detrimental, causing distortion of the expected antenna pattern. See the **Transmission Line System Techniques** for additional details on this problem.

27.8.2 TEST SITE SET-UP AND EVALUATION

Since an antenna is a reciprocal device, measurements of gain and radiation patterns can be made with the test antenna used either as a transmitting or as a receiving antenna. In general and for practical reasons, the test antenna is used in the receiving mode, and the source or transmitting antenna is located at a specified fixed remote site and unattended. In other words the source antenna, energized by a suitable transmitter, is simply required to illuminate or flood the receiving site in a controlled and constant manner.

As mentioned earlier, antenna measurements ideally should be made under free-space conditions. A further restriction is that the illumination from the source antenna be a *plane wave* over the effective aperture (capture area) of the test antenna. A plane wave by definition is one in which the magnitude and phase of the fields are uniform, and in the test-antenna situation, *uniform over the effective area plane of the test antenna.* Since it is the nature of all radiation to expand in a spherical manner at great distance from the source, it would seem to be most desirable to locate the source antenna as far from the test site as possible. However, since for practical reasons the test site and source location will have to be near the Earth and not in outer space, the environment must include the effects of the ground surface and other obstacles in the vicinity of both antennas. These effects almost always dictate that the test range (spacing between source and test antennas) be as short as possible consistent with maintaining a nearly error-free plane wave illuminating the test *aperture*.

A nearly error-free plane wave can be specified as one in which the phase and amplitude, from center to edge of the illuminating field over the test aperture, do not deviate by more than about 30° and 1 dB, respectively. These conditions will result in a gain-measurement error of no more than a few percent less than the true gain. Based on the 30° phase error alone, it can be shown that the minimum range distance is approximately

$$S_{min} = 2\frac{D^2}{\lambda} \qquad (19)$$

where D is the largest aperture dimension and λ is the free-space wavelength in the same units as D. The phase error over the aperture D for this condition is ¹⁄₁₆ wavelength.

Since aperture size and gain are related by

$$Gain = \frac{4\pi A_c}{\lambda^2} \qquad (20)$$

where A_e is the effective aperture area, the dimension D may be obtained for simple aperture configurations. For a square aperture

$$D^2 = G\frac{\lambda^2}{4\pi} \qquad (21)$$

that results in a minimum range distance for a square aperture of

$$S_{min} = G\frac{\lambda}{2\pi} \qquad (22)$$

and for a circular aperture of

$$S_{min} = G\frac{2\lambda}{\pi^2} \qquad (23)$$

For apertures with a physical area that is not well defined or is much larger in one dimension that in other directions, such as a long thin array for maximum directivity in one plane, it is advisable to use the maximum estimate of D from either the expected gain or physical aperture dimensions.

Up to this point in the range development, only the conditions for minimum range length, S_{min}, have been established, as though the ground surface were not present. This minimum S is therefore a necessary condition even under free-space environment. The presence of the ground further complicates the range selection, not in the determination of S but in the exact location of the source and test antennas above the Earth.

It is always advisable to select a range whose intervening terrain is essentially flat, clear of obstructions, and of uniform surface conditions, such as all grass or all pavement. The extent of the range is determined by the illumination of the source antenna, usually a Yagi, whose gain is no greater than the lowest gain antenna to be measured. For gain measurements the range consists essentially of the region in the beam of the test antenna. For radiation-pattern measurements, the range is considerably larger and consists of all that area illuminated by the source antenna, especially around and behind the test site. Ideally you should choose a site where the test-antenna location is near the center of a large open area and the source antenna is located near the edge where most of the obstacles (trees, poles, fences, etc.) lie.

The primary effect of the range surface is that some of the energy from the source antenna will be reflected into the test antenna, while other energy will arrive on a direct line-of-sight path. This is illustrated in **Figure 27.53**. The use of a flat, uniform ground surface assures that there will be essentially a mirror reflection, even though the reflected energy may be slightly weakened (absorbed) by the surface material (ground). In order to perform an analysis you should realize that horizontally polarized waves undergo a 180° phase reversal upon reflection from the Earth. The resulting illumination amplitude at any point in the test aperture is the vector sum of the electric fields arriving from the two directions, the direct path and the reflected path.

If a perfect mirror reflection is assumed from the ground (it is nearly that for practical ground conditions at VHF/UHF) and the source antenna is isotropic, radiating equally in all directions, then a simple geometric analysis of the two path lengths will show that at various points in the vertical plane

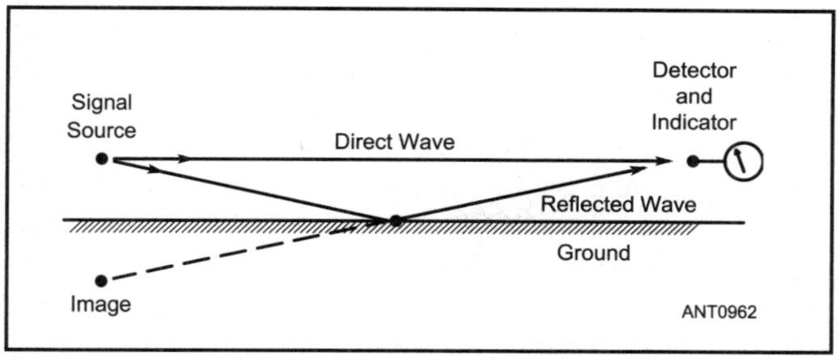

Figure 27.53 — On an antenna test range, energy reaching the receiving equipment may arrive after being reflected from the surface of the ground, as well as by the direct path. The two waves may tend to cancel each other, or may reinforce one another, depending on their phase relationship at the receiving point.

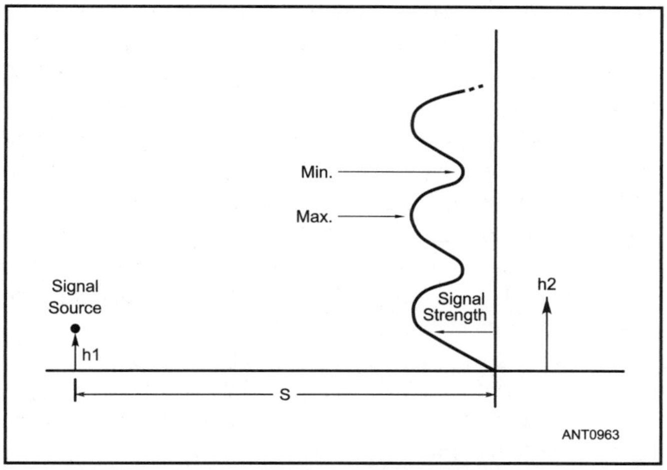

Figure 27.54 — The vertical profile, or plot of signal strength versus test-antenna height, for a fixed height of the signal source above ground and at a fixed distance. See text for definitions of symbols.

at the test-antenna site the waves will combine in different phase relationships. At some points the arriving waves will be in phase, and at other points they will be 180° out of phase. Since the field amplitudes are nearly equal, the resulting phase change caused by path length difference will produce an amplitude variation in the vertical test site direction similar to a standing wave, as shown in **Figure 27.54**.

The simplified formula relating the location of h2 for maximum and minimum values of the two-path summation in terms of h1 and S is

$$h2 = n\frac{\lambda}{4} \times \frac{S}{h1} \tag{24}$$

with n = 0, 2, 4, . . . for minimums and n = 1, 3, 5, . . . for maximums, and S is much larger than either h1 or h2.

The significance of this simple ground reflection formula is that it permits you to determine the approximate location of the source antenna to achieve a nearly plane-wave amplitude distribution *in the vertical direction* over a particular test *aperture size*. It should be clear from examination of the height formula that as h1 is decreased, the vertical distribution pattern of signal at the test site, h2, expands. Also note that the signal level for h2 equal to zero is always zero on the ground regardless of the height of h1.

The objective in using the height formula then is, given an effective antenna aperture to be illuminated from which a minimum S (range length) is determined and a suitable range site chosen, to find a value for h1 (source antenna height). The required value is such that the first maximum of vertical distribution at the test site, h2, is at a practical distance above the ground, and at the same time the signal amplitude over the aperture in the vertical direction does not vary more than about 1 dB. This last condition is not absolutely necessary but is closely related to the particular antenna under test.

In practice these formulas are useful only to initialize the range setup. A final check of the vertical distribution at the test site must be made by direct measurement. This measurement should be conducted with a small low-gain but unidirectional probe antenna such as a corner reflector or 2-element Yagi that you move along a vertical line over the intended aperture site. Care should be exercised to minimize the effects of local environment around the probe antenna and that the beam of the probe be directed at the source antenna at all times for maximum signal. A simple dipole is undesirable as a probe antenna because it is susceptible to local environmental effects.

The most practical way to instrument the vertical distribution measurement is to construct some kind of vertical track, preferably of wood, with a sliding carriage or platform that may be used to support and move the probe antenna. It is assumed of course that a stable source transmitter and calibrated receiver or detector are available so variations of the order of ½ dB can be clearly distinguished.

Once you conduct these initial range measurements successfully, the range is now ready to accommodate any aperture size less in vertical extent than the largest for which S_{min} and the vertical field distribution were selected. Place the test antenna with the center of its aperture at the height h2 where maximum signal was found. Tilt the test antenna so that its main beam is pointed in the direction of the source antenna. The final tilt is found by observing the receiver output for maximum signal. This last process must be done empirically since the apparent location of the source is somewhere between the actual source and its image, below the ground.

An example will illustrate the procedure. Assume that we wish to measure a 7-foot diameter parabolic reflector antenna at 1296 MHz (λ = 0.75 foot). The minimum range distance, S_{min}, can be readily computed from the formula for a circular aperture.

$$S_{min} = 2\frac{D^2}{\lambda} = 2 \times \frac{49}{0.75} = 131 \text{ feet}$$

Now a suitable site is selected based on the qualitative discussion given before.

Next determine the source height, h1. The procedure is to choose a height h1 such that the first minimum above ground (n = 2 in formula) is at least two or three times the aperture size, or about 20 feet.

$$h1 = n\frac{\lambda S}{4\,h2} = 2 \times \frac{0.75}{4} \times \frac{131}{20} = 2.5 \text{ feet}$$

Place the source antenna at this height and probe the vertical distribution over the 7-foot aperture location, which will be about 10 feet off the ground.

$$h2 = n\frac{\lambda S}{4\,h1} = 1 \times \frac{0.75}{4} \times \frac{131}{2.5} = 9.8 \text{ feet}$$

Plot the measured profile of vertical signal level versus height. From this plot, empirically determine whether the 7-foot aperture can be fitted in this profile such that the 1-dB variation is not exceeded. If the variation exceeds 1 dB over the 7-foot aperture, the source antenna should be lowered and h2 raised. Small changes in h1 can quickly alter the distribution at the test site. **Figure 27.55** illustrates the points of the previous discussion.

The same set-up procedure applies for either horizontal or vertical linear polarization. However, it is advisable to check by direct measurement at the site for each polarization to be sure that the vertical distribution is satisfactory. Distribution probing in the horizontal plane is unnecessary as little or no variation in amplitude should be found, since the reflection geometry is constant. Because of this, antennas with apertures that are long and thin, such as a stacked collinear vertical, should be measured with the long dimension parallel to the ground.

A particularly difficult range problem occurs in measurements of antennas that have depth as well as cross-sectional aperture area. Long end-fire antennas such as long Yagis, rhombics, V-beams, or arrays of these antennas, radiate as volumetric arrays and it is therefore even more essential that the illuminating field from the source antenna be reasonably uniform in depth as well as plane wave in cross section. For measuring these types of antennas it is advisable to make several vertical profile measurements that cover the depth of the array. A qualitative check on the integrity of the illumination for long end-fire antennas can be made by moving the array or antenna axially (forward and backward) and noting the change in received signal level. If the signal level varies less than 1 or 2 dB for an axial movement of several wavelengths then the field can be considered satisfactory for most demands on accuracy. Large variations indicate that the illuminating field is badly distorted over the array depth and subsequent measurements are questionable. It is interesting to note in connection with gain measurements that any illuminating field distortion will always result in measurements that are lower than true values.

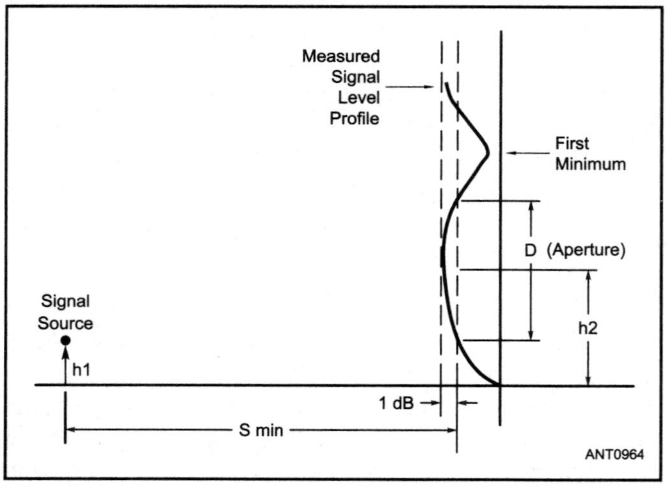

Figure 27.55 — Sample plot of a measured vertical profile.

27.8.3 ABSOLUTE GAIN MEASUREMENT

Having established a suitable range, the measurement of gain relative to an isotropic (point source) radiator is almost always accomplished by direct comparison with a calibrated standard-gain antenna. That is, the signal level with the test antenna in its optimum location is noted. Then you remove the test antenna and place the standard-gain antenna with its aperture at the center of location where the test antenna was located. Measure the difference in signal level between the standard and the test antennas and add to or subtract from the gain of the standard-gain antenna to obtain the absolute gain of the test antenna. Here, *absolute* means with respect to a point source with a gain of unity, by definition. The reason for using this reference rather than a dipole, for instance, is that it is more useful and convenient for system engineering. We assume that both standard and test antennas have been carefully matched to the appropriate impedance and an accurately calibrated and matched detecting device is being used.

A standard-gain antenna may be any type of unidirectional, preferably planar-aperture, antenna, which has been calibrated either by direct measurement or in special cases by accurate construction according to computed dimensions. A standard-gain antenna for VHF and low-UHF bands has been suggested by Richard F. H. Yang (see Bibliography). Shown in **Figure 27.56**, it consists of two in-phase dipoles ½ λ apart and backed up with a ground plane 1 λ square. (It is recommended that the builder cut the dipoles close to their free-space length and trim to resonance.)

In Yang's original design, the stub at the center is a balun formed by cutting two longitudinal slots of ⅛-inch width, diametrically opposite, on a ¼-λ section of ⅞-inch rigid 50-Ω coax. An alternative method of feeding is to feed RG-8 or RG-213 coax through slotted ¾-inch copper tubing with a ⅞-inch OD. (Due to variations in ID/OD for stock copper tubing, either bring a section of the rigid coax or take careful measurements with a caliper to check for fit between the coax and the balun tubing.)

Be sure to leave the outer jacket on the coax to insulate it from the copper-tubing balun section. When constructed accurately to scale for the frequency of interest, this type of standard will have an absolute gain of 9.85 dBi (7.7 dBd gain over a dipole in free space) with an accuracy of ± 0.25 dB. (The balun is described in detail in the original article.)

At 1296 MHz it may be more practical to build a reference horn out of sheet metal as described by Paul Wade, W1GHZ on his website. (**www.w1ghz.org**) The waveguide section can also be made out of sheet metal.

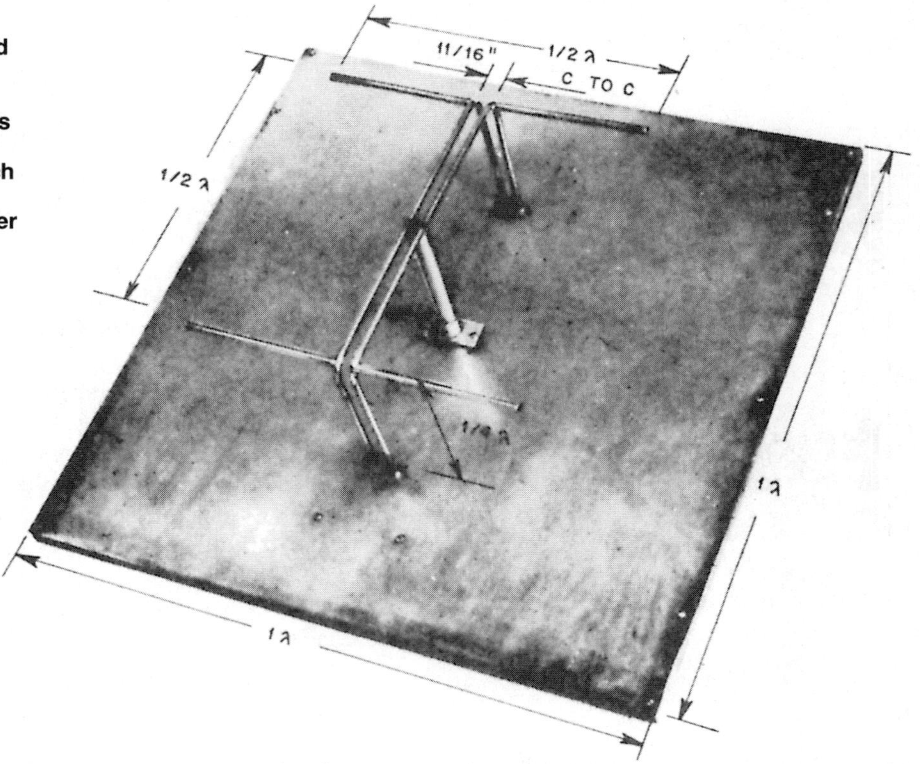

Figure 27.56 — Standard-gain antenna. When accurately constructed for the desired frequency, this antenna will exhibit a gain of 7.7 dB over a dipole radiator, plus or minus 0.25 dB. In this model, constructed for 432 MHz, the elements are ⅜-inch diameter tubing. The phasing and support lines are of 5⁄16-inch diameter tubing or rod.

27.8.4 RADIATION PATTERN MEASUREMENTS

Of all antenna measurements, the radiation pattern is the most demanding in measurement and the most difficult to interpret. Any antenna radiates to some degree in all directions into the space surrounding it. Therefore, the radiation pattern of an antenna is a three-dimensional representation of the magnitude, phase and polarization. In general, and in practical cases for Amateur Radio communications, the polarization is well defined and only the magnitude of radiation is important.

Furthermore, in many of these cases the radiation in one particular plane is of primary interest, usually the plane corresponding to that of the Earth's surface, regardless of polarization. Because of the nature of the range setup, measurement of radiation pattern can be successfully made only in a plane nearly parallel to the Earth's surface. With beam antennas it is advisable and usually sufficient to take two radiation pattern measurements, one in the polarization plane and one at right angles to the plane of polarization. These radiation patterns are referred to in antenna literature as the principal E-plane and H-plane patterns, respectively. *E-plane* means parallel to the electric field that is the polarization plane and *H-plane* means parallel to the magnetic field in free space. The electric field and magnetic field are always perpendicular to each other in a plane wave as it propagates through space.

When the antenna is located over real Earth, the terms *azimuth* and *elevation* planes are commonly used, since the frame of reference is the Earth itself, rather than the electric and magnetic fields in free space. For a horizontally polarized antenna such as a Yagi mounted with its elements parallel to the ground, the azimuth plane is the E-plane and the elevation plane is the H-plane.

The technique to obtain these patterns is simple in procedure but requires more equipment and patience than does making a gain measurement. First, a suitable mount is required that can be rotated in the azimuth plane (horizontal) with some degree of accuracy in terms of azimuth-angle positioning. Second, a signal-level indicator calibrated over at least a 20-dB dynamic range with a readout resolution of at least 2 dB is required. A dynamic range of up to about 40 dB would be desirable but does not add greatly to the measurement significance.

With this much equipment, the procedure is to locate first the area of maximum radiation from the beam antenna by carefully adjusting the azimuth and elevation positioning. These settings are then arbitrarily assigned an azimuth angle of zero degrees and a signal level of zero decibels. Next, without changing the elevation setting (tilt of the rotating axis), the antenna is carefully rotated in azimuth in small steps that permit signal-level readout of 2 or 3 dB per step. These points of signal level corresponding with an azimuth angle are recorded and plotted on polar coordinate paper. A sample of the results is shown on ARRL coordinate paper in

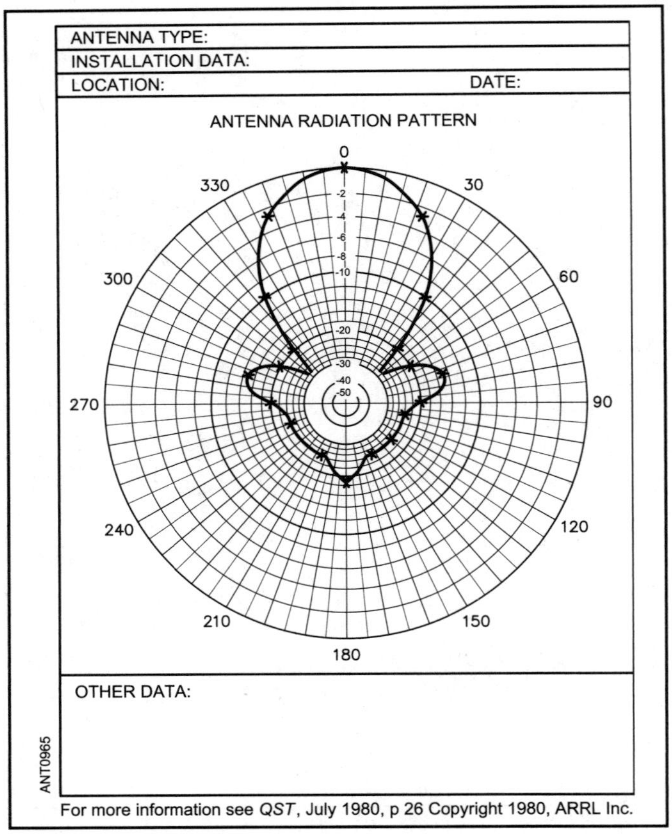

Figure 27.57 — Sample plot of a measured radiation pattern, using techniques described in the text.

Figure 27.57. (See the **Antenna Fundamentals** chapter for more information on coordinate scales.)

On the sample radiation pattern the measured points are marked with an X and a continuous line is drawn in, since the pattern is a continuous curve. Radiation patterns should preferably be plotted on a logarithmic radial scale, rather than a voltage or power scale. The reason is that the log scale approximates the response of the ear to signals in the audio range. Also many receivers have AGC systems that are somewhat logarithmic in response; therefore the log scale is more representative of actual system operation.

Having completed a set of radiation-pattern measurements, one is prompted to ask, "Of what use are they?" The primary answer is as a diagnostic tool to determine if the antenna is functioning as it was intended to. A second answer is to know how the antenna will discriminate against interfering signals from various directions.

Consider now the diagnostic use of the radiation patterns. If the radiation beam is well defined, then there is an approximate formula relating the antenna gain to the measured half-power beamwidth of the E- and H-plane radiation patterns. The half-power beamwidth is indicated on the polar plot where the radiation level falls to 3 dB below the main beam 0-dB reference on either side. The formula is

$$\text{Gain (isotropic)} \cong \frac{41{,}253}{\theta_E \phi_H} \qquad (25)$$

where θ_E and ϕ_H are the half-power beamwidths in degrees of the E- and H-plane patterns, respectively. This equation assumes a lossless antenna system, where any side-lobes are well suppressed. (To obtain gain in dBi, take the log of isotropic gain and multiply by 10.)

To illustrate the use of this equation, assume that we have a Yagi antenna with a boom length of two wavelengths. From known relations (described in the **HF Yagi and Quad Antennas** chapter) the expected free-space gain of a Yagi with a boom length of 2 λ is about 13 dBi; its gain, G, equals 20. Using the above relationship, the product of $\theta_E \times \phi_H \approx 2062$ square degrees. Since a Yagi produces a nearly symmetric beam shape in cross section, $\theta_E = \phi_H = 45°$. Now if the measured values of θ_E and ϕ_H are much larger than 45°, then the gain will be much lower than the expected 13 dBi.

As another example, suppose that the same antenna (a 2-wavelength-boom Yagi) gives a measured gain of 9 dBi but the radiation pattern half power beamwidths are approximately 45°. This situation indicates that although the radiation patterns seem to be correct, the low gain shows inefficiency somewhere in the antenna, such as lossy materials or poor connections.

Large broadside collinear antennas can be checked for excessive phasing-line losses by comparing the gain computed from the radiation patterns with the direct-measured gain. It seems paradoxical, but it is indeed possible to build a large array with a very narrow beamwidth indicating high gain, but actually having very low gain because of losses in the feed distribution system.

In general, and for most VHF/UHF Amateur Radio communications, gain is the primary attribute of an antenna. However, radiation in directions other than the main beam, called *sidelobe radiation*, should be examined by measurement of radiation patterns for effects such as nonsymmetry on either side of the main beam or excessive magnitude of sidelobes. (Any sidelobe that is less than 10 dB below the main beam reference level of 0 dB should be considered excessive.) These effects are usually attributable to incorrect phasing of the radiating elements or radiation from other parts of the antenna that was not intended, such as the support structure or feed line.

The interpretation of radiation patterns is intimately related to the particular type of antenna under measurement. Reference data should be consulted for the antenna type of interest, to verify that the measured results are in agreement with expected results.

To summarize the use of pattern measurements, if a beam antenna is first checked for gain (the easier measurement to make) and it is as expected, then pattern measurements may be academic. However, if the gain is lower than expected it is advisable to make pattern measurements to help determine the possible causes for low gain.

Regarding radiation pattern measurements, remember that the results measured under proper range facilities will not necessarily be the same as observed for the same antenna at a home-station installation. The reasons may be obvious now in view of the preceding information on the range setup, ground reflections, and the vertical-field distribution profiles. For long paths over rough terrain where many large obstacles may exist, the effects of ground reflection tend to become diffused, although they still can cause unexpected results. For these reasons it is usually unjust to compare VHF/UHF antennas over long paths.

27.9 BIBLIOGRAPHY

Source material and more extended discussion of topics covered in this chapter can be found in the references given below.

Agilent Technologies, "Understanding the Fundamental Principles of Vector Network Analysis," Application Note AN 1287-1. Other application notes with further information on network analyzers are AN 1287-2 through AN 1287-10 and AN 1287-12, and also 5965-7917E, and 5990-5446EN, available from **www.keysight.com** (enter the application note number in the search box).

J. Althouse, "The Noise Bridge," *QST*, Sep 1992, pp 75-78.

G. Badger, et al, "SWR Analyzer Tips, Tricks and Techniques: SWR Analyzer Hints," *QST*, Sep 1996, p 36-40.

T. Baier, "A Small, Simple USB-Powered Vector Network Analyzer Covering 1 kHz to 1.3 GHz," *QEX*, Jan/Feb 2009, pp 32-36.

T. Baier, "A Simple S-Parameter Test Set for the VNWA2 Vector Network Analyzer," *QEX*, May/Jun 2009, pp 29-32.

A. Bailey, "The Antenna Lab, Parts 1 and 2," *Radio Communication*, Aug and Sep 1983.

J. Belrose, "On Tuning, Matching and Measuring Antenna System Impedance Using a Hand-Held SWR Analyzer," *QST*, Sep 2006, pp 56-68.

L. Blake, *Transmission Lines and Waveguides* (New York: John Wiley & Sons, 1969), pp 244-251.

J. H. Bowen, "A Calorimeter for VHF and UHF Power Measurements," *QST*, Dec 1975, pp 11-13.

D. Bramwell, "An RF Step Attenuator," *QST*, Jun 1995, pp 33-34.

T. Brock-Fisher, "Build a Super-Simple SWR Indicator," *QST*, Jun 1995, pp 40-41.

F. Brown, "A Reflectometer for Twin-Lead," *QST*, Oct 1980, p 15-17.

W. Bruene, "An Inside Picture of Directional Wattmeters," *QST*, Apr 1959, pp 24-28.

CCIR Recommendation 368, Documents of the CCIR XII Plenary assembly, ITU, Geneva, 1967.

J. Carr, "Find Fault with Your Coax," *73*, Oct 1984, pp 10-14.

S. Cooper, "A Compensated, Modular RF Voltmeter," *QEX*, Mar/Apr 2001, pp 26-34.

P. Danzer, "A Simple Transformer to Measure Your Antenna Current," *QST*, Sep 2009, p 35.

D. DeMaw, "In-Line RF Power Metering," *QST*, Dec 1969, pp 11-16.

D. DeMaw, "A QRP Person's VSWR Indicator," *QST*, Aug 1982, p. 45.

D. Fayman, "A Simple Computing SWR Meter," *QST*, Jul 1973, pp 23-33.

J. Gibbons and H. Horn, "A Circuit With Logarithmic Response Over Nine Decades," *IEEE Transactions on Circuit Theory*, Vol CT-11, No. 3, Sep 1964, pp 378-384.

J. Grebenkemper, "Calibrating Diode Detectors," *QEX*, Aug 1990, pp 3-8.

J. Grebenkemper, "The Tandem Match — An Accurate Directional Wattmeter," *QST*, Jan 1987, pp 18-26. Also see corrections in Technical Correspondence, *QST*, Jan 1988, p 49 and "An Updated Tandem Match" in Technical Correspondence, *QST*, Jul 1993, p 50.

J. Grebenkemper, "Improving and Using R-X Noise Bridges," *QST*, Aug 1989, pp 27-32, 52; Feedback, *QST*, Jan 1990, p 27.

J. Hallas, *Understanding Your Antenna Analyzer,* ARRL, 2013.

E. Hare, "A Current Probe for the RF-Survey Meter," *QST*, Aug 2000, p 43.

F. Hauff, "The Gadget — an SWR Analyzer Add-On," *QST*, Oct 1996, pp 33-35.

W. Kaune, "A Modern Directional Power/SWR Meter," *QST*, Jan 2011, pp 39-43.

T. King, "A Practical Time-Domain Reflectometer," *QST*, May 1989, pp 22-24.

M. Knitter, "The DG5MK IV Meter — An Accurate Antenna Analyzer," *QEX*, May/June 2017, pp 3-14.

Z. Lau, "A Relative RF Ammeter for Open-Wire Lines," *QST*, Oct 1988, pp 15-17, 20.

Z. Lau and C. Hutchinson, "Improving the HW-9 Transceiver," *QST*, Apr 1988, pp 26-29.

V. G. Leenerts, "Automatic VSWR and Power Meter," *Ham Radio*, May 1980, pp 34-43.

J. Lenk, *Handbook of Oscilloscopes* (Englewood Cliffs, NJ: Prentice-Hall, 1982), pp 288-292.

R. Lewallen, "Notes on Phased Verticals," Technical Correspondence, *QST*, Aug 1979, pp 42-43.

I. Lindell, E. Alanen, K. Mannerslo, "Exact Image Method for Impedance Computation of Antennas Above the Ground," *IEEE Trans. On Antennas and Propagation*, AP-33, Sep 1985.
R. Littlefield, "A Wide-Range RF-Survey Meter," *QST*, Aug 2000, pp 42-44.
L. McCoy, "A Linear Field-Strength Meter," *QST*, Jan 1973, pp 18-20, 35.
T. McDermott and K. Ireland, "A Low-Cost 100 MHz Vector Network Analyzer with USB Interface," *QEX*, Jul/Aug 2004, pp 3-13.
T. McMullen, "The Line Sampler, an RF Power Monitor for VHF and UHF," *QST*, Apr 1972, pp 21-23, 25.
M. W. Maxwell, *Reflections* (Newington: ARRL, 1990), p 20-3. [Out of print.]
C. Michaels, "Determining Line Lengths," Technical Correspondence, *QST*, Sep 1985, pp 43-44.
J. Noakes, "The "No Fibbin" RF Field Strength Meter," *QST*, Aug 2002, pp 28-29.
Orr and Cowan, *Vertical Antennas*, Radio Amateur Call Book, 1986, pp 148-150.
P. Ostapchuk, "A Rugged, Compact Attenuator," *QST*, May 1998, pp 41-43. Also see Technical Correspondence, *QST*, Dec 1998, p 64.
H. Perras, "Broadband Power-Tracking VSWR Bridge," *Ham Radio*, Aug 1979, pp 72-75.
D. Pozar, *Microwave Engineering* (New York: John Wiley & Sons, 2004).
S. Ramo, J. Whinnery and T. Van Duzer, *Fields and Waves in Communication Electronics* (New York: John Wiley & Sons, 1967), Chap 1.
Reference Data for Radio Engineers, 5th edition (Indianapolis: Howard W. Sams, 1968), Chapter 28.
W. Sabin, "The Lumped-Element Directional Coupler," *QEX*, Mar 1995, pp 3-11.
P. Salas, "A Compact 100-W Z-Match Antenna Tuner," *QST*, Jan 2003, p 28-30.
P. N. Saveskie, *Radio Propagation Handbook* (Blue Ridge Summit, PA: TAB Books, 1960).
P. Schuch, "The SWR Analyzer and Transmission Lines," *QST*, Jul 1997, p 68.
J. Sevick, "Short Ground-Radial Systems for Short Verticals," *QST*, Apr 1978, pp 30-33.
J. Sevick, "Measuring Soil Conductivity," *QST*, Mar 1981, pp 38-39.
W. Silver, "Hands-On Radio: Experiment #52 — SWR Meters," *QST*, May 2007, pp 57-58.
R. Skelton, Ron, "Measuring HF Balun Performance," *QEX*, Nov/Dec 2010, pp 39-41.
S. Sparks, "An RF Current Probe for Amateur Use," *QST*, Feb 1999, p 34.
W. Spaulding, "A Broadband Two-Port S-Parameter Test Set," *Hewlett-Packard Journal*, Nov 1984.
F. Sutter, "What, No Meters?," *QST*, Oct 1938, pp 49-50.
D. Turrin, "Antenna Performance Measurements," *QST*, Nov 1974, pp 35-41.
F. Van Zant, "High-Power Operation with the Tandem Match Directional Coupler," Technical Correspondence, *QST*, Jul 1989, pp 42-43.
P. Wade, "Directional Couplers," Microwavelengths, *QST*, Jan 2007, pp 87-88.
P. Wade, "Microwave System Test," Microwavelengths, *QST*, Aug 2010, pp 96-97.
C. Wright, "The Twin-Lamp," *QST*, Oct 1947, pp 22-23, 110, 112.
R. F. H. Yang, "A Proposed Gain Standard for VHF Antennas," *IEEE Transactions on Antennas and Propagation*, Nov 1966.

TABLE OF CONTENTS

Chapter 28

Antenna System Troubleshooting

Even with commercial equipment, there is not a single amateur who, at some time, has not introduced an error into the antenna system either during installation or use. Similarly, of course, nothing remains faultless forever and those are the subjects of this chapter — finding the errors and faults. The first section of the chapter is directed at the beginner, providing a structured process to hunt for and find the problem. It is adapted from the Wireless Institute of Australia *Amateur Radio* magazine's excellent series of "Foundation Corner" articles for new hams. It was originally written by Ted Thrift, VK2ARA, and Ross Pittard, VK3CE. The second section of the chapter is more detailed and assumes more technical background on the part of the reader. It is adapted from material written by Tom Schiller, N6BT, as part of his book *Array of Light, 3rd Edition* (**www.n6bt.com**).

The goal of this chapter is not to provide an exhaustive procedure that can be followed "cookbook-style" to troubleshoot any antenna or antenna system. There are just too many variables and configurations for that to be possible. Rather, this chapter suggest systematic approaches and general guidelines to apply in order to find problems. Once problems are identified, the solution is usually obvious and even trivial.

Anyone with experience in maintaining or building systems of more than a few parts — whether related to Amateur Radio or not — will recognize the value of a systematic approach to troubleshooting. The underlying lesson in this material is that carefully analyzing a problem with a step-by-step approach pays off in effective troubleshooting, saving time and expense. This is true for antennas, transceivers, computer systems — any sort of technology. Whether the reader is just getting on the air or has a lifetime of experience, there is something for everyone in this chapter.

The material on troubleshooting and repair of antenna tuners was contributed by Matt Kastigar, N9ES. Antenna tuners operate at the same power levels as the final amplifier, so they are subjected to the same stresses plus higher SWR levels. This material helps you find problems and repair the affected components.

The final section of this chapter is more about maintenance than troubleshooting but the two are so closely linked that the information will be helpful. It is another adaptation from the WIA *Amateur Radio* "Foundation Corner" columns, this one written by Ross Pittard, VK3CE, and Geoff Emery, VK4ZPP.

28.1 ANTENNA SYSTEM TROUBLESHOOTING FOR BEGINNERS

So you can no longer hear anything and you think your antenna system is faulty. It is very likely that it is, or at least some part of it is faulty. To repair the fault, we first have to find it. To do this we have to treat your antenna system in exactly the same way as fault finding inside a radio. After all, it is an electrical circuit and if not completely correct, will not work in the way that you expect. The process described in the rest of this section can be adapted to most simple antenna systems similar to that shown in **Figure 28.1**.

Start with an inventory of the antenna system. Any of these can be the cause of your problem:

- The support poles and ropes
- The antenna insulators
- The antenna elements
- The feed point or balun
- The feed line
- The entry point to the shack
- The jumper cable to the radio

A *jumper cable* (also called a *patch cable*) is a short piece of coaxial cable with RF connectors on each end. It is used to connect two pieces of equipment together. The discussion below assumes that you have a coaxial feed line to the antenna.

Determine the characteristics of the antenna you are troubleshooting:

- Is it a balanced half-wave dipole?
- Is it an off-center-fed (OCF) dipole?
- Is it a multiband antenna, for example, a G5RV?
- What is the primary band it is designed for?

Consider the characteristics of the radio as well:

- Does it have a built in antenna tuner or do you use an add-on antenna tuner?
- Can you transmit a carrier signal on any band?
- Can you adjust the power level of the carrier?

During the following sequence of testing, be alert for mistaken or loose connections, loose or disconnected power and control cables, wires touching each other that shouldn't be, and so forth. Your main system components may be just fine but not connected properly. This is *very* common!

If you haven't started one yet, this is a great time to start your "shack notebook" in which you record how your station is built. This is where you write down test results, color codes of control cables, modifications to equipment, dates of installation, etc. This information can be a huge time-saver in the future when you are troubleshooting or designing an addition to the station. A spiral-bound or composition book of graph paper is the best option, but a loose-leaf binder works well, too. Remember to put the date on each page as you make an entry.

28.1.1 BEFORE TESTING

If your radio has a built in auto tuner it has by now attempted to match your antenna system, faults and all. You may have also tried other bands to see if you can get "something" to work. To find the fault we must test the system *on the primary band for which it was designed.* Keep this in mind when you start testing. If your testing indicates that the tuner may be at fault, see the section on Antenna Tuner Troubleshooting and Repair later in this chapter.

Test Equipment

In addition to your radio, you will need at least the following items.

- A suitable power/SWR meter.
- A volt-ohm meter to check continuity of cables and wires.
- A suitable 50-Ω dummy load.
- At least two tested and known-good 50-Ω jumper cables.

28.1.2 INITIAL TESTING

This is to ensure that both your radio and your test equipment are working correctly.

1) Remove the antenna coax and connect your test jumper cable.

2) Connect the other end of the jumper cable to your power/SWR meter.

3) Connect your dummy load to the power/SWR meter.

4) Set the power range on the meter to a high scale to prevent overload.

5) Set the radio to the antenna's primary band.

6) Set your radio to CW, AM or FM.

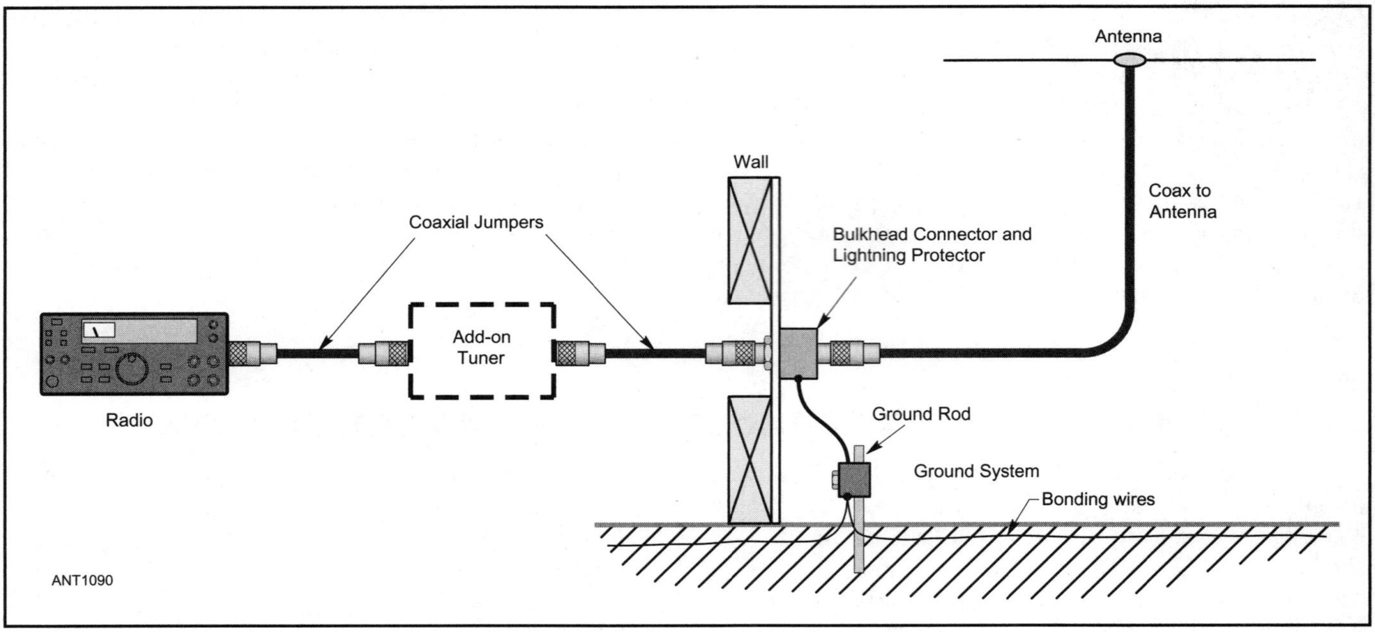

Figure 28.1 — A typical simple antenna system. If the transceiver does not have a built-in auto tuner, an external add-on tuner may be included in the system. It is good practice for the antenna cable to enter the shack through a connector on a grounded wall panel. This bulkhead connector is often a lightning arrestor, as well. Coax jumpers connect the various pieces of equipment together.

7) Adjust output power to minimum.

8) Press (PTT) and adjust output power to (say) 5-10 W.

9) Check that the power indication in the radio and the power/SWR meter are similar.

10) If your radio passes this test, activate whatever tuner you use, either the transceiver's internal tuner or an external tuner. Then repeat steps 8 and 9 after the internal tuner has adjusted to match the 50 Ω load or you have adjusted the manual tuner to match the 50 Ω load. If the internal or external tuner experience difficulty tuning to the 50 Ω load, proceed to the section Antenna Tuner Troubleshooting and Repair.

You have now set a benchmark with known output into a 50-Ω load. *This is an important step.* Do not change any settings on your radio until all tests are completed and the faults fixed.

28.1.3 ANTENNA SYSTEM TESTING

Your Second Test

Here is where we start to eliminate possible causes of your problems. Start by simplifying your antenna system. Remove any extra equipment (switches, filters, etc) between the radio and the antenna, reducing your antenna system to a single connection similar to that in Figure 28.1.

It is likely that you have some kind of receptacle or bulkhead connector (such as a UG-363 adaptor or Amphenol 83-1F) where your antenna coax enters the shack. From there you have a jumper cable to your radio. We test this next.

1) Remove the test jumper cable from the radio to the power/SWR meter.

2) Connect your normal jumper cable from the radio to the power/SWR meter.

3) Press (PTT) and observe the power reading. It should be exactly the same as step 8, above. If not, your jumper cable is faulty or not suitable.

Test and Fix

First, perform a continuity check of the inner and outer conductors of the jumper cable. Then check the cable insulation — there should be no continuity from the inner to outer conductor. Check that the pins on each PL-259 plug are correctly soldered and fit firmly in the SO-239 receptacles. Look for markings on the jacket of the cable to ensure that it is a 50-Ω cable. *If you find a fault and fix it, retest steps 1-3 above.*

Your Third Test

Here is another elimination step. It is very common to have bulkhead connectors that are also lightning arrestors. These are not totally fool-proof and can fail due to a lightning hit or moisture. Even non-arrestor connectors fail from moisture or other reasons. We do need to test this connector. If you do not have any connectors between the antenna and your transceiver, skip this test and proceed to the fourth test below.

1) Disconnect the coax to the antenna from the bulkhead connector.

2) Using your "now tested OK" jumper cable, perform a dc test (continuity test) on the connector using the following steps.

3) Connect the jumper cable to the connector on the inside.

4) Test the insulation from inner to outer conductor using a high resistance scale. If the connector is also a lightning arrestor, test the inner conductor to earth ground (should be an open circuit) then test the outer conductor to earth ground (should be a short circuit or very low resistance).

5) The easiest way to test continuity of the connector is to connect your 50-Ω dummy load to the outside of the connector. Look for 50 Ω from the inner to outer conductor.

6) Using two jumper cables and the power/SWR meter, apply power from your transmitter to the dummy load on the outside of the connector.

7) Power should be the same as when you tested your jumper lead.

8) SWR must be no higher than 1.1:1 or the connector is faulty at RF.

Before the Fourth Test

When are we going to test the antenna? Very soon but since it does not work we need to perform a visual inspection. Assuming you have some kind of wire antenna, you need to lower it and in the process, inspect and ensure that:

- On the insulators at each end, there is no possibility of contact between the antenna wire and the supporting wire/ropes.
- If there are any splices in the wire elements, they are well crimped or soldered.
- At the center insulator, there is no possibility of contact between the element wires.
- At the balun or coax connection the element connections are soldered or firmly connected.
  - If it is a center-fed dipole it should be a 1:1 choke balun.
  - If it is an OCF dipole, it should be a 4:1 or 6:1 balun.

Cut away the waterproofing around the coax termination and inspect for water damage. If the connector is discolored or corroded it will need to be cleaned if not replaced and the cable checked as well.

Similar steps apply if you have a Yagi or vertical antenna.

Your Fourth Test

Now we are going to carefully test the main antenna coax cable *and* its connectors. First some dc tests, then we can RF test.

1) With the coax disconnected from the antenna *and* bulkhead connector (or radio), test continuity overall of the inner conductor, then the outer conductor. Test the insulation from the inner to outer conductor on the highest scale.

2) Connect the 50-Ω dummy load to the antenna end of the main coax. At the radio end, measure resistance from the inner to outer conductor. You should see close to 50 Ω.

3) Reconnect the bulkhead connector or radio end of the main coax. You should now have connected in sequence; radio, jumper, power/SWR meter, jumper, bulkhead/wall connector, main coax and dummy load as in **Figure 28.2**.

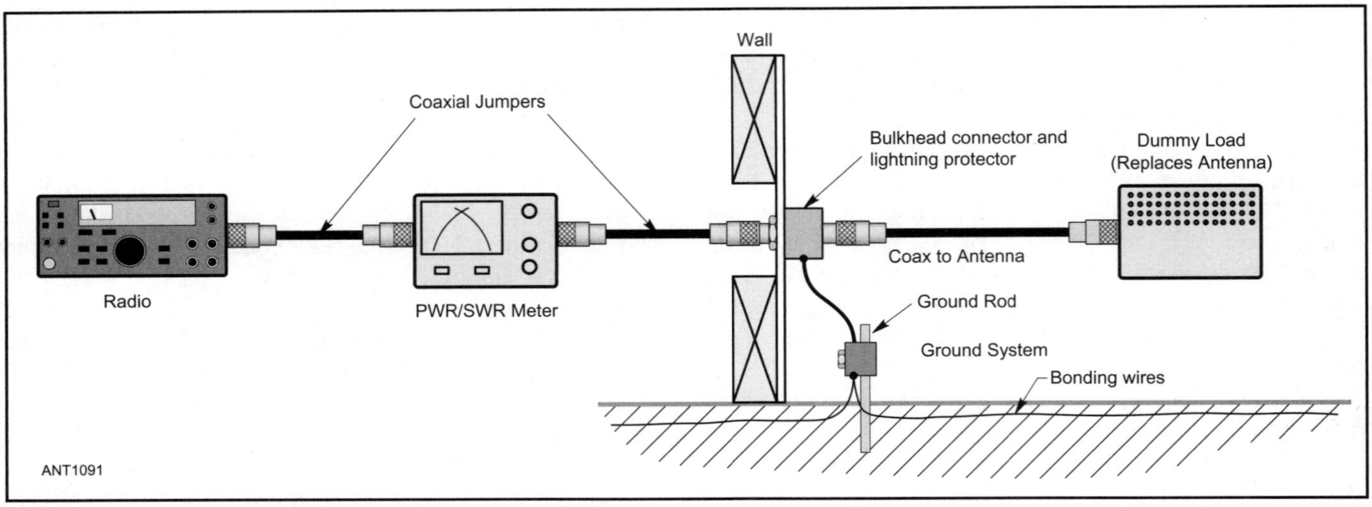

Figure 28.2 — Test setup to check SWR with the antenna replaced by a dummy load.

4) Press PTT and note the power reading: It should be very close to your preset 5 or 10 W. Check SWR; it should be no higher than 1.1:1. Be very wary of seeing no reflected power at all. This could mean that the coax is so lossy that reflected power is unreadable. One more test will determine this.

5) Relocate the power/SWR meter from the shack to the antenna end of your main coax but put it where it can be seen. The sequence is now: radio, jumper, bulkhead/wall connector, main coax, power/SWR meter, dummy load as in Figure 28.3.

6) Press PTT and note power reading: it should be at least 75% of your preset 5 or 10 W. If much less, the coax is lossy and should be replaced.

7) Check SWR and it should be no higher than 1.1:1.

8) If you do replace the main coax, repeat all of steps 1 to 7 above.

We are nearly done. Reapply the waterproofing to the connection of coax to balun, or at least some temporary tape. (If it now works you will get so busy you may forget to finish it all!) Pull your antenna back up into position, taking care not to put *any* stress on the coax cable. We are going to test the SWR on the primary band *without* the help of the tuner in the radio.

The Final Test

Initially we are going to test without the tuner engaged, so we can see how well the antenna is working on the main band that it was designed for. It is only on this band that we can make any adjustments to the length of the wire elements. Before we start adjusting we need to know which direction to go, so we will test the high end, middle and low end of the band.

Connect the power/SWR meter between the radio and the

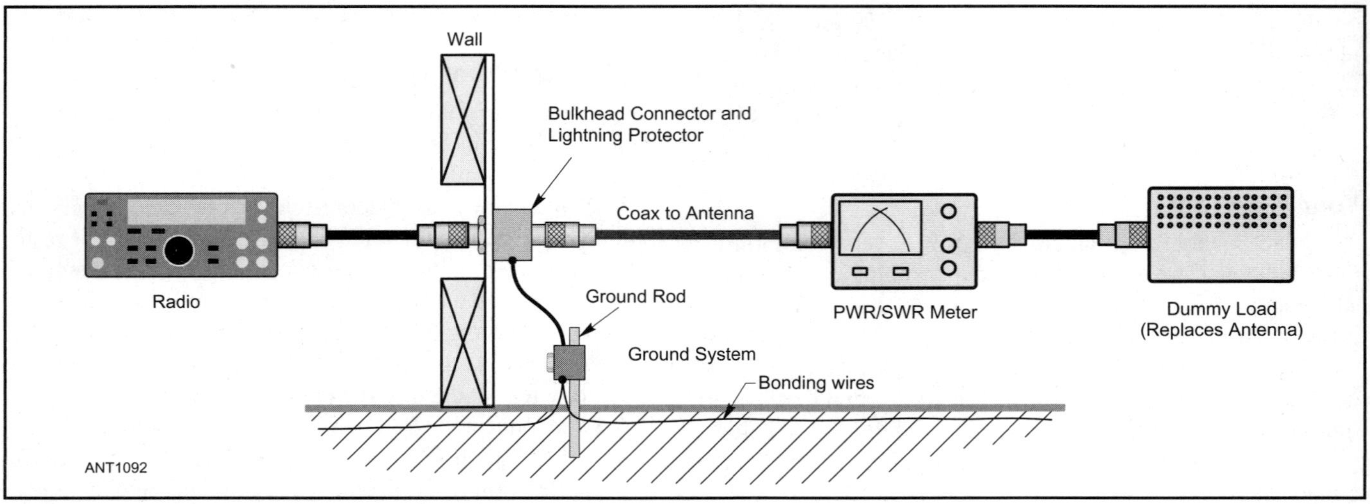

Figure 28.3 — Test setup to check if the main coax is lossy.

bulkhead connector or between the radio and the coax to the antenna. *Remember that we are now going to be testing "On Air" so we need to consider others and ask if the frequency is in use.* (You can also use an SWR analyzer as described in the **Antenna and Transmission Line Measurements** chapter.)

Assuming that the main band is 40 meters, tune the radio to, say, 7250 kHz (near the top of the band) and find a quiet spot. Check/ask if the frequency is in use. If it is not, announce, "[Your call] testing."

- Set carrier power to a low value such as 10 W.
- Set SWR meter calibrate control to near maximum and increase power just enough to be able to set the calibration reading to full-scale.
- Return the meter to read SWR and write down the reading.

Now tune the radio to the middle of the band and find a quiet spot. Repeat the test procedure using an appropriate mode. Repeat near the bottom of the band.

Compare the three SWR readings and decide if the antenna is long (SWR too high at the high end of the band) or short (SWR too high at the low end of the band), or if no adjustment is required. Note that if all SWR readings are 1.5:1 or lower, very little will be gained by adjusting the length. If SWR is uniformly high everywhere in the band, the antenna itself is at fault.

If the antenna SWR measurements are acceptable, it is now time to let the radio and auto tuner operate. If you use an add-on antenna tuner, you'll need to make sure that the jumper between it and the radio is good as described previously, then reinstall it between the radio and antenna. The following paragraph assumes the auto tuner is internal to the radio.

Remove the power/SWR meter from the antenna feed line so that the antenna is connected directly to the radio through the bulkhead connector and jumper. Engage the auto tuner and let it set up on a convenient frequency. Set the output power control to about 75-80% of maximum, then find a clear frequency as before and initiate the auto tuner operation as instructed for your radio. Since you have confirmed your antenna system presents a reasonable SWR to the radio, your tuner should operate normally and you can resume operating! If the tuner does not operate properly, there may be excessive RF current on the feed line's outer surface. Add a choke balun at the output of the radio or antenna tuner and try again. (See the **Transmission Line System Techniques** chapter.) If the tuner still doesn't work, you may have a defective tuner.

If the antenna SWR measurements indicate an antenna fault, the exact troubleshooting sequence will depend on the type of antenna. Remember to write everything down in case you need to contact the manufacturer or ask for other help. Start with a visual inspection of the entire antenna looking for loose or corroded elements and joints. Perform a continuity check of all coils, clamps, and capacitors. Wiggle the various pieces while making measurements to look for intermittent connections. If nothing is obviously wrong, try disassembling the antenna, cleaning the various metal-to-metal surfaces using a nonferrous, nonabrasive synthetic cleaning pad such as a Scotch-Brite pad, then reassemble (checking for proper dimensions and orientation of parts) and test. If this fails to restore normal operation, you should contact the manufacturer's customer service department or ask for help from your local club.

28.2 GUIDELINES FOR ANTENNA SYSTEM TROUBLESHOOTING

The antenna is an electrical device implemented via a mechanical construction; therefore, if it is built properly, it should "work" (especially for production units). There are five general categories of problems:

- Test measurements
- Mechanical
- Proximity
- Feed system
- Misunderstandings

Guidelines for dealing with and approaching each type of problem are presented in the following sections. They will be used in subsequent sections in different ways to address different types of problems. Think of them as a kind of toolbox for troubleshooting. Many of them assume you are testing some type of Yagi or other beam antenna but the general guidelines apply to all types of antennas

It is important to remember this simple rule for adjustments and troubleshooting: Do the simplest and easiest adjustment or correction *first*, and only *one* at a time.

When making on-air comparisons, select signals that are at the "margin" and not pushing your receiver well over S9 where it can be difficult to measure differences of a few dB. Terrain has a lot to do with performance as well. If you are comparing with large stations, keep in mind that station location was probably selected carefully and the antennas were placed exactly where they should be for optimum performance on the property.

Remember the Law of Conservation of Energy: Energy can neither be created, nor destroyed. Therefore, the *sum* of all the energies in a system (an antenna system) is a constant. From the perspective of transmitting, we start with so many watts and the energy will go somewhere, either emitted from the antenna and on its way to the destination, or dissipated as heat due to loss.

If you increase your antenna efficiency, you will expand your performance envelope, and thus be able to hear *and* work more stations, providing more enjoyment from radio. If you increase only your transmit power, you will expand your "transmit envelope," but you won't be able to hear any better!

28.2.1 TEST MEASUREMENTS

A. Test the antenna at a minimum height of 15-20 feet. (See **Figure 28.4**) This will move the antenna far enough away from the ground (which acts to add capacitance to the antenna) and enable meaningful measurements. Use sawhorses *only* for construction purposes.

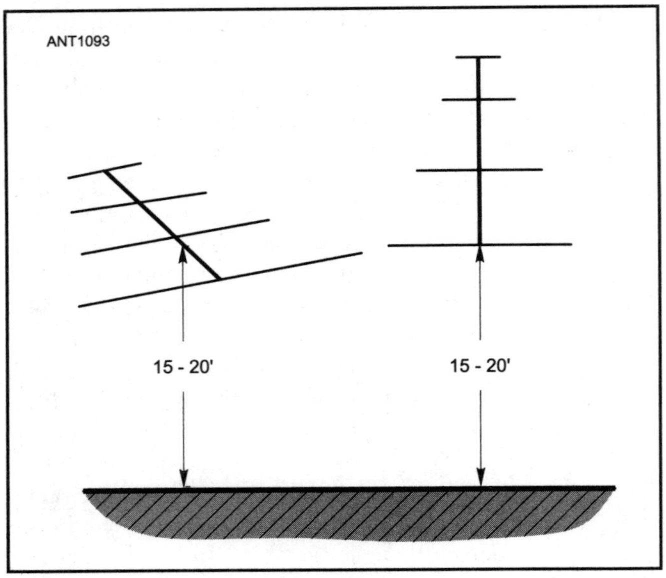

Figure 28.4 — When testing a Yagi or quad antenna, make sure it is at least 15 to 20 feet above ground. If oriented vertically, the reflector should be the closest to ground. Performance will still change as the antenna is raised.

- A minimum height of 15-20 feet above ground does not mean 5 feet above a 10-15 foot high roof, it means above ground with nothing in between.
- Antenna resonant frequency will shift upward as it is raised.
- Feed point impedance will change with a change in height and this applies to both horizontal and vertical antennas.
- Some antennas are more sensitive to proximity to ground than others.
- Some antennas are more sensitive to nearby conductive objects (i.e. other antennas) than others.

B. Aiming the antenna upward with the reflector on the ground might coincide with some measurements on rare occasions, but there are no guarantees with this method. The reflector is literally touching a large capacitor (earth) and the driven element is very close, too. Raise the antenna at least 15-20 feet off the ground.

C. When using a hand-held SWR analyzer you are looking for the dip in SWR, not where the impedance or resistance meter indicates 50 Ω. ("Dip" = frequency of lowest SWR value, or lowest swing on the meter.) On the MFJ-259/269 series, the left-hand meter (SWR) is the one you want to watch, not the right-hand meter (IMPEDANCE).

D. Check for nearby broadcast transmitters. The small amount of power used by the hand-held metering devices is no match for several thousand watts. The front-ends of the devices are broadband and will receive this out-of-band broadcast energy and "assume" it is reflected energy. This will manifest itself as the meter never showing a low SWR — sometimes as low as 1.3:1 or higher than 5:1 — all the while the antenna is actually matched properly. The broadcast transmitter will change its power and direction at sunset/sunrise, making daytime and nighttime measurements different. If the signal is from an AM transmitter, you may see the meters move with the programming audio amplitude.

E. Does the SWR and frequency of lowest dip change when the coax length is changed? If so, the balun might be faulty, as in not isolating the load from the coax feed line. Additionally. with an added length of coax and its associated small (hopefully small) amount of loss:

- The value of SWR is expected to be lower with the additional coax and,
- The width of the SWR curve is expected to be wider with the additional coax *when measured at the transmitter end of the coax.*

F. Be sure you are watching for the right dip, as some antennas can have a secondary resonance (another "dip"). It is quite possible to see a Yagi reflector's resonant frequency, or some other dip caused by interaction with adjacent antennas.

28.2.2 MECHANICAL

A. Are the dimensions correct? Production units should match the documentation (within reason). When using tubing elements, measure each *exposed* element section during assembly and the element *half-length* (the total length of each half of the element) after assembly. Measuring the entire length is sometimes tricky depending on the center attachment to the boom on Yagis, as the element can bow, or the tape might not lie flat along the tubing sections. Self-designed units might have a taper error.

B. Making the average taper diameter larger will make the equivalent electrical element longer. This makes the antenna act as if the physical element is too long.

C. Making the average taper diameter smaller will make the equivalent electrical element shorter. This makes the antenna act as if the physical element is too short.

D. If the element is a mono-taper (tubing element is the same for the entire length), larger diameter elements will be physically shorter than smaller diameter mono-taper elements to give the same electrical performance at the same frequency.

E. The type of mounting of the element to the boom affects the element length, whether it is attached directly to the boom, or insulated from the boom. Incorrect mounting/mounting plate allocation will upset the antenna tuning:

- A mounting plate 4 × 8 inches has an equivalent diameter of approximately 2.5 inches and 4 inches in length for each element half.
- A mounting plate that is 3 × 6 inches has an equivalent diameter of about 1.8 inches and a length of 3 inches for each element half.
- The mounting plate equivalent will be the first section in a model of the element half.

F. In a Yagi, if the elements are designed to be touching, are the elements touching the boom in the correct locations?

G. In a Yagi, if the elements are designed to be insulated, are the elements insulated from the boom in the correct locations?

H. The center of hairpin matching devices (i.e. on a Yagi) can be grounded to the boom.

I. The boom is "neutral," but it is still a conductor! The center of a dipole element is also "neutral" and can be touched while tuning without affecting the reading. With a hairpin match, the center of the hairpin can also be touched while tuning and touching the whole hairpin might not affect the readings much at all.

J. Tests have shown that in installations with several Yagis on a common mast, insulating the elements from the boom can reduce interaction between the individual antennas.

K. Sufficient spacing between Yagis on a common mast is critical to not lose gain and F/B. Even 10 foot spacing between a 20 meter monoband Yagi and a 15 meter Yagi can significantly reduce the gain on 15 (sometimes by 50%), plus almost completely eliminating the F/B on 15.

L. The higher frequency Yagi in a common stack is the one that will be affected by the lower frequency Yagi(s). If a stack of 20, 15 and 10 meter Yagis (20 being the lowest on the mast — which is the correct stacking sequence), the 15 will be affected by the 20, the 10 will be affected by the 15 and possibly also by the 20.

28.2.3 PROXIMITY

A. What else is nearby (roof, wires, guy lines, gutters)? If it can conduct at all, it can and probably will couple to the antenna!

B. Does the SWR change when the antenna is rotated? If so, this indicates interaction. Note that in some combinations of antennas, there can be destructive interaction even if the SWR does not change. Computer models can be useful here.

C. What is within ¼ wavelength of the antenna? Imagine a sphere (like a big ball) with the antenna in question at the center of the sphere, with the following as a radius, depending on frequency. Think in three dimensions like a sphere — up and down and front and rear as in **Figure 28.5**.

160 meters = 140 foot *radius* for ¼ wavelength
80 meters = 70 foot *radius*
40 meters = 35 foot *radius*
20 meters = 18 foot *radius*
15 meters = 12 foot *radius*
10 meters = 9 foot *radius*

D. Interaction occurs whether or not you are transmitting on the adjacent antennas. When receiving, it simply is not as apparent as when transmitting.

E. Wire antennas under a Yagi can easily affect it. This includes inverted V dipoles for the low bands and multiband dipoles. The wire antennas are typically for lower frequency band(s) and will not be affected by the Yagi(s), as the Yagis are used for the higher bands.

F. Are the higher frequency antennas (Yagis) above the lower frequency ones in the stack? Is there adequate distance between the various antennas? Remember, anything within ¼ wavelength in any direction is a potential problem. Careful modeling might not necessarily indicate the interaction in found in the actual installation. Cross polarization between VHF antennas and HF Yagis on the same mast is OK.

G. An 80 meter rotatable dipole should be parallel to nearby Yagi boom(s) so that it is essentially transparent.

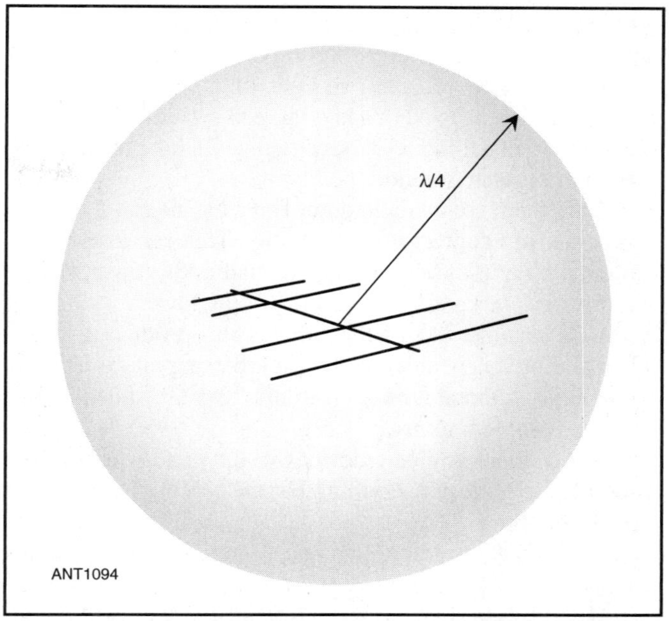

Figure 28.5 — Any conductive material within λ/4 that has a medium to low impedance at the frequency of operation has the potential of interacting with the antenna.

Other antennas that could interfere *might be able* to be positioned at right angles. Orienting the 80 meter dipole parallel to the boom also makes the installation more neutral in the wind. Most Yagis have more wind load from the elements than from the boom which tends to make them "hunt" in the wind. Adding area to the boom can, therefore, help the installation be more manageable in the wind.

28.2.4 FEED SYSTEM

The feed system includes:

- the feed line
- switching mechanisms
- pigtails from the feed point on the antenna to the main feed line or switch
- all feed lines inside the radio room

The feed system is the *entire connection* between the radio and the feed point of the antenna.

A. Is the feed line (coax) known to be good? (Start with the easiest first.) Is there water in the coax? This can give strange readings, even frequency-dependent ones. If there is any question, swap the feed line for a known good one and test again.

B. Are the connectors installed properly? Has a connector been stressed (pulled)? Is the rotation loop done properly to not stress the coax? Is it an old existing loop or a new one? Usually it's alright if new. Type N connectors (especially the older type) are prone to having the center conductor pull out due to the weight of the coax pulling down on the connector. Connectors are easy to do, using the right technique.

C. Is there a "barrel" connector (a PL-258 dual-SO-239 adapter) in the feed line *anywhere*? Has a new or different barrel been inserted? These are a common failure point, even with new barrels. The failures range from micro-bridges across the face of the barrel shorting out the center and shield, to resistance between the two ends of the barrel. Have the new barrels been tested in a known feed system? Always test them before installing. Use only quality RF adapters as these are common system failure points.

D. Is the coax intact and not frayed such that the shield can come into contact with anything? This can cause intermittent problems as the coax shield touches the tower, such as on rotation loops and coax on telescoping towers.

E. Is the tuner OFF on the radio? This is often overlooked when adding a new antenna. If you are using an external antenna tuner, remove it or set it to the "Bypass" position and see if the problem remains.

F. Are there any new devices in the line? It might be a good idea to remove everything but the essential items when troubleshooting.

G. Is there a remote antenna switch? Swap to another port.

H. Are there band-pass or low-pass filters in the line? Filters can become defective, causing strange SWR readings.

28.2.5 MISUNDERSTANDINGS

The antenna can be working properly but there may be a misunderstanding of the anticipated readings versus the actual readings. There can also be discrepancies between the observed "performance" (i.e. F/B ratio) and the specification(s). Having an open mind here is a great asset and will aid in understanding and resolving the situation. "Open mind" means no preconceived ideas or bias, which is sometimes difficult. Remember that we are working toward a solution to improve performance. Common misunderstandings:

A. "A low SWR means the antenna has gain." No, it only means it is matched to the feed line. Remember that a dummy load also has low SWR.

B. "A high SWR means the antenna does not have gain." No, it only means it is not matched or is fed improperly.

C. "An SWR that does not go to 1:1 is a serious problem." No, as long as your rig can tune it, use it. Reflected power is not totally lost. As long as the feed line loss is acceptable, SWR does not need to be 1:1. (See the **Transmission Lines** chapter for more information on matched line loss with varying SWR.)

D. "My antenna has a great pattern, so it must have a lot of gain." No, these two antenna aspects are not necessarily related. The Beverage receiving antenna has an excellent pattern, but its gain is about –20 dBd.

E. "Once the antenna is up, it will stay there forever." An antenna is an electrical device implemented via a mechanical structure. Mechanical devices require periodic maintenance, just like your car.

28.3 ANALYZING AN ANTENNA PROBLEM

Having a specific sequence of steps to take for a systematic resolution of installation questions will make the process easier with less frustration. It will also provide a learning environment and future projects will run smoother and be enjoyable, as the prospect of a higher performance envelope is anticipated!

The following typical debugging sequence is divided into five parts. Each one uses the guidelines to address a specific aspect of the resolution process. Not all the steps will be used each time a new antenna is installed; however, reading through them will be beneficial.

The length of this material and the steps noted should not deter anyone from reading — installation difficulties are usually simple to resolve.

28.3.1 PART 1 — SWR

A. The usual reason for debugging is that the SWR is not as expected. This is the only measurement that can be reliably made by the majority of people.

- If the SWR is showing high values (4:1 or higher), do not attempt any adjustment of the antenna before *first* certifying the feed system is correct.
- High values like this are so far away from the expected values that they essentially eliminate the antenna from being the current problem.

B. Remove all devices in the feed system to eliminate possible components with problems, such as low pass filters (especially if 10 meter SWR readings are not as expected); therefore, we want to work as directly as possible with the antenna in a good location.

C. Isolate the feed system as the first step.

- Place a 50-Ω dummy load at the antenna end of the coax feed line.
- Measure the SWR of the coax feed line at the transmitter end (dummy load at the other).
- If you measure anything other than a low SWR (1.2:1 or less), the coax should be changed and/or;
  - If you see a significant drop in power through the coax (use a wattmeter), the coax should be replaced.
  - If the coax is good, proceed to the next steps.

D. Is the antenna at a reasonable height above ground?

- 15-20 feet above ground and roof.
- If not, place it as high as possible and watch for proximity effects.

E. Does the SWR change as it is rotated?

- What else is on the mast?
- Are there any wire antennas nearby?
- What it is rotating above or below to cause a change in measurement?

F. Are the element lengths correct?

G. Are the elements in the proper location?

H. If a hand-held test unit is used, is there a broadcast transmitter within several miles? This is very important on 160, 80/75 or 40 meter antennas.

28.3.2 PART 2 — FEED SYSTEM AND ANTENNA ASSEMBLY

A. Stay calm.

B. Do the easiest thing(s) first.

C. If a simple change was made (i.e. moved an element a few inches), the problem is most often in the feed system.

D. Swap the coax, even if it takes some effort.

E. Try to remove the parts of the antenna feed system one at a time to isolate the culprit.

F. Be sure to track the correct dip in SWR readings.

G. On production antennas, most problems are identified by checking for:

- Element length and tuning (and location on the boom, but extremely rare).
- A local broadcast transmitter affecting the readings — use your transmitter and its SWR meter.
- Antenna mounted properly; clear of proximity issues, including conductive guy wires.
- Correct feed line and matching system adjusted properly.

28.3.3 PART 3 — KEEPING RECORDS

A. Keep sequential notes of each step taken.

- A legal pad or notebook is excellent — number the steps and each page.
- Write down what was done and then write down the observed result.
- Underline the amount of a change and use a + or – sign, or say "longer" or "shorter."

B. If you make a change, do only one item at a time.

- If you change more than one item, you will not know what caused the observed change.
- If nothing appeared to change and more than one item was changed, it is possible that the items changed countered the effect(s) of each other.
- Changing more than one item at a time makes it *impossible* to track.

C. Write on your notepad the initial observation(s) and the conditions, such as height and proximity.

- This increases your situational awareness and it will provide a documented starting point.

28.3.4 PART 4 — HOME-MADE ANTENNAS

A. For noncommercial, home-brew, or "one-off" antennas:

- Follow same procedures for production units.
- Element tapering needs to be verified.
- Element mountings might not be properly accounted for (i.e. insulating boots when using old Hy-Gain mounts for a new design)
- Matching techniques might not be working as expected. Check directly at the feed point without the matching device in place.
  - A hairpin will step up the impedance and might just move it to the high side of 50 Ω, making adjustment (down) to 50 Ω impossible.
  - If the design is a "forward stagger" type, the forward Yagi needs to be shorted across the feed point (i.e. hairpin); otherwise, the driver will have an open or shorted coaxial stub (the pigtail feeding it) attached across it.

B. Keeping a design notebook, with as much detail as possible using the same note-taking procedure as described earlier is invaluable.

28.3.5 PART 5 — ON-AIR OBSERVATIONS

A. F/B is less than expected.

- Antenna height affects F/B, so does the angle being used. Refer to typical plots to acquaint yourself with these issues.
- F/B specification might be too ambitious. Some specifications are given as peak values, available only across a narrow frequency range (if not tuned properly, might be out of band).
- How much to expect?
  - A 2-element full-size parasitic Yagi will be around 12-16 dB and A 2-element shortened, loaded Yagi can be >20 dB if tuned properly.
  - A 3-element full-size Yagi "naturally" wants to be around 20 dB.
- Stacked Yagis on one mast (for example, 20-15-10 meters) can greatly affect the F/B.
- Rotator clamps not secure, mast slipping.
- Antenna attachment might not be secure, even with the clamps tight, and the antenna is slipping on the mast (typical with hard steel masts).

B. How much gain (redistribution of the constant energy) to expect? **Table 28.1** lists real-life, reasonable, verifiable figures for full-size 20 meter antennas, with gain specified as dB compared to a full size dipole at the same height, same location:

These figures are increased by 2.14 dB when comparing to the isotropic source (4.5 dB + 2.14 = 6.64 dBi); and if ground reflection gain is also included (i.e. at 1 wavelength above ground), add another 5.8 dB. Using both

Table 28.1
Expected Performance Values of Full-Size Antennas

Gain (dBd)	*Antenna Type*	*Full Size Boom Length (20 meter antenna)*
0	Dipole	Reference*
4.5	2 element	10' boom
5.5	3 element	20' boom
6.5	4 element	30' boom
7.5	5/6 element	42' boom
8.5	7 element	60' boom
9.5	8 element	80' boom
10.5	9 element	105' boom
12.5	12 element	175' boom
14.5	20 element	330' boom

*The Reference is a dipole is in the exact same location as the Yagi, such as over ground)

of these, the 5.5 dB figure for a 3-element Yagi becomes 13.44 dBi. Whichever the case, the reference must be specified; otherwise, you know nothing about the antenna.

C. Does not seem to be competitive or crack pileups.

- Not aimed in the right direction (being off 30 degrees can be a lot).
- Gain specification in error or loss in the antenna system.
- Coax, switches, antenna tuning, antenna components, radial system.
- Could it be a problem with the operator?

28.3.6 TROUBLESHOOTING HIGH SWR IN YAGI ANTENNAS

This section applies mainly to Yagi antennas; however, it should be useful for other types as well. There are additional sections for other types of antennas.

One thought to keep in mind when tuning a Yagi is that in a Yagi, the primary purpose of the driver (driven element) is to excite the array. The driver tuning has very little to do with the gain and pattern, although the spacing between the driver and adjacent elements is quite important to the Yagi design. In a 2-element Yagi, the driver location does impact the gain and pattern, because it sets the boom length; however, the parasitic element (either a reflector or director) is the primary "controller."

To locate the problem of a high SWR, we need a scope of reasonableness. We need to keep our mind open to locate where the problem is and where the problem is not. Let us say we have just put up a commercially produced Yagi antenna and it has a high SWR at the rig end of the coax. The first thing that comes to mind is that it is the antenna. Perhaps it is, but we need to follow a plan.

Let us say our rig, with the example new antenna, is showing an SWR of 3:1. If the antenna is the culprit, it means the feed line is seeing a load (antenna feed point) that is not close to the characteristic impedance of the coax. In simple form, if the coax is 50 Ω, a 3:1 SWR means the antenna feed point impedance is either 150 Ω or 17 Ω. The feed point impedance of a Yagi can be as low as 17 Ω, but not as high as 150 Ω; therefore, we need to make a choice and we choose that the feed point is 17 Ω. We need to consider there might be an impedance transformation device at the feed point, but this device most likely will never transform the feed point to as high as 150 Ω for an expected 50-Ω feed.

There are times when the feed point will be intentionally transformed high. Band-specific 4:1 coaxial baluns can reduce even harmonics. These baluns require the Yagi feed point to be four times the impedance of the coax, or 200 Ω. This is accomplished using a hairpin across the Yagi feed point. The circuit is: 50-Ω coax up the tower, mast and out to the driver, through the 4:1 coaxial balun and attached to the feed point, which also has the hairpin across the feed point. Back to our example with a 3:1 SWR.

Impedance transformation devices (matching circuits) are used to step up the feed point impedance to match the feed line (some matching circuits step down the impedance, but almost all used in Yagi antennas step up the feed point impedance). If the Yagi feed point impedance is 17 Ω, a hairpin (inductive reactance across the feed point) can be used to increase the feed point to match the 50-Ω feed line. So, if the Yagi really has 17-Ω feed point impedance and there is a hairpin-matching device, one might want to be sure the hairpin is properly attached and adjusted (if there is an adjustment). An important piece of information is to know the untransformed feed point impedance.

Yagis can be designed with a very low feed point impedance, but most production antennas are not. In our example, let us assume the feed point impedance is in the range of 35 Ω. Now what do we do?

The Yagi, without a hairpin, would have a SWR of about 1.4:1, derived by dividing the characteristic impedance of the coax by the feed point: 50 / 35 = 1.4. Therefore, if we remove the impedance transformation device and measure the driven element directly (at a reasonable test height above ground), we should see an SWR of about 1.4:1. If we do, we can eliminate the Yagi as the cause of the 3:1 SWR we saw at the rig end of the coax feed line. This means the problem is elsewhere, so we can go to the common section below.

28.3.7 TROUBLESHOOTING HIGH SWR IN NON-YAGI ANTENNAS

Full-size dipole antennas will not have a matching device, because their impedance is usually between 45 and 90 Ω, depending on the shape and height above ground. The lower values will be for dipoles that are inverted Vs with the ends not far from the ground. If you have a high SWR on one of these antennas, it is almost sure to be in the feed system.

You should check all the components from the antenna to the rig. This includes the balun (rare to have a problem here), connectors, coax and all equipment in the line, such as SWR meter, antenna switch, etc.

There can be several reasons for a higher than expected SWR. What "a higher than expected SWR" means is that the SWR exceeds the specification by a large margin, such as 2:1, when a 1.3:1 is expected. A difference of a few tenths should not be a serious concern. We are addressing a more major difference. Let us continue the example above for a purchased antenna. If the antenna is one that has been in production, then it is reasonable to expect the antenna to meet the specifications. If the antenna does not meet the specifications, then try the following step first, then move to the longer list below:

Remove the driver element from the array (Yagi), place it on a wooden stepladder. Measure the element to be certain it is built properly, with the correct dimensions. Check the SWR. If the SWR remains at 3:1, the problem is not in the antenna. It must be in the delivery system, because the driver is a dipole and it will not be 3:1 under any circumstances. A dipole's feed point impedance can be between 40 to 90 Ω, depending on its height above ground, which translates into an SWR of not more than 1.8:1. If the SWR is noticeably higher, then the delivery system is suspect and must be checked. This consists of the rig, amplifier, tuner(s), antenna selector(s), all metering equipment (SWR/power meter), all coax lines and connections.

The usual questions to move through the process are:

1) Is the tuner in the line? Many times, a tuner has been left in with settings that cause the rig's SWR indicator to read improperly.

2) Is the SWR/power meter battery powered? A low battery can cause erratic readings.

3) How sure are you that the coax connections are properly made? How good are the solder joints?

4) Is there water in the coax?

5) Is there an RF choke or balun being used to decouple the coax feed line from the antenna?

If the problem is still not solved, here is the longer list:

1) Remember that an antenna is an electrical design implemented in a mechanical structure; therefore, be sure all joints are mechanically secure, making a solid connection.

2) Remember that an antenna is simply an airborne conductor. There is no "magic"!

3) Be sure the new antenna is at a reasonable test height. Having a Yagi antenna a few feet above ground, such as on sawhorses, will not provide much useful information. An antenna covering 20 through 10 meters should be in the clear about 12 feet above ground, preferably higher. A 40 meter dipole or Yagi can be effectively tested down to 15 feet, but will probably shift upward in frequency as the antenna is raised to its final height. The ground contributes a very large amount of capacitance!

4) Aiming a Yagi upward at the sky with the reflector laying on the ground is also not a good idea. The reflector is very closely coupled to the ground and it will not be properly tuned. If the reflector can be raised several feet above the ground (a quarter wave is perfect), the entire antenna can be accurately tuned. Of course, it might be easier to raise the whole antenna horizontally 12-15 feet.

5) Check the dimensions of the assembled antenna to ensure they are reasonably close to the drawings. Unless a particular design is extremely sensitive, a difference of an inch on 20 meter elements should not cause a serious SWR change.

6) Check for other antennas within proximity to the new antenna. Antennas that are related to the new one are of particular interest. A few guidelines are provided in **Table 28.2**. "New Antenna" refers to the one just put up and assumes it is a horizontal design."Watch These" means other antennas that can be influencing the new one. "Coupling Distance" is the distance that the new antenna can effectively couple through the air to another antenna. The coupling distance implies distance to the closest point between the antennas.

7) If the new antenna is a horizontal type, a vertical antenna within near proximity will not usually cause any problems. The anticipated isolation between horizontal and vertical polarization is 20 dB and this is sufficient to isolate the antennas from causing harmful interference, or sufficient influence as to cause a high SWR on either antenna.

8) There are some new SWR meters on the market that make antenna adjustments and testing quite easy. These instruments provide a direct SWR readout, along with the frequency. At least one can display a graph of the SWR curve. If one of the new SWR meters is being utilized, caution should be observed. These instruments send out a low level signal to the antenna under test then sense the reflected power, computing the return loss and the resulting SWR at that point on the feed line. The SWR indicated is the SWR at that point on the line, not necessarily at the actual feed point.

The difficulty using these instruments arises when there is RF energy in the area from sources other than from the antenna under test. Some are so sensitive that a SWR reading of 1:1 on the instrument is not possible. The stray RF energy does not have to be near the frequency being tested, as the front end of the instruments are basically untuned and, therefore, very wide.

During the day, AM broadcast stations can dramatically influence these instruments. At dusk, most AM stations reduce their power and redirect the antenna patterns; however, the redirected energy might just now be in the direction of the antenna under test, whereas during the day the energy was directed somewhere else and was not noticed.

AM broadcast harmonics can be a problem up through 40 meters; maybe higher harmonics are multiples of the operating (fundamental) frequency, such as 1200 kHz (AM band) with harmonics at 2400 kHz and 3600 kHz. Although the harmonics are greatly reduced by the filters at the AM transmitter, reducing a harmonic from a 50 kW transmitter so that it is insignificant compared to the reflected power from a 5 mW signal from one of these SWR devices is a tough order.

Any of these instruments can be used as long as one is aware of this possible problem. Using a transmitter at a few watts will be the most accurate, as the energy from other sources will be substantially less than that of the transmitter.

9) If the antenna is physically correct and the antenna is commercially made, then the problem must be due to other conductors or antennas within close proximity, the match, or feed system. The feed system includes the balun or RF choke and the feed line. The feed line has connectors. Some feed lines purchased pre-made use connectors that are only crimped. Some amateurs believe they should be soldered.

10) A balun should have its leads as short as possible, usually about 2½ inches. An RF choke balun should be wound on a cylinder (solenoidal) to be most effective. (See the **Transmission Line System Techniques** chapter.)

11) The split portion attached to the feed point needs to be waterproofed so that water will not wick down inside the coax. If there are guy wires, they should be broken up with insulators into nonresonant lengths, or use nonconductive guy cable.

12) If the coax feed line is old, it is possibly contaminated.

Table 28.2
Potential Interactions

New Antenna	*Watch These*	*Coupling Distance (ft)*
40 meters	80, 160 meters	35
20 meters	20, 40, 80 meters	18
15 meters	20, 40 meters	12
10 meters	15, 20, 80 meters	10

The contamination comes from the jacket of the coax contaminating the interior dielectric.

13) The coax might also have water inside. This can happen when the end is split (i.e. such as for an RF choke or pigtail connection) and the water wicks up the braid and goes inside the coax cable. Water can also find a path on the inner dielectric and flow inside the coax cable. Air-dielectric coax is especially sensitive and vulnerable to water. It has even been suggested that water can condense inside coaxial cable with an air dielectric. An air-dielectric cable is one that uses air, rather than a solid material for the space between the center conductor and the shield.

The above information pertains to antennas you design and build as well, except that the actual SWR specification will probably not be readily known but it will be anticipated. Keep in mind that a vast majority of Yagi designs have an impedance of less than 50 Ω at the feed point. It is rare to find any that are even in the 40+ Ω range. Some go as low as 10 Ω. This means the SWR can be as high as 5:1 without a matching circuit.

28.3.8 YAGI FEED POINT IMPEDANCE NOTES

Most Yagi designs are in the high teens to mid 20-Ω range and the unmatched SWR will be a maximum of 2.5:1 for a 20-Ω feed point (assuming no reactance). The matching systems usually utilized (hairpin, gamma, T) are step-up circuits, which means the matching circuit raises feed point impedance. The feed point can be transformed to values above 50 Ω, even as high at 200 Ω if a 4:1 balun is desired to be used (50-Ω coax × 4 = 200 Ω).

Please note that transformed impedance is not the same as "native" impedance, meaning untransformed. An antenna that has a native impedance of 10 Ω will have the same current flowing in it when the feed point is transformed to 50 Ω to match the coax feed line's characteristic impedance of 50 Ω.

A "dual-driven" 2-element driver design with crossed-over feed straps between the driver elements is a way of transforming the feed point impedance to a higher value, such as 200 Ω. The "native" feed point impedance of that antenna will be much lower, possibly even way below 50 Ω.

28.4 ANTENNA TUNER TROUBLESHOOTING AND REPAIR

Antenna tuners are usually well designed and built with adequately rated parts. Most will last a lifetime but even QRP power levels can result in arcing if the tuner is trying to match a very high impedance or accidentally disconnected from an antenna. *Hot switching* can cause damage when contacts in the tuner are moved while transmitting. Lightning transients and excessive power beyond the tuner's ratings cause damage. Frequently adjusted components and contacts can wear out over time or just get dirty. Any of these can cause problems with normal operation.

For more information on the different types of circuits used in tuners, see the section on Impedance Matching Networks in the chapter on **Transmission Line System Techniques**. Remember that "tuner" is the most common term, but ATU, transmatch, antenna coupler, impedance matching unit, matchbox, and other terms also refer to the same piece of equipment.

If you think your tuner is misbehaving, begin the process of troubleshooting according to the section "Guidelines for Antenna System Troubleshooting." Make sure the problem really is in the tuner! Once you're sure the tuner has a problem, give it a good checkout to get an idea of what you're looking for. Keep notes as you test since these will provide clues to what the problem may be and also point to tests you should perform after repairs to be sure you've fixed the problem.

Whether the tuner is internal to your transceiver or an external unit, start with a close and detailed visual inspection. Are the connectors clean? Do any look like there has been an arc or are they discolored from heat or corrosion? If there are multiple antenna connectors, does the unit perform differently when the antenna is connected to different connectors? Are there any loose parts inside that rattle when the unit is tipped or shaken? Smell the unit, too — if anything smells burned, you may have a damaged component inside. These are also excellent inspections to make before buying a used tuner.

Operate the tuner into a dummy load at low and high power. Does it behave the same way at both power levels? Does it operate erratically? Does wiggling any of the feed lines to or from the tuner cause SWR to change at the transmitter output? Operate the tuner into a known-good antenna and feed line, then repeat the tests.

T network tuners have a reputation of being able to "tune up into themselves" meaning they can match even an open circuit because they have such a wide tuning range. This results in very high voltages and currents inside the tuner, creating all sorts of problems.

Once you've put the tuner through its paces, you'll have a better idea of what problems you're facing. It is also worth considering that there may be more than one problem. When you find something wrong and fix it, repeat your tests to see if the problem is still there or has changed.

28.4.1 CONNECTORS

A "problem" can be chased for hours only to find a connector that is partially seated or loose and is now intermittent. Start by carefully checking them and any connecting cables.

The SO-239 UHF receptacle center socket usually has four fingers that compress around an inserted pin. Check to make sure all of the fingers are still present. Over time or with mechanical stress, a frequently used connector can develop a loose fit between the fingers and pin. You may be able to use a jeweler's screwdriver to bend the finger back toward the center but eventually this will break off the finger. If the fingers are missing or broken, your only option is to replace the entire connector.

Corrosion usually appears as a dark film of tarnish. Silver-plated connectors sometimes develop tarnish that is conductive. Nickel-plated connectors should be clean and bright. Do not use a drill or sandpaper to scrape the socket or connector surfaces — plating will be removed. Use a cotton swab dipped in a contact cleaning solution and insert a test connector several times. Corrosion from water often appears light-colored and crusty. This type of corrosion can be removed with a brush (on the outside of the connector) or swab. Corrosion that can't be removed or that pits the connector surface requires that the connector be replaced.

Replacing the SO-239 entails de-soldering the center pin and the removal of four (sometimes only two) 4-40 screws, nuts, and lock washers. Be sure to use lock washers when reassembling using internal- or external-tooth types so they can make a solid contact to the enclosure. Do not use the split-O lock washers which do not ensure good enclosure contact. If lock washers are not present, consider adding them. If rivets were used, you can substitute screws or re-rivet the connector, making sure the mating metal surfaces are clean.

Internal cables are often smaller TMP connectors that are friction fit into board-mounted jacks. Once installed, these cables are rarely changed or moved and may become intermittent due to oxidation. The cable connector can come loose due to vibration or shock. If the cable is under tension (not recommended) it may pull loose or put stress on the jack.

28.4.2 MANUAL ANTENNA TUNERS

In a manual tuner, there is generally at least one variable inductor (whether a switch selects taps or continuously adjustable) and one variable capacitor. Usually, there are two variable capacitors with the inductor, forming a T network. If there is a power or SWR meter, switches will select power ranges and forward or reflected power. Some tuners have more than one output antenna connector. Some also have a balun to feed a balanced transmission line and that is selected by a switch, as well. This section will focus on the switches and adjustable inductor and capacitor(s).

Switches

In the presence of high voltage or if a switch is changed while transmitting, arcing of switch contacts is common. Eventually, the arcing results in pitting or burning away of the fixed or sliding contact metal as shown for the *rotary wafer switch* in **Figure 28.6**. Until the contact becomes completely open it will operate more and more erratically. A corroding contact will act the same way. The symptom of failing switches is intermittent high SWR to the transceiver, whether the contact is in the matching circuit or in an antenna select switch. Another possible symptom is SWR that increases during long transmissions as the switch contacts heat up.

Moving the switch to a different position and back again can eventually clear away enough oxide or burned material to make contact again. As the contacts degrade, it becomes more and more difficult to maintain consistent operation and eventually the contact will fail completely. If contact cleaner spray is used be sure it does not leave a residue that can break down from high voltage between and around the contacts.

Most rotary switches have "open" contacts, meaning they are not sealed in a housing, so they can usually be repaired or at least cleaned. Toggle, slide, and rocker switches are not reparable

Figure 28.6 — The switch on the left shows the effects of destructive arcing compared to the new switch at the right. Even heavy-duty switches used in amplifiers and high-power tuners can arc under overload and high-SWR conditions.

Figure 28.7 — A repaired wafer switch section using #2 hardware and contacts removed from another switch. See text for repair instructions.

and must be replaced. The only option for smaller rotary switches may be replacement; this is switch-specific.

The contacts of larger rotary switches can be filed, polished, and restored. Note that any sharp points from arcing can make contact distances just slightly smaller or reduce breakdown voltage and arcs can re-occur. Be sure to make all air-insulating gaps as smooth as possible by minimizing the size and sharpness of these points.

For a custom switch for which replacement parts are unavailable, repair is sometimes the only option. Remove the switch and drill-out the rivets holding the contacts. If you can find unused contacts on the same switch, or good contacts on another similar switch, remove a set of contacts and mount them on the switch being repaired with #2 hardware (bolt, washer, and nut) in the needed location. (See **Figure 28.7**.) Do not overtighten the fasteners, as ceramic and older Bakelite or plastics are brittle. If the insulating wafer cracks, it can be repaired with a very small dab of cyanoacrylate. Ceramic can be repaired with white glue or epoxy.

Inductors

Most tuners use fixed-value *air-wound* inductors as in **Figure 28.8** with turns spaced for cooling and higher Q. A switch selects a tap on the coil to change inductance. Impact (tuner was dropped) can cause coil failure by making the plastic or ceramic coil form or formers (strips which holds the turns in place) crack or split. The usual symptom of a broken air-wound coil is a sudden change in coil value that requires a different setting be used for an antenna that hasn't changed. Arcing can also occur between turns if they move closer together.

Figure 28.8 — An air-wound coil showing the plastic formers (white strips) that hold the wire turns. Note the large wire gauge and spacing between the turns. In this homebrew tuner, an alligator clip makes the adjustable contact. Commercial tuners use a multi-position switch to select different values of inductance.

If the coil can be bent back into shape (as uniformly as possible), the former can be glued together (literally) — plastic with modeling cement, ceramic with white glue or epoxy. Plastic forms sometimes crack with age and heat, as well.

If necessary, one (or two) turns can be unwound to replace a connecting lead, then replace the missing section with the proper number of turns and gauge of wire. An "extension" of the coil form made of plastic or wood can be added as a replacement or reinforcement. Glue it so the coil diameter stays as uniform and consistent as possible. If you need to remove and replace many turns, consider replacing the coil.

Toroid core inductors are used in low-power tuners, and the cores can be damaged by impact or by overheating. The symptom of a cracked or broken toroid is usually a large change in inductance that prevents achieving a match.

If the core is just cracked with clean surfaces that fit snugly together, you may be able to glue it back together with a very small amount of glue along the outside edges of the crack. The individual pieces must be fit as closely and tightly as possible. The inductance will be reduced but might still be sufficient to perform its former function — replacement is a better choice if practical. If a core is crushed or partially missing, it will have to be replaced.

If you do not have an original part number or specification for the core, assess any paint color and the core's size. Then, carefully remove the coil from its mounting (typically a PC board) and unwind the coil, counting the turns and noting the placement of turns. Taking a photo of the coil in place before it is removed can be very helpful in duplicating the winding. Procure another core of the same material and as close to the same size as possible, then rewind the coil. If the wire is not damaged, i.e. the enamel is still consistently covering the wire and it is not kinked, re-use it; if not, replace with as close to the same size and type of wire (enameled magnet wire, Teflon-covered, solid or stranded). It can be tedious work, but take your time and spread the turns around the core in the same pattern as the original. Replace the coil and test.

Roller inductors as seen in **Figure 28.9** present their own unique challenges. A roller or wiper contacts the coil turns as either it or the roller is moved to increase or decrease inductance. Roller inductors typically develop problems either from corrosion of the coil or moving contact or from overheating at one or more positions on the coil. The usual symptoms of a failing roller inductor are erratic SWR when adjusting inductance or when using high power as the resistance of the moving contact changes.

Corrosion is usually fixable with silver polish or a nonmetallic scuffing pad, such as Scotchbrite. If a crust of corrosion has formed, an old toothbrush and contact cleaner can be used. Do not use steel bristle brushes as they will scratch or remove any plating. A brass bristle brush may be used, but gently. The roller contact can also corrode and be cleaned in a similar way. If contact cleaner spray is used, be sure it does not leave a residue that can break down from high voltage between the turns. A polish compound should be flushed from

Figure 28.9 — The roller inductor coil turns while the contact at the top rolls along the wire, moving back and forth along the shaft. The contact is held against the wire by a spring.

the coil with clean water or alcohol and the coil carefully dried.

If the coil or movable contact has developed a burned spot from prolonged high-power use in one position, repair may be difficult or impossible. Try cleaning the burned spot with a brass bristle brush or toothbrush and contact cleaner. If the contact point is pitted, it is likely to develop additional burning after repair. If replacing the inductor is not an option, try adding a small amount of inductance in series with the roller inductor so that operation takes place at a different location on the inductor. Otherwise, you will probably have to replace the inductor entirely

The spring holding the roller contact against the coil can weaken due to metal fatigue and age. This is often the cause of erratic SWR as the contact moves. Remove the roller for cleaning and add a slight bend to the spring to restore operation; be cautious as over-bending may snap the spring. Test with a continuity checker while running through the length of the coil. If a bad spot with weak or erratic contact is found, adjust the roller to make consistent, solid contact. If the roller rides on a shaft, clean the shaft as well.

Capacitors

Air-variable capacitors are almost always present, with or without fixed capacitors that can be switched in for wider ranges or for different bands. Arcing from excessive voltage is most likely to occur on the edges of the capacitor plates, usually on the rounded edges as shown in **Figure 28.10**. Arcing can be from plate to plate or from plates to wiring or chassis hardware. Once an arc develops, prolonged arcing can eat away a capacitor plate (or switch contact), causing ragged edges and points that enable arcs to form at even lower voltages.

The symptom of arcing is proper matching at low power and a sudden jump in SWR as power is increased. You may also be able hear or even smell the arc. At the first sign of arcing, remove power and try to determine what is causing the high voltage in the tuner. High SWR from disconnected or incorrect antennas and bad cables are possible causes, so make sure those aren't the cause before continuing to transmit through the tuner and damaging it.

When there has been an arc, it is fairly obvious. File down the arced section and smooth to a rounded shape. The amount of capacitance lost to this repair is minimal, versus the cost of repairing the capacitor. Check the bearings, where the shaft of the rotor contacts the frame — clean them with alcohol or safe solvent and add a very slight amount of lubricant. Also check the stator (stationary plates) contacts for connections broken due to fatigue or physical damage.

Fixed transmitting capacitors ('door knob' or vacuum capacitors) can fail, typically at the contacts; test with an LCR meter to verify. The only option is replacement. Carefully remove the screws from the contacts or clamps and replace the entire component. If the original value is unavailable, series or parallel combinations of capacitors can be used although the extra inductance may affect performance above 20 MHz.

Baluns

Some tuners also include a balun for use of balanced feed lines. The symptom of a balun problem is similar to toroid inductor failures — a sudden change in settings or SWR. If the

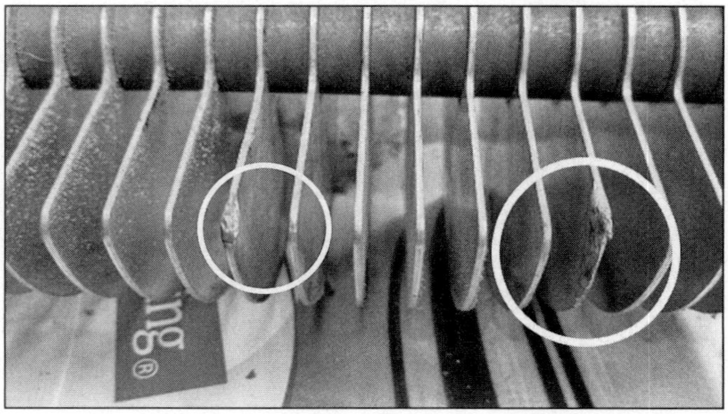

Figure 28.10 — The air-variable capacitor plates in the white circles show the effect of persistent arcing. The edges of the plates are pitted and ragged. The plate on the left is discolored from heat.

balun is suspect, measure the winding resistances or count turns. The impedance ratio of a transformer is the square of the turns ratio. If the balun is sealed, estimate the turns ratio as the ratio of the input and output winding resistances. See the previous section on Inductors for repair information. Most failures are from overheating the core, so if the windings are okay, the core is suspect; verify with replacement. If the windings fail, replace with Teflon-covered wire using the same number of (uniformly wound) turns.

28.4.2 AUTOMATIC ANTENNA TUNERS

Most of the same components in a manual tuner are present in an automatic tuner along with sensing, selection and indicating circuits. **Figure 28.11** shows the inside of a typical model. The most important new moving parts are relays. Automatic tuners are a bit more difficult to diagnose, but by breaking them down into functional parts, troubleshooting is straightforward.

Typically, automatic tuners have fixed-value capacitors and inductors in an L network. A phase sensor and voltage detectors are read by a microprocessor, which switches in L and C based on an algorithm to arrive at the best SWR match. The inductors and capacitors are switched in or out by relays. In "zero-power" tuners (tuners that do not draw much, if any current once tuning is complete) latching relays are used. These remain open or closed once power is removed.

There are three usual symptoms for automatic tuner problems. The tuner may not be able to achieve a match at all and display some kind of error condition. The tuner can "hunt" without stopping for a match according to its control program — you'll hear the relays clicking or buzzing without stopping. Or the tuner will suddenly start re-tuning at higher power levels during transmission because a component or relay is failing.

If the tuner cannot find a match or keeps hunting to find a match, the issue is typically a bad relay contact. The controller thinks it has the correct L or C value switched-in, but the contact is not being made. A relay driver line can also be open. Also check for a bad interconnect cable between the external antenna connector and the main board.

Figure 28.11 — Typical construction of an automatic tuner (manufactured by LDG) using toroid inductors and fixed-value capacitors. Controlled by a microcontroller, relays (the dark blocks) switch in different values and configurations of L and C to effect the match.

The most common issue is relay failure. Relays have a coil that is energized to move an *armature* holding the contacts. The usual relay acts as a DPDT switch with a set of NC (*normally closed*) and NO (*normally open)* contacts. To test the coils, first measure the coil resistance. Then energize each relay one at a time and measure the resistance across the contacts with and without power. A coil failure (usually an open-circuit) requires relay replacement.

If the coil is good and you can get to the relay contacts, a strip of bond paper and cleaning solution can sometimes clean the contacts of corrosion or oxide. Carefully remove the cover using a hobby knife along the bottom edge, not poking too far into the relay — you do not want to cut the coil. In miniature relays in particular, be careful to avoid bending the armature while cleaning. Put some cleaning solution on the paper strip, slide the strip between one set of contacts, hold them together, then move the strip back and forth. If there is a dark deposit on the paper, keep sliding it back and forth until no additional deposit is seen. Repeat with the other set of contacts. If the contacts are severely pitted or there is large buildup of material on the contact from arcing, the relay should be replaced. Filing the contacts should be avoided because it removes any plating from the contact surfaces.

If the relays are good, they may not be being actuated by the controller. Check the printed-circuit board traces for burned or open traces. Then work your way back to the driver transistors and test them; microcontrollers do not drive relays directly. Typically, a transistor is used to energize the relay coils. There should be a suppressor diode across each coil, as well. Replace components as necessary.

Tuner Controller

The microcontroller controls the relays based on its inputs, usually a pair of voltages connected to an analog-to-digital conversion pin. The sensing circuits are made up of a sensing coil, diodes and possibly an operational amplifier. (See the **Antenna and Transmission Line Measurements** chapter material on SWR bridges.) The usual symptom of failed sensing circuits is no forward or reflected power reading, even when the tuner is bypassed. (Most tuners will act as power meters when in the bypass configuration.) Test the sensing coil with an ohmmeter, then the diodes (a common failure especially in a high RF environment). If all check good, replace the op amp that conditions the signals for the microcontroller input.

The last and least likely to fail part is the microcontroller. Testing this component requires a high-impedance oscilloscope and probe, a schematic, and basic logic of how the tuner should work. While trying to tune a dummy load at very low power, verify the inputs (from the sensors) and the outputs (to the driver transistors); as the inputs change, the outputs should also change to adapt. You should hear the relays chatter as the tuner attempts to lower the SWR.

Internal Antenna Tuners

Internal antenna tuners are automatic antenna tuners (as described above), mounted inside a transceiver. They are typically small assemblies, since most transceivers today are of the 100 W class. This complicates troubleshooting only slightly, since the components are smaller. It also makes it slightly easier since internal tuners typically will only correct a mismatch of 3:1 — reducing the number of inductors and capacitors to switch. Use the same techniques to troubleshoot, but be careful of other circuits in the transceiver and be sure than any connecting cables are securely seated. Check the printed-circuit board mounting screws, as they can work themselves loose due to thermal cycling, becoming faulty grounds.

28.4.4 MAINTENANCE AND OPERATION

Think of your antenna tuner as the output stage of an amplifier — it contains many of the same type of components, operates at the same power levels, and needs the same care to operate reliably.

In large manual tuners, keep air-variable capacitors, exposed inductors, and switches clean. Dirt and dust can form paths for arcing and cause heat buildup. Remove dust with a gentle brush and vacuum. If the tuner has been in a smoking environment, smoke deposits can accumulate — clean with a brush first, then apply cleaning solution using a brush and thoroughly dry before operation. Lightly re-oil any bearings in air-variable capacitors after using cleaning solution. Don't put oil on a roller inductor shaft or contact. Check for arcing, broken or heated connections and wires; repair or replace as needed. Use a high-quality cleaning solution on switch contacts, but not to excess and remove any residue. Check connectors and the cables in and out of the tuner.

Check grounding and bonding. The cabinet of an (external) tuner should be bonded to the transceiver, and to any RF bonding bus or plane in the station. If common-mode RF current is upsetting SWR measurements, use ferrite beads or a toroid to block it.

Proper Operation

It sounds backwards, but "tuning a tuner" is the best way to avoid interfering with other stations and is easier on the transceiver, too. There are many antenna analyzer products out today that will put out a very small signal and measure the health of your antenna — they will work in much the same way with the tuner. Connect the analyzer to the input of the tuner (the transmitter port), adjust the analyzer for the desired band / frequency, and tune the tuner for minimum SWR. The result is very low output (reduced interference) and a tuner that is very close to optimal.

If you do not have an antenna analyzer, turn down the transmitter output and use very low power to tune the tuner while your keyer to send a series of 30 WPM dits (followed by your call sign). This is a lower duty cycle than continuous carrier, but will do the same job.

Once you determine the optimal setting for your tuner, write the control settings down by band and frequency — you then have a starting-point for tuning on that band or frequency. Cut an index card to fit over the **TUNE** and **LOAD** controls and mark the locations for each band. This way, you are not damaging the front of your tuner. The less time you spend tuning, the less stress you place on your tuner.

28.5 REFURBISHING ALUMINUM ANTENNAS

Whether passed on by another amateur, recovered from the local recycling shop, grabbed as a bargain at a swap meet or just needing to do maintenance, the average amateur often has to bring up to scratch antennas that are the worse for wear.

Two of the most detrimental factors to aluminum are the results of electrolysis caused by poor choice of connectors and the chemistry of the air. Salt near the coast or industrial/automotive particulates can, when mixed with the normal moisture content, eat away at the shiny aluminum. If allowed to progress far enough, the mechanical integrity of the structure is impaired beyond simple repair.

The first procedure is to inspect the antenna. Look for the dreaded white oxide powder around connectors and joints. This points the way to the areas that need particular attention. Next is to try and remove the connector hardware which may be seized beyond recovery. This is particularly the case where steel plated with cadmium or zinc/galvanized hardware has been used. Before struggling with wrenches and screwdrivers, spray the area with penetrating oil such as Kroil or other modern preparations. These are more effective than some of the older preparations such as WD40 and CRC-556.

If the items release, you have had a win. If not then you have to find a suitable method of removal. Sometimes, heating the area with a blowtorch may cause sufficient expansion for the frozen joint to be loosened. Clamps may be cut free using a cutting wheel on a high speed grinding tool — before cutting into the underlying aluminum, try leverage with a small bladed screwdriver and hopefully you will be able to break the metal along the cut without bruising or deformation of the aluminum. Even an old fashioned hacksaw with a fine toothed blade might be suitable in making the cut.

Metal threads that are frozen because of corrosion can be a great frustration. This can be made more difficult if they pass through plastic insulators, as trying to grind the heads off will melt the plastic. A method that has been found helpful is to drill though the head of the metal thread with a sharp drill slightly smaller in diameter than the shank. The hole only needs to be slightly deeper than the depth of the head. Then use a drill slightly smaller than the diameter of the head to remove the head. This method generates less heat from friction than most other methods and is particularly easy to use on PoziDriv or Phillips head hardware as the drill is automatically centered.

Having disassembled the antenna, it is necessary to further inspect its condition and repair and/or treat areas that are damaged. Areas of oxidation need to be removed by abrasion. This can generally be done using a kitchen plastic scouring pad such as Scotch-Brite, if the oxidation is superficial. The advantage of using the plastic pad is that it does not impregnate the surfaces with metal particles of dissimilar metal which will only cause further corrosion later on.

If the pitting is deep, it may be necessary to remove the damaged area and insert a suitable sleeve just to restore mechanical strength. Pitted areas can sometimes be cleaned and an internal sleeve of PVC or similar used but remember to ensure balance if the element or boom section is undamaged on the opposite end. Remember that crystallization occurs in aluminum subjected to constant vibration, a lesson learned from the aircraft industry but obvious in aluminum antennas mounted in windy sites.

If the metal has to be cut, it must be joined to be electrically continuous and particularly at VHF and UHF, the outside diameter must be maintained to keep the tuning characteristics within specification. For this reason, internal sleeves are usually preferable with use of aluminum pop rivets that have aluminum mandrels. Some bargain rivets use steel mandrels and in the right conditions you will have a loose fastening, a nonconductive joint and a noisy antenna.

Once the various components have been cleaned and mended they are ready for reassembly. Replace the hardware with stainless steel and use nylon insert (Nylok) nuts that remain tight without deforming the tubing. Worm drive stainless steel hose clamps are used but not the ones with plain steel worm drives. Boom clamps using U-bolts are expensive items and a wire brush can be used on the threads to remove any rust, followed with a light spray of aluminum-based paint and replacing the washers and nuts with bright steel ones which are then also painted. If possible, after assembly, a further coat of paint is applied to keep the moisture from these components.

Remember that UV light causes many wire jackets to degrade and so any pigtails, whether insulated or not, benefit from having heat shrink tubing applied.

All swaged joints should be cleaned to bright metal on the mating surfaces, remembering the RF skin effect. Use a thin coating of anti-oxidation compound at all metal-to-metal joints as described in the section on Corrosion in the chapter **Building Antenna Systems and Towers**.

On the exterior, if there are concerns of moisture ingress, clean the surface of any contaminants and apply neutral-cure silicone sealant or cover with butyl rubber self-vulcanizing tape. See the section on Waterproofing in the chapter **Building Antenna Systems and Towers**. Do not be tempted to use hot melt glue on external applications as it deteriorates rapidly from UV radiation.

Although there are warnings about painting antennas, particularly where there is evidence of pitting or scratching on the surface a light spray of aluminum-based paint provides added protection against additional damage. The point is that you are not painting a rusty hulk and brushing paint on thickly but lightly coating the surfaces and paint runs will not occur to cause insulation of parts of your antenna.

It is probably wise to have a progressive program of inspection and maintenance of all antenna systems. Birds find our structures good perches, wind can bend things and moisture which is trapped can all cause damage. At least every couple of years is a good program. Look after your antennas and they will serve you well and long.

APPENDIX

This appendix contains a glossary of terms, a list of common abbreviations, length conversion information (feet and inches), metric equivalents and antenna-gain-reference data.

Glossary of Terms

This glossary provides a handy list of terms that are used frequently in Amateur Radio conversation and literature about antennas. With each item is a brief definition of the term. Most terms given here are discussed more thoroughly in the text of this book, and may be located by using the index.

Actual ground — The point within the earth's surface where effective ground conductivity exists. The depth for this point varies with frequency and the condition of the soil.

Antenna — An electrical conductor or array of conductors that radiates signal energy (transmitting) or collects signal energy (receiving).

Antenna tuner — A device containing variable reactances (and perhaps a balun). It is connected between the transmitter and the feed point of an antenna system, and adjusted to transform the impedance at the end of the feed line, usually to 50 Ω.

Aperture, effective — An area enclosing an antenna, on which it is convenient to make calculations of field strength and antenna gain. Sometimes referred to as the "capture area."

Apex — The feed-point region of a V type of antenna.

Apex angle — The included angle between the wires of a V, an inverted-V dipole, and similar antennas, or the included angle between the two imaginary lines touching the element tips of a log periodic array.

Azimuthal pattern — The radiation pattern of an antenna in all horizontal directions around it.

Balanced line — A symmetrical two-conductor feed line for which each conductor has the same impedance to ground.

Balun — A device for transferring power between a balanced and unbalanced system while isolating the two systems, such as feeding a balanced antenna with an unbalanced coaxial feed line, or vice versa. Often used in antenna systems to interface a coaxial transmission line to the feed point of a balanced antenna, such as a dipole. Current baluns create equal currents in the output terminals and voltage baluns create equal voltages at the output terminals. Baluns may or may not effect an impedance transformation between the balanced and unbalanced systems.

Base loading — A lumped reactance that is inserted at the base (ground end) of a vertical antenna to resonate the antenna.

Beamwidth — Related to directive antennas. The width, in degrees, of the major lobe between the two directions at which the relative radiated power is equal to one half its value at the peak of the lobe (half power = –3 dB).

Beta match — A form of hairpin match. The two conductors straddle the boom of the antenna being matched, and the closed end of the matching-section conductors is strapped to the boom.

Bridge — A circuit with two or more ports that is used in measurements of impedance, resistance or standing waves in an antenna system. When the bridge is adjusted for a balanced condition, the unknown factor can be determined by reading its value on a calibrated scale or meter.

Capacitance hat — A conductor of large surface area that is connected at the high-impedance end of an antenna to effectively increase the electrical length. It is sometimes mounted directly above a loading coil to reduce the required inductance for establishing resonance. It usually takes the form of a series of wheel spokes or a solid circular disc. Sometimes referred to as a "top hat."

Capture area — See aperture.

Center fed — Feed point at the electrical center of an antenna.

Center loading — A scheme for inserting inductive reactance (coil) at or near the center of an antenna element for the purpose of lowering its resonant frequency. Used with elements that are less than ¼ wavelength at the operating frequency.

Choke balun — A balun that works by presenting a high impedance to common-mode current on a feed line.

Coaxial cable or coax — Any of the coaxial transmission lines that have the outer shield (solid or braided) on the same axis as the inner or center conductor. The insulating material can be a gas, a series of spacers, or solid or foamed plastic.

Collinear array — A linear array of radiating elements (usually dipoles) with their axes arranged in a straight line. Popular at VHF and above.

Common-mode current — Current that flows equally on all conductors of a group or that flows on the outside of the shield of a coaxial feed line.

Conductor — A metal body, surface, or wire that permits current to travel.

Counterpoise — A wire or group of wires mounted close to ground, but insulated from ground, to form a low-impedance, high-capacitance path to ground. Used at MF and HF to provide an RF ground for an antenna. Also see ground plane.

Current loop — A point of current maximum (antinode) on an antenna.

Current node — A point of current minimum on an antenna.

D layer — The lowest layer of the ionosphere that forms during daylight hours and acts primarily to absorb RF at MF and HF.

Decade — A factor of ten or frequencies having a 10:1 harmonic relationship

Decibel — A logarithmic power ratio, abbreviated dB. May also represent a voltage or current ratio if the voltages or currents are measured across (or through) identical impedances. Suffixes to the abbreviation indicate references: dBi, isotropic radiator; dBic, isotropic radiator circular; dBm, milliwatt; dBW, watt.

Delta loop — A full-wave loop shaped like a triangle or delta.

Delta match — Center-feed technique used with radiators that are not split at the center. The feed line is fanned near the radiator center and connected to the radiator symmetrically. The fanned area is delta shaped.

Dielectrics — Various insulating materials used in antenna systems, such as found in insulators and transmission lines.

Diffraction — The bending of a wave by the abrupt edge or corner at a change in the medium through which the wave is traveling.

Dipole — An antenna, usually a half wavelength long, with opposing voltages on each half. The term "doublet" refers more generally to a symmetrical, center-fed antenna.

Direct ray — Transmitted signal energy that arrives at the receiving antenna directly rather than being reflected by any object or medium.

Directivity — The property of an antenna that concentrates the radiated energy to form one or more major lobes.

Director — A conductor placed in front of a driven element to cause directivity. Frequently used singly or in multiples with Yagi or cubical-quad beam antennas.

Doublet — See dipole.

Driven array — An array of antenna elements which are all driven or excited by means of a transmission line, usually to achieve directivity.

Driven element — A radiating element of an antenna system to which the transmission line is connected.

Dummy load — A nonradiating substitute for an antenna. Also known as a dummy antenna.

E layer — The ionospheric layer nearest Earth from which radio signals can be reflected to a distant point, generally a maximum of 2000 km (1250 miles).

E plane — Related to a linearly polarized antenna, the plane containing the electric field vector of the antenna and its direction of maximum radiation. For terrestrial antenna systems, the direction of the E plane is also taken as the polarization of the antenna. The E plane is at right angles to the H plane.

Efficiency — The ratio of radiated power to input power, determined in antenna systems by losses in the system, including in nearby objects.

EIRP — Effective isotropic radiated power. The power radiated by an antenna in its favored direction, taking the gain of the antenna into account as referenced to isotropic.

Elements — The conductive parts of an antenna system that determine the antenna characteristics. For example, the reflector, driven element and directors of a Yagi antenna.

Elevation pattern — The radiation pattern of an antenna at all vertical angles along a fixed direction.

End effect — A condition caused by capacitance at the ends of an antenna element. Insulators and related support wires contribute to this capacitance and lower the resonant frequency of the antenna. The effect increases with conductor diameter and must be considered when cutting an antenna element to length.

End fed — An end-fed antenna is one to which power is applied at one end, rather than at some point between the ends.

F layer — The ionospheric layer that lies above the E layer. Radio waves can be refracted from it to provide communications distances of several thousand miles by means of single- or double-hop propagation.

Feed line, feeders — See Transmission Line.

Field strength — The intensity of a radio wave as measured at a point some distance from the antenna. This measurement is usually made in microvolts per meter.

Front to back — The ratio of power at the peak of an antenna's main lobe to that in the opposite direction. For example, a beam that radiates 20 times more power to the front than to the back would have a front-to-back ratio of $10 \log 20 = 13$ dB.

Front to rear — The ratio of radiated power at the peak of the antenna's main lobe to that of the largest lobe in the 180° sector to the rear.

Front to side — The ratio of radiated power at the peak of the antenna's main lobe to that 90° to the side of the antenna.

Gain — The increase in effective radiated power in the direction of an antenna's main lobe.

Gamma match — A matching system used with driven antenna elements to effect a match between the transmission line and the feed point of the antenna. It consists of a series capacitor and a rod or tube that is mounted close to the driven element and in parallel with it near the feed point.

Ground plane — A system of conductors placed beneath an elevated monopole to serve as return path for signal current. A ground-mounted vertical monopole uses a ground plane to reduce signal loss in the soil.

Ground screen — A wire mesh counterpoise.

Ground wave — Radio waves that travel along the earth's surface.

H plane — Related to a linearly polarized antenna. The plane containing the magnetic field vector of an antenna and its direction of maximum radiation. The H plane is at right angles to the E plane.

HAAT — Height above average terrain. A term used mainly in connection with repeater antennas in determining coverage area.

Hairpin match — A U-shaped conductor that is connected to the two inner ends of a split dipole for the purpose of creating an impedance match to a balanced feed line.

Hardline — A type of low-loss coaxial feed line with a rigid or semi-rigid outer shield.

Harmonic antenna — An antenna that will operate on its fundamental frequency and the harmonics of the fundamental frequency for which it is designed.

Heliax — Trade name for a type of hardline coaxial cable with a center insulator wrapped helically around the center conductor.

Helical — A helically wound antenna, one that consists of a spiral conductor. If it has a very large winding length to diameter ratio it provides broadside radiation. If the length-to-diameter ratio is small, it will operate in the axial mode and radiate off the end opposite the feed point. The polarization will be circular for the axial mode, with left or right circularity, depending on whether the helix is wound clockwise or counterclockwise.

Image antenna — The imaginary counterpart of an actual antenna. It is assumed for mathematical purposes to be located below the earth's surface beneath the antenna, and is considered symmetrical with the antenna above ground.

Impedance (feed point) — The impedance at an antenna's feed point, which may be composed of both resistance and reactance.

Impedance matching unit — see Antenna Tuner.

Inverted-V (dipole) — A half-wavelength dipole erected in the form of an upside-down V, with the feed point at the apex. Its radiation pattern is similar to that of a horizontal dipole.

Isotropic — An imaginary or hypothetical point-source antenna that radiates equal power in all directions. It is used as a reference for the directive characteristics of actual antennas.

Ladder line — see Open-wire Line.

Lambda — Greek symbol (λ) used to represent wavelength.

Line loss — The power lost in a transmission line, usually expressed in decibels.

Line of sight — Transmission path of a wave that travels directly from the transmitting antenna to the receiving antenna.

Litz wire — Stranded wire with individual strands insulated; small wire provides a large surface area for current flow, so losses are reduced for the wire size.

Load — The electrical entity to which power is delivered. The antenna system is a load for the transmitter.

Loading — The effect a load has on a power source. Increasing an antenna's electrical length by adding reactance.

Lobe — A region of radiated signal from a directive antenna between two minimum points. The main lobe is the region with the highest gain or in the preferred direction. Minor or side lobes have less gain and are oriented in other directions. The rear lobe is directly opposite the antenna's preferred direction.

Log-periodic antenna — A broadband directive antenna with impedance and radiation characteristics that repeat periodically as the logarithm of frequency.

Long wire — A single-wire antenna that is one wavelength or greater in electrical length.

Marconi antenna — A shunt-fed monopole operated against ground or a radial system. In modern jargon, the term refers loosely to any type of vertical antenna.

Matchbox — see Antenna Tuner

Matching — The process of effecting an impedance match between two electrical circuits of unlike impedance. One example is matching a transmission line to the feed point of an antenna. Maximum power transfer to the load (antenna system) will occur when a matched condition exists.

Monopole — Literally, one pole, an antenna that operates with a single voltage with respect to ground, such as a vertical radiator operated against the Earth or a counterpoise.

Null — A condition during which an electrical quantity is at a minimum. A null in an antenna radiation pattern is a point in the radiation pattern where a minimum in field intensity is observed.

Octave — A factor of two or frequencies having a 2:1 harmonic relationship.

Open-wire line — Consists of parallel, symmetrical wires with insulating spacers at regular intervals to maintain the line spacing. The dielectric is principally air, making it a low-loss type of line.

Parabolic reflector — An antenna reflector that is a portion of a parabolic revolution or curve. Used mainly at UHF and higher.

Parallel-conductor line — see Open-wire Line.

Parasitic array — A directive antenna that has a driven element and at least one independent director or reflector, or a combination of both. The directors and reflectors are not connected to the feed line. A Yagi antenna is one example of a parasitic array.

Patch antenna — A type of microwave antenna made from flat pieces of conductive material suspended above a ground-plane.

Phase — The relative time relationship of two signals.

Phasing lines — Sections of transmission line that are used to ensure the correct phase relationship between the elements of a driven array, or between bays of an array of antennas. Also used to effect impedance transformations while maintaining the desired phase.

Polarity — The assigned convention of positive and negative for a signal or system.

Polarization — The orientation of the E field radiated by an antenna. This can be horizontal, vertical, elliptical or circular (left or right hand circularity), depending on the design and application.

Q section — A quarter-wavelength section of feed line used for impedance matching.

Quad — A parasitic array using rectangular or diamond shaped full-wave wire loop elements. Another version uses trangular elements, and is called a delta loop beam.

Radiation pattern — The distribution of an antenna's radiated or received signal strength around the antenna. Usually presented as a graph in circular coordinates.

Radiation resistance — The ratio of the power radiated by an antenna to the square of the RMS antenna current, referred to a specific point, usually the feed point, and assuming no losses. Alternatively, the resistive portion of the feed point impedance representing power radiated by the antenna.

Radiator — A discrete conductor that radiates RF energy in an antenna system.

Random wire — A random length of wire used as an antenna and fed at one end by means of an antenna tuner.

Reflected ray — A radio wave that is reflected from the earth, ionosphere or a man-made medium, such as a passive reflector.

Reflector — A parasitic antenna element or a metal assembly that is located behind the driven element to enhance forward directivity. Hillsides and large man-made structures such as buildings and towers may act as reflectors.

Refraction — Process by which a radio wave is bent and returned to earth from an ionospheric layer or other medium after entering the medium.

Resonator — In antenna terminology, a loading assembly consisting of a coil and a short radiator section. Used to lower the resonant frequency of an antenna, usually a vertical or a mobile whip.

Rhombic — A rhomboid or diamond-shaped antenna consisting of sides (legs) that are each one or more wavelengths long. The antenna is usually erected parallel to the ground. A rhombic antenna is bidirectional unless terminated by a resistance, which makes it unidirectional.

Shunt feed — A method of feeding an antenna driven element with a parallel conductor mounted adjacent to a low-impedance point on the radiator. Frequently used with grounded quarter-wave vertical antennas to provide an impedance match to the feed line.

Sleeve balun — A type of choke balun consisting of a ¼-wavelength metal tube or sleeve around a coaxial feed line that acts as an open-circuit to RF current.

Stacking — The process of placing similar directive antennas atop or beside one another, forming a "stacked array." Stacking provides more gain or directivity than a single antenna.

Stub — A section of transmission line used to tune an antenna element to resonance or to aid in obtaining an impedance match.

SWR — Standing-wave ratio on a transmission line in an antenna system. Usually referes to VSWR, or voltage standing-wave ratio. The ratio of the forward to reflected voltage on the line, and not a power ratio. A VSWR of 1:1 occurs when the feed line and antenna impedances are the same.

T match — Method for matching a transmission-line to the center of an unbroken driven element. In effect it is a double gamma match in the shape of a T.

Top hat — See Capacitance hat.

Top loading — Addition of a reactance (usually a capacitance hat) at the end of an antenna element opposite the feed point to increase the electrical length of the radiator.

Transmatch — See Antenna tuner.

Transmission line — A cable that transfers electrical energy between sources and loads.

Trap — Parallel L-C network inserted in an antenna element to provide multiband operation with a single conductor.

Tuner — see Antenna Tuner

Twinlead — A type of open-wire line encased in plastic insulation for its entire length. See also open-wire line.

Uda — Co-inventor of the Yagi antenna.

Unun — Unbalanced-to-unbalanced impedance transformer.

Velocity factor — The ratio of the velocity of radio wave propagation in a dielectric medium to that in free space.

Vivaldi antenna — A type of microwave antenna that uses an exponential cutout as the radiating element, similar to an exponential horn.

VSWR — Voltage standing-wave ratio. See SWR.

Wave — A disturbance or variation that is a function of time or space, or both, transferring energy progressively from point to point. A radio wave, for example.

Wave angle — The angle above the horizon at which a radio wave is launched from or received by an antenna. Also called elevation angle.

Wave front — A surface on which all the points in a wave have the same phase at a given instant in time.

Window line — A type of open-wire line with regular rectangular holes or "windows" in the insulation between conductors.

Yagi — A directive antenna that utilizes a number of parasitic directors and a reflector. Named after one of the two Japanese inventors (Yagi and Uda).

Zepp antenna — A half-wave wire antenna fed at one end by means of open-wire feeders. The name evolved from its popularity as an antenna on Zeppelins. In modern jargon the term refers loosely to any horizontal half-wave section.

ABBREVIATIONS

Abbreviations and acronyms that are commonly used throughout this book are defined in the list below. Periods are not part of an abbreviation unless the abbreviation otherwise forms a common English word. When appropriate, abbreviations as shown are used in either singular or plural construction.

A

A — ampere
ac — alternating current
ANT — antenna
ARRL — American Radio Relay League
ATV — amateur television
AWG — American wire gauge
az-el — azimuth-elevation

B

balun — balanced to unbalanced
BC — broadcast
BCI — broadcast interference
BW — bandwidth

C

c — centi (prefix)
ccw — counterclockwise
cm — centimeter
coax — coaxial cable
CT — center tap
cw — clockwise
CW — continuous wave

D

D — ionospheric layer
dB — decibel
dBd — decibels referenced to a dipole
dBi — decibels referenced to isotropic
dBic — decibels referenced to isotropic, circular
dBm — decibels referenced to one milliwatt
dBW — decibels referenced to one watt
dc — direct current
DE — driven element
deg — degree
DF — direction finding
dia — diameter
DPDT — double pole, double throw
DPST — double pole, single throw
DVM — digital voltmeter
DX — long distance communication

E

E — ionospheric layer, electric field
ed. — edition
Ed. — editor
EIRP — effective isotropic radiated power
ELF — extremely low frequency
EMC — electromagnetic compatibility
EME — earth-moon-earth
EMF — electromotive force
EMI — electromagnetic interference
ERP — effective radiated power
E_S or Es — sporadic E

F

f — frequency
F — ionospheric layer, farad
F/B — front to back (ratio)
ff — index abbreviation for topic appears on subsequent pages
F/R — worst-case front to rear (ratio)
FM — frequency modulation
FOT — frequency of optimum transmission
ft — foot or feet (unit of length)
F1 — ionospheric layer
F2 — ionospheric layer

G

G — giga (prefix)
GDO — grid- or gate-dip oscillator
GHz — gigahertz
GND — ground

H

H — magnetic field, henry
HAAT — height above average terrain
HF — high frequency (3-30 MHz)
Hz — hertz (unit of frequency)

I

I — current
ID — inside diameter
IEEE — Institute of Electrical and Electronic Engineers
in. — inch
IRE — Institute of Radio Engineers (now IEEE)

J

j — square root of –1, used in complex and vector math

K

k — kilo (prefix)
kHz — kilohertz
km — kilometer
kW — kilowatt
kΩ — kilohm

L

L — inductance
lb — pound (unit of mass)
LF — low frequency (30-300 kHz)
LHCP — left-hand circular polarization
ln — natural logarithm
log — common logarithm
LP — log periodic
LPDA — log periodic dipole array
LUF — lowest usable frequency

M

m — meter (unit of length), milli (prefix)
M — mega (prefix)
m/s — meters per second
mA — milliampere
max — maximum
MF — medium frequency (0.3-3 MHz)
mH — millihenry
MHz — megahertz
mi — mile
min — minute
mm — millimeter
MPE — maximum permissible exposure
ms — millisecond
mS — millisiemens
MS — meteor scatter
MUF — maximum usable frequency
mW — milliwatt
MΩ — megohm

N

n — nano (prefix)
NC — no connection, normally closed
NiCd — nickel cadmium
NiMH — nickel metal hydride
NIST — National Institute of Standards and Technology
NO — normally open
no. — number

O

OD — outside diameter

P

p — page (bibliography reference), pico (prefix)
P-P — peak to peak
PC — printed circuit
pF — picofarad
pk-to-pk — peak-to-peak
pot — potentiometer
pp — pages (bibliography reference)
Proc — Proceedings

Q

Q — ratio of energy stored to energy lost (or radiated) per cycle; ratio of reactance to loss resistance

R

R — resistance, resistor
RF — radio frequency
RFC — radio frequency choke
RFI — radio frequency interference
RHCP — right-hand circular polarization
RLC — resistance-inductance-capacitance
r/min — revolutions per minute
RMS — root mean square
r/s — revolutions per second
RSGB — Radio Society of Great Britain
RX — receiver

S

s — second
S — siemen
S/N, SNR — signal-to-noise ratio
SAR — specific absorption rate
SASE — self-addressed stamped envelope
SINAD — signal-to-noise and distortion
SPDT — single pole, double throw
SPST — single pole, single throw
SWR — standing wave ratio
sync — synchronous

T

tpi — turns per inch
TR — transmit-receive
TVI — television interference
TVRO — Television Receive-Only
TX — transmitter

U

UHF — ultra-high frequency (300-3000 MHz)
US — United States
UTC — Universal Time, Coordinated

V

V — volt
VF — velocity factor
VHF — very-high frequency (30-300 MHz)
VLF — very-low frequency (3-30 kHz)
Vol — volume (bibliography reference)
VOM — volt-ohm meter
VSWR — voltage standing-wave ratio
VTVM — vacuum-tube voltmeter

W

W — watt
WRC — World Radio Conference

X

X — reactance
XCVR — transceiver
XFMR — transformer
XMTR — transmitter

Z

Z — impedance

Other Symbols and Greek Letters

° — degrees
λ — wavelength
ε — permittivity
ε_0 — permittivity of free space
ε_r — relative permittivity or dielectric constant
e — 2.71828
μ_0 — permeability of free space
μ — permeability, micro (prefix)
μF — microfarad
μH — microhenry
μV — microvolt
Ω — ohm
ϕ, θ — angles
π — 3.14159
ρ, Γ — reflection coefficient

Length Conversions

Throughout this book, equations may be found for determining the design length and spacing of antenna elements. For convenience, the equations are written to yield a result in feet. (The answer may be converted to meters simply by multiplying the result by 0.3048.) If the result in feet is not an integral number, however, it is necessary to make a conversion from a decimal fraction of a foot to inches and fractions before the physical distance can be determined with a conventional tape measure. Table 1 may be used for this conversion, showing inches and fractions for increments of 0.01 foot. The table deals with only the fractional portion of a foot. The integral number of feet remains the same.

For example, say a calculation yields a result of 11.63 feet, and we wish to convert this to a length we can find on a tape measure. For the moment, consider only the fractional part of the number, 0.63 foot. In Table 1 1ocate the line with "0.6" appearing in the left column. (This is the 7th line down in the body of the table.) Then while staying on that line, move over to the column headed "0.03." Note here that the sum of the column and line heads, 0.6 + 0.03, equals the value of 0.63 that we want to convert. In the body of the table for this column and line we read the equivalent fraction for 0.63 foot, 7 9/16 inches. To that value, add the number of whole feet from the value being converted, 11 in this case. The total length equivalent of 11.63 feet is thus 11 feet 7 9/16 inches.

Similarly, Table 2 may be used to make the conversion from inches and fractions to decimal fractions of a foot. This table is convenient for using measured distances in equations. For example, say we wish to convert a length of 19 feet 7¾ inches to a decimal fraction. Considering only the fractional part of this value, 7¾ inches, locate the decimal value on the line identified as "7-" and in the column headed "¾," where we read 0.646. This decimal value is equivalent to 7 + ¾ = 7¾ inches. To this value add the whole number of feet from the value being converted for the final result, 19 in this case. In this way, 19 feet 7¾ inches converts to 19 + 0.646 = 19.646 feet.

Table 1

Conversion, Decimal Feet to Inches (Nearest 16th)

	Decimal Increments									
	0.00	*0.01*	*0.02*	*0.03*	*0.04*	*0.05*	*0.06*	*0.07*	*0.08*	*0.09*
0.0	00	0⅛	0¼	0⅜	0½	0⅝	0¾	0 13/16	0 15/16	1 1/16
0.1	1 3/16	1 5/16	1 7/16	1 9/16	1 11/16	1 13/16	1 15/16	2 1/16	2 3/16	2¼
0.2	2⅜	2½	2⅝	2¾	2⅞	3 0	3⅛	3¼	3⅜	3½
0.3	3⅝	3¾	3 13/16	3 15/16	4 1/16	4 3/16	4 5/16	4 7/16	4 9/16	4 11/16
0.4	4 13/16	4 15/16	5 1/16	5 3/16	5¼	5⅜	5½	5⅝	5¾	5⅞
0.5	60	6⅛	6¼	6⅜	6½	6⅝	6¾	6 13/16	6 15/16	7 1/16
0.6	7 3/16	7 5/16	7 7/16	7 9/16	7 11/16	7 13/16	7 15/16	8 1/16	8 3/16	8¼
0.7	8⅜	8½	8⅝	8¾	8⅞	9 0	9⅛	9¼	9⅜	9½
0.8	9⅝	9¾	9 13/16	9 15/16	10 1/16	10 3/16	10 5/16	10 7/16	10 9/16	10 11/16
0.9	10 13/16	10 15/16	11 1/16	11 3/16	11¼	11⅜	11½	11⅝	11¾	11⅞

Table 2

Conversion, Inches and Fractions to Decimal Feet

	Fractional Increments							
	0	*⅛*	*¼*	*⅜*	*½*	*⅝*	*¾*	*⅞*
0-	0.000	0.010	0.021	0.031	0.042	0.052	0.063	0.073
1-	0.083	0.094	0.104	0.115	0.125	0.135	0.146	0.156
2-	0.167	0.177	0.188	0.198	0.208	0.219	0.229	0.240
3-	0.250	0.260	0.271	0.281	0.292	0.302	0.313	0.323
4-	0.333	0.344	0.354	0.365	0.375	0.385	0.396	0.406
5-	0.417	0.427	0.438	0.448	0.458	0.469	0.479	0.490
6-	0.500	0.510	0.521	0.531	0.542	0.552	0.563	0.573
7-	0.583	0.594	0.604	0.615	0.625	0.635	0.646	0.656
8-	0.667	0.677	0.688	0.698	0.708	0.719	0.729	0.740
9-	0.750	0.760	0.771	0.781	0.792	0.802	0.813	0.823
10-	0.833	0.844	0.854	0.865	0.875	0.885	0.896	0.906
11-	0.917	0.927	0.938	0.948	0.958	0.969	0.979	0.990

Metric Equivalents

Throughout this book, distances and dimensions are usually expressed in English units—the mile, the foot, and the inch. Conversions to metric units may be made by using the following equations:

km = mi × 1.609

m = ft (') × 0.3048

mm = in. (") × 25.4

An inch is $\frac{1}{12}$ of a foot. Tables in the previous section provide information for accurately converting inches and fractions to decimal feet, and vice versa, without the need for a calculator.

Gain Reference

Throughout this book, gain references are as follows:

- to a dipole in free space (dBd)
- to an isotropic radiator (dBi)
- to an isotropic radiator with circular polarization (dBic)

Gain in dBi is converted to dBd by subtracting 2.15 dB and gain in dBd is converted to dBi by adding 2.15 dB. Comparisons of gain for antennas over a reflecting surface such as ground must include the effects of ground.

Advertisers Index

Advertising Department Staff

Janet Rocco, W1JLR, *Advertising Sales Manager*
Lisa Tardette, KB1MOI, *Account Executive*
Diane Szlachetka, KB1OKV, *Advertising Graphic Design*

800-243-7768

Direct Line: 860-594-0207 ■ Fax: 860-594-4285 ■ e-mail: ads@arrl.org ■ Web: www.arrl.org/ads

If your company provides products or services of interest to our readers,
please contact the ARRL Advertising Department today for information on building your business.

ADVANCED SPECIALTIES INC.

New Jersey's Communications Store

YAESU
The radio
Authorized Dealer

• OPEK • COMET • MALDOL • MFJ •
• UNIDEN • ANLI • YAESU • WHISTLER •

FT-2980R
80W 2M Mobile

Yaesu FTM-7250DR
Digital
Dual Band

Uniden Bearcat
SDS100
Police Scanner

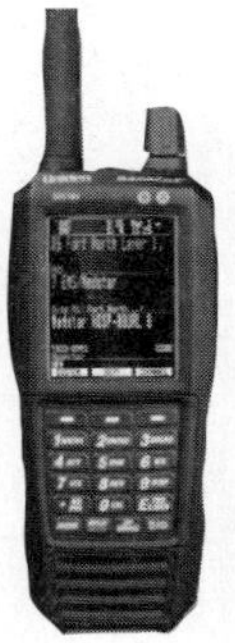

VX-6R
Tri Band
Submersible
HT

FT-857D
HF, 6M, 2M, 70 CM

Yaesu
FT3DR
System
Fusion
Digital
Dual Band
Radio

Orders/Quotes: (201)-VHF-2067
Closed Sunday & Monday – 114 Essex Street ■ Lodi, NJ 07644

Big **Online Catalog** at: **www.advancedspecialties.net**

AMATEUR RADIO – SCANNERS – BOOKS – ANTENNAS – MOUNTS
FILTERS – ACCESSORIES AND MORE!

MasterCard VISA DISCOVER AMERICAN EXPRESS

ALFA ROTATORS

WWW.ALFARADIO.CA

High Torque, Self braking worm drive
USB, TCPIP (MD-0x), 720 degrees
Programmable limits, Simple wiring
12 - 24 Volt operation
Small footprint for controller
ALFA RADIO LTD. 780 466 5779
sales@alfaradio.ca

The NEW EZ HANG Square Shot Kit
www.ezhang.com

Suggestions from thousands of HAM'S and Cable installers around the world, led to a complete redesign of the **EZ Hang**. Custom designed for YOU, the user in mind. Now safer and easier to use, you will hit your mark every time, with less chance of misfires hitting the yoke.

OVER 13,900 SOLD AROUND THE WORLD!

$99.95 + $9.05 for shipping when paying by check

304-856-1026
www.ezhang.com
EZ HANG
75 Goldfinch Way
Capon Bridge, WV 26711

MasterCard AMERICAN EXPRESS VISA

CURE RFI NOW

RFI Kits—Home, Mobile or Portable operation
Audio/home theater, AM Broadcast, Marine/RV, Ham Radio, Consumer Electronics, Computer, Solar Systems, Garage Door, Grow Lights, Sprinkler, HVAC, LED, Ethernet/Cable TV/DSL

Ferrites—Toroid Rings, Snap-on, Slip-on
On-line tutorials show you how to stop RFI from 100 KHz to 2000 GHz - Group discounts, OEM, dealer, quantity pricing

Noise Filters—reduce radio noise, work more DX
AC/DC power, coax noise filters, wall wart, generator

Antenna Kits—Feed Line Chokes & Transformers
BULLET™ end fed antennas from QRP to Kilowatts on all bands

Download FREE RFI Tip Sheet

Palomar-Engineers®.com
760-747-3343

Index

Editor's Note: Except for commonly used phrases and abbreviations, topics are indexed by their noun names. Many topics are also cross-indexed.

The letters "ff" after a page number indicate coverage of the indexed topic on succeeding pages.

A separate Project Index and Author Index follow the main index.

B

C

D

H

I

N

O

P

Q

R

S

T

U

V

Project Index

Author Index

The following individuals contributed material to this edition of the *ARRL Antenna Book* or material from previous editions that is included here, or are referenced in the text. Note that in some cases the authors have changed call signs, or have become Silent Keys and their call signs have been reassigned.

Notes

Notes

Notes

Notes

Notes

Notes

Notes

Notes

Notes

Notes